WHY YOU SHOULD CONSIDER

Geometry

■ This comprehensive course in geometry is enhanced by emphasizing and integrating logical reasoning and spatial visualization skills. (See Contents, pages iv-ix, and also pages 8 and 147.)

■ Lessons include numerous worked-out examples to guide student learning. (See pages 127-128 and 241-242.)

■ Material that incorporates hands-on activities and encourages visual thinking is integrated throughout the text. (See pages 96, 135, and 485.) Real-world applications are stressed throughout. (See pages 196, 343, and 390-391.)

■ Classroom Exercises clarify and review concepts. (See pages 14, 75, and 119.) Written Exercises provide practice with skills, applications, and theory. Graded at the A, B, and C levels of difficulty, they provide plenty of practice for every level student. (See pages 21-22, 46-47, and 97-99.)

■ Chapter Reviews and Mixed Reviews occur in every chapter. (See pages 30 and 151.) Algebra Reviews review algebra skills for upcoming lessons, and Cumulative Reviews review material from previous chapters. (See pages 280, and 281-283.)

■ A substantial technology strand includes Calculator Key-In and Computer Key-In features extending and applying geometry concepts by means of calculators and computers. (See pages 226-227 and 496.) Explorations enable students to discover and study geometric relationships using computer software that draws and measures geometric figures. (See pages 89, 176, and 254.)

■ A new Handbook for Integrating Coordinate and Transformational Geometry, with supporting pages in the Teacher's Edition, has been added. (See pages 657-675.)

Supplementary Materials (See pages T4-T5 for a description.)

The Teacher's Edition includes *Strategies For Teaching*, *Lesson Commentary*, and annotated student book pages with side-column notes. (See Contents, page T3, and pages T8-T9.)

The new Study Guide for Reteaching and Practice accommodates students who need reteaching or miss a class lesson. Colorful Overhead Visuals help you present difficult geometric concepts in an exciting fashion. The disk Geometry Grapher, Coordinates and Transformations, helps you and your students graph and transform geometric figures with ease.

Other ancillaries include the Resource Book, Practice Masters, Tests, and Solution Key.

Geometry

Teacher's Edition

Ray C. Jurgensen
Richard G. Brown
John W. Jurgensen

Teacher Consultants
Jean A. Giarrusso
Byron E. Gunsallus, Jr.
James R. Keeney
David Molina
Patricia Onodera Nicholson

McDougal Littell
A HOUGHTON MIFFLIN COMPANY
EVANSTON, ILLINOIS BOSTON ◆ DALLAS

THE AUTHORS

Ray C. Jurgensen is former Chairman of the Mathematics Department and holder of the Eppley Chair of Mathematics, Culver Academies, Culver, Indiana.

Richard G. Brown teaches mathematics at Phillips Exeter Academy in Exeter, New Hampshire, and is currently a member of the COMAP Consortium Council.

John W. Jurgensen teaches mathematics at the University of Houston-Downtown and is a mathematician for the National Aeronautics and Space Administration (NASA) at the Johnson Space Center.

TEACHER CONSULTANTS

Jean A. Giarrusso, Mathematics Teacher, Spanish River High School, Boca Raton, Florida

Byron E. Gunsallus, Jr., Mathematics Supervisor, Harrisburg High School, Harrisburg, Pennsylvania

James R. Keeney, Mathematics Teacher, Hillcrest High School, Country Club Hills, Illinois

David Molina, Assistant Professor of Education, Trinity University, San Antonio, Texas

Patricia Onodera Nicholson, Mathematics Teacher, Glen A. Wilson High School, Hacienda Heights, California

The authors wish to thank Celia Lazarski, Mathematics Teacher, Glenbard North High School, Carol Stream, Illinois, and Roger L. McClintock, Chairman of the Mathematics Department, Jacksonville High School, Jacksonville, Illinois, for their valuable contributions to this Teacher's Edition. They also wish to thank Jonathan Choate, Chairman of the Mathematics Department, Groton School, Groton, Massachusetts, for contributing the article and paragraphs on technology, and David L. Myers, Computer Coordinator and Mathematics Teacher, Winsor School, Boston, Massachusetts, for writing the Portfolio Projects.

Printed in U.S.A.

ISBN: 0-395-77121-8

123456789-RT-00 99 98 97 96

Contents

Materials

An explanation of the contents of the student textbook, Teacher's Edition, and additional publications in the program.

Assessment

A set of tests and reviews to help you teach the course.

Scheduling

Guides suggesting a variety of ways you can cover the material presented in this text during the academic year.

Strategies for Teaching

A set of articles designed to help you teach geometry.

Lesson Commentary

Interleaved Teacher Pages

Annotated Student Text

Geometry for the 90's

Balanced Approach

A number of questions have been raised about the geometry curriculum in recent years. For example: How should formal proof be taught? What place do informal activities have in a geometry course? How much emphasis should be put on coordinate and transformational geometry? What role should technology play?

There are, of course, no right or wrong answers to these questions. Your answers depend on the goals of your curriculum, the abilities and interests of your students, and your teaching preferences. Our goal, therefore, has been to develop a textbook that gives you the **flexibility** to teach the course that is right for you and your students. *Geometry* offers you this flexibility because of its **comprehensive topic coverage** and its **balanced treatment** of the different aspects of geometry: theory and application; informal and formal reasoning; symbolic and visual thinking; synthetic, coordinate, and transformational methods.

Flexible course that meets your needs

A Course for Today's Students

In planning this new program, we have spoken with many geometry teachers throughout the country and have been guided by their suggestions. We have also been guided by the recommendations of professional organizations, such as the *Standards* of the National Council of Teachers of Mathematics. The result is a contemporary course that works in the classroom.

Contemporary curriculum

In this book, **principles of logical reasoning** are introduced early, *before* the study of proof. Students develop their **deductive reasoning skills** throughout the course, by providing informal justifications (for example, using paper-folding) and informal arguments as well as by writing formal two-column and paragraph proofs. **Real-life applications** illustrate geometric concepts in the text, exercises, and *Application* lessons. Of special interest are the **Exploration** exercises, designed for use with draw-and-measure software. **Algebra** concepts and skills are interwoven with the geometry. The *Handbook for Integrating Coordinate and Transformational Geometry* enables you to integrate work with coordinates and transformations throughout the course.

Promotes Effective Learning

This book has been designed to make geometry accessible to a wide range of students — without sacrificing complete content and challenge for capable students. The following features aid learning: **gradual introduction to proof**, with careful development of the skills needed to write proofs; **numerous worked-out examples**; exercise sets that provide plenty of **practice** for all ability levels, and include exercises to develop **visualization skills** and **hands-on activities** to build understanding; **Algebra Reviews** that prepare for upcoming lessons; **Mixed Reviews** that help students retain what they have learned.

Accessible to a wide range of students

Geometry

Houghton Mifflin

Teaching the Course

Teacher's Edition

- Special articles discuss a variety of teaching strategies.
- Guides for integrating constructions, coordinate and transformational geometry, and software throughout the course.
- Pages interleaved between chapters provide explorations that present content informally.
- Assignment and Supplementary materials guides interleaved between chapters.
- Contains reduced facsimiles of key supplementary materials.
- Includes extra tests and reviews.

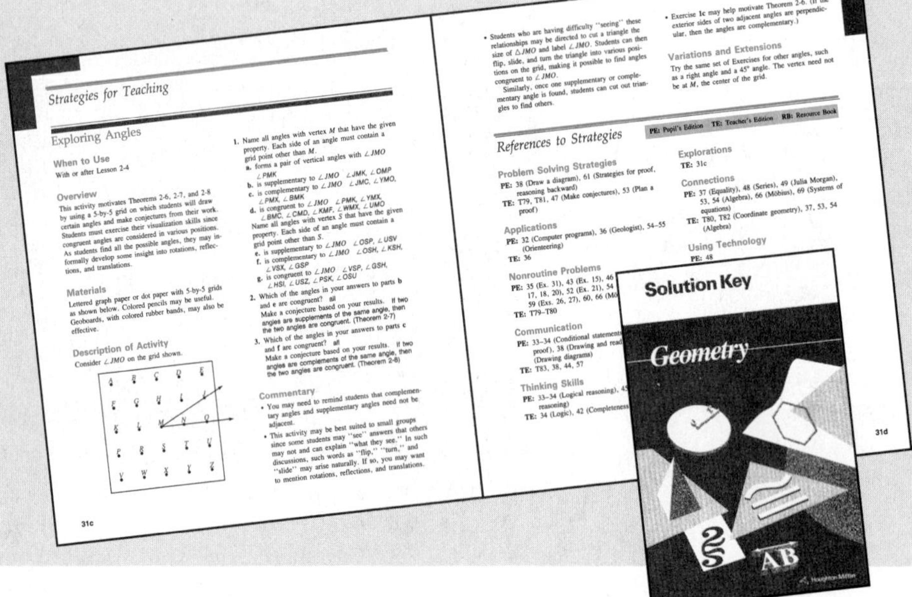

Strategies for Teaching

Exploring Angles

When to Use
With or after Lesson 2-4

Overview
This activity motivates Theorems 2-6, 2-7, and 2-8 by using a 5-by-5 grid on which students will draw certain angles and make conjectures from their work. Students must exercise their visualization skills since congruent angles are considered in various positions. As students find all the possible angles, they may informally develop some insight into rotations, reflections, and translations.

Materials
Lettered graph paper or dot paper with 5-by-5 grids as shown below. Colored pencils may be useful. Geoboards, with colored rubber bands, may also be effective.

Description of Activity
Consider $\angle JMO$ on the grid shown.

1. Name all angles with vertex M that have the given property. Each side of an angle must contain a grid point other than M.
   a. forms a pair of vertical angles with $\angle JMO$ $\angle PMK$
   b. is supplementary to $\angle JMO$ $\angle JMK$, $\angle OMP$
   c. is complementary to $\angle JMO$ $\angle JMC$, $\angle YMO$, $\angle PMX$, $\angle BMK$
   d. is congruent to $\angle JMO$ $\angle PMK$, $\angle YMX$, $\angle BMC$, $\angle CMD$, $\angle KMF$, $\angle WMX$, $\angle UMO$

   Name all angles with vertex S that have the given property. Each side of an angle must contain a grid point other than S.
   e. is supplementary to $\angle JMO$ $\angle OSP$, $\angle USV$
   f. is complementary to $\angle JMO$ $\angle OSH$, $\angle KSH$, $\angle VSX$, $\angle GSP$
   g. is congruent to $\angle JMO$ $\angle VSP$, $\angle GSH$, $\angle HSI$, $\angle USZ$, $\angle PSK$, $\angle OSU$
2. Which of the angles in your answers to parts **b** and **e** are congruent? all
   Make a conjecture based on your results. If two angles are supplements of the same angle, then the two angles are congruent. (Theorem 2-7)
3. Which of the angles in your answers to parts **c** and **f** are congruent? all
   Make a conjecture based on your results. If two angles are complements of the same angle, then the two angles are congruent. (Theorem 2-8)

Commentary
- You may need to remind students that complementary angles and supplementary angles need not be adjacent.
- This activity may be best suited to small groups since some students may "see" answers that others may not and can explain "what they see." In such discussions, such words as "flip," "turn," and "slide" may arise naturally. If so, you may want to mention rotations, reflections, and translations.

31c

- Students who are having difficulty "seeing" these relationships may be directed to cut a triangle the size of $\triangle JMO$ and label $\angle JMO$. Students can then flip, slide, and turn the triangle into various positions on the grid, making it possible to find angles congruent to $\angle JMO$.
  Similarly, once one supplementary or complementary angle is found, students can cut out triangles to find others.
- Exercise **1c** may help motivate Theorem 2-6. (If the exterior sides of two adjacent angles are perpendicular, then the angles are complementary.)

Variations and Extensions
Try the same set of Exercises for other angles, such as a right angle and a 45° angle. The vertex need not be at M, the center of the grid.

References to Strategies

PE: Pupil's Edition TE: Teacher's Edition RB: Resource Book

Problem Solving Strategies
PE: 38 (Draw a diagram), 61 (Strategies for proof, reasoning backward)
TE: T79, T81, 47 (Make conjectures), 53 (Plan a proof)

Applications
PE: 32 (Computer programs), 36 (Geologist), 54–55 (Orienteering)
TE: 36

Nonroutine Problems
PE: 35 (Ex. 31), 43 (Ex. 15), 46 17, 18, 20), 52 (Ex. 21), 54 59 (Exs. 26, 27), 60, 66 (Mö
TE: T79–T80

Communication
PE: 33–34 (Conditional statements proof), 38 (Drawing and read (Drawing diagrams)
TE: T83, 38, 44, 57

Thinking Skills
PE: 33–34 (Logical reasoning), 45 reasoning)
TE: 34 (Logic), 42 (Completeness

Explorations
TE: 31c

Connections
PE: 37 (Equality), 48 (Series), 49 (Julia Morgan), 53, 54 (Algebra), 66 (Möbius), 69 (Systems of equations)
TE: T80, T82 (Coordinate geometry), 37, 53, 54 (Algebra)

Using Technology
PE: 48

31d

Overhead Visuals

- Full-color overhead transparencies, some with moving parts, provide concrete modeling to enhance presentations.
- Printed folders include objectives, textbook references, and questions and answers for using the visuals.

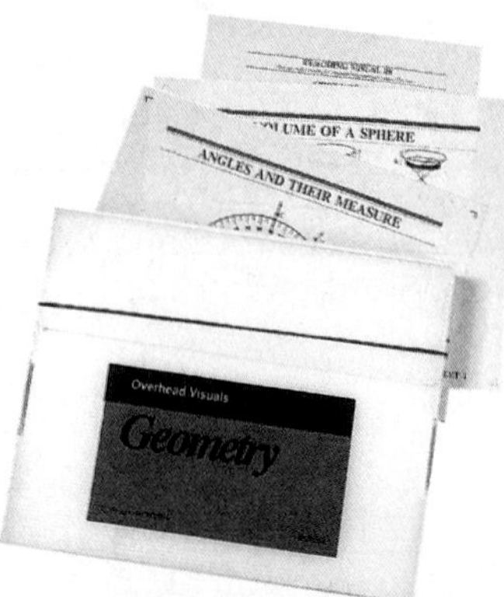

Study Guide for Reteaching and Practice

- Contains alternative two-page lessons for each textbook lesson.
- Provides vocabulary review.
- Has worked-out examples, exercises mainly at the "A" level, and mixed reviews.
- Accompanied by a separate *Answer Key.*

Geometry Grapher

- *Disk* can be used independently by students or by the teacher for classroom presentations.
  - Constructs points, segments, polygons, and circles.
  - Measures lengths, slopes, angles, and areas.
  - Transforms by reflection, translation, rotation, and dilation.
  - Apple II and IBM versions.
  - Available for 5 1/4" or 3 1/2" disk drives.
- *Using Geometry Grapher* booklet includes worked sample exercises, classroom demonstrations, activity sheets, and user's manual.

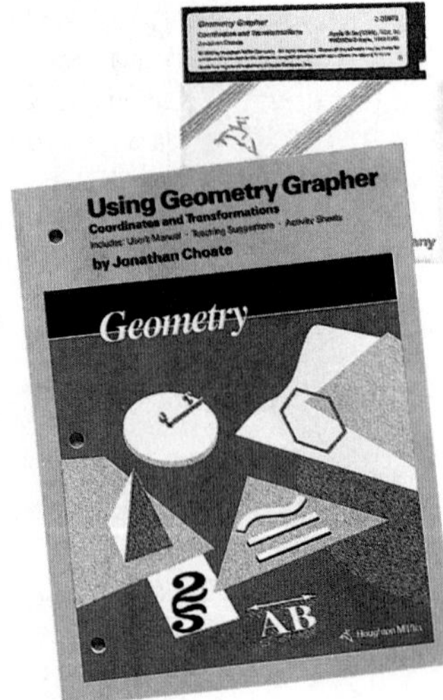

Additional Support

Teacher's Resource Files

Includes:

- *Teachers Resource Book*
  tests, practice, mixed review, college entrance exam preparation, enrichment, technology, diagram masters
- *Study Guide for Reteaching and Practice*
- *Geometry Grapher* Demo disk and booklet
- *Overhead Visuals* sample
- Topic and Chapter folders

Practice Masters

offer concentrated practice in worksheet format including periodic cumulative reviews on blackline masters and duplicating masters.

Tests

contain quizzes, chapter tests (in two parallel forms,) and cumulative tests on black-line masters and duplicating masters.

Computer Activities

provide activities that extend and reinforce students' understanding of geometric concepts through BASIC programming.

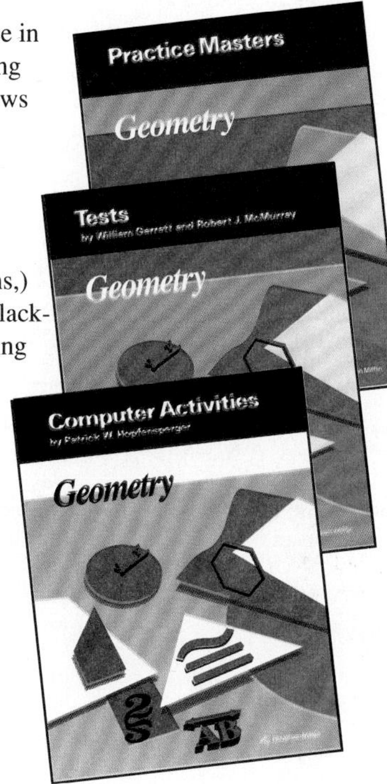

Test Generator

software for generating your own tests either manually or by random selection, with options for customizing the format and level of difficulty.

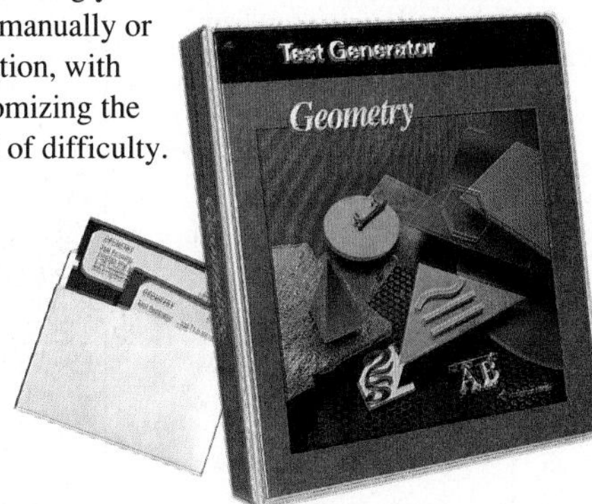

Texas Instruments Calculators

further enhance the technology strand.

- TI-34 a scientific calculator with fraction capability.
- TI-81 a graphing calculator with powerful mathematical capabilities.

Organization of the Textbook

Each of the fourteen chapters has been divided into two or three groups of related lessons. For example, 8-1 *Similarity in Right Triangles* is one of four lessons in the section subtitled *Right Triangles* in Chapter 8.

The objectives for each group of lessons are stated.

The lesson text introduces vocabulary, using **boldface** and *italic*. Color is used for clarity and emphasis.

Worked-out examples illustrate and reinforce the concepts and skills presented in the text.

Statements of postulates, theorems, and corollaries are given in color. Postulates and theorems are also set off by colored bars.

Summaries of important information are given in tint blocks for easy reference and review.

Right Triangles

SIMULATED PAGE

Objectives

1. Determine the geometric mean between two numbers.
2. State and apply the relationships that exist when the altitude is drawn to the hypotenuse of a right triangle.

8-1 *Similarity in Right Triangles*

Recall that in the proportion $\frac{a}{x} = \frac{y}{b}$, the terms shown in red are called the *means*. If a, b, and x are positive numbers and $\frac{a}{x} = \frac{x}{b}$, then x is called the **geometric mean** between a and b. If you solve this proportion for x, you will find that $x = \sqrt{ab}$, a positive number.

Example 1 Find the geometric mean between 5 and 11.

Solution 1 Solve the proportion $\frac{5}{x} = \frac{x}{11}$: $x^2 = 5 \cdot 11$; $x = \sqrt{55}$.

Solution 2 Use the equation $x = \sqrt{ab} = \sqrt{5 \cdot 11} = \sqrt{55}$.

Theorem 8-1

If the altitude is drawn to the hypotenuse of a right triangle, then the two triangles formed are similar to the original triangle and to each other.

Given: $\triangle ABC$ with rt. $\angle ACB$; altitude $\overline{CN}$

Prove: $\triangle ACB \sim \triangle ANC \sim \triangle CNB$

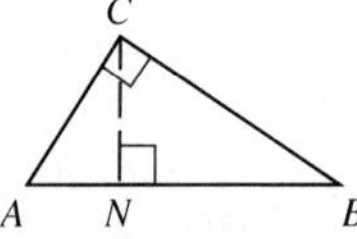

Corollary 1

When the altitude is drawn to the hypotenuse of a right triangle, the length of the altitude is the geometric mean between the segments of the hypotenuse.

Some Common Right Triangle Lengths

3, 4, 5	5, 12, 13	8, 15, 17	7, 24, 25
6, 8, 10	10, 24, 26		
9, 12, 15			
12, 16, 20			
15, 20, 25			

The different types of material within the textbook have been color-coded to emphasize their function.

Exercises are printed under a light blue bar. Written Exercises are graded.

Classroom Exercises

Written Exercises

Mixed Review Exercises

Explorations

Challenge problems provide extensions for students.

Challenge

The **Calculator** and **Computer Key-Ins** (green bars) indicate ways of using technology to enhance the geometry course.

♦ Calculator Key-In

♦ Computer Key-In

Careers (orange bar), **Applications,** and **Biographical Notes** (blue bars) relate geometry to people and everyday life by providing historical background and human interest.

Extras present topics of high interest.

Career	*Carpenter*
Application	*Technical Drawing*
Biographical Note	*Julia Morgan*
Extra	*Möbius Bands*

The testing strand is color-coded with green bars.

Each group of lessons in the book is followed by a **Self-Test.** Questions are keyed to the objectives.

Each chapter has a **Chapter Summary, Chapter Review, Chapter Test,** and **Cumulative Review** (after Chapter 1).

Preparing for College Entrance Exams pages appear at the end of even-numbered chapters. They help students review concepts and develop test-taking skills.

Self-Test 2

Chapter Summary

Chapter Review

Chapter Test

Cumulative Review: Chapters 1–8

Preparing for College Entrance Exams

Algebra Review exercises (dark red bar) are placed strategically to remind students of algebraic skills they will need in the next lesson or chapter.

Algebra Review: *Linear Equations*

Using the Teacher's Edition

This Teacher's Edition provides Lesson Commentary for every lesson followed by nearly full-size textbook pages with annotated answers and accompanying side column material. As illustrated below, the side columns include time-saving references and material on which you can model your lesson presentation.

Further information about when to use technology is indicated by a logo and given under **Using a Computer** (or **Using a Calculator**).

For each lesson, page references are given for the corresponding **Lesson Commentary,** which includes teaching suggestions and ideas for making connections, applications, problem solving, enrichment, and reinforcement, as well as those topics shown.

Page references are also given for specific **Cooperative Learning, Exploring Activity,** and **Communication Skills** suggestions.

References to **Supplementary Materials** are provided for the sets of blackline and duplicating masters available for each lesson.

Lesson Focus informally states the purpose of the lesson.

Suggested Assignments are given for minimum, average, and maximum courses.

Using a Model includes teaching suggestions about hands-on manipulative aids that can be used in the lesson.

Using a Computer

This Exploration introduces the properties of isosceles triangles that are developed in Lesson 4-4.

Teaching Suggestions, p. T90

Objective
Presenting the Lesson
Using Technology
Extension

Cooperative Learning, p. T91

Supplementary Materials

Test 14
Resource Book, pp. 19, 122
Study Guide, pp. 43–46

Lesson Focus

Two important theorems involving isosceles triangles are presented in this lesson and are used to further enhance students' abilities to write proofs.

Suggested Assignments

Minimum
Day 1: 137/1–8
Day 2: 137–138/9, 11, 13–15
Average
Day 1: 137/1–9 odd, 10, 12
Maximum
Day 1: 137–138/3, 4, 6, 9, 12, 14, 15, 17, 22

Using a Model

Students can create a useful model of an isosceles triangle by doing this paper-folding activity.

SIMULATED PAGE

Explorations

These exploratory exercises can be done using a computer with a program that draws and measures geometric figures.

Draw several isosceles triangles. For each triangle, measure all sides and angles. What do you notice?

What is the relationship between the congruent sides and some of the angles?
The $\triangle$ opposite the $\cong$ sides are $\cong$.

Some Theorems Based on Congruent Triangles

Objectives

1. Apply the theorems and corollaries about isosceles triangles.
2. Use the AAS Theorem to prove two triangles congruent.

4-4 *The Isosceles Triangle Theorems*

The photograph shows the Transamerica Pyramid in San Francisco. Each of its four faces is an isosceles triangle, with two congruent sides. These congruent sides are called **legs** and the third side is called the **base.** The angles at the base are called *base angles* and the angle opposite the base is called the *vertex angle* of the isosceles triangle.

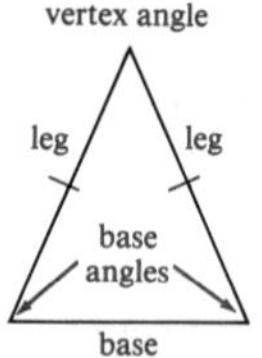

You can use the steps described below to form an isosceles tringle. Refer to the diagram shown.

(1) Fold a sheet of paper in half.
(2) Cut off a double-thickness corner piece along the dashed line.
(3) Open the corner piece and lay it flat. You will have a triangle, which is labeled $\triangle PRS$. The fold line is labeled $\overline{PQ}$.
(4) Since $\overline{PR}$ and $\overline{PS}$ were formed by the same cut line, you can conclude that they are congruent segments and that $\triangle PRS$ is isosceles.

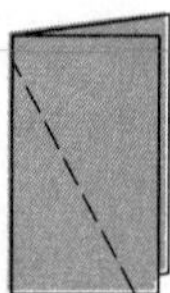

In addition to the elements displayed on these pages, side columns include:

Application	Group Activity	Teaching Note
Assessment	Problem Solving	Thinking Skills
Cultural Note	Proof Note	Using a Calculator
Exercise Note	Quick Quiz	

SIMULATED PAGE

Theorem 4-1 *The Isosceles Triangle Theorem*
If two sides of a triangle are congruent, then the angles opposite those sides are congruent.

Given: $\overline{AB} \cong \overline{AC}$

Prove: $\angle B \cong \angle C$

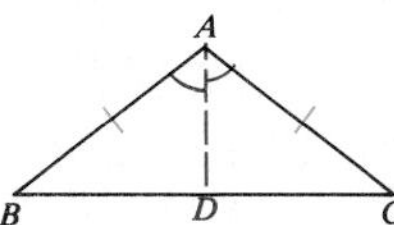

Plan for Proof: You can show that $\angle B$ and $\angle C$ are corresponding parts of congruent triangles if you draw an auxiliary line that will give you such triangles. For example, draw the bisector of $\angle A$.

Classroom Exercises

1. If $\triangle AOD$ is isosceles, with $\overline{OA} \cong \overline{OD}$, then $\angle$ _?_ $\cong \angle$ _?_. **A, D**
2. If $\triangle BOC$ is isosceles, with $\overline{OB} \cong \overline{OC}$, then $\angle$ _?_ $\cong \angle$ _?_. **2. $\angle OBC \cong \angle OCB$**
3. If $\triangle AOD$ is an isosceles right triangle with right $\angle AOD$, then the measure of $\angle A$ is _?_. **45**
4. Explain how Corollary 1 follows from Theorem 4-1.
5. Explain how Corollary 2 follows from Corollary 1.

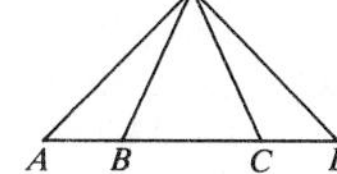

Written Exercises

Find the value of *x*.

1. **80**

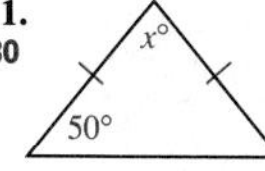

2. **45**

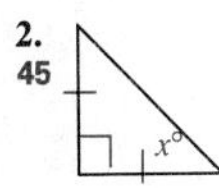

3. **53**

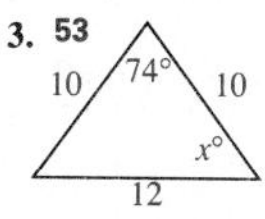

4. **11**

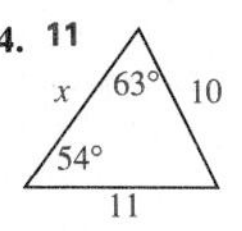

For each exercise place the statements in an appropriate order for a proof. (There may be more than one correct order.) **Answers may vary.**

5. Given: $\overline{RS} \cong \overline{RT}$
   Prove: $\angle 3 \cong \angle 4$ **c, d, b, a**
   (a) $\angle 3 \cong \angle 4$
   (b) $\angle 3 \cong \angle 1$; $\angle 2 \cong \angle 4$
   (c) $\overline{RS} \cong \overline{RT}$
   (d) $\angle 1 \cong \angle 2$

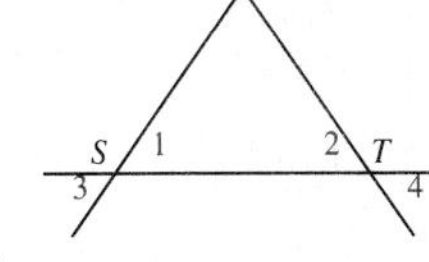

$m\angle 2 = 40$
$m\angle 7 = 100$
$m\angle 5 = 40$
$m\angle 6 = 40$

B 6. Given: $\overline{PO} \cong \overline{QO}$; $\overline{RO} \cong \overline{SO}$
   a. If you are also given that $m\angle 1 = 40$, find the measures of $\angle 2$, $\angle 7$, $\angle 5$, and $\angle 6$. Then decide whether $\overline{PQ}$ must be parallel to $\overline{SR}$. **Yes**
   b. Repeat part (a), but use $m\angle 1 = k$.
   $m\angle 2 = m\angle 5 = m\angle 6 = k$, $m\angle 7 = 180 - 2k$; yes

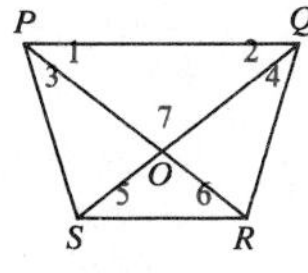

Communication Skills

The use of an auxiliary line can be introduced by means of informal language such as "draw a line through the middle of the triangle."

Chalkboard Examples

In Exs. 1 and 2, $\overline{BC} \cong \overline{AC}$.

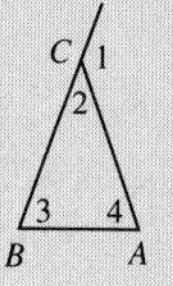

1. If $m\angle 1 = 140$, $m\angle 2 =$ 40, $m\angle 3 =$ 70, $m\angle 4 =$ 70
2. If $m\angle 4 = 65$, $m\angle 3 =$ 65, $m\angle 2 =$ 50, $m\angle 1 =$ 130.

Additional Answers Classroom Exercises

4. $\triangle ABC$ is equilateral. $\overline{AB} \cong \overline{AC}$, so $\angle B \cong \angle C$. $\overline{AB} \cong \overline{BC}$, so $\angle A \cong \angle C$. Then $\angle A \cong \angle B \cong \angle C$.

Guided Practice

Find the value of *x*.

1. 75

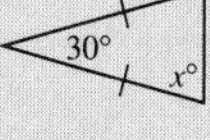

Making Connections

In Ex. 6, students extend a specific case to the general variable *k*. Exercises such as this strengthen students' algebraic and geometric thinking skills.

Communication Skills includes notes about oral and written expression, and meanings of terminology.

Chalkboard Examples are additional examples for classroom presentation.

Additional Answers supplement the answers printed on the student pages.

Guided Practice provides additional "A" exercises for students to do under the teacher's guidance after the presentation of the lesson.

Making Connections notes relationships between various topics in geometry *and* between geometry and other branches of mathematics, such as algebra.

Key Topics and Approaches

Problem Solving

Problem Solving Strategies

Applications

Nonroutine Problems

Reasoning

Thinking Skills

Explorations

Communication

Reading

Scale drawings, 248, 262
Two-column proof, 38
Venn diagrams, 208–209

Discussion

Convincing argument, 9 (Challenge), 86 (Ex. 20), 88 (Ex. 30), 132 (Ex. 15), 179 (Ex. 1)

Writing

Conditional statements, 33–34
Drawing and reading diagrams, 19, 38, 61, 319–320
Drawing geometric figures, 485, 492, 493
Drawing space figures, 8, 77
Isometric drawings, 90–92
Key steps of proof, 147
Paragraph proof, 147
Rewording, 24 (Exs. 2–4), 25 (Ex. 12)

Connections

Mathematics

Algebra, 10, 13, 16, 37, 48, 53, 54, 69, 120, 163, 175 (Exs. 19–22), 203–233, 237, 241–248, 261, 280, 287, 290 (Ex. 45), 299, 419, 451, 534, 571, 606
Analytic geometry, 27, 66, 113, 273, 356, 523, 338, 434, 516, 525, 657–672
Arithmetic, 11–12
Discrete mathematics, 332, 506, 564
Non-Euclidean geometry, 233–234, 304
Probability, 461–464
Trigonometry, 317–320

Other Disciplines

Architecture, 9, 20 (Ex. 26), 90–92, 105 (Exs. 18–20), 133, 248, 262, 253, 265, 298 (Ex. 22), 321, 505–506
Art, 116, 253, 263 (Ex. 9), 422
Biology, 104 (Ex. 11), 410 (Ex. 24)
Business, 400, 481
Communications, 343 (Exs. 23, 24)
Computers, 32, 261, 598
Engineering, 173 (Exs. 12, 13), 174 (Ex. 7), 196, 284, 303 (Ex. 28), 309 (Exs. 19, 20), 427 (Exs. 29, 30, 35, 36), 500–502, 512 (Ex. 16), 514, 515, 564
Geography, 27, 157 (Ex. 19), 213, 240, 340, 343
Geology, 36
Logic, 1–2
Navigation, 27–28, 54–55, 157 (Ex. 19), 132 (Ex. 16), 256 (Ex. 13), 257 (Ex. 15), 258 (Exs. 16, 17, 20), 224, 259 (Ex. 32), 273 (Ex. 24), 310 (Exs. 29, 30), 315, 317–320, 342 (Exs. 17–20), 367–368, 467–469, 539–541
Physics, 16 (Ex. 48), 202, 260 (Ex. 35), 319 (Ex. 12), 328, 374, 390–391, 497, 582–583, 614
Sports, 104 (Ex. 9), 449, 454

Technology

Calculator

Exercises, 163, 189, 244 (Ex. 33), 247 (Exs. 21–28), 253, 297 (Exs. 1–8), 306 (Ex. 7), 313 (Ex. 7), 343 (Exs. 23, 24), 368 (Exs. 1–5), 500 (Ex. 17), 551 (Exs. 25–30)
Explorations, 552
Key-Ins, 109, 253, 434, 445, 451, 488, 496, 503, 514

Computer

Exercises, 20, 108 (Exs. 15–25, 27), 185
Explorations, 78, 89, 99, 134, 158, 176, 189, 195, 225, 254, 268, 298, 310, 338, 361, 385, 392, 433, 552, 576
Key-Ins, 48, 109, 183, 226–227, 261, 299, 428, 438–439, 481, 488–489, 504, 515, 528

Using Geometry Grapher

Suggested Textbook Exercises

525–528 (Cl. Exs. 4–10; Wr. Exs. 5–16, 27–32, 39–42, 44)
531–534 (Cl. Exs. 1–3; Wr. Exs. 3–15, 20, 21, 26–29, 32)
537–538 (Wr. Exs. 1, 2, 5, 7–18)
545–547 (Cl. Exs. 1–5; Wr. Exs. 1–3, 5, 7–9, 13–21, 24)
550–552 (Cl. Exs. 1–13; Wr. Exs. 1–35)
554–556 (Cl. Exs. 1–12; Wr. Exs. 1–32, 34–39)
562 (Wr. Exs. 4, 5, 7–10)
579–582 (Cl. Exs. 13, 14; Wr. Exs. 1–12, 15, 16, 21, 22, 24, 32–39)
585–587 (Cl. Exs. 1–3, 8; Wr. Exs. 1–12, 15–18, 20, 22)
589–591 (Cl. Exs. 12, 13; Wr. Exs. 27–30, 32–34)
595–597 (Cl. Exs. 5–10; Wr. Exs. 1–8, 18–21, 27)
602–605 (Cl. Exs. 3–8; Wr. Exs. 10, 17–29)
613–614 (Wr. Exs. 21–23, 25)

Sample Textbook Exercise Demonstrations

The Distance Formula, 528 (Ex. 44)
Slope of a Line, 533 (Ex. 21)
Parallel and Perpendicular Lines, 538 (Ex. 12)
The Midpoint Formula, 546 (Ex. 15)
Graphing Linear Equations, 552 (Ex. 35c)
Writing Linear Equations, 555 (Ex. 27)
Coordinate Geometry Proofs, 562 (Ex. 5)
Reflections, 582 (Ex. 38)
Translations and Glide Reflections, 586 (Ex. 8)
Rotations, 590 (Ex. 29)
Dilations, 596 (Ex. 5)
Composites of Mappings, 605 (Ex. 28)
Symmetry in the Plane and in Space, 614 (Ex. 25)

Classroom Demonstrations

Theorem 3-2, Transversal, 78
Theorem 5-9, Parallels, 177
Theorem 6-2, Inequalities, 219
Theorem 7-4, Angle Bisector, 270
Theorem 9-11, Intersecting Chords, 362
Theorem 10-4, Medians, 387
Lesson 14-2, Reflection, 577
Lesson 14-4, Rotation, 588
Lesson 14-5, Double Dilation, 592
Lesson 14-8, Point Symmetry, 609

Activity Sheets

Lessons 13-2, 13-3; Activity 1
Lessons 13-1, 13-5; Activity 2
Lessons 13-6, 13-7; Activity 3
Lesson 14-2; Activity 4
Lesson 14-3; Activity 5
Lesson 14-4; Activity 6
Lesson 14-5; Activity 7
Lessons 14-6, 14-8; Activity 8

Diagnostic Test Ch. 1

This test covers Chapter 1. It can be used either to assess a class's background before beginning the course or as an alternative test for Chapter 1.

1. Name three points that are collinear.
2. The intersection of $\overline{JM}$ and $\overline{TQ}$ is _?_.
3. A ray opposite to $\overrightarrow{RS}$ is _?_.
4. The sides of $\angle 1$ are _?_ and _?_.
5. The vertex of $\angle JQP$ is _?_.
6. Give two different names for $\angle 2$.
7. $m\angle KQJ =$ _?_
8. Classify each angle.
   a. $\angle JKQ$ is a(n) _?_ angle.
   b. $\angle SML$ is a(n) _?_ angle.
   c. $\angle RSM$ is a(n) _?_ angle.
   d. $\angle KJQ$ and $\angle QJP$ are _?_ angles.

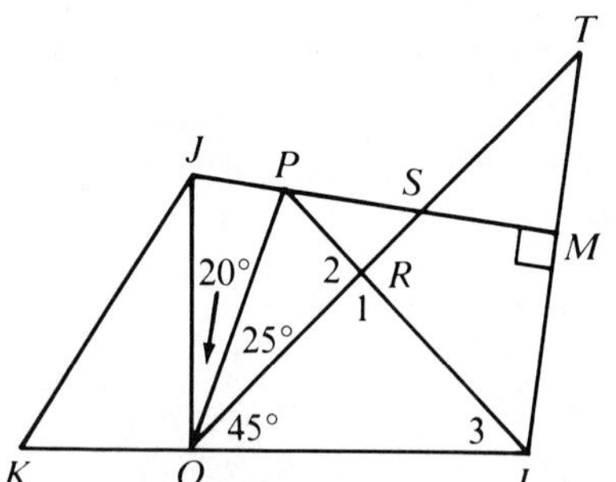

Exs. 1–8

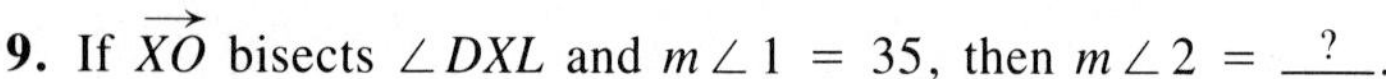

9. If $\overrightarrow{XO}$ bisects $\angle DXL$ and $m\angle 1 = 35$, then $m\angle 2 =$ _?_.

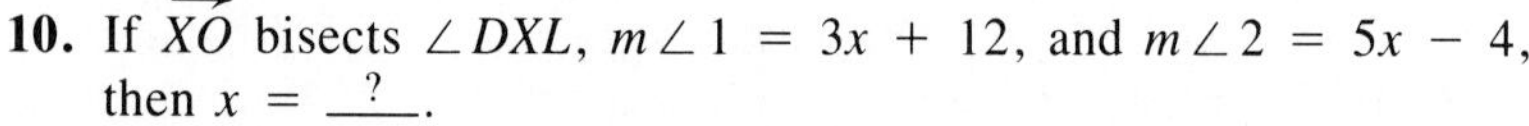

10. If $\overrightarrow{XO}$ bisects $\angle DXL$, $m\angle 1 = 3x + 12$, and $m\angle 2 = 5x - 4$, then $x =$ _?_.

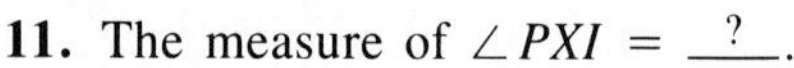

11. The measure of $\angle PXI =$ _?_.
12. If $m\angle HXL = 90$, then $m\angle 3 =$ _?_.
13. According to the Angle Addition Postulate, $m\angle DXO +$ _?_ $= m\angle DXH$.

Exs. 9–13

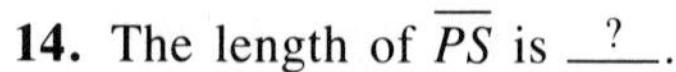

14. The length of $\overline{PS}$ is _?_.
15. The coordinate of the midpoint of $\overline{IT}$ is _?_.
16. Name a point on $\overrightarrow{NT}$ that is not on $\overline{NT}$.

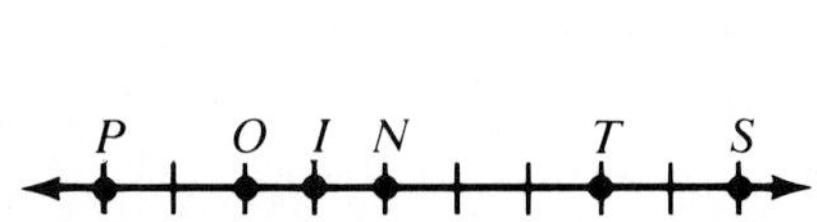

Exs. 14–16

Classify each statement as true or false.

17. $\overleftrightarrow{EF}$ is in plane Y.
18. Plane X intersects plane Y in $\overleftrightarrow{CD}$.
19. C, G, D, and H are noncoplanar points.
20. Point D is in X and Y.

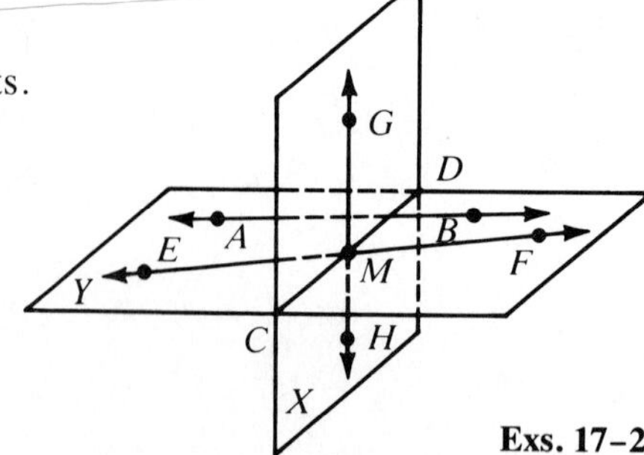

Exs. 17–20

Complete.

21. The distance between two points is always given by a __?__ number.
22. Two planes can intersect to form a __?__.
23. Congruent figures have the same size and the same __?__.
24. The set of all points is called __?__.
25. A statement that is accepted as true without a proof is called a __?__.
26. The measure of an angle can be found by using a __?__.
27. Adjacent angles have a common vertex and a common side but no common __?__ points.
28. Through any two points there is exactly one __?__.
29. $\overrightarrow{MN}$ and $\overrightarrow{MP}$ are called opposite rays if M is __?__ N and P.
30. The measure of a straight angle is __?__.

Answer each question by writing *yes* or *no*.

31. Is it possible for six points to be collinear?
32. Is it possible for a segment not to have an endpoint?
33. Is it possible to find the absolute value of a negative number?
34. Is it possible for two angles to have the same vertex?
35. Is it possible for three points to be noncoplanar?

Given the diagram, tell whether you can reach the conclusion shown.

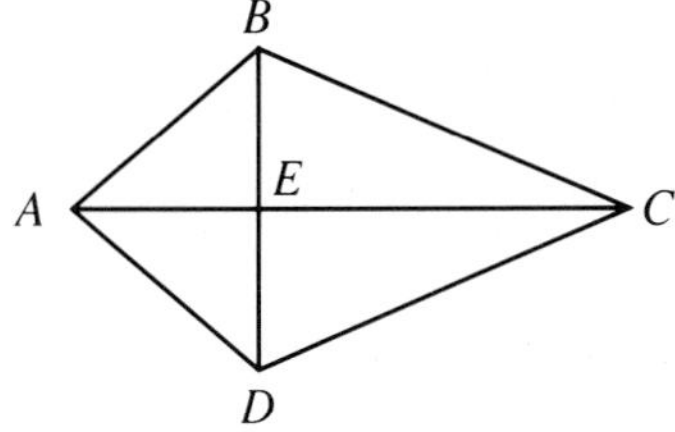

36. $AB = AD$
37. $\angle AEB$ is a right angle.
38. Point E is between points A and C.
39. Point E is the midpoint of $\overline{BD}$.
40. $\overline{ED}$ lies in the interior of $\angle ABC$.

Chapter Tests

Chapter 1

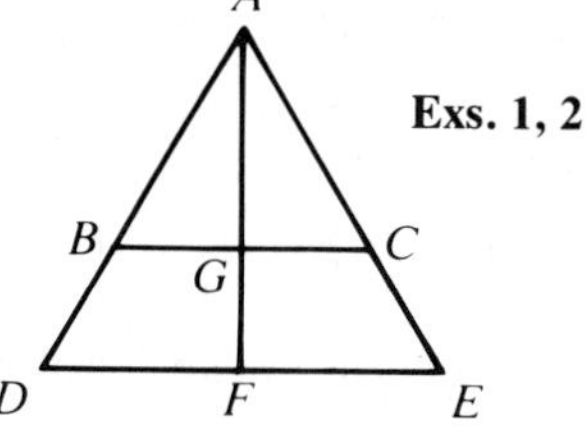

Exs. 1, 2

1. Name three collinear points.
2. Name three coplanar points that are noncollinear.

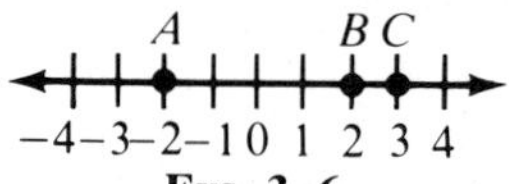

Exs. 3–6

3. Name the coordinate of point A.
4. Name the coordinate of the midpoint of $\overline{AC}$.
5. Complete: $AB + BC =$ __?__
6. Name a ray opposite to $\overrightarrow{BC}$.

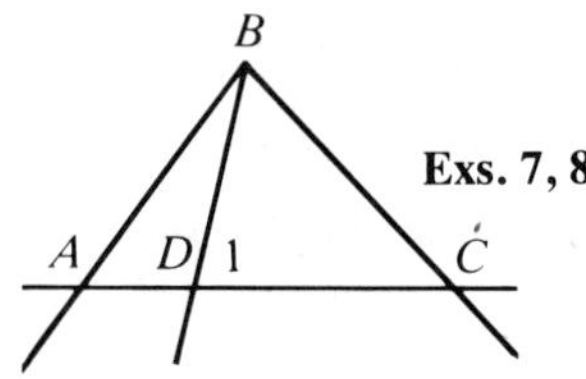

Exs. 7, 8

7. Name a pair of adjacent angles.
8. Name the sides of $\angle 1$.

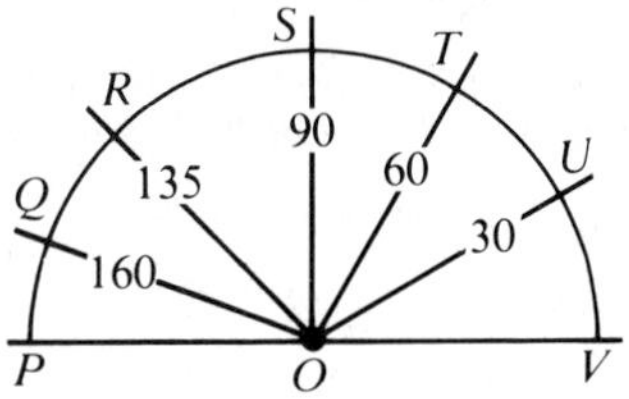

Exs. 9–12

9. Name the vertex of $\angle ROS$.
10. Name a right angle.
11. Name the postulate that justifies the following statement:
 $m\angle ROS + m\angle SOU = m\angle ROU.$
12. Find the measure of $\angle SOU$.

Complete.

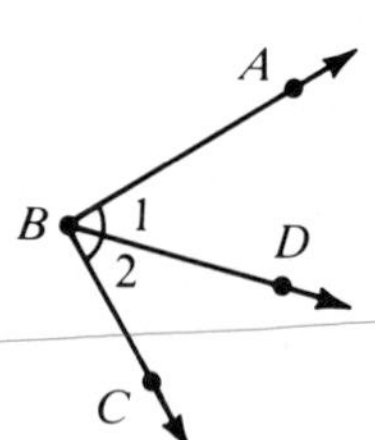

Exs. 13–15

13. If $\overrightarrow{BD}$ bisects $\angle ABC$, then __?__ = __?__.
14. If $\overrightarrow{BD}$ bisects $\angle ABC$ and $m\angle 1 = 45$, then $m\angle 2 =$ __?__.
15. If $\overrightarrow{BD}$ bisects $\angle ABC$, $m\angle 1 = 4x + 8$, and $m\angle 2 = 7x - 1$, then $x =$ __?__.

Classify each statement as true or false.

16. Any three points lie in exactly one plane.
17. A line and a point not on that line lie in more than one plane.
18. The intersection of two lines is exactly one point.
19. The intersection of two planes is exactly one point.
20. The length of $\overline{AB}$ is denoted by AB.
21. If an angle appears to be a 90° angle, then you can conclude it is a right angle.
22. If a point C is between points A and B, then C must lie on $\overrightarrow{AB}$.

Chapter 2

1. Write the hypothesis and the conclusion of the conditional statement:
   If $\angle A$ is a right angle, then $m\angle A = 90$.

2. Write the converse of the following statement:
   If $x < 0$, then $x^2 > 0$.

3. Justify each statement with a property from algebra.
   a. If $2x = 7$, then $7 = 2x$.
   b. If $-3y + x = 12$ and $x = 2y$, then $-3y + 2y = 12$.

4. $\overrightarrow{YK}$ is the bisector of $\angle XYZ$, $\overrightarrow{YD}$ is the bisector of $\angle KYZ$, and $m\angle XYZ = 144$. Find $m\angle KYD$.

5. Name a pair of complementary angles.
6. Name two perpendicular rays.
7. Name a pair of adjacent supplementary angles.
8. $\overrightarrow{PE}$ bisects $\angle DPC$. Find $m\angle EPC$.
9. Complete: $m\angle APD + m\angle BPC = \underline{\ ?\ }$
10. Name a pair of vertical angles.

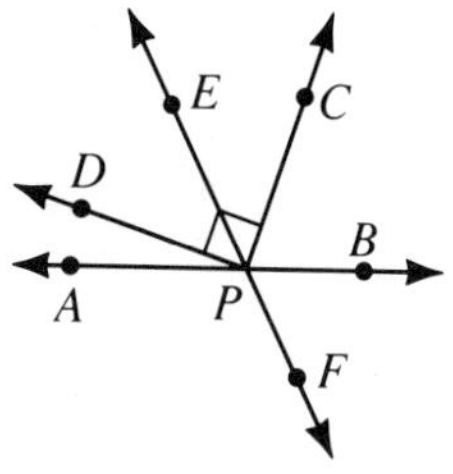

Exs. 5–10

Complete.

11. If M is the midpoint of $\overline{PL}$, then $PM = \underline{\ ?\ }$.
12. If $\angle A$ and $\angle B$ are complementary and $m\angle A = 47$, then $m\angle B = \underline{\ ?\ }$.
13. If $\angle 1$ and $\angle 2$ are vertical angles, then $\angle 1 \underline{\ ?\ } \angle 2$.
14. If two lines form congruent adjacent angles, then the lines are $\underline{\ ?\ }$.
15. Supplements of congruent angles are $\underline{\ ?\ }$.

Classify each statement as true or false.

16. Perpendicular lines form right angles.
17. Adjacent angles must be complementary.
18. Two segments are congruent if and only if their lengths are equal.
19. Theorems that have already been proved can be used as reasons in proofs.

Write a proof in two-column form.

20. Given: $\overline{AB} \perp \overline{BC}$;
    $\angle 1$ and $\angle 2$ are complementary angles.
    Prove: $\angle 1 \cong \angle 3$

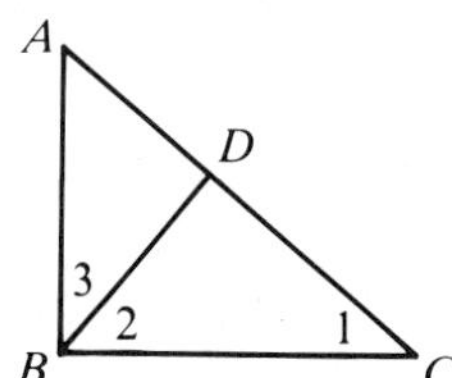

Chapter 3

Complete each statement with the word *always, sometimes,* or *never.*

1. Two lines that do not intersect are __?__ parallel.
2. Two lines parallel to the same plane __?__ intersect.
3. Through a point not on a line, one can __?__ draw a line parallel to the line.
4. An acute triangle is __?__ a right triangle.
5. Two lines parallel to a third line are __?__ parallel to each other.
6. If two lines are cut by a transversal, then corresponding angles are __?__ congruent.
7. Two lines perpendicular to the same line are __?__ parallel.

Find the measures of the numbered angles in the diagrams shown.

8.

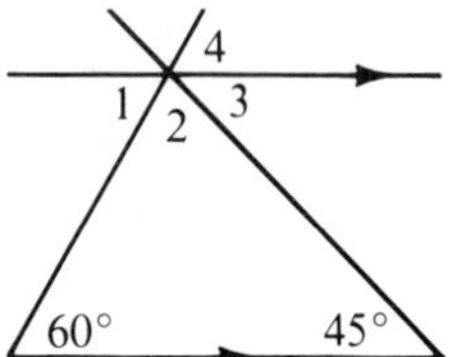

9.

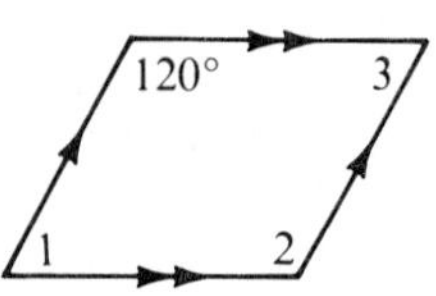

10. Explain why $\overleftrightarrow{AC}$ and $\overleftrightarrow{DE}$ must be parallel.

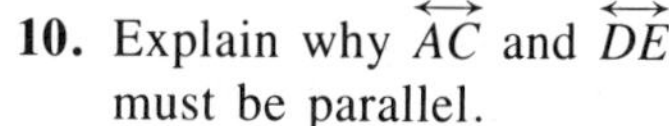

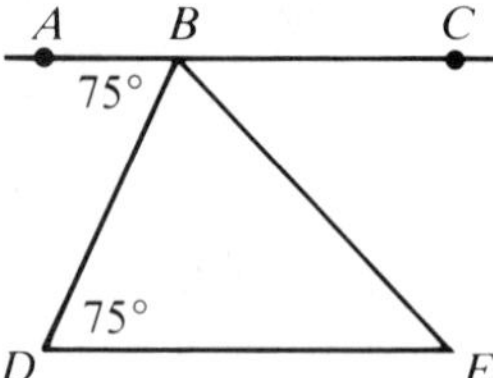

11. Find the value of x.

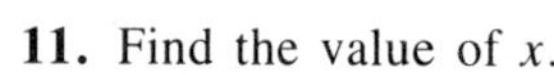

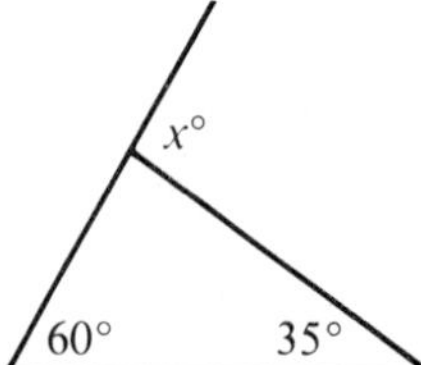

12. A polygon has 7 sides. Find the sum of the measures of the interior angles.

13. A regular polygon has 15 sides. Find the measure of each exterior angle.

14. Use inductive reasoning to predict the next two numbers in each sequence.

a. 1, 6, 10, 13, . . .   **b.** $\frac{1}{4}$, 1, 4, 16, . . .

Write a proof in two-column form.

15. Given: $\overline{BC} \parallel \overline{DE}$; $\angle D \cong \angle B$

Prove: $\overline{AB} \parallel \overline{CD}$

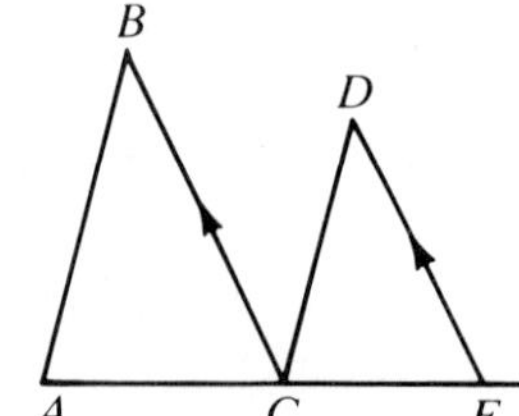

Chapter 4

Complete.

1. If $\triangle TAR \cong \triangle DEW$, then $\angle A \cong$ __?__, $\overline{RT} \cong$ __?__, and $\triangle ART \cong$ __?__.
2. If $\overline{PA} \cong \overline{AT}$, then $\triangle PAT$ is a(n) __?__ triangle.
3. If $\overline{SP} \cong \overline{PT}$, then $\overline{RP}$ is a(n) __?__ of $\triangle RST$.
4. If $m\angle RPS = 90$, then $\overline{RP}$ is a(n) __?__ of $\triangle RST$.
5. If X is equidistant from the sides of $\angle RST$, then $\overrightarrow{SX}$ is the __?__ of $\angle$ __?__.

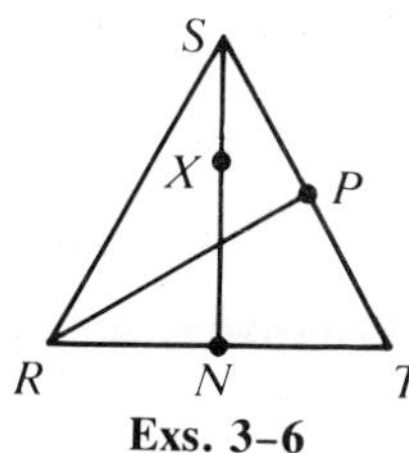

Exs. 3–6

6. If $\overline{SN}$ is a perpendicular bisector of $\overline{RT}$, then X is equidistant from __?__ and __?__.
7. If $m\angle 1 = 50$, find the measures of $\angle 2$ and $\angle 3$.

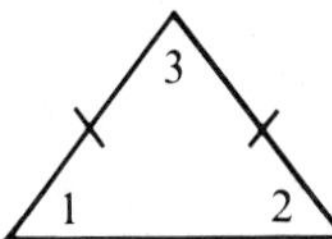

Can the triangles be proved congruent? If so, by which method, SSS, SAS, ASA, AAS, or HL?

8.

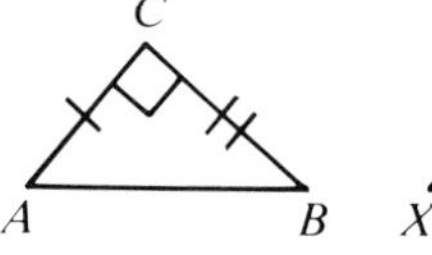

9.

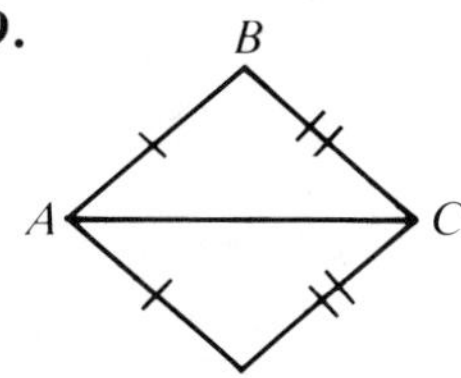

10.

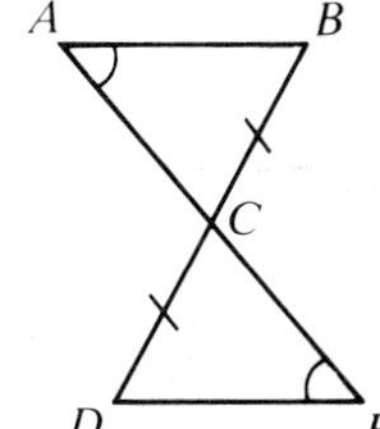

11.

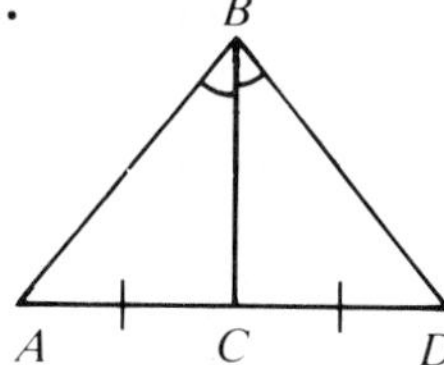

12.

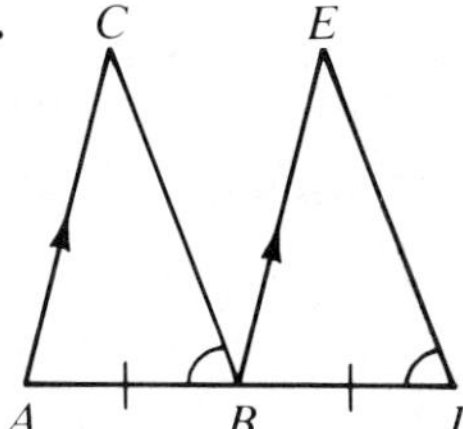

13.

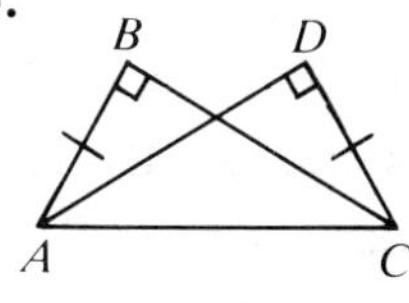

14. Given: H is the midpoint of $\overline{DK}$ and $\overline{PG}$.
    Prove: $\overline{DG} \cong \overline{KP}$

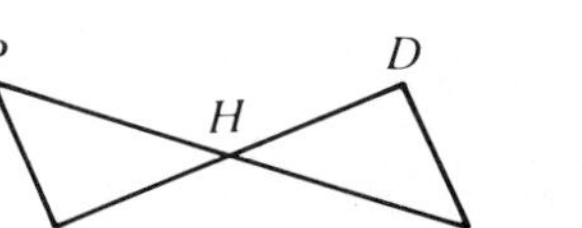

15. Given: $\overline{CS}$ and $\overline{AT}$ are altitudes; $\overline{CS} \cong \overline{AT}$
    Prove: $\overline{AS} \cong \overline{CT}$

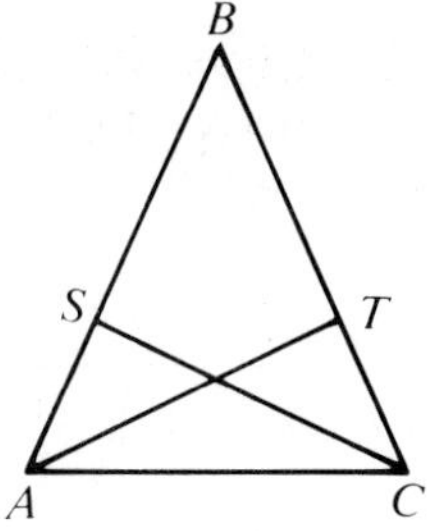

Chapter 5

Complete each statement with the word *always, sometimes,* or *never.*

1. A rectangle is __?__ a square.
2. The diagonals of a square are __?__ perpendicular.
3. A rhombus is __?__ equiangular.
4. If $\overline{AD} \parallel \overline{BC}$ and $\overline{AB} \cong \overline{CD}$, then quadrilateral $ABCD$ is __?__ a parallelogram.
5. A trapezoid __?__ has congruent bases.

Quadrilateral *ABCD* is a parallelogram. Complete.

6. If $DC = 8$ and $AD = 6$, then $AB =$ __?__ and $BC =$ __?__.
7. If $RC = 10$ and $DR = 7$, then $BD =$ __?__ and $AR =$ __?__.
8. If $m\angle CDA = 100$, then $m\angle ABC =$ __?__ and $m\angle DAB =$ __?__.
9. If $m\angle 1 = 30$ and $m\angle 2 = 40$, then $m\angle 3 =$ __?__ and $m\angle 4 =$ __?__.

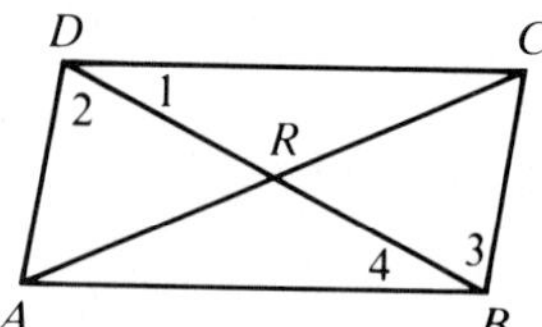

Exs. 6–9

Trapezoid *TRAP* has median $\overline{MN}$.

10. If $m\angle T = 60$ and $m\angle A = 150$, then $m\angle P =$ __?__ and $m\angle R =$ __?__.
11. If $PM = 12$ and $NR = 15$, then $MT =$ __?__ and $AN =$ __?__.
12. If $PA = 3x - 6$, $MN = x + 5$, and $TR = 5x - 2$, then $x =$ __?__.

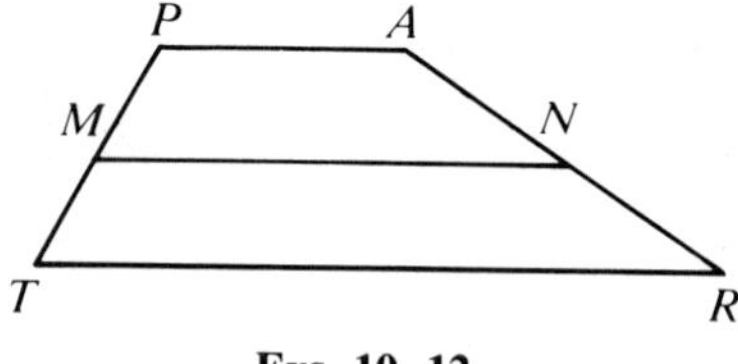

Exs. 10–12

Complete.

13. The segment that joins the midpoints of two sides of a triangle is __?__ to the third side and __?__ as long as the third side.
14. If two lines are parallel, then all points on one line are __?__ from the other line.
15. Given: $\square PQRS$; $\angle 1 \cong \angle 2$
    Prove: $\overline{ST} \cong \overline{QU}$

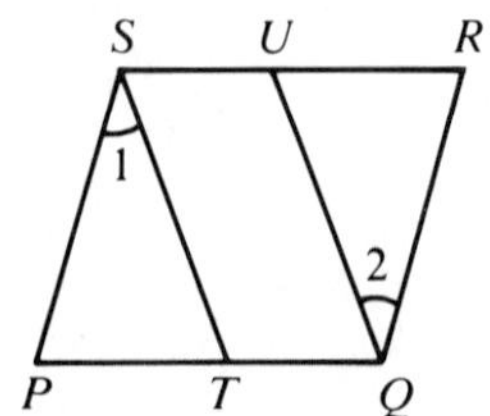

16. Given: $\square CDEF$; S and T are the midpoints of $\overline{EF}$ and $\overline{ED}$.
    Prove: $\overline{SR} \cong \overline{FD}$

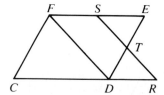

Chapter 6

Classify each statement as true or false.

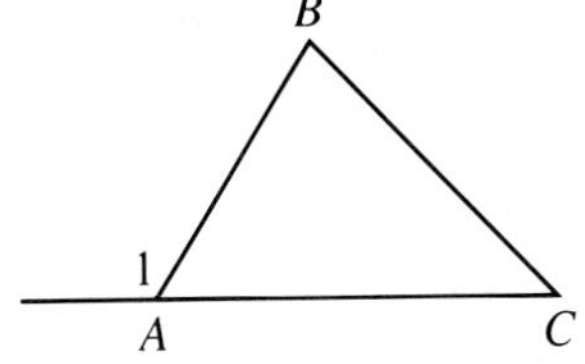

1. $m\angle 1 = m\angle BAC + m\angle B$
2. $m\angle B + m\angle C > m\angle 1$
3. $m\angle 1 < m\angle B$
4. $m\angle 1 > m\angle C$

Consider the true statement: Two skew lines do not intersect.

5. Write the statement in if-then form.
6. Write the converse. Is the converse true or false?
7. Write the inverse. Is the inverse true or false?
8. Write the contrapositive. Is the contrapositive true or false?

Complete each sentence on how to write an indirect proof.

9. Assume temporarily that the conclusion is __?__.
10. Reason logically until you reach a contradiction of a __?__.
11. Point out that the temporary assumption must be __?__, and that the conclusion must then be __?__.
12. To write an indirect proof of "If x is an integer and x^2 is even, then x is even," you begin by writing: Assume temporarily that __?__.

Complete each statement by writing <, =, or >. In Exercises 13 and 15 the diagrams are not drawn to scale.

13. If $BC > AC$, then $m\angle B$ __?__ $m\angle A$.

14. $RS + ST$ __?__ RT

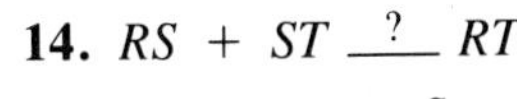

15. If $\overline{PQ} \cong \overline{RQ}$ and $PT > TR$, then $m\angle 1$ __?__ $m\angle 2$.

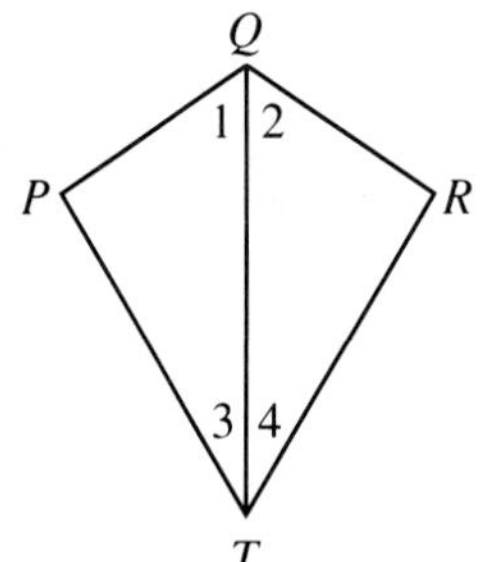

16. Use $m\angle 1$, $m\angle 2$, and $m\angle 3$ to complete: __?__ > __?__ > __?__

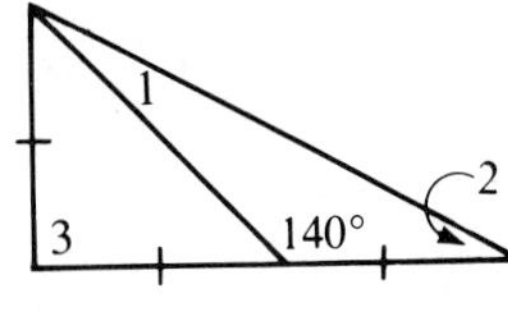

17. The lengths of two sides of a triangle are 16 and 10. The length of the third side must be greater than __?__, but less than __?__.

Chapter 7

1. Express the ratio $\frac{9}{12}$ in simplest form.

2. Find the value of x if: **a.** $\frac{7}{8} = \frac{x}{12}$ **b.** $\frac{9}{x+1} = \frac{6}{x}$

3. If $\triangle ABC \sim \triangle DEF$, then $\angle B \cong$ __?__ and $\frac{AB}{DE} = \frac{?}{DF}$.

4. If $\frac{a}{b} = \frac{4}{9}$, then:

   a. $\frac{a}{4} = \frac{?}{?}$ **b.** $\frac{a+b}{b} = \frac{?}{?}$ **c.** $\frac{3a}{4} = \frac{?}{9}$

5. $ABCD$ and $EFGH$ are squares with $AB = 3$ and $EF = 5$. Find, in simplest form, the ratio of:
   a. the length of a side of $ABCD$ to its perimeter
   b. the perimeter of $ABCD$ to the perimeter of $EFGH$

6. The ratio of the measures of the angles of a triangle is 1:4:7. Find the measure of the largest angle.

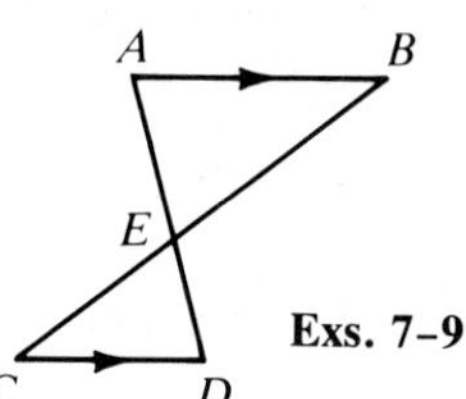

Exs. 7–9

7. What postulate or theorem justifies the statement $\triangle ABE \sim \triangle DCE$?

8. **a.** $\frac{AE}{DE} = \frac{BE}{?}$ **b.** $\frac{AE}{AB} = \frac{DE}{?}$

9. The scale factor $\triangle AEB$ to $\triangle DEC$ is 5:2. If $DE = 7$, then $AE =$ __?__.

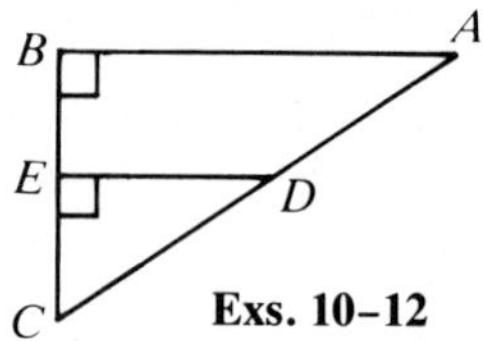

Exs. 10–12

10. What postulate or theorem justifies each statement?
    a. $\overleftrightarrow{AB} \parallel \overleftrightarrow{DE}$ **b.** $\frac{CD}{DA} = \frac{CE}{EB}$

11. If $CD = 4$, $DA = 3$, and $DE = 3$, then $AB =$ __?__.

12. If $CB = 12$, $EB = 8$, and $CD = 6$, then $DA =$ __?__.

Find the value of x.

13. 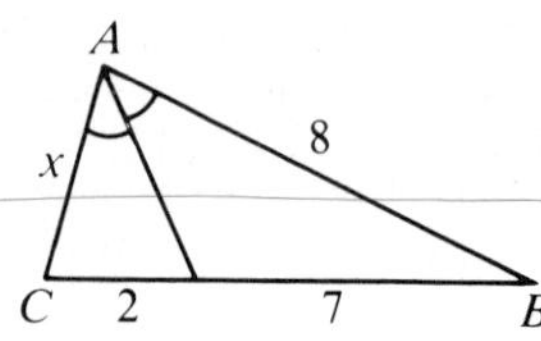

14. 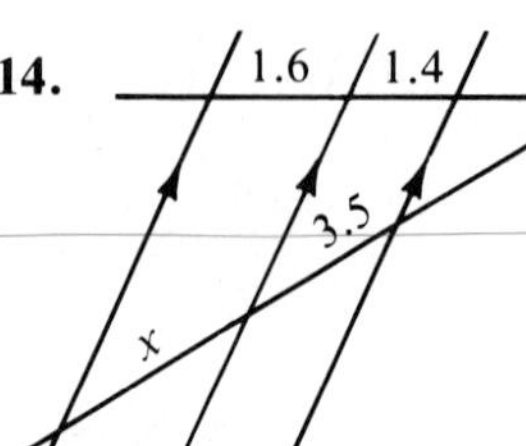

15. Given: $\overline{MN} \perp \overline{NO}$; $\overline{MO} \perp \overline{LN}$
    Prove: $MN \cdot LN = ML \cdot NO$

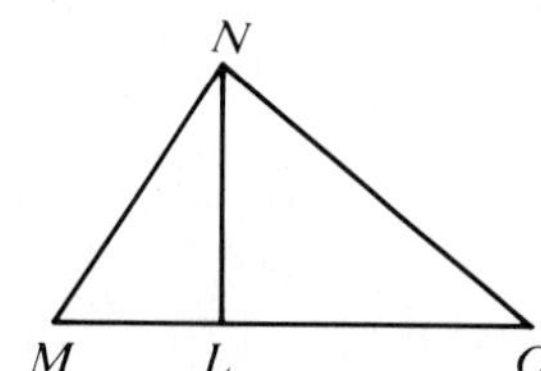

Chapter 8

Find the geometric mean between the numbers.

1. 8 and 18 **2.** 9 and 80

3. Simplify the radical expressions.

a. $\sqrt{75}$ **b.** $\frac{2}{\sqrt{3}}$

In the diagram, $\angle ACB$ is a right angle and $\overline{CD} \perp \overline{AB}$.

4. $\triangle ADC \sim \triangle$ _?_, and $\triangle ADC \sim \triangle$ _?_.

5. CD is the geometric mean between _?_ and _?_.

6. CB is the geometric mean between _?_ and _?_.

7. If $AD = 9$ and $CD = 6$, then $DB =$ _?_.

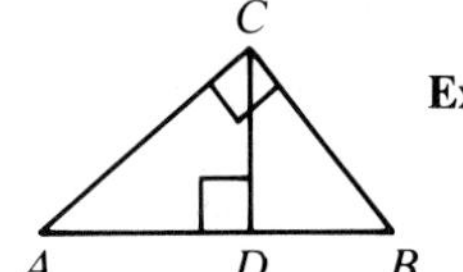

Exs. 4–7

Tell whether a triangle formed with sides having the lengths named is acute, obtuse, or right. If a triangle can't be formed, write *not possible*.

8. 2, 7, 10 **9.** 6, 6, 2 **10.** 5, 12, 13 **11.** 5, 8, 15

Find the value of x.

12.

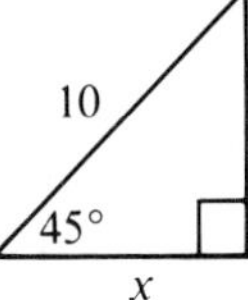

13.

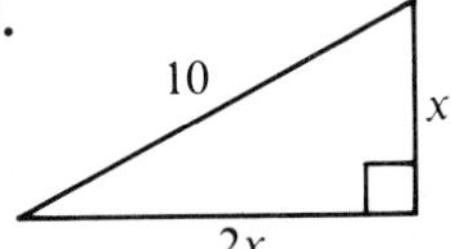

14.

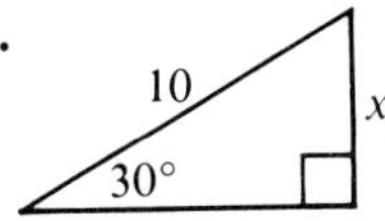

15.

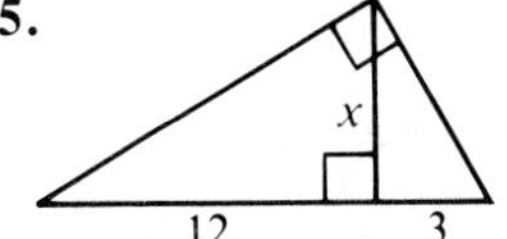

For Exercises 16–23 find angle measures and lengths correct to the nearest integer.

16.

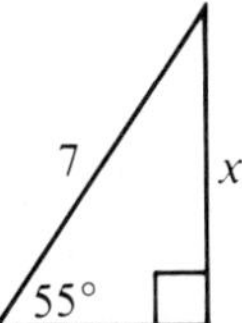

17.

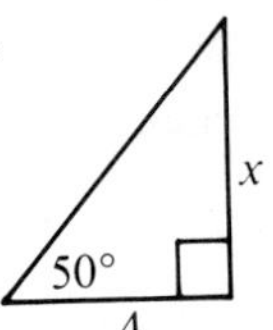

18.

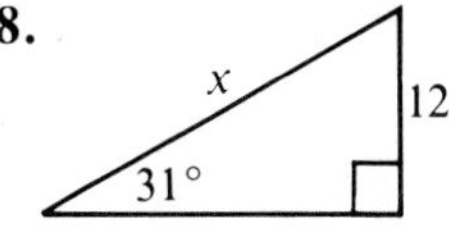

19.

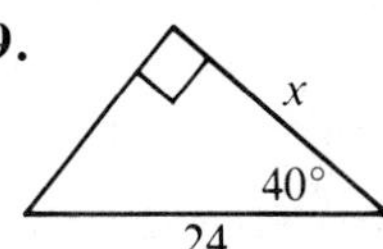

20.

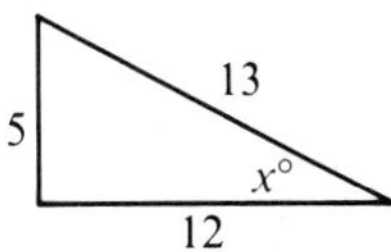

21.

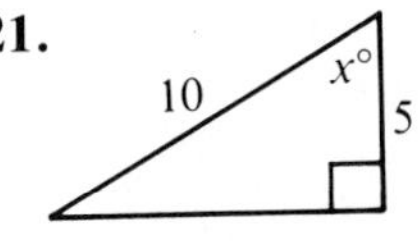

22.

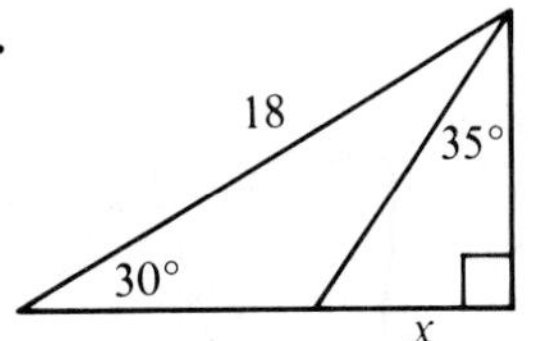

23. A building casts a shadow 40 ft long when the sun's angle of elevation is 58°. Find the height of the building.

Chapter 9

In the diagram, $\overline{DA} \perp \overleftrightarrow{AB}$.

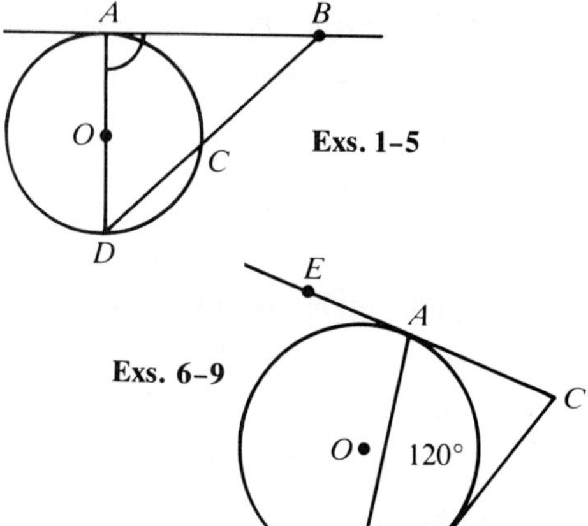

1. Name a chord that is not a diameter.
2. Name a diameter.
3. Name a radius.
4. Name a tangent.
5. Name a secant.

$\overrightarrow{CA}$ and $\overrightarrow{CB}$ are tangent to $\odot O$.

6. $m\angle AOB =$ _?_
7. $m\angle ADB =$ _?_
8. $m\angle ACB =$ _?_
9. $m\angle EAD =$ _?_

10. If $m\angle AEB = 20$, then $m\angle AFB =$ _?_.
11. If $m\widehat{AB} = 95$ and $m\widehat{EF} = 25$, then $m\angle AGB =$ _?_.
12. If $m\widehat{AB} = 70$ and $m\widehat{EF} = 30$, then $m\angle AHB =$ _?_.
13. If $m\widehat{AB} = 85$ and $m\angle EHF = 59$, then $m\widehat{EF} =$ _?_.

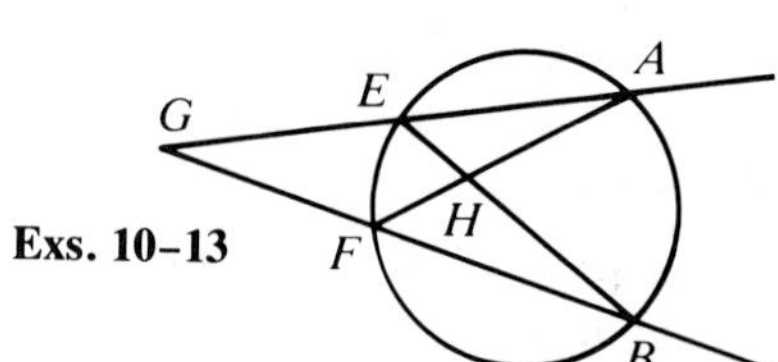

For Exercises 14–17 find the value of x.

14.

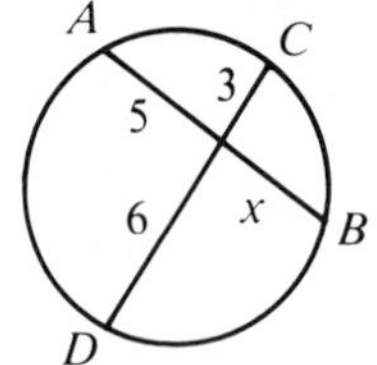

15.

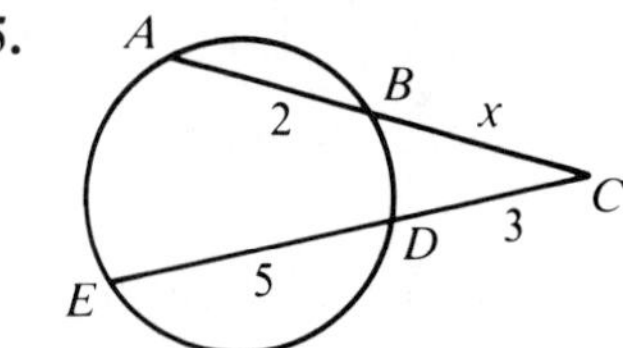

16. $\overline{BA}$ is tangent to the circle.

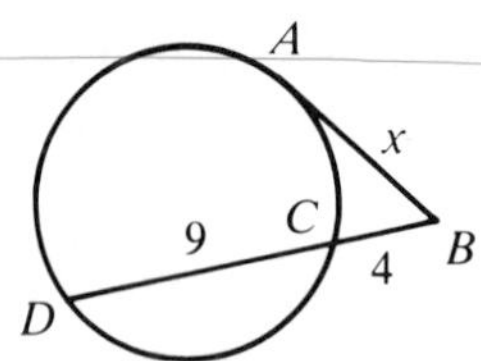

17. $\overline{CA}$ and $\overline{CB}$ are tangent to the circle.

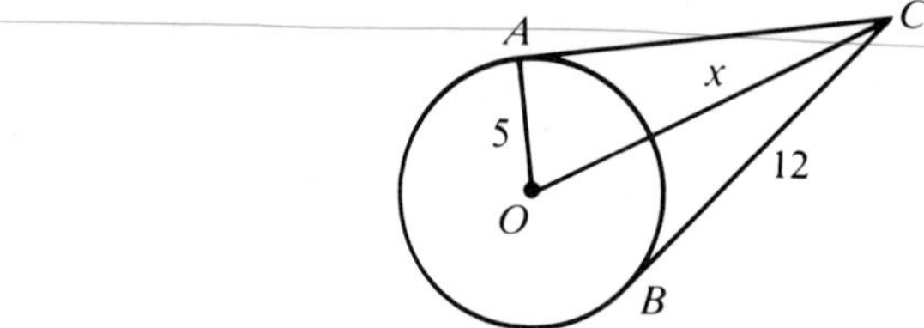

18. Given: $\overline{AD}$ and $\overline{BE}$ are chords intersecting at C.
    Prove: $\triangle BCA \sim \triangle DCE$

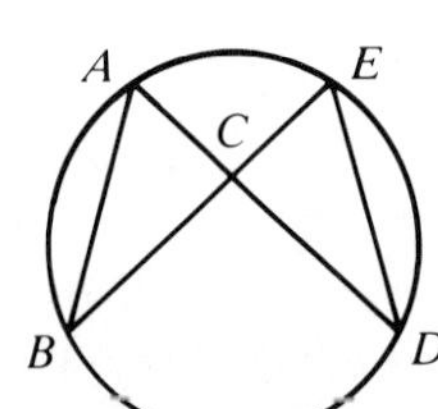

Chapter 10

Begin by drawing segments and angles roughly like those shown.

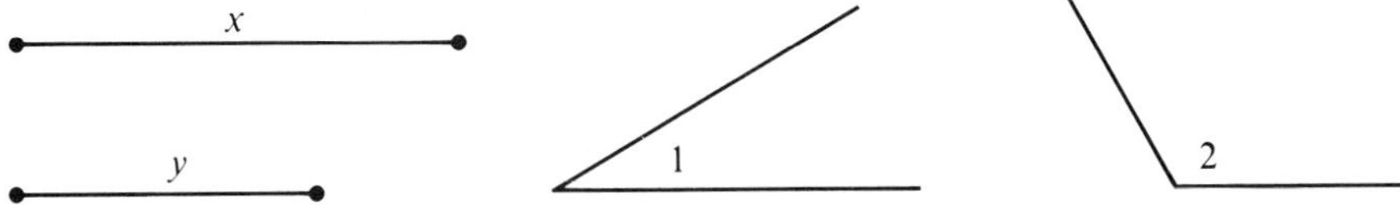

1. Construct an angle A such that $m\angle A = \frac{1}{2}m\angle 2$.
2. Construct a segment of length $x + 3y$.
3. Construct an isosceles right triangle with legs of length x.
4. Construct $\triangle ABC$ with $\angle A \cong \angle 1$, $\angle B \cong \angle 2$, and $AB = x$.
5. Construct $\triangle DEF$ so that $DE = x$, $EF = y$, and $\angle E \cong \angle 1$.
6. Construct an angle having measure 60°.
7. Draw a line l, and select a point A on l. Construct a line perpendicular to l at point A.
8. Refer to Exercise 7, and select a point B not on l. Construct a line parallel to l through point B.
9. Draw a large circle and a point M not on the circle. From point M, construct a tangent to the circle.
10. Draw a large acute triangle. Construct a circle that circumscribes the triangle.
11. What is the locus of points in a plane at a given distance from a given line?
12. What is the locus of points in space at a given distance from a given point?
13. What is the locus of points in a plane equidistant from two intersecting lines?
14. What is the locus of all points in space equidistant from two points?

Chapter 11

Find the area of each figure described.

1. A square with perimeter 28 cm
2. A rectangle with width 7 and diagonal 25
3. A parallelogram with sides 16 and 20 that form a 30° angle
4. A trapezoid with bases 6 and 10 and height 4
5. A rhombus with diagonals 8 and 5
6. A right triangle with legs 25 cm and 6 cm
7. A circle with diameter 18
8. A triangle with sides 5, 5, and 8
9. A circle with circumference 22π cm
10. A regular hexagon with radius 12
11. Sector AOB of $\odot O$ with radius 8 and $m\widehat{AB} = 40$
12. An equilateral triangle with radius $6\sqrt{3}$

Find the area of each shaded region.

13.

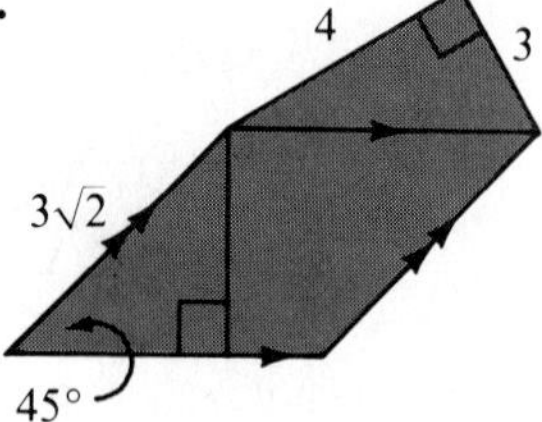

14.

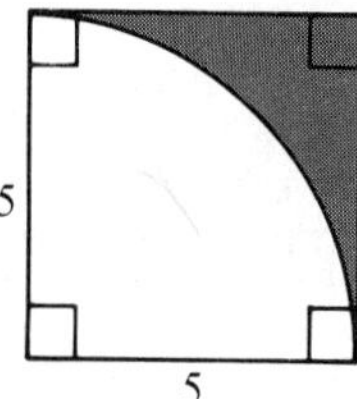

15. In $\odot O$, $m\widehat{AB} = 72$, and the area of sector AOB is 20π. Find the length of $\widehat{AB}$.

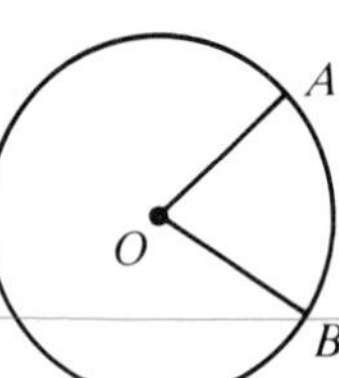

16. Two circles have radii 8 and 11. What is the ratio of the areas?
17. Two corresponding sides of two similar polygons have lengths 3 and 7. The perimeter of the larger polygon is 91 cm. What is the perimeter of the smaller polygon?
18. The dimensions of the small rectangle are one-third those of the large rectangle. A point is picked at random within the large rectangle. What is the probability that it is within the small rectangle?

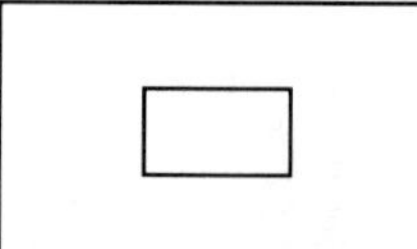

Chapter 12

1. Find the volume of a rectangular solid with length 6 cm, width 5 cm, and height 12 cm.
2. Find the volume and the total area of a cube with edge $5a$.
3. A right triangular prism has height 15 and base edges 5, 12, and 13. Find the volume and the total area.
4. Find the volume of a cone with radius 4 and height 7.
5. Find the lateral area and the total area of the cone in Exercise 4.
6. Find the lateral area of a cylinder with radius 4 cm and height 6 cm.
7. A regular square pyramid has base edge 8 and lateral edge 6. Find the lateral area and the total area.
8. Find the area and the volume of a sphere with radius 6 cm.
9. Two similar regular triangular pyramids have total areas of 20 cm^2 and 80 cm^2. Find the volume of the smaller pyramid if the volume of the larger one is 10 cm^3.
10. The volumes of two spheres have a ratio of 27:64. Find the area of the larger sphere if the area of the smaller is 18.
11. The radii of two similar cylinders are 2 and 5. Find the ratio of their volumes and of their lateral areas.
12. Find the area of a sphere with volume 36π.
13. A cone with radius 5 cm has total area 90π cm^2. Find its height.
14. The volumes of two similar rectangular solids are 125 cm^3 and 64 cm^3. Find the ratio of their base perimeters.

Chapter 13

Given points $A(1, 3)$ and $B(4, -1)$, complete each statement.

1. The y-coordinate of point B is __?__.
2. The distance between A and B equals __?__.
3. The midpoint of $\overline{AB}$ is (__?__, __?__).
4. The slope of $\overleftrightarrow{AB}$ is __?__.
5. An equation of $\overleftrightarrow{AB}$ is __?__.
6. The circle with diameter $\overline{AB}$ has equation __?__.
7. An equation of the line through $G(3, -2)$ and perpendicular to $\overleftrightarrow{AB}$ is __?__.
8. An equation of the line that is parallel to $\overleftrightarrow{AB}$ and has y-intercept -3 is __?__.
9. If B is the midpoint of $\overline{AC}$, then C has coordinates (__?__, __?__).

10. Given points $L(3, 3)$, $M(6, 5)$, and $N(3, 8)$, find **(a)** $\overrightarrow{LM}$, **(b)** $|\overrightarrow{MN}|$, and **(c)** $\overrightarrow{LM} + 3\overrightarrow{MN}$.
11. Draw the graph of the equation $4x - 3y = 9$.
12. Find the point of intersection of the lines $3x + 2y = 17$ and $x - 3y = 2$.
13. Find the radius and the center of the circle with the equation $(x + 1)^2 + (y - 5)^2 = 49$.
14. Parallelogram $ORST$ is shown. Give the missing coordinates of point S without introducing any new letters.

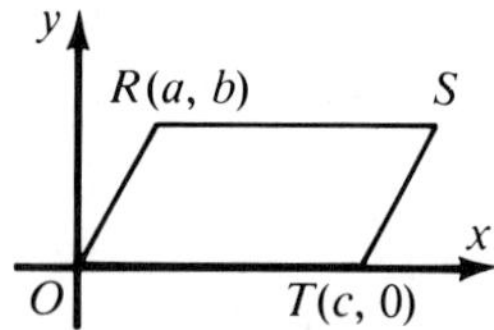

15. Consider points $D(3, 3)$, $E(-1, 2)$, and $F(0, -2)$. Show that $\triangle DEF$ is a right triangle by using slopes.
16. Use coordinate geometry to prove the statement: If a point lies on the perpendicular bisector of a segment, then the point is equidistant from the endpoints of the segment.

Chapter 14

T is the transformation mapping (x, y) to $(x + 1, 3y)$.

1. The image of $(2, -2)$ is $(\underline{\ ?\ }, \underline{\ ?\ })$.
2. The preimage of $(6, -3)$ is $(\underline{\ ?\ }, \underline{\ ?\ })$.
3. Is T an isometry? Give a reason to justify your answer.

Give the coordinates of the image of P under reflection in the lines specified.

4. The x-axis
5. The y-axis
6. The line $y = x$

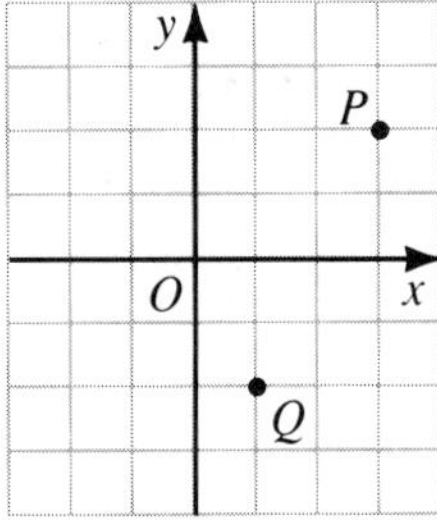

Give the coordinates of the image of point Q under the transformations specified. Use the diagram above.

7. R_y
8. $\mathcal{R}_{O, 90}$
9. $\mathcal{R}_{O, -90}$
10. H_O
11. $D_{O, \frac{1}{2}}$
12. $H_O \circ \mathcal{R}_{O, 90}$
13. $\mathcal{R}_{O, 180} \circ H_O$
14. $R_x \circ H_O$
15. $R_x \circ R_y$
16. $R_x \circ D_{O, 2}$

Give the inverse of each transformation.

17. $D_{O, 3}$
18. $\mathcal{R}_{O, 90}$
19. R_l

T is the translation mapping $(-1, 5)$ to $(2, 1)$. Find the coordinates of the origin under each mapping.

20. T
21. T^{-1}
22. T^2

Hexagon $ABCDEF$ is shown below. Does the hexagon have the symmetry named?

23. point symmetry
24. line symmetry
25. 90° rotational symmetry
26. 180° rotational symmetry

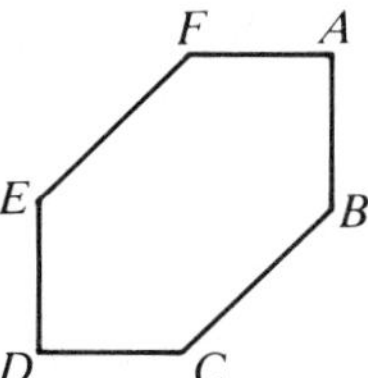

27. How many planes of symmetry does a square pyramid have?

Cumulative Reviews

Chapters 1–3

Complete.

A 1. If Q is between P and R, then $PQ + \underline{\ ?\ } = \underline{\ ?\ }$.

2. Four or more points lying in one plane are said to be $\underline{\ ?\ }$.

3. In $\triangle DEF$, the angle included between $\overline{DF}$ and $\overline{EF}$ is $\angle \underline{\ ?\ }$.

4. If two parallel lines are cut by a transversal, then $\underline{\ ?\ }$ angles are congruent.

5. If $\overrightarrow{BE}$ bisects $\angle ABC$, then $\angle \underline{\ ?\ } \cong \angle \underline{\ ?\ }$.

6. If point D lies between points A and C, then $\angle ADC$ is a(n) $\underline{\ ?\ }$ angle.

7. Two lines parallel to a third line are $\underline{\ ?\ }$.

8. One of two congruent adjacent supplementary angles is called a(n) $\underline{\ ?\ }$ angle.

9. The measure of an $\underline{\ ?\ }$ angle of a triangle equals the sum of the measures of the two remote interior angles.

10. If $m\angle A = 57$, what is the measure of a complement of $\angle A$?

11. On a number line point A has coordinate -4 and point B has coordinate 8.
    a. Find the length of $\overline{AB}$.
    b. Find the coordinate of the midpoint of $\overline{AB}$.

12. If two angles of a triangle have measures 23 and 110, what is the measure of the third angle?

13. Find the sum of the measures of the angles of a polygon with 11 sides.

14. If seven exterior angles of an octagon each have measure 42, what is the measure of the eighth exterior angle?

15. Consider the statement: Any equilateral triangle has congruent sides.
    a. Write the statement in if-then form.
    b. Write the converse of the statement.

Exercises 16 and 17 refer to the diagram.

16. Find the measure of $\angle RXT$. State the theorem that justifies your answer.

17. Name two pairs of supplementary angles.

State the definition or theorem that justifies the statement about the diagram at the right.

18. If $\overline{XS} \perp \overline{RT}$, then $\angle 1 \cong \angle 2$.

19. If $\angle 1 \cong \angle 2$, then $\overline{XS} \perp \overline{RT}$.

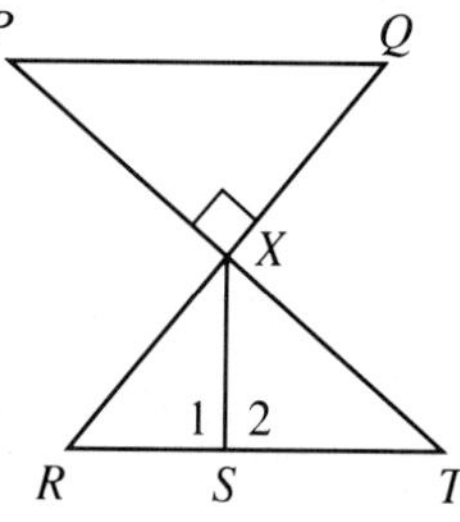

Exs. 16–19

Justify each statement with a property from algebra or a property of congruence.

20. If $\angle A \cong \angle B$ and $\angle B \cong \angle C$, then $\angle A \cong \angle C$.

21. If $RS = XY$ and $ST = YZ$, then $RS + ST = XY + YZ$.

22. If $m\angle 1 + m\angle 2 = m\angle 3$ and $m\angle 2 = m\angle 4$, then $m\angle 1 + m\angle 4 = m\angle 3$.

Find the value of x.

B **23.**

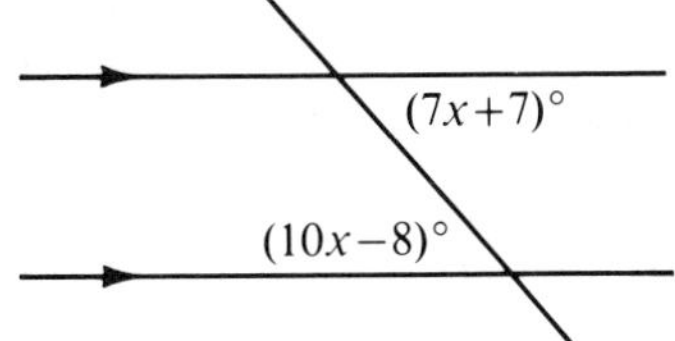

24.

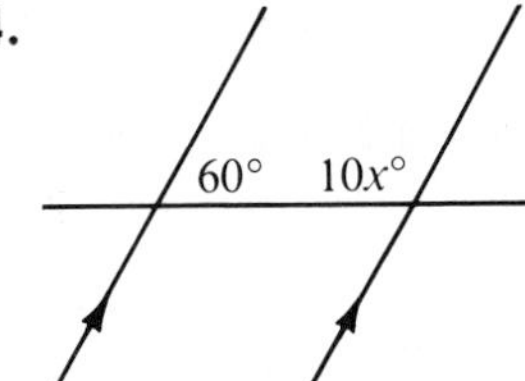

25. A supplement of an angle is four times as large as a complement of the angle. Find the measure of the angle.

26. If each interior angle of a regular polygon has measure 135, find the number of sides of the polygon.

What can you conclude from the given information?

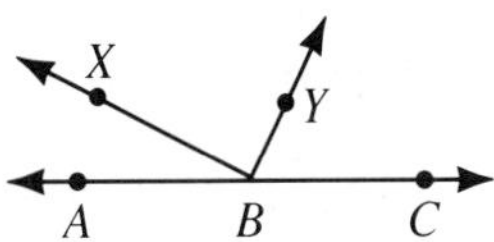

27. Given: $\overrightarrow{BX} \perp \overrightarrow{BY}$

28. Given: $\angle ABX$ and $\angle YBC$ are comp. ∠s.

29. Given: $\angle 1$ and $\angle 2$ are comp. ∠s;
$\angle 1$ and $\angle 4$ are comp. ∠s;
$\angle 2$ and $\angle 3$ are comp. ∠s.

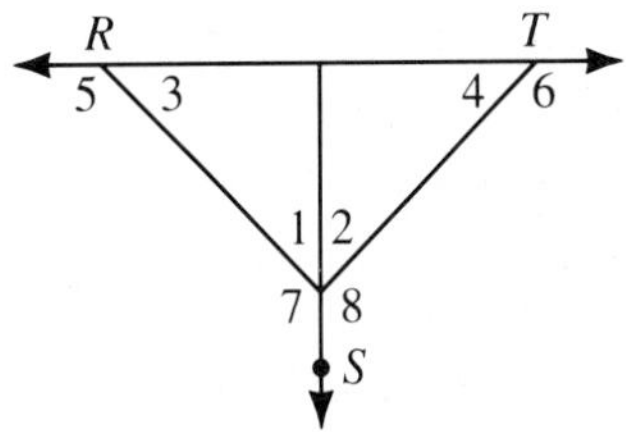

a. $\angle 1 \cong \angle$ _?_

b. $\angle 2 \cong \angle$ _?_

c. $\angle 5 \cong \angle$ _?_

d. $\angle 6 \cong \angle$ _?_

e. If $m\angle 8 = 150$, then $m\angle 7 =$ _?_.

f. If $m\angle 1 = 45$, then $m\angle 6 =$ _?_.

Write a two-column proof.

C **30.** Given: $\angle 2 \cong \angle 3$;
$\angle 4 \cong \angle 5$
Prove: $\angle 1$ is supp. to $\angle 6$.

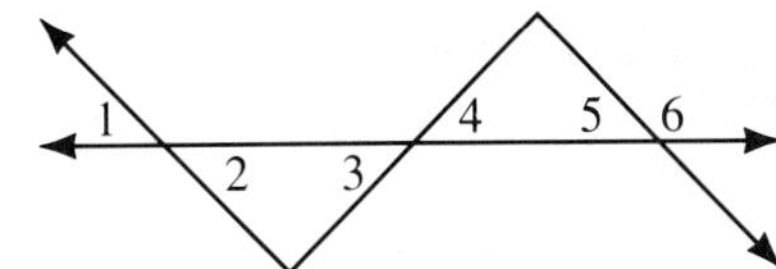

Chapters 4–7

Complete each statement with the word *always*, *sometimes*, or *never*.

A 1. A square is ___?___ a rhombus.

2. The inverse of a true statement is ___?___ true.

3. Similar figures are ___?___ congruent.

4. An acute triangle and an obtuse triangle are ___?___ similar.

5. The base angles of an isosceles trapezoid are ___?___ congruent.

Refer to the diagram at the right. Tell whether each statement must be true.

6. $\overline{PQ} \cong \overline{SR}$ and $\overline{PS} \cong \overline{QR}$

7. $\angle RSP \cong \angle PQR$

8. $\angle SPQ \cong \angle PQR$

9. $\angle SPQ$ and $\angle PQR$ are supp. $\angle$s.

10. $\overline{PR} \perp \overline{SQ}$

11. $\overline{SO} \cong \overline{OQ}$

12. $\overline{PS} \cong \overline{SR}$

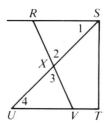

13. Supply the reasons.

Given: $\overline{ST} \perp \overline{RS}$; $\overline{ST} \perp \overline{UT}$; $\overline{RS} \cong \overline{UV}$

Prove: $\overline{RV}$ and $\overline{US}$ bisect each other.

Proof:

1. $\overline{ST} \perp \overline{RS}$; $\overline{ST} \perp \overline{UT}$
2. $\overline{RS} \parallel \overline{UT}$
3. $\angle 1 \cong \angle 4$
4. $\angle 2 \cong \angle 3$
5. $\overline{RS} \cong \overline{UV}$
6. $\triangle SXR \cong \triangle UXV$
7. $\overline{RX} \cong \overline{VX}$; $\overline{SX} \cong \overline{UX}$
8. $\overline{RV}$ and $\overline{US}$ bisect each other.

$\overline{MN}$ is the median of trapezoid *ABCD*.

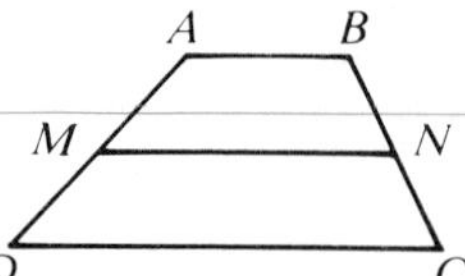

14. If $AM = 3$ and $BN = 2$, then $MD =$ ___?___ and $NC =$ ___?___.

15. If $AB = 10$ and $DC = 14$, then $MN =$ ___?___.

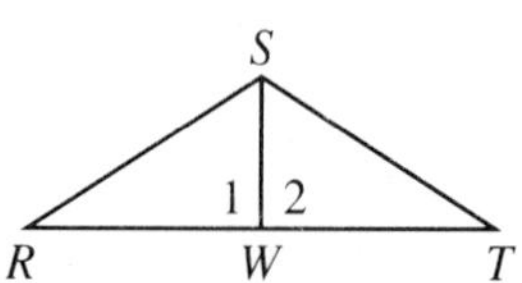

16. If $\overline{SW}$ is an altitude of $\triangle RST$, then $m\angle 2 =$ ___?___.

17. If $\overline{SW}$ is a median of $\triangle RST$, then ___?___ $\cong$ ___?___.

18. If S is equidistant from R and T, then S lies on the ___?___ of $\overline{RT}$.

B 19. The lengths of two sides of a triangle are 10 and 13. The length of the third side must be greater than ___?___, but less than ___?___.

20. If two angles of a triangle are congruent to two angles of another triangle, then the triangles are __?__.

21. The ratio of a side of a square to the perimeter of the square is __?__.

22. The measures of the angles of a quadrilateral are in the ratio 2:4:5:7. Find the measures of the angles.

23. Write (a) the inverse and (b) the contrapositive of the following statement: If $\triangle ABC$ is acute, then $m\angle A \neq 90$. Then classify each as true or false.

24. Write an indirect proof in paragraph form.
Given: $\triangle RST$; $RT > RS$
Prove: $m\angle S \neq m\angle T$

25. Given: $\overleftrightarrow{BE} \parallel \overleftrightarrow{AF} \parallel \overleftrightarrow{CG}$;
$\overrightarrow{AF}$ bisects $\angle BAC$.
Prove: $\dfrac{AB}{AC} = \dfrac{EF}{FG}$

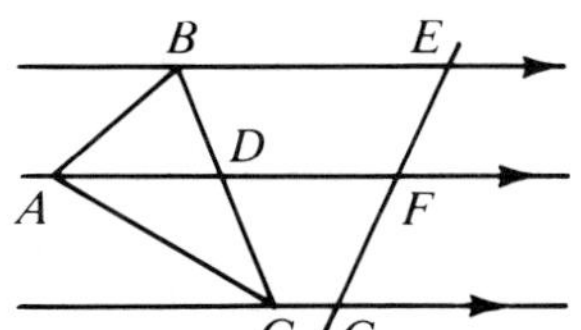

26. Given: $\triangle QRT \cong \triangle VST$; S is the midpoint of $\overline{PV}$.
Prove: Quadrilateral $PQRS$ is a parallelogram.

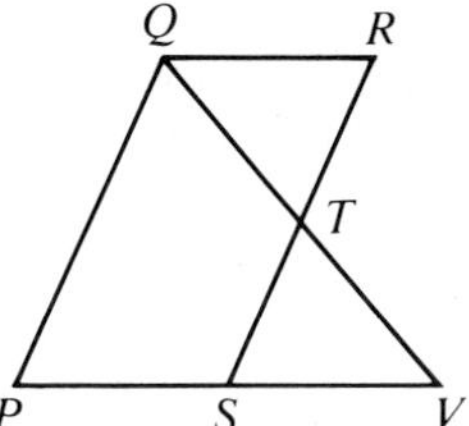

27. Given: $\overline{AD} \cong \overline{AE}$; $\overline{PX} \cong \overline{QX}$; $\overline{PD} \cong \overline{EQ}$
Prove: $\overline{BD} \cong \overline{CE}$

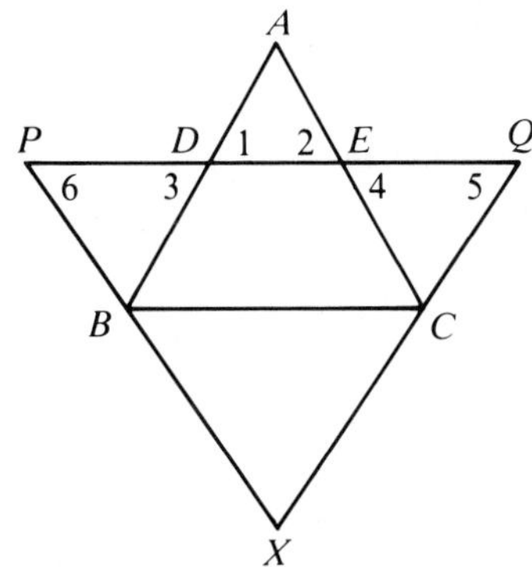

28. Given: $\overline{DC} \cong \overline{FC}$; $\overline{DE} \cong \overline{FE}$; $\overline{DA} \cong \overline{FB}$
Prove: $\triangle DAC \cong \triangle FBC$

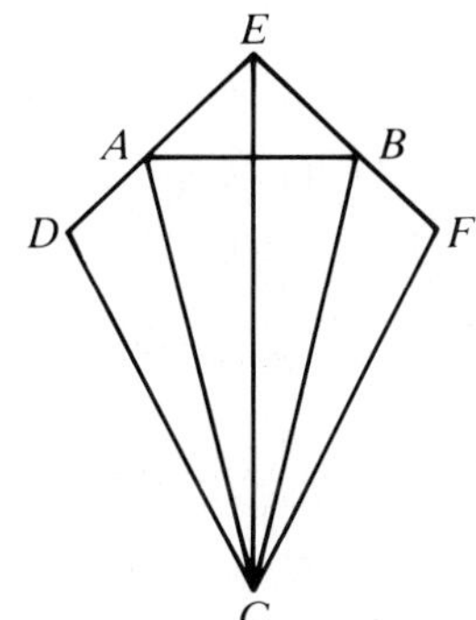

Chapters 8–10

Classify each statement as true or false.

A 1. In a plane, the locus of points 5 units from line l is another line m parallel to l.

2. A radius perpendicular to a chord of a circle bisects the chord.

3. A tangent to a circle and a chord drawn to the point of tangency are perpendicular.

4. If s is the geometric mean between r and t, then $r:s = t:s$.

5. In right $\triangle ABC$, the tangent of $\angle B$ is $\dfrac{\text{leg opposite } \angle B}{\text{leg adjacent to } \angle B}$.

6. When two or more lines intersect in one point, the lines are concurrent.

Find the value of x.

7. x is the geometric mean between 6 and 15.

8. 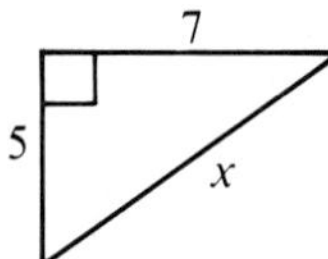

9. 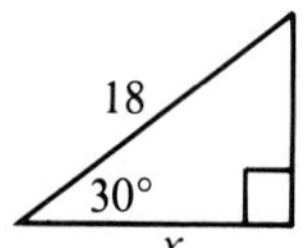

10. 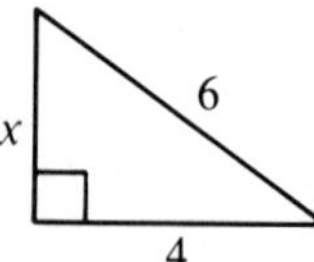

11. 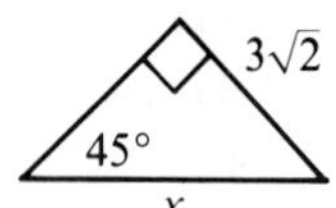

Find the value of x to the nearest tenth or to the nearest degree. Use a calculator or the table on page 311.

12. 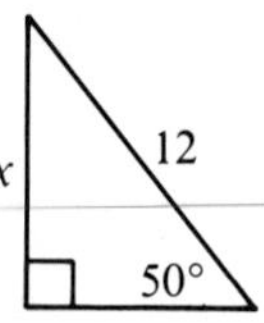

13. 

14. 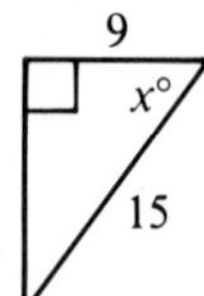

15. 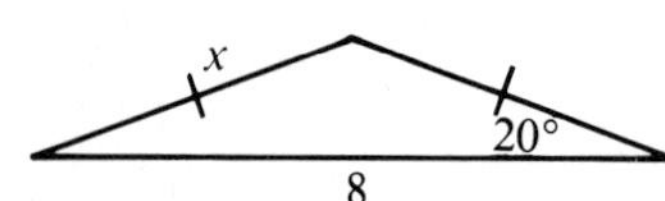

Tell whether a triangle formed with sides having the lengths named is acute, right, or obtuse. If a triangle can't be formed, write *not possible*.

16. 2, 3, 3 **17.** 4, 5, 10 **18.** 5, 12, 13

19. Describe the locus of points in a plane that are equidistant from the sides of $\triangle ABC$.

20. Construct a 30° angle.

21. Draw a large obtuse triangle. Construct a circle that circumscribes the triangle.

22. Supply the reasons.

Given: $\odot O$

Prove: $XZ \cdot VW = VZ \cdot XY$

Proof:

1. $\angle 1 \cong \angle 2$
2. $\angle 3 \cong \angle 4$
3. $\triangle XYZ \sim \triangle VWZ$
4. $\frac{XZ}{VZ} = \frac{XY}{VW}$
5. $XZ \cdot VW = VZ \cdot XY$

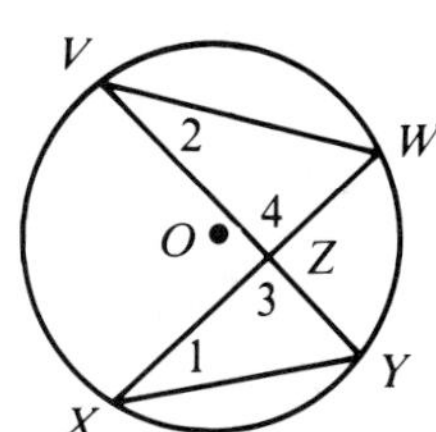

Draw segments roughly like those shown.

B **23.** Construct a right triangle with legs of lengths a and b.

24. Construct a segment of length d such that $ad = bc$.

In Exercises 25–30 $m\widehat{DA} = 80$, $m\widehat{BC} = 20$, and $m\widehat{AB} = 100$. Complete.

25. $m\angle P =$ _?_.

26. $m\angle A + m\angle D =$ _?_.

27. $m\angle DXC =$ _?_.

28. $m\angle DAB =$ _?_.

29. If $BX = 3$ and $AX = 9$, then $XC =$ _?_.

30. If $DC = 15$, then $PC =$ _?_.

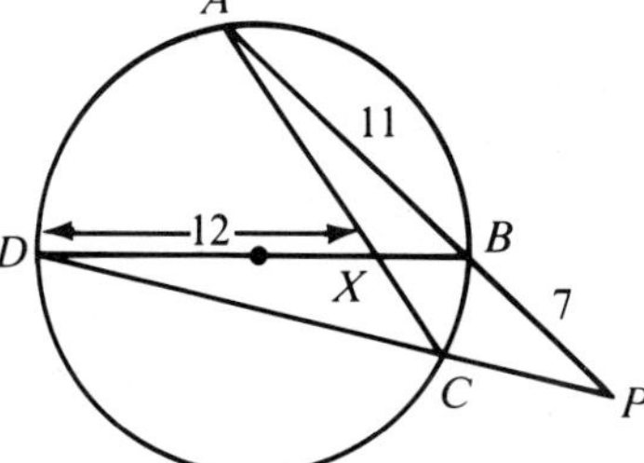

Exs. 25–30

31. If $AC = 15$, find AD.

32. If $AD = 4$, find DB.

33. If $DB = 16$, find BC.

34. If $AB = 26$ and $AD < BD$, find AD.

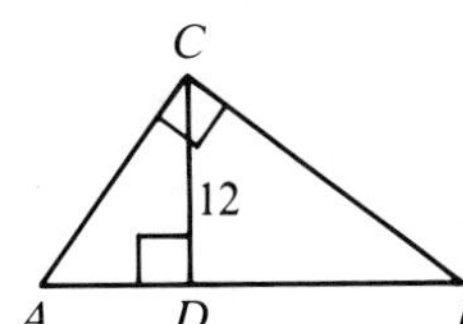

35. Given: $\overrightarrow{AB}$ is tangent to $\odot O$ at B;
$\angle BAO \cong \angle CBD$
Prove: $\triangle BAO \sim \triangle CBD$

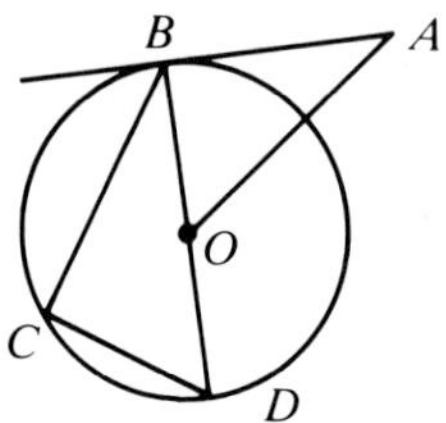

36. Given: $\overline{AB}$ is tangent to $\odot P$ at B;
$\overline{BC}$ is tangent to $\odot O$ at B.
Prove: $\triangle ABD \sim \triangle BCD$

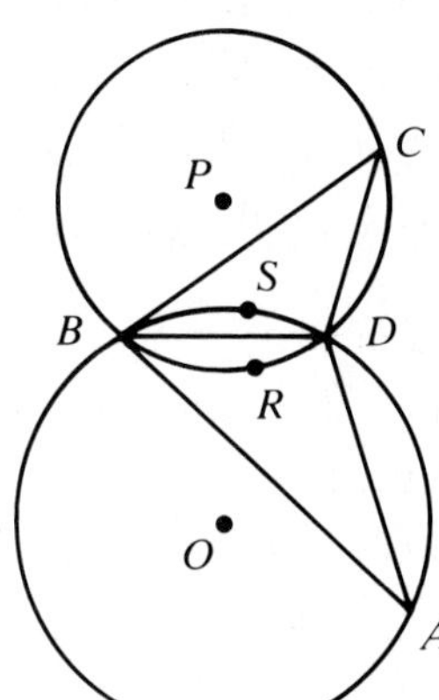

C 37. Given: O is the center of concentric circles;
$\overline{BC}$ is tangent to the smaller $\odot O$ at X.
Prove: $\frac{CX}{CB} = \frac{OX}{AC}$

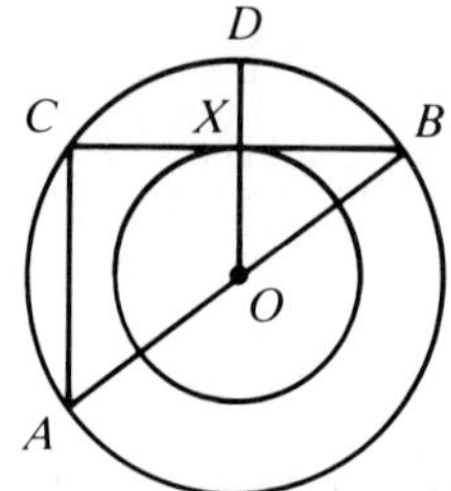

38. Given: $\overleftrightarrow{XY}$ is tangent to $\odot O$ at B;
$\overline{AB} \parallel \overline{CD}$; $\overline{XY} \parallel \overline{AE}$
Prove: $\overline{DC} \cong \overline{DE}$

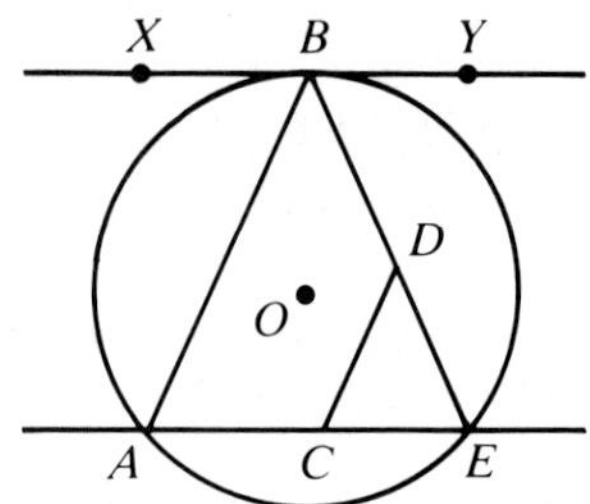

Chapters 11–14

Find each of the following.

A 1. The volume of a sphere with radius 10 cm

2. The center of the circle $x^2 + (y - 2)^2 = 16$

3. The volume of a cylinder with height 10 and diameter 10

4. The volume of a regular square pyramid with base edges 8 and height 3

5. The total area of the pyramid in Exercise 4

6. The lateral area of a cone with slant height 14 and radius 9

7. The slope of the line $3x - 4y = 7$

8. The distance between the points (3, 6) and (−3, 7)

9. The area of a rhombus with diagonals 8 and 18

10. The slope of a line that is perpendicular to $\overline{PQ}$, where P is point (−4, 5) and Q is point (6, 3)

11. The area of a sphere with radius 5

12. An equation of the circle with center (−1, 2) and radius 12

13. The length of $\widehat{AB}$ in $\odot O$ with radius 3 and $m\angle AOB = 45$

Give the coordinates of the image of (4, −1) under the transformation specified.

14. $T:(x, y) \rightarrow (x + 5, y - 3)$

15. R_x

16. H_O

17. $D_{O,3}$

Complete.

B 18. An equation of the line with slope $\frac{5}{2}$ that passes through point (−2, −3) is _?_.

19. The perpendicular bisector of the line segment with endpoints (5, 3) and (−7, 9) has equation _?_.

20. The ratio of the volumes of two similar prisms is $\frac{64}{27}$. The ratio of their lateral areas is _?_.

21. Find the area of a right triangle with hypotenuse 13 and leg 5.

22. Find the intersection point of the lines $3x + 2y = 10$ and $-x + 4y = 6$.

23. If the distance between the points $(a, 3)$ and (0, −1) is 5 units, find all possible values of a.

24. Find the area of a triangle with vertices $A(0, 0)$, $B(4, 0)$, and $C(2, 8)$.

25. Find the height of a trapezoid with bases 9 cm and 15 cm long and area 60 cm^2.

26. A right triangular prism has height 6 and base edges 5, 5, and 8. Find the total area.

27. A regular square pyramid has lateral edge $\sqrt{34}$ and base edge 6. Find the volume.

28. A cone with radius 6 has lateral area 60π. Find the volume.

29. Find the circumference of the circle that can be circumscribed about a square with side 3 cm.

30. The lateral areas of two similar square pyramids are 20 m^2 and 125 m^2, respectively. The volume of the smaller pyramid is 8 m^3. Find the volume of the larger pyramid.

Find the area of each shaded region.

31.
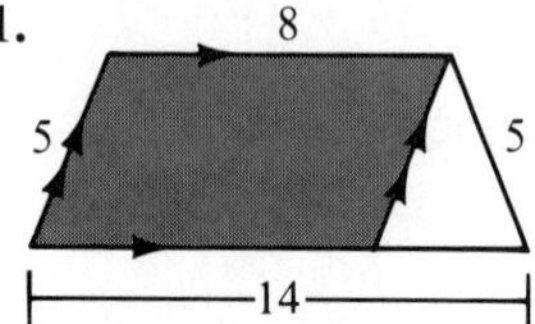

32.
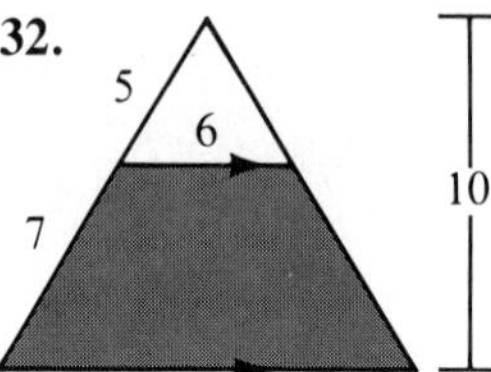

33.
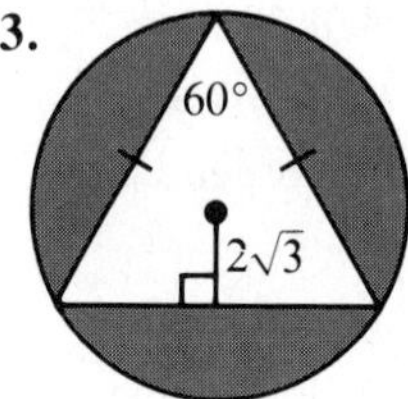

Give the coordinates of the image of (4, −2) under the transformation specified.

34. $R_x \circ H_O$

35. $\mathcal{R}_{O, -90} \circ D_{O, -3}$

36. $D_{O, \frac{1}{2}} \circ R_y$

37. $\mathcal{R}_{O, 90} \circ (R_y \circ R_x)$

C 38. Find the edge of a cube with total area 150 cm^2.

39. Write a coordinate geometry proof.
Given: Trapezoid $ABCD$ with $\overline{DC} \parallel \overline{AB}$; $\overline{CE} \cong \overline{CB}$
Prove: Quadrilateral $AECD$ is a ▱.
(*Hint*: Express d in terms of a and b.)

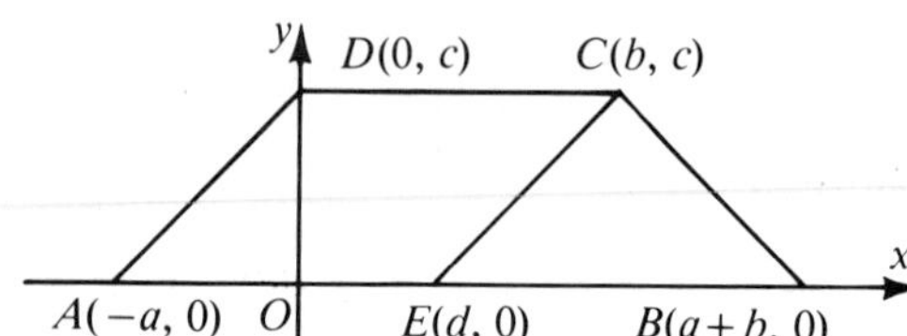

Answers to Chapter Tests

Diagnostic Test

1. Answers may vary; for example, *J*, *P*, and *S*, or *Q*, *R*, and *T*. **2.** *S* **3.** $\overrightarrow{RQ}$ **4.** $\overrightarrow{RQ}$ and $\overrightarrow{RL}$ **5.** *Q* **6.** $\angle PRQ$, $\angle QRP$ **7.** 90 **8. a.** acute **b.** right **c.** obtuse **d.** adjacent **9.** 35 **10.** 8 **11.** 85 **12.** 45 **13.** $m\angle OXH$ **14.** 9 **15.** 1 **16.** *S* **17.** True **18.** True **19.** False **20.** True **21.** positive **22.** line **23.** shape **24.** space **25.** postulate **26.** protractor **27.** interior **28.** line **29.** between **30.** 180 **31.** yes **32.** no **33.** yes **34.** yes **35.** no **36.** no **37.** no **38.** yes **39.** no **40.** yes

Chapter 1

1. Answers may vary; for example, *B*, *G*, and *C*, or *A*, *C*, and *E*. **2.** Answers may vary; for example, *A*, *B*, and *F*, or *D*, *G*, and *E*. **3.** -2 **4.** $\frac{1}{2}$ **5.** *AC* or 5 **6.** $\overrightarrow{BA}$ **7.** $\angle ADB$ and $\angle BDC$, or $\angle ABD$ and $\angle DBC$ **8.** $\overrightarrow{DB}$ and $\overrightarrow{DC}$ **9.** *O* **10.** $\angle POS$, $\angle SOP$, $\angle SOV$ or $\angle VOS$ **11.** Angle Add. Post. **12.** 60 **13.** $m\angle ABD$, $m\angle DBC$, or $m\angle 1$, $m\angle 2$ **14.** 45 **15.** 3 **16.** False **17.** False **18.** True **19.** False **20.** True **21.** False **22.** True

Chapter 2

1. $\angle A$ is a rt. $\angle$; $m\angle A = 90$ **2.** If $x^2 > 0$, then $x < 0$. **3. a.** Symmetric Prop. **b.** Subst. Prop. **4.** 36 **5.** $\angle DPE$ and $\angle CPE$, or $\angle APD$ and $\angle CPB$ **6.** $\overrightarrow{PD}$ and $\overrightarrow{PC}$ **7.** Answers may vary; for example, $\angle APD$ and $\angle DPB$ **8.** 45 **9.** 90 **10.** $\angle APE$ and $\angle FPB$, or $\angle APF$ and $\angle EPB$ **11.** $\frac{1}{2}PL$ or *ML* **12.** 43 **13.** $\cong$ **14.** perpendicular **15.** congruent **16.** True **17.** False **18.** True **19.** True **20.** 1. $\overline{AB} \perp \overline{BC}$ (Given) 2. $\angle 2$, $\angle 3$ are comp. (If the ext. sides of 2 adj. acute ∠s are $\perp$, then the ∠s are comp.) 3. $\angle 1$, $\angle 2$ are comp. (Given) 4. $\angle 1 \cong \angle 3$ (If 2 ∠s are comp. of the same $\angle$, then the 2 ∠s are $\cong$.)

Chapter 3

1. sometimes **2.** sometimes **3.** always **4.** never **5.** always **6.** sometimes **7.** sometimes **8.** $m\angle 1 = 60$, $m\angle 2 = 75$, $m\angle 3 = 45$, $m\angle 4 = 60$ **9.** $m\angle 1 = 60$, $m\angle 2 = 120$, $m\angle 3 = 60$ **10.** If 2 lines are cut by a trans. and alt. int. ∠s are $\cong$, then the lines are $\parallel$. **11.** 95 **12.** 900 **13.** 24 **14. a.** 15, 16 **b.** 64, 256 **15.** 1. $\overline{BC} \parallel \overline{DE}$ (Given) 2. $\angle BCD \cong \angle D$ (If 2 $\parallel$ lines are cut by a trans., then alt. int. ∠s are $\cong$.) 3. $\angle D \cong \angle B$ (Given) 4. $\angle BCD \cong \angle B$ (Trans. Prop.) 5. $\overline{AB} \parallel \overline{CD}$ (If 2 lines are cut by a trans. and alt. int. ∠s are $\cong$, then the lines are $\parallel$.)

Chapter 4

1. $\angle E$; $\overline{WD}$; $\triangle EWD$ **2.** isosceles **3.** median **4.** altitude **5.** bisector, *RST* **6.** *R*; *T* **7.** $m\angle 2 = 50$, $m\angle 3 = 80$ **8.** Yes; SAS **9.** Yes; SSS **10.** Yes; AAS **11.** No **12.** Yes; ASA **13.** Yes; HL or AAS **14.** 1. *H* is the midpt. of $\overline{DK}$ and $\overline{PG}$. (Given) 2. $\overline{DH} \cong \overline{KH}$ and $\overline{GH} \cong \overline{PH}$ (Def. of midpt.) 3. $\angle DHG \cong \angle KHP$ (Vert. ∠s are $\cong$.) 4. $\triangle DHG \cong \triangle KHP$ (SAS) 5. $\overline{DG} \cong \overline{KP}$ (Corr. parts of $\cong$ △s are $\cong$.) **15.** 1. $\overline{CS}$ and $\overline{AT}$ are altitudes. (Given) 2. $\overline{CS} \perp \overline{BA}$; $\overline{AT} \perp \overline{BC}$ (Def. of alt.) 3. $\angle ASC$, $\angle CTA$ are rt. ∠s (Def. of $\perp$ lines) 4. $\triangle ASC$, $\triangle CTA$ are rt. △s (Def. of rt. $\triangle$) 5. $\overline{AC} \cong \overline{AC}$ (Reflex. Prop.) 6. $\overline{CS} \cong \overline{AT}$ (Given) 7. $\triangle ASC \cong \triangle CTA$ (HL) 8. $\overline{AS} \cong \overline{CT}$ (Corr. parts of $\cong$ △s are $\cong$.)

Chapter 5

1. sometimes **2.** always **3.** sometimes **4.** sometimes **5.** never **6.** 8; 6 **7.** 14; 10 **8.** 100; 80 **9.** 40; 30 **10.** 120; 30 **11.** 12; 15 **12.** 3 **13.** parallel, half **14.** equidistant **15.** 1. Quad. *PQRS* is a ▱ (Given) 2. $\overline{SP} \cong \overline{QR}$ (Opp. sides of a ▱ are $\cong$.) 3. $\angle SPT \cong \angle QRU$ (Opp. ∠s of a ▱ are $\cong$.) 4. $\angle 1 \cong \angle 2$ (Given) 5. $\triangle SPT \cong \triangle QRU$ (ASA) 6. $\overline{ST} \cong \overline{QU}$ (Corr. parts of $\cong$ △s are $\cong$.) **16.** 1. ▱*CDEF* (Given) 2. $\overline{FS} \parallel \overline{DR}$ (*CDEF* is a ▱.) 3. *S* and *T* are midpts. of $\overline{EF}$ and $\overline{ED}$. (Given) 4. $\overline{ST} \parallel \overline{FD}$ (The seg. that joins the midpts. of 2 sides of a $\triangle$ is $\parallel$ to the 3rd side.) 5. $\overline{SR} \parallel \overline{FD}$ ($\overline{ST} \parallel \overline{FD}$) 6. *DRSF* is a ▱. (Def. of ▱) 7. $\overline{SR} \cong \overline{FD}$ (Opp. sides of a ▱ are $\cong$.)

Chapter 6

1. False **2.** False **3.** False **4.** True **5.** If two lines are skew, then they do not intersect. **6.** If two lines do not intersect, then they are skew. False **7.** If two lines are not skew, then they intersect. False **8.** If two lines intersect, then they are not skew. True **9.** not true **10.** known fact **11.** false, true **12.** x is odd **13.** $<$ **14.** $>$ **15.** $>$ **16.** $m\angle 3 > m\angle 2 > m\angle 1$ **17.** 6, 26

Chapter 7

1. $\frac{3}{4}$ **2. a.** $10\frac{1}{2}$ **b.** 2 **3.** $\angle E$; AC **4. a.** $\frac{b}{9}$ **b.** $\frac{13}{9}$ **c.** $3b$ **5. a.** $\frac{1}{4}$ **b.** $\frac{3}{5}$ **6.** 105 **7.** AA Similarity Post. **8. a.** CE **b.** DC **9.** $2\frac{4}{5}$ **10. a.** In a plane, 2 lines $\perp$ to the same line are $\parallel$; or, If 2 lines are cut by a trans. and corr. $\angle$s are $\cong$, then the lines are $\parallel$. **b.** $\triangle$ Proportionality Thm. **11.** $5\frac{1}{4}$ **12.** 12 **13.** $2\frac{2}{7}$ **14.** 4 **15.** 1. $\overline{MN} \perp \overline{NO}$; $\overline{MO} \perp \overline{LN}$ (Given) 2. $\angle MNO$ and $\angle MLN$ are rt. $\angle$s. (Def. of $\perp$ lines) 3. $m\angle MNO = 90 = m\angle MLN$ (Def. of rt. $\angle$) 4. $\angle MNO \cong \angle MLN$ (Def. of $\cong$ $\angle$s) 5. $\angle M \cong \angle M$ (Reflex. Prop.) 6. $\triangle MNO \sim \triangle MLN$ (AA $\sim$ Post.) 7. $\frac{MN}{ML} = \frac{NO}{LN}$ (Corr. sides of $\sim$ $\triangle$s are in proportion.) 8. $MN \cdot LN = ML \cdot NO$ (Prop. of proportions)

Chapter 8

1. 12 **2.** $12\sqrt{5}$ **3. a.** $5\sqrt{3}$ **b.** $\frac{2\sqrt{3}}{3}$ **4.** ACB; CDB **5.** AD, DB **6.** AB, DB **7.** 4 **8.** not possible **9.** acute **10.** right **11.** not possible **12.** $5\sqrt{2}$ **13.** $2\sqrt{5}$ **14.** 5 **15.** 6 **16.** 6 **17.** 5 **18.** 23 **19.** 18 **20.** 23 **21.** 60 **22.** 6 **23.** 64 ft

Chapter 9

1. $\overline{DC}$ **2.** $\overline{AD}$ **3.** $\overline{OA}$ or $\overline{OD}$ **4.** $\overleftrightarrow{AB}$ **5.** $\overleftrightarrow{DB}$ **6.** 120 **7.** 60 **8.** 60 **9.** 100 **10.** 20 **11.** 35 **12.** 50 **13.** 33 **14.** $3\frac{3}{5}$ **15.** 4 **16.** $2\sqrt{13}$ **17.** 13 **18.** 1. $\angle BAD \cong \angle DEB$; $\angle ABE \cong \angle EDA$ (If 2 inscr. $\angle$s int. the same arc, the $\angle$s are $\cong$.) 2. $\triangle BCA \sim \triangle DCE$ (AA $\sim$)

Chapter 10

1. Use Const. 2 to construct an $\angle \cong \angle 2$; use Const. 3 to bisect this $\angle$. **2.** Draw a line; use Const. 1 to construct a seg. of length x; from one of its endpts. use Const. 1 to mark off the length y three times. **3.** Draw a line; use Const. 5 to construct a $\perp$ to the line; use Const. 1 to construct the legs of the $\triangle$ along the $\perp$ lines, each with length x; draw the hypotenuse. **4.** Use Const. 1 to construct $\overline{AB}$ with length x; use Const. 2 to construct an $\angle \cong \angle 1$ at A and an $\angle \cong \angle 2$ at B; locate C at their int. **5.** Use Const. 1 to construct $\overline{DE}$ with length x; use Const. 2 to construct an $\angle \cong \angle 1$ at E; use Const. 1 to locate F such that $\overline{EF}$ has length y; draw $\overline{DF}$. **6.** Draw a seg. $\overline{AB}$; using A and B as centers and AB as the radius, swing two arcs; label their int. C; each $\angle$ of $\triangle ABC$ is a 60° $\angle$. **7.** Use Const. 5. **8.** Use Const. 7. **9.** Use Const. 9. **10.** Use Const. 10. **11.** 2 lines ($\parallel$ to and on opp. sides of the given line, at the given dist. from the given line) **12.** a sphere (with center at the given pt. and radius the given distance) **13.** 2 lines (that bisect each of the 4 $\angle$s formed by the given int. lines) **14.** a plane (that is $\perp$ to and bisects the seg. joining the 2 given pts.)

Chapter 11

1. 49 cm^2 **2.** 168 **3.** 160 **4.** 32 **5.** 20 **6.** 75 cm^2 **7.** 81π **8.** 12 **9.** 121π cm^2 **10.** $216\sqrt{3}$ **11.** $\frac{64\pi}{9}$ **12.** $81\sqrt{3}$ **13.** 21 **14.** $25 - \frac{25\pi}{4}$ **15.** 4π **16.** 64:121 **17.** 39 cm **18.** $\frac{1}{9}$ or about 0.11

Chapter 12

1. 360 cm^3 **2.** $V = 125a^3$; T.A. $= 150a^2$ **3.** $V = 450$; T.A. $= 510$ **4.** $\frac{112\pi}{3}$ **5.** L.A. $= 4\pi\sqrt{65}$; T.A. $= 16\pi + 4\pi\sqrt{65}$ **6.** 48π cm^2 **7.** L.A. $= 32\sqrt{5}$; T.A. $= 64 + 32\sqrt{5}$ **8.** $A = 144\pi$ cm^2; $V = 288\pi$ cm^3 **9.** 1.25 cm^3 **10.** 32 **11.** ratio of volumes is 8:125; ratio of lateral areas is 4:25 **12.** 36π **13.** 12 cm **14.** 5:4

Chapter 13

1. -1 **2.** 5 **3.** $\left(\frac{5}{2}, 1\right)$ **4.** $-\frac{4}{3}$ **5.** Form of equation may vary; for example, $y - 3 = -\frac{4}{3}(x - 1)$, $y + 1 = -\frac{4}{3}(x - 4)$, or $y = -\frac{4}{3}x + \frac{13}{3}$ **6.** $\left(x - \frac{5}{2}\right)^2 + (y - 1)^2 = \frac{25}{4}$ **7.** $y + 2 = \frac{3}{4}(x - 3)$ **8.** $y = -\frac{4}{3}x - 3$
9. $(7, -5)$ **10. a.** $(3, 2)$ **b.** $3\sqrt{2}$ **c.** $(-6, 11)$
11. The line passes through $(0, -3)$ and $(3, 1)$. **12.** $(5, 1)$
13. $r = 7$; ctr. $= (-1, 5)$ **14.** $(a + c, b)$ **15.** slope of $\overline{DE} = \frac{3 - 2}{3 - (-1)} = \frac{1}{4}$; slope of $\overline{EF} = \frac{2 - (-2)}{-1 - 0} = -4$; slope of $\overline{DF} = \frac{3 - (-2)}{3 - 0} = \frac{5}{3}$; $\frac{1}{4}(-4) = -1$, so $\overline{DE} \perp \overline{EF}$, $\angle DEF$ is a rt. $\angle$, and $\triangle DEF$ is a rt. $\triangle$. **16.** Given: P is on the $\perp$ bis. of $\overline{XY}$. Prove: $PX = PY$. Let the coordinates of the seg. be $X(-a, 0)$ and $Y(a, 0)$; then the x-coord. of $P = \frac{-a + a}{2} = 0$; let the y-coord. of P be b; $PX = \sqrt{(0 - (-a))^2 + (b - 0)^2} = \sqrt{a^2 + b^2}$; $PY = \sqrt{(0 - a)^2 + (b - 0)^2} = \sqrt{a^2 + b^2}$; $PX = PY$.

Chapter 14

1. $(3, -6)$ **2.** $(5, -1)$ **3.** No; T distorts distances (for example, if $P(2, 1)$ and $Q(2, 3)$, then $P'(3, 3)$ and $Q'(3, 9)$ gives $PQ = 2$, $P'Q' = 6$, $PQ \neq P'Q'$). **4.** $(3, -2)$
5. $(-3, 2)$ **6.** $(2, 3)$ **7.** $(-1, -2)$ **8.** $(2, 1)$
9. $(-2, -1)$ **10.** $(-1, 2)$ **11.** $\left(\frac{1}{2}, -1\right)$ **12.** $(-2, -1)$
13. $(1, -2)$ **14.** $(-1, -2)$ **15.** $(-1, 2)$ **16.** $(2, 4)$
17. $D_{O,\frac{1}{3}}$ **18.** $\mathcal{R}_{O,-90}$ **19.** R_l **20.** $(3, -4)$
21. $(-3, 4)$ **22.** $(6, -8)$ **23.** Yes **24.** Yes
25. No **26.** Yes **27.** 4

Answers to Cumulative Reviews

Chapters 1–3

1. QR; PR **2.** coplanar **3.** F **4.** corresponding or alternate interior **5.** ABE, EBC **6.** straight **7.** parallel **8.** right **9.** exterior **10.** 33 **11. a.** 12 **b.** 2 **12.** 47 **13.** 1620 **14.** 66 **15. a.** If a △ is equilateral, then the sides of the △ are ≅. **b.** If the sides of a △ are ≅, then the △ is equilateral. **16.** 90; Vertical ∠s are ≅. **17.** Answers may vary. ∠1 and ∠2, ∠PXQ and ∠QXT **18.** If 2 lines are ⊥, then they form ≅ adj. ∠s. **19.** If 2 lines form ≅ adj. ∠s, then the lines are ⊥. **20.** Trans. Prop. **21.** Add. Prop. of = **22.** Subst. Prop. **23.** 5 **24.** 12 **25.** 60 **26.** 8 Answers may vary in Exs. 27–28. **27.** $m\angle XBY = 90$, ∠ABX and ∠YBC are complementary. **28.** ∠XBY is a rt. ∠, $\overrightarrow{BX} \perp \overrightarrow{BY}$ **29. a.** 3 **b.** 4 **c.** 7 **d.** 8 **e.** 120 **f.** 135 **30.** 1. ∠1 ≅ ∠2 (Vert. ∠s are ≅.) 2. ∠2 ≅ ∠3 (Given) 3. ∠3 ≅ ∠4 (Vert. ∠s are ≅.) 4. ∠4 ≅ ∠5 (Given) 5. ∠1 ≅ ∠5 or $m\angle 1 = m\angle 5$ (Trans. Prop. used several times) 6. $m\angle 5 + m\angle 6 = 180$ (∠ Add. Post.) 7. $m\angle 1 + m\angle 6 = 180$ (Subst. Prop.) 8. ∠1 is supp. to ∠6. (Def. of supp. ∠s)

Chapters 4–7

1. always **2.** sometimes **3.** sometimes **4.** never **5.** always **6.** Yes **7.** Yes **8.** No **9.** Yes **10.** No **11.** Yes **12.** No **13.** 1. Given 2. In a plane, 2 lines ⊥ to the same line are ∥. 3. If 2 ∥ lines are cut by a trans., then alt. int. ∠s are ≅. 4. Vert. ∠s are ≅. 5. Given 6. AAS Thm. 7. Corr. parts of ≅ △s are ≅. 8. Def. of segment bisector, def. of midpt. **14.** 3; 2 **15.** 12 **16.** 90 **17.** $\overline{RW}$, $\overline{WT}$ **18.** ⊥ bisector **19.** 3; 23 **20.** similar **21.** 1:4 **22.** 40, 80, 100, 140 **23. a.** If △ABC is not acute, then $m\angle A = 90$. (False) **b.** If $m\angle A = 90$, then △ABC is not acute. (True) **24.** Assume temp. that $m\angle S = m\angle T$. Then $\overline{RT} \cong \overline{RS}$ by the converse of the Isos. △ Thm, and $RT = RS$. But this contradicts the given info. that $RT > RS$. The temp. assumption that $m\angle S = m\angle T$ must be false. It follows that $m\angle S \neq m\angle T$. **25.** 1. $\overleftrightarrow{BE} \parallel \overleftrightarrow{AF} \parallel \overleftrightarrow{CG}$ (Given) 2. $\frac{BD}{DC} = \frac{EF}{FG}$ (If 3 ∥ lines int. 2 trans., then they divide the trans. proportionally.) 3. $\overrightarrow{AF}$ bisects ∠BAC. (Given) 4. $\frac{BD}{DC} = \frac{AB}{AC}$ (△ ∠-Bis. Thm.) 5. $\frac{AB}{AC} = \frac{EF}{FG}$ (Subst. Prop.)

26. 1. △QRT ≅ △VST (Given) 2. ∠RQT ≅ ∠SVT (Corr. parts of ≅ △s are ≅.) 3. $\overline{PV} \parallel \overline{QR}$ (If 2 lines are cut by a trans. and alt. int. ∠s are ≅, then the lines are ∥.) 4. $\overline{PS} \parallel \overline{QR}$ ($\overline{PS}$ lies on $\overline{PV}$.) 5. S is the midpt. of $\overline{PV}$. (Given) 6. $\overline{PS} \cong \overline{SV}$ (Def. of midpt.) 7. $\overline{SV} \cong \overline{QR}$ (Corr. parts of ≅ △s are ≅.) 8. $\overline{PS} \cong \overline{QR}$ (Trans. Prop.) 9. Quad. $PQRS$ is a ▱. (If one pair of opp. sides of a quad. are both ≅ and ∥, then the quad. is a ▱.) **27.** 1. $\overline{AD} \cong \overline{AE}$; $\overline{PX} \cong \overline{QX}$ (Given) 2. ∠1 ≅ ∠2; ∠6 ≅ ∠5 (Isosceles △ Thm.) 3. ∠3 ≅ ∠1; ∠2 ≅ ∠4 (Vert. ∠s are ≅.) 4. ∠3 ≅ ∠4 (Trans. Prop.) 5. $\overline{PD} \cong \overline{EQ}$ (Given) 6. △PDB ≅ △QEC (ASA) 7. $\overline{BD} \cong \overline{CE}$ (Corr. parts of ≅ △s are ≅.) **28.** 1. $\overline{DC} \cong \overline{FC}$; $\overline{DE} \cong \overline{FE}$ (Given) 2. $\overline{EC} \cong \overline{EC}$ (Reflex. Prop.) 3. △ECD ≅ △ECF (SSS) 4. ∠D ≅ ∠F (Corr. parts of ≅ △s are ≅.) 5. $\overline{DA} \cong \overline{FB}$ (Given) 6. △DAC ≅ △FBC (SAS)

Chapters 8–10

1. False **2.** True **3.** False **4.** False **5.** True **6.** True **7.** $3\sqrt{10}$ **8.** $\sqrt{74}$ **9.** $9\sqrt{3}$ **10.** $2\sqrt{5}$ **11.** 6 **12.** 9.2 **13.** 30.1 **14.** 53 **15.** 4.3 **16.** acute **17.** not possible **18.** right **19.** 1 point, the intersection of the ∠ bisectors of △ABC (also the center of the circle inscribed in △ABC) **20.** Draw a seg. $\overline{AB}$; using A and B as centers and AB as the radius, draw two arcs; label their int. C; draw $\overline{CA}$; use Const. 3 to bisect ∠CAB; each of the two resulting ∠s is a 30° ∠. **21.** Const. 10 **22.** 1. If 2 inscr. ∠s int. the same arc, then the ∠s are ≅. 2. Vert. ∠s are ≅. 3. AA ~ Post. 4. Corr. sides of ~ △s are in proportion. 5. Prop. of proportions **23.** Use Const. 1 to construct a seg. $\overline{XY}$ with length a; use Const. 5 to construct line l ⊥ to $\overline{XY}$ at X; use Const. 1 to construct a seg. $\overline{XZ}$ with length b along l; draw $\overline{ZY}$. **24.** Use Const. 13. **25.** 30 **26.** 20 **27.** 130 **28.** 90 **29.** 4 **30.** 6 **31.** 9 **32.** 36 **33.** 20 **34.** 8 **35.** 1. $\overrightarrow{AB}$ is tangent to ⊙O at B. (Given) 2. $\overline{AB} \perp \overline{BO}$ (If a line is tangent to a ⊙, then the line is ⊥ to the radius drawn to the pt. of tangency.) 3. $m\angle ABO = 90$ (Def. of ⊥ lines; def. of rt. ∠) 4. $m\angle BCD = 90$ (An ∠ inscribed in a semicircle is a rt. ∠; def. of rt. ∠) 5. $m\angle ABO = m\angle BCD$ (Subst. Prop.) 6. ∠BAO ≅ ∠CBD (Given) 7. △BAO ~ △CBD (AA ~ Post.) **36.** 1. $\overline{AB}$ is tangent to ⊙P at B. $\overline{BC}$ is tangent to ⊙O at B. (Given) 2. In ⊙O, $m\angle CBD = \frac{1}{2} m\widehat{BSD}$;

in $\odot P$, $m\angle ABD = \frac{1}{2}m\widehat{BRD}$. (The meas. of an $\angle$ formed by a chord and a tangent $= \frac{1}{2}$ the meas. of the intercepted arc.) 3. In $\odot O$, $m\angle A = \frac{1}{2}m\widehat{BSD}$; in $\odot P$, $m\angle C = \frac{1}{2}m\widehat{BRD}$. (The meas. of an inscribed $\angle = \frac{1}{2}$ the meas. of its intercepted arc.) 4. $m\angle CBD = m\angle A$; $m\angle ABD = m\angle C$ (Subst. Prop.) 5. $\triangle ABD \sim \triangle BCD$ (AA $\sim$ Post.) **37.** 1. $\odot$ centers at O; $\overline{BC}$ is tangent to the smaller $\odot O$ at X. (Given) 2. $\overline{OX} \perp \overline{BC}$ (If a line is tangent to a $\odot$, then the line is $\perp$ to the radius drawn to the pt. of tangency.) 3. $\overline{OD}$ bisects $\overline{CB}$. (A diam. that is $\perp$ to a chord bisects the chord and its arc.) 4. $CX = \frac{1}{2}CB$ (Def. of seg. bisector; Midpt. Thm.) 5. $AO = \frac{1}{2}AB$ (Def. of diameter of a $\odot$) 6. $OX = \frac{1}{2}AC$ (The seg. that joins the midpts. of 2 sides of a $\triangle$ has length $= \frac{1}{2}$ the length of the 3rd side.) 7. $\frac{CX}{CB} = \frac{1}{2}$; $\frac{OX}{AC} = \frac{1}{2}$ (Div. Prop. of $=$) 8. $\frac{CX}{CB} = \frac{OX}{AC}$ (Subst. Prop.) **38.** 1. $\overleftrightarrow{XY}$ is tangent to $\odot O$ at B; $\overline{XY} \parallel \overline{AE}$ (Given) 2. $\angle XBA \cong \angle BAE$ (If 2 $\parallel$ lines are cut by a trans., then alt. int. $\angle$s are $\cong$.) 3. $m\angle XBA = \frac{1}{2}m\widehat{AB}$ (The meas. of an $\angle$ formed by a chord and a tangent $= \frac{1}{2}$ the meas. of the intercepted arc.) 4. $m\angle E = \frac{1}{2}m\widehat{AB}$ (meas. of inscr. $\angle$ = half meas. of int. arc) 5. $\angle A \cong \angle E$ (Subst. Prop.) 6. $\overline{AB} \parallel \overline{CD}$ (Given) 7. $\angle A \cong \angle DCE$ (If 2 $\parallel$ lines are cut by a trans., then corr. $\angle$s are $\cong$.) 8. $\angle E \cong \angle DCE$ (Trans. Prop.) 9. $\overline{DC} \cong \overline{DE}$ (If 2 $\angle$s of a $\triangle$ are $\cong$, the sides opp. the $\angle$s are $\cong$.)

Chapters 11–14

1. $\frac{4000\pi}{3}$ cm^3 **2.** (0, 2) **3.** 250π **4.** 64 **5.** 144 **6.** 126π **7.** $\frac{3}{4}$ **8.** $\sqrt{37}$ **9.** 72 **10.** 5 **11.** 100π **12.** $(x + 1)^2 + (y - 2)^2 = 144$ **13.** $\frac{3}{4}\pi$ **14.** $(9, -4)$ **15.** (4, 1) **16.** $(-4, 1)$ **17.** $(12, -3)$ **18.** $y + 3 = \frac{5}{2}(x + 2)$ **19.** $y - 6 = 2(x + 1)$ **20.** $\frac{16}{9}$ **21.** 30 **22.** (2, 2) **23.** 3, -3 **24.** 16 **25.** 5 cm **26.** 132 **27.** 48 **28.** 96π **29.** $3\pi\sqrt{2}$ cm **30.** 125 m^3 **31.** 32 **32.** $59\frac{1}{2}$ **33.** $48\pi - 36\sqrt{3}$ **34.** $(-4, -2)$ **35.** (6, 12) **36.** $(-2, -1)$ **37.** $(-2, -4)$ **38.** 5 cm **39.** $\triangle CEB$ is an isosceles $\triangle$ since $\overline{CE} \cong \overline{CB}$. The alt. from vertex $C(b, c)$ intersects base $\overline{EB}$ at $(b, 0)$, which must be the midpt. of $\overline{EB}$. Therefore, $b - d = a + b - b$, so $d = b - a$. $DC = b$ and $AE = d + a = b$, so $\overline{DC} \cong \overline{AE}$. Since $\overline{DC} \parallel \overline{AB}$, $\overline{DC} \parallel \overline{AE}$. $AECD$ is a $\square$ since one pair of opp. sides are both $\cong$ and $\parallel$.

Assignment Guide

No one time schedule or one list of daily assignments is suitable for all classes. In this section you will find separate suggested time schedules and assignment guides for a minimum course, an average course, and a maximum course. They are intended to serve as guides to help you plan the course that best meets the particular needs of your students.

A 160-day time schedule is shown for each course with each schedule divided into (a) two approximately 80-day semesters and (b) three roughly equivalent trimesters. Since each lesson in the book includes more exercises than students would normally be expected to complete within a single assignment, the suggested daily assignments include only a portion of the exercises. Most concepts are covered by several exercises, and thus an assignment of selected exercises still provides sufficient practice to master skills. Some assignments include spiraled exercises that help students review concepts learned in previous sections. Spiraled exercises also provide the opportunity to distribute the more difficult exercises over a period of several days so that daily assignments are not too lengthy. These exercises are denoted by the symbol S. A sample entry from the assignment guide is given below.

2-3 46–47/2–18 even, 19, 20
S 42/12–14
49/Self-Test 1

This is a suggested daily assignment for Lesson 2-3: Exercises 2–18 even, 19, and 20 on pages 46–47, Exercises 12–14 on page 42 (spiraled exercises), and Self-Test 1 on page 49.

Classroom Exercises are not mentioned in any suggested assignment. These exercises continue the development of the concepts introduced in the discussion of each lesson and sometimes prepare students for the Written Exercises. Therefore, we expect that most teachers will use these exercises in class. If it suits your method of teaching, however, the Classroom Exercises may be assigned as homework.

For the minimum and the average courses, the Self-Tests are assigned to enable students to check their own progress. All answers to these tests are at the back of the student book. The assignment of the Self-Tests for the maximum course is optional. You may wish to tell students to work the Self-Tests on their own. The minimum and average courses also are assigned the brief sets of Mixed Review Exercises that appear one to three times in each chapter. Again, the assignment of these exercises for the maximum course is optional. Each Chapter Test in the student book is assigned as a diagnostic aid to prepare students for testing of the concepts presented in the chapter. Whenever you plan to test your students, you may wish to use the alternate chapter tests in this teacher's edition. Page references for these tests are given in the assignment guide in color. Answers for the tests are on pages T35–T37.

The minimum course covers Chapters 1–12 while the average and maximum courses cover Chapters 1–14. Although the average course covers almost all of the lessons in Chapters 13 and 14, the number and type of exercises assigned are less demanding than the assignments for the maximum course. The maximum course covers the last two chapters of the book thoroughly. If you wish to distribute the coordinate and transformational geometry material of Chapters 13 and 14 throughout the course, see pages T56–T57 for a Suggested Integrated Curriculum that uses the *Handbook* found on pages 657–675.

Suggested Schedule for Minimum Course

|←——— Semester 1 ———→|←——— Semester 2 ———→|

Chapter	1	2	3	4	5	6	7	8	9	10	11	12
Days	10	9	13	18	10	10	13	17	16	15	15	14

|←— Trimester 1 —→|←— Trimester 2 —→|←— Trimester 3 —→|

Suggested Schedule for Average Course

|←——— Semester 1 ———→|←——— Semester 2 ———→|

Chapter	1	2	3	4	5	6	7	8	9	10	11	12	13	14
Days	10	8	13	15	9	9	11	15	15	14	13	13	8	7

|←— Trimester 1 —→|←— Trimester 2 —→|←— Trimester 3 —→|

Suggested Schedule for Maximum Course

|←——— Semester 1 ———→|←——— Semester 2 ———→|

Chapter	1	2	3	4	5	6	7	8	9	10	11	12	13	14
Days	6	7	12	13	9	8	9	14	13	14	13	13	15	14

|←— Trimester 1 —→|←— Trimester 2 —→|←— Trimester 3 —→|

Day	Minimum Course	Average Course	Maximum Course
1	**1-1** pp. 3–4/exs. 1–10	**1-1** pp. 3–4/exs. 1–10	**1-1** pp. 3–4/exs. 1–10
2	**1-2** 7–8/1–26	**1-2** 7–9/1–25 odd, 26–28	**1-2** 7–9/2–26 even, 27–36
3	**1-2** 9/27–30 10/Self-Test 1	**1-2** 9/29–35 odd 10/Self-Test 1	**1-3** 15–16/1–45 odd, 46–48
4	**1-3** 15/1–26	**1-3** 15–16/1–39 odd	**1-4** 21–22/10–24 even, 25–36
5	**1-3** 15–16/27–35	**1-3** 16/40–46 even	**1-5** 25–26/1–13 odd, 14–20
6	**1-4** 21/1–25	**1-4** 21/1–25 odd, 26–28	**1-5** 31/Chapter Test Test, page T12
7	**1-4** 21–22/26–34 even **S** 9/31–33	**1-4** 22/29–35 **S** 16/41–47 odd	**2-1** 35/3, 5, 7, 9, 12, 15, 16, 18, 21, 24, 27, 30
8	**1-5** 25/1–12	**1-5** 25/1–15 odd, 16	**2-1** 35/20, 22, 26, 28, 29, 31
9	**1-5** 25/13, 14 29/Self-Test 2	**1-5** 26/17–19 29/Self-Test 2	**2-2** 41–43/6, 8, 10, 11–15
10	**1-5** 31/Chapter Test Test, page T12	**1-5** 31/Chapter Test Test, page T12	**2-3** 46–47/12–22
11	**2-1** 35/2–16 even	**2-1** 35/1–15 odd, 16–22	**2-4** 53–54/19–31 odd, 32–35
12	**2-1** 35/7–25 odd 37/Mixed Review 1–4	**2-1** 35/23–30 37/Mixed Review 1–4	**2-5** 58–60/4–24 even, 25–29
13	**2-2** 41–42/1, 4, 5, 7–10	**2-2** 41–42/1, 4, 6, 7–11	**2-6** 63–65/15–25 odd 68–69/Chapter Test Test, page T13
14	**2-3** 46–47/1–12, 13, 15, 17 **S** 42/11 49/Self-Test 1	**2-3** 46–47/2–18 even, 19, 20 **S** 42/12–14 49/Self-Test 1	**3-1** 76–77/1–41 odd
15	**2-4** 52–53/1–20, 23, 25	**2-4** 52–53/7–25 odd, 28, 29	**3-2** 80–81/1–15 odd
16	**2-5** 58–59/1–13 **S** 53/27, 28, 30, 31 60/Mixed Review 1–7	**2-5** 58–60/2–8 even, 9–25 odd, 26, 28 **S** 54/32–34 60/Mixed Review 1–7	**3-2** 82/17–25 odd
17	**2-6** 63–64/1–17 odd **S** 59/14–17	**2-6** 63–65/2–18 even, 21, 23 65/Self-Test 2	**3-3** 87–88/1–23 odd

Day	Minimum Course	Average Course	Maximum Course
18	**2-6** 63–64/2–20 even 65/Self-Test 2	**2-6** 68–69/Chapter Test Test, page T13	**3-3** 88/24–31
19	**2-6** 68–69/Chapter Test Test, page T13	**3-1** 76–77/1–29 odd	**3-4** 97–98/1, 3, 9, 11, 12, 15, 17–19, 21, 24
20	**3-1** 76/1–20	**3-1** 77/22–42 even	**3-4** 98–99/25, 27–29, 31, 33
21	**3-1** 76–77/21–38	**3-2** 80–81/1–13 odd	**3-5** 104/4, 6–8, 9–13 odd **S** 99/30, 32
22	**3-2** 80–81/1–6, 7, 9, 11, 12	**3-2** 81–82/14–24 even 82/Mixed Review 1–4	**3-5** 105/16, 18, 20, 21, 24–28
23	**3-2** 81–82/13–19 82/Mixed Review 1–4	**3-3** 87/1–19 odd **S** 81–82/15, 17	**3-6** 107–108/3, 5, 8, 12, 15, 16–22 even
24	**3-3** 87/1–17	**3-3** 87–88/12–28 even 89/Self-Test 1	**3-6** 108–109/17–29 odd
25	**3-3** 87–88/18–21 89/Self-Test 1	**3-4** 97–98/1, 2, 6, 9, 12–15, 17, 18, 20	**3-6** 112–113/Chapter Test Test, page T14
26	**3-4** 97/1–13 **S** 88/22, 24	**3-4** 98–99/22–32 even	**4-1** 120–121/1–19 odd, 20–23
27	**3-4** 97–98/14–24, 30	**3-5** 104–105/2, 4–9, 11, 15, 16	**4-2** 124–126/1–17 odd
28	**3-5** 104/1–11	**3-5** 105/18, 19, 22, 25, 26	**4-2** 126–127/18–26 even **S** 121/24
29	**3-5** 104–105/12–20	**3-6** 107–108/1–17 odd	**4-3** 130–131/2, 5, 9, 10, 12 **S** 126–127/23, 25, 27
30	**3-6** 107/1–14	**3-6** 108/18–27 **S** 105/20, 23	**4-3** 131–132/7, 11, 13–15
31	**3-6** 108/15–17 **S** 105/22 110/Self-Test 2	**3-6** 110/Self-Test 2 112–113/Chapter Test Test, page T14	**4-4** 137–138/3, 4, 6, 9, 12, 14, 15, 17, 22 **S** 132/16
32	**3-6** 112–113/Chapter Test Test, page T14	**4-1** 120/1–13	**4-4** 138–139/16, 19, 21, 24, 25, 27, 31
33	**4-1** 120/1–10	**4-1** 120–121/14–22 121/Mixed Review 1, 2	**4-5** 144/3–9, 13 **S** 139/33–34
34	**4-1** 120/11–15, 18, 19 121/Mixed Review 1, 2	**4-2** 124–125/1–15 odd, 16 **S** 121/23, 24	**4-5** 144–145/10–22 even

Day	Minimum Course	Average Course	Maximum Course
35	**4-2** 124–125/1–16	**4-2** 126/17–23 odd	**4-6** 149/3–8 **S** 145/19, 21
36	**4-2** 126/17–19	**4-3** 130–131/1–3, 6	**4-6** 150–151/9–16
37	**4-3** 130/1–4	**4-3** 131/7, 8, 10, 12	**4-7** 156–158/6–13, 15, 19, 23, 25
38	**4-3** 131/5–8	**4-3** 132/13, 14 132–133/Self-Test 1	**4-7** 158/26–28 162–163/Chapter Test Test, page T15
39	**4-3** 131–132/9, 11, 13 132–133/Self-Test 1	**4-4** 137/1–9 odd, 10, 12	**5-1** 169–170/3, 6, 9, 12, 15, 16, 19–27 odd
40	**4-4** 137/1–8	**4-4** 137–139/13, 14, 17, 18–21, 25, 27	**5-1** 170–171/20–38 even
41	**4-4** 137–138/9, 11, 13–15	**4-5** 143–144/1, 3, 5, 8, 10 **S** 139/29, 31	**5-2** 174–176/9, 11, 13, 15, 17, 18, 21, 24
42	**4-4** 138/17, 18, 21	**4-5** 144–145/11, 13, 15, 16, 18, 19, 21 146/Self-Test 2	**5-3** 180–181/5–19 odd **S** 176/25
43	**4-5** 143–144/1–4	**4-6** 148–150/1, 3, 5, 6, 8, 10	**5-3** 181–182/20–25
44	**4-5** 144/5–7, 9–12	**4-6** 150–151/12–16 151/Mixed Review 1–11	**5-4** 187–188/1–10, 14, 17, 28, 30, 34 **S** 181/18
45	**4-5** 144–145/13, 15, 16 146/Self-Test 2	**4-7** 156–157/1–14, 18	**5-4** 188–189/32, 33, 36, 37, 40–42
46	**4-6** 148–149/1–5	**4-7** 159/Self-Test 3 162/Chapter Test, 1–18 Test, page T15	**5-5** 192–193/4, 8, 11, 12, 16, 17, 19, 20, 25
47	**4-6** 149–150/6–9, 11, 12 **S** 145/14 151/Mixed Review 1–11	**5-1** 169/2–16 even	**5-5** 193–194/21–29, 32, 33 199/Chapter Test Test, page T16
48	**4-7** 156/1–9	**5-1** 170/17–31 odd	**6-1** 206–207/1–13 odd
49	**4-7** 156/10–14	**5-2** 174–175/3–5, 9, 10, 12, 15, 19, 22	**6-2** 210–211/3, 5–8, 10, 12, 15
50	**4-7** 159/Self-Test 3 162/Chapter Test, 1–17 odd Test, page T15	**5-3** 180/2–14 even **S** 175/18, 20	**6-2** 211–212/11, 13, 16, 17, 20–22
51	**5-1** 169/1–13	**5-3** 181/16–22 even 182/Self-Test 1	**6-3** 216–217/2, 4–6, 9, 10, 13 **S** 212/18, 19

Day	Minimum Course	Average Course	Maximum Course
52	**5-1** 170/17, 19, 20, 22–26 even	**5-4** 187–188/1–11, 14, 17, 20–23	**6-3** 217/11, 15–20
53	**5-2** 174/1–7, 9	**5-4** 188/24–34 even 189/Mixed Review 1–9	**6-4** 222–223/4, 9, 12, 13, 15–17, 19, 21, 23
54	**5-2** 174–175/8, 10, 11, 14, 19	**5-5** 192–193/1, 3, 6, 7, 9, 11, 12, 14, 16	**6-5** 231–232/1–15 odd **S** 223/20, 22
55	**5-3** 180/1–11	**5-5** 193/15, 17–19, 21–25, 27 195/Self-Test 2 199/Chapter Test Test, p. T16	**6-5** 236–237/Chapter Test Test, page T17
56	**5-3** 180–181/12, 13–21 odd 182/Self-Test 1	**6-1** 206–207/1–9	**7-1** 243–244/5, 10, 14, 15, 20, 25, 28, 30, 33, 35, 36
57	**5-4** 187/1–13 **S** 181/20	**6-2** 210–211/3–9, 11 **S** 207/10	**7-2** 247–248/4, 8, 12, 15, 20, 25, 30, 35, 37, 40 **S** 244/34
58	**5-4** 187–188/14, 17, 18, 20–22 189/Mixed Review 1–9	**6-2** 211–212/12, 13, 15, 16, 18, 19 212/Mixed Review 1–9	**7-3** 250–251/5, 10, 12, 15, 19, 21, 23, 25, 26 **S** 248/41, 43
59	**5-5** 192–193/1–11	**6-3** 216/1–10	**7-3** 251/20, 24, 27, 29, 31–37 odd
60	**5-5** 193/13, 14, 16, 17, 21–23 195/Self-Test 2 199/Chapter Test Test, p. T16	**6-3** 217/11, 13, 15–18 218/Self-Test 1	**7-4** 257–259/5, 9, 14, 15, 20, 21, 24, 27, 29, 31
61	**6-1** 206–207/1–6, 8	**6-4** 222–223/1, 4–7, 10, 13, 16, 19	**7-5** 266–267/5, 10, 14, 16, 17, 20, 22, 23 **S** 260/33
62	**6-2** 210–211/2, 4, 6–8 **S** 206/7	**6-5** 231/1–8 **S** 223/14, 17	**7-6** 272–273/6, 11, 12, 15, 20, 21, 25, 27, 31 **S** 267/18
63	**6-2** 210–211/3, 5, 9, 11, 13 212/Mixed Review 1–9	**6-5** 232/9–13 233/Self-Test 2	**7-6** 273/29, 30, 32, 33 **S** 267/19, 21
64	**6-3** 216/1–8	**6-5** 236–237/Chapter Test Test, page T17	**7-6** 279/Chapter Test Test, page T18
65	**6-3** 216–217/9–13 218/Self-Test 1	**7-1** 243–244/1–35 odd	**8-1** 288–289/3, 8, 11, 15, 16, 19, 22, 25–43 odd
66	**6-4** 222/1–9	**7-2** 247/2–8 even, 11, 12, 16, 20 **S** 244/34, 36	**8-2** 292–293/5, 8, 10, 16, 19, 21–24, 26, 31
67	**6-4** 222–223/10–16	**7-2** 247–248/21–29 odd, 32, 33, 35–37	**8-2** 293–294/27, 28, 33–38

Day	Minimum Course	Average Course	Maximum Course
68	**6-5** 231/1–8 **S** 223/17	**7-3** 250–251/1–12, 13–19 odd, 21–24	**8-3** 297/1–15 odd **S** 294/39
69	**6-5** 232/9–12 233/Self-Test 2	**7-3** 251/25, 26, 29, 31 252/Self-Test 1	**8-3** 297–298/12–20 even, 21, 22
70	**6-5** 236–237/Chapter Test Test, page T17	**7-4** 257–259/5–15 odd, 16–24 even	**8-4** 302/5–7, 11–13, 17–20 **S** 297/19
71	**7-1** 243–244/1–20	**7-5** 266–267/1–15 odd **S** 259/25–31 odd	**8-4** 302–303/21–23, 25, 27–30, 32, 35, 38
72	**7-1** 244/21–31	**7-5** 266–267/14–22 even 268/Mixed Review 1, 2	**8-5** 308/1–15
73	**7-2** 247/1–8, 9–15 odd **S** 244/32, 33	**7-6** 272–273/2–6 even, 7–15 odd, 16–18 **S** 267/22	**8-5** 308–310/16–30 even
74	**7-2** 247/16–20 even, 21–27 odd, 29	**7-6** 273/19, 20, 22, 25, 27, 29, 30 274/Self-Test 2	**8-6** 314–315/2–10 even, 11–14 **S** 309/25, 27
75	**7-3** 250–251/1–12, 14–20 even	**7-6** 279/Chapter Test Test, page T18	**8-6** 315–316/16–26 even
76	**7-3** 251/21–25 252/Self-Test 1	**8-1** 288–289/1–29 odd, 22–36 even, 40, 41	**8-7** 318–319/1–9 **S** 316/21, 25
77	**7-4** 257–258/1–16	**8-2** 292/2–16 even, 17–20 **S** 289/42	**8-7** 319–320/10–14
78	**7-4** 258–259/18–20, 23, 24	**8-2** 292–293/21, 22, 24, 25, 28, 33–36 294/Mixed Review 1–7	**8-7** 324–325/Chapter Test Test, page T19
79	**7-5** 266/1–10 **S** 258/17 268/Mixed Review 1, 2	**8-3** 297/1–7, 10, 12, 13	**9-1** 330–331/1–11 odd, 12–20 even
80	**7-6** 272/1–8 **S** 266/11, 13	**8-3** 297–298/11, 14–20	**9-2** 335–336/5–15 odd
81	**7-6** 272–273/10–20 even	**8-4** 302/2–14 even, 15, 16, 18, 19, 21, 22	**9-2** 337/17–23
82	**7-6** 273/21, 24, 25 274/Self-Test 2	**8-4** 302–303/20, 23, 25, 28, 31 304/Self-Test 1	**9-3** 341–343/2–12 even, 13–21 odd, 22 **S** 337/16
83	**7-6** 279/Chapter Test Test, page T18	**8-5** 308/1–6, 9, 10, 12 **S** 303/30	**9-4** 347/1–7 odd, 8, 10, 14 **S** 342–343/16, 23
84	**8-1** 288/1–21	**8-5** 308–309/7, 8, 11, 13–15, 17, 19, 25	**9-4** 347–348/11, 13, 15, 16–26 even

Day	Minimum Course	Average Course	Maximum Course
85	**8-1** 288–289/22–33	**8-6** 314–315/1–10, 12–14	**9-5** 354–355/1–9 odd, 10, 12, 13 **S** 348/23, 25
86	**8-2** 292/1–8, 9–15 odd	**8-6** 315–316/11, 15–25 odd	**9-5** 355–356/14, 15, 19–21, 25, 27
87	**8-2** 292/10–16 even, 17–22, 24 294/Mixed Review 1–7	**8-7** 318–319/1–6	**9-6** 359–360/2–20 even, 21, 22
88	**8-3** 297/1–9 odd	**8-7** 319/7–12	**9-6** 360/23, 25–30
89	**8-3** 297/2–12 even, 13, 15	**8-7** 320/13, 14 320/Self-Test 2	**9-7** 364–365/1–10, 12, 13
90	**8-4** 302/1–16 **S** 297/14, 16	**8-7** 324–325/Chapter Test Test, page T19	**9-7** 365–366/11, 15–27
91	**8-4** 302/17–24 304/Self-Test 1	**9-1** 330–331/1–12, 13–17 odd	**9-7** 371/Chapter Test Test, page T20
92	**8-5** 308/1–9	**9-1** 330–331/18–20	**10-1** 378/2–10 even, 11–14, 17–21
93	**8-5** 308/10–18	**9-2** 335–336/5–11 **S** 331/14, 16	**10-1** 378–379/22–25
94	**8-6** 314/1–9 **S** 309/19, 20	**9-2** 336–337/12–20 even 337/Mixed Review 1–3	**10-2** 383–384/5–8, 11–16 **S** 379/26
95	**8-6** 315/10–17	**9-3** 341–342/1–9 odd, 10, 12	**10-2** 384/17–25 odd
96	**8-6** 316/18–24 even	**9-3** 342–343/13–21	**10-2** 384–385/18–26 even, 27
97	**8-7** 318–319/1–6 **S** 316/19	**9-4** 347/2–8 even, 9–15 odd	**10-3** 388–389/1–7 odd, 8, 9, 11, 13
98	**8-7** 319/7–12	**9-4** 348/16–22 even 349/Self-Test 1	**10-3** 389/10, 12, 14–16 **S** 385/28
99	**8-7** 320/Self-Test 2 324–325/Chapter Test 1–12	**9-5** 354/1–12	**10-4** 395/5, 6, 9–11, 13, 16–18
100	**8-7** 325/Chapter Test 13–27 Test, page T19	**9-5** 355/13–15, 19–23 357/Mixed Review 1–6	**10-5** 399/3, 6, 7, 9–11 **S** 396/19, 20
101	**9-1** 330–331/1–12	**9-6** 359–360/1–17	**10-5** 399/12, 14–17
102	**9-2** 335–336/1–8	**9-6** 360/18–21, 22–30 even	**10-6** 404–405/1–12, 14–20 even, 21

Day	Minimum Course	Average Course	Maximum Course
103	**9-2** 336/9–12 337/Mixed Review 1–3	**9-7** 364–365/1–11, 13, 15	**10-7** 408–409/5–11 odd, 14, 16–18, 20, 22
104	**9-3** 341–342/1–10	**9-7** 365–366/16–21 367/Self-Test 2	**10-8** 413/6, 9, 12, 15, 16–19
105	**9-3** 342/11–16	**9-7** 371/Chapter Test Test, page T20	**10-8** 418/Chapter Test Test, page T21
106	**9-4** 347/1–9	**10-1** 378/1–9, 11–16	**11-1** 426–427/11, 15, 17–19, 20–28 even, 29–31, 35, 37
107	**9-4** 347/10–15 349/Self-Test 1	**10-1** 378–379/17–21, 23 380/Mixed Review 1–6	**11-2** 431–432/10, 11, 14, 15–21 odd
108	**9-5** 354/1–9	**10-2** 383–384/3, 4, 6, 7, 9–14	**11-2** 432–433/23–27 odd, 28, 30, 32, 33, 35, 37 **S** 427/36
109	**9-5** 354–355/10–13 357/Mixed Review 1–6	**10-2** 384/15, 16, 17–23 odd, 24	**11-3** 436–437/8, 10, 14, 16, 18, 21, 24, 26–28
110	**9-6** 359/1–14 **S** 355/16	**10-3** 388–389/1–7, 10 **S** 384/25	**11-4** 443–444/7, 10, 13–15, 17 **S** 437/25, 30
111	**9-6** 360/15–23	**10-3** 389/8, 11–14 390/Self-Test 1 391/Mixed Review 1–4	**11-4** 444/18–22
112	**9-6** 360/24–30	**10-4** 395/1–3, 5, 6, 10, 11, 13, 15	**11-5** 448–450/7, 11, 12, 15, 17, 18, 20, 22–24, 26
113	**9-7** 364/1–9	**10-5** 399/1, 3, 5–8 **S** 395/16	**11-5** 450/27, 29–34
114	**9-7** 365/10, 11, 13–18	**10-5** 399/9–13, 15 401/Self-Test 2	**11-6** 453–455/12, 14, 16–20, 22–26
115	**9-7** 367/Self-Test 2	**10-6** 404–405/1–19 odd	**11-7** 458–459/5, 8, 10, 13, 15, 17, 19, 20 **S** 455/27, 29
116	**9-7** 371/Chapter Test Test, page T20	**10-7** 407–409/1, 4, 6–10 even, 11–17 odd, 18	**11-7** 459–460/21–31 odd
117	**10-1** 378/1–6	**10-8** 412–413/2, 4–7	**11-8** 463–464/2–10 even, 11–17 odd
118	**10-1** 378/7–9, 11–14, 16 380/Mixed Review 1–6	**10-8** 413/9, 12, 15 414/Self-Test 3	**11-8** 465/Self-Test 2 471/Chapter Test Test, page T22
119	**10-2** 383/1–8 **S** 378/15, 17	**10-8** 418/Chapter Test Test, page T21	**12-1** 478–479/4, 12, 13, 16, 18, 19, 21–24

Day	Minimum Course	Average Course	Maximum Course
120	**10-2** 384/9–18	**11-1** 426/1, 3, 4, 7, 10, 12, 15, 17, 19, 21	**12-1** 479–480/26, 27, 30–34
121	**10-3** 388/1–5	**11-1** 426–427/18, 20, 22–26, 28, 29, 31, 33	**12-2** 485/4, 10, 13, 15, 17
122	**10-3** 389/6, 8 390/Self-Test 1 391/Mixed Review 1–4	**11-2** 431/2, 4, 5, 8, 9–11, 13–15, 17, 19	**12-2** 486/18, 23–25, 27 **S** 480/35, 37
123	**10-4** 395/1–3, 6, 9	**11-2** 432–433/21, 22–26, 28, 30, 32, 34	**12-3** 492–493/7, 8, 12–14, 16, 17 **S** 486/28, 30
124	**10-4** 395/5, 8, 10, 11, 14	**11-3** 436–437/1, 2, 5, 10–12, 15, 17, 21, 24, 26 440/Mixed Review, 1–8	**12-3** 493–494/19–21, 23, 25, 26
125	**10-5** 399/1–4	**11-4** 443/1, 3, 5, 6, 10–13	**12-3** 494–495/27–39
126	**10-5** 399/5–7, 9 401/Self-Test 2	**11-4** 443–444/14, 15, 18–22 444/Self-Test 1	**12-4** 500–501/6–14 even, 16–18
127	**10-6** 404/1–8	**11-5** 448–449/2, 5–13 odd, 16–19, 21	**12-4** 501–502/19–25 odd, 26, 28, 29, 31
128	**10-6** 404/9–15	**11-5** 449–450/23–27, 29, 30, 32	**12-5** 511/4, 7, 9, 11–13 **S** 502/30
129	**10-7** 407–408/1–5 odd	**11-6** 453–455/3, 4, 6, 10, 11, 13, 14, 16–19, 21, 22, 25	**12-5** 511–512/14, 16–22
130	**10-7** 408/6, 7, 9 414/Self-Test 3, 1–6	**11-7** 458–459/1–15 odd **S** 455/26	**12-5** 512–513/23–26, 28
131	**10-7** 418/Chapter Test 1–11 Test, page T21	**11-7** 459–460/16, 18–21, 23, 26, 30	**12-5** 519/Chapter Test Test, page T23
132	**11-1** 426/1–15 odd, 17–19	**11-8** 463/1–7 odd 465/Self-Test 2 471/Chapter Test Test, page T22	**13-1** 526–527/2–40 even
133	**11-1** 426–427/2, 10, 14, 16, 20, 22, 23, 25, 28	**12-1** 478/3, 5, 8, 9, 13, 15, 17, 18	**13-2** 532–533/5, 8, 11, 14–16, 18, 20–24
134	**11-2** 431/1–9	**12-1** 478–480/19, 21–23, 25, 26, 28–30, 32	**13-2** 533–534/25–32
135	**11-2** 431–432/10–13, 18, 19, 22, 23, 25 **S** 427/26, 29	**12-2** 485/1, 4, 5, 7, 10–15	**13-3** 537–538/4, 5, 7, 10–12, 15
136	**11-3** 436/1–7, 9–11	**12-2** 485–486/16–18, 19–25 odd 487/Mixed Review 1–10	**13-3** 538/13, 17, 20, 21, 23

Day	Minimum Course	Average Course	Maximum Course
137	**11-3** 436–437/12–19 440/Mixed Review 1–8	**12-3** 492–493/3, 5–8, 10, 11, 13, 16, 17	**13-4** 541–542/8, 10, 16, 20, 26, 27, 31 **S** 538/19
138	**11-4** 443/1–12	**12-3** 493–494/18–21, 23, 24, 26	**13-5** 545–547/4, 5, 8, 12, 13, 15, 19, 23 **S** 542/29, 32
139	**11-4** 443/13, 15 444/Self-Test 1	**12-3** 494/25, 27 496/Self-Test 1	**13-6** 550–551/3, 5, 8, 13, 16, 19, 24
140	**11-5** 448–449/1–8, 9–15 odd	**12-4** 500/2, 3, 5, 8, 9, 11, 14, 15	**13-6** 551–552/25–37 odd
141	**11-5** 448–449/10–16 even, 17, 18, 21	**12-4** 500–501/16–18, 20–23, 26 507/Mixed Review 1–6	**13-7** 555/2, 6, 9, 15, 17–25 odd
142	**11-6** 453–454/1–13 odd, 15–17	**12-5** 511/1–6, 8, 10–12	**13-7** 555–556/27, 31, 34–36, 38
143	**11-6** 454/18, 19, 21	**12-5** 511–512/14–17, 19, 22, 23	**13-8** 558–559/1–9
144	**11-7** 458/1–8	**12-5** 513/Self-Test 2 519/Chapter Test 1–4	**13-8** 559/10–13 **S** 556/37
145	**11-7** 458–459/9–12, 14, 15, 18	**12-5** 519/Chapter Test 5–16 Test, page T23	**13-9** 562/1, 4, 5, 7–10
146	**11-7** 465/Self-Test 2, 1–8 471/Chapter Test 1–18 Test, page T22	**13-1** 526–527/1–27 odd	**13-9** 562–563/3, 6, 11–14 568/Chapter Test Test, page T24
147	**12-1** 478/1–12	**13-2** 532–533/1–5, 7, 8, 10, 11, 14, 16, 18, 19	**14-1** 574–575/1–7, 10, 11, 14
148	**12-1** 478/13–18	**13-3** 537/2, 3, 5, 7, 9	**14-1** 575–576/12, 13, 15–19, 21
149	**12-1** 478–479/22, 24, 26	**13-4** 541–542/1–17 odd 543/Mixed Review 2–10 even	**14-2** 580–581/4–6, 8–18 even, 21, 23
150	**12-2** 485/2, 4–10	**13-5** 545–546/3, 5–7, 9, 12, 13 547/Self-Test 1	**14-2** 581–582/25–30, 32–35, 38
151	**12-2** 485–486/11–15, 19, 20 487/Mixed Review 1–10	**13-6** 550–551/2, 5, 8, 15, 19, 25	**14-3** 586–587/2, 3, 6, 7, 9, 11, 14, 15, 17, 18, 21
152	**12-3** 492/1, 3, 5–8 **S** 486/18, 21	**13-7** 555/1–25 odd	**14-4** 590/7–21 odd, 24–27
153	**12-3** 493/9–14, 16–19, 21	**13-8** 558–559/1–7 563/Self-Test 2, 1–6	**14-4** 590–592/28, 29, 31, 33, 35–38

Day	Minimum Course	Average Course	Maximum Course
154	**12-3** 493/15, 20 496/Self-Test 1	**14-1** 574–575/1–10	**14-5** 596/2, 4, 7, 8, 10, 14, 16, 17, 19, 22
155	**12-4** 500/1–9	**14-2** 580/1–15	**14-5** 596–597/18, 21, 23–28
156	**12-4** 500/10–17 507/Mixed Review 1–6	**14-3** 586/1–10 **S** 580/17	**14-6** 603–604/2, 4, 6, 7–19 odd
157	**12-5** 511/1–5 **S** 501/18–22	**14-4** 590/1–23 odd 592/Mixed Review 1–7	**14-7** 607–608/1–29 odd **S** 604–605/21–30
158	**12-5** 511/6, 8, 9, 11–13	**14-5** 596/2–8 even, 9–21 odd 597/Self-Test 1	**14-7** 607–608/2–30 even
159	**12-5** 512/15, 16 513/Self-Test 2	**14-6** 603–604/1–4, 6–8, 10, 12	**14-8** 612–613/1–29 odd
160	**12-5** 519/Chapter Test 1–15 odd Test, page T23	**14-7** 607–608/1–13 odd, 14–19 615/Self-Test 2, 1–10	**14-8** 613–614/20–28 even 620/Chapter Test Test, page T25

Guide to Distribution of Constructions

The text teaches constructions all together in Chapter 10. The following guide offers a suggested sequence for those teachers who wish to distribute work with constructions throughout the first nine chapters.

Introduce after	Constructions
Lesson 1-3	1
Lesson 2-5	4, 5, 6
Lesson 4-2	2, 3, 7
Lesson 4-7	10, 11
Lesson 7-6	12, 13
Lesson 8-1	14
Lesson 9-2	8
Lesson 9-5	9

Supplementary Materials Guide

For Use after Lesson	Practice Masters	Tests	Study Guide (Reteaching)	Resource Book: Tests	Resource Book: Practice Exercises	Resource Book: Mixed Review (MR) Prep. for College Entrance Exams (Col) Enrichment (E) Computer (C)	Computer Activities
1-1			pp. 1–2				Activity 1
1-2	Sheet 1	Test 1	pp. 3–4	p. 1	p. 109		
1-3			pp. 5–6				Activity 2
1-4	Sheet 2	Test 2	pp. 7–8	p. 2	p. 110		
1-5	Sheet 3	Test 3	pp. 9–10	p. 3	p. 111		
Chapter 1	Sheet 4	Test 4		pp. 4–5	p. 112	p. 190 (Col) p. 204 (E)	
2-1	Sheet 5		pp. 11–12				Activity 3
2-2	Sheet 6		pp. 13–14				
2-3	Sheet 7	Test 5	pp. 15–16	p. 6	p. 113		
2-4	Sheet 8		pp. 17–18				Activity 4
2-5		Test 6	pp. 19–20	p. 7	p. 114		
2-6	Sheet 9	Test 7	pp. 21–22	p. 8	p. 115		
Chapter 2	Sheet 10	Test 8		pp. 9–10	p. 116	p. 191 (Col) pp. 205–206 (E) p. 237 (C)	
Chapters 1–2	Sheet 11						
3-1			pp. 23–24				
3-2	Sheet 12		pp. 25–28				
3-3	Sheet 13	Test 9	pp. 29–32	p. 11	p. 117		
3-4			pp. 33–34				Activity 5
3-5	Sheet 14	Test 10	pp. 35–36	p. 12	p. 118		Activity 6
3-6	Sheet 15	Test 11	pp. 37–38	p. 13	p. 119		Activities 7, 8
Chapter 3	Sheet 16	Test 12		pp. 14–15	p. 120	p. 192 (Col) pp. 207–209 (E) pp. 238–239 (C)	
Chapters 1–3		Test 13		pp. 16–18	p. 121	pp. 173–174 (MR)	
4-1			pp. 39–40				
4-2	Sheet 17		pp. 41–42				Activity 9
4-3	Sheet 18	Test 14	pp. 43–46	p. 19	p. 122		
4-4			pp. 47–50				
4-5	Sheet 19	Test 15	pp. 51–54	p. 20	p. 123		Activity 10
4-6	Sheet 20		pp. 55–56				
4-7	Sheet 21	Test 16	pp. 57–58	p. 21	p. 124		
Chapter 4	Sheet 22	Test 17		pp. 22–23	p. 125	p. 193 (Col) p. 210 (E) pp. 240–241 (C)	
Chapters 3–4	Sheets 23, 24						

For Use after Lesson	Practice Masters	Tests	Study Guide (Reteaching)	Resource Book			Computer Activities
				Tests	Practice Exercises	Mixed Review (MR) Prep. for College Entrance Exams (Col) Enrichment (E) Computer (C)	
5-1			pp. 59–60				
5-2	Sheet 25		pp. 61–62				
5-3	Sheet 26	Test 18	pp. 63–64	pp. 24–25	p. 126		
5-4	Sheet 27		pp. 65–66				
5-5	Sheet 28	Test 19	pp. 67–68	pp. 26–27	p. 127		Activity 11
Chapter 5	Sheet 29	Test 20		pp. 28–29	p. 128	p. 194 (Col) pp. 211–215 (E) p. 242 (C)	
Chapters 4–5		Test 21		pp. 30–32	p. 129		
Chapters 1–5						pp. 175–176 (MR)	
6-1			pp. 69–70				
6-2	Sheet 30		pp. 71–72				
6-3	Sheet 31	Test 22	pp. 73–74	p. 33	p. 130		
6-4	Sheet 32		pp. 75–76				Activity 12
6-5	Sheet 33	Test 23	pp. 77–78	p. 34	p. 131		
Chapter 6	Sheet 34	Test 24		pp. 35–36	p. 132	p. 195 (Col) p. 216 (E)	
Chapters 5–6	Sheets 35, 36						
7-1			pp. 79–80				Activity 13
7-2	Sheet 37		pp. 81–82				
7-3	Sheet 38	Test 25	pp. 83–84	p. 37	p. 133		
7-4	Sheet 39		pp. 85–86				Activity 14
7-5	Sheet 40	Test 26	pp. 87–88	p. 38	p. 134		
7-6	Sheet 41	Test 27	pp. 89–90	p. 39	p. 135		
Chapter 7	Sheet 42	Test 28		pp. 40–41	p. 136	p. 196 (Col) p. 217 (E) p. 243 (C)	
Chapters 6–7		Test 29		pp. 42–44	p. 137		
Chapters 1–7		Test 30		pp. 45–49	pp. 138–139	pp. 177–179 (MR)	
8-1			pp. 91–92				Activity 15
8-2	Sheet 43	Test 31	pp. 93–94	p. 50	p. 140		Activity 16
8-3			pp. 95–96				
8-4	Sheet 44	Test 32	pp. 97–98	p. 51	p. 141		
8-5			pp. 99–100, 105				
8-6	Sheet 45		pp. 101–102, 106				Activity 17
8-7	Sheet 46	Test 33	pp. 103–104	p. 52	p. 142		Activity 18
Chapter 8	Sheet 47	Test 34		pp. 53–54	p. 143	p. 197 (Col) pp. 218–219 (E) pp. 244–249 (C)	
Chapters 7–8	Sheets 48, 49						

For Use after Lesson	Practice Masters	Tests	Study Guide (Reteaching)	Resource Book: Tests	Resource Book: Practice Exercises	Resource Book: Mixed Review (MR) Prep. for College Entrance Exams (Col) Enrichment (E) Computer (C)	Computer Activities
9-1			pp. 107–108				
9-2	Sheet 50		pp. 109–110				
9-3			pp. 111–112				
9-4	Sheet 51	Test 35	pp. 113–114	pp. 55–56	p. 144		Activity 19
9-5	Sheet 52		pp. 115–116				
9-6	Sheet 53		pp. 117–118				
9-7	Sheet 54	Test 36	pp. 119–120	pp. 57–58	p. 145		Activity 20
Chapter 9	Sheet 55	Test 37		pp. 59–60	p. 146	p. 198 (Col) pp. 220–221 (E) pp. 250–253 (C)	
10-1			pp. 121–122				
10-2	Sheet 56		pp. 123–124				
10-3	Sheet 57	Test 38	pp. 125–126	pp. 61–62	p. 147		
10-4			pp. 127–128				
10-5	Sheet 58	Test 39	pp. 129–130	pp. 63–64	p. 148		
10-6			pp. 131–132				Activity 21
10-7	Sheet 59		pp. 133–134				
10-8	Sheet 60	Test 40	pp. 135–136	p. 65	p. 149		
Chapter 10	Sheet 61	Test 41		pp. 66–69	p. 150	p. 199 (Col) pp. 222–224 (E) p. 254 (C)	
Chapters 8–10		Test 42		pp. 70–72	p. 151		
Chapters 9–10	Sheets 62, 63						
Chapters 1–10						pp. 180–182 (MR)	
11-1			pp. 137–138				Activity 22
11-2	Sheet 64		pp. 139–140				
11-3	Sheet 65		pp. 141–142				
11-4	Sheet 66	Test 43	pp. 143–144	p. 73	p. 152		
11-5	Sheet 67		pp. 145–146				Activity 23
11-6	Sheet 68	Test 44	pp. 147–148	p. 74	p. 153		
11-7	Sheet 69		pp. 149–150				
11-8	Sheet 70	Test 45	pp. 151–152	p. 75	p. 154		Activity 24
Chapter 11	Sheet 71	Test 46		pp. 76–77	p. 155	p. 200 (Col) pp. 210, 225–227 (E) p. 255 (C)	
12-1			pp. 153–154				
12-2	Sheet 72		pp. 155–156				Activity 25
12-3	Sheet 73	Test 47	pp. 157–158	pp. 78–79	p. 156		
12-4	Sheet 74		pp. 159–160				
12-5	Sheet 75	Test 48	pp. 161–162	p. 80	p. 157		Activity 26
Chapter 12	Sheet 76	Test 49		pp. 81–82	p. 158	p. 201 (Col) pp. 228–229 (E) p. 256 (C)	

For Use after Lesson	Practice Masters	Tests	Study Guide (Reteaching)	Resource Book			Computer Activities
				Tests	**Practice Exercises**	**Mixed Review (MR) Prep. for College Entrance Exams (Col) Enrichment (E) Computer (C)**	
Chapters 11–12	Sheets 77, 78	Test 50		pp. 83–85	pp. 159–160		
Chapters 1–12						pp. 183–185 (MR)	
13-1	Sheet 79		pp. 163–164				Activities 27, 28
13-2			pp. 165–166				
13-3	Sheet 80	Test 51	pp. 167–168	pp. 86–87	p. 161		Activity 29
13-4			pp. 169–170				
13-5	Sheet 81	Test 52	pp. 171–172	pp. 88–89	p. 162		Activity 30
13-6			pp. 173–174				
13-7	Sheet 82	Test 53	pp. 175–176	pp. 90–91	p. 163		Activities 31, 32
13-8			pp. 177–178				
13-9	Sheet 83	Test 54	pp. 179–180	pp. 92–93	p. 164		
Chapter 13	Sheet 84	Test 55		pp. 94–95	p. 165	p. 202 (Col) pp. 230–236 (E) pp. 243, 257–259 (C)	Activity 33
14-1	Sheet 85		pp. 181–182				Activity 34
14-2			pp. 183–184				
14-3	Sheet 86	Test 56	pp. 185–186	p. 96	p. 166		
14-4			pp. 187–188				
14-5	Sheet 87	Test 57	pp. 189–190	p. 97	p. 167		Activity 35
14-6			pp. 191–192				Activity 36
14-7	Sheet 88		pp. 193–194				
14-8	Sheet 89	Test 58	pp. 195–196	p. 98	p. 168		
Chapter 14	Sheet 90	Test 59		pp. 99–100	p. 169	p. 203 (Col)	
Chapters 13–14	Sheets 91, 92	Test 60		pp. 101–103	p. 170		
Chapters 8–14		Test 61		pp. 104–108	pp. 171–172		
Chapters 1–14						pp. 186–189 (MR)	
Logic							Activity 37

Integrating Synthetic, Coordinate, and Transformational Geometry

Coordinate and Transformational Geometry

The study of coordinates and transformations appears as the last two chapters of the text, and you may wish to maintain this standard sequence. However, these chapters may easily be used in whole or in part very much earlier in the text. To facilitate such an integration, we have included a *Handbook for Integrating Coordinate and Transformational Geometry* on pages 657–675 of the student text. The Handbook is divided into sections to be completed after Chapters 3, 4, 5, 6, 7, 8, 9, 10, 11, and 13. Each section indicates how coordinate or transformational approaches may be used in conjunction with the ideas of the most recently completed chapter.

Value of an Integrated Approach

Many teachers integrate coordinate and transformational points of view with the synthetic approach throughout their geometry course. As students see how coordinates and transformations interconnect with synthetic ideas and with each other, they begin to see the unity in mathematics. Such integration has the additional benefit of solidifying algebraic ideas and skills. Algebra and geometry are made richer by building on each other.

Problem solving skills are enhanced as students have more resources to call upon. The integrated approach offers students a variety of strategies for solving problems. For a particular problem, some students may use a synthetic approach while others will use coordinates or transformations. The integrated approach encourages students to value and accept a diversity of problem solving strategies.

Using the Suggested Integrated Curriculum

The Suggested Integrated Curriculum (see next page) lists how to integrate the Handbook and Chapters 13 and 14 throughout your geometry course.

For example, Item I suggests that once the Chapter 7 material on similarity has been completed, you can cover Lesson 14-5, assigning Classroom Exercises 1–12 and 14–17, and Written Exercises 1–21 and 25–28. Also, the Handbook section on dilations and similarity on pages 664–665 can be assigned.

Note that the Suggested Curriculum omits only those exercises in Chapters 13 and 14 that are not suitable for their place in the new sequence. Omitted exercises are listed at the ends of later Handbook sections as soon as appropriate.

Also, two theorems of Chapter 13 depend on synthetic results that students will not have studied if you follow the suggested integration. The derivation of the distance formula that is given in Lesson 13-1 uses the Pythagorean Theorem, which is not proven until Chapter 8. Also, the derivation of the midpoint formula that appears in Lesson 13-5 relies on Theorem 5-10. You may wish to present these items briefly when using the integrated curriculum.

Features of the Integrated Curriculum

The integration begins after Chapter 3, with an informal introduction to transformations. After Chapter 4, when students are familiar with the concepts of distance, midpoint, and parallel lines, you may assign the first seven lessons of Chapter 13. Following Chapter 5, you may assign the first four lessons of Chapter 14. At this point students will have mastered the concepts of congruence and perpendicular bisector needed for a more formal treatment of transformations, and they will have enough familiarity with triangles and quadrilaterals to do many exercises.

Presentation of dilations (Lesson 14-5) is delayed until after the chapter on similarity (Chapter 7), and coordinate work with circles (part of Lesson 13-1) is delayed until after the circles chapter (Chapter 9). The later portions of Chapters 13 and 14 are covered at the end of the course.

The final section of the Handbook (pages 672–675) offers students the opportunity to decide which approach they feel is best suited to a problem. The exercises included in this section can often be solved in a number of ways. Page 673 features a summary outline that students can use as a heuristic aid.

Suggested Integrated Curriculum

	Subjects	Lessons	Text Pages	Handbook Pages
A	*Basic Figures*	**Chapter 1**	1–31	
B	*Deductive Reasoning*	**Chapter 2**	33–71	
C	*Parallel Lines and Planes*	**Chapter 3**	73–115	
		Handbook: Translation and Rotation		657–659
D	*Congruent Triangles*	**Chapter 4**	117–165	
		Handbook: Reflection and Symmetry		659–660
E	*Coordinate Geometry*	**13-1** Cl. Ex. 1–10; Wr. Ex. 1–16, 27, 30, 33, 43, 44	523–528	
		13-2 Cl. Ex. 1–6; Wr. Ex. 1–27, 32, 34	529–534	
		13-3 Cl. Ex. 1–10; Wr. Ex. 1, 2, 7–10, 21, 22	535–538	
		13-4 Cl. Ex. 1, 2, 4, 6–8; Wr. Ex. 1–25, 27–32, 34	539–543	
		13-5 Cl. Ex. 1–10; Wr. Ex. 1–14, 16, 17, 20, 22–24	544–547	
		13-6 Cl. Ex. 1–13; Wr. Ex. 1–33	548–552	
		13-7 Cl. Ex. 1–13; Wr. Ex. 1–33, 36–37c, 38, 39	553–556	
F	*Quadrilaterals*	**Chapter 5**	167–201	
		Handbook: Quadrilaterals		660–662
G	*Transformations*	**14-1** Cl. Ex. 1–10; Wr. Ex. 1–23	571–576	
		14-2 Cl. Ex. 1–20; Wr. Ex. 1–20, 23–40	577–583	
		14-3 Cl. Ex. 1–8; Wr. Ex. 1–17, 19, 22, 23	583–587	
		14-4 Cl. Ex. 1–15; Wr. Ex. 1–30, 32–37	588–592	
H	*Inequalities in Geometry*	**Chapter 6**	203–239	
		Handbook: Minimal Paths		662–664
I	*Similarity*	**Chapter 7**	241–283	
		14-5 Cl. Ex. 1–12, 14–17; Wr. Ex. 1–21, 25–28	592–598	
		Handbook: Dilations and Similarity		664–665
J	*Right Triangles*	**Chapter 8**	285–327	
		Handbook: Right Triangles		665–667
K	*Circles*	**Chapter 9**	329–373	
		13-1 Cl. Ex. 11, 12; Wr. Ex. 17–26, 34–40, 45	526–528	
		Handbook: Circles		667–669
L	*Constructions and Locus*	**Chapter 10**	375–421	
		Handbook: Constructions		669–670
M	*Area*	**Chapter 11**	423–473	
		Handbook: Areas		670–672
N	*Volume*	**Chapter 12**	475–521	
		14-5 Wr. Ex. 22, 23	596	
O	*Composition and Symmetry*	**14-6 through 14-8**	599–620	
P	*Coordinate Proofs*	**13-8 through 13-9**	556–569	
		14-2 Wr. Ex. 30, 31	581	
Q	*Choosing an Approach*	**Handbook:** Deciding Which Method to Use in a Problem		672–675
R	*Final Review*	**Cumulative Review**	622–625	

Strategies for Teaching

The following pages present a group of articles intended to help you teach geometry successfully. These articles cover a variety of topics of current interest, including methods of teaching and learning, classroom management, and curriculum.

Teaching Students to Value Mathematics

Introduction

The mathematical education of students at all levels should include information and experiences that will help them appreciate and value the role of mathematics in the development of modern society. Students need to hear and read about the history of mathematics, as well as learn about its applications to real-world problems. Thus, the study of geometry should include more than its definitions, postulates, and theorems—it should include experiences and activities that allow students to finish the course with an understanding of and feeling for the value of geometry in their lives.

Exploring the History of Geometry

Most teachers would agree that geometry cannot be appreciated properly without some acquaintance with the history of the subject. Students can explore this history through independent reading assignments and by writing short historical papers. The general aims of these assignments can be as follows: (1) to make students aware of the empirical basis of geometry before the time of Euclid; (2) to show Euclid as an organizer and codifier of the geometry of his time; (3) to study Descartes and the significance of analytic geometry; and (4) to study Bolyai and Lobachevsky and the import of non-Euclidean geometry.

The Role of Geometry in Today's World

Students need to be made aware of the fact that the study of geometry arose in response to certain human needs, and that it has survived for centuries because it is still useful in solving many practical problems in the physical and life sciences, the social sciences, and the humanities. Throughout the textbook there are many special features that discuss the uses of geometry in different careers and show its applications to other fields of study (see, for example, pages 36, 133, 262, 390, 598). To help students gain an appreciation of the role of geometry in today's world, some class time should be spent in discussing these special features. Also, at the beginning of the course, students can be given the assignment of always being alert to articles in newspapers or magazines that discuss applications of geometry (or other fields of mathematics) to real-world situations. Instruct students to bring this information to class for display and discussion.

Project Questions

You can help students to develop an awareness of and appreciation for the role geometry has played in the development of modern society by assigning them questions to research, study, think about, and discuss. Questions such as those below can be assigned at various times during the year. Students should provide facts to support their answers.

1. How and where was geometry first used?
2. Is the development of modern society dependent on the development of science and technology?
3. Is the development of science and technology dependent on the development of mathematics?
4. List five professions that use geometry.
5. Does the subject of geometry contain problems that have not been solved?
6. How has geometry influenced art?

Teaching Students to Reason Mathematically

Introduction

Geometry provides abundant opportunities to teach students how to reason mathematically. Reasoning mathematically means thinking as a mathematician would think. Mathematicians take as their responsibility the creation of new mathematics, and they do this by making and testing conjectures. Conjectures are either proved to be true by using deductive reasoning or proved to be false by a counterexample. The study of geometry historically has been concerned with teaching students the method of deductive proof. However, the goal of teaching students to make conjectures has received very little attention until recently.

What strategies can be used to teach students to make conjectures?

Teaching students to make conjectures requires a spirit of experimentation and exploration in the classroom. Students will need to participate actively in the creation of the geometry they are learning. Participation may take place in a variety of activities ranging from working with manipulatives to paper and pencils to computers. Allow students to suggest statements that might be true about the figures they are studying. Such suggestions can be made by using inductive reasoning, that is, by examining a number of special cases, observing a pattern in the special cases, and then generalizing from the pattern to form a conjecture. Once a conjecture is stated, a problem exists for students to solve. The conjecture needs to be proved by using deductive methods or disproved by a counterexample.

What other activities can teach students to reason mathematically?

The ability to reason mathematically can be developed by engaging students in a variety of activities. Once students are introduced to the idea of deductive reasoning, they need to be taught what a counterexample is and what it means to disprove a statement by using a counterexample. Students need to be given many opportunities to construct counterexamples of both mathematical and nonmathematical statements. Students also need to learn how to follow a proof and to judge whether a proof is valid or invalid. At first, students should be assigned simple proofs to write; then, with experience, they can attempt to write more difficult proofs. Many students experience a great deal of difficulty with the proof-writing aspect of geometry; they need encouragement and support in order not to lose their motivation to continue studying the subject. One strategy for helping students learn how to write proofs is to have them work together in small groups.

What emphasis should be placed on writing proofs?

By encouraging students to make and test conjectures, you will be nurturing a problem-solving attitude toward the study of geometry. When students put forth their own ideas about the properties of a figure, for example, they are motivated to solve their problems by thinking and reasoning deductively. Then the focus shifts from writing proofs to solving problems that are real for students. Many geometry students can achieve success in reasoning through the solution (proof) of a problem, yet cannot write a proof successfully. You may wish to give students the option of writing the key steps of a proof or a paragraph proof rather than a detailed two-column proof. Developing a student's ability to reason correctly, to try new ideas, and to solve problems is a fundamental goal of all mathematics instruction and should take priority over the mechanics of writing proofs.

Research on How Students Learn Geometry

Introduction

Recent education research has many profound implications for the teaching of geometry. The most influential research on how students learn geometry is that of the van Hieles, which will be the focus of this article. Other research concerning mathematics education will be mentioned at the end, and a list of selected references is included.

What are the van Hiele levels of understanding?

In the late 1950's, Dutch mathematics educators Pierre Marie van Hiele and Dina van Hiele-Geldof developed a model of geometric thought that can be used to understand how students learn geometry, and consequently how geometry can be taught to students. The model consists of five levels of understanding that students pass through in learning geometric concepts.

Level 0: Visualization

At the basic level of visualization, students see geometric figures as a *whole*. They can recognize and name a square, rectangle, triangle, and other figures, but they cannot identify the parts or properties of a figure. A student at this level sees a square and a rectangle as two completely distinct figures.

At Level 0, students cannot understand that a square is a rectangle because they cannot identify, and thus compare, the common properties of the two figures.

Level 1: Analysis

At this level, students can think about the properties of a figure. Thus, a student can think in terms of a square having four equal sides and a rectangle having four right angles. Students can also notice that a square and a rectangle have opposite sides that are equal and both have four right angles, but they are still unable to understand that every square is a rectangle.

At Level 1, the parts and properties of a figure can be recognized, and students can name and draw a figure given its properties. Thus, at this level students can make an analysis of figures that were perceived only as a whole at Level 0. However, they still cannot see the interrelationships among figures and cannot understand definitions.

Level 2: Informal Deduction

At the Level 2 stage of understanding, students can understand definitions and establish the interrelationships among figures. Thus, students can now understand that a square is a rectangle because it possesses all the properties of a rectangle. They can also understand that both squares and rectangles are parallelograms.

At Level 2, students cannot see the logical connection of one statement with another, and thus they cannot yet construct a proof. Nevertheless, a formal proof can be followed with the help of the teacher, but there is no understanding of how the sequence of statements in a proof can be altered. Deductive methods are mixed with results obtained through experimentation, and there is no understanding of the role of axioms.

Level 3: Deduction

At Level 3, deductive methods and the need for proof are understood. Students can deduce one statement from another, and in so doing develop a sequence of statements to form a proof. The role of axioms, definitions, and theorems is understood.

Students can see how to vary the steps in a proof to construct yet another logical proof. Necessary and sufficient conditions are understood and students can understand the distinction between a statement and its converse. At Level 3, however, students do not understand the need for rigor.

Level 4: Rigor

At Level 4, students have a sophisticated understanding of mathematical methods and are able to generalize concepts without any reference to concrete interpretations. A variety of axiomatic systems can be understood. Non-Euclidean geometry can be studied and the properties of a deductive system, such as the consistency, independence, and completeness of the postulates, can be understood.

It is probably safe to assume that in a typical geometry class there are students at the first three levels of geometric thinking. Teachers who understand the van Hiele levels can sort out the students according to their levels. This is particularly important at the beginning of the school year so instruction and other class activities can be matched to a student's level. If there is a mismatch between the instruction and the level of thinking of the student, the desired learning outcomes may not occur.

Another implication for teaching is the need to engage students in conversations about the topics being studied. The teacher needs to listen to what students are saying in order to arrive at some judgments about what their levels of thinking might be. Students will use the vocabulary appropriate to a particular level and cannot understand the terms specific to a higher level. Difficulties with vocabulary are a clue to the teacher that a student is at a lower level than the terms being used.

As students' levels of thinking are identified, the teacher can direct instruction at these levels with the goal of advancing each student to the next level. Students will not be able to skip a level; they must proceed through the levels in order. The van Hieles proposed five sequential phases of learning which can help advance a student to the next higher level.

What are the van Hiele phases of learning?

Instruction developed according to the following sequence can lead to a higher level of thinking, according to the van Hieles.

Phase 1: Inquiry/Information

The teacher and students discuss the figures being studied. The teacher asks questions such as the following: "What is a square? A rectangle? A parallelogram? How are they alike? How are they different?" These kinds of questions introduce the figures to be studied and the vocabulary appropriate to the level. The students' responses indicate to the teacher their levels of thinking.

Phase 2: Direct Orientation

At this phase, physical materials such as a geoboard can be used to explore the topic of study. Short one-step tasks that require a specific response should be used. Properties of figures are investigated experimentally.

Phase 3: Explication

The goal of this phase is to have students make observations about the topics being studied. Teacher lectures should be very brief. Care must be taken to see that students use the new vocabulary and symbols correctly. Students are beginning to form a network of relations regarding the topics being studied.

Phase 4: Free Orientation

Students are now working on multistep tasks. They can understand explicitly the relationships among the figures studied. More complex problems can be solved independently by students.

Phase 5: Integration

The teacher helps students form an overview of what they have learned. The use of summaries and reviews is important to help students integrate their knowledge about a particular topic. The van Hieles state that no new information should be introduced at this time. At the end of this phase, students will have reached the next higher level of understanding. Then the new level of thinking replaces the old level, and the teacher starts over again by repeating the five learning phases at the new level.

What are some of the crucial pedagogical factors in the van Hiele model?

There are a number of factors that are crucial to the teaching of geometry.

1. The language used by the teacher and students is very important for the development of geometric thinking and for assessing students' understandings.
2. All activities performed by the teacher and students should set the stage for further development and learning.
3. Geometry should be taught for understanding and not rote response.
4. The teaching of geometry should engage the students actively in the subject, asking questions, working with physical materials, reading the book, interacting with classmates, solving problems, writing proofs, making conjectures, drawing diagrams, verbally describing geometric shapes, and so on.

Other research

Recent research on left- and right-brain functions has important implications for the teaching of mathematics. Stressing the visual aspects of mathematics as well as the logical and symbolic aspects can help students achieve a broader understanding of mathematics through use of both left- and right-brain capabilities. Therefore, this textbook offers many opportunities for students to visualize and draw both two- and three-dimensional figures as an integral part of solving geometric problems. Suggestions for drawing and reading diagrams appear on pages 19, 38, 61, 77, 90, 485, and 492. You will find examples of problems requiring visualization on pages 9 (Exs. 29–36), 77 (Ex. 22), and 485 (Exs. 7–16), and also in Challenge problems such as those found on pages 139, 194, 260, and 495.

Research in geometry education indicates that the most difficult ideas in geometry, usually those related to rigorous geometric deduction, should be introduced in a gentle, gradual manner and then reinforced and extended throughout the course. The textbook includes a variety of strategies to help students explore problems numerically, explain ideas intuitively, generalize results by induction, fill in reasons for two-column proofs whose statements are given, and finally to construct their own more complex proofs. Samples of this variety can be found on the following pages: 104 (Ex. 7), 47 (Ex. 20), 26 (Ex. 19), and 40 (Ex. 12).

List of references

NCTM Publications for Teachers

Geddes, Dorothy; David Fuys; and Rosamond Tischler. *The van Hiele Model of Thinking in Geometry among Adolescents,* 1988.

Grouws, Douglas; Thomas J. Cooney; and Douglas Jones, eds. *Effective Mathematics Teaching,* 1988.

Joint committee of the MAA and the NCTM. *A Sourcebook of Applications of School Mathematics,* 1980.

Kastner, Bernice. *Applications of Secondary School Mathematics,* 1978.

Lindquist, Mary, and Albert Shulte, eds. *Learning and Teaching Geometry, K–12,* 1987 Yearbook.

Shumway, Richard, ed. *Research in Mathematics Education,* 1980.

NCTM Publications for Students

Engelhardt, John. *Geometry in Our World,* 1987.

Kespohl, Ruth. *Geometry Problems My Students Have Written,* 1979.

Virginia State Dept. of Education, Div. of Sciences and Elementary Administration. *Mathematics Enrichment Activities: Grades 3 through 12,* 1986.

Wills, Herbert, III. *Leonardo's Dessert: No Pi.,* 1985.

Journal Articles and Collections

Burger, William F., and J. Michael Shaughnessy. "Characterizing the van Hiele Levels of Development in Geometry." *Journal for Research in Mathematics Education* 17 (January 1986): 31–48.

Hoffer, Alan. "Geometry is More Than Proof." *Mathematics Teacher* 74 (January 1981): 11–18.

van Hiele, P. M. "A Child's Thought and Geometry." In *English Translation of Selected Writings of Dina van Hiele-Geldof and Pierre M. van Hiele,* edited by Dorothy Geddes, David Fuys, and Rosamond Tischler. Brooklyn: Brooklyn College, C.U.N.Y., 1984.

Wirszup, Izaak. "Breakthroughs in the Psychology of Learning and Teaching Geometry." In *Space and Geometry,* edited by J. L. Martin and D. A. Bradbard, pp. 75–97. Columbus: ERIC Center for Science, Mathematics and Environmental Education, 1976.

Mathematics Teacher 78 (September 1985). Entire issue is devoted to geometry.

Enrichment for students

Barbeau, Edward J. "Which Method is Best?" *Mathematics Teacher* 81 (February 1988): 87–90.

Bern, Marshall W., and Ronald L. Graham. "The Shortest-Network Problem." *Scientific American* 260 (January 1989): 84–89.

Carroll, William M. "Cross Sections of Clay Solids." *Arithmetic Teacher* 35 (March 1988): 6–11.

Gadanidis, George. "Problem Solving: The Third Dimension in Mathematics Teaching." *Mathematics Teacher* 81 (January 1988): 16–21.

Thinking Skills

Introduction

Thinking skills are woven into the whole fabric of geometry. In your lesson presentations you can help students improve their thinking skills, use them more efficiently, and acquire additional skills.

Thinking Skills in Geometry

In the Index under "Thinking Skills" you will find a list of some of the areas in which these skills are applied by students.

Reasoning	Applying concepts
Analysis	Classification
Interpreting	Spatial perception
Recall and transfer	Synthesis

Deductive reasoning in the form of if-then statements and proofs is a thinking skill that is introduced in Chapter 2 and applied throughout the course. Students use this kind of *reasoning* to come to conclusions based on accepted statements (definitions, postulates, previous theorems, corollaries, and given information). Encourage your students to use sketches and to try to find counterexamples when deciding whether or not a statement is true (see, for example, Exercises 18–25 on page 108). When appropriate, suggest that students use inductive reasoning as a problem solving strategy. They must be aware of the limits of inductive reasoning, however. To this end, Exercise 26 on page 108 shows how a conclusion based on several past observations may not be true.

Throughout the course, the skills of *analysis* and *interpretation* of information will be called upon. Encourage your students to be on the lookout for likenesses, differences, and patterns and to recognize similarities between problems that appear at first glance to be different. In attacking a problem students will need to examine and interpret the given information and discard any irrelevant material (see, for example, Exercises 9–10 on page 131). In the Logic appendix (pages 644–654) students expand their thinking skills through analysis and interpretation of truth tables. Students also analyze whether reasoning is valid or flawed and apply their logic skills to electrical circuits.

Other thinking skills applied by students are the *recall* of methods learned earlier in the course or in algebra and their *transfer* or extension to new material.

Classification of geometric shapes is required of students throughout the course. Exercises 1–4 on page 186 and Exercises 1–10 on page 187 ask students to identify figures with shared characteristics.

Spatial perception is required to understand how lines and planes relate to each other in space. This thinking skill is vital in sketching and understanding geometric diagrams (see Exercise 22 on page 77 and pages 90–92 for examples).

Synthesis is employed when ideas come together to form something new; for example, when definitions, theorems, postulates, and algebraic properties are put together to form a proof.

Helping Students Develop Thinking Skills

1. *Be a role model.* Talk through the steps in your own proof or solution to an exercise. By following your reasoning, a student can often learn to organize his or her own thinking more logically.
2. *Use helpful questioning techniques.* Be sure that many of your questions to students are directed to the way in which they have arrived at their answers rather than to their recall of specific information.
3. *Encourage active participation by students.* Take full advantage of Classroom and Written Exercises that ask students to "explain" or "show." These words indicate that an informal proof is expected of the students. As the basis for a group activity such exercises provide the opportunity for one student to present an explanation and the others to judge whether the argument is convincing.

You will need to emphasize the importance of attacking a problem analytically—of trying to see the problem as a whole and planning a solution. Point out that there may be a variety of ways of approaching a problem, and that there is nothing wrong with abandoning one strategy and trying another. This course offers you a great opportunity to guide your students to develop good thinking skills.

Using Cooperative Learning Groups

Introduction

Cooperative learning groups, ranging in size from three to six students, are formed to help students learn mathematics. Such groups can be formed within a traditional classroom structure at any time. Students in cooperative learning groups learn mathematics by taking more responsibility for their own learning and by doing and discussing mathematics with other students. Leaders in industrial management have recognized that the ability to work with others in solving problems is a characteristic to be nurtured.

How are groups formed?

At first, the best approach is to allow students to form their own groups. Point out to students that a group is a voluntary coming-together, and that the purpose of a group is to work together to learn mathematics. If some students choose to work alone, this choice should be respected; however, as time passes, encourage all students to join a group. In order to achieve certain learning goals, it may be necessary at times for you to change the assignment of students to groups.

What can groups do?

Learning groups can do many different kinds of things. For example, students in general have difficulty learning to write proofs. Students working in groups can share their ideas about the proof of a theorem and, in so doing, develop a proof that any single student might not have been able to write. Groups can work on the same or different problems, exploring and investigating possible solutions and then communicating their results to the class. Sometimes it is helpful to differentiate the tasks assigned to students in the group. Let students decide who will record observations, who will do research, and who will present findings to the class. In this way, students can gain confidence in their ability to make a unique contribution suited to their talents. Assign student tutors to groups where students are having trouble. Form enrichment groups to solve challenging problems. Other possible group activities might involve working on exercises in the textbook, self-evaluation using the Self-Tests, Chapter Reviews, or Chapter Tests, working with manipulative aids to illustrate concepts concretely, or simply reading and discussing topics together. Specific suggestions are given in the Lesson Commentary under the heading "Cooperative Learning," and throughout the side-column notes under the heading "Group Activity." (See page T80 and student page 66 for examples.)

How should groups work?

Students should have access to a wide variety of learning materials: reference books, articles in periodicals, manipulative aids, filmstrips, and whatever else pertains to the topic being studied. Encourage a group to solve its problems independently by using these materials. If answers to problems have been provided, students can sometimes work backward from the answer to find the solution. All of these activities assist students in learning how to learn. If all attempts by a group to do the work fail, provide some assistance so that students will not become discouraged and waste time.

What are the advantages of using learning groups?

1. Students take responsibility for their own learning.
2. Students actively do mathematics with other students.
3. Students improve their skills in using mathematical language as they work with others in the group.
4. Students share their ideas with others.
5. Students become less fearful of making errors in a small group.
6. Students become more confident in their own abilities by successful group participation.
7. Students learn that a group can often solve problems that an individual cannot solve.
8. Students learn how to work in a group.
9. Students learn better how to learn.
10. Students learn more mathematics, enjoy learning it more, and develop a positive attitude toward mathematics.

Teaching Students Communication Skills

Introduction

Learning to communicate mathematical ideas effectively is an essential skill for achieving success in the subject. The communication skills required to learn, to use, and to enjoy geometry are *listening, reading, speaking,* and *writing*. A deficiency in any one of these four skills will create learning problems for a student. This fact should be pointed out to students as they start their study of geometry. Then explicit strategies for developing these skills in students need to be implemented throughout the course.

What strategies can be used to help students learn to read geometry?

Students can learn to read geometry if they are given consistent reading assignments and are held accountable for doing the assignments. Homework assignments can include reading and studying the text, and students can be questioned in class on the text material as a check on their reading. At various times, students can be asked to read short sections of the text aloud in class. Silent reading sessions in class, followed by questions, will also encourage students to read their books.

A class discussion with students about the importance of reading the textbook can be used to provide some suggestions on how to read geometry successfully. Since geometry contains many special symbols, stress to students that they must learn the meanings of all symbols. Encourage them to stop reading and look up the meaning of any symbol that is not understood. Page xi gives a list of symbols with page references. Students should also be encourged to ask questions in class about the meanings of all symbols they do not understand.

Another area of difficulty for many students is in understanding the meanings of technical terms. Geometry contains many specialized terms whose meanings must be understood in order to solve problems and to continue learning new content. Encourage students to look up terms in the Glossary at the back of the student book. Emphasize the importance of understanding the meaning of each new term.

Geometry cannot be learned without using and understanding drawings of figures. Encourage students to study the drawings in the book as they read the textual material. Encourage them also to make their own drawings as they read or try to solve problems. Accurate drawings are a prerequisite to understanding many geometric concepts and to solving many problems.

Reading proofs is an essential skill for success in geometry. Have students read aloud the initial proofs presented in the book. This kind of activity will expose any difficulties students may have in understanding the organization of a proof.

Point out to students that they cannot read a geometry book as they would read a newspaper or magazine. Reading mathematics must be done slowly, checking calculations and drawings, working through the steps of an example or proof, thinking about the definitions of new terms, and taking time to understand and write new symbols. These kinds of activities need to be part of the reading process for understanding to develop.

Students will learn to read geometry if they are expected to do so, and if they are tested both formally and informally on their reading. As students gain proficiency in reading geometry, their understanding of concepts and their ability to solve problems will grow substantially.

Is listening a communication skill?

Listening is perhaps the most important of all the communication skills. Students need to learn how to listen in order to learn geometry effectively. They need to listen to the teacher and their classmates carefully and critically. Encourage students to listen with a pen or pencil in hand and to take notes about key ideas. They can return to their notes and ask questions about things they do not understand. In this way, a question can be asked that otherwise may have been forgotten; or a comment can be made to clarify a statement made by the speaker. Stress to students the importance of allowing a speaker to finish speaking before making a comment or asking a question. Clearly, most of the time a student spends in class is spent listening. Students with good listening habits will benefit most from instruction and discussions in class.

How can students be helped to verbalize geometric ideas?

Learning geometry is an active process in which students need to ask questions, explain solutions to problems, discuss concepts and theorems, make conjectures, and take part in small group activities. The ability to verbalize thoughts is essential to all these learning activities, and students need to learn how to do this in a clear and correct way. In many classrooms, students are passive observers of a very active teacher who explains the content of the course. For students to learn how to verbalize geometric ideas, it is necessary that they be fully engaged in the learning process. They must be encouraged to speak in class without fear of making an error and looking foolish to their classmates. They should also be encouraged to express geometric ideas in their own words. An approach to teaching geometry that places value on making conjectures and solving problems in small groups will encourage more students to speak up in class. A spirit of inquiry and a climate of trust and openness in the classroom will lessen the fear that many students have in verbalizing geometric ideas.

What writing skills do students need to acquire in geometry?

More than most other branches of mathematics, learning geometry requires good writing skills because of the need to write proofs. Students need to be able to reproduce statements of theorems, postulates, and definitions accurately in order to construct logical proofs. They also need to learn to write paragraph proofs. If students understand the meanings of theorems, postulates, and definitions, they should be able to reproduce them correctly in written form without having to memorize the book's version. Understanding rather than rote memorization should be the goal, and students should be encouraged to restate what they have learned in their own words.

Since mathematics is a symbolic language, the correct use of the symbols that represent mathematical ideas is crucial for successful learning. In studying geometry, students will learn many new symbols that are unique to the subject. These symbols must be mastered and written correctly when solving problems or writing proofs. If students use a symbol incorrectly, it may be an indication that they do not understand the idea it represents.

Students should be encouraged to write their homework and test papers neatly and in an organized way. Lack of organization and carelessness in writing answers to questions, solutions to problems, and two-column proofs often introduce errors that could have been avoided.

What strategies can be used in a multilingual classroom?

With encouragement and assistance, students who are not proficient in English can develop communication skills. The following ideas may help. When you introduce new geometric terms in class, allow students time to ask questions about them and to use them in sentences. Whenever possible, use concrete models to illustrate new terms. Take time for frequent summaries of key points during class discussions. Some bilingual students may enjoy giving a short presentation on a geometric topic in their native language, using visual aids to illustrate their comments. Cooperative learning groups provide an ideal setting for students of varying degrees of proficiency in English to discuss the process involved in solving assigned problems. Bilingual members of the group who are proficient in English can help those less proficient express their ideas.

Teaching Students to Solve Problems

Introduction

The fundamental goal of all instruction in mathematics is to teach students to solve problems. The study of geometry provides daily opportunities for students to solve interesting and challenging problems. One technique to use in developing problem solving skills in students is to engage them in making conjectures, and then have them try to prove or disprove their conjectures (see Exercises 33 and 34 on page 171 and Exercise 28 on page 193 for examples). Students are more interested in solving problems of their own than they are in accepting theorems and proofs given in the textbook.

What approach is necessary to create a positive attitude toward solving problems?

Many students do not like to solve mathematics problems. Very often, these students have not had many successful experiences in solving problems. The study of geometry, however, presents students with new subject matter that is visual, involving drawings of figures, rather than numeric or symbolic. Thus, a good opportunity exists for a new start with many students. Also, in geometry, students can often reason correctly through part of a proof or solution and thus attain partial success, whereas in arithmetic or algebra a single correct answer may be demanded. With encouragement from the teacher and from other students, partial success is likely to develop into complete success, and students will discover that problem solving is an enjoyable activity.

Is solving problems or learning to write proofs more important?

One of the major goals of instruction in geometry is to teach students the concept and methods of deductive reasoning. This can be done successfully in the context of a course oriented toward stating and solving problems. A theorem, after all, can be presented as an unsolved problem, or students can be led to discover geometric relationships by using physical materials, drawings, measuring instruments, and inductive reasoning—generalizing from specific cases to the statement of a conjecture. Thus, instead of writing a proof for a given theorem, the focus shifts to finding a solution to a problem. And the solution does not have to be written out in a two-column proof format. Instead, a series of logical statements can be written down in paragraph form, which is a more natural way to give a solution to a problem.

What specific strategies can be used to solve geometry problems?

A problem solving strategy is a plan for solving a problem. One of the goals of a geometry course is to familiarize students with the strategies that are useful in solving geometry problems. The general strategies listed below provide an approach to solving a problem for which the method of solution is not obvious. Students should understand that solving a problem requires critical thinking, and that if one strategy does not work, then another one should be tried.

- Look for a pattern
- Use a table or a chart
- Draw a diagram
- Generalize from specific examples
- Apply a standard formula
- Solve a simpler, related problem
- Use trial and error and the process of elimination
- Reason backward
- Make a deductive argument
- Recognize the possibility of no solution
- Construct a counterexample

Specific comments on problem solving are given in the Lesson Commentary and in the side-column notes for many lessons (see the Problem Solving paragraph on page T81 and the side-column note on page 77 for examples).

Helping Students Become Independent Learners

Introduction

Teachers have a responsibility to help students become confident in their own abilities and to help them take more responsibility for their own learning; that is to say, a student's education should always be directed toward helping him or her become an independent learner.

When a student asks for help in learning geometry, the teacher must first ascertain what the problem is. Very often, students' learning problems involve their study habits in doing homework, preparing for a test, using a textbook, solving problems, or working with others. The latter two problems are discussed in the articles on problem solving and cooperative learning groups.

Doing Homework

Many students may understand the class discussion of a topic yet cannot do their homework independently. As soon as these students encounter a problem they find difficult, they are likely to stop working. The suggestions that follow can help students learn how to do their homework. You may want to discuss them as a class activity and ask students to suggest other learning methods they have used.

1. Take notes in class so you can use your notebook as a reference when doing problems at home. Before your teacher or another student explains a problem in class, write the problem in your notebook. Then listen to the explanation of the solution. Try not to take notes while the explanation is being given, but listen carefully. When the explanation is finished, write the solution in your notebook.
2. Read the material preceding the exercises in the textbook and be sure to study the book's examples. Go over the notes you made in class.
3. Before starting your homework, review the assignment from the previous day. Pay particular attention to those exercises you could not solve. Are you now able to solve them?
4. Remember, there can be more than one way to do a mathematics problem. If the first method you try does not work, try another method.

Preparing for a Test

Point out to students that most preparation for tests actually takes place through daily homework assignments and classwork. Emphasize that the preparation for a test should not take place only on the night before. The following are some suggestions for students when preparing for a test.

1. Review the meanings of the boldface words in the book.
2. Work the examples in the book by covering up each solution and writing out your solution. Then see if you have the right answer.
3. Review your notebook.
4. Do the chapter review exercises.
5. Pick out the problems from your homework that you tried to work but did not get correct. Can you do them now?
6. Have another student make up a problem for you to do. Then make up one for him or her. Explain your solutions to one another.

Using Textbooks Effectively

The following strategies can be presented to students to help them use their textbooks effectively:

1. Be an active reader. When you read an example in the book, write out the solution in your notebook and study it. In doing so, you will understand why certain steps are needed. Check the calculations and look up the meanings of any symbols you do not understand.
2. Learn the boldface words and their meanings. Look up the words you do not know in the Glossary or in the Index at the back of the book.
3. Describe to someone else how a problem in the book was solved. Be sure to use the correct mathematical terms.

Multicultural Aspects of Geometry

Respecting Cultural Diversity

As today's classrooms become more and more culturally diverse, teachers are realizing the value of having students explore the contributions of different groups of people to our wealth of knowledge. Research has shown that all students benefit from a multicultural approach to learning, and that learning is enhanced in classrooms where cultural diversity is respected and emphasized in the curriculum.

Geometry lends itself well to the goal of emphasizing cultural diversity. Because geometry has important applications for so many aspects of our lives—art, architecture, astronomy, mapmaking—many cultures have helped further its development. By studying the contributions of these cultures, students gain a better understanding and appreciation for the importance of geometry to society.

Cultural Notes

At the beginning of each chapter and throughout the book, cultural notes have been provided to help teachers interweave cultural themes with their teaching of specific topics. For example, the Cultural Note on page xvi discusses the contribution of Egyptian astronomy to our modern calendar system.

Student Projects

You may want to use some of the Cultural Notes as starting points for student projects. For example, the Cultural Note on page 451 suggests that students research some of the methods used throughout history to calculate the value of π. The Cultural Note on page 293 discusses the understanding and application of the Pythagorean relationship in ancient China, Babylon, and Egypt. Having students research and report on historical topics such as these not only helps increase their understanding of geometry topics, but also helps them learn to communicate effectively. You may want to have students work on some projects in cooperative groups.

Suggested Resources

Eves, Howard. *An Introduction to the History of Mathematics*, 5th ed. New York: Saunders College Publishing, 1983.

Gillings, Richard J. *Mathematics in the Time of the Pharaohs*. New York: Dover Publications, 1982.

Grinstein, Louise S., and Paul J. Campbell. *Women of Mathematics: A Biobibliographic Sourcebook*. Westport, CT: Greenwood Press, 1987.

Kline, Morris. *Mathematical Thought from Ancient to Modern Times*. New York: Oxford University Press, 1972.

Lǐ, Yǎn, and Dù, Shírán. *Chinese Mathematics: A Concise History*. Oxford, England: Clarendon Press, 1987.

National Council of Teachers of Mathematics. *Historical Topics for the Mathematics Classroom*. Reston, VA: NCTM, 1989.

Naylor, Maria, ed. *Authentic Indian Designs*. New York: Dover Publications, Inc., 1975.

Steen, Lynn Arthur, ed. *For All Practical Purposes: Introduction to Contemporary Mathematics*. New York: W. H. Freeman and Company, 1988.

Whitlock, Ralph. *Everyday Life of the Maya*. New York: Dorset Press, 1976.

Zaslavsky, Claudia. *Africa Counts: Number and Pattern in African Culture*. Boston, MA: Prindle, Weber & Schmidt, 1973.

Teaching Students to Make Connections

Introduction

Students are more likely to become fully involved in the study of geometry if they see that it is related to other academic disciplines and to practical problems from everyday life. Whenever possible, teachers should emphasize connections: connections among various approaches to geometry, connections with other branches of mathematics, and connections with other disciplines and fields. Specific comments about making connections are given under the heading "Making Connections" in the lesson commentary on pages T74–T144 and in the side-column notes.

Connections with Coordinate and Transformational Geometry

Geometry can be presented in many ways: synthetic geometry, coordinate geometry, and transformational geometry are all possible approaches. However, developing geometry from a synthetic point of view, with connections to coordinate and transformational ideas, is the approach favored by the majority of geometry teachers.

This textbook presents coordinate geometry in Chapter 13 and transformational geometry in Chapter 14, but it is possible to integrate this material throughout the course. To assist this process, a *Handbook for Integrating Coordinate and Transformational Geometry* is included on pages 657–675 of the student textbook, and complete instructions for an integrated order of topics and assignments are presented on pages T56 and T57.

Connections with Other Branches of Math

Not only are connections among different approaches important, but students need to understand the connections between geometry and other branches of mathematics. Thus, algebra, metric geometry, and even trigonometry are used to support and enhance the content of a course in geometry. Unless explicit mention is made of the connections that are implicit in the content itself, few students will be aware of them. Students may continue to think of arithmetic, algebra, and geometry as unrelated subjects. Explicit attention given to these content connections by the teacher will create in students a sense of awareness, and an appreciation for the interrelationships of mathematical ideas. The interplay among various branches of mathematics can strengthen students' understanding of geometry and increase their abilities to solve problems.

Connections with Algebra

Students see their first formal connection with algebra in Lesson 1-3, when every point on a line is paired with a real number. The use of a coordinate system for a line introduces algebraic ideas that allow teachers to discuss the concepts of length, distance, midpoints of segments, and graphs of inequalities.

Lesson 2-2 introduces the properties of equality of real numbers that are used as postulates in writing proofs. The properties of inequalities are given in Lesson 6-1, and a brief review of inequality symbols together with a few numerical examples of each property would be appropriate at that time. Students are often surprised to see inequalities used as reasons in proofs involving the sides and angles of triangles because they are accustomed to proving segments or angles congruent.

The early introduction of real numbers and their properties is a strong connection between algebraic and geometric ideas that will influence the presentation of the geometry throughout the course. For example, a purely synthetic development that follows Euclid would not use the properties of the real numbers. However, this approach is not appropriate today because the real numbers are available, and students have studied their properties in previous mathematics courses.

Another goal that motivates the use of algebra in the textbook is to help students retain their algebraic skills. Therefore, algebra reviews are placed throughout the book. These reviews should be completed as they appear, since they usually review algebraic concepts that will be used in the lessons immediately following.

For example, the Algebra Review on page 280 prepares students for the Pythagorean Theorem and its converse by reviewing the manipulation of radical expressions and the solving of quadratic equations such as $x^2 + 5^2 = (5\sqrt{2})^2$. Such work will help students in solving right triangle problems where variables occur in the expressions for side lengths.

Connections with Metric Geometry

Students have studied topics from metric geometry in many of their earlier mathematics courses. Students calculated perimeters, areas, and volumes of simple figures in elementary school. At that time, connections between arithmetic and geometry were made. These connections allowed students to apply their newly learned arithmetic skills in a geometric context.

At the high school level, areas of plane figures, and areas and volumes of solids, are studied in more detail and with greater sophistication. General formulas are derived to calculate areas and volumes. The derivation of these formulas very often requires algebraic symbols and techniques. Also, students again use their arithmetic skills to calculate answers.

Many students will not have seen geometric probability problems involving areas of the type presented in Lesson 11-8. Here metric geometry is linked to another branch of mathematics: probability. Representing abstract events of chance by geometric figures is helpful to some students.

Connections with Trigonometry

Although some students may have had a brief exposure to the basic trigonometric ratios in an earlier mathematics course, many students may not have had any contact with trigonometry. Yet the tangent, sine, and cosine ratios for an acute angle of a right triangle can be integrated naturally into a geometry course. These ratios are presented in Lessons 8-5 and 8-6.

Both geometry and trigonometry consider various measurements of triangles. Geometry is essentially the mathematics of size and shape, while trigonometry started its development as the art of calculating the dimensions of triangles. (The word *trigonometry* literally means *triangle measuring*.) These connections between the two oldest branches of mathematics are interesting for students to know. If students continue their study of mathematics, they will learn a great deal more about the trigonometric ratios, but their learning will be from the modern point of view of trigonometric *functions*.

Connections with Other Disciplines

Since its beginning, the development of geometry has been linked to a variety of real-world applications. The word *geometry* literally means *earth measurement*, and the textbook discusses contemporary examples of this earliest application, such as geology (page 36), orienteering (page 54), and cartography (page 213).

Geometry as a tool for architects also has a rich heritage, including the use of the golden ratio in the Parthenon (page 253), the use of proportions and similar figures in preparing scale drawings (page 262) and technical drawings (page 90), the use of trigonometry in passive solar design (page 321), and the use of Euler's formula in geodesic domes (page 505).

Scientific applications of geometry are far-ranging; the textbook includes examples from optics (page 260) and the navigation of space shuttle landings (page 467).

Geometry can influence arts such as painting, photography, and sculpture as well. Many exercises in the text involve folding and cutting paper, or the creation of three-dimensional models. The concepts of symmetry and tessellation (page 609) are particularly adaptable to the visual arts.

Utilizing geometry to represent the world around us has involved tools as ancient as the pantograph (page 265) and as recent as the computer-generated fractal (page 598). Indeed, geometry—as the premier example of expressing the physical form of the natural world in abstract terms—may be seen as the archetype of all mathematical inquiry.

Using Software with Geometry

Introduction

Excellent software programs are now available to be used in teaching geometry. For example, there are geometric construction programs such as *Geometry Grapher* (Houghton Mifflin), *Geometric Supposer* (Sunburst), and *GeoDraw* (IBM). These programs provide exciting opportunities for teaching geometry because students can construct and analyze geometric figures, form conjectures, and then test their conjectures on other figures. This process allows students to disprove conjectures by counterexample or to find some information useful in proving them.

About Geometry Grapher

The *Geometry Grapher* software has been designed specifically to support this geometry textbook, and in particular the topics of coordinate and transformational geometry. The program is available for both IBM and Apple computers.

Geometry Grapher can be used independently by students or as a classroom presentation device. *Geometry Grapher*'s coordinate geometry features allow students to plot points, segments, lines, polygons, and circles; measure slopes, lengths, and areas; plot midpoints, perpendicular bisectors, and angle bisectors; explore the relation between lines and their equations; and investigate the properties of polygons. *Geometry Grapher*'s transformation capabilities allow students to explore the effects of reflections, translations, rotations, and dilations on figures they have drawn.

A booklet included with the *Geometry Grapher* software provides Activity Sheets designed for use with Chapters 13 and 14. The booklet also contains descriptions of how to use *Geometry Grapher* throughout your course for Classroom Demonstrations. In addition, nearly all of the Explorations features of this textbook can be examined using *Geometry Grapher*. The chart in the next column summarizes the ways in which *Geometry Grapher* can support your teaching. No doubt you will find the program powerful enough to use in many other ways as well.

When To Use Geometry Grapher			
Ch.	Classroom Demonstrations	Textbook Explorations	Activity Sheets
3	p. 78 (Thm. 3-2)	p. 78 p. 89 p. 99	
4		p. 134 p. 158	
5	p. 177 (Thm. 5-9)	p. 176 p. 189 p. 195	
6	p. 219 (Thm. 6-2)		
7	p. 270 (Thm. 7-4)	p. 268	
8		p. 298 p. 310	
9	p. 362 (Thm. 9-11)	p. 338 p. 361	
10	p. 387 (Thm. 10-4)	p. 385 p. 392	
11		p. 433	
12		p. 552	
13	Lessons 13-1, 2, 3, 5, 6, 7, 9		Activities 1–3
14	Lessons 14-2, 3, 4, 5, 6, 8	p. 576	Activities 4–8

Computer Support in the Teacher's Edition

Whether you already have experience with computer-assisted instruction or are a newcomer to software technology, this Teacher's Edition has features that can help you incorporate computers into your geometry course.

In the Lesson Commentary under the "Using Technology" heading appear suggestions on how to use computers to augment the teaching of particular lessons.

"Using Technology" contains suggested Experiments to use with a class and information about the Explorations in the student text. (See pages T89 and T90 for examples.)

The "Using a Computer" heading in the side columns of the Teacher's Edition gives further information about specific Explorations and Computer Key-Ins, and about exercises in the student textbook where computers might be used. (See pages 188 and 189 for examples.)

The Explorations in the student textbook are designed to be investigated with a geometric construction program, though if necessary drawings may be done by hand. The Explorations promote discovery learning when used as an introduction to a lesson. (See pages 78 and 89 for examples.)

Instructional Settings

Construction programs can be used both to present new concepts and to have students discover new results as a class, in small groups, or individually.

If you have only one computer and a large display device, you can use the computer to demonstrate concepts for the entire class. If you have a lab setup with several computers, students can do their own explorations. Have them work in groups of two or three. Each student can assume a different task: one can be recorder, another can type at the computer. From time to time encourage students to switch roles, so they see that others may learn at a different pace or approach investigations with different procedures.

Discovery Learning

Don't be surprised if students discover things that were not part of your original lesson plan. Listen carefully to what they say. Encourage their pursuits even if they wander from the given subject. Allow them the chance to discover geometry on their own. After all, discovery is what mathematics is all about.

Experiment vs. Proof

You may wish to point out that construction programs don't prove anything. They merely provide a convenient tool for performing constructions and generating conjectures. Students should be encouraged to complete a more traditional proof before any hypothesis can be known to be true.

Some Technical Issues

Geometric construction programs give approximate measurements only. Sometimes two quantities that are equal will have measurements that differ in the last decimal place.

Various construction programs may label figures differently. For example, some programs will construct isosceles $\triangle ABC$ with $AB = AC$ and others with $AB = BC$. Successful learning from the activities is not dependent on having the same lettering. You may wish to remind your students, however, that they should keep track of any differences that they see in labeling.

Other Available Software

Other types of software may be appropriate for the teaching and learning of geometry. Spreadsheets, for example, may be useful in treating the computational aspects of area and volume. The chart below shows some common software programs and chapters where they may apply.

Chapter	Geometric Supposer	GeoDraw	spreadsheet
1	P	√	
2	P	√	
3	P, △	√	
4	△	√	
5	△, ▱	√	
6	△	√	
7	△	√	×
8	△, ▱	√	×
9	▱, ⊙	√	
10	△	√	
11	▱	√	×
12			×
13		√	×
14	△	√	×

P: PreSupposer
△: Triangles
▱: Quadrilaterals
⊙: Circles

Lesson Commentary

1 *Points, Lines, Planes, and Angles*

The chapter begins by discussing a certain stage in a game. The student, regarded as a participant in the game, does some thinking that is geometrical—not geometrical in the sense of involving mathematics that has been learned, but geometrical in the sense of investigating some relationships among certain points and lines. Thus, at the very beginning of the course, the student learns that critical thinking is important in the study of geometry.

The second lesson further develops the basic concepts of points and lines, and introduces the concept of a plane. Most students are familiar with these three geometric terms. However, the notion that most terms are defined but that the terms *point*, *line*, and *plane* are accepted as intuitive ideas and are not defined will be new to almost all students.

Lesson 1-3 introduces the definitions and notations for rays and segments. The Ruler Postulate and the Segment Addition Postulate are presented in the development of the idea of distance (length).

Angles and their degree measurements are presented in Lesson 1-4, along with the Protractor Postulate and the Angle Addition Postulate. The two angle postulates are like the Ruler Postulate and the Segment Addition Postulate. All four postulates establish relationships among geometric ideas and the set of real numbers, thus allowing the introduction of the concept of measure into the study of geometry.

The last lesson of the chapter introduces the incidence postulates. These postulates discuss ways in which points, lines, and planes can lie on, contain, or intersect one another. Consequences of the postulates are considered also. The three theorems stated on page 23 introduce the idea that geometric relationships can be proved by applying the postulates. Direct student involvement with writing proofs does not begin until Chapter 2. The goal in Chapter 1 is to teach students that once some propositions are accepted as true (that is, are assumed to be true), then other propositions follow from them and must also be true. Students will grow in their understanding of the way some truths lead to other truths if, at this beginning stage in the study of deductive reasoning, they don't attempt to write proofs for intuitively clear theorems. Incidence theorems sound simple, but their proofs can confuse many students so they are often omitted.

Algebra will play an important role in the course. For example, the first four postulates bring numbers and algebra into geometry. The Algebra Reviews are placed where particular skills are needed. Thus, the first Algebra Review, on linear equations, is positioned just before the Ruler Postulate and the Protractor Postulate. Students can sharpen their skills by solving the equations provided.

Students enrolled in geometry begin the course with vastly different backgrounds. The first chapters can be covered as quickly or as deliberately as the needs of a class suggest. The goal is to promote maximum mathematical learning in students regardless of their starting points.

1-1 pages 1–4

Teaching Suggestions

Objectives

1. Use the term *equidistant*.
2. Use the terms *point* and *line*.
3. Draw representations of points and lines.

Presenting the Lesson

Reproduce the drawing on page 1 on the chalkboard as a model to initiate the discussion of the game. Then have students reproduce the drawing on page 2, using a compass and ruler. Illustrate points and lines with chalkboard drawings, and have students reproduce these figures with pencil and paper. For example, show three lines intersecting in exactly two points.

Problem Solving

The conditions of the game present an interesting problem for students to solve. After solving the problem with the class, point out the need to be aware of making hidden, unwarranted assumptions in solving problems. The fact that the next clue is at "a point" does not imply that the possible solution to the problem consists of only a single point. In fact, two different points are possible solutions.

Communication Skills

The objectives of this first lesson identify three geometric terms for students to learn. The terms are introduced informally and intuitively. Students first need to learn the vocabulary of geometry and understand the concepts involved on an intuitive level. Experiences with physical objects and pictorial representations of geometric ideas will help students to learn and to understand ideas intuitively. Then, it is appropriate to introduce more symbolic, abstract, and general representations of geometric concepts. Encourage students to speak the language of geometry, using the terms introduced in each section until they are a natural part of students' mathematical vocabulary.

1-2 pages 5–9

Teaching Suggestions

Objectives

1. Use the undefined terms *point*, *line*, and *plane*.
2. Draw representations of points, lines, and planes.
3. Use the terms *collinear*, *coplanar*, and *intersection*.

Presenting the Lesson

Many physical objects can be used to illustrate points, lines, and planes. Marbles, for example, can be used to represent points. A taut piece of string can represent a line. A sheet of paper or a poster board can represent a plane. Also, the sides of a cardboard box represent intersecting planes. Ask students to suggest other physical representations of points, lines, and planes using familiar objects.

Reinforcement

Since the concept of a plane has been studied less than the concepts of point and line in prior mathematics courses, it is suggested that sufficient time be spent discussing planes. To illustrate the concept, use examples of planes within the classroom, such as walls and book pages. Ask: Would the plane represented by the floor of the classroom extend outside the building? down the street? How wide is this plane? Does it have thickness?

Cooperative Learning

Arrange the class into small groups of three to five students each. Have each group prepare one or two of the drawings for Exercises 29–33. Encourage students having a strong visual ability to help those students in their group who may be having difficulty drawing three-dimensional figures.

1-3 pages 11–16

Teaching Suggestions

Objectives

1. Use symbols for lines, segments, rays, and distances.
2. Find distances.
3. State and use the Ruler Postulate and the Segment Addition Postulate.

Presenting the Lesson

The diagrams presented in the textbook can be reproduced on the chalkboard to serve as effective models for discussing the concepts of segment, ray, and distance. To illustrate the idea of a ray, suggest that students think of the sun's rays. The endpoint of a ray of light from the sun is the sun itself. The ray of light goes out into space and has no other end, unless it strikes an object in space. If a ray of the sun strikes the earth, it ceases to be a geometric ray.

Rulers can be used to develop an understanding of Postulates 1 and 2. Use two different rulers, one marked off in inches and the other in centimeters, to illustrate both the Ruler Postulate and the Segment Addition Postulate.

Initiate a discussion of the concept of congruent figures by having students suggest different objects that have the same size and shape. There are usually many congruent objects in a typical classroom, such as sheets of writing paper, panes of window glass, and chalkboard erasers.

Making Connections

Students need to learn where and how the different branches of mathematics come together to reinforce and strengthen one another. The number line pairs geometric points with numbers (arithmetic) and introduces the ideas of coordinates, length, distance, and absolute value (algebra) into geometry. The Ruler Postulate and the Segment Addition Postulate use the concepts of number and absolute value.

The Example on page 13 uses algebraic notation in a problem involving the length of a line segment. The connections between algebra and geometry are enhanced further in many of the exercises.

Reinforcement

The notions of segment, ray, and distance on a number line will be familiar to most students. However, many students will need to review the notations AC, $\overline{AC}$, $\overleftrightarrow{AC}$, and $\overrightarrow{AC}$. For a ray, it is helpful to note that, as the arrow suggests, the ray starts at point A. Point A is the initial point, called the endpoint. Ask students to suggest some examples of rays in the real world.

Communication Skills

Lesson 1-3 introduces many geometric words and symbols. As an introduction, ask students to skim the first three pages and find important terms in boldface type or unfamiliar words and symbols. You may write these on the chalkboard. Examples of symbols and corresponding word forms may be:

$\overleftrightarrow{AC}$	"line AC"
$\overline{AC}$	"segment AC"
$\overrightarrow{AC}$	"ray AC"
JL	"length of segment JL"
$\lvert x - y \rvert$	"the absolute value of the difference of x and y"

After writing each symbol on the chalkboard, say its word form. Note that a mathematical symbol sometimes has more than one correct word form. For example, x^3 may be read "x cubed" or "the cube of x" or "the third power of x" or "x to the third power." Remind students to be alert for familiar words, such as "between," that have a more precise meaning in mathematics than in ordinary conversation.

Before students begin the exercises, you may want to ask them to express the following symbols verbally. Allow any word form that expresses the meaning clearly.

$$\overleftrightarrow{ST}$$
$$AC = 12$$
$$\overline{RS} \cong \overline{ST}$$
$$AC = DE$$
$$JM = |4 - (-3)| = |7| = 7$$
$$-2 \leqslant x < 3$$

1-4 pages 17–22

Teaching Suggestions

Objectives

1. Name angles and find their measures.
2. State and use the Angle Addition Postulate.
3. Recognize what can be concluded from a diagram.

Presenting the Lesson

As you begin to discuss angle measure, review the use of the protractor. This can be accomplished by asking students to draw angles of various measures, including some greater than 90. Point out to students that the lengths of the rays drawn for the sides of an angle do not affect the measure of the angle.

Problem Solving

Solving a problem in geometry almost always involves the drawing of a figure. A common error made by students is to assume that certain information is true based upon the figure itself. As the discussion on page 19 makes clear, there are certain facts that can be stated to be true based upon a diagram and there are other facts that cannot be assumed to be true.

Making Connections

The Protractor Postulate and the Angle Addition Postulate introduce the use of numbers (arithmetic) and absolute value (algebra) into the study of angles. This interplay among arithmetic, algebraic, and geometric concepts enriches the study of geometry and provides students with a variety of ideas to solve problems.

Extension

More advanced students might be challenged to find the value of x using the diagram for Exercises 29–34 on page 22 and the information given below.

(a) $m\angle 1 = 4x$, $m\angle 3 = x^2$ **10**

(b) $m\angle 2 = 3x + 6$, $m\angle 3 = x^2 + 56$ **8**

(c) $m\angle 1 = x^2$, $m\angle 2 = 30 - x$ **5, −6**

Finding the value of x requires solving a quadratic equation and then rejecting any root that leads to a negative angle measure. Students may oversimplify the problem by rejecting all negative values of x. Notice that in (c), where the equation $x^2 = 30 - x$ has roots 5 and -6, both roots should be kept. When $x = -6$, $m\angle 1 = 36$ and $m\angle 2 = 36$.

Using Technology

Here are three possible introductory experiments designed to acquaint students with the different features of geometric construction software and to have students begin to make conjectures. (See "Getting Started with Computers" on pages T72–T73.) Complete understanding of the terminology used and the conjectures reached is not as important as the experimentation process itself. Many of the ideas in the experiments will, of course, be treated completely later in the course.

Experiment 1 Draw any right triangle. Measure each side and each angle. Label the midpoint of the longest side. Connect the midpoint of the longest side to the vertex containing the right angle. Measure all segments and angles formed. Name all congruent segments and all congruent angles. Repeat the experiment for another right triangle and make some conjectures.

Experiment 2 Draw any triangle. Label the midpoints of the three sides and draw three segments, joining pairs of midpoints. Measure all segments and angles formed. Name all congruent segments and all congruent angles. Repeat the experiment for a different type of triangle and make some conjectures.

Experiment 3 Draw any triangle. Label the midpoints of two sides. Draw the segments from each midpoint to the opposite vertex. (These segments are called medians.) Label the intersection of the two medians. Draw the segment connecting the third vertex to the intersection of the medians, then extend the segment to intersect the third side of the triangle. Is this segment a median? How can you tell? What do you notice about the medians of a triangle?

Communication Skills

Mathematics is communicated most often in written form. Sometimes there are different ways to express the same idea symbolically, and students need to know and understand the use of equivalent notation. For example, since a straight angle does not have an interior, the statement of the Angle Addition Postulate has two parts, covering both types of angles. The conclusion of the second part, covering the case when $\angle AOC$ is a straight angle, could have been stated as

$$m\angle AOB + m\angle BOC = m\angle AOC.$$

However, the form

$$m\angle AOB + m\angle BOC = 180$$

is the one that will be most useful in proofs.

We use $m\angle DEF = m\angle GEH$ and $\angle DEF \cong \angle GEH$ interchangeably, as we do $\overline{AB} \cong \overline{CD}$ and $AB = CD$. The form "$m\angle DEF = m\angle GEH$" is most useful when angle measures are to be added (or subtracted).

1-5 pages 22–26

Teaching Suggestions

Objective

Use postulates and theorems relating points, lines, and planes.

Presenting the Lesson

The best teaching models to illustrate Postulates 5–9 and Theorems 1-1, 1-2, and 1-3 are drawings and physical models that illustrate the relationships involved. As the postulates and theorems are illustrated on the chalkboard, have students make their own drawings.

Through the construction of many examples, students will begin to develop powers of visualization to the point where they can "see" how to complete sentences when asked, for example, "If two planes intersect, then . . . ."

In addition to using drawings, demonstrate the postulates and theorems using objects, such as a piece of string, a piece of cardboard, and marbles. Remind students during these demonstrations that objects are imperfect representations of abstract geometric ideas, but they are helpful in thinking about geometry. Point out also that geometric ideas are precise models for physical objects.

Extension

Ask students to prove Theorem 1-3: If two lines intersect, then exactly one plane contains the lines. Hint: Use the diagrams below and Exercise 20 as a guide.

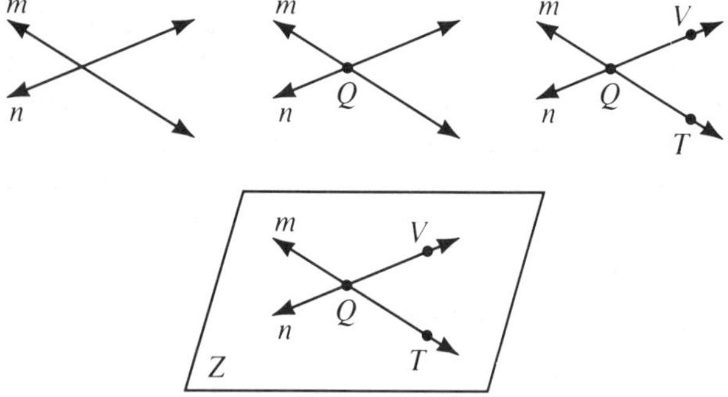

Problem Solving

Emphasize to students that theorems are problems that have been solved and that the solution is called a proof. Students are introduced to the idea of proof in Classroom Exercise 1 and Written Exercise 20. However, it is not necessary to dwell on the idea of proof in this lesson. Proofs of the incidence theorems are subtle and consequently difficult for beginning students of geometry.

The ideas of this lesson are important because they are at the foundation of geometry. Students should study the postulates and theorems relating points, lines, planes to the extent that they can do so successfully and with a feeling of achievement. In particular, students should understand that the first three theorems follow from the postulates. To demonstrate how Theorem 1-1 follows from the postulates, go through Classroom Exercise 1 in class. Then tell students that demonstrations of the other two theorems are similar. With this approach, students can work the exercises with zest, applying the postulates and theorems in appropriate situations.

Cooperative Learning

You may wish to form groups of about four students each to review the answers to Written Exercises 1–12 in class. Monitor the groups by listening to their discussions, providing assistance when needed. Observe who the group leaders are for further reference in setting up groups. Encourage all students to participate in offering their solutions to the exercises. Encourage them also to ask questions and to make comments on other students' solutions.

2 *Deductive Reasoning*

Chapter 2 introduces students to deductive reasoning and the deductive method in writing proofs. Although some students may have had a few experiences in writing proofs in algebra, the content of this chapter will be new to almost all students. The intent of the chapter is simply to give students a first taste of the nature of mathematical proof.

The chapter opens with a discussion of *if-then statements* because of their central role in teaching students to think logically. Sometimes the illustrative material is geometric, sometimes it is algebraic, and sometimes it involves ordinary concerns that are not mathematical. The nonmathematical examples will help many students understand the ideas on an intuitive level.

The second lesson is devoted to algebraic properties, examples, and exercises that show how the properties can be applied to prove simple statements involving segment length and angle measure. Students are introduced to the idea of a proof written in two-column form.

Lesson 2-3 states and proves the Midpoint Theorem and the Angle Bisector Theorem, using the properties from algebra, as well as previously introduced definitions and postulates. The properties from algebra are treated as postulates. Thus, students see their first examples of deductive reasoning and learn that statements can be proved by reasoning from postulates, definitions, theorems that have already been proved, and given information.

Complementary and supplementary angles are defined in Lesson 2-4 and the theorem that vertical angles are congruent is proved. Then, in Lesson 2-5, three theorems involving perpendicular lines are stated with their proofs left for students to do as exercises. Throughout these two lessons, the theorems as well as the exercises help students to understand deductive reasoning and mathematical proof.

The concluding lesson of the chapter, Lesson 2-6, focuses attention on the process of planning a proof. In so doing, students have an opportunity to review the parts of a proof introduced in previous lessons of the chapter.

2-1 pages 33–35

Teaching Suggestions

Objectives

1. Recognize the hypothesis and the conclusion of an if-then statement.
2. State the converse of an if-then statement.
3. Use a counterexample to disprove an if-then statement.
4. Understand the meaning of *if and only if*.

Presenting the Lesson

The circle diagram that follows (also called a Venn diagram or Euler circle) can be used as a model to help students understand if-then statements. For example, suppose the conditional "If p, then q" is true. Then the circle for p is inside the circle for q, and whenever the hypothesis p is true, the conclusion q is also true.

When p is true, tell students to think of a point inside circle p. That point is automatically inside circle q. The conclusion q is true.

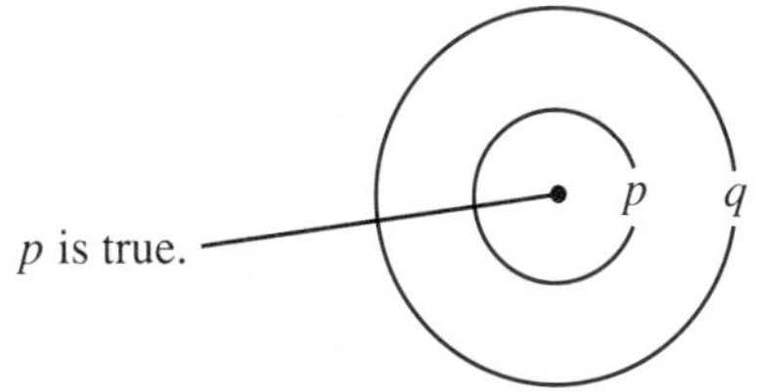

If p, then q.

Explain that a circle diagram also illustrates the relationship of a statement and its converse. A point inside q is not necessarily inside p, and thus a true statement may have a false converse. Venn diagrams are also used in Lesson 6-2.

Problem Solving

Some problems can be solved by finding an example that shows the statement of the problem to be false. Many students are not familiar with this procedure, but they need to be in order to understand deductive reasoning and mathematical proof. Point out to students that a counterexample solves a problem in a negative sense by disproving it. Ask students to give a counterexample to this statement: If four points are in a plane, then the points are in a line.

Using Technology

Geometric construction programs can be used to create counterexamples. Below are some statements that can be disproved by using counterexamples.

1. If a triangle is isosceles, then it is a right triangle.
2. The sum of the lengths of any two sides of a triangle is always less than the length of the third side of the triangle.
3. The bisector of an angle of a triangle bisects the opposite side.

Extension

With a very capable class of students, you may want to introduce the language of *necessary* and *sufficient* conditions. For example, let r and s represent the following statements:

r: Springfield is a town in Ohio.
s: Springfield is a town in the USA.

Point out that the truth of r guarantees the truth of s. Knowing that r is true gives you sufficient information to conclude that s is true. We say that r is *sufficient* for s. But r is not *necessary* for s. The particular Springfield could be the one in Massachusetts, Illinois, Missouri, or several other states; such a town satisfies s without satisfying r. Although r is not necessary for s, s is necessary for r.

In general, the following circle diagram shows that p is sufficient for q and q is necessary for p whenever we have the conditional "If p, then q."

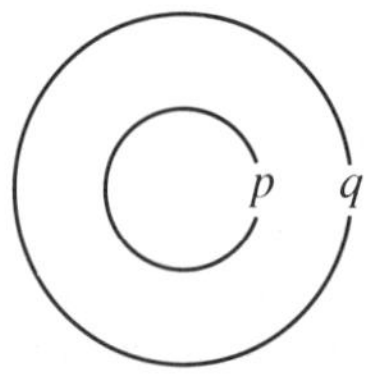

2-2 pages 37–43

Teaching Suggestions

Objective

Use properties from algebra and properties of congruence in proofs.

Presenting the Lesson

The two-column form for writing a geometric proof serves well as a model for teaching students how to organize their thoughts into a proof. The first proofs students see are very simple. Some students will need all the steps given in the text in order to understand the flow of a proof. Other students will understand the flow better if they are permitted to write shortened proofs. Allowing students to shorten a proof by combining some steps helps them to concentrate on the essence of the proof without being distracted by minor steps. However, it will take effort, time, and patience for students to achieve success in writing proofs.

Making Connections

Some students may be surprised to see properties from algebra in a geometry book. They should understand that work in geometry involves the real numbers. The text helps keep algebraic skills sharp by providing in the exercise sets frequent problems that require the use of algebraic techniques. Substantial sets of algebra review exercises are also provided throughout the book.

Cooperative Learning

Classroom Exercises 11 and 12 and Written Exercises 1–10 give students practice in supplying reasons and statements before they have to attempt to write their own "original" proofs. Although the four exercises of the latter type (Written Exercises 11–14) are classified as B exercises, all students who take enough time and who have proper guidance should be able to have some success with the proofs. You may wish to have students work in pairs or small groups on the proofs. Students can take turns supplying a statement or a reason for each proof. You may wish to assign only one or two proofs to each group. Volunteers from four groups can demonstrate each of the four proofs at the chalkboard.

2-3 pages 43–48

Teaching Suggestions

Objectives

1. Use the Midpoint Theorem and the Angle Bisector Theorem.
2. Know the kinds of reasons that can be used in proofs.

Presenting the Lesson

The Midpoint Theorem and the Angle Bisector Theorem are introduced in this lesson to provide more examples of two-column proofs and to shorten future proofs involving midpoints and angle bisectors.

Many students have difficulty understanding proofs and how to write them. The proofs of the two theorems in this lesson should be discussed thoroughly with students. When you discuss the reasons that are used in the proofs, point out that each reason is one of the types listed in the summary box on page 45.

Using Technology

The first Computer Key-In is on page 48. Students who do the Key-In should understand that Line 50 is based on the relationship developed in Exercise 19, page 47. P(N) is the midpoint, the average of the two previous positions P(N − 1) and P(N − 2). Most of the Computer Key-Ins can be done independently by students, even by those who have not had much experience in programming in BASIC. Some of the Key-Ins will require more familiarity with the language.

Problem Solving

Students need to learn to make conjectures in their mathematics courses and then to try to prove or disprove their conjectures. A good strategy to use throughout the course to develop students' abilities to make conjectures is to choose almost any proof, copying the "Given" on the chalkboard but omitting the "Prove." Then ask students what deductions they can make.

Reinforcement

One of the reasons why students have difficulty in writing proofs is that they must remember many facts introduced earlier in the course to use in a proof. Thus, it is very important to continually review and reinforce the meanings of key definitions, postulates, and theorems that will appear as reasons in proofs.

Communication Skills

Reading and writing proofs are important communication skills that are necessary for success in geometry. Students should be asked occasionally to read aloud in class the statements and reasons in a proof in order for you to check their ability to read geometry correctly. Written proofs should be reviewed with students so they can make corrections and improve their ability to write a proof.

2-4 pages 50–55

Teaching Suggestions

Objectives

1. Apply the definitions of complementary and supplementary angles.
2. State and use the theorem about vertical angles.

Presenting the Lesson

Students sometimes want to apply the term *complementary* to three or more angles whose measures total 90. You will need to point out that the terms *complementary* and *supplementary* apply only to pairs of angles. If a student asks what name is used for three or more angles whose measure sum is 90, you can reply that no one has dealt with such sets of angles enough to find it desirable or useful to assign a name to them.

Problem Solving

Some students have difficulty solving problems involving supplements or complements. Suppose a student who uses x for the measure of an angle has trouble figuring out what to use for the measure of the supplement. Ask students to look for a pattern when answering this series of questions.

a. If the measure of an angle is 20, what is the measure of the supplement?

b. If the measure of an angle is 80, what is the measure of the supplement?

c. If the measure of an angle is 120, what is the measure of the supplement?

d. If the measure of an angle is 179, what is the measure of the supplement?

e. What did you do in each case to get your answer?

Explain to students that when the measure of one angle is x, they need to subtract x from 180. Indicate the subtraction by writing $180 - x$.

Reinforcement

The following exercises can be used to reinforce the concepts of this lesson.

In the diagram, $\overrightarrow{YG}$ bisects $\angle FYH$. Complete.

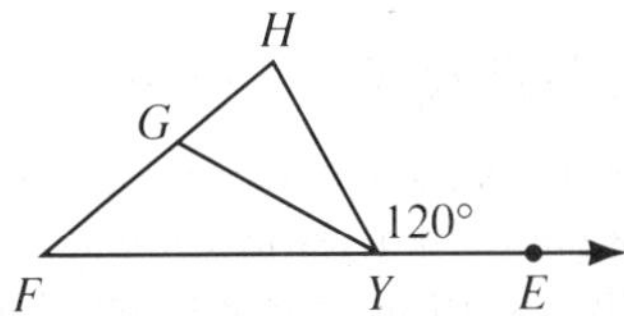

1. $m\angle FYH$ = 60

2. $m\angle FYG$ = 30

3. $m\angle GYE$ = 150

2-5 pages 56–60

Teaching Suggestions

Objective

Apply the definition and theorems about perpendicular lines.

Presenting the Lesson

Many examples of perpendicular lines exist in the real world. After discussing the presentation in the book, ask students to suggest physical examples of perpendicular lines, for example, the lines represented by the edges of a sheet of writing paper. In drawing perpendicular lines on the chalkboard, use illustrations that have many different orientations in the plane of the chalkboard. Some students seem to think that all perpendicular lines need to be drawn like those shown on page 56.

Using Technology

The experiments on page T77 introduce students to geometric construction programs. In the experiment below, students will draw angle bisectors and discover perpendicular lines.

Experiment Draw any triangle. Extend one of the sides. This extended side forms a new angle with a side of the triangle and is called an exterior angle. Bisect the exterior angle just formed. Bisect the angle of the triangle adjacent to this exterior angle. Measure the angles formed by the two angle bisectors. Repeat the experiment on another triangle and make a conjecture. Try to prove your conjecture.

Cooperative Learning

Proofs of the three theorems in this lesson can be done in small groups. Have each group draw and label a diagram, list what is given and what is to be proved, and write a two-column proof for Theorem 2-4. Choose a representative from each group to write the proof on the chalkboard. Try to have all proofs of this theorem on the chalkboard at the same time. Compare and discuss the different proofs as a class. Then repeat this procedure for the other two theorems.

2-6 pages 60–65

Teaching Suggestions

Objectives

1. State and apply the theorems about angles supplementary to, or complementary to, congruent angles.
2. Plan proofs and then write them in two-column form.

Presenting the Lesson

This lesson summarizes the parts of a proof and lays the foundation for writing proofs. Students will need a great deal of experience in planning proofs before they will be able to do original proofs that do not follow a pattern they have observed in the book's proofs.

Begin the lesson by reviewing the five parts of the proof of a theorem. Ask students to explain each part in their own words. Then introduce the idea of developing a plan for a proof before any attempt is made to write the proof. Provide students with some examples of plans, such as reasoning back from what needs to be proved, or studying the proofs of previously proven theorems. Ask students if they can suggest any plans they may have used in previous mathematics courses to *solve problems*. Point out that planning a proof is really planning how to solve a problem; thus, any problem-solving strategies students know can be discussed in this lesson.

Making Connections

One of the reasons why students have major difficulties in learning to write proofs is that there is no guiding method they can learn to use in constructing a proof. To a student, each proof is an original that requires a new insight or display of ingenuity. To help students over this hurdle, this Teacher's Edition suggests the use of coordinate techniques whenever appropriate to prove theorems and do exercises. Coordinate geometry introduces a methodology for proving geometric theorems, and students should be allowed to use both analytic as well as synthetic methods in proving theorems.

Communication Skills

When a proof is planned during class discussion, it is appropriate to encourage informal language. Emphasize that there is more than one way to present a proof. Certainly the wording and the order of presenting statements will vary from one student to the next; sometimes basic strategies will be different.

Some students like to begin proofs by listing all the given information in the statement column. This procedure may help some students to get started. However, when information is introduced at the point where it is used, a proof flows more logically.

3 *Parallel Lines and Planes*

The chapter begins by considering the notion of parallelism. After a discussion of parallel lines and planes, the concept of a transversal is introduced. Interior, exterior, alternate interior, same-side interior, and corresponding angles are then defined, and students are given practice in identifying these angles.

The second lesson discusses the properties of parallel lines. Students who have used protractors in experiments with parallel lines will readily accept the postulate: "If two parallel lines are cut by a transversal, then corresponding angles are congruent." This postulate enables students to prove a number of theorems, establishing ways to prove angles congruent or supplementary.

Lesson 3-3 analyzes the converse of the postulate used in Lesson 3-2. This postulate is used to develop several theorems that lines are parallel given certain information about the angles formed by a transversal. It is also used to develop the key theorems that through a point outside a line there is exactly one line parallel to the given line and one line perpendicular to the given line.

The fourth lesson discusses the different types of triangles, and applies properties of parallel lines to prove the important theorem about the sum of the measures of the angles of a triangle. The notion of angle sums in other convex polygons is presented in Lesson 3-5.

The last lesson is about inductive reasoning. Inductive and deductive reasoning are compared and contrasted.

At the end of this chapter, you will find two useful reviews. The Algebra Review on the coordinate plane is designed to reinforce students' knowledge of algebra, and to sharpen algebraic skills that the students will need in subsequent geometry work. The Cumulative Review provides another opportunity for students to practice the geometric skills taught in the current chapter and in previous chapters.

3-1 pages 73–78

Teaching Suggestions

Objectives

1. Distinguish between intersecting lines, parallel lines, and skew lines.
2. State and apply the theorem about the intersection of two parallel planes by a third plane.
3. Identify the angles formed when two lines are cut by a transversal.

Presenting the Lesson

Because students often have an intuitive grasp of the concept of parallel lines, this lesson can be a confidence-builder for the entire chapter. In a class discussion, ask students to define in their own terms lines that are parallel, not parallel, coplanar, or skew. Ask how they think parallel segments should be defined. Having students give definitions in their own words often helps them understand and remember concepts.

When you sketch lines cut by a transversal on the chalkboard, it is best to use numbers to name the angles formed so that students can identify them more quickly. Be sure to vary your drawings, sometimes making the parallel lines vertical with the transversal cutting across diagonally, and sometimes making the lines not parallel. Students often have the mistaken idea that a transversal cuts only parallel lines.

Applications

There are several examples in your classroom that can be used to illustrate parallel planes, parallel lines, and skew lines—the ceiling, floor, walls, and their intersections. For a further discussion of these concepts, you can label the corners of a cardboard box and ask students to identify various lines and planes. To demonstrate skew lines, use two pencils or pointers.

Communication Skills

With the introduction of a transversal, point out that the prefix *trans* means *across*. Ask students to think of other words that use the prefix *trans*.

3-2 pages 78–82

Teaching Suggestions

Objective

State and apply a postulate and theorems about parallel lines.

Presenting the Lesson

We begin deductive work with parallels by assuming a property with considerable intuitive appeal. You may wish to prepare copies of several diagrams representing transversals cutting parallel lines for your students to use. By measuring many different sets of corresponding angles with a protractor, students should become comfortable with Postulate 10. Then ask them to consider which other angles are congruent when lines are parallel. If they have not done Written Exercise 19 in Lesson 3-1, suggest that they test their hypotheses by using a protractor and the parallel lines on their notebook pages, or on the copies of parallel lines you have prepared.

Reinforcement

When considering same-side interior angles, some students may think that these angles are also congruent to each other. Again, measuring angles will be helpful, and the drawing of some extreme cases should convince most students that same-side angles are not usually congruent. Ask students when the angles will be congruent. The drawing activity provides an opportunity to review with students what information can and cannot be assumed from a diagram.

Communication Skills

A student may misstate Theorem 3-4 by saying: "If a *line* is perpendicular to one of two parallel lines, then it is perpendicular to the other one also." To show that this statement is incorrect, you can draw two parallel lines on the chalkboard; then, at a point on one of the lines, hold a pointer perpendicular to the chalkboard. This is a case where students can recognize the need for precision of language. Review the fact that the term *transversal* refers to intersecting coplanar lines and thus cannot be replaced by the term *line* in the statement of Theorem 3-4.

3-3 pages 83–88

Teaching Suggestions

Objectives

1. State and apply the postulates and theorems about parallel lines.
2. State and apply the theorems about a parallel and a perpendicular to a given line through a point outside the line.

Presenting the Lesson

There are two postulates and six theorems presented in this lesson. After discussing Postulates 10 and 11, you can prove Theorems 3-5, 3-6, and 3-7 by using Postulate 11. When presenting Theorems 3-8, 3-9, and 3-10, ask students to suggest ways that these theorems can be proved.

Theorem 3-10 is very useful in subsequent exercises and one that students can understand and remember easily. The coplanar case is proved in Classroom Exercise 20. A proof for the noncoplanar case is not appropriate for a first-year geometry book. If you do not like to have students use a theorem in which one case is unproved, then you may wish to have your students regard the noncoplanar case as a postulate.

Using Technology

Encourage students to practice drawing parallel lines with a construction program and proving that lines in a construction are parallel. The following triangle experiments give students such practice.

Experiment 1 Draw any triangle. Label the midpoints of the three sides and draw three segments, joining pairs of midpoints. List all sets of parallel lines and use various ways to prove that the lines are parallel.

Experiment 2 Draw any triangle. Extend a side to form an exterior angle. Through the vertex not on the extended side, draw a line parallel to the extended side. Draw the bisector of the exterior angle and the bisector of the exterior angle formed by the parallel line. Label the intersection of the two bisectors and find the measure of the angle formed. Repeat the experiment on a different type of triangle.

Making Connections

The original statement of Euclid's Fifth Postulate is: "If a straight line falling on two straight lines makes the interior angles on the same side less than two right angles, the two straight lines, if produced indefinitely, meet on that side on which are the angles less than the two right angles." Some modern books on geometry state this postulate in the form: "Through a point outside a line, there is exactly one line parallel to the given line." For historical reasons, this statement is often called the *Parallel Postulate*, but there are other possible choices for making assumptions about parallels. Because Euclid's Fifth Postulate is open to different interpretations, we have chosen to make the necessary assumptions about parallels in Postulates 10 and 11 and state the existence and uniqueness of a parallel line as Theorem 3-8. This theorem can be used immediately to prove Theorem 3-11 (the sum of the measures of the angles of a triangle is 180), which allows us to study angles of a polygon earlier in the course. If we had chosen instead to state Postulate 10 as a theorem, we would have needed to postpone the proof of this statement until the study of triangle congruence. A more complete discussion of the rationale for our development of a geometry can be found in the Extra entitled "Non-Euclidean Geometries" on pages 233–234.

Communication Skills

Postulate 11 is the converse of Postulate 10, and Theorem 3-5 is the converse of Theorem 3-2. Emphasizing what is given and what is concluded in each case provides a good review of converses and sharpens students' communication skills.

3-4 pages 93–99

Teaching Suggestions

Objectives

1. Classify triangles according to sides and to angles.
2. State and apply the theorem and the corollaries about the sum of the measures of the angles of a triangle.
3. State and apply the theorem about the measure of an exterior angle of a triangle.

Presenting the Lesson

Many students are awed by the fact that no matter how obtuse or how acute a triangle is, the sum of the measures of the angles is always 180. You can ask students if they can conceive of any way of proving Theorem 3-11 without drawing an auxiliary line, or conceive of any way of proving the theorem without using parallel lines.

Using Technology

The following experiment involves identifying parallel lines, perpendicular lines, and different types of triangles.

Experiment Draw an equilateral triangle. Trisect each side. Join all the points of trisection to form a six-sided figure (hexagon) with all the diagonals drawn in. Label the vertices of the hexagon. Find (and verify) parallel lines and perpendicular lines. Also find (and verify) equilateral, isosceles, scalene, right, obtuse, and acute triangles. Repeat the experiment with a scalene triangle. Which lines are still parallel? Which lines are still perpendicular?

Enrichment

Using a large globe, have a student trace the path a plane takes when it flies from a South American point on the equator directly to the North Pole. Ask another to trace the path of a plane that flies from a point on the equator in Africa directly to the North Pole. Ask: What angle does each flight make with the equator? What is the measure of the angle formed at the North Pole by the flight paths? Tell students that the two flight paths and the equator form a *spherical triangle*.

Point out that the sum of the measures in a spherical triangle is always more than 180. In a plane, the sum of the measures of a triangle is always exactly 180.

3-5 pages 101–105

Teaching Suggestions

Objectives

1. Recognize and name convex polygons and regular polygons.
2. Find the measures of interior angles and exterior angles of convex polygons.

Presenting the Lesson

The idea of a convex polygon is grasped quickly by students. You can draw one on the chalkboard and say: "This is a convex polygon." Then draw a concave polygon and say: "This figure is a polygon, but it is not convex; it is concave." Finally, draw a couple of figures that aren't polygons at all.

Students need to know what a polygon is intuitively, and a precise definition is unimportant. Some definitions are important because they are applied in proofs—for example, the definition of perpendicular lines. But the definition of a convex polygon will not be used in proofs.

Problem Solving

When students work with angle measures of polygons they usually reveal preferences for different approaches. For example, consider this problem: Find the measure of each interior angle of a regular polygon with 20 sides.

A student who memorizes formulas will write: "sum of measures = $(n - 2)180$," and proceed from there. This student may even have memorized the formula $\frac{(n-2)180}{n}$. Another student may simply think: "Clearly an exterior angle has measure 360/20 or 18. That leaves 180 − 18, or 162, for the interior angle." No one is obligated to use a particular approach. He or she has the privilege of choosing any correct method.

Cooperative Learning

Groups of students can be used to illustrate the meaning of Theorem 3-14. Each group can select a different convex polygon for the theorem. Then a student volunteer from each group can help his or her classmates learn Theorem 3-14 in a way that promotes retention. Use the largest open floor space in a room and draw (on suitable floors) a large polygon. On other floors, you can lay books for the vertices and ask students to imagine the sides. Label the vertices with consecutive letters. Let the demonstrator move slowly from A to B, executing in a deliberate way, a turn at B before proceeding to C, and so on until the person reaches A and turns to face B. Ask students to tell how much the demonstrator's body turned or rotated in total. (One complete rotation, or 360 degrees.) Point out that the amount of turn is determined by the exterior angle at that vertex.

3-6 pages 106–109

Teaching Suggestions

Objective

Understand and use inductive reasoning.

Presenting the Lesson

In addition to using number sequences when teaching this lesson, use alphabetic sequences such as O, T, T, F, F, . . . (One, Two, Three, Four, Five, . . .) or S, M, T, W, T, . . . (Sunday, Monday, Tuesday, Wednesday, Thursday, . . .). Written Exercise 26 demonstrates the fallacy of drawing conclusions from a limited set of data.

Point out that an infant learns many things during the first year of life, most of them by thinking inductively. Ask students to name some conclusions a typical infant would be apt to reach inductively.

Enrichment

When giving examples of number sequences, include some that have more than one plausible rule by which to select the next number. For example, the pattern 3, 5, 7, . . . could be continued as 3, 5, 7, 9, 11, . . . using consecutive odd integers, or it could be continued as 3, 5, 7, 11, 13, . . . using consecutive prime numbers. Encourage students to develop more sequences such as this one.

Making Connections

Call attention to the three examples on page 106, and point out the similarities between these examples and the following: A physician takes a case history, hoping that a diagnosis will be suggested. A professional athlete pays attention to the moves an opponent has made in the past, hoping to do better next time. A scientist records measurements and draws graphs, hoping to discover an underlying relationship.

Cooperative Learning

Divide your class into four groups. Have two groups create examples of deductive reasoning for presentation to the class and the other two groups create examples of inductive reasoning for presentation to the class. Tell students that they can use examples from both mathematics and real life. Have one of the deductive groups and one of the inductive groups present examples with valid reasoning, and the other two groups present examples with invalid reasoning. The group looking for examples of invalid deductive reasoning (see Classroom Exercise 14 on page 80) should contain some of your better students.

Have each of several groups of students make out a list of problems that permit a conclusion based on inductive reasoning. Then have groups exchange lists and solve the problems.

4 *Congruent Triangles*

This chapter extends the concept of congruence, moving from the segments and angles studied earlier to triangles and other polygons. An intuitive feeling for *same size and shape* leads to a precise definition of congruent triangles. Students, in general, have difficulty with an abstract development of the notion of a correspondence and then of congruence as a type of correspondence. Students need to acquire the skill of looking at diagrams carefully and making visual judgments about which figures seem to be congruent. The exercises develop such skills as well as the ability to use precise terminology.

The second lesson states three postulates for congruence—SSS, SAS, and ASA. Each postulate will seem reasonable to students who think critically about figures. After practice in proving triangles congruent, students are ready, in Lesson 4-3, to use congruent triangles to prove certain segments congruent and certain angles congruent. Visual judgment continues to be important. First a student needs to decide—by looking at a figure—what triangles to work with so that particular segments and angles can be treated as corresponding parts. Then a proof is written to show that the corresponding parts are congruent.

Lesson 4-4 deals with the Isosceles Triangle Theorem and its converse. Again, visual judgment is involved. The theorems and their corollaries are applied in proof exercises. Other exercises provide for meaningful use of equation-solving skills. The final two methods for proving triangles congruent (AAS and HL) are presented as theorems in Lesson 4-5.

The fact that congruence problems can be quite involved becomes evident in Lesson 4-6. Sometimes it is necessary to prove one pair of triangles congruent in order to get corresponding congruent parts that are used in another pair of triangles. Listing only the key steps of a proof, or writing a proof in paragraph form, can help students keep the main ideas in mind.

The final lesson of the chapter introduces and defines medians, altitudes, and perpendicular bisectors. The exercises permit students to complete the chapter by planning and writing more proofs.

4-1 pages 117–121

Teaching Suggestions

Objective

Identify the corresponding parts of congruent figures.

Presenting the Lesson

After pages 117 and 118 have been discussed, you can hold up two textbooks and point out that it would be reasonable to apply the word *congruent* to them, even though the congruence of three-dimensional objects has not been defined yet. Ask students to name other pairs of objects in the classroom that can be described as congruent. (Some possible answers: two new pieces of chalk, two paper clips, two student desk tops)

Applications

Point out that using graph paper or a template to draw diagrams yields congruent figures. The spark plugs in the engine of a new car are interchangeable; they are congruent. Ask students to name congruent objects they have encountered outside of school. If students have trouble thinking of examples, you can suggest that they think of building materials, hardware, or items in a grocery story or a clothing store.

Using Technology

If your geometric construction program can draw reflections of points in lines or lines in other lines, now is a good time to introduce geometric transformations using reflections. Students will see the connection between reflections and congruence in the following experiment.

Experiment Draw any $\triangle ABC$ and do the following:

(a) Reflect point A in $\overline{BC}$ and label image D. Draw $\overline{DB}$ and $\overline{DC}$. $\triangle DBC$ is the reflection of $\triangle ABC$ in $\overline{BC}$. $\triangle DBC$ is also called the *image* of $\triangle ABC$.

(b) Reflect point B in $\overline{AC}$ and label image E. Draw $\overline{EA}$ and $\overline{EC}$.

(c) Reflect point C in $\overline{AB}$ and label image F. Draw $\overline{FA}$ and $\overline{FB}$.

(d) Measure all segments. What sides correspond to $\overline{AB}$? to $\overline{BC}$? to $\overline{AC}$? What is the relationship between each side of $\triangle ABC$ and its reflections?

(e) List all congruent triangles.

Enrichment

Ask students what they think about the possibility of two snowflakes being congruent. Ask also if the word *congruent* is suitable for a pair of gloves. It is not necessary for all students to agree. Have students describe in their own words the relationship between a left-hand and right-hand glove.

Making Connections

In this chapter, the word *congruent* and the symbol $\cong$ are used for two polygons that have the same size and shape. In Chapter 7, the word *similar* and the symbol $\sim$ are used for two polygons that have the same shape. In the diagram below, triangles ABC and DEF are congruent whereas triangles ABC and RST are similar. Point out to students that the equal sign is a part of the congruence symbol.

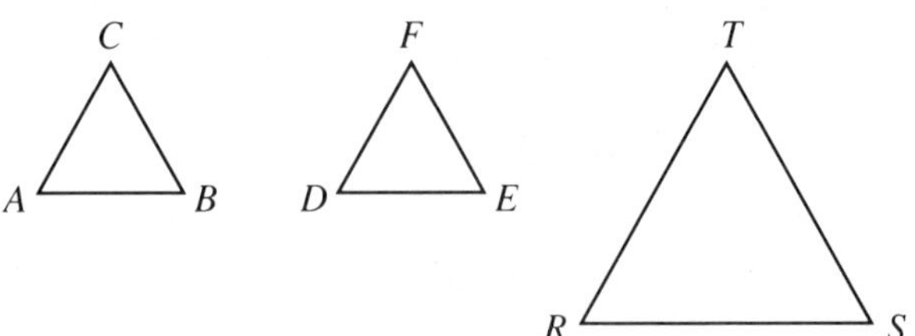

Cooperative Learning

Draw on the chalkboard a diagram like the one shown below. Then form groups of four or five students each, and tell each group to list all possible ways of stating a congruence between the triangles. Give the groups five minutes to do this.

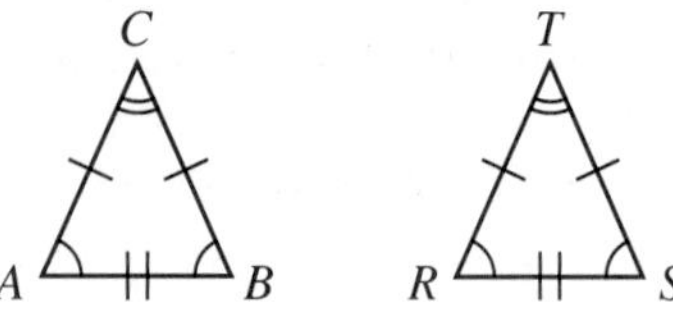

Agree in advance that $\triangle ABC \cong \triangle RST$ and $\triangle RST \cong \triangle ABC$ can be counted as different ways. After the effort, students should realize that some time first spent in assigning parts of the listing to individuals or pairs would have been time well spent. (Twenty-four statements are possible. If equilateral triangles are drawn, seventy-two statements are possible.)

4-2 pages 122–127

Teaching Suggestions

Objective

Prove two triangles congruent by using the SSS Postulate, the SAS Postulate, and the ASA Postulate.

Presenting the Lesson

Some students have such a good sense of size and shape that they know intuitively the truth of the SSS Postulate. Other students may need to see a demonstration with objects. You can use sticks or straws for this activity. Give one student three sticks of varying lengths and ask him or her to form a triangle. Give a second student a duplicate set with the challenge of forming a triangle not congruent to the first one. The class will observe that the challenge cannot be met; therefore it is reasonable to accept Postulate 12.

Using Technology

Students can practice the different ways to draw triangles with a program and at the same time reinforce their understanding of the postulates in this lesson. To those using the Supposer series, three choices are given under the YOUR OWN option to draw a new triangle: SSS, SAS, and ASA.

Extension

When working Exercises 5, 6, 8, 12, and 13 on page 125, some students may insist that the triangles have to be congruent. Suggest that students draw a diagram showing that the triangles do not have to be congruent. For example, the following hint will be useful for Exercise 8: Try to draw the triangles so the included angles, $\angle B$ and $\angle Q$, are clearly not congruent.

Reinforcement

Suggest that students write proofs in two-column form for the diagrams shown under the statements of the postulates on pages 122 and 123. Each of the six proofs needs only four steps. In the second diagram after Postulate 12, the reason for $\overline{OP} \cong \overline{RT}$ can be either "Given" or "Def. of $\cong$ segments."

4-3 pages 127–133

Teaching Suggestions

Objective

Deduce information about segments and angles after proving that two triangles are congruent.

Presenting the Lesson

The language "Corresponding parts of congruent triangles are congruent" is well established in geometry textbooks. Unfortunately, students who learn the statement by rote treat it as a special rule to use as a reason in proofs. Stress to students that it is the definition of congruent triangles that guarantees the congruence of corresponding parts. (See the definition near the top of page 118.) The use of the reason "Definition of congruent triangles" is an excellent alternative wording; students who use it are communicating well. In any event, all students should understand that the definition of congruent triangles specifies that corresponding parts are congruent.

Applications

Average students should try some C exercises, and all students will benefit from an application they can recognize as one they might have thought of themselves. Exercise 15 on page 132 offers an opportunity for you to stimulate your students' thinking.

Problem Solving

Some students begin proofs by automatically copying down everything that is given. To the extent that the process is automatic, it is distinct from reasoning. Encourage students to think of a plan first and then use a fact when and where it helps to implement the plan. Stress that any fact not relevant to a plan is not worth stating in the proof. Ask students to think of a lawyer. A lawyer does not state every fact known to be true in pleading a case. Facts are stated if and when they fit with supporting a goal.

Cooperative Learning

The exercises in this lesson provide a good opportunity for students to help each other learn. Probably the whole class will work together on the Classroom Exercises. Then you can designate groups of four or five students each to do preliminary planning for some of the Written Exercises, beginning with Exercise 3. Suggest that each student assume responsibility for devising a plan for a particular exercise. After preparation time is over, he or she can present the plan to the group. Later, individual students should write their own proofs.

4-4 pages 134–139

Teaching Suggestions

Objective

Apply the theorems and corollaries about isosceles triangles.

Presenting the Lesson

Some students may ask when they see the Plan for Proof for Theorem 4-1: "How do you know you're supposed to draw that line?" The point to get across to students is that a person is not obligated to draw an auxiliary line. Rather, the person has an opportunity to try any approach to solve the problem. Suggest that students think of a football team which scores a touchdown by unexpectedly passing the ball. The spectators applaud the plan and the execution. That does not mean, however, that a pass is always a good idea. Similarly, in mathematics, there are times when drawing an auxiliary line works and there are other times when it does not work.

Using Technology

The following experiment provides a verification of the Isosceles Triangle Theorem, its corollaries, and its converse.

Experiment Draw any triangle with two congruent sides; draw the bisector of the angle between the congruent sides. Measure the angles opposite the congruent sides. What theorem have you verified? In a similar way, verify the three corollaries and the converse of this theorem (see pages 135–136).

Extension

Some students will find a radically different strategy for proving Theorem 4-1 stimulating.

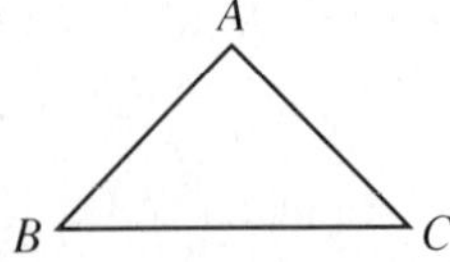

Consider $\triangle BAC$ and $\triangle CAB$. From $\overline{AB} \cong \overline{AC}$, $\overline{BC} \cong \overline{CB}$, and $\overline{AC} \cong \overline{AB}$, we get $\triangle BAC \cong \triangle CAB$ (SSS Postulate). Then, $\angle B \cong \angle C$ (CPCT).

4-5 pages 140–146

Teaching Suggestions

Objectives

1. Use the AAS Theorem to prove two triangles congruent.
2. Use the HL Theorem to prove two right triangles congruent.
3. Prove that two overlapping triangles are congruent.

Presenting the Lesson

One of the most convincing ways to present the AAS Theorem is through the use of numerical examples. Explain to students that this method of proving triangles congruent is a *theorem*, since unlike the previous methods, it can be proved. Students should understand that the AAS Theorem does not apply in all cases in which two angles and a side of one triangle are congruent to two angles and a side of another triangle. Draw diagrams on the chalkboard to help students understand that the AAS Theorem requires that congruent parts must *correspond*. For example, in the diagrams shown below, the first two triangles are congruent to each other, but there is no combination of slide, turn, or flip that will match the third triangle with the first two.

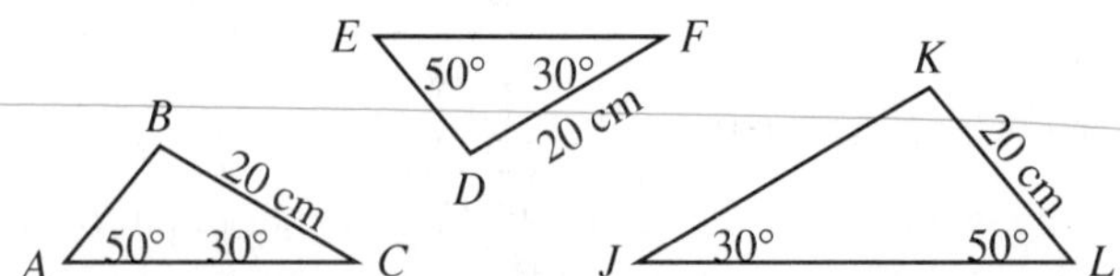

When discussing the summary of ways to prove two triangles congruent given on page 141, you may want to mention to students that all five methods are available for right triangles. The HL method, available for right triangles only, is sometimes the only method that will work.

Extension

The Isosceles Triangle Theorem studied in the previous lesson is used so often that it must have the status of a theorem. You may wish to point out to students that other propositions could be incorporated into the book's list of theorems, but their infrequent use in proofs makes this unnecessary. Classroom Exercise 14 on page 143 shows three propositions that could be called theorems. Not one of these statements would save many steps for students in writing subsequent proofs, so they are not listed as theorems.

A brief discussion of these ideas will extend students' knowledge and understanding of how a deductive system is organized and presented in a geometry textbook. Point out also that the propositions in Exercise 14 may be theorems in other geometry textbooks.

4-6 pages 146–151

Teaching Suggestions

Objective

Prove two triangles congruent by first proving two other triangles congruent.

Presenting the Lesson

Students who draw figures well sometimes do so only because their teacher requires neat papers. In this lesson, you have an opportunity to present the idea that carefully drawn figures can actually save time and effort. Students can use color to emphasize particular relationships. They can redraw parts of diagrams to focus attention on these parts.

Problem Solving

Once the solution to a problem is clear, writing a proof becomes a secondary aspect of the problem-solving process. The two-column form of proofs is used as a pedagogical device to help students learn to write their first proofs. Paragraph proofs, discussed on page 147, are effective because they focus on key ideas and omit unnecessary details. Students should be encouraged to write some proofs in paragraph form.

Communication Skills

The phrases *key steps of a proof*, *paragraph proof*, and *proof in two-column form* should become meaningful to students. Stress to students that the point of view to take in listing a key step in a proof is <u>not</u> to list details that a reader should be able to supply. In a paragraph proof, the goal is to write exactly those facts that give the clearest idea of the reasoning. Most reasons are omitted in the interest of overall effectiveness, and because it is assumed the reader knows the reasons.

4-7 pages 152–158

Teaching Suggestions

Objectives

1. Apply the definitions of the median and the altitude of a triangle and the perpendicular bisector of a segment.
2. State and apply the theorem about a point on the perpendicular bisector of a segment, and the converse.
3. State and apply the theorem about a point on the bisector of an angle, and the converse.

Presenting the Lesson

Some students may find it difficult to draw the altitudes of an obtuse triangle, such as $\triangle ABC$ below.

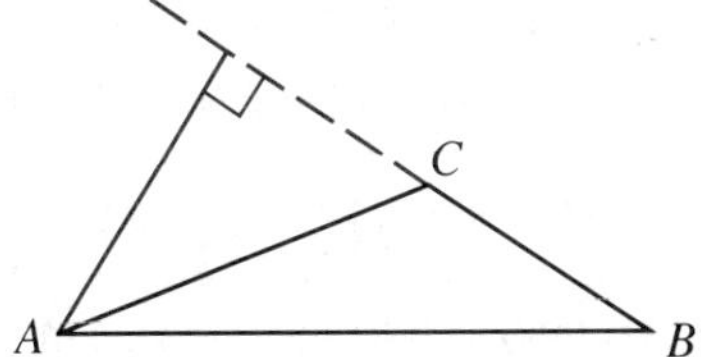

One way to help these students is to reinforce the idea that the altitude is not defined as a perpendicular from point A to segment BC, but as a perpendicular to the *line that contains* $\overline{BC}$. Have students extend the segment BC, in color if necessary. Then the task is simply to draw a perpendicular from point A to the line. Students usually do not have difficulty drawing altitudes if they remember that an altitude does not have to lie in the interior of a triangle.

Making Connections

The relationship expressed in Theorem 4-6 is one that many students recognize without assistance. You may wish to refer students to the diagrams for the game discussed on pages 1 and 2 of the student textbook.

Using Technology

Although the topic of concurrent lines is developed in Lesson 10-3, now is a good time for students to become acquainted with it and to show that medians, altitudes, angle bisectors, and perpendicular bisectors of a triangle are concurrent. See the following experiment and related Exercises 1–6 on page 156.

Experiment For each part, complete the experiment for three different types of triangles and then make a conjecture.

(a) Draw a triangle and its three medians.
(b) Draw a triangle and its three altitudes.
(c) Draw a triangle and the bisectors of its three angles.
(d) Draw a triangle and the perpendicular bisectors of its three sides.

Extension

For a given angle there is just one bisector, and the bisector must lie in the plane of the angle. For a given segment, with no particular plane specified, there are infinitely many perpendicular bisectors, one for each plane that contains the segment. Ask students to describe the figure made up of all the perpendicular bisectors of a segment not lying in any particular plane.

5 *Quadrilaterals*

This chapter begins with a study of the properties of a parallelogram. The proofs of three theorems that introduce the properties also reinforce and extend previous work with congruent triangles and parallel lines.

The second lesson presents the five ways to prove that a quadrilateral is a parallelogram. Students are asked to explore various combinations of angles and segments that are congruent in parallelograms, including some combinations that review algebraic skills.

Four additional theorems involving parallel lines are presented in Lesson 5-3, including the important midpoint theorems for triangles.

The properties of special parallelograms, including the rectangle, rhombus, and square, are developed and proved in Lesson 5-4. Students are encouraged to organize the properties in chart form and to use the properties to calculate the measures of angles and segments in parallelograms.

The chapter concludes with a lesson on trapezoids. The proofs of the theorems, which are done in more than one way and use auxiliary lines, should encourage students to draw several diagrams, if possible, before starting a proof.

5-1 pages 167–171

Teaching Suggestions

Objective

Apply the definition of a parallelogram and the theorems about properties of a parallelogram.

Presenting the Lesson

Most students find the study of properties of parallelograms interesting since it shows the importance of using congruent triangles in proofs. Before discussing Theorems 5-1, 5-2, and 5-3, you may want to provide students with the opportunity to discover the properties themselves. First, write the definition of a parallelogram on the chalkboard and then provide each student with a protractor, a ruler, and one or more sheets of paper that contain diagrams of various parallelograms. Ask students to try to discover as many properties as they can. Encourage drawing lines on the diagrams and give as few instructions as possible. At the end of the allotted time, list the discovered properties on the chalkboard and discuss them. You can then relate them to the theorems and include any properties that were not discovered.

Students frequently believe that the diagonals of a parallelogram are congruent. One convincing way to show that this is not true in general is to build a model of a parallelogram, using tongue depressors for sides, paper fasteners for vertices, and colored rubber bands for diagonals. As the parallelogram is shifted, students will see the diagonals stretch and shrink.

Using Technology

If your program does not draw quadrilaterals but draws triangles, you can use either of the following methods to construct a parallelogram. *Method 1:* Draw $\triangle ABC$. Draw a parallel to $\overline{AC}$ through B with length $2 \cdot AC$. Draw the segment connecting C with the endpoint of the constructed parallel on the same side of $\overline{AB}$ as C. Both $ABEC$ and $ADBC$ are parallelograms. *Method 2:* Draw $\triangle ABC$. Draw a parallel to $\overline{AC}$ through B, then draw a parallel to $\overline{AB}$ through C. Label the intersection of the parallels. This point of intersection, A, B, and C are the vertices of a parallelogram.

Extension

Ask students to explain how Theorem 5-3 can be used to center a picture on a wall. Locate the point of intersection of the diagonals of the wall and place the picture so that its diagonals intersect at the same point on the wall.

Communication Skills

The Classroom Exercises on page 168 provide an excellent opportunity for reviewing symbols and their word forms. When exercises refer to diagrams, it may be beneficial for students to read what is said about the figure and then to say in their own words what they know about the figure. Students should be encouraged to give answers in complete sentences rather than in one or two words.

Cooperative Learning

You may wish to form groups of three to five students to go over Written Exercises 13–16 and 29–32 on pages 169–170. You can assign each group two problems (they are all proofs). Each group should do the following:

1. Assign one person the task of recording the proofs done by the group.
2. Assign another member of the group the leadership position. This student should ask for suggested proof plans, then lead the group in a discussion of the proof, step by step.
3. Each member of the group should be encouraged to make suggestions, offer corrections, or present both alternatives for the plan for proof and each step of the proof to the other members of the group.
4. The leader should continue soliciting ideas until the proof is done. The proof should include full statements of theorems or definitions used.
5. The recorder should record the proof and write it on the chalkboard or on an overhead projector sheet.
6. Another group member can be responsible for presenting the proof to the class.

After the groups have presented their proofs, the class as a whole can discuss and evaluate them.

5-2 pages 172–176

Teaching Suggestions

Objective

Prove that certain quadrilaterals are parallelograms.

Presenting the Lesson

In discussing Theorems 5-4, 5-5, 5-6, and 5-7, it might be helpful to use a hinged-model parallelogram like the one shown in Classroom Exercise 12 or like the one described in Presenting the Lesson, Lesson 5-1 on page T92. Since the sides are hinged at the vertices, the distance between the sides can be varied.

Be sure students understand that the goal of this lesson is to find ways to prove that certain quadrilaterals are parallelograms when it is not known that the opposite sides are parallel. This is in contrast to the goal of Lesson 5-1, where characteristics of parallelograms were deduced on the basis of the definition. Point out to students that it is not necessary to know that both pairs of opposite sides are parallel. Then you may want to have students discover for themselves what given information is sufficient to determine if a quadrilateral is a parallelogram. For example, ask students: "If one pair of opposite sides of a quadrilateral are congruent, then would the quadrilateral necessarily be a parallelogram?" Some students may see that the answer is no and show a counterexample. Then ask: "What can you conclude if both pairs of opposite sides are congruent?" Continuing on in this manner, students should be able to understand the five ways to prove that a quadrilateral is a parallelogram, stated on page 172.

Extension

Have students do the following experiment. Draw a parallelogram with a square along each of its sides. A side of the square should be congruent to each adjacent side of the parallelogram. Connect the midpoints of the diagonals of the squares. What shape is formed? (square) Repeat the experiment for other parallelograms.

Cooperative Learning

Students can demonstrate Theorems 5-4, 5-5, 5-6, and 5-7 by using the models as described in Presenting the Lesson, Lesson 5-1 on page T92. Groups of three or four students can work together. Two pairs of congruent tongue depressors or sticks can be used to demonstrate Theorem 5-4. Theorem 5-5 would need one pair of tongue depressors or sticks, a third tongue depressor or stick to act as a transversal, and a protractor. Theorem 5-6 would need a protractor as well as two pairs of tongue depressors or sticks. The last theorem, Theorem 5-7, would need the same two pairs of tongue depressors, but they would need to be fastened at the middle. Have the groups decide what supplies they will need before you provide them.

5-3 pages 177–182

Teaching Suggestions

Objectives

1. Apply theorems about parallel lines.
2. Apply the midpoint theorems for triangles.

Presenting the Lesson

You can demonstrate Theorem 5-8 by using the same hinged models described in Presenting the Lesson, Lesson 5-1 on page T92. Theorem 5-11 can be investigated by having students find the midpoints of various types of triangles drawn on a sheet of paper. Students should measure the segments connecting the midpoints of the triangle and the sides of the triangle and compare them. They should also note that the segments connecting the midpoints are parallel to the side opposite them in the original triangle.

Using Technology

The following experiment introduces limits using nested triangles. It is also related to Theorem 5-11.

Experiment Draw any triangle, the midpoints of its three sides, and the triangle formed by the three midpoints. Now, draw the midpoints of this new triangle and then the triangle formed by these three midpoints. Repeat this process as many times as you can. You will form a sequence of nested triangles. As the triangles get smaller, they converge on a point. What point is it? Prove the result.

Applications

To illustrate the idea in Theorem 5-9, tell students to think of the grid pattern formed by many city streets.

5-4 pages 184–189

Teaching Suggestions

Objectives

1. Apply the definitions and identify the special properties of a rectangle, a rhombus, and a square.
2. Determine when a parallelogram is a rectangle, rhombus, or square.

Presenting the Lesson

Before discussing the theorems about special parallelograms, you may wish to have students draw and measure rectangles, rhombuses, and squares. This activity helps students develop an intuitive understanding of the theorems and also provides them with an opportunity to develop ruler and protractor skills.

If you made the model of a parallelogram as described in Lesson 5-1 on page T92, you can use it now to show that when the model is adjusted to the shape of a rectangle, the diagonals become congruent.

Using Technology

The Computer Key-In on page 183 has a short BASIC program that given the coordinates of the four vertices of a quadrilateral will output the length of the sides and the diagonals. This provides a good introduction to the coordinate geometry of quadrilaterals.

Problem Solving

You may wish to show the relationships among special types of quadrilaterals by means of the following diagram.

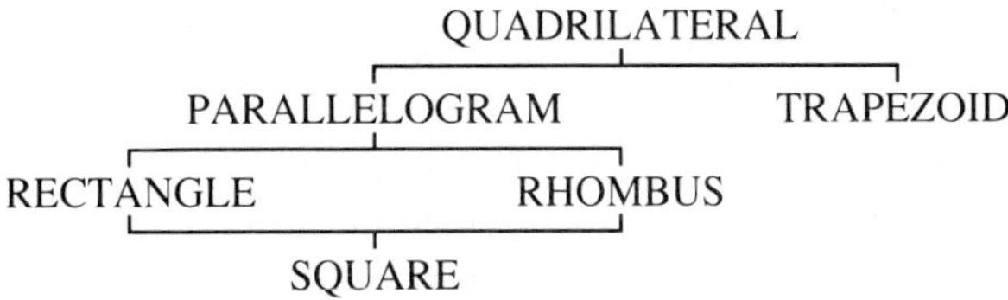

Even though the trapezoid is not defined until the next lesson, you may want to include it in the diagram at this time. Later, you can use the diagram to motivate the study of trapezoids and to summarize the concepts in the chapter.

Reinforcement

It will be helpful for some students to use the diagram above when doing Written Exercises 1–10 and when studying the properties of parallelograms. If students are still having difficulty with the properties, it may be worthwhile to have them answer questions such as the following, which relate more than one special parallelogram.

1. If a parallelogram has congruent diagonals, then it is a rectangle or a square.
2. If a parallelogram has perpendicular diagonals, then it is a rhombus or a square.
3. If a parallelogram has congruent and perpendicular diagonals, then it is a square.
4. If a parallelogram has diagonals that bisect the angles, then it is a rhombus or a square.
5. If a parallelogram has four congruent angles, then it is a rectangle or a square.
6. If a parallelogram has four congruent sides, then it is a rhombus or a square.

Enrichment

Students may wish to explore which parallelograms tessellate a plane (cover it without gaps or overlapping). Patterns that emerge can be very interesting. See Lesson 14-8 for more on tessellations.

5-5 pages 190–194

Teaching Suggestions

Objective

Apply the definitions and identify the properties of a trapezoid and an isosceles trapezoid.

Presenting the Lesson

Your students may understand and appreciate the properties of an isosceles trapezoid better if it is described informally as a "truncated isosceles triangle." A paper model can be made of an isosceles triangle, and then the vertex angle can be cut off or folded over to form an isosceles trapezoid with congruent base angles.

You can use as a model a quadrilateral with four telescoping sides to demonstrate how one pair of parallel sides is sufficient to form a trapezoid from a general quadrilateral. If you form a parallelogram with the model, make a pair of opposite sides noncongruent to show that the quadrilateral becomes a trapezoid.

Using Technology

Have students practice drawing the different types of quadrilaterals using their construction programs. Have them experiment with various methods. For example, to draw a rectangle, start with a right triangle; then from the rectangle, draw a square. They will improve their skills with the programs while reinforcing their understanding of special quadrilaterals and their properties.

Problem Solving

Written Exercises 28 and 29 on page 193 present problems about kites. For those students who have worked these exercises, you may wish to assign the following problem. Prove or disprove this statement: If a diagonal of a quadrilateral divides it into two congruent triangles, then the quadrilateral is a parallelogram. Some students may suggest the following "proof": If a diagonal of a quad. divides it into 2 congruent triangles, the opposite sides of the quad. are congruent. (Corr. parts of $\cong$ $\triangle$s are $\cong$.) Therefore, the quad. is a ▱ by Thm. 5-4.

After discussing any proofs that students may suggest, show them this counterexample. $\overline{AD}$ and $\overline{BC}$ are not congruent and $\overline{DC}$ and $\overline{AB}$ are not congruent.

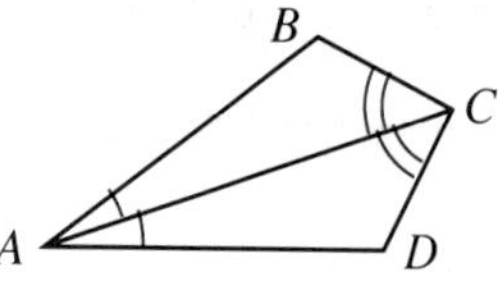

Extension

Written Exercises 21–25 extend the idea that connecting the midpoints of the adjacent sides of a quadrilateral forms a parallelogram. You may need to discuss the justifications for the special kinds of quadrilaterals found in these exercises as well as for trapezoids. Encourage students to choose the most special parallelogram and to justify their choices.

Enrichment

Have students try to draw the shape formed by rotating an isosceles trapezoid about a vertical axis passing through the center. Ask what the solid shape formed is called. (frustum) This shape is a truncated cone. The volume of a cone will be studied in Chapter 12.

Communication Skills

When you introduce the definition of the median of a trapezoid, point out to students that they use the word differently for a triangle. With trapezoids, medians do not originate from vertices but from the midpoints of the legs. Remind students that a trapezoid has only one median, and a triangle has three medians.

6 *Inequalities in Geometry*

The importance of algebraic properties in geometry is emphasized throughout this chapter. Properties of inequality taken from algebra are reviewed in the first lesson and then applied to segment lengths and to angle measures.

The second lesson presents two types of conditionals, the inverse and the contrapositive. The truth or falsity of these statements is discussed, and Venn diagrams are used to help determine whether arguments lead to valid conclusions. Two valid inference patterns are given along with two invalid patterns.

Lesson 6-3 introduces indirect proof with an everyday example of indirect reasoning. Three steps are then given as a summary of the procedure for writing an indirect proof.

Inequalities for one triangle, including the Triangle Inequality theorem, are presented in Lesson 6-4. Two theorems establish the inequality relationships between unequal sides and the angles opposite them in a triangle. All three theorems use the notion that if the sides of a triangle are unequal, the angles opposite them are also "unequal in the same order." Corollaries to these theorems establish that the shortest segment from a point to a line or plane is the perpendicular segment.

In the last lesson of this chapter, the SAS Inequality Theorem and its converse, the SSS Inequality Theorem, describe the inequality relationships between two triangles. The proofs of these theorems reinforce the basic goals of the chapter: to apply algebraic properties of inequality to segment lengths and angle measures, to write indirect proofs, and to state and apply inequality theorems for one or two triangles.

6-1 pages 203–207

Teaching Suggestions

Objectives

1. Apply properties of inequality to positive numbers, lengths of segments, and measures of angles.
2. State and use the Exterior Angle Inequality Theorem.

Presenting the Lesson

Before discussing inequalities in segment lengths and angle measures, be sure to review the algebraic properties of inequality on page 204. Encourage the use of numerical examples for the properties of inequality, and then show how the numbers can represent segment lengths or angle measures. This can be done by using physical models or drawings of segments having the same lengths or angles having the same measures as the numbers used in the numerical examples.

Properties of parallel lines can be used to help students understand the Exterior Angle Inequality Theorem. Draw the following diagram on the chalkboard or make a model out of sticks.

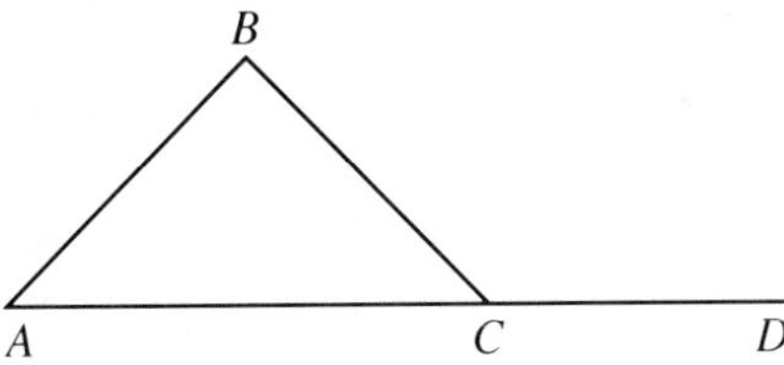

"Slide" a copy of $\overline{AB}$ along $\overrightarrow{AD}$ until point A = point C and $\overline{EC} \parallel \overline{BA}$, as shown below.

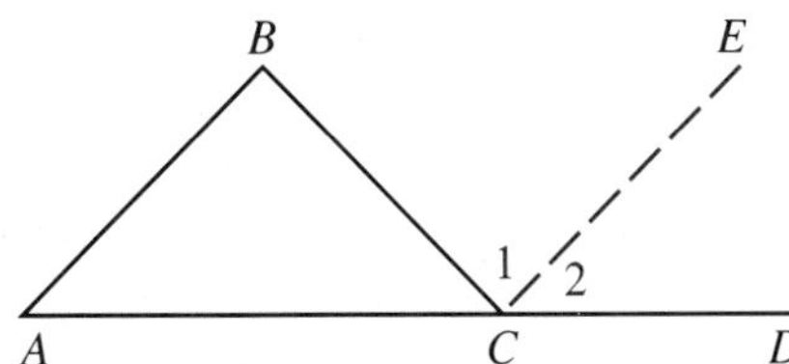

It is easy to see that $\angle BCD$ is larger than either $\angle 1$ or $\angle 2$. Since $\angle 2 \cong \angle A$ and $\angle 1 \cong \angle B$, $\angle BCD$, an exterior angle to $\triangle ABC$, is greater than either of the remote interior angles, $\angle A$ and $\angle B$.

Making Connections

The properties of inequality reinforce the role of algebra in geometry by using numbers and algebraic properties to study segments and angles in geometry.

Extension

Use Theorem 3-12 to find the least possible value for the exterior angle y if $x > 40$.

By Thm. 3-12, $y = x + 10 + x$.
Since $x > 40$, $y > 40 + 10 + 40$.
So, $y > 90$.

Cooperative Learning

Groups of two to three students may review the properties of inequality on page 204 and discuss Classroom Exercises 1–16 on page 205 and Written Exercises 1–4 on page 206. Encourage students to draw diagrams often and to replace the variables with geometric quantities, segment lengths, or angle measures.

6-2 pages 208–212

Teaching Suggestions

Objectives

1. State the contrapositive and inverse of an if-then statement.
2. Understand the relationship between logically equivalent statements.
3. Draw correct conclusions from given statements.

Presenting the Lesson

Venn diagrams provide excellent models for representing conditionals and diagramming the arguments presented on page 209. Emphasize that argument 3, for example, is not valid because Linda can be placed inside or outside the inner circle. If the conclusion can result from either of two contradictory positions in the Venn diagram, the argument is not valid. Encourage students to think of and diagram their own valid or invalid arguments.

Making Connections

Formulating the contrapositive of a conditional is basic to understanding how to prove statements indirectly, the topic of Lesson 6-3. Symbolically, "If p, then q" is logically equivalent to its contrapositive, "If not q, then not p." In an indirect proof, you assume that not q is true and show that a contradiction results because p cannot be true, too.

Reinforcement

The following exercise may be used to review converses and practice formulating the inverse and contrapositive of a statement. For example, the entry in the upper left box of the table states that the converse of the converse of a statement is the original statement. Have students copy and complete the table.

	conv.	inv.	cont.
conv.	orig.	cont.	inv.
inv.	cont.	orig.	conv.
cont.	inv.	conv.	orig.

Extension

Have students diagram each of the following arguments.

1. Given: All runners are athletes.
   Some runners are women.
   Conclusion: Some women are athletes.

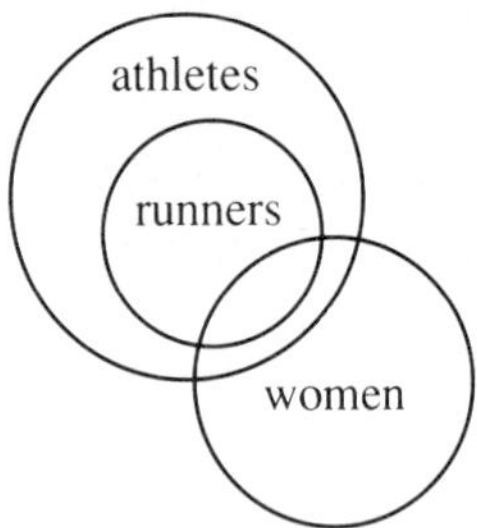

2. Given: Rainy days are tiresome.
   Some holidays are rainy.
   Conclusion: Some holidays are tiresome.

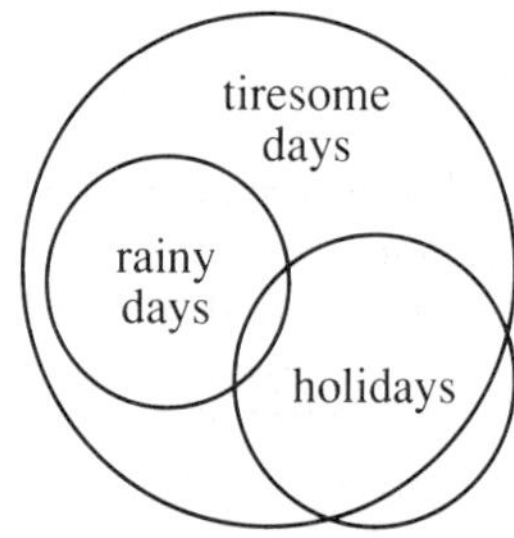

Enrichment

Lewis Carroll wrote the following logic exercise:

Given: Babies are illogical.
Nobody is despised who can manage a crocodile.
Illogical persons are despised.
Conclusion: Babies cannot manage crocodiles.

Although Lewis Carroll deliberately made the statements difficult to follow by not putting the statements in "if-then" form, make the proof understandable by drawing a Venn diagram.

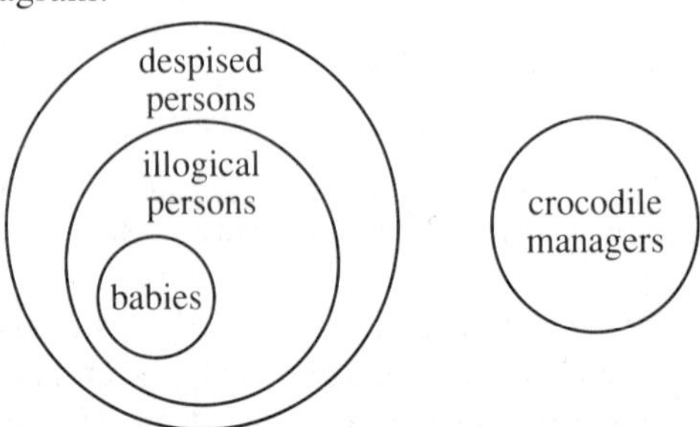

Communication Skills

Symbolic logic is a branch of mathematics in which the statements of a proof are often represented in symbols instead of words. This keeps the content from influencing how the statements are used in inference patterns or proofs. For example, the conditional statement "If two lines are parallel, then the corresponding angles are congruent," might be represented by "If p, then q," where p is the phrase "two lines are parallel," and q is the phrase "corresponding angles are congruent."

Point out to students that there is an appendix on logic that begins on page 644.

6-3 pages 214–217

Teaching Suggestions

Objective

Write indirect proofs in paragraph form.

Presenting the Lesson

A good way to begin this lesson is with an example of your own, perhaps relating it to the class or school. You might use an example similar to the following one:

Alicia's name is on the honor roll for the first semester. Knowing the requirement for making the honor roll, you would conclude that Alicia did not receive any grade lower than an A or B for the first semester. Your reasoning would be as follows:

1. Assume Alicia received a C in at least one course for the first semester.
2. Since one requirement for making the honor roll is to receive only A or B grades, Alicia did not make the honor roll. But this contradicts the known fact that Alicia did make the honor roll.
3. Therefore, the assumption that Alicia received at least one C grade is false. Therefore, Alicia received only A or B grades.

Making Connections

Indirect proofs, along with paragraph and two-column proofs, are the methods of proof now available to your students. They can be used whenever appropriate throughout the course. Note that an indirect proof is used to prove the SSS Inequality Theorem in the next lesson.

Extension

List all possibilities for valid conclusions which could be proved indirectly for the following.

Given: $\triangle ABC$ and $\triangle AYX$ are equilateral; $\overline{AX} < \overline{AB}$

Prove: Answers will vary.
$\triangle ABC \not\cong \triangle AYX$;
$\overline{XA} < \overline{CA}$; $\overline{YX} < \overline{BC}$

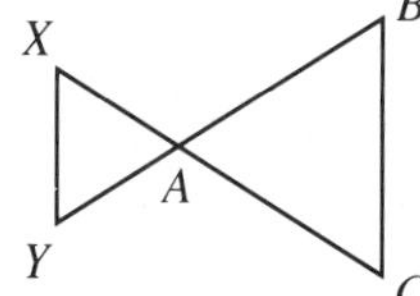

Enrichment

Students usually enjoy logic puzzles like the one below. You might want to bring in logic puzzles on a regular basis to reinforce indirect reasoning and the methods of indirect proof.

Who Found It?
Three detectives were searching a house for the diary of a murder victim. While looking in a safe, a secret passage, and a drawer, they found one real diary and two other fake books. One book was red, one was orange, and one was black. Who found the diary? What color was it? Where was it found? Detective Adams; orange; drawer

1. Detective Cody did not find the black book.
2. Detective Adams found the orange book.
3. Detective Bean found a book, but he hadn't searched the safe.
4. The book Detective Cody found was a fake.
5. The black book was not the diary.
6. One book was found in a secret passage.
7. The book found in a drawer was not black.
8. Detective Adams could not open the safe.

Communication Skills

The first step in an indirect proof is to add "not" to a conclusion, the Prove statement. As you discuss how to write indirect proofs, it might be worthwhile to show equivalent forms of adding "not" to a conclusion.

Conclusion	Equivalent Form After Adding "Not"
$\angle A \cong \angle B$	$\angle A \not\cong \angle B$
$x \geq y$	$x < y$
$a + b < c$	$a + b \geq c$
$\overrightarrow{XY}$ bisects $\angle ZXW$.	$\overrightarrow{XY}$ does not bisect $\angle ZXW$.
Planes S and T are parallel.	Planes S and T do intersect.
$\overline{AB} \parallel \overline{CD}$	$\overline{AB}$ intersects $\overline{CD}$ or $\overline{AB}$ and $\overline{CD}$ are skew.
$m\angle XYZ = 50$	$m\angle XYZ > 50$ or $m\angle XYZ < 50$

6-4 pages 219–223

Teaching Suggestions

Objective

State and apply the inequality theorems and corollaries for one triangle.

Presenting the Lesson

An excellent teaching model to illustrate Theorems 6-2 and 6-3 is a triangle with hinged, telescoping sides. Some commercially available models even have protractors at the hinged vertices. As you "pull out" or increase the length of one side, it is easy to see that the angle opposite that side increases.

In addition to using drawings to illustrate the triangle inequality, encourage students to make stick models of triangles with sides of various lengths. As different lengths for sides are put together, some combinations might not work. Those lengths which do not fit the conditions of the triangle inequality will not form triangles.

Using Technology

The following experiments can be used to introduce or reinforce the three theorems in this lesson. Experiments 2 and 3 deal specifically with The Triangle Inequality.

Experiment 1 Draw any triangle and measure all sides and angles. List the lengths of the sides and the measures of the angles in decreasing order. See the example below. What relationships between the sides and angles of $\triangle ABC$ do you see?

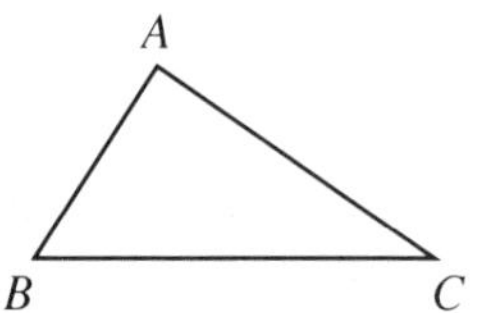

Sides	Angles
$\overline{BC}$	$\angle BAC$
$\overline{AC}$	$\angle ABC$
$\overline{AB}$	$\angle ACB$

Experiment 2 Input various possible lengths for the three sides of a triangle and observe whether a triangle can be constructed. Try to imagine (or sketch) what the triangle you are asking the program to construct will look like before it appears on the screen.

Experiment 3 Draw an acute triangle and measure one of its sides. Then estimate the lengths of the other two sides and check your estimate by measuring. Repeat several times to improve your skill. Then do the experiment with various right triangles and obtuse triangles.

Making Connections

Point out that in addition to being able to determine the order of angle measures in a triangle according to the lengths of the sides, there is much to be learned about triangles. Students who study trigonometry will not only order angle measures or side lengths, but will also calculate the angles based on the lengths of the sides (see Lessons 8-5 and 8-6).

Extension

Ask students to verify that if a and b are the lengths of the sides of a triangle with $a < b$, then the third side c will be between $b - a$ and $b + a$, or $b - a < c < b + a$.

6-5 pages 228–232

Teaching Suggestions

Objective

State and apply the inequality theorems for two triangles.

Presenting the Lesson

You can help students to develop an intuitive understanding of the two inequality theorems for triangles by using physical examples that students can measure. The theorems can also be demonstrated by using folding yardsticks. Encourage students to reach their own conclusions. Discuss with students why these theorems are frequently called *hinge theorems*.

Extension

More capable students might try to prove Theorem 6-5 for the case in which point X is inside $\triangle ABC$. The proof is similar to Case 2.

7 *Similar Polygons*

This chapter begins with a review of ratio and proportion. Ratios are defined as quotients that can be expressed in fraction form. The notation $a:b$ and $a:b:c$ is introduced. A proportion is defined as an equation stating that two ratios are equal. Lesson 7-2 expands on the topic of proportions, listing equivalent forms and the important property that the product of the extremes is equal to the product of the means.

The focus of Lesson 7-3 is the definition of similar polygons. The definition requires a matching of vertices, the congruence of pairs of corresponding angles, and the same ratio (scale factor) for pairs of corresponding sides. The relation *similarity* is compared to equality and congruence. All three relations are reflexive, symmetric, and transitive.

Lesson 7-4 concentrates on applying the definition of similar polygons to a special case, similar triangles. An experiment suggests that two pairs of congruent angles are sufficient for triangles to be similar. This fact is stated as the AA Similarity Postulate.

Necessary and sufficient conditions for triangle similarity are considered in Lesson 7-5. The SAS and SSS similarity theorems are presented and hints for proving these theorems are provided.

Identifying proportional segments in similar triangles is covered in Lessons 7-4 and 7-5. Lesson 7-6 deals with proportional segments within a single triangle.

7-1 pages 241–244

Teaching Suggestions

Objective

Express a ratio in simplest form.

Presenting the Lesson

Explain that doubling a recipe requires doubling each ingredient. Ask students to think of other combinations in which a constant ratio of components is important. Suggestions might include chemistry experiments or ecological systems. Remind students that fractions offer a convenient way to describe ratios.

Continue the lesson by asking students to consider ratios that compare different units, such as rates, conversion factors, or map scales. Explain that a rate of 30 has no meaning unless the units are known; for example, the rate needs to be expressed as 30 miles per hour or 30 kilometers per hour or 30 feet per second. In geometry we often wish to compare measures. If the units are the same, they are not needed in the ratio to convey meaning. In Example 1, the ratio 1 to 2 makes sense because both angles are measured in degrees. In Example 2, the ratio $\frac{13}{25}$ describes the comparison as long as the width and length are measured in the same unit.

Students may question the use of x in Example 3. The x represents a common factor in the ratios. For example, the ratio $\frac{2}{3}$ could come from $\frac{2 \cdot 5}{3 \cdot 5}$ or $\frac{2 \cdot x}{3 \cdot x}$. We solve for the common factor (in this case, ten degrees) and then find the measure of each angle.

Using Technology

This is a good place to use the ratio feature of construction programs. The following experiment introduces ratio and proportion.

Experiment Draw any triangle ABC. Label the midpoint of $\overline{AB}$ as D and the midpoint of $\overline{AC}$ as E. Find the ratios $AD:AB$, $AD:DB$, $AE:AC$, $AE:EC$, and $DE:BC$ and see how many proportions you can come up with. Repeat on several triangles. Now, assume $AD:AB = 1:3 = AE:AC$ and repeat the experiment.

As an extension, draw a right $\triangle ABC$ with $m\angle C = 90$ and altitude $\overline{CD}$. Again, come up with as many proportions as you can.

Applications

Example 3 demonstrates a way to divide 180 degrees according to a required proportion. A nutritionist studies ratios of fats, proteins, carbohydrates and fiber to design a diet that will divide a patient's calorie quota into healthy proportions. A financial analyst determines the proportional share of each item in a budget and then calculates amounts based on the total budget. Circle graphs illustrate visually the process of dividing a whole into proportional parts.

Making Connections

The comparison of the circumference of a circle to its diameter yields a scale factor of approximately 22:7. Although an exact fraction of integers to name this famous ratio does not exist, we use approximations to solve problems. The number π will be discussed in Chapter 9 on circles.

Reinforcement

You may want to review with students how to find equivalent ratios using common factors: $\frac{4}{5} = \frac{4 \cdot 2}{5 \cdot 2} = \frac{4 \cdot 3}{5 \cdot 3} = \frac{4 \cdot 4}{5 \cdot 4}$, and so on. Since $\frac{m\angle 1}{m\angle 2} = \frac{4}{5} = \frac{4x}{5x}$, the measures of two angles that are in the ratio 4 to 5 must have a common factor. In this case, the common factor is x.

7-2 pages 245–248

Teaching Suggestions

Objectives

1. Solve for an unknown term in a given proportion.
2. Express a given proportion in an equivalent form.

Presenting the Lesson

You can begin the lesson by illustrating properties of a proportion with numerical examples. Since students have studied these properties in algebra, this review should stimulate their recall as well as build confidence in each statement's validity.

Next, present an algebraic proof of the statement that in a proportion, the product of the means is equal to the product of the extremes. In symbols, if $a:b = c:d$, then $bc = ad$.

Proof

1. If $\frac{a}{b} = \frac{c}{d}$, then $bd \cdot \frac{a}{b} = bd \cdot \frac{c}{d}$.
2. If $bd \cdot \frac{a}{b} = bd \cdot \frac{c}{d}$, then $da = bc$.
3. If $da = bc$, then $bc = ad$.

Students can read the steps of the proof aloud and offer reasons for each step.

Communication Skills

Most students are familiar with the basic arithmetic and algebraic ideas and skills that can be used to understand the concepts of ratio and proportion. The major differences are mostly with the language.

A proportion is a special kind of equation with several time-saving equivalent forms; however, these forms apply only to proportions. Many errors in algebra are made by students who incorrectly try to "cross-multiply" or "invert" in certain situations. Emphasize to students that they must learn the following: (1) to recognize a proportion as a special kind of equation; (2) to use correct names for the parts of a proportion; (3) to recognize that any three terms will determine the fourth term; and (4) to know that only proportions may be manipulated according to the list of properties on page 245.

7-3 pages 248–252

Teaching Suggestions

Objective

State and apply the properties of similar polygons.

Presenting the Lesson

Draw figures A, B, C, D, E, and F on the chalkboard or prepare cutouts. Begin the discussion with the first five figures; figure F is introduced later.

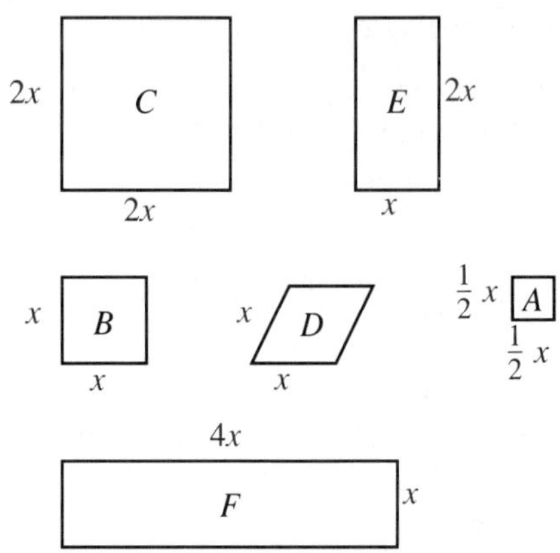

Ask a volunteer to explain the terms *reduce* and *enlarge*, using any of the first five figures to illustrate these terms. The intuitive idea of shape is preserved in these transformations. Ask students to compare the five figures. Their observations should include the following: all the figures are quadrilaterals; figures B and D have congruent sides and equal perimeters; figures B and E have congruent angles and unequal perimeters, and figures A, B, and C have congruent angles and proportional sides. Read the definition of similar polygons and point out that figures A, B, and C are similar. Introduce figure F and ask if it is similar to E.

Write the definition of similar polygons as two if-then statements, pointing out that one form can be used to establish similarity and the other, used after similarity has been established, to identify relations between corresponding parts.

Using Technology

In this experiment, students draw similar figures (by changing the scale of a figure) and verify the similarity.

Experiment Draw any quadrilateral. Measure all sides, all angles, and the perimeter. Change the scale to form a second quadrilateral. Repeat the measurements. To verify that the two quadrilaterals are similar, answer the following questions. Are all corresponding angles congruent? Are all corresponding sides in proportion? Now, find the scale factor of the similarity and the ratio of the perimeters, and compare these ratios. Repeat the experiment on different types of polygons.

Making Connections

Congruent polygons are similar, and the ratio of their corresponding sides is 1:1. The symbol for congruence ($\cong$) is a combination of the symbol for similarity ($\sim$) and the symbol for equality ($=$).

It is possible to approach congruence relationships by studying similarity first and then defining congruence as a 1:1 similarity. This is not the usual sequence of topics in elementary geometry, but students should understand that this approach could have been taken.

Cooperative Learning

The notion of similarity can be introduced by having students work together in small groups. Have students cut different polygons out of heavy construction paper, measure the angles and the sides of each polygon, and record the measurements. Using an overhead projector, project a triangle, for example, on a screen. Have one student from each group measure the angles and the sides of the triangle projected on the screen and record the results. After doing this experiment several times using different polygons, ask students to compare the measurements of the original figures with the corresponding measurements of the projected figures. Suggest that students in each group study their results and present their findings to the entire class. They should have discovered that the corresponding angles are congruent and the corresponding sides are in proportion.

7-4 pages 254–260

Teaching Suggestions

Objectives

1. Use the AA Similarity Postulate to prove triangles similar.
2. Use similar triangles to deduce information about segments or angles.

Presenting the Lesson

Have each student cut a triangle from a 3 × 5 index card. The triangles may not be congruent, but each student should label his or her vertices A, B, and C. Direct students to draw on a piece of paper a segment $\overline{B'C'}$ with length twice that of $\overline{BC}$. At B', trace $\angle B$; at C', trace $\angle C$. Extend the noncommon rays of the angles and call their intersection A'. Point out that $\angle A'$ is congruent to $\angle A$.

Review the criteria for similar polygons. In the case of triangles ABC and $A'B'C'$, the angles are matched as congruent pairs. If the ratios of the corresponding sides are equal (in this case, 1:2), then the triangles are similar. Point out that A' was determined when the other two angles were traced (ASA). If there is a triangle similar to $\triangle ABC$ with a scale factor 2, then such a triangle must be congruent to $\triangle A'B'C'$.

The existence of such a triangle seems to be a reasonable assumption. Thus, the criterion of AA (two pairs of corresponding congruent angles) guarantees the triangles are similar.

Carefully go through the steps of the Example proof following the AA Similarity Postulate. Point out that Reason 6 is part of the definition of similar polygons. The strategy for doing proofs and exercises in this lesson is to establish similar triangles using AA first, and then to identify the proportions.

Using Technology

The following experiment demonstrates the AA Similarity Postulate.

Experiment Draw $\triangle ABC$ with $m\angle A = 30$, $AB = 4$, and $m\angle B = 45$. Measure $\overline{AC}$ and $\overline{BC}$. Now draw $\triangle A'B'C'$ with $m\angle A' = 30$, $A'B' = 5$, and $m\angle B' = 45$. Measure $\overline{A'C'}$ and $\overline{B'C'}$. Compare the ratios $AC{:}A'C'$, $BC{:}B'C'$, and $AB{:}A'B'$. Repeat the experiment with $A'B' = 6$. Make a conjecture.

Applications

Some measurements are very difficult to obtain directly. Examples include the height of a building or a mountain, the width of a gorge or body of water, and the distance from the earth to a planet or star. Similar triangles can help us to calculate these measures. Finding the height of a flagpole or a tree by using a meter stick and the corresponding shadows can be a meaningful class project.

Communication Skills

To make sure that students understand the symbols used in this chapter, be sure to have them read some of the material aloud. Two of the benefits derived from oral reading are the following. Point out these advantages to students.

1. Hearing the pronunciation can assist with conceptualization as symbols are connected with words and sentences.
2. A slowing down of the reading process allows for careful thought.

Select some symbolic expressions such as the following and have students read them aloud.

$4:3:9 \qquad 9:4 = 18:s \qquad \frac{3x-2}{6} = \frac{1}{5} \qquad \frac{AB}{UV} = \frac{BC}{VW}$

$\frac{a}{b} = \frac{c}{d}$ is equivalent to $\frac{a+b}{b} = \frac{c+d}{d}$.

Quad. $ABCD \sim$ quad. $A'B'C'D'$.

7-5 pages 263–268

Teaching Suggestions

Objective

Use the SAS Similarity Theorem and the SSS Similarity Theorem to prove triangles similar.

Presenting the Lesson

Ask students to list the ways they know to prove triangles similar. The list should include the definition of similarity, the AA Postulate, and knowing that the triangles are congruent. Write each of the statements in if-then form and add to the list Theorems 7-1 and 7-2. If students try to prove these theorems, they will find the original list very helpful.

Work through the Example on page 264 carefully, pointing out techniques for assigning correspondence. Written Exercises 7–10 offer more practice. Make sure students read and write statements about similarity correctly by labeling triangles with the corresponding vertices in the same order.

Making Connections

Compare the ways to prove triangles similar with the ways to prove triangles congruent. Point out that the ASA Congruence Postulate is a special case of the AA Similarity Postulate with scale factor 1.

Problem Solving

Overlapping triangles and triangles that share sides can be redrawn to make the naming of proportional sides easier. Demonstrate this technique using Classroom Exercise 5.

Once the similarity of triangles has been established, corresponding angles in a diagram should be marked with the same symbol. Corresponding sides are opposite corresponding angles and can be identified easily.

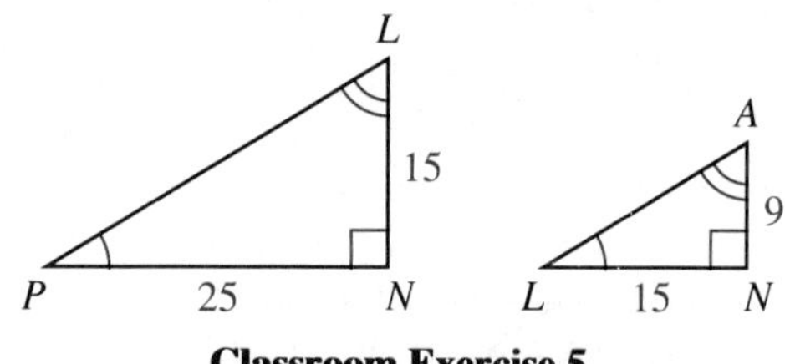

Classroom Exercise 5

Cooperative Learning

A project that uses the varying abilities of students may be developed around Classroom Exercise 9. The project could be worked on over several days while the class is covering this chapter. Group activities might include: (1) constructing a pantograph; (2) collecting pictures to enlarge and/or reduce; (3) hands-on experience in using this instrument; (4) a discussion of the questions suggested in the exercise; and (5) arranging a bulletin board display of the final products.

7-6 pages 269–273

Teaching Suggestions

Objectives

1. Apply the Triangle Proportionality Theorem and its corollary.
2. State and apply the Triangle Angle-Bisector Theorem.

Presenting the Lesson

You may wish to propose the following problem. Two brothers, Brad and Ty, want to buy a long loaf of French bread which costs one dollar. Ty has 40¢ and Brad has 60¢, so they pool their money and make the purchase. How should they divide the loaf of bread? Be sure students understand the problem. They need to find a method for dividing the bread (segment) into lengths with a ratio of 40:60, or 2:3.

One solution is based on Theorem 7-3. Borrow a piece of ruled notebook paper from a student and use the parallel lines to mark off units on the vertical margin line. On this line, label a segment $\overline{AB}$ which has five units. A triangle can be formed by using $\overline{AB}$, the line perpendicular at B, and the loaf of bread. The line that cuts $\overline{AB}$ in the ratio 2:3 also divides the bread in the same ratio. You may want to refer students to the illustration on page 179, Classroom Exercise 1.

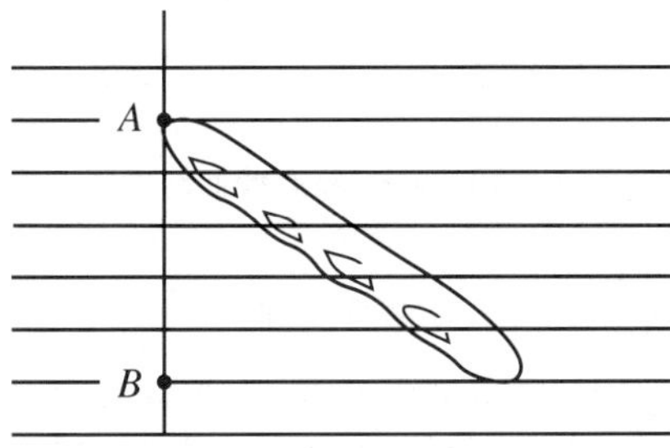

Another solution is based on Theorem 7-4. Draw a segment $\overline{XY}$ on the chalkboard to represent the bread. Choosing a unit length longer than one fifth of $\overline{XY}$, use a compass to draw an arc with center X and radius 2. With center Y and radius 3, draw another arc and call the point where the arcs intersect Z. Bisect $\angle Z$ and the bisector will divide $\overline{XY}$ into the desired ratio.

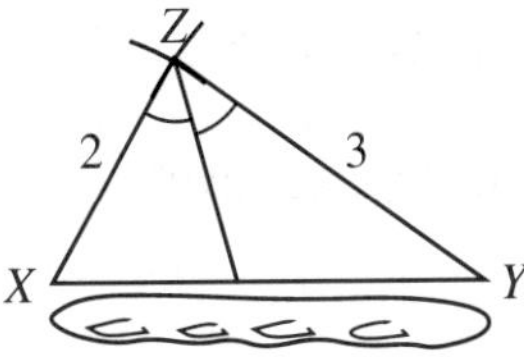

In each of the two solutions, a triangle is created that meets the conditions of the hypotheses of a theorem, and the conclusion is used to solve the problem.

Making Connections

Your students have studied special cases of the theorems presented in this lesson. Suggest comparing Theorem 5-9 and Theorem 5-10 on pages 177 and 178 with Theorem 7-3 and its corollary on pages 269 and 270. One of the conclusions of Corollary 3 to Theorem 4-1 on page 135 can be stated as follows: The bisector of the vertex angle of an isosceles triangle also bisects the base. Consider that this statement could be a corollary to Theorem 7-4.

Problem Solving

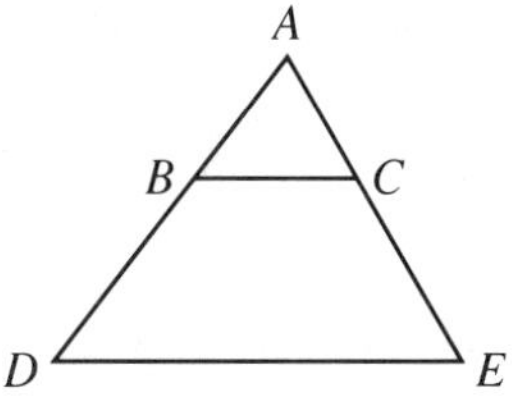

In solving certain problems, students need to consider if a problem requires one triangle with a line parallel to one of its sides or two triangles which are similar to each other. If $\overline{BC} \parallel \overline{DE}$, we can conclude that $AB:BD = AC:CE$, but the Triangle Proportionality Theorem does not consider the ratio $BC:DE$. If a problem involves this ratio, we need to compare similar triangles $\triangle ABC$ and $\triangle ADE$. The proportion is $AB:AD = AC:AE = BC:DE$.

Extension

You may wish to extend the study of the Triangle Proportionality Theorem by asking students to state the converse of this theorem. Since the converse of this theorem is also true, some of your better students may be interested in proving it.

Using Technology

The following experiments extend the topics of Chapter 7 while applying properties of quadrilaterals.

Experiment 1 Draw any parallelogram and its diagonals. What do you notice about the four triangles formed? Look for congruent and similar triangles. Repeat this experiment on a rectangle, a rhombus, a square, a trapezoid, an isosceles trapezoid, and a kite. Make some conjectures.

Experiment 2 In Chapter 7 you learned to show two triangles similar by the AA, SAS, and SSS Similarity theorems. What similarity theorems might there be for quadrilaterals? For example, AAA is not enough:

a square and a rectangle may not be similar. SSSS is not enough: a rectangle and a parallelogram may not be similar. Try to discover a similarity theorem for quadrilaterals.

8 *Right Triangles*

Chapter 8 begins with the similarities produced when the altitude is drawn to the hypotenuse of a right triangle. The various geometric means found in these similarities are developed along with the algebraic techniques with radicals that will be needed throughout the chapter.

In Lesson 8-2, geometric means are used to prove the Pythagorean Theorem. Most of the applications of the theorem are confined to two dimensions, although some of the exercises use the theorem to find diagonals of rectangular solids.

Lesson 8-3 proves the converse of the Pythagorean Theorem that tells when a triangle is a right triangle, as well as related theorems that tell when a triangle is acute or obtuse. The common Pythagorean triples are also studied.

In Lesson 8-4, the special 45°-45°-90° and 30°-60°-90° triangles are studied. The relationships among the sides of these triangles will be useful when students study areas and volumes of figures having square or equilateral triangular faces.

The last three lessons of the chapter deal with right triangle trigonometry. Lesson 8-5 begins with the tangent ratio, considered by most people to be easier than the sine and cosine ratios studied in Lesson 8-6. Lesson 8-7 gives many applications of right triangle trigonometry.

8-1 pages 285–290

Teaching Suggestions

Objectives

1. Determine the geometric mean between two numbers.
2. State and apply the relationships that exist when the altitude is drawn to the hypotenuse of a right triangle.

Presenting the Lesson

You can make a simple model to illustrate Theorem 8-1 by cutting a rectangular piece of paper or cardboard along a diagonal. This produces two congruent right triangles. Cut one of these right triangles along the altitude to its hypotenuse so that you now have three right triangles. The two smaller ones are easily visualized as similar by rotating the smaller of the two clockwise 90° about point N, shown in the drawing for Theorem 8-1. If you flip the two smaller triangles over, they will have the same orientation as the largest right triangle, and the similarity is more easily visualized.

Using Technology

In this experiment, students explore (and possibly discover) Theorem 8-1 and related results.

Experiment Draw any right triangle. Draw one line segment that divides the triangle into two similar triangles. How many different segments can you find that will work? Next, draw one line segment that will divide the right triangle into *three* similar triangles. (Hint: Three triangles includes the original triangle.) Now try to divide a right triangle into similar triangles by drawing *two* line segments. How many similar triangles can you create? Repeat the experiment for other types of triangles.

Making Connections

This section has many connections with algebra. The geometric mean involves work with radicals. The types of radical simplification techniques shown in Example 3 are all that will be needed in this and later chapters.

Enrichment

Students may be challenged to try to find an inequality relation between the arithmetic mean and the geometric mean of any two positive numbers.

$$\text{If } a > 0 \text{ and } b > 0, \text{ then } (a - b)^2 \geq 0.$$
$$a^2 - 2ab + b^2 \geq 0$$
$$a^2 + 2ab + b^2 \geq 4ab$$
$$(a + b)^2 \geq 4ab$$
$$|a + b| \geq 2\sqrt{ab}$$
$$\frac{a + b}{2} \geq \sqrt{ab}$$

Communication Skills

It is important that students understand the paragraph preceding Corollary 1. Without agreeing to use the words *segment*, *side*, *leg*, and *hypotenuse* in two ways, the statements of theorems and corollaries can become very complicated. For example, Corollary 2 would have to be worded as follows: When the altitude is drawn to the hypotenuse of a right triangle, the length of each leg is the geometric mean between the length of the hypotenuse and the length of the segment of the hypotenuse that is adjacent to that leg.

8-2 pages 290–294

Teaching Suggestions

Objective

State and apply the Pythagorean Theorem.

Presenting the Lesson

When early geometers discovered the Pythagorean Theorem, they visualized it as a statement about areas of squares and not about squares of numbers such as $3^2 + 4^2 = 5^2$. They saw a figure, perhaps like the one in the Challenge on page 294, in which the squares on the legs of a right triangle could be cut and reassembled to form the square on the hypotenuse.

You might consider introducing the Pythagorean Theorem by enlarging and reproducing the figure in the Challenge so each student has one. Then let students cut and reassemble the five pieces and ask one or two students to show their solutions on an overhead projector. This approach conveys very clearly the geometric meaning of the theorem. Now you can prove the theorem by discussing page 290 or by discussing Exercise 41 on page 289.

Making Connections

The Pythagorean Theorem is one of the most useful theorems in mathematics. The theorem will be used in this book to do right triangle trigonometry and to calculate dimensions for finding areas and volumes. The Written Exercises anticipate some of these uses. The theorem is used in Chapter 13 to derive the distance formula. In trigonometry, it will be used to derive the so-called Pythagorean Identities: (1) $\sin^2 x + \cos^2 x = 1$, (2) $1 + \tan^2 x = \sec^2 x$, and (3) $1 + \cot^2 x = \csc^2 x$.

Enrichment

Students may be fascinated to learn that there are hundreds of different proofs of the Pythagorean Theorem. One of them is by James A. Garfield, written before he became President of the United States. It is given as Written Exercise 32 in Lesson 11-3. An interesting research project for some students would be to study a few of the different proofs of the theorem. Many proofs are given in *The Pythagorean Proposition* by Elisha Loomis, published by the National Council of Teachers of Mathematics.

Cooperative Learning

Before students have read the example preceding Written Exercises 33–36, use the following group learning exercise. Show the students a rectangular box, preferably one whose length, width, and height are all different. Give them the three dimensions (or let them measure them) and ask if they can find the length of a diagonal of the box without any further measuring. Encourage each group to first draw a picture of the box, label the known dimensions, and indicate on their drawing the unknown dimension.

8-3 pages 295–298

Teaching Suggestions

Objective

State and apply the converse of the Pythagorean Theorem and related theorems about obtuse and acute triangles.

Presenting the Lesson

You can begin the lesson by asking a student to write a statement of the Pythagorean Theorem on the chalkboard. Then ask another student to write the converse. After stressing that the converse of a theorem is not necessarily true, ask the class whether they think the converse of the Pythagorean Theorem is true. Since some may say "yes," a proof is in order. A good way to illustrate Theorems 8-3, 8-4, and 8-5 is to pin together at the right angle two straws with lengths a and b. Join the other end of each straw with a rubber band having length c so that $c^2 = a^2 + b^2$. Then open the angle at the pin and students will see that as the angle becomes obtuse, c gets longer and $c^2 > a^2 + b^2$.

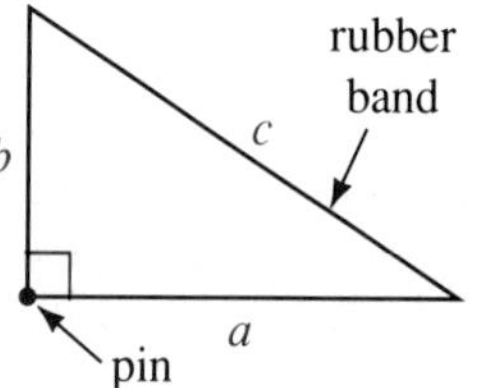

Applications

The word *geometry* literally means earth measurement. When the Nile River annually overflowed its banks, land had to be resurveyed, and knowing how to determine a right angle was crucial to surveying. One device that the Egyptians used for determining right angles was a rope with knots indicating twelve equal segments. They then formed a right angle by arranging the rope to form a triangle with sides 3, 4, and 5 "knot units" long.

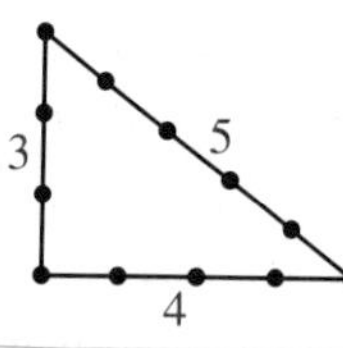

Knowing that an angle measures 90° is also important in carpentry, navigation, and situations that require distances to be minimized.

Making Connections

Theorems 8-3, 8-4, and 8-5 are special cases of the Law of Cosines, which states that if a triangle has sides a, b, and c, then $c^2 = a^2 + b^2 - 2ab \cdot \cos C$.

If $m\angle C = 90$, then $\cos C = 0$ and $c^2 = a^2 + b^2$.
If $m\angle C < 90$, then $\cos C > 0$ and $c^2 < a^2 + b^2$.
If $m\angle C > 90$, then $\cos C < 0$ and $c^2 > a^2 + b^2$.

Reinforcement

The following exercises can be used to help students become more familiar with the Pythagorean triples. Each exercise uses more than one triple, and students must find the values of the variables.

1. $x = 8$, $y = 17$ **2.** $x = 5$, $y = 13$

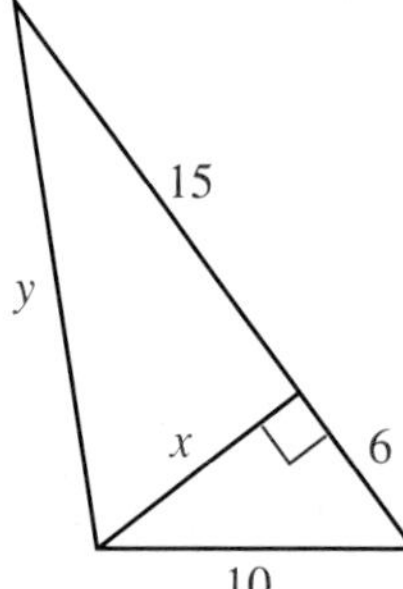

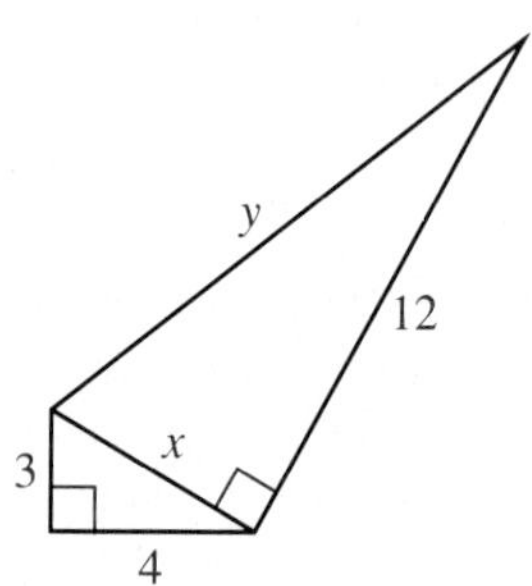

8-4 pages 300–303

Teaching Suggestions

Objective

Determine the lengths of two sides of a 45°-45°-90° or a 30°-60°-90° triangle when the length of the third side is known.

Presenting the Lesson

In presenting the material of this lesson, you may wish to ask students to find the diagonal of a square with side 8 and then with side s. This approach leads to Theorem 8-6. Similarly, asking students to find the altitude of an equilateral triangle with side 10 and then with side s leads them to Theorem 8-7.

Before the widespread use of calculators, the material in this lesson was quite important because 45°-45°-90° and 30°-60°-90° were special triangles that required no knowledge of trigonometry. The advent of calculators has made it so easy to do right triangle trigonometry that the need to spend time on the special triangles is not nearly as important. In fact, you may want to do this lesson *after* doing Lessons 8-5 and 8-6, treating the relationships of Lesson 8-4 as special relationships in trigonometry. However, if this strategy is adopted, then many areas and volumes of special figures that are calculated in Chapters 11 and 12 will contain $\sqrt{2}$ and $\sqrt{3}$ in the answers given. These, of course, can be converted to decimal form.

Applications

Wherever regular polygons of three, four, six, eight, and twelve sides appear, you can find one of the special triangles of this lesson. The special triangles also can be found in three-dimensional figures because many solids have these regular polygons as faces.

Reinforcement

There are always some students who become very anxious over facts they think must be memorized. Tell these students that the relationships in the 45°-45°-90° and 30°-60°-90° triangles do not have to be memorized. Point out that the Pythagorean Theorem can be applied to find the relationships for the special triangles. (Also help students to recognize that a 30°-60°-90° triangle is "half" of an equilateral triangle.) After using this method to do problems such as those in the Classroom and Written Exercises, students generally see that the theorems of the lesson are very useful and not hard to remember. Certain students are reassured by knowing that they can always use another method should their memories fail them.

Enrichment

The figure shown in Written Exercise 27 can be extended to include more 45°-45°-90° triangles. The result is a spiral of such triangles which is reminiscent of the spirals of the chambered nautilus shell. Have students research other things in nature with spirals and find out how the spirals are formed.

Cooperative Learning

The facts about special right triangles can be learned by students working together in small groups. Have students make many drawings of isosceles right triangles. Then ask students to find the hypotenuse of each triangle, using the Pythagorean Theorem, and make a conjecture based on the results. Introduce the 30°-60°-90° Theorem in the same way. Have students examine the altitudes of many drawings of equilateral triangles and then make a conjecture based on the results. Be sure to point out that all isosceles right triangles are similar and all 30°-60°-90° triangles are similar.

8-5 pages 305–310

Teaching Suggestions

Objectives

1. Define the tangent ratio for an acute angle.
2. Solve right triangle problems by using the tangent ratio.

Presenting the Lesson

This textbook develops the sine, cosine, and tangent ratios for angles between 0° and 90°. Of these, the tangent seems the easiest for students to understand. Teachers of accelerated classes may wish to introduce all three ratios in the same class period, assigning exercises from both Lessons 8-5 and 8-6.

You can introduce the tangent ratio by having students accurately draw a 20°-70°-90° triangle of their choice, measure the legs, and calculate the ratio of opposite side to adjacent side. By calculating the opposite to adjacent ratio for each triangle, students will see that the ratio is constant; of course, it *must* be since the triangles are all similar. Since the ratio is constant, it is given a name: tangent of 20° or tan 20°.

Communication Skills

The tangent ratio of an angle is defined as the leg opposite the angle divided by the leg adjacent to the angle. After you are certain that students understand the meaning of the tangent ratio, allow them to abbreviate the ratio as $\tan A = \frac{\text{opposite}}{\text{adjacent}}$.

8-6 pages 312–316

Teaching Suggestions

Objectives

1. Define the sine and cosine ratios for an acute angle.
2. Solve right triangle problems by using the sine and cosine ratios.

Presenting the Lesson

You can use the same type of introduction to this lesson as was suggested for the previous lesson. Have students calculate the opposite side to hypotenuse ratio and adjacent side to hypotenuse ratio for several 20°-70°-90° triangles. Then you can name these ratios sine and cosine.

Problem Solving

Problems in right triangle trigonometry fall into two categories. In the first, an acute angle and one side are given and an unknown side must be found. Relative to the given angle, the student must decide what the given side and unknown side are. If neither is the hypotenuse, the tangent ratio is required; otherwise, either the sine or the cosine is used, depending on whether the opposite or adjacent side is given or unknown.

In the second category of problems, two sides of a right triangle are given and an acute angle must be found. Again, the student must ask how these sides are related to the angle—opposite, adjacent, or hypotenuse—and choose the correct ratio.

8-7 pages 317–320

Teaching Suggestions

Objective

Solve right triangle problems by correct selection and use of the tangent, sine, and cosine ratios.

Presenting the Lesson

The difference between this lesson and the previous two is that all the problems of this lesson are real-life applications of right triangle trigonometry. The problems of the previous lessons were more abstract—various measurements were found without relating the measurements to applied situations.

The only new terminology introduced in this lesson is *angle of depression* and *angle of elevation*. One way to introduce this terminology is by discussing the problem situation described on page 317. Point out to students that if they do not use a calculator, then Method 2, which involves multiplication, is easier than Method 1, which involves division by a decimal.

Making Connections

The *grade* of a road was introduced in Example 3 on page 306 and is related to Exercises 10–12 on page 319. A measure of a road's steepness is analogous to the slope of a line, except that unlike the slope of a line, the grade of a road is never negative.

Applications

Here is an easy application of trigonometry. Your students can make a *height sight* for tall objects by taping a straw to the hypotenuse of a 70°-20°-90° cardboard triangle, as shown at the left below. Be sure they make the triangle large enough to be handled easily. Have them attach a weighted string to the vertex of the 20° angle.

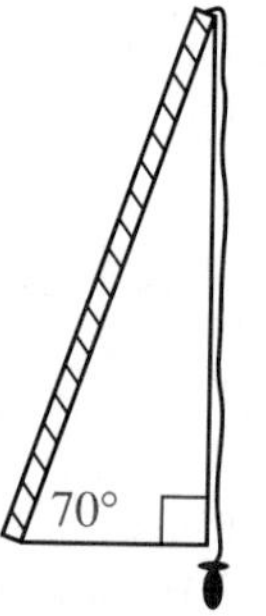

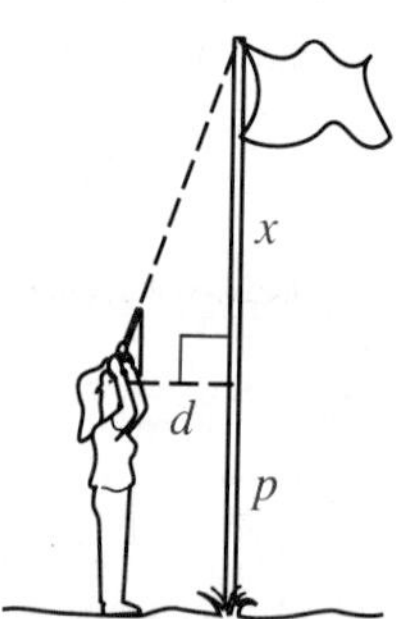

In order to use the "height sight," the observer holds the lower end of the straw at eye level and tilts the triangle until the weighted string coincides with the longer leg. The observer then moves forward or backward until the object whose height is to be measured comes into view through the straw. The horizontal distance from the observer's eye to the object is measured. Call this distance d. Call the person's height, up to eye level, p. Then the height of the object equals $d \tan 70° + p$.

Enrichment

Written Exercise 13 relates right triangle trigonometry to soccer. Students might enjoy compiling a list of sports applications of trigonometry. If three-dimensional problems are introduced, they become more interesting and realistic. For example, consider the problem of serving a tennis ball over the middle of the net (height 3 feet) from a height of 7 feet if the server stands in the middle of or at the end of the baseline. Another problem for students to solve is the following: The crossbar $\overline{XY}$ of a football goalpost is 10′ above the ground and 23′4″ long. If a field goal is to be kicked from a point F, 20 yards in front of the right-hand goalpost, find $m\angle XFY$.

Communication Skills

Although the ideas of an angle of depression and an angle of elevation seem rather obvious, students can have difficulty using these ideas correctly in problem-solving situations. Suggest that the problems in the exercises be read very carefully and that accurate drawings be made before any solution is attempted. Also, ask students to express the meaning of an angle of depression and an angle of elevation in their own words. This will enable you to detect faulty thinking.

9 *Circles*

The goal of this chapter is to establish the numerical relationships between arcs and angles of a circle and to provide ways of calculating segments related to circles. The definitions of circle and sphere and terms related to them are presented in the first lesson. Congruent and concentric circles are defined, and the concepts of an inscribed polygon and circumscribed circle are introduced.

The next lesson discusses tangents, tangent circles, and common tangents. Theorems that are converses of each other establish the relationship between tangents and radii. Arcs and central angles are presented in the third lesson along with the Arc Addition Postulate. Theorem 9-3 states the relationship between the congruence of minor arcs and the congruence of their central angles.

Arcs and chords are introduced in Lesson 9-4 with three theorems that discuss congruent arcs and chords, diameters perpendicular to chords, and chords equally distant from the center of a circle.

The second part of the chapter deals with angles formed from segments. In Lesson 9-5, students solve problems and prove statements involving inscribed angles. Three corollaries develop ideas about inscribed angles, right angles, and inscribed quadrilaterals. The measure of an angle formed by a chord and a tangent is proved to be equal to half the measure of the intercepted arc.

Lesson 9-6 discusses other angles related to circles. These angles are formed from chords, secants, or tangents having their vertices either inside or outside a circle.

The last lesson of the chapter presents three theorems that give the numerical relationships involving products of different segments related to circles. All the theorems are proved by using similar triangles and thus provide an excellent review of the properties of similar triangles.

9-1 pages 329–332

Teaching Suggestions

Objectives

1. Define a circle, a sphere, and terms related to them.
2. Recognize inscribed polygons and circumscribed circles.

Presenting the Lesson

A good way to introduce the definitions of a circle and a sphere is to use a piece of string with chalk tied to one end. Tape one end of the string on the chalkboard and draw a circle. Discuss how the points that are a string length away from the taped end are all the same distance from the center of the circle. Discuss what figure results if the points need not lie on the chalkboard. (hemisphere)

Extension

Guided Practice Exercise 4 on page 331 assumes the following theorem: If a plane intersects a sphere in more than one point, the intersection is a circle.

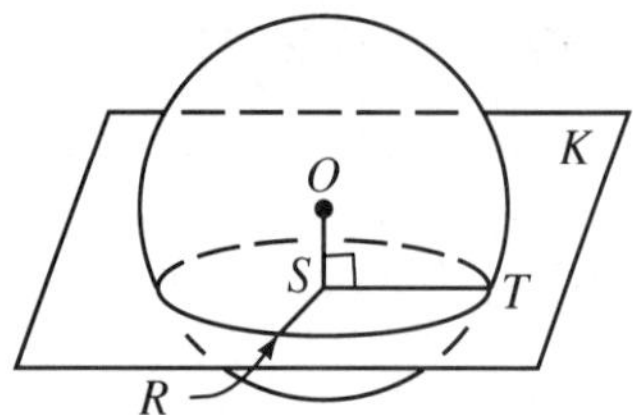

The case in which plane K passes through the center of the sphere is covered in Written Exercise 4, page 331. If K does not pass through the center of sphere O, draw a perpendicular from point O to plane K intersecting K at S, with R and T any two points of the intersection of the sphere with the plane. Then $\overline{OR} \cong \overline{OT}$ because they are radii of the sphere. Because $\overline{OS} \cong \overline{OS}$, $\triangle ORS \cong \triangle OTS$ by the HL Theorem. Thus $\overline{RS} \cong \overline{TS}$, making them $\cong$ radii of a circle.

Using Technology

Since this chapter contains many proofs and problems in which students are asked to draw a figure and discover something, it provides lots of opportunity for discovery by construction. If your students are using the *Geometric Supposer: Circles*, then *Geometry Problems and Projects: Circles* is a source of many more activities. Note that some programs will give an arc measurement in both degrees and radians, but list as data only the radian measure. In that case, students will need to record the degree measures themselves.

Communication Skills

Many new words are defined in the early lessons of this chapter. Encourage students to look for clues to the meaning of the words within the words themselves. They can do this by watching for prefixes they know.

As you discuss Lesson 9-1, write the boldface words on the chalkboard, pronounce them, and explain their meanings by using other diagrams. If possible, point out prefixes that provide clues to meaning. For example:

Words	Clue
inscribed polygon	*Inscribed* suggests that the polygon is *inside* the circle.
concentric circles	*Concentric* suggests that the circles have the same *center*.

9-2 pages 333–338

Teaching Suggestions

Objectives

1. Apply theorems that relate tangents and radii.
2. Recognize circumscribed polygons and inscribed circles.

Presenting the Lesson

Theorem 9-1 on page 333 can be discovered by students who perform the following experiment. Have each student draw a circle and a tangent to it. Then have them draw the radius to the point of tangency and measure the angle formed by the tangent and the radius, using a protractor. This can be done several times with different circles. Then have students compare their results and make a conjecture about their findings.

Making Connections

Presenting the intuitive definition of a tangent line as the limiting position of a secant line whose chord becomes shorter and shorter is a useful geometric example of the concept of a limit. Limits are studied in pre-calculus and calculus courses.

Communication Skills

The importance of accurate notation in communicating mathematical ideas is evident when discussing the many segments and lines that relate to circles. For example, $\overline{AB}$ denotes a segment, while $\overleftrightarrow{AB}$ denotes a line. If $\overline{AB}$ is a chord, then it is a subset of secant $\overleftrightarrow{AB}$. Careless use of notation can lead to inaccurate conclusions. Remind students that only segments have lengths, not lines.

Cooperative Learning

You may wish to form groups of three or four students to encourage the discovery of the relationships between tangents and radii in Written Exercises 7, 8, 12, and 14 on page 336. One student should record any conjectures made while all students discuss the exercises.

Each student should make conjectures about the relationships and try to prove them to the rest of the group. Other students in the group can offer counterexamples if the conjectures are not true and suggest alternate statements. Each group can present its conjectures to the class for further discussion.

9-3 pages 339–343

Teaching Suggestions

Objective

Define and apply properties of arcs and central angles.

Presenting the Lesson

This lesson can be introduced by using a protractor and an overhead projector to help students understand the measure of arcs. Place the protractor on the projector surface and draw a 40° angle. As you draw the angle, also trace along the curve of the protractor, thus producing an arc whose measure is 40. Point out that drawing an angle of 40° with a protractor is the same as drawing a central angle of 40°.

Extension

Capable students might enjoy calculating the angle between the hands of a clock for any time given. The angle between the hands of a clock when the time is on the hour is always a multiple of 30° ($\frac{360}{12}$), and the minute hand moves 30° for each number on a 12-hour clock. Since the hour hand moves more slowly during a one-hour period, students will have to consider adding (or subtracting) a fraction of 30° to calculate the angle between the hands at certain times. Two examples are: 5:15 ($67\frac{1}{2}$°); 1:45 ($142\frac{1}{2}$°).

Communication Skills

If students are to become proficient in the silent reading of mathematical material, they will need frequent supervised practice in this skill. Ask students to read the first page of Lesson 9-3. Tell them to read silently and to try to remember as many details as they can. Then ask selected students to try to reconstruct the content of the paragraphs on the chalkboard.

Cooperative Learning

Students can work in small groups of two or three on measuring central angles to see that the measure of an arc is independent of the size of the circle. Have them use protractors to measure central angles and their related arcs for various sets of concentric circles. Have the groups discuss their measurements and try to explain why the size of a circle does not determine the measure of the arc.

9-4 pages 344–349

Teaching Suggestions

Objective

Apply theorems about the chords of a circle.

Presenting the Lesson

Theorem 9-4 can be demonstrated by using paper models of circles and a ruler. Cut off a part of a circle and measure its chord. Then place the cut part of the circle so that it overlaps the original circle or a congruent circle. This will demonstrate clearly that congruent arcs have congruent chords and that congruent chords have congruent arcs. You can also demonstrate Theorem 9-6 by showing that congruent chords are always the same distance from the center of a circle.

You can demonstrate the phrase "in the same circle or in congruent circles" in a similar manner by cutting off parts of two noncongruent circles with the same chord measure. Show that the arcs have different measures. Similarly, in noncongruent circles, show that congruent chords or chords of congruent arcs are not the same distance from the center of the circle.

Enrichment

Ask students to state how many chords can be drawn connecting pairs of points in the circles below. (10; 15)

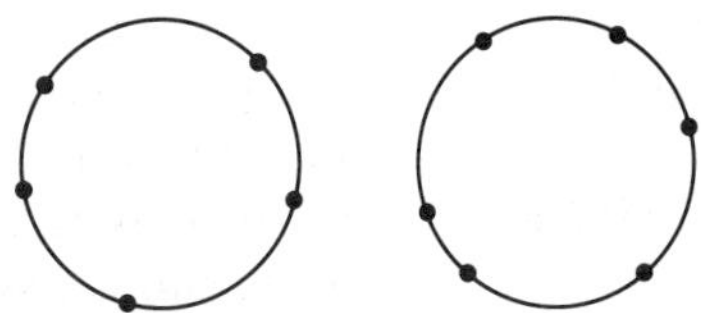

Have students predict how many chords can be drawn between seven points of a circle. (21) Challenge students to find the formula for the number of chords for n points.

$$\left(\frac{n(n-1)}{2} \text{ or } (n-1) + (n-2) + \cdots + 1\right)$$

9-5 pages 349–357

Teaching Suggestions

Objectives

1. Solve problems and prove statements involving inscribed angles.
2. Solve problems and prove statements involving angles formed by chords, secants, and tangents.

Presenting the Lesson

You can begin the lesson by discussing Theorem 9-7 and the key steps of its proof. Then have students verify the theorem experimentally by drawing inscribed angles in circles and making measurements.

Corollaries 1–3 also can be verified by drawing diagrams and making measurements. On the chalkboard, draw several diagrams similar to the one at the left below, varying the size of the circle and the placement of points A and B. Have students use a protractor to measure the inscribed angles in each circle and make some conjectures based upon their measurements. In so doing, they should verify Corollary 1.

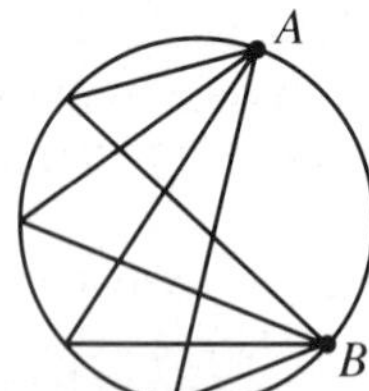

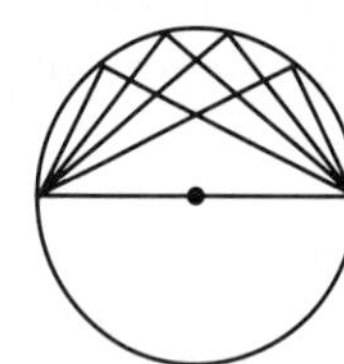

You can have students go through a similar process to verify Corollary 2. They should draw several diagrams similar to the one at the right above and measure the angles with a protractor.

To motivate Corollary 3, ask students to draw three different quadrilaterals in each of three circles and measure the angles. They should pay careful attention to the measures of the opposite angles. Theorem 9-8 also can be verified by having students draw diagrams and make measurements.

Reinforcement

Some students may need practice in recognizing inscribed angles. Students should know the two conditions that an angle must satisfy before it can be called an inscribed angle, namely that the vertex must be a point of the circle and that the sides must contain chords of the circle. Have students prepare a worksheet full of circles with inscribed angles and angles that are not inscribed, drawn in many different positions relative to the circle. Ask students to label the inscribed angles and to trace their intercepted arcs. Also include circles with inscribed angles that illustrate the corollaries of this lesson.

9-6 pages 357–361

Teaching Suggestions

Objective

Solve problems and prove statements involving angles formed by chords, secants, and tangents.

Presenting the Lesson

Students will enjoy discovering Theorem 9-9 for themselves. Draw the diagram shown below on the chalkboard, and ask the class to find the measures of $\angle 2$, $\angle 3$, and $\angle 1$ in order. (15, 25, 40) To find the measure of $\angle 1$, some students may need a hint to recall that the measure of the exterior angle of a triangle is equal to the sum of the measures of the two remote interior angles.

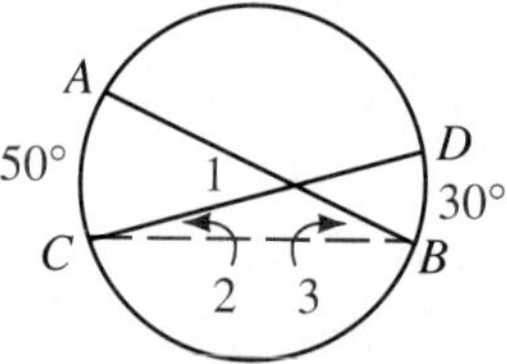

At this point, you can erase the degree measures from the diagram and ask students to express the measures of the numbered angles in terms of $\overset{\frown}{AC}$ and $\overset{\frown}{BD}$.

When they arrive at $m\angle 1 = \frac{1}{2}(m\widehat{AC} + m\widehat{BD})$, ask them to state a theorem about an angle formed by two chords intersecting inside a circle.

Reinforcement

For many students, it might be helpful to discuss the following summary.

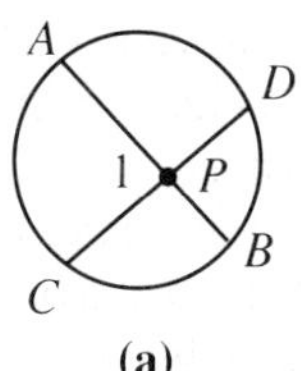

(a)

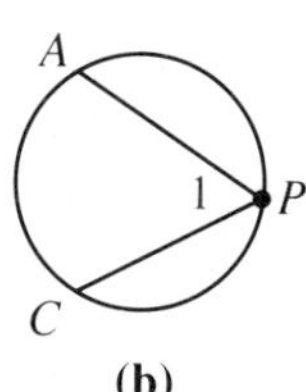

(b)

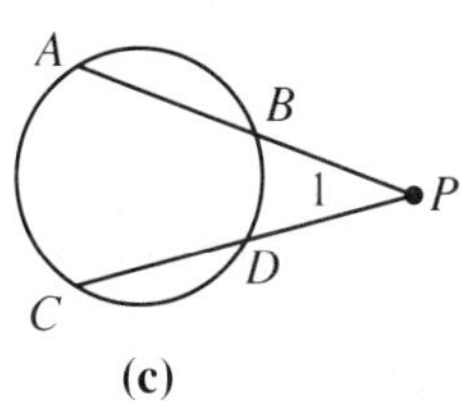

(c)

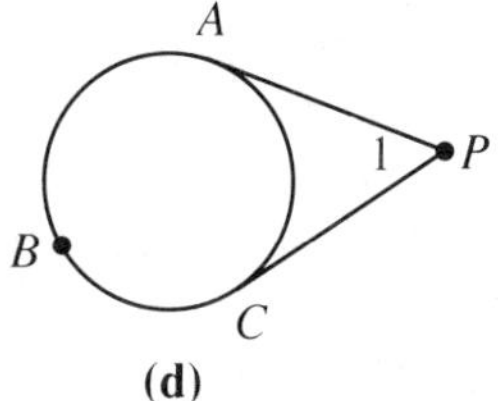

(d)

(a) Let P be the point of intersection of chords, secants, or tangents. If P is inside the circle, then $m\angle 1 = \frac{1}{2}(m\widehat{AC} + m\widehat{BD})$.

(b) If P is on the circle, then $m\angle 1 = \frac{1}{2}m\widehat{AC}$.

(c) If P is outside the circle and $m\widehat{AC} > m\widehat{BD}$, then $m\angle 1 = \frac{1}{2}(m\widehat{AC} - m\widehat{BD})$.

(d) If P is outside the circle and $\overline{AP}$ and $\overline{PC}$ are tangents, then $m\angle 1 = \frac{1}{2}(m\widehat{ABC} - m\widehat{AC})$.

Cooperative Learning

You may wish to form groups of four students to explore Theorems 9-9 and 9-10.

1. Ask each of the four students in the groups to prepare a worksheet with various examples of one of the following:
   a. Theorem 9-9
   b. Theorem 9-10, Case I
   c. Theorem 9-10, Case II
   d. Theorem 9-10, Case III
2. Ask students to measure the various arcs and angles on their worksheets. The goal is to discover the relationships stated in the theorems.
3. Each member of the group is then responsible for teaching the other members of the group the relationships that have been discovered.

9-7 pages 361–368

Teaching Suggestions

Objective

Solve problems involving lengths of chords, secant segments, and tangent segments.

Presenting the Lesson

Theorems 9-11, 9-12, and 9-13 can be demonstrated on the chalkboard by drawing circles with the appropriate chords, segments, or tangents. A ruler can be used to verify the relationships stated in the theorems. Following the demonstration, have students draw their own figures to verify the statements of the theorems.

Reinforcement

Theorems 9-11 and 9-12 can be combined into a single theorem: If A, B, C, and D are points on circle O, and if $\overline{AB}$ intersects $\overline{CD}$ at point P, then $PA \cdot PB = PC \cdot PD$. Students may find this easier to remember than two separate theorems.

Using Technology

Here is an interesting project your students might want to explore, especially if they do the Application on page 367.

1. TV stations can broadcast only to the horizon. So, to broadcast to as large an audience as possible they must place their antennas as high as possible. Have your students write a computer program that calculates the distance to the horizon, and hence the broadcast range, given the height of the transmitter. Students should then do some research on their local stations and find out how far they transmit and how high their transmitters are.
2. Same as (1) but applied to satellites.

Cooperative Learning

Theorems 9-11, 9-12, and 9-13 can be studied in a cooperative-learning environment. Place drawings of the theorems on the chalkboard and do not allow students to open their textbooks. Form groups of three students and assign the following tasks. Have each student in a group copy a different drawing shown on the chalkboard. Tell them to make additional drawings of the same type but having different sizes. Let the students experiment with the drawings to see if they can form any conjectures. Provide hints if students are having difficulties. At an appropriate time, ask each group to present its findings to the entire class.

10 *Constructions and Loci*

The basic geometric constructions are presented in Lessons 10-1, 10-2, 10-4, and 10-5. Construction activities include copying a segment and an angle; bisecting an angle and a segment (perpendicular bisector); constructing perpendicular, parallel, and tangent lines; and finding the circumscribed and inscribed circles of given triangles. Constructions resulting in proportional line segments and geometric means are also covered. Lesson 10-3 discusses four theorems concerning concurrent lines pertaining to triangles. These theorems provide the justifications for later constructions.

The concept of locus is introduced following these constructions. Practice with locus problems that satisfy only one condition is given before locus problems involving more than one condition are studied. The chapter concludes with a study of construction problems that can be solved using locus concepts.

This material may be presented throughout the course (see page T51) or it may be approached as a separate chapter. Many students enjoy the hands-on approach of doing constructions. Like theorems, constructions require analysis, but the results are more artistic, colorful, and fun to display in the classroom.

10-1 pages 375–380

Teaching Suggestions

Objectives

1. Perform three basic constructions.
2. Use these basic constructions in original construction exercises.

Presenting the Lesson

To introduce the straightedge use a meter stick with masking tape covering the markings, explaining to students that they will use rulers but should disregard the markings.

Show students how to use a compass by planting the point firmly on a piece of paper with some kind of pad underneath. Notebooks can serve this purpose. Tell students to control the compass at the top with the thumb and index finger, thus allowing a free, twirling motion. Supervise a practice session in the use of both instruments. Put the constructions on the board while students work on them independently.

Making Connections

Circle constructions can be used to double and halve angles. For example, given $\angle X$ we can find $\angle Y$ such that $m\angle Y = 2m\angle X$. Select point Y in the interior of $\angle X$. Then draw a circle with center Y and radius $\overline{YX}$. Draw the two radii to points where the sides of $\angle X$ intercept the circle.

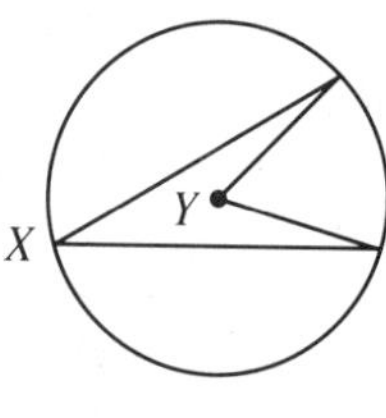

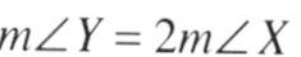

$m\angle Y = 2m\angle X$

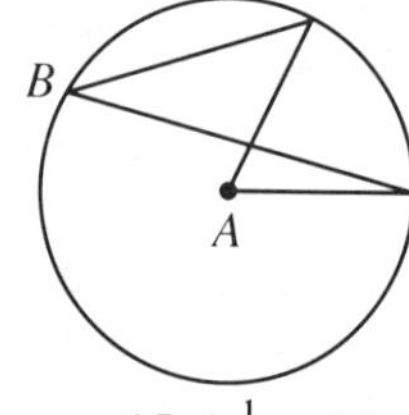

$m\angle B = \frac{1}{2}m\angle A$

The following problem can also be demonstrated. Given $\angle A$, find $\angle B$ such that $m\angle B = \frac{1}{2}m\angle A$. Using any radius, draw a circle with center A. Select point B on the circle anywhere but the interior of $\angle A$. Draw chords to the points where the sides of $\angle A$ intercept the circle.

Communication Skills

Students who have difficulty in reading expository material often benefit from hearing the words spoken first. As you demonstrate the first three constructions at the chalkboard, talk through the procedure step by step. After you have demonstrated Construction 1, have students pair off. Let one student in each pair do the construction and talk through it while the other student writes the steps of the procedure. Then ask the students to read the description of Construction 1 in the book and compare it with their own written steps.

Making Connections

The corollary stating that angles inscribed in semicircles are right angles (Corollary 2, page 351) suggests another way to construct right angles.

First, select points O and A and construct a circle with center O and radius OA. Draw any diameter that does not contain A. Draw chords from A to the endpoints of the diameter. The chords form a right angle at vertex A.

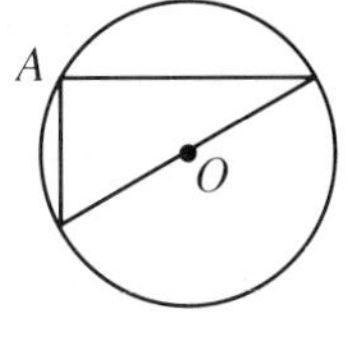

This method offers an alternate approach to Written Exercise 24 on page 384. It is also part of Construction 9 in Lesson 10-4.

Extension

Challenge students to create instruments other than the straightedge and compass that will produce circles and lines. For example, a folded piece of paper makes a straightedge, and a piece of string and chalk or a stick with one endpoint fixed can produce a circle. See how many different tools students can devise.

10-2 pages 380–385

Teaching Suggestions

Objectives

1. Perform four basic constructions.
2. Use these basic constructions in original construction exercises.

Presenting the Lesson

Review the postulate and theorem stated at the beginning of this lesson. Demonstrate Construction 4, pointing out that the perpendicular that is created locates the midpoint of the segment. The next two constructions may be considered special cases of Construction 4. For a point on the line (Construction 5), use any radius to create a segment; for a point outside the line (Construction 6), use any radius that is long enough to create a segment. These constructions are used to produce right angles and to locate midpoints of segments, as well as to create perpendicular lines.

Constructions 6 and 7 involve a line and a point outside the line as the given. Discuss ways to determine a plane before discussing these constructions.

Also, review ways to prove lines parallel (page 85) and Theorem 3-8 before doing Construction 7. The method used in Construction 7 requires constructing congruent corresponding angles with any transversal. Classroom Exercise 1 suggests discussing alternate ways to do this construction.

10-3 pages 386–392

Teaching Suggestions

Objective

State and apply theorems involving concurrent lines.

Presenting the Lesson

Direct each student to construct a circle and name three points on it. Draw the triangle determined by the three points and construct the perpendicular bisectors of the sides (chords of the circle). Point out that these lines are concurrent—they meet at a common point. In fact, this point is the center of the circle. Since the center lies at the same distance from any two points on the circle, it must lie on the perpendicular bisector of any chord (Theorem 4-6, page 153).

Ask this question: "If you began with a triangle, would the perpendicular bisectors be concurrent and could you construct the circle?" Allow time for the students to experiment with different triangles; to ensure a variety of types, you may prefer to provide the triangles. Suggest that the point of concurrency could be called the circumcenter, since it is the center of the circumscribed circle.

Collect the students' work and compare results. Point out that the circumcenter can be inside, outside or on the triangle. Consider angle bisectors of a triangle; are they also concurrent? If you assigned Exercise 15, page 378, students can answer this question by checking their homework.

Discuss the four theorems in this lesson and invite students to speculate about the locations of incenters, orthocenters, and centroids. Which of these points, if any, must be inside the triangle?

Enrichment

Paper-folding activities can reinforce the ideas in this lesson. Demonstrate how to fold angle bisectors, perpendicular bisectors, altitudes, and medians, and then provide each student with four cutouts of acute triangles. Each of the four centers should fall within the triangles. Next, provide equilateral, right, and obtuse triangles with which students may experiment. Encourage students to make and test hypotheses based on their observations.

Make available other polygons, both regular and not regular, for students who complete their work more quickly than others. Students may assume that perpendicular bisectors will always be concurrent. They should discover that this is not necessarily true in polygons that are not triangles.

Using Technology

Experiment Draw any triangle. Draw the four special points discussed on page 387: incenter, circumcenter, orthocenter, and centroid. Three of these four points are collinear and lie on what is called the Euler line. Which points are they? How do they lie on the Euler line in relation to each other? Repeat on several types of triangles.

Communication Skills

Key words encountered in this chapter include concurrent, equidistant, and circumcenter. Review the meanings and spellings of these words. Many students confuse *equidistant* with *given distance*. A student may say incorrectly, "A circle is all the points in a plane equidistant from a given point." Explain the difference between these concepts.

10-4 pages 392–396

Teaching Suggestions

Objectives

1. Perform four additional basic constructions.
2. Use the basic constructions in original construction exercises.

Presenting the Lesson

Introduce the four constructions of this lesson by pointing out that the first two produce tangents to circles and that the last two produce circles.

A tangent to a circle is perpendicular to the radius drawn at the point of tangency. Therefore, when the point of tangency is given, as in Construction 8, constructing the tangent applies Construction 5. When the point of tangency is not given, as in Construction 9, drawing a sketch reveals a right triangle that can be constructed by constructing a semicircle with diameter $\overline{OP}$. The right angle of the triangle is an inscribed angle of the semicircle.

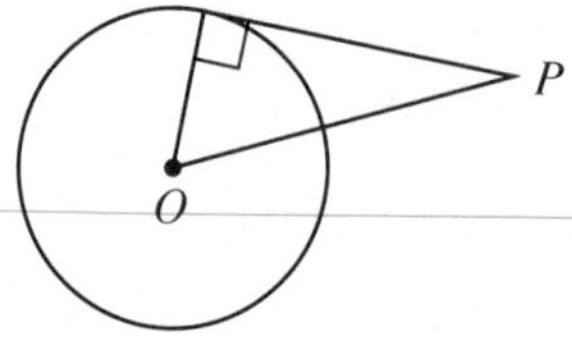

To analyze Constructions 10 and 11, remind students that to construct a circle requires both a center and a radius. If the sides of a triangle are all chords of a circle (a circumscribed circle), then the perpendicular bisectors of any two sides will locate the center. The center and any one of the vertices will give the radius. An inscribed circle is one for which the sides of the triangle are tangents. Since the points of tangency are not known, a sketch is helpful.

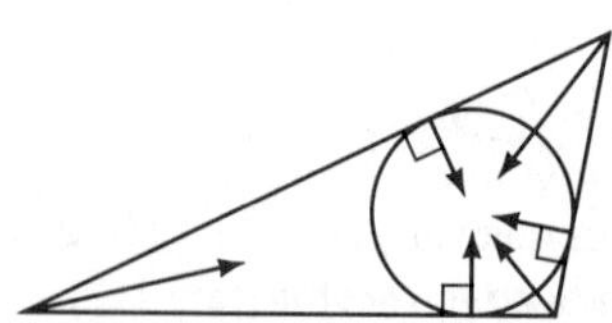

Explain to students that two tangents from an external point form an angle whose bisector passes through the circle's center. Therefore, any two such angle bisectors will locate the center. To find the radius, a perpendicular to a side from the center must be constructed. Stress to students that this radius is not just estimated; it must be constructed.

10-5 pages 396–401

Teaching Suggestions

Objectives

1. Perform three additional basic constructions.
2. Use the basic constructions in original construction exercises.

Presenting the Lesson

The constructions in this lesson may seem complicated to some students. As a preparation for the discussion of these constructions, you may want to review the following theorems:

1. If parallel lines cut off congruent segments on one transversal, then they cut off congruent segments on every transversal. (Theorem 5-9)
2. If a line parallel to one side of a triangle intersects the other two sides, then it divides those sides proportionally. (Theorem 7-3)
3. When the altitude is drawn to the hypotenuse of a right triangle, the length of the altitude is the geometric mean between the segments of the hypotenuse. (Theorem 8-1, Corollary 1)

You can demonstrate Construction 12 in class by using sheets of lined notebook paper. Have students draw a line down the paper from the top edge to the bottom edge. Students should verify that this line is divided into congruent segments by the horizontal parallel lines. Then ask students to fold over a corner of the paper and study the crease made. Again, they should see that the line made by the fold is divided into congruent segments.

Making Connections

On a number line, every point is paired with a number and every number is paired with a point. Ask students to suggest ways to use a compass and a straightedge to locate the points that correspond to 3, $\frac{1}{3}$, and $\sqrt{3}$, given points for 0 and 1.

Extension

Written Exercise 18 is a challenging problem to be assigned to very capable students. However, you may want to comment on the trisection of a general angle to the entire class. Research on the history of this problem would be an interesting assignment for some students.

10-6 pages 401–405

Teaching Suggestions

Objectives

1. Describe the locus that satisfies a given condition.
2. Describe the locus that satisfies more than one given condition.

Presenting the Lesson

You can begin the lesson by writing the definition of a circle on the chalkboard: A circle is the set of all points in a plane at a given distance from a given point. Point out that the plane, the radius, and the center are all *conditions* that determine the circle. The circle itself does not include the center or the radius, and although it encloses a portion of the plane, that area is not a part of the circle. The definition of a circle is an example of a locus, the set of all points that satisfy one or more conditions. If we remove one condition, *in a plane*, then the locus changes and we have a sphere.

Making Connections

Conic sections, namely the circle, parabola, ellipse, and hyperbola have loci definitions. Students can try to locate the points in a plane equidistant from a line and a point (parabola), or they may enjoy constructing an ellipse. First, have them fix two points on a piece of cardboard with two thumbtacks. Then use a loop of string and pencil to trace the path of a point as it moves under the condition that the sum of the distances from the two thumbtacks is constant.

Reinforcement

Describe the locus of points in a plane satisfying the given condition.

1. the locus of points that are equidistant from three noncollinear points A, B, and C center of a circle containing pts. A, B, and C
2. the locus of the midpoints of all chords of length 6 in a circle with radius 6 a concentric circle with radius $= 3\sqrt{3}$

Communication Skills

Students should practice describing the loci defined in the examples and in the Classroom Exercises. One student can read the description while another sketches a diagram. Have them use contrasting colors for the conditions and the locus.

Making Connections

Coordinate geometry describes the location of a point in terms of the directed distance it lies from each of two perpendicular lines (axes). This is the intersection of two loci.

The linear equation $y = \frac{2}{3}x + 4$ has many ordered pairs of numbers as solutions. We can choose a convenient point, say (0, 4), and then allow the point to move with a constant slope of $\frac{2}{3}$. The path of this moving point traces a line which is a locus described by the equation.

The inequality $y > \frac{2}{3}x + 4$ describes the set of all points above the line $y = \frac{2}{3}x + 4$. This is a locus.

If two equations are considered simultaneously, we are interested in their common solutions. Graphically, we look for the points the equations have in common. Using different colors for each graph helps to keep the separate loci defined. The points of intersection of the graphs are the solutions of the system. Stress to students that these are locus problems.

10-7 pages 405–410

Teaching Suggestions

Objectives

1. Describe the locus that satisfies a given condition.
2. Describe the locus that satisfies more than one given condition.

Presenting the Lesson

This lesson on intersections of loci can be introduced by using the following problem. Forest rangers stationed at points A and B, 10 mi apart, each spot the same fire. The ranger at A calculates the angle at A on $\overrightarrow{AB}$ to be 30°. The ranger at B calculates the angle at B on $\overrightarrow{BA}$ to be 127°. Together they can report the location to firefighters.

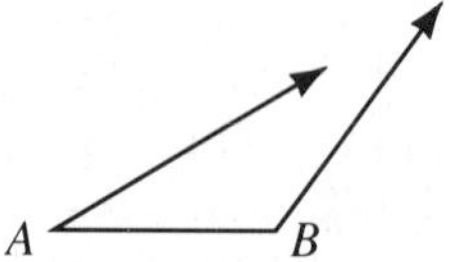

Lesson 1-1 and the Application on pages 27 and 28 also provide related problems.

Cooperative Learning

After introducing the lesson, you might find it helpful to allow students to work in small groups on the following problem. The solution can then be illustrated on either an overhead projector or on the chalkboard.

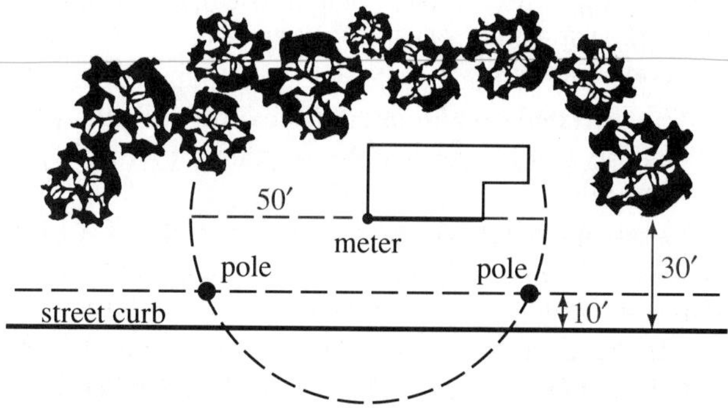

Utility employees from the local power company need to place a telephone pole near a new house in order to provide service. They have been instructed to place the pole exactly 50 ft from the meter located at a corner of the house. The meter side of the house is parallel to and 30 ft from the street curb. Zoning laws require that the pole be 10 ft from the street curb. Locate the possible positions for the pole.

10-8 pages 410–415

Teaching Suggestions

Objective

Apply the concept of locus in the solution of construction exercises.

Presenting the Lesson

In this lesson, students apply locus concepts to the solving of construction problems. Suggest to students that they read each exercise carefully and note all of the conditions required by the problem. After they have constructed a figure, urge them to reread the exercise and check that all requirements have been satisfied.

Before approaching the more complicated constructions of this lesson, take time to review the fourteen basic constructions. Ask students to demonstrate the following, in each case explaining the procedure in terms of locus. First, show how to use the straightedge correctly. Second, use the compass to produce a circle. Third, demonstrate how to copy a segment. Fourth, show the method used to copy an angle. Fifth, bisect a given angle, and sixth, bisect a segment.

Consider the remaining constructions as either direct applications of or combinations of these six constructions. For example, the perpendicular to a line at a point (Construction 5) is a special case of the angle bisector (Construction 3) where the angle is a straight angle. Construction 9 requires drawing a segment, bisecting a segment, drawing a circle, and drawing another line.

The constructions in this lesson can be very difficult for some students. You may want to suggest that they first draw a rough sketch of the completed construction. Knowing what the finished construction should look like may help students to formulate a plan for the construction. Encourage students not to give up trying to solve any construction problem for which they cannot immediately find an answer.

Reinforcement

1. Given $\angle A$, $\overline{BC}$, and the altitude h to side $\overline{AC}$, construct $\triangle ABC$.

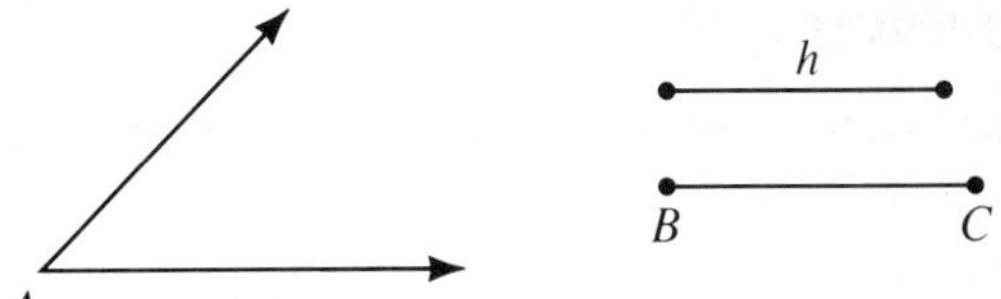

Const. $\angle A$. Const. a $\perp$ to one side of $\angle A$ at A. Locate pt. D on the $\perp$ such that $AD = h$. Const. the $\perp$ to $\overline{AD}$ at D, which int. one side of $\angle A$ at B. With ctr. B and rad. BC, locate pt. C on the other side of $\angle A$. There are two possible pts. for C.

2. Given a segment of length a, construct a 45°-45°-90° triangle with the altitude to the hypotenuse having length a.

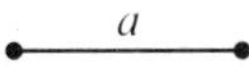

Draw a line. Mark off $AB = 2a$. Const. $\perp$ bis. of $\overline{AB}$. Let M be the midpt. of $\overline{AB}$. On the $\perp$ of $\overline{AB}$, mark off $MC = a$. Draw $\overline{AC}$ and $\overline{BC}$.

Extension

The Challenge problems on pages 385 and 410 change the rules for constructions by limiting the student to just one tool. Students might like to research the topic "Constructions with Restrictions on Tools" by reading the chapter with this title in *Geometric Constructions* by Alfred S. Posamentier and William Wernick (J. Weston Walch: Portland, Maine, 1973). Suggestions include compass only, straightedge only, compass and straightedge with two marks, the collapsible compass and the rusty compass (only one choice of radius).

Enrichment

Constructing the nine-point circle (Extra, page 414) provides review and practice for the constructions in this chapter. Offer extra credit to students who produce this demanding construction correctly.

Using Technology

The topic of the Extra on page 414 is the nine-point circle. Have students use a construction program with this Extra to help with the proofs. Also, have them do the Experiment described in Lesson Commentary for 10-3 if they haven't already done so. Show that the center of the nine-point circle lies on the Euler line. Where is the center located with respect to the other points on the line?

11 *Areas of Plane Figures*

The study of area in this chapter provides excellent opportunities to discuss real-life applications of geometry and geometric probability. The area formulas in the chapter will allow students to use their computational skills in learning some metric geometry.

The first three lessons of the chapter present the formulas for finding areas of polygons, including rectangles, parallelograms, triangles, and trapezoids. Only the key steps in proofs are given so students can see how the formulas are derived. A sequential development of the area formulas is a powerful example of the structure of geometry. Several exercises involve 30°-60°-90° and 45°-45°-90° triangles and trigonometric ratios, thus reviewing some previously presented concepts and skills.

In Lesson 11-4, the formula for finding areas of regular polygons is derived from congruent triangles and is then used in Lesson 11-5 to show how the area of an inscribed polygon gets closer and closer to a limiting number, defined to be the area of a circle. Circles and sectors of circles are then explored in Lesson 11-6, and the formulas for finding arc lengths and areas of sectors of a circle are presented. After all formulas are studied, students learn to compare the areas of figures by finding and using ratios.

The final lesson introduces applications of geometric probability. Two methods for solving problems are discussed: (1) by finding the ratio of the lengths of segments, and (2) by finding the ratio of areas of regions. The exercises in this lesson provide interesting applications of area and should help to review the concepts of ratio and proportion.

11-1 pages 423–428

Teaching Suggestions

Objectives

1. Understand what is meant by the area of a polygon.
2. Understand the area postulates.
3. Know and use the formula for the area of a rectangle.

Presenting the Lesson

Some students may still be confused by the distinction between units and square units. The following example may help to illustrate the difference. To wrap a package, wrapping paper is used to cover the area and string is used to tie it. The wrapping paper and the string are not measured with the same unit of measure. Filling the package requires still a third unit (volume), which will be discussed in Chapter 12.

Locating the bases and altitudes of certain polygons can be effectively presented by first having students draw various triangles, parallelograms, trapezoids, rectangles, and squares on a worksheet. The bases of the figures should be drawn with various orientations (not all horizontal). Then have each student draw in the altitudes.

Using Technology

Chapters 11 and 12 contain many Calculator and Computer Key-Ins, some of which can be done using a spreadsheet. The topics provide an excellent computational introduction to the use of limits. The Computer Key-In on page 428 studies the area under the curve $y = x^2$ while applying the topic of this lesson, area of a rectangle.

Enrichment

In ancient Egypt, the amount of taxes that farmers paid was based on the areas of their plots of land. Historians have researched how ancient Egyptian surveyors developed a method to calculate the area of a region. One theory is that they learned three facts.

1. A region of any shape bounded by straight lines can be divided into triangles.

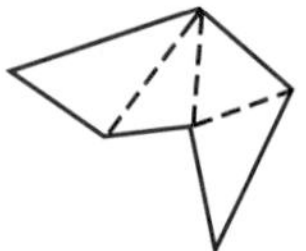

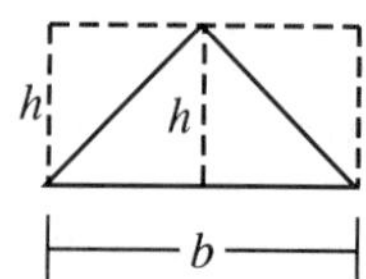

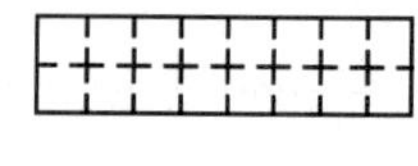

2. The area of a triangular region is half the area of a rectangular region that has the same height and the same base.
3. Any rectangular region can be measured in square units.

Students might wish to research how the Egyptians

combined these three facts to arrive at a method for measuring the area of any plot of land bounded by straight lines.

11-2 pages 429–434

Teaching Suggestions

Objective

Know and use the formulas for the areas of parallelograms, triangles, and rhombuses.

Presenting the Lesson

You can demonstrate Theorem 11-2 by the cut-and-paste method. Cut a right triangle from one side of a rectangular sheet of paper, as shown below, and slide it along the paper to the other side, where it completes the parallelogram.

Theorem 11-3 can be demonstrated by cutting a paper parallelogram in half along a diagonal to form two triangles (hence, $\frac{1}{2}$ × base × height). Conversely, start with any paper triangle and show how it is one half of some parallelogram. To demonstrate this, use two congruent paper triangles. Tape one to the chalkboard and then position the other one next to it until a parallelogram is formed. Repeat this experiment with different types of triangles to show students that a triangle is half a parallelogram.

You might need to emphasize that the area of a parallelogram is not the product of its sides.

Using Technology

The Calculator Key-In on page 434 introduces Heron's Formula, which is useful for calculating the area of a triangle given the lengths of its sides. Heron's Formula and a spreadsheet or computer program can be used to do the following experiment.

Experiment Of all triangles with perimeter 100, which one has the maximum area? Is there a triangle of minimum area? Why not?

11-3 pages 435–440

Teaching Suggestions

Objective

Know and use the formula for the area of a trapezoid.

Presenting the Lesson

You can use the cut-and-paste method to justify the formula for the area of a trapezoid. Cut two congruent paper trapezoids and show how they form a parallelogram, as shown below.

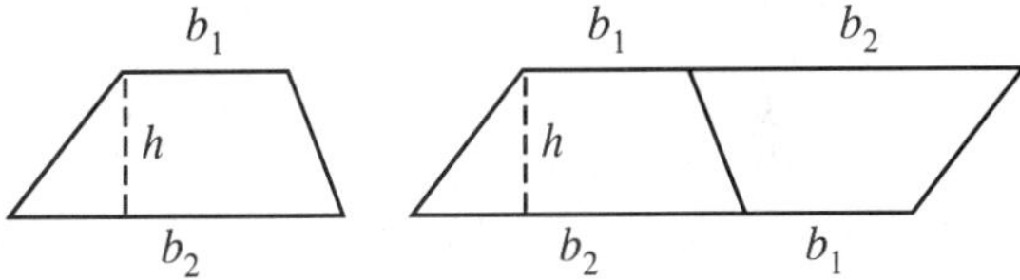

Area $= \frac{1}{2}h(b_1 + b_2)$, where $b_1 + b_2$ is the base of the parallelogram.

You can also cut a single trapezoid along its median and paste the two pieces together to form a parallelogram, as shown below.

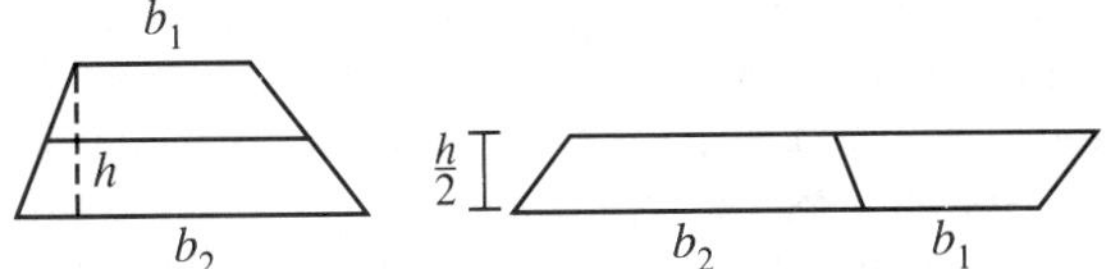

Area $= \frac{1}{2}h(b_1 + b_2)$, where $b_1 + b_2$ is the base of the parallelogram.

Using Technology

The Computer Key-In on pages 438–439 continues the study of the area under the curve $y = x^2$ begun on page 428, but uses trapezoids instead of rectangles.

11-4 pages 440–445

Teaching Suggestions

Objective

Know and use the formula for the areas of regular polygons.

Presenting the Lesson

You might want to use a drawing activity to help illustrate the relationship between circles and regular polygons. Have students draw large circles around regular polygons. Then have students use a compass and protractor to explore their drawings. With some help, they may be able to discover the following relationships.

1. The center of the circumscribed circle is the intersection of the perpendicular bisectors of two consecutive sides of the regular polygon.
2. The apothems of the regular polygon are all congruent and are the perpendicular bisectors of its sides.
3. The radius of the regular polygon is also the radius of the circumscribed circle.
4. The radii of the regular polygon bisect the angles of the polygon.

If students also experiment with the circle inscribed in the polygon, they might discover that the apothem is its radius.

Making Connections

The formula for the area of a regular polygon, $A = \frac{1}{2}ap$, will be useful for the development of the area of a circle in the next lesson. Written Exercises 18–22 should be thought of as a unit, leading into the Calculator Key-In on page 445 and into the next lesson.

Point out to students that increasing the number of sides causes the perimeter of an inscribed polygon to become larger, but the perimeter will never be as large as the circumference of its circumscribed circle. Likewise, the area of an inscribed polygon will increase, but it will never be as large as the area of its circumscribed circle.

Reinforcement

It might be helpful for some students to review all the area formulas for polygons.

Triangle:	$\frac{1}{2}bh$
Parallelogram:	bh
Rectangle:	bh
Trapezoid:	$\frac{1}{2}h(b_1 + b_2)$
Regular Polygon:	$\frac{1}{2}ap$

Extension

Students might enjoy finding the apothem of a regular polygon by using trigonometry. For a regular octagon $ABCDEFGH$, $a = OA \cdot \cos \angle AOX$ (or equivalently, $a = OA \cdot \sin \angle OAX$).

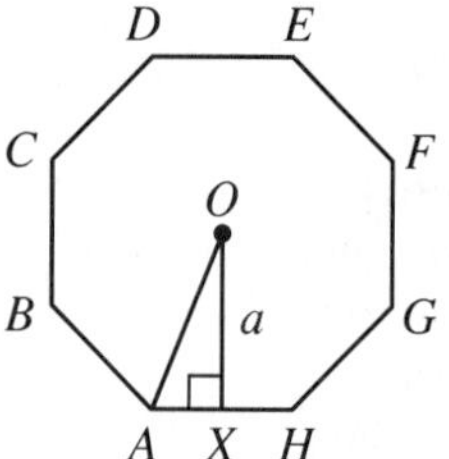

The measure of $\angle AOX = \frac{180}{n}$, where n is the number of sides of the polygon. For an octagon with radius 6, $a = 6 \cdot \cos \frac{180°}{8} = 6 \cos 22.5° \approx 6(0.9239)$ or 5.54.

Cooperative Learning

After completing this lesson, you may wish to organize students into small groups to review the material covered in the first four lessons of the chapter. Self-Test 1 on page 444 can be used for this purpose. Assign at least one capable student to each group to serve as a tutor.

11-5 pages 445–451

Teaching Suggestions

Objective

Know and use the formulas for the circumferences and areas of circles that are derived from the perimeter and area formulas for regular polygons.

Presenting the Lesson

You can demonstrate how to approximate π by taping a piece of string around a wooden or metal hoop. Measure the diameter of the hoop and then carefully unwind the string and measure it also. The ratio of the string measure to the diameter of the hoop will approximate π. Repeat this experiment with several different size hoops to show that π is a constant.

You can also use hoops to discuss the circumference of a circle. Wrap string around a hoop and then carefully measure the diameter of the hoop. Have students predict the circumference of the hoop by using the circumference formula. Unwrap the string and compare its measure with the number found by using the formula.

Reinforcement

The discussion on page 446 is concerned with the inscribed polygon approximating or "fitting" a circle. Explain that the perimeter of the inscribed polygon approaches the circumference of the circle as a limit. You may need to discuss some other basic examples of limits to help students with this concept. For example, ask students to determine what happens to the value of the number $\frac{1}{x}$ as x becomes larger and larger.

Enrichment

Students might be interested in exploring the history of π as well as current computer approximations.

Communication Skills

You may wish to review the definition of an irrational number with students and to mention that π is an irrational number. When discussing different approximate values for π, point out that since these values are indeed approximations, students should use the symbol for "approximately equal to" ($\approx$). Mention also that the most appropriate approximation to use for π will depend upon the facts given in any particular problem.

11-6 pages 452–455

Teaching Suggestions

Objective

Know and use the formulas for arc lengths and the areas of sectors of a circle.

Presenting the Lesson

You may wish to introduce this lesson by demonstrating a variety of ways to divide a pizza. A fair way to divide a pizza seems to be to cut from the center out—to divide the pizza into sectors of equal area, as shown at the right below.

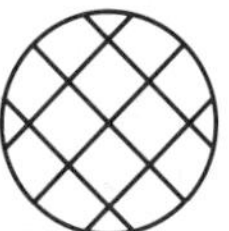

If pizza is cut into nine congruent pieces, each central angle will have a measure of 40. Ask your students to generalize and find the central angle for n pieces. $\left(\frac{360}{n}\right)$

Reinforcement

Students might need extra help in remembering the formulas for arc length and arc measure. Since sectors represent fractional parts of a circular region, have students think of arc length as a fractional part of the circumference, and the area of a sector as a fractional part of the area of a circle. They can then use fractions with the circle formulas to derive the arc length and sector formulas quickly.

Cooperative Learning

Students can work in a cooperative-learning environment on the following experiment: Find (a) the area of a sector, and (b) the area of the region bounded by a chord on one side and its arc on the other side.

To do the experiment, all students will need protractors, rulers, and scissors. Have each group begin by cutting out at least four large paper circles of different sizes. Each member of a group should choose a different central angle to work with. All students should do the following.

1. Measure the radius of the circle.
2. Draw in the appropriate central angle of the circle and cut out a sector with that angle.
3. Calculate the area of the sector and length of the arc of the sector.
4. Cut the sector along the chord connecting points of the original circle.
5. Measure the height and the corresponding base of the resulting triangle, and use the measurements to calculate the area of the triangle ($A = \frac{1}{2}bh$).

6. Find (b) by subtracting the area of the triangle from the area of the sector (from Step 3).

Encourage each member of the group to offer comments and make suggestions.

11-7 pages 456–460

Teaching Suggestions

Objectives

1. Find the ratio of the areas of two triangles.
2. Understand and apply the relationship between scale factors, perimeters, and areas of similar figures.

Presenting the Lesson

Have students do exploratory exercises by comparing the areas of two triangles using graph paper. Instruct students to draw pairs of similar triangles and pairs of triangles that have equal bases or equal heights. Then have students calculate the areas of the triangles by counting squares. The areas should have the ratios described on the bottom of page 456.

Theorem 11-7 can be explored on graph paper also. Give each student the dimensions of two rectangles that are similar, ask them to draw the rectangles on graph paper, and then have them determine the ratio of their perimeters and areas. The explorations can be extended to two equilateral triangles. Encourage students to make conjectures about the ratios of the perimeters and areas of similar figures.

Enrichment

An interesting reference book is *How to Lie with Statistics* by Darrell Huff and Irving Geis, published by W. W. Norton Company, Inc., New York. Chapter 6 explains how bar graphs and other types of graphs can be misleading. To indicate a size twice as large, only one dimension should be doubled. The book contains illustrations showing that even when the numerical facts are stated correctly, the graphs with two dimensions give a far different impression to the reader. If the graph is sketched with a third-dimension perspective, the ratios, of course, are changed even more dramatically.

For a special project assignment, you might want to encourage some students to look for misleading graphical representations. Possible sources for examples are newspapers and periodicals.

Communication Skills

It may be necessary to review the meaning of the term *ratio* before discussing this lesson. Also, have students read the statements on comparing areas of triangles silently and then call upon specific students to explain what they have read. There are many terms in this lesson that must be understood and communicated in order to work the exercises. For example, ask students to explain the meaning of a *scale factor*.

11-8 pages 461–469

Teaching Suggestions

Objective

Use areas to solve problems involving geometric probability.

Presenting the Lesson

Example 3 can be demonstrated by using a dime and a checkerboard. Have students drop the coin on the board 10, 25, 50, or 100 times while keeping track of how many times it lands on the edge of a square or totally within the square. Calculate the ratio of the results. This experiment can lead to a discussion of how the number of times an experiment is performed affects how close the experimental probability is to the theoretical probability. The more times an experiment is repeated, the closer the experimental results will get to the computed theoretical value of the probability.

Cooperative Learning

This is an excellent lesson to motivate by a cooperative-learning environment. Example 3 and Written Exercises 9, 10, 12, and 15 can be done in the classroom. The exercises using darts and arrows can be done also, if they are replaced with coins and concentric circles.

Divide the class into groups of three to four students and provide the materials listed in each exercise. Each group should perform a different experiment. Assign one student the task of being the recorder and the others the task of performing the repeated experiments of the problem. Prior to breaking up into groups, stress that the experimental probability calculation will approach the theoretical probability only after a large number of trials are done. You can combine results from several classes to increase the number of trials.

As the students perform as many trials as time permits, many problems and concerns should arise. For example, when dropping a coin on a table, it may roll off. It is important that the recorder keep a record of all problems that occur in the experimental setting.

At the end of the time allotted, students should discuss their results. As a group they should summarize their results, perform the experimental and theoretical probability calculations, and prepare to explain and discuss their experiment with the entire class.

12 *Areas and Volumes of Solids*

This chapter contains formulas for surface areas and volumes of prisms, pyramids, cylinders, cones, and spheres. The development focuses on right solids; however, an Extra on Cavalieri's Principle is included for teachers who wish to extend the formulas to oblique cases. The final lesson deals with similar solids and comparisons of their linear measures, areas, and volumes.

Instead of proving the theorems, informal arguments and examples are presented and the formulas are stated. This approach is different from the one used throughout the rest of the book and is explained to the student at the beginning of the chapter. Most students will accept this approach and be satisfied using the formulas to solve problems. Each lesson does contain optional material that lays the foundation for deriving the formulas by using calculus. Students need to understand that the theorems can be proved by using mathematics that is beyond the scope of a course in geometry.

A study of three-dimensional solids includes an examination of their one-dimensional and two-dimensional parts. The measures in each case are different and require different kinds of units. Also, the perception of solids drawn in a plane may create unique learning difficulties for some students. Polygons can be seen clearly, but polyhedra present only partial views.

Cones and spheres offer new surfaces to explore. If you did not talk about non-Euclidean geometries when presenting material on parallel lines, you may wish to do so now.

12-1 pages 475–481

Teaching Suggestions

Objectives

1. Identify the parts of prisms.
2. Find the lateral areas, total areas, and volumes of right prisms.

Presenting the Lesson

Provide a variety of three-dimensional models for students to study and manipulate. Include any solids that may be available for classroom demonstration purposes. If possible, use polyhedra folded from opaque materials, such as construction paper or lightweight cardboard. Models that have one face missing will allow students to see the interior spaces of solids. Allow time for handling the models and discussing vertices, edges, faces, surface area, and volume.

Discuss the definition of a prism, and use the models as examples. Include the classroom also, checking to see if the floor and ceiling are portions of parallel planes. Consider opposite walls as well. Explain that prisms do not necessarily rest on bases and that some prisms have more than one set of bases.

Point out to students that in the previous chapters they have been working primarily with plane geometry. The study of solid figures introduces a third dimension and the concepts of surface area and volume. To be sure that students can distinguish between the surface area and volume of a prism, compare the covering and filling of a container. Point out that volume requires a new unit of measurement, namely, the cube.

Members of the packaging industry are very interested in total surface areas and volumes. The Computer Key-In on page 481 involves searching for a container that will provide maximum volume using a given area. Other considerations for an ideal container would include cost of materials, shipping costs, shelf space, and attractiveness to the consumer.

Cooperative Learning

Students can work together to make models of solids. The models may be used as manipulatives, or they may be turned into attractive mobiles for the classroom. One reference is *Paper Folding for the Mathematics Class* by D. A. Johnson, published by NCTM.

Encourage pupils to count and record the number of vertices, edges, and faces of each model. Continued activities of this kind will help students to appreciate Euler's Formula ($F + V - E = 2$), discussed later in the chapter on page 506.

12-2 pages 482–489

Teaching Suggestions

Objectives

1. Identify the parts of pyramids.
2. Find lateral areas, total areas, and volumes of regular pyramids.

Presenting the Lesson

Prepare a paper cutout of a regular pentagon whose sides are bases for congruent isosceles triangles, as shown. Fold into a pyramid, identifying the pentagon as the base, the five triangles as lateral faces, and the point of intersection of the lateral edges as the vertex. Discuss lateral area, using both methods explained on page 482. Read together the list of properties for regular pyramids on the same page.

For most students, the factor of $\frac{1}{3}$ in the formula for the volume of a pyramid will seem mysterious. Experimentation with models is probably the best way to convince students that this factor is correct. One experiment, which can be done before the lesson is presented, is as follows:

1. Cut a standard milk carton so that it has the dimensions shown at the left below.

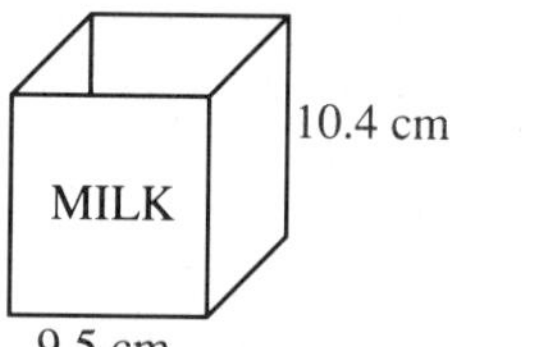

2. Cut out four cardboard triangles with the dimensions given at the right above. Tape the triangles together so as to form a regular square pyramid without a base. The height of the pyramid and the length of a base edge match those of the milk carton.
3. Fill the model of a pyramid three times with rice or sand, emptying it into the milk carton each time. The milk carton will be approximately full, thus demonstrating that the volume of the pyramid is one-third that of the prism which has the same base and height.

Reinforcement

Linear measures, area, and volume all require different types of units. A box of wooden cubes can help to illustrate this idea for students who are having difficulty.

Have students build a rectangular solid with the cubes and then find the perimeter of the base, the total surface area, and the volume by counting the appropriate edges, faces, and cubes. The perimeter, total surface area, and volume should be found as well by using the formulas, and the results compared.

If models of a prism and a pyramid with congruent bases and altitudes are available, fill each with rice and compare the volumes. Students should understand that the volume of a pyramid is given in cubic units.

Using Technology

The Computer Key-In on page 488 approximates the volume of a pyramid by adding the volumes of layered right prisms. The "slicing" technique is also found in this chapter on pages 498, 504, 516, and 517. Students compare the approximate volume with the actual volume of the pyramid. In the Calculator Key-In on page 488, students find an approximate percent of volume.

12-3 pages 490–496

Teaching Suggestions

Objective

Find the lateral areas, total areas, and volumes of right cylinders and right cones.

Presenting the Lesson

In the discussion of cylinders and cones, the book gives intuitive, informal descriptions and not formal definitions. You may want to extend the discussion by using a "limit" approach similar to the one used in Lesson 11-5. You can compare a cylinder to a prism with the same height and consider what happens as you add more and more sides to the polygonal base of the prism. As the figure of the base approaches a circle, the rectangular faces become narrower, approximating a smooth and round surface. Similarly, you can compare a cone to a pyramid. Since prisms and pyramids approximate cylinders and cones, respectively, it seems reasonable that the formulas for their volumes and surface areas are related.

Again, experimentation with models may help students to understand the formulas. The dimensions of a standard soup can with height about 9.5 cm and radius about 3.2 cm can be used to make useful models of a cylinder and a cone, as illustrated below. To make the cone, cut a circle with radius 10 cm out of heavy construction paper. Cut along a radius of the circle and then form a cone whose base is congruent to the base of the soup can.

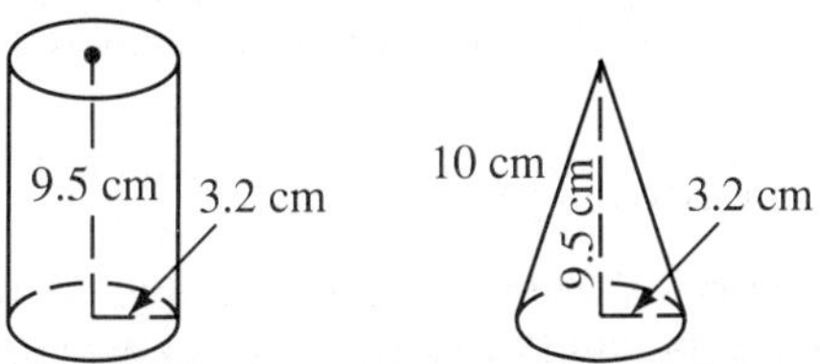

The experiment described for Lesson 12-2 may be repeated using a soup can and the model cone described above to show that the formula $V = \frac{1}{3}\pi r^2 h$ is reasonable for a cone.

Making Connections

The intersection of a plane and a cone creates a conic section. You may wish to talk about circles, ellipses, parabolas, and hyperbolas in this context, especially if models or sketches are available. Students study these curves in their second course in algebra.

Using Technology

The Calculator Key-In on page 496 makes a connection between the area of a rectangle and the lateral area of a cylinder to solve a practical problem involving volume of paint.

Communication Skills

Students may notice that the book discusses right prisms, right cylinders, and right cones, but *regular* pyramids. A discussion of this use of language will help students to understand better the properties of these figures.

Cooperative Learning

Students can work together on the following experiment to see that the volume of a cone is one-third that of a cylinder having the same base and height. Bring one empty soup can to class for each group. Make sure the labels can be removed. Instruct students to do the following.

1. Remove the label carefully and use it to draw a segment with length h, the height of the can.
2. Trace around the bottom of the can. Using a compass and straightedge, locate the circle center and draw a radius r.
3. Construct a right triangle with legs h and r. Call the hypotenuse k.
4. Construct a circle with radius k.
5. With a thin wire, measure the circumference of the can. Use the measured piece of wire to mark off an arc length of $2\pi r$ on the circle with radius k.
6. Add a tab and cut out this sector.
7. Form a cone. Glue or tape the tab.

The cone has the same base and height as the can. Fill the cone with rice and pour it into the can. Three cones of rice will fill the can.

12-4 pages 497–507

Teaching Suggestions

Objective

Find the area and the volume of a sphere.

Presenting the Lesson

To show that four times the area of a circle equals the surface area of a sphere, use a sphere and a circle with the same radius. Wrap yarn in a spiral pattern beginning at the center and working outward until the entire circle is covered, as shown below. Do this four times without cutting the yarn. Then wrap the yarn around the sphere working from the "equator" to each pole. A 12-inch playground ball would make a suitable sphere.

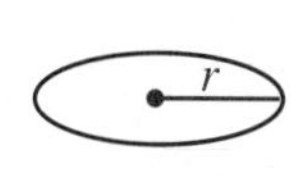

Many students will have difficulty following the argument presented for the justification of the volume formula. It suggests the type of thinking students will encounter later in calculus. Allow students to accept and use the formula without justification.

Enrichment

If you have a student interested in presenting a special report to the class, suggest that the mathematician Archimedes is a good subject to research. Having compiled some remarkable achievements, Archimedes is remembered for his discovery of how to calculate the volume of a sphere.

Making Connections

A solid generated by revolving a plane area about a line (called the axis) is a solid of revolution. Volumes of such solids (the cylinder, cone, and sphere are examples) can be calculated by using integral calculus. Students who study calculus will prove the volume formulas of Lessons 12-3 and 12-4.

Using Technology

The Calculator and Computer Key-Ins on pages 503–505 further explore the volume of a sphere. They give students another informal exposure to limits.

Communication Skills

In this chapter, students have learned three formulas (lateral area, total area, and volume) for each of five solids (right prisms, right cylinders, regular pyramids, right cones, and spheres). Before going on to the lesson about comparing areas and volumes, students should organize this information, looking for clues to help them remember the formulas.

12-5 pages 508–517

Teaching Suggestions

Objective

State and apply the properties of similar solids.

Presenting the Lesson

Discuss the requirements for similarity of solids and the comparison of scale factors for linear measure, area, and volume as listed in Theorem 12-11. Build similar prisms with wooden cubes and compare the scale factors for perimeter, total area, and volume.

Direct students to construct two similar equilateral triangles with a scale factor of 1:2. Remind them that all corresponding linear measures (sides, altitudes, medians, perimeters) have the same scale factor. Next, students should locate the midpoint of each side and draw the segments determined by them. Point out that each area is divided into four congruent triangles and that $\triangle XYZ \cong \triangle A'B'C'$. Thus, the areas of $\triangle A'B'C'$ and $\triangle ABC$ have a scale factor 1:4. Locate the points where the altitudes of each triangle meet, and label these points O and O'. Students may find these points by construction or by folding.

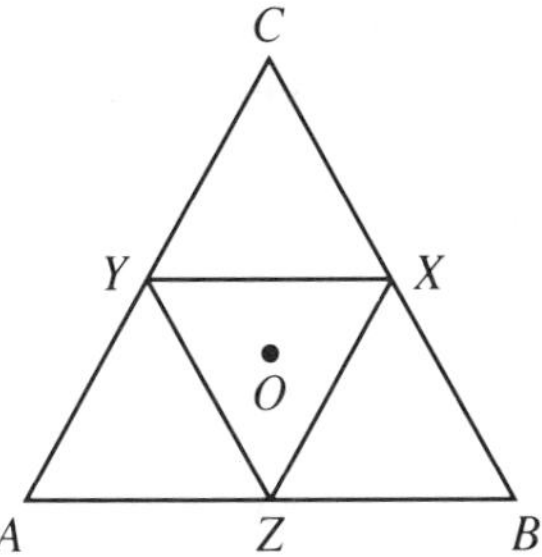

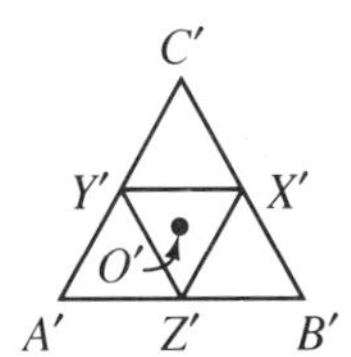

Cut out the triangles, fold along the midlines and form two pyramids. The bases, $\triangle YXZ$ and $\triangle Y'X'Z'$ are similar. The altitudes have a scale factor of 1:2. To demonstrate this, use toothpicks (insert each at the points where the altitudes of each triangle meet, which is the foot of the perpendicular dropped from the vertex to the plane of the base). Break the toothpicks off at the vertices, remove them, and compare their lengths.

Ask students to estimate how many of the smaller pyramids are required to fill the larger one. If B represents the area of $\triangle XYZ$ and h is the height of the pyramid, then the volume of the larger pyramid is $\frac{1}{3}Bh$, and the volume of the smaller one is $\frac{1}{3} \cdot \frac{B}{4} \cdot \frac{h}{2}$, or $\frac{1}{3}Bh(\frac{1}{8})$.

This experiment may be done with any acute triangle, but the construction of the models is easier if the orthocenter lies within $\triangle XYZ$.

Application

Shoppers know that judging the volumes of two different containers can be difficult when trying to determine the best buy. Comparison shopping involves calculating price per unit (volume or weight). You might collect a few containers, mark prices, and ask students to determine the best buy.

13 *Coordinate Geometry*

This chapter contains the important elementary topics of coordinate geometry. The distance formula is developed in the first lesson as a natural application of the Pythagorean Theorem. The distance formula is then used to find the equation of a circle with a given center and radius.

The slope of a line is derived in Lesson 13-2 informally as the ratio of the vertical change to the horizontal change between two points. This notion is used to help develop an intuitive understanding of slope before presenting the formula. The third lesson explores the slopes of parallel and perpendicular lines.

In Lesson 13-4, vectors in the coordinate plane are defined as quantities that have both magnitude and direction. Scalar multiples and the addition of vectors are presented, and vectors are used in application problems. Because vectors have many real-life physical applications, this is an important lesson for students.

In Lesson 13-5, the midpoint formula is developed by averaging coordinates of horizontal and vertical segments and extending the ideas to the coordinate plane.

In Lesson 13-6, slopes are used in graphing lines. Students are asked to write linear equations both in standard and in slope-intercept form and are encouraged to convert from one form to another in order to make graphing more convenient.

Writing linear equations using the point-slope form is presented in Lesson 13-7. Students are given various conditions and asked to write equations of lines fulfilling the conditions.

The chapter concludes with a presentation of the methods of coordinate proofs. Students are given practice placing figures on coordinate axes and are then asked to prove theorems or statements using coordinate methods.

13-1 pages 523–528

Teaching Suggestions

Objectives

1. State and apply the distance formula.
2. State and apply the general equation of a circle.

Presenting the Lesson

You might want to introduce the distance formula, Theorem 13-1, by providing students with graphed line segments drawn in various positions not parallel to the vertical or the horizontal axis. Have them draw in the right triangle associated with the line segment, label the points, and show the values $y_2 - y_1$ and $x_2 - x_1$ for points (x_1, y_1) and (x_2, y_2). This should help students apply the distance formula better and also prepare them for slope in the next lesson.

In order to demonstrate Theorem 13-2, you might want to cut out paper circles or transparency film circles and use an overhead projector to show circles in various positions on a coordinate plane. Give the radius and the coordinates of the center of each circle. Ask students to note relationships and then generalize from these examples the equation of a circle of radius r and center (a, b). Point out that the equation $(x - a)^2 + (y - b)^2 = r^2$ indicates that when a and b are positive, the center lies a units to the right of and b units up from the origin. Then consider examples such as $(x + 1)^2 + (y + 3)^2 = 16$ and have students guess the center and radius. Point out that this equation is the same as $(x - (-1))^2 + (y - (-3))^2 = 4^2$. The center is $(-1, -3)$, and the radius is 4.

Making Connections

Coordinate geometry establishes a strong relationship between algebraic and geometric concepts. Most of the geometry in this chapter is defined or verified by algebraic means and encourages students to review geometric concepts from an algebraic point of view. This should help them both in this chapter and in their future study of mathematics.

Extension

1. Extend and apply the distance formula to three dimensions, and use it to find the distance between the following points, using the distance formula for three dimensions,

$$d = \sqrt{(x_2 - x_1)^2 + (y_2 - y_1)^2 + (z_2 - z_1)^2}.$$

   a. (0, 0, 0) and (12, 4, 3) 13
   b. (5, −3, 2) and (7, 3, −1) 7

2. You might suggest to capable students that they identify the radius and center of a circle in general form by completing the square. For example,

$$x^2 + y^2 - 6x - 8y = 0$$
$$x^2 - 6x + 9 + y^2 - 8y + 16 = 0 + 9 + 16$$
$$(x - 3)^2 + (y - 4)^2 = 25$$

   The center is (3, 4), and the radius is 5. Have students do the following problems.
   a. $x^2 + y^2 - 24x - 10y = 0$
   center (12, 5); radius 13
   b. $x^2 + y^2 + 2x - 12y + 28 = 0$
   center (−1, 6); radius 3

Enrichment

Some students might be interested in doing a special report on René Descartes and the development of the Cartesian coordinate system. A particularly good source is *Mathematics* by David Bergamini and the Editors of *Life*, published by Time Inc., New York.

Communication Skills

When discussing the development of the distance formula in Theorem 13-1, you may need to review the meaning of the absolute value symbol. In addition, you may need to explain why $d^2 = |x_2 - x_1|^2 + |y_2 - y_1|^2$ is equivalent to $d^2 = (x_2 - x_1)^2 + (y_2 - y_1)^2$.

13-2 pages 529–534

Teaching Suggestions

Objective

State and apply the slope formula.

Presenting the Lesson

To introduce slope and to show that the slope of a line is constant, you can use the following activity. Sketch the line through (0, 1) and (3, 3) on the chalkboard and have students copy it on a piece of graph paper. Ask students to select any two points on the line and label the points P_1 and P_2. Next, ask students to draw a horizontal path and then a vertical path that will lead from P_1 to P_2 and compute the ratio of the vertical distance to the horizontal distance. Ask several students to reproduce their work on the chalkboard.

Although students will have different points and different right triangles, everyone should have the same ratio.

Application

You can explore the intuitive notion of slope by discussing the pitch of a roof or the grade of a hill. Some students understand the concept of *rise* for the change in y and *run* for the change in x better than the mathematical definition.

Reinforcement

An alternate way to illustrate slope is to find other points on a line graphically by defining slope to be the ratio $\frac{\text{rise}}{\text{run}}$. One example could be: Given the line with slope $-\frac{1}{3}$ that passes through $(-1, 2)$, find three other points on the line. Be sure to point out that all triangles formed will be similar since their sides have the same ratio.

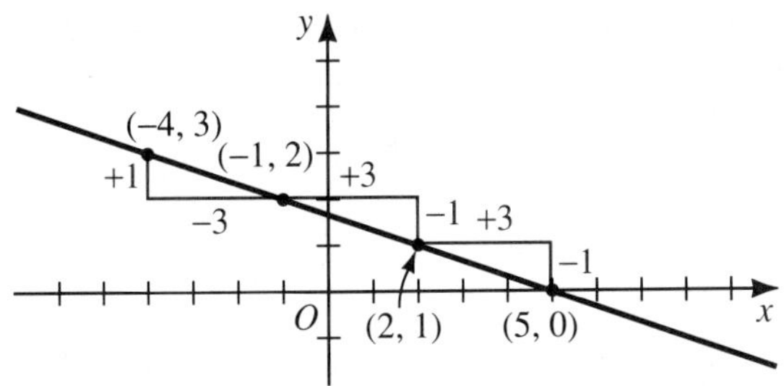

The distance formula and the slope formula both involve the quantities $(x_2 - x_1)$ and $(y_2 - y_1)$, often called "the change in x" and "the change in y."

$$d = \sqrt{(x_2 - x_1)^2 + (y_2 - y_1)^2}$$
$$= \sqrt{(\text{change in } x)^2 + (\text{change in } y)^2}$$

$$m = \frac{y_2 - y_1}{x_2 - x_1} = \frac{\text{change in } y}{\text{change in } x}$$

When calculating the changes in x and y, you may choose either point to be (x_1, y_1).

Communication Skills

To check students' understanding of the definition of slope, ask them to express verbally the definition of slope. Then give students the following sets of two points and ask them to give the slope.

1. $Q(a, b)$, $R(c, d)$ $\frac{d - b}{c - a}$
2. $S(j - k, m)$, $T(j, n)$ $\frac{n - m}{k}$
3. $U(k, m)$, $V(j, m)$ 0
4. $W(k, m)$, $X(k, n)$ not defined

13-3 pages 535–538

Teaching Suggestions

Objective

Determine whether two lines are parallel, perpendicular, or neither.

Presenting the Lesson

You might want to demonstrate the following alternate proof of the "only if" part of Theorem 13-3 by constructing similar triangles with parallel sides on a coordinate plane. Start by constructing two parallel lines, as shown below.

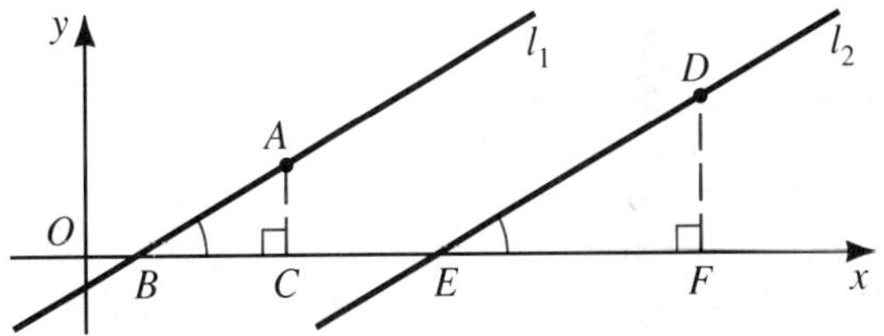

Prove that $\triangle ABC$ and $\triangle DEF$ are similar by using the AA Similarity Theorem. Since corresponding sides are in proportion, $\frac{AC}{BC} = \frac{DF}{EF}$. Since $\frac{AC}{BC}$ is the slope of $\overline{AB}$ and $\frac{DF}{EF}$ is the slope of $\overline{DE}$, the slopes are equal.

You can demonstrate the idea that perpendicular lines have slopes that are negative reciprocals of each other by graphing a line on the chalkboard. At any point of the line, construct a perpendicular line. Use the graphical method described in the Reinforcement for Lesson 13-2 on this page to determine the slope of this perpendicular line. Then verify Theorem 13-4 algebraically. You can have students repeat the demonstration by drawing lines on their own graph paper.

Reinforcement

You can summarize the formulas developed so far in this chapter with the following chart:

Description	Formula
Distance d between points (x_1, y_1) and (x_2, y_2)	$d = \sqrt{(x_2 - x_1)^2 + (y_2 - y_1)^2}$
Equation of a circle with center (a, b) and radius r.	$(x - a)^2 + (y - b)^2 = r^2$
Slope m of a line through (x_1, y_1) and (x_2, y_2)	$m = \frac{y_2 - y_1}{x_2 - x_1}$

13-4 pages 539–543

Teaching Suggestions

Objective

Understand the basic properties of vectors.

Presenting the Lesson

You can introduce vectors by having students think of moving point A to point B on the coordinate plane. Demonstrate the movement of point A to point B by tracing out its path, an arrow from A to B.

Once students understand that a movement can be represented by a vector, you can reinforce this idea by using a physical application. Have students think of a river as the coordinate plane and point A as the initial location of a canoe. If the canoe moves from point A on one side of the river to point B across the river, propelled solely by the force of paddling (with no current), the vector $\overrightarrow{AB}$ of its path is represented by the ordered pair (change in x values, change in y values).

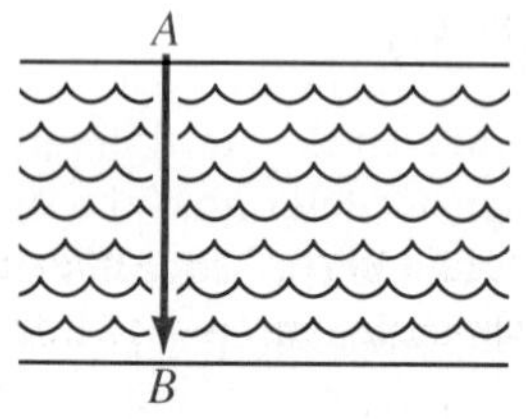

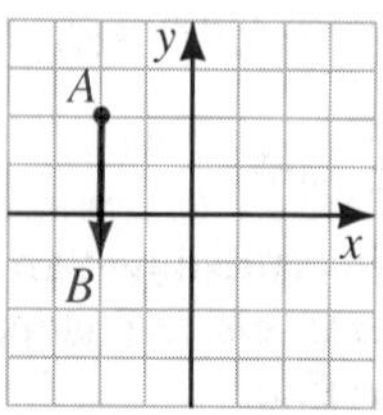

If the canoe is paddled at a rate of 3 mi/h perpendicular to a 4 mi/h current of the river, it will follow a path that will put it farther downstream than if there were no current. The vector $\overrightarrow{AB}$, representing its path, is the vector sum of the "paddle" vector and the "current" vector, and its magnitude is the Pythagorean distance between A and B, namely 5 (5 mi/h).

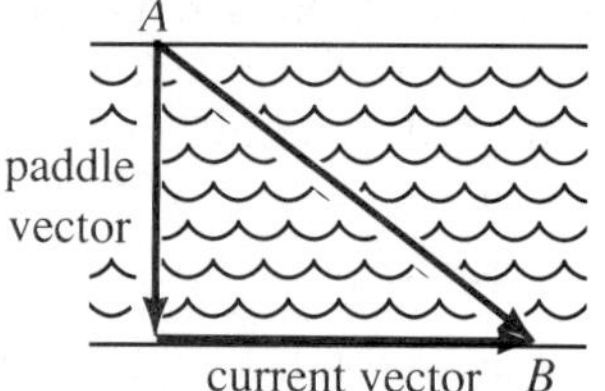

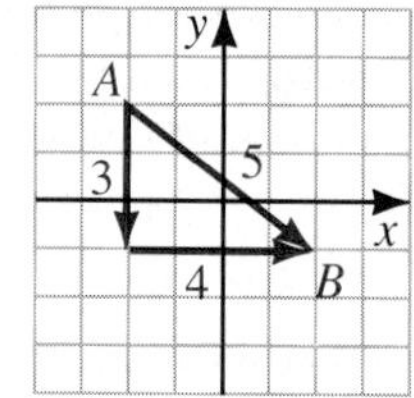

Cooperative Learning

Students can explore "the parallelogram law" for vectors (Written Exercise 26) by working in groups of two or three. Each student can draw the vectors that are equivalent to the sum of various pairs of vectors by (1) first drawing the vectors in standard position (that is, with the origin as the initial point) on a coordinate plane, and then (2) finding the diagonal of a parallelogram that can be formed by the two vectors. After determining the "resultant" vector, students should explain to members of their groups how they reached their conclusions.

13-5 pages 544–547

Teaching Suggestions

Objective

State and apply the midpoint formula.

Presenting the Lesson

When presenting the midpoint formula, Theorem 13-5, emphasize that each coordinate of the midpoint is the average of the respective coordinates of the endpoints of the segment. You can do this by having students check carefully graphed vertical and nonvertical segments for which the midpoints can be determined easily by inspection. A check of the coordinates of the endpoints of the segments and their midpoints can verify the midpoint formula.

Finding the coordinates of the midpoint of a nonvertical segment is then a natural extension of the averaging method. For a nonvertical segment, the coordinates of the midpoint are the averages of the respective coordinates of the endpoints.

Enrichment

Challenge some students to prove the midpoint formula by using vectors. The proof is as follows.

Let $M(a, b)$ be the midpoint of the segment joining $P(x_1, y_1)$ and $Q(x_2, y_2)$. Then $\overrightarrow{PM} = \frac{1}{2}\overrightarrow{PQ}$. $\overrightarrow{PQ} = (x_2 - x_1, y_2 - y_1)$, and $\overrightarrow{PM} = (a - x_1, b - y_1)$. Substituting, $(a - x_1, b - y_1) = \frac{1}{2}(x_2 - x_1, y_2 - y_1)$, or $a - x_1 = \frac{1}{2}(x_2 - x_1)$ and $b - y_1 = \frac{1}{2}(y_2 - y_1)$, which yields $a = \frac{x_1 + x_2}{2}$ and $b = \frac{y_1 + y_2}{2}$. Thus, the coordinates of M are $\left(\frac{x_1 + x_2}{2}, \frac{y_1 + y_2}{2}\right)$.

13-6 pages 548–552

Teaching Suggestions

Objectives

1. Identify the slope and y-intercept of the line specified by a given equation.
2. Draw the graph of the line specified by a given equation.
3. Determine the intersection of two lines.

Presenting the Lesson

After working through the two examples given in the lesson, you can provide extra practice both in graphing lines with equations in standard form and lines with equations in slope-intercept form by having students graph the equations of the lines given in Classroom Exercises 3–11. Point out that values other than $x = 0$ and $y = 0$ may be used to determine points on a line and that a third point can be used to check the sketch of a line. For example, the point $(6, -2)$ may be used to verify that the sketch is correct for the line $2x + 3y = 6$.

You can illustrate graphs with the same intercepts or graphs with the same slopes (parallel lines) by drawing the following sequence of graphs on the chalkboard: (1) graphs with the same intercept, different slopes: $y = mx - 1$, with $m = 1, 2, -2, -3$; (2) graphs with the same slope, different intercepts: $y = \frac{2}{3}x + b$, with $b = 0, 1, -1, 3, -3$.

Reinforcement

You might wish to provide extra practice in converting the equation of a line in standard form to the equation of a line in slope-intercept form. Emphasize the need to convert to the slope-intercept form to make graphing more convenient. The y-intercept can be plotted first and then the slope can be used to plot another point. The line is drawn by connecting the two points.

Using Technology

Have students set up spreadsheets or computer programs that perform the tasks listed below. This Experiment combines the main results of the first six lessons of Chapter 13.

Experiment

1. Take as inputs the coordinates of two points P and Q and output (a) the length of $\overline{PQ}$, (b) the slope of $\overline{PQ}$, (c) the midpoint of $\overline{PQ}$, and (d) the y-intercept of $\overleftrightarrow{PQ}$.
2. Take as inputs the slopes and y-intercepts of two lines and output their point of intersection.
3. Take as inputs the coordinates of three points P, Q, and R, and output for $\triangle PQR$ (a) the length of each side, (b) the perimeter, and (c) the area (For area, use Heron's Formula on page 434.).

13-7 pages 553–556

Teaching Suggestions

Objective

Write the equation of a line when given either one point and the slope of the line, or two points on the line.

Presenting the Lesson

Demonstrate how to determine the equation of a line from its graph. Graph several lines on the chalkboard and then show students how to do each of the following.

1. Determine the slope of each line and a point on the line.
2. Using a point on the line and its slope, determine the equation of the line.
3. Determine two points on the line.
4. Using two points on the line, determine the equation of the line.

Repeat the demonstration with vertical and horizontal lines, and with lines having various slopes.

Reinforcement

You can summarize the formulas for the equation of a line with the following chart.

Form	Equation
Standard	$Ax + By = C$
Slope-Intercept	$y = mx + b$
Point-Slope	$y - y_1 = m(x - x_1)$

The restriction on the standard form is that A and B are not both zero. The slope-intercept form and the point-slope form cannot be used for vertical lines.

Enrichment

In the equation $3x - 4y + k = 0$, if any real number is substituted for k, a unique line is determined. Since all the lines determined by substituting k into $3x - 4y + k = 0$ are parallel (they have the same slope), $3x - 4y + k$ is called the equation of the "family of lines" of slope $\frac{3}{4}$, and k is the "parameter" of the family.

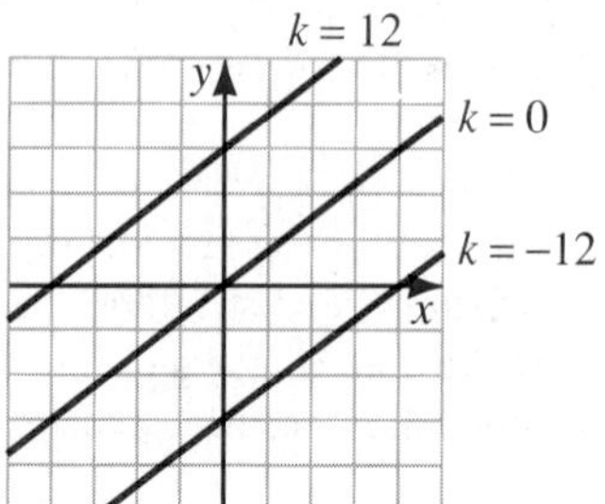

Have students find the equation of the family of lines perpendicular to $11x - 3y = 0$. $(3x + 11y + k = 0)$

13-8 pages 556–559

Teaching Suggestions

Objective

Given a polygon, choose a convenient placement of coordinate axes and assign appropriate coordinates.

Presenting the Lesson

You might want to demonstrate good placement of coordinate axes versus awkward placement with the following examples.

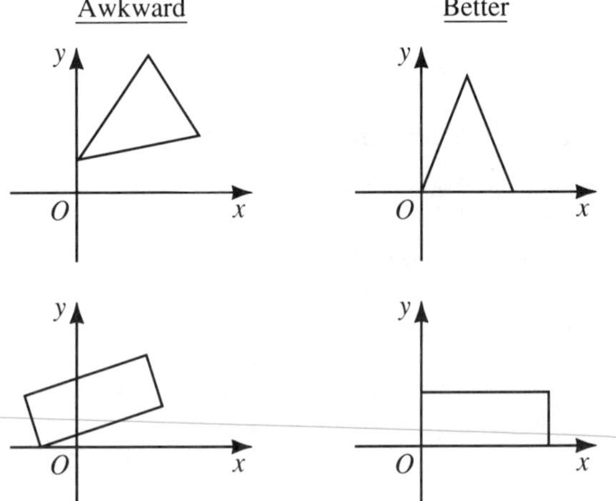

Communication Skills

Students must be very careful not to assume more than is given in the hypothesis of a theorem. Emphasize that points must be chosen in the most general way. For example, if the hypothesis is about quadrilaterals, the coordinates should not reflect any special properties that would make the sides congruent, parallel, or perpendicular. However, it is desirable to choose the coordinates so that the algebra is simplest.

When you discuss the various ways that coordinate axes can be placed on figures, point out the rationale for some of the coordinates. For example, if a parallelogram with consecutive vertices $(a, 0)$, $(0, 0)$, and (b, c) is given, the fourth vertex must be $(a + b, c)$. Always stress the advantages of choosing convenient coordinates.

13-9 pages 560–563

Teaching Suggestions

Objective

Prove statements by using coordinate geometry methods.

Presenting the Lesson

You can compare how coordinate geometry proofs are usually easier than synthetic proofs once a polygon has been given coordinates. Write a coordinate proof and a paragraph proof side by side on the chalkboard. You can use Example 2 and the proof of Theorem 5-11 on page 178.

Making Connections

In coordinate geometry, problems are solved by using algebra. Coordinate geometry is an important part of analytic geometry, a subject in which algebra, geometry, and trigonometry are studied together. Emphasize that it is important to study coordinate geometry because it illustrates the interrelationships of algebra and geometry, as well as providing new and interesting mathematics that contains powerful problem-solving techniques.

Cooperative Learning

You may wish to form groups of three or four students to go over the Written Exercises on pages 562 and 563. Each member of the group can perform some of the following tasks.

1. Read the problem and identify the hypothesis and conclusion in the proof.
2. Give coordinates to the polygon with convenient axes.
3. Identify the algebraic statements necessary to form the key deductive steps of the proof.
4. Discuss how the proof might have been written without using coordinate geometry methods.

14 *Transformations*

This final chapter explores many concepts from the subject of transformational geometry. Lesson 14-1 starts out by discussing some basic mappings, including projections on the plane. It defines a one-to-one mapping and develops the general concept of a transformation of the plane.

Specific transformations that are isometries, namely reflections, translations, and rotations, are developed in the next three lessons. These transformations are studied geometrically and on the coordinate plane. Ample material is provided so that capable students can explore the underlying algebraic structure of the transformations.

Dilations are explored in Lesson 14-5. They are presented as expansions or contractions of the plane by using both geometric and coordinate methods. Dilations provide an excellent opportunity to review the topic of similarity.

The second part of the chapter, Lessons 14-6 through 14-8, presents the composition of transformations, inverses and the identity transformation, and describes the symmetry of figures and solids. The composition of transformations is compared to the composition of functions in algebra, and then geometric examples are presented. Translations and rotations are redefined to be the composition of two reflections either in parallel lines (for translations) or in intersecting lines (for rotations). The inverse of a transformation and the identity transformation are then defined and used in mappings in much the same way that they are used for numbers.

The chapter concludes with a discussion of line symmetry, rotational symmetry, point symmetry, translational symmetry, and glide symmetry.

The Extra following Lesson 14-8 provides capable students with challenging problems on symmetry groups that relate algebra and geometry.

Chapter 14 provides an excellent opportunity to conclude a geometry course with a new look at the fundamental concepts of congruence and similarity. Students who study the chapter may gain a better awareness of the close relationship between algebra and geometry.

Suggestions on how to integrate transformational geometry throughout the year are presented on pages T56–T57.

14-1 pages 571–576

Teaching Suggestions

Objectives

1. Recognize and use the terms *image*, *preimage*, *mapping*, *one-to-one mapping*, *transformation*, *isometry*, and *congruence mapping*.
2. Recognize the properties of the basic mappings.

Presenting the Lesson

You can demonstrate the idea of a transformation by drawing a figure on an elastic sheet (like balloon material) and stretching it. The figure will lose its shape, but students will be able to see easily that the transformation is one to one. The transformation is not an isometry, however, because the image is larger than the preimage.

Another one-to-one transformation you can demonstrate is finding the shadow of an object. Use a light source and various objects to project the shadow of each object. You can also show different transformations on the same object by demonstrating how the shadow of the object changes as you change the position of the light source.

Reinforcement

To help students understand the relationships between the different types of transformations, you may want to introduce the following chart in this lesson and then use it throughout the chapter as the terms are defined.

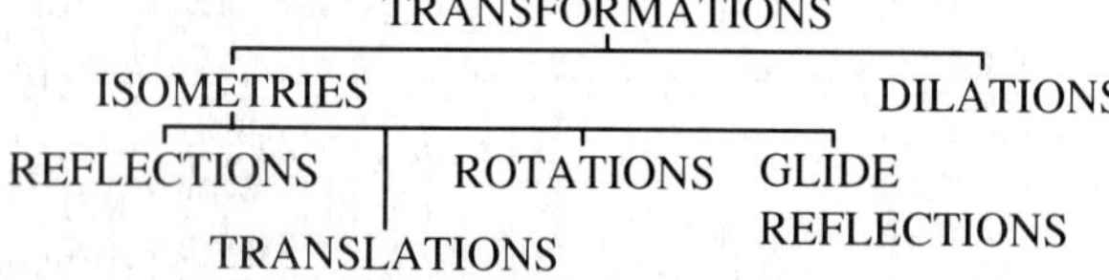

Extension

You might want to have students practice making projections onto a plane by sketching the projections of objects placed on a table or floor as they look down on them or look at them from different angles. For example, the projection of the following figure onto the plane of *ABCD* would be as shown.

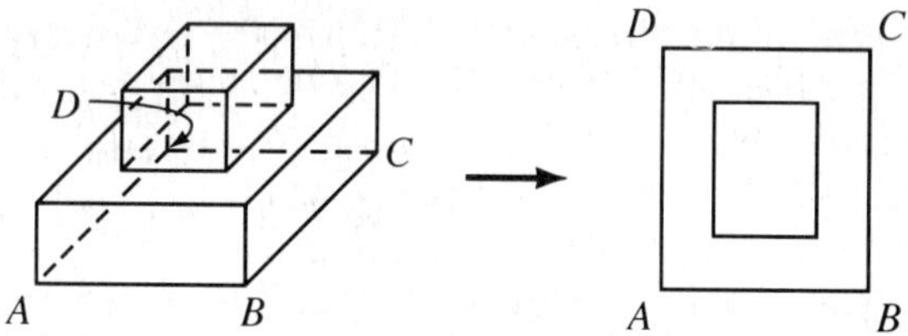

Communication Skills

The language of transformations suggests motion such as stretching, contracting, sliding, rotating, or reflecting. While transformations can occur without apparent motion, a transformation that is not the identity involves the idea of moving points. Motion for an *isometry* then implies rigidity and can be thought of that way.

Tell students that the term *isometry*, which identifies distance-preserving transformations, comes from the Greek *iso* (meaning *equal*) and *metry* (meaning *measure*).

14-2 pages 577–582

Teaching Suggestions

Objective

Locate images of figures by reflection.

Presenting the Lesson

Reflections can be demonstrated by using several methods. The most obvious one is to show the reflection of an object in a mirror. A thin, transparent plastic mirror is best. Either reflect actual objects or objects drawn on a piece of paper. For the latter case, you can demonstrate different reflections of a simple segment drawn on a piece of paper. Place the mirror perpendicular to the paper and intersecting the endpoint of the segment, as shown below.

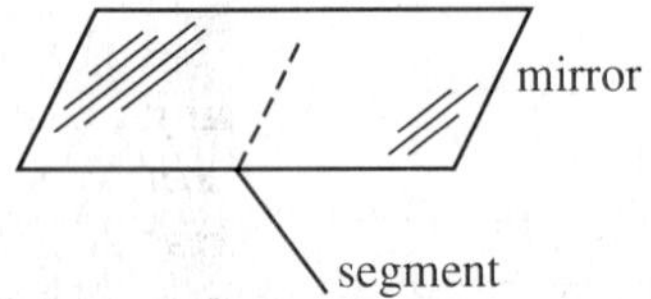

The reflection makes the segment look like an angle. Then move the mirror to get different angles. Ask students when the reflection will look like a straight angle. (Mirror is ⊥ to segment.)

Another way to demonstrate a reflection is to draw a line of reflection on the chalkboard and reflect various polygons (either drawn or cut out of cardboard). Each polygon will "flip" over the line and change orientation. Students will observe the motion as this is done.

A third method to demonstrate a reflection is to use constructions to locate reflection images. Draw a polygon on the chalkboard along with the line of reflection. Use a compass and straightedge to construct perpendiculars to the line of reflection from each vertex of the polygon and to construct segments on the other side of the line of reflection that are equal to the length of the perpendicular segments.

Applications

Excellent applications of reflections are the patterns called *frieze patterns* obtained by continually reflecting over parallel lines in a row. They are often used in architecture and interior decorating. You might want students to do some research on frieze patterns (which can also be made by using other transformations) and try to generate a pattern of their own.

Stress that reflections can be found in many real-life applications. For example, reflections have applications in miniature golf, billiards, and other games of aiming at a particular target via a reflected path. Satellite transmissions are also reflected, as are certain beams of laser light.

Extension

At this time, you might want to explore the identity reflection with students. Have students find all possible lines of reflection that map a triangle onto itself for each of the following triangles: isosceles, equilateral, and scalene. You can then extend the idea to include other polygons. Introduce the concept of "line symmetry" and ask students to draw a figure (not a polygon) with exactly one, two, three, or four lines of symmetry.

Enrichment

Ask students to plot the following points, by column, connect them in order to form a picture, and then reflect the points over the y-axis.

(−8, 4)	(−3, 14)	(−8, 7)	(−10, 11)	STOP
(−10, 4)	(−6, 14)	(−10, 7)	(−12, 11)	(−12, 15)
(−11, 5)	(−5, 12)	(−10, 6)	(−12, 12)	(−12, 14)
(−11, 8)	(−5, 9)	(−8, 6)	(−10, 12)	STOP
(−13, 9)	(−7, 8)	STOP	(−10, 11)	(−6, 15)
(−13, 12)	(−7, 5)	(−9, 6)	STOP	(−6, 14)
(−12, 14)	(−8, 4)	(−9, 7)	(−7, 8)	STOP
(−15, 14)	STOP	STOP	(−8, 11)	
(−15, 18)	(−11, 5)	(−11, 8)	(−6, 11)	
(−14, 15)	(−7, 5)	(−7, 8)	(−6, 12)	
(−4, 15)	STOP	STOP	(−8, 12)	
(−3, 18)	(−8, 6)	(−11, 8)	(−8, 11)	

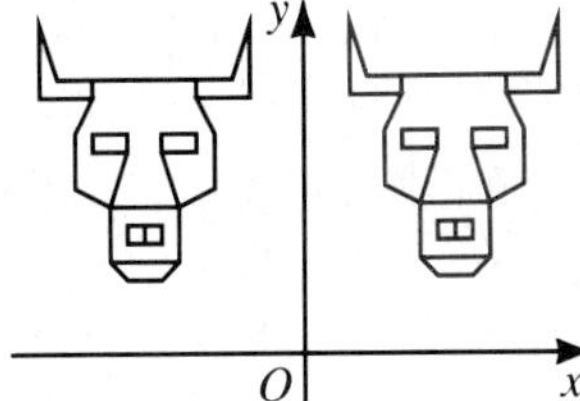

14-3 pages 583–587

Teaching Suggestions

Objective

Locate images of figures by translation and glide reflection.

Presenting the Lesson

You may want to demonstrate translations by placing a cardboard cutout of a triangle on a chalkboard coordinate plane. Place coordinates on the triangle and then slide it to another position and locate the new coordinates. Have students describe the translation by giving the equivalent vector and by giving a coordinate description. Use their description to translate other points or figures. Repeat the demonstration for other translations.

A translation can also be demonstrated by showing that it is the composite of reflections over two parallel lines. You can draw two parallel lines on the chalkboard, draw a figure, and then show the actual reflections. The result is the same as if a glide were performed (without the reflecting lines showing). By using this method, the magnitude of the translation is twice the distance between the reflecting lines, and its direction is along a perpendicular to the reflecting lines. This method is a nice preview of the composition of transformations, a topic introduced in Lesson 14-6.

Communication Skills

The definition of a translation implies that the distances between points and the measures of angles are *invariant* under a translation. You may wish to remind students of the term invariant and then continue to use it throughout the chapter.

14-4 pages 588–592

Teaching Suggestions

Objective

Locate images of figures by rotation.

Presenting the Lesson

An excellent way to demonstrate rotations is on an overhead projector, using a transparency and a pin as a pivot. Indicate the image and preimage points of various figures and discuss whether angles, distances, or orientation are preserved before proving Theorem 14-4.

You can also demonstrate rotations by using congruent cardboard triangles taped to the chalkboard. Show the various possible positions for the center of rotation by showing pairs of triangles in the positions shown below.

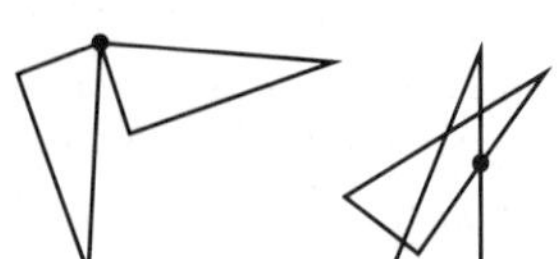

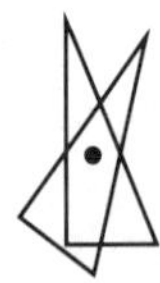

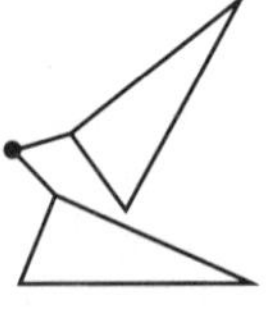

You can then use the triangles on a chalkboard coordinate plane to demonstrate half-turns about the origin. Have students try to predict the new coordinates under the half-turn.

The "turning" nature of rotations can be demonstrated by having students work with compasses and various pairs of rotated figures. Have them place the compass points on the centers and use the compasses to connect the image points to the preimage points.

Applications

Because a rotation is a mathematical model for the motion of turning, there are many applications. Objects that operate by a rotation are a radio dial, a pulley, a key, a water faucet, a compact disc player, and the wheels of a car. Ask students to suggest other examples.

Extension

You can trace various figures on a geoboard, as shown below, and ask students to predict the location of the figures after the entire geoboard is rotated through angles of 45°, 90°, and 180°.

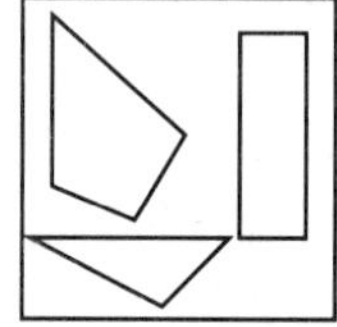

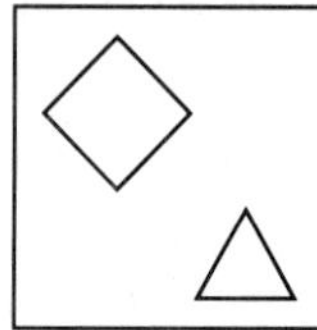

Enrichment

With reflections, unlike translations and rotations, an asymmetrical figure does not have an exact duplicate because the orientation of the figure is reversed even though the image is congruent. One way to match a figure with the image produced by a reflection is to lift it off the plane, flip it over, and put it back on the corresponding image. This cannot be done with three-dimensional figures because a fourth dimension would be required to transport the preimage figure (in order to reverse the orientation). This concept of reverse orientation is dealt with in a fascinating book entitled *Sphereland*, written by Dionys Burger as a sequel to Edwin Abbott's *Flatland*. You might want to ask some students to read these books and share what they have learned with the class.

14-5 pages 592–597

Teaching Suggestions

Objective

Locate images of figures by dilation.

Presenting the Lesson

You can use an overhead projector as a model for a dilation. It acts as the center of the dilation, and as the projector is moved forward or backward, the image on the screen gets smaller or larger.

You might want to demonstrate dilations by using constructions. Draw a figure on the chalkboard and locate the center of the dilation. Using a compass and straightedge, show how the image points under an expansion or a contraction can be found. Use various scale factors and show that the definition of a dilation applies. Then use these same examples to verify Theorem 14-5 and its three corollaries by comparing the image and preimage angle measures and distances.

Applications

Expanding or contracting the size of a figure is basic to many occupations, such as an architect, cartographer (mapmaker), engineer, clothes designer, interior decorator, photographer, and artist. Hobbyists who build miniature models also need to be able to determine the new dimensions of an object. Ask students for other examples and use them to motivate the lesson.

Reinforcement

Properties of figures that are preserved under a transformation can be summarized by the following chart.

	Isometry	Dilation
Angle Measure	✓	✓
Distance	✓	
Parallelism	✓	✓
Ratio of Distances	✓	✓
Area	✓	
Orientation		✓

Extension

Ask students to sketch a figure with at least 20 points on a piece of graph paper, assign coordinates to the points, and then dilate it with a scale factor of -2. (See the Enrichment in Lesson 14-2, page T139, for an example of a figure with coordinates.)

14-6 pages 599–605

Teaching Suggestions

Objective

Locate the images of figures by composites of mappings.

Presenting the Lesson

You can introduce the concept of composites of mappings by having students do the following experiment. Ask students to cut out an arrow and a square using heavy construction paper, and attach the arrow to the center of the square with a paper fastener.

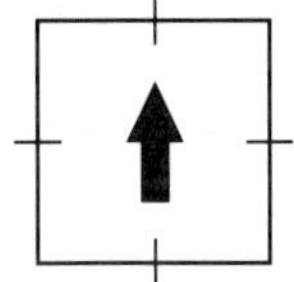

Give the students a list of directions for rotating the arrow, such as: S (stand still), RT (right turn, 90 degrees clockwise), LT (left turn, 90 degrees counterclockwise), and H (half turn, 180-degree turn). Ask students to combine any two motions and record the results. Remind students that when writing compositions the first operation goes rightmost and later operations are placed to the left. For example, a left turn followed by a right turn is symbolized $RT \circ LT$. But this is equivalent to standing still, so $RT \circ LT = S$. Similarly, $RT \circ RT = H$ and $RT \circ S = RT$. You can extend this exercise by asking students to combine three motions, such as $RT \circ H \circ RT = S$.

You might want to demonstrate reflections in parallel lines and in intersecting lines before discussing Theorems 14-7 and 14-8. Use a compass and straightedge to reflect various figures drawn on the chalkboard. Demonstrate that the product of two reflections is not commutative by performing the reflections in different orders.

Making Connections

The discussion of the material in this lesson will probably be the first introduction to the concept of compositions of mappings for most students. The notation for the composition of mappings is consistent with the usual treatment of the composition of functions in algebra: In evaluating the composite function $f \circ g$, g is applied first and then f. Very few students will have studied composition of functions in algebra.

Reinforcement

Use the experiment in the Presenting the Lesson section of this lesson to illustrate the identity property and also to check for the commutative and associative properties. Point out that the composition of transformations is associative because the transformations are always performed sequentially. The compositions of rotations about the same center are commutative, but the compositions of rotations about different centers are not.

Extension

Ask students to draw two congruent triangles on graph paper as shown below and find the composition of isometries that will make them coincide.

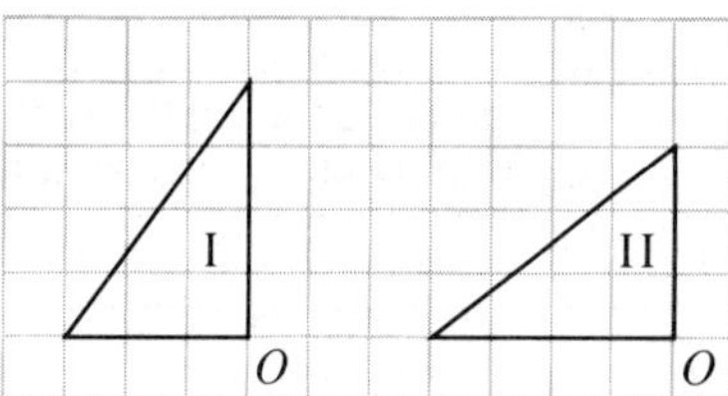

(Answers will vary. One composition is to translate triangle I seven spaces to the right horizontally, rotate it 90° clockwise about the vertex O, and then reflect in the shortest side.)

Cooperative Learning

The proofs of Theorems 14-7 and 14-8 can be discussed in a group environment. Have students form discussion groups of three or four students. Students should test various examples of translations done by a composition of reflections to show that the magnitude of the translation is twice the distance between the parallel reflecting lines. They should then test various examples of rotations done by a composition of reflections to verify that the magnitude of the rotation is twice the measure of the angle between the reflecting lines. Encourage the groups to come up with their own proofs of the Corollary of Theorem 14-8.

14-7 pages 605–608

Teaching Suggestions

Objective

Recognize and use the terms *identity* and *inverse* in relation to mappings.

Presenting the Lesson

You can give students a more intuitive feeling for the concept of inverse by showing the following list of examples on the chalkboard.

Motion	*Inverse*
Reflect in line x	Reflect in line x
Rotate 60°	Rotate $-60°$
Translate 2 up	Translate 2 down
Turn 180°	Turn $-180°$

Have students add their own examples to the list.

Use the teaching model from Lesson 14-6 in Presenting the Lesson to list various composite transformations that are inverses of each other. For example, *RT* (right turn, 90° clockwise) and *LT* (left turn, 90° counterclockwise) are inverses of each other.

Communication Skills

Students have learned the terms *inverse* and *identity* in previous mathematics courses. The use of these same terms in geometry will help them to understand that some concepts are fundamental to more than one branch of mathematics. These kinds of concepts not only help to unify mathematics but also develop students' use of a more general mathematical vocabulary.

14-8 pages 609–614

Teaching Suggestions

Objective

Describe the symmetry of figures and solids.

Presenting the Lesson

Paper folding can be used to demonstrate line symmetry. Copy the following shapes onto lightweight paper and trace over the lines with a dark marking pen so that the lines can be seen through the paper. Then fold the shapes along their lines of symmetry, as shown in red below. Students should be able to see through the paper to verify that each figure has line symmetry.

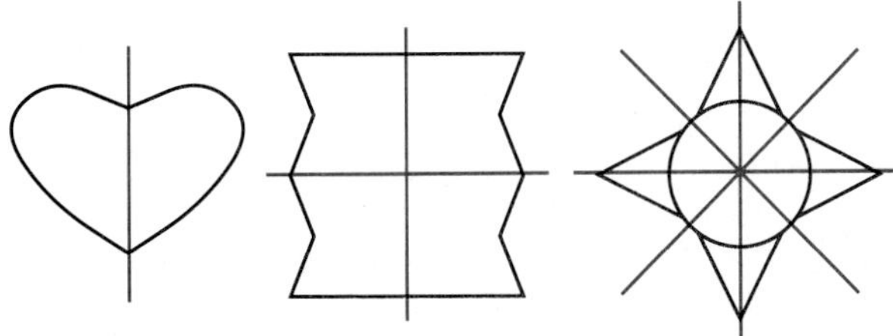

Rotational symmetry can be demonstrated by using large paper models of various polygons. Locate their centers of rotation by finding the intersection points of the diagonals. Then place a large dot on one corner of each polygon. Cut a congruent polygon out of transparent film (the clear material used for transparencies) and make the figures coincide. Draw the large dot on the clear film as well. Now place a pin in the center and rotate the film. If the film and the original shape coincide after rotating the film by a certain angle, the figure has rotational symmetry. The angles can be measured with a protractor or calculated algebraically if the figures are regular polygons.

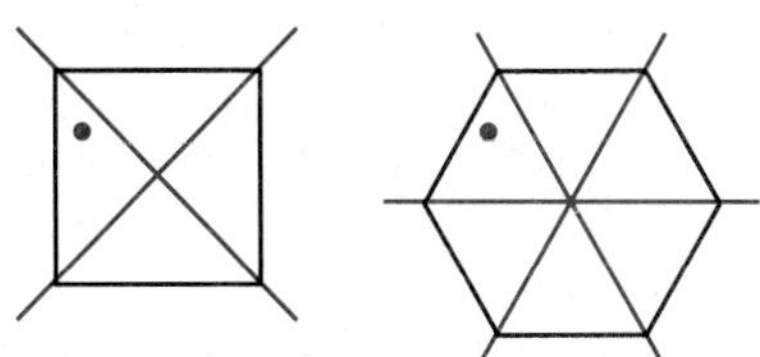

Applications

Symmetry can be found everywhere in nature and in objects made by people. Plants, animals, art, architecture, music, dance, poetry, and chemical structure are some examples. Ask students for some specific examples and use them as a basis for discussion.

Cooperative Learning

You might want to have students explore the line and rotational symmetries of various quadrilaterals by working in groups of four. On the chalkboard draw diagrams similar to those shown below and have students copy them on a worksheet.

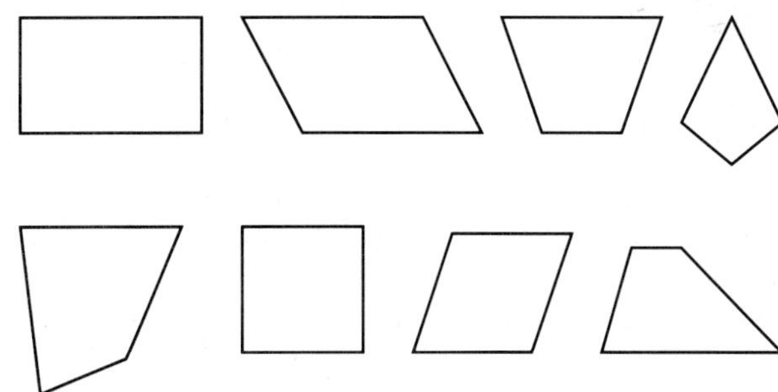

Tell students to divide up the task of drawing all lines of symmetry and filling in the following chart. They should consider and discuss questions such as, "Why don't rectangles have four lines of symmetry? Why aren't the diagonals of a parallelogram lines of symmetry?" Students should compile their questions and present them to the class. Encourage them to use paper folding to find lines of symmetry and rotational symmetry.

Shape	Lines of Symmetry	Rotation Symm. (other than 360°)
Quadrilateral	0	—
Kite	1	—
Trapezoid	0	—
Isosceles Trap.	1	—
Parallelogram	0	180°
Rhombus	2	180°
Rectangle	2	180°
Square	4	90°, 180°, 270°

Nonroutine Problems

Nonroutine problems appear in other publications for this program as well: Enrichment Activities in the *Resource Book*, Extensions and Enrichments in the *Teacher's Edition*, and certain of the activities in the *Computer Activities.* This chart lists nonroutine problems in the student textbook that we would like to call to your attention. The column marked "Other" contains references to Applications, Challenges, Mixed Reviews, and other features.

Ch.	Class Exercises	Written Exercises	Other
1	2–3 (Exs. 1–8), 14 (Exs. 21, 22), 20 (Exs. 26, 27), 24 (Exs. 13–15)	4 (Exs. 7–10), 9 (Ex. 28), 16 (Ex. 47), 21 (Ex. 28), 22 (Ex. 35), 26 (Ex. 19)	9
2	52 (Ex. 21)	35 (Ex. 31), 43 (Ex. 15), 46 (Ex. 12), 47 (Exs. 17, 18, 20), 54 (Exs. 34, 35), 59 (Exs. 26, 27)	55, 60, 66
3	80 (Ex. 14), 96 (Exs. 16, 17), 103 (Exs. 1–7)	76 (Exs. 18–21), 88 (Exs. 20, 21, 30), 99 (Exs. 31–34), 104 (Ex. 7), 105 (Exs. 18–20), 108 (Exs. 15–17, 26, 27), 109 (Exs. 28, 30)	92
4	119 (Exs. 17–20), 124 (Ex. 11)	120 (Exs. 12–19), 121 (Exs. 22, 24), 130 (Ex. 2), 131 (Exs. 9–12), 132 (Exs. 15, 16), 137 (Exs. 9, 10), 138 (Exs. 15, 16), 139 (Exs. 26, 30–32, 34), 143 (Ex. 2), 144 (Exs. 9, 10), 151 (Ex. 17), 156 (Exs. 1–6), 157 (Ex. 19)	121, 139
5	168 (Exs. 15, 17, 18), 173 (Exs. 10–13), 179 (Exs. 1, 9), 186 (Exs. 1–4, 11)	170 (Exs. 17, 18), 171 (Exs. 33–36), 174 (Exs. 7, 8), 188 (Exs. 20–23, 36–39), 189 (Exs. 40–42), 193 (Exs. 19–26, 28, 29), 194 (Exs. 33–36)	194
6	221 (Ex. 13), 230 (Exs. 9, 10)	223 (Exs. 20, 23), 231 (Exs. 1, 2), 232 (Exs. 12, 15)	207, 217, 225
7	243 (Ex. 6), 265 (Ex. 9), 271 (Ex. 8),	244 (Ex. 33), 251 (Exs. 32, 33), 252 (Exs. 35–37), 258 (Ex. 20), 259 (Ex. 32), 273 (Exs. 27, 29, 30)	260, 262, 274, 276, 280

Ch.	Class Exercises	Written Exercises	Other
8	291 (Ex. 1), 301 (Ex. 12), 307 (Exs. 10, 11), 313 (Ex. 11), 314 (Exs. 12, 14, 15), 318 (Ex. 7)	297 (Exs. 16, 17), 298 (Ex. 22), 303 (Exs. 32–34), 309 (Ex. 25)	294, 316, 321, 322
9	335 (Ex. 5), 353 (Ex. 14)	330 (Exs. 1–3), 331 (Exs. 16, 20), 336 (Exs. 7–9, 12, 13), 337 (Ex. 19), 342 (Exs. 12, 13, 17–20), 343 (Exs. 22–24), 360 (Ex. 30), 361 (Exs. 31, 32), 366 (Ex. 21)	332, 368
10	403 (Exs. 11, 12)	384 (Ex. 26), 389 (Exs. 8–10), 399 (Ex. 18), 410 (Ex. 24)	385, 391, 410, 415
11	425 (Ex. 15), 436 (Ex. 7), 462 (Exs. 1–4)	427 (Exs. 35, 36), 433 (Ex. 34), 438 (Ex. 32), 455 (Exs. 26, 27), 463–464 (Exs. 1–17)	455, 464, 466, 469
12	484 (Exs. 1, 16–18)	494 (Ex. 28), 495 (Exs. 30, 31, 39, 40)	480, 487, 495, 502, 506, 513, 517
13	532 (Ex. 7), 541 (Ex. 8)	527 (Exs. 41, 42), 538 (Exs. 15–18), 543 (Exs. 33, 34)	552, 564, 565
14	574 (Exs. 6–8), 612 (Ex. 15)	576 (Exs. 16–19, 22), 581 (Exs. 26–29), 587 (Exs. 16, 17), 612 (Exs. 8–11), 614 (Ex. 24)	583, 614, 616–617
Handbook	658–659 (Exs. 1–7), 659–660 (Exs. 1–9), 662 (Ex. 12), 663–664 (Exs. 1–5), 666 (Ex. 9), 668 (Exs. 7–9), 670 (Exs. 6, 7), 671–672 (Exs. 1–7), 674–675 (Exs. 1–20)		

Geometry

Ray C. Jurgensen
Richard G. Brown
John W. Jurgensen

Teacher Consultants
Jean A. Giarrusso
Byron E. Gunsallus, Jr.
James R. Keeney
David Molina
Patricia Onodera Nicholson

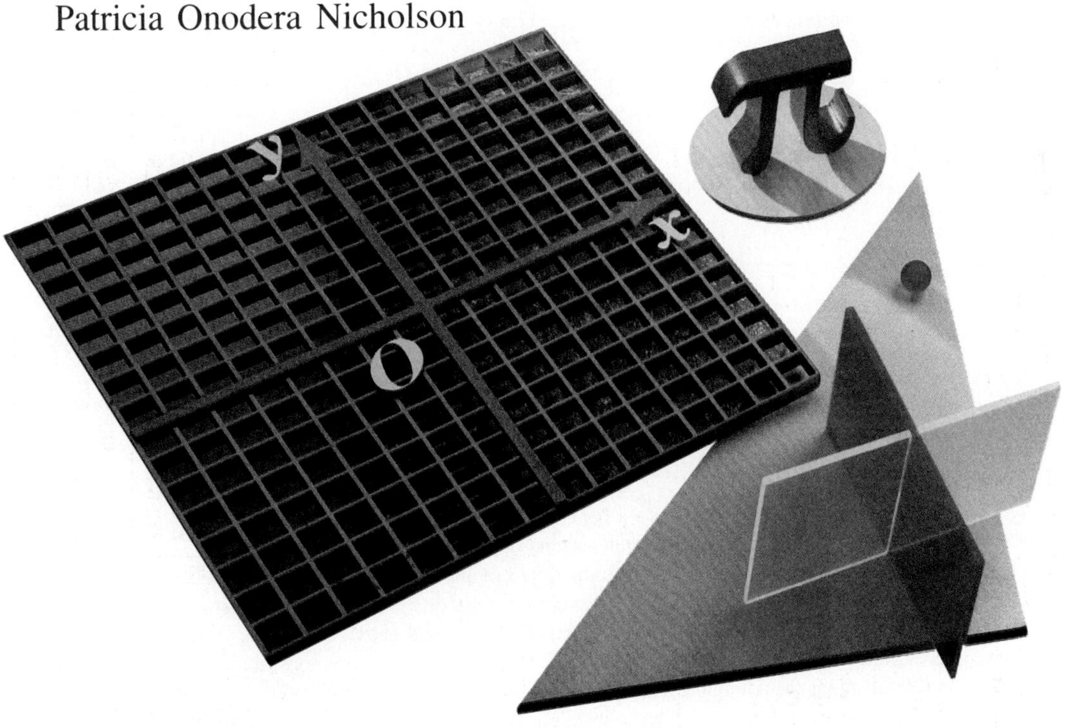

McDougal Littell
A HOUGHTON MIFFLIN COMPANY
EVANSTON, ILLINOIS BOSTON • DALLAS

THE AUTHORS

Ray C. Jurgensen is former Chairman of the Mathematics Department and holder of the Eppley Chair of Mathematics, Culver Academies, Culver, Indiana.

Richard G. Brown teaches mathematics at Phillips Exeter Academy in Exeter, New Hampshire, and is currently a member of the COMAP Consortium Council.

John W. Jurgensen teaches mathematics at the University of Houston-Downtown and is a mathematician for the National Aeronautics and Space Administration (NASA) at the Johnson Space Center.

TEACHER CONSULTANTS

Jean A. Giarrusso, Mathematics Teacher, Spanish River High School, Boca Raton, Florida

Byron E. Gunsallus, Jr., Mathematics Supervisor, Harrisburg High School, Harrisburg, Pennsylvania

James R. Keeney, Mathematics Teacher, Hillcrest High School, Country Club Hills, Illinois

David Molina, Assistant Professor of Education, Trinity University, San Antonio, Texas

Patricia Onodera Nicholson, Mathematics Teacher, Glen A. Wilson High School, Hacienda Heights, California

The authors wish to thank **David L. Myers**, Computer Coordinator and Mathematics Teacher, Winsor School, Boston, Massachusetts, for writing the Portfolio Projects.

Printed in U.S.A.

ISBN: 0-395-77120-X

Contents

1 POINTS, LINES, PLANES, AND ANGLES

2 DEDUCTIVE REASONING

5 QUADRILATERALS

Parallelograms

Special Quadrilaterals

6 INEQUALITIES IN GEOMETRY

Inequalities and Indirect Proof

Inequalities in Triangles

7 SIMILAR POLYGONS

8 RIGHT TRIANGLES

9 CIRCLES

Tangents, Arcs, and Chords

Angles and Segments

www.mathopenref.com/constructions.html

10 CONSTRUCTIONS AND LOCI

Basic Constructions

More Constructions

Locus

11 AREAS OF PLANE FIGURES

12 AREAS AND VOLUMES OF SOLIDS

13 COORDINATE GEOMETRY

Geometry and Algebra

Lines and Coordinate Geometry Proofs

14 TRANSFORMATIONS

Some Basic Mappings

Composition and Symmetry

Using Technology with This Course

There are two types of optional computer material in this book: Explorations and Computer Key-Ins. The Explorations sections are intended for use with computer software that draws and measures geometric figures, such as *Geometry Grapher* and *Geometric Supposer*. These sections provide exploratory exercises that lead students to discover geometric properties and develop geometric intuition.

The Computer Key-Ins do not require any supplementary computer software. These features teach some programming in BASIC and usually include a program that students can run to explore a topic covered in the chapter. Some writing of programs may be required in some of these features.

Calculator Key-In features and certain exercise sets also suggest appropriate use of scientific calculators with this course.

Symbols

$\|x\|$	absolute value of x (p. 12)
adj. ∠s	adjacent angles (p. 19)
alt. int. ∠s	alternate interior angles (p. 74)
∠, ∠s	angle(s) (pp. 17, 19)
a	apothem (p. 441)
$\approx$	is approximately equal to (p. 306)
$\overset{\frown}{BC}$	arc with endpoints B and C (p. 339)
A	area (p. 423)
B	area of base (p. 476)
b	length of base; y-intercept (p. 424; p. 548)
$\odot O$	circle with center O (p. 329)
C	circumference (p. 446)
comp. ∠s	complementary angles (p. 50)
$S \circ T$	composite of S and T (p. 599)
$\cong$	congruent, is congruent to (p. 13)
$\leftrightarrow$	corresponds to (p. 117)
corr. ∠s	corresponding angles (p. 74)
cos	cosine (p. 312)
$^\circ$	degrees (p. 17)
diag.	diagonal (p. 187)
d	diameter; distance; length of diagonal (p. 446; p. 524; p. 430)
$D_{O,k}$	dilation with center O and scale factor k (p. 592)
e	edge length (p. 478)
$=$	equal(s); equality (pp. 13, 37)
ext. ∠	exterior angle (p. 103)
$>, \geq$	greater than; greater than or equal to (p. 16)
H_O	half turn about point O (p. 589)
h	height; length of altitude (p. 424; p. 435)
hyp.	hypotenuse (p. 141)
T^{-1}	inverse of transformation T (p. 605)
I	identity transformation (p. 605)
int. ∠	interior angle (p. 103)
L.A.	lateral area (p. 476)
JL	length of $\overline{JL}$, distance between points J and L (p. 11)
$<, \leq$	less than; less than or equal to (p. 16)
$\overleftrightarrow{AB}$	line containing points A and B (p. 5)
$S: A \rightarrow A'$	S maps point A to point A'. (p. 571)
$m\angle A$	measure of $\angle A$ (p. 17)
$\not\cong$	not congruent (p. 215)
$\neq$	not equal (p. 37)
$\not>$	not greater than (p. 220)
$\nparallel$	not parallel (p. 216)
opp. ∠s	opposite angles (p. 187)
(x, y)	ordered pair (p. 113)
$\parallel$	parallel, is parallel to (p. 73)
▱	parallelogram (p. 167)
p	perimeter (p. 426)
$\perp$	perpendicular, is perpendicular to (p. 56)
π	pi (p. 446)
n-gon	polygon with n sides (p. 101)
quad.	quadrilateral (p. 168)
r	radius (p. 446)
$\frac{a}{b}$, $a:b$	ratio of a to b (pp. 241, 242)
$\overrightarrow{AB}$	ray with endpoint A, passing through point B (p. 11)
R_j	reflection in line j (p. 577)
rt. ∠	right angle (p. 19)
rt. △	right triangle (p. 290)
$\mathcal{R}_{O,90}$	rotation about point O through 90° (p. 588)
s-s. int. ∠s	same-side interior angles (p. 74)
$\overline{AB}$	segment with endpoints A and B (p. 11)
s	length of a side of a regular polygon (p. 423)
$\sim$	similar, is similar to (p. 249)
sin	sine (p. 312)
l	slant height (p. 482)
m	slope (p. 529)
$\sqrt{x}$	positive square root of x (p. 280)
supp. ∠s	supplementary angles (p. 50)
T.A.	total area (p. 476)
tan	tangent (p. 305)
trap.	trapezoid (p. 198)
△, △s	triangle(s) (pp. 93, 118)
$\overrightharpoon{AB}$	vector from A to B (p. 539)
vert. ∠s	vertical angles (p. 51)
V	volume (p. 476)

Reading Your Geometry Book

Reading mathematics is different from reading the newspaper or reading a novel because mathematics has its own vocabulary and symbols. You will find many new words in this book. Some of them are unique to mathematics, for example, *hypotenuse*, *isosceles*, and *secant*. Other words are used in everyday speech but have a different meaning in geometry, for example, *plane*, *line*, and *construction*. It is important to understand each new vocabulary word because ideas in geometry are built from the vocabulary and ideas that come before. If you don't remember the meaning of a word, you can look it up in the Glossary or Index.

Symbols

In order to read geometry, you must also know how to read its symbols. If you have trouble reading a statement expressed in symbols, first make sure you understand all the symbols. Use the list of symbols on page xi if you need to refresh your memory. Then, reread the statement. Sometimes you may find it helpful to write the statement out in words or just to say the words aloud.

Reading a Lesson

When you read a geometry lesson, first skim the lesson for main ideas. This book is organized to help you find the main ideas easily. Look for the title of the chapter and lesson. Each section of this book lists the objectives for the next two or three lessons. Look for displayed material in boxes or color, including postulates, theorems, and summaries. Look for any vocabulary words in **boldface** or *italic*. And look for any new symbols. Skimming the lesson should allow you to build a general framework of the information you are about to read.

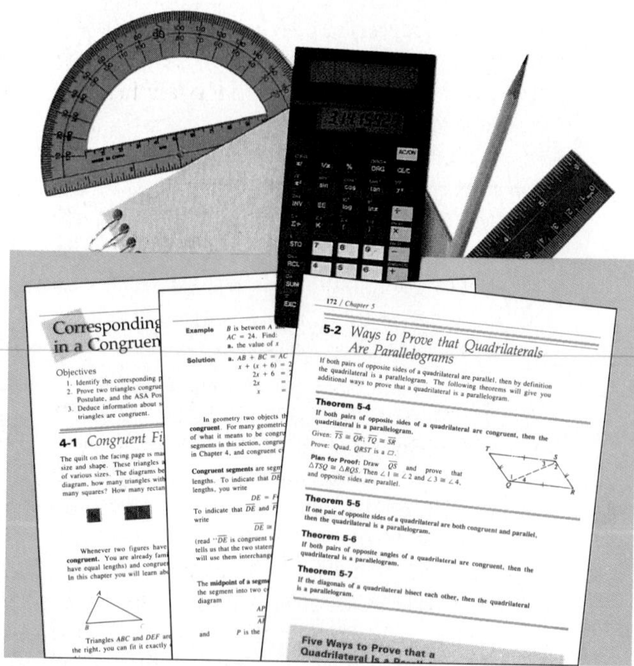

Now read the section. Think about each block of information as you read. Try to place it in the framework you built while skimming. There are many worked-out examples that can help you in doing the exercises. Think about how you would solve each example before reading its solution. Keep paper and pencil handy for doing the examples, taking notes, or writing down questions. If there is anything you don't understand after reading and rereading, make a note to ask your teacher or a classmate later.

After reading the lesson, but before attempting any of the exercises, ask yourself, "What did I just read?" Say the main words and ideas aloud to yourself or write down the ideas in your own words.

Diagrams

It is important to be able to read a diagram and to draw a diagram from given information. Look carefully for all the information given by a diagram, but be sure you don't read more into a diagram than is actually there. For example, don't assume that two segments are the same length just because they *look* that way; if the segments are the same length, they will be marked to show it. Other suggestions about reading and drawing diagrams are given on pages 19, 61, and 140.

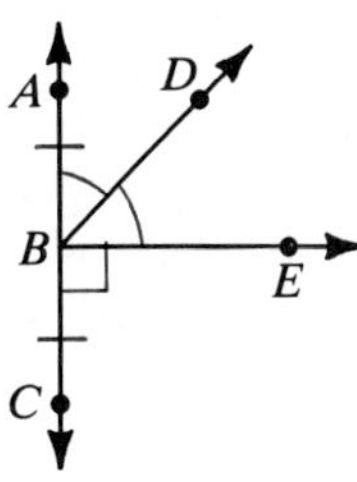

Exercises, Tests, and Reviews

Each lesson is followed by Classroom and Written Exercises. Self-Tests are mid-chapter progress tests. At the end of each chapter are other checks of your understanding and mastery: the Chapter Review and the Chapter Test. There are lesson numbers in the margin of the Chapter Review to indicate which lesson a group of exercises covers. Each chapter also has a Cumulative Review of the material covered through that chapter. And, at the end of the book, there are multiple-choice examinations for each chapter.

Other features you will find helpful are the Mixed Review Exercises and the Algebra Reviews, which review material you will need in the next lesson or chapter. Even-numbered chapters have multiple-choice tests, called Preparing for College Entrance Exams, with questions similar to those in some college entrance tests. There are also Chapter Summaries (at the end of each chapter), the list of symbols (page xi), the Glossary, the Index, and lists of postulates, theorems, and constructions (at the back of the book). Answers for all the Mixed Review Exercises, Self-Tests, and Preparing for College Entrance Exams, and for selected Written Exercises, Chapter Review Exercises, and Cumulative Review Exercises are also at the back of the book.

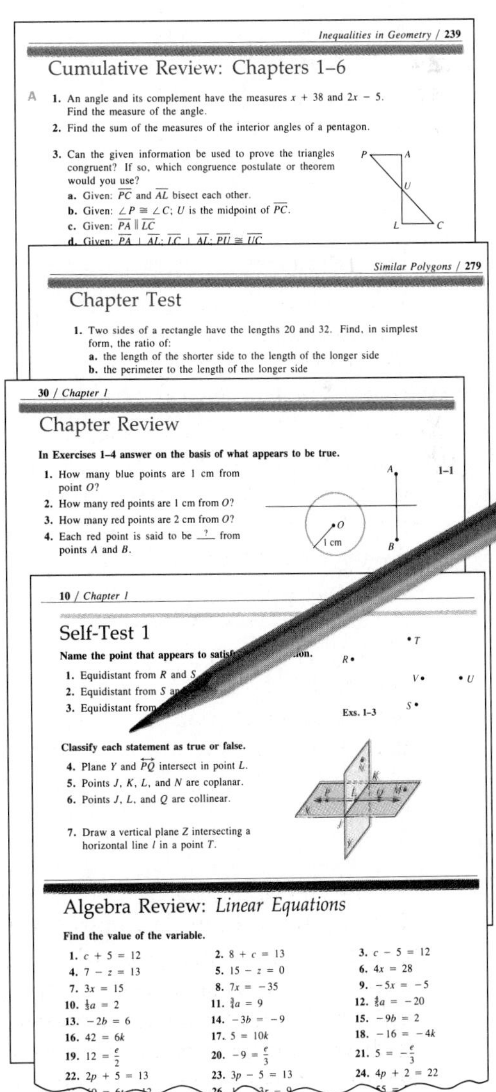

Inequalities in Geometry / 239

Cumulative Review: Chapters 1–6

A 1. An angle and its complement have the measures $x + 38$ and $2x - 5$. Find the measure of the angle.

2. Find the sum of the measures of the interior angles of a pentagon.

3. Can the given information be used to prove the triangles congruent? If so, which congruence postulate or theorem would you use?

a. Given: $\overline{PC}$ and $\overline{AL}$ bisect each other.

b. Given: $\angle P \cong \angle C$; U is the midpoint of $\overline{PC}$.

c. Given: $\overline{PA} \parallel \overline{LC}$

d. Given: $\overline{PA} \perp \overline{AL}$; $\overline{LC} \perp \overline{AL}$; $\overline{PU} \cong \overline{UC}$

Similar Polygons / 279

Chapter Test

1. Two sides of a rectangle have the lengths 20 and 32. Find, in simplest form, the ratio of:

a. the length of the shorter side to the length of the longer side

b. the perimeter to the length of the longer side

30 / *Chapter 1*

Chapter Review

In Exercises 1–4 answer on the basis of what appears to be true. 1–1

1. How many blue points are 1 cm from point O?
2. How many red points are 1 cm from O?
3. How many red points are 2 cm from O?
4. Each red point is said to be __?__ from points A and B.

10 / *Chapter 1*

Self-Test 1

Name the point that appears to satis... **...ion.**

1. Equidistant from R and S...
2. Equidistant from S a...
3. Equidistant fro...

Exs. 1–3

Classify each statement as true or false.

4. Plane Y and $\overleftrightarrow{PQ}$ intersect in point L.
5. Points J, K, L, and N are coplanar.
6. Points J, L, and Q are collinear.
7. Draw a vertical plane Z intersecting a horizontal line l in a point T.

Algebra Review: *Linear Equations*

Find the value of the variable.

1. $c + 5 = 12$	2. $8 + c = 13$	3. $c - 5 = 12$
4. $7 - z = 13$	5. $15 - z = 0$	6. $4x = 28$
7. $3x = 15$	8. $7x = -35$	9. $-5x = -5$
10. $\frac{1}{2}a = 2$	11. $\frac{1}{3}a = 9$	12. $\frac{4}{5}a = -20$
13. $-2b = 6$	14. $-3b = -9$	15. $-9b = 2$
16. $42 = 6k$	17. $5 = 10k$	18. $-16 = -4k$
19. $12 = \frac{e}{2}$	20. $-9 = \frac{e}{3}$	21. $5 = -\frac{e}{3}$
22. $2p + 5 = 13$	23. $3p - 5 = 13$	24. $4p + 2 = 22$

Table of Measures

Time

60 seconds (s) = 1 minute (min)
60 minutes = 1 hour (h)
24 hours = 1 day (d)
7 days = 1 week

365 days, 52 weeks (approx.), 12 months = 1 year

10 years = 1 decade
100 years = 1 century

Metric Units

Length	10 millimeters (mm)	=	1 centimeter (cm)
	100 centimeters, 1000 millimeters	=	1 meter (m)
	1000 meters	=	1 kilometer (km)
Area	100 square millimeters (mm^2)	=	1 square centimeter (cm^2)
	10,000 square centimeters	=	1 square meter (m^2)
	10,000 square meters	=	1 hectare (ha)
Volume	1000 cubic millimeters (mm^3)	=	1 cubic centimeter (cm^3)
	1,000,000 cubic centimeters	=	1 cubic meter (m^3)
Liquid Capacity	1000 milliliters (mL)	=	1 liter (L)
	1000 cubic centimeters	=	1 liter
	1000 liters	=	1 kiloliter (kL)
Mass	1000 milligrams (mg)	=	1 gram (g)
	1000 grams	=	1 kilogram (kg)
	1000 kilograms	=	1 metric ton (t)
Temperature: Degrees Celsius (°C)	0°C	=	freezing point of water
	37°C	=	normal body temperature
	100°C	=	boiling point of water

Notice that the same prefixes are used in many metric units of measure.

Examples milli = thousandth: millimeter, milliliter, milligram
centi = hundredth: centimeter
kilo = thousand: kilometer, kiloliter, kilogram

United States Customary Units

Length	12 inches (in.)	=	1 foot (ft)
	36 inches 3 feet	=	1 yard (yd)
	5280 feet 1760 yards	=	1 mile (mi)
Area	144 square inches (in.^{2})	=	1 square foot (ft^2)
	9 square feet	=	1 square yard (yd^2)
	43,560 square feet 4840 square yards	=	1 acre (A)
Volume	1728 cubic inches (in.^{3})	=	1 cubic foot (ft^3)
	27 cubic feet	=	1 cubic yard (yd^3)
Liquid Capacity	8 fluid ounces (fl oz)	=	1 cup (c)
	2 cups	=	1 pint (pt)
	2 pints	=	1 quart (qt)
	4 quarts	=	1 gallon (gal)
Weight	16 ounces (oz)	=	1 pound (lb)
	2000 pounds	=	1 ton (t)
Temperature: **Degrees Fahrenheit (°F)**	32°F	=	freezing point of water
	98.6°F	=	normal body temperature
	212°F	=	boiling point of water

Compound units of metric units or U.S. customary units may be formed by multiplication or division.

Examples		
	square centimeters	cm^2
	cubic yards	yd^3
	kilometers per hour	km/h
	feet per minute	ft/min

1 Points, Lines, Planes, and Angles

Objectives

1-1 Use the term *equidistant*.
Use the terms *point* and *line*.
Draw representations of points and lines.

1-2 Use the undefined terms *point*, *line*, and *plane*.
Draw representations of points, lines, and planes.
Use the terms *collinear*, *coplanar*, and *intersection*.

1-3 Use symbols for lines, segments, rays, and distances.
Find distances.
State and use the Ruler Postulate and the Segment Addition Postulate.

1-4 Name angles and find their measures.
State and use the Angle Addition Postulate.
Recognize what can be concluded from a diagram.

1-5 Use postulates and theorems relating points, lines, and planes.

Assignment Guide

See page T40 for information about the Assignment Guide.

Day	Minimum Course	Average Course	Maximum Course
1	**1-1** pp. 3–4/exs. 1–10	**1-1** pp. 3–4/exs. 1–10	**1-1** pp. 3–4/exs. 1–10
2	**1-2** 7–8/1–26	**1-2** 7–9/1–25 odd, 26–28	**1-2** 7–9/2–26 even, 27–36
3	**1-2** 9/27–30 10/Self-Test 1	**1-2** 9/29–35 odd 10/Self-Test 1	**1-3** 15–16/1–45 odd, 46–48
4	**1-3** 15/1–26	**1-3** 15–16/1–39 odd	**1-4** 21–22/10–24 even, 25–36
5	**1-3** 15–16/27–35	**1-3** 16/40–46 even	**1-5** 25–26/1–13 odd, 14–20
6	**1-4** 21/1–25	**1-4** 21/1–25 odd, 26–28	**1-5** 31/Chapter Test Test, page T12
7	**1-4** 21–22/26–34 even **S** 9/31–33	**1-4** 22/29–35 **S** 16/41–47 odd	
8	**1-5** 25/1–12	**1-5** 25/1–15 odd, 16	
9	**1-5** 25/13, 14 29/Self-Test 2	**1-5** 26/17–19 29/Self-Test 2	
10	**1-5** 31/Chapter Test Test, page T12	**1-5** 31/Chapter Test Test, page T12	

Supplementary Materials Guide

For Use after Lesson	Practice Masters	Tests	Study Guide (Reteaching)	Resource Book: Tests	Resource Book: Practice Exercises	Resource Book: Prep. for College Entrance Exams (Col) Enrichment (E)	Computer Activities
1-1			pp. 1–2				Activity 1
1-2	Sheet 1	Test 1	pp. 3–4	p. 1	p. 109		Activity 2
1-3			pp. 5–6				
1-4	Sheet 2	Test 2	pp. 7–8	p. 2	p. 110		
1-5	Sheet 3	Test 3	pp. 9–10	p. 3	p. 111		
Chapter 1	Sheet 4	Test 4		pp. 4–5	p. 112	p. 190 (Col) p. 204 (E)	

Overhead Visuals

Guided Discovery Visuals (lettered) and Teaching Visuals (numbered) available for Chapter 1.

Lessons	Visual	Title
1-2, 1-5	A	Lines and Planes in Space
1-2	B	Points, Lines, and Planes
1-3, 1-4	C	Angles and Their Measure
1-1, 1-2	1	How to Draw 3-D Figures
1-3, 1-4, 1-5	2	Polar Coordinates

Software Guide

Houghton Mifflin software for Chapter 1
Test Generator (Apple or IBM): 75 test items

Other software appropriate for Chapter 1
Geometric Supposer (Apple): PreSupposer
GeoDraw (IBM)

Guide to Integrated Curriculum

Although the text presents coordinate and transformational geometry in Chapters 13 and 14 and in the Handbook on pp. 657–675, teachers wishing to integrate this material throughout the course may do so easily using the information on **pp. T56–T57**. The integration begins after Chapter 3.

With this integrated curriculum, students learn concepts, solve problems, and prove theorems using alternate approaches. Students make connections between geometry and algebra, and they learn the valuable skill of deciding which method to use in a problem (**pp. 672–673**).

Guide to Distribution of Constructions

The text teaches constructions in Chapter 10. Teachers wishing to distribute work with constructions throughout the first nine chapters can use this guide.

Introduce after	Construction	Page
Lesson 1-3	1	375

Exploring Interesting Intersections

When to Use

Before or with Lesson 1-5

Overview

This activity will:

- reinforce concepts of point, line, collinear, intersection, and "exactly one"
- provide practice in drawing diagrams of possible cases
- lead students to discover ideas related to Postulate 6 (Through any two points there is exactly one line.) and Theorem 1-1 (If two lines intersect, then they intersect in exactly one point.)

Description of Activity

Guide students through the exploration by using the following activities and questions.

1. Two lines can determine 0 or 1 point of intersection, as shown below.

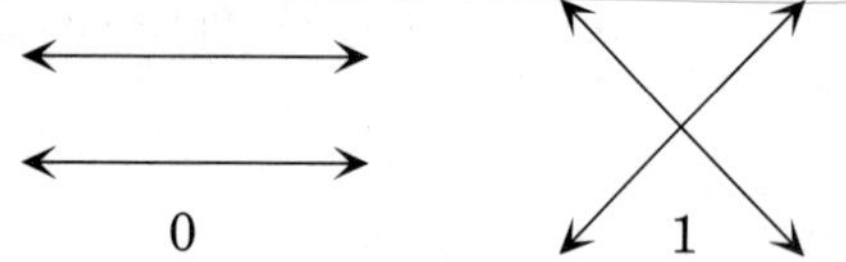

   a. Three lines can determine 0, 1, 2, or 3 points of intersection. Draw a diagram of each possible case. See answer next column.

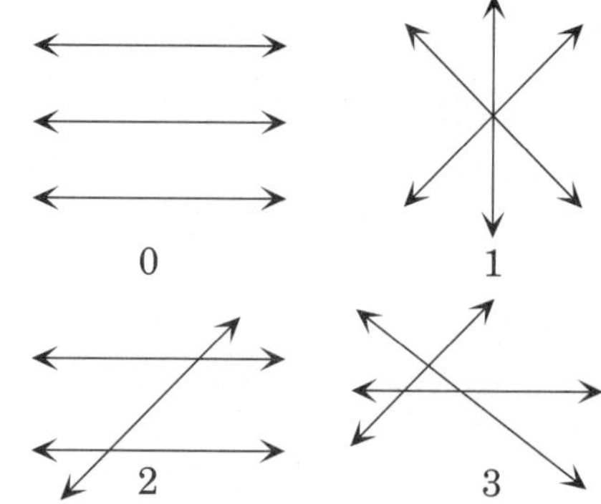

   b. How many points of intersection can you find using four lines? Draw a diagram of each possible case. If you think a case is impossible, try to give a reason why. 0, 1, 3, 4, 5, and 6 points of intersection are possible; 2 points of intersection is an impossible case.

   c. How many points of intersection can you find using five lines? Draw a diagram of each possible case. If you think a case is impossible, try to give a reason why. 0, 1, 4, 6, 7, 8, 9, and 10 points of intersection are possible.

2. Draw two lines *l* and *m*. Choose three points *A*, *B*, *C* on *l* and three points *D*, *E*, *F* on *m*. The six points must lie on exactly one of the lines *l* or *m*. Locate the points of intersection: *X* of $\overline{AE}$ and $\overline{BD}$; *Y* of $\overline{AF}$ and $\overline{CD}$; *Z* of $\overline{BF}$ and $\overline{CE}$.

   a. Repeat this construction for several different pairs of lines. What do you discover about the relationship between *X*, *Y*, and *Z*? They are collinear points.

   b. Can you locate the six points *A*, *B*, *C* on *l* and *D*, *E*, *F* on *m* so that none of the three points of intersection *X*, *Y*, or *Z* exist?

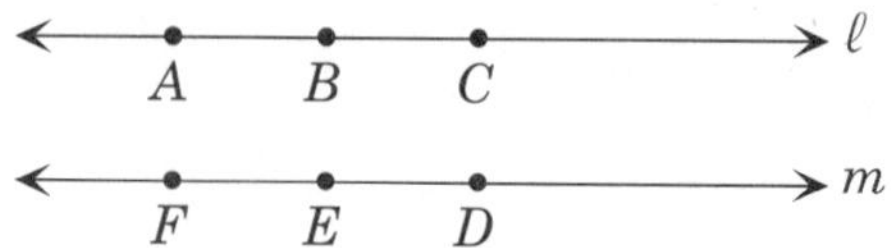

c. Can you locate the six points A, B, C on l and D, E, F on m so that exactly one of the three points of intersection X, Y, or Z exist?
impossible

d. Can you locate the six points A, B, C on l and D, E, F on m so that exactly two of the three points of intersection X, Y, or Z exist?

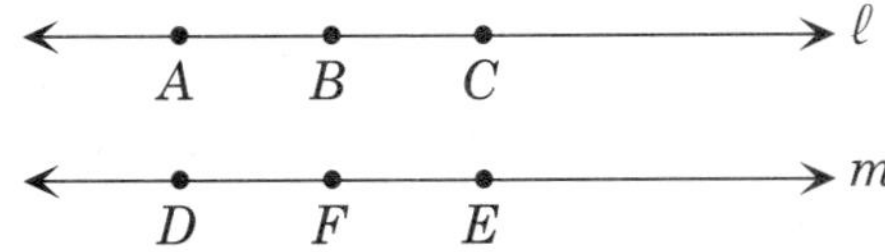

e. Repeat parts **a–d** using a circle instead of two lines. Choose A, B, C, D, E, F on one circle.

Commentary

1. b. You may wish to give students the hint: "One of the cases is impossible."

1, 2. Students can practice writing convincing arguments as they describe the impossible cases.

2. e. The answers are similar to those of parts **a–d.** This version of using circles rather than lines is called Pascal's Theorem, discovered by Blaise Pascal (1623–1662) at the age of 16. Have students research some of Pascal's other work.

References to Strategies

PE: Pupil's Edition **TE:** Teacher's Edition **RB:** Resource Book

Problem Solving Strategies

PE: 1–2 (Mathematical model), 19 (Draw a diagram), 22, 26 (Recognize a pattern), 27 (Mathematical model)
TE: T75, T76, 8 (Interpret diagrams)

Applications

PE: 1–2 (Clue game), 9 (Architecture), 16 (Ex. 48, Temperature), 20 (Ex. 26, Architecture), 24 (Exs. 14, 15, Carpentry), 27 (Grids)

Nonroutine Problems

PE: 2–3 (Exs. 1–8), 4 (Exs. 7–10), 9 (Ex. 28, Challenge), 14 (Exs. 21, 22), 16 (Exs. 47, 48), 20 (Exs. 26–27), 21 (Ex. 28), 22 (Ex. 35), 24 (Exs. 13–15), 26 (Ex. 19)
TE: T77, T78

Communication

PE: 8 (Drawing space figures), 9 (Challenge, Convincing argument), 19 (Drawing and reading diagrams), 24 (Exs. 2–4, Rewording), 25 (Ex. 12, Rewording)
TE: T75–T77, 7, 11, 13, 19, 25
RB: 204

Thinking Skills

PE: 22, 26 (Analysis of patterns)
TE: 1 (Understand conditions), 9 (Relate to an earlier problem), 13 (Look for counterexamples), 18 (Analyze postulates), 19 (Limits of diagrams)

Explorations

TE: c

Connections

PE: 10 (Algebra), 11–12 (Number line, absolute value), 13, 16 (Algebra), 27 (Polar coordinates)
TE: T76, T77, 13, 16, 27

Using Technology

PE: 20
TE: T77, 20
Computer Activities: 1–5

Using Manipulatives/Models

PE: 5, 8, 9 (Exs. 29–36), 14 (Ex. 21), 20 (Ex. 27), 21
TE: T75, T77, 2, 4, 6, 7, 9, 14, 17, 20
Overhead Visuals: A, B, C, 1, 2

Cooperative Learning

TE: T75, T78, 9

Teaching Resources

For use in implementing the teaching strategies referenced on the previous page.

Exploration
Study Guide, p. 1

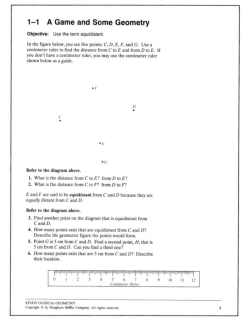

1–1 A Game and Some Geometry

Objective: Use the term *equidistant.*

In the figure below, you see five points: *C, D, E, F,* and *G.* Use a centimeter ruler to find the distance from *C* to *E* and from *D* to *E.* If you don't have a centimeter ruler, you may use the centimeter ruler shown below as a guide.

Refer to the diagram above.

1. What is the distance from *C* to *E*? from *D* to *E*?
2. What is the distance from *C* to *F*? from *D* to *F*?

E and *F* are said to be **equidistant** from *C* and *D* because they are equally distant from *C* and *D.*

Refer to the diagram above.

3. Find another point on the diagram that is equidistant from *C* and *D.*
4. How many points exist that are equidistant from *C* and *D*? Describe the geometric figure the points would form.
5. Point *G* is 5 cm from *C* and *D.* Find a second point, *H,* that is 5 cm from *C* and *D.* Can you find a third one?
6. How many points exist that are 5 cm from *C* and *D*? Describe their location.

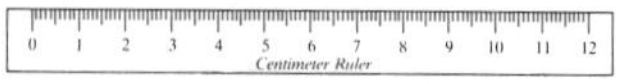

STUDY GUIDE for GEOMETRY

1

Exploration
Study Guide, p. 2

1–1 A Game and Some Geometry *(continued)*

Mark a point *P* on your paper.

7. Mark a point 4 cm from *P.*
8. Mark another point 4 cm from *P.*
9. Mark several other points that are 4 cm from *P.* How many points exist that are 4 cm from *P*? Describe the geometric figure the points would form.

You are given the points *X, Y,* and *Z,* below.

10. a. Draw a line to indicate all points equidistant from *X* and *Y.*
    b. Draw a circle to indicate all points 5 cm from *Z.* If you don't have a compass, draw freehand as well as you can.
    c. How many points are equidistant from *X* and *Y* and are also 5 cm from *Z*?
11. Repeat Exercise 10(c), but use 1 cm instead of 5 cm.

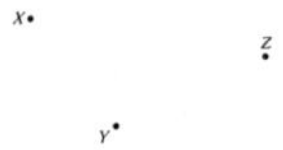

Your eyes may mislead you in the exercises that follow, but you are asked to make estimates. You may want to check your estimates by measuring.

12. Which is greater, the distance from *A* to *B* or the distance from *C* to *D*?

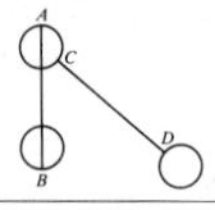

13. How does the area of the circle on the left compare to the area of the circle on the right?

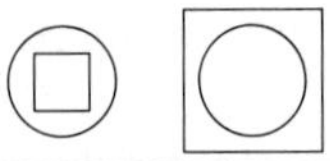

2
STUDY GUIDE for GEOMETRY

Using Technology
Computer Activities, p. 1

ACTIVITY 1. ***Counting Squares*** (for use with Lesson 1-1)

Directions: Write all answers in the spaces provided.

PROBLEM

People usually say there are 64 squares on a regular checkerboard. But there are many more if you count squares with sides longer than one unit. The following program calculates the total number of squares (of all sizes) in a square checkerboard pattern.

PROGRAM

```
10  LET T = 0
20  PRINT "ENTER THE NUMBER OF SQUARES ALONG EACH SIDE OF
    THE CHECKERBOARD ";
30  INPUT N
40  FOR I=N TO 1 STEP -1
50  LET S=I*I
60  PRINT "NUMBER OF "; N - I + 1 ;" × " ; N - I + 1;" SQUARES IS ";S
70  LET T = T + S
80  NEXT I
90  PRINT "TOTAL NUMBER OF SQUARES IS ";T
100  END
```

PROGRAM CHECK

Type in the program and run it. After the question mark enter 2. The computer should print

```
NUMBER OF 1×1 SQUARES IS 4
NUMBER OF 2×2 SQUARES IS 1
TOTAL NUMBER OF SQUARES IS 5
```

USING THE PROGRAM

One way to solve this problem is to start with a simpler case, organize your findings in a table, and look for a pattern.

1. Use the program and complete the chart below.

	1×1 checkerboard	2×2 checkerboard	3×3 checkerboard	4×4 checkerboard
number of 1×1 squares				
number of 2×2 squares				
number of 3×3 squares				
number of 4×4 squares				
total number of squares				

COMPUTER ACTIVITIES for GEOMETRY

(continued)
1

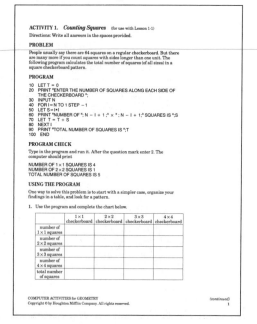

Thinking Skills
Teaching Visual 1

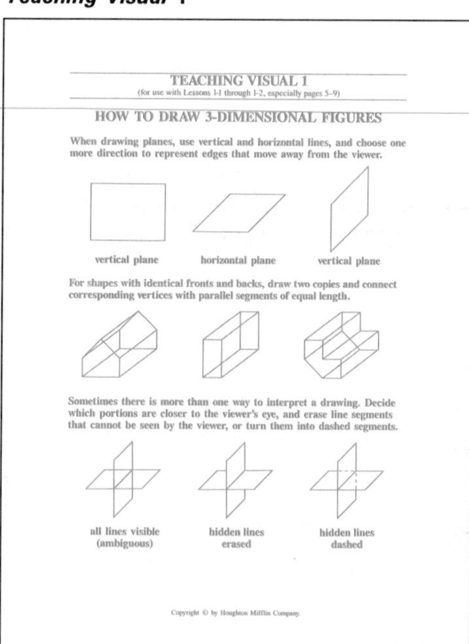

TEACHING VISUAL 1
(for use with Lessons 1-1 through 1-2, especially pages 5–9)

HOW TO DRAW 3-DIMENSIONAL FIGURES

When drawing planes, use vertical and horizontal lines, and choose one more direction to represent edges that move away from the viewer.

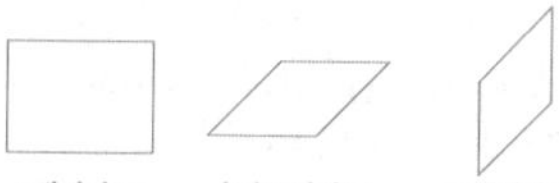

For shapes with identical fronts and backs, draw two copies and connect corresponding vertices with parallel segments of equal length.

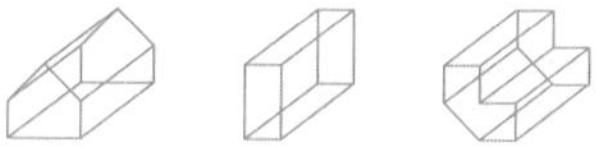

Sometimes there is more than one way to interpret a drawing. Decide which portions are closer to the viewer's eye, and erase line segments that cannot be seen by the viewer, or turn them into dashed segments.

Using Models

***Guided Discovery Visual* A, Sheets 1–3**

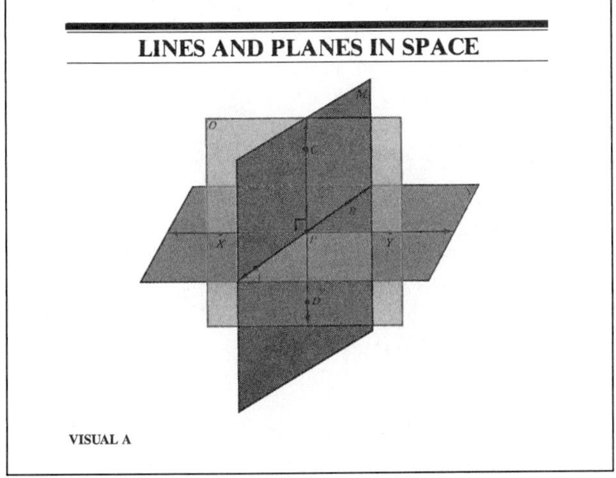

Using Models

***Guided Discovery Visual* C, Sheets 1 and 2**

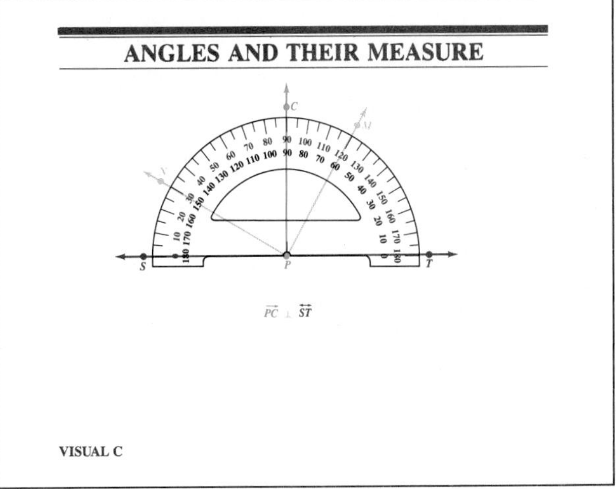

Using Models

***Guided Discovery Visual* B, Sheet 1**

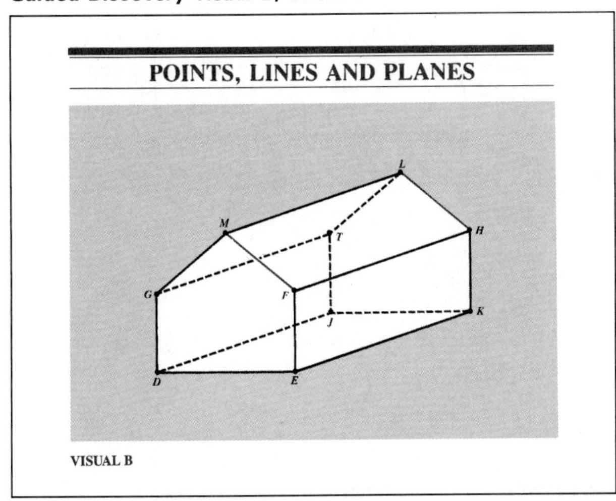

Using Models

***Guided Discovery Visual* B, Sheet 2**

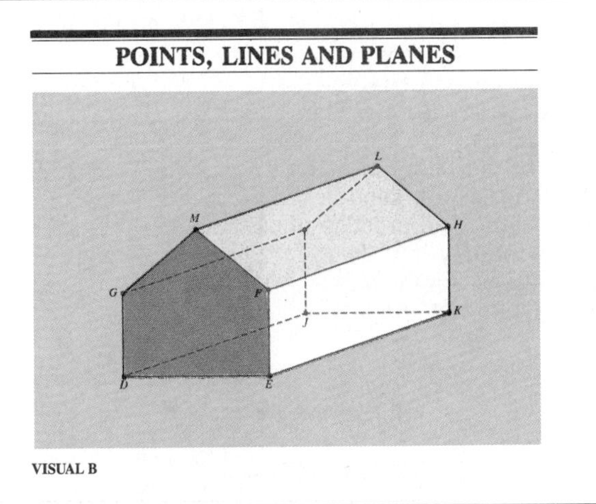

Teaching References

Lesson Commentary, pp. T74–T78

Assignment Guide, p. T42

Software Guide, p. T73

Alternate Test, p. T12

Supplementary Materials

Practice Masters 1–4

Tests 1–4

Resource Book
- Tests, pp. 1–5
- Practice, pp. 109–112
- Preparing for College Entrance Exams, p. 190
- Enrichment Activity, p. 204

Study Guide, pp. 1–10

Overhead Visuals A–C, 1, 2

Computer Activities
1. Counting Squares
2. Finding the Midpoint of a Segment

Cultural Note

Our modern calendar has its roots in ancient astronomy. It is estimated that as early as 4241 B.C., an Egyptian calendar dividing the year into $365\frac{1}{4}$ days was used to predict the annual rising of the waters of the Nile River. This calendar system was based in part on observations of the star Sirius. The Egyptians also used observations of the rising of stars in the night sky to keep track of time. The practice of dividing the day into 24 hours has its origins in ancient Egyptian astronomy.

1 POINTS, LINES, PLANES, AND ANGLES

As ancient people studied the heavens, they saw and named many patterns of points, lines, and angles formed by the stars. Although modern astronomers use sophisticated observatories and equipment, they still base their calculations on geometric principles that have been known for many centuries.

Some Basic Figures

Objectives

1. Use the term *equidistant*.
2. Use the undefined terms *point*, *line*, and *plane*.
3. Draw representations of points, lines, and planes.
4. Use the terms *collinear*, *coplanar*, and *intersection*.

1-1 *A Game and Some Geometry*

Suppose that you and Pat are partners in a game in which you must locate various clues to win. You are told to pick up your next clue at a point that

1. is as far from the fountain as from the oak tree

   and

2. is 10 m (meters) from the flag pole.

You locate X, which satisfies both requirements, but grumble because there simply isn't any clue to be found at X.

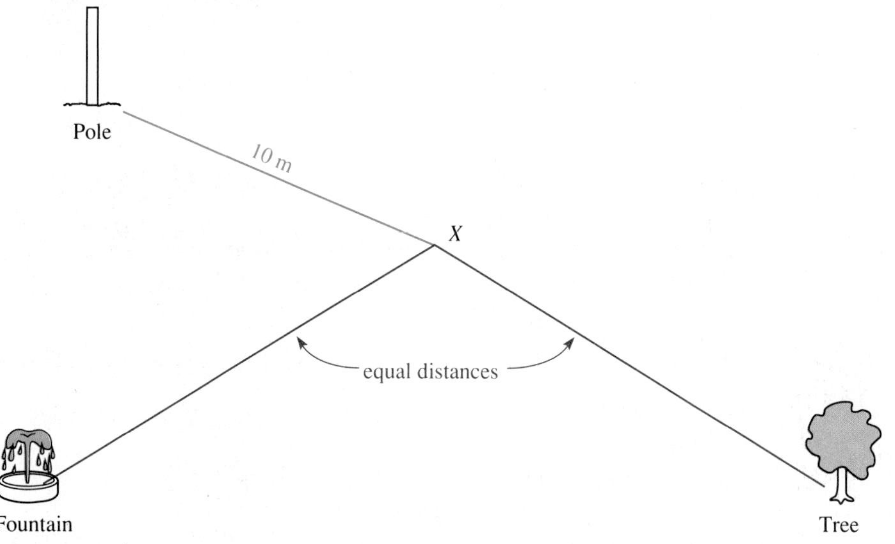

Then Pat realizes that there may be a different location that satisfies both requirements. (Before reading on, see if you can find another point that meets requirements 1 and 2.)

Teaching Suggestions,
pp. T74–T75
Objectives
Presenting the Lesson
Problem Solving

Communication Skills,
p. T75

Supplementary Materials

Study Guide, pp. 1–2

Computer Activity 1

Lesson Focus

This lesson introduces some basic ideas in geometry, such as points and lines. The lesson also shows that an important skill in learning geometry is to learn to think very carefully about the figures being studied.

Suggested Assignments

Minimum
3–4/1–10

Average
3–4/1–10

Maximum
3–4/1–10

Teaching Note

If the diagrams on pages 1 and 2 are drawn on the chalkboard, they should be drawn to scale.

Thinking Skills

Point out to students that the expression "a point" does not imply that just one point is possible. All points that meet the conditions of the game are possible solutions.

Using a Model

Students should reproduce the diagram, using a compass and ruler. Make sure students understand the notion of a scale drawing. Ask why the particular scale used in the diagram was chosen for this problem.

Mention that geometric ideas can be used to represent physical objects. Thus, the fountain is represented by point *F*. In the same way, a mapmaker can represent a city by a point on a map. Students need to understand that points and other geometric figures can serve as *models* for many real-world objects.

Exercise Note

Here, and throughout the text, classroom exercises can lead to discussions that will increase understanding and prepare students to do the written exercises. Because the classroom exercises continue the development of concepts covered in the section, it is important to go over these exercises with students during class time.

Suppose that you concentrate on points that satisfy requirement 1 while Pat works on points that meet requirement 2. In the diagram below, 1 cm represents 2 m, so the blue arc shows points that are 10 m from the pole. Each red point is equally distant, or *equidistant*, from *F* and *T*. Point *Y*, as well as *X*, meets both requirements. You and Pat find your clue at *Y* and proceed with the game.

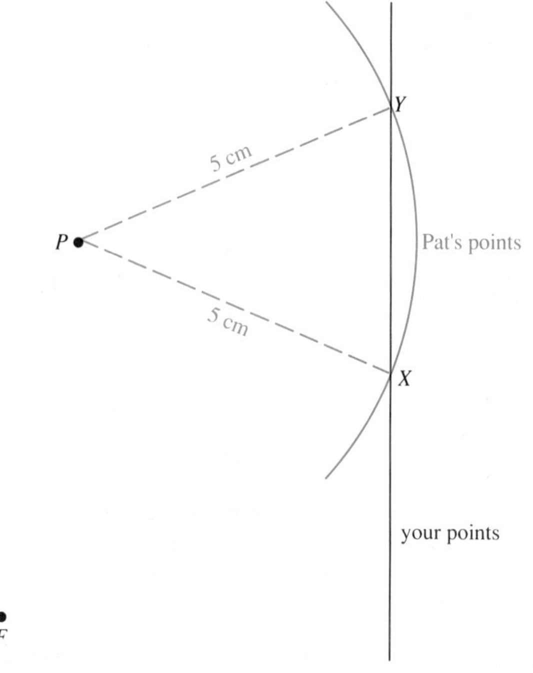

The game discussed above involves *points* and *distances*. When you approach the game systematically, you use *lines* and *circles*. Understanding the properties of geometric figures like these is an important part of geometry. The rest of this chapter will deal with the most basic figures of geometry.

Classroom Exercises

For Exercises 1–8 refer to the diagram above.

1. Suppose that the diagram showed, in blue, *all* the points that are 5 cm from *P*. What geometric figure would the points form? **a circle**
2. In a more complete diagram, would there be a red point 15 cm from both *F* and *T*? How many such points? **Yes; 2**
3. It appears as if points *P*, *X*, and *T* might lie on a straight line. Use a ruler or the edge of a sheet of paper to see if they do. **No**

4. It looks as if P might be equidistant from F and X. Is it? **No**
5. Suppose Pat spoke of a line l joining F and T while you thought of a line n joining F and T. Is it better to say that l and n are two different lines, or to say that we have one line with two different names? **one line with two different names**
6. Point X is equidistant from F and T. Furthermore, point Y is equidistant from F and T. Does that mean that X and Y are equally distant from F? **No**
7. Suppose you were asked to find a point 5 cm from P, 5 cm from F, and 5 cm from T. Is there such a point? **No**
8. Do you believe there is any point that is equidistant from P, F, and T? **Yes**

Written Exercises

A 1. Copy and complete the table. Refer to the diagrams on pages 1 and 2.

Distance between	*Diagram distance*	*Ground distance*
X and P	5 cm	10 m
X and F	7 cm	**14** ? m
X and T	**7** ? cm	**14** ? m
Y and F	**9.5** ? cm	19 m
F and T	12 cm	**24** ? m

For Exercises 2–4 use a centimeter ruler. If you don't have a centimeter ruler, you may use the centimeter ruler shown below as a guide. Either open your compass to the appropriate distance or mark the appropriate distance on the edge of a sheet of paper.

2. Copy the points F, T, and P from the diagram on page 2. If you lay your paper over the page, you can see through the paper well enough to get the points.
   a. Draw a line to indicate all points equidistant from F and T.
   b. Draw a circle to indicate points 6 cm from P. If you don't have a compass, draw as well as you can freehand. **Check students' drawings.**
   c. How many points are equidistant from F and T, and are also 6 cm from P? **2**
3. Repeat Exercise 2, but use 2 cm instead of 6 cm. **c. none**
4. There is a distance you could use in parts (b) and (c) of Exercise 2 that would lead to the answer *one point* in part (c). Estimate that distance. **about 4.7 cm**

Guided Practice

Suppose the diagram on page 2 is drawn so that 1 cm represents 3 m. Complete.

1. diagram distance = 2 cm
   ground distance = 6 m
2. ground distance = 30 m
   diagram distance = 10 cm
3. diagram distance = 5 cm
   ground distance = 15 m
4. ground distance = 60 m
   diagram distance = 20 cm

Exercise Note

Exercise 1 is an exercise in thinking, not in mechanics. The numbers are simple enough so that the arithmetic can be done mentally.

The word *estimate* is used in Ex. 4. Diverse answers such as 4.3, 4.4, . . . , 4.8 are acceptable. On the other hand, answers such as 4.68 or 4.71 are not desirable as they suggest a degree of precision not appropriate for an estimate.

Point out that answers to selected exercises are given at the back of the book.

The spoon in the photograph appears to be broken because light rays bend as they go from air to water. As in the photograph, your eyes may mislead you in some of the exercises that follow, but you are asked to make estimates. You may want to check your estimates by measuring.

Using a Model

The role of Exs. 5–10 is to arouse interest and stimulate thinking. For Ex. 7, a student can prepare at home a large paper square with creases for the sides of the smaller square. In class, the four triangles can be folded in to cover the smaller square. Also, a student can draw the diagram on the chalkboard. Then, the teacher can draw the diagonals of the smaller square.

5. Which is greater, the distance from R to S or the distance from T to U? ***RS***

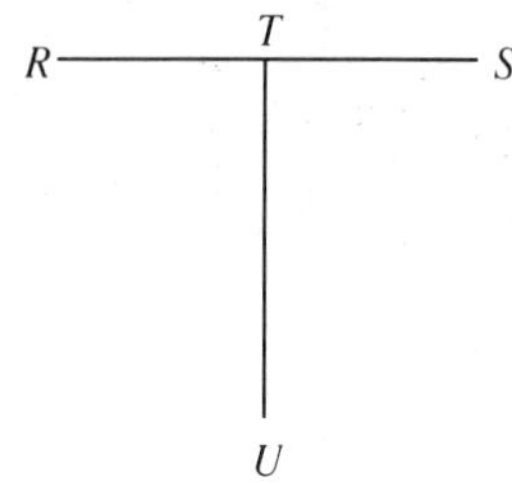

6. Which is greater, the distance from A to B or the distance from A to C? ***AB = AC***

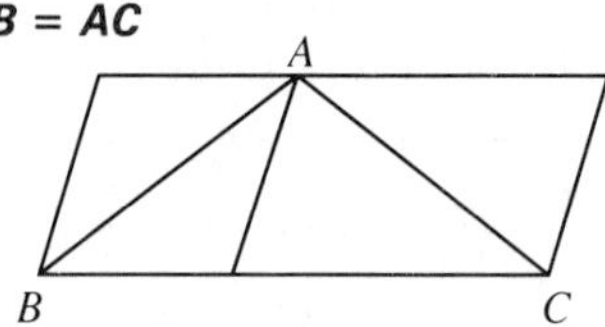

B

7. How does the area of the outer square compare with the area of the inner square?

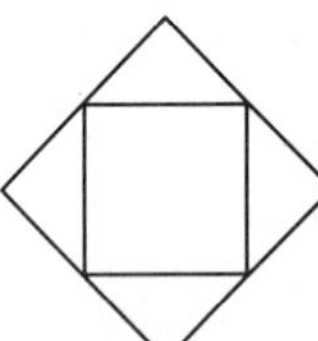

It is twice the area of the inner square.

8. Compare the areas of the red and blue regions. (Area of circle $= \pi r^2$.)

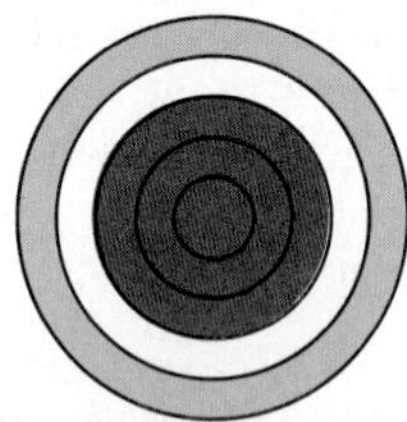

The areas are equal.

9. In the diagram a, b, c, and d are lengths. Which is greater, the product ab or the product cd? ***ab = cd***

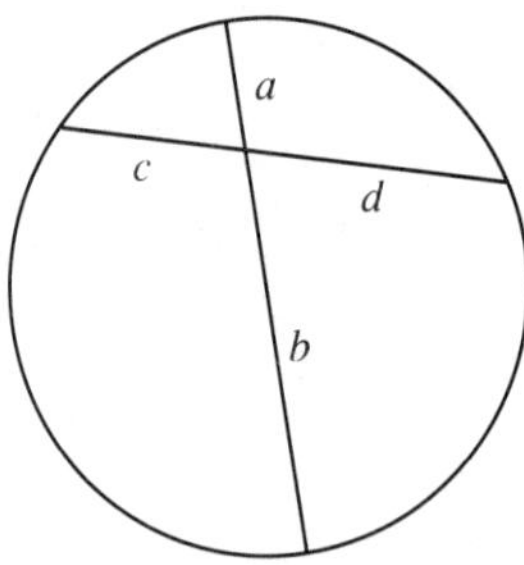

10. A path between opposite vertices of the square is made up of hundreds of horizontal and vertical segments. (The diagram shows a simplified version.) What is the best approximation to the length of the path—24, 34, 44, or more than 44? **34**

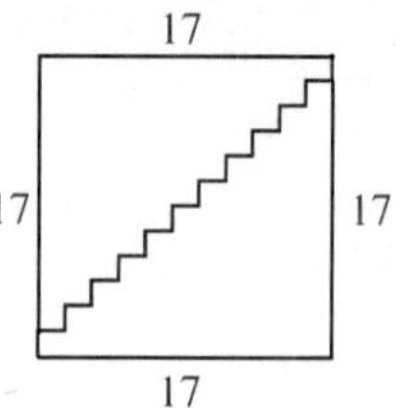

1-2 *Points, Lines, and Planes*

When you look at a color television picture, how many different colors do you see? Actually, the picture is made up of just three colors—red, green, and blue. Most color television screens are covered with more than 300,000 colored dots, as shown in the enlarged diagram below. Each dot glows when it is struck by an electron beam. Since the dots are so small, and so close together, your eye sees a whole image rather than individual dots.

Each dot on a television screen suggests the simplest figure studied in geometry—a *point*. Although a point doesn't have any size, it is often represented by a dot that does have some size. You usually name points by capital letters. Points A and B are pictured at the right.

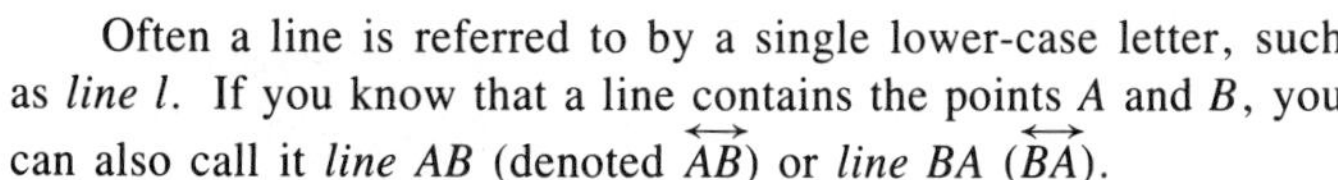

All geometric figures consist of points. One familiar geometric figure is a *line*, which extends in two directions without ending. Although a picture of a line has some thickness, the line itself has no thickness.

Often a line is referred to by a single lower-case letter, such as *line l*. If you know that a line contains the points A and B, you can also call it *line AB* (denoted $\overleftrightarrow{AB}$) or *line BA* ($\overleftrightarrow{BA}$).

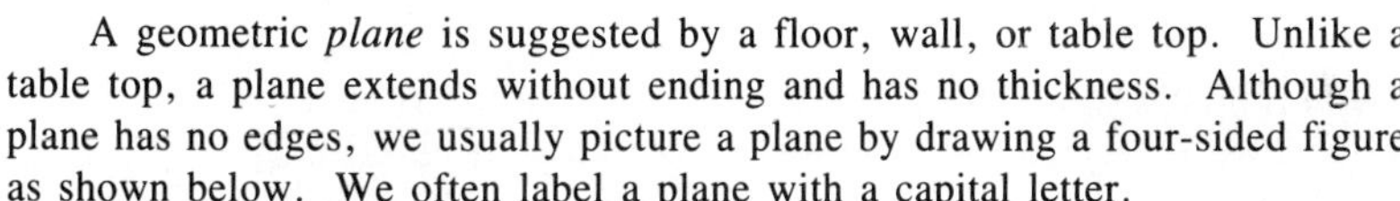

A geometric *plane* is suggested by a floor, wall, or table top. Unlike a table top, a plane extends without ending and has no thickness. Although a plane has no edges, we usually picture a plane by drawing a four-sided figure as shown below. We often label a plane with a capital letter.

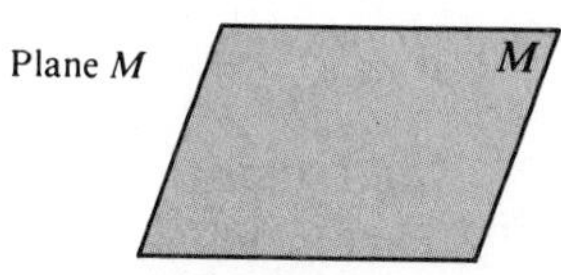

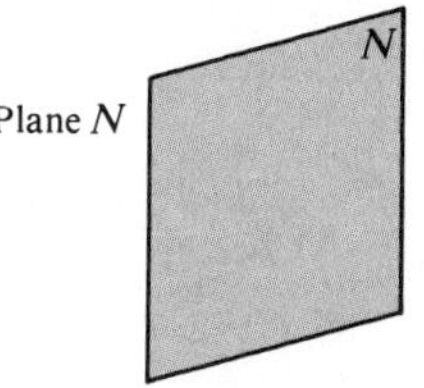

In geometry, the terms *point*, *line*, and *plane* are accepted as intuitive ideas and are not defined. These *undefined terms* are then used in the definitions of other terms, such as those at the top of the next page.

Teaching Suggestions,
p. T75

Objectives
Presenting the Lesson
Reinforcement

Cooperative Learning,
p. T75

Supplementary Materials

Practice Master 1
Test 1
Resource Book, pp. 1, 109
Study Guide, pp. 3–4
Overhead Visuals A, B

Lesson Focus

The three most basic figures in geometry are points, lines, and planes. This lesson illustrates how these three basic figures are related to one another.

Suggested Assignments

Minimum
Day 1: 7–8/1–26
Day 2: 9/27–30
10/Self-Test 1

Average
Day 1: 7–9/1–25 odd, 26–28
Day 2: 9/29–35 odd
10/Self-Test 1

Maximum
7–9/2–26 even, 27–36

Teaching Note

Some students will come to class with a strong intuitive understanding of the terms point, line, and plane. For this reason, it may be difficult for them to accept that these terms are undefined in a formal geometric system.

Chalkboard Examples

Classify each statement as true or false.

1. $\overleftrightarrow{PF}$ ends at P. F
2. Point S is on an infinite number of lines. T
3. A plane has no thickness. T
4. Collinear points are coplanar. T
5. Planes have edges. F
6. Two planes intersect in a line segment. F
7. Two intersecting lines meet in exactly one point. T
8. Points have no size. T
9. Line XY can be denoted as $\overleftrightarrow{XY}$ or $\overleftrightarrow{YX}$. T

Using a Model

Some students will need to see physical models of lines in space. You can use a marble and a pointer, and two pointers. To illustrate plane M with line j intersecting it, push a pencil through a sheet of paper or use a piece of poster board—with a hole in it—and a pointer. For two intersecting planes, use two poster boards, one cut through from C to B, the other from D to E.

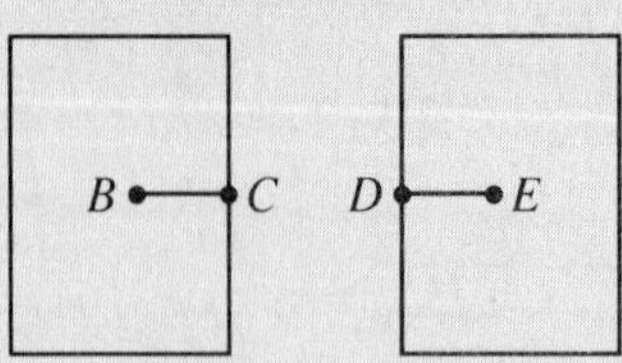

With one board vertical and the other one horizontal, fit the two together so that points D and E fall on points B and C, respectively.

Space is the set of all points. **Collinear points** are points all in one line.

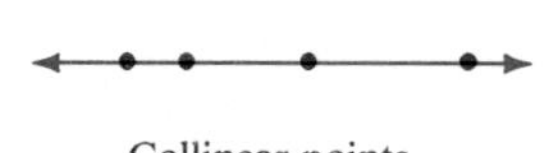

Collinear points

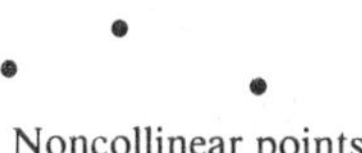

Noncollinear points

Coplanar points are points all in one plane.

Coplanar points

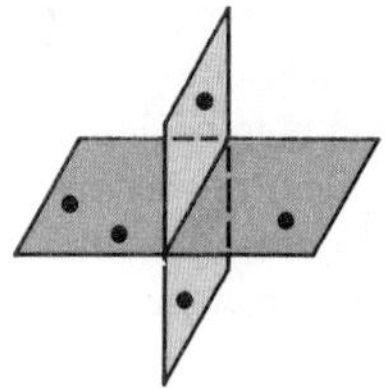

Noncoplanar points

Some expressions commonly used to describe relationships between points, lines, and planes follow. In these expressions, *intersects* means "meets" or "cuts." The **intersection** of two figures is the set of points that are in both figures. Dashes in the diagrams indicate parts hidden from view in figures in space.

A is in l, or A is on l.
l contains A.
l passes through A.

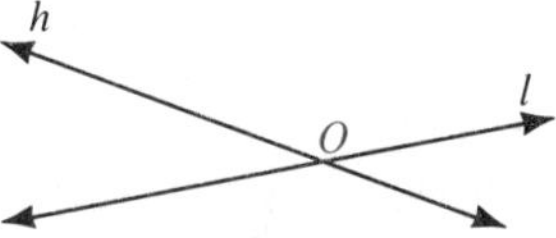

l and h intersect in O.
l and h intersect at O.
O is the intersection of l and h.

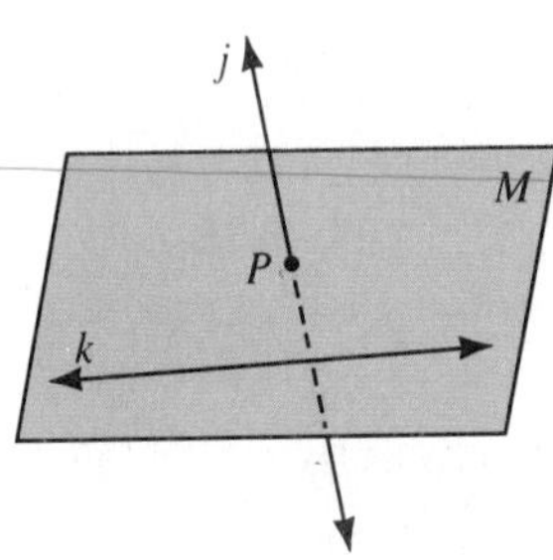

k and P are in M.
M contains k and P.
j intersects M at P.
P is the intersection of j and M.

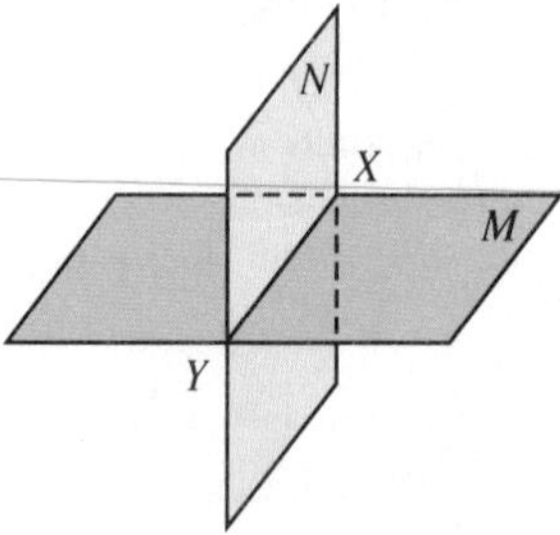

M and N intersect in $\overleftrightarrow{XY}$.
$\overleftrightarrow{XY}$ is the intersection of M and N.
$\overleftrightarrow{XY}$ is in M and N.
M and N contain $\overleftrightarrow{XY}$.

In this book, whenever we refer, for example, to "two points" or "three lines," we will mean *different* points or lines (or other geometric figures).

Classroom Exercises

Classify each statement as true or false.

1. $\overleftrightarrow{XY}$ intersects plane *M* at point *O*. **True**
2. Plane *M* intersects $\overleftrightarrow{XY}$ in more than one point. **False**
3. *T*, *O*, and *R* are collinear. **False**
4. *X*, *O*, and *Y* are collinear. **True**
5. *R*, *O*, *S*, and *W* are coplanar. **True**
6. *R*, *S*, *T*, and *X* are coplanar. **False**
7. *R*, *X*, *O*, and *Y* are coplanar. **True**

Exs. 1–7

8. Does a plane have edges? **No**
9. Can a given point be in two lines? in ten lines? **Yes; Yes**
10. Can a given line be in two planes? in ten planes? **Yes; Yes**

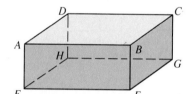

Name a fourth point that is in the same plane as the given points.

11. *A*, *B*, *C* ***D*** 12. *E*, *F*, *H* ***G*** 13. *D*, *C*, *H* ***G***
14. *A*, *D*, *E* ***H*** 15. *B*, *E*, *F* ***A*** 16. *B*, *G*, *C* ***F***

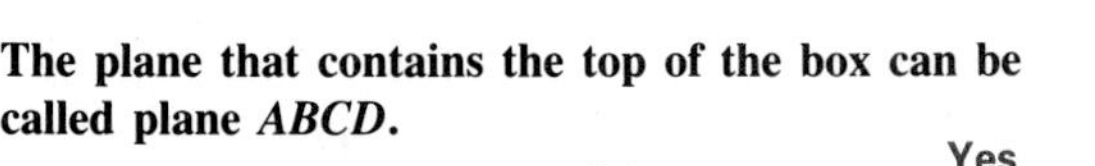

The plane that contains the top of the box can be called plane *ABCD*.

17. Are there any points in $\overleftrightarrow{CG}$ besides *C* and *G*? **Yes**
18. Are there more than four points in plane *ABCD*? **Yes**
19. Name the intersection of planes *ABFE* and *BCGF*. $\overleftrightarrow{BF}$
20. Name two planes that do not intersect. ***ABCD* and *EFGH*, or *ADHE* and *BCGF*, or *ABFE* and *DCGH***

Exs. 11–20

Written Exercises

Classify each statement as true or false.

A
1. $\overleftrightarrow{AB}$ is in plane *R*. **True** 2. *S* contains $\overleftrightarrow{AB}$. **True**
3. *R* and *S* contain *D*. **True** 4. *D* is on line *h*. **True**
5. *h* is in *S*. **True** 6. *h* is in *R*. **False**
7. Plane *R* intersects plane *S* in $\overleftrightarrow{AB}$. **True**
8. Point *C* is in *R* and *S*. **False**
9. *A*, *B*, and *C* are collinear. **False**
10. *A*, *B*, *C*, and *D* are coplanar. **True**

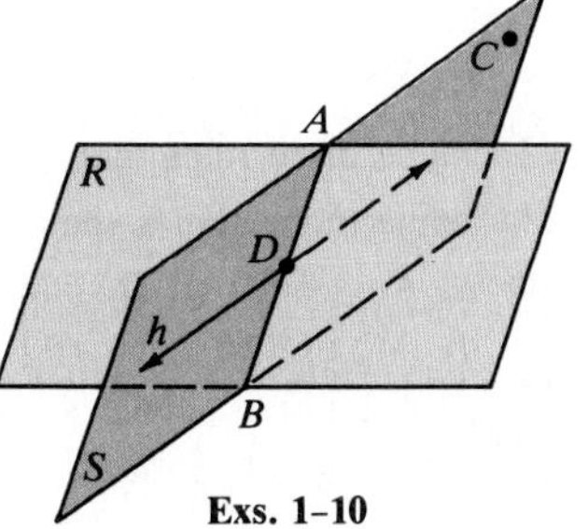

Exs. 1–10

Communication Skills

Point out that collinear points are automatically coplanar, but coplanar points are not necessarily collinear.

Using a Model

For variety, you can use the floor for plane *M* and a pointer for $\overleftrightarrow{XY}$. Students will see the part of the line above point *O*. They can imagine the continuation of the line below the floor.

For Exs. 11–20, some rectangular-shaped classrooms can serve as good models. An empty shoe box also serves well as a model.

Guided Practice

Use the diagram below to classify each statement as true or false.

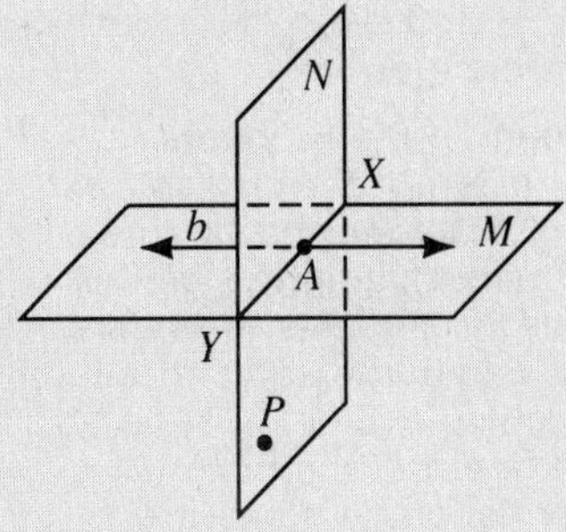

1. *P* is in *M*. F
2. *b* is in *M*. T
3. $\overleftrightarrow{YX}$ contains *P*. F
4. *M* contains $\overleftrightarrow{YX}$. T
5. *A* is on *b*. T
6. *A* and *P* are in *M*. F
7. *N* contains *P*. T

11. Make a sketch showing four coplanar points such that three, but not four, of them are collinear.

12. Make a sketch showing four points that are not coplanar.

A plane can be named by three or more noncollinear points it contains. In Chapter 12 you will study *pyramids* like the one shown at the right below.

13. Name five planes that contain sides of the pyramid shown. ***VWT, VST, VRS, VWR, WRST***

14. Of the five planes containing sides of the pyramid, are there any that do not intersect? **No**

15. Name three lines that intersect at point R. ***$\overleftrightarrow{RW}$, $\overleftrightarrow{RV}$, $\overleftrightarrow{RS}$***

16. Name two planes that intersect in $\overleftrightarrow{ST}$. ***VST, WRST***

17. Name three planes that intersect at point S. ***VRS, VST, WRST***

18. Name a line and a plane that intersect in a point.
Answers may vary; for example, $\overleftrightarrow{VS}$ and *WRST*

Exs. 13–18

Follow the steps shown to draw the figure named.

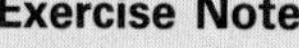

Exercise Note

The procedure for making the drawings in Exs. 19–20 should be demonstrated at the chalkboard. Then have students attempt to do their own drawings.

Problem Solving

Many of the problems throughout the student text are accompanied by three-dimensional drawings. In order for students to understand how to solve these problems, they must be able to interpret the pictorial information. In some instances, they may have to sketch their own diagrams. Encourage students to practice drawing three-dimensional figures by copying the diagrams in the textbook.

19. a rectangular solid or box

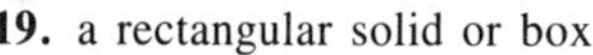

Step 1 Step 2 Step 3

20. a barn

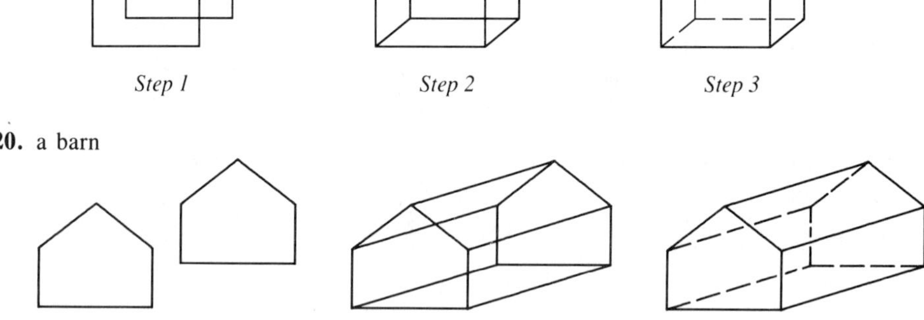

Step 1 Step 2 Step 3

Note: After drawing more figures in space, you will probably be able to go directly from Step 1 to Step 3.

21. Name two planes that intersect in $\overleftrightarrow{FG}$. ***RSGF* and *FGCB***

22. Name three lines that intersect at point E. ***$\overleftrightarrow{EA}$, $\overleftrightarrow{ER}$, $\overleftrightarrow{EH}$***

23. Name three planes that intersect at point B.

24. **a.** Are points A, D, and C collinear? **No**
b. Are points A, D, and C coplanar? **Yes**

25. **a.** Are points R, S, G, and F coplanar? **Yes**
b. Are points R, S, G, and C coplanar? **No**

Exs. 21–26

26. **a.** Name two planes that do not intersect.
b. Name two other planes that do not intersect.

Answers may vary; for example, a. *REABF, SHDCG* b. *AEHD, BFGC*

23. *ABCD, REABF, GFBC*

You can think of the ceiling and floor of a room as parts of *horizontal planes*. The walls are parts of *vertical planes*. Vertical planes are represented by figures like those shown in which two sides are vertical. A horizontal plane is represented by a figure like that shown, with two sides horizontal and no sides vertical.

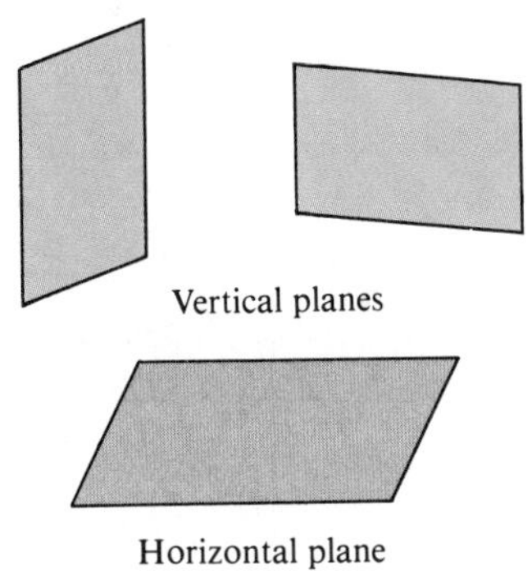
Vertical planes

Horizontal plane

B **27.** Can two horizontal planes intersect? **No**

28. **a.** Can two vertical planes intersect? **Yes**

b. Suppose a line is known to be in a vertical plane. Does the line have to be a vertical line? **No**

Sketch and label the figures described. Use dashes for hidden parts.

29. Vertical line l intersects a horizontal plane M at point O.

30. Horizontal plane P contains two lines k and n that intersect at point A.

31. Horizontal plane Q and vertical plane N intersect.

32. Vertical planes X and Y intersect in $\overleftrightarrow{AB}$.

33. Point P is not in plane N. Three lines through point P intersect N in points A, B, and C.

C **34.** Three vertical planes intersect in a line.

35. A vertical plane intersects two horizontal planes in lines l and n.

36. Three planes intersect in a point.

Challenge

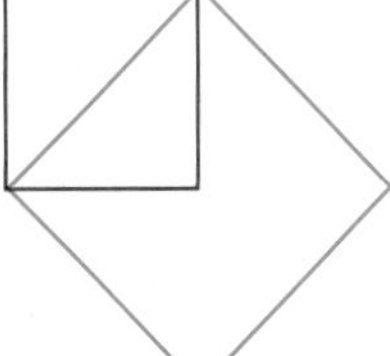

If the area of the red square is 1 square unit, what is the area of the blue square? Give a convincing argument.
2 square units

Using a Model

Box dividers serve to illustrate families of intersecting planes. Ask a student to manipulate the dividers to illustrate various possibilities.

Ask students if planes suggested by parts of the classroom can help in doing Exs. 27–28. For Ex. 27, examples of horizontal planes are the ceiling and floor, or a desktop and the floor. For Ex. 28(a), use a front wall and side wall. For Ex. 28(b), the chalkboard and the trough for chalk can serve as an example.

Group Activity

It is easy to underestimate the difficulty some students have with drawing three-dimensional figures. If you can spare class time, divide the class into several groups and have a representative of each group draw Ex. 29 on the chalkboard. Later, the class as a whole can discuss the relative merits of the different versions. You can repeat this procedure for Exs. 30–36.

Another approach is to assign only two exercises the first day. Then display and discuss a few of the solutions the next day. Continue in this way until all the exercises have been completed.

Thinking Skills

Some students will observe that the challenge problem is related to Ex. 7 on page 4. For insightful students, the numerical answer is found easily; however, providing a convincing argument will be a challenge for most students.

Quick Quiz

Classify each statement as true or false.

1. All points on a line are coplanar. T
2. A line has one endpoint. F
3. A point is named by a capital letter. T
4. Two lines intersect in two points. F
5. The edge of a plane is a line. F

Teaching Note

Self-Tests are not intended to be graded or marked. Encourage students to use these tests to check their mastery of basic facts.

Exercise Note

The goal of an Algebra Review is to strengthen students' algebraic skills and build their confidence in applying these skills in a geometric context. Encourage students to do mentally as many of the exercises as they can. Steps should be written down only when necessary.

Self-Test 1

Name the point that appears to satisfy the description.

1. Equidistant from R and S **T**
2. Equidistant from S and U **T**
3. Equidistant from U and T **V**

T
R
V U
S
Exs. 1–3

Classify each statement as true or false.

4. Plane Y and $\overleftrightarrow{PQ}$ intersect in point L. **True**
5. Points J, K, L, and N are coplanar. **True**
6. Points J, L, and Q are collinear. **False**

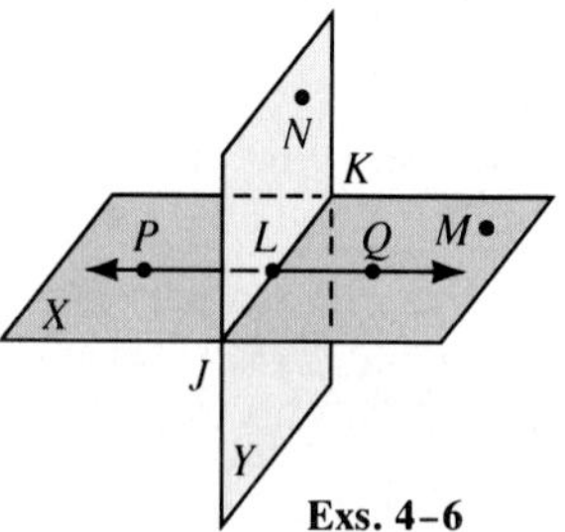

Exs. 4–6

7. Draw a vertical plane Z intersecting a horizontal line l in a point T.

Algebra Review: *Linear Equations*

Find the value of the variable. **31. $g = 8$ 32. $u = 3$ 33. $w = 8$**

1. $c + 5 = 12$ **$c = 7$**
2. $8 + c = 13$ **$c = 5$**
3. $c - 5 = 12$ **$c = 17$**
4. $7 - z = 13$ **$z = -6$**
5. $15 - z = 0$ **$z = 15$**
6. $4x = 28$ **$x = 7$**
7. $3x = 15$ **$x = 5$**
8. $7x = -35$ **$x = -5$**
9. $-5x = -5$ **$x = 1$**
10. $\frac{1}{3}a = 2$ **$a = 6$**
11. $\frac{3}{4}a = 9$ **$a = 12$**
12. $\frac{4}{5}a = -20$ **$a = -25$**
13. $-2b = 6$ **$b = -3$**
14. $-3b = -9$ **$b = 3$**
15. $-9b = 2$ **$b = -\frac{2}{9}$**
16. $42 = 6k$ **$k = 7$**
17. $5 = 10k$ **$k = \frac{1}{2}$**
18. $-16 = -4k$ **$k = 4$**
19. $12 = \frac{e}{2}$ **$e = 24$**
20. $-9 = \frac{e}{3}$ **$e = -27$**
21. $5 = -\frac{e}{3}$ **$e = -15$**
22. $2p + 5 = 13$ **$p = 4$**
23. $3p - 5 = 13$ **$p = 6$**
24. $4p + 2 = 22$ **$p = 5$**
25. $60 = 6t + 12$ **$t = 8$**
26. $12 = 3r - 9$ **$r = 7$**
27. $55 = 7s - 8$ **$s = 9$**
28. $8x + 2x = 90$ **$x = 9$**
29. $8x - 2x = 90$ **$x = 15$**
30. $x + 9x = 5$ **$x = \frac{1}{2}$**
31. $(2g - 15) + g = 9$
32. $3u + (u - 2) = 10$
33. $(w - 20) + 5w = 28$
34. $3x = 2x - 17$ **$x = -17$**
35. $5y = 3y + 26$ **$y = 13$**
36. $7z = 180 - 2z$ **$z = 20$**
37. $12 + 3b = 2 + 5b$ **$b = 5$**
38. $4c + 23 = 9c - 7$ **$c = 6$**
39. $7h + (90 - h) = 210$ **$h = 20$**
40. $5x + (180 - x) = 300$ **$x = 30$**
41. $(4f + 5) + (5f + 40) = 180$ **$f = 15$**
42. $(3g - 4) + (4g + 10) = 90$ **$g = 12$**
43. $2(4d + 4) = d + 1$ **$d = -1$**
44. $2(d + 5) = 3(d - 2)$ **$d = 16$**
45. $180 - x = 3(90 - x)$ **$x = 45$**
46. $3(180 - y) = 2(90 - y)$ **$y = 360$**

Definitions and Postulates

Objectives

1. Use symbols for lines, segments, rays, and distances; find distances.
2. Name angles and find their measures.
3. State and use the Segment Addition Postulate and the Angle Addition Postulate.
4. Recognize what you can conclude from a diagram.
5. Use postulates and theorems relating points, lines, and planes.

1-3 *Segments, Rays, and Distance*

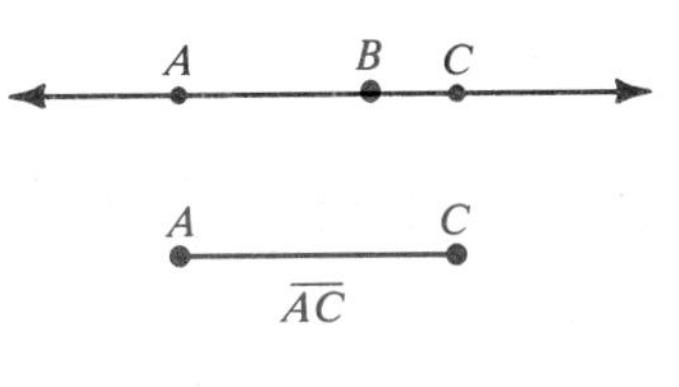

In the diagram, point B is *between* points A and C. Note that B must lie on $\overleftrightarrow{AC}$.

Segment *AC*, denoted $\overline{AC}$, consists of points A and C and all points that are between A and C. Points A and C are called the *endpoints* of $\overline{AC}$.

Ray *AC*, denoted $\overrightarrow{AC}$, consists of $\overline{AC}$ and all other points P such that C is between A and P. The *endpoint* of $\overrightarrow{AC}$ is A, the point named first.

$\overrightarrow{SR}$ and $\overrightarrow{ST}$ are called **opposite rays** if S is between R and T.

The hands of the clock shown suggest opposite rays.

On a *number line* every point is paired with a number and every number is paired with a point. In the diagram, point J is paired with -3, the *coordinate* of J.

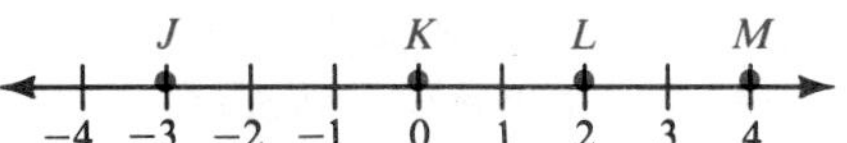

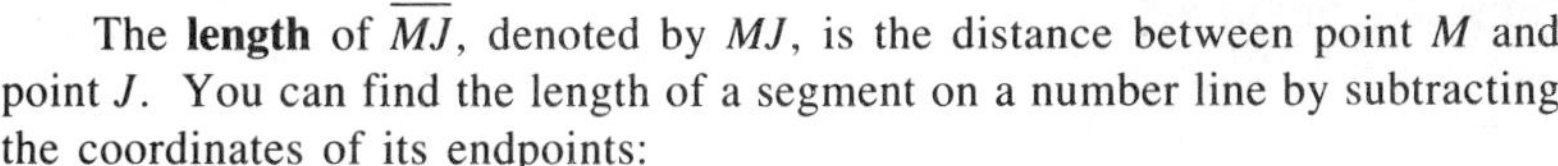

The **length** of $\overline{MJ}$, denoted by MJ, is the distance between point M and point J. You can find the length of a segment on a number line by subtracting the coordinates of its endpoints:

$$MJ = 4 - (-3) = 7$$

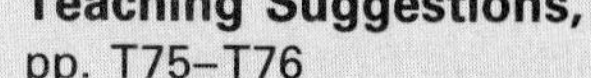

Teaching Suggestions,
pp. T75–T76

Objectives
Presenting the Lesson
Making Connections
Reinforcement

Communication Skills,
p. T76

Supplementary Materials

Study Guide, pp. 5–6
Overhead Visual C
Computer Activity 2

Lesson Focus

This lesson shows how numbers can be related to points on a line. In so doing, the ideas of distance, length, and congruence can be discussed.

Suggested Assignments

Minimum
Day 1: 15/1–26
Day 2: 15–16/27–35

Average
Day 1: 15–16/1–39 odd
Day 2: 16/40–46 even

Maximum
15–16/1–45 odd, 46–48

You may wish to introduce Construction 1 on page 375 after covering this lesson.

Communication Skills

You may need to remind students repeatedly that AB is a length (number), $\overline{AB}$ is a segment, $\overrightarrow{AB}$ is a ray, and $\overleftrightarrow{AB}$ is a line. The arrowheads suggest that $\overrightarrow{AB}$ goes on past B, and that $\overleftrightarrow{AB}$ goes on past A and on past B.

Notice that since a length must be a positive number, you subtract the lesser coordinate from the greater one. Actually, the distance between two points is the absolute value of the difference of their coordinates. When you use absolute value, the order in which you subtract coordinates doesn't matter.

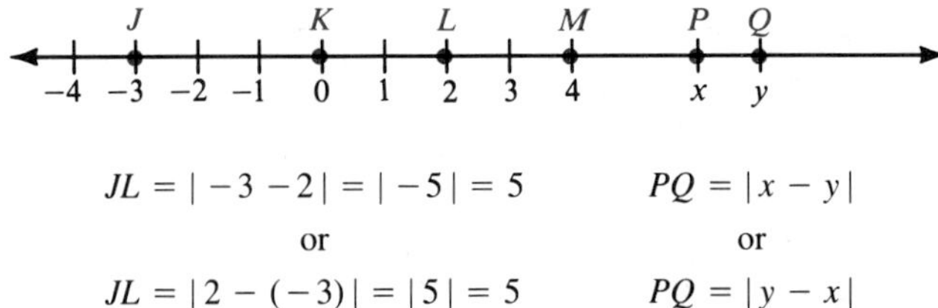

$JL = |-3-2| = |-5| = 5$ or $JL = |2-(-3)| = |5| = 5$

$PQ = |x-y|$ or $PQ = |y-x|$

There are many different ways to pair the points on a line with numbers. For example, the red coordinates shown below would give distances in centimeters. The blue coordinates would give distances in inches.

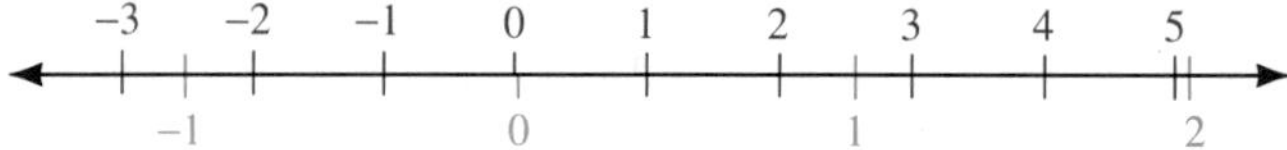

Once you have chosen a unit of measure, the distance between any two points will be the same no matter where you place the coordinate 0. For example, the black coordinates below show another way of assigning coordinates to points on the line so that distances will be measured in inches.

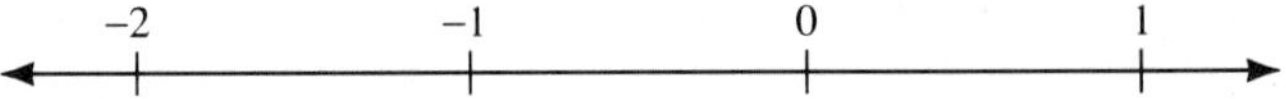

Using number lines involves the following basic assumptions. Statements such as these that are accepted without proof are called **postulates** or **axioms.** Notice that the Ruler Postulate below allows you to measure distances using centimeters or inches or any other convenient unit. But once a unit of measure has been chosen for a particular problem, you must use that unit throughout the problem.

Postulate 1 *Ruler Postulate*

1. The points on a line can be paired with the real numbers in such a way that any two points can have coordinates 0 and 1.

2. Once a coordinate system has been chosen in this way, the distance between any two points equals the absolute value of the difference of their coordinates.

Postulate 2 *Segment Addition Postulate*

If *B* is between *A* and *C*, then

$$AB + BC = AC.$$

Chalkboard Examples

Fill in the blank with *always, sometimes,* or *never.*

1. The length of a segment is never negative.
2. If point *S* is between points *R* and *V*, then *S* always lies on $\overleftrightarrow{RV}$.
3. A coordinate can always be paired with a point on a number line.
4. A bisector of a segment is sometimes a line.
5. A ray never has a midpoint.
6. Congruent segments always have equal lengths.
7. $\overrightarrow{AB}$ and $\overrightarrow{BA}$ never denote the same ray.

Proof Note

More can be said later about accepting statements without proof, that is, about basic assumptions. After students have seen some proofs, they will understand the role of assumptions better.

Teaching Note

Students should be told not to memorize Postulate 1. They can refer to it as the Ruler Postulate. Postulate 2 should be memorized (the letters used need not be *A, B, C*) even though everyone can refer to it as the Segment Addition Postulate.

You may wish to point out that real numbers are the numbers students used in their first-year algebra course. There is no need to discuss real numbers in terms of rational and irrational numbers.

Example B is between A and C, with $AB = x$, $BC = x + 6$, and $AC = 24$. Find:
a. the value of x **b.** BC

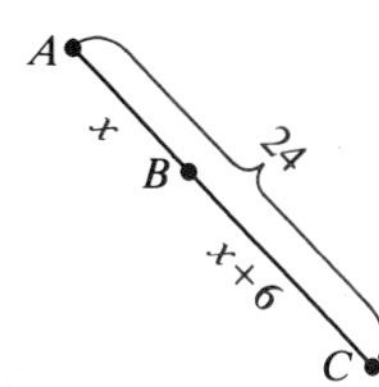

Solution

a.
$$\begin{aligned} AB + BC &= AC \\ x + (x + 6) &= 24 \\ 2x + 6 &= 24 \\ 2x &= 18 \\ x &= 9 \end{aligned}$$

b.
$$\begin{aligned} BC &= x + 6 \\ &= 9 + 6 \\ &= 15 \end{aligned}$$

In geometry two objects that have the same size and shape are called **congruent**. For many geometric figures we can give a more precise definition of what it means to be congruent. For example, we will define congruent segments in this section, congruent angles in the next section, congruent triangles in Chapter 4, and congruent circles and arcs in Chapter 9.

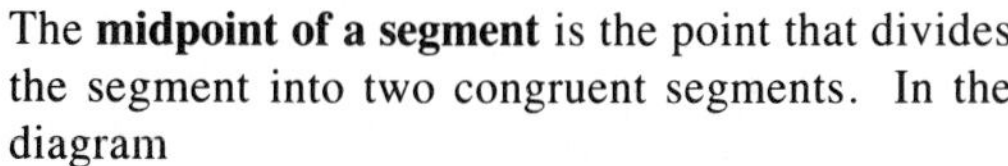

Congruent segments are segments that have equal lengths. To indicate that $\overline{DE}$ and $\overline{FG}$ have equal lengths, you write

$$DE = FG.$$

To indicate that $\overline{DE}$ and $\overline{FG}$ are congruent, you write

$$\overline{DE} \cong \overline{FG}$$

(read "$\overline{DE}$ is congruent to $\overline{FG}$"). The definition tells us that the two statements are equivalent. We will use them interchangeably.

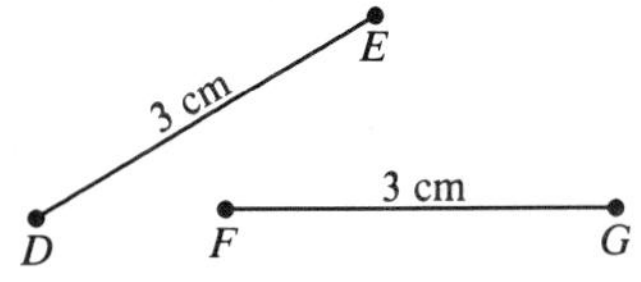

The **midpoint of a segment** is the point that divides the segment into two congruent segments. In the diagram

$$AP = PB,$$
$$\overline{AP} \cong \overline{PB},$$

and P is the midpoint of $\overline{AB}$.

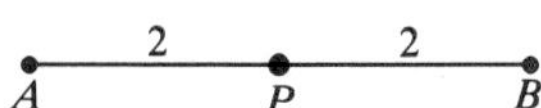

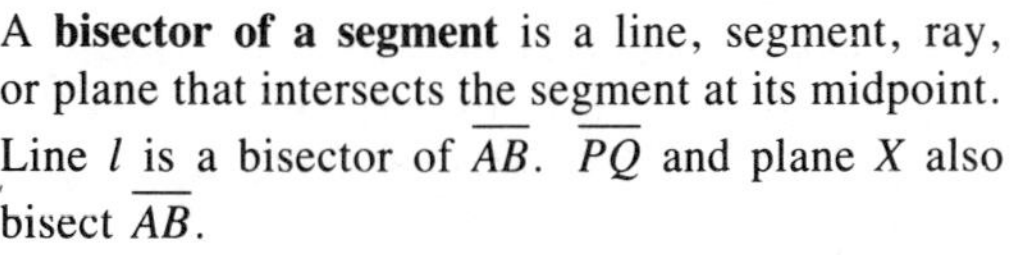

A **bisector of a segment** is a line, segment, ray, or plane that intersects the segment at its midpoint. Line l is a bisector of $\overline{AB}$. $\overline{PQ}$ and plane X also bisect $\overline{AB}$.

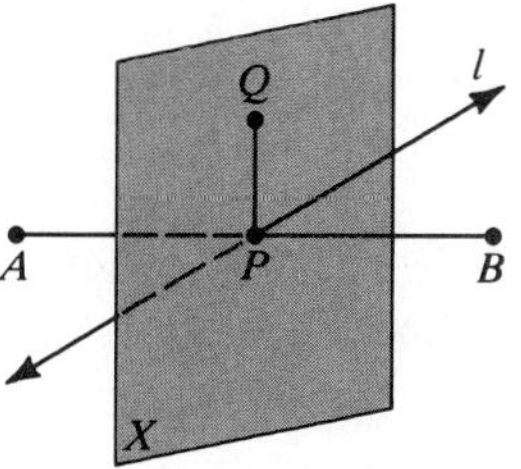

Making Connections

Students who did the Algebra Review on page 10 will be able to apply their algebra here. Typically, a text example shows more steps than most students need. They might write only

$$\begin{aligned} x + (x + 6) &= 24 \\ x &= 9 \\ BC &= 15 \end{aligned}$$

Communication Skills

The equivalence of $DE = FG$ and $\overline{DE} \cong \overline{FG}$ permits us to choose, in a particular case, the more convenient statement ($AP = PB$ or $\overline{AP} \cong \overline{PB}$) as the translation of "P is the midpoint of $\overline{AB}$."

Thinking Skills

Students should observe that when P is the midpoint of $\overline{AB}$, $AP = PB$. Then they may be tempted to believe the converse, that when $SM = MT$, M is the midpoint of $\overline{ST}$. Ask for a volunteer to draw a figure on the chalkboard that shows clearly this is not true.

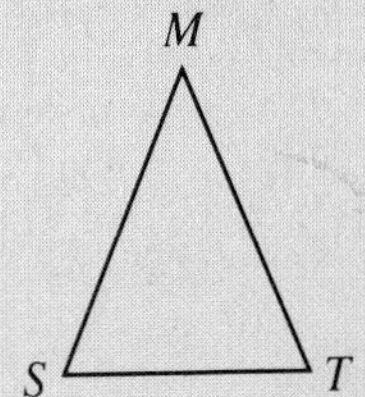

Exercise Note

For Ex. 3, draw points A and B on the chalkboard. Have one student draw $\overline{AB}$ in red and another student draw $\overline{BA}$ in yellow. Students will see that $\overline{AB}$ and $\overline{BA}$ are the same. Exs. 4–5 can be handled in a similar way.

Classroom Exercises

1. Does the symbol represent a line, segment, ray, or length?
   a. $\overline{PQ}$ **segment** **b.** $\overrightarrow{PQ}$ **ray** **c.** $\overleftrightarrow{PQ}$ **line** **d.** PQ **length**
2. How many endpoints does a segment have? a ray? a line? **2; 1; 0**
3. Is $\overline{AB}$ the same as $\overline{BA}$? **Yes**
4. Is $\overrightarrow{AB}$ the same as $\overrightarrow{BA}$? **No**
5. Is $\overleftrightarrow{AB}$ the same as $\overleftrightarrow{BA}$? **Yes**
6. Is AB the same as BA? **Yes**

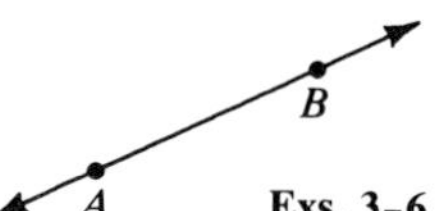

Exs. 3–6

7. What is the coordinate of P? of R? **−2; 0**
8. Name the point with coordinate 2. ***T***
9. Find each distance: **a.** RS **b.** RQ **c.** PT **1; 1; 4**
10. Name three segments congruent to $\overline{PQ}$. $\overline{QR}, \overline{RS}, \overline{ST}$
11. Name the ray opposite to $\overrightarrow{SP}$. $\overrightarrow{ST}$
12. Name the midpoint of $\overline{PT}$. ***R***
13. **a.** What number is halfway between 1 and 2? **1.5**
    b. What is the coordinate of the midpoint of $\overline{ST}$? **1.5**

P Q R S T
−2 −1 0 1 2

Exs. 7–14

14. **a.** Could you list all the numbers between 1 and 2? **No**
    b. Is there a point on the number line for every number between 1 and 2? **Yes**
    c. Is there any limit to the number of points between S and T? **No**

State whether the figures *appear* to be congruent (that is, appear to have the same size and shape).

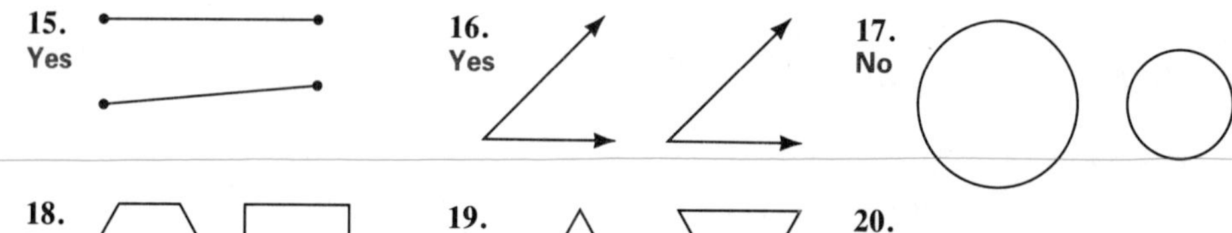

15. **Yes** 16. **Yes** 17. **No**

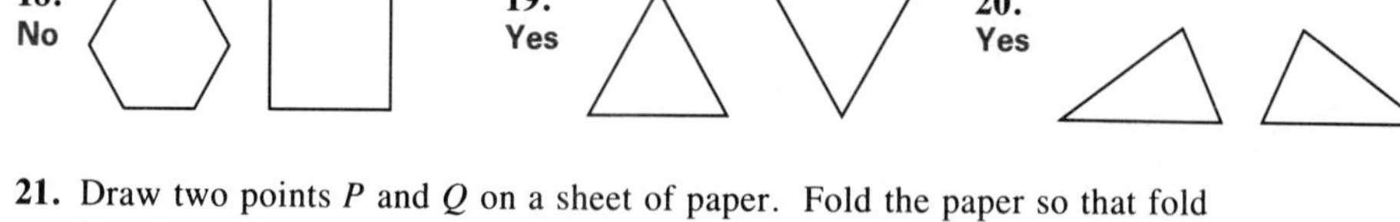

18. **No** 19. **Yes** 20. **Yes**

Using a Model

If you use a large sheet of paper for Ex. 21, you will interest students and have an effective demonstration.

21. Draw two points P and Q on a sheet of paper. Fold the paper so that fold line f contains both P and Q. Unfold the paper. Now fold so that P falls on Q. Call the second fold g. Lay the paper flat and label the intersection of f and g as point X. How are points P, Q, and X related? Explain. ***X*** **is the midpoint of** $\overline{PQ}$.
22. If $AB = BC$, must point B be the midpoint of $\overline{AC}$? Explain. **No; *B* does not have to be on** $\overline{AC}$.

The given numbers are the coordinates of two points on a number line. State the distance between the points.

23. −2 and 6 **8** 24. −2 and −6 **4** 25. 2 and −6 **8** 26. 7 and −1 **8**

Written Exercises

The numbers given are the coordinates of two points on a number line. State the distance between the points.

A 1. −6 and 9 **15** 2. −3 and −17 **14** 3. −1.2 and −5.7 **4.5** 4. −2.5 and 4.6 **7.1**

In the diagram, $\overline{HL}$ and $\overleftrightarrow{KT}$ intersect at the midpoint of $\overline{HL}$. Classify each statement as true or false.

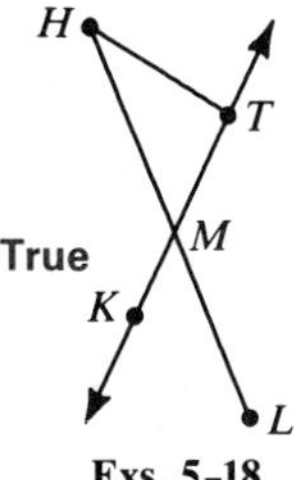

Exs. 5-18

5. $\overline{LM} \cong \overline{MH}$ **True**
6. KM must equal MT. **False**
7. $\overline{MT}$ bisects $\overline{LH}$. **True**
8. $\overleftrightarrow{KT}$ is a bisector of $\overline{LH}$. **True**
9. $\overrightarrow{MT}$ and $\overrightarrow{TM}$ are opposite rays. **False**
10. $\overrightarrow{MT}$ and $\overrightarrow{MK}$ are opposite rays. **True**
11. $\overleftrightarrow{LH}$ is the same as $\overline{HL}$. **False**
12. $\overrightarrow{KT}$ is the same as $\overrightarrow{KM}$. **True**
13. $\overleftrightarrow{KT}$ is the same as $\overleftrightarrow{KM}$. **True**
14. $\overline{KT}$ is the same as $\overline{KM}$. **False**
15. $HM + ML = HL$ **True**
16. $TM + MH = TH$ **False**
17. T is between H and M. **False**
18. M is between K and T. **True**

Name each of the following.

19. The point on $\overrightarrow{DA}$ whose distance from D is 2 ***B***
20. The point on $\overrightarrow{DG}$ whose distance from D is 2 ***F***
21. Two points whose distance from E is 2 ***C, G***
22. The ray opposite to $\overrightarrow{BE}$ $\overrightarrow{BA}$
23. The midpoint of $\overline{BF}$ ***D***
24. The coordinate of the midpoint of $\overline{BD}$ **−1**
25. The coordinate of the midpoint of $\overline{AE}$ **−1**
26. A segment congruent to $\overline{AF}$ $\overline{BG}$

A B C D E F G
−3 −2 −1 0 1 2 3
Exs. 19–26

In Exercises 27–30 draw $\overline{CD}$ and $\overline{RS}$ so that the conditions are satisfied.

27. $\overline{CD}$ and $\overline{RS}$ intersect, but neither segment bisects the other.
28. $\overline{CD}$ and $\overline{RS}$ bisect each other.
29. $\overline{CD}$ bisects $\overline{RS}$, but $\overline{RS}$ does not bisect $\overline{CD}$.
30. $\overline{CD}$ and $\overline{RS}$ do not intersect, but $\overrightarrow{CD}$ and $\overrightarrow{RS}$ do intersect.

B 31. In the diagram, $\overline{PR} \cong \overline{RT}$, S is the midpoint of $\overline{RT}$, $QR = 4$, and $ST = 5$. Complete.
a. RS = ? **5** b. RT = ? **10**
c. PR = ? **10** d. PQ = ? **6**

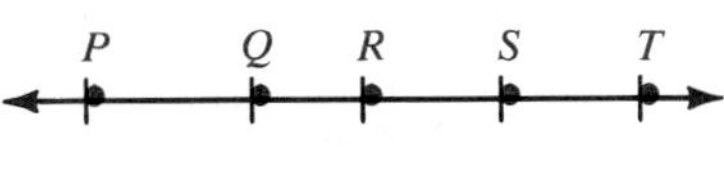

32. In the diagram, X is the midpoint of $\overline{VZ}$, $VW = 5$, and $VY = 20$. Find the coordinates of W, X, and Y. **−7, 5, 8**

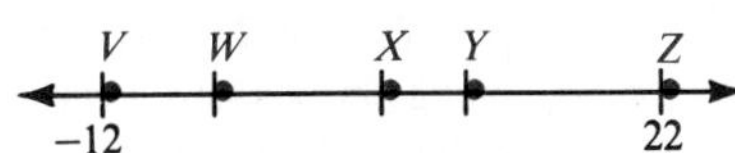

Guided Practice

Write a symbol to represent each of the following.

1. Segment MN $\overline{MN}$
2. Point R R
3. Line ST $\overleftrightarrow{ST}$
4. Ray AB $\overrightarrow{AB}$
5. Ray BA $\overrightarrow{BA}$

State the distance between the following coordinates on a number line.

6. −3 and −8 5
7. 4 and −1 5
8. −2.2 and 2.2 4.4
9. 0 and −17 17
10. 12 and −1.5 13.5

Making Connections

Students must have good algebraic skills to solve various problems found in geometry. It is important that these skills, once learned, are maintained in other mathematics courses. Exs. 33–40 are designed to give students an opportunity to practice and apply their algebraic skills. Similar exercises that integrate geometry and algebra are provided throughout the book.

Exercise Note

After completing Ex. 48, ask students to name other temperature scales. The Kelvin scale is the one they are most likely to name. The Rankine scale is another.

E is the midpoint of $\overline{DF}$. Find the value of x.

33. $DE = 5x + 3,\ EF = 33$ **$x = 6$**
34. $DE = 45,\ EF = 5x - 10$ **$x = 11$**
35. $DE = 3x,\ EF = x + 6$ **$x = 3$**
36. $DE = 2x - 3,\ EF = 5x - 24$ **$x = 7$**

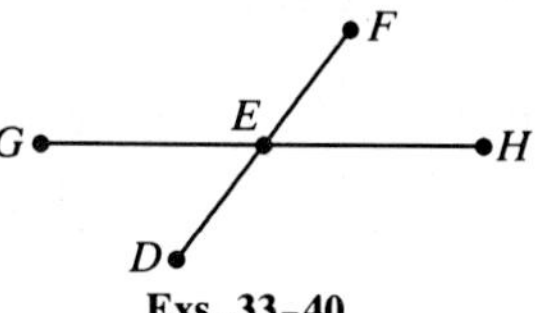

Exs. 33–40

Find the value of y.

37. $GE = y,\ EH = y - 1,\ GH = 11$ **$y = 6$**

38. $GE = 3y,\ GH = 7y - 4,\ EH = 24$ **$y = 7$**

Find the value of z. Then find GE and EH and state whether E is the midpoint of $\overline{GH}$.

39. $GE = z + 2,\ GH = 20,\ EH = 2z - 6$ **$z = 8$; $GE = 10$; $EH = 10$; yes**
40. $GH = z + 6,\ EH = 2z - 4,\ GE = z$ **$z = 5$; $GE = 5$; $EH = 6$; no**

Name the graph of the given equation or inequality.

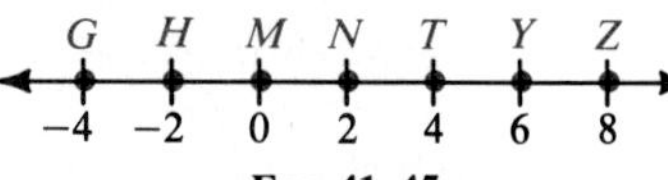

Exs. 41–45

Example a. $x \geq 2$ b. $4 \leq x \leq 6$

Solution a. $\overrightarrow{NT}$ b. $\overline{TY}$

41. $-2 \leq x \leq 2$ **$\overline{HN}$**
42. $x \leq 0$ **$\overrightarrow{MH}$ or $\overrightarrow{MG}$**
43. $|x| \leq 4$ **$\overline{GT}$**
44. $|x| \geq 0$ **Answers may vary; $\overleftrightarrow{GT}$**
45. $|x| = 0$ **M**

In Exercises 46 and 47 draw a diagram to illustrate your answer.

46. a. On $\overrightarrow{AB}$, how many points are there whose distance from point A is 3 cm? **1**
    b. On $\overleftrightarrow{AB}$, how many points are there whose distance from point A is 3 cm? **2**

C 47. On $\overrightarrow{AB}$, how many points are there whose distance from point B is 3 cm? **2 if $AB \geq 3$ cm, 1 if $AB < 3$ cm**

48. The Ruler Postulate suggests that there are many ways to assign coordinates to a line. The Fahrenheit and Celsius temperature scales on a thermometer indicate two such ways of assigning coordinates. A Fahrenheit temperature of 32° corresponds to a Celsius temperature of 0°. The formula, or rule, for converting a Fahrenheit temperature F into a Celsius temperature C is

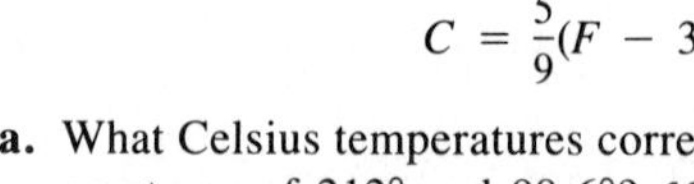

$$C = \frac{5}{9}(F - 32).$$

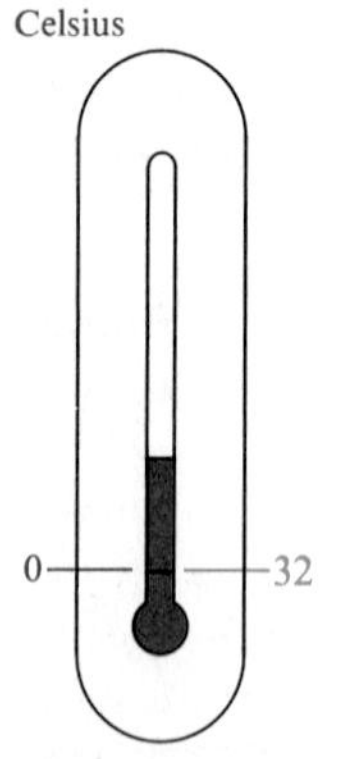

a. What Celsius temperatures correspond to Fahrenheit temperatures of 212° and 98.6°? **100°C; 37°C**
b. Solve the equation above for F to obtain a rule for converting Celsius temperatures to Fahrenheit temperatures.
c. What Fahrenheit temperatures correspond to Celsius temperatures of −40° and 2000°? **−40°F, 3632°F**

b. $F = \frac{9}{5}C + 32$

1-4 *Angles*

An **angle** (∠) is the figure formed by two rays that have the same endpoint. The two rays are called the **sides** of the angle, and their common endpoint is the **vertex** of the angle.

The sides of the angle shown are $\overrightarrow{BA}$ and $\overrightarrow{BC}$. The vertex is point B. The angle can be called $\angle B$, $\angle ABC$, $\angle CBA$, or $\angle 1$. If three letters are used to name an angle, the middle letter must name the vertex.

When you talk about this $\angle B$, everyone knows what angle you mean. But if you tried to talk about $\angle E$ in the diagram at the right, people wouldn't know which angle you meant. There are three angles with vertex E. To name any particular one of them you need to use either three letters or a number.

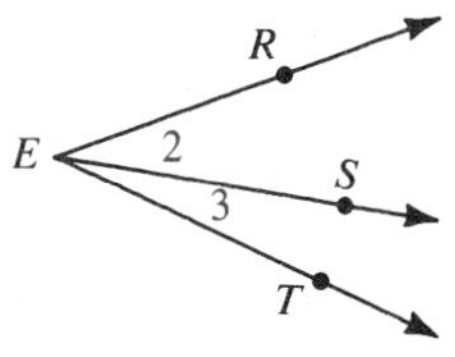

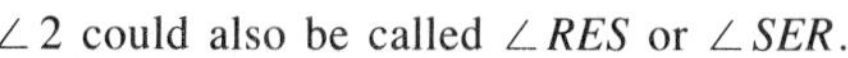

$\angle 2$ could also be called $\angle RES$ or $\angle SER$.
$\angle 3$ could also be called $\angle SET$ or $\angle TES$.
$\angle RET$ could also be called $\angle TER$.

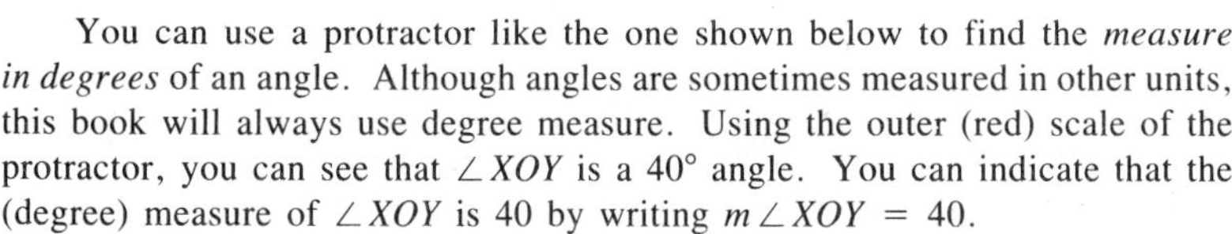

You can use a protractor like the one shown below to find the *measure in degrees* of an angle. Although angles are sometimes measured in other units, this book will always use degree measure. Using the outer (red) scale of the protractor, you can see that $\angle XOY$ is a 40° angle. You can indicate that the (degree) measure of $\angle XOY$ is 40 by writing $m\angle XOY = 40$.

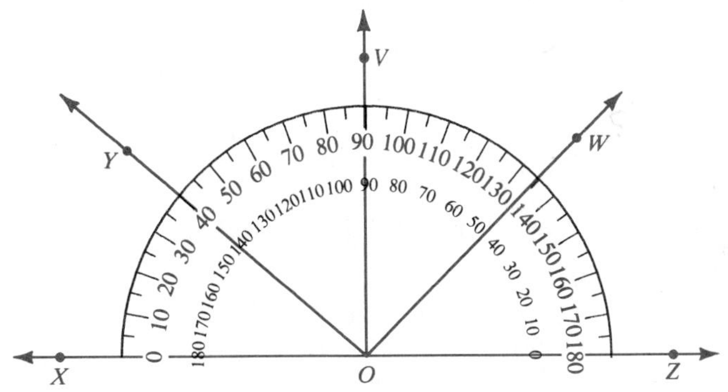

Using the inner scale of the protractor, you find that:

$m\angle YOZ = 140$ $\quad m\angle WOZ = 45$ $\quad m\angle YOW = 140 - 45 = 95$

Angles are classified according to their measures.

Acute angle:	Measure between 0 and 90	**Examples:** $\angle XOY$ and $\angle VOW$
Right angle:	Measure 90	**Examples:** $\angle XOV$ and $\angle VOZ$
Obtuse angle:	Measure between 90 and 180	**Examples:** $\angle XOW$ and $\angle YOW$
Straight angle:	Measure 180	**Example:** $\angle XOZ$

Teaching Suggestions,
pp. T76–T77

Objectives
Presenting the Lesson
Problem Solving
Making Connections
Extension
Using Technology

Communication Skills,
p. T77

Supplementary Materials

Practice Master 2
Test 2
Resource Book, pp. 2, 110
Study Guide, pp. 7–8
Overhead Visual C

Lesson Focus

In this lesson, the idea of an angle and its measure is introduced and given mathematical meaning.

Suggested Assignments

Minimum
Day 1: 21/1–25
Day 2: 21–22/26–34 even
S 9/31–33
Average
Day 1: 21/1–25 odd, 26–28
Day 2: 22/29–35
S 16/41–47 odd
Maximum
21–22/10–24 even, 25–36

Using a Model

Students can use the corner of an index card or the corner of a sheet of paper to compare a right angle to an angle shown in a diagram. It is then easy to tell whether an angle is acute or obtuse.

Teaching Note

It is not necessary for students to memorize Postulate 3. This postulate gives an imaginary protractor to use in geometric thinking, just as the Ruler Postulate gives an imaginary ruler.

Thinking Skills

It will be worthwhile for students to see that the first part of Postulate 4 is made necessary by cases such as the one pictured below.

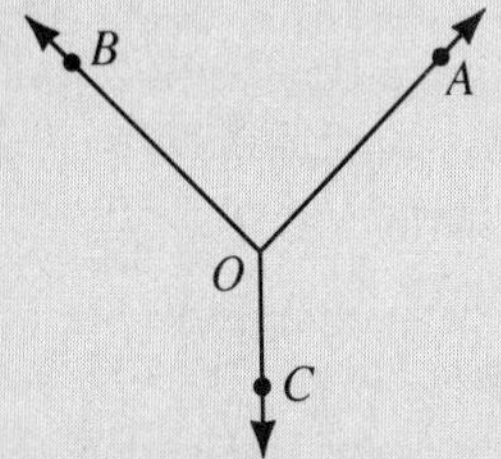

If students ask why the second part of Postulate 4 ends with 180, not $m\angle AOC$, tell them that 180 is more convenient when applying the postulate in proofs.

Chalkboard Examples

Give another name for each angle.

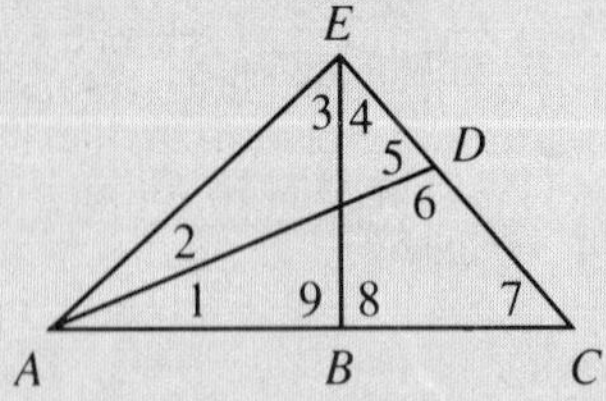

1. $\angle DEB$ $\angle 4$ **2.** $\angle CBE$ $\angle 8$
3. $\angle BEA$ $\angle 3$ **4.** $\angle DAB$ $\angle 1$
5. $\angle 7$ $\angle C$ **6.** $\angle 9$ $\angle ABE$
7. $m\angle 1 + m\angle 2 = m\angle$ <u>EAB</u>
8. $m\angle 3 + m\angle 4 = m\angle$ <u>AEC</u>
9. $m\angle 5 + m\angle 6 = m\angle$ <u>EDC</u> or <u>180</u>

The two angle postulates below are very much like the Ruler Postulate and the Segment Addition Postulate on page 12.

Postulate 3 *Protractor Postulate*

On $\overleftrightarrow{AB}$ in a given plane, choose any point O between A and B. Consider $\overrightarrow{OA}$ and $\overrightarrow{OB}$ and all the rays that can be drawn from O on one side of $\overleftrightarrow{AB}$. These rays can be paired with the real numbers from 0 to 180 in such a way that:

a. $\overrightarrow{OA}$ is paired with 0, and $\overrightarrow{OB}$ with 180.

b. If $\overrightarrow{OP}$ is paired with x, and $\overrightarrow{OQ}$ with y, then $m\angle POQ = |x - y|$.

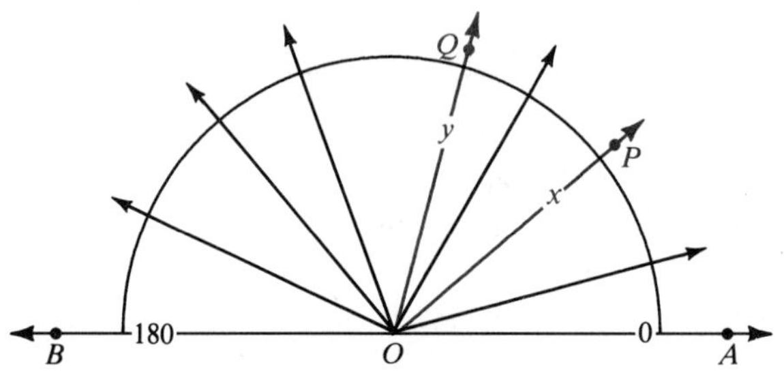

Postulate 4 *Angle Addition Postulate*

If point B lies in the interior of $\angle AOC$, then

$$m\angle AOB + m\angle BOC = m\angle AOC.$$

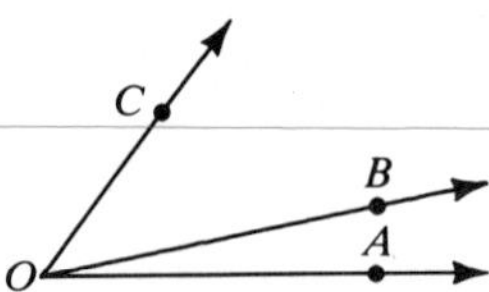

If $\angle AOC$ is a straight angle and B is any point not on $\overleftrightarrow{AC}$, then

$$m\angle AOB + m\angle BOC = 180.$$

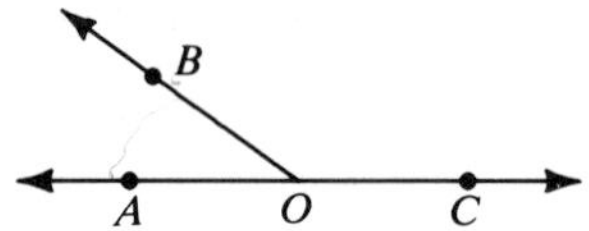

Congruent angles are angles that have equal measures. Since $\angle R$ and $\angle S$ both have measure 40, you can write

$$m\angle R = m\angle S \text{ or } \angle R \cong \angle S.$$

The definition of congruent angles tells us that these two statements are equivalent. We will use them interchangeably.

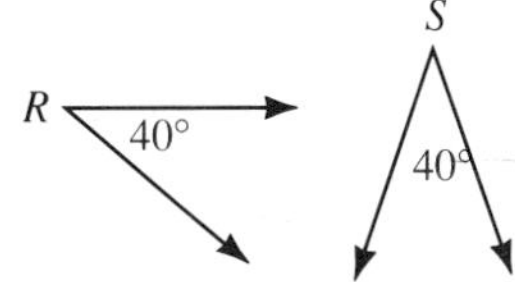

Adjacent angles (adj. $\angle$s) are two angles in a plane that have a common vertex and a common side but no common interior points.

$\angle 1$ and $\angle 2$ are adjacent angles.

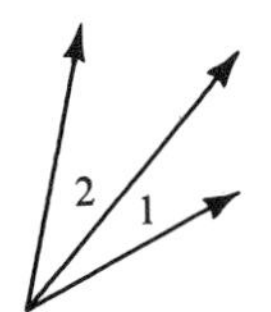

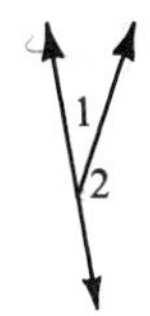

$\angle 3$ and $\angle 4$ are not adjacent angles.

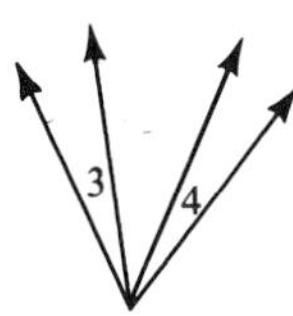

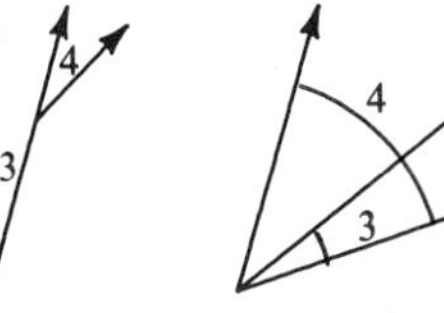

The **bisector of an angle** is the ray that divides the angle into two congruent adjacent angles. In the diagram,

$$m\angle XYW = m\angle WYZ,$$
$$\angle XYW \cong \angle WYZ,$$

and $\overrightarrow{YW}$ bisects $\angle XYZ$.

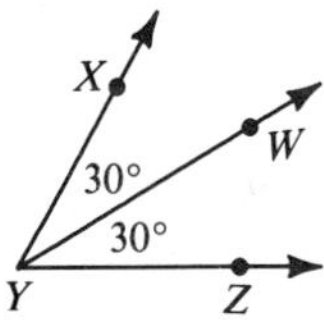

There are certain things that you can conclude from a diagram and others that you can't. The following are things you can conclude from the diagram shown below.

All points shown are coplanar.
$\overleftrightarrow{AB}$, $\overrightarrow{BD}$, and $\overrightarrow{BE}$ intersect at B.
A, B, and C are collinear.
B is between A and C.
$\angle ABC$ is a straight angle.
D is in the interior of $\angle ABE$.
$\angle ABD$ and $\angle DBE$ are adjacent angles.

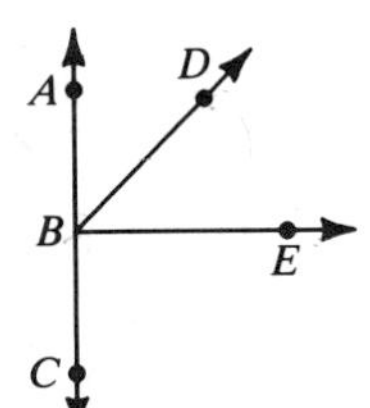

The diagram above does *not* tell you that $\overline{AB} \cong \overline{BC}$, that $\angle ABD \cong \angle DBE$, or that $\angle CBE$ is a right angle. These three new pieces of information can be indicated in a diagram by using marks as shown at the right. Note that a small square is used to indicate a right angle (rt. $\angle$).

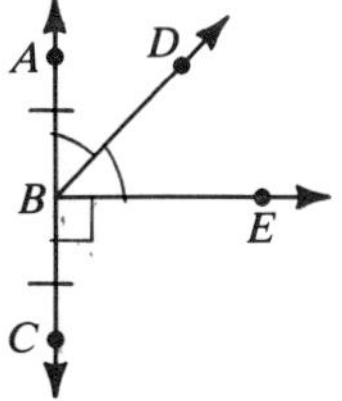

Teaching Note

Point out to students how closely related the definition of congruent angles is to the definition of congruent segments.

Communication Skills

Emphasize the interchangeability of the equality and congruence statements associated with angle XYZ. When the fact that $\overrightarrow{YW}$ bisects $\angle XYZ$ is used in a proof and we want to deal with measures, we can at once assert that $m\angle XYW = m\angle WYZ$ by definition of angle bisector. We also can assert $\angle XYW \cong \angle WYZ$ when we want to talk about congruence, again by definition of angle bisector.

Thinking Skills

In using diagrams, students need to understand the following rule: You can draw conclusions about position, but not about size, from a diagram.

Teaching Note

Explain that marks are used to indicate conclusions about *size* in a diagram.

Using a Computer

See page T77 for three experiments involving measuring segments and angles.

This is the first of the "Using a Computer" paragraphs that occur periodically throughout the side columns of this Teacher's Edition. Designed to help teachers wishing to emphasize technology, these paragraphs typically offer teaching commentary on computer material in the student textbook, point out Written Exercises that may be studied profitably using a computer, or refer teachers to additional computer material that appears in the "Using Technology" paragraphs at the front of this Teacher's Edition. In most cases, access to geometric construction software, such as the *Geometric Supposer* or *GeoDraw*, is required. (See "Getting Started with Computers" on pages T72–T73.) Exceptions to the software requirement are "Using a Computer" paragraphs referring to "Computer Key-Ins," where students work with simple BASIC programs.

Using a Model

For Ex. 27, the use of a large sheet of wrapping paper can provide an effective demonstration. Have an angle cut out in advance. Then, in class, put bold labels *O*, *A*, and *B* on the paper.

Classroom Exercises

Name the vertex and the sides of the given angle.

1. ∠4 **C; $\overrightarrow{CD}$, $\overrightarrow{CB}$** 2. ∠1 **A; $\overrightarrow{AD}$, $\overrightarrow{AB}$** 3. ∠6 **D; $\overrightarrow{DC}$, $\overrightarrow{DB}$**

4. Name all angles adjacent to ∠6. **∠7, ∠5**
5. Name three angles that have *B* as the vertex. **∠ABC, ∠DBA, ∠DBC**
6. How many angles have *D* as the vertex? **6**

Exs. 1-16

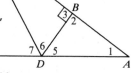

State whether the angle appears to be acute, right, obtuse, or straight. Then estimate its measure. **Accept reasonable estimates.**

7. ∠1 **acute; about 35** 8. ∠2 **right; 90** 9. ∠*EDB* **obtuse; about 125**
10. ∠*CDB* **acute; about 65** 11. ∠*ADC* **obtuse; about 120** 12. ∠*ADE* **straight; 180**

Complete.

13. $m\angle 7 + m\angle 6 = m\angle$ ___?___ **EDB** 14. $m\angle 6 + m\angle 5 = m\angle$ ___?___ **ADC**
15. $m\angle 2 + m\angle 3 =$ ___?___ **180** 16. If $\overrightarrow{DB}$ bisects ∠*CDA*, then ∠ ___?___ ≅ ∠ ___?___. **5, 6**

23. ∠GOH, ∠COF, ∠FOB, and ∠FOA

State the measure of each angle.

17. ∠*BOC* **70** 18. ∠*GOH* **20**
19. ∠*FOG* **40** 20. ∠*COF* **30**
21. ∠*GOB* **140** 22. ∠*HOA* **180**
23. Name four angles that are adjacent to ∠*FOG*. **See above.**
24. What ray bisects which two angles? **$\overrightarrow{OC}$ bisects ∠HOA and ∠GOB.**
25. Name a pair of congruent: **See below.**
    a. acute angles b. right angles c. obtuse angles

Exs. 17–25

26. Study a corner of your classroom where two walls and the ceiling meet. How many right angles can you see at the corner? **3**
27. Draw an angle, ∠*AOB*, on a sheet of paper. Fold the paper so that $\overrightarrow{OA}$ falls on $\overrightarrow{OB}$. Lay the paper flat and call the fold line $\overleftrightarrow{OK}$. How is $\overrightarrow{OK}$ related to ∠*AOB*? Explain. **$\overrightarrow{OK}$ bisects ∠AOB.**

Given the diagram, state whether you can reach the conclusion shown.

28. $m\angle FOB = 50$ **Yes** 29. $m\angle AOC = 90$ **No**
30. $m\angle DOC = 180$ **Yes** 31. $AO = OB$ **No**
32. $\angle AOC \cong \angle BOC$ **No** 33. $m\angle AOF = 130$ **Yes**
34. Points *E*, *O*, and *F* are collinear. **Yes**
35. Point *C* is in the interior of ∠*AOF*. **Yes**
36. ∠*AOE* and ∠*AOD* are adjacent angles. **No**

Exs. 28–38

37. ∠*AOB* is a straight angle. **Yes** 38. $\overrightarrow{OA}$ and $\overrightarrow{OB}$ are opposite rays. **Yes**

25. a. ∠GOH and ∠BOA, or ∠GOC and ∠COB b. ∠HOC and ∠COA c. ∠HOB and ∠GOA

Written Exercises

A 1. Name the vertex and the sides of $\angle 5$. **E; $\overrightarrow{EL}$, $\overrightarrow{EA}$**

2. Name all angles adjacent to $\angle ADE$. **$\angle ADL$, $\angle EDT$**

Answers may vary in Exs. 3–8.

State another name for the angle.

3. $\angle 1$ **$\angle DLT$** 4. $\angle 3$ **$\angle LAT$** 5. $\angle 5$ **$\angle AEL$**

6. $\angle ALD$ **$\angle 2$** 7. $\angle AST$ **$\angle 7$** 8. $\angle LES$ **$\angle 6$**

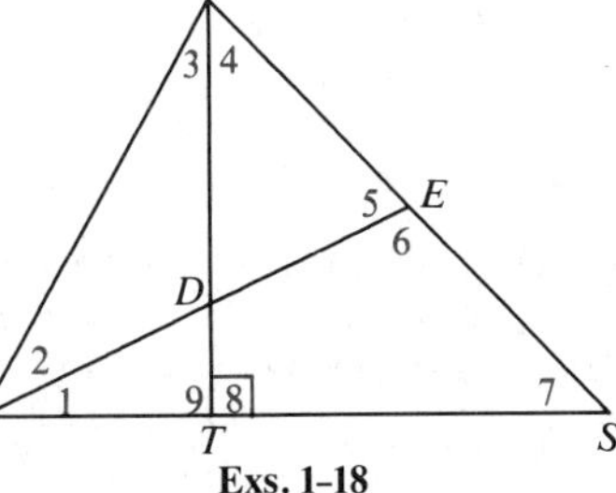

Exs. 1-18

State whether the angle appears to be acute, right, obtuse, or straight.

9. $\angle 2$ **acute** 10. $\angle LAS$ **acute** 11. $\angle ATL$ **right**

12. $\angle S$ **acute** 13. $\angle LTS$ **straight** 14. $\angle EDT$ **obtuse**

Complete.

15. $m\angle 3 + m\angle 4 = m\angle$ _?_ **LAS**

16. $m\angle ALS - m\angle 2 = m\angle$ _?_ **1**

17. If $m\angle 1 = m\angle 2$, then _?_ bisects _?_. **$\overrightarrow{LE}$** **$\angle ALS$**

18. $m\angle LDA + m\angle ADE =$ _?_ **180**

Without measuring, sketch each angle. Then use a protractor to check your accuracy. **Check students' drawings.**

19. 90° angle 20. 45° angle 21. 150° angle 22. 10° angle

Draw a line, $\overleftrightarrow{AB}$. Choose a point O between A and B. Use a protractor to investigate the following questions.

23. In the plane represented by your paper, how many lines can you draw through O that will form a 30° angle with $\overrightarrow{OB}$? **2**

24. In the plane represented by your paper, how many lines can you draw through O that will form a 90° angle with $\overrightarrow{OB}$? **1**

B 25. Using a ruler, draw a large triangle. Then use a protractor to find the approximate measure of each angle and compute the sum of the three measures. Repeat this exercise for a triangle with a different shape. Did you get the same result? **Yes**

26. Find $m\angle 2$, $m\angle 3$, and $m\angle 4$ when the measure of $\angle 1$ is:
a. 90 **90, 90, 90** b. 93 **87, 93, 87**

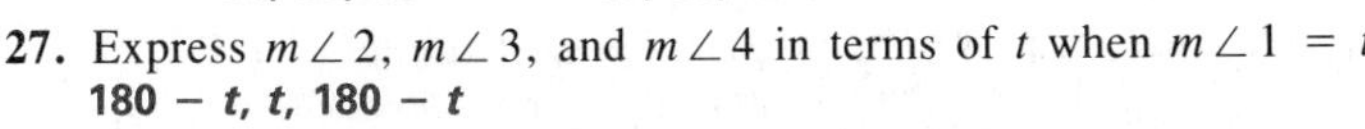

27. Express $m\angle 2$, $m\angle 3$, and $m\angle 4$ in terms of t when $m\angle 1 = t$.
180 − *t*, *t*, 180 − *t*

28. A careless person wrote, using the figure shown,

$$m\angle AOB + m\angle BOC = m\angle AOC.$$

What part of the Angle Addition Postulate did that person overlook?
***B* must be in the interior of $\angle AOC$.**

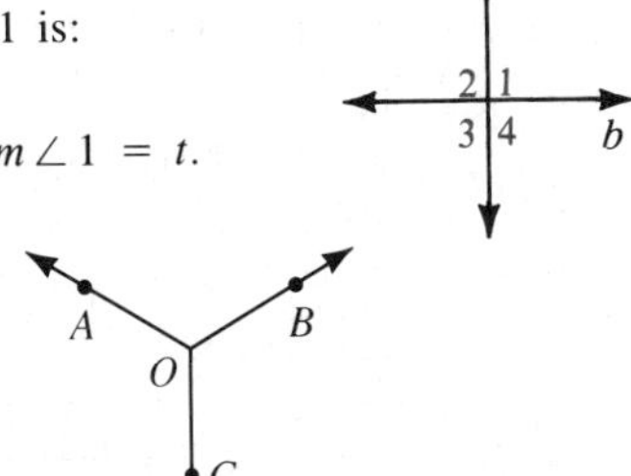

Guided Practice

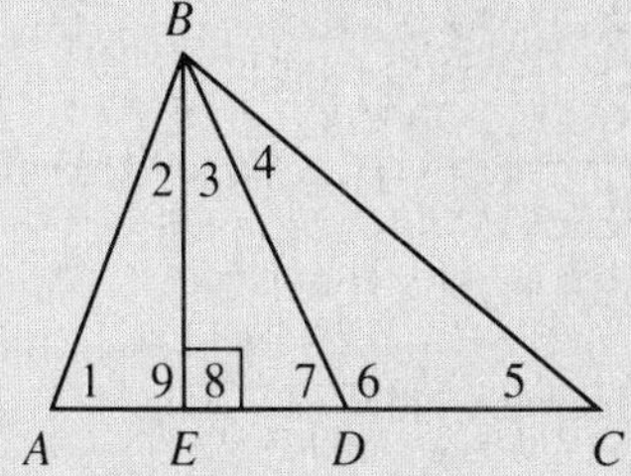

1. Name the vertex of $\angle 3$. *B*
2. Name the right angle. $\angle 8$

State another name for each angle.

3. $\angle 1$ $\angle A$
4. $\angle 6$ $\angle BDC$
5. $\angle 3$ $\angle EBD$
6. $\angle 4$ $\angle DBC$
7. $\angle 7$ $\angle EDB$
8. $\angle 2$ $\angle ABE$
9. $\angle 5$ $\angle C$
10. $\angle 9$ $\angle AEB$

$\overrightarrow{AL}$ bisects $\angle KAT$. Find the value of x.

29. $m\angle 3 = 6x$, $m\angle KAT = 90 - x$ **$x = 18$**
30. $m\angle 1 = 7x + 3$, $m\angle 2 = 6x + 7$ **$x = 4$**
31. $m\angle 1 = 5x - 12$, $m\angle 2 = 3x + 6$ **$x = 9$**
32. $m\angle 1 = x$, $m\angle 3 = 4x$ **$x = 30$**
33. $m\angle 1 = 2x - 8$, $m\angle 3 = 116$ **$x = 20$**
34. $m\angle 2 = x + 12$, $m\angle 3 = 6x - 20$ **$x = 22$**

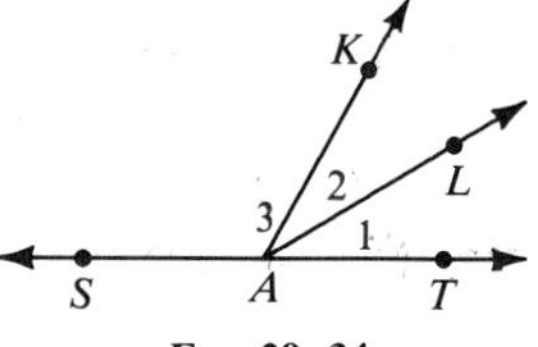

Exs. 29–34

Exercise Note

Some students may observe that all the figures drawn in Ex. 35 show rays in a half-plane. This restriction, however, does not affect the answer.

C 35. **a.** Complete.

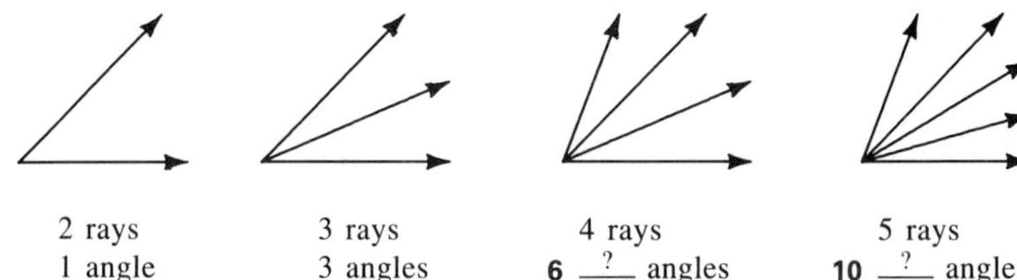

2 rays	3 rays	4 rays	5 rays
1 angle	3 angles	**6** _?_ angles	**10** _?_ angles

b. Study the pattern in the four cases shown, and predict the number of angles formed by six noncollinear rays that have the same endpoint. **15**

c. Which of the expressions below gives the number of angles formed by n noncollinear rays that have the same endpoint?

$n - 1$ $2n - 3$ $n^2 - 3$ $\frac{n(n-1)}{2}$ (circled)

36. $\overrightarrow{OC}$ bisects $\angle AOB$, $\overrightarrow{OD}$ bisects $\angle AOC$, $\overrightarrow{OE}$ bisects $\angle AOD$, $\overrightarrow{OF}$ bisects $\angle AOE$, and $\overrightarrow{OG}$ bisects $\angle FOC$.
a. If $m\angle BOF = 120$, then $m\angle DOE =$ _?_. **16**
b. If $m\angle COG = 35$, then $m\angle EOG =$ _?_. **25**

Teaching Suggestions, pp. T77–T78

Objectives
Presenting the Lesson
Problem Solving
Extension

Cooperative Learning, p. T78

Exploring Activity, p. c

1-5 *Postulates and Theorems Relating Points, Lines, and Planes*

Recall that we have accepted, without proof, the following four basic assumptions.

The Ruler Postulate	The Segment Addition Postulate
The Protractor Postulate	The Angle Addition Postulate

These postulates deal with segments, lengths, angles, and measures. The following five basic assumptions deal with the way points, lines, and planes are related.

Postulate 5
A line contains at least two points; a plane contains at least three points not all in one line; space contains at least four points not all in one plane.

Postulate 6
Through any two points there is exactly one line.

Postulate 7
Through any three points there is at least one plane, and through any three noncollinear points there is exactly one plane.

Postulate 8
If two points are in a plane, then the line that contains the points is in that plane.

Postulate 9
If two planes intersect, then their intersection is a line.

Important statements that are *proved* are called **theorems.** In Classroom Exercise 1 you will see how Theorem 1-1 follows from the postulates. In Written Exercise 20 you will complete an argument that justifies Theorem 1-2. You will learn about writing proofs in the next chapter.

Theorem 1-1
If two lines intersect, then they intersect in exactly one point.

Theorem 1-2
Through a line and a point not in the line there is exactly one plane.

Theorem 1-3
If two lines intersect, then exactly one plane contains the lines.

The phrase "exactly one" appears several times in the postulates and theorems of this section. The phrase "one and only one" has the same meaning. For example, here is another correct form of Theorem 1-1:

If two lines intersect, then they intersect in one and only one point.

The theorem states that a point of intersection *exists* (there is *at least one* point of intersection) and the point of intersection is *unique* (*no more than one* such point exists).

Supplementary Materials
Practice Master 3
Test 3
Resource Book, pp. 3, 111
Study Guide, pp. 9–10
Overhead Visual A

Lesson Focus
Postulates are statements accepted as true without proof. Postulates are then used to prove theorems. This lesson begins the study of using postulates to prove theorems.

Suggested Assignments
Minimum
Day 1: 25/1–12
Day 2: 25/13–14
29/Self-Test 2
Day 3: 31/Chapter Test

Average
Day 1: 25/1–15 odd, 16
Day 2: 26/17–19
29/Self-Test 2
Day 3: 31/Chapter Test

Maximum
Day 1: 25–26/1–13 odd, 14–20
Day 2: 31/Chapter Test

Chalkboard Examples

Classify each statement as true or false and give the definition, postulate or theorem that supports your conclusion.

1. A given triangle can lie in more than one plane. F
   Through a line and a point not in the line there is exactly 1 plane.
2. Any two points are collinear. T
   Through any 2 pts. there is exactly 1 line.
3. Two planes can intersect in only one point. F
   If 2 planes int., then their int. is a line.
4. Two lines can intersect in two points. F
   If 2 lines int., then they int. in exactly 1 pt.

Additional Answers Classroom Exercises

13. The ends of three legs determine a plane (the floor); the end of the fourth leg might not be in that plane.

Cultural Note

Surveying was a highly developed science in many ancient societies. Egyptian surveyors, for example, were able to measure straight lines over great distances of terrain of varying elevations.

Classroom Exercises

1. Theorem 1-1 states that two lines intersect in exactly one point. The diagram suggests what would happen if you tried to show two "lines" drawn through two points. State the postulate that makes this situation impossible. **See below.**

2. State Postulate 6 using the phrase *one and only one*. **See below.**
3. Reword the following statement as two statements, one describing existence and the other describing uniqueness: **Every segment has at least one midpoint. A segment has no more than one midpoint.**

   A segment has exactly one midpoint.

Postulate 6 is sometimes stated as "Two points *determine* a line."

4. Restate Theorem 1-2 using the word *determine*. **A line and a point not in the line determine a plane.**
5. Do two intersecting lines determine a plane? **Yes**
6. Do three points determine a line? **Yes; at least 1 line**
7. Do three points determine a plane? **No; unless the pts. are noncoll.**

State a postulate, or part of a postulate, that justifies your answer to each exercise.

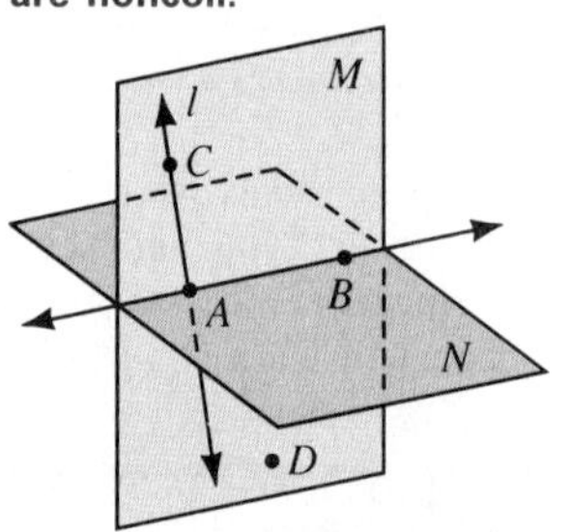

8. Name two points that determine line l. **C, A; Post. 6**
9. Name three points that determine plane M. **See below.**
10. Name the intersection of planes M and N. **$\overleftrightarrow{AB}$; Post. 9**
11. Does $\overleftrightarrow{AD}$ lie in plane M? **Yes; Post. 8**
12. Does plane N contain any points not on $\overleftrightarrow{AB}$? **Yes; A plane contains at least 3 pts. not all in 1 line.**

Surveyors and photographers use a *tripod* for support.

13. Why does a three-legged support work better than one with four legs?
14. Explain why a four-legged table may rock even if the floor is level. **The legs may not be the same length and their ends may not be coplanar.**
15. A carpenter checks to see if a board is warped by laying a straightedge across the board in several directions. State the postulate that is related to this procedure. **Post. 8**
16. Think of the intersection of the ceiling and the front wall of your classroom as line l. Let the point in the center of the floor be point C.
    a. Is there a plane that contains line l and point C? **Yes**
    b. State the theorem that applies. **Theorem 1-2**

1. Through any 2 pts. there is exactly 1 line.
2. Through any 2 pts. there is one and only one line.
9. Answers may vary; any 3 of *A*, *B*, *C*, and *D*. Through any 3 noncollinear pts. there is exactly 1 plane.

Written Exercises

A **1.** State Theorem 1-2 using the phrase *one and only one*. **If there is a line and a point not on the line, then one and only one plane contains them.**

2. Reword Theorem 1-3 as two statements, one describing existence and the other describing uniqueness. **See below.**

3. Planes M and N are known to intersect.

a. What kind of figure is the intersection of M and N? **a line**

b. State the postulate that supports your answer to part (a). **If two planes intersect, then their intersection is a line.**

4. Points A and B are known to lie in a plane.

a. What can you say about $\overleftrightarrow{AB}$? **$\overleftrightarrow{AB}$ is in the plane.**

b. State the postulate that supports your answer to part (a). **If 2 pts. are in a plane, then the line that contains the pts. is in that plane.**

In Exercises 5-11 you will have to visualize certain lines and planes not shown in the diagram of the box. When you name a plane, name it by using four points, no three of which are collinear.

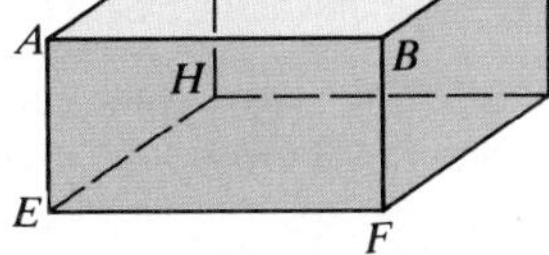

Exs. 5–12

5. Write the postulate that assures you that $\overleftrightarrow{AC}$ exists. **See below.**

6. Name a plane that contains $\overleftrightarrow{AC}$. ***ABCD***

7. Name a plane that contains $\overleftrightarrow{AC}$ but that is not shown in the diagram. **ACGE**

8. Name the intersection of plane *DCFE* and plane *ABCD*. **$\overleftrightarrow{CD}$**

9. Name four lines shown in the diagram that don't intersect plane *EFGH*. **$\overleftrightarrow{AB}$, $\overleftrightarrow{CD}$, $\overleftrightarrow{AD}$, $\overleftrightarrow{BC}$**

10. Name two lines that are not shown in the diagram and that don't intersect plane *EFGH*. **$\overleftrightarrow{AC}$, $\overleftrightarrow{BD}$**

11. Name three planes that don't intersect $\overleftrightarrow{EF}$ and don't contain $\overleftrightarrow{EF}$. ***ABCD, DCGH, ABGH***

12. If you measure $\angle EFG$ with a protractor you get more than 90°. But you know that $\angle EFG$ represents a right angle in a box. Using this as an example, complete the table.

	$\angle EFG$	$\angle AEF$	$\angle DCB$	$\angle FBC$
In the diagram	obtuse	? **rt.**	? **ac.**	? **obt.**
In the box	right	? **rt.**	? **rt.**	? **rt.**

State whether it is possible for the figure described to exist. Write *yes* or *no*.

B **13.** Two points both lie in each of two lines. **No**

14. Three points all lie in each of two planes. **Yes**

15. Three noncollinear points all lie in each of two planes. **No**

16. Two points lie in a plane X, two other points lie in a different plane Y, and the four points are coplanar but not collinear. **Yes**

2. If two lines intersect, then at least one plane contains the lines. If two lines intersect, then no more than one plane contains the lines.

5. Through any 2 pts. there is exactly 1 line.

Guided Practice

Classify each statement as true or false.

1. A postulate is a statement assumed to be true without proof. T
2. The phrase "exactly one" has the same meaning as the phrase "one and only one." T
3. Three points determine a plane. F
4. Through any two points there is exactly one plane. F
5. Through a line and a point not on the line there is one and only one plane. T

Communication Skills

Point out to students that it takes only three noncollinear points to determine a plane, but that each plane shown in the drawing contains four labeled points. If a student chooses to name the upper base as the answer for Ex. 6, the name *plane ABCD* will be more readily understood by a person than a three-letter name such as *plane ABC.*

17. Points R, S, and T are noncollinear points.

a. State the postulate that guarantees the existence of a plane X that contains R, S, and T. **Through any 3 pts. there is at least 1 plane.**

b. Draw a diagram showing plane X containing the noncollinear points R, S, and T. **Check students' drawings.**

c. Suppose that P is any point of $\overleftrightarrow{RS}$ other than R and S. Does point P lie in plane X? Explain. **Yes. If 2 pts. are in a plane, then the line that contains the pts. is in that plane.**

d. State the postulate that guarantees that $\overleftrightarrow{TP}$ exists. **Through any 2 pts. there is exactly 1 line.**

e. State the postulate that guarantees that $\overleftrightarrow{TP}$ is in Plane X. **See 17. c.**

18. Points A, B, C, and D are four noncoplanar points.

a. State the postulate that guarantees the existence of planes ABC, ABD, ACD, and BCD. **See 17. a.**

b. Explain how the Ruler Postulate guarantees the existence of a point P between A and D.

c. State the postulate that guarantees the existence of plane BCP. **See 17. a.**

d. Explain why there are an infinite number of planes through $\overline{BC}$. **There are an infinite number of pts. P on $\overleftrightarrow{AD}$. For each P there exists a plane BCP.**

C **19.** State how many segments can be drawn between the points in each figure. No three points are collinear.

a.

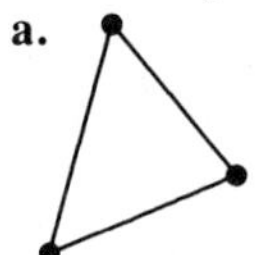

3 points

3 ___?___ segments

b.

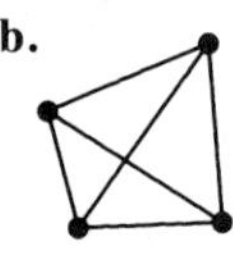

4 points

6 ___?___ segments

c.

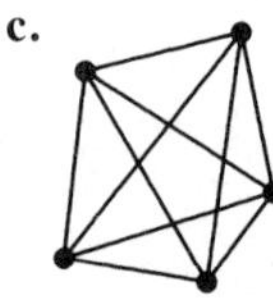

5 points

10 ___?___ segments

d.

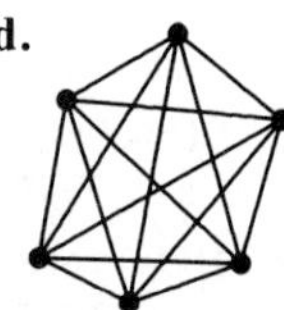

6 points

15 ___?___ segments

e. Without making a drawing, predict how many segments can be drawn between seven points, no three of which are collinear. **21**

f. How many segments can be drawn between n points, no three of which are collinear? $\frac{n(n-1)}{2}$

Exercise Note

It is suggested that only the most capable students work on Exs. 19–20.

20. Parts (a) through (d) justify Theorem 1-2: Through a line and a point not in the line there is exactly one plane.

a. If P is a point not in line k, what postulate permits us to state that there are two points R and S in line k? **Post. 5**

b. Then there is at least one plane X that contains points P, R, and S. Why? **See below.**

c. What postulate guarantees that plane X contains line k? Now we know that there is a plane X that contains both point P and line k. **Post. 8**

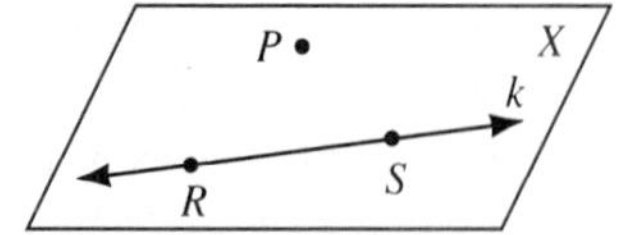

d. There can't be another plane that contains point P and line k, because then *two* planes would contain noncollinear points P, R, and S. What postulate does this contradict? **See below.**

20. b. Through any 3 pts. there is at least 1 plane.

20. d. Through any 3 noncoll. pts. there is exactly 1 plane.

Application

Locating Points

Suppose you lived in an area with streets laid out on a grid. If you lived in a house located at point P in the diagram at the right below, you could tell someone where you lived by saying:

From the crossing at the center of town, go three blocks east and two blocks north.

A friend of yours living at Q might say she lives two blocks west and three blocks north of the town center.

Mathematicians make such descriptions shorter by using a grid system and *coordinates*. They use (3, 2) for your house at point P, and $(-2, 3)$ for your friend's house at Q. Point O at the center of town is (0, 0). Points R and S are (3, 0) and $(-1, -2)$.

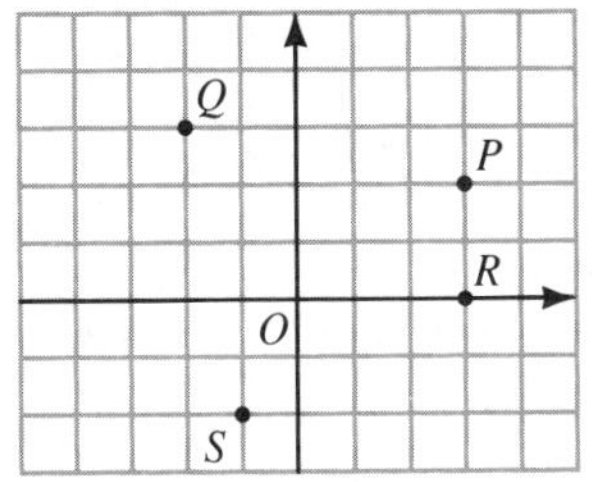

This grid system is not always the easiest way to describe a position. If you were a pilot and saw another airplane while flying, it would be difficult to give its position in this system. However, you might say the other plane is 4 km away at 11 o'clock, with 12 o'clock being straight ahead.

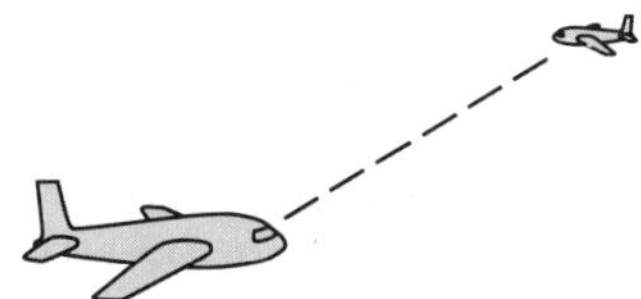

Mathematicians sometimes find it convenient to describe a point by a distance and an angle. Rotation in a clockwise direction is represented by a negative angle. Counterclockwise rotation is represented by a positive angle. A complete rotation, all the way around once, is 360° (or −360°). The labeled points in the diagram at the right are described as shown below.

A	(3, 60°)
B	(2, 120°)
C	(1.5, 210°) or (1.5, −150°)
D	(3, 315°) or (3, −45°)

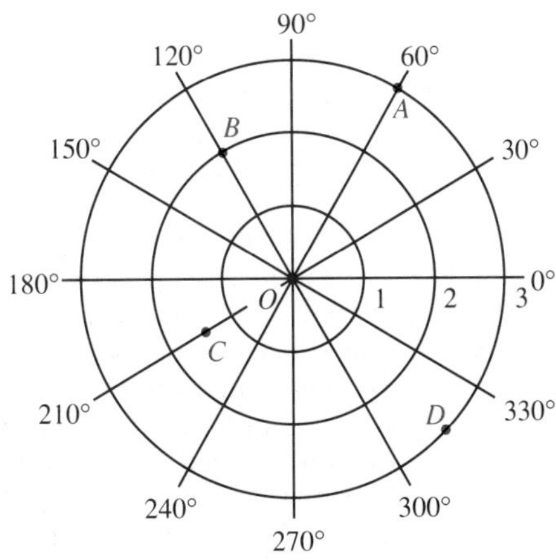

Making Connections

It is a good learning experience for students to consider a situation in which angles are related to rotations. In this context, negative numbers and negative angles make sense, allowing students to see that a concept can be broadened. This brief exposure to ideas to be studied in trigonometry and coordinate geometry (polar coordinates) will help students to grow mathematically.

Sometimes you may want to change from one system to the other. For example, if you were at the town center and walked two blocks east and three blocks north, what would your position be in the distance-angle system? Use a centimeter ruler and draw the triangle suggested by your path. If you measure the triangle, you will get about (3.6, 56°).

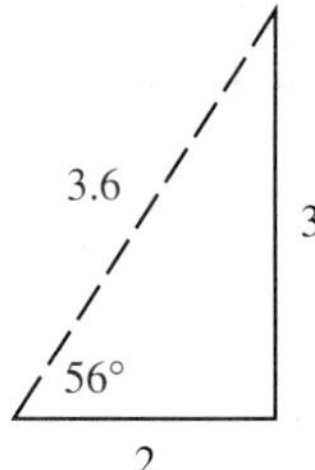

Exercises

1. Copy the grid system shown on the previous page onto a piece of graph paper. Then locate the following points. **Check students' drawings. Coordinates are given.**
   a. A point T five blocks due west of the center of town **(−5, 0)**
   b. A point U five blocks east and two blocks south of the center of town **(5, −2)**
   c. A point V two blocks west and one block north of your house, which is located at point P **(1, 3)**

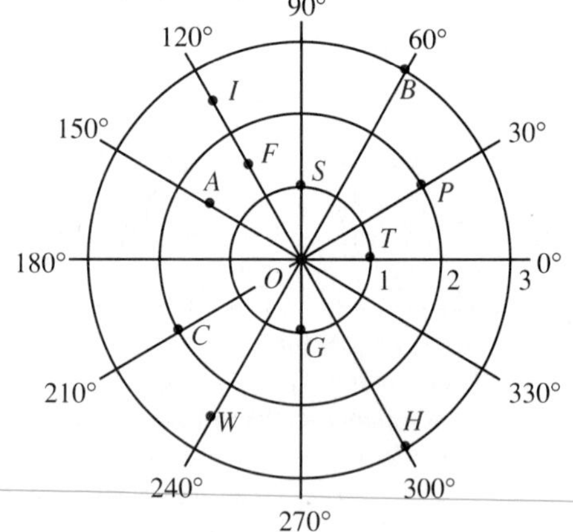

2. Give the letter that names each point.
   a. (2, 30°) ***P***
   b. (2.5, 120°) ***I***
   c. (1, −90°) ***G***
3. Give the distance and angle for each point.
   a. C **(2, 210°) or (2, −150°)**
   b. A **(1.5, 150°) or (1.5, −210°)**
   c. T **(1, 0°)**
4. Give another way of naming each point.
   a. (1, −120°) **(1, 240°)** b. (2, 300°) **(2, −60°)** c. (2.5, −180°) **(2.5, 180°)**
5. A point is given in the grid system. What would it be called in the distance-angle system? (*Hint*: See the discussion at the top of the page. Use a protractor and a centimeter ruler to help you answer the question.) **In Exs. 5 and 6, accept reasonable answers.**
   a. (3, 4) **(5, 53°)**
   b. (−2, 5) **(5.4, 112°)**
   c. (4, 0) **(4, 0°)**
   d. (8, −6) **(10, −37°)**
6. A point is given in the distance-angle system. What would it be called, approximately, in the grid system? (*Hint*: Use a protractor and a centimeter ruler to draw the triangle suggested by the angle and distance. Measure the sides of the triangle.)
   a. (2, 50°) **(1.3, 1.5)**
   b. (1.5, −70°) **(0.5, −1.4)**
   c. (3, 90°) **(0, 3)**
   d. (1, 120°) **(−0.5, 0.9)**

Self-Test 2

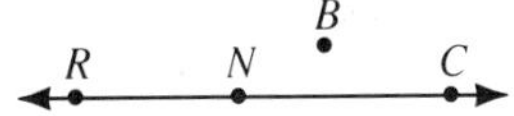

1. Write three names for the line pictured. **$\overleftrightarrow{RN}$, $\overleftrightarrow{RC}$, $\overleftrightarrow{NC}$**
2. Name the ray that is opposite to $\overrightarrow{NC}$. **$\overrightarrow{NR}$**
3. Is it correct to say that point B lies between points N and C? **No**
4. When $RN = 7$, $NC = 3x + 5$, and $RC = 18$, what is the value of x? **$x = 2$**

Complete.

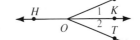

5. $m\angle 1 + m\angle 2 = m\angle$ _?_ **JOT**
6. If $\angle 1 \cong \angle 2$, then _?_ is the bisector of $\angle$ _?_. **$\overrightarrow{OK}$, JOT**
7. $m\angle HOK =$ _?_, and $\angle HOK$ is called a(n) _?_ angle. **180, straight**

J, H, K, O, T, 1, 2

8. Which of the four things stated *can't* you conclude from the diagram?
   a. A, B, and C are collinear. b. $\angle DBC$ is a right angle.
   (c.) B is the midpoint of $\overline{AC}$. d. E is in the interior of $\angle DBA$.

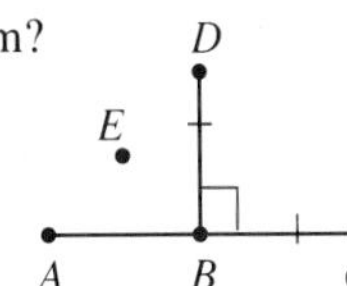

Apply postulates and theorems to complete the statements.

9. Through any two points _?_.
10. If points A and B are in plane Z, _?_. **then $\overleftrightarrow{AB}$ is in Z**
11. If two planes intersect, then _?_. **their intersection is a line**
12. If there is a line j and a point P not in the line, then _?_. **there is exactly one plane that contains j and P**

9. there is exactly one line

Chapter Summary

1. The concepts of *point*, *line*, and *plane* are basic to geometry. These undefined terms are used in the definitions of other terms.
2. $\overleftrightarrow{AB}$ represents a line, $\overline{AB}$ a segment, and $\overrightarrow{AB}$ a ray. AB represents the length of $\overline{AB}$; AB is a positive number.
3. Two rays with the same endpoint form an angle.
4. Congruent segments have equal lengths. Congruent angles have equal measures.
5. Angles are classified as acute, right, obtuse, or straight, according to their measures.
6. Diagrams enable you to reach certain conclusions. However, judgments about segment length and angle measure must not be made on the basis of appearances alone.
7. Statements that are accepted without proof are called postulates. Statements that are proved are called theorems.
8. Postulates and theorems in this chapter deal with distances, angle measures, points, lines, and planes.

Quick Quiz

Complete with *always*, *sometimes*, or *never*.

1. Two points always lie in exactly one line.
2. Three points sometimes lie in exactly one line.
3. Three points sometimes lie in exactly one plane.
4. Three collinear points never lie in exactly one plane.
5. Two planes sometimes intersect.
6. Two intersecting planes never intersect in exactly one point.
7. Two intersecting lines always intersect in exactly one point.
8. Two lines sometimes intersect in exactly one point.
9. Two intersecting lines always lie in exactly one plane.
10. A line and a point not on that line never lie in more than one plane.
11. A line never contains exactly one point.
12. When A and B are in a plane, $\overleftrightarrow{AB}$ is always in that plane.

Teaching Note

The Chapter Summary provides a review of the most important ideas in the chapter. Use of the summary in class can help to reinforce students' understanding of the material covered in the chapter.

Supplementary Materials

Practice Master 4

Test 4

Resource Book, pp. 4–5, 112, 190

Chapter Review

In Exercises 1–4 answer on the basis of what appears to be true.

1. How many blue points are 1 cm from point O? **infinitely many** 1–1

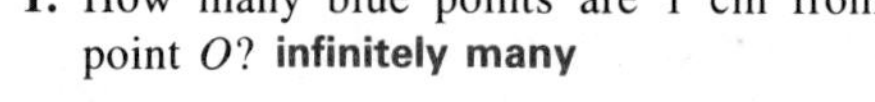

2. How many red points are 1 cm from O? **2**
3. How many red points are 2 cm from O? **2**
4. Each red point is said to be _?_ from points A and B. **equidistant**

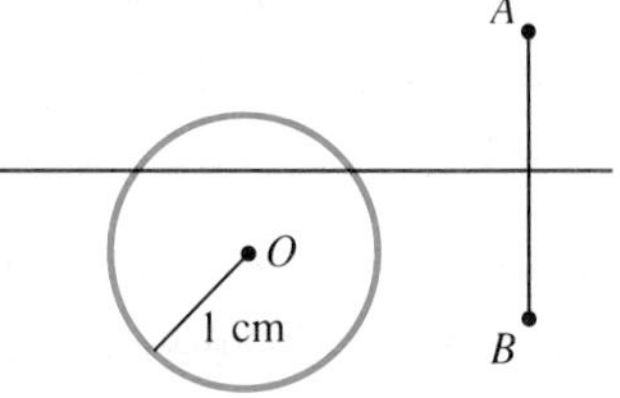

Sketch and label the figures described. **Check students' drawings.**

5. Points A, B, C, and D are coplanar, but A, B, and C are the only three of those points that are collinear. 1–2
6. Line l intersects plane X in point P.
7. Plane M contains intersecting lines j and k.
8. Planes X and Y intersect in $\overleftrightarrow{AB}$.

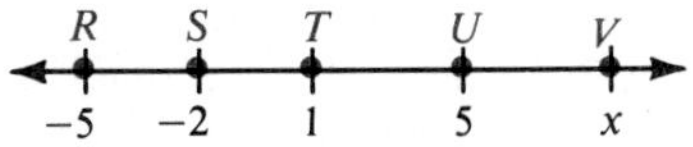

9. Name a point on $\overrightarrow{ST}$ that is not on $\overline{ST}$. **U or V** 1–3
10. Complete: RS = _?_ and ST = _?_ **3, 3**
11. Complete: $\overline{RS}$ and $\overline{ST}$ are called _?_ segments. **congruent**
12. If U is the midpoint of $\overline{TV}$, find the value of x. **$x = 9$**

R S T U V
−5 −2 1 5 x

13. Name three angles that have vertex D. Which angles with vertex D are adjacent angles? **∠1, ∠2, ∠ADC; ∠1, ∠2** 1–4
14. **a.** $m\angle CBD$ = _?_ **92**

    b. Name the postulate that justifies your answer in part (a). **Angle Addition Postulate**

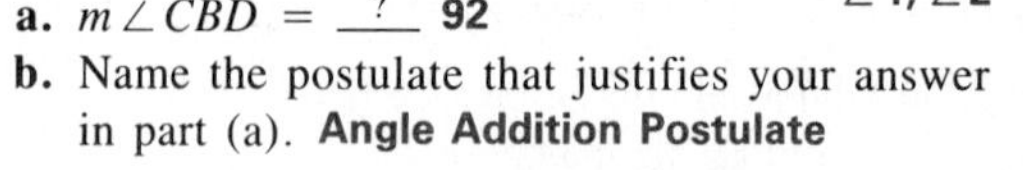

15. What kind of angle is $\angle CBD$? **obtuse**

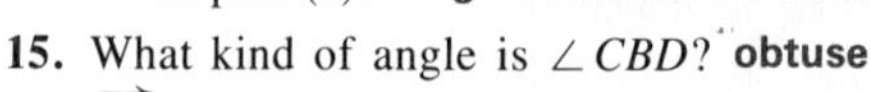

16. $\overrightarrow{DB}$ bisects $\angle ADC$, $m\angle 1 = 5x - 3$, and $m\angle 2 = x + 25$. Find the value of x. **$x = 7$**

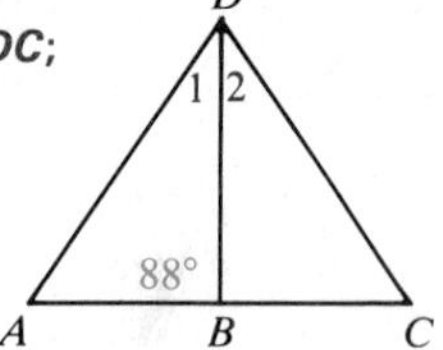

Classify each statement as true or false.

17. It is possible to locate three points in such a position that an unlimited number of planes contain all three points. **True** 1–5
18. It is possible for two intersecting lines to be noncoplanar. **False**
19. Through any three points there is at least one line. **False**
20. If points A and B lie in plane P, then so does any point of $\overrightarrow{AB}$. **True**

Chapter Test

State how many points meet the requirements. For each answer write *none*, *one*, or *an unlimited number*.

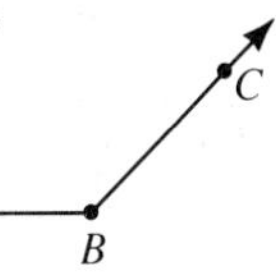

1. Equidistant from points A and B **an unlimited number**
2. On $\overrightarrow{BC}$ and equidistant from points A and B **none**

Given the diagram, tell whether you can reach the conclusion shown.

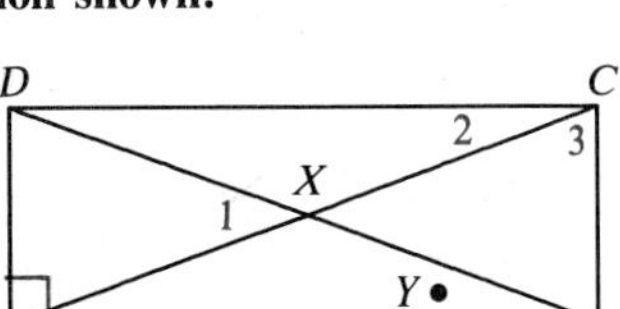

Exs. 3-15

3. $\angle AXC$ is a straight angle. **Yes**
4. Point Y lies in the interior of $\angle 3$. **Yes**
5. $\angle ADC$ is a right angle. **No**
6. X is the midpoint of $\overline{AC}$. **No**
7. Point Y lies between points A and B. **No**
8. Name three collinear points. ***A*, *X*, and *C*; or *D*, *X*, and *B***

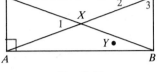

9. Name the intersection of $\overrightarrow{CX}$ and $\overleftrightarrow{AB}$. ***A***
10. Which postulate justifies the statement $AX + XC = AC$? **Segment Addition Postulate**
11. If $\overline{AC}$ bisects $\overline{BD}$, name two congruent segments. **$\overline{DX}$, $\overline{XB}$**
12. Name the vertex and sides of $\angle 1$. **X; $\overrightarrow{XD}$, $\overrightarrow{XA}$**
13. Name a right angle. **$\angle DAB$**
14. If $m\angle 1 = 46$, find $m\angle DXC$ and $m\angle CXB$. **134, 46**
15. If $m\angle DAX = 70$, find the measure of $\angle XAB$. **20**

Exercises 16–20 refer to a number line that is not pictured here. Point A has coordinate 2 and point B has coordinate 5.

16. What is the length of $\overline{AB}$? **3**
17. What is the coordinate of the midpoint of $\overline{AB}$? **3.5**
18. If A is the midpoint of $\overline{PB}$, what is the coordinate of P? **−1**
19. What is the coordinate of a point that is on $\overrightarrow{AB}$ and is 4 units from B? **9**
20. What is the coordinate of a point that is 4 units from B, but is not on $\overrightarrow{AB}$? **1**
21. Is it possible for a line and a point to be noncoplanar? **No**
22. Is it possible for the intersection of two planes to consist of a segment? **No**
23. Is a postulate an important proved statement, or is it a basic assumption? **basic assumption**
24. Complete the statement of the postulate: If two points are in a plane, then __?__. **the line that contains the points is in that plane**

Teaching References

Alternate Test, p. T12

2 Deductive Reasoning

Objectives

2-1 Recognize the hypothesis and the conclusion of an if-then statement.

State the converse of an if-then statement.

Use a counterexample to disprove an if-then statement.

Understand the meaning of *if and only if.*

2-2 Use properties from algebra and properties of congruence in proofs.

2-3 Use the Midpoint Theorem and the Angle Bisector Theorem.

Know the kinds of reasons that can be used in proofs.

2-4 Apply the definitions of complementary and supplementary angles.

State and use the theorem about vertical angles.

2-5 Apply the definition and theorems about perpendicular lines.

2-6 State and apply the theorems about angles supplementary to, or complementary to, congruent angles.

Plan proofs and then write them in two-column form.

Assignment Guide

See page T40 for information about the Assignment Guide.

Day	Minimum Course	Average Course	Maximum Course
1	**2-1** 35/2–16 even	**2-1** 35/1–15 odd, 16–22	**2-1** 35/3, 5, 7, 9, 12, 15, 16, 18, 21, 24, 27, 30
2	**2-1** 35/7–25 odd 37/Mixed Review 1–4	**2-1** 35/23–30 37/Mixed Review 1–4	**2-1** 35/20, 22, 26, 28, 29, 31
3	**2-2** 41–42/1, 4, 5, 7–10	**2-2** 41–42/1, 4, 6, 7–11	**2-2** 41–43/6, 8, 10, 11–15
4	**2-3** 46–47/1–12, 13, 15, 17 **S** 42/11 49/Self-Test 1	**2-3** 46–47/2–18 even, 19, 20 **S** 42/12–14 49/Self-Test 1	**2-3** 46–47/12–22
5	**2-4** 52–53/1–20, 23, 25	**2-4** 52–53/7–25 odd, 28, 29	**2-4** 53–54/19–31 odd, 32–35
6	**2-5** 58–59/1–13 **S** 53/27, 28, 30, 31 60/Mixed Review 1–7	**2-5** 58–60/2–8 even, 9–25 odd, 26, 28 **S** 54/32–34 60/Mixed Review 1–7	**2-5** 58–60/4–24 even, 25–29
7	**2-6** 63–64/1–17 odd **S** 59/14–17	**2-6** 63–65/2–18 even, 21, 23 65/Self-Test 2	**2-6** 63–65/15–25 odd 68–69/Chapter Test Test, page T13
8	**2-6** 63–64/2–20 even 65/Self-Test 2	**2-6** 68–69/Chapter Test Test, page T13	
9	**2-6** 68–69/Chapter Test Test, page T13		

Supplementary Materials Guide

For Use after Lesson	Practice Masters	Tests	Study Guide (Reteaching)	Resource Book			Computer Activities
				Tests	Practice Exercises	Prep. for College Entrance Exams (Col) Enrichment (E) Computer (C)	
2-1	Sheet 5		pp. 11–12				Activity 3
2-2	Sheet 6		pp. 13–14				
2-3	Sheet 7	Test 5	pp. 15–16	p. 6	p. 113		
2-4	Sheet 8		pp. 17–18				Activity 4
2-5		Test 6	pp. 19–20	p. 7	p. 114		
2-6	Sheet 9	Test 7	pp. 21–22	p. 8	p. 115		
Chapter 2	Sheet 10	Test 8		pp. 9–10	p. 116	p. 191 (Col) pp. 205–206 (E) p. 237 (C)	
Chapters 1–2	Sheet 11						

Overhead Visuals

Guided Discovery Visuals (lettered) and Teaching Visuals (numbered) available for Chapter 2.

Lessons	Visual	Title
2-5	A	Lines and Planes in Space
2-5	C	Angles and Their Measure
2-1, 2-2, 2-3	3	Reasons Used in Proofs
2-4, 2-5, 2-6	4	Supplements, Complements, and Vertical Angles

Software Guide

Houghton Mifflin software for Chapter 2
Test Generator (Apple or IBM): 90 test items

Other software appropriate for Chapter 2
Geometric Supposer (Apple): PreSupposer
GeoDraw (IBM)

Guide to Integrated Curriculum

Although the text presents coordinate and transformational geometry in Chapters 13 and 14 and in the Handbook on pp. 657–675, teachers wishing to integrate this material throughout the course may do so easily using the information on **pp. T56–T57.** The integration begins after Chapter 3.

With this integrated curriculum, students learn concepts, solve problems, and prove theorems using alternate approaches. Students make connections between geometry and algebra, and they learn the valuable skill of deciding which method to use in a problem **(pp. 672–673).**

Guide to Distribution of Constructions

The text teaches constructions in Chapter 10. Teachers wishing to distribute work with constructions throughout the first nine chapters can use this guide.

Introduce after	Constructions	Pages
Lesson 2-5	4, 5, 6	380, 381

Strategies for Teaching

Exploring Angles

When to Use

With or after Lesson 2-4

Overview

This activity motivates Theorems 2-6, 2-7, and 2-8 by using a 5-by-5 grid on which students will draw certain angles and make conjectures from their work. Students must exercise their visualization skills since congruent angles are considered in various positions. As students find all the possible angles, they may informally develop some insight into rotations, reflections, and translations.

Materials

Lettered graph paper or dot paper with 5-by-5 grids as shown below. Colored pencils may be useful. Geoboards, with colored rubber bands, may also be effective.

Description of Activity

Consider ∠*JMO* on the grid shown.

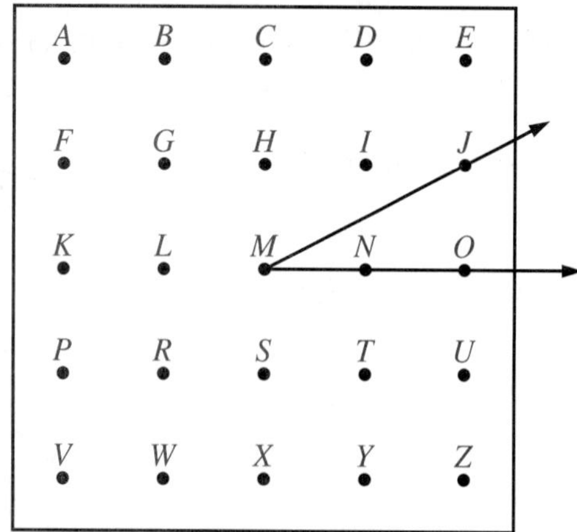

1. Name all angles with vertex *M* that have the given property. Each side of an angle must contain a grid point other than *M*.
   a. forms a pair of vertical angles with ∠*JMO* ∠PMK
   b. is supplementary to ∠*JMO* ∠JMK, ∠OMP
   c. is complementary to ∠*JMO* ∠JMC, ∠YMO, ∠PMX, ∠BMK
   d. is congruent to ∠*JMO* ∠PMK, ∠YMX, ∠BMC, ∠CMD, ∠KMF, ∠WMX, ∠UMO

   Name all angles with vertex *S* that have the given property. Each side of an angle must contain a grid point other than *S*.
   e. is supplementary to ∠*JMO* ∠OSP, ∠USV
   f. is complementary to ∠*JMO* ∠OSH, ∠KSH, ∠VSX, ∠GSP, ∠XSZ, ∠ISU
   g. is congruent to ∠*JMO* ∠VSP, ∠GSH, ∠HSI, ∠USZ, ∠PSK, ∠OSU
2. Which of the angles in your answers to parts **b** and **e** are congruent? all

   Make a conjecture based on your results. If two angles are supplements of the same angle, then the two angles are congruent. (Theorem 2-7)
3. Which of the angles in your answers to parts **c** and **f** are congruent? all

   Make a conjecture based on your results. If two angles are complements of the same angle, then the two angles are congruent. (Theorem 2-8)

Commentary

- You may need to remind students that complementary angles and supplementary angles need not be adjacent.
- This activity may be best suited to small groups since some students may "see" answers that others may not and can explain "what they see." In such discussions, such words as "flip," "turn," and "slide" may arise naturally. If so, you may want to mention rotations, reflections, and translations.

- Students who are having difficulty "seeing" these relationships may be directed to cut a triangle the size of $\triangle JMO$ and label $\angle JMO$. Students can then flip, slide, and turn the triangle into various positions on the grid, making it possible to find angles congruent to $\angle JMO$.

  Similarly, once one supplementary or complementary angle is found, students can cut out triangles to find others.

- Exercise **1c** may help motivate Theorem 2-6. (If the exterior sides of two adjacent angles are perpendicular, then the angles are complementary.)

Variations and Extensions

Try the same set of Exercises for other angles, such as a right angle and a 45° angle. The vertex need not be at M, the center of the grid.

References to Strategies

PE: Pupil's Edition **TE:** Teacher's Edition **RB:** Resource Book

Problem Solving Strategies

PE: 38 (Draw a diagram), 61 (Strategies for proof, reasoning backward)
TE: T79, T81, 47 (Make conjectures), 53 (Plan a proof)

Applications

PE: 32 (Computer programs), 36 (Geologist), 54–55 (Orienteering)
TE: 36

Nonroutine Problems

PE: 35 (Ex. 31), 43 (Ex. 15), 46 (Ex. 12), 47 (Exs. 17, 18, 20), 52 (Ex. 21), 54 (Exs. 34, 35), 55, 59 (Exs. 26, 27), 60, 66 (Möbius bands)
TE: T79–T80

Communication

PE: 33–34 (Conditional statements), 38 (Two-column proof), 38 (Drawing and reading diagrams), 61 (Drawing diagrams)
TE: T83, 38, 44, 57

Thinking Skills

PE: 33–34 (Logical reasoning), 45 (Deductive reasoning)
TE: 34 (Logic), 42 (Completeness of proof)

Explorations

TE: 31c

Connections

PE: 37 (Equality), 48 (Series), 49 (Julia Morgan), 53, 54 (Algebra), 66 (Möbius), 69 (Systems of equations)
TE: T80, T82 (Coordinate geometry), 37, 53, 54 (Algebra)

Using Technology

PE: 48
TE: T79, T80–T81, T82, 33, 48, 59
RB: 237
Computer Activities: 6–10

Using Manipulatives/Models

PE: 47 (Ex. 20), 55 (Orienteering), 66 (Möbius bands)
TE: T82
Overhead Visuals: A, C, 3, 4

Cooperative Learning

TE: T80, T82, 42, 47, 64, 66

Teaching Resources

For use in implementing the teaching strategies referenced on the previous page.

Communication/Thinking Skills
Resource Book, p. 204

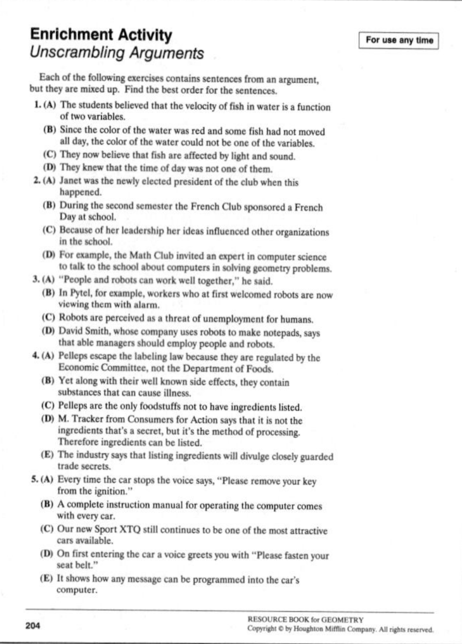

Enrichment Activity
Unscrambling Arguments

For use any time

Each of the following exercises contains sentences from an argument, but they are mixed up. Find the best order for the sentences.

1. (A) The students believed that the velocity of fish in water is a function of two variables.
   (B) Since the color of the water was red and some fish had not moved all day, the color of the water could not be one of the variables.
   (C) They now believe that fish are affected by light and sound.
   (D) They knew that the time of day was not one of them.
2. (A) Janet was the newly elected president of the club when this happened.
   (B) During the second semester the French Club sponsored a French Day at school.
   (C) Because of her leadership her ideas influenced other organizations in the school.
   (D) For example, the Math Club invited an expert in computer science to talk to the school about computers in solving geometry problems.
3. (A) "People and robots can work well together," he said.
   (B) In Pytel, for example, workers who at first welcomed robots are now viewing them with alarm.
   (C) Robots are perceived as a threat of unemployment for humans.
   (D) David Smith, whose company uses robots to make notepads, says that able managers should employ people and robots.
4. (A) Pelleps escape the labeling law because they are regulated by the Economic Committee, not the Department of Foods.
   (B) Yet along with their well known side effects, they contain substances that can cause illness.
   (C) Pelleps are the only foodstuffs not to have ingredients listed.
   (D) M. Tracker from Consumers for Action says that it is not the ingredients that's a secret, but it's the method of processing. Therefore ingredients can be listed.
   (E) The industry says that listing ingredients will divulge closely guarded trade secrets.
5. (A) Every time the car stops the voice says, "Please remove your key from the ignition."
   (B) A complete instruction manual for operating the computer comes with every car.
   (C) Our new Sport XTQ still continues to be one of the most attractive cars available.
   (D) On first entering the car a voice greets you with "Please fasten your seat belt."
   (E) It shows how any message can be programmed into the car's computer.

204 RESOURCE BOOK for GEOMETRY

Using Technology
Resource Book, p. 237

Computer Activity
Angles, Supplements, Complements

For use with Chapter 2

1. Write a program that will print a table giving the measure of an angle, the measure of its complement, and the measure of its supplement. Run your program to obtain values for all integral angle measures from 0 to 90. Then use the table to answer each true-false question below.

   a. The measure of the supplement of an angle is always greater than the measure of its complement.

   b. Whenever the measure of an angle increases, so does the measure of its supplement.

   c. If the measure of an angle is doubled, then the measure of its complement is halved.

   d. The measure of the complement of an angle is always exactly 90 less than the measure of its supplement.

   e. If the measure of the complement of an angle increases by 10, then the measure of its supplement increases by 20.

   f. When the measure of the supplement of an angle decreases, so does the measure of its complement.

   g. The measure of an angle, the measure of its supplement, and the measure of its complement always have three different values.

   h. The sum of the measure of the supplement of an angle and the measure of its complement is always more than twice the measure of the angle.

RESOURCE BOOK for GEOMETRY
 237

Thinking Skills
Study Guide, p. 21

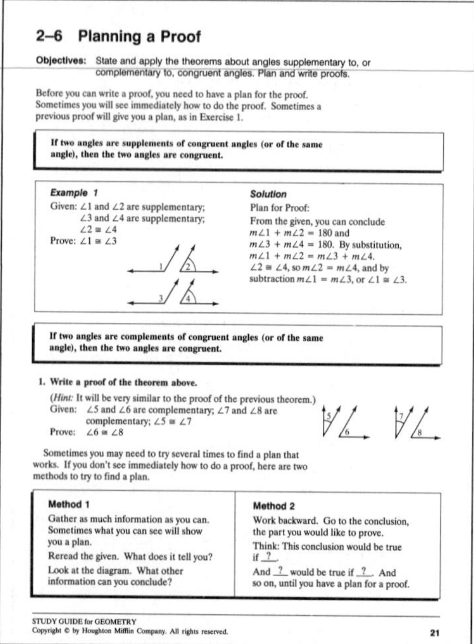

2–6 Planning a Proof

Objectives: State and apply the theorems about angles supplementary to, or complementary to, congruent angles. Plan and write proofs.

Before you can write a proof, you need to have a plan for the proof. Sometimes you will see immediately how to do the proof. Sometimes a previous proof will give you a plan, as in Exercise 1.

If two angles are supplements of congruent angles (or of the same angle), then the two angles are congruent.

Example 1
Given: $\angle 1$ and $\angle 2$ are supplementary; $\angle 3$ and $\angle 4$ are supplementary; $\angle 2 \cong \angle 4$
Prove: $\angle 1 \cong \angle 3$

Solution
Plan for Proof:
From the given, you can conclude $m\angle 1 + m\angle 2 = 180$ and $m\angle 3 + m\angle 4 = 180$. By substitution, $m\angle 1 + m\angle 2 = m\angle 3 + m\angle 4$. $\angle 2 \cong \angle 4$, so $m\angle 2 = m\angle 4$, and by subtraction $m\angle 1 = m\angle 3$, or $\angle 1 \cong \angle 3$.

If two angles are complements of congruent angles (or of the same angle), then the two angles are congruent.

1. **Write a proof of the theorem above.**
   (*Hint:* It will be very similar to the proof of the previous theorem.)
   Given: $\angle 5$ and $\angle 6$ are complementary; $\angle 7$ and $\angle 8$ are complementary; $\angle 5 \cong \angle 7$
   Prove: $\angle 6 \cong \angle 8$

Sometimes you may need to try several times to find a plan that works. If you don't see immediately how to do a proof, here are two methods to try to find a plan.

Method 1	Method 2
Gather as much information as you can. Sometimes what you can see will show you a plan. Reread the given. What does it tell you? Look at the diagram. What other information can you conclude?	Work backward. Go to the conclusion, the part you would like to prove. Think: This conclusion would be true if _?_. And _?_ would be true if _?_. And so on, until you have a plan for a proof.

STUDY GUIDE for GEOMETRY
 21

Thinking Skills
Study Guide, p. 22

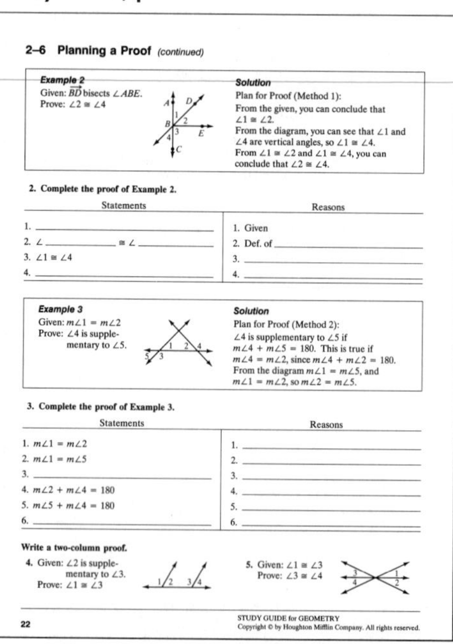

2–6 Planning a Proof *(continued)*

Example 2
Given: $\overrightarrow{BD}$ bisects $\angle ABE$.
Prove: $\angle 2 \cong \angle 4$

Solution
Plan for Proof (Method 1):
From the given, you can conclude that $\angle 1 \cong \angle 2$.
From the diagram, you can see that $\angle 1$ and $\angle 4$ are vertical angles, so $\angle 1 \cong \angle 4$.
From $\angle 1 \cong \angle 2$ and $\angle 1 \cong \angle 4$, you can conclude that $\angle 2 \cong \angle 4$.

2. **Complete the proof of Example 2.**

Statements	Reasons
1. ______	1. Given
2. $\angle$ ______ $\cong \angle$ ______	2. Def. of ______
3. $\angle 1 \cong \angle 4$	3. ______
4. ______	4. ______

Example 3
Given: $m\angle 1 = m\angle 2$
Prove: $\angle 4$ is supplementary to $\angle 5$.

Solution
Plan for Proof (Method 2):
$\angle 4$ is supplementary to $\angle 5$ if $m\angle 4 + m\angle 5 = 180$. This is true if $m\angle 4 = m\angle 2$, since $m\angle 4 + m\angle 2 = 180$. From the diagram $m\angle 1 = m\angle 5$, and $m\angle 1 = m\angle 2$, so $m\angle 2 = m\angle 5$.

3. **Complete the proof of Example 3.**

Statements	Reasons
1. $m\angle 1 = m\angle 2$	1. ______
2. $m\angle 1 = m\angle 5$	2. ______
3. ______	3. ______
4. $m\angle 2 + m\angle 4 = 180$	4. ______
5. $m\angle 5 + m\angle 4 = 180$	5. ______
6. ______	6. ______

Write a two-column proof.

4. Given: $\angle 2$ is supplementary to $\angle 3$.
   Prove: $\angle 1 \cong \angle 3$

5. Given: $\angle 1 \cong \angle 3$
   Prove: $\angle 3 \cong \angle 4$

22 STUDY GUIDE for GEOMETRY

Exploration/Using Technology
Computer Activities, p. 9

ACTIVITY 4. ***Supplement/Complement Word Problems*** (for use with Lesson 2-4)

Directions: Write all answers in the spaces provided.

PROBLEM

The supplement of an angle is three times as large as the angle. Find the measure of the angle.

PROGRAM

```
10 PRINT
20 PRINT "WHAT IS THE MEASURE OF THE ANGLE";
30 INPUT G
40 LET S = 3 • G
50 LET R = 180 - G
60 PRINT
70 PRINT "THE SUPPLEMENT OF YOUR ANSWER IS ";R
80 IF S = R THEN 150
90 PRINT "SORRY, YOUR ANSWER IS NOT CORRECT"
100 PRINT "DO YOU WISH TO TRY AGAIN (Y OR N)";
110 INPUT A$
120 IF A$ = "Y" THEN 10
130 PRINT "SORRY YOU DON'T WANT TO CONTINUE"
140 GOTO 160
150 PRINT "VERY GOOD — YOU ARE RIGHT!!!"
160 END
```

PROGRAM CHECK

Type in the program and run it. After the question mark type in 80. The computer should print

```
THE SUPPLEMENT OF YOUR ANSWER IS 100
SORRY, YOUR ANSWER IS NOT CORRECT
DO YOU WISH TO TRY AGAIN (Y OR N)?
```

USING THE PROGRAM

Type Y to continue. By adjusting your estimate you should be able to find the angle.

1. If your estimate is 50, what value does the computer find for S in line 40? ______
2. If your estimate is 50, what is the value for R in line 70? ______
3. How does the computer decide if your estimate is correct? (*Hint:* Line 80.) ______
4. What is the measure of the angle? ______

By changing line 40 you can use this program to solve other word problems of this type.

5. The supplement of an angle is eight times as large as the angle. Find the measure of the angle.

   40 LET S = 8 • ______

   Your first estimate ______ The measure of the angle ______

COMPUTER ACTIVITIES for GEOMETRY (continued)

9

Exploration/Using Technology
Computer Activities, p. 10

(Activity 4 continued)

6. The supplement of an angle is five times as large as the angle. Find the measure of the angle.

   40 ______

   Your first estimate ______ The measure of the angle ______
7. The supplement of an angle is seven times as large as the angle. Find the measure of the angle.

   40 ______

   Your first estimate ______ The measure of the angle ______
8. The supplement of an angle is one fifth as large as the angle. Find the measure of the angle.

   40 ______

   Your first estimate ______ The measure of the angle ______

EXTENSION

In order to solve word problems concerning complements you must make a change in the program. Type in the following lines.

```
50 LET R = 90 - G
70 PRINT "THE COMPLEMENT OF YOUR ANSWER IS ";R
```

Use this new program and continue to change line 40 to solve the following problems.

1. The complement of an angle is five times as large as the angle. Find the measure of the angle.

   40 LET S = ______

   The measure of the angle ______
2. Two angles are complementary. The measure of one is eight times the measure of the other. Find the measure of each angle.

   40 ______

   The measure of each angle ______ ______
3. Two angles are complementary. The measure of one is one-fourth the measure of the other. Find the measure of each angle.

   40 ______

   The measure of each angle ______ ______
4. The complement of an angle is 50% more than the angle. Find the measure of the angle.

   40 ______

   The measure of the angle ______

10
COMPUTER ACTIVITIES for GEOMETRY

Thinking Skills
Teaching Visual 3

TEACHING VISUAL 3
(for use with Lessons 2-1 through 2-3, especially page 45)

REASONS USED IN PROOFS

Given information
Definitions
Postulates (including properties from algebra)
Theorems that have already been proved

A PROOF THAT USES THESE REASONS

Complete the proof of Theorem 2-2.
Given: $\overrightarrow{BX}$ is the bisector of $\angle ABC$.
Prove: $m\angle ABX = \frac{1}{2}m\angle ABC$; $m\angle XBC = \frac{1}{2}m\angle ABC$

Proof:

Statements	Reasons
1. $\overrightarrow{BX}$ is the bisector of $\angle ABC$.	1. ?
2. $\angle ABX \cong$?, or $m\angle ABX =$?	2. ?
3. $m\angle ABX + m\angle XBC = m\angle ABC$	3. ?
4. $m\angle ABX + m\angle ABX = m\angle ABC$, or $2m\angle ABX = m\angle ABC$	4. ?
5. $m\angle ABX = \frac{1}{2}m\angle ABC$	5. ?
6. $m\angle XBC = \frac{1}{2}m\angle ABC$	6. Substitution Prop. (Steps ? and ?)

Thinking Skills
Teaching Visual 4

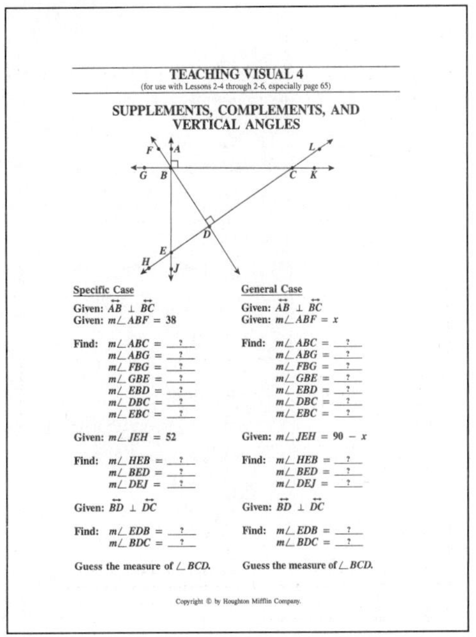

TEACHING VISUAL 4
(for use with Lessons 2-4 through 2-6, especially page 65)

SUPPLEMENTS, COMPLEMENTS, AND VERTICAL ANGLES

Specific Case	General Case
Given: $\overleftrightarrow{AB} \perp \overleftrightarrow{BC}$	Given: $\overleftrightarrow{AB} \perp \overleftrightarrow{BC}$
Given: $m\angle ABF = 38$	Given: $m\angle ABF = x$
Find: $m\angle ABC =$?	Find: $m\angle ABC =$?
$m\angle ABG =$?	$m\angle ABG =$?
$m\angle FBG =$?	$m\angle FBG =$?
$m\angle GBE =$?	$m\angle GBE =$?
$m\angle EBD =$?	$m\angle EBD =$?
$m\angle DBC =$?	$m\angle DBC =$?
$m\angle EBC =$?	$m\angle EBC =$?
Given: $m\angle JEH = 52$	Given: $m\angle JEH = 90 - x$
Find: $m\angle HEB =$?	Find: $m\angle HEB =$?
$m\angle BED =$?	$m\angle BED =$?
$m\angle DEJ =$?	$m\angle DEJ =$?
Given: $\overleftrightarrow{BD} \perp \overleftrightarrow{DC}$	Given: $\overleftrightarrow{BD} \perp \overleftrightarrow{DC}$
Find: $m\angle EDB =$?	Find: $m\angle EDB =$?
$m\angle BDC =$?	$m\angle BDC =$?
Guess the measure of $\angle BCD$.	Guess the measure of $\angle BCD$.

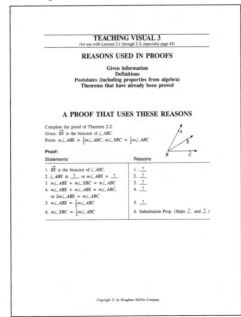

Teaching References

Lesson Commentary, pp. T78–T83
Assignment Guide, pp. T42–T43
Software Guide, p. T73
Alternate Test, p. T13

Supplementary Materials

Practice Masters 5–11
Tests 5–8
Resource Book
- Tests, pp. 6–10
- Practice, pp. 113–116
- Preparing for College Entrance Exams, p. 191
- Enrichment Activity, pp. 205–206
- Computer Activity, p. 237

Study Guide, pp. 11–22
Overhead Visuals A, C, 3, 4
Computer Activities
- 3 Conditional Statements
- 4 Supplement/Complement Word Problems

Cultural Note

Significant contributions to computer programming were made by the mathematician Augusta Ada Lovelace (1815–1852). Among them are descriptions of looping and recursion techniques. The computer programming language Ada, which was developed in the 1980s, is named after Lovelace.

2 DEDUCTIVE REASONING

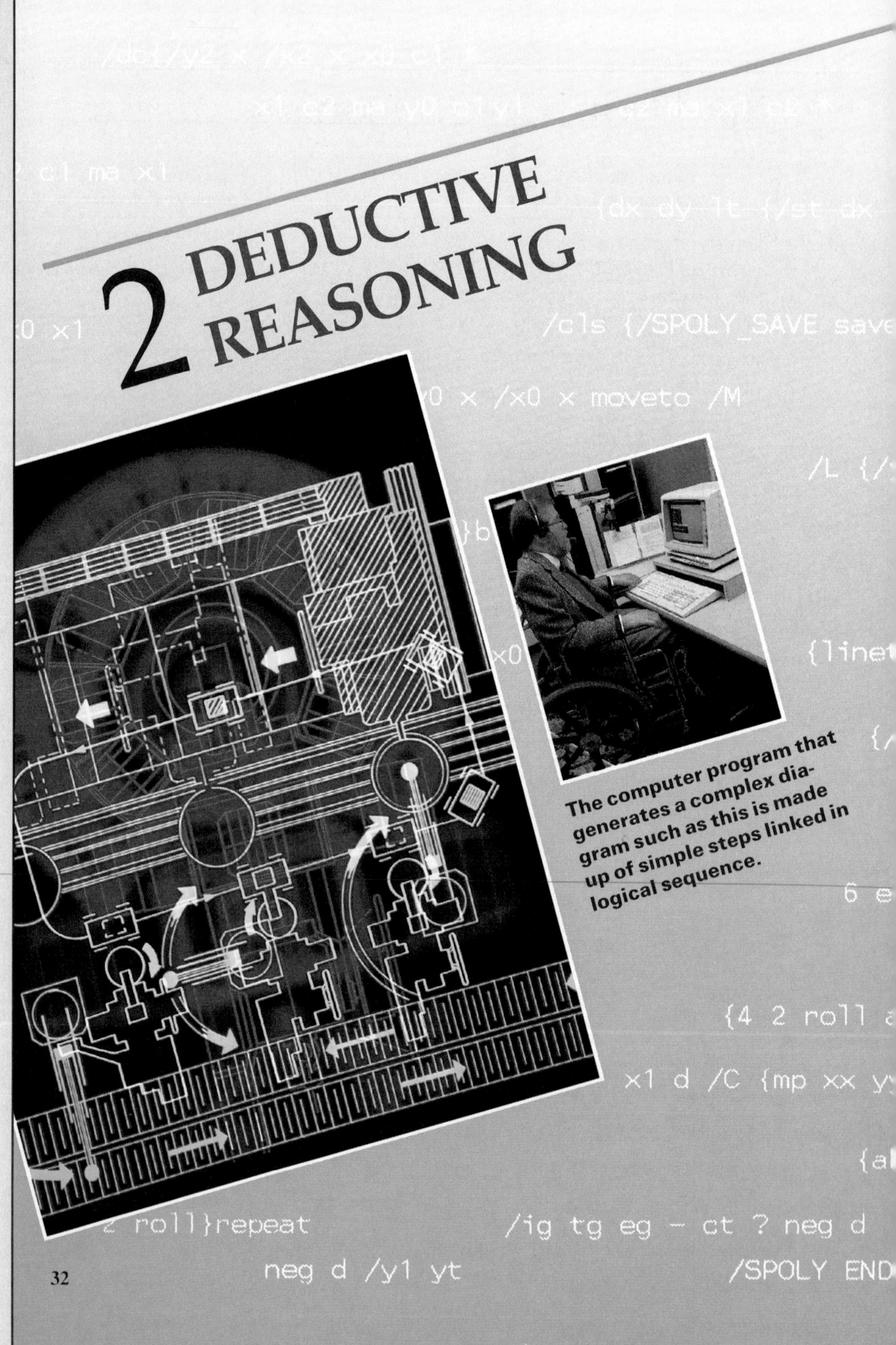

The computer program that generates a complex diagram such as this is made up of simple steps linked in logical sequence.

Using Deductive Reasoning

Objectives

1. Recognize the hypothesis and the conclusion of an if-then statement.
2. State the converse of an if-then statement.
3. Use a counterexample to disprove an if-then statement.
4. Understand the meaning of *if and only if.*
5. Use properties from algebra and properties of congruence in proofs.
6. Use the Midpoint Theorem and the Angle Bisector Theorem.
7. Know the kinds of reasons that can be used in proofs.

2-1 *If-Then Statements; Converses*

Your friend says, "If it rains after school, then I will give you a ride home."

A geometry student reads, "If B is between A and C, then AB + BC = AC."

These are examples of **if-then statements,** which are also called **conditional statements** or simply **conditionals.**

To represent an if-then statement symbolically, let p represent the **hypothesis,** shown in red, and let q represent the **conclusion,** shown in blue. Then we have the basic form of an if-then statement shown below:

If p, then q.

↑ ↑

p: **hypothesis** q: **conclusion**

The **converse** of a conditional is formed by interchanging the hypothesis and the conclusion.

Statement: If p, then q. Converse: If q, then p.

A statement and its converse say different things. In fact, some true statements have false converses.

Statement: If Ed lives in Texas, then he lives south of Canada.
False Converse: If Ed lives south of Canada, then he lives in Texas.

An if-then statement is false if an example can be found for which the hypothesis is true and the conclusion is false. Such an example is called a **counterexample.** It takes only one counterexample to disprove a statement. We know the converse above is false because we can find a counterexample: Ed could live in Kansas City, which *is* south of Canada and *is not* in Texas.

Some true statements have true converses.

Statement: If $4x = 20$, then $x = 5$.
True Converse: If $x = 5$, then $4x = 20$.

Teaching Suggestions,
pp. T79–T80

Objectives
Presenting the Lesson
Problem Solving
Using Technology
Extension

Supplementary Materials

Practice Master 5
Study Guide, pp. 11–12
Computer Activity 3

Lesson Focus

In order to learn mathematics, it is necessary to learn to think logically. The purpose of this lesson is to study different *forms* of if-then statements that are used extensively in geometry and all other branches of mathematics.

Suggested Assignments

Minimum
Day 1: 35/2–16 even
Day 2: 35/7–25 odd
37/Mixed Review 1–4

Average
Day 1: 35/1–15 odd, 16–22
Day 2: 35/23–30
37/Mixed Review 1–4

Maximum
Day 1: 35/3, 5, 7, 9, 12, 15, 16, 18, 21, 24, 27, 30
Day 2: 35/20, 22, 26, 28, 29, 31

Using a Computer

See p. T79 for some statements to disprove by counterexample using a program that draws and measures geometric figures.

Thinking Skills

The form "*p* only if *q*" will prove troublesome to students who look for the single word *if* and then call the next statement the hypothesis. Point out that *only if* means something completely different from *if.* Use an example such as: A person is president only if he or she is well known.

Proof Note

You can use Ex. 10 to reinforce the point that one counterexample disproves a statement but that infinitely many favorable examples cannot prove it. List the numbers 12, 24, 36, 48, 60, and so on, which are all divisible by 4 and 6. Then ask students to name one counterexample, namely 16, that proves the conditional false.

Additional Answers Classroom Exercises

12. If tomorrow is Saturday, then today is Friday. T
13. If $x^2 > 0$, then $x > 0$. F
14. If a number is divisible by 3, then it is divisible by 6. F
15. If $x = 3$, then $6x = 18$. T

Conditional statements are not always written with the "if" clause first. Here are some examples. All these conditionals mean the same thing.

General Form	*Example*
If p, then q.	If $x^2 = 25$, then $x < 10$.
p implies q.	$x^2 = 25$ implies $x < 10$.
p only if q.	$x^2 = 25$ only if $x < 10$.
q if p.	$x < 10$ if $x^2 = 25$.

If a conditional and its converse are both true they can be combined into a single statement by using the words "if and only if." A statement that contains the words "if and only if" is called a **biconditional.** Its basic form is shown below.

p if and only if q.

Every definition can be written as a biconditional as the statements below illustrate.

Definition: Congruent segments are segments that have equal lengths.

Biconditional: Segments are congruent if and only if their lengths are equal.

Classroom Exercises

State the hypothesis and the conclusion of each conditional.

1. If $2x - 1 = 5$, then $x = 3$.
2. If she's smart, then I'm a genius.
3. $8y = 40$ implies $y = 5$.
4. $RS = \frac{1}{2}RT$ if S is the midpoint of $\overline{RT}$.
5. $\angle 1 \cong \angle 2$ if $m\angle 1 = m\angle 2$.
6. $\angle 1 \cong \angle 2$ only if $m\angle 1 = m\angle 2$.
7. Combine the conditionals in Exercises 5 and 6 into a single biconditional.
   $m\angle 1 = m\angle 2$ if and only if $\angle 1 \cong \angle 2$.

Provide a counterexample to show that each statement is false. You may use words or draw a diagram. **Answers will vary. Examples are given.**

8. If $\overline{AB} \cong \overline{BC}$, then B is the midpoint of $\overline{AC}$.
9. If a line lies in a vertical plane, then the line is vertical.
10. If a number is divisible by 4, then it is divisible by 6. **$n = 16$**
11. If $x^2 = 49$, then $x = 7$. **$x = -7$**

State the converse of each conditional. Is the converse true or false?

12. If today is Friday, then tomorrow is Saturday. **True**
13. If $x > 0$, then $x^2 > 0$. **False**
14. If a number is divisible by 6, then it is divisible by 3. **False**
15. If $6x = 18$, then $x = 3$. **True**
16. Give an example of a false conditional whose converse is true.
    Answers will vary. An example is given:
    If $\overline{AB} \cong \overline{BC}$, then B is the midpoint of $\overline{AC}$.

Written Exercises

Write the hypothesis and the conclusion of each conditional.

A 1. If $3x - 7 = 32$, then $x = 13$.
2. I can't sleep if I'm not tired.
3. I'll try if you will.
4. If $m\angle 1 = 90$, then $\angle 1$ is a right angle.
5. $a + b = a$ implies $b = 0$.
6. $x = -5$ only if $x^2 = 25$.

Rewrite each pair of conditionals as a biconditional.

7. If B is between A and C, then $AB + BC = AC$. If $AB + BC = AC$, then B is between A and C. **B is between A and C if and only if $AB + BC = AC$.**
8. If $m\angle AOC = 180$, then $\angle AOC$ is a straight angle. If $\angle AOC$ is a straight angle, then $m\angle AOC = 180$. **$m\angle AOC = 180$ if and only if $\angle AOC$ is a straight angle.**

Write each biconditional as two conditionals that are converses of each other.

9. Points are collinear if and only if they all lie in one line. **If points are collinear, then they all lie in 1 line. If pts. all lie in 1 line, then they are collinear.**
10. Points lie in one plane if and only if they are coplanar. **If pts. lie in 1 plane, then they are coplanar. If pts. are coplanar, then they lie in 1 plane.**

Provide a counterexample to show that each statement is false. You may use words or a diagram. Answers will vary. Examples are given.

11. If $ab < 0$, then $a < 0$. **$a = 1, b = -1$**
12. If $n^2 = 5n$, then $n = 5$. **$n = 0$**
13. If point G is on $\overrightarrow{AB}$, then G is on $\overrightarrow{BA}$.
14. If $xy > 5y$, then $x > 5$. **$x = -1, y = -1$**
15. If a four-sided figure has four right angles, then it has four congruent sides.
16. If a four-sided figure has four congruent sides, then it has four right angles.

Tell whether each statement is true or false. Then write the converse and tell whether it is true or false.

17. If $x = -6$, then $|x| = 6$. **True; False**
18. If $x^2 = 4$, then $x = -2$. **False; True**
19. If $b > 4$, then $5b > 20$. **True; True**
20. If $m\angle T = 40$, then $\angle T$ is not obtuse. **True, False**
21. If Pam lives in Chicago, then she lives in Illinois. **True; False**
22. If $\angle A \cong \angle B$, then $m\angle A = m\angle B$. **True; True**

B 23. $a^2 > 9$ if $a > 3$. **True; False**
24. $x = 1$ only if $x^2 = x$. **True; False**
25. $n > 5$ only if $n > 7$. **False; True**
26. $ab = 0$ implies that $a = 0$ or $b = 0$. **True; True**
27. If points D, E, and F are collinear, then $DE + EF = DF$. **False; True**
28. P is the midpoint of $\overline{GH}$ implies that $GH = 2PG$. **True; False**
29. Write a definition of congruent angles as a biconditional. **Two $\angle$s are $\cong$ if and only if their measures are =.**
30. Write a definition of a right angle as a biconditional. **An $\angle$ is a rt. $\angle$ if and only if its measure is 90.**

C 31. What can you conclude if the following sentences are all true? **Possible conclusions are: q, not r, s**
(1) If p, then q. (2) p (3) If q, then not r. (4) s or r.

Guided Practice

Write the hypothesis and the conclusion of each conditional.

1. $VW = XY$ implies $\overline{VW} \cong \overline{XY}$.
2. K is the midpoint of $\overline{JL}$ only if $JK = KL$.
3. $n > 8$ only if n is greater than 7.
4. I'll dive if you dive.
5. If $a = b$, then $a + c = b + c$.
6. If $a + c = b + c$, then $a = b$.
7. $r = s$ only if $r + n = s + n$.
8. $r + n = s + n$ if $r = s$.

Additional Answers Written Exercises

17. T; If $|x| = 6$, then $x = -6$. F
18. F; If $x = -2$, then $x^2 = 4$. T
19. T; If $5b > 20$, then $b > 4$. T
20. T; If $\angle T$ is not obtuse, then $m\angle T = 40$. F
21. T; If Pam lives in Illinois, then she lives in Chicago. F
22. T; If $m\angle A = m\angle B$, then $\angle A \cong \angle B$. T
23. T; If $a^2 > 9$, then $a > 3$. F
24. T; If $x^2 = x$, then $x = 1$. F
25. F; If $n > 7$, then $n > 5$. T
26. T; If $a = 0$ or $b = 0$, then $ab = 0$. T
27. F; If $DE + EF = DF$, then points D, E, and F are collinear. T
28. T; If $GH = 2PG$, then P is the midpoint of $\overline{GH}$. F

Application

A discussion of the question about determining the position of a stratum of rock beneath the surface of the earth can lead students to think about the relationship of geometric ideas as mathematical models of physical objects. A stratum of rock is modeled by a geometric plane. Then the properties of a plane can be used to think about a solution to the geologist's problem. Remind students that any three noncollinear points fix or determine a plane, and that this fact permits an approach to determining the position of a stratum of rock beneath the Earth.

Cultural Note

Students may be interested in studying photographs of geological formations that show stratification of rock layers. Students can research such areas as the Grand Canyon in North America and the Rift Valley in Africa.

Career

Geologist

Geologists study rock formations like those at Checkerboard Mountain in Zion National Park. Rock formations often occur in *strata*, or layers, beneath the surface of the Earth. Earthquakes occur at *faults*, breaks in the strata. In search of a fault, how would you determine the position of a stratum of rock buried deep beneath the surface of the Earth?

A geologist might start by picking three noncollinear points, A, B, and C, on the surface and drilling holes to find the depths of points A', B', and C' on the stratum. These three points determine the plane of the surface of the stratum.

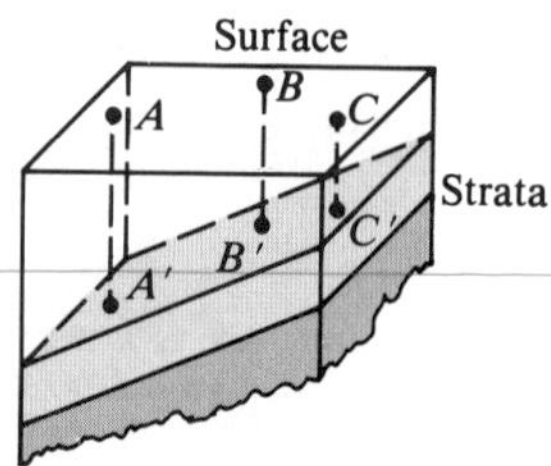

Geologists may work for industry, searching for oil or minerals. They may work in research centers, developing ways to predict earthquakes.

Today, geologists are trying to locate sources of geothermal energy, energy generated by the Earth's internal heat. A career in geology usually requires knowledge of mathematics, physics, and chemistry, as well as a degree in geology.

Mixed Review Exercises

Complete. You may find that drawing a diagram will help you.

1. If M is the midpoint of $\overline{AB}$, then __?__ ≅ __?__. **$\overline{AM}$; $\overline{MB}$**
2. If $\overrightarrow{BX}$ is the bisector of $\angle ABC$, then __?__ ≅ __?__. **$\angle ABX$; $\angle XBC$**
3. If point B lies in the interior of $\angle AOC$, then $m\angle$ __?__ + $m\angle$ __?__ = $m\angle$ __?__. **AOB; BOC; AOC**
4. If $\angle POQ$ is a straight angle and R is any point not on $\overleftrightarrow{PQ}$, then $m\angle$ __?__ + $m\angle$ __?__ = __?__. **POR; ROQ; 180**

2-2 *Properties from Algebra*

Since the length of a segment is a real number and the measure of an angle is a real number, the facts about real numbers and equality that you learned in algebra can be used in your study of geometry. The properties of equality that will be used most often are listed below.

Properties of Equality

Addition Property	If $a = b$ and $c = d$, then $a + c = b + d$.
Subtraction Property	If $a = b$ and $c = d$, then $a - c = b - d$.
Multiplication Property	If $a = b$, then $ca = cb$.
Division Property	If $a = b$ and $c \neq 0$, then $\frac{a}{c} = \frac{b}{c}$.
Substitution Property	If $a = b$, then either a or b may be substituted for the other in any equation (or inequality).
Reflexive Property	$a = a$
Symmetric Property	If $a = b$, then $b = a$.
Transitive Property	If $a = b$ and $b = c$, then $a = c$.

Recall that $DE = FG$ and $\overline{DE} \cong \overline{FG}$ can be used interchangeably, as can $m\angle D = m\angle E$ and $\angle D \cong \angle E$. Thus the following properties of congruence follow directly from the related properties of equality.

Properties of Congruence

Reflexive Property	$\overline{DE} \cong \overline{DE}$ $\quad\angle D \cong \angle D$
Symmetric Property	If $\overline{DE} \cong \overline{FG}$, then $\overline{FG} \cong \overline{DE}$. If $\angle D \cong \angle E$, then $\angle E \cong \angle D$.
Transitive Property	If $\overline{DE} \cong \overline{FG}$ and $\overline{FG} \cong \overline{JK}$, then $\overline{DE} \cong \overline{JK}$. If $\angle D \cong \angle E$ and $\angle E \cong \angle F$, then $\angle D \cong \angle F$.

Teaching Suggestions,
p. T80

Objective
Presenting the Lesson
Making Connections

Cooperative Learning,
p. T80

Supplementary Materials

Practice Master 6
Study Guide, pp. 13–14

Lesson Focus

There are many connections between algebra and geometry. This lesson reviews the algebraic properties of equality that will be used to write proofs and solve problems.

Suggested Assignments

Minimum
41–42/1, 4, 5, 7–10
Average
41–42/1, 4, 6, 7–11
Maximum
41–43/6, 8, 10, 11–15

Making Connections

Geometry students who have studied two years of algebra can review quickly properties of equality and then concentrate on the properties of congruence. This book treats $\overline{DE} \cong \overline{DE}$ and $DE = DE$ as interchangeable, which should help students remember that the properties of congruence follow directly from the properties of equality.

Communication Skills

Suppose a student writes a valid geometric proof that uses the Distributive Property, but he or she cannot recall the name of the property to justify the step. Allow the student to write "Algebraic Property" as the reason. Students should try to remember the correct terms to use as reasons in proofs, but they should be given some latitude if their reasoning is good and a property is used correctly.

Chalkboard Examples

Justify each step in solving the equation $3y + 4 = \frac{2y}{5}$.

1. $3y + 4 = \frac{2y}{5}$ Given
2. $15y + 20 = 2y$ Mult. Prop. of =
3. $13y + 20 = 0$ Subtr. Prop. of =
4. $13y = -20$ Subtr. Prop. of =
5. $y = \frac{-20}{13}$ Div. Prop. of =

Proof Note

You may wish to permit students to use a shortened proof in which Statement 3 in Example 2 is omitted (Version 1) or Statements 2 and 3 are omitted (Version 2).

Version 1

1. $RS = PS$; $ST = SQ$ (Given)
2. $RS + ST = PS + SQ$ (Addition Prop. of =)
3. $RT = PQ$ (Seg. Add. Post. and Substitution)

Version 2

1. $RS = PS$, $ST = SQ$ (Given)
2. $RT = PQ$ (Seg. Add. Post.)

The properties of equality and other properties from algebra, such as the **Distributive Property,**

$$a(b + c) = ab + ac,$$

can be used to justify your steps when you solve an equation.

Example 1 Solve $3x = 6 - \frac{1}{2}x$ and justify each step.

Solution

Steps	*Reasons*
1. $3x = 6 - \frac{1}{2}x$	1. Given equation
2. $6x = 12 - x$	2. Multiplication Property of Equality
3. $7x = 12$	3. Addition Property of Equality
4. $x = \frac{12}{7}$	4. Division Property of Equality

Example 1 shows a proof of the statement "If $3x = 6 - \frac{1}{2}x$, then x *must* equal $\frac{12}{7}$." In other words, when given the information that $3x = 6 - \frac{1}{2}x$ we can use the properties of algebra to conclude, or *deduce*, that $x = \frac{12}{7}$.

Many proofs in geometry follow this same pattern. We use certain given information along with the properties of algebra and accepted statements, such as the Segment Addition Postulate and Angle Addition Postulate, to show that other statements *must* be true. Often a geometric proof is written in two-column form, with statements on the left and a reason for each statement on the right.

In the following examples, congruent segments are marked alike and congruent angles are marked alike. For example, in the diagram below, the marks show that $\overline{RS} \cong \overline{PS}$ and $\overline{ST} \cong \overline{SQ}$. In the diagram for Example 3 the marks show that $\angle AOC \cong \angle BOD$.

Example 2

Given: $\overline{RT}$ and $\overline{PQ}$ intersecting at S so that $RS = PS$ and $ST = SQ$.

Prove: $RT = PQ$

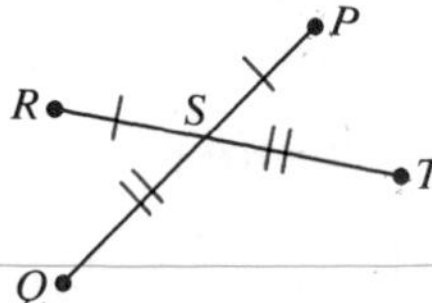

Proof:

Statements	Reasons
1. $RS = PS$; $ST = SQ$	1. Given
2. $RS + ST = PS + SQ$	2. Addition Prop. of =
3. $RS + ST = RT$; $PS + SQ = PQ$	3. Segment Addition Postulate
4. $RT = PQ$	4. Substitution Prop.

In Steps 1 and 3 of Example 2, notice how statements can be written in pairs when justified by the same reason.

Example 3

Given: $m\angle AOC = m\angle BOD$

Prove: $m\angle 1 = m\angle 3$

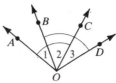

Proof:

Statements	Reasons
1. $m\angle AOC = m\angle BOD$	1. Given
2. $m\angle AOC = m\angle 1 + m\angle 2$; $m\angle BOD = m\angle 2 + m\angle 3$	2. Angle Addition Postulate
3. $m\angle 1 + m\angle 2 = m\angle 2 + m\angle 3$	3. Substitution Prop.
4. $m\angle 2 = m\angle 2$	4. Reflexive Prop.
5. $m\angle 1 = m\angle 3$	5. Subtraction Prop. of =

Notice that the reason given for Step 4 is "Reflexive Property" rather than "Reflexive Property of Equality." Since the reflexive, symmetric, and transitive properties of equality are so closely related to the corresponding properties of congruence, we will simply use "Reflexive Property" to justify either

$$m\angle BOC = m\angle BOC \quad \text{or} \quad \angle BOC \cong \angle BOC.$$

Suppose, in a proof, you have made the statement that

$$m\angle R = m\angle S$$

and also the statement that

$$m\angle S = m\angle T.$$

You can then deduce that $m\angle R = m\angle T$ and use as your reason either "Transitive Property" or "Substitution Property." Similarly, if you know that

(1) $m\angle R = m\angle S$
(2) $m\angle S = m\angle T$
(3) $m\angle T = m\angle V$

you can go on to write (4) $m\angle R = m\angle V$

and use either "Transitive Property" or "Substitution Property" as your reason. Actually, you use the Transitive Property twice or else make a double substitution.

There are times when the Substitution Property is the simplest one to use. If you know that

(1) $m\angle 4 + m\angle 2 + m\angle 5 = 180$
(2) $m\angle 4 = m\angle 1$; $m\angle 5 = m\angle 3$

you can make a double substitution and get

(3) $m\angle 1 + m\angle 2 + m\angle 3 = 180.$

Note that you can't use the Transitive Property here.

Proof Note

Here is a shortened version of the proof for Example 3.

1. $m\angle AOC = m\angle BOD$ (Given)
2. $m\angle 1 + m\angle 2 = m\angle 2 + m\angle 3$ (Angle Addition Post.)
3. $m\angle 1 = m\angle 3$ (Subtraction Prop. of =)

Teaching Note

You may need to remind students occasionally that there is no substitution property of congruence. Substitution deals with numbers, not congruence. An example can help.

Given: $\overline{AB}$ and $\overline{CD}$ intersect; $\overline{XY} \cong \overline{AB}$

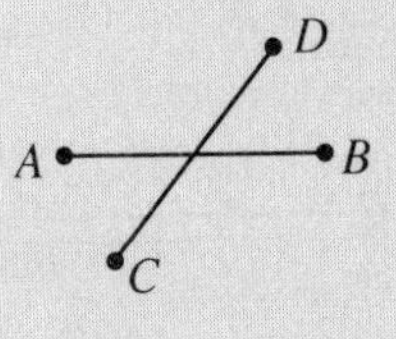

We *cannot* substitute $\overline{XY}$ for $\overline{AB}$ and assert that $\overline{XY}$ and $\overline{CD}$ intersect.

Teaching Note

When the Division Property is used as a reason, the Multiplication Property always can be used instead. In Ex. 5, students can either divide by 5 or multiply by $\frac{1}{5}$. The same is true for the Subtraction and Addition Properties.

Proof Note

During the discussion of Ex. 11, you can—if you wish to permit your class to write shortened proofs—remind students of your policy. If Statement 3 is omitted, then the final reason should be Angle Addition Postulate. In Ex. 12, Statement 2 can be omitted.

Classroom Exercises

Justify each statement with a property from algebra or a property of congruence. **2. Trans. Prop. 3. Sym. Prop. 5. Div. Prop. of = 7. Distributive Prop.**

1. $\angle P \cong \angle P$ **Reflexive Prop.**

2. If $\overline{AB} \cong \overline{CD}$ and $\overline{CD} \cong \overline{EF}$, then $\overline{AB} \cong \overline{EF}$.

3. If $RS = TW$, then $TW = RS$.

4. If $x + 5 = 16$, then $x = 11$. **Subtr. Prop. of =**

5. If $5y = -20$, then $y = -4$.

6. If $\frac{z}{5} = 10$, then $z = 50$. **Mult. Prop. of =**

7. $2(a + b) = 2a + 2b$

8. If $2z - 5 = -3$, then $2z = 2$. **Add. Prop. of =**

9. If $2x + y = 70$ and $y = 3x$, then $2x + 3x = 70$. **Substitution Prop.**

10. If $AB = CD$, $CD = EF$, and $EF = 23$, then $AB = 23$. **Trans. Prop.**

Complete each proof by supplying missing reasons and statements.

11. Given: $m\angle 1 = m\angle 3$; $m\angle 2 = m\angle 4$

Prove: $m\angle ABC = m\angle DEF$

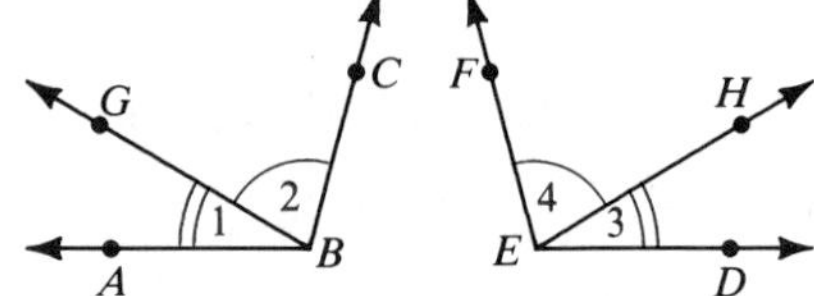

Proof:

Statements	Reasons
1. $m\angle 1 = m\angle 3$; $m\angle 2 = m\angle 4$	1. ? **Given**
2. $m\angle 1 + m\angle 2 = m\angle 3 + m\angle 4$	2. ? **Addition Prop. of =**
3. $m\angle 1 + m\angle 2 = m\angle ABC$; $m\angle 3 + m\angle 4 = m\angle DEF$	3. ? **Angle Addition Post.**
4. $m\angle ABC = m\angle DEF$	4. ? **Substitution Prop.**

12. Given: $ST = RN$; $IT = RU$

Prove: $SI = UN$

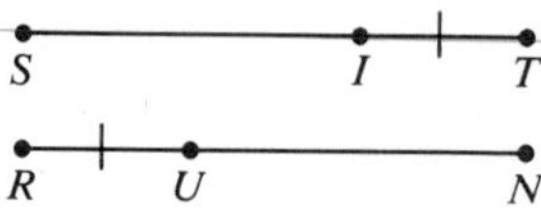

Proof:

Statements	Reasons
1. $ST = RN$	1. ? **Given**
2. ? $= SI + IT$; **ST** ? $= RU + UN$ **RN**	2. ? **Segment Addition Post.**
3. $SI + IT = RU + UN$	3. ? **Substitution Prop.**
4. $IT = RU$	4. ? **Given**
5. ? ***SI = UN***	5. ? **Subtraction Prop. of =**

Written Exercises

Justify each step.

A

1.
$4x - 5 = -2$ **Given**
$4x = 3$ **Add. Prop. of =**
$x = \frac{3}{4}$ **Div. Prop. of =**

2.
$\frac{3a}{2} = \frac{6}{5}$ **Given**
$3a = \frac{12}{5}$ **Mult. Prop. of =**
$a = \frac{4}{5}$ **Div. Prop. of =**

3.
$\frac{z + 7}{3} = -11$
$z + 7 = -33$
$z = -40$

4.
$15y + 7 = 12 - 20y$ **Given**
$35y + 7 = 12$ **Add. Prop. of =**
$35y = 5$ **Subtr. Prop. of =**
$y = \frac{1}{7}$ **Div. Prop. of =**

5.
$\frac{2}{3}b = 8 - 2b$
$2b = 3(8 - 2b)$
$2b = 24 - 6b$
$8b = 24$
$b = 3$

6.
$x - 2 = \frac{2x + 8}{5}$
$5(x - 2) = 2x + 8$
$5x - 10 = 2x + 8$
$3x - 10 = 8$
$3x = 18$
$x = 6$

Copy everything shown and supply missing statements and reasons.

7. Given: $\angle AOD$ as shown
Prove: $m\angle AOD = m\angle 1 + m\angle 2 + m\angle 3$

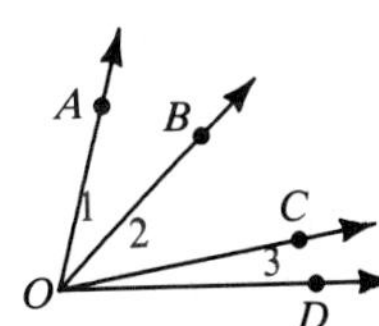

Proof:

Statements	Reasons
1. $m\angle AOD = m\angle AOC + m\angle 3$	1. __?__ **Angle Addition Postulate**
2. $m\angle AOC = m\angle 1 + m\angle 2$	2. __?__ **Angle Addition Postulate**
3. __?__ **$m\angle AOD = m\angle 1 + m\angle 2 + m\angle 3$**	3. __?__ **Substitution Prop.**

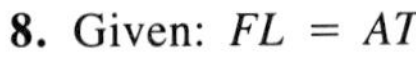

8. Given: $FL = AT$
Prove: $FA = LT$

Proof:

Statements	Reasons
1. __?__ **$FL = AT$**	1. Given
2. $LA = LA$	2. __?__ **Reflexive Prop.**
3. $FL + LA = AT + LA$	3. __?__ **Addition Prop. of =**
4. $FL + LA = FA$; $LA + AT = LT$	4. __?__ **Segment Addition Post.**
5. __?__ **$FA = LT$**	5. Substitution Prop.

Guided Practice

Justify each step.

1.
$2x + 3 = 11$ Given
$2x = 8$ Subtr. Prop. of =
$x = 4$ Div. Prop. of =

2.
$\frac{3}{4}x = 6 + 2x$ Given
$3x = 4(6 + 2x)$ Mult. Prop. of =
$3x = 24 + 8x$ Dist. Prop.
$-5x = 24$ Subt. Prop. of =
$x = -\frac{24}{5}$ Div. Prop. of =

Additional Answers Written Exercises

3. Given
Mult. Prop. of =
Subtr. Prop. of =

5. Given
Mult. Prop. of =
Dist. Prop.
Add. Prop. of =
Div. Prop. of =

6. Given
Mult. Prop. of =
Dist. Prop.
Subtr. Prop. of =
Add. Prop. of =
Div. Prop. of =

9. Given: $DW = ON$
Prove: $DO = WN$

Proof:

Statements	Reasons
1. $DW = ON$	1. _?_ **Given**
2. $DW = DO + OW$; $ON = \underline{?} + \underline{?}$ ***OW, WN***	2. _?_ **Segment Addition Post.**
3. _?_ $\boldsymbol{DO + OW = OW + WN}$	3. Substitution Prop.
4. $OW = OW$	4. _?_ **Reflexive Prop.**
5. _?_ $\boldsymbol{DO = WN}$	5. _?_ **Subtraction Prop. of =**

10. Given: $m\angle 4 + m\angle 6 = 180$
Prove: $m\angle 5 = m\angle 6$

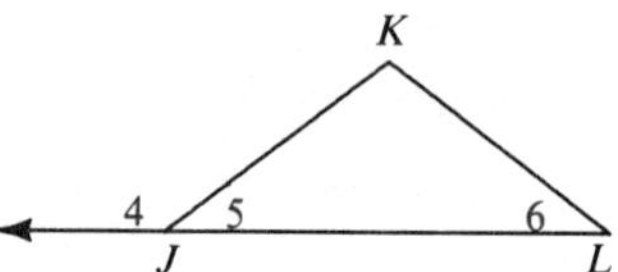

Proof:

Statements	Reasons
1. $m\angle 4 + m\angle 6 = 180$	1. _?_ **Given**
2. $m\angle 4 + m\angle 5 = 180$	2. _?_ **Angle Addition Post.**
3. $m\angle 4 + m\angle 5 = m\angle 4 + m\angle 6$	3. _?_ **Substitution Prop.**
4. $m\angle 4 = m\angle 4$	4. _?_ **Reflexive Prop.**
5. _?_ $\boldsymbol{m\angle 5 = m\angle 6}$	5. _?_ **Subtraction Prop. of =**

Copy everything shown and write a two-column proof.

B **11.** Given: $m\angle 1 = m\angle 2$; $m\angle 3 = m\angle 4$
Prove: $m\angle SRT = m\angle STR$

12. Given: $RP = TQ$; $PS = QS$
Prove: $RS = TS$

13. Given: $RQ = TP$; $ZQ = ZP$
Prove: $RZ = TZ$

14. Given: $m\angle SRT = m\angle STR$; $m\angle 3 = m\angle 4$
Prove: $m\angle 1 = m\angle 2$

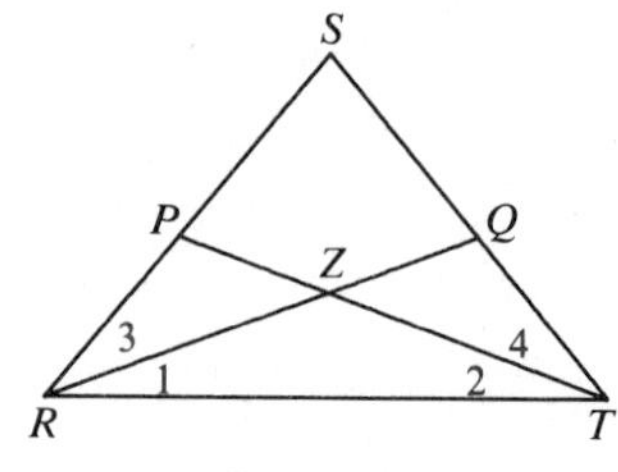

Exs. 11–14

Thinking Skills

In Ex. 10, students may ask why Statement 2 has been written. Explain that Angle 5 needs to be brought into the proof because of what is being proved. Statement 2 is the natural one to make about angle 5.

In Ex. 11, point out to students that angles 1, 2, 3, and 4 are parts of $\angle SRT$ and $\angle STR$, which need to be proved equal in measure. The one property that looks as if it may help really does help, namely the Addition Property of Equality.

Group Activity

Students can learn to write proofs by sharing their ideas with classmates in small groups. You may wish to use Exs. 11–14 as a group activity. Point out to students that the purpose of the group is to allow its members to help each other learn geometry. As the students work together trying to construct the proofs, suggest that each student play a role in the work by giving at least one statement or reason for each proof. As the students work on the proofs, you may wish to walk around the class, talking to a student or a group as you do so.

C **15.** Consider the following statements:

Reflexive Property: Robot A is as rusty as itself.
Symmetric Property: If Robot A is as rusty as Robot B, then Robot B is as rusty as Robot A.
Transitive Property: If Robot A is as rusty as Robot B and Robot B is as rusty as Robot C, then Robot A is as rusty as Robot C.

A *relation* such as "is as rusty as" that is reflexive, symmetric, and transitive is an *equivalence relation*. Which of the following are equivalence relations?

a. is rustier than (**b.**) has the same length as
c. is opposite (for rays) **d.** is coplanar with (for lines)

2-3 *Proving Theorems*

Chapter 1 included three *theorems*, statements that are proved. The theorems were deduced from *postulates*, statements that are accepted without proof. We will prove additional theorems throughout the book. When writing proofs, we will treat properties from algebra as postulates.

Suppose you are told that Y is the midpoint of $\overline{XZ}$ and that $XZ = 12$. You probably realize that $XY = 6$. Your conclusion about one particular situation suggests the general statement shown below as Theorem 2-1. The theorem uses the definition of a midpoint to prove additional properties of a midpoint that are not explicitly included in the definition. In this case, the theorem states something obvious. Later theorems may not be so obvious. In fact, some of them may surprise you.

Theorem 2-1 *Midpoint Theorem*

If M is the midpoint of $\overline{AB}$, then $AM = \frac{1}{2}AB$ and $MB = \frac{1}{2}AB$.

Given: M is the midpoint of $\overline{AB}$.
Prove: $AM = \frac{1}{2}AB$; $MB = \frac{1}{2}AB$

A M B

Proof:

Statements	Reasons
1. M is the midpoint of $\overline{AB}$.	1. Given
2. $\overline{AM} \cong \overline{MB}$, or $AM = MB$	2. Definition of midpoint
3. $AM + MB = AB$	3. Segment Addition Postulate
4. $AM + AM = AB$, or $2AM = AB$	4. Substitution Prop. (Steps 2 and 3)
5. $AM = \frac{1}{2}AB$	5. Division Prop. of =
6. $MB = \frac{1}{2}AB$	6. Substitution Prop. (Steps 2 and 5)

Teaching Suggestions,
pp. T80–T81
Objectives
Presenting the Lesson
Using Technology
Problem Solving
Reinforcement

Communication Skills,
p. T81

Supplementary Materials
Practice Master 7
Test 5
Resource Book, pp. 6, 113
Study Guide, pp. 15–16

Lesson Focus
A theorem is a statement that can be proved by using information that is known to be true. The purpose of this lesson is to begin the topic of what a proof is and how theorems are proved.

Suggested Assignments

Minimum
46–47/1–12, 13, 15, 17
S 42/11
49/Self-Test 1

Average
46–47/2–18 even, 19, 20
S 42/12–14
49/Self-Test 1

Maximum
46–47/12–22

Proof Note

On page 38, students were introduced to geometric proofs written in two-column form. Point out that the solution of Example 1 is a valid argument leading from what is given to a true conclusion. Therefore, the solution is a proof. Tell students that this proof is written in paragraph form, and that the paragraph form of proof is used most often in advanced mathematics courses.

Communication Skills

Remind students that a definition is really a biconditional statement, that is, both the statement (conditional) and its converse are true. Informally speaking, tell students that a definition works both ways. This idea is brought out in Exs. 6 and 7. In Ex. 9, the statements "$\angle BEC \cong \angle CEF$" and "$\overrightarrow{EC}$ is the bisector of $\angle BEF$" express the same idea.

Example 1 Given: M is the midpoint of $\overline{AB}$;
N is the midpoint of $\overline{CD}$;
$AB = CD$
What can you deduce?

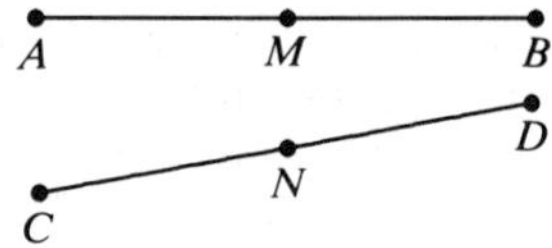

Solution Because M and N are midpoints, you know that $AM = MB$ and $CN = ND$. From the Midpoint Theorem, you know that $AM = \frac{1}{2}AB$ and $CN = \frac{1}{2}CD$. Since $AB = CD$, you know that $\frac{1}{2}AB = \frac{1}{2}CD$. By substitution, you get $AM = CN$. Thus you can deduce that AM, MB, CN, and ND are all equal.

The next theorem is similar to the Midpoint Theorem. It proves properties of the angle bisector that are not given in the definition. The proof is left as Classroom Exercise 10.

Theorem 2-2 *Angle Bisector Theorem*

If $\overrightarrow{BX}$ is the bisector of $\angle ABC$, then

$$m\angle ABX = \tfrac{1}{2}m\angle ABC \text{ and } m\angle XBC = \tfrac{1}{2}m\angle ABC.$$

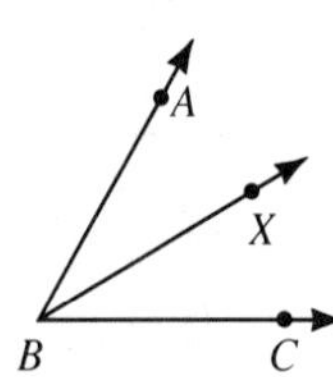

Given: $\overrightarrow{BX}$ is the bisector of $\angle ABC$.

Prove: $m\angle ABX = \frac{1}{2}m\angle ABC$; $m\angle XBC = \frac{1}{2}m\angle ABC$

In addition to postulates and definitions, theorems may be used to justify steps in a proof. Notice the use of the Angle Bisector Theorem in Example 2.

Example 2

Given: $\overrightarrow{EG}$ is the bisector of $\angle DEF$;
$\overrightarrow{SW}$ is the bisector of $\angle RST$;
$m\angle DEG = m\angle RSW$

Prove: $m\angle DEF = m\angle RST$

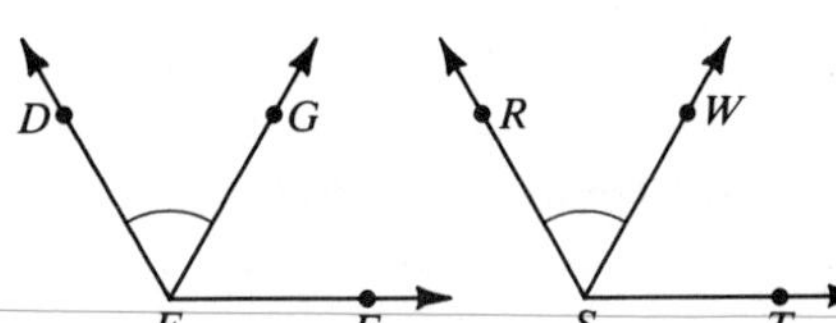

Proof:

Statements	Reasons
1. $\overrightarrow{EG}$ is the bisector of $\angle DEF$; $\overrightarrow{SW}$ is the bisector of $\angle RST$.	1. Given
2. $m\angle DEG = \frac{1}{2}m\angle DEF$; $m\angle RSW = \frac{1}{2}m\angle RST$	2. Angle Bisector Theorem
3. $m\angle DEG = m\angle RSW$	3. Given
4. $\frac{1}{2}m\angle DEF = \frac{1}{2}m\angle RST$	4. Substitution Prop. (Steps 2 and 3)
5. $m\angle DEF = m\angle RST$	5. Multiplication Prop. of =

The two-column proofs you have seen in this section and the previous one are examples of **deductive reasoning.** We have proved statements by reasoning from postulates, definitions, theorems, and given information. The kinds of reasons you can use to justify statements in a proof are listed below.

Reasons Used in Proofs

Given information

Definitions

Postulates (These include properties from algebra.)

Theorems that have already been proved

Teaching Note

Point out to students that once a theorem has been proved, it can be used as a reason in a proof.

Classroom Exercises

4. Def. of midpt. 5. Midpt. Thm. 6, 7, Def. of segment bisector

What postulate, definition, or theorem justifies the statement about the diagram?

1. $m\angle AEB + m\angle BEC = m\angle AEC$ **Angle Add. Post.**
2. $AE + EF = AF$ **Segment Add. Post.**
3. $m\angle AEB + m\angle BEF = 180$ **Angle Add. Post.**
4. If E is the midpoint of $\overline{AF}$, then $\overline{AE} \cong \overline{EF}$.
5. If E is the midpoint of $\overline{AF}$, then $AE = \frac{1}{2}AF$.
6. If E is the midpoint of $\overline{AF}$, then $\overrightarrow{EC}$ bisects $\overline{AF}$.
7. If $\overrightarrow{EB}$ bisects $\overline{AF}$, then E is the midpoint of $\overline{AF}$.
8. If $\overrightarrow{EB}$ is the bisector of $\angle AEC$, then $m\angle AEB = \frac{1}{2}m\angle AEC$. **Angle Bisector Thm.**
9. If $\angle BEC \cong \angle CEF$, then $\overrightarrow{EC}$ is the bisector of $\angle BEF$. **Def. of angle bisector**

Exs. 1–9

10. Complete the proof of Theorem 2-2.
    Given: $\overrightarrow{BX}$ is the bisector of $\angle ABC$.
    Prove: $m\angle ABX = \frac{1}{2}m\angle ABC$; $m\angle XBC = \frac{1}{2}m\angle ABC$

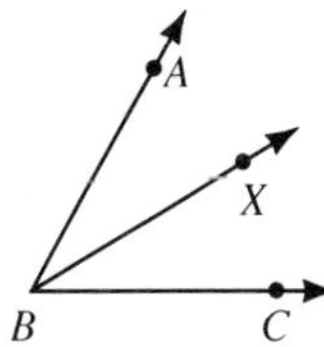

Proof:

Statements	Reasons
1. $\overrightarrow{BX}$ is the bisector of $\angle ABC$.	1. ? **Given**
2. $\angle ABX \cong$? **$\angle XBC$**, or $m\angle ABX =$? **$m\angle XBC$**	2. ? **Def. of angle bisector**
3. $m\angle ABX + m\angle XBC = m\angle ABC$	3. ? **Angle Addition Post.**
4. $m\angle ABX + m\angle ABX = m\angle ABC$, or $2m\angle ABX = m\angle ABC$	4. ? **Substitution Prop.**
5. $m\angle ABX = \frac{1}{2}m\angle ABC$	5. ? **Mult. Prop. of =**
6. $m\angle XBC = \frac{1}{2}m\angle ABC$	6. Substitution Prop. (Steps ? **2** and ? **5**)

Chalkboard Examples

1. Given: $m\angle 1 = m\angle 2$; $\overrightarrow{AD}$ bisects $\angle CAB$; $\overrightarrow{BD}$ bisects $\angle CBA$
Prove: $m\angle 3 = m\angle 4$

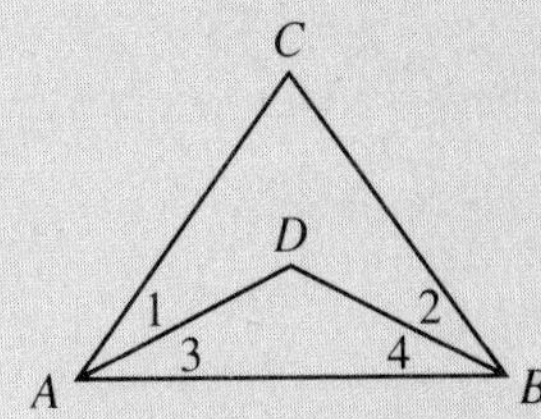

1. $m\angle 1 = m\angle 2$; $\overrightarrow{AD}$ bisects $\angle CAB$; $\overrightarrow{BD}$ bisects $\angle CBA$ (Given)
2. $m\angle 1 = m\angle 3$; $m\angle 2 = m\angle 4$ (Def. of $\angle$ bisector)
3. $m\angle 3 = m\angle 4$ (Subst. Prop.)

2. Given: $WX = YZ$; Y is the midpoint of $\overline{XZ}$
Prove: $WX = XY$

1. $WX = YZ$; Y is the midpt. of $\overline{XZ}$ (Given)
2. $XY = YZ$ (Def. of midpt.)
3. $WX = XY$ (Subst. Prop.)

Exercise Note

Alert students to the fact that they are to *name* the definition, postulate, or theorem for Exs. 1–8, and not write the full statements. A full statement for Ex. 8 of the Segment Addition Postulate would be confusing because of the use of letters *A*, *B*, and *C*, which would have to be replaced by *B*, *C*, and *D*.

Guided Practice

The coordinates of points *P*, *Q*, and *M* are given in the table. *M* is the midpoint of $\overline{PQ}$. Complete the table.

P	1	19	−2	a	1	b
Q	25	7	24	3a	?	?
M	?	?	?	?	−2	4b
	13	13	11	2a	−5	7b

Additional Answers Written Exercises

12.d. Since $m\angle LMP + m\angle PMN = 180$, then $\frac{1}{2}m\angle LMP + \frac{1}{2}m\angle PMN = \frac{1}{2}(m\angle LMP + m\angle PMN) = \frac{1}{2}(180) = 90$

Written Exercises

Name the definition, postulate, or theorem that justifies the statement about the diagram. **2. Def of ∠ bisector 5. Def. of midpoint 6. Midpoint Thm.**

A

1. If D is the midpoint of $\overline{BC}$, then $\overline{BD} \cong \overline{DC}$. **Def. of midpoint**
2. If $\angle 1 \cong \angle 2$, then $\overrightarrow{AD}$ is the bisector of $\angle BAC$.
3. If $\overrightarrow{AD}$ bisects $\angle BAC$, then $\angle 1 \cong \angle 2$. **Def. of ∠ bis.**
4. $m\angle 3 + m\angle 4 = 180$ **Angle Addition Post.**
5. If $\overline{BD} \cong \overline{DC}$, then D is the midpoint of $\overline{BC}$.
6. If D is the midpoint of $\overline{BC}$, then $BD = \frac{1}{2}BC$.
7. $m\angle 1 + m\angle 2 = m\angle BAC$ **Angle Add. Post.**
8. $BD + DC = BC$ **Segment Addition Post.**

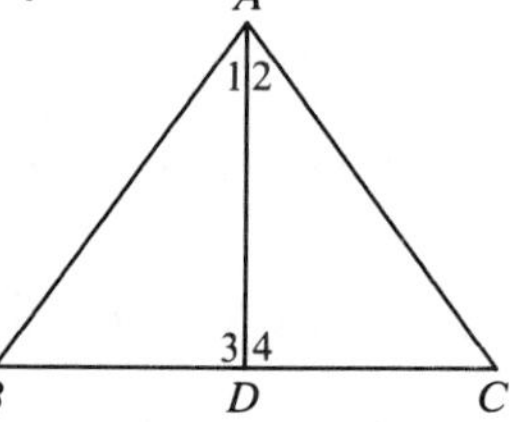

Exs. 1–8

Write the number that is paired with the bisector of ∠CDE.

9. **60**

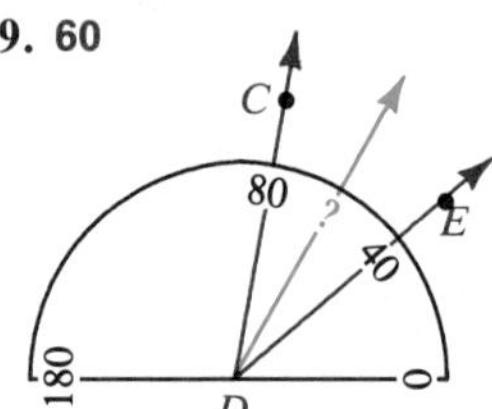

10. **75**

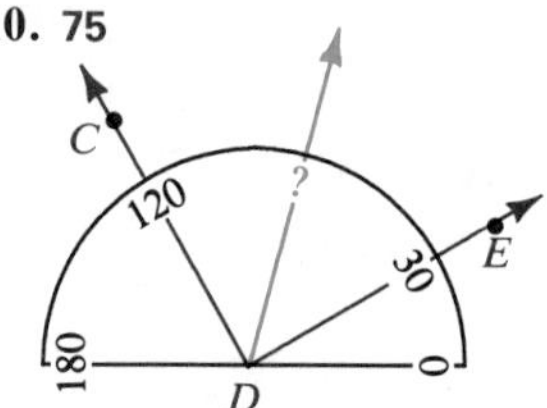

11. **70**

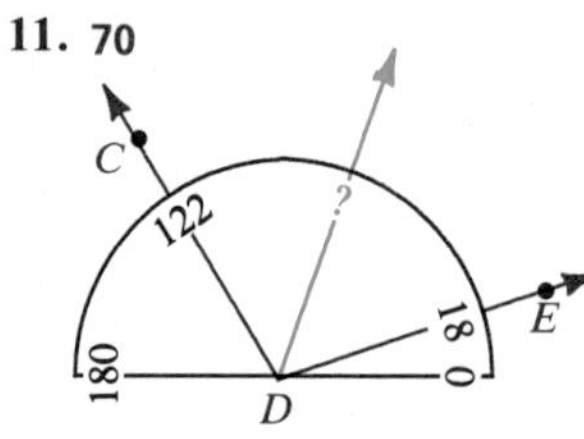

12. a. Draw a diagram similar to the one shown.
    b. Use a protractor to draw the bisectors of $\angle LMP$ and $\angle PMN$. **Check students' drawings.**
    c. What is the measure of the angle formed by these bisectors? **90**
    d. Explain how you could have known the answer to part (c) without measuring.

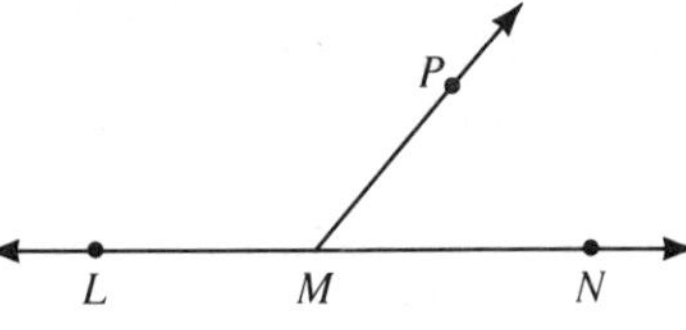

B

13. The coordinates of points L and X are 16 and 40, respectively. N is the midpoint of $\overline{LX}$, and Y is the midpoint of $\overline{LN}$. Sketch a diagram and find: **a.** LN **12** **b.** the coordinate of N **28** **c.** LY **6** **d.** the coordinate of Y **22**

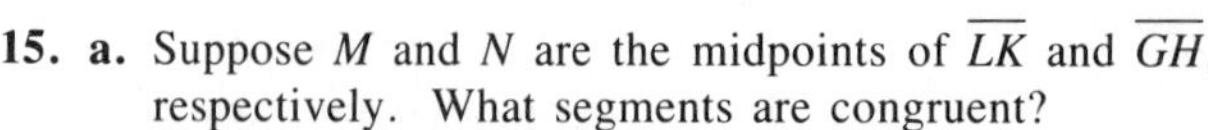

14. $\overrightarrow{SW}$ bisects $\angle RST$ and $m\angle RST = 72$. $\overrightarrow{SZ}$ bisects $\angle RSW$, and $\overrightarrow{SR}$ bisects $\angle NSW$. Sketch a diagram and find $m\angle RSZ$ and $m\angle NSZ$. **18, 54**

15. a. Suppose M and N are the midpoints of $\overline{LK}$ and $\overline{GH}$, respectively. What segments are congruent?
    b. What additional information about the figure would enable you to deduce that $LM = NH$?

16. a. Suppose $\overrightarrow{SV}$ bisects $\angle RST$ and $\overrightarrow{RU}$ bisects $\angle SRT$. What angles are congruent?
    b. What additional information would enable you to deduce that $m\angle VSU = m\angle URV$?

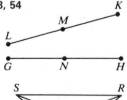

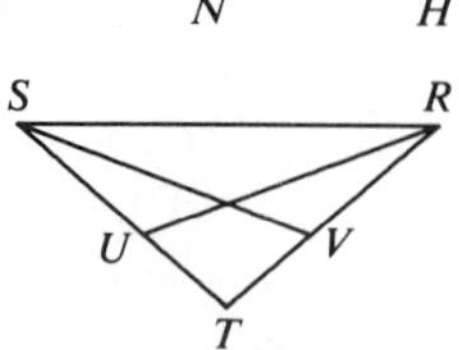

15. a. $\overline{LM}$ **and** $\overline{MK}$, $\overline{GN}$ **and** $\overline{NH}$ **b.** $\overline{LK} \cong \overline{GH}$

16. a. $\angle RSV$ **and** $\angle VST$, $\angle SRU$ **and** $\angle URT$ **b.** $\angle RST \cong \angle SRT$

What can you deduce from the given information?

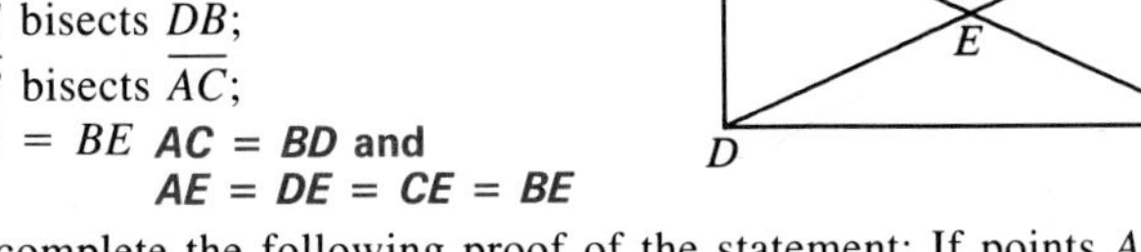

17. Given: $AE = DE$;
$CE = BE$ **$AC = BD$**

18. Given: $\overline{AC}$ bisects $\overline{DB}$;
$\overline{DB}$ bisects $\overline{AC}$;
$CE = BE$ **$AC = BD$ and $AE = DE = CE = BE$**

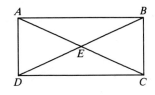

19. Copy and complete the following proof of the statement: If points A and B have coordinates a and b, with $b > a$, and the midpoint M of $\overline{AB}$ has coordinate x, then $x = \frac{a + b}{2}$.

Given: Points A and B have coordinates a and b;
$b > a$; midpoint M of $\overline{AB}$ has coordinate x.

Prove: $x = \frac{a + b}{2}$

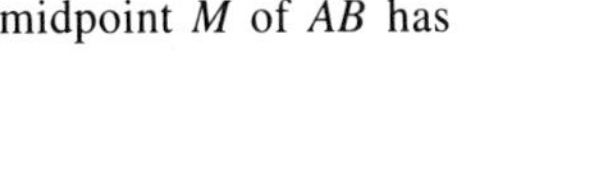

Proof:

Statements	Reasons
1. A, M, and B have coordinates a, x, and b respectively; $b > a$	1. __?__ **Given**
2. $AM = x - a$; $MB = b - x$	2. __?__ **Ruler Postulate**
3. M is the midpoint of $\overline{AB}$.	3. __?__ **Given**
4. $\overline{AM} \cong \overline{MB}$, or $AM = MB$	4. __?__ **Def. of midpoint**
5. $x - a = b - x$	5. __?__ **Substitution Prop.**
6. $2x =$ __?__ **$a + b$**	6. __?__ **Addition Prop. of =**
7. $x = \frac{a + b}{2}$	7. __?__ **Division Prop. of =**

C **20.** Fold down a corner of a rectangular sheet of paper. Then fold the next corner so that the edges touch as in the figure. Measure the angle formed by the fold lines. Repeat with another sheet of paper, folding the corner at a different angle. Explain why the angles formed are congruent.

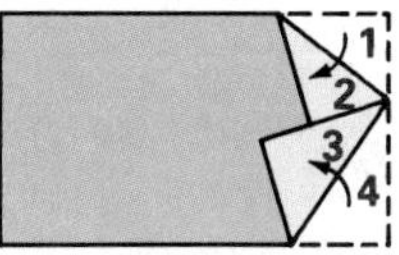

21. M is the midpoint of $\overline{AB}$, Q is the midpoint of $\overline{AM}$, and T is the midpoint of $\overline{QM}$. If the coordinates of A and B are a and b, find the coordinates of Q and T in terms of a and b. **Q: $\frac{3a + b}{4}$ T: $\frac{5a + 3b}{8}$**

22. Point T is the midpoint of $\overline{RS}$, W is the midpoint of $\overline{RT}$, and Z is the midpoint of $\overline{WS}$. If the length of $\overline{TZ}$ is x, find the following lengths in terms of x. (*Hint*: Sketch a diagram and let $y = WT$.)

a. RW **$2x$** **b.** ZS **$3x$** **c.** RS **$8x$** **d.** WZ **$3x$**

20. $m\angle 1 + m\angle 2 + m\angle 3 + m\angle 4 = 180$; $m\angle 1 = m\angle 2$; $m\angle 3 = m\angle 4$; $2m\angle 2 + 2m\angle 3 = 180$; $m\angle 2 + m\angle 3 = 90$

Problem Solving

Exs. 17 and 18 allow students to make some conjectures about the properties of the figure shown. Making conjectures is an important problem-solving activity. Students should be encouraged to pose their own questions and problems and then attempt to prove them deductively or to disprove them by giving a counterexample.

In Ex. 17, a student might conclude that $AE + BE = CE + DE$. This conclusion is not wrong. On the other hand, it is less significant than the conclusion that $AC = BD$.

If time permits, you may wish to have students try to prove their conclusions for Exs. 17 and 18.

Group Activity

Exs. 20–22 can be worked as a group activity. However, if a student chooses to work alone, this choice should be respected. Also, it is important to allow students to form their own groups so that they begin to take responsibility for their own learning. Emphasize that the members of a group are to support one another in order to derive mutual benefits from working together. Each group member also has a responsibility to participate in the work of the group.

Using a Computer

This computer activity is designed to give students an opportunity to explore new mathematical concepts. With the use of the computer, students can direct their energy towards understanding new concepts instead of exerting a large amount of time and energy on tedious or complicated calculations.

♦ Computer Key-In

A bee starts at point P_0, flies to point P_1, and lands. The bee then returns half of the way to P_0, landing at P_2. From P_2, the bee returns half of the way to P_1, landing at P_3, and so forth. Can you predict the bee's location after 10 trips?

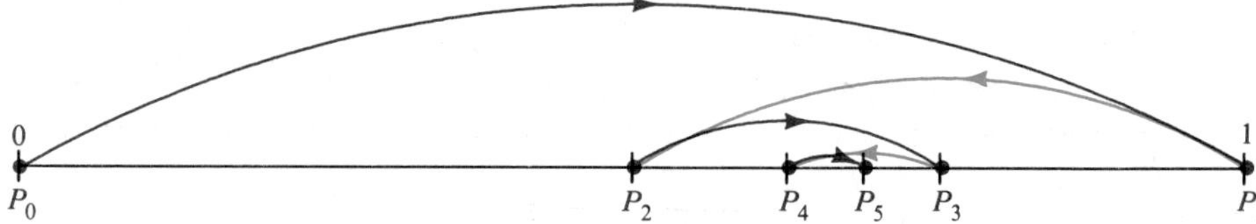

Assuming that P_0 and P_1 have coordinates 0 and 1, respectively, the BASIC program below will compute and print the bee's location at the end of trips 2 through 10. P_n represents the position of the bee after n trips. Since P_n is the midpoint of the bee's previous two positions, P_{n-1} and P_{n-2}, line 50 calculates $P(N)$ by using the statement proved in Exercise 19, page 47.

```
10 DIM P(50)
20 LET P(0) = 0
30 LET P(1) = 1
40 FOR N = 2 TO 10
50 LET P(N) = (1/2) * (P(N - 2) + P(N - 1))
60 PRINT N, P(N)
70 NEXT N
80 END
```

Exercises

1. Enter the program on your computer and RUN it. Do you notice any patterns or trends in the coordinates? Change line 40 so that the computer will print the coordinates up to P_{40}. What simple fraction is approximated by P_{40}? **40 FOR N = 2 to 40; $\frac{2}{3}$**

2. In line 50, $P(n)$ could instead be computed from the *series*
$$1 - \tfrac{1}{2} + \tfrac{1}{4} - \tfrac{1}{8} + \cdots + (-\tfrac{1}{2})^{n-1}$$
where each term of the series reflects the bee's return half of the way from P_{n-1} to P_{n-2}. Replace line 50 with the line below and RUN the new program.

```
50 LET P(N) = P(N - 1) + (-1/2) ↑ (N - 1)
```

Check that both programs produce the same results. (Some slight variations will be expected, due to rounding off.)

3. Suppose that on each trip the bee returned one third of the way to the previous point instead of half of the way. How would the series in Exercise 2 be modified? How would line 50 of Exercise 2 be modified? RUN a modified program for 30 trips and determine what point the bee seems to be approaching. **$1 - \frac{1}{3} + \frac{1}{9} - \frac{1}{27} + \cdots + (-\frac{1}{3})^{n-1}$; P(N) = P(N − 1) + (−1/3) ↑ (N − 1); $\frac{3}{4}$**

Self-Test 1

2. If $\overrightarrow{AB}$ and $\overrightarrow{CD}$ intersect, then $\overline{AB}$ and $\overline{CD}$ intersect; False

Use the conditional: If $\overline{AB}$ and $\overline{CD}$ intersect, then $\overrightarrow{AB}$ and $\overrightarrow{CD}$ intersect.

1. Write the hypothesis and the conclusion of the conditional. **H: $\overline{AB}$ and $\overline{CD}$ intersect C: $\overrightarrow{AB}$ and $\overrightarrow{CD}$ intersect**
2. Write the converse of the conditional. Is the converse true or false?
3. Rewrite the following pair of conditionals as a biconditional: **$\overline{AB} \cong \overline{CD}$ if and only if $AB = CD$.**
   $\overline{AB} \cong \overline{CD}$ if $AB = CD$; $\overline{AB} \cong \overline{CD}$ only if $AB = CD$.
4. Provide a counterexample to disprove the statement: **Answers may vary; $m\angle A = 95$**
   If $m\angle A$ is less than 100, then $\angle A$ is an acute angle.
5. Given: $m\angle A + m\angle B = 180$; $m\angle C = m\angle B$
   What property of equality justifies the statement $m\angle A + m\angle C = 180$? **Substitution Prop.**
6. Point M is the midpoint of $\overline{RT}$. $RM = x$ and $RT = 4x - 6$. Find the value of x. **$x = 3$**
7. The measure of $\angle ABC$ is 108. $\overrightarrow{BD}$ is the bisector of $\angle ABC$, and $\overrightarrow{BE}$ is the bisector of $\angle ABD$. Find the measure of $\angle EBC$. **81**
8. You can use given information and theorems as reasons in proofs. Name two other kinds of reasons you can use. **definitions, postulates**

Biographical Note — *Julia Morgan*

Julia Morgan (1872–1959), the first successful woman architect in the United States, was born in San Francisco. Though best known for her design of San Simeon, the castle-like former home of William Randolph Hearst pictured at the left, she designed numerous public buildings and private homes. Even today, to own "a Julia Morgan house" carries considerable prestige.

To become an architect, Morgan needed great determination as well as a brilliant mind. Since the University of California did not have an architecture curriculum at that time, she prepared for graduate work in Paris by studying civil engineering. In Paris the École des Beaux-Arts, which had just begun to admit foreigners, was particularly reluctant to admit a foreign woman. She persisted, however, and became the school's first woman graduate.

Assessment

Self-Test 1 provides an opportunity for students to informally assess their understanding of the main ideas presented in the first three lessons of this chapter. Review the answers to the test items with students to make sure they understand the concepts involved. Students showing any deficiencies in their grasp of the material will need to restudy the appropriate parts of the chapter.

Quick Quiz

Classify each statement as true or false.

1. The converse of a true statement is sometimes false. T
2. Only one counterexample is needed to disprove a statement. T
3. Properties of numbers cannot be used in geometric proofs. F
4. Postulates are deduced from theorems. F
5. Every angle has only one bisector. T

Teaching Suggestions, p. T81

Objectives
Presenting the Lesson
Problem Solving
Reinforcement

Exploring Activity, p. 31c

Supplementary Materials

Practice Master 8
Study Guide, pp. 17–18
Computer Activity 4

Lesson Focus

Pairs of angles whose measures have the sum 90 or 180 appear frequently in geometric situations. For this reason, they are given special names. This lesson studies these special angles and solves problems involving them.

Suggested Assignments

Minimum
52–53/1–20, 23, 25

Average
52–53/7–25 odd, 28, 29

Maximum
53–54/19–31 odd, 32–35

Theorems about Angles and Perpendicular Lines

Objectives

1. Apply the definitions of complementary and supplementary angles.
2. State and use the theorem about vertical angles.
3. Apply the definition and theorems about perpendicular lines.
4. State and apply the theorems about angles supplementary to, or complementary to, congruent angles.
5. Plan proofs and then write them in two-column form.

2-4 *Special Pairs of Angles*

Complementary angles (comp. ∠s) are two angles whose measures have the sum 90. Each angle is called a *complement* of the other.

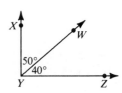

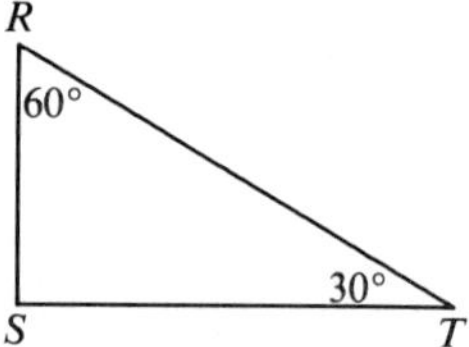

$\angle R$ and $\angle T$ are complementary.

$\angle XYW$ is a complement of $\angle WYZ$.

Supplementary angles (supp. ∠s) are two angles whose measures have the sum 180. Each angle is called a *supplement* of the other.

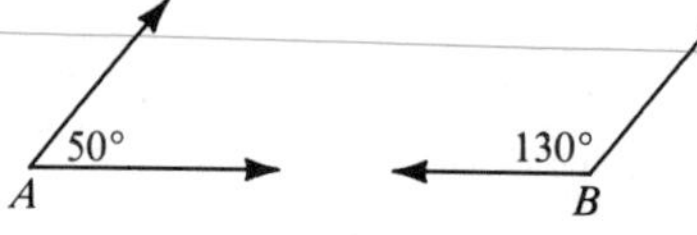

$\angle A$ and $\angle B$ are supplementary.

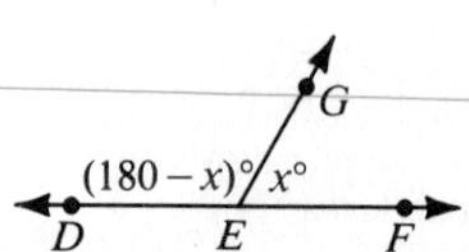

$\angle DEG$ is a supplement of $\angle GEF$.

Example 1 A supplement of an angle is three times as large as a complement of the angle. Find the measure of the angle.

Solution Let x = the measure of the angle.
Then $180 - x$ = the measure of its supplement,
and $90 - x$ = the measure of its complement.

$$180 - x = 3(90 - x)$$
$$180 - x = 270 - 3x$$
$$2x = 90$$
$$x = 45$$

The measure of the angle is 45.

Vertical angles (vert. ∠s) are two angles such that the sides of one angle are opposite rays to the sides of the other angle. When two lines intersect, they form two pairs of vertical angles.

∠1 and ∠3 are vert. ∠s. ∠2 and ∠4 are vert. ∠s.

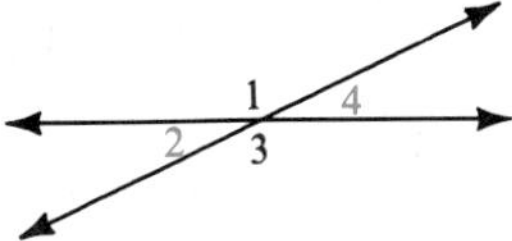

Theorem 2-3

Vertical angles are congruent.

Given: ∠1 and ∠2 are vertical angles.

Prove: ∠1 ≅ 2

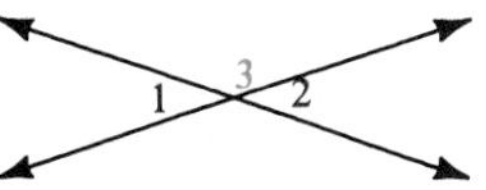

Proof:

Statements	Reasons
1. $m\angle 1 + m\angle 3 = 180$; $m\angle 2 + m\angle 3 = 180$	1. Angle Addition Postulate
2. $m\angle 1 + m\angle 3 = m\angle 2 + m\angle 3$	2. Substitution Prop.
3. $m\angle 3 = m\angle 3$	3. Reflexive Prop.
4. $m\angle 1 = m\angle 2$, or $\angle 1 \cong \angle 2$	4. Subtraction Prop. of =

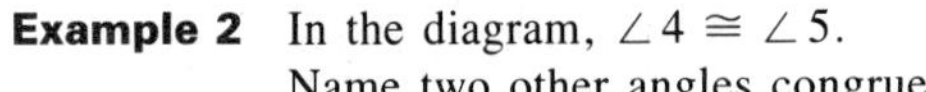

Example 2 In the diagram, ∠4 ≅ ∠5. Name two other angles congruent to ∠5.

Solution ∠8 ≅ ∠5 since vertical angles are congruent. Since ∠7 ≅ ∠4 and ∠4 ≅ ∠5, ∠7 ≅ ∠5 by the Transitive Property.

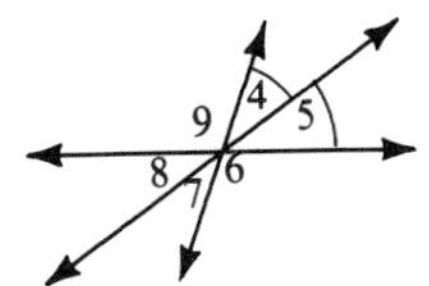

Classroom Exercises

Find the measures of a complement and a supplement of ∠A.

1. $m\angle A = 10$ **80, 170**
2. $m\angle A = 75$ **15, 105**
3. $m\angle A = 89$ **1, 91**
4. $m\angle A = y$ **90 − y, 180 − y**
5. Name two right angles. ***∠M, ∠QPM***
6. Name two adjacent complementary angles. ***∠LPQ, ∠LPM***
7. Name two complementary angles that are not adjacent. ***∠LPM, ∠MLP***
8. **a.** Name a supplement of ∠MLQ. ***∠LQP***
   b. Name another pair of supplementary angles. ***∠M and ∠MPQ***

L M 40° 60° 50° 80° 40° Q P

9. In the diagram, $m\angle AXB = 90$. Name:
   a. two congruent supplementary angles ***∠AXB and ∠BXD***
   b. two supplementary angles that are not congruent ***∠AXC and ∠CXD***
   c. two complementary angles ***∠BXC and ∠CXD***
   d. a straight angle ***∠AXD***

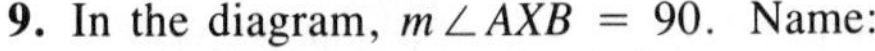

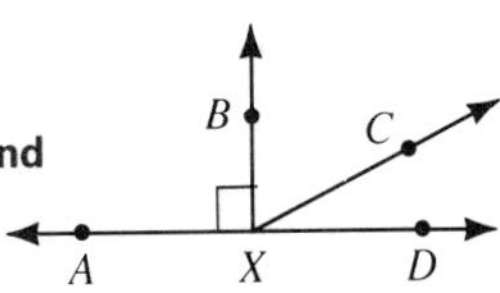

Chalkboard Examples

Give the complement and the supplement of each angle measure.

1. 32 58; 148
2. 87 3; 93
3. *b* 90 − *b*; 180 − *b*

Classify each statement as true or false.

4. If $m\angle A + m\angle B + m\angle C = 180$, then ∠A, ∠B, and ∠C are supplementary. F
5. Vertical angles have the same measure. T
6. If ∠1 and ∠2 are vertical angles, $m\angle 1 = 2x + 18$, and $m\angle 2 = 3x + 4$, then $x = 14$. T

Proof Note

Most students will understand that an identical proof can be given for the other pair of vertical angles, and that it is not necessary to write down the steps.

Complete.

10. $\angle AOB \cong$ _?_ $\angle$ ***EOD***
11. $\angle AOE \cong$ _?_ $\angle$ ***BOD***
12. $\angle FOB \cong$ _?_ $\angle$ ***EOC***
13. $\angle COA \cong$ _?_ $\angle$ ***FOD***
14. $m\angle FOE =$ _?_ **60**
15. $m\angle COD =$ _?_ **40**
16. $m\angle DOB =$ _?_ **100**
17. $m\angle AOB =$ _?_ **80**
18. $m\angle COE =$ _?_ **120**
19. $m\angle FOB =$ _?_ **120**

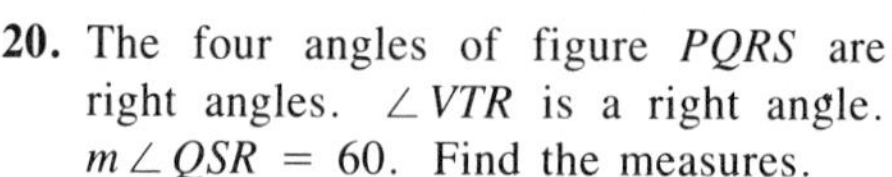

20. The four angles of figure $PQRS$ are right angles. $\angle VTR$ is a right angle. $m\angle QSR = 60$. Find the measures.
    a. $m\angle VTP$ **90**
    b. $m\angle XSY$ **60**
    c. $m\angle RSX$ **120**
    c. $m\angle PSY$ **90**

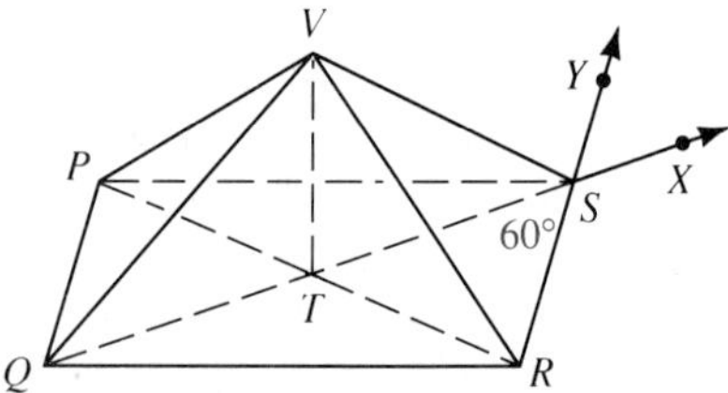

21. Given: $\angle 2 \cong \angle 3$
    a. What can you deduce? **∠1 ≅ ∠4**
    b. Explain how you would prove your conclusion. **∠1 ≅ ∠2 and ∠3 ≅ ∠4 because vertical ∠s are ≅. ∠1 ≅ ∠4 by the Transitive Prop.**

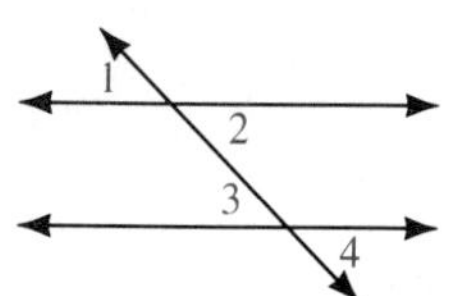

Written Exercises

Find the measures of a complement and a supplement of $\angle K$.

2. $17\frac{1}{2}$, $107\frac{1}{2}$
3. $90 - x$, $180 - x$

A

1. $m\angle K = 20$ **70, 160**
2. $m\angle K = 72\frac{1}{2}$
3. $m\angle K = x$
4. $m\angle K = 2y$ **$90 - 2y$, $180 - 2y$**
5. Two complementary angles are congruent. Find their measures. **45, 45**
6. Two supplementary angles are congruent. Find their measures. **90, 90**

In the diagram, $\angle AFB$ is a right angle. Name the figures described.

7. Another right angle **∠AFD**
8. Two complementary angles
9. Two congruent **∠AFD and** supplementary angles **∠AFB**
10. Two noncongruent supplementary angles
11. Two acute vertical angles **∠BFC and ∠EFD**
12. Two obtuse vertical angles **∠BFE and ∠CFD**

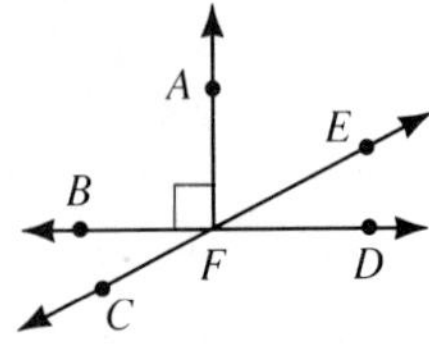

In the diagram, $\overrightarrow{OT}$ bisects $\angle SOU$, $m\angle UOV = 35$, and $m\angle YOW = 120$. Find the measure of each angle.

13. $m\angle ZOY$ **35**
14. $m\angle ZOW$ **155**
15. $m\angle VOW$ **25**
16. $m\angle SOU$ **120**
17. $m\angle TOU$ **60**
18. $m\angle ZOT$ **85**

8. ∠AFE and ∠EFD, or ∠AFE and ∠BFC
10. ∠BFE and ∠EFD, ∠CFA and ∠AFE, ∠DFC and ∠CFB

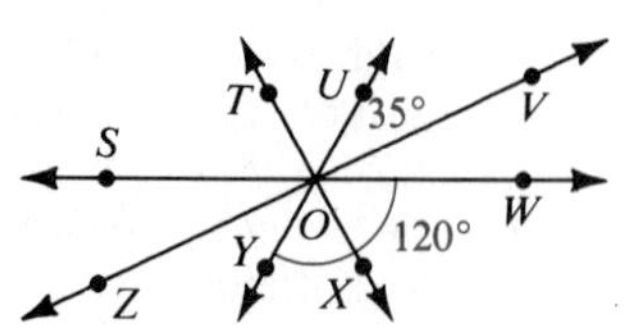

Guided Practice

Find the measure of a complement and a supplement of $\angle T$.

1. $m\angle T = 40$ 50; 140
2. $m\angle T = 89$ 1; 91
3. $m\angle T = 75$ 15; 105
4. $m\angle T = a$ $90 - a$; $180 - a$
5. $m\angle T = 3x$ $90 - 3x$; $180 - 3x$

Complete with *always*, *sometimes*, or *never*.

6. Vertical angles always have a common vertex.
7. Two right angles are never complementary.
8. Right angles are sometimes vertical angles.
9. Angles A, B, and C are never complementary.
10. Vertical angles always have a common supplement.

Find the value of x.

19. 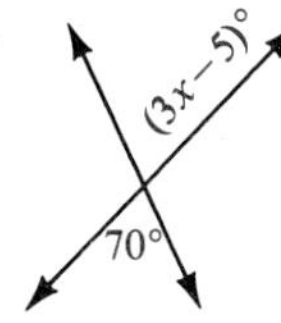

$x = 25$

20. 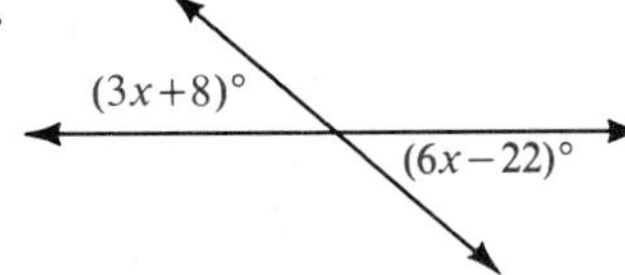

$x = 10$

21. 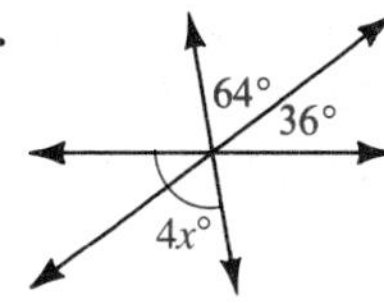

$x = 25$

22. $\angle 1$ and $\angle 2$ are supplements.
$\angle 3$ and $\angle 4$ are supplements.

a. If $m\angle 1 = m\angle 3 = 27$, find $m\angle 2$ and $m\angle 4$. **153; 153**

b. If $m\angle 1 = m\angle 3 = x$, find $m\angle 2$ and $m\angle 4$ in terms of x. **$180 - x$; $180 - x$**

c. If two angles are congruent, must their supplements be congruent? **Yes**

23. Copy everything shown. Complete the proof.

Given: $\angle 2 \cong \angle 3$
Prove: $\angle 1 \cong \angle 4$

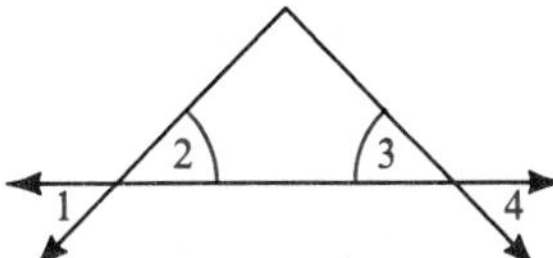

Proof:

Statements	Reasons
1. $\angle 1 \cong \angle 2$	1. ? **Vertical $\angle$s are $\cong$.**
2. $\angle 2 \cong \angle 3$	2. ? **Given**
3. $\angle 3 \cong \angle 4$	3. ? **Vertical $\angle$s are $\cong$.**
4. ? **$\angle 1 \cong \angle 4$**	4. Transitive Property (used twice)

If $\angle A$ and $\angle B$ are supplementary, find the value of x, $m\angle A$, and $m\angle B$.

B **24.** $m\angle A = 2x$, $m\angle B = x - 15$
$x = 65$, $m\angle A = 130$, $m\angle B = 50$

25. $m\angle A = x + 16$, $m\angle B = 2x - 16$
$x = 60$, $m\angle A = 76$, $m\angle B = 104$

If $\angle C$ and $\angle D$ are complementary, find the value of y, $m\angle C$, and $m\angle D$.

26. $m\angle C = 3y + 5$, $m\angle D = 2y$
$y = 17$, $m\angle C = 56$, $m\angle D = 34$

27. $m\angle C = y - 8$, $m\angle D = 3y + 2$
$y = 24$, $m\angle C = 16$, $m\angle D = 74$

Use the given information to write an equation and solve the problem.

28. Find the measure of an angle that is twice as large as its supplement. **$x = 2(180 - x)$; 120**

29. Find the measure of an angle that is half as large as its complement. **$x = \frac{1}{2}(90 - x)$; 30**

30. The measure of a supplement of an angle is 12 more than twice the measure of the angle. Find the measures of the angle and its supplement. **$180 - x = 2x + 12$; 56; 124**

31. A supplement of an angle is six times as large as a complement of the angle. Find the measures of the angle, its supplement, and its complement. **$180 - x = 6(90 - x)$; 72; 108; 18**

Problem Solving

Point out to students that moving the word *must* to follow the word *supplements* in Ex. 22c, and replacing the question mark with a period, yields a statement that could be a theorem. Ask students to give a verbal explanation of the proof of this theorem. For any problem, encourage students to think through the solution of the problem, trying to understand intuitively how to solve the problem, before attempting to write out a formal proof.

Making Connections

Exs. 24–33 allow students to see that algebraic techniques can play an important role in solving geometric problems. Over time, students need to understand and appreciate the fact that algebraic and geometric ideas can join together to form powerful problem-solving tools.

Making Connections

Exs. 32 and 33 involve two unknowns, but one of the equations that can be written has the single unknown x. Once that equation is solved, the value of x can be substituted for x in the measures shown. Then an equation in the single unknown y can be written.

Find the values of x and y for each diagram.

32. **33.**

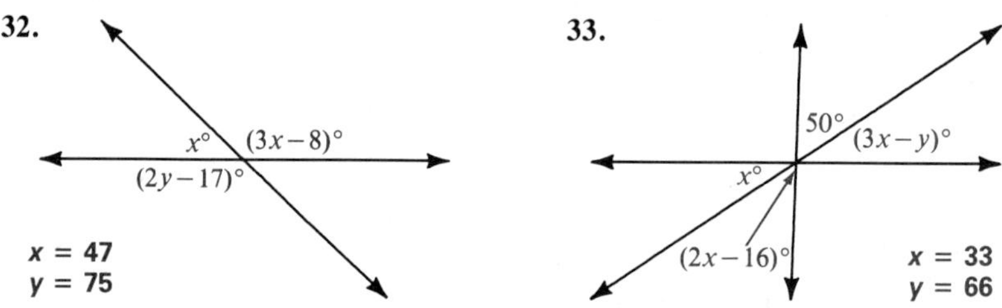

32. $x = 47$, $y = 75$

33. $x = 33$, $y = 66$

C **34.** Can the measure of a complement of an angle ever equal exactly half the measure of a supplement of the angle? Explain. **No. If $90 - x = \frac{1}{2}(180 - x)$ then $x = 0$.**

35. You are told that the measure of an acute angle is equal to the difference between the measure of a supplement of the angle and twice the measure of a complement of the angle. What can you deduce about the angle? Explain. **No conclusion is possible. For any angle that has a complement, it is true that $x = (180 - x) - 2(90 - x)$, or $x = x$.**

Cultural Note

The compass was first invented in China, probably around 500 B.C. A piece of lodestone was first used as the part of the compass that pointed north. Later, around the 5th century A.D., magnetized needles began to be used. Compasses were not used for navigating ships until around the 9th century.

Application — *Orienteering*

The sport of orienteering involves finding your way from control point to control point in a wilderness area, using a map and protractor-type compass. Similar methods can be used by hikers, hunters, boaters, and backpackers.

One thing you want to be able to do is locate your position on the map. This can be done by taking sightings of specific objects. For example, suppose you can see a lookout tower (on Number Four Mountain at • on the map shown below).

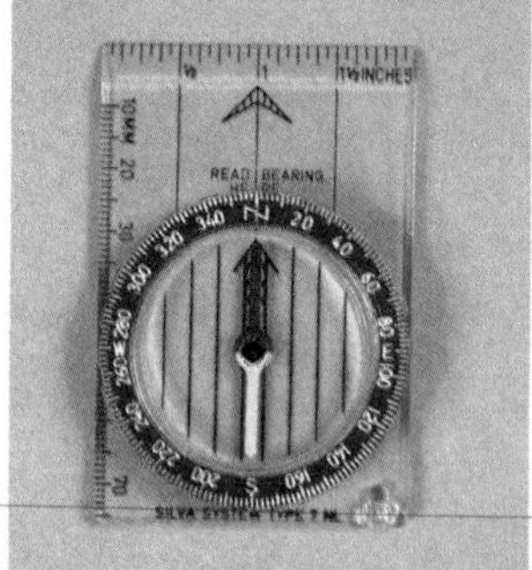

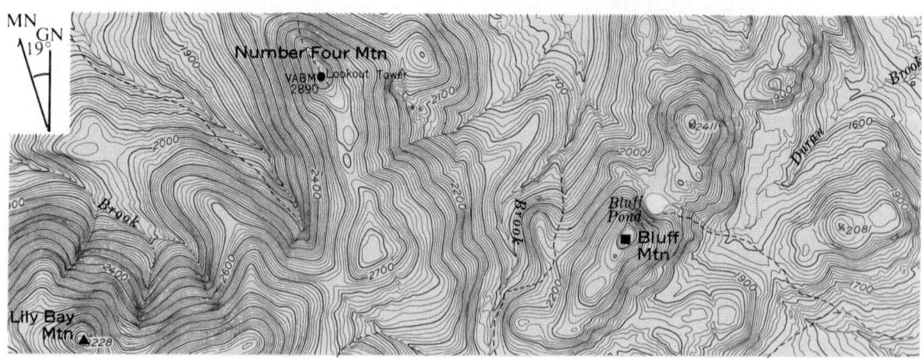

You sight across your compass and discover the tower is 33° east of magnetic north (MN). On your map you draw a line through the tower at a 33° angle to magnetic north. Be sure to use magnetic north rather than true north, for they may differ by as much as 20°. Hiking maps and nautical charts usually give both. All compass readings here are given in terms of magnetic north.

You are somewhere on the line you have drawn. If there is a feature near you (a trail, stream or pond), then your position is where the line crosses the feature on the map. Otherwise, you will need to take a second sighting, on the peak of Lily Bay Mountain (at ▲ on the map). It is 50° west of north. Draw a line on your map through the peak at a 50° angle with magnetic north. You are close to the point where the lines cross.

Since a third landmark is visible, the summit of Bluff Mountain (■ on the map), you can check your position with a third sighting. The three lines might cross at a single point. However, there is usually some error in sighting and drawing the angles, so instead of meeting exactly at a point, the three lines drawn often form a triangle. If the triangle is small, it gives you a good idea of your true position.

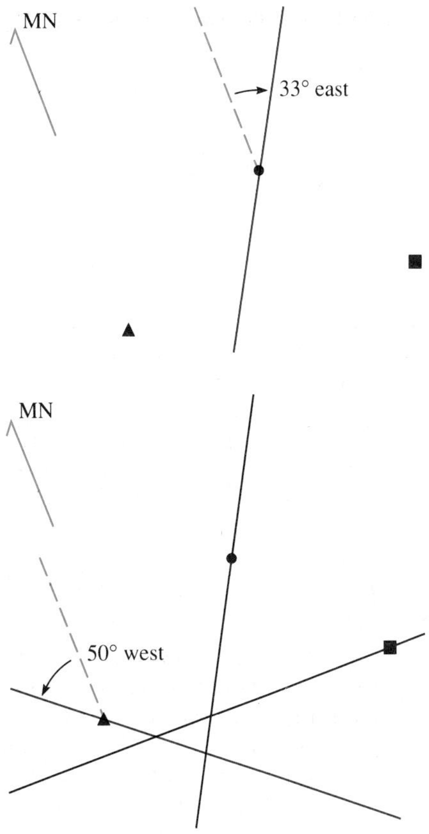

Exercises

1. Another orienteering party sights on Lily Bay Mountain and the lookout tower and finds the following angles: mountain, 58° west of north; tower, 40° east of north. Are they north or south of you? **north**
2. If you head due east from Lily Bay Mountain (90° east of magnetic north), will you pass Bluff Mountain on your right or on your left? **right**
3. Lillian and Ray both sight Lily Bay Mountain at 70° west of north, but Lillian sees the lookout tower at 40° east of north, while Ray sees it at 20° east of north. Which person is closer to Bluff Mountain? **Ray**
4. Sailors use this method of finding their position when they are navigating near shore, sighting on lighthouses, smokestacks, and other landmarks shown on their charts. They call the small triangle formed by the three sighting lines a ''cocked hat,'' and usually mark their position at the corner closest to the nearest hazard. Why is this a sensible rule?
It allows them the greatest margin of safety.

2-5 *Perpendicular Lines*

In the town shown, roads that run east-west are called streets, while those that run north-south are called avenues. Each of the streets is *perpendicular* to each of the avenues.

Perpendicular lines are two lines that intersect to form right angles (90° angles). Because lines that form one right angle always form four right angles (see Exercise 26, page 21), you can conclude that two lines are perpendicular, by definition, once you know that any one of the angles they form is a right angle. The definition of perpendicular lines can be used in the two ways shown below.

1. If $\overleftrightarrow{JK}$ is perpendicular to $\overleftrightarrow{MN}$ (written $\overleftrightarrow{JK} \perp \overleftrightarrow{MN}$), then each of the numbered angles is a right angle (a 90° angle).
2. If any one of the numbered angles is a right angle (a 90° angle), then $\overleftrightarrow{JK} \perp \overleftrightarrow{MN}$.

The word *perpendicular* is also used for intersecting rays and segments. For example, if $\overleftrightarrow{JK} \perp \overleftrightarrow{MN}$ in the diagram, then $\overline{JK} \perp \overline{MN}$ and the sides of $\angle 2$ are perpendicular.

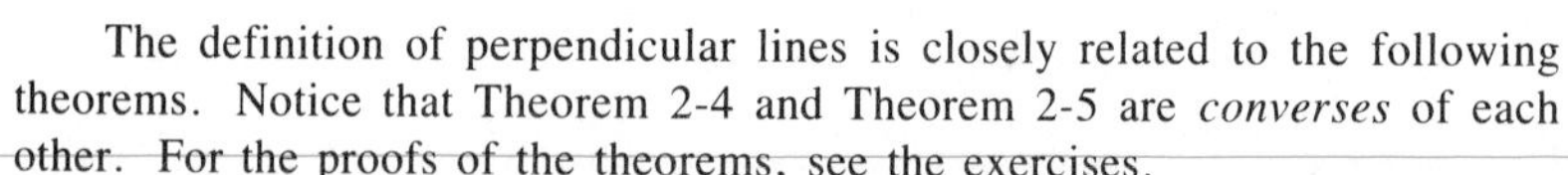

The definition of perpendicular lines is closely related to the following theorems. Notice that Theorem 2-4 and Theorem 2-5 are *converses* of each other. For the proofs of the theorems, see the exercises.

Theorem 2-4

If two lines are perpendicular, then they form congruent adjacent angles.

Theorem 2-5

If two lines form congruent adjacent angles, then the lines are perpendicular.

Theorem 2-6

If the exterior sides of two adjacent acute angles are perpendicular, then the angles are complementary.

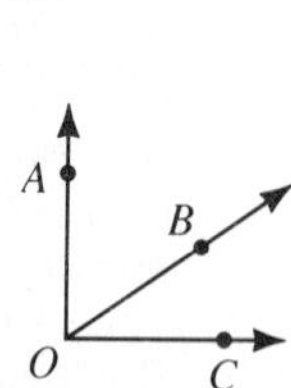

Given: $\overrightarrow{OA} \perp \overrightarrow{OC}$

Prove: $\angle AOB$ and $\angle BOC$ are comp. $\angle$s.

Teaching Suggestions,
p. T82

Objective
Presenting the Lesson
Using Technology

Cooperative Learning,
p. T82

Supplementary Materials

Test 6
Resource Book, pp. 7, 114
Study Guide, pp. 19–20
Overhead Visuals A, C

Lesson Focus

The focus of this lesson is the study and use of three theorems about perpendicular lines. Such lines intersect to form right angles.

Suggested Assignments

Minimum
58–59/1–13
S 53/27, 28, 30, 31
60/Mixed Review 1–7

Average
58–60/2–8 even, 9–25 odd, 26, 28
S 54/32–34
60/Mixed Review 1–7

Maximum
58–60/4–24 even, 25–29

You may wish to introduce Constructions 4, 5, and 6 on pages 380–381 after covering this lesson.

Classroom Exercises

1. Complete the proof of Theorem 2-4: If two lines are perpendicular, then they form congruent adjacent angles.

Given: $l \perp n$

Prove: $\angle 1$, $\angle 2$, $\angle 3$, and $\angle 4$ are congruent angles.

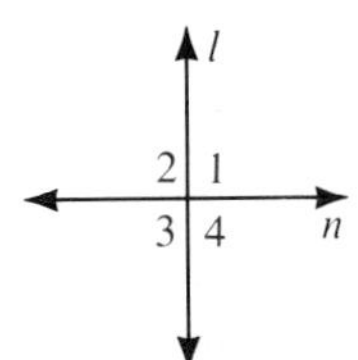

Proof:

Statements	Reasons
1. $l \perp n$	1. ? **Given**
2. $\angle 1$, $\angle 2$, $\angle 3$, $\angle 4$ are 90° ∠s.	2. Definition of ? **⊥ lines**
3. $\angle 1$, $\angle 2$, $\angle 3$, $\angle 4$ are ≅ ∠s.	3. Definition of ? **≅ ∠s**

2. In the diagram, $\overleftrightarrow{AB} \perp \overleftrightarrow{CD}$ and $\overleftrightarrow{EF} \perp \overleftrightarrow{GH}$. Name eight right angles.

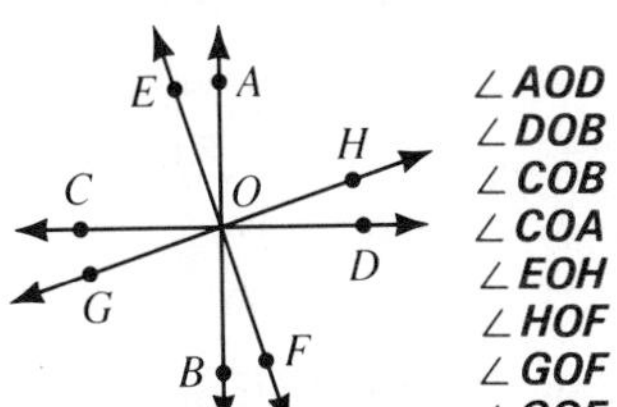

∠AOD
∠DOB
∠COB
∠COA
∠EOH
∠HOF
∠GOF
∠GOE

3. In the diagram, $\overrightarrow{OZ} \perp \overleftrightarrow{PQ}$, $\overrightarrow{OZ} \perp \overleftrightarrow{XY}$, and $\overleftrightarrow{PQ} \perp \overleftrightarrow{XY}$. Name eight right angles.

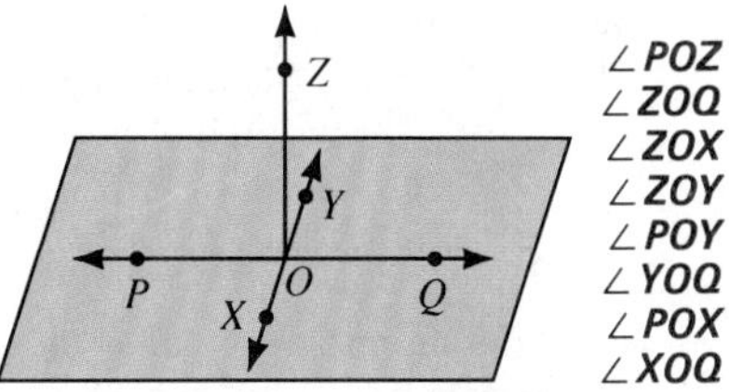

∠POZ
∠ZOQ
∠ZOX
∠ZOY
∠POY
∠YOQ
∠POX
∠XOQ

In the diagram, $\overrightarrow{BE} \perp \overleftrightarrow{AC}$ and $\overrightarrow{BD} \perp \overrightarrow{BF}$. Find the measures of the following angles.

	$m\angle CBF$	$m\angle EBF$	$m\angle DBE$	$m\angle DBA$	$m\angle DBC$
4.	40	? **50**	? **40**	? **50**	? **130**
5.	x	?	?	?	?
		90 − x	**x**	**90 − x**	**90 + x**

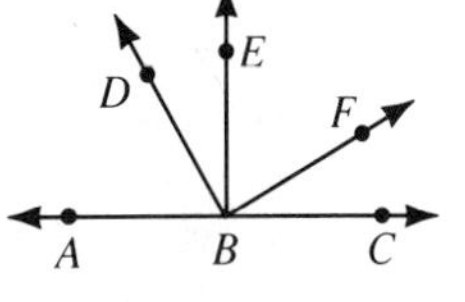

Name the definition or state the theorem that justifies the statement about the diagram.

6. If $\angle 6$ is a right angle, then $\overleftrightarrow{RS} \perp \overleftrightarrow{TV}$. **6., 7. Def of ⊥ lines**

7. If $\overleftrightarrow{RS} \perp \overleftrightarrow{TV}$, then $\angle 5$, $\angle 6$, $\angle 7$, and $\angle 8$ are right angles.

8. If $\overleftrightarrow{RS} \perp \overleftrightarrow{TV}$, then $\angle 8 \cong \angle 7$.

9. If $\overleftrightarrow{RS} \perp \overleftrightarrow{TV}$, then $m\angle 6 = 90$. **Def. of ⊥ lines**

10. If $\angle 5 \cong \angle 6$, then $\overleftrightarrow{RS} \perp \overleftrightarrow{TV}$.

11. If $m\angle 5 = 90$, then $\overleftrightarrow{RS} \perp \overleftrightarrow{TV}$. **Def. of ⊥ lines**

8. If 2 lines are ⊥, then they form ≅ adj. ∠s.
10. If 2 lines form ≅ adj. ∠s, then the lines are ⊥.

R
T 5 6 V
8 7
S

Communication Skills

Have students suggest other statements that can be used to express the meaning of Theorem 2-4. One possible wording is: Perpendicular lines form congruent adjacent angles. Both statements are correct, and students should understand that the wording of a theorem can be changed provided that its meaning is not altered.

Chalkboard Examples

$\overleftrightarrow{AB} \perp \overleftrightarrow{CD}$. Use the diagram to classify each statement as true or false.

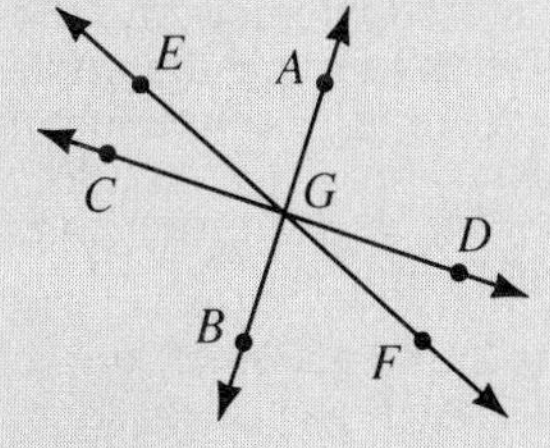

1. $\overline{AB} \perp \overline{EF}$ F
2. $\angle CGB$ is a right angle. T
3. $\angle CGA$ is a right angle. T
4. $m\angle DGB = 90$. T
5. $\angle EGC$ and $\angle EGA$ are complements. T
6. $\angle DGF$ is complementary to $\angle DGA$. F
7. $\angle EGA$ is complementary to $\angle DGF$. T

Guided Practice

Complete with *always*, *sometimes*, or *never.*

1. Perpendicular lines sometimes lie in the same plane.
2. Two lines are perpendicular if and only if they always form congruent adjacent angles.
3. Perpendicular lines never form 60° angles.
4. If the exterior sides of two adjacent angles are perpendicular, then the angles are never supplementary.
5. If a pair of vertical angles are supplementary, the lines forming the angles are always perpendicular.

Proof Note

Ask students which one of the four types of reasons listed on page 45 is not used in the proof for Ex. 2 (theorems that have already been proved).

Written Exercises

A **1.** In the diagram, $\overrightarrow{UL} \perp \overleftrightarrow{MJ}$ and $m\angle JUK = x$. Express in terms of x the measures of the angles named.

a. $\angle LUK$ **90 − x** **b.** $\angle MUK$ **180 − x**

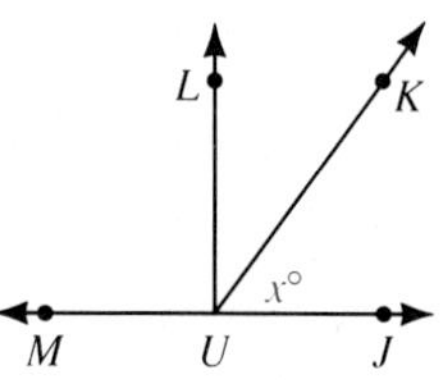

2. Copy and complete the proof of Theorem 2-5: If two lines form congruent adjacent angles, then the lines are perpendicular.

Given: $\angle 1 \cong \angle 2$

Prove: $l \perp n$

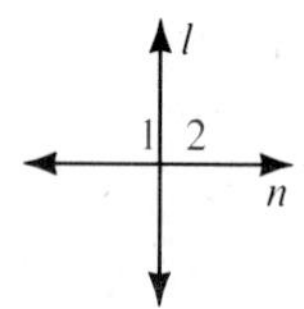

Proof:

Statements	Reasons
1. $\angle 1 \cong \angle 2$, or $m\angle 1 = m\angle 2$	1. _?_ **Given**
2. $m\angle 1 + m\angle 2 = 180$	2. _?_ **Angle Addition Post.**
3. $m\angle 2 + m\angle 2 = 180$, or $2m\angle 2 = 180$	3. _?_ **Substitution Prop.**
4. $m\angle 2 = 90$	4. _?_ **Division Prop. of =**
5. _?_ **$l \perp n$**	5. Def. of $\perp$ lines

Name the definition or state the theorem that justifies the statement about the diagram. **5. If the ext. sides of 2 adj. ∠s are ⊥, then the ∠s are comp.**

3. If $\angle EBC$ is a right angle, then $\overrightarrow{BE} \perp \overleftrightarrow{AC}$. **Def. of ⊥ lines**

4. If $\overleftrightarrow{AC} \perp \overrightarrow{BE}$, then $\angle ABE$ is a right angle. **Def. of ⊥ lines**

5. If $\overrightarrow{BE} \perp \overleftrightarrow{AC}$, then $\angle ABD$ and $\angle DBE$ are complementary.

6. If $\angle ABD$ and $\angle DBE$ are complementary angles, then $m\angle ABD + m\angle DBE = 90$. **Def. of comp. ∠s**

7. If $\overrightarrow{BE} \perp \overleftrightarrow{AC}$, then $m\angle ABE = 90$. **Def. of ⊥ lines**

8. If $\angle ABE \cong \angle EBC$, then $\overleftrightarrow{AC} \perp \overrightarrow{BE}$.
If 2 lines form ≅ adj. ∠s, then the lines are ⊥.

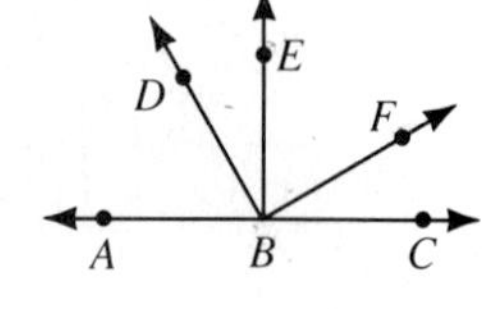

Exs. 3–12

In the diagram, $\overrightarrow{BE} \perp \overleftrightarrow{AC}$ and $\overrightarrow{BD} \perp \overrightarrow{BF}$. Find the value of x.

9. $m\angle ABD = 2x - 15$, $m\angle DBE = x$ **x = 35**

10. $m\angle DBE = 3x$, $m\angle EBF = 4x - 1$ **x = 13**

11. $m\angle ABD = 3x - 12$, $m\angle DBE = 2x + 2$, $m\angle EBF = 2x + 8$ **x = 20**

12. $m\angle ABD = 6x$, $m\angle DBE = 3x + 9$, $m\angle EBF = 4x + 18$, $m\angle FBC = 4x$ **x = 9**

13. Copy and complete the proof of Theorem 2-6: If the exterior sides of two adjacent acute angles are perpendicular, then the angles are complementary.

Given: $\overrightarrow{OA} \perp \overrightarrow{OC}$
Prove: $\angle AOB$ and $\angle BOC$ are comp. $\angle$s.

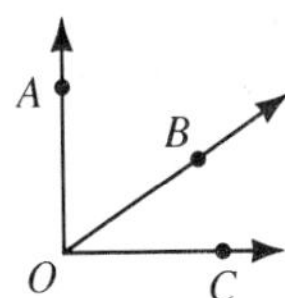

Proof:

Statements	Reasons
1. $\overrightarrow{OA} \perp \overrightarrow{OC}$	1. ? **Given**
2. $m\angle AOC = 90$	2. Def. of $\perp$ lines
3. $m\angle AOB + m\angle BOC = m\angle AOC$	3. ? **Angle Addition Post.**
4. ? **$m\angle AOB + m\angle BOC = 90$**	4. Substitution Prop.
5. ? **$\angle AOB$ and $\angle BOC$ are comp. $\angle$s.**	5. Def. of comp. $\angle$s

In the figure $\overleftrightarrow{BF} \perp \overleftrightarrow{AE}$, $m\angle BOC = x$, and $m\angle GOH = y$. Express the measure of the angle in terms of x, y, or both.

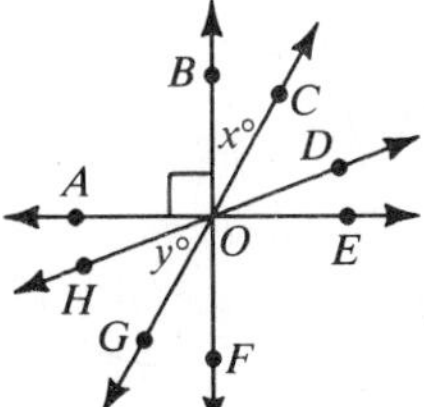

B **14.** $\angle COA$ **$x + 90$**

15. $\angle COH$ **$180 - y$**

16. $\angle HOF$ **$x + y$**

17. $\angle DOE$ **$90 - (x + y)$**

Can you conclude from the information given for each exercise that $\overrightarrow{XY} \perp \overrightarrow{XZ}$?

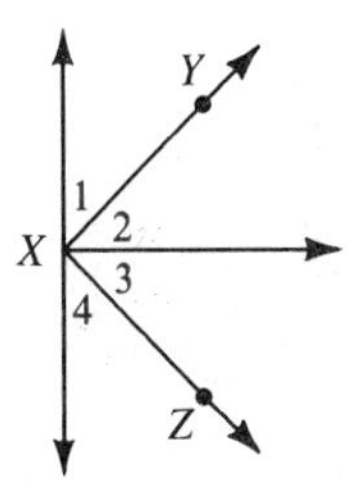

18. $m\angle 1 = 46$ and $m\angle 4 = 44$ **Yes**

19. $\angle 1$ and $\angle 3$ are complementary. **No**

20. $\angle 2 \cong \angle 3$ **No**

21. $m\angle 1 = m\angle 4$ **No**

22. $\angle 1$ and $\angle 3$ are congruent and complementary. **No**

23. $m\angle 1 = m\angle 2$ and $m\angle 3 = m\angle 4$ **Yes**

24. $\angle 1 \cong \angle 3$ and $\angle 2 \cong \angle 4$ **Yes**

25. $\angle 1 \cong \angle 4$ and $\angle 2 \cong \angle 3$ **No**

What can you conclude from the information given? **Answers may vary.**

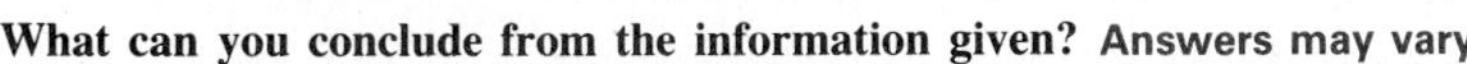

26. Given: $\overrightarrow{AB}$ bisects $\angle DAC$; $\overrightarrow{CB}$ bisects $\angle ECA$; **$m\angle 1 = 45$; $m\angle 4 = 45$; $\angle DAC$ is a rt. $\angle$; $\angle ECA$ is a rt. $\angle$; $m\angle 2 = 45$; $m\angle 3 = 45$; $\overrightarrow{AD} \perp \overleftrightarrow{AC}$; $\overrightarrow{CE} \perp \overleftrightarrow{AC}$**

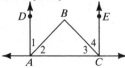

27. Given: $\overrightarrow{AD} \perp \overleftrightarrow{AC}$; $\overrightarrow{CE} \perp \overleftrightarrow{AC}$; $m\angle 1 = m\angle 4$
$m\angle 2 = m\angle 3$; $m\angle DAC = 90$; $m\angle ECA = 90$

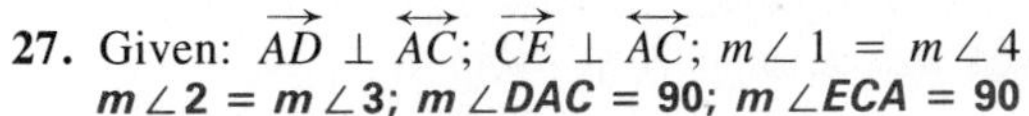

Exercise Note

An effective approach to Exs. 14–17 is to have students initially ignore the particular angle measures that are to be found. Instead, have students draw a figure on scratch paper and label the measures of all eight nonoverlapping angles in terms of x and y. Then, students can express the measures of the angles specified in the exercises more easily.

Using a Computer

See p. T82 for an experiment involving angle bisectors and perpendicular lines.

28. Copy everything shown and write a two-column proof.
Given: $\overleftrightarrow{AO} \perp \overleftrightarrow{CO}$
Prove: ∠1 and ∠3 are comp. ∠s.

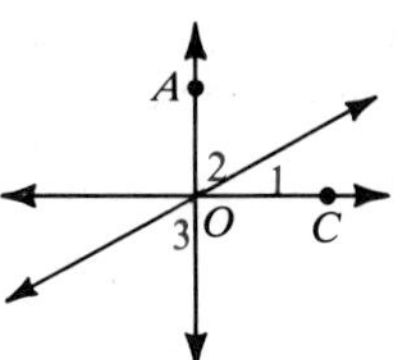

C **29.** First find two lines (other than $\overleftrightarrow{YD}$ and $\overleftrightarrow{YF}$) that are perpendicular. Then write a two-column proof that the lines are perpendicular.
Given: $\overleftrightarrow{YD} \perp \overleftrightarrow{YF}$;
$m\angle 7 = m\angle 5$;
$m\angle 8 = m\angle 6$
Prove: __?__ ⊥ __?__ **$\overleftrightarrow{XD}$, $\overleftrightarrow{XF}$**

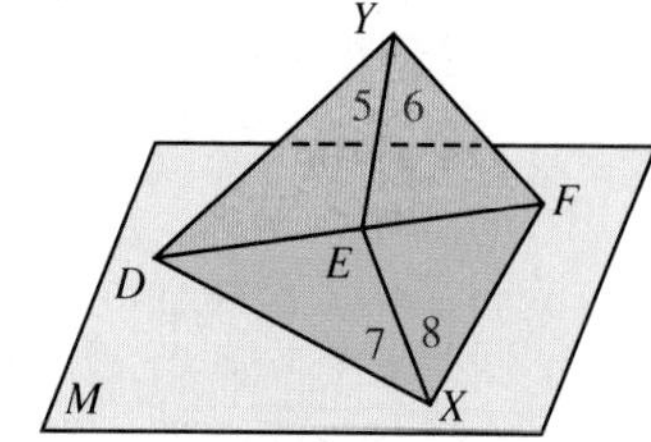

Mixed Review Exercises

Answers may vary.

Write something you can conclude from the given information.

1. Given: $m\angle 1 = m\angle 4$; $m\angle 2 = m\angle 3$ **∠CBF ≅ ∠BCG**
2. Given: $AB = CD$ **AC = BD**
3. Given: $m\angle 6 = m\angle 4$ **∠3 ≅ ∠4**
4. Given: $\overline{FB} \perp \overline{AD}$; $\overrightarrow{BE}$ bisects ∠FBC. **m∠1 = m∠2 = 45**
5. Given: $BE = EF$; E is the midpoint of $\overline{FC}$. **CE = BE**
6. Given: ∠1 and ∠2 are complements. **$\overleftrightarrow{AB} \perp \overline{BF}$**
7. Given: ∠4 and ∠6 are complements. **m∠5 = 90**

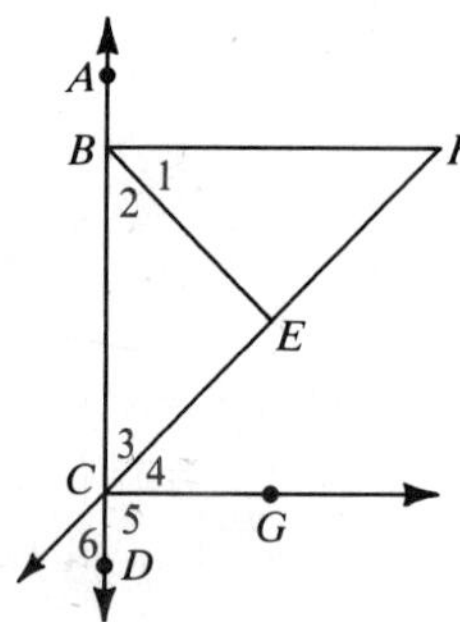

Teaching Suggestions,
pp. T82–T83

Objectives
Presenting the Lesson
Making Connections

Communication Skills,
p. T83

Supplementary Materials

Practice Master 9
Test 7
Resource Book, pp. 8, 115
Study Guide, pp. 21–22

2-6 *Planning a Proof*

As you have seen in the last few sections, a proof of a theorem consists of five parts:

1. *Statement* of the theorem
2. A *diagram* that illustrates the given information
3. A list, in terms of the figure, of what is *given*
4. A list, in terms of the figure, of what you are to *prove*
5. A series of *statements and reasons* that lead from the given information to the statement that is to be proved

In many of the proofs in this book, the diagram and the statements of what is given and what is to be proved will be supplied for you. Sometimes you will be asked to provide them.

When you draw a diagram, try to make it reasonably accurate, avoiding special cases that might mislead. For example, when a theorem refers to an angle, don't draw a *right* angle.

Before you write the steps in a two-column proof you will need to plan your proof. Sometimes you will read the statement of a theorem and see immediately how to prove it. Other times you may need to try several approaches before you find a plan that works.

If you don't see a method of proof immediately, try reasoning back from what you would like to prove. Think: "This conclusion will be true if __?__ is true. This, in turn, will be true if __?__ is true . . . ." Sometimes this procedure leads back to a given statement. If so, you have found a method of proof.

Studying the proofs of previous theorems may suggest methods to try. For example, the proof of the theorem that vertical angles are congruent suggests the proof of the following theorem.

Theorem 2-7

If two angles are supplements of congruent angles (or of the same angle), then the two angles are congruent.

Given: $\angle 1$ and $\angle 2$ are supplementary;
$\angle 3$ and $\angle 4$ are supplementary;
$\angle 2 \cong \angle 4$

Prove: $\angle 1 \cong \angle 3$

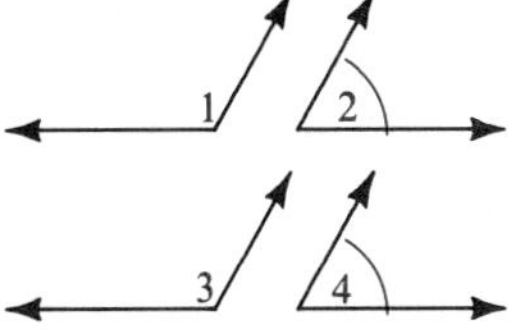

Proof:

Statements	Reasons
1. $\angle 1$ and $\angle 2$ are supplementary; $\angle 3$ and $\angle 4$ are supplementary.	1. Given
2. $m\angle 1 + m\angle 2 = 180$; $m\angle 3 + m\angle 4 = 180$	2. Def. of supp. $\angle$s
3. $m\angle 1 + m\angle 2 = m\angle 3 + m\angle 4$	3. Substitution Prop.
4. $\angle 2 \cong \angle 4$, or $m\angle 2 = m\angle 4$	4. Given
5. $m\angle 1 = m\angle 3$, or $\angle 1 \cong \angle 3$	5. Subtraction Prop. of =

The proof of the following theorem is left as Exercise 18.

Theorem 2-8

If two angles are complements of congruent angles (or of the same angle), then the two angles are congruent.

Lesson Focus

Before a proof is written, a plan for the proof should be developed. A plan is a method that can be tried to write a proof. If the plan does not work, a new plan should be developed and tried.

Suggested Assignments

Minimum
Day 1: 63–64/1–17 odd
S 59/14–17
Day 2: 63–64/2–20 even
65/Self-Test 2
Day 3: 68–69/Chapter Test

Average
Day 1: 63–65/2–18 even, 21, 23
65/Self-Test 2
Day 2: 68–69/Chapter Test

Maximum
63–65/15–25 odd
68–69/Chapter Test

Chalkboard Examples

Explain your plan for proof.

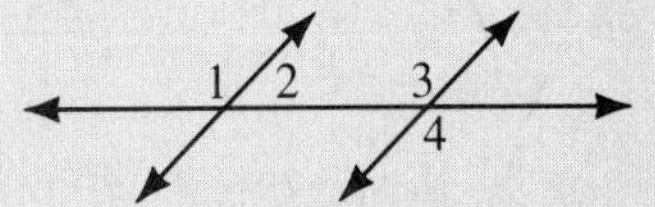

Exs. 1, 2

1. Given: $\angle 2$ and $\angle 3$ are supplementary
Prove: $m\angle 1 = m\angle 3$
$\angle 2$ is supp. to $\angle 1$; $\angle 2$ is supp. to $\angle 3$; therefore $\angle 1 \cong \angle 3$
2. Given: $m\angle 1 = m\angle 4$
Prove: $\angle 4$ is supp. to $\angle 2$
$m\angle 1 = m\angle 4$; $\angle 1$ is supp. to $\angle 2$; therefore $\angle 4$ is supp. to $\angle 2$

There is often more than one way to prove a particular statement, and the amount of detail one includes in a proof may differ from person to person. You should show enough steps so the reader can follow your argument and see why the theorem you are proving is true. As you gain more experience in writing proofs, you and your teacher may agree on what steps may be combined or omitted.

Classroom Exercises

1. a. $\angle 6 \cong \angle 7$ **2. a.** $\angle 5 \cong \angle 7$ **3. a.** $\angle 8 \cong \angle 9$

a. In each exercise use the information given to conclude that two angles are congruent.

b. Name or state the definition or theorem that justifies your conclusion.

1. $\angle 6$ is comp. to $\angle 10$; $\angle 7$ is comp. to $\angle 10$.
2. $m\angle 5 = 31$; $m\angle 7 = 31$
3. $\overline{AB} \perp \overline{CD}$
4. $\overrightarrow{XZ}$ bisects $\angle WXY$.
5. $\angle 4$ is supp. to $\angle 6$; $\angle 2$ is supp. to $\angle 7$; $\angle 6 \cong \angle 7$
6. Given only the diagrams, and no additional information

4. a. $\angle 6 \cong \angle 7$ **5. a.** $\angle 2 \cong \angle 4$ **6. a.** $\angle 1 \cong \angle 3$

Describe your plan for proving the following. You don't need to give all the details.

7. Given: $\angle 2 \cong \angle 3$
   Prove: $\angle 1 \cong \angle 4$

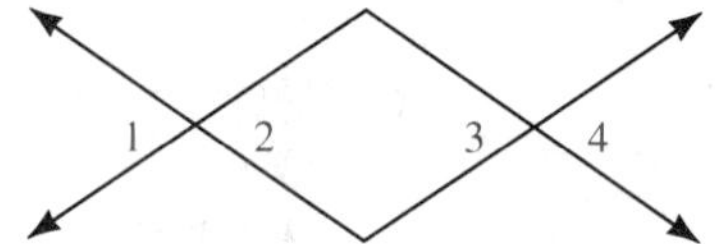

8. Given: $\angle 3$ is supp. to $\angle 1$; $\angle 4$ is supp. to $\angle 2$.
   Prove: $\angle 3 \cong \angle 4$

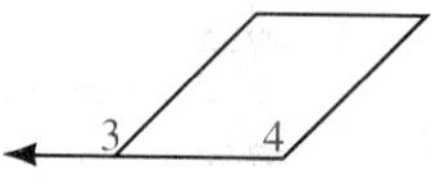

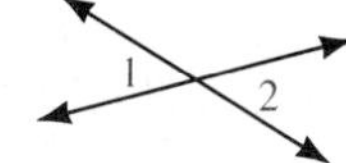

9. Given: $\overline{AC} \perp \overline{BC}$; $\angle 3$ is comp. to $\angle 1$.
   Prove: $\angle 3 \cong \angle 2$

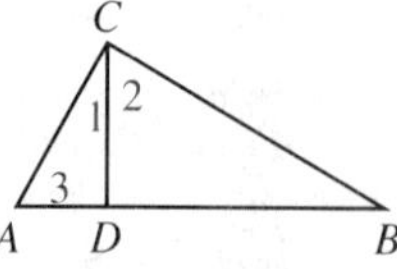

10. Given: $m\angle 1 = m\angle 4$
    Prove: $m\angle 2 = m\angle 3$

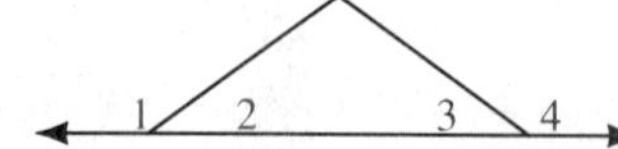

Assessment

Many students feel more comfortable writing detailed proofs at first. With experience, they will be able to omit the minor steps in a proof. Encourage students to write proofs they think are logically sound, and assess their understanding by having them give verbal explanations. If a student can explain a proof with correct reasoning, then the omission of some written steps is acceptable.

Additional Answers Classroom Exercises

1.b. If two angles are complements of the same angle, then the two angles are congruent.

2.b. Def. of congruent angles

3.b. If two lines are perpendicular, then they form congruent adjacent angles.

4.b. Def. of angle bisector

5.b. If two angles are supplements of congruent angles, then the two angles are congruent.

6.b. Vertical angles are congruent.

Exercise Note

For Ex. 7, a good student plan is: Use vertical angles to show that $\angle 1$ and $\angle 4$ are congruent to congruent angles. Another student may have a good plan involving the Transitive Property.

For Ex. 8, some students may think of using Theorem 2-7 when others think of the Angle Addition Postulate.

Written Exercises

Write the name or statement of the definition, postulate, property, or theorem that justifies the statement about the diagram.

Exs. 1–14

A **1.** $AD + DB = AB$ **Segment Addition Post.**

2. $m\angle 1 + m\angle 2 = m\angle CDB$ **Angle Addition Post.**

3. $\angle 2 \cong \angle 6$ **Vertical angles are $\cong$.**

4. If D is the midpoint of $\overline{AB}$, then $AD = \frac{1}{2}AB$. **Midpoint Thm.**

5. If $\overrightarrow{DF}$ bisects $\angle CDB$, then $\angle 1 \cong \angle 2$. **Def. of $\angle$ bisector**

6. $m\angle ADF + m\angle FDB = 180$ **Angle Addition Post.**

7. If $\overline{CD} \perp \overline{AB}$, then $m\angle CDB = 90$. **Def. of $\perp$ lines**

8. If $\angle 4 \cong \angle 3$, then $\overrightarrow{DG}$ bisects $\angle BDE$. **Def. of $\angle$ bisector**

9. If $m\angle 3 + m\angle 4 = 90$, then $\angle 3$ and $\angle 4$ are complements. **Def. of comp. $\angle$s**

10. If $\angle ADF$ and $\angle 4$ are supplements, then $m\angle ADF + m\angle 4 = 180$. **Def. of supp. $\angle$s**

11. If $\overline{AB} \perp \overline{CE}$, then $\angle ADC \cong \angle ADE$. **If 2 lines are $\perp$, then they form $\cong$ adj. $\angle$s.**

12. If $\angle 4$ is complementary to $\angle 5$ and $\angle 6$ is complementary to $\angle 5$, then $\angle 4 \cong \angle 6$. **If 2 $\angle$s are comp. of the same $\angle$, then the 2 $\angle$s are $\cong$.**

13. If $\angle FDG$ is a right angle, then $\overrightarrow{DF} \perp \overrightarrow{DG}$. **Def. of $\perp$ lines**

14. If $\angle FDG \cong \angle GDH$, then $\overrightarrow{DG} \perp \overleftrightarrow{HF}$. **If 2 lines form $\cong$ adj. $\angle$s, then the lines are $\perp$.**

15. Copy everything shown and complete the proof of Theorem 2-7 for the case where two angles are supplements of the same angle.

Given: $\angle 1$ and $\angle 5$ are supplementary;
$\angle 3$ and $\angle 5$ are supplementary.

Prove: $\angle 1 \cong \angle 3$

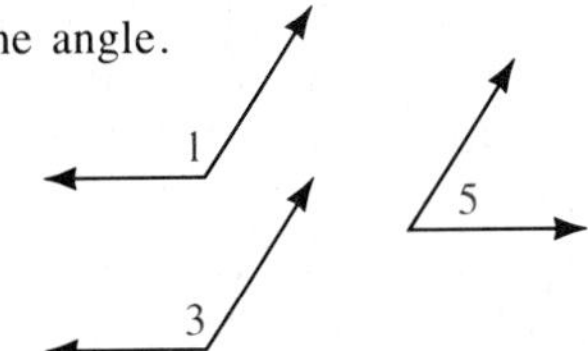

Proof:

Statements	Reasons
1. $\angle 1$ and $\angle 5$ are supplementary; $\angle 3$ and $\underline{?}$. **$\angle 5$ are supplementary**	1. $\underline{?}$ **Given**
2. $m\angle 1 + m\angle 5 = 180$; $m\angle 3 + m\angle 5 = 180$	2. $\underline{?}$ **Def. of supp. $\angle$s**
3. $m\angle 1 + m\angle 5 = m\angle 3 + m\angle 5$	3. $\underline{?}$ **Substitution Prop.**
4. $m\angle 5 = m\angle 5$	4. Reflexive Prop.
5. $m\angle 1 = m\angle 3$, or $\angle 1 \cong \angle 3$	5. $\underline{?}$ **Subtraction Prop. of =**

16. a. Are there any angles in the diagram that must be congruent to $\angle 4$? Explain. **$\angle 2$; Vert. $\angle$s are $\cong$.**

b. If $\angle 4$ and $\angle 5$ are supplementary, name all angles shown that must be congruent to $\angle 4$. **$\angle 2$, $\angle 6$, $\angle 8$**

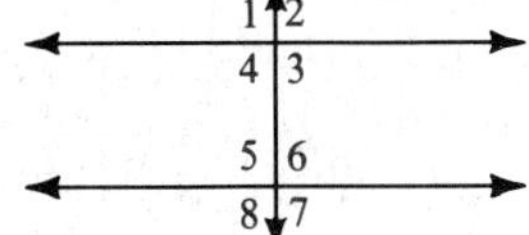

Guided Practice

1. Use the diagram below.

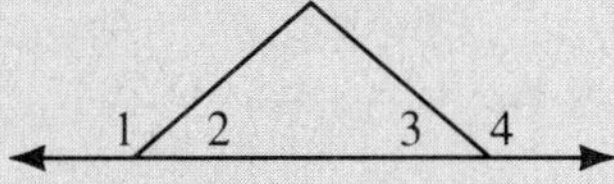

a. Name a supplement of $\angle 2$. $\angle 1$

b. Name a supplement of $\angle 3$. $\angle 4$

c. What postulate or theorem, along with the definition of supplementary angles, justifies your answers to parts (a) and (b)? Angle Addition Postulate

d. If $\angle 2 \cong \angle 3$, write the theorem that allows you to conclude that $\angle 1 \cong \angle 4$. If 2 $\angle$s are supp. of $\cong$ $\angle$s, then the 2 $\angle$s are $\cong$.

2. In the diagram below, $\overline{LM} \perp \overline{MN}$ and $\overline{KN} \perp \overline{MN}$.

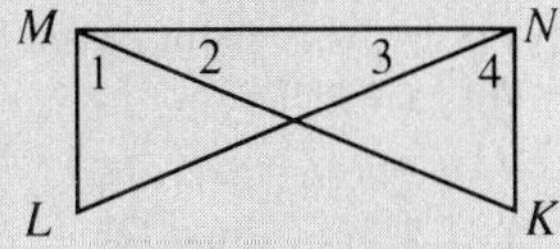

a. Name a complement of $\angle 2$. $\angle 1$

b. Name a complement of $\angle 3$. $\angle 4$

c. Write the theorem that justifies your answers to parts (a) and (b). If the ext. sides of 2 adj. acute $\angle$s are $\perp$, then the $\angle$s are complementary.

d. If $\angle 2 \cong \angle 3$, write the theorem that allows you to conclude that $\angle 1 \cong \angle 4$. If 2 $\angle$s are comp. of $\cong$ $\angle$s, then the 2 $\angle$s are $\cong$.

17. a. Copy everything shown and complete the proof.

Given: $\overline{PQ} \perp \overline{QR}$;
$\overline{PS} \perp \overline{SR}$;
$\angle 1 \cong \angle 4$

Prove: $\angle 2 \cong \angle 5$

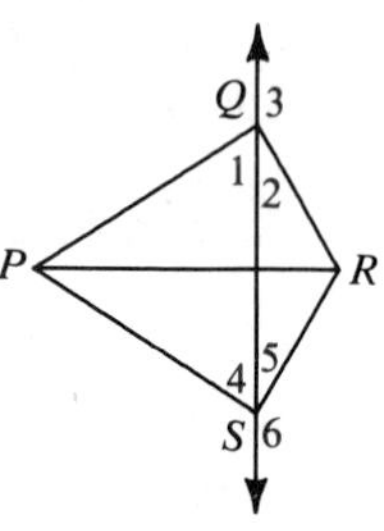

Proof:

Statements	Reasons
1. $\overline{PQ} \perp \overline{QR}$; $\overline{PS} \perp \overline{SR}$	1. ? **Given**
2. $\angle 2$ is comp. to $\angle 1$; $\angle 5$ is comp. to $\angle 4$.	2. ? **If the ext. sides of 2 adj. acute ∡ are ⊥, then the ∡ are comp.**
3. $\angle 1 \cong \angle 4$	3. ? **Given**
4. $\angle 2 \cong \angle 5$	4. ? **If 2 ∡ are comp. of ≅ ∡, then the 2 ∡ are ≅.**

b. After proving that $\angle 2 \cong \angle 5$ in part (a), tell how you could go on to prove that $\angle 3 \cong \angle 6$. **Show that $\angle 3$ and $\angle 6$ are supps. of ≅ ∡.**

B 18. Prove Theorem 2-8: If two angles are complements of congruent angles, then the two angles are congruent. *Note*: You will need to draw your own diagram and state what is given and what you are to prove in terms of your diagram. (*Hint*: See the proof of Theorem 2-7 on page 61.)

Copy everything shown and write a two-column proof.

19. Given: $\angle 2 \cong \angle 3$
Prove: $\angle 1 \cong \angle 4$

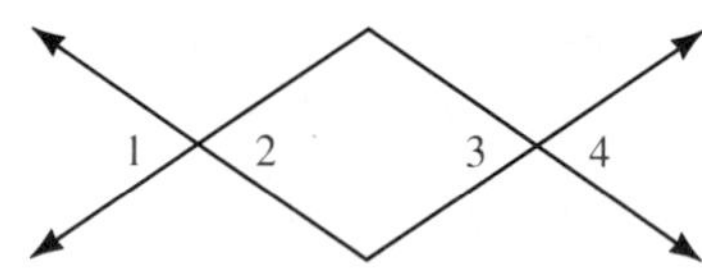

20. Given: $\angle 3$ is supp. to $\angle 1$;
$\angle 4$ is supp. to $\angle 2$.
Prove: $\angle 3 \cong \angle 4$

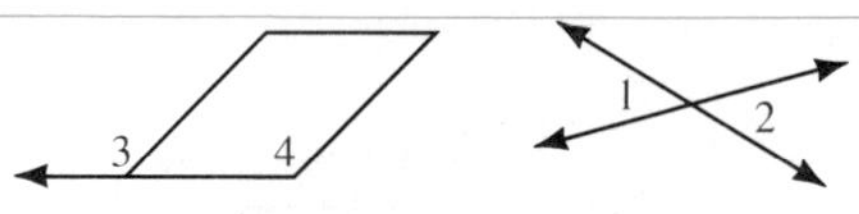

21. Given: $\overline{AC} \perp \overline{BC}$;
$\angle 3$ is comp. to $\angle 1$.
Prove: $\angle 3 \cong \angle 2$

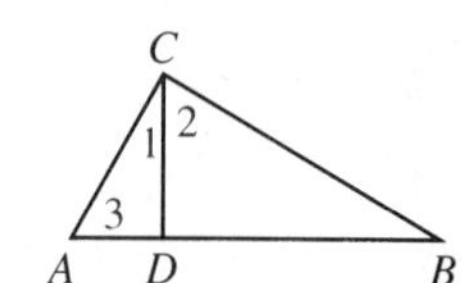

22. Given: $m\angle 1 = m\angle 2$;
$m\angle 3 = m\angle 4$
Prove: $\overrightarrow{YS} \perp \overleftrightarrow{XZ}$

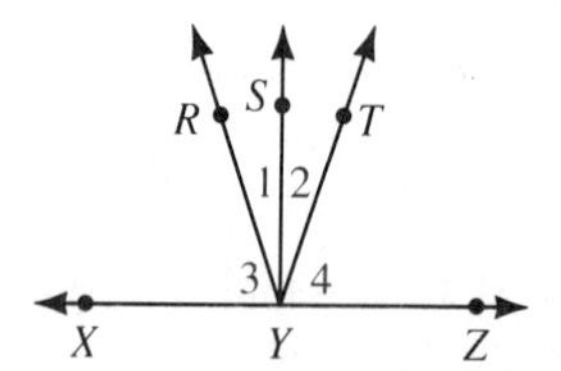

Exercise Note

Some students will need a lot of time to write a proof for Ex. 18 even after you advise them that the proof is step by step like the book's proof of Theorem 2-7. (*Complementary* and 90 replace *supplementary* and 180.)

In Exs. 19–21, students will write proofs that were planned on page 62 (Exs. 7–9).

Group Activity

You may wish to continue the procedure of teaching students to write proofs, using small groups. The interaction of ideas among students in a group who participate actively in the proof-writing process will enhance the ability of all students to write proofs. Allow the groups to use their textbooks and any other materials you wish to make available. Try to provide help as needed to keep the work of each group productive. Encourage all students to try to make a contribution to each proof being written.

23. Draw any $\angle AOB$ and its bisector $\overrightarrow{OE}$. Now draw the rays opposite to $\overrightarrow{OA}$, $\overrightarrow{OB}$, and $\overrightarrow{OE}$. What can you conclude about the part of the diagram shown in red? Prove your conclusion. **$\overrightarrow{OF}$ bisects $\angle COD$.**

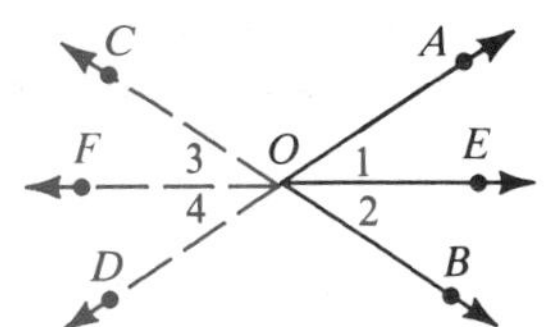

C **24.** Make a diagram showing $\angle PQR$ bisected by $\overrightarrow{QX}$. Choose a point Y on the ray opposite to $\overrightarrow{QX}$.
Prove: $\angle PQY \cong \angle RQY$

25. Given: $m\angle DBA = 45$;
$m\angle DEB = 45$
Prove: $\angle DBC \cong \angle FEB$

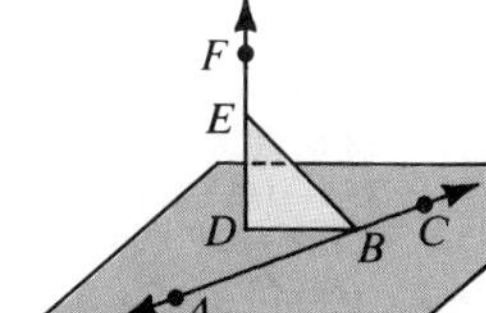

Self-Test 2

1. It is known that $\angle HOK$ has a supplement, but can't have a complement. Name one possible measure for $\angle HOK$. **Answers may vary; $90 \le m\angle HOK < 180$**

2. $m\angle 1 = 3x - 5$ and $m\angle 2 = x + 25$
a. $x =$ __?__ **15** **b.** $m\angle 1 =$ __?__ (numerical value) **40**

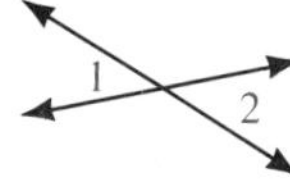

For Exercises 3 and 4 you are given that $\overrightarrow{OB} \perp l$ and $\overrightarrow{OA} \perp \overrightarrow{OC}$.

3. If $m\angle 3 = 37$, complete:
$m\angle 4 =$ __?__ **53** $m\angle 5 =$ __?__ **37** $m\angle 6 =$ __?__ **53**

4. If $m\angle 3 = t$, express the measures of the other numbered angles in terms of t. **$m\angle 4 = 90 - t$, $m\angle 5 = t$, $m\angle 6 = 90 - t$**

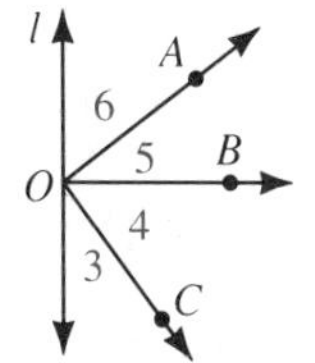

In the diagram, $\overline{DE} \perp n$. State the theorem or name the definition that justifies the statement about the diagram.

5. $\angle 8$ is a 90° angle. **Def. of ⊥ lines**

6. $\angle 7 \cong \angle 10$ **Vertical angles are ≅.**

7. $\angle 9$ and $\angle 10$ are complementary. **If the ext. sides of 2 adj. ∠s are ⊥, then the ∠s are comp.**

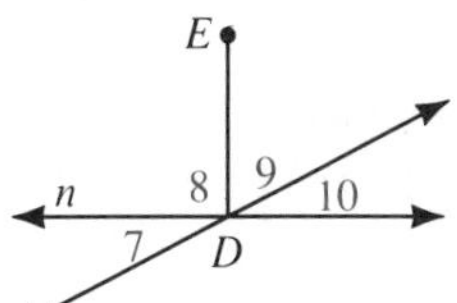

8. Give a plan for the following proof.
Given: $\angle 1$ is supp. to $\angle 3$;
$\angle 2$ is supp. to $\angle 3$.
Prove: $j \perp k$ **$\angle 1 \cong \angle 2$, so $j \perp k$.**

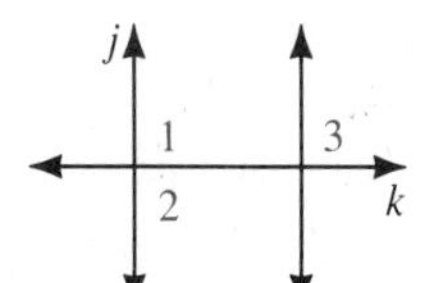

9. Write a proof for Exercise 8 in two-column form.

Exercise Note

In Ex. 25, some students may use the Angle Addition Postulate. Other students may translate to the language of congruence and apply Theorem 2-7. Either approach is acceptable.

Quick Quiz

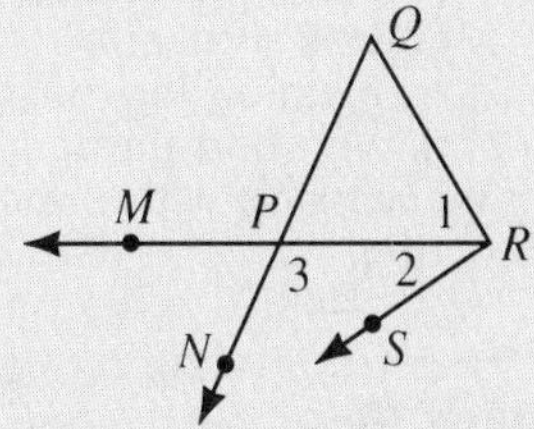

Complete.

1. If $\angle 1$ and $\angle 3$ are supplementary, then $\angle 1$ and $\angle$ MPQ are supplementary.
2. If $MR = NQ$ and $MP = NP$, then $PR = PQ$.
3. If $\angle QRS$ is a right angle, then $\angle 1$ and $\angle 2$ are adjacent complementary angles.

Complete with *always*, *sometimes*, or *never*.

4. Vertical angles are always congruent.
5. Perpendicular lines never form 45° angles.
6. A theorem is always a true statement.
7. A postulate is sometimes used as a reason in a proof.
8. Supplements of congruent angles are always congruent.
9. Two angles are sometimes complements.
10. A statement in a proof always has a reason.

Extra — *Möbius Bands*

Take a long narrow strip of paper. Give the strip a half-twist. Tape the ends together. The result is a *Möbius band.*

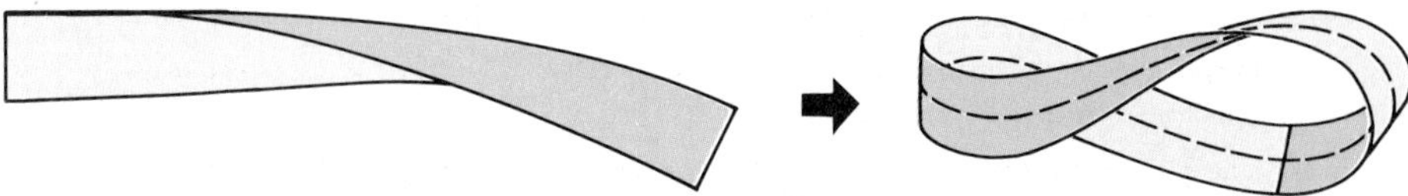

Exercises

2. The result is a non-Möbius (2-sided) band that is twice as long. The band separates into 2 non-Möbius bands that are linked together.
3. 2; The result is 2 non-Möbius (2-sided) bands linked together.

1. Make a Möbius band. Color one side of the Möbius band. How much of the band is left uncolored? The original strip of paper had two sides. How many sides does a Möbius band have? **None of it; one**
2. Cut the Möbius band lengthwise down the middle. (Start at a point midway between the edges and cut around the band.) What is the result? Cut the band a second time down the middle. Write a sentence or two describing what happens. **See above.**
3. Give a full twist to a long, narrow strip of paper. Tape the ends together. How many sides does this band have? Cut this band lengthwise down the middle. Write a brief description of what is formed.
4. Make a Möbius band. Let the band be 3 cm wide. Make a lengthwise cut, staying 1 cm from the right-hand edge. Describe the result. **See below.**
5. Take two long narrow strips of paper. Fasten them together so they are perpendicular and form a plus sign. Twist one strip so it is a Möbius band and fasten its ends together. Don't twist the other strip at all, just fasten its ends. Cut the Möbius band down the middle lengthwise. Then cut the other band down the middle. Describe the final result. **The result is a rectangular frame.**

Chapter Summary

1. *If p, then q* is a conditional statement. p is the hypothesis and q is the conclusion. *If q, then p* is the converse. The statement *p if and only if q* is a biconditional that means both the conditional and its converse are true.
2. Properties of algebra (see page 37) can be used to reach conclusions in geometry. Properties of congruence are related to some of the properties of equality.
3. Deductive reasoning is a process of proving conclusions. Given information, definitions, postulates, and previously proved theorems are the four kinds of reasons that can be used to justify statements in a proof.

4. The result is a short 1 cm wide Möbius band linked with a longer 1 cm wide non-Möbius band.

Group Activity

Students may enjoy working together in small groups on the Möbius Band exercises.

The physical activity of creating a Möbius band helps students appreciate mathematics at a concrete level. Opportunities are provided also for students to communicate their experiences verbally and in writing. Möbius bands are highly motivating for most students who find the results of working with them fascinating.

Cultural Note

August Ferdinand Möbius (1790–1868) was a German mathematician and theoretical astronomer. He was particularly well known for his work in geometry and helped pioneer the study of topology. (For more on topology, see pages 275–276.) Möbius's description of the properties of the so-called Möbius band was discovered after his death.

4. When $m\angle A + m\angle B = 90$, $\angle A$ and $\angle B$ are complementary. When $m\angle C + m\angle D = 180$, $\angle C$ and $\angle D$ are supplementary. Complements (or supplements) of the same angle or of congruent angles are congruent.
5. Vertical angles are congruent.
6. Perpendicular lines are two lines that form right angles (90° angles). If two lines are perpendicular, then they form congruent adjacent angles. If two lines form congruent adjacent angles, then the lines are perpendicular.
7. If the exterior sides of two adjacent acute angles are perpendicular, then the angles are complementary.
8. The proof of a theorem consists of five parts, which are listed on page 60.

Chapter Review

Use the conditional: If $m\angle 1 = 120$, then $\angle 1$ is obtuse.

1. Write the hypothesis and the conclusion of the conditional. **H: $m\angle 1 = 120$ C: $\angle 1$ is obtuse** 2–1
2. Write the converse of the conditional. **If $\angle 1$ is obtuse, then $m\angle 1 = 120$.**
3. Provide a counterexample to disprove the converse. **Answers may vary; $m\angle 1 = 100$**
4. Write a definition of a straight angle as a biconditional.
An angle is a straight angle if and only if the measure of the angle is 180.

Justify each statement with a property from algebra or a property of congruence.

5. If $m\angle A + m\angle B + m\angle C = 180$ and $m\angle C = 50$, then $m\angle A + m\angle B + 50 = 180$. **Substitution Prop.** 2–2
6. If $m\angle A + m\angle B + 50 = 180$, then $m\angle A + m\angle B = 130$. **Subtr. Prop. of =**
7. If $6x = 18$, then $x = 3$. **Division Prop. of =**
8. If $\overline{AB} \cong \overline{CD}$ and $\overline{CD} \cong \overline{EF}$, then $\overline{AB} \cong \overline{EF}$. **Transitive Prop.**

Name the definition, postulate, or theorem that justifies the statement.

9. If $\overline{RS} \cong \overline{ST}$, then S is the midpoint of $\overline{RT}$. **Def. of midpoint** 2–3
10. If $\overrightarrow{SW}$ bisects $\angle VST$, then $\angle VSW \cong \angle WST$.
11. If $\overrightarrow{SW}$ bisects $\angle VST$, then $m\angle WST = \frac{1}{2}m\angle VST$.

10. Def. of $\angle$ bisector 11. Angle Bisector Thm.

12. If $\angle BOC$ is a right angle and $m\angle COD = 58$, then $m\angle DOE =$ _?_, $m\angle BOA =$ _?_, and $m\angle AOC =$ _?_. **32; 32; 122** 2–4
13. Name a supplement of $\angle AOE$. **$\angle BOA$ or $\angle DOE$**

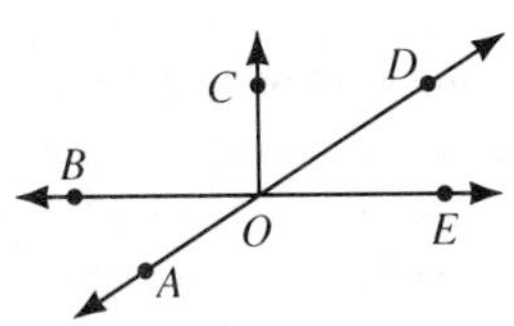

14. A supplement of a given angle is four times as large as a complement of the angle. Find the measure of the given angle. **60**

Supplementary Materials

Practice Master 10

Test 8

Resource Book, pp. 9–10, 116

Name the definition or state the theorem that justifies the statement about the diagram. **15., 16. Def. of ⊥ lines** **17. If 2 lines are ⊥, they form ≅ adj. ∠s.**

2–5

15. If $\overrightarrow{KJ} \perp \overleftrightarrow{GH}$, then ∠1 is a right angle.

16. If ∠2 is a 90° angle, then $\overrightarrow{KJ} \perp \overleftrightarrow{GH}$.

17. If $\overrightarrow{NM} \perp \overleftrightarrow{GH}$, then ∠MNK ≅ ∠MNH.

18. If $\overrightarrow{NM} \perp \overleftrightarrow{GH}$, then ∠3 and ∠4 are complementary. **If the ext. sides of 2 adj. ∠s are ⊥, then the ∠s are comp.**

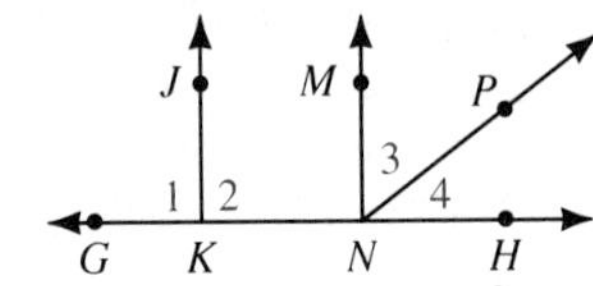

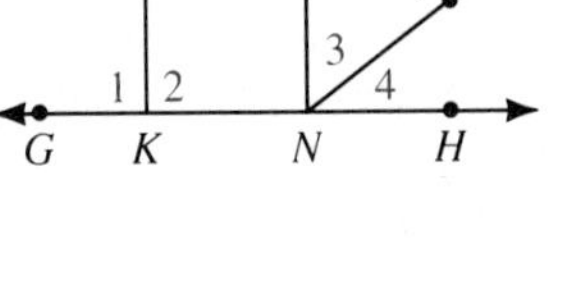

2–6

19. Write a plan for a proof.
Given: ∠3 is a supplement of ∠1;
∠4 is a supplement of ∠2.
Prove: ∠3 ≅ ∠4

20. Write a proof in two-column form for Exercise 19.

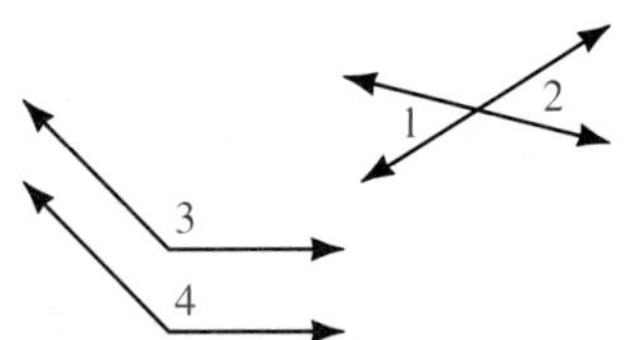

Teaching References

Alternate Test, p. T13

Chapter Test

a. 2 ∠s are vert. ∠s **b. If 2 ∠s are ≅, then they are vert. ∠s.**

1. Use the conditional: Two angles are congruent if they are vertical angles.
a. Write the hypothesis. **b.** Write the converse.

2. Provide a counterexample to disprove the statement:
If $x^2 > 4$, then $x > 2$. **Answers may vary; $x = -3$**

3. Write the biconditional as two conditionals that are converses of each other:
Angles are congruent if and only if their measures are equal.

3. If ∠s are ≅, then their measures are =.
If ∠s have = measures, then they are ≅.

4. Supply reasons to justify the steps:

	Steps	*Reasons*
	1. $y = 12$	1. Given
	2. $5x = 2x + y$	2. Given
Subst. Prop.	3. $5x = 2x + 12$	3. ?
Subtr. Prop. of =	4. $3x = 12$	4. ?
Div. Prop. of =	5. $x = 4$	5. ?

5. $\overrightarrow{OB}$ is the bisector of ∠AOC and $\overrightarrow{OC}$ is the bisector of ∠BOD. $m\angle AOC = 60$. Find $m\angle COD$. **30**

6. S is the midpoint of $\overline{RT}$ and W is the midpoint of $\overline{ST}$. If $RT = 32$, find ST, WT, and RW. **16; 8; 24**

7. In the diagram, $\overline{AB} \perp \overline{BC}$. Name:
a. two supplementary angles **∠3 and ∠4**
b. two complementary angles **∠1 and ∠2**

8. Given: ∠5 is supplementary to ∠4.
a. What can you conclude about ∠5 and ∠3? **≅**
b. State the theorem that justifies your conclusion.

A
3
4
2
1
B
C

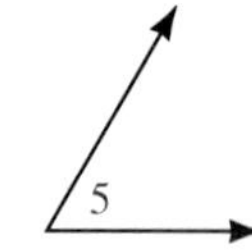

Exs. 7–9

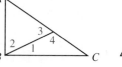

9. Suppose $m\angle 3 = 3x + 5$ and $m\angle 4 = 6x + 13$. Find the value of x. **$x = 18$**

8. b. If 2 ∠s are supp. of the same ∠, the 2 ∠s are ≅.

10. State the theorem that justifies the statement $\angle 6 \cong \angle 7$. **Vert. ∠s are ≅.**

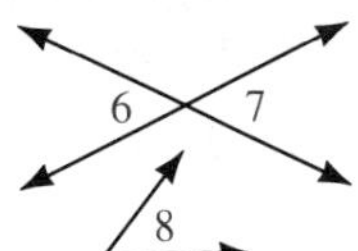

11. Suppose you have already stated that $\angle 6 \cong \angle 7$ and $\angle 7 \cong \angle 8$. What property of congruence justifies the conclusion that $\angle 6 \cong \angle 8$? **Transitive Prop.**

12. Write a proof in two-column form.
Given: $\overrightarrow{DC} \perp \overleftrightarrow{BD}$; $\angle 1 \cong \angle 2$
Prove: $\overrightarrow{BA} \perp \overleftrightarrow{BD}$

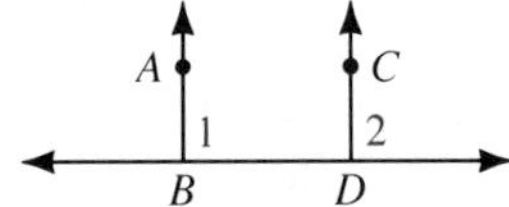

Algebra Review: *Systems of Equations*

Solve each system of equations by the substitution method.

Example 1 (1) $y = 5 - 2x$
(2) $5x - 6y = 21$

Solution Substitute $5 - 2x$ for y in (2): $5x - 6(5 - 2x) = 21$
$17x - 30 = 21;\ x = 3$

Substitute 3 for x in (1): $y = 5 - 2(3) = -1$

The solution is $x = 3,\ y = -1$.

1. $y = 3x$; $5x + y = 24$ **x = 3, y = 9**
2. $y = 2x + 5$; $3x - y = 4$ **x = 9, y = 23**
3. $x = 8 + 3y$; $2x - 5y = 8$ **x = −16, y = −8**
4. $3x + 2y = 71$; $y = 4 + 2x$ **x = 9, y = 22**
5. $4x - 5y = 92$; $x = 7y$ **x = 28, y = 4**
6. $y = 3x + 8$; $x = y$ **x = −4, y = −4**
7. $8x + 3y = 26$; $2x = y - 4$ **x = 1, y = 6**
8. $x - 7y = 13$; $3x - 5y = 23$ **x = 6, y = −1**
9. $3x + y = 19$; $2x - 5y = -10$ **x = 5, y = 4**

Solve each system by the method of addition or subtraction.

Example 2 (1) $3x - y = 13$
(2) $4x + y = 22$

Solution Add (1) and (2):
$7x = 35;\ x = 5$
Substitute 5 for x in (2):
$4(5) + y = 22;\ y = 2$
The solution is $x = 5,\ y = 2$.

Example 3 (1) $6x + 15y = 90$
(2) $6x - 14y = 32$

Solution Subtract (2) from (1):
$29y = 58;\ y = 2$
Substitute 2 for y in (1):
$6x + 15(2) = 90;\ x = 10$
The solution is $x = 10,\ y = 2$.

10. $5x - y = 20$; $3x + y = 12$ **x = 4, y = 0**
11. $x + 3y = 7$; $x + 2y = 4$ **x = −2, y = 3**
12. $3x - 2y = 11$; $3x - y = 7$ **x = 1, y = −4**
13. $7x + y = 29$; $5x + y = 21$ **x = 4, y = 1**
14. $8x - y = 17$; $6x + y = 11$ **x = 2, y = −1**
15. $9x - 2y = 50$; $6x - 2y = 32$ **x = 6, y = 2**
16. $7y = 2x + 35$; $3y = 2x + 15$ **x = 0, y = 5**
17. $2y = 3x - 1$; $2y = x + 21$ **x = 11, y = 16**
18. $19 = 5x + 2y$; $1 = 3x - 4y$ **x = 3, y = 2**

Supplementary Materials

Practice Master 11

Resource Book, p. 191

Preparing for College Entrance Exams

Strategy for Success

When you are taking a college entrance exam, be sure to read the directions, the questions, and the answer choices very carefully. In the test booklet, you may want to underline important words such as *not, exactly, false, never,* and *except,* and to cross out answer choices that are clearly incorrect.

Indicate the best answer by writing the appropriate letter.

C **1.** On a number line, point M has coordinate -3 and point R has coordinate 6. Point Z is on $\overrightarrow{RM}$ and $RZ = 4$. Find the coordinate of Z.
(A) -7 **(B)** 1 **(C)** 2 **(D)** 10 **(E)** cannot be determined

C **2.** $\angle 1$ and $\angle 2$ are complementary. $m\angle 1 = 5x + 15$ and $m\angle 2 = 10x$. The measure of $\angle 1$ is:
(A) 5 **(B)** 11 **(C)** 40 **(D)** 70 **(E)** 30

D **3.** Vertical angles are never:
(A) complementary **(B)** supplementary **(C)** right angles
(D) adjacent **(E)** congruent

E **4.** A reason that cannot be used to justify a statement in a proof is:
(A) a postulate **(B)** a definition **(C)** given information
(D) yesterday's theorem **(E)** tomorrow's theorem

D **5.** Which of the following must be true?
(I) If two lines form congruent adjacent angles, then the lines are perpendicular.
(II) If two lines are perpendicular, then they form congruent adjacent angles.
(III) If the exterior sides of two adjacent obtuse angles are perpendicular, then the angles are complementary.
(A) I only **(B)** II only **(C)** III only
(D) I and II only **(E)** I, II, and III

B **6.** $\angle 1$ and $\angle 2$ are congruent angles. $m\angle 1 = 10x - 20$ and $m\angle 2 = 8x + 2$. $\angle 1$ is a(n) __?__ angle.
(A) acute **(B)** right **(C)** obtuse **(D)** straight
(E) answer cannot be determined

E **7.** If you know that $m\angle A = m\angle B$ and $m\angle B = m\angle C$, then what reason can you give for the statement that $m\angle A = m\angle C$?
(I) Reflexive Property (II) Transitive Property (III) Substitution Property
(A) I only **(B)** II only **(C)** III only
(D) either I or II **(E)** either II or III

C **8.** Which of the following is *not* the converse of the statement: If b, then c.
(A) If c, then b. **(B)** b if c. **(C)** c if and only if b.
(D) c only if b. **(E)** c implies b.

Cumulative Review: Chapters 1 and 2

Name or state the postulate, property, definition, or theorem that justifies the statement.

A **1.** If $8x = 16$, then $x = 2$. **Division Prop. of =**

2. If $\angle K \cong \angle L$ and $\angle L \cong \angle M$, then $\angle K \cong \angle M$. **Transitive Prop.**

3. If $\angle AOB$ is a right angle, then $\overleftrightarrow{OA} \perp \overleftrightarrow{OB}$. **Def. of ⊥ lines**

4. If $a + 7 = b$ and $b = 4$, then $a + 7 = 4$. **Substitution Prop.**

5. If $a + 7 = 4$, then $a = -3$. **Subtraction Prop. of =**

6. There is a line through F and H. **Through any 2 points there is exactly 1 line.**

7. The intersection of plane $CDEH$ and plane $FGHE$ is $\overleftrightarrow{EH}$. **If 2 planes intersect, then their intersection is a line.**

8. If W is the midpoint of $\overline{XV}$, then $XW = \frac{1}{2}XV$. **Midpoint Thm.**

9. $MW + WN = MN$ **Segment Add. Post.**

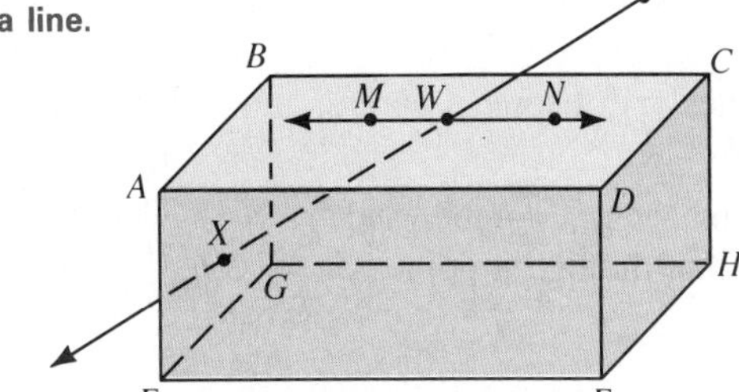

Exs. 6–14

Classify each statement as true or false.

10. $\overrightarrow{WV}$ contains point X. **False**

11. $\overline{MN}$ lies in plane $ABCD$. **True**

12. $\overleftrightarrow{WV}$ intersects plane $ABGF$. **True**

13. F, E, H, and C are coplanar. **False**

14. A, B, and V are coplanar. **True**

Examples may vary.

Classify each statement as true or false. If it is false, provide a counterexample.

15. Through any three points, there is exactly one plane. **False; 3 collinear points**

16. Perpendicular lines form congruent adjacent angles. **True**

17. If points A and B are in plane M, then $\overline{AB}$ is in plane M. **True**

18. Complementary angles must be adjacent. **False**

B **19.** If $m\angle A = 45$, then the complement of $\angle A$ is one third of its supplement. **True**

20. If $m\angle RUN = m\angle SUN$, then $\overrightarrow{UN}$ is the bisector of $\angle RUS$. **False; *R*, *U*, *N*, and *S* need not be coplanar.**

In the diagram, $\overrightarrow{OB}$ bisects $\angle AOC$ and $\overleftrightarrow{EC} \perp \overrightarrow{OD}$. Find the value of x.

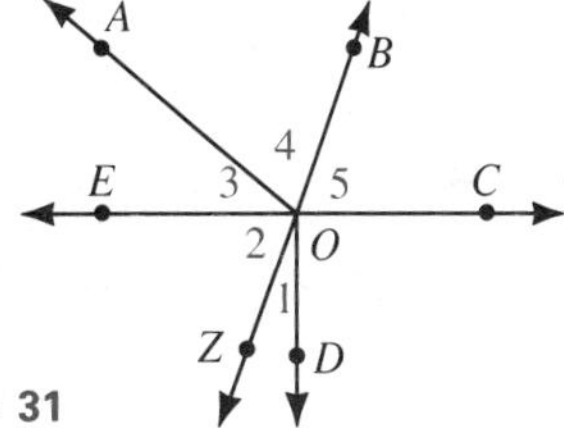

21. $m\angle 5 = 2x$, $m\angle 3 = x$ **$x = 36$**

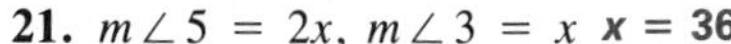

22. $m\angle 1 = 2x$, $m\angle 2 = 6x + 2$ **$x = 11$**

23. $m\angle 2 = 6x + 9$, $m\angle 5 = 2x + 49$ **$x = 10$**

24. $m\angle 2 = 3x$, $m\angle 3 = 2x - 4$ **$x = 23$**

25. $m\angle 1 = x - 8$, $m\angle 2 = 2x + 5$, $m\angle 4 = 3x - 26$ **$x = 31$**

3 Parallel Lines and Planes

Objectives

3-1 Distinguish between intersecting lines, parallel lines, and skew lines.

State and apply the theorem about the intersection of two parallel planes by a third plane.

Identify the angles formed when two lines are cut by a transversal.

3-2 State and apply a postulate and theorems about parallel lines.

3-3 State and apply the postulates and theorems about parallel lines.

State and apply the theorems about a parallel and a perpendicular to a given line through a point outside the line.

3-4 Classify triangles according to sides and to angles.

State and apply the theorem and the corollaries about the sum of the measures of the angles of a triangle.

State and apply the theorem about the measure of an exterior angle of a triangle.

3-5 Recognize and name convex polygons and regular polygons.

Find the measures of interior angles and exterior angles of convex polygons.

3-6 Understand and use inductive reasoning.

Assignment Guide

See page T40 for information about the Assignment Guide.

Day	Minimum Course	Average Course	Maximum Course
1	**3-1** 76/1–20	**3-1** 76–77/1–29 odd	**3-1** 76–77/1–41 odd
2	**3-1** 76–77/21–38	**3-1** 77/22–42 even	**3-2** 80–81/1–15 odd
3	**3-2** 80–81/1–6, 7, 9, 11, 12	**3-2** 80–81/1–13 odd	**3-2** 82/17–25 odd
4	**3-2** 81–82/13–19 82/Mixed Review 1–4	**3-2** 81–82/14–24 even 82/Mixed Review 1–4	**3-3** 87–88/1–23 odd
5	**3-3** 87/1–17	**3-3** 87/1–19 odd **S** 81–82/15, 17	**3-3** 88/24–31
6	**3-3** 87–88/18–21 89/Self-Test 1	**3-3** 87–88/12–28 even 89/Self-Test 1	**3-4** 97–98/1, 3, 9, 11, 12, 15, 17–19, 21, 24
7	**3-4** 97/1–13 **S** 88/22, 24	**3-4** 97–98/1, 2, 6, 9, 12–15, 17, 18, 20	**3-4** 98–99/25, 27–29, 31, 33
8	**3-4** 97–98/14–24, 30	**3-4** 98–99/22–32 even	**3-5** 104/4, 6–8, 9–13 odd **S** 99/30, 32
9	**3-5** 104/1–11	**3-5** 104–105/2, 4–9, 11, 15, 16	**3-5** 105/16, 18, 20, 21, 24–28
10	**3-5** 104–105/12–20	**3-5** 105/18, 19, 22, 25, 26	**3-6** 107–108/3, 5, 8, 12, 15, 16–22 even
11	**3-6** 107/1–14	**3-6** 107–108/1–17 odd	**3-6** 108–109/17–29 odd
12	**3-6** 108/15–17 **S** 105/22 110/Self-Test 2	**3-6** 108/18–27 **S** 105/20, 23	**3-6** 112–113/Chapter Test Test, page T14

Assignment Guide (continued)

Day	Minimum Course	Average Course	Maximum Course
13	**3-6** 112–113/Chapter Test Test, page T14	**3-6** 110/Self-Test 2 112–113/Chapter Test Test, page T14	**3-6** 112–113/Chapter Test Test, page T14

Supplementary Materials Guide

				Resource Book			
For Use after Lesson	Practice Masters	Tests	Study Guide (Reteaching)	Tests	Practice Exercises	Mixed Review (MR) Prep. for College Entrance Exams (Col) Enrichment (E) Computer (C)	Computer Activities
3-1			pp. 23–24				
3-2	Sheet 12		pp. 25–28				
3-3	Sheet 13	Test 9	pp. 29–32	p. 11	p. 117		
3-4			pp. 33–34				Activity 5
3-5	Sheet 14	Test 10	pp. 35–36	p. 12	p. 118		Activity 6
3-6	Sheet 15	Test 11	pp. 37–38	p. 13	p. 119		Activities 7, 8
Chapter 3	Sheet 16	Test 12		pp. 14–15	p. 120	p. 192 (Col) pp. 207–209 (E) pp. 238–239 (C)	
Chapters 1–3		Test 13		pp. 16–18	p. 121	pp. 173–174 (MR)	

Overhead Visuals

Guided Discovery Visuals (lettered) and Teaching Visuals (numbered) available for Chapter 3.

Lessons	Visual	Title
3-1	B	Points, Lines, and Planes
3-1, 3-2, 3-3	5	Ways to Prove Two Lines Parallel
3-4, 3-5, 3-6	6	Triangle Classification

Software Guide

Houghton Mifflin software for Chapter 3

Geometry Grapher (Apple or IBM)

Use with	**Booklet**
p. 78 (Theorem 3-2)	Classroom Demonstration, p. 14
p. 78 (Explorations)	
p. 89 (Explorations)	
p. 99 (Explorations)	

Test Generator (Apple or IBM): 90 test items

Other software appropriate for Chapter 3

Geometric Supposer (Apple): PreSupposer, Triangles

GeoDraw (IBM)

Guide to Integrated Curriculum

Teachers wishing to integrate coordinate and transformational geometry throughout the course can use the following lessons after Chapter 3. See pages T56–T57 and 657 for more information.

Handbook: Translation and Rotation, pp. 657–659

Exploring Angles of Polygons

When to Use

Before Lesson 3-4

Overview

Activity motivates Theorems 3-11, 3-13, and 3-14.

Description of Activity

Guide students through the exploration by using the following activities and questions.

1. Draw $\triangle ABC$ and place your pencil as in Figure 1. First rotate your pencil counterclockwise through $\angle A$ (Figure 2). Then rotate your pencil through $\angle C$ (Figure 3). Finally, rotate your pencil through $\angle B$ (Figure 4). You have rotated the pencil through the three interior angles of $\triangle ABC$.

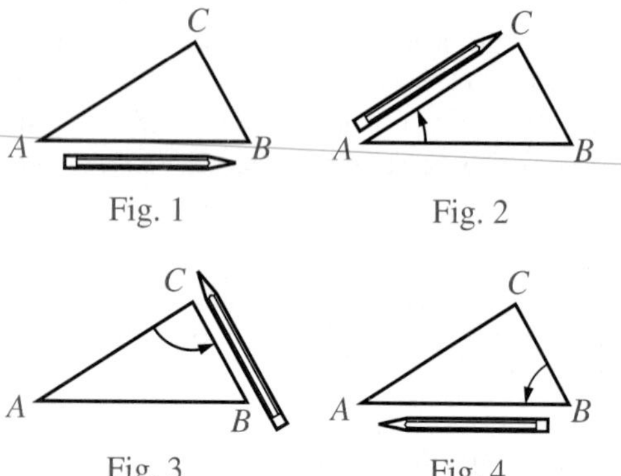

a. In what direction was your pencil pointing at the beginning? right

b. What was the final direction of your pencil? left

c. Through how many degrees has your pencil rotated? 180

d. Make a conjecture about the sum of the measures of the angles of $\triangle ABC$. Sum equals 180.

e. Is your conjecture true for any triangle? Yes

2. Draw a convex quadrilateral $ABCD$. (A convex quadrilateral is a four-sided figure such that no line containing a side of the figure contains a point in the interior of the figure.) Repeat Activity 1, rotating the pencil counterclockwise through the four angles of this quadrilateral. Through how many degrees has your pencil rotated? 360 Make a conjecture about the sum of the angles of a convex quadrilateral. The sum of the measures of the angles of a convex quadrilateral is 360.

3. Draw an n-gon (a convex polygon with n sides) for $n = 5, 6, 7, \ldots$. Repeat Activity 1, rotating the pencil counterclockwise through the angles of the n-gon. Through how many degrees has your pencil rotated? Make a conjecture about the sum of the angles of a convex n-gon. The sum of the measures of the angles of a convex polygon with n sides is $(n - 2)180$.

4. Do a similar experiment to investigate the sum of the three exterior angles as shown below.

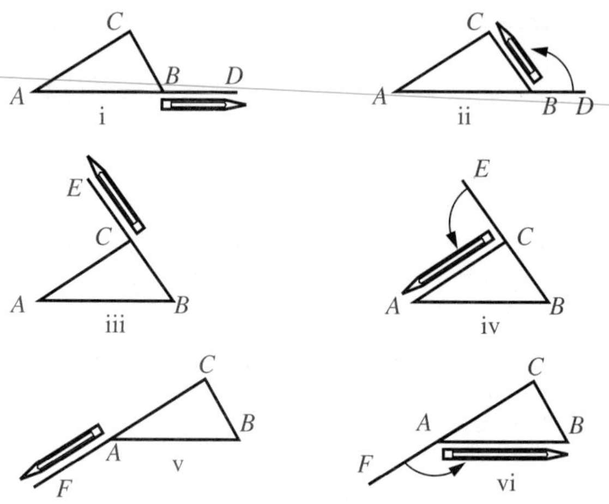

a. In what direction was your pencil pointing at the beginning? right

b. What was the final direction of your pencil? right

c. Through how many degrees has your pencil rotated? 360

d. Make a conjecture about the sum of the measures of the exterior angles of $\triangle ABC$. The sum is 360.

e. Is your conjecture true about any triangle? Yes

5. Draw a convex n-gon for $n = 4, 5, 6, 7, \ldots$. Repeat Activity 4, rotating the pencil through the exterior angles of the n-gon. Through how many degrees has your pencil rotated? Make a conjecture about the sum of the exterior angles of a convex n-gon. The sum of the measures of the exterior angles of any convex polygon is 360.

Commentary

This exploration can be teacher-led on an overhead projector or used as a small group discovery activity.

References to Strategies

PE: Pupil's Edition **TE:** Teacher's Edition **RB:** Resource Book

Problem Solving Strategies

PE: 85 (Strategies for proof), 90–91 (Draw a diagram), 94 (Strategies for proof), 103 (Choose a method of solution), 106–109 (Recognize a pattern)
TE: T86, 75, 77 (Reasoning backward), 105 (Extend a problem), 108 (Draw a diagram)
RB: 207–208 (Generalize from a specific example)

Applications

PE: 90–92 (Technical drawing), 100 (Carpenter), 104 (Ex. 9, Baseball), 104 (Ex. 11, Honeycomb), 105 (Exs. 18–20, Tiling), 657–658 (Tiling)
TE: 90, T83–T84

Nonroutine Problems

PE: 76 (Exs. 18–21), 80 (Ex. 14), 88 (Exs. 20, 21, 30), 92, 96 (Exs. 16, 17), 99 (Exs. 31–34), 103 (Exs. 1–7), 104 (Ex. 7), 105 (Exs. 18–20), 108 (Exs. 15–17, 26, 27), 109 (Exs. 28, 30), 658–659 (Exs. 1–7)
TE: T85 (Spherical triangles), T86–T87 (Ambiguous patterns)
RB: 207–209

Communication

PE: 77 (Drawing space figures), 86 (Ex. 20, Convincing argument), 88 (Ex. 30, Convincing argument), 90–92 (Isometric drawings)
TE: T84, 75, 77, 87, 103

Thinking Skills

PE: 93 (Classification), 106 (Deductive and inductive reasoning), 106–109 (Analysis of patterns)
TE: 98 (Multiple answers)
RB: 261 (Van Hiele activity)

Explorations

PE: 78, 89, 99
TE: 71c

Connections

PE: 113 (Coordinate plane), 657–659 (Transformational geometry)
TE: T85 (Non-Euclidean geometry), T87 (Reasoning), 80 (Fallacies), 84, 103 (Reference to Ch. 7)

Using Technology

PE: 78, 88, 89, 99, 104, 108, 109
TE: T84–T85, 78, 88, 93, 99, 105, 108, 109
RB: 238–239
Using Geometry Grapher: 14
Computer Activities: 11–19

Using Manipulatives/Models

PE: 77, 90–92, 96 (Exs. 16, 17), 104 (Ex. 7), 657–659
TE: T83, 74
RB: 209

Cooperative Learning

TE: T86, T87, 77

Teaching Resources

For use in implementing the teaching strategies referenced on the previous page.

Problem Solving
***Resource Book*, p. 207**

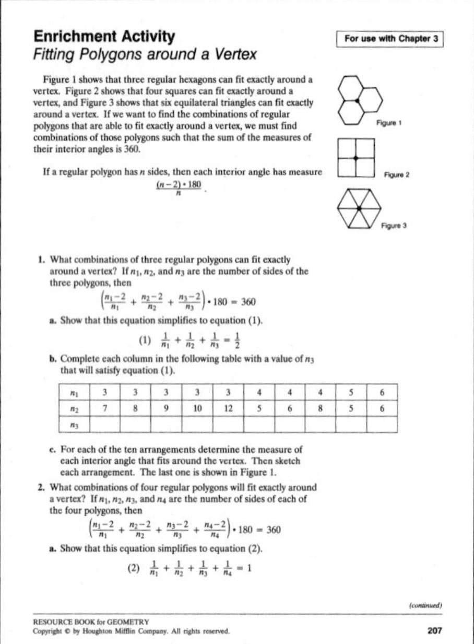

Enrichment Activity
Fitting Polygons around a Vertex

For use with Chapter 3

Figure 1 shows that three regular hexagons can fit exactly around a vertex. Figure 2 shows that four squares can fit exactly around a vertex, and Figure 3 shows that six equilateral triangles can fit exactly around a vertex. If we want to find the combinations of regular polygons that are able to fit exactly around a vertex, we must find combinations of those polygons such that the sum of the measures of their interior angles is 360.

If a regular polygon has n sides, then each interior angle has measure $\frac{(n-2)\cdot 180}{n}$.

Figure 1

Figure 2

Figure 3

1. What combinations of three regular polygons can fit exactly around a vertex? If n_1, n_2, and n_3 are the number of sides of the three polygons, then

$$\left(\frac{n_1-2}{n_1} + \frac{n_2-2}{n_2} + \frac{n_3-2}{n_3}\right)\cdot 180 = 360$$

a. Show that this equation simplifies to equation (1).

$$(1)\quad \frac{1}{n_1} + \frac{1}{n_2} + \frac{1}{n_3} = \frac{1}{2}$$

b. Complete each column in the following table with a value of n_3 that will satisfy equation (1).

n_1	3	3	3	3	3	4	4	4	5	6
n_2	7	8	9	10	12	5	6	8	5	6
n_3										

c. For each of the ten arrangements determine the measure of each interior angle that fits around the vertex. Then sketch each arrangement. The last one is shown in Figure 1.

2. What combinations of four regular polygons will fit exactly around a vertex? If n_1, n_2, n_3, and n_4 are the number of sides of each of the four polygons, then

$$\left(\frac{n_1-2}{n_1} + \frac{n_2-2}{n_2} + \frac{n_3-2}{n_3} + \frac{n_4-2}{n_4}\right)\cdot 180 = 360$$

a. Show that this equation simplifies to equation (2).

$$(2)\quad \frac{1}{n_1} + \frac{1}{n_2} + \frac{1}{n_3} + \frac{1}{n_4} = 1$$

(continued)

RESOURCE BOOK for GEOMETRY

207

Exploration
***Resource Book*, p. 209**

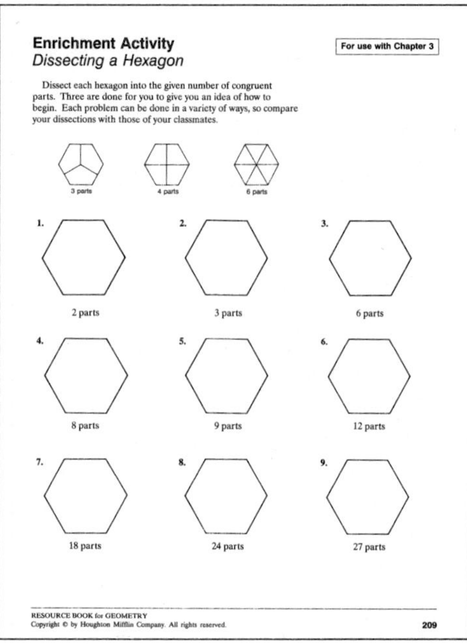

Enrichment Activity
Dissecting a Hexagon

For use with Chapter 3

Dissect each hexagon into the given number of congruent parts. Three are done for you to give you an idea of how to begin. Each problem can be done in a variety of ways, so compare your dissections with those of your classmates.

3 parts 4 parts 6 parts

1. 2 parts
2. 3 parts
3. 6 parts
4. 8 parts
5. 9 parts
6. 12 parts
7. 18 parts
8. 24 parts
9. 27 parts

RESOURCE BOOK for GEOMETRY

209

Thinking Skills
***Resource Book*, p. 261**

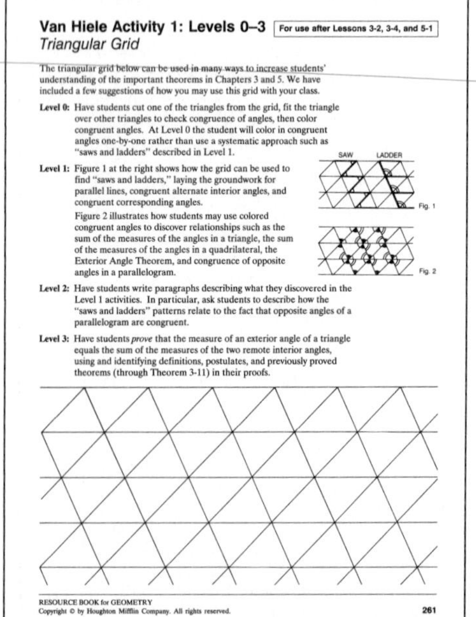

Van Hiele Activity 1: Levels 0–3
Triangular Grid

For use after Lessons 3-2, 3-4, and 5-1

The triangular grid below can be used in many ways to increase students' understanding of the important theorems in Chapters 3 and 5. We have included a few suggestions of how you may use this grid with your class.

Level 0: Have students cut one of the triangles from the grid, fit the triangle over other triangles to check congruence of angles, then color congruent angles. At Level 0 the student will color in congruent angles one-by-one rather than use a systematic approach such as "saws and ladders" described in Level 1.

Level 1: Figure 1 at the right shows how the grid can be used to find "saws and ladders," laying the groundwork for parallel lines, congruent alternate interior angles, and congruent corresponding angles.

Figure 2 illustrates how students may use colored congruent angles to discover relationships such as the sum of the measures of the angles in a triangle, the sum of the measures of the angles in a quadrilateral, the Exterior Angle Theorem, and congruence of opposite angles in a parallelogram.

SAW LADDER

Fig. 1

Fig. 2

Level 2: Have students write paragraphs describing what they discovered in the Level 1 activities. In particular, ask students to describe how the "saws and ladders" patterns relate to the fact that opposite angles of a parallelogram are congruent.

Level 3: Have students *prove* that the measure of an exterior angle of a triangle equals the sum of the measures of the two remote interior angles, using and identifying definitions, postulates, and previously proved theorems (through Theorem 3-11) in their proofs.

RESOURCE BOOK for GEOMETRY

261

Using Technology
***Using Geometry Grapher*, p. 14**

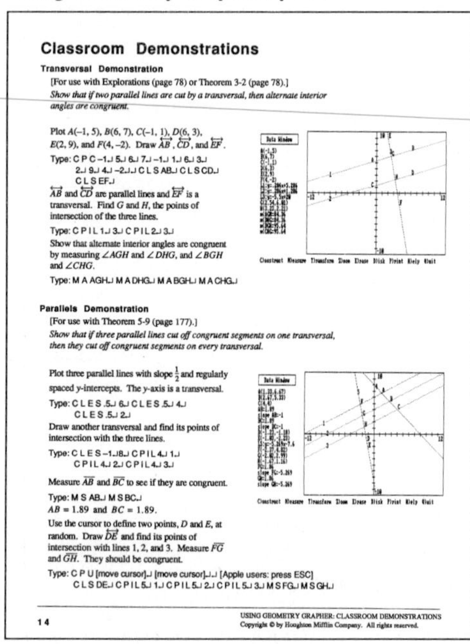

Classroom Demonstrations

Transversal Demonstration

[For use with Explorations (page 78) or Theorem 3-2 (page 78).]

Show that if two parallel lines are cut by a transversal, then alternate interior angles are congruent.

Plot $A(-1, 5)$, $B(6, 7)$, $C(-1, 1)$, $D(6, 3)$, $E(2, 9)$, and $F(4, -2)$. Draw $\overleftrightarrow{AB}$, $\overleftrightarrow{CD}$, and $\overleftrightarrow{EF}$.

Type: C P C −1↵ 5↵ 6↵ 7↵ −1↵ 1↵ 6↵ 3↵ 2↵ 9↵ 4↵ −2↵↵ C L S AB↵ C L S CD↵ C L S EF↵

$\overleftrightarrow{AB}$ and $\overleftrightarrow{CD}$ are parallel lines and $\overleftrightarrow{EF}$ is a transversal. Find G and H, the points of intersection of the three lines.

Type: C P I L 1↵ 3↵ C P I L 2↵ 3↵

Show that alternate interior angles are congruent by measuring $\angle AGH$ and $\angle DHG$, and $\angle BGH$ and $\angle CHG$.

Type: M A AGH↵ M A DHG↵ M A BGH↵ M A CHG↵

Parallels Demonstration

[For use with Theorem 5-9 (page 177).]

Show that if three parallel lines cut off congruent segments on one transversal, then they cut off congruent segments on every transversal.

Plot three parallel lines with slope $\frac{1}{2}$ and regularly spaced y-intercepts. The y-axis is a transversal.

Type: C L E S .5↵ 6↵ C L E S .5↵ 4↵ C L E S .5↵ 2↵

Draw another transversal and find its points of intersection with the three lines.

Type: C L E S −1↵8↵ C P I L 4↵ 1↵ C P I L 4↵ 2↵ C P I L 4↵ 3↵

Measure $\overline{AB}$ and $\overline{BC}$ to see if they are congruent.

Type: M S AB↵ M S BC↵
$AB = 1.89$ and $BC = 1.89$.

Use the cursor to define two points, D and E, at random. Draw $\overleftrightarrow{DE}$ and find its points of intersection with lines 1, 2, and 3. Measure $\overline{FG}$ and $\overline{GH}$. They should be congruent.

Type: C P U [move cursor]↵ [move cursor]↵↵ [Apple users: press ESC] C L S DE↵ C P I L 5↵ 1↵ C P I L 5↵ 2↵ C P I L 5↵ 3↵ M S FG↵ M S GH↵

14
USING GEOMETRY GRAPHER: CLASSROOM DEMONSTRATIONS

Thinking Skills
Study Guide, p. 37

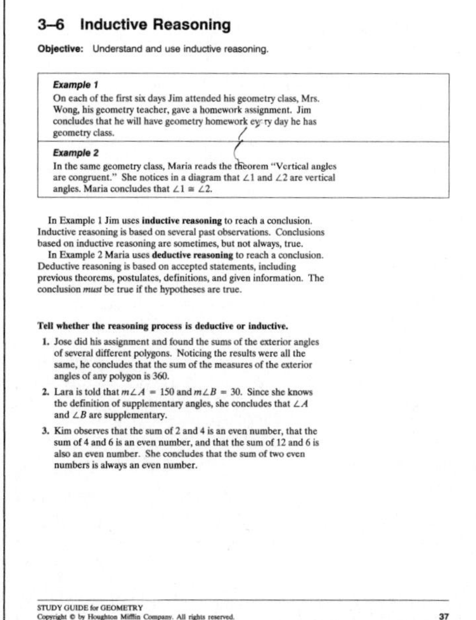

3–6 Inductive Reasoning

Objective: Understand and use inductive reasoning.

Example 1
On each of the first six days Jim attended his geometry class, Mrs. Wong, his geometry teacher, gave a homework assignment. Jim concludes that he will have geometry homework every day he has geometry class.

Example 2
In the same geometry class, Maria reads the theorem "Vertical angles are congruent." She notices in a diagram that $\angle 1$ and $\angle 2$ are vertical angles. Maria concludes that $\angle 1 \cong \angle 2$.

In Example 1 Jim uses **inductive reasoning** to reach a conclusion. Inductive reasoning is based on several past observations. Conclusions based on inductive reasoning are sometimes, but not always, true.

In Example 2 Maria uses **deductive reasoning** to reach a conclusion. Deductive reasoning is based on accepted statements, including previous theorems, postulates, definitions, and given information. The conclusion *must* be true if the hypotheses are true.

Tell whether the reasoning process is deductive or inductive.

1. Jose did his assignment and found the sums of the exterior angles of several different polygons. Noticing the results were all the same, he concludes that the sum of the measures of the exterior angles of any polygon is 360.
2. Lara is told that $m\angle A = 150$ and $m\angle B = 30$. Since she knows the definition of supplementary angles, she concludes that $\angle A$ and $\angle B$ are supplementary.
3. Kim observes that the sum of 2 and 4 is an even number, that the sum of 4 and 6 is an even number, and that the sum of 12 and 6 is also an even number. She concludes that the sum of two even numbers is always an even number.

STUDY GUIDE for GEOMETRY

37

Thinking Skills
Study Guide, p. 38

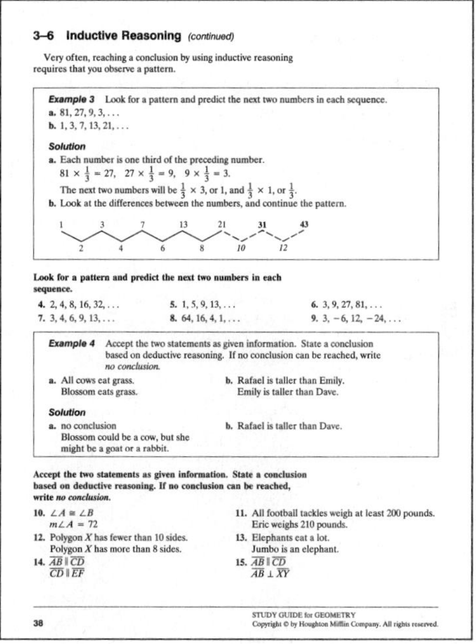

3–6 Inductive Reasoning *(continued)*

Very often, reaching a conclusion by using inductive reasoning requires that you observe a pattern.

Example 3 Look for a pattern and predict the next two numbers in each sequence.

a. 81, 27, 9, 3, . . .
b. 1, 3, 7, 13, 21, . . .

Solution

a. Each number is one third of the preceding number.
$81 \times \frac{1}{3} = 27, \quad 27 \times \frac{1}{3} = 9, \quad 9 \times \frac{1}{3} = 3.$
The next two numbers will be $\frac{1}{3} \times 3$, or 1, and $\frac{1}{3} \times 1$, or $\frac{1}{3}$.
b. Look at the differences between the numbers, and continue the pattern.

Look for a pattern and predict the next two numbers in each sequence.

4. 2, 4, 8, 16, 32, . . .
5. 1, 5, 9, 13, . . .
6. 3, 9, 27, 81, . . .
7. 3, 4, 6, 9, 13, . . .
8. 64, 16, 4, 1, . . .
9. 3, −6, 12, −24, . . .

Example 4 Accept the two statements as given information. State a conclusion based on deductive reasoning. If no conclusion can be reached, write *no conclusion.*

a. All cows eat grass.
Blossom eats grass.

b. Rafael is taller than Emily.
Emily is taller than Dave.

Solution

a. no conclusion
Blossom could be a cow, but she might be a goat or a rabbit.

b. Rafael is taller than Dave.

Accept the two statements as given information. State a conclusion based on deductive reasoning. If no conclusion can be reached, write *no conclusion.*

10. $\angle A \cong \angle B$
$m\angle A = 72$
11. All football tackles weigh at least 200 pounds.
Eric weighs 210 pounds.
12. Polygon X has fewer than 10 sides.
Polygon X has more than 8 sides.
13. Elephants eat a lot.
Jumbo is an elephant.
14. $\overline{AB} \parallel \overline{CD}$
$\overline{CD} \parallel \overline{EF}$
15. $\overline{AB} \parallel \overline{CD}$
$\overline{AB} \perp \overline{XY}$

38
STUDY GUIDE for GEOMETRY

Thinking Skills
Teaching Visual 5

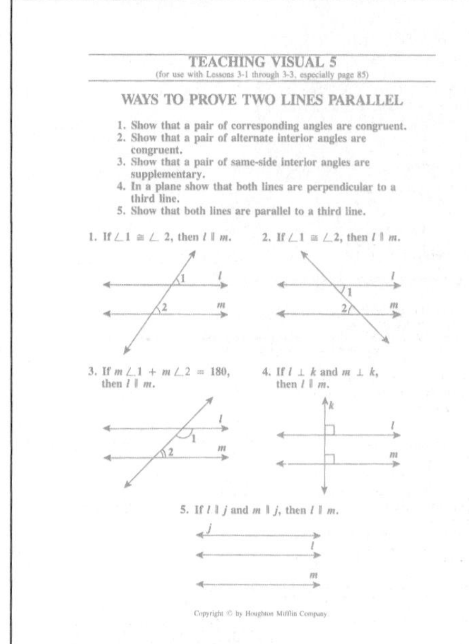

TEACHING VISUAL 5
(for use with Lessons 3-1 through 3-3, especially page 85)

WAYS TO PROVE TWO LINES PARALLEL

1. Show that a pair of corresponding angles are congruent.
2. Show that a pair of alternate interior angles are congruent.
3. Show that a pair of same-side interior angles are supplementary.
4. In a plane show that both lines are perpendicular to a third line.
5. Show that both lines are parallel to a third line.

1. If $\angle 1 \cong \angle 2$, then $l \parallel m$.
2. If $\angle 1 \cong \angle 2$, then $l \parallel m$.
3. If $m\angle 1 + m\angle 2 = 180$, then $l \parallel m$.
4. If $l \perp k$ and $m \perp k$, then $l \parallel m$.
5. If $l \parallel j$ and $m \parallel j$, then $l \parallel m$.

Thinking Skills
Teaching Visual 6

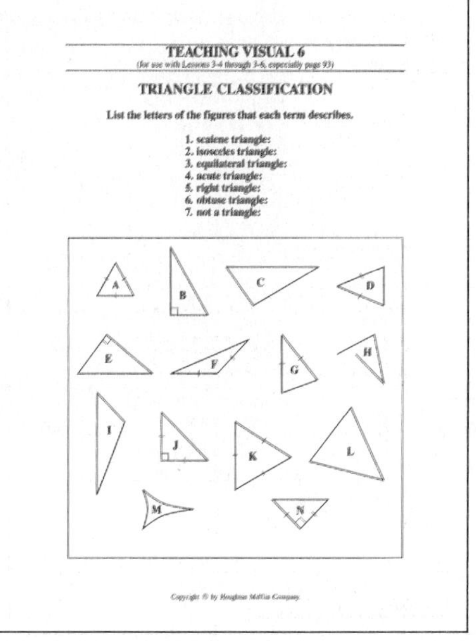

TEACHING VISUAL 6
(for use with Lessons 3-4 through 3-6, especially page 93)

TRIANGLE CLASSIFICATION

List the letters of the figures that each term describes.

1. scalene triangle:
2. isosceles triangle:
3. equilateral triangle:
4. acute triangle:
5. right triangle:
6. obtuse triangle:
7. not a triangle:

Teaching References

Lesson Commentary, pp. T83–T87

Assignment Guide, pp. T42–T43

Software Guide, p. T73

Alternate Test, p. T14

Supplementary Materials

Practice Masters 12–16

Tests 9–13

Resource Book
- Tests, pp. 11–18
- Practice, pp. 117–121
- Mixed Rev., pp. 173–174
- Preparing for College Entrance Exams, p. 192
- Enrichment Activity, pp. 207–209
- Computer Activity, pp. 238–239
- van Hiele Activity, p. 261

Study Guide, pp. 23–38

Overhead Visuals B, 5, 6

Computer Activities
- 5 Conditions on Triangles
- 6 Angles of a Polygon
- 7 Pascal's Triangle
- 8 Twenty-three Matches

Handbook for Integrating Coordinate and Transformational Geometry

Translation and Rotation, pp. 657–659

Cultural Note

The word *parallel* comes from a Greek word meaning *beside one another,* or *side by side.* The word *skew* is related to a Middle English word, *skewen,* which means *to escape,* or *to slip away.*

3 PARALLEL LINES AND PLANES

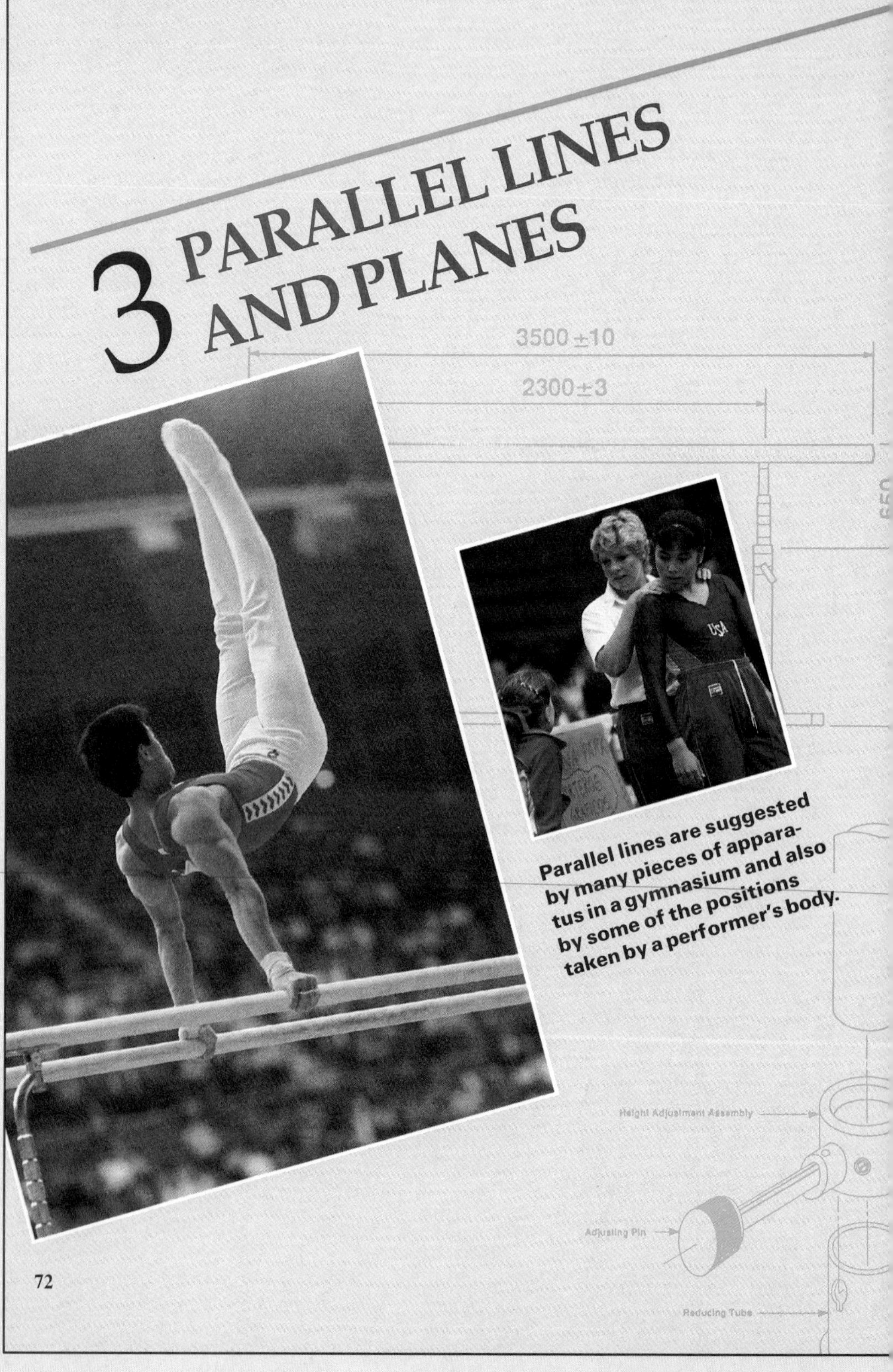

Parallel lines are suggested by many pieces of apparatus in a gymnasium and also by some of the positions taken by a performer's body.

72

When Lines and Planes Are Parallel

Objectives

1. Distinguish between intersecting lines, parallel lines, and skew lines.
2. State and apply the theorem about the intersection of two parallel planes by a third plane.
3. Identify the angles formed when two lines are cut by a transversal.
4. State and apply the postulates and theorems about parallel lines.
5. State and apply the theorems about a parallel and a perpendicular to a given line through a point outside the line.

3-1 *Definitions*

Two lines that do not intersect are either *parallel* or *skew*.

Parallel lines (∥ lines) are coplanar lines that do not intersect.

Skew lines are noncoplanar lines. Therefore, they are neither parallel nor intersecting.

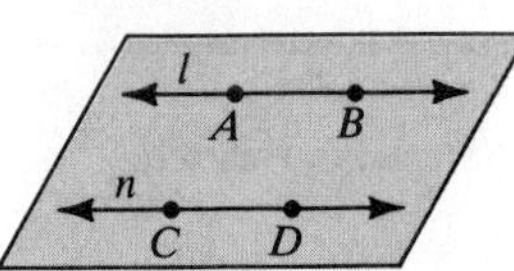

l and *n* are parallel lines.
l is parallel to *n* ($l \parallel n$).

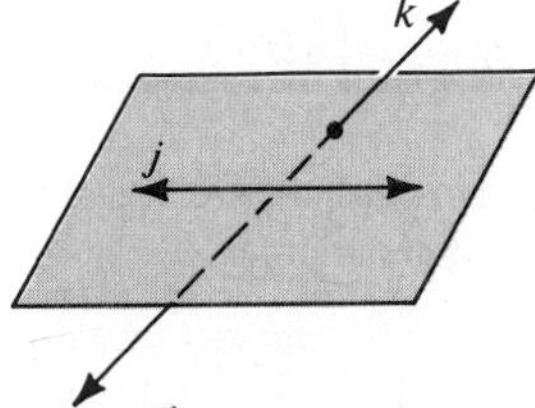

j and *k* are skew lines.

Segments and rays contained in parallel lines are also called parallel. For example, in the figure at the left above, $\overline{AB} \parallel \overline{CD}$ and $\overrightarrow{AB} \parallel \overrightarrow{CD}$.

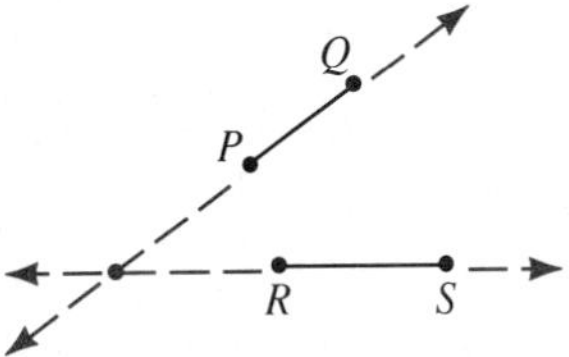

In the diagram at the right, $\overline{PQ}$ and $\overline{RS}$ do not intersect, but they are parts of lines, $\overleftrightarrow{PQ}$ and $\overleftrightarrow{RS}$, that do intersect. Thus $\overline{PQ}$ is *not* parallel to $\overline{RS}$.

The box pictured below may help you understand the following definitions. Think of the top of the box as part of plane *X* and the bottom of the box as part of plane *Y*.

Parallel planes (∥ planes) do not intersect.
Plane *X* is parallel to plane *Y* ($X \parallel Y$).

A line and a plane are parallel if they do not intersect.
For example, $\overleftrightarrow{EF} \parallel Y$ and $\overleftrightarrow{FG} \parallel Y$.
Also, $\overleftrightarrow{AB} \parallel X$ and $\overleftrightarrow{BC} \parallel X$.

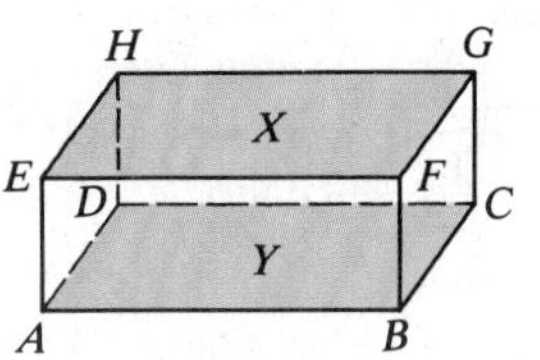

Teaching Suggestions,
pp. T83–T84

Objectives
Presenting the Lesson
Applications

Communication Skills,
p. T84

Supplementary Materials

Study Guide, pp. 23–24
Overhead Visual B

Lesson Focus

Lines and planes have different relationships to themselves and each other. This lesson presents the definitions that describe these basic relationships.

Suggested Assignments

Minimum
Day 1: 76/1–20
Day 2: 76–77/21–38

Average
Day 1: 76–77/1–29 odd
Day 2: 77/22–42 even

Maximum
76–77/1–41 odd

Teaching Note

Some diagrams in this chapter represent plane figures and some are two-dimensional representations of space figures. Students may need help in relating objects (models), diagrams, ideas, words, and symbols. Call students' attention to the following four ways of representing Theorem 3-1: (1) object or model; (2) diagram in text; (3) statement of the theorem; (4) the symbols and words in the Given/Prove part.

Using a Model

An excellent model to illustrate Theorem 3-1 is the cardboard separator used to divide and protect jars that are shipped in large cartons. When discussing this theorem, stress that two planes either intersect or are parallel.

Chalkboard Examples

Classify each statement as true or false.

1. A transversal intersects only parallel lines. F
2. Skew lines are not coplanar. T
3. If two lines are coplanar, then they are parallel. F
4. If two lines are parallel, then exactly one plane contains them. T

If *j*, *k*, and *l* are coplanar, name the transversal(s).

5. *l*

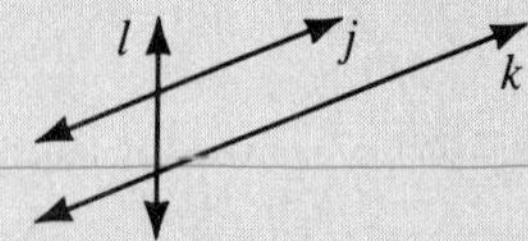

6. *j*, *k*, *l*

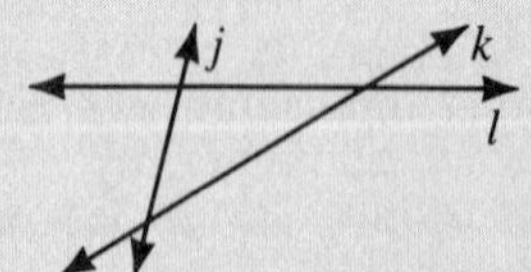

7. none

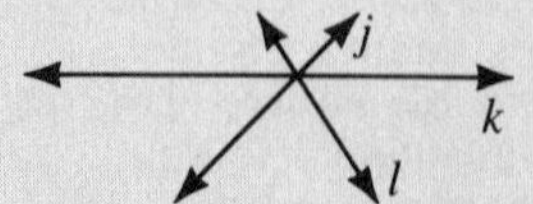

Our first theorem about parallel lines and planes is given below. Notice the importance of definitions in the proof.

Theorem 3-1

If two parallel planes are cut by a third plane, then the lines of intersection are parallel.

Given: Plane $X \parallel$ plane Y;
plane Z intersects X in line l;
plane Z intersects Y in line n.

Prove: $l \parallel n$

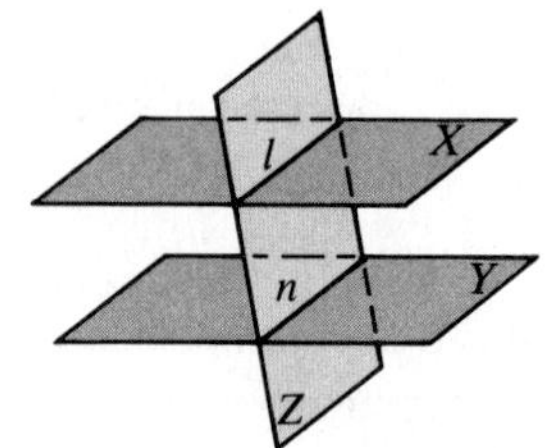

Proof:

Statements	Reasons
1. l is in Z; n is in Z.	1. Given
2. l and n are coplanar.	2. Def. of coplanar
3. l is in X; n is in Y; $X \parallel Y$.	3. Given
4. l and n do not intersect.	4. Parallel planes do not intersect. (Def. of $\parallel$ planes)
5. $l \parallel n$	5. Def. of $\parallel$ lines (Steps 2 and 4)

The following terms, which are needed for future theorems about parallel lines, apply only to coplanar lines.

A **transversal** is a line that intersects two or more coplanar lines in different points. In the next diagram, t is a transversal of h and k. The angles formed have special names.

Interior angles: angles 3, 4, 5, 6

Exterior angles: angles 1, 2, 7, 8

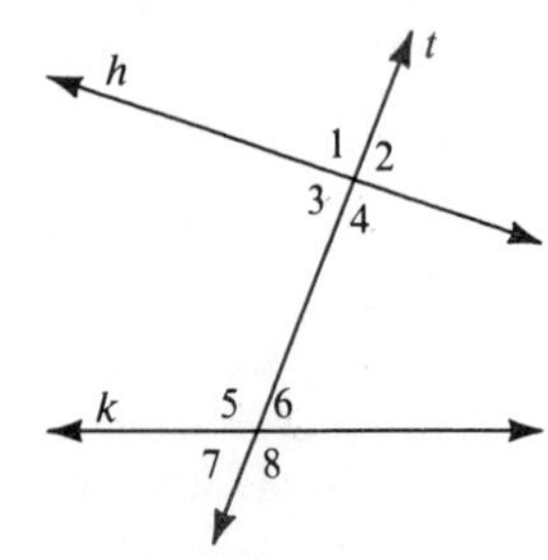

Alternate interior angles (alt. int. $\angle$s) are two nonadjacent interior angles on opposite sides of the transversal.

$\angle 3$ and $\angle 6$ $\quad$ $\angle 4$ and $\angle 5$

Same-side interior angles (s-s. int. $\angle$s) are two interior angles on the same side of the transversal.

$\angle 3$ and $\angle 5$ $\quad$ $\angle 4$ and $\angle 6$

Corresponding angles (corr. $\angle$s) are two angles in corresponding positions relative to the two lines.

$\angle 1$ and $\angle 5$ $\quad$ $\angle 2$ and $\angle 6$ $\quad$ $\angle 3$ and $\angle 7$ $\quad$ $\angle 4$ and $\angle 8$

Classroom Exercises

1. The blue line is a transversal.
   a. Name four pairs of corresponding angles.
   b. Name two pairs of alternate interior angles.
   c. Name two pairs of same-side interior angles. ∠2, ∠5; ∠3, ∠8
   d. Name two pairs of angles that could be called *alternate exterior angles.* ∠1, ∠7; ∠4, ∠6
   e. Name two pairs of angles that could be called *same-side exterior angles.* ∠1, ∠6; ∠4, ∠7
   a. ∠1, ∠5; ∠2, ∠6; ∠3, ∠7; ∠4, ∠8   b. ∠2, ∠8; ∠3, ∠5

Classify each pair of angles as alternate interior angles, same-side interior angles, corresponding angles, or none of these.

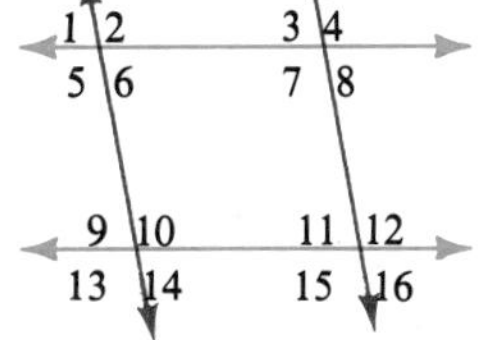

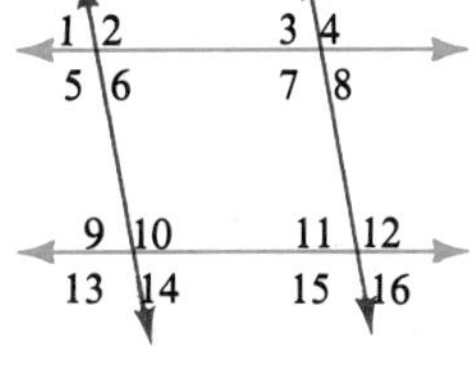

2. ∠7 and ∠11 **s-s int.**
3. ∠14 and ∠16 **corr.**
4. ∠4 and ∠10 **none**
5. ∠3 and ∠6 **alt. int.**
6. ∠6 and ∠11 **none**
7. ∠2 and ∠10 **corr.**
8. ∠2 and ∠3 **s-s int.**
9. ∠7 and ∠12 **alt. int.**

10. Classify each pair of lines as intersecting, parallel, or skew.
    a. $\overleftrightarrow{AB}$ and $\overleftrightarrow{EJ}$ ∥
    b. $\overleftrightarrow{AB}$ and $\overleftrightarrow{FK}$ ∥
    c. $\overleftrightarrow{AB}$ and $\overleftrightarrow{ID}$ **skew**
    d. $\overleftrightarrow{EF}$ and $\overleftrightarrow{IH}$ **int.**
    e. $\overleftrightarrow{EF}$ and $\overleftrightarrow{NM}$ **skew**
    f. $\overleftrightarrow{CN}$ and $\overleftrightarrow{FG}$ **skew**

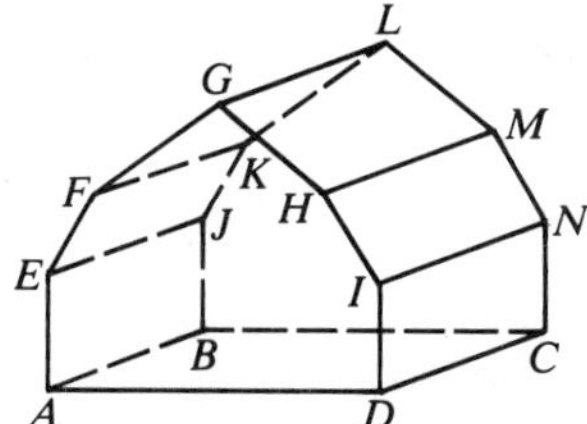

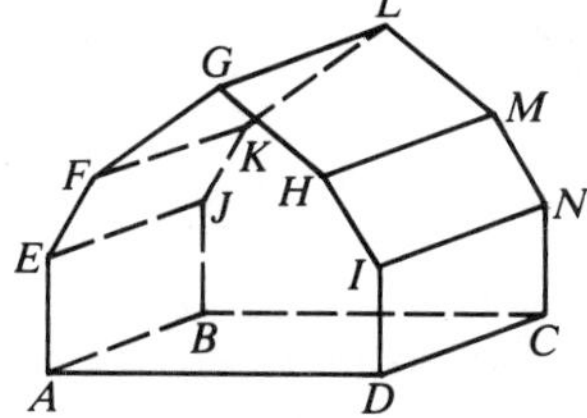

11. Name six lines parallel to $\overleftrightarrow{GL}$.
12. Name several lines skew to $\overleftrightarrow{GL}$.
13. Name five lines parallel to plane *ABCD*.
14. Name two coplanar segments that do not intersect and yet are not parallel.
    Answers may vary; $\overline{EF}$, $\overline{HI}$; $\overline{BJ}$, $\overline{LM}$

Complete each statement with the word *always, sometimes,* or *never.*

15. Two skew lines are _?_ parallel. **never**
16. Two parallel lines are _?_ coplanar. **always**
17. A line in the plane of the ceiling and a line in the plane of the floor are _?_ parallel. **sometimes**
18. Two lines in the plane of the floor are _?_ skew. **never**
19. A line in the plane of a wall and a line in the plane of the floor are
    a. _?_ parallel. **sometimes**
    b. _?_ intersecting. **sometimes**
    c. _?_ skew. **sometimes**

11. $\overleftrightarrow{AB}$, $\overleftrightarrow{EJ}$, $\overleftrightarrow{FK}$, $\overleftrightarrow{HM}$, $\overleftrightarrow{IN}$, $\overleftrightarrow{DC}$ **12.** $\overleftrightarrow{HI}$, $\overleftrightarrow{ID}$, $\overleftrightarrow{FE}$, $\overleftrightarrow{EA}$, $\overleftrightarrow{JK}$, $\overleftrightarrow{JB}$, $\overleftrightarrow{MN}$, $\overleftrightarrow{NC}$, $\overleftrightarrow{BC}$, $\overleftrightarrow{AD}$
13. $\overleftrightarrow{EJ}$, $\overleftrightarrow{FK}$, $\overleftrightarrow{GL}$, $\overleftrightarrow{HM}$, $\overleftrightarrow{IN}$

Problem Solving

To strengthen students' understanding of the definition of a transversal and their ability to solve problems involving transversals, tell students to think of coplanar lines *l* and *k* and transversal *t*. Call the plane containing *l* and *k* plane *X*, the intersection of *l* and *t* point *A*, and the intersection of *k* and *t* point *B*. Ask the following questions:
Is point *A* in plane *X*? Yes
Is point *B* in plane *X*? Yes
Is line *t* in plane *X*? Yes

Teaching Note

Encourage students to bring to class models and pictures that illustrate the concepts under discussion, and to describe the relationships in their own words.

Exercise Note

For Exs. 11–14, you may wish to have students name some planes that are not shown in the diagram, such as plane ABMH, or plane EJNI.

Guided Practice

Name the two lines and the transversal that form each pair of angles.

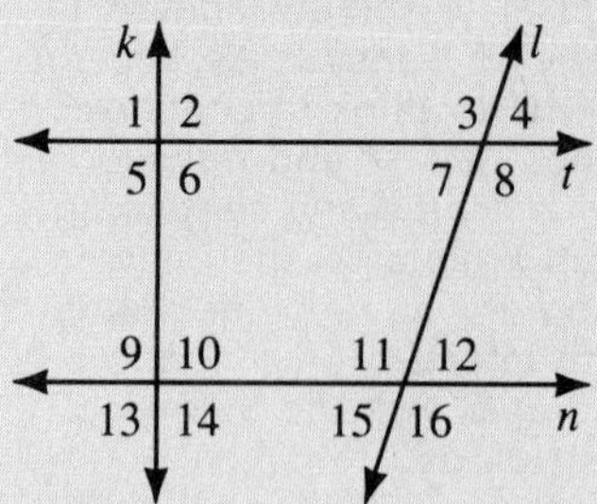

1. ∠1 and ∠3 *l, k; t*
2. ∠3 and ∠11 *t, n; l*
3. ∠10 and ∠11 *k, l; n*
4. ∠6 and ∠9 *t, n; k*
5. ∠8 and ∠11 *t, n; l*

Classify each pair of angles as alternate interior angles, same-side interior angles, or corresponding angles.

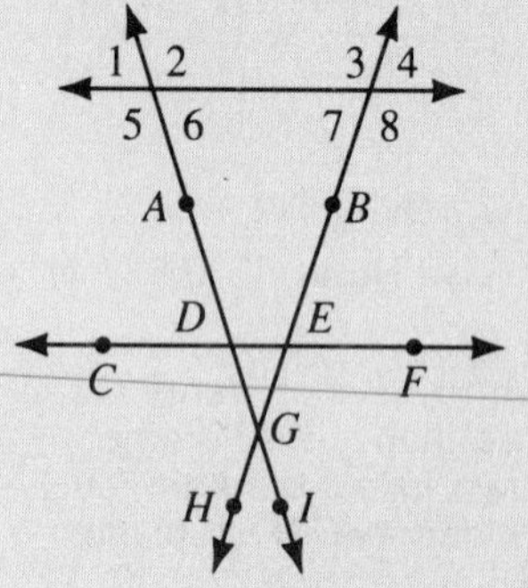

6. ∠1 and ∠3 C
7. ∠6 and ∠7 SSI
8. ∠2 and ∠7 AI
9. ∠ADE and ∠DEB SSI
10. ∠BEF and ∠EGI C

Exercise Note

Exs. 18–20 introduce the topics in the next lesson. Time allocated to these exercises can reduce the time required for the next lesson.

Written Exercises

Classify each pair of angles as alternate interior angles, same-side interior angles, or corresponding angles.

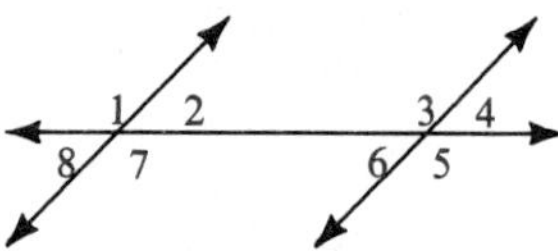

A

1. ∠2 and ∠6 **alt. int.**
2. ∠8 and ∠6 **corr.**
3. ∠2 and ∠3 **s-s int.**
4. ∠3 and ∠7 **alt. int.**
5. ∠5 and ∠7 **corr.**
6. ∠3 and ∠1 **corr.**

Name the two lines and the transversal that form each pair of angles.

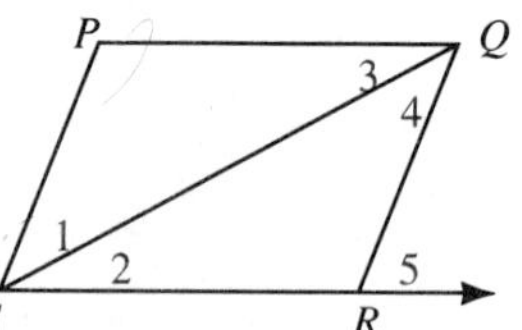

7. ∠2 and ∠3 $\overleftrightarrow{PQ}$, $\overleftrightarrow{SR}$; $\overleftrightarrow{SQ}$
8. ∠1 and ∠4 $\overleftrightarrow{PS}$, $\overleftrightarrow{QR}$; $\overleftrightarrow{SQ}$
9. ∠P and ∠PSR $\overleftrightarrow{PQ}$, $\overleftrightarrow{SR}$; $\overleftrightarrow{PS}$
10. ∠5 and ∠PSR $\overleftrightarrow{PS}$, $\overleftrightarrow{QR}$; $\overleftrightarrow{SR}$
11. ∠5 and ∠PQR $\overleftrightarrow{PQ}$, $\overleftrightarrow{SR}$; $\overleftrightarrow{QR}$

Classify each pair of angles as alternate interior, same-side interior, or corresponding angles.

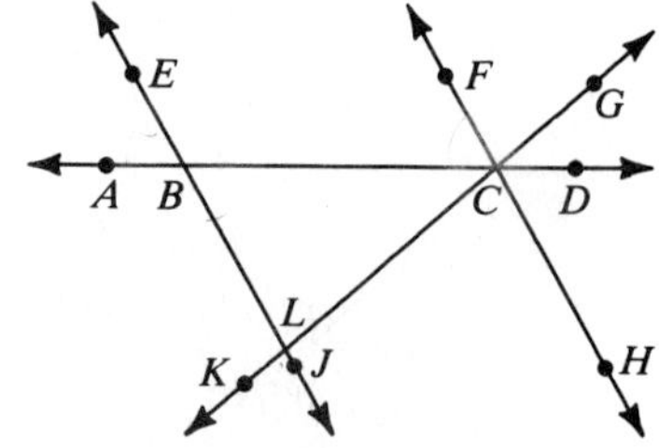

12. ∠EBA and ∠FCB **corr.**
13. ∠DCH and ∠CBJ **corr.**
14. ∠FCB and ∠CBL **alt. int.**
15. ∠FCL and ∠BLC **s-s int.**
16. ∠HCB and ∠CBJ **s-s int.**
17. ∠GCH and ∠GLJ **corr.**

In Exercises 18–20 use two lines of notebook paper as parallel lines and draw any transversal. Use a protractor to measure.

18. Measure one pair of corresponding angles. Repeat the experiment with another transversal. What appears to be true? **Corr. ∠s are congruent.**
19. Measure one pair of alternate interior angles. Repeat the experiment with another transversal. What appears to be true? **Alt. int. ∠s are congruent.**
20. Measure one pair of same-side interior angles. Repeat the experiment with another transversal. What appears to be true? **S-s int. ∠s are supplementary.**

B

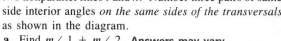

21. Draw a large diagram showing three transversals intersecting two nonparallel lines *l* and *n*. Number three pairs of same-side interior angles *on the same sides of the transversals*, as shown in the diagram.

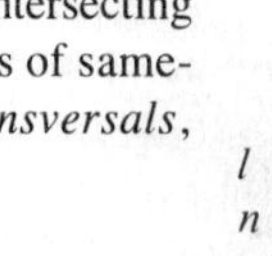

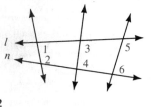

a. Find $m\angle 1 + m\angle 2$. **Answers may vary.**
b. Find $m\angle 3 + m\angle 4$. **Same as $m\angle 1 + m\angle 2$**
c. Predict the value of $m\angle 5 + m\angle 6$. Then check your prediction by measuring. **Same as $m\angle 1 + m\angle 2$**
d. What do you conclude? **When 2 nonparallel lines are cut by transversals, the sum of the measures of s-s int. ∠s is a constant.**

22. Draw a diagram of a six-sided box by following the steps below.

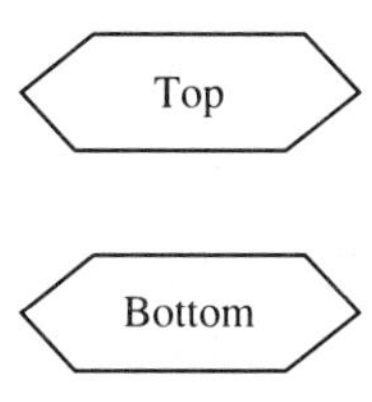

Step 1

Draw a six-sided top. Then draw an exact copy of the top directly below it.

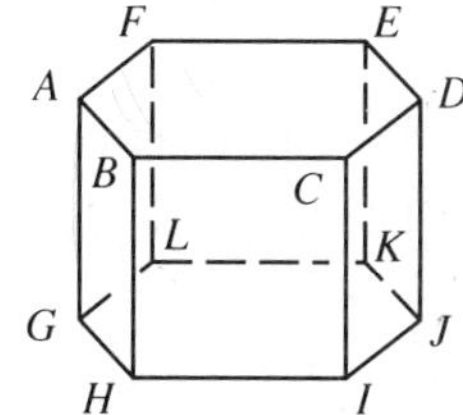

Step 2

Draw vertical edges. Make invisible edges dashed.

25. Answers may vary. $\overleftrightarrow{FL}$, $\overleftrightarrow{EK}$, $\overleftrightarrow{DJ}$, $\overleftrightarrow{CI}$, $\overleftrightarrow{GL}$, $\overleftrightarrow{LK}$, $\overleftrightarrow{JI}$, $\overleftrightarrow{IH}$

Exercises 23–29 refer to the diagram in Step 2 of Exercise 22.

23. Name five lines that appear to be parallel to $\overline{AG}$. **$\overleftrightarrow{BH}$, $\overleftrightarrow{CI}$, $\overleftrightarrow{DJ}$, $\overleftrightarrow{EK}$, $\overleftrightarrow{FL}$**

24. Name three lines that appear to be parallel to $\overline{AB}$. **$\overleftrightarrow{GH}$, $\overleftrightarrow{ED}$, $\overleftrightarrow{KJ}$**

25. Name four lines that appear to be skew to $\overline{AB}$. **See above.**

26. Name two planes parallel to $\overleftrightarrow{AF}$. ***CDJI*, *GHIJKL***

27. Name four planes parallel to $\overleftrightarrow{FL}$. ***ABHG*, *BCIH*, *CDJI*, *DEKJ***

28. How many pairs of parallel planes are shown? **4**

29. Suppose the top and bottom of the box lie in parallel planes. Explain how Theorem 3-1 can be used to prove $\overline{CD} \parallel \overline{IJ}$.

Complete each statement with the word *always*, *sometimes*, or *never*.

30. When there is a transversal of two lines, the three lines are __?__ coplanar. **always**

31. Three lines intersecting in one point are __?__ coplanar. **sometimes**

32. Two lines that are not coplanar __?__ intersect. **never**

33. Two lines parallel to a third line are __?__ parallel to each other. **always**

34. Two lines skew to a third line are __?__ skew to each other. **sometimes**

35. Two lines perpendicular to a third line are __?__ perpendicular to each other. **sometimes**

36. Two planes parallel to the same line are __?__ parallel to each other. **sometimes**

37. Two planes parallel to the same plane are __?__ parallel to each other. **always**

38. Lines in two parallel planes are __?__ parallel to each other. **sometimes**

39. Two lines parallel to the same plane are __?__ parallel to each other. **sometimes**

Draw each figure described. Check students' drawings.

C **40.** Lines a and b are skew, lines b and c are skew, and $a \parallel c$.

41. Lines d and e are skew, lines e and f are skew, and $d \perp f$.

42. Line $l \parallel$ plane X, plane $X \parallel$ plane Y, and l is not parallel to Y. ***l* must lie in *Y*.**

Group Activity

It is easy to underestimate the difficulty some students have with drawing three-dimensional figures. If you can spare class time, divide the class into several groups and have a representative from each group draw Ex. 22 on the chalkboard. Later, the class as a whole can discuss the relative merits of the different versions, and all students should practice drawing the figure.

Additional Answers Written Exercises

29. If the top and bottom lie in $\parallel$ planes, then $\overline{CD}$ and $\overline{IJ}$ are the lines of intersection of *DCIJ* with 2 $\parallel$ planes, and therefore are $\parallel$.

Exercise Note

For Exs. 30–39, encourage students to use physical models such as pieces of cardboard and pencils to illustrate the relationships stated.

Problem Solving

Many students approach problems by using information in the order it is presented. In Ex. 40, if you encourage students to work backwards, starting with lines *a* and *c*, then more students will be able to solve this C-level problem. This approach reinforces the importance of *thinking* about each problem.

Explorations

These exploratory exercises can be done using a computer with a program that draws and measures geometric figures.

Draw two parallel segments and a transversal and label the points of intersection. Measure all eight angles formed. Repeat several times. Do you notice any patterns? What kinds of angles are congruent? What kinds of angles are supplementary? **cong. ∠s: corr., alt. int., vertical, alt. ext.**
suppl. ∠s: s-s int., s-s ext., adj.

Using a Computer

These exercises explore properties of parallel lines that are developed in Lesson 3-2.

3-2 *Properties of Parallel Lines*

By experimenting with parallel lines, transversals, and a protractor in Exercise 18, page 76, you probably discovered that corresponding angles are congruent. There is not enough information in our previous postulates and theorems to deduce this property as a theorem. We will accept it as a postulate.

Postulate 10

If two parallel lines are cut by a transversal, then corresponding angles are congruent.

From this postulate we can easily prove the next three theorems.

Theorem 3-2

If two parallel lines are cut by a transversal, then alternate interior angles are congruent.

Given: $k \parallel n$; transversal t cuts k and n.
Prove: $\angle 1 \cong \angle 2$

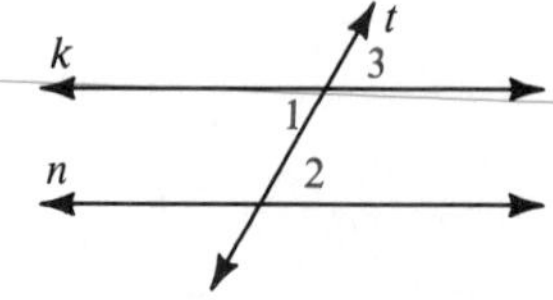

Proof:

Statements	Reasons
1. $k \parallel n$	1. Given
2. $\angle 1 \cong \angle 3$	2. Vert. ∠s are ≅.
3. $\angle 3 \cong \angle 2$	3. If two parallel lines are cut by a transversal, then corr. ∠s are ≅.
4. $\angle 1 \cong \angle 2$	4. Transitive Property

Teaching Suggestions, p. T84

Objectives
Presenting the Lesson
Reinforcement

Communication Skills, p. T84

Supplementary Materials
Practice Master 12
Resource Book, p. 261
Study Guide, pp. 25–28

Lesson Focus

Parallel lines have many interesting properties. This lesson discusses four properties of parallel lines. One is presented as a postulate, and the other three as theorems.

Suggested Assignments

Minimum
Day 1: 80–81/1–6, 7, 9, 11, 12
Day 2: 81–82/13–19
82/Mixed Review 1–4

Average
Day 1: 80–81/1–13 odd
Day 2: 81–82/14–24 even
82/Mixed Review 1–4

Maximum
Day 1: 80–81/1–15 odd
Day 2: 82/17–25 odd

Theorem 3-3

If two parallel lines are cut by a transversal, then same-side interior angles are supplementary.

Given: $k \parallel n$; transversal t cuts k and n.

Prove: $\angle 1$ is supplementary to $\angle 4$.

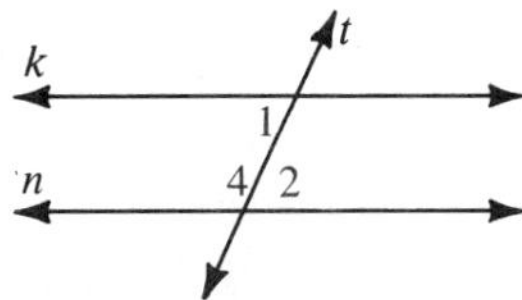

The proof is left as Exercise 22.

Theorem 3-4

If a transversal is perpendicular to one of two parallel lines, then it is perpendicular to the other one also.

Given: Transversal t cuts l and n;
$t \perp l$; $l \parallel n$

Prove: $t \perp n$

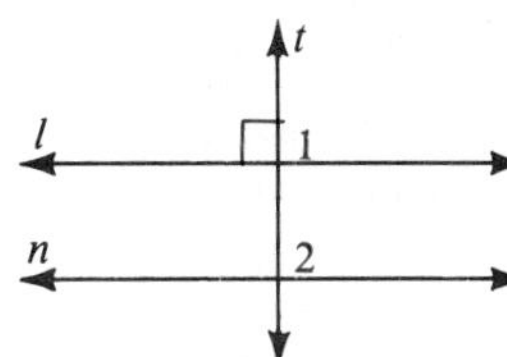

The proof is left as Exercise 13.

For the rest of this book, arrowheads will no longer be used in diagrams to suggest that a line extends in both directions without ending. Instead, pairs of arrowheads (and double arrowheads when necessary) will be used to indicate parallel lines, as shown in the following examples.

Example 1 Find the measure of $\angle PQR$.

Solution The diagram shows that

$$\overleftrightarrow{QR} \perp \overleftrightarrow{RS} \text{ and } \overleftrightarrow{QP} \parallel \overleftrightarrow{RS}.$$

Then by Theorem 3-4, $\overleftrightarrow{QR} \perp \overleftrightarrow{QP}$ and $m\angle PQR = 90$.

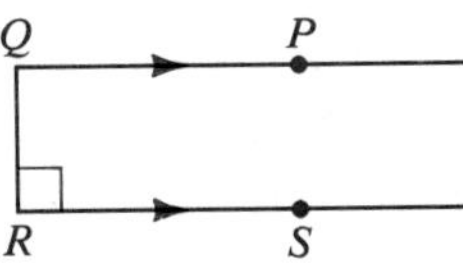

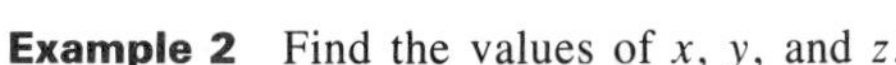

Example 2 Find the values of x, y, and z.

Solution Since $a \parallel b$, $2x = 40$. (Why?)
Thus, $x = 20$.
Since $c \parallel d$, $y = 40$. (Why?)
Since $a \parallel b$, $y + z = 180$. (Why?)
$40 + z = 180$
$z = 140$

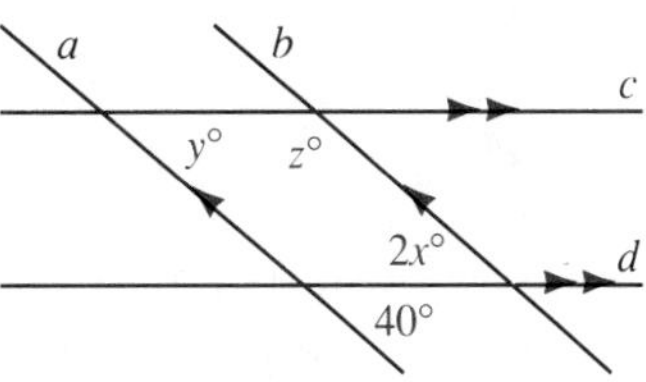

Proof Note

This lesson continues the development of deductive reasoning by proving statements about parallel lines. After completing the lesson, students should begin to understand the structure of a deductive proof.

Chalkboard Examples

Find the measures of the angles named.

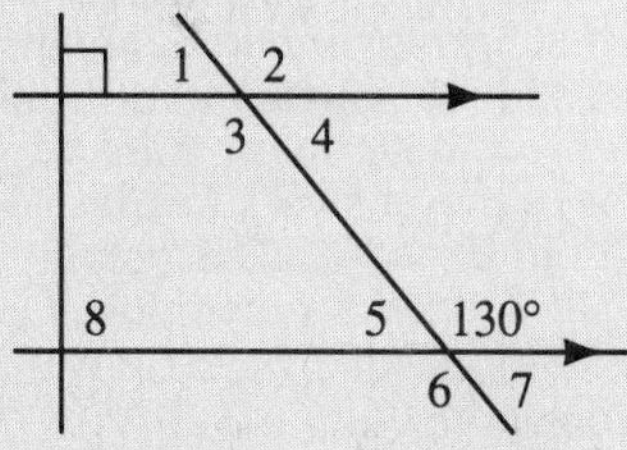

1. $m\angle 1$ 50 2. $m\angle 2$ 130
3. $m\angle 3$ 130 4. $m\angle 4$ 50
5. $m\angle 5$ 50 6. $m\angle 6$ 130
7. $m\angle 7$ 50 8. $m\angle 8$ 90
9. Find the values of x, y, and z.
$x = 70$, $y = 35$, $z = 55$

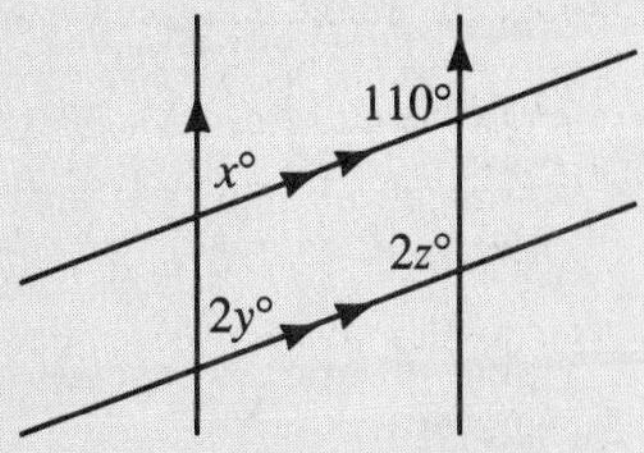

Teaching Note

When discussing Example 2, ask students to suggest an alternate equation to use for finding the values of x, y, and z. $(2x + z = 180)$

Making Connections

Classroom Ex. 14 discusses a proof that is not valid. The fallacy involved in the proof is called circular reasoning. Emphasize to students that a logical system must be developed with sequentially proved statements. Therefore, since Postulate 10 was used to prove Theorem 3-2, they cannot use Theorem 3-2 to prove Postulate 10.

Assessment

As an informal assessment of students' understanding of the ideas presented in the lesson, have them state verbally the answers to Classroom Exs. 2–9. The postulate or theorem should be stated in full. Correct any misunderstandings at this time.

Guided Practice

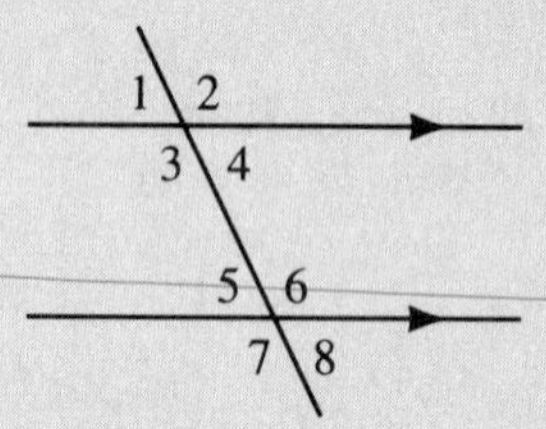

1. Name all angles that are congruent to ∠1. ∠4, ∠5, ∠8
2. Name all angles that are supplementary to ∠1. ∠2, ∠3, ∠6, ∠7

Complete.

3. If $m\angle 5 = 60$, then $m\angle 4 =$ 60 and $m\angle 2 =$ 120.
4. If $m\angle 7 = 110$, then $m\angle 3 =$ 110, and $m\angle 4 =$ 70.
5. If $m\angle 6 = x$, then $m\angle 2 =$ x, and $m\angle 1 =$ $180 - x$.

Classroom Exercises

10. $m\angle 4 = m\angle 5 = m\angle 8 = 130$; $m\angle 2 = m\angle 3 = m\angle 6 = m\angle 7 = 50$

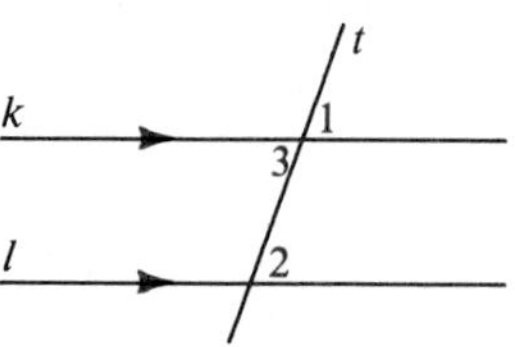

Exs. 1-13

1. What do the arrowheads in the diagram tell you? **$l \parallel p$**
4. Thm. 3-3

State the postulate or theorem that justifies each statement.

2. ∠1 ≅ ∠5 **Post. 10**
3. ∠3 ≅ ∠6 **Thm. 3-2**
4. $m\angle 4 + m\angle 6 = 180$
5. $m\angle 4 = m\angle 8$ **Post. 10**
6. $m\angle 4 = m\angle 5$ **Thm. 3-2**
7. ∠6 ≅ ∠7 **Thm. 2-3**
8. $k \perp p$ **Thm. 3-4**
9. ∠3 is supplementary to ∠5. **Thm. 3-3**
10. If $m\angle 1 = 130$, what are the measures of the other numbered angles? **See above.**
11. If $m\angle 1 = x$, what are the measures of the other numbered angles? **11. $m\angle 4 = m\angle 5 = m\angle 8 = x$; $m\angle 2 = m\angle 3 = m\angle 6 = m\angle 7 = 180 - x$**
12. If $m\angle 4 = 2m\angle 3$, find $m\angle 6$. **60**
13. If $m\angle 5 = m\angle 6 + 20$, find $m\angle 1$. **100**
14. Alan tried to prove Postulate 10 as shown below. However, he did *not* have a valid proof. Explain why not.

If two parallel lines are cut by a transversal, then corresponding angles are congruent.

Given: $k \parallel l$; transversal t cuts k and l.

Prove: ∠1 ≅ ∠2

In Step 2 he used Thm. 3-2 that relies on Post. 10.

Proof:

Statements	Reasons
1. $k \parallel l$	1. Given
2. ∠3 ≅ ∠2	2. If two parallel lines are cut by a transversal, then alt. int. ∠s are ≅.
3. ∠1 ≅ ∠3	3. Vert. ∠s are ≅.
4. ∠1 ≅ ∠2	4. Transitive Prop.

Written Exercises

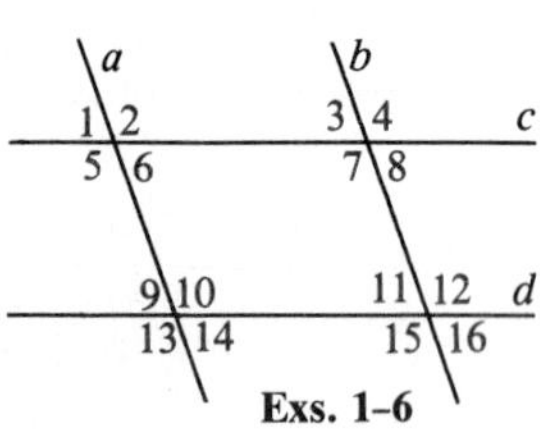

A

1. If $a \parallel b$, name all angles that must be congruent to ∠1. **∠3, ∠6, ∠8**
2. If $c \parallel d$, name all angles that must be congruent to ∠1. **∠6, ∠9, ∠14**

Assume that $a \parallel b$ and $c \parallel d$.

3. Name all angles congruent to ∠2. **∠4, ∠5, ∠7, ∠10, ∠12, ∠13, ∠15**
4. Name all angles supplementary to ∠2.
5. If $m\angle 13 = 110$, then $m\angle 15 =$ _?_ and $m\angle 3 =$ _?_. **110, 70**
6. If $m\angle 7 = x$, then $m\angle 12 =$ _?_ and $m\angle 6 =$ _?_. **x, $180 - x$**

4. ∠1, ∠3, ∠6, ∠8, ∠9, ∠11, ∠14, ∠16

Find the values of x and y.

7.

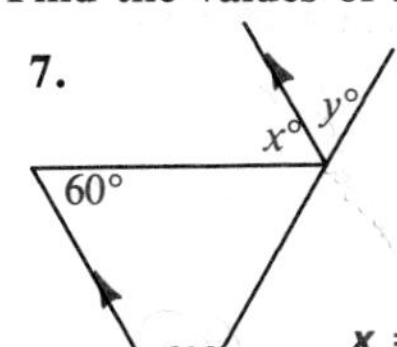

x = 60
y = 61

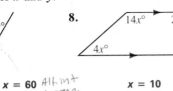

8. 14x° 2y° 4x°

x = 10
y = 45

9.

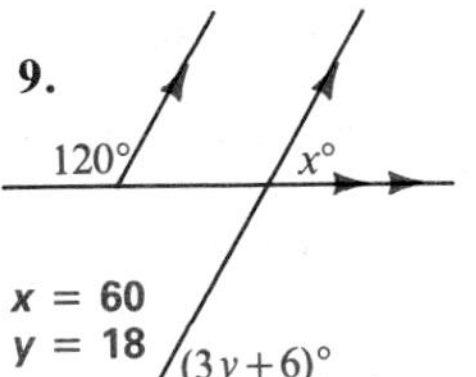

x = 60
y = 18

10.

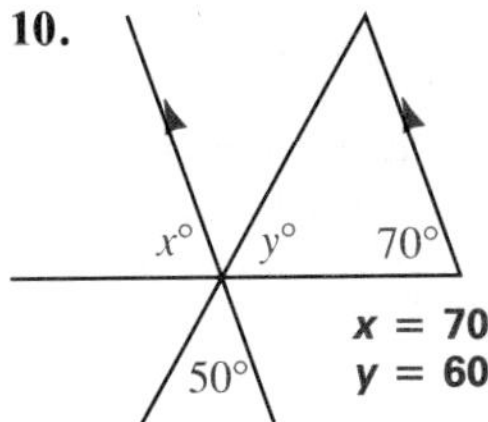

x = 70
y = 60

11.

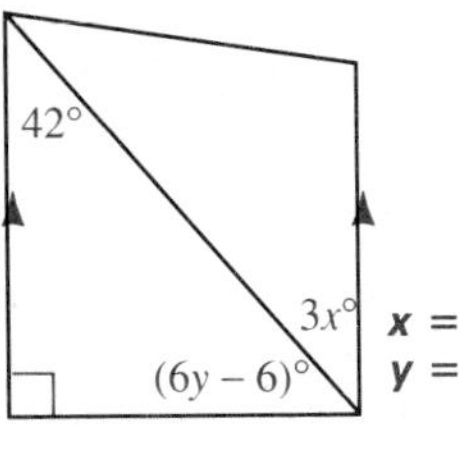

x = 14
y = 9

12.

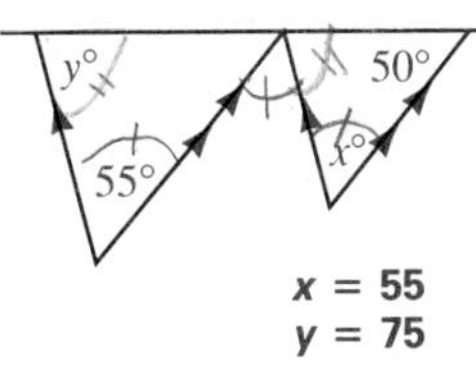

x = 55
y = 75

13. Copy and complete the proof of Theorem 3-4.

Given: Transversal t cuts l and n;
$t \perp l$; $l \parallel n$

Prove: $t \perp n$

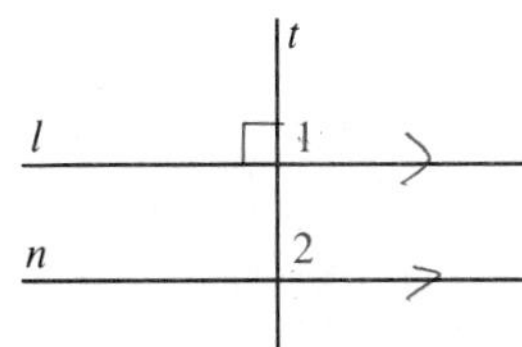

Proof:

Statements	Reasons
1. $t \perp l$	1. ? **Given**
2. $m\angle 1 = 90$	2. ? **Def. of ⊥ lines**
3. ? **$l \parallel n$**	3. Given
4. $\angle 2 \cong \angle 1$ or $m\angle 2 = m\angle 1$	4. ? **If 2 ∥ lines are cut by a trans., then corr. ∠s are ≅.**
5. ? **$m\angle 2 = 90$**	5. Substitution Property
6. $t \perp n$	6. ? **Def. of ⊥ lines**

Find the values of x, y, and z.

B **14.**

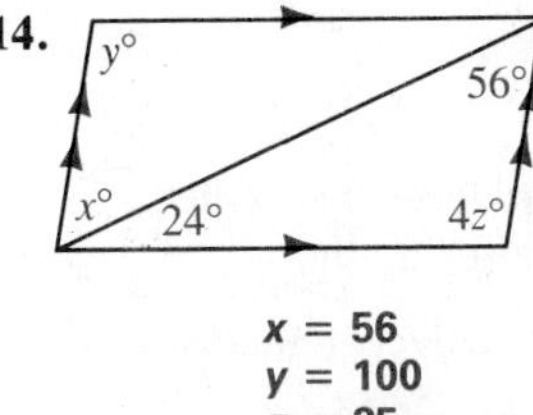

x = 56
y = 100
z = 25

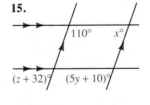

15. 110° x° (z + 32)° (5y + 10)°

x = 70
y = 12
z = 38

16.

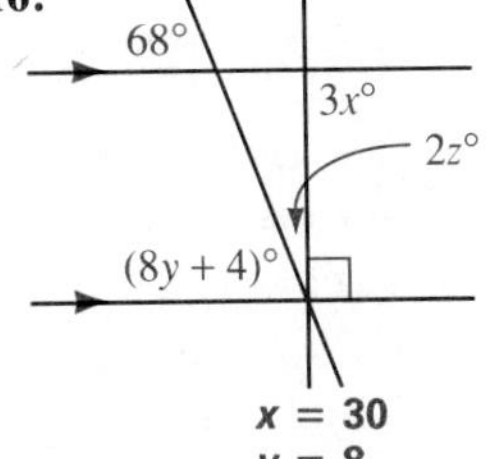

x = 30
y = 8
z = 11

Guided Practice

Find the values of x and y.

1. $x = 100$, $y = 40$

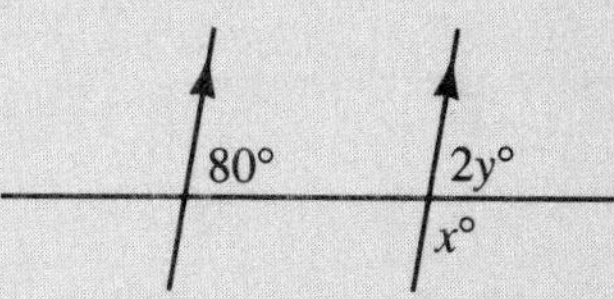

2. $x = 90$, $y = 30$

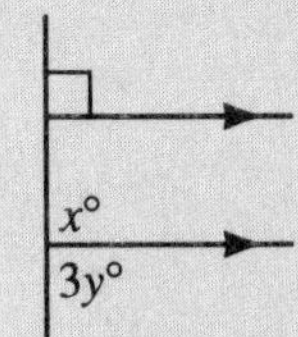

3. $x = 60$, $y = 130$

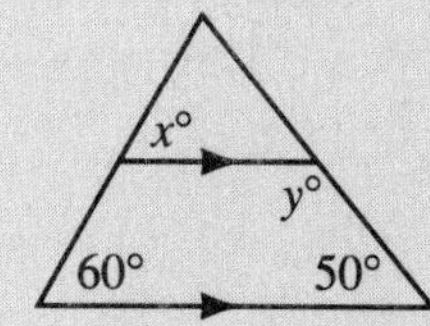

4. $x = 110$, $y = 55$

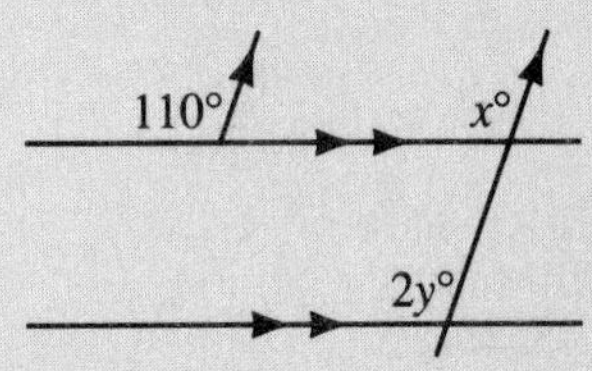

Proof Note

Some students may find the statements given in Exs. 13, 20, and 21 to be obvious, and thus they may find writing the proofs to be tedious. However, several of these short proofs have been included in the exercise sets for the beginning chapters of the book because many students need practice with supplying reasons for statements in proofs.

17. Given: $\overline{AB} \parallel \overline{CD}$; $m\angle D = 116$;
$\overrightarrow{AK}$ bisects $\angle DAB$.
a. Find the measures of $\angle DAB$, $\angle KAB$, and $\angle DKA$. **64 32 32**
b. Is there enough information for you to conclude that $\angle D$ and $\angle C$ are supplementary, or is more information needed? **More info. is needed.**

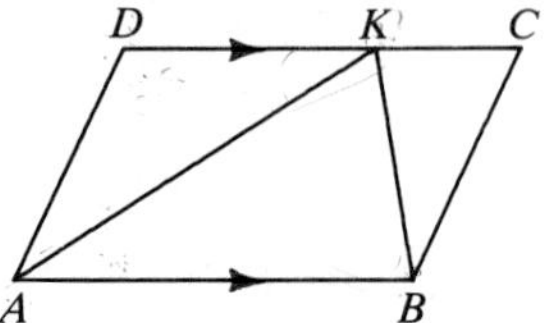

Find the values of x and y.

18.

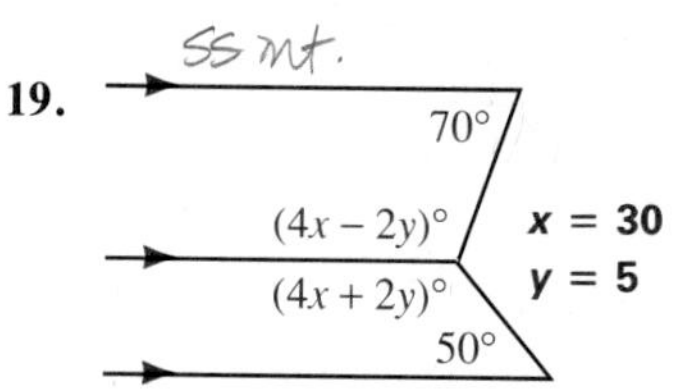

$x = 25$
$y = 10$

19.

$x = 30$
$y = 5$

Write proofs in two-column form.

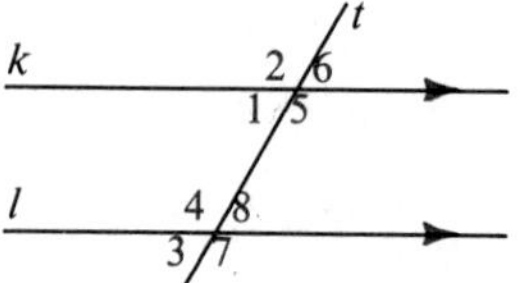

20. Given: $k \parallel l$
Prove: $\angle 2 \cong \angle 7$

21. Given: $k \parallel l$
Prove: $\angle 1$ is supplementary to $\angle 7$.

22. Copy what is shown for Theorem 3-3 on page 79. Then write a proof in two-column form.

23. Draw a four-sided figure $ABCD$ with $\overline{AB} \parallel \overline{DC}$ and $\overline{AD} \parallel \overline{BC}$.
a. Prove that $\angle A \cong \angle C$.
b. Is $\angle B \cong \angle D$? **Yes**

C 24. Given: $\overline{AS} \parallel \overline{BT}$;
$m\angle 4 = m\angle 5$
Prove: $\overrightarrow{SA}$ bisects $\angle BSR$.

25. Given: $\overline{AS} \parallel \overline{BT}$;
$m\angle 4 = m\angle 5$;
$\overrightarrow{SB}$ bisects $\angle AST$.
Find the measure of $\angle 1$. **60**

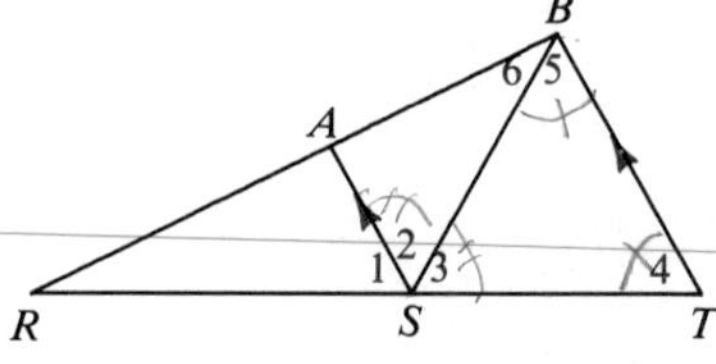

Mixed Review Exercises

For each statement (a) tell whether the statement is true or false, (b) write the converse, and (c) tell whether the converse is true or false.

1. If two lines are perpendicular, then they form congruent adjacent angles. **a. True c. True**
2. If two lines are parallel, then they are not skew. **a. True c. False**
3. Two angles are supplementary if the sum of their measures is 180. **a. True c. True**
4. Two planes are parallel only if they do not intersect. **a. True c. True**

3-3 *Proving Lines Parallel*

In the preceding section you saw that when two lines are parallel, you can conclude that certain angles are congruent or supplementary. In this section the situation is reversed. From two angles being congruent or supplementary you will conclude that certain lines forming the angles are parallel. The key to doing this is Postulate 11 below. Postulate 10 is repeated so you can compare the wording of the postulates. Notice that these two postulates are converses of each other.

Postulate 10

If two parallel lines are cut by a transversal, then corresponding angles are congruent.

Postulate 11

If two lines are cut by a transversal and corresponding angles are congruent, then the lines are parallel.

The next three theorems can be deduced from Postulate 11.

Theorem 3-5

If two lines are cut by a transversal and alternate interior angles are congruent, then the lines are parallel.

Given: Transversal t cuts lines k and n; $\angle 1 \cong \angle 2$

Prove: $k \parallel n$

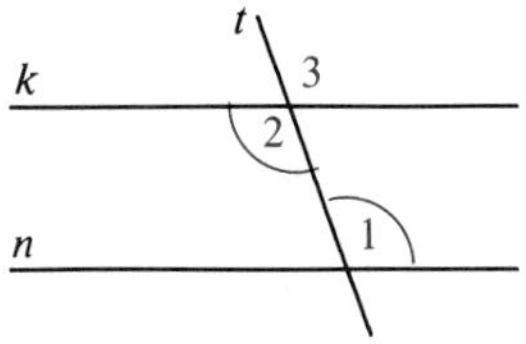

Proof:

Statements	Reasons
1. $\angle 1 \cong \angle 2$	1. Given
2. $\angle 2 \cong \angle 3$	2. Vert. ∠s are ≅.
3. $\angle 1 \cong \angle 3$	3. Transitive Property
4. $k \parallel n$	4. If two lines are cut by a transversal and corr. ∠s are ≅, then the lines are ∥.

You may have recognized that Theorem 3-5 is the converse of Theorem 3-2, "If two parallel lines are cut by a transversal, then alternate interior angles are congruent." The next theorem is the converse of Theorem 3-3, "If two parallel lines are cut by a transversal, then same-side interior angles are supplementary."

Teaching Suggestions, pp. T84–T85

Objectives
Presenting the Lesson
Using Technology
Making Connections

Communications Skills, p. T85

Supplementary Materials

Practice Master 13
Test 9
Resource Book pp. 11, 117
Study Guide, pp. 29–32

Lesson Focus

The purpose of this lesson is to study different ways in which two lines can be shown to be parallel.

Suggested Assignments

Minimum
Day 1: 87/1–17
Day 2: 87–88/18–21
89/Self-Test 1

Average
Day 1: 87/1–19 odd
S 81–82/15, 17
Day 2: 87–88/12–28 even
89/Self-Test 1

Maximum
Day 1: 87–88/1–23 odd
Day 2: 88/24–31

Theorem 3-6

If two lines are cut by a transversal and same-side interior angles are supplementary, then the lines are parallel.

Given: Transversal t cuts lines k and n;
$\angle 1$ is supplementary to $\angle 2$.

Prove: $k \parallel n$

The proof is left as Exercise 22.

Theorem 3-7

In a plane two lines perpendicular to the same line are parallel.

Given: $k \perp t$; $n \perp t$

Prove: $k \parallel n$

The proof is left as Exercise 23.

Example 1 Which segments are parallel?

Solution (1) $\overline{HI}$ and $\overline{TN}$ are parallel since corresponding angles have the same measure:

$m\angle HIL = 23 + 61 = 84$

$m\angle TNI = 22 + 62 = 84$

(2) $\overline{WI}$ and $\overline{AN}$ are *not* parallel since $61 \neq 62$.

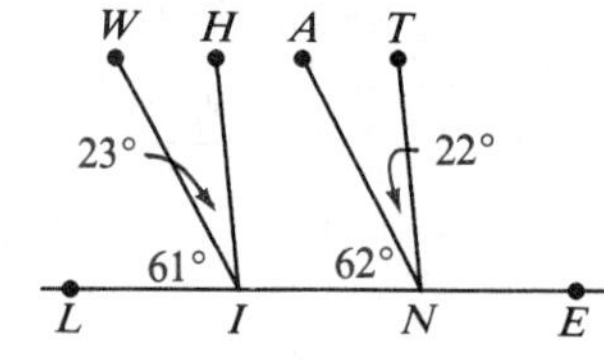

Example 2 Find the values of x and y that make $\overline{AC} \parallel \overline{DF}$ and $\overline{AE} \parallel \overline{BF}$.

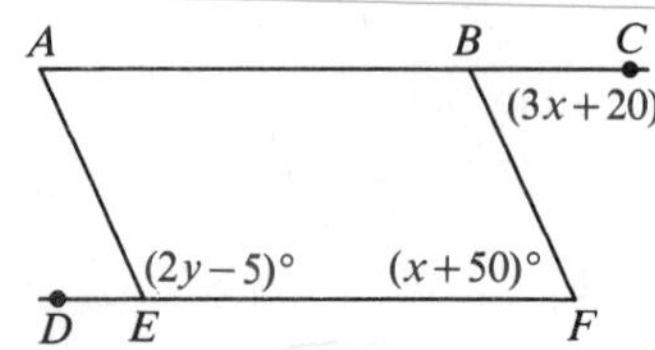

Solution If $m\angle CBF = m\angle BFE$, then $\overline{AC} \parallel \overline{DF}$. (Why?)

$$3x + 20 = x + 50$$
$$2x = 30$$
$$x = 15$$

If $\angle AEF$ and $\angle F$ are supplementary, then $\overline{AE} \parallel \overline{BF}$. (Why?)

$$(2y - 5) + (x + 50) = 180$$
$$(2y - 5) + (15 + 50) = 180$$
$$2y = 120$$
$$y = 60$$

Chalkboard Examples

1. Which segments are parallel? $\overline{AC} \parallel \overline{BE}$

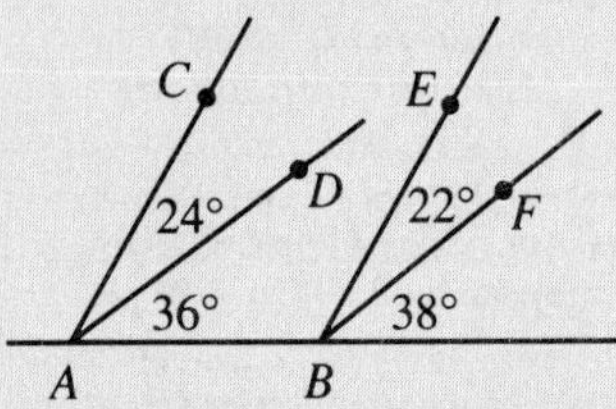

2. What value of x makes $\overline{AB}$ parallel to $\overline{CD}$? 50

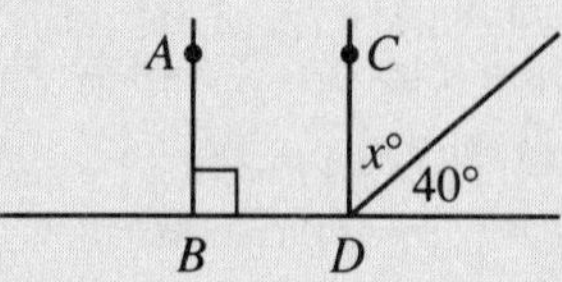

3. Find the values of x and y that make $j \parallel k$ and $l \parallel t$. $x = 20$, $y = 30$

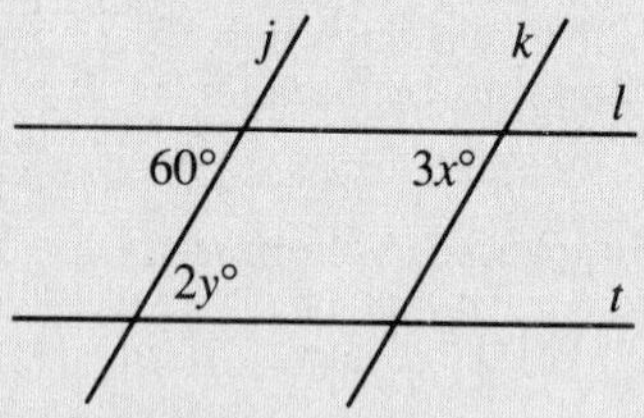

Making Connections

An extensive discussion of the approach taken in this lesson as to why Theorem 3-8 is stated as a theorem and not a postulate is given on page T85.

The following theorems can be proved using previous postulates and theorems. We state the theorems without proof, however, for you to use in future work.

Theorem 3-8

Through a point outside a line, there is exactly one line parallel to the given line.

Theorem 3-9

Through a point outside a line, there is exactly one line perpendicular to the given line.

Given this: P • ; line k

Theorem 3-8 says that line n exists and is unique.

Given this: P • ; line k

Theorem 3-9 says that line h exists and is unique.

Theorem 3-10

Two lines parallel to a third line are parallel to each other.

Given: $k \parallel l$; $k \parallel n$

Prove: $l \parallel n$

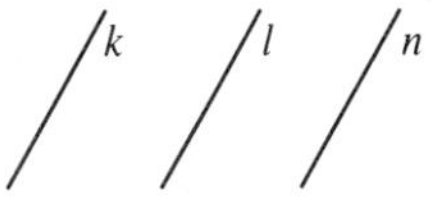

In Classroom Exercise 20 you will explain why this theorem is true when all three lines are coplanar. The theorem also holds true for lines in space.

Ways to Prove Two Lines Parallel

1. Show that a pair of corresponding angles are congruent.
2. Show that a pair of alternate interior angles are congruent.
3. Show that a pair of same-side interior angles are supplementary.
4. In a plane show that both lines are perpendicular to a third line.
5. Show that both lines are parallel to a third line.

Proof Note

Theorems 3-8 and 3-9 are given without proof. The surprising history of the attempts to prove Theorem 3-8 without making some assumption about parallels may fascinate some students. The special topic Extra entitled "Non-Euclidean Geometries," pages 233–234, discusses this topic and concludes with a proof of Theorem 3-8 based on Postulate 11. This proof requires the ability to follow indirect reasoning. Clear thinkers can intuitively understand an indirect proof before studying the method in Chapter 6.

The uniqueness part of Theorem 3-9 is proved using indirect reasoning in Ex. 10 of Self-Test 1 for Chapter 6 (page 218). You may wish to discuss the following suggested proof of the existence part (1) of Theorem 3-9 with your students.

Given: Point P outside line k

Prove: (1) There is a line through P perpendicular to k (existence).
(2) There is only one line through P perpendicular to k (uniqueness).

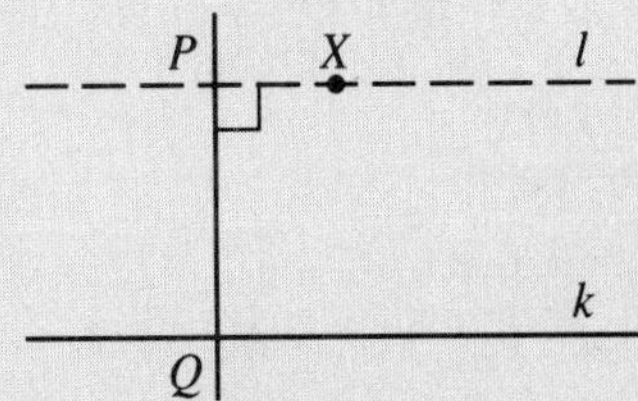

Outline of proof of (1):

1. Draw a line l through $P \parallel$ to k. (Theorem 3-8)
2. At point P, draw $\angle XPQ$ so that $m\angle XPQ = 90$. (Protractor Postulate).
3. $\overrightarrow{PQ} \perp l$ (Def. of $\perp$ lines)
4. $\overrightarrow{PQ} \perp k$ (Theorem 3-4)

Classroom Exercises

State which segments (if any) are parallel. State the postulate or theorem that justifies your answer.

1. 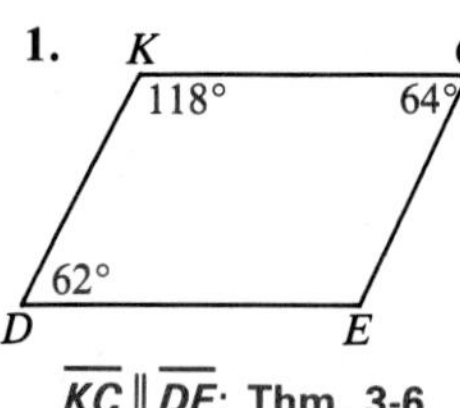

$\overline{KC} \parallel \overline{DE}$; Thm. 3-6

2. 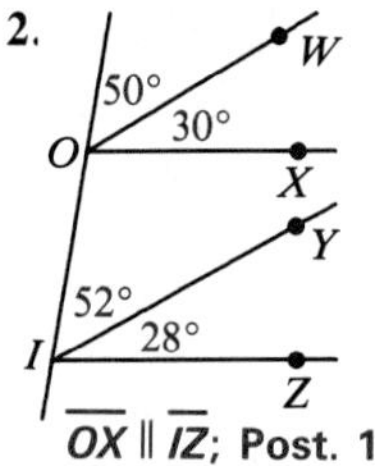

$\overline{OX} \parallel \overline{IZ}$; Post. 11

3. 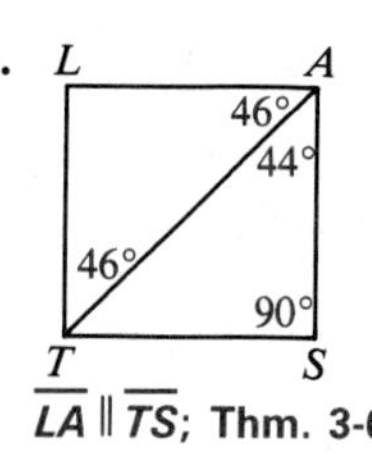

$\overline{LA} \parallel \overline{TS}$; Thm. 3-6

4. 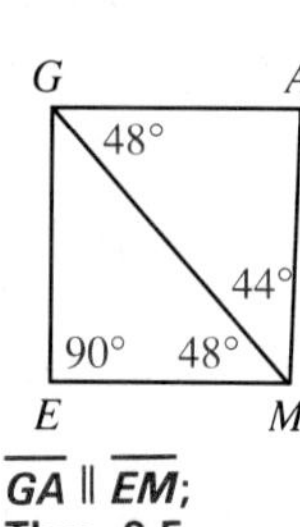

$\overline{GA} \parallel \overline{EM}$; Thm. 3-5

In each exercise some information is given. Use this information to name the segments that must be parallel. If there are no such segments, say so.

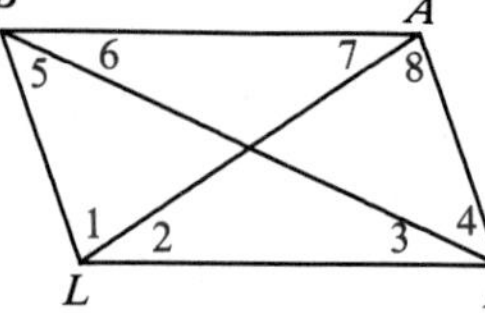

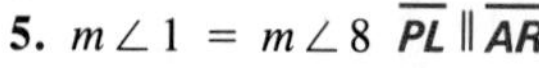

5. $m\angle 1 = m\angle 8$ $\overline{PL} \parallel \overline{AR}$

6. $\angle 2 \cong \angle 7$ $\overline{PA} \parallel \overline{LR}$

7. $\angle 5 \cong \angle 3$ no segs. ∥

8. $m\angle 5 = m\angle 4$ $\overline{PL} \parallel \overline{AR}$

9. $m\angle 5 + m\angle 6 = m\angle 3 + m\angle 4$ no segs. ∥

10. $m\angle APL + m\angle PAR = 180$ $\overline{PL} \parallel \overline{AR}$

11. $m\angle 1 + m\angle 2 + m\angle 5 + m\angle 6 = 180$ $\overline{PA} \parallel \overline{LR}$

12. Reword Theorem 3-8 as two statements, one describing existence and the other describing uniqueness.

13. Reword Theorem 3-9 as two statements, one describing existence and the other describing uniqueness.

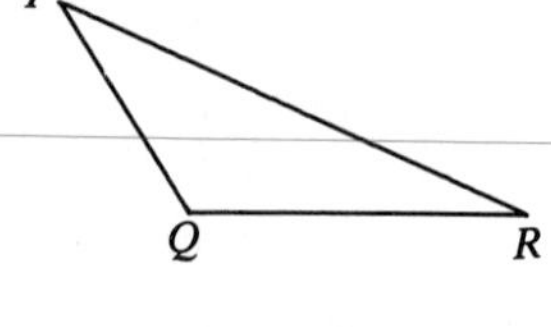

14. How many lines can be drawn through *P* parallel to $\overleftrightarrow{QR}$? 1

15. How many lines can be drawn through *Q* parallel to $\overleftrightarrow{PR}$? 1

16. How many lines can be drawn through *P* perpendicular to $\overleftrightarrow{QR}$? 1

17. In the plane of *P*, *Q*, and *R*, how many lines can be drawn through R perpendicular to $\overleftrightarrow{QR}$? What postulate or theorem justifies your answer? 1; Protractor Post.

18. In space, how many lines can be drawn through *R* perpendicular to $\overleftrightarrow{QR}$? Infinitely many

19. True or false?

a. Two lines perpendicular to a third line must be parallel. False

b. In a plane two lines perpendicular to a third line must be parallel. True

c. In a plane two lines parallel to a third line must be parallel. True

d. Any two lines parallel to a third line must be parallel. True

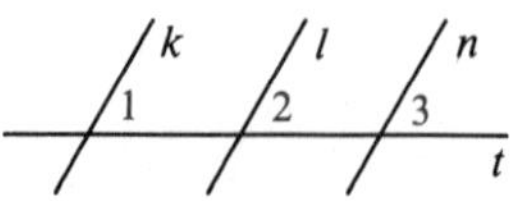

20. Use the diagram to explain why Theorem 3-10 is true for coplanar lines. That is, if $k \parallel l$ and $k \parallel n$, why does it follow that $l \parallel n$? If $k \parallel l$, then $\angle 1 \cong \angle 2$. If $k \parallel n$, then $\angle 1 \cong \angle 3$. Therefore $\angle 2 \cong \angle 3$ and $l \parallel n$. (Trans. Prop. of $\cong$ and Post. 11)

Additional Answers Classroom Exercises

12. Through a point outside a line, there is a line ∥ to the given line. Through a point outside a line, there is no more than one line ∥ to the given line.

13. Through a point outside a line, there is a line ⊥ to the given line. Through a point outside a line, there is no more than one line ⊥ to the given line.

Written Exercises

In each exercise some information is given. Use this information to name the segments that must be parallel. If there are no such segments, write *none*.

A

1. $\angle 2 \cong \angle 9$ **1., 3.** $\overline{AB} \parallel \overline{FC}$
2. $\angle 6 \cong \angle 7$ $\overline{AE} \parallel \overline{BD}$
3. $m\angle 1 = m\angle 8 = 90$
4. $\angle 5 \cong \angle 9$ $\overline{FB} \parallel \overline{EC}$
5. $m\angle 2 = m\angle 5$ **none**
6. $\angle 3 \cong \angle 11$ $\overline{AE} \parallel \overline{BD}$
7. $m\angle 1 = m\angle 4 = 90$ **none**
8. $m\angle 10 = m\angle 11$ **none**
9. $m\angle 8 + m\angle 5 + m\angle 6 = 180$ $\overline{AE} \parallel \overline{BD}$
10. $\overline{FC} \perp \overline{AE}$ and $\overline{FC} \perp \overline{BD}$ $\overline{AE} \parallel \overline{BD}$
11. $m\angle 5 + m\angle 6 = m\angle 9 + m\angle 10$ $\overline{AE} \parallel \overline{BD}$
12. $\angle 7$ and $\angle EFB$ are supplementary. $\overline{FB} \parallel \overline{EC}$
13. $\angle 2$ and $\angle 3$ are complementary and $m\angle 1 = 90$. $\overline{AE} \parallel \overline{BD}$
14. $m\angle 2 + m\angle 3 = m\angle 4$ **none**
15. $m\angle 7 = m\angle 3 = m\angle 10$ $\overline{FB} \parallel \overline{EC}$; $\overline{AE} \parallel \overline{BD}$
16. $m\angle 4 = m\angle 8 = m\angle 1$ $\overline{AB} \parallel \overline{FC}$; $\overline{AE} \parallel \overline{BD}$
17. Write the reasons to complete the proof: If two lines are cut by a transversal and alternate exterior angles are congruent, then the lines are parallel.

    Given: Transversal t cuts lines l and n; $\angle 2 \cong \angle 1$

    Prove: $l \parallel n$

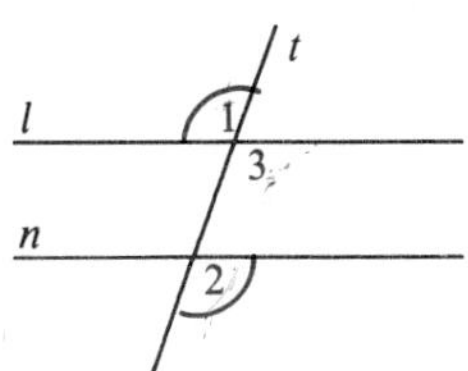

Proof:

Statements	Reasons
1. $\angle 2 \cong \angle 1$	1. ___?___ **Given**
2. $\angle 1 \cong \angle 3$	2. ___?___ **Vert. ∠s are ≅**
3. $\angle 2 \cong \angle 3$	3. ___?___ **Trans. Prop.**
4. $l \parallel n$	4. ___?___ **If 2 lines are cut by a trans. and corr. ∠s are ≅, then the lines are ∥.**

Find the values of x and y that make the red lines parallel *and* the blue lines parallel.

B

18.

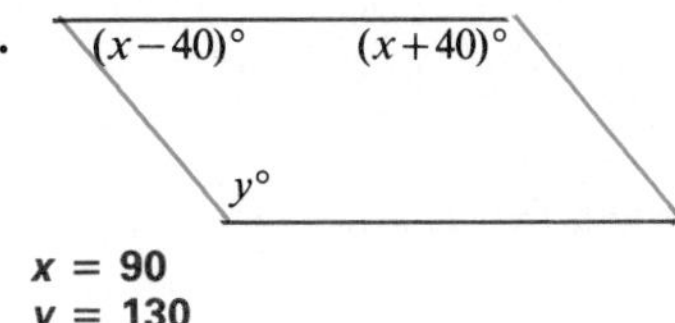

x = 90
y = 130

19.

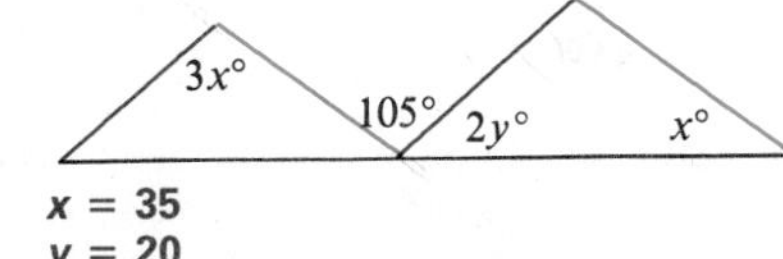

x = 35
y = 20

Guided Practice

What two lines (if any) are parallel if the given information is true?

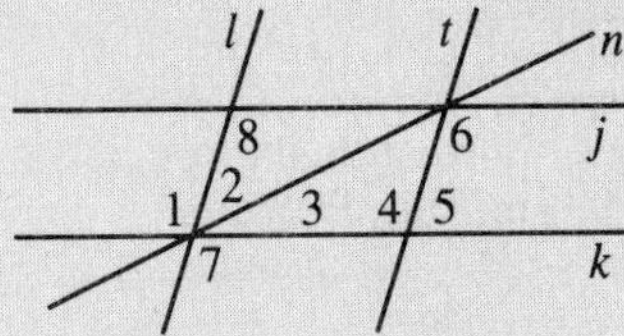

1. $m\angle 1 = m\angle 4$ *l, t*
2. $m\angle 6 = m\angle 4$ *j, k*
3. $m\angle 2 + m\angle 3 = m\angle 5$ *l, t*
4. $m\angle 2 + m\angle 3 + m\angle 8 = 180$ *j, k*
5. $\angle 6 \cong \angle 8$ *l, t*
6. $\angle 7 \cong \angle 1$ none
7. $m\angle 1 = m\angle 8 = 75$ *j, k*
8. $\angle 5$ and $\angle 6$ are supplementary. *j, k*
9. $\angle 4$ and $\angle 5$ are supplementary. none
10. $\angle 2$ and $\angle 3$ are complementary and $m\angle 5 = 90$. *l, t*

Communication Skills

After completing Ex. 17, ask students to put into their own words what has been proved.

Proof Note

When assigning proofs, you might want to mention to students that if they are trying to prove certain lines perpendicular (or parallel), they should not mark those lines perpendicular (or parallel) on the diagram.

20. Given: $\angle 1 \cong \angle 2$; $\angle 4 \cong \angle 5$
What can you prove about $\overline{PQ}$ and $\overline{RS}$? Be prepared to give your reasons in class, if asked. **$\overline{PQ} \parallel \overline{RS}$**

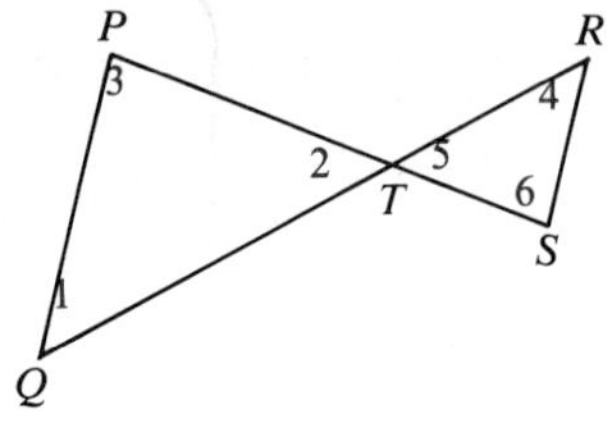

21. Given: $\angle 3 \cong \angle 6$
What can you prove about other angles? Be prepared to give your reasons in class, if asked.
$\angle 1 \cong \angle 4$; $\angle 2 \cong \angle 5$

22. Copy what is shown for Theorem 3-6 on page 84. Then write a proof in two-column form.

23. Copy what is shown for Theorem 3-7 on page 84. Then write a proof in two-column form.

24. Given: $\overline{BE}$ bisects $\angle DBA$; $\angle 3 \cong \angle 1$
Prove: $\overline{CD} \parallel \overline{BE}$

25. Given: $\overline{BE} \perp \overline{DA}$; $\overline{CD} \perp \overline{DA}$
Prove: $\angle 1 \cong \angle 2$

26. Given: $\angle C \cong \angle 3$; $\overline{BE} \perp \overline{DA}$
Prove: $\overline{CD} \perp \overline{DA}$

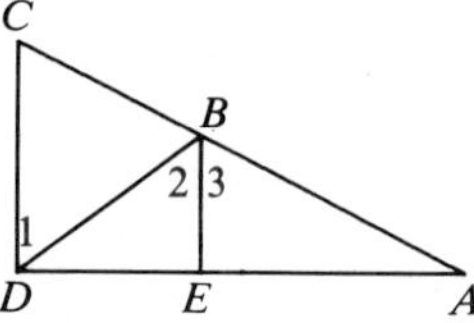

Find the measure of $\angle RST$. (*Hint*: Draw a line through S parallel to $\overline{RX}$ and $\overline{TY}$.)

27.
110

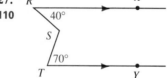

28.
130

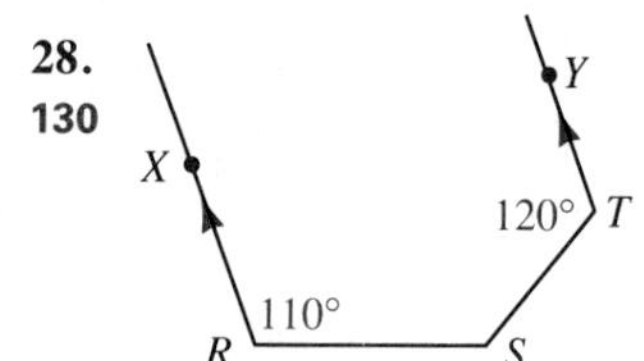

29. Find the values of x and y that make the lines shown in red parallel. **$x = 50$, $y = 20$**

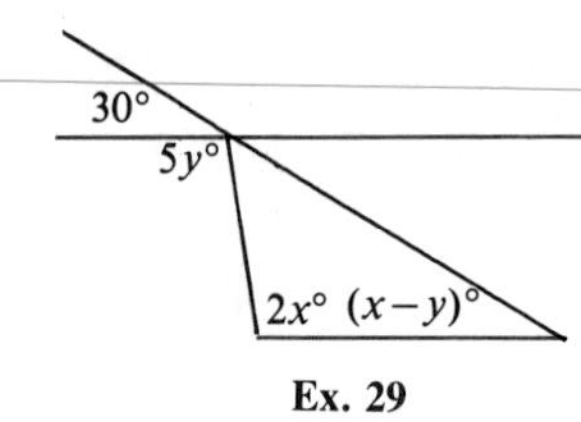

Ex. 29

Using a Computer

Ex. 30 can be done using a construction program. Refer students to the table on page 85 for the possible ways to prove that the bisectors are parallel. See Experiment 2 on page T85 for a similar exercise.

C **30.** Draw two parallel lines cut by a transversal. Then draw the bisectors of two corresponding angles. What appears to be true about the bisectors? Prove that your conclusion is true. **The bisectors appear to be ∥.**

31. Find the value of x that makes the lines shown in red parallel. **$x = 12$**

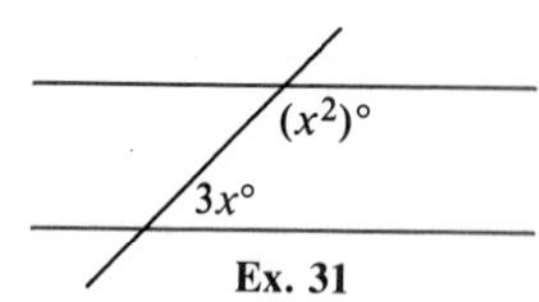

Ex. 31

Self-Test 1

Complete each statement with the word *always*, *sometimes*, or *never*.

1. Two lines that do not intersect are ___?___ parallel. **sometimes**
2. Two skew lines ___?___ intersect. **never**
3. Two lines parallel to a third line are ___?___ parallel. **always**
4. If a line is parallel to plane X and also to plane Y, then plane X and plane Y are ___?___ parallel. **sometimes**
5. Plane X is parallel to plane Y. If plane Z intersects X in line l and Y in line n, then l is ___?___ parallel to n. **always**
6. Name two pairs of congruent alternate interior angles. **∠3, ∠6; ∠4, ∠5**
7. Name two pairs of congruent corresponding angles. **See below.**
8. Name a pair of supplementary same-side interior angles. **∠3, ∠5 or ∠4, ∠6**

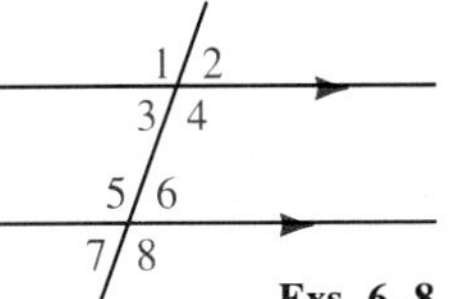

Exs. 6–8

9. Complete: If $\overline{AE} \parallel \overline{BD}$, then $\angle 1 \cong$ ___?___ and $\angle 9 \cong$ ___?___. **∠4; ∠3**
10. If $\overline{ED} \parallel \overline{AC}$, name all pairs of angles that must be congruent.
11. If $\overline{ED} \parallel \overline{AC}$ and $\overline{EB} \parallel \overline{DC}$, name all angles that must be congruent to $\angle 5$. **∠2, ∠8**
12. Complete: If $\overline{ED} \parallel \overline{AC}$, $\overline{EB} \parallel \overline{DC}$, and $m\angle 2 = 65$, then $m\angle 8 =$ ___?___ and $m\angle EDC =$ ___?___. **65; 115**

10. ∠2, ∠8; ∠4, ∠7

E D A B C, 1–9

Exs. 9–15

Use the given information to name the segments (if any) that must be parallel.

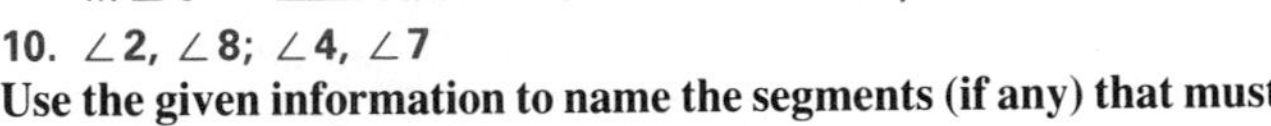

13. $\angle 3 \cong \angle 6$ **$\overline{EB} \parallel \overline{DC}$**
14. $\angle 9 \cong \angle 6$ **none**
15. $m\angle 7 + m\angle AED = 180$ **$\overline{AE} \parallel \overline{BD}$**

16. Complete: Through a point outside a line, ___?___ line(s) can be drawn parallel to the given line, and ___?___ line(s) can be drawn perpendicular to the given line. **one, one**

7. Examples: ∠1, ∠5; ∠2, ∠6; ∠3, ∠7; ∠4, ∠8

Explorations

These exploratory exercises can be done using a computer with a program that draws and measures geometric figures.

Draw a triangle ABC. At each vertex extend one side, as shown in the diagram. Measure all six angles formed. Repeat on several triangles. What do you notice?
What is the sum of the measures of the angles inside the triangle? of the angles outside the triangle?

180 **360**

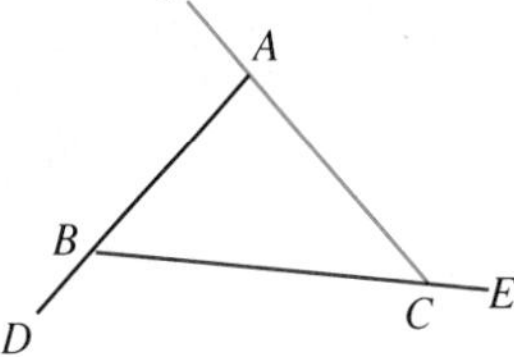

Quick Quiz

Complete with *always*, *sometimes*, or *never*.

1. Two skew lines are <u>never</u> parallel.
2. In a plane, two lines perpendicular to a third line are <u>always</u> parallel.

Exs. 3–5 refer to the diagram below.

3. Name a pair of congruent alternate interior angles. ∠2, ∠7; or ∠3, ∠6
4. Name a pair of supplementary same-side interior angles. ∠2, ∠3; or ∠6, ∠7
5. Name a pair of congruent corresponding angles. ∠1, ∠3; ∠2, ∠4; ∠5, ∠7; or ∠6, ∠8

Exs. 6–10 refer to the diagram below.

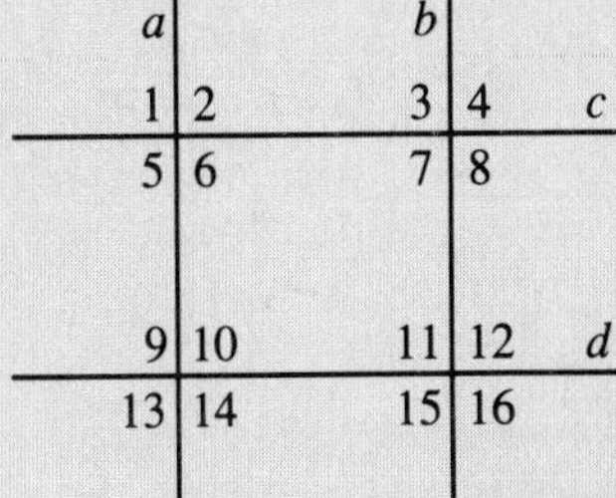

6. If $a \parallel b$, name all angles congruent to ∠1. ∠3, ∠6, ∠8
7. If $c \parallel d$ and $m\angle 6 = 90$, then $m\angle 5 =$ <u>90</u> and $m\angle 9 =$ <u>90</u>.
8. If $\angle 7 \cong \angle 15$, then $c \parallel d$.
9. If $\angle 11 \cong \angle 14$, then $a \parallel b$.
10. If $m\angle 8 + m\angle 12 = 180$, then $c \parallel d$.

Application

The activities in this lesson can be done in or out of class. As a final project, students can choose an object in the classroom to draw.

Application — *Technical Drawing*

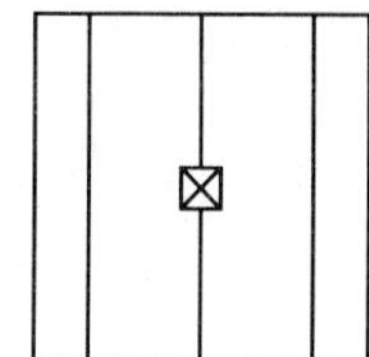

Can the shape of a three-dimensional object be determined from a single two-dimensional image? For example, if you photographed the barn shown on page 75 from a point directly above, then your photograph might look something like the sketch shown at the right. You cannot tell from this one photograph how the roof slopes or anything about the sides of the barn. You would have a much better idea of the shape of the barn if you could also see it from the front and from one side.

The three views of the barn are the parts of an *orthographic projection*, a set of projections of an object into three planes perpendicular to one another. They show the actual shape of the building much more clearly than any single picture.

To make an orthographic projection of an object, draw a top view, a front view, and a side view. Arrange the three views in an ''L'' shaped pattern as illustrated in the figure on the left below. Some corresponding vertices have been connected with red lines.

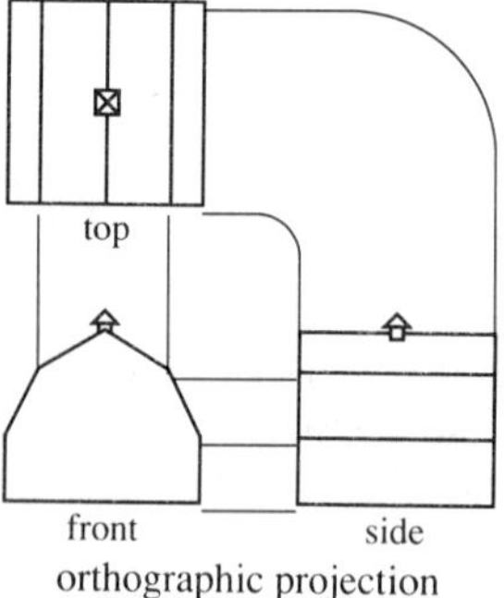

orthographic projection

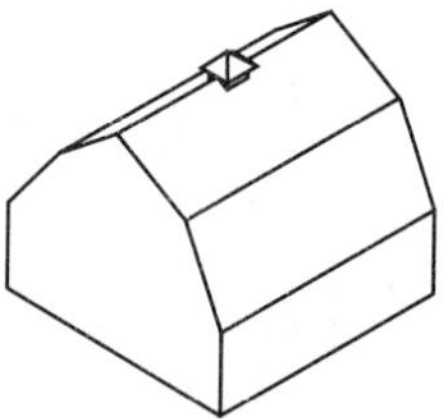

isometric drawing

A related method of representing a three-dimensional object by a two-dimensional image is an *isometric drawing*. In this type of representation the object is viewed at an angle that allows simultaneous vision of the top, front, and one side. Unlike most drawings, however, an isometric drawing does not show perspective. Rather, congruent sides are drawn congruent. Because we are accustomed to seeing objects in perspective, an isometric representation can appear distorted to us. The following figures illustrate the difference between a perspective drawing (left) and an isometric drawing (right).

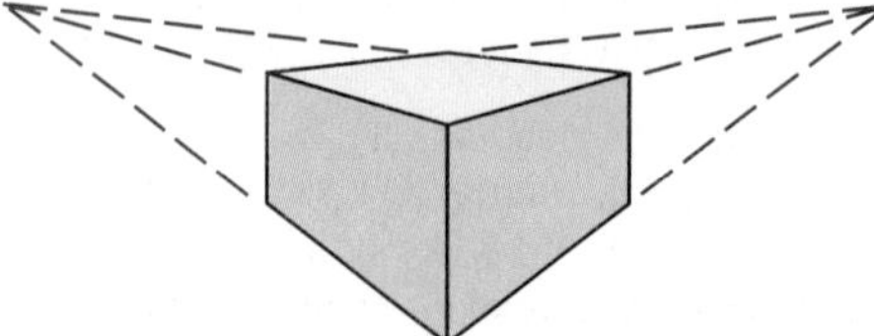

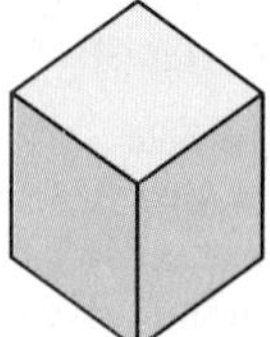

To make an orthographic projection into an isometric drawing, we fold the top, front, and side together. The base of the box becomes angled, but vertical lines remain vertical, parallel lines remain parallel, and congruence is preserved.

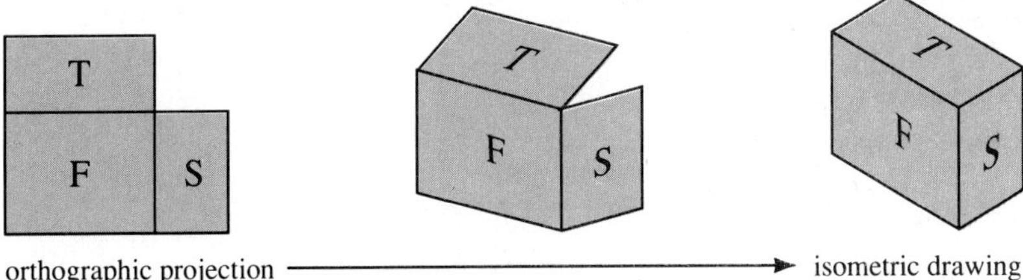

orthographic projection ⟶ isometric drawing

To illustrate, we shall make an isometric drawing of the solid whose orthographic projection is shown below. Visible edges and intersections are shown as solid lines. Hidden edges are shown as dashed lines.

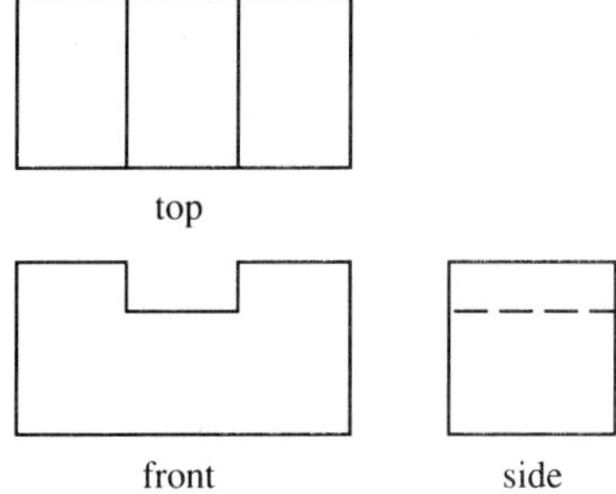

Begin by drawing three rays with a common endpoint such that one ray is vertical and the other two rays are 30° off of horizontal. Mark off the lengths of the front, side, and height of the solid. By drawing congruent segments and by showing parallel edges as parallel in the figure, you can finish the isometric drawing. The figures that follow suggest the procedure.

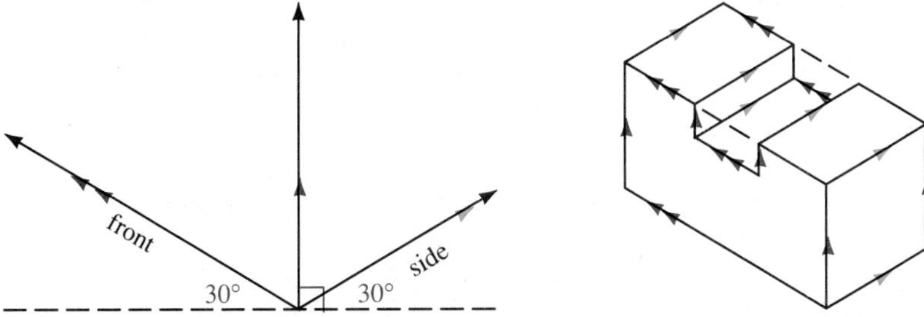

Industry requires millions of drawings similar to these each year. The drafters who make these drawings professionally combine the knowledge of parallel lines with the skills of using a compass, a protractor, and a ruler. More recently, drafters make drawings like these using a computer and a special printer.

Additional Answers Application Exercises

1.

4.

7.

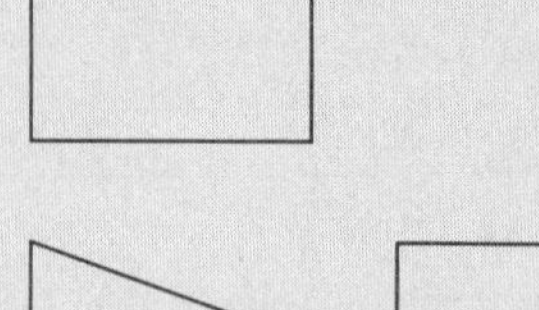

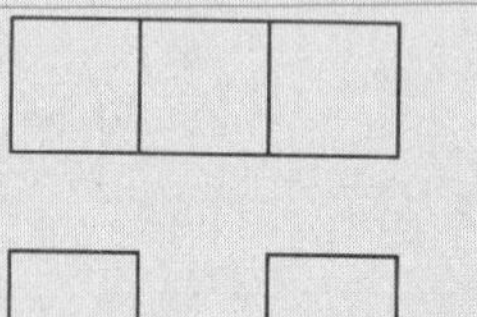

8.

Exercises

Match the orthographic projections with their isometric drawings. If there is no isometric drawing, then make one.

1.

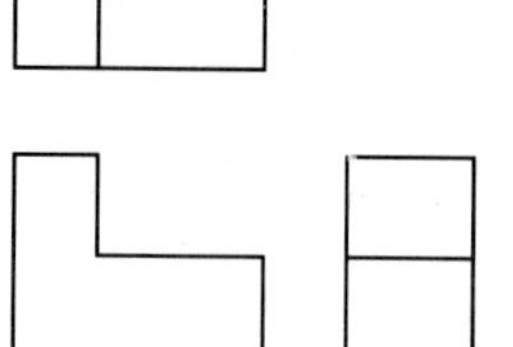

2. d

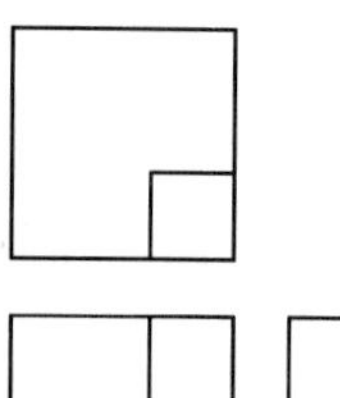

a.

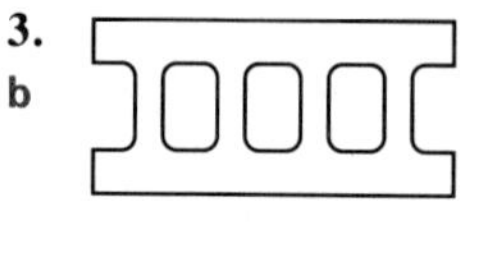

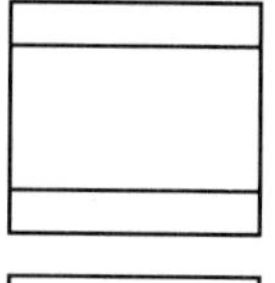

b.

3. b

4.

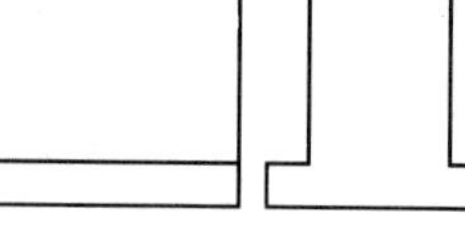

c.

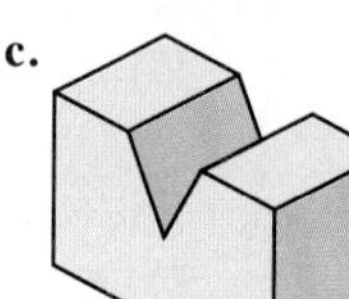

5. c

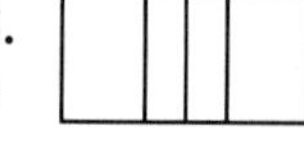

6. a

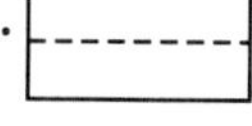

d.

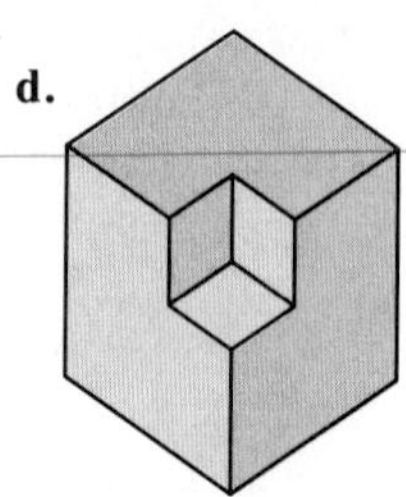

Trace each figure. Then make an orthographic projection of the figure.

7.

8.

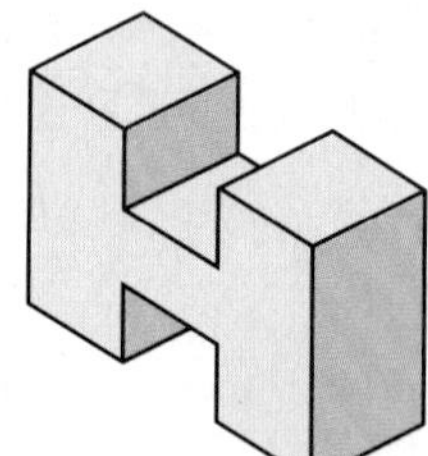

Applying Parallel Lines to Polygons

Objectives

1. Classify triangles according to sides and to angles.
2. State and apply the theorem and the corollaries about the sum of the measures of the angles of a triangle.
3. State and apply the theorem about the measure of an exterior angle of a triangle.
4. Recognize and name convex polygons and regular polygons.
5. Find the measures of interior angles and exterior angles of convex polygons.
6. Understand and use inductive reasoning.

3-4 *Angles of a Triangle*

A **triangle** is the figure formed by three segments joining three noncollinear points. Each of the three points is a **vertex** of the triangle. (The plural of *vertex* is *vertices*.) The segments are the **sides** of the triangle.

Triangle ABC ($\triangle ABC$) is shown.

Vertices of $\triangle ABC$: points A, B, C

Sides of $\triangle ABC$: $\overline{AB}$, $\overline{BC}$, $\overline{CA}$

Angles of $\triangle ABC$: $\angle A$, $\angle B$, $\angle C$

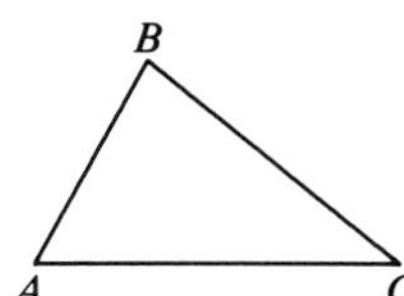

A triangle is sometimes classified by the number of congruent sides it has.

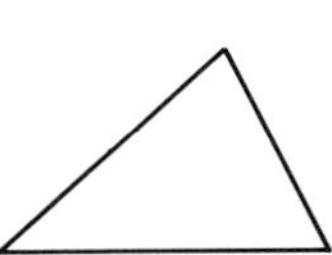

Scalene triangle
No sides congruent

Isosceles triangle
At least two sides congruent

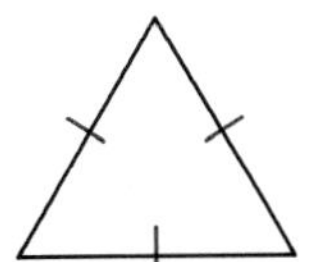

Equilateral triangle
All sides congruent

Triangles can also be classified by their angles.

Acute △
Three acute ∠s

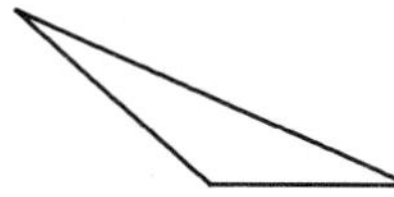

Obtuse △
One obtuse ∠

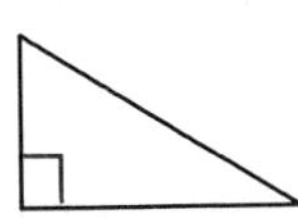

Right △
One right ∠

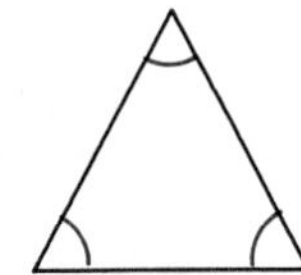

Equiangular △
All ∠s congruent

Teaching Suggestions, pp. T85–T86

Objectives
Presenting the Lesson
Using Technology
Enrichment

Exploring Activity, p. 71c

Supplementary Materials

Resource Book, p. 261
Study Guide, pp. 33–34
Computer Activity 5

Lesson Focus

A very common figure in geometry is the triangle. Triangles are seen in many objects in the real world, such as bridges and buildings. This lesson presents many facts about triangles, including a very well-known theorem.

Suggested Assignments

Minimum
Day 1: 97/1–13
S 88/22, 24
Day 2: 97–98/14–24, 30

Average
Day 1: 97–98/1, 2, 6, 9, 12–15, 17, 18, 20
Day 2: 98–99/22–32 even

Maximum
Day 1: 97–98/1, 3, 9, 11, 12, 15, 17–19, 21, 24
Day 2: 98–99/25, 27–29, 31, 33

Using a Computer

See page T85 for an experiment involving the identification of various types of triangles within a constructed figure.

An **auxiliary line** is a line (or ray or segment) added to a diagram to help in a proof. An auxiliary line is used in the proof of the next theorem, one of the best-known theorems of geometry. The auxiliary line is shown as a dashed line in the diagram.

Theorem 3-11

The sum of the measures of the angles of a triangle is 180.

Given: $\triangle ABC$

Prove: $m\angle 1 + m\angle 2 + m\angle 3 = 180$

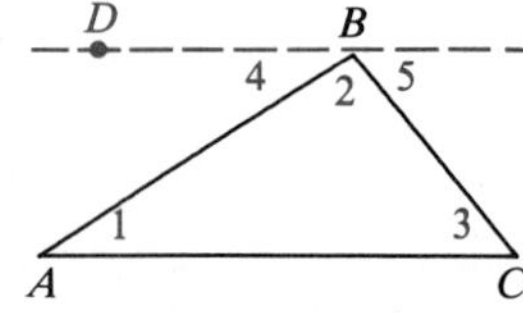

Proof:

Statements	Reasons
1. Through B draw $\overleftrightarrow{BD}$ parallel to $\overleftrightarrow{AC}$.	1. Through a point outside a line, there is exactly one line ∥ to the given line.
2. $m\angle DBC + m\angle 5 = 180$; $m\angle DBC = m\angle 4 + m\angle 2$	2. Angle Addition Postulate
3. $m\angle 4 + m\angle 2 + m\angle 5 = 180$	3. Substitution Property
4. $\angle 4 \cong \angle 1$, or $m\angle 4 = m\angle 1$; $\angle 5 \cong \angle 3$, or $m\angle 5 = m\angle 3$	4. If two parallel lines are cut by a transversal, then alt. int. ∠s are ≅.
5. $m\angle 1 + m\angle 2 + m\angle 3 = 180$	5. Substitution Property

A statement that can be proved easily by applying a theorem is often called a **corollary** of the theorem. Corollaries, like theorems, can be used as reasons in proofs. Each of the four statements that are shown below is a corollary of Theorem 3-11.

Corollary 1

If two angles of one triangle are congruent to two angles of another triangle, then the third angles are congruent.

Corollary 2

Each angle of an equiangular triangle has measure 60.

Corollary 3

In a triangle, there can be at most one right angle or obtuse angle.

Corollary 4

The acute angles of a right triangle are complementary.

Proof Note

A shortened version of the proof of Theorem 3-11 is:

1. Through B draw $\overleftrightarrow{BD}$ parallel to $\overleftrightarrow{AC}$. (Through a pt. outside a line, there is exactly one line ∥ to the given line.)
2. $m\angle 4 = m\angle 1$; $m\angle 5 = m\angle 3$ (Alt. int. ∠s are ≅.)
3. $m\angle 4 + m\angle 2 + m\angle 5 = 180$ (Angle Add. Post., used twice.)
4. $m\angle 1 + m\angle 2 + m\angle 3 = 180$ (Substitution Prop.)

Chalkboard Examples

State whether a triangle with two angles having the given measures is acute, right, or obtuse.

1. 55, 43 acute
2. 47, 43 right
3. 80, 75 acute
4. 33, 33 obtuse
5. 24, 66 right
6. $10 - t$, $60 + 3t$ obtuse

In the classroom exercises you will explain how these corollaries follow from Theorem 3-11.

Example 1 Is $\angle P \cong \angle V$?

Solution $\angle R \cong \angle E$ (Given in diagram)

$\angle 1 \cong \angle 2$ (Vertical angles are congruent.)

Thus two angles of $\triangle PRO$ are congruent to two angles of $\triangle VEO$, and therefore $\angle P \cong \angle V$ by Corollary 1.

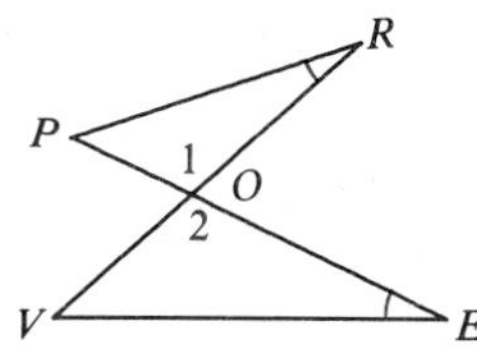

When one side of a triangle is extended, an *exterior angle* is formed as shown in the diagrams below. Because an exterior angle of a triangle is always a supplement of the adjacent interior angle of the triangle, its measure is related in a special way to the measure of the other two angles of the triangle, called the *remote interior angles*.

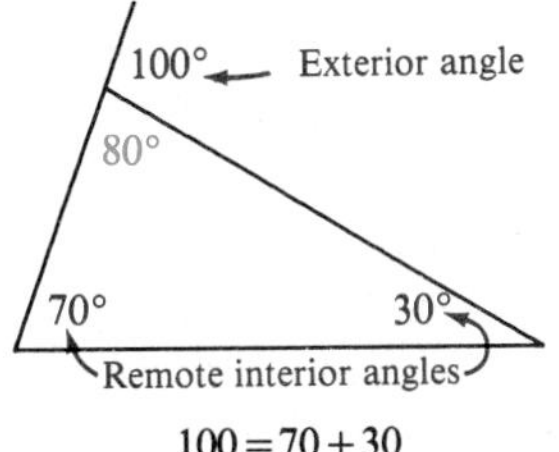

$100 = 70 + 30$

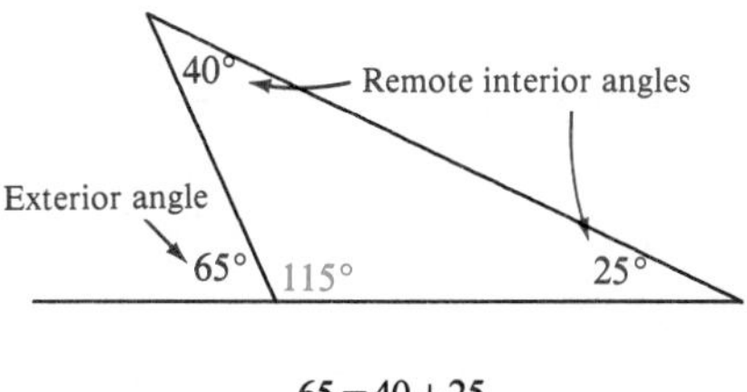

$65 = 40 + 25$

Theorem 3-12

The measure of an exterior angle of a triangle equals the sum of the measures of the two remote interior angles.

The proof of Theorem 3-12 is left as Classroom Exercise 15.

Example 2 In $\triangle ABC$, $m\angle A = 120$ and an exterior angle at C is five times as large as $\angle B$. Find $m\angle B$.

Solution Let $m\angle B = x$.

Draw a diagram that shows the given information. Then apply Theorem 3-12.

$$5x = 120 + x$$
$$4x = 120$$
$$x = 30$$
$$m\angle B = 30$$

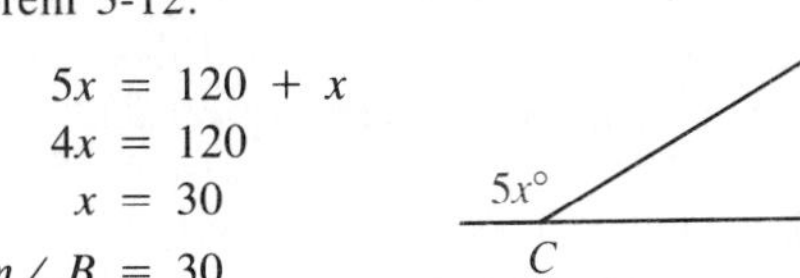

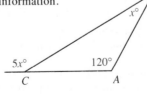

Find the $m\angle A$.

7. 80

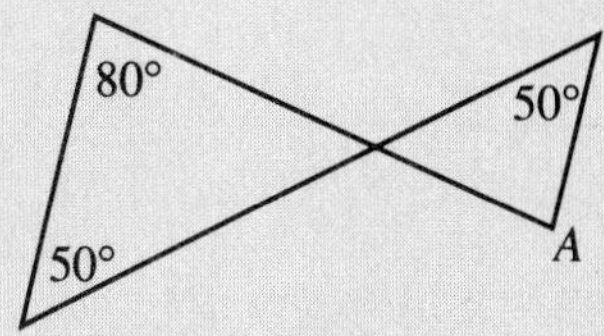

8. 60

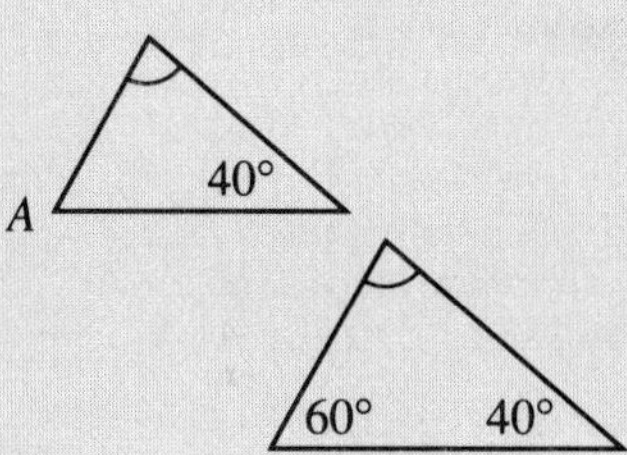

9. 110

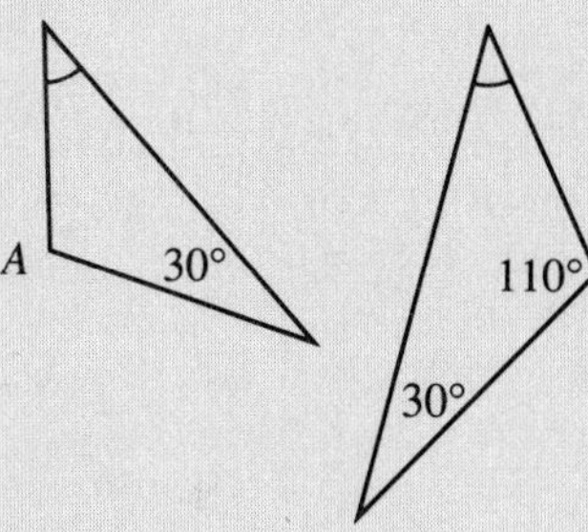

10. 40

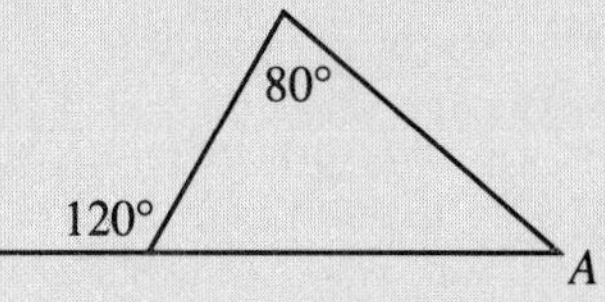

11. In $\triangle EFG$, $m\angle G = 100$, and $m\angle FEH = 3 \cdot m\angle F$. Find $m\angle F$. 50

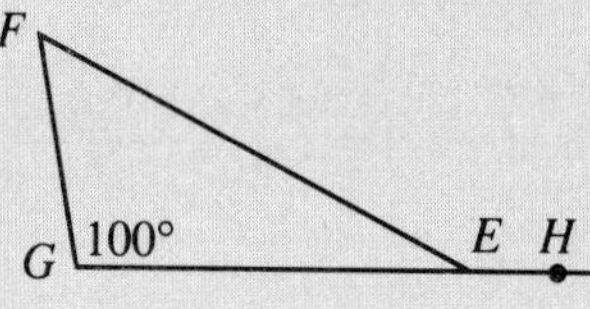

Classroom Exercises

Complete each statement with the word *always*, *sometimes*, or *never*.

1. If a triangle is isosceles, then it is __?__ equilateral. **sometimes**
2. If a triangle is equilateral, then it is __?__ isosceles. **always**
3. If a triangle is scalene, then it is __?__ isosceles. **never**
4. If a triangle is obtuse, then it is __?__ isosceles. **sometimes**

Explain how each corollary of Theorem 3-11 follows from the theorem.

5. Corollary 1
6. Corollary 2
7. Corollary 3
8. Corollary 4

Find the value of x.

9. **90**
10. **105**
11. **75**

What is wrong with each of the following instructions?

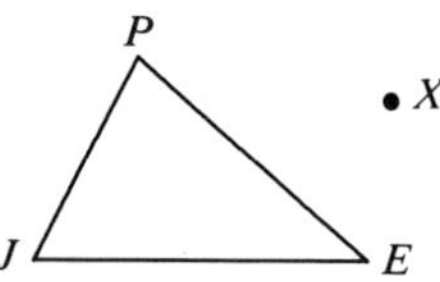

12. Draw the bisector of $\angle J$ to the midpoint of $\overline{PE}$.
13. Draw the line from P perpendicular to $\overline{JE}$ at its midpoint.
14. Draw the line through P and X parallel to $\overleftrightarrow{JE}$.

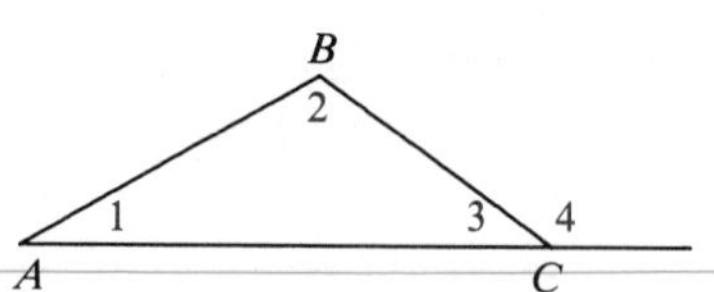

15. In the diagram you know that
(1) $m\angle 1 + m\angle 2 + m\angle 3 = 180$
(2) $m\angle 3 + m\angle 4 = 180$
Explain how these equations allow you to prove Theorem 3-12.

16. Fold a corner of a sheet of paper and then cut along the fold to get a right triangle. Let the right angle be $\angle C$. Fold each of the other two vertices so that they coincide with point C. What result of this section does this illustrate? **The acute ∠s of a rt. △ are comp.**

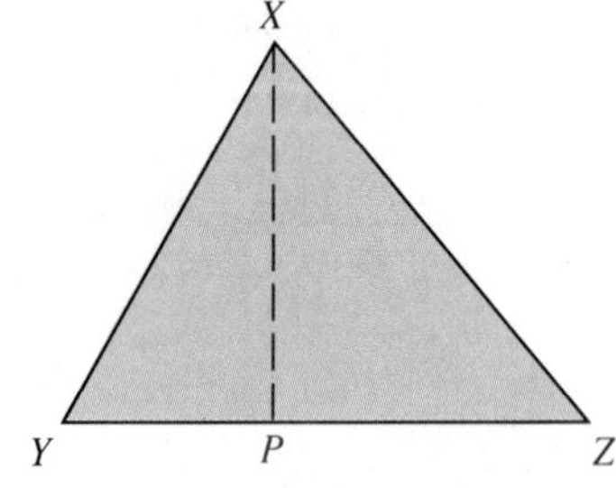

17. Cut out any large $\triangle XYZ$. (If the triangle has a longest side, let that side be $\overline{YZ}$.) Fold so that X lies on the fold line and Y falls on $\overrightarrow{YZ}$. Let P be the intersection of $\overline{YZ}$ and the fold line. Unfold. Now fold the paper so that Y coincides with P. Fold it twice more so that both X and Z coincide with P. What result of this section does this illustrate? **The sum of the meas. of the ∠s of a △ is 180.**

Additional Answers Classroom Exercises

5. The sums of the meas. of the 2 ∠s in each △ are =. The meas. of the third ∠ in each △ = 180 − sum.
6. Let meas. of each ∠ = x; $3x = 180$, $x = 60$.
7. In $\triangle ABC$, if $m\angle A \geq 90$ and $m\angle B \geq 90$, then $m\angle A + m\angle B + m\angle C > 180$ since $m\angle C > 0$.
8. In $\triangle ABC$, if $m\angle C = 90$, then $m\angle A + m\angle B = 180 - 90 = 90$.
12. The bisector of $\angle J$ may not contain the midpoint of $\overline{PE}$.
13. The line through $P \perp$ to $\overline{JE}$ may not contain the midpoint of $\overline{JE}$.
14. $\overleftrightarrow{PX}$ may not be $\parallel$ to $\overleftrightarrow{JE}$.
15. By the Substitution Prop., $m\angle 1 + m\angle 2 + m\angle 3 = m\angle 3 + m\angle 4$. By the Subtraction Prop. of =, $m\angle 1 + m\angle 2 = m\angle 4$, which proves Thm. 3-12.

Written Exercises

Draw a triangle that satisfies the conditions stated. If no triangle can satisfy the conditions, write *not possible*. **Check students' drawings.**

A **1. a.** An acute isosceles triangle
b. A right isosceles triangle
c. An obtuse isosceles triangle

2. a. An acute scalene triangle
b. A right scalene triangle
c. An obtuse scalene triangle

3. A triangle with two acute exterior angles **not possible**

4. A triangle with two obtuse exterior angles

Complete.

5. $m\angle 6 + m\angle 7 + m\angle 8 = \underline{\ ?\ }$. **180**

6. If $m\angle 6 = 52$ and $m\angle 11 = 82$, then $m\angle 7 = \underline{\ ?\ }$. **30**

7. If $m\angle 6 = 55$ and $m\angle 10 = 150$, then $m\angle 8 = \underline{\ ?\ }$. **95**

8. If $m\angle 6 = x$, $m\angle 7 = x - 20$, and $m\angle 11 = 80$, then $x = \underline{\ ?\ }$. **50**

9. If $m\angle 8 = 4x$, $m\angle 7 = 30$, and $m\angle 9 = 6x - 20$, then $x = \underline{\ ?\ }$. **25**

10. $m\angle 9 + m\angle 10 + m\angle 11 = \underline{\ ?\ }$. **360**

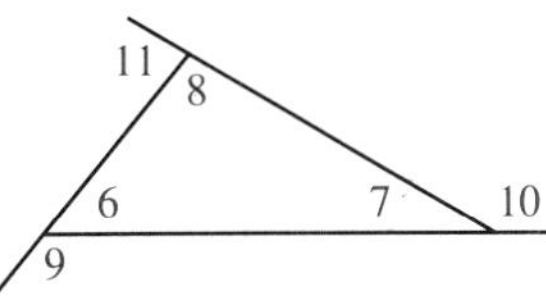

Exs. 5-10

Find the values of x and y.

11.
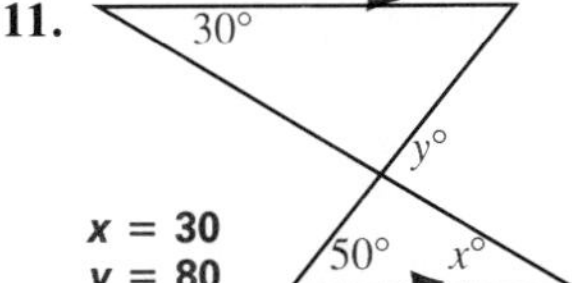

x = 30
y = 80

12.
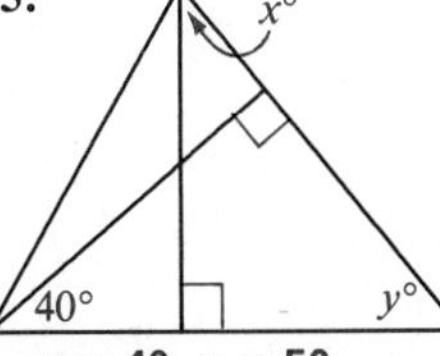

x = 110
y = 70

13.
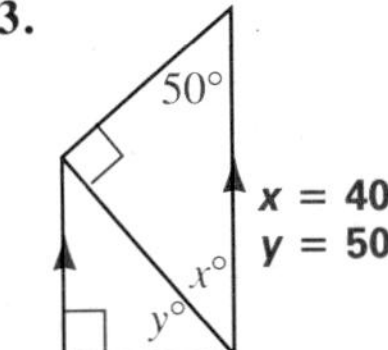

x = 40
y = 50

B **14.**
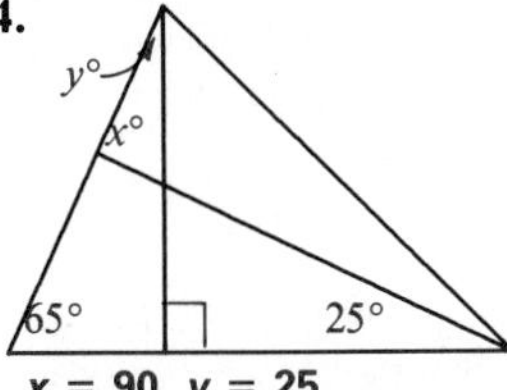

x = 90, y = 25

15.
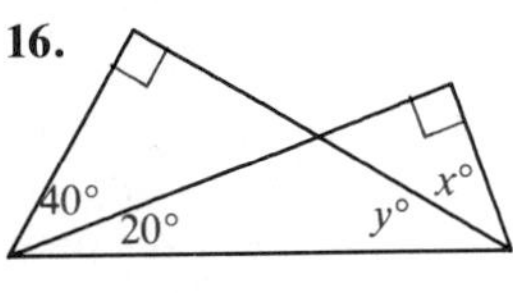

x = 40, y = 50

16.

x = 40, y = 30

17. The lengths of the sides of a triangle are $4n$, $2n + 10$, and $7n - 15$. Is there a value of n that makes the triangle equilateral? Explain. **Yes, $n = 5$**

18. The lengths of the sides of a triangle are $3t$, $5t - 12$, and $t + 20$.
a. Find the value(s) of t that make the triangle isosceles. **$t = 6$, $t = 8$, $t = 10$**
b. Does any value of t make the triangle equilateral? Explain. **No; there is no value of t such that $3t = 5t - 12 = t + 20$.**

Guided Practice

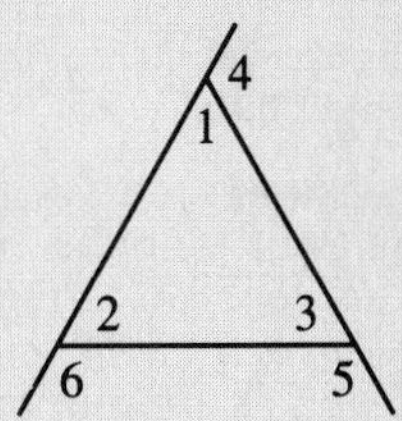

Complete.

1. $m\angle 1 + m\angle 2 + m\angle 3 = \underline{180}$

2. If $m\angle 1 = m\angle 2 = m\angle 3$, then each of the three angles has measure $\underline{60}$, and the triangle is $\underline{\text{equiangular}}$.

3. $m\angle 4 = m\angle 2 + m\underline{\angle 3}$

4. If $m\angle 1 = 55$ and $m\angle 2 = 60$, then $m\angle 3 = \underline{65}$.

5. If $m\angle 5 = 120$, $m\angle 1 = x$, and $m\angle 2 = x + 10$, then $x = \underline{55}$.

6. If $m\angle 6 = 3x - 5$, $m\angle 1 = x + 20$, and $m\angle 3 = 55$, then $x = \underline{40}$.

Find the values of x and y.

7. $x = 110$, $y = 65$

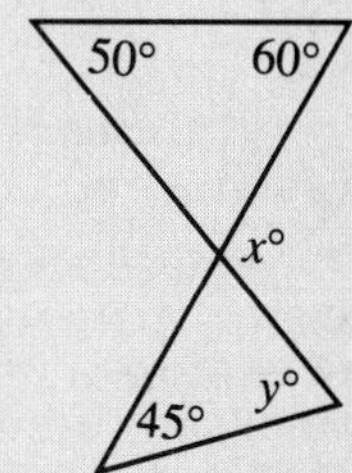

8. $x = 60$, $y = 30$

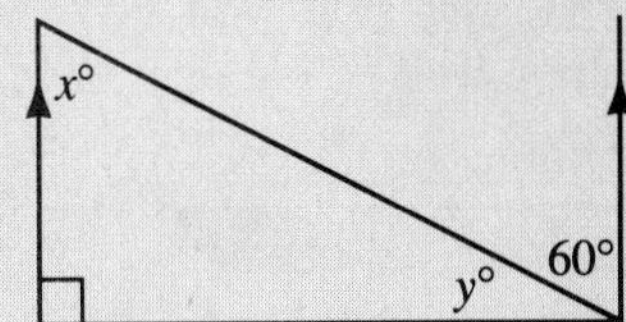

Thinking Skills

Most students tend to think that parts of triangles are described only in terms of congruence. Exs. 21 and 22 give students the opportunity to use an inequality statement to describe the measure of an angle. This enables students to see that sometimes a range of values can be given for an answer instead of one value.

19. The largest two angles of a triangle are two and three times as large as the smallest angle. Find all three measures. **30, 60, 90**

20. The measure of one angle of a triangle is 28 more than the measure of the smallest angle of the triangle. The measure of the third angle is twice the measure of the smallest angle. Find all three measures. **38, 66, 76**

21. In $\triangle ABC$, $m\angle A = 60$ and $m\angle B < 60$. What can you say about $m\angle C$? **$m\angle C > 60$**

22. In $\triangle RST$, $m\angle R = 90$ and $m\angle S > 20$. What can you say about $m\angle T$? **$m\angle T < 70$**

23. Given: $\overline{AB} \perp \overline{BC}$; $\overline{BD} \perp \overline{AC}$
    a. If $m\angle C = 22$, find $m\angle ABD$. **22**
    b. If $m\angle C = 23$, find $m\angle ABD$. **23**
    c. Explain why $m\angle ABD$ always equals $m\angle C$. **$\angle ABD$ and $\angle C$ are complements of $\angle CBD$.**

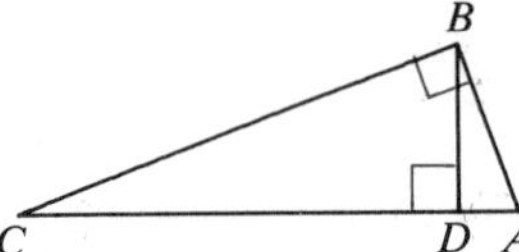

24. The bisectors of $\angle EFG$ and $\angle EGF$ meet at I.
    a. If $m\angle EFG = 40$, find $m\angle FIG$. **130**
    b. If $m\angle EFG = 50$, find $m\angle FIG$. **130**
    c. Generalize your results in (a) and (b). **If $m\angle E = 80$, then $m\angle FIG$ will always be 130.**

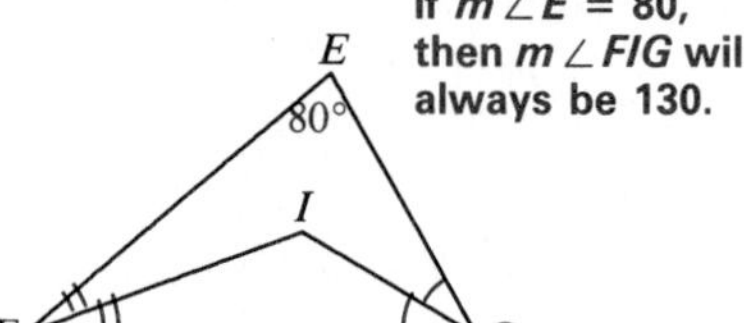

25. Given: $\angle ABD \cong \angle AED$
    Prove: $\angle C \cong \angle F$

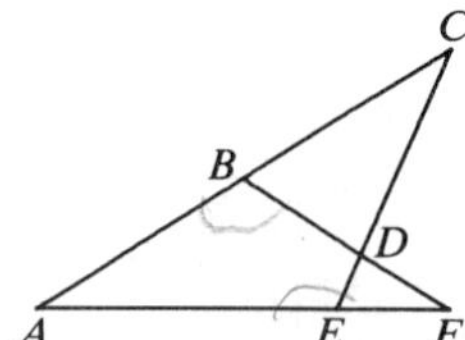

26. Find the measures of $\angle 1$ and $\angle 2$. **35** **125**

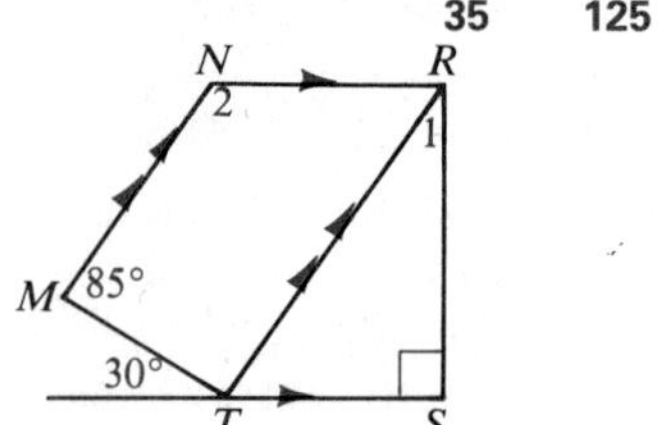

Proof Note

Ex. 27 illustrates that sometimes there is more than one way to prove a theorem. All students should be aware of this, and the more capable students should be encouraged to find alternative proofs whenever they can.

27. Prove Theorem 3-11 by using the diagram below. (Begin by stating what is given and what is to be proved. Draw the auxiliary ray shown.)

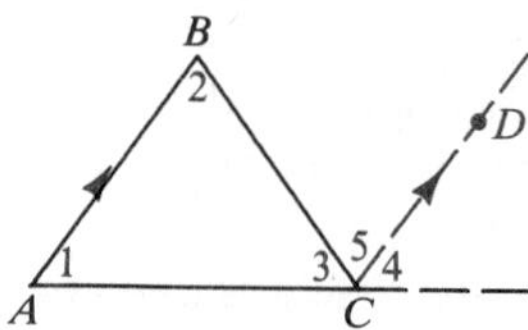

28. Given: $\overrightarrow{GK}$ bisects $\angle JGI$;
    $m\angle H = m\angle I$
    Prove: $\overline{GK} \parallel \overline{HI}$

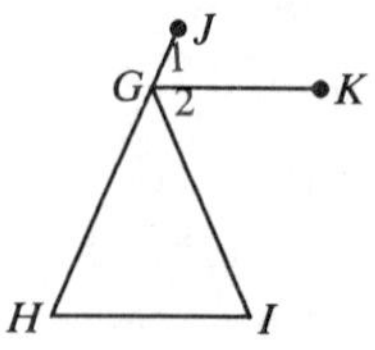

Find the values of x and y.

29. 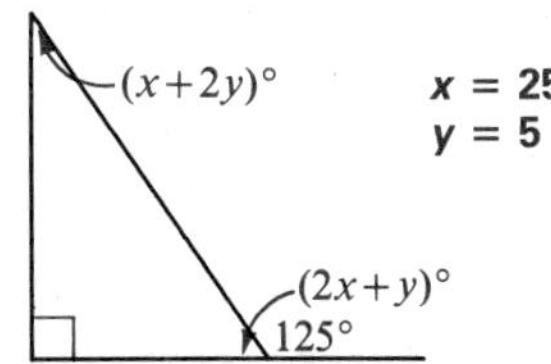

$x = 25$
$y = 5$

30. 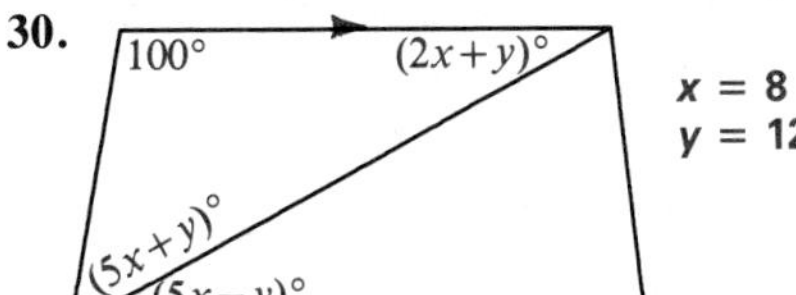

$x = 8$
$y = 12$

31. Given: $\overline{AB} \perp \overline{BF}$; $\overline{HD} \perp \overline{BF}$; $\overline{GF} \perp \overline{BF}$; $\angle A \cong \angle G$

Which numbered angles must be congruent? **$\angle 1 \cong \angle 2 \cong \angle 5$; $\angle 3 \cong \angle 4 \cong \angle 6$**

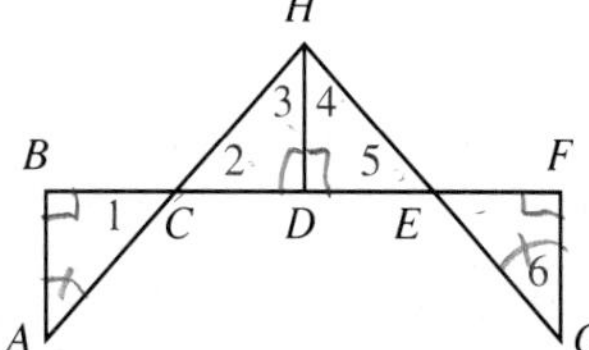

C **32.** Given: $\overrightarrow{PR}$ bisects $\angle SPQ$; $\overline{PS} \perp \overline{SQ}$; $\overline{RQ} \perp \overline{PQ}$

Which numbered angles must be congruent? **$\angle 7 \cong \angle 8$, $\angle 11 \cong \angle 12$**

Ex. 32

33. a. Draw two parallel lines and a transversal.

b. Use a protractor to draw bisectors of two same-side interior angles.

c. Measure the angles formed by the bisectors. What do you notice? **The angles measure 90, so the bisectors are $\perp$.**

d. Prove your answer to part (c).

34. A pair of same-side interior angles are *trisected* (divided into three congruent angles) by the red lines in the diagram. Find out what you can about the angles of *ABCD*.

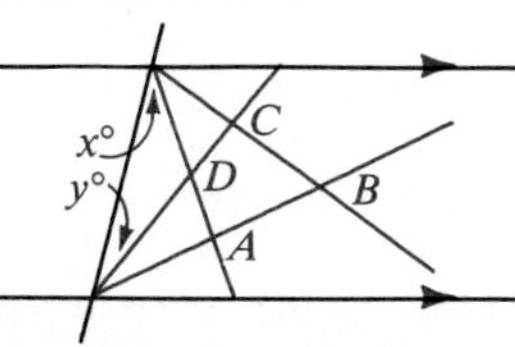

Explorations

These exploratory exercises can be done using a computer with a program that draws and measures geometric figures.

Decide if the following statements are true or false. If you think the statement is true, give a convincing argument to support your belief. If you think the statement is false, make a sketch and give all the measurements of the triangle that you find as your counterexample. For each false statement, also discover if there are types of triangles for which the statement is true.

1. The measure of an exterior angle is greater than the measure of any interior angle of a triangle. **False; true for acute triangles.**
2. An exterior angle is always an obtuse angle. **False; true for acute triangles.**
3. An exterior angle and some interior angle are supplementary. **True**
4. The sum of the measures of an exterior angle and the remote interior angles is 180. **False; true for right triangles.**

Additional Answers Written Exercises

34. $m\angle C + m\angle A = (2x + y) + (2y + x) = 180$. $m\angle B + m\angle D = 60 + 120 = 180$. Opposite angles of *ABCD* are supplementary.

Using a Computer

These exercises extend the topics just learned. Students use a construction program to verify true statements and to disprove false statements by counterexample.

Career

Carpenter

Carpenters work in all parts of the construction industry. A self-employed carpenter may work on relatively small-scale projects—for example, remodeling rooms or making other

alterations in existing houses or even building new single-family houses. As an employee of a large building contractor, a carpenter may be part of the work force building apartment or office complexes, stores, factories, and other major projects. Some carpenters are employed solely to provide maintenance to a large structure, where they do repairs and upkeep and make any alterations in the structure that are required.

Carpenters with adequate experience and expertise may become specialists in some skill of their own choice, for example, framing, interior finishing, or cabinet making. A carpenter who learns all aspects of the building industry thoroughly may decide to go into business as a general contractor, responsible for all work on an entire project.

Although some carpenters learn the trade through four-year apprenticeships, most learn on the job. These workers begin as laborers or as carpenters' helpers. While they work in these jobs they gradually acquire the skills necessary to become carpenters themselves. Carpenters must be able to measure accurately and to apply their knowledge of arithmetic, geometry, and informal algebra. They also benefit from being able to read and understand plans, blueprints, and charts.

3-5 *Angles of a Polygon*

The word **polygon** means "many angles." Look at the figures at the left below and note that each polygon is formed by coplanar segments (called *sides*) such that:

(1) Each segment intersects exactly two other segments, one at each endpoint.

(2) No two segments with a common endpoint are collinear.

Polygons

Not Polygons

Can you explain why each of the figures at the right above is *not* a polygon?

A **convex polygon** is a polygon such that no line containing a side of the polygon contains a point in the interior of the polygon. The outline of the state flag of Arizona, shown at the left below, is a convex polygon. At the right below is the state flag of Ohio, whose outline is a nonconvex polygon.

When we refer to a polygon in this book we will mean a convex polygon.

Polygons are classified according to the number of sides they have. Listed below are some of the special names for polygons you will see in this book.

Number of Sides	*Name*
3	triangle
4	quadrilateral
5	pentagon
6	hexagon
8	octagon
10	decagon
n	*n*-gon

A triangle is the simplest polygon. The terms that we applied to triangles (such as *vertex* and *exterior angle*) also apply to other polygons.

Teaching Suggestions, p. T86

Objectives
Presenting the Lesson
Problem Solving

Cooperative Learning, p. T86

Supplementary Materials

Practice Master 14
Test 10
Resource Book, pp. 12, 118
Study Guide, pp. 35–36
Computer Activity 6

Lesson Focus

This lesson discusses the meaning of the term *polygon* and then presents two theorems that involve the interior and exterior angles of convex polygons.

Suggested Assignments

Minimum
Day 1: 104/1–11
Day 2: 104–105/12–20

Average
Day 1: 104–105/2, 4–9, 11, 15, 16
Day 2: 105/18, 19, 22, 25, 26

Maximum
Day 1: 104/4, 6–8, 9–13 odd
S 99/30, 32
Day 2: 105/16, 18, 20, 21, 24–28

Teaching Note

You might wish to mention that a 12-sided polygon is called a *dodecagon.* Also, point out that a nonconvex polygon can be called a *concave* polygon.

Chalkboard Examples

Find (a) the sum of the measures of the interior angles, and (b) the sum of the measures of the exterior angles, one angle at each vertex.

1. For a polygon with 7 sides 900; 360
2. For a 17-gon 2700; 360

Proof Note

To prove Theorem 3-14, we reason as follows. At each vertex of a polygon, the interior and exterior angles are supplementary.

$m\angle 1 + m\angle 2 = 180$,
$m\angle 3 + m\angle 4 = 180$,
and so on.

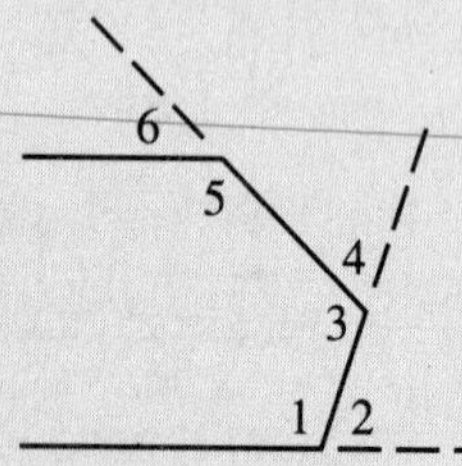

If the polygon has n vertices, then there are n pairs of supplementary angles and the sum of the measures of all these angles is $180n$. Thus,

$180n$ = (interior angle sum) + (exterior angle sum)
$180n = 180(n - 2)$ + (exterior angle sum)
$180n = 180n - 360$ + (exterior angle sum)
360 = exterior angle sum

When referring to a polygon, we list its consecutive vertices in order. Pentagon *ABCDE* and pentagon *BAEDC* are two of the many correct names for the polygon shown at the right.

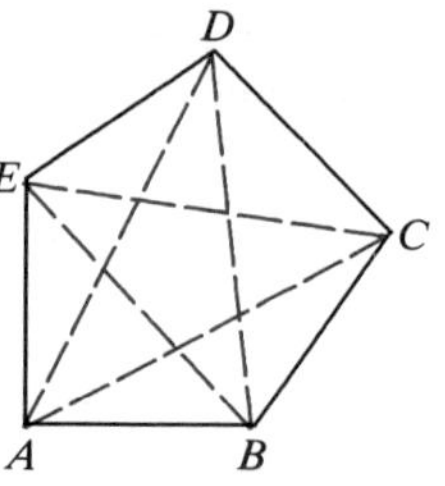

A segment joining two nonconsecutive vertices is a **diagonal** of the polygon. The diagonals of the pentagon at the right are indicated by dashes.

To find the sum of the measures of the angles of a polygon draw all the diagonals from just *one* vertex of the polygon to divide the polygon into triangles.

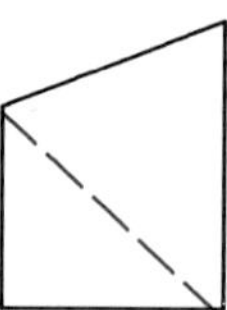

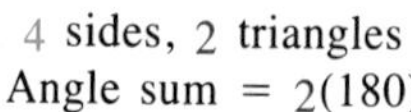
4 sides, 2 triangles
Angle sum = 2(180)

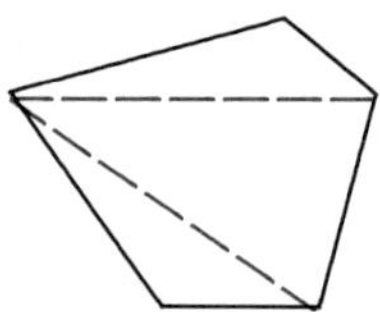

5 sides, 3 triangles
Angle sum = 3(180)

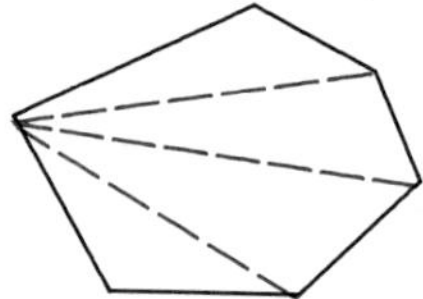

6 sides, 4 triangles
Angle sum = 4(180)

Note that the number of triangles formed in each polygon is two less than the number of sides. This result suggests the following theorem.

Theorem 3-13

The sum of the measures of the angles of a convex polygon with n sides is $(n - 2)180$.

Since the sum of the measures of the *interior* angles of a polygon depends on the number of sides, n, of the polygon, you would think that the same is true for the sum of the exterior angles. This is *not* true, as Theorem 3-14 reveals. The experiment suggested in Exercise 7 should help convince you of the truth of Theorem 3-14.

Theorem 3-14

The sum of the measures of the exterior angles of any convex polygon, one angle at each vertex, is 360.

Example 1 A polygon has 32 sides. Find (a) the sum of the measures of the interior angles and (b) the sum of the measures of the exterior angles, one angle at each vertex.

Solution (a) Interior angle sum = $(32 - 2)180 = 5400$ (Theorem 3-13)
(b) Exterior angle sum = 360 (Theorem 3-14)

Polygons can be equiangular or equilateral. If a polygon is both equiangular and equilateral, it is called a **regular polygon.**

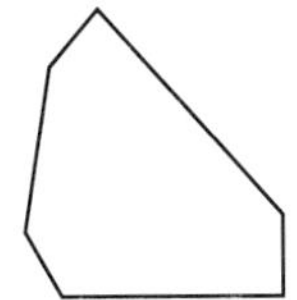
Hexagon that is neither equiangular nor equilateral

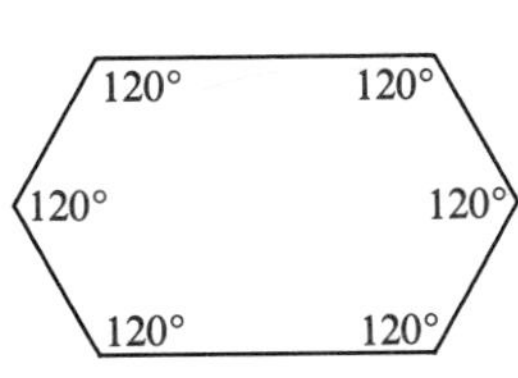

Equiangular hexagon

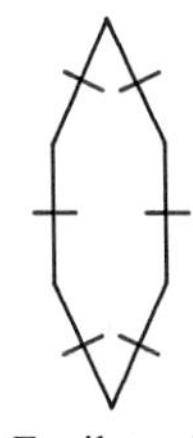
Equilateral hexagon

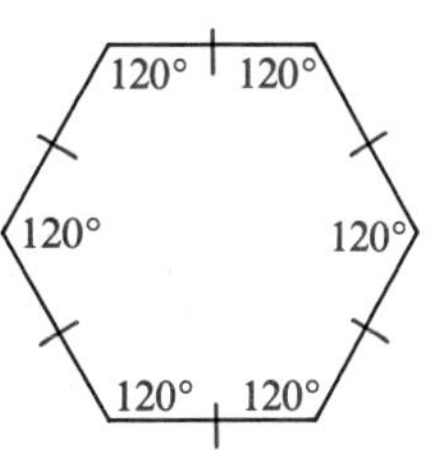

Regular hexagon

Example 2 A regular polygon has 12 sides. Find the measure of each interior angle.

Solution 1 Interior angle sum = (12 − 2)180 = 1800
Each of the 12 congruent interior angles has measure 1800 ÷ 12, or 150.

Solution 2 Each exterior angle has measure 360 ÷ 12, or 30.
Each interior angle has measure 180 − 30, or 150.

Classroom Exercises

Is the figure a convex polygon, a nonconvex polygon, or neither?

1.  **Convex polygon**

2.  **Nonconvex polygon**

3. 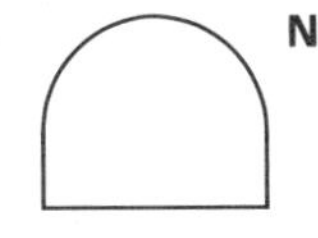 **Not a polygon**

4.  **Nonconvex polygon**

5. 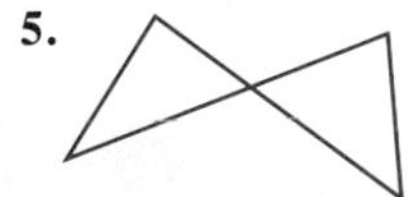 **Not a polygon**

6.  **Nonconvex polygon**

7. Imagine stretching a rubber band around each of the figures in Exercises 1–6. What is the relationship between the rubber band and the figure when the figure is a convex polygon? **It has the same shape.**

8. A polygon has 102 sides. What is the interior angle sum? the exterior angle sum? **18,000; 360**

9. Complete the table for regular polygons.

Number of sides	6	10	20	? **36**	? **18**	? **360**	? **4**
Measure of each ext. ∠	? **60**	? **36**	? **18**	10	20	? **1**	? **90**
Measure of each int. ∠	? **120**	? **144**	? **162**	? **170**	? **160**	179	90

Making Connections

When discussing the terms *equilateral* and *equiangular*, you may wish to emphasize that an equilateral polygon is not necessarily equiangular and vice versa. Draw examples to show this. It will be important when students encounter the definition of similarity of polygons in Chapter 7.

Chalkboard Examples

Find the measure of an interior angle.

1. for a regular quadrilateral 90
2. for a regular octagon 135
3. for a regular polygon with 15 sides 156
4. for a regular polygon with 20 sides 162

Communication Skills

Sometimes there is more than one way to define a term. A convex polygon might be defined as a "polygon such that no line containing a side of the polygon intersects another side of the polygon except at a vertex." Ask students if this definition is equivalent to the definition on page 101. That is, must a polygon that is convex according to one definition be convex according to the other definition also? Remind students that they must check "both ways"—that is, definition 1 works if and only if definition 2 works.

Guided Practice

Complete with *always*, *sometimes*, or *never*.

1. The sum of the measures of the exterior angles of any polygon, one angle at each vertex, is always 360.
2. The sum of the measures of the angles of a convex polygon is sometimes 360.
3. A segment joining two vertices of a polygon is sometimes a diagonal.
4. The sum of the measures of the exterior angles of a polygon never depends on the number of sides of the polygon.
5. A regular polygon is always equilateral.
6. An equiangular polygon is sometimes regular.

Find the interior angle sum and the exterior angle sum for:

7. a triangle 180; 360
8. a 20-gon 3240; 360
9. a 27-gon 4500; 360

Complete.

10. An exterior angle of a regular polygon has measure 10. The polygon has 36 sides.
11. An interior angle of a regular polygon has measure 160. The polygon has 18 sides.
12. Three of the angles of a quadrilateral have measures 90, 60, and 115. The fourth angle has measure 95.

Written Exercises

For each polygon, find (a) the interior angle sum and (b) the exterior angle sum.

A

1. Quadrilateral **360; 360**
2. Pentagon **540; 360**
3. Hexagon **720; 360**
4. Octagon **1080; 360**
5. Decagon **1440; 360**
6. n-gon **(n − 2)180; 360**
7. Draw a pentagon with one exterior angle at each vertex. Cut out the exterior angles and arrange them so that they all have a common vertex, as shown at the far right. What is the sum of the measures of the exterior angles? Repeat the experiment with a hexagon. Do your results support Theorem 3-14? **360; yes**

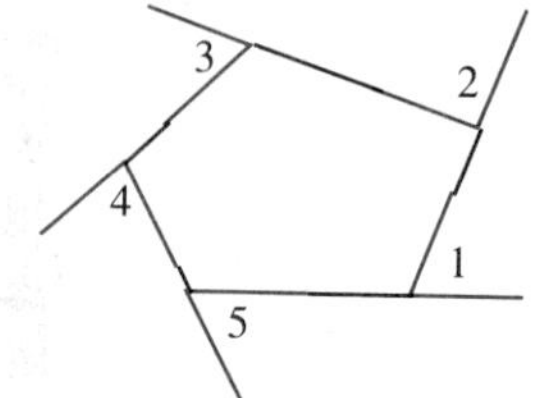

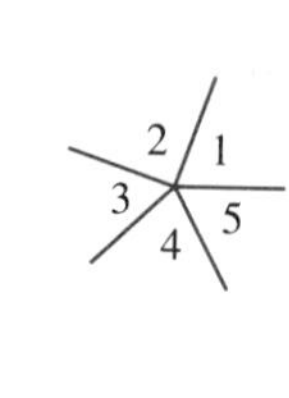

8. Complete the table for regular polygons.

Number of sides	9	15	30	? **60**	? **45**	? **24**	? **180**
Measure of each ext. ∠	?**40**	?**24**	?**12**	6	8	?**15**	? **2**
Measure of each int. ∠	? **140**	? **156**	? **168**	? **174**	? **172**	165	178

9. A baseball diamond's home plate has three right angles. The other two angles are congruent. Find their measure. **135**

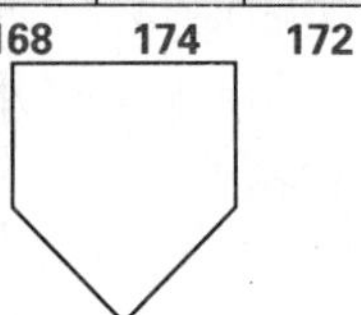

10. Four of the angles of a pentagon have measures 40, 80, 115, and 165. Find the measure of the fifth angle. **140**
11. The face of a honeycomb consists of interlocking regular hexagons. What is the measure of each angle of these hexagons? **120**

Sketch the polygon described. If no such polygon exists, write *not possible*.

12. A quadrilateral that is equiangular but not equilateral
13. A quadrilateral that is equilateral but not equiangular
14. A regular pentagon, one of whose angles has measure 120 **not poss.**
15. A regular polygon, one of whose angles has measure 130 **not poss.**

B **16.** The sum of the measures of the interior angles of a polygon is five times the sum of the measures of its exterior angles, one angle at each vertex. How many sides does the polygon have? **12**

17. The measure of each interior angle of a regular polygon is eleven times that of an exterior angle. How many sides does the polygon have? **24**

18. **a.** What is the measure of each interior angle of a regular pentagon? **108**
b. Can you tile a floor with tiles shaped like regular pentagons? **No** (Ignore the difficulty in tiling along the edges of the room.)

19. Make a sketch showing how to tile a floor using both squares and regular octagons.

20. The cover of a soccerball consists of interlocking regular pentagons and regular hexagons, as shown at the right. The second diagram shows that regular pentagons and hexagons cannot be interlocked in this pattern to tile a floor. Why not?

Possible

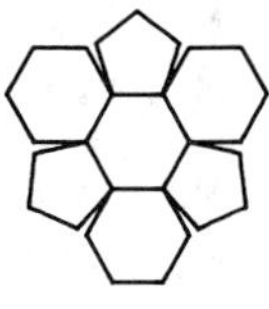

Impossible

21. In quadrilateral $ABCD$, $m\angle A = x$, $m\angle B = 2x$, $m\angle C = 3x$, and $m\angle D = 4x$. Find the value of x and then state which pair of sides of $ABCD$ must be parallel. **$x = 36$; $\overline{AB} \parallel \overline{CD}$**

22. In pentagon $PQRST$, $m\angle P = 60$ and $m\angle Q = 130$. $\angle S$ and $\angle T$ are each three times as large as $\angle R$.
a. Find the measures of $\angle R$, $\angle S$, and $\angle T$. **50, 150, 150**
b. Which pair of sides of $PQRST$ must be parallel? **$\overline{PQ} \parallel \overline{RS}$**

23. $ABCDEFGHIJ$ is a regular decagon. If sides $\overline{AB}$ and $\overline{CD}$ are extended to meet at K, find the measure of $\angle K$. **108**

24. $\overline{BC}$ is one side of a regular n-gon. The sides next to $\overline{BC}$ are extended to meet at W. Find the measure of $\angle W$ in terms of n. **$\frac{180(n-4)}{n}$**

25. The sum of the measures of the interior angles of a polygon is known to be between 2100 and 2200. How many sides does the polygon have? **14**

C **26.** The sum of the measures of the interior angles of a polygon with n sides is S. Without using n in your answer, express in terms of S the sum of the measures of the angles of a polygon with:
a. $n + 1$ sides **$S + 180$** **b.** $2n$ sides **$2(S + 180)$**

27. The formula $S = (n - 2)180$ can apply to nonconvex polygons if you allow the measure of an interior angle to be more than 180.
a. Illustrate this with a diagram that shows interior angles with measures greater than 180.
b. Does the reasoning leading up to Theorem 3-13 apply to your figure? **Yes**

28. Given: The measure of each interior angle of a regular n-gon is x times that of an exterior angle.
a. Express x in terms of n. **$x = \frac{n-2}{2}$**
b. For what values of n will x be an integer? **Even values ≥ 4**

Using a Computer

Encourage students to write a program for Ex. 8 that calculates the measure of each exterior angle and the measure of each interior angle for all polygons with 360 or fewer sides. Ask students how many of these polygons have integral interior (exterior) angle measures.

Additional Answers Written Exercises

20. The sum of the measures of the int. ∠s of 2 hexagons and one pentagon at any common vertex is 2(120) + 108 = 348. A sum of 360 is necessary to tile a plane.

Problem Solving

As an extension to Ex. 24, you may wish to have students consider the following problems.

1. Sides $\overline{KL}$ and $\overline{MN}$ of regular octagon $KLMNOPQR$ are extended to meet at S. Use your results in Ex. 24 to explain why $\overrightarrow{KL} \perp \overrightarrow{MN}$. The rays intersect to form a 90° angle.
2. $TUVXYZ$ is a regular hexagon. Use your results in Ex. 24 to explain why $\overline{TU} \parallel \overline{YX}$. $\overrightarrow{TU}$ and $\overrightarrow{XV}$ intersect to form a 60° angle. $m\angle YXV = 120$, therefore the exterior angle with vertex X is 60°. The 60° angles are alternate interior angles of transversal $\overleftrightarrow{XV}$.

Teaching Suggestions, pp. T86–T87

Objectives
Presenting the Lesson
Enrichment
Making Connections

Cooperative Learning, p. T87

Supplementary Materials

Practice Master 15
Test 11
Resource Book, pp. 13, 119
Study Guide, pp. 37–38
Computer Activities 7, 8

Lesson Focus

Deductive reasoning is used in mathematics to prove theorems. This lesson compares deductive reasoning with inductive reasoning. Inductive reasoning can be used to make conjectures about what relationships might be theorems.

Suggested Assignments

Minimum
Day 1: 107/1–14
Day 2: 108/15–17
S 105/22
Day 3: 110/Self-Test 2
112–113/Chapter Test

Average
Day 1: 107–108/1–17 odd
Day 2: 108/18–27
S 105/20, 23
Day 3: 110/Self-Test 2
112–113/Chapter Test

Maximum
Day 1: 107–108/3, 5, 8, 12, 15, 16–22 even
Day 2: 108–109/17–29 odd
Day 3: 112–113/Chapter Test

3-6 *Inductive Reasoning*

Throughout these first three chapters, we have been using deductive reasoning. Now we'll consider **inductive reasoning,** a kind of reasoning that is widely used in science and in everyday life.

Example 1 After picking marigolds for the first time, Connie began to sneeze. She also began sneezing the next four times she was near marigolds. Based on this past experience, Connie reasons inductively that she is allergic to marigolds.

Example 2 Every time Pitch has thrown a high curve ball to Slugger, Slugger has gotten a hit. Pitch concludes from this experience that it is not a good idea to pitch high curve balls to Slugger.

In coming to this conclusion, Pitch has used inductive reasoning. It may be that Slugger just happened to be lucky those times, but Pitch is too bright to feed another high curve to Slugger.

From these examples you can see how inductive reasoning differs from deductive reasoning.

Deductive Reasoning	**Inductive Reasoning**
Conclusion based on accepted statements (definitions, postulates, previous theorems, corollaries, and given information)	Conclusion based on several past observations
Conclusion *must* be true if hypotheses are true.	Conclusion is *probably* true, but not necessarily true.

Often in mathematics you can reason inductively by observing a pattern.

Example 3 Look for a pattern and predict the next number in each sequence.
a. 3, 6, 12, 24, __?__ **b.** 11, 15, 19, 23, __?__ **c.** 5, 6, 8, 11, 15, __?__

Solution

a. Each number is twice the preceding number. The next number will be 2×24, or 48.

b. Each number is 4 more than the preceding number. The next number will be $23 + 4$, or 27.

c. Look at the differences between the numbers.

Numbers	5		6		8		11		15		?
Differences		1		2		3		4		?	

The next difference will be 5, and thus the next number will be $15 + 5$, or 20.

Classroom Exercises

Tell whether the reasoning process is deductive or inductive.

1. Ramon noticed that spaghetti had been on the school menu for the past five Wednesdays. Ramon decides that the school always serves spaghetti on Wednesday. **inductive**
2. Ky did his assignment, adding the lengths of the sides of triangles to find the perimeters. Noticing the results for several equilateral triangles, he guesses that the perimeter of every equilateral triangle is three times the length of a side. **inductive**
3. By using the definitions of equilateral triangle (a triangle with three congruent sides) and of perimeter (the sum of the lengths of the sides of a figure), Katie concludes that the perimeter of every equilateral triangle is three times the length of a side. **deductive**
4. Linda observes that $(-1)^2 = +1$, $(-1)^4 = +1$, and $(-1)^6 = +1$. She concludes that every even power of (-1) is equal to $+1$. **inductive**
5. John knows that multiplying a number by -1 merely changes the sign of the number. He reasons that multiplying a number by an even power of -1 will change the sign of the number an even number of times. He concludes that this is equivalent to multiplying a number by $+1$, so that every even power of -1 is equal to $+1$. **deductive**
6. Look at the discussion leading up to the statement of Theorem 3-13 on page 102. Is the thinking inductive or deductive? **inductive**

Written Exercises

1. 256, 1024 2. 6, 3 3. $\frac{1}{81}, \frac{1}{243}$ 4. 25, 36 5. 17, 23 6. 40, 52

Look for a pattern and predict the next two numbers in each sequence.

A

1. 1, 4, 16, 64, . . .
2. 18, 15, 12, 9, . . .
3. $1, \frac{1}{3}, \frac{1}{9}, \frac{1}{27}, \ldots$
4. 1, 4, 9, 16, . . .
5. 2, 3, 5, 8, 12, . . .
6. 10, 12, 16, 22, 30, . . .
7. 40, 39, 36, 31, 24, . . . **15, 4**
8. $8, -4, 2, -1, \frac{1}{2}, \ldots$ **$-\frac{1}{4}, \frac{1}{8}$**
9. 2, 20, 10, 100, 50, . . . **500, 250**

Accept the two statements as given information. State a conclusion based on *deductive* reasoning. If no conclusion can be reached, write *none*.

10. Chan is older than Pedro.
    Pedro is older than Sarah.
11. Valerie is older than Greg.
    Dan is older than Greg. **none**
12. Polygon G has more than 6 sides.
    Polygon G has fewer than 8 sides.
13. Polygon G has more than 6 sides.
    Polygon K has more than 6 sides. **none**
14. There are three sisters. Two of them are athletes and two of them like tacos. Can you be sure that both of the athletes like tacos? Do you reason deductively or inductively to conclude the following? *At least one of the athletic sisters likes tacos.* **No; deductively**

10. Chan is older than Sarah.
12. Polygon *G* has 7 sides.

Chalkboard Examples

Complete.

1. Mary has given Jimmy a present on each of his birthdays. He reasons inductively that she will give him a present on his next birthday.
2. Jerry has gotten a sunburn every time he has gone fishing. He reasons inductively that he will get a sunburn the next time he goes fishing.

Fill in the blanks for the given sequence.

3. 10, 20, 30, 40, 50
4. 7, 4, 1, −2, −5
5. 0, 0.1, 0.01, 0.001, 0.0001, 0.00001
6. 2, 4, 8, 16, 32, 64
7. 1, 4, 9, 16, 25, 36, 49
8. $\frac{1}{2}, \frac{2}{3}, \frac{3}{4}, \frac{4}{5}, \frac{5}{6}$

Guided Practice

Look for a pattern and predict the next two numbers in each sequence.

1. 1, 1, 2, 3, 5, 8, 13
2. 1, 3, 5, 7, 9
3. 1, 8, 27, 64, 125
4. 2, 5, 8, 11, 14
5. 8, 4, 0, −4, −8
6. 12, 7, 2, −3, −8
7. 3, 6, 12, 24, 48
8. 5, 15, 45, 135, 405

Accept the two statements as given information. State a conclusion based on deductive reasoning.

9. $\overline{AB}$ is longer than $\overline{BC}$. $\overline{BC}$ is longer than $\overline{CD}$. $\overline{AB}$ is longer than $\overline{CD}$.
10. 12 is greater than integer *I*. *I* is greater than 8. *I* is 9, 10, or 11.

For each exercise, write the equation you think should come next. Check your prediction with a calculator.

15. $1 \times 9 + 2 = 11$
$12 \times 9 + 3 = 111$
$123 \times 9 + 4 = 1111$
$1234 \times 9 + 5 = 11111$

16. $9 \times 9 + 7 = 88$
$98 \times 9 + 6 = 888$
$987 \times 9 + 5 = 8888$
$9876 \times 9 + 4 = 88888$

17. $9^2 = 81$
$99^2 = 9801$
$999^2 = 998001$
$9999^2 = 99980001$

Draw several diagrams to help you decide whether each statement is true or false. If it is false, show a counterexample. If it is true, draw and label a diagram you could use in a proof. List, in terms of the diagram, what is given and what is to be proved. Do *not* write a proof.

B

18. If a triangle has two congruent sides, then the angles opposite those sides are congruent. **True**

19. If a triangle has two congruent angles, then the sides opposite those angles are congruent. **True**

20. If two triangles have equal perimeters, then they have congruent sides. **False**

21. All diagonals of a regular pentagon are congruent. **True**

22. If both pairs of opposite sides of a quadrilateral are parallel, then the diagonals bisect each other. **True**

23. If the diagonals of a quadrilateral are congruent and also perpendicular, then the quadrilateral is a regular quadrilateral. **False**

24. The diagonals of an equilateral quadrilateral are congruent. **False**

25. The diagonals of an equilateral quadrilateral are perpendicular. **True**

26. a. Study the diagrams below. Then guess the number of regions for the fourth diagram. Check your answer by counting.

2 points	3 points	4 points	5 points
2 regions	4 regions	8 regions	? regions **16**

b. Using 6 points on a circle as shown, guess the number of regions within the circle. Carefully check your answer by counting. **Guess: 32 Actual count: 31**
Important note: This exercise shows that a pattern predicted on the basis of a few cases may be incorrect. To be sure of a conclusion, use a deductive proof.

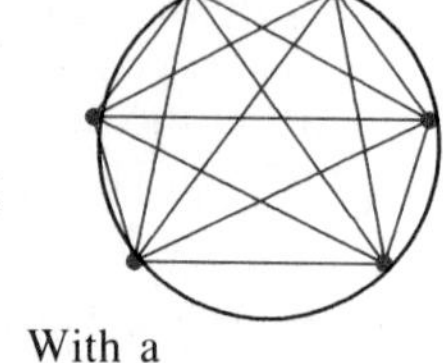

27. a. Draw several quadrilaterals whose opposite sides are parallel. With a protractor measure both pairs of opposite angles of each figure. On the basis of the diagrams and measurements, what do you guess is true for all such quadrilaterals? (*Note*: See Exercise 23, page 82.) **Opposite ∠s are ≅.**

b. State and prove the converse of your conclusion about opposite angles in part (a).

c. Write a biconditional about pairs of opposite angles of a quadrilateral.
Both pairs of opposite ∠s of a quad. are ≅ if and only if opposite sides are ∥.

Using a Calculator

A calculator is ideal for verifying equations like those in Exs. 15–17, and for searching for patterns in equations.

Using a Computer

Exs. 18–25, 27 can be done effectively using a construction program.

Problem Solving

When students investigate the truth of a statement involving two triangles, it is often a good strategy to draw one triangle first, then try to draw a second triangle that violates the relationship being considered. In Ex. 20, suggest that students draw the following:

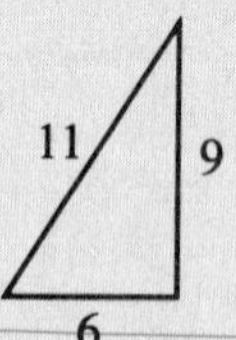

11

Ask students if they can always complete the second triangle so that the perimeter is 26. (Yes) Can they find two sides whose lengths total 15? (5 and 10, for instance)

Additional Answers Written Exercises

27.b. If both pairs of opposite angles of a quad. are ≅, then opposite sides are ∥.

C **28. a.** Substitute each of the integers from 1 to 9 for n in the expression $n^2 + n + 11$. **13, 17, 23, 31, 41, 53, 67, 83, 101**

b. Using inductive reasoning, guess what kind of number you will get when you substitute any positive integer for n in the expression $n^2 + n + 11$. **a prime number**

c. Test your guess by substituting 10 and 11 for n. **121, 143, neither of which is prime**

29. Complete the table for convex polygons.

Number of sides	3	4	5	6	7	8	n
Number of diagonals	0	2	?	?	?	?	?
			5	**9**	**14**	**20**	$\frac{n(n-3)}{2}$

30. Find the sum of the measures of the angles formed at the tips of each star.

a. five-pointed star **180**

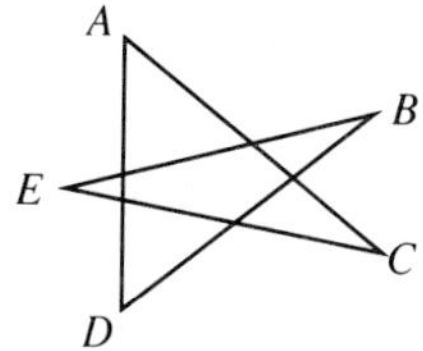

b. six-pointed star **360**

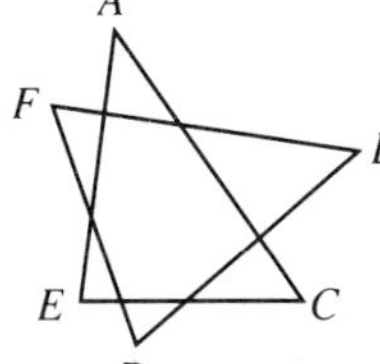

c. Using inductive reasoning, suggest a formula for the sum of the angle measures at the tips of an n-pointed star. **180(*n* − 4)**

d. Using deductive reasoning, justify your formula.

♦ Calculator Key-In

Complete the right side of the first three equations in each exercise. Then use inductive reasoning to predict what the fourth equation would be if the pattern were continued. Check your prediction with your calculator.

1. $1 \times 1 =$ _?_ **1**
$11 \times 11 =$ _?_ **121**
$111 \times 111 =$ _?_ **12321**
_?_ × _?_ = _?_ **1234321**
1111 1111

2. $6 \times 7 =$ _?_ **42**
$66 \times 67 =$ _?_ **4422**
$666 \times 667 =$ _?_ **444222**
_?_ × _?_ = _?_ **44442222**
6666 6667

3. $8 \times 8 =$ _?_ **64**
$98 \times 98 =$ _?_ **9604**
$998 \times 998 =$ _?_ **996004**
_?_ × _?_ = _?_ **99960004**
9998 9998

4. $7 \times 9 =$ _?_ **63**
$77 \times 99 =$ _?_ **7623**
$777 \times 999 =$ _?_ **776223**
_?_ × _?_ = _?_ **77762223**
7777 9999

Using a Calculator

This Calculator Key-In provides more examples of equations well suited for verification by a calculator. Exs. 1 and 3 illustrate the advantages of a calculator with more than four functions—in this case, the capability to square a number.

Self-Test 2

Complete.

1. If the measure of each angle of a triangle is less than 90, the triangle is called ___?___. **acute**
2. If a triangle has no congruent sides, it is called ___?___. **scalene**
3. Each angle of an equiangular triangle has measure ___?___. **60**
4. In the diagram, m∠1 = ___?___ and m∠2 = ___?___. **105, 35**
5. If the measures of the acute angles of a right triangle are $2x + 4$ and $3x - 9$, then x = ___?___. **19**

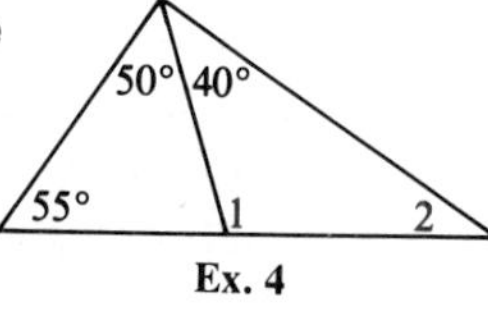

Ex. 4

6. Find the values of y and z. **$y = 50$, $z = 60$**
7. The lengths of the sides of a triangle are $2x + 5$, $3x + 10$, and $x + 12$. Find all values of x that make the triangle isosceles. **$x = 1$, $x = 7$**
8. An octagon has ___?___ sides. **8**
9. A regular polygon is both ___?___ and ___?___. **equilateral, equiangular**
10. In a regular decagon, the sum of the measures of the exterior angles is ___?___ and the measure of each interior angle is ___?___. **360, 144**

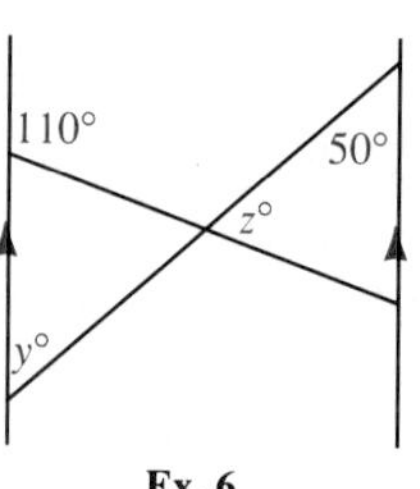

Ex. 6

11. If the measure of each angle of a polygon is 174, then the measure of each exterior angle is ___?___ and the polygon has ___?___ sides. **6** **60**

Use inductive reasoning to predict the next number in each sequence.

12. 2, −4, 8, −16, . . . **32**
13. 7, 12, 17, 22, 27, . . . **32**
14. 1, 4, 9, 16, 25, . . . **36**
15. 1, 4, 2, 8, 4, 16, 8, 32, . . . **16**

Chapter Summary

1. Lines that do not intersect are either parallel or skew.
2. When two parallel lines are cut by a transversal:
   a. corresponding angles are congruent;
   b. alternate interior angles are congruent;
   c. same-side interior angles are supplementary;
   d. if the transversal is perpendicular to one of the two parallel lines, it is also perpendicular to the other one.
3. The chart on page 85 lists five ways to prove lines parallel.
4. Through a point outside a line, there is exactly one line parallel to, and exactly one line perpendicular to, the given line.
5. Two lines parallel to a third line are parallel to each other.

Quick Quiz

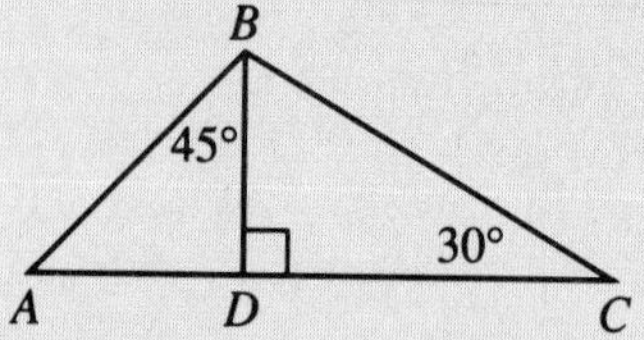

Complete.

1. m∠A = 45
2. m∠CBD = 60
3. m∠ABC = 105
4. △CBD is a(n) scalene right triangle.
5. △ABC is a(n) scalene obtuse triangle.
6. △ABD is a(n) isosceles right triangle.
7. If each angle of a regular polygon measures 140, then the polygon has 9 sides.
8. Find the values of x, y, and z.
   $x = 65$, $y = 55$, $z = 25$

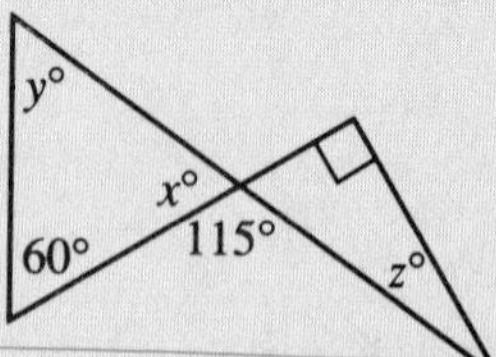

9. The lengths of the sides of a triangle are $2x$, $x + 5$, and $3x - 10$. Find all values of x that make the triangle isosceles.
   5, 7.5, 10
10. A decagon has 10 sides.
11. In a regular hexagon, the sum of the measures of the exterior angles is 360 and the measure of each interior angle is 120.
12. If the measure of each angle of a polygon is 170, then the measure of each exterior angle is 10 and the polygon has 36 sides.

6. Triangles are classified (page 93) by the lengths of their sides and by the measures of their angles. In any $\triangle ABC$, $m\angle A + m\angle B + m\angle C = 180$.
7. The measure of an exterior angle of a triangle equals the sum of the measures of the two remote interior angles.
8. The sum of the measures of the angles of a convex polygon with n sides is $(n - 2)180$. The sum of the measures of the exterior angles, one angle at each vertex, is 360.
9. Polygons that are both equiangular and equilateral are regular polygons.
10. Inductive reasoning is the process of observing individual cases and then reaching a general conclusion suggested by them. The conclusion is probably, but not necessarily, true.

Chapter Review

1. $\angle 5$ and $\angle$ _?_ are same-side interior angles. **2** 3–1
2. $\angle 5$ and $\angle 1$ are _?_ angles. **corr.**
3. $\angle 5$ and $\angle 3$ are _?_ angles. **alt. int.**
4. Line j, not shown, does not intersect line r. Must lines r and j be parallel? **No, they can be skew.**

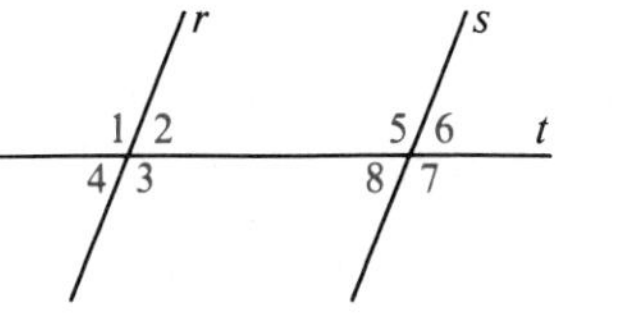

Exs. 1–7

In the diagram above, $r \parallel s$.

5. If $m\angle 1 = 105$, then $m\angle 5 =$ _?_ **105** and $m\angle 7 =$ _?_. **105** 3–2
6. Solve for x: $m\angle 2 = 70$ and $m\angle 8 = 6x - 2$ **$x = 12$**
7. Solve for y: $m\angle 3 = 8y - 40$ and $m\angle 8 = 2y + 20$ **$y = 20$**
8. Lines a, b, and c are coplanar, $a \parallel b$, and $a \perp c$. What can you conclude? Explain. **$b \perp c$; Thm. 3-4**
9. Which line is parallel to $\overleftrightarrow{AB}$? Why? **$\overleftrightarrow{DE}$; $\angle A$ is suppl. to $\angle ADE$.** 3–3
10. Name a pair of parallel lines other than the pair in Exercise 9. Why must they be parallel? **$\overleftrightarrow{BE} \parallel \overleftrightarrow{CF}$; both are $\perp$ to $\overleftrightarrow{DF}$.**

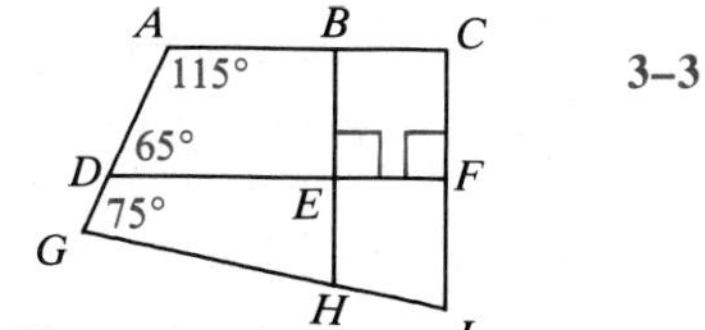

Exs. 9, 10

11. Name five ways to prove two lines parallel. **See p. 85.**
12. If x and $2x - 15$ represent the measures of the acute angles of a right triangle, find the value of x. **$x = 35$** 3–4
13. $m\angle 6 + m\angle 7 + m\angle 8 =$ _?_ **180**
14. If $m\angle 1 = 30$ and $m\angle 4 = 130$, then $m\angle 2 =$ _?_. **100**
15. If $\angle 4 \cong \angle 5$ and $\angle 1 \cong \angle 7$, name two other pairs of congruent angles and give a reason for each answer.
    $\angle 3 \cong \angle 6$ (Thm. 2-7)

    $\angle 2 \cong \angle 8$ (Thm. 3-11, Cor. 1, p. 94)

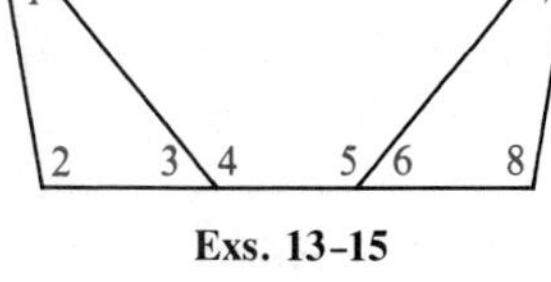

Exs. 13–15

Use inductive reasoning to predict the next number of each sequence.

13. 7, 9, 11, 13

14. 3, 9, 27, 81

15. 64, 16, 4, 1

Supplementary Materials

Practice Master 16

Test 12

Resource Book, pp. 14–15, 120

16. **a.** Sketch a hexagon that is equiangular but not equilateral. 3–5
b. What is its interior angle sum? **720**
c. What is its exterior angle sum? **360**

17. A regular polygon has 18 sides. Find the measure of each interior angle. **160**

18. A regular polygon has 24 sides. Find the measure of each exterior angle. **15**

19. Each interior angle of a regular polygon has measure 150. How many sides does the polygon have? **12**

Use inductive reasoning to predict the next two numbers in each sequence.

20. 15, 30, 45, 60, . . . **75, 90**

21. 100, -10, 1, $-\frac{1}{10}$, . . . $\frac{1}{100}$, $-\frac{1}{1000}$ 3–6

Teaching References

Alternate Test, p. T14

Chapter Test

Complete each statement with the word *always*, *sometimes*, or *never*.

1. Two lines that have no points in common are __?__ parallel. **sometimes**
2. If a line is perpendicular to one of two parallel lines, then it is __?__ perpendicular to the other one. **sometimes**
3. If two lines are cut by a transversal and same-side interior angles are complementary, then the lines are __?__ parallel. **never**
4. An obtuse triangle is __?__ a right triangle. **never**
5. In $\triangle ABC$, if $\overline{AB} \perp \overline{BC}$, then $\overline{AC}$ is __?__ perpendicular to $\overline{BC}$. **never**
6. As the number of sides of a regular polygon increases, the measure of each exterior angle __?__ decreases. **always**

Find the value of *x*.

7. $m\angle 1 = 3x - 20$, $m\angle 2 = x$ **50**
8. $m\angle 2 = 2x + 12$, $m\angle 3 = 4(x - 7)$ **20**

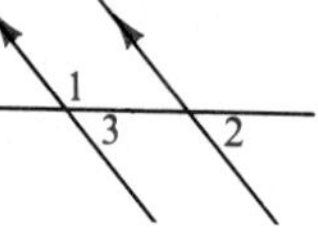

11. $m\angle 1 = 72$
$m\angle 2 = 72$
$m\angle 3 = 36$
$m\angle 4 = 108$
$m\angle 5 = 36$

Find the measures of the numbered angles.

9. *XYZ* is regular.

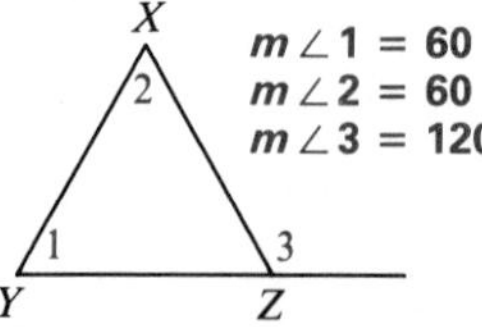

$m\angle 1 = 60$
$m\angle 2 = 60$
$m\angle 3 = 120$

10. **See below.**

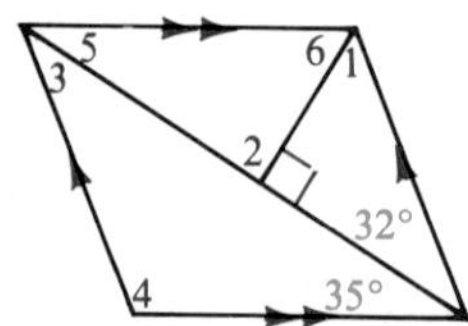

11. *ABCDE* is regular.

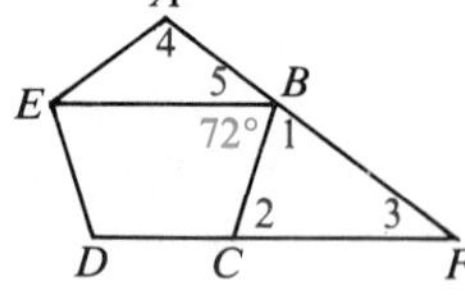

12. In the diagram for Exercise 11, explain why $\overline{EB}$ and $\overline{DF}$ must be parallel. **∠*EBC* ≅ ∠2 (Thm. 3-5), or ∠5 ≅ ∠3 (Post. 11)**

10. $m\angle 1 = 58$, $m\angle 2 = 90$, $m\angle 3 = 32$, $m\angle 4 = 113$, $m\angle 5 = 35$, $m\angle 6 = 55$

13. Given: $\overleftrightarrow{AB} \parallel \overleftrightarrow{CD}$; $\overrightarrow{BF}$ bisects $\angle ABE$;
$\overrightarrow{DG}$ bisects $\angle CDB$.
Prove: $\overleftrightarrow{BF} \parallel \overleftrightarrow{DG}$

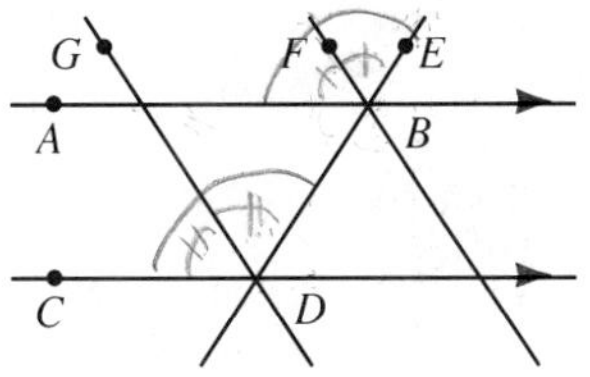

14. Predict the next two numbers in the sequence 7, 9, 11, 13, ... **15, 17**

5. (3, 5) **6.** (4, 3) **7.** (4, 0) **8.** (0, 4) **9.** (−5, 0)
10. (−4, 3) **11.** (−2, 2) **12.** (−4, −2) **13.** (−2, −3) **14.** (3, −2)

Algebra Review: *The Coordinate Plane*

15. ***K, O, S*** **16.** ***O, R, Z***

1. What is the x-coordinate of point P? **3**

2. What is the y-coordinate of point P? **2**

3. What are the coordinates of the origin, point O? **(0, 0)**

4. Name the graph of the ordered pair (0, −2). ***Z***

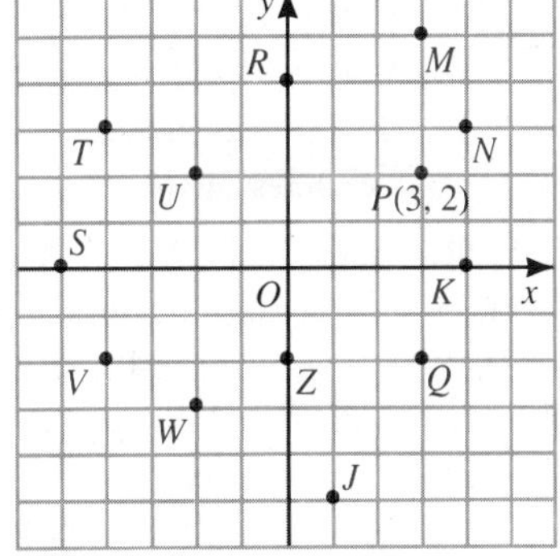

Exs. 1–22

Name the coordinates of each point.

5. M	**6.** N	**7.** K	**8.** R	**9.** S
10. T	**11.** U	**12.** V	**13.** W	**14.** Q

15. Name all the points shown that lie on the x-axis.

16. Name all the points shown that lie on the y-axis.

17. What is the x-coordinate of every point that lies on a vertical line through P? **3**

18. Which of the following points lie on a horizontal line through W?
a. (−2, 1) **b.** (2, 3) **(c.)** (1, −3) **d.** (−2, 0) **(e.)** (0, −3) **f.** (2, 0)

Name all the points shown that lie in the quadrant indicated. (A point on an axis is not in any quadrant.)

19. Quadrant I ***M, N, P*** **20.** Quadrant II ***T, U*** **21.** Quadrant III ***V, W*** **22.** Quadrant IV ***J, Q***

Plot each point on graph paper. **Check students' drawings.**

23. O (0, 0)	**24.** A (2, 1)	**25.** B (3, 4)	**26.** C (5, 0)
27. D (0, 3)	**28.** E (−3, 1)	**29.** F (−2, −1)	**30.** G (1, −2)
31. H (0, −4)	**32.** I (−4, 0)	**33.** J (4, −2)	**34.** K (−4, −3)

Find the coordinates of the midpoint of $\overline{AB}$. (You may want to draw a diagram.)

35. A (0, 1), B (4, 1) **(2, 1)** **36.** A (2, 0), B (2, 10) **(2, 5)** **37.** A (0, 1), B (0, 5) **(0, 3)**

38. A (−3, 4), B (−3, −4) **(−3, 0)** **39.** A (−5, −2), B (−3, −2) **(−4, −2)** **40.** A (4, −1), B (−2, −1) **(1, −1)**

∠CDB ≅ ∠ABE corr. ∠'s
m∠GDB = ½ m∠CDB
m∠FBE = ½ m∠ABE
m∠GDB = m∠FBE
$\overleftrightarrow{EF} \parallel \overleftrightarrow{DG}$ corr. ∠'s ≅, so lines ∥

Supplementary Materials

Test 13

Resource Book, pp. 16–18, 121, 173–174, 192

Exercise Note

Many students draw diagrams that are so small that they become cluttered and do not assist the learning process. Encourage students to draw large diagrams—and different diagrams when they start to get cluttered. This guidance will be particularly beneficial for Exs. 14–22.

Cumulative Review: Chapters 1–3

Complete each statement with the word *always*, *sometimes*, or *never*.

A

1. If $\overleftrightarrow{AB}$ intersects $\overline{CD}$, then $\overline{AB}$ _?_ intersects $\overline{CD}$. **sometimes**

2. If two planes intersect, their intersection is _?_ a line. **always**

3. If $a \perp c$ and $b \perp c$, then a and b are _?_ parallel. **sometimes**

4. If two parallel planes are cut by a third plane, then the lines of intersection are _?_ coplanar. **always**

5. A scalene triangle _?_ has an acute angle. **always**

Draw a diagram that satisfies the conditions stated. If the conditions cannot be satisfied, write *not possible*.

6. $\overline{AB}$ and $\overline{XY}$ intersect and A is the midpoint of $\overline{XY}$.

7. A triangle is isosceles but not equilateral.

8. Three points all lie in both plane M and plane N.

9. Two lines intersect to form adjacent angles that are not supplementary. **not possible**

10. Points A and B on a number line have coordinates -3.5 and 8.5. Find the coordinate of the midpoint of $\overline{AB}$. **2.5**

11. $\overrightarrow{QX}$ bisects $\angle PQR$, $m\angle PQX = 5x + 13$, and $m\angle XQR = 9x - 39$. Find (a) the value of x and (b) $m\angle PQR$. **$x = 13$; $m\angle PQR = 156$**

12. The measure of a supplement of an angle is 35 more than twice the complement of the angle. Find the measures of the angle, its supplement, and its complement. **35, 145, 55**

13. The measures of two angles of a triangle are five and six times as large as the measure of the smallest angle. Find all three measures. **15, 75, 90**

In the diagram $\overleftrightarrow{AB}$ bisects $\angle DHF$, $\overleftrightarrow{AB} \perp \overline{GH}$, $\overleftrightarrow{AB} \parallel \overleftrightarrow{CD}$, and $m\angle AHD = 60$. Find the measure of each angle.

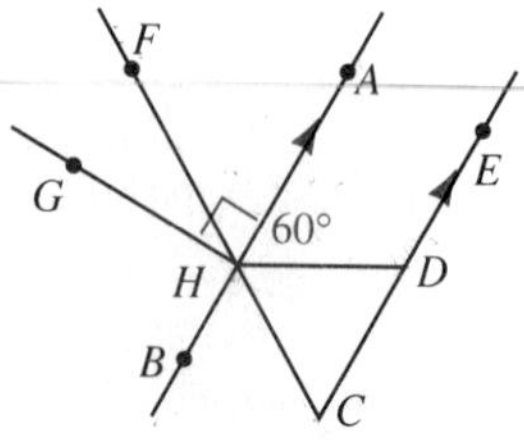

14. $\angle FHD$ **120**	**15.** $\angle AHG$ **90**	**16.** $\angle FHG$ **30**
17. $\angle GHB$ **90**	**18.** $\angle BHC$ **60**	**19.** $\angle DHC$ **60**
20. $\angle HDE$ **120**	**21.** $\angle HDC$ **60**	**22.** $\angle HCD$ **60**

Tell whether each statement is true or false. Then write the converse and tell whether it is true or false.

23. If two lines do not intersect, then they are parallel. **False; converse true**

24. If two lines intersect to form right angles, then the lines are perpendicular. **True; converse true**

25. An angle is acute only if it is not obtuse. **True; converse false**

26. A triangle is isosceles if it is equilateral. **True; converse false**

Name or state the postulate, definition, or theorem that justifies each statement about the diagram.

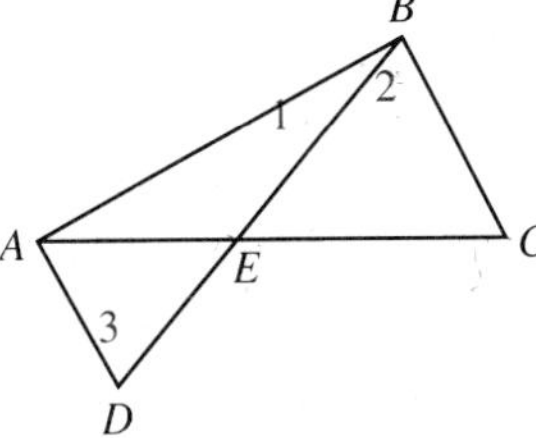

27. $\angle AED \cong \angle BEC$ **Thm. 2-3**

28. $AE + EC = AC$ **Segment Add. Post.**

29. $m\angle 1 + m\angle 2 = m\angle ABC$ **Angle Add. Post.**

30. If $\angle 2 \cong \angle 3$, then $\overline{AD} \parallel \overline{BC}$. **Thm. 3-5**

31. $m\angle AEB = m\angle 2 + m\angle C$ **Thm. 3-12**

32. If $\overline{DA} \perp \overline{AB}$, then $m\angle DAB = 90$. **Def. of ⊥ lines**

33. $m\angle 1 + m\angle 3 + m\angle DAB = 180$ **Thm. 3-11**

34. If $\angle ABC$ is a right angle, then $\overline{AB} \perp \overline{BC}$. **Def. of ⊥ lines**

Complete.

35. The endpoint of $\overrightarrow{XY}$ is point __?__. **X**

36. If the sum of the measures of two angles is 180, then the angles are __?__. **supplementary**

37. If the measure of each interior angle of a regular polygon is 108, then the polygon is a(n) __?__. **pentagon**

38. If M is the midpoint of $\overline{AB}$ and $AM = 12$, then $AB =$ __?__. **24**

39. If two parallel lines are cut by a transversal, then alternate interior angles are __?__. **congruent**

40. The process of forming a conclusion based on past observations or patterns is called __?__ reasoning. **inductive**

41. When a statement and its converse are both true, they can be combined into one statement called a __?__. **biconditional**

42. In a decagon the sum of the measures of the exterior angles is __?__. **360**

43. In an octagon the sum of the measures of the interior angles is __?__. **1080**

44. Every triangle has at least two __?__ angles. **acute**

Write a two column proof.

B **45.** Given: $\overline{WX} \perp \overline{XY}$;
$\angle 1$ is comp. to $\angle 3$.
Prove: $\angle 2 \cong \angle 3$

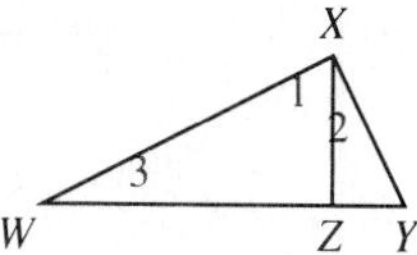

46. Given: $\overline{RU} \parallel \overline{ST}$; $\angle R \cong \angle T$
Prove: $\overline{RS} \parallel \overline{UT}$

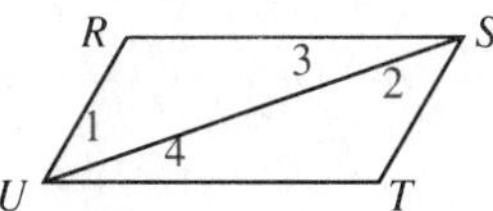

4 Congruent Triangles

Objectives

4-1 Identify corresponding parts of congruent figures.

4-2 Prove two triangles congruent by using the SSS, the SAS, and the ASA Postulates.

4-3 Deduce information about segments and angles after proving that two triangles are congruent.

4-4 Apply the theorems and corollaries about isosceles triangles.

4-5 Use the AAS Theorem to prove two triangles congruent. Use the HL Theorem to prove two right triangles congruent. Prove that two overlapping triangles are congruent.

4-6 Prove two triangles congruent by first proving two other triangles congruent.

4-7 Apply the definitions of the median and the altitude of a triangle and the perpendicular bisector of a segment. State and apply the theorem about a point on the perpendicular bisector of a segment, and the converse. State and apply the theorem about a point on the bisector of an angle, and the converse.

Assignment Guide

See page T40 for information about the Assignment Guide.

Day	Minimum Course	Average Course	Maximum Course
1	**4-1** 120/1–10	**4-1** 120/1–13	**4-1** 120–121/1–19 odd, 20–23
2	**4-1** 120/11–15, 18, 19 121/Mixed Review 1, 2	**4-1** 120–121/14–22 121/Mixed Review 1, 2	**4-2** 124–126/1–17 odd
3	**4-2** 124–125/1–16	**4-2** 124–125/1–15 odd, 16 **S** 121/23, 24	**4-2** 126–127/18–26 even **S** 121/24
4	**4-2** 126/17–19	**4-2** 126/17–23 odd	**4-3** 130–131/2, 5, 9, 10, 12 **S** 126–127/23, 25, 27
5	**4-3** 130/1–4	**4-3** 130–131/1–3, 6	**4-3** 131–132/7, 11, 13–15
6	**4-3** 131/5–8	**4-3** 131/7, 8, 10, 12	**4-4** 137–138/3, 4, 6, 9, 12, 14, 15, 17, 22 **S** 132/16
7	**4-3** 131–132/9, 11, 13 132–133/Self-Test 1	**4-3** 132/13, 14 132–133/Self-Test 1	**4-4** 138–139/16, 19, 21, 24, 25, 27, 31
8	**4-4** 137/1–8	**4-4** 137/1–9 odd, 10, 12	**4-5** 144/3–9, 13 **S** 139/33–34
9	**4-4** 137–138/9, 11, 13–15	**4-4** 137–139/13, 14, 17, 18–21, 25, 27	**4-5** 144–145/10–22 even
10	**4-4** 138/17, 18, 21	**4-5** 143–144/1, 3, 5, 8, 10 **S** 139/29, 31	**4-6** 149/3–8 **S** 145/19, 21
11	**4-5** 143–144/1–4	**4-5** 144–145/11, 13, 15, 16, 18, 19, 21; 146/Self-Test 2	**4-6** 150–151/9–16
12	**4-5** 144/5–7, 9–12	**4-6** 148–150/1, 3, 5, 6, 8, 10	**4-7** 156/6–13, 15, 19, 23, 25
13	**4-5** 144–145/13, 15, 16 146/Self-Test 2	**4-6** 150–151/12–16 151/Mixed Review 1–11	**4-7** 158/26–28 162–163/Chapter Test Test, page T15

14	**4-6** 148–149/1–5	**4-7** 156–157/1–14, 18	
15	**4-6** 149–150/6–9, 11, 12 **S** 145/14 151/Mixed Review 1–11	**4-7** 159/Self-Test 3 162/Chapter Test, 1–18 Test, page T15	
16	**4-7** 156/1–9		
17	**4-7** 156/10–14		
18	**4-7** 159/Self-Test 3 162/Chapter Test, 1–17 odd Test, page T15		

Supplementary Materials Guide

For Use after Lesson	Practice Masters	Tests	Study Guide (Reteaching)	Resource Book			Computer Activities
				Tests	Practice Exercises	College Entrance (Col) Enrichment (E)	
4-1			pp. 39–40				
4-2	Sheet 17		pp. 41–42				Activity 9
4-3	Sheet 18	Test 14	pp. 43–46	p. 19	p. 122		
4-4			pp. 47–50				
4-5	Sheet 19	Test 15	pp. 51–54	p. 20	p. 123		Activity 10
4-6	Sheet 20		pp. 55–56				
4-7	Sheet 21	Test 16	pp. 57–58	p. 21	p. 124		
Chapter 4	Sheet 22	Test 17		pp. 22–23	p. 125	p. 193 (Col); p. 210 (E)	
Chapters 3–4	Sheets 23, 24						

Overhead Visuals

Guided Discovery Visuals (lettered) and Teaching Visuals (numbered) available for Chapter 4.

Lessons	Visual	Title
4-3	A	Lines and Planes in Space
4-3	D	Segments and Angles in Space Figures
4-3	F	Diagonals of Prisms
4-1, 4-2, 4-3	7	A Way to Prove Two Segments or Two Angles Congruent
4-4, 4-5	8	Summary of Ways to Prove Triangles Congruent
4-6, 4-7	9	Equidistant Points Using Perpendicular Bisectors

Software Guide

Houghton Mifflin software for Chapter 4

Geometry Grapher (Apple or IBM)
Use With pp. 134, 158 (Explorations)

Test Generator (Apple or IBM): 105 test items

Other software appropriate for Chapter 4

Geometric Supposer (Apple): Triangles

GeoDraw (IBM)

Guide to Integrated Curriculum

Teachers wishing to integrate coordinate and transformational geometry throughout the course can use the following lessons after Chapter 4. See pages T56–T57 and 657 for more information.

Handbook: Reflection and Symmetry, pp. 659–660
13-1 Cl. Ex. 1–10; Wr. Ex. 1–16, 27, 30, 33, 43, 44
13-2 Cl. Ex. 1–6; Wr. Ex. 1–27, 32, 34
13-3 Cl. Ex. 1–10; Wr. Ex. 1, 2, 7–10, 21, 22
13-4 Cl. Ex. 1, 2, 4, 6–8; Wr. Ex. 1–25, 27–32, 34
13-5 Cl. Ex. 1–10; Wr. Ex. 1–14, 16, 17, 20, 22–24
13-6 Cl. Ex. 1–13; Wr. Ex. 1–33
13-7 Cl. Ex. 1–13; Wr. Ex. 1–33, 36–37c, 38, 39

Guide to Distribution of Constructions

The text teaches constructions in Chapter 10. Teachers wishing to distribute work with constructions throughout the first nine chapters can use this guide.

Introduce after	Constructions	Pages
Lesson 4-2	2, 3, 7	376, 382
Lesson 4-7	10, 11	393, 393

Exploring Congruent Triangles

When to Use

Before Lesson 4-2

Overview

This activity motivates the SSS, SAS, ASA, and AAS Postulates. It is related to Written Exercise 22 on page 121.

Materials

Cardboard, scissors, paper bag, protractor, ruler

Description of Activity

Make a cardboard triangle and measure its angles and sides. Label the vertices A, B, C and its sides a, b, c, as shown below.

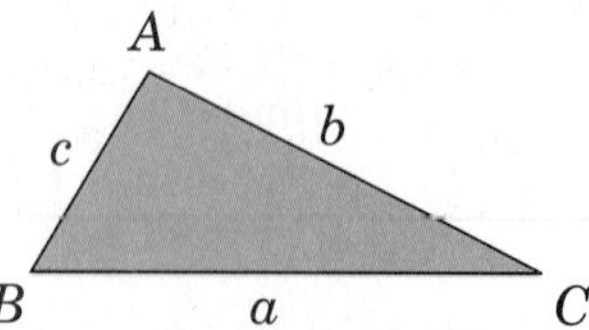

1. Place the triangle in a paper bag. Challenge students to make a copy of the triangle (a congruent triangle) by asking you for as few measurements of the triangle as possible. For example, the students could ask for a, b, and $\angle C$. Encourage students to find more than one set of measurements that will allow them to make a copy of the triangle. Also ask them to find one set of measurements that will allow them to make several different triangles, including the one in the paper bag.
2. Discuss the following questions with students.
   a. Were you able to make a copy of the triangle knowing only two sides? two angles? one side and one angle?
   b. Were you able to make a copy of the triangle knowing all three sides? all three angles?
   c. Could you make a copy knowing one angle and the side opposite that angle? What other information do you need?
   d. For cases in which four measurements seem to be necessary, are all four required? Which measurement may not be needed? Is that the only one?

Commentary

1. This activity is ideal for use in small groups. Compare solutions found by each group. In most cases, students will find SSS first, followed by versions of SAS. Lead a discussion that guides students to realizing that with each triangle there are three examples of the same general case for SAS and ASA.

2. Students should discover that two measurements are not sufficient. Some may think that only two angles are needed (the third is implied). Guide them to understanding that while this may give a copy, it may also produce a similar triangle; thus, AA and AAA do not guarantee congruence. You might further demonstrate this by using two of the original angle measurements to construct various similar triangles.

2. c. Some students may notice that an angle, its opposite side, and another angle give a congruent copy. This is the AAS Theorem presented in Lesson 4-5.

2. d. Encourage students to answer these questions in relation to the rules they have just "discovered" (SSS, SAS, ASA, and AAS Postulates). If four measurements are given, one can be discarded, but the three that remain must satisfy the conditions of one of the postulates that guarantee congruence.

Variations and Extensions

- You can use this activity throughout the course by adding new measurements such as median, angle bisector, altitude, perimeter, and area. Side-Side-Perimeter, Side-Median-Side, Angle-Side-Area, and Altitude-Bisector-Median may be discovered.
- You can use an activity similar to this for quadrilaterals. Have students discover congruence conditions such as SASAS, ASASA, SSSSA, etc.
- You can use the idea of having students ask questions to guess the contents of a bag in many ways. One way is to restrict the number of questions that can be asked, and/or restrict the questions to those that can be answered "Yes" or "No." Adopt rules to discourage the question "Is it a __?" The "object" in the bag can be something like a postulate or a theorem rather than a real object.

References to Strategies

PE: Pupil's Edition **TE:** Teacher's Edition **RB:** Resource Book

Problem Solving Strategies

PE: 121 (Use a model), 147 (Strategies for proof, reason backward), 157 (Ex. 19, Mathematical model)

TE: T89, T91, 128 (Reason backward), 129 (Plan a proof), 143 (Find a counterexample)

Applications

PE: 116 (Quiltmaking), 132 (Ex. 16, Estimating distance), 133 (Bracing with triangles), 157 (Ex. 19, City planning)

TE: T88, T89

Nonroutine Problems

PE: 119 (Exs. 17–20), 120 (Exs. 12–19), 121 (Exs. 22, 24, Challenge), 124 (Ex. 11), 130 (Ex. 2), 131 (Exs. 9–12), 132 (Exs. 15, 16), 137 (Exs. 9, 10), 138 (Exs. 15, 16), 139 (Exs. 26, 30–32, 34, Challenge), 143 (Ex. 2), 144 (Exs. 9, 10), 151 (Ex. 17), 156 (Exs. 1–6), 157 (Ex. 19), 659–660 (Exs. 1–9)

TE: T88, T89, T90, T92

RB: 210

Communication

PE: 132 (Ex. 15, Convincing argument), 147 (Key steps of proof, paragraph proof)

TE: T91, 118, 122, 124, 144, 153, 154, 157

Thinking Skills

TE: 118 (Limits of diagrams), 126 (Translate words into diagrams), 131 (Recognize unnecessary givens), 132, 153 (Compose new definitions)

Explorations

PE: 134, 158

TE: 115c

Connections

PE: 120 (Graphing), 150 (Euclid), 163 (Quadratic equations), 659–660 (Transformational geometry)

TE: T88, T91, 120 (Coordinate geometry), 121 (Equivalence relations), 153 (Reference to Ch. 10)

Using Technology

PE: 134, 158

TE: T88, T89, T90, T92, 121, 126, 134, 138, 139, 144, 150, 155, 158, 163

RB: 240–241

Computer Activities: 20–24

Using Manipulatives/Models

PE: 121 (Challenge), 135, 156 (Exs. 5, 6), 157 (Ex. 19), 659–660

TE: 141

RB: 210

Overhead Visuals: A, D, F, 7, 8, 9

Cooperative Learning

TE: T88, T89, 144

Teaching Resources

For use in implementing the teaching strategies referenced on the previous page.

Problem Solving
Resource Book, p. 205

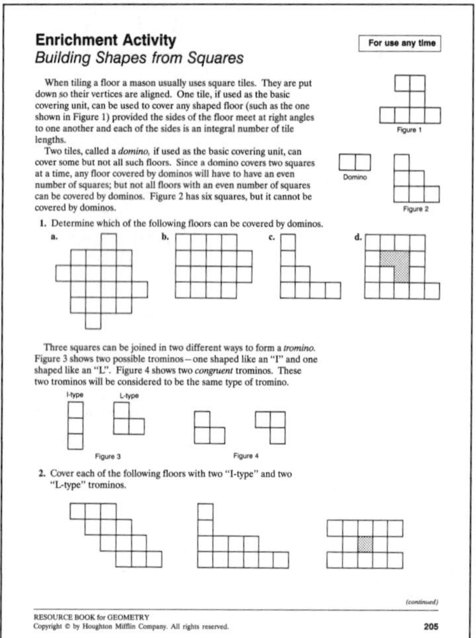

Enrichment Activity
Building Shapes from Squares

For use any time

When tiling a floor a mason usually uses square tiles. They are put down so their vertices are aligned. One tile, if used as the basic covering unit, can be used to cover any shaped floor (such as the one shown in Figure 1) provided the sides of the floor meet at right angles to one another and each of the sides is an integral number of tile lengths.

Figure 1

Two tiles, called a *domino,* if used as the basic covering unit, can cover some but not all such floors. Since a domino covers two squares at a time, any floor covered by dominos will have to have an even number of squares; but not all floors with an even number of squares can be covered by dominos. Figure 2 has six squares, but it cannot be covered by dominos.

Domino

Figure 2

1. Determine which of the following floors can be covered by dominos.
   a. b. c. d.

Three squares can be joined in two different ways to form a *tromino.* Figure 3 shows two possible trominos—one shaped like an "I" and one shaped like an "L". Figure 4 shows two *congruent* trominos. These two trominos will be considered to be the same type of tromino.

I-type L-type

Figure 3 Figure 4

2. Cover each of the following floors with two "I-type" and two "L-type" trominos.

(continued)

RESOURCE BOOK for GEOMETRY

205

Problem Solving
Resource Book, p. 206

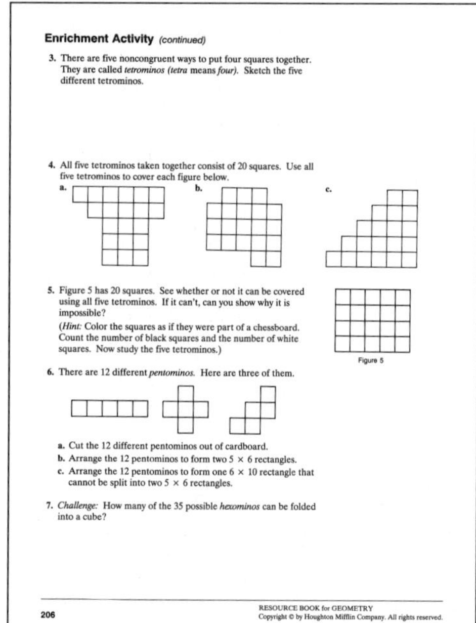

Enrichment Activity *(continued)*

3. There are five noncongruent ways to put four squares together. They are called *tetrominos (tetra* means *four).* Sketch the five different tetrominos.
4. All five tetrominos taken together consist of 20 squares. Use all five tetrominos to cover each figure below.
   a. b. c.
5. Figure 5 has 20 squares. See whether or not it can be covered using all five tetrominos. If it can't, can you show why it is impossible?
   (*Hint:* Color the squares as if they were part of a chessboard. Count the number of black squares and the number of white squares. Now study the five tetrominos.)

   Figure 5
6. There are 12 different *pentominos.* Here are three of them.
   a. Cut the 12 different pentominos out of cardboard.
   b. Arrange the 12 pentominos to form two 5 × 6 rectangles.
   c. Arrange the 12 pentominos to form one 6 × 10 rectangle that cannot be split into two 5 × 6 rectangles.
7. *Challenge:* How many of the 35 possible *hexominos* can be folded into a cube?

206
RESOURCE BOOK for GEOMETRY

Using Manipulatives
Resource Book, p. 210

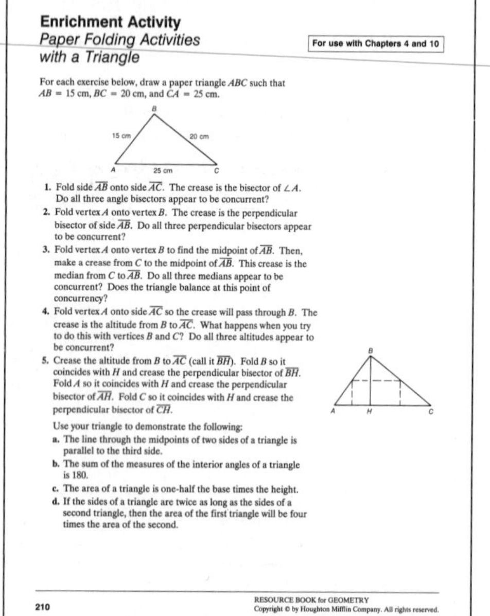

Enrichment Activity
Paper Folding Activities with a Triangle

For use with Chapters 4 and 10

For each exercise below, draw a paper triangle ABC such that $AB = 15$ cm, $BC = 20$ cm, and $CA = 25$ cm.

1. Fold side $\overline{AB}$ onto side $\overline{AC}$. The crease is the bisector of $\angle A$. Do all three angle bisectors appear to be concurrent?
2. Fold vertex A onto vertex B. The crease is the perpendicular bisector of side $\overline{AB}$. Do all three perpendicular bisectors appear to be concurrent?
3. Fold vertex A onto vertex B to find the midpoint of $\overline{AB}$. Then, make a crease from C to the midpoint of $\overline{AB}$. This crease is the median from C to $\overline{AB}$. Do all three medians appear to be concurrent? Does the triangle balance at this point of concurrency?
4. Fold vertex A onto side $\overline{AC}$ so the crease will pass through B. The crease is the altitude from B to $\overline{AC}$. What happens when you try to do this with vertices B and C? Do all three altitudes appear to be concurrent?
5. Crease the altitude from B to $\overline{AC}$ (call it $\overline{BH}$). Fold B so it coincides with H and crease the perpendicular bisector of $\overline{BH}$. Fold A so it coincides with H and crease the perpendicular bisector of $\overline{AH}$. Fold C so it coincides with H and crease the perpendicular bisector of $\overline{CH}$.

Use your triangle to demonstrate the following:
a. The line through the midpoints of two sides of a triangle is parallel to the third side.
b. The sum of the measures of the interior angles of a triangle is 180.
c. The area of a triangle is one-half the base times the height.
d. If the sides of a triangle are twice as long as the sides of a second triangle, then the area of the first triangle will be four times the area of the second.

210
RESOURCE BOOK for GEOMETRY

Communication
Study Guide, p. 57

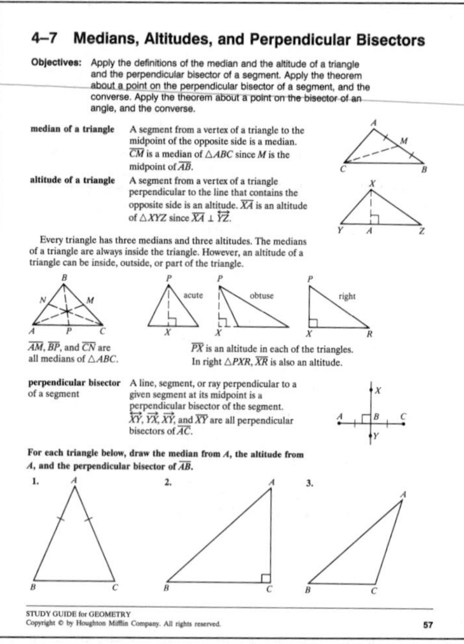

4–7 Medians, Altitudes, and Perpendicular Bisectors

Objectives: Apply the definitions of the median and the altitude of a triangle and the perpendicular bisector of a segment. Apply the theorem about a point on the perpendicular bisector of a segment, and the converse. Apply the theorem about a point on the bisector of an angle, and the converse.

median of a triangle A segment from a vertex of a triangle to the midpoint of the opposite side is a median. $\overline{CM}$ is a median of $\triangle ABC$ since M is the midpoint of $\overline{AB}$.

altitude of a triangle A segment from a vertex of a triangle perpendicular to the line that contains the opposite side is an altitude. $\overline{XA}$ is an altitude of $\triangle XYZ$ since $\overline{XA} \perp \overleftrightarrow{YZ}$.

Every triangle has three medians and three altitudes. The medians of a triangle are always inside the triangle. However, an altitude of a triangle can be inside, outside, or part of the triangle.

$\overline{AM}$, $\overline{BP}$, and $\overline{CN}$ are all medians of $\triangle ABC$.

$\overline{PX}$ is an altitude in each of the triangles. In right $\triangle PXR$, $\overline{XR}$ is also an altitude.

perpendicular bisector of a segment A line, segment, or ray perpendicular to a given segment at its midpoint is a perpendicular bisector of the segment. $\overleftrightarrow{XY}$, $\overrightarrow{YX}$, $\overrightarrow{XY}$, and $\overline{XY}$ are all perpendicular bisectors of $\overline{AC}$.

For each triangle below, draw the median from A, the altitude from A, and the perpendicular bisector of $\overline{AB}$.

1. 2. 3.

STUDY GUIDE for GEOMETRY

57

Thinking Skills
Teaching Visual 8

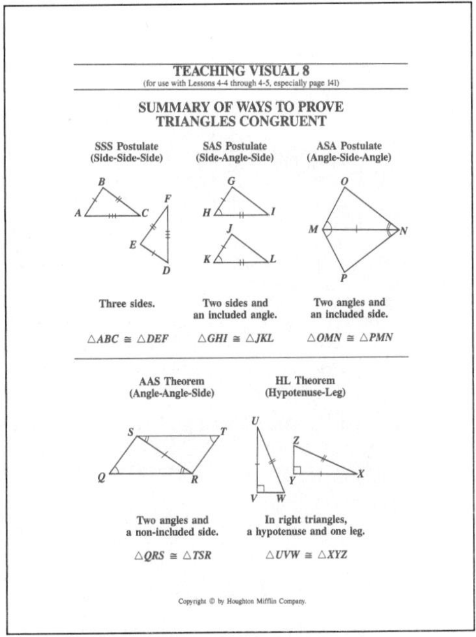

Using Models
Teaching Visual 9

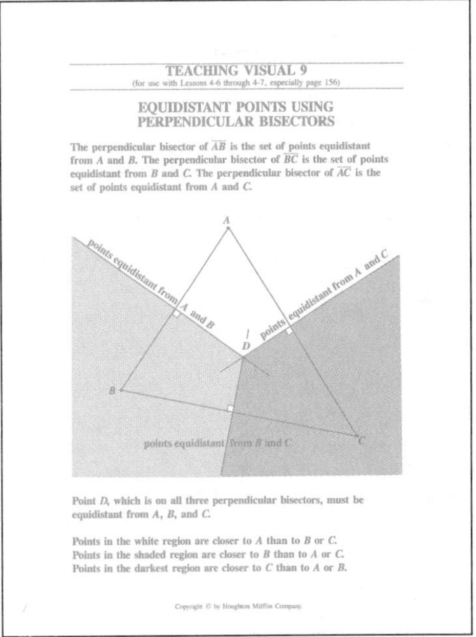

Using Models
Guided Discovery Visual D, Sheets 1 and 2

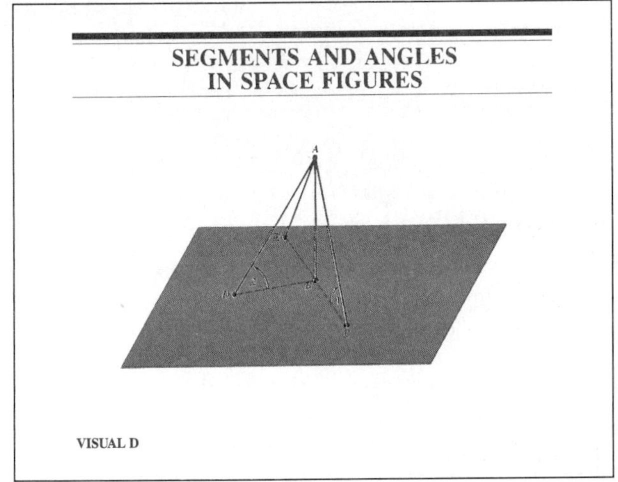

Using Models
Guided Discovery Visual F, Sheet 1

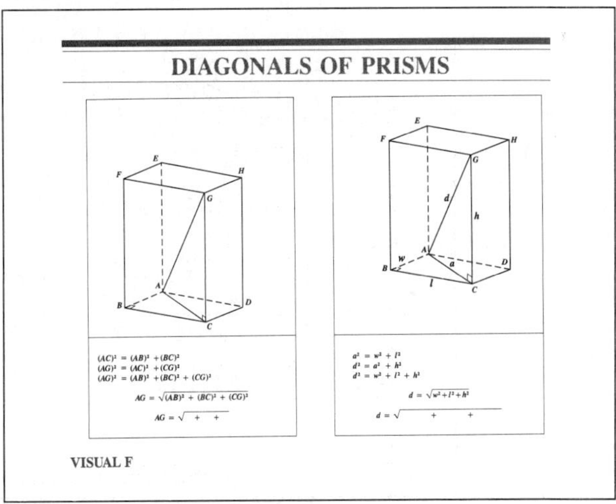

Teaching References

Lesson Commentary, pp. T87–T92

Assignment Guide, pp. T43–T44

Software Guide, p. T73

Alternate Test, p. T15

Supplementary Materials

Practice Masters 17–24

Tests 14–17

Resource Book
- Tests, pp. 19–23
- Practice, pp. 122–125
- Preparing for College Entrance Exams, p. 193
- Enrichment Activity, p. 210
- Computer Activity, pp. 240–241

Study Guide, pp. 39–58

Overhead Visuals A, D, F, 7–9

Computer Activities
- 9 Congruence Conditions on Triangles, Part 1
- 10 Part 2

Handbook for Integrating Coordinate and Transformational Geometry

Reflection and Symmetry, pp. 659–660

Cultural Note

Euclid made a distinction between common notions (or *axioms,* after the Greek word *axiōma,* meaning *worthy*) and postulates. For Euclid, a common notion was applicable to all sciences. A postulate (from the Latin verb *postulare,* meaning *to request*) was a truth applicable to geometry.

4 CONGRUENT TRIANGLES

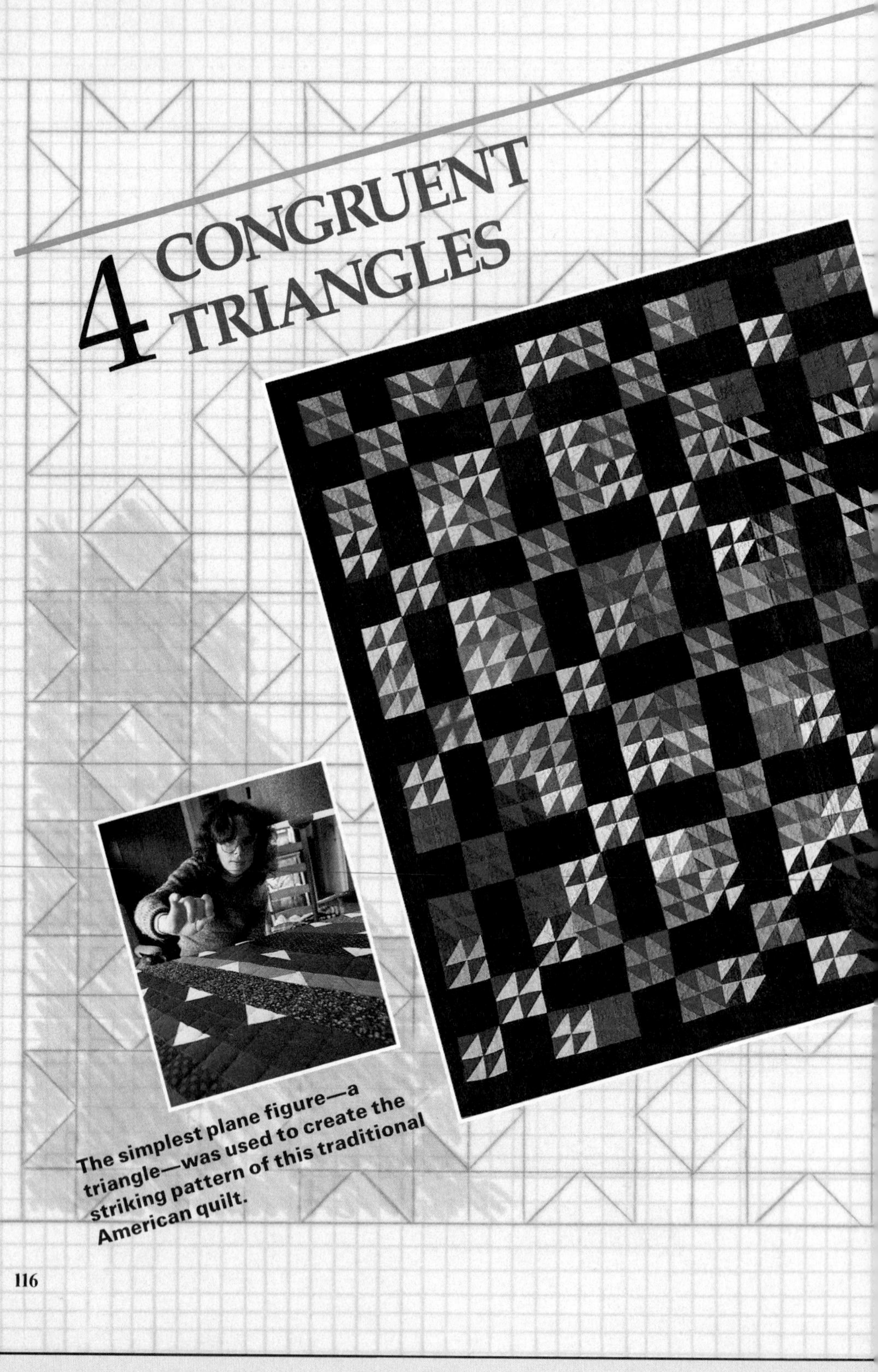

The simplest plane figure—a triangle—was used to create the striking pattern of this traditional American quilt.

Corresponding Parts in a Congruence

Objectives

1. Identify the corresponding parts of congruent figures.
2. Prove two triangles congruent by using the SSS Postulate, the SAS Postulate, and the ASA Postulate.
3. Deduce information about segments and angles after proving that two triangles are congruent.

4-1 *Congruent Figures*

The quilt on the facing page is made up of many triangles that are all the same size and shape. These triangles are arranged to form squares and rectangles of various sizes. The diagrams below feature the pattern in the quilt. In each diagram, how many triangles with the same size and shape do you see? How many squares? How many rectangles?

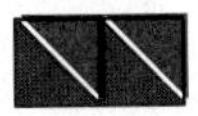
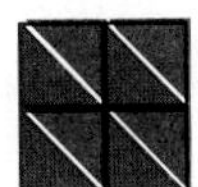
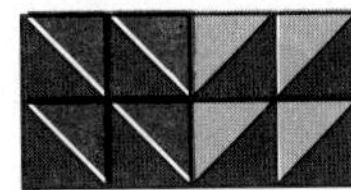

Whenever two figures have the same size and shape, they are called **congruent.** You are already familiar with congruent segments (segments that have equal lengths) and congruent angles (angles that have equal measures). In this chapter you will learn about congruent triangles.

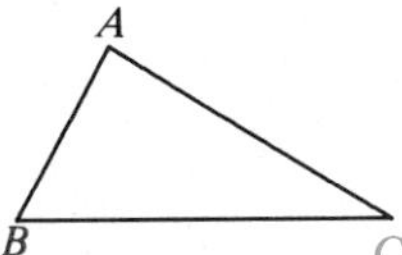

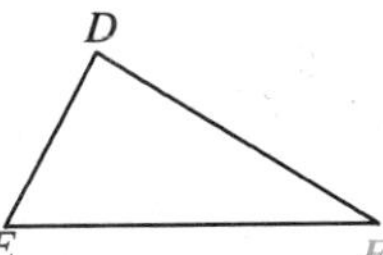

Triangles ABC and DEF are congruent. If you mentally slide $\triangle ABC$ to the right, you can fit it exactly over $\triangle DEF$ by matching up the vertices like this:

$A \longleftrightarrow D$ $\quad$ $B \longleftrightarrow E$ $\quad$ $C \longleftrightarrow F$

The sides and angles will then match up like this:

Corresponding angles	*Corresponding sides*
$\angle A \longleftrightarrow \angle D$	$\overline{AB} \longleftrightarrow \overline{DE}$
$\angle B \longleftrightarrow \angle E$	$\overline{BC} \longleftrightarrow \overline{EF}$
$\angle C \longleftrightarrow \angle F$	$\overline{AC} \longleftrightarrow \overline{DF}$

Teaching Suggestions, pp. T87–T88

Objective
Presenting the Lesson
Applications
Using Technology
Enrichment
Making Connections

Cooperative Learning, p. T88

Supplementary Materials

Study Guide, pp. 39–40

Lesson Focus

This lesson begins the study of congruent figures. The idea of figures, or objects, being congruent, that is, having the same size and shape, is important in geometry and in the world.

Suggested Assignments

Minimum
Day 1: 120/1–10
Day 2: 120/11–15, 18–19
121/Mixed Review 1, 2

Average
Day 1: 120/1–13
Day 2: 120–121/14–22
121/Mixed Review 1, 2

Maximum
120–121/1–19 odd, 20–23

Teaching Note

The illustration and the first sentence of the chapter will help students understand congruence. With the idea of *same size and shape,* a student knows when two rectangular solids can be called congruent.

Thinking Skills

Point out to students that if the diagram showed no marks on segments or angles, then the strongest statement that could be made is: The triangles look congruent. No assertion about congruence could be made in a proof.

Chalkboard Examples

Fill in the blank with *always*, *sometimes*, or *never*.

1. An acute triangle is never congruent to an obtuse triangle.
2. A polygon is always congruent to itself.
3. A right triangle is sometimes congruent to another right triangle.
4. If $\triangle ABC \cong \triangle XYZ$, $\angle A$ is sometimes congruent to $\angle Y$.
5. If $\triangle ABC \cong \triangle XYZ$, $\angle B$ is always congruent to $\angle Y$.
6. If $\triangle ABC \cong \triangle XYZ$, $\overline{AB}$ is sometimes congruent to $\overline{YZ}$.

Communication Skills

Make sure students understand the significance of the position of letters in a congruence statement. The statement $\triangle XYZ \cong \triangle ABC$ means that the letters X and A, which appear first, name corresponding vertices and that $\angle X \cong \angle A$. The letters Y and B come next, so $\angle Y \cong \angle B$ and $\overline{XY} \cong \overline{AB}$.

Do you see that the following statements are true?

(1) Since congruent triangles have the same shape, their corresponding angles are congruent.

(2) Since congruent triangles have the same size, their corresponding sides are congruent.

We have the following definition for *congruent triangles*.

Two triangles are **congruent** if and only if their vertices can be matched up so that the *corresponding parts* (angles and sides) of the triangles are congruent.

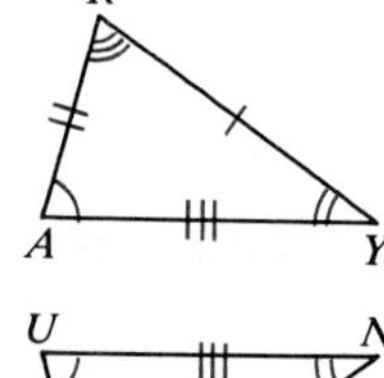

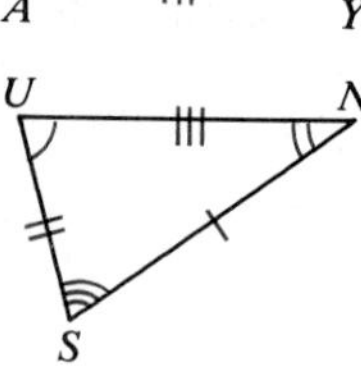

The congruent parts of the triangles shown are marked alike. Imagine sliding $\triangle SUN$ up until $\overline{UN}$ falls on $\overline{AY}$ and then flipping $\triangle SUN$ over so that point S falls on point R. The vertices are matched like this:

$$S \longleftrightarrow R \qquad U \longleftrightarrow A \qquad N \longleftrightarrow Y$$

$\triangle SUN$ fits over $\triangle RAY$. The corresponding parts are congruent, and the triangles are congruent.

When referring to congruent triangles, we name their corresponding vertices in the same order. For the triangles shown,

$\triangle SUN$ is congruent to $\triangle RAY$.
$\triangle SUN \cong \triangle RAY$

The following statements about these triangles are also correct, since corresponding vertices of the triangles are named in the same order.

$$\triangle NUS \cong \triangle YAR \qquad \triangle SNU \cong \triangle RYA$$

Suppose you are given that $\triangle XYZ \cong \triangle ABC$. From the definition of congruent triangles you know, for example, that

$$\overline{XY} \cong \overline{AB} \quad \text{and} \quad \angle X \cong \angle A.$$

When the definition of congruent triangles is used to justify either of these statements, the wording commonly used is

Corresponding parts of congruent triangles are congruent,

which is often written:

Corr. parts of $\cong$ $\triangle$s are $\cong$.

Two *polygons* are **congruent** if and only if their vertices can be matched up so that their corresponding parts are congruent. Just as for triangles, there are many ways to list the congruence between the two pentagons at the right so that corresponding vertices are written in the same order.

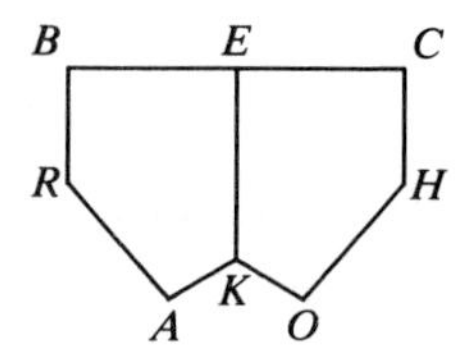

$BRAKE \cong CHOKE$

Notice that side $\overline{KE}$ of pentagon $BRAKE$ corresponds to side $\overline{KE}$ of pentagon $CHOKE$. $\overline{KE}$ is called a *common side* of the two pentagons.

Classroom Exercises

9. Yes; *O* is the midpt. of $\overline{AC}$ and of $\overline{DB}$ because *AO* = *OC* and *DO* = *OB*.

Suppose you know that $\triangle FIN \cong \triangle WEB$.

1. Name the three pairs of corresponding sides. **$\overline{FI}$, $\overline{WE}$; $\overline{IN}$, $\overline{EB}$; $\overline{FN}$, $\overline{WB}$**
2. Name the three pairs of corresponding angles. **$\angle F$, $\angle W$; $\angle I$, $\angle E$; $\angle N$, $\angle B$**
3. Is it correct to say $\triangle NIF \cong \triangle BEW$? **Yes**
4. Is it correct to say $\triangle INF \cong \triangle EWB$? **No**

10. If 2 lines are cut by a trans. and alt. int. $\angle$s are $\cong$, then the lines are $\parallel$.

The two triangles shown are congruent. Complete.

5. $\triangle ABO \cong$ __?__ **$\triangle CDO$**
6. $\angle A \cong$ __?__ **$\angle C$**
7. $\overline{AO} \cong$ __?__ **$\overline{CO}$**
8. $BO =$ __?__ **DO**
9. Can you deduce that *O* is the midpoint of any segment? Explain. **See above.**

10. Explain how you can deduce that $\overline{DC} \parallel \overline{AB}$. **See above.**

Exs. 5-11

11. Suppose you know that $\overline{DB} \perp \overline{DC}$. Explain how you can deduce that $\overline{DB} \perp \overline{BA}$. **If $\overline{DB} \perp \overline{DC}$, then $m\angle D = 90$. But $m\angle D = m\angle B$, so $m\angle B = 90$. Therefore, $\overline{DB} \perp \overline{BA}$.**

The pentagons shown are congruent. Complete.

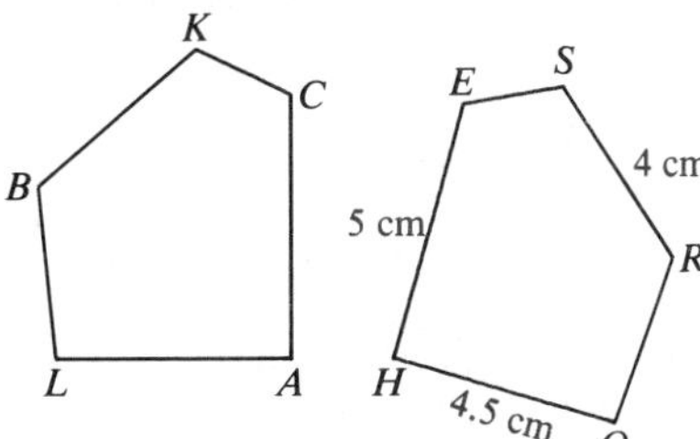

12. *B* corresponds to __?__. **R**
13. $BLACK \cong$ __?__ **ROHES**
14. __?__ $= m\angle E$ **$m\angle C$**
15. $KB =$ __?__ cm **4**
16. If $\overline{CA} \perp \overline{LA}$, name two right angles in the figures. **$\angle A$, $\angle H$**

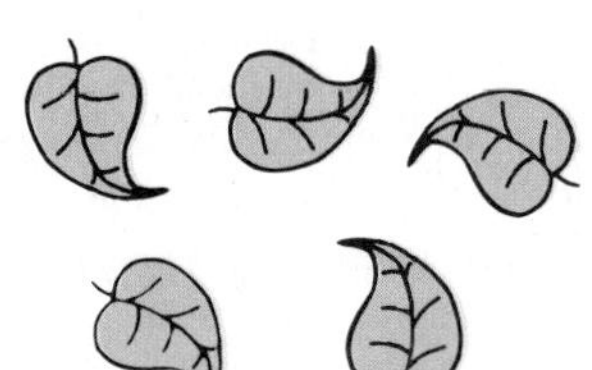

17. The five leaves shown are all congruent, but one differs from the others. Which one is different and how?
The leaf in the lower left-hand corner is flipped over.

A(1, 2), B(4, 2), C(2, 4)

18. **a.** Name the coordinates of points *A*, *B*, and *C*.
    b. Name the coordinates of a point *D* such that $\triangle ABC \cong \triangle ABD$. **D(2, 0)**
19. Name the coordinates of a point *G* such that $\triangle ABC \cong \triangle EFG$. Is there another location for *G* such that $\triangle ABC \cong \triangle EFG$? **G(6, 5) or G(6, 1)**
20. Name the coordinates of two possible points *H* such that $\triangle ABC \cong \triangle FEH$. **H(7, 5) or H(7, 1)**

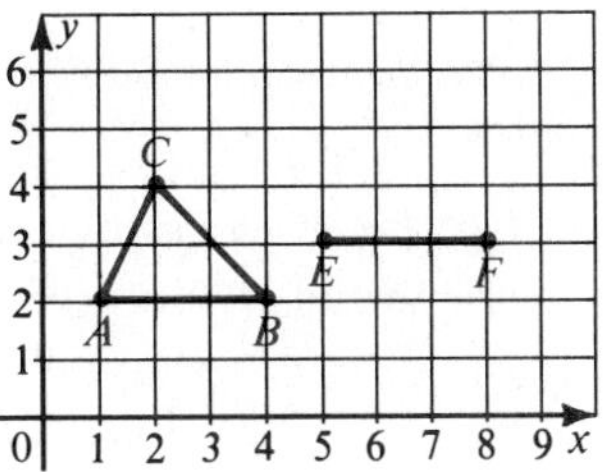

Teaching Note

Draw two congruent segments $\overline{TP}$ and $\overline{SF}$ and write $\triangle TIP \cong \triangle$ __U__ on the chalkboard. Tell students you will hold a finger at a point of $\triangle TIP$ and state a congruence, using either *SUF* or *FUS*. Call on students to show two possible positions for point *U*, using both hands. Then position your finger and say, "$\triangle TIP \cong \triangle SUF$." Repeat the activity using other positions. Sometimes you should use *SUF*, and other times use *FUS*.

Exercise Note

For Exs. 5–11, students will see that the following matching is the one to use.

$A \leftrightarrow C \quad B \leftrightarrow D \quad O \leftrightarrow O$

It may help to write this matching on the chalkboard and to call attention to the fact that a point can correspond to itself.

Guided Practice

Suppose $\triangle TIM \cong \triangle BER$. Complete.

1. $\overline{IM} \cong$ $\overline{ER}$
2. $\angle M \cong \angle R$
3. $\triangle MTI \cong \triangle$ RBE
4. If $\triangle ABC \cong \triangle XYZ$, $m\angle B = 80$, and $m\angle C = 50$, name four congruent angles.
   $\angle A$, $\angle C$, $\angle X$, and $\angle Z$
5. What definition underlies the statement: "Corresponding parts of congruent triangles are congruent"? Def. of $\cong$ ⚠s
6. Write six congruences that must be correct when $\triangle ABC \cong \triangle DEF$.
   $\overline{AB} \cong \overline{DE}$, $\overline{BC} \cong \overline{EF}$, $\overline{AC} \cong \overline{DF}$, $\angle A \cong \angle D$, $\angle B \cong \angle E$, $\angle C \cong \angle F$
7. The two triangles shown are congruent. Complete.

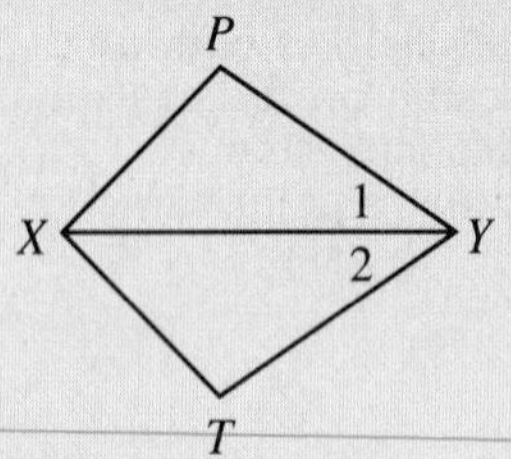

a. $\triangle PXY \cong \triangle$ TXY
b. $\angle P \cong$ $\angle T$ because Corr. parts of $\cong$ ⚠s are $\cong$.
c. $\overline{XP} \cong$ $\overline{XT}$ because Corr. parts of $\cong$ ⚠s are $\cong$.
d. $\angle 1 \cong \angle 2$ because Corr. parts of $\cong$ ⚠s are $\cong$.
e. Then $\overline{YX}$ bisects $\angle PYT$ because Def. of $\angle$ bisector.

Making Connections

Exs. 12–19 not only help to develop an understanding of congruence, but they also provide meaningful practice in plotting points.

Written Exercises

Note: CPCT is used below for "corr. parts of $\cong$ ⚠ are $\cong$."

Suppose $\triangle BIG \cong \triangle CAT$. Complete.

A

1. $\angle G \cong$ _?_ $\angle T$
2. _?_ $= m\angle A$ $m\angle I$
3. $BI =$ _?_ CA
4. _?_ $\cong \overline{AT}$ $\overline{IG}$
5. $\triangle IGB \cong$ _?_ $\triangle ATC$
6. _?_ $\cong \triangle CTA$ $\triangle BGI$
7. If $\triangle DEF \cong \triangle RST$, $m\angle D = 100$, and $m\angle F = 40$, name four congruent angles. $\angle E$, $\angle F$, $\angle S$, $\angle T$
8. Is the statement "Corresponding parts of congruent triangles are congruent" based on a definition, postulate, or theorem? **Def. (of $\cong$ ⚠)**
9. Suppose $\triangle LXR \cong \triangle FNE$. List six congruences that can be justified by the following reason: Corr. parts of $\cong$ ⚠ are $\cong$. $\angle L \cong \angle F$, $\angle X \cong \angle N$, $\angle R \cong \angle E$, $\overline{LX} \cong \overline{FN}$, $\overline{XR} \cong \overline{NE}$, $\overline{LR} \cong \overline{FE}$
10. The two triangles shown are congruent. Complete.

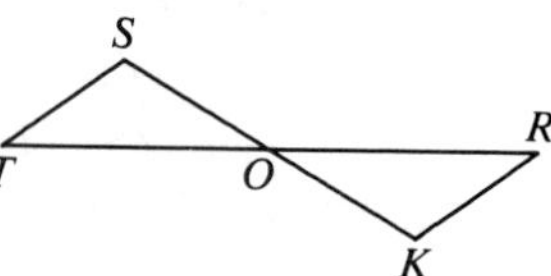

a. $\triangle STO \cong$ _?_ $\triangle KRO$
b. $\angle S \cong$ _?_ because _?_. $\angle K$, CPCT
c. $\overline{SO} \cong$ _?_ because _?_. $\overline{KO}$, CPCT
   Then point O is the midpoint of _?_. $\overline{SK}$
d. $\angle T \cong$ _?_ because _?_. $\angle R$, CPCT
   Then $\overline{ST} \parallel \overline{RK}$ because _?_. alt. int. ⚠ are $\cong$

11. The two triangles shown are congruent. Complete.

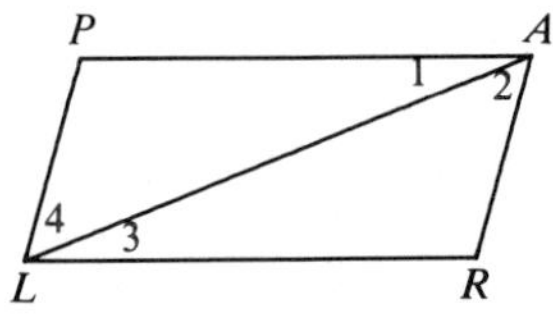

a. $\triangle PAL \cong$ _?_ $\triangle RLA$
b. $\overline{PA} \cong$ _?_ $\overline{RL}$
c. $\angle 1 \cong$ _?_ because _?_. $\angle 3$, CPCT
   Then $\overline{PA} \parallel$ _?_ because _?_. $\overline{LR}$, alt. int. ⚠ are $\cong$
d. $\angle 2 \cong$ _?_ because _?_. $\angle 4$, CPCT
   Then _?_ $\parallel$ _?_ because _?_.
   $\overline{PL}$, $\overline{AR}$; alt. int. ⚠ are $\cong$

Plot the given points on graph paper. Draw $\triangle FAT$. Locate point C so that $\triangle FAT \cong \triangle CAT$.

12. $F(1, 2)$ $A(4, 7)$ $T(4, 2)$ $C(7, 2)$
13. $F(7, 5)$ $A(-2, 2)$ $T(5, 2)$ $C(7, -1)$

Plot the given points on graph paper. Draw $\triangle ABC$ and $\triangle DEF$. Copy and complete the statement $\triangle ABC \cong$ _?_. 14. $\triangle ABC \cong \triangle FDE$

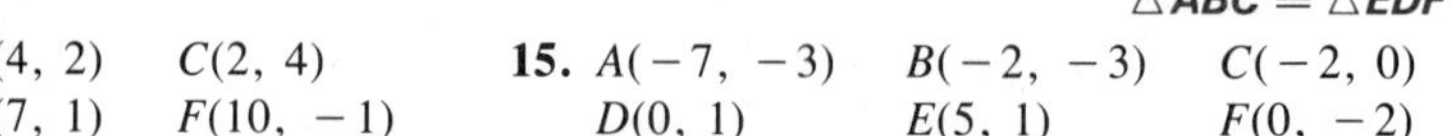

B

14. $A(-1, 2)$ $B(4, 2)$ $C(2, 4)$
    $D(5, -1)$ $E(7, 1)$ $F(10, -1)$
15. $A(-7, -3)$ $B(-2, -3)$ $C(-2, 0)$
    $D(0, 1)$ $E(5, 1)$ $F(0, -2)$
    $\triangle ABC \cong \triangle EDF$
16. $A(-3, 1)$ $B(2, 1)$ $C(2, 3)$
    $D(4, 3)$ $E(6, 3)$ $F(6, 8)$
    $\triangle ABC \cong \triangle FED$
17. $A(1, 1)$ $B(8, 1)$ $C(4, 3)$
    $D(3, -7)$ $E(5, -3)$ $F(3, 0)$
    $\triangle ABC \cong \triangle FDE$

Plot the given points on graph paper. Draw $\triangle ABC$ and $\overline{DE}$. Find two locations of point F such that $\triangle ABC \cong \triangle DEF$.

18. $A(1, 2)$ $B(4, 2)$ $C(2, 4)$ $D(6, 4)$ $E(6, 7)$ $F(4, 5)$, $F(8, 5)$
19. $A(-1, 0)$ $B(-5, 4)$ $C(-6, 1)$ $D(1, 0)$ $E(5, 4)$ $F(2, 5)$, $F(6, 1)$

$\overline{OR}$ is a common side of two congruent quadrilaterals.

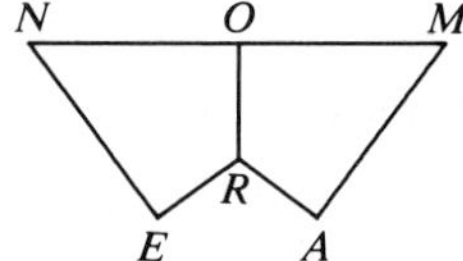

Exs. 20, 21

20. Complete: quad. $NERO \cong$ quad. __?__ **MARO**

21. In your own words explain why each of the following statements must be true.

a. O is the midpoint of $\overline{NM}$. **See below.**

b. $\angle NOR \cong \angle MOR$ **They are corr. ∠s of ≅ quads.**

c. $\overline{RO} \perp \overline{NM}$ **If 2 lines form ≅ adj. ∠s, then the lines are ⊥.**

22. Accurately draw each triangle described. Predict whether your triangle will be congruent to your classmates'.

a. In $\triangle RST$, $RS = 4$ cm, $m\angle S = 45$, and $ST = 6$ cm. **Yes**

b. In $\triangle UVW$, $m\angle U = 30$, $UV = 5$ cm, and $m\angle V = 100$. **Yes**

c. In $\triangle DEF$, $m\angle D = 30$, $m\angle E = 68$, and $m\angle F = 82$. **No**

d. In $\triangle XYZ$, $XY = 3$ cm, $YZ = 5$ cm, and $XZ = 6$ cm. (Try for a reasonably accurate drawing. You may find it helpful to cut a thin strip of paper for each side, then form the triangle.) **Yes**

23. Does congruence of triangles have the reflexive property? the symmetric property? the transitive property? **Yes; yes; yes**

C **24.** Suppose you are given a scalene triangle and a point P on some line l. How many triangles are there with one vertex at P, another vertex on l, and each triangle congruent to the given triangle? **24**

21. a. Since $NERO \cong MARO$, $\overline{NO} \cong \overline{OM}$. By the def. of midpt., O is the midpoint of $\overline{NM}$.

Challenge

Twelve toothpicks are arranged as shown to form a regular hexagon.

a. Copy the figure and show how six more toothpicks of the same size could be used to divide it into three congruent regions.

b. Keeping two of the toothpicks from part (a) in the same place and moving four, use the six toothpicks to divide the figure into two congruent regions.

Mixed Review Exercises

Write proofs in two-column form.

1. Given: $\overline{AD} \perp \overline{BC}$; $\overline{BA} \perp \overline{AC}$
Prove: $\angle 1 \cong \angle 2$

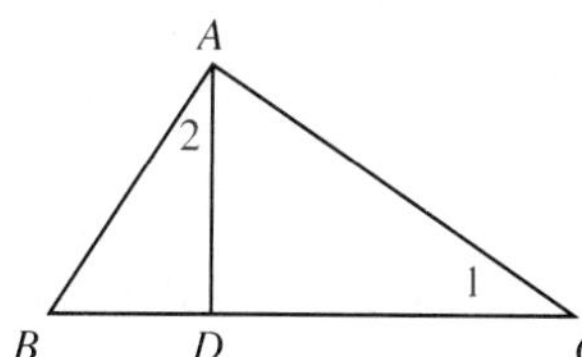

2. Given: $\overline{FC}$ and $\overline{SH}$ bisect each other at A; $FC = SH$
Prove: $SA = AC$

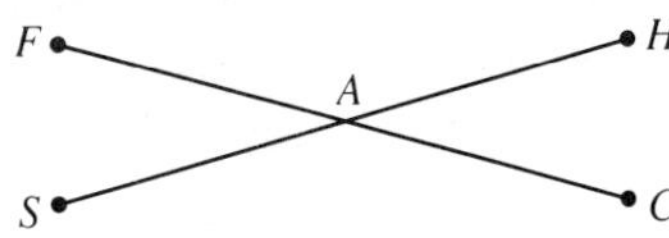

Making Connections

Students who do Ex. 23 can be told that a relation that has all three properties is called an *equivalence relation.*

Using a Computer

See page T88 for an Experiment involving congruent triangles constructed by reflection.

4-2 *Some Ways to Prove Triangles Congruent*

If two triangles are congruent, the six parts of one triangle are congruent to the six corresponding parts of the other triangle. If you are not sure whether two triangles are congruent, however, it is not necessary to compare all six parts. As you saw in Written Exercise 22 of the preceding section, sometimes three pairs of congruent corresponding parts will guarantee that two triangles are congruent. The following postulates give you three ways to show that two triangles are congruent by comparing only three pairs of corresponding parts.

Postulate 12 *SSS Postulate*

If three sides of one triangle are congruent to three sides of another triangle, then the triangles are congruent.

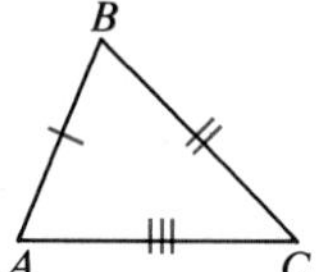

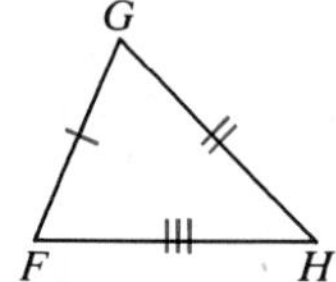

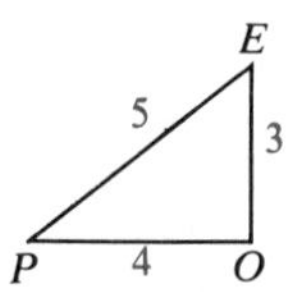

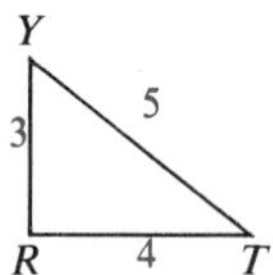

By the SSS Postulate, $\triangle ABC \cong \triangle FGH$ and $\triangle POE \cong \triangle TRY$.

Sometimes it is helpful to describe the parts of a triangle in terms of their relative positions.

$\overline{AB}$ is *opposite* $\angle C$.

$\overline{AB}$ is *included* between $\angle A$ and $\angle B$.

$\angle A$ is *opposite* $\overline{BC}$.

$\angle A$ is *included* between $\overline{AB}$ and $\overline{AC}$.

B

A C

Postulate 13 *SAS Postulate*

If two sides and the included angle of one triangle are congruent to two sides and the included angle of another triangle, then the triangles are congruent.

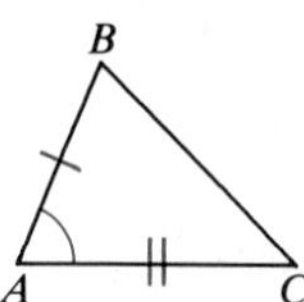

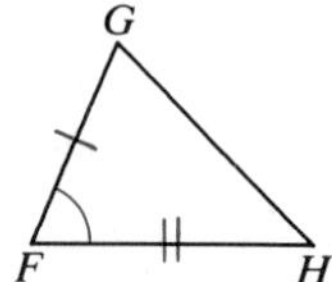

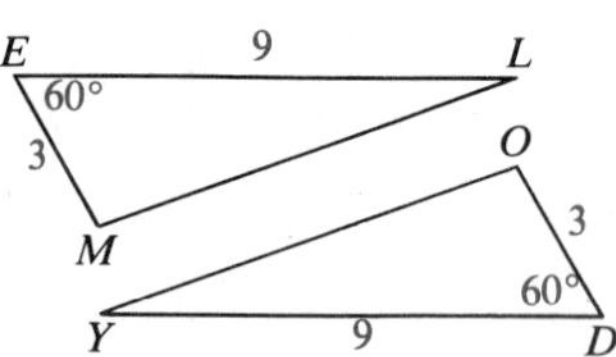

By the SAS Postulate, $\triangle ABC \cong \triangle FGH$ and $\triangle MEL \cong \triangle ODY$.

Teaching Suggestions, pp. T88–T89

Objective
Presenting the Lesson
Using Technology
Extension
Reinforcement

Exploring Activity, p. 115c

Supplementary Materials

Practice Master 17
Study Guide, pp. 41–42
Computer Activity 9

Lesson Focus

Figures cannot be assumed to be congruent because they look congruent. It is necessary to use deductive reasoning to show congruence.

Suggested Assignments

Minimum
Day 1: 124–125/1–16
Day 2: 126/17–19

Average
Day 1: 124–125/1–15 odd, 16
S 121/23–24
Day 2: 126/17–23 odd

Maximum
Day 1: 124–126/1–17 odd
Day 2: 126–127/18–26 even
S 121/24

You may wish to introduce Constructions 2 and 3 on page 376 and Construction 7 on page 382 after covering this lesson.

Communication Skills

An alternate statement of Postulate 13 is: "If two sides and the included angle of one triangle are congruent to the corresponding parts of another triangle, then the triangles are congruent."

Postulate 14 *ASA Postulate*

If two angles and the included side of one triangle are congruent to two angles and the included side of another triangle, then the triangles are congruent.

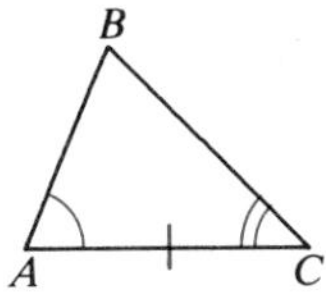

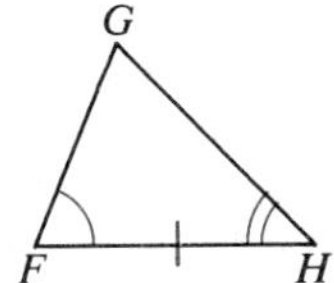

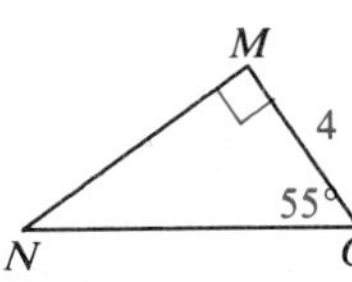

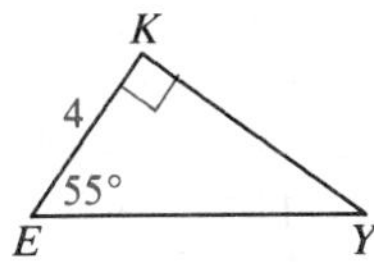

By the ASA Postulate, $\triangle ABC \cong \triangle FGH$ and $\triangle MON \cong \triangle KEY$.

Example Supply the missing statements and reasons in the following proof.

Given: E is the midpoint of $\overline{MJ}$;
$\overline{TE} \perp \overline{MJ}$

Prove: $\triangle MET \cong \triangle JET$

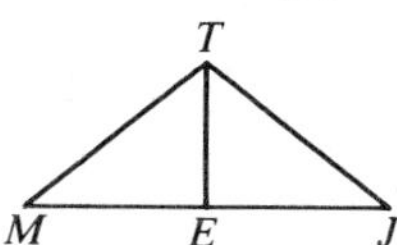

Proof:

Statements	Reasons
1. E is the midpoint of $\overline{MJ}$.	1. Given
2. _?_ $\cong$ _?_	2. Def. of midpoint
3. $\overline{TE} \perp \overline{MJ}$	3. _?_
4. $\angle MET \cong \angle JET$	4. _?_
5. $\overline{TE} \cong$ _?_	5. _?_
6. $\triangle MET \cong \triangle JET$	6. _?_

Solution

Statement 2	$\overline{ME} \cong \overline{JE}$
Reason 3	Given
Reason 4	If two lines are $\perp$, then they form $\cong$ adj. $\angle$s.
Statement 5	$\overline{TE}$
Reason 5	Reflexive Prop.
Reason 6	SAS Postulate

Classroom Exercises

Does the SAS Postulate justify that the two triangles are congruent?

1.

Yes

2.

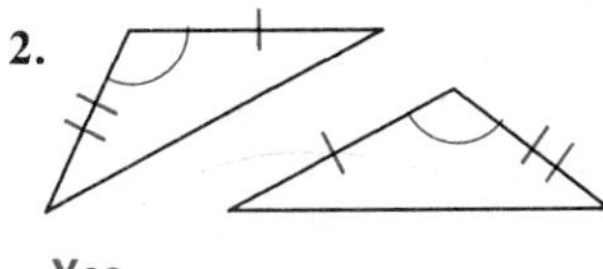

Yes

3.

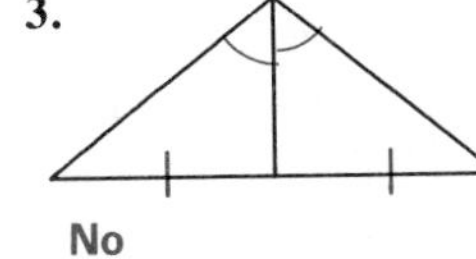

No

Teaching Note

An effective way to present the parts of a triangle in terms of their relative positions is as follows. Draw a large scalene triangle *RST* on the chalkboard. Put prominent red dots at *R* and *S*. Draw slowly and heavily from *R* to *S* as you say "This side is included between $\angle R$ and $\angle S$." Then lay one hand at *T* and say "$\angle T$ is opposite side $\overline{RS}$." Use a new triangle *XYZ* with $\overline{XY}$ and $\overline{XZ}$ colored to show that $\angle X$ is included between $\overline{XY}$ and $\overline{XZ}$, while $\overline{YZ}$ is opposite $\angle X$.

Chalkboard Example

Supply the missing statements and reasons in the following proof.

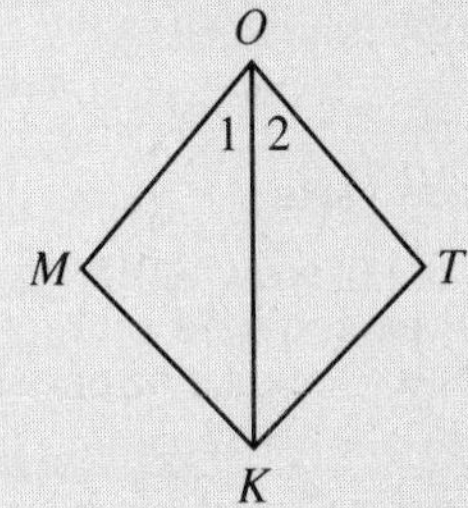

Given: $\overline{OK}$ bisects $\angle MOT$;
$\overline{OM} \cong \overline{OT}$

Prove: $\triangle MOK \cong \triangle TOK$

Proof:

1. $\overline{OK}$ bisects $\angle MOT$. (Given)
2. $\angle 1 \cong \angle 2$ (Def. of $\angle$ bisector)
3. $\overline{OK} \cong \overline{OK}$ (Reflexive Prop.)
4. $\overline{OM} \cong \overline{OT}$ (Given)
5. $\triangle MOK \cong \triangle TOK$ (SAS Post.)

Exercise Note

None of our postulates can be applied to Ex. 7. Draw a large diagram like the one shown in the book on the chalkboard. Remind students that they cannot judge angle measure from the appearance of a figure.

Communication Skills

A brief statement of the idea of the proof for Ex. 10 is acceptable. For example, a student might communicate the idea of the proof by saying: "using vertical angles, alternate interior angles, and the ASA Postulate."

Exercise Note

For Ex. 11, draw $\triangle YTR$ and $\triangle XTR$ as separate triangles and mark congruent parts.

Assessment

A thorough discussion of Exs. 1–15 will reveal any misunderstandings by students regarding the key postulates developed in this lesson. Students will have difficulties in subsequent lessons if they do not master the concepts of this lesson.

Can the two triangles be proved congruent? If so, what postulate can be used?

4.  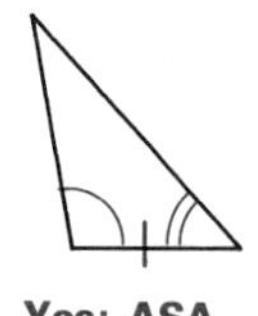

Yes; ASA

5. 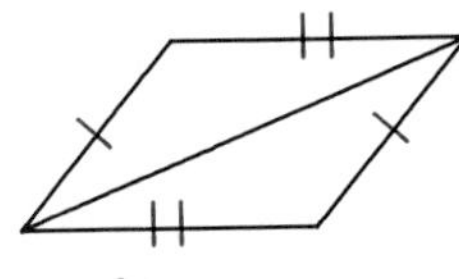

Yes; SSS

6. 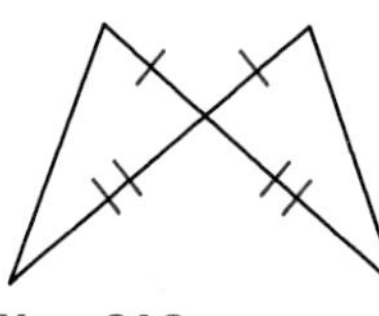

Yes; SAS

7. 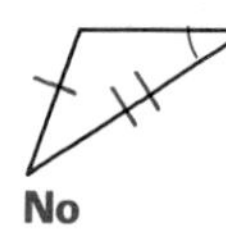 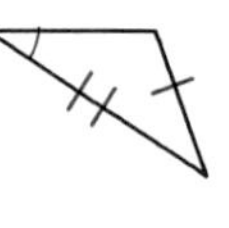

No

8. 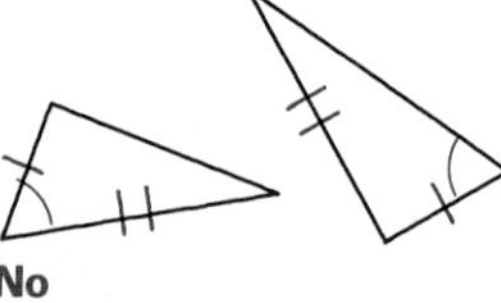

No

9. 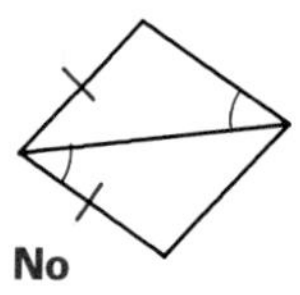

No

10. Explain how you would prove the following.
    Given: $\overline{HY} \cong \overline{LY}$; $\overline{WH} \parallel \overline{LF}$
    Prove: $\triangle WHY \cong \triangle FLY$
    Use vert. ∠s and alt. int. ∠s to prove the △s ≅ by ASA.

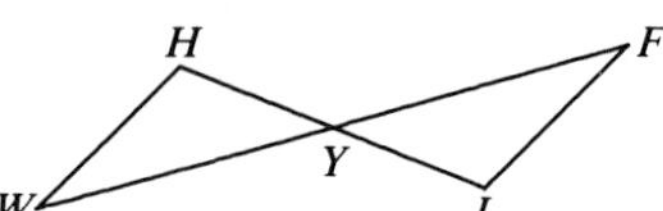

11. **a.** List two pairs of congruent corresponding sides and one pair of congruent corresponding angles in $\triangle YTR$ and $\triangle XTR$. **See below.**
    b. Notice that, in each triangle, you listed two sides and a *nonincluded* angle. Do you think that SSA is enough to guarantee that two triangles are congruent? **No**

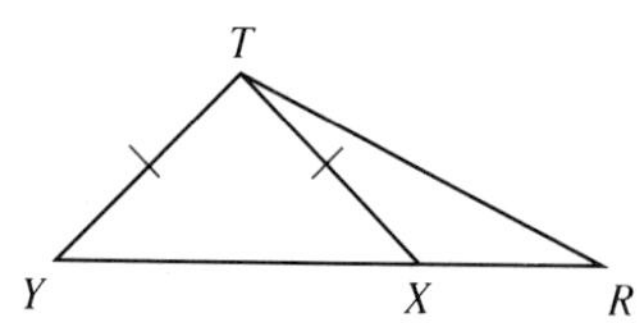

a. $\overline{TR}, \overline{TR}$; $\overline{YT}, \overline{XT}$; $\angle R, \angle R$

Written Exercises

Decide whether you can deduce by the SSS, SAS, or ASA Postulate that another triangle is congruent to $\triangle ABC$. If so, write the congruence and name the postulate used. If not, write *no congruence can be deduced*.

A

1. 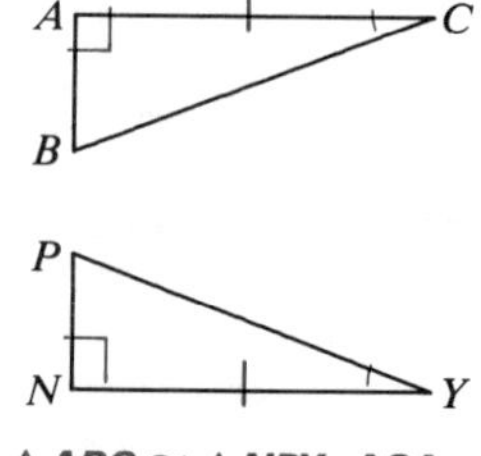

$\triangle ABC \cong \triangle NPY$; ASA

2. 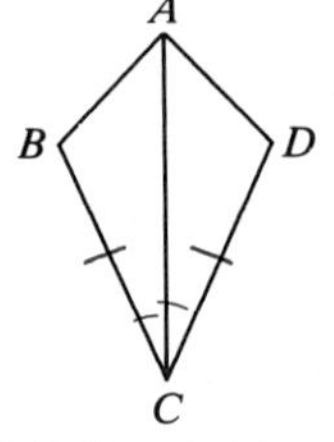

$\triangle ABC \cong \triangle ADC$; SAS

3. 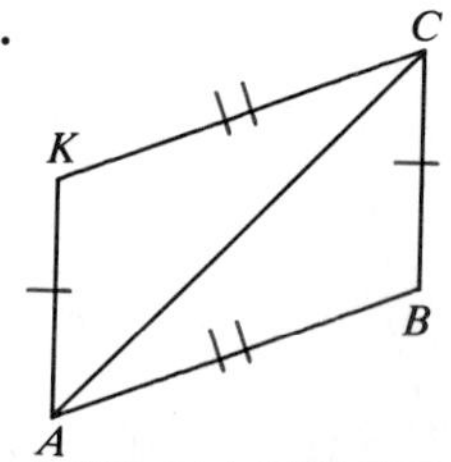

$\triangle ABC \cong \triangle CKA$; SSS

4.

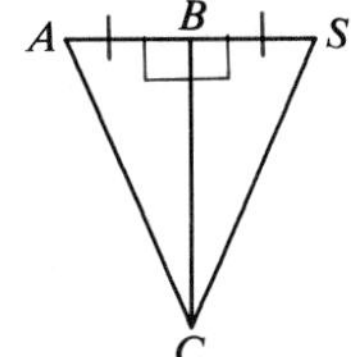

△*ABC* ≅ △*SBC*; SAS

5.

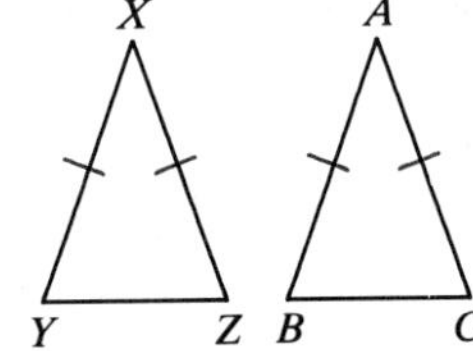

No ≅ can be deduced.

6.

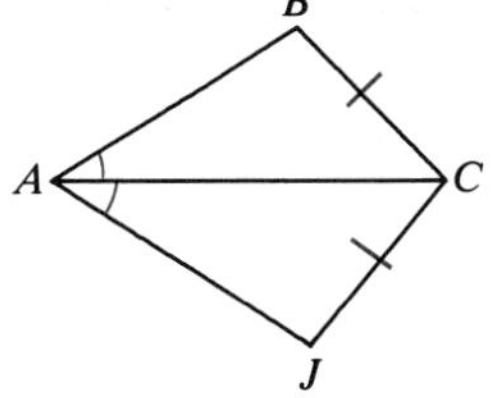

No ≅ can be deduced.

7.

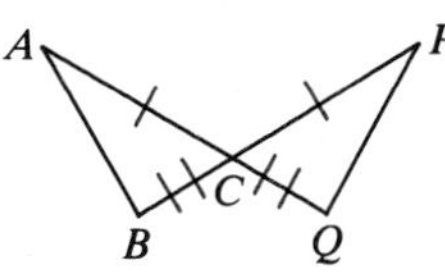

△*ABC* ≅ △*PQC*; SAS

8.

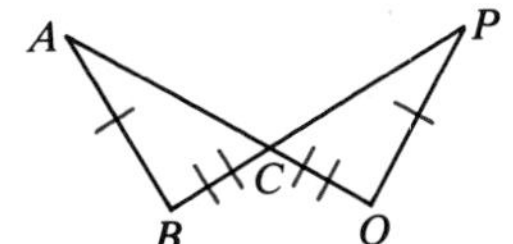

No ≅ can be deduced.

9.

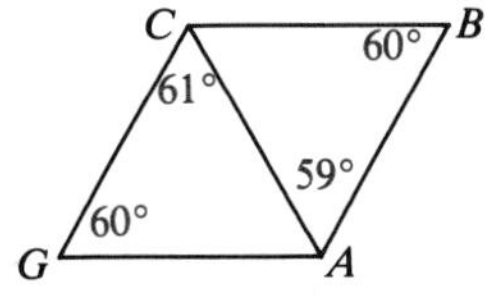

△*ABC* ≅ △*AGC*; ASA

10.

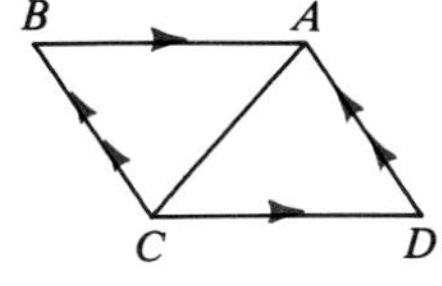

△*ABC* ≅ △*CDA*; ASA

11.

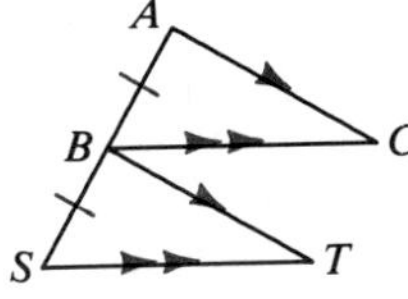

△*ABC* ≅ △*BST*; ASA

12.

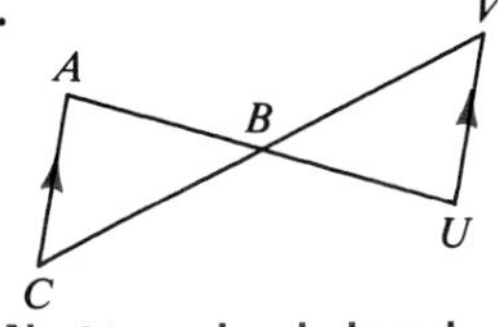

No ≅ can be deduced.

13.

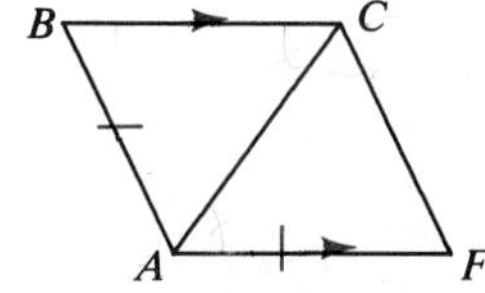

No ≅ can be deduced.

14.

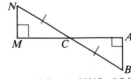

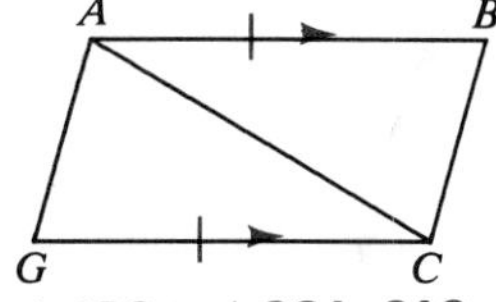

△*ABC* ≅ △*CGA*; SAS

15.

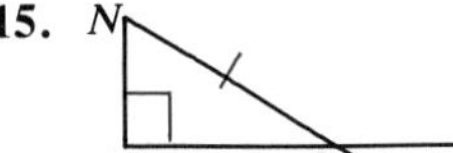

△*ABC* ≅ △*MNC*; ASA

16. Supply the missing reasons.
Given: $\overline{AB} \parallel \overline{DC}$; $\overline{AB} \cong \overline{DC}$
Prove: $\triangle ABC \cong \triangle CDA$

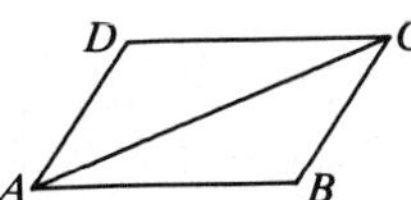

Proof:

Statements	Reasons
1. $\overline{AB} \cong \overline{DC}$	1. ? **Given**
2. $\overline{AC} \cong \overline{AC}$	2. ? **Reflexive Prop.**
3. $\overline{AB} \parallel \overline{DC}$	3. ? **Given**
4. $\angle BAC \cong \angle DCA$	4. ? **If 2 ∥ lines are cut by a trans., then alt. int. ∠s are ≅.**
5. $\triangle ABC \cong \triangle CDA$	5. ? **SAS Post.**

Guided Practice

Decide whether you can deduce by the SSS, SAS, or ASA Postulate that another triangle is congruent to △*ABC.* If so, write the congruence and name the postulate used. If not, write *no congruence.*

1.

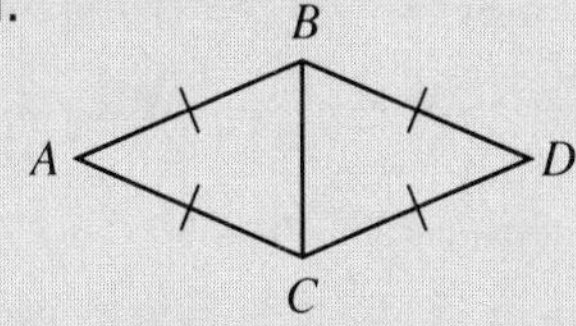

△*DBC* ≅ △*ABC*; SSS

2.

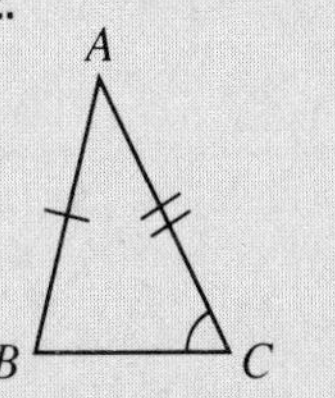

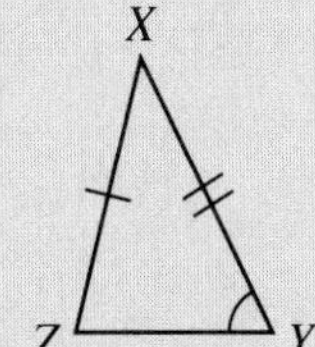

no congruence

3. Supply the missing statements and reasons.

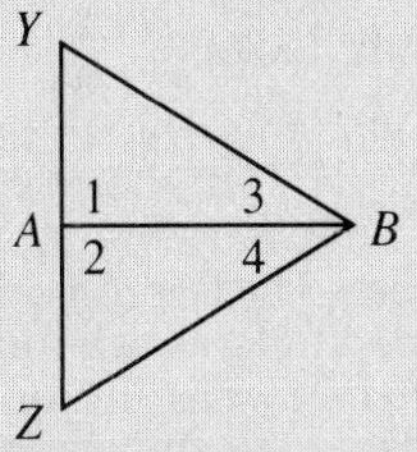

Given: $\overline{BA} \perp \overline{YZ}$;
$\overline{BA}$ bisects ∠ *YBZ.*
Prove: △*AYB* ≅ △*AZB*
Proof:

1. $\overline{BA} \perp \overline{YZ}$ (Given)
2. ∠1 ≅ ∠2 (If two lines are ⊥, they form ≅ adj. ∠s.)
3. $\overline{BA}$ bisects ∠ *YBZ.* (Given)
4. ∠3 ≅ ∠4 (Def. of ∠ bisector)
5. $\overline{AB} \cong \overline{AB}$ (Reflexive Prop.)
6. △*AYB* ≅ △*AZB* (ASA Post.)

17. Supply the missing statements and reasons.
Given: $\overline{RS} \perp \overline{ST}$; $\overline{TU} \perp \overline{ST}$;
V is the midpoint of $\overline{ST}$.
Prove: $\triangle RSV \cong \triangle UTV$

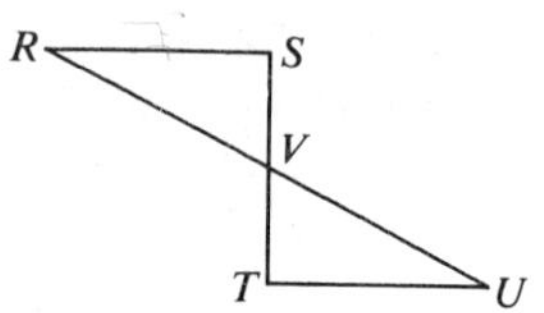

Proof:

Statements	Reasons
1. $\overline{RS} \perp \overline{ST}$; $\overline{TU} \perp \overline{ST}$	1. _?_ **Given**
2. $m\angle S = 90$; $m\angle$ _?_ $= 90$ ***T***	2. _?_ **Def. of ⊥ lines**
3. $\angle S \cong \angle T$	3. _?_ **Def. of ≅ ∠s**
4. V is the midpoint of $\overline{ST}$.	4. _?_ **Given**
5. $\overline{SV} \cong$ _?_ ***VT***	5. _?_ **Def. of midpoint**
6. $\angle RVS \cong \angle$ _?_ ***UVT***	6. _?_ **Vert. ∠s are ≅.**
7. $\triangle$ _?_ $\cong \triangle$ _?_ ***RSV, UTV***	7. _?_ **ASA Post.**

Write proofs in two-column form.

B **18.** Given: $\overline{TM} \cong \overline{PR}$; $\overline{TM} \parallel \overline{RP}$
Prove: $\triangle TEM \cong \triangle PER$

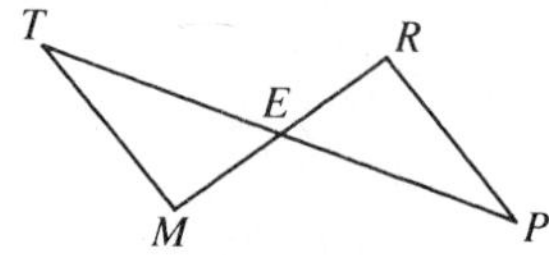

19. Given: E is the midpoint of $\overline{TP}$;
E is the midpoint of $\overline{MR}$.
Prove: $\triangle TEM \cong \triangle PER$

20. Given: Plane M bisects $\overline{AB}$; $\overline{PA} \cong \overline{PB}$
Prove: $\triangle POA \cong \triangle POB$

21. Given: Plane M bisects $\overline{AB}$; $\overline{PO} \perp \overline{AB}$
Prove: $\triangle POA \cong \triangle POB$

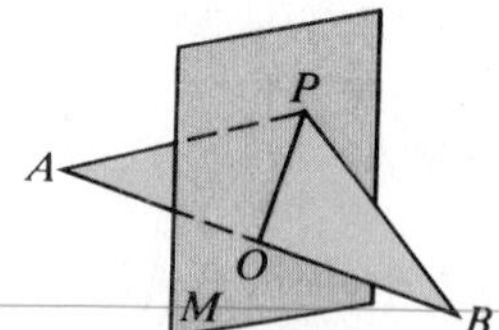

Draw and label a diagram. List, in terms of the diagram, what is given and what is to be proved. Then write a two-column proof.

22. In an isosceles triangle, if the angle between the congruent sides is bisected, then two congruent triangles are formed.

23. In an isosceles triangle, if a segment is drawn from the vertex of the angle between the congruent sides to the midpoint of the opposite side, then congruent triangles are formed.

24. If a line perpendicular to $\overline{AB}$ passes through the midpoint of $\overline{AB}$, and segments are drawn from any other point on that line to A and B, then two congruent triangles are formed.

25. If pentagon $ABCDE$ is equilateral and has right angles at B and E, then diagonals $\overline{AC}$ and $\overline{AD}$ form congruent triangles.

Thinking Skills

Most students will enjoy Exs. 22–25, but they will need sufficient time to work on them. These problems provide students with valuable experiences in translating verbal statements into diagrams and geometric statements.

Using a Computer

In Exs. 22–25, students may find it helpful to use a program to draw the given figures and then look for congruent triangles. They will see the difference between Exs. 22 and 23 because of how the figures must be constructed. Ex. 25 provides a challenging construction.

Copy each three-dimensional figure and with colored pencils outline the triangles listed. What postulate proves that these triangles are congruent?

C **26.**

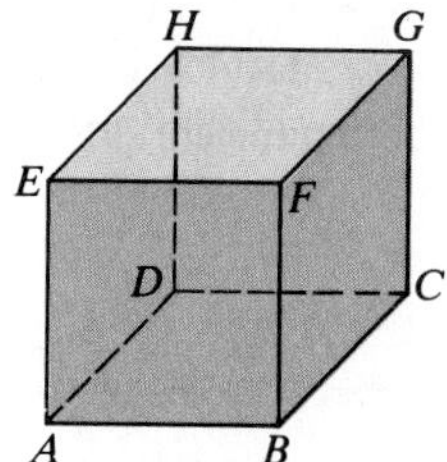

Given: Cube whose faces are congruent squares
Show: $\triangle ABF$, $\triangle BCG$ **SAS**

27.

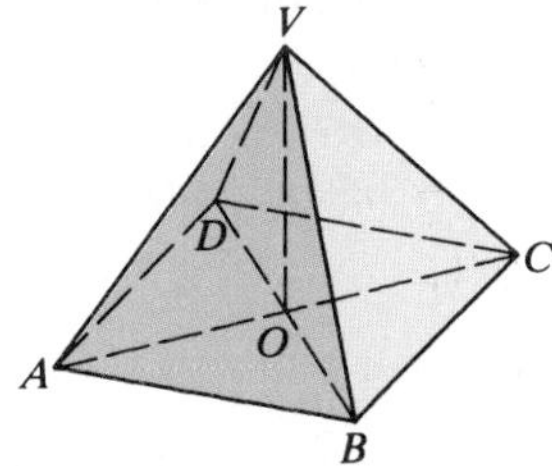

Given: Pyramid with square base; $VA = VB = VC = VD$
Show: $\triangle VAB$, $\triangle VBC$ **SSS**

4-3 *Using Congruent Triangles*

Our goal in the preceding section was to prove that two triangles are congruent. Our goal in this section is to deduce information about segments or angles once we have shown that they are corresponding parts of congruent triangles.

Example 1

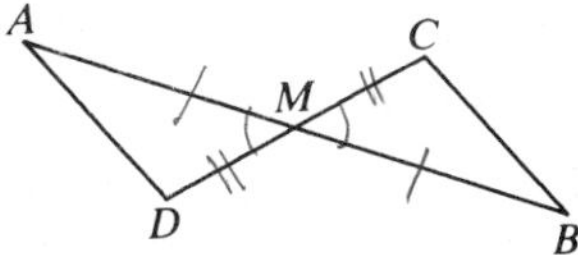

Given: $\overline{AB}$ and $\overline{CD}$ bisect each other at M.
Prove: $\overline{AD} \parallel \overline{BC}$

Plan for Proof: You can prove $\overline{AD} \parallel \overline{BC}$ if you can show that alternate interior angles $\angle A$ and $\angle B$ are congruent. You will know that $\angle A$ and $\angle B$ are congruent if they are corresponding parts of congruent triangles. The diagram suggests that you try to prove $\triangle AMD \cong \triangle BMC$.

Proof:

Statements	Reasons
1. $\overline{AB}$ and $\overline{CD}$ bisect each other at M.	1. Given
2. M is the midpoint of $\overline{AB}$ and of $\overline{CD}$.	2. Def. of a bisector of a segment
3. $\overline{AM} \cong \overline{MB}$; $\overline{DM} \cong \overline{MC}$	3. Def. of midpoint
4. $\angle AMD \cong \angle BMC$	4. Vertical ∠s are ≅.
5. $\triangle AMD \cong \triangle BMC$	5. SAS Postulate
6. $\angle A \cong \angle B$	6. Corr. parts of ≅ △s are ≅.
7. $\overline{AD} \parallel \overline{BC}$	7. If two lines are cut by a transversal and alt. int. ∠s are ≅, then the lines are ∥.

Exercise Note

Most students should be able to do Exs. 26 and 27 successfully. Students should draw a large diagram carefully and use color as suggested to bring clarity to the problems.

Teaching Suggestions, p. T89

Objective
Presenting the Lesson
Applications
Problem Solving

Cooperative Learning, p. T89

Supplementary Materials

Practice Master 18
Test 14
Resource Book, pp. 19, 122
Study Guide, pp. 43–46
Overhead Visuals A, D, F

Lesson Focus

One of the reasons for proving that triangles are congruent is to show that certain sides or angles of the triangles are congruent. This lesson introduces and develops how congruent triangles are used to deduce other facts about geometric figures.

Some proofs require the idea of a line perpendicular to a plane. **A line and a plane are perpendicular** if and only if they intersect and the line is perpendicular to all lines in the plane that pass through the point of intersection. Suppose you are given $\overleftrightarrow{PO} \perp$ plane X. Then you know that $\overleftrightarrow{PO} \perp \overleftrightarrow{OA}$, $\overleftrightarrow{PO} \perp \overleftrightarrow{OB}$, $\overleftrightarrow{PO} \perp \overleftrightarrow{OC}$, $\overline{PO} \perp \overline{OC}$, and so on. The ice-fishing equipment shown below suggests a line perpendicular to a plane.

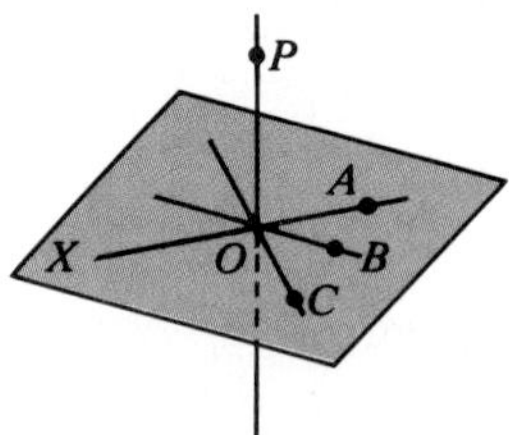

Example 2

Given: $\overline{PO} \perp$ plane X;
$\overline{AO} \cong \overline{BO}$

Prove: $\overline{PA} \cong \overline{PB}$

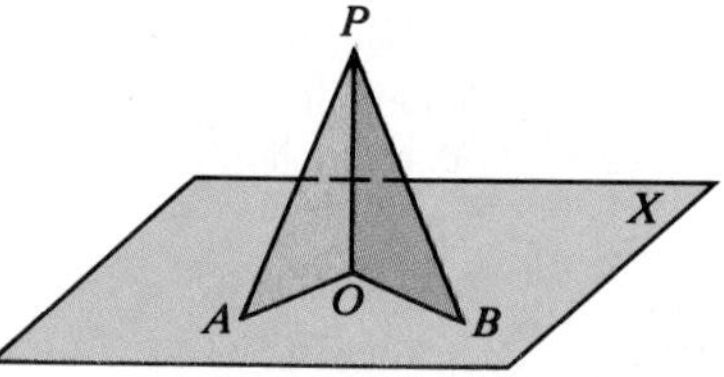

Plan for Proof: You can prove $\overline{PA} \cong \overline{PB}$ if you can show that these segments are corresponding parts of congruent triangles. The diagram suggests that you try to prove $\triangle POA \cong \triangle POB$.

Proof:

Statements	Reasons
1. $\overline{PO} \perp$ plane X	1. Given
2. $\overline{PO} \perp \overline{OA}$; $\overline{PO} \perp \overline{OB}$	2. Def. of a line perpendicular to a plane
3. $m\angle POA = 90$; $m\angle POB = 90$	3. Def. of $\perp$ lines
4. $\angle POA \cong \angle POB$	4. Def. of $\cong$ $\angle$s
5. $\overline{AO} \cong \overline{BO}$	5. Given
6. $\overline{PO} \cong \overline{PO}$	6. Reflexive Prop.
7. $\triangle POA \cong \triangle POB$	7. SAS Postulate
8. $\overline{PA} \cong \overline{PB}$	8. Corr. parts of $\cong$ $\triangle$s are $\cong$.

Suggested Assignments

Minimum
Day 1: 130/1–4
Day 2: 131/5–8
Day 3: 131–132/9, 11, 13
132–133/Self-Test 1

Average
Day 1: 130–131/1–3, 6
Day 2: 131/7, 8, 10, 12
Day 3: 132/13, 14
132–133/Self-Test 1

Maximum
Day 1: 130–131/2, 5, 9, 10, 12
S 126–127/23, 25, 27
Day 2: 131–132/7, 11, 13–15

Problem Solving

Point out that in the Plan for Proof, reasoning backward is the strategy used. The plan starts from the desired conclusion and works backward until a preliminary goal is realized. It is more important for students to understand this plan than to see a proof.

Proof Note

You can discuss with students why Step 3 is necessary. Ask: "Why can't you jump to Step 4 and use the reason: If two lines are perpendicular, they form congruent adjacent angles?" Because $\overline{OA}$ and $\overline{OB}$ are not in one line.

A Way to Prove Two Segments or Two Angles Congruent

1. Identify two triangles in which the two segments or angles are corresponding parts.
2. Prove that the triangles are congruent.
3. State that the two parts are congruent, using the reason

Corr. parts of ≅ ▲ are ≅.

Classroom Exercises

Note: CPCT is used below for "corr. parts of ≅ ▲ are ≅."

Describe your plan for proving the following.

1. Given: $\overleftrightarrow{PR}$ bisects $\angle QPS$; $\overline{PQ} \cong \overline{PS}$
   Prove: $\angle Q \cong \angle S$ **See below.**
2. Given: $\overleftrightarrow{PR}$ bisects $\angle QPS$ and $\angle QRS$
   Prove: $\overline{RQ} \cong \overline{RS}$
   $\triangle PQR \cong \triangle PSR$ by ASA, so $\overline{RQ} \cong \overline{RS}$ (CPCT).

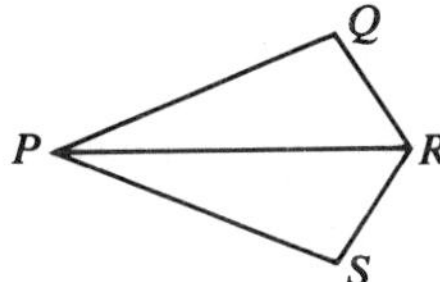

3. Given: $\overline{WX} \cong \overline{YZ}$; $\overline{ZW} \cong \overline{XY}$
   Prove: $\overline{WX} \parallel \overline{ZY}$ **See below.**
4. Given: $\overline{ZW} \parallel \overline{YX}$; $\overline{ZW} \cong \overline{XY}$
   Prove: $\overline{ZY} \parallel \overline{WX}$
   $\overline{ZW} \parallel \overline{YX}$, so $\angle 3 \cong \angle 4$ by Thm. 3-2. Then $\triangle ZWX \cong \triangle XYZ$ by SAS, and $\angle 1 \cong \angle 2$ (CPCT). Therefore, $\overline{ZY} \parallel \overline{WX}$ by Thm. 3-5.

Z Y 3 2 4 1 W X

5. Given: $\overline{CD} \perp \overline{AB}$;
   D is the midpoint of $\overline{AB}$.
   Prove: $\overline{CA} \cong \overline{CB}$
   $\triangle CAD \cong \triangle CBD$ by SAS, so $\overline{CA} \cong \overline{CB}$ (CPCT).

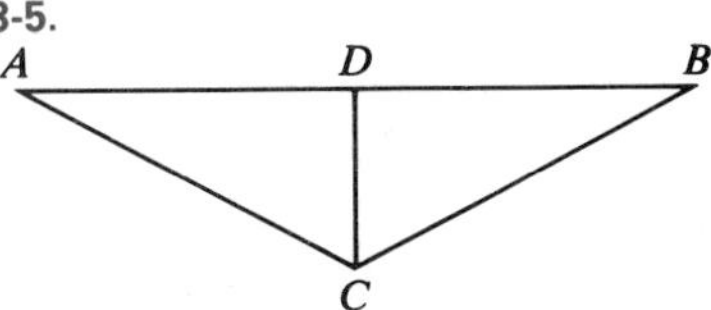

6. Given: M is the midpoint of $\overline{AB}$;
   plane X ⊥ $\overline{AB}$ at M.
   What can you deduce about $\overline{AP}$ and $\overline{BP}$? **$\overline{AP} \cong \overline{BP}$**
   Describe a plan for proving that your conclusion is correct.
   $\triangle APM \cong \triangle BPM$ by SAS, so $\overline{AP} \cong \overline{BP}$ (CPCT).

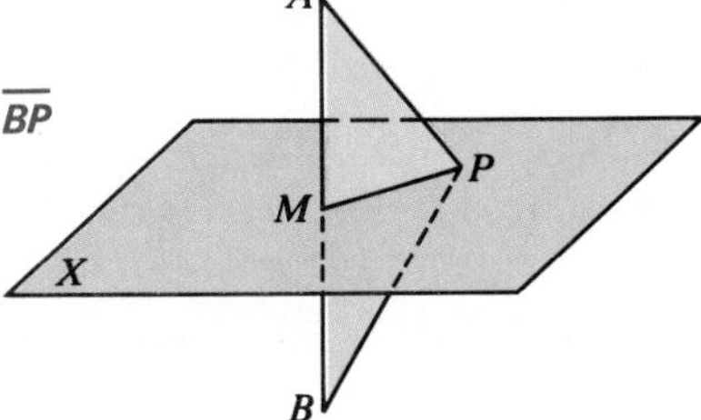

1. $\triangle PQR \cong \triangle PSR$ by SAS, so $\angle Q \cong \angle S$ (CPCT).
3. $\triangle ZWX \cong \triangle XYZ$ by SSS, so $\angle 1 \cong \angle 2$ (CPCT). Therefore, $\overline{WX} \parallel \overline{ZY}$ by Thm. 3-5.

Chalkboard Examples

1. Given: $m\angle 1 = m\angle 2$; $m\angle 3 = m\angle 4$
Prove: M is the midpoint of $\overline{JK}$.

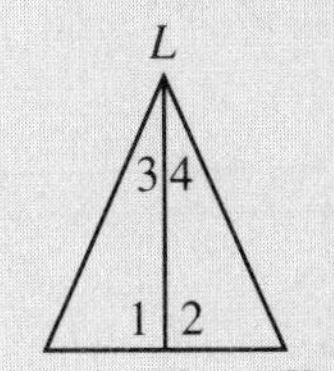

1. $m\angle 1 = m\angle 2$; $m\angle 3 = m\angle 4$ (Given)
2. $\angle 1 \cong \angle 2$; $\angle 3 \cong \angle 4$ (Def. of ≅ ▲)
3. $\overline{LM} \cong \overline{LM}$ (Refl. Prop.)
4. $\triangle LMJ \cong \triangle LMK$ (ASA)
5. $\overline{JM} \cong \overline{KM}$ (Corr. parts of ≅ ▲ are ≅.)
6. M is midpt. of $\overline{JK}$. (Def. of midpt.)

2. Given: $m\angle 1 = m\angle 2$; $m\angle 3 = m\angle 4$
Prove: $\triangle JKL$ is isosceles.

1–4. (Use steps in Ex. 1.)
5. $\overline{JL} \cong \overline{KL}$ (Corr. parts of ≅ ▲ are ≅.)
6. $\triangle JKL$ is isos. (Def. of isos. △)

Problem Solving

A good plan enables a student to write a proof. One satisfactory plan for Ex. 1 is: Since $\angle QPS$ is bisected, the two triangles can be proved congruent by the SAS method and the use of corresponding parts.

Guided Practice

1. Copy and complete the proof.

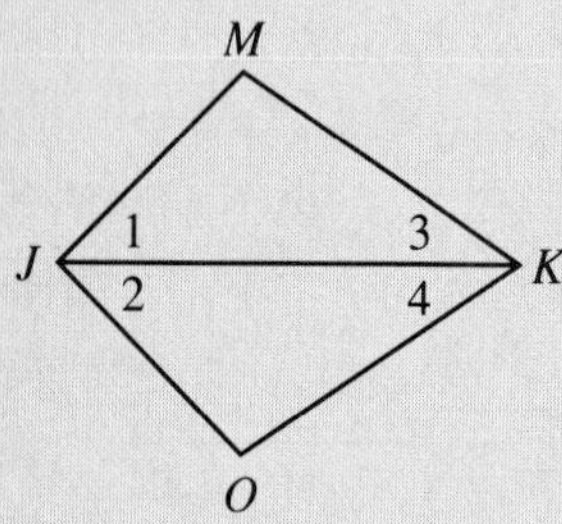

Given: $\overline{MK} \cong \overline{OK}$;
$\overline{KJ}$ bisects $\angle MKO$.
Prove: $\overline{JK}$ bisects $\angle MJO$.
Proof:
1. $\overline{MK} \cong \overline{OK}$ (Given)
2. $\overline{KJ}$ bisects $\angle MKO$. (Given)
3. $\angle 3 \cong \angle 4$ (Def. of $\angle$ bis.)
4. $\overline{JK} \cong \overline{JK}$ (Reflexive Prop.)
5. $\triangle MJK \cong \triangle OJK$ (SAS Post.)
6. $\angle 1 \cong \angle 2$ (Corr. parts of $\cong$ △s are $\cong$.)
7. $\overline{JK}$ bisects $\angle MJO$. (Def. of $\angle$ bis.)

2. Write the statements in a correct order for a proof.

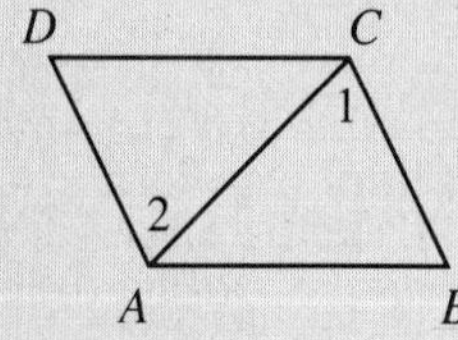

Given: $\overline{AD} \parallel \overline{BC}$; $\overline{AD} \cong \overline{BC}$
Prove: $\overline{AB} \cong \overline{CD}$
(a) $\overline{AD} \parallel \overline{BC}$
(b) $\overline{AB} \cong \overline{CD}$
(c) $\triangle ABC \cong \triangle CDA$
(d) $\overline{AD} \cong \overline{BC}$
(e) $\overline{AC} \cong \overline{AC}$
(f) $\angle 1 \cong \angle 2$
Answer may vary.
d, a, f, e, c, b

Written Exercises

Copy and complete the proof.

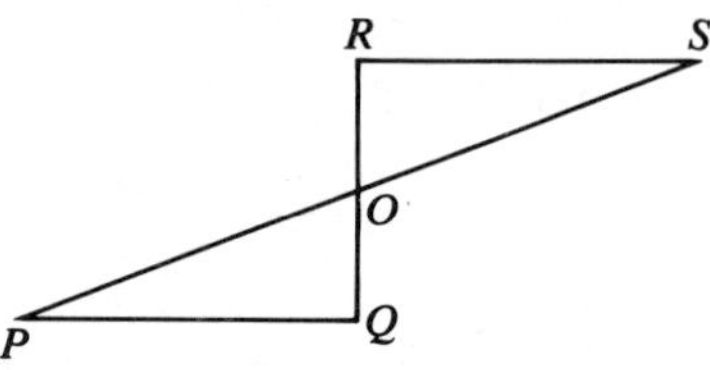

A **1.** Given: $\angle P \cong \angle S$;
O is the midpoint of $\overline{PS}$.
Prove: O is the midpoint of $\overline{RQ}$.

Proof:

Statements	Reasons
1. $\angle P \cong \angle S$	1. ? **Given**
2. O is the midpoint of $\overline{PS}$.	2. ? **Given**
3. $\overline{PO} \cong \overline{SO}$	3. ? **Def. of midpoint**
4. $\angle POQ \cong \angle SOR$	4. ? **Vert. △s are ≅.**
5. $\triangle POQ \cong \triangle SOR$	5. ? **ASA Post.**
6. $\overline{QO} \cong \overline{RO}$	6. ? **Corr. parts of ≅ △s are ≅.**
7. O is the midpoint of $\overline{RQ}$.	7. ? **Def. of midpoint**

The statements in Exercise 2 might be used as statements in a proof but they are given out of order. Find an appropriate order for the statements. (There may be more than one correct order.)

2. Given: $\overline{AM} \cong \overline{BM}$; $\overline{TM} \perp \overline{AB}$ **Answers may vary. a, e, c, f, b, d**
Prove: $\overline{AT} \cong \overline{BT}$
(a) $\overline{AM} \cong \overline{BM}$
(b) $\triangle AMT \cong \triangle BMT$
(c) $\angle 1 \cong \angle 2$
(d) $\overline{AT} \cong \overline{BT}$
(e) $\overline{TM} \perp \overline{AB}$
(f) $\overline{TM} \cong \overline{TM}$

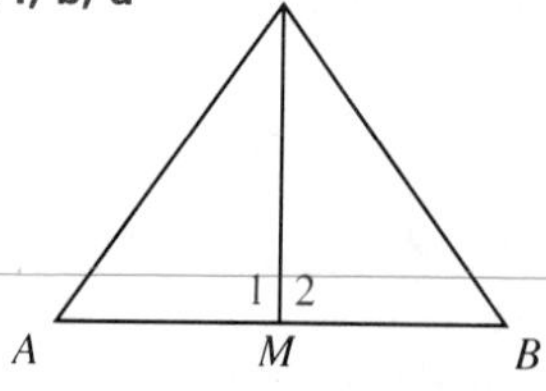

Write proofs in two-column form.

3. Given: $\overline{WO} \cong \overline{ZO}$; $\overline{XO} \cong \overline{YO}$
Prove: $\angle W \cong \angle Z$

4. Given: M is the midpoint of $\overline{AB}$;
$\angle 1 \cong \angle 2$; $\angle 3 \cong \angle 4$
Prove: $\overline{AC} \cong \overline{BD}$

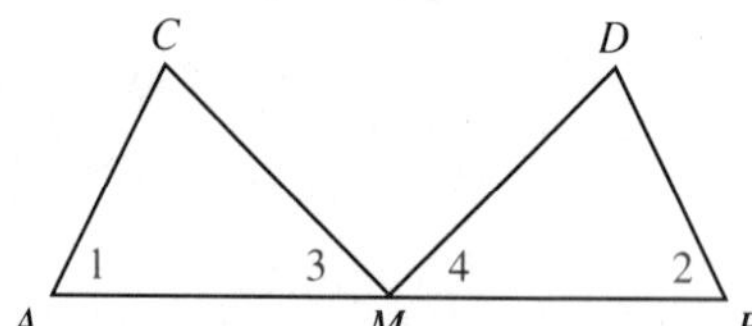

5. Prove the following statement: If both pairs of opposite sides of a quadrilateral are parallel, then they are also congruent.
Given: $\overline{SK} \parallel \overline{NR}$; $\overline{SN} \parallel \overline{KR}$
Prove: $\overline{SK} \cong \overline{NR}$; $\overline{SN} \cong \overline{KR}$

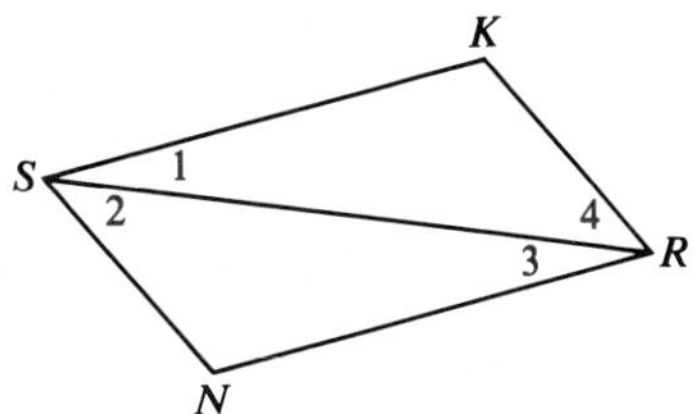

6. Prove the converse of the statement in Exercise 5: If both pairs of opposite sides of a quadrilateral are congruent, then they are also parallel.
Given: $\overline{SK} \cong \overline{NR}$; $\overline{SN} \cong \overline{KR}$
Prove: $\overline{SK} \parallel \overline{NR}$; $\overline{SN} \parallel \overline{KR}$

Write proofs in two-column form.

7. Given: $\overline{AD} \parallel \overline{ME}$; $\overline{MD} \parallel \overline{BE}$;
M is the midpoint of $\overline{AB}$.
Prove: $\overline{MD} \cong \overline{BE}$

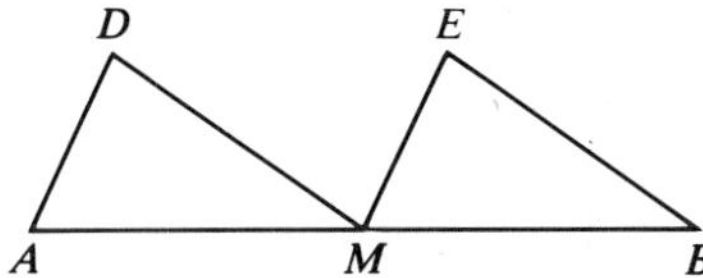

B **8.** Given: M is the midpoint of $\overline{AB}$;
$\overline{AD} \cong \overline{ME}$; $\overline{AD} \parallel \overline{ME}$
Prove: $\overline{MD} \parallel \overline{BE}$

In Exercises 9 and 10 you are given more information than you need. For each exercise state one piece of given information that you do not need for the proof. Then give a two-column proof that does not use that piece of information.

9. Given: $\overline{PQ} \cong \overline{PS}$; $\overline{QR} \cong \overline{SR}$;
$\angle 1 \cong \angle 2$
Prove: $\angle 3 \cong \angle 4$

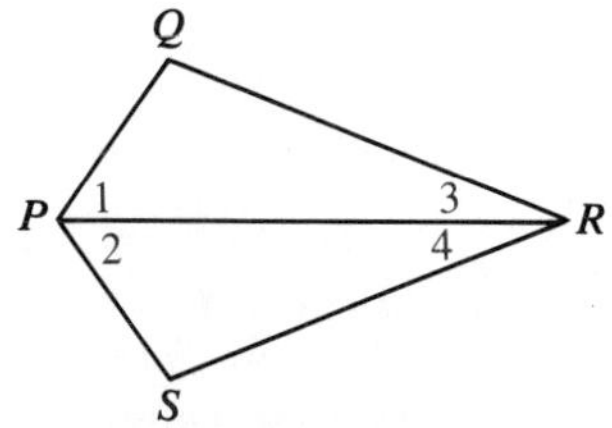

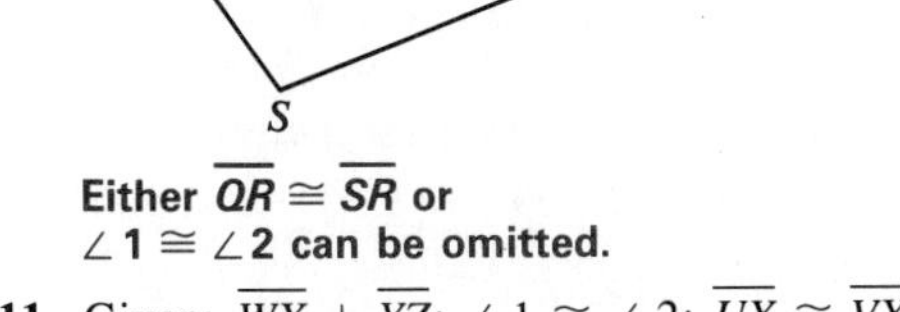

Either $\overline{QR} \cong \overline{SR}$ or $\angle 1 \cong \angle 2$ can be omitted.

10. Given: $\overline{LM} \cong \overline{LN}$; $\overline{KM} \cong \overline{KN}$;
$\overrightarrow{KO}$ bisects $\angle MKN$.
Prove: $\overrightarrow{LO}$ bisects $\angle MLN$.

$\overrightarrow{KO}$ bisects $\angle MKN$ can be omitted. (A more complex proof can be written if $\overline{LM} \cong \overline{LN}$ is omitted instead of $\overrightarrow{KO}$ bisects $\angle MKN$.)

11. Given: $\overline{WX} \perp \overline{YZ}$; $\angle 1 \cong \angle 2$; $\overline{UX} \cong \overline{VX}$
Which one(s) of the following statements *must* be true?
(1) $\overline{XW} \perp \overline{UV}$ (2) $\overline{UV} \parallel \overline{YZ}$ (3) $\overline{VX} \perp \overline{UX}$

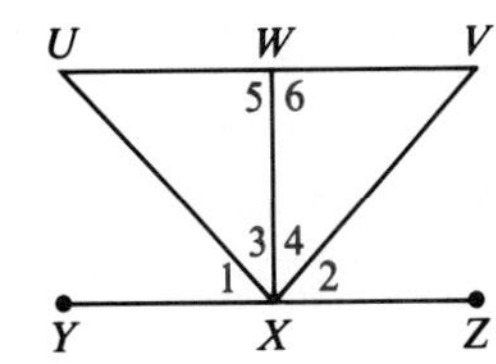

12. Given: $\overline{WX} \perp \overline{UV}$; $\overline{WX} \perp \overline{YZ}$; $\overline{WU} \cong \overline{WV}$
Prove whatever you can about angles 1, 2, 3, and 4.
$\angle 1 \cong \angle 2$, $\angle 3 \cong \angle 4$

Thinking Skills

For Exs. 9 and 10, the directions prevent students from starting out mechanically by listing everything that is given. Students must think about the information that is essential to writing a proof.

13. Given: $\overline{RS} \perp$ plane Y;
$\angle TRS \cong \angle VRS$
Prove: $\triangle RTV$ is isosceles.

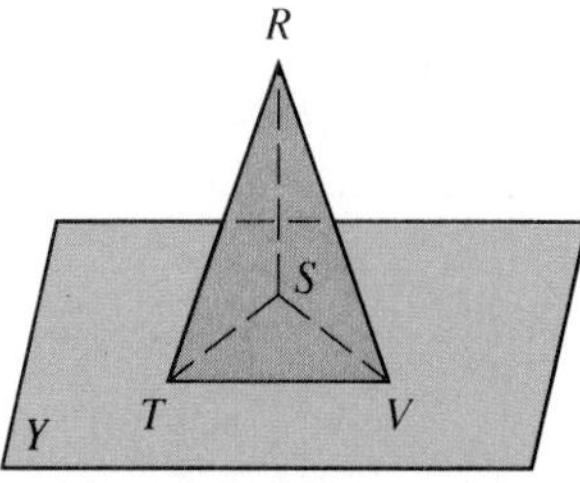

14. Given: $\overline{PA} \perp$ plane X; $\overline{QB} \perp$ plane X;
O is the midpoint of $\overline{AB}$.
Prove: O is the midpoint of $\overline{PQ}$.

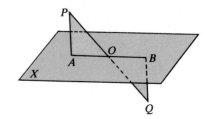

15. A young tree on level ground is supported at P by three wires of equal length. The wires are staked to the ground at points A, B, and C, which are equally distant from the base of the tree, T. Explain in a paragraph how you can prove that the angles the wires make with the ground are all congruent.

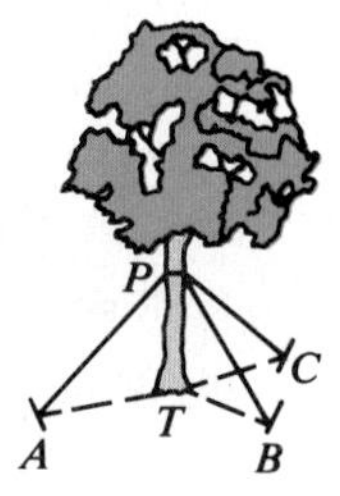

C 16. Napoleon, on a river bank, wanted to know the width of the stream. A young soldier faced directly across the stream and adjusted the visor of his cap until the tip of the visor was in line with his eye and the opposite bank. Next he did an about-face and noted the spot on the ground now in line with his eye and visor-tip. He paced off the distance to this spot, made his report, and earned a promotion. What postulate is this method based on? Draw a diagram to help you explain. **ASA**

Self-Test 1

Given: $\triangle KOP \cong \triangle MAT$

1. What can you conclude about $\angle P$? Why? **$\angle P \cong \angle T$; Corr. parts of $\cong$ △ are $\cong$.**
2. Name three pairs of corresponding sides. **$\overline{KO}$, $\overline{MA}$; $\overline{OP}$, $\overline{AT}$; $\overline{KP}$, $\overline{MT}$**

Decide whether the two triangles must be congruent. If so, write the congruence and name the postulate used. If not, write *no congruence can be deduced.*

3.

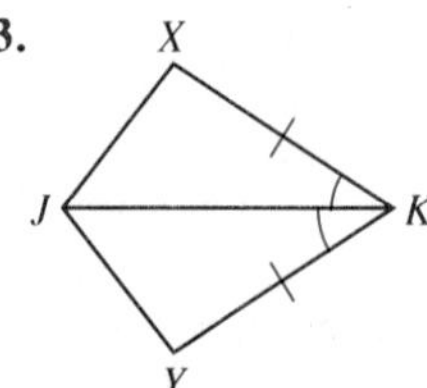

$\triangle JKX \cong \triangle JKY$; SAS

4.

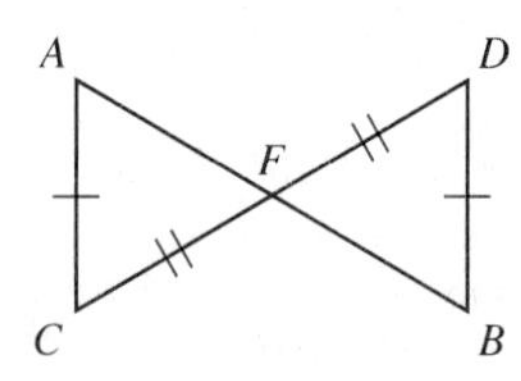

No $\cong$ can be deduced.

5.

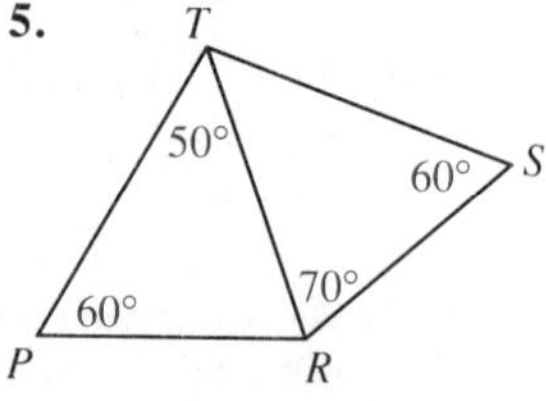

$\triangle TRP \cong \triangle TRS$; ASA

Additional Answers Written Exercises

15. The wires are of equal length, so $PA = PB = PC$. The stakes are equidistant from the base of the tree, so $TA = TB = TC$. $PT = PT = PT$ by the Refl. Prop., so $\triangle PTA \cong \triangle PTB \cong \triangle PTC$ by SSS. The △ the 3 wires make with the ground are corr. parts of $\cong$ △.

Thinking Skills

Students will understand intuitively what is meant by the angle a wire makes with the ground. You can use this problem: Define, for a line $\overleftrightarrow{RS}$ that intersects a plane M at S, the angle that $\overleftrightarrow{RS}$ makes with M.

Quick Quiz

Given: $\triangle DOG \cong \triangle RAN$

1. What can you conclude about $\overline{OG}$? Why? $\overline{OG} \cong \overline{AN}$; Corr. parts of $\cong$ △ are $\cong$.
2. Name three pairs of corresponding angles. $\angle D$, $\angle R$; $\angle O$, $\angle A$; $\angle G$, $\angle N$

For Exs. 3–5, decide whether the two triangles must be congruent. If so, write the congruence and name the postulate used. If not, write *no congruence.*

3.

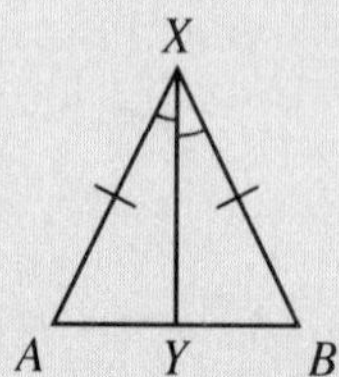

$\triangle AXY \cong \triangle BXY$; SAS Post.

Write proofs in two-column form.

6. Given: $\angle 1 \cong \angle 2$; $\angle 3 \cong \angle 4$
Prove: $\triangle ADB \cong \triangle CBD$

7. Given: $\overline{CD} \cong \overline{AB}$; $\overline{CB} \cong \overline{AD}$
Prove: $\angle 1 \cong \angle 2$

8. Given: $\overline{AD} \parallel \overline{BC}$; $\overline{AD} \cong \overline{CB}$
Prove: $\overline{DC} \parallel \overline{AB}$

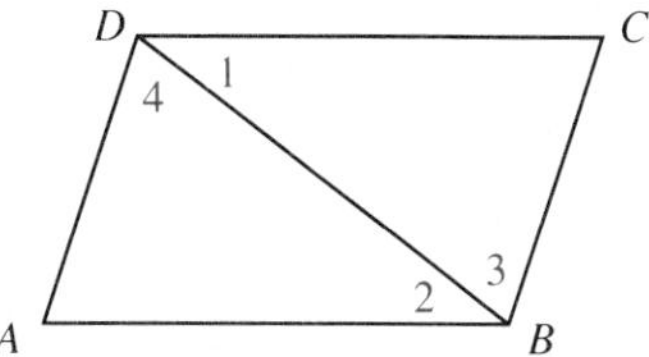

Application — *Bracing With Triangles*

The two famous landmarks pictured above have much in common. They were completed within a few years of each other, the Eiffel Tower in 1889 and the Statue of Liberty in 1886. The French engineer Gustave Eiffel designed both the tower's sweeping form and the complex structure that supports Liberty's copper skin. And both designs gain strength from the rigidity of the triangular shape.

The strength of triangular bracing is related to the SSS Postulate, which tells us that a triangle with given sides can have only one shape. A rectangle formed by four bars joined at their ends can flatten into a parallelogram, but the structural triangle cannot be deformed except by bending or stretching the bars.

The Eiffel Tower's frame is tied together by a web of triangles. A portion of the statue's armature is shown in the photograph at the right. The inner tower of wide members is strengthened by double diagonal bracing. A framework of lighter members, also joined in triangular patterns, surrounds this core.

Structural engineers use geometry in designing bridges, towers, and large-span roofs. See what you can find out about Eiffel's bridges and about the work of some of the other great modern builders.

4.

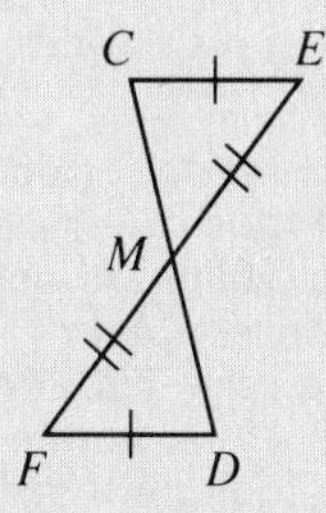

no congruence

5.

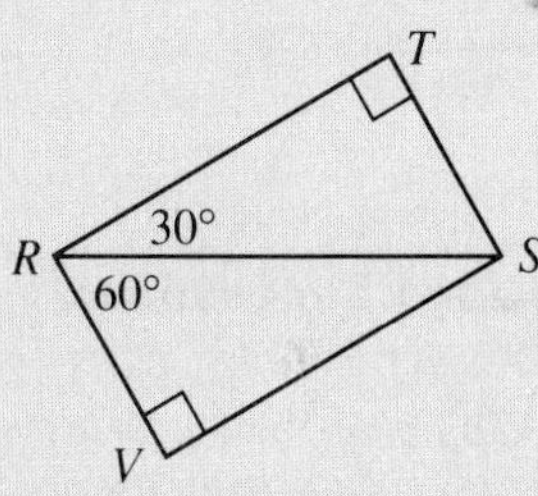

$\triangle RTS \cong \triangle SVR$; ASA Post.

Write a proof in two-column form.

6. Given: $\overline{AE} \cong \overline{BE}$; $\overline{DE} \cong \overline{CE}$
Prove: $\angle D \cong \angle C$

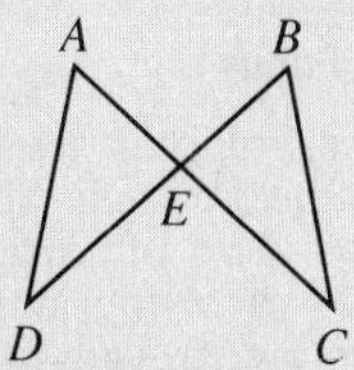

1. $\overline{AE} \cong \overline{BE}$; $\overline{DE} \cong \overline{CE}$ (Given)
2. $\angle AED \cong \angle BEC$ (Vert. ∠s are ≅.)
3. $\triangle AED \cong \triangle BEC$ (SAS)
4. $\angle D \cong \angle C$ (Corr. parts of ≅ △s are ≅.)

Using a Computer

This Exploration introduces the properties of isosceles triangles, which are developed in Lesson 4-4.

Also see page T90 for an Experiment that verifies the isosceles triangle theorems and corollaries.

Teaching Suggestions, p. T90

Objective
Presenting the Lesson
Using Technology
Extension

Supplementary Materials

Study Guide, pp. 47–50

Lesson Focus

Isosceles triangles are used by architects to help design buildings. Two important theorems involving isosceles triangles are presented in this lesson and are used to further enhance students' abilities to write proofs.

Suggested Assignments

Minimum
Day 1: 137/1–8
Day 2: 137–138/9, 11, 13–15
Day 3: 138/17, 18, 21

Average
Day 1: 137/1–9 odd, 10, 12
Day 2: 137–139/13, 14, 17, 18–21, 25, 27

Maximum
Day 1: 137–138/3, 4, 6, 9, 12, 14, 15, 17, 22
S 132/16
Day 2: 138–139/16, 19, 21, 24, 25, 27, 31

Explorations

These exploratory exercises can be done using a computer with a program that draws and measures geometric figures.

Draw several isosceles triangles. For each triangle, measure all sides and angles. What do you notice?

What is the relationship between the congruent sides and some of the angles? **The ∠s opposite the ≅ sides are ≅.**

Draw several triangles with two congruent angles. Measure all sides. What do you notice?

What is the relationship between the congruent angles and some of the sides? **The sides opposite the ≅ ∠s are ≅.**

Some Theorems Based on Congruent Triangles

Objectives

1. Apply the theorems and corollaries about isosceles triangles.
2. Use the AAS Theorem to prove two triangles congruent.
3. Use the HL Theorem to prove two right triangles congruent.
4. Prove that two overlapping triangles are congruent.

4-4 *The Isosceles Triangle Theorems*

The photograph shows the Transamerica Pyramid in San Francisco. Each of its four faces is an isosceles triangle, with two congruent sides. These congruent sides are called **legs** and the third side is called the **base.** The angles at the base are called *base angles* and the angle opposite the base is called the *vertex angle* of the isosceles triangle.

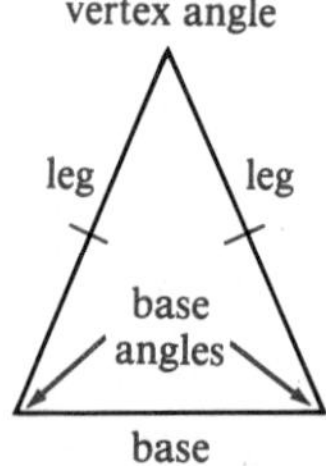

You can use the steps described below to form an isosceles triangle. Refer to the diagrams shown.

(1) Fold a sheet of paper in half.
(2) Cut off a double-thickness corner piece along the dashed line.
(3) Open the corner piece and lay it flat. You will have a triangle, which is labeled $\triangle PRS$ in the diagram. The fold line is labeled $\overline{PQ}$.
(4) Since $\overline{PR}$ and $\overline{PS}$ were formed by the same cut line, you can conclude that they are congruent segments and that $\triangle PRS$ is isosceles.

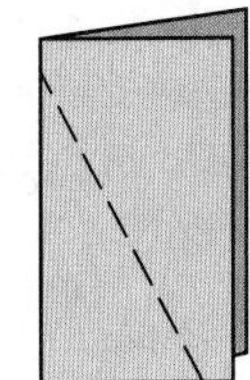

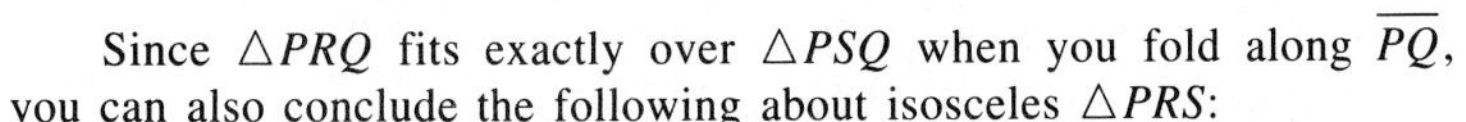

Since $\triangle PRQ$ fits exactly over $\triangle PSQ$ when you fold along $\overline{PQ}$, you can also conclude the following about isosceles $\triangle PRS$:

$\angle PRS \cong \angle PSR$
$\overline{PQ}$ bisects $\angle RPS$.
$\overline{PQ}$ bisects $\overline{RS}$.
$\overline{PQ} \perp \overline{RS}$ at Q.
$\triangle PQR \cong \triangle PQS$

These observations suggest some of the following results.

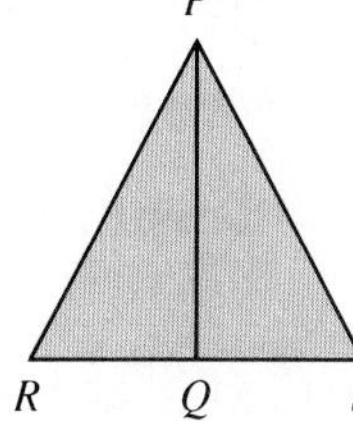

Theorem 4-1 *The Isosceles Triangle Theorem*

If two sides of a triangle are congruent, then the angles opposite those sides are congruent.

Given: $\overline{AB} \cong \overline{AC}$

Prove: $\angle B \cong \angle C$

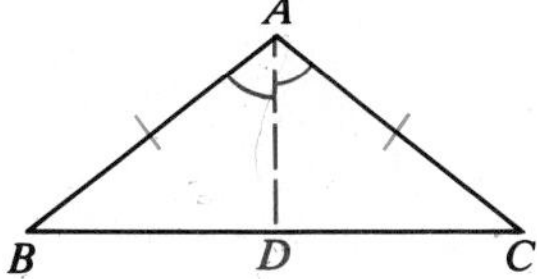

Plan for Proof: You can show that $\angle B$ and $\angle C$ are corresponding parts of congruent triangles if you draw an auxiliary line that will give you such triangles. For example, draw the bisector of $\angle A$.

Theorem 4-1 is often stated as follows: Base angles of an isosceles triangle are congruent. The following corollaries of Theorem 4-1 will be discussed as classroom exercises.

Corollary 1

An equilateral triangle is also equiangular.

Corollary 2

An equilateral triangle has three 60° angles.

Corollary 3

The bisector of the vertex angle of an isosceles triangle is perpendicular to the base at its midpoint.

Teaching Note

Draw figures like those shown below to reinforce the idea that the base of an isosceles triangle does not have to be at the "bottom" of the figure.

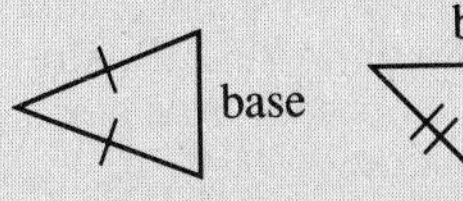

Chalkboard Examples

In Exs. 1 and 2, $\overline{BC} \cong \overline{AC}$.

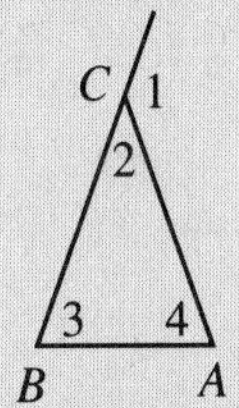

1. If $m\angle 1 = 140$, $m\angle 2 = \underline{40}$, $m\angle 3 = \underline{70}$, $m\angle 4 = \underline{70}$.
2. If $m\angle 4 = 65$, $m\angle 3 = \underline{65}$, $m\angle 2 = \underline{50}$, $m\angle 1 = \underline{130}$.
3. Given: $j \parallel k$; $\overline{AB} \cong \overline{CB}$
   Prove: $m\angle 1 = m\angle 2$

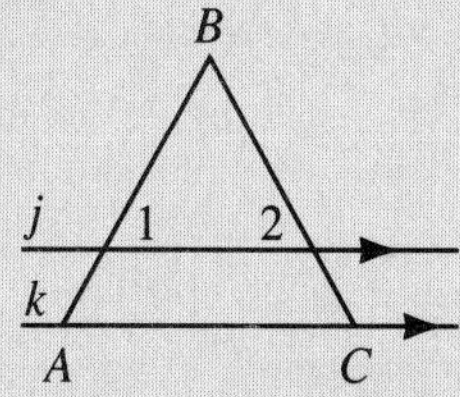

1. $j \parallel k$; $\overline{AB} \cong \overline{CB}$ (Given)
2. $\triangle ABC$ is isos. (Def. of isos. $\triangle$)
3. $\angle A \cong \angle C$ (Isos. $\triangle$ Thm.)
4. $\angle 1 \cong \angle A$; $\angle 2 \cong \angle C$ (If 2 $\parallel$ lines are cut by a trans. corr. $\angle$s are $\cong$.)
5. $\angle 1 \cong \angle 2$ (Trans. Prop.)
6. $m\angle 1 = m\angle 2$ (Def. of $\cong$ $\angle$s)

Theorem 4-2

If two angles of a triangle are congruent, then the sides opposite those angles are congruent.

Given: $\angle B \cong \angle C$

Prove: $\overline{AB} \cong \overline{AC}$

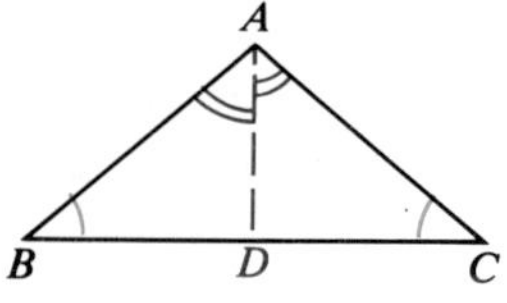

Plan for Proof: You can show that $\overline{AB}$ and $\overline{AC}$ are corresponding parts of congruent triangles. Draw the bisector of $\angle A$ as your auxiliary line, show that $\angle ADB \cong \angle ADC$, and use ASA.

Corollary

An equiangular triangle is also equilateral.

Notice that Theorem 4-2 is the converse of Theorem 4-1, and the corollary of Theorem 4-2 is the converse of Corollary 1 of Theorem 4-1.

Classroom Exercises

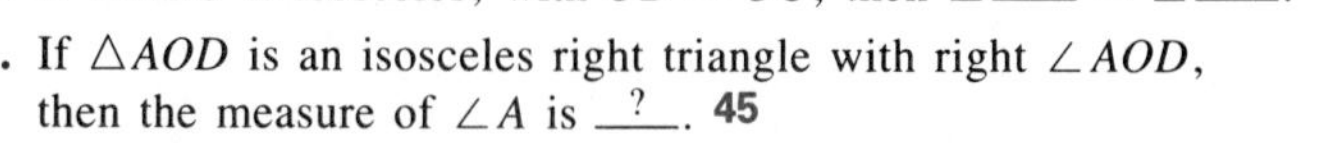

2. $\angle OBC \cong \angle OCB$

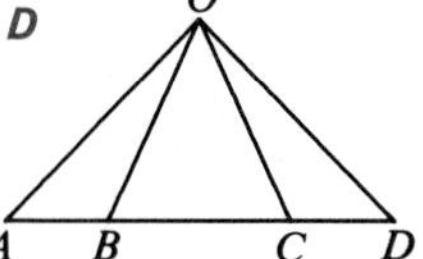

1. If $\triangle AOD$ is isosceles, with $\overline{OA} \cong \overline{OD}$, then $\angle$ _?_ $\cong \angle$ _?_. **A, D**
2. If $\triangle BOC$ is isosceles, with $\overline{OB} \cong \overline{OC}$, then $\angle$ _?_ $\cong \angle$ _?_.
3. If $\triangle AOD$ is an isosceles right triangle with right $\angle AOD$, then the measure of $\angle A$ is _?_. **45**
4. Given the triangles at the right, which of the following can you conclude are true? **b, c, d, f**

   a. $\angle D \cong \angle R$ b. $\overline{DE} \cong \overline{DF}$

   c. $\overline{DF} \cong \overline{RT}$ d. $\angle E \cong \angle F$

   e. $\angle E \cong \angle S$ f. $\angle S \cong \angle T$

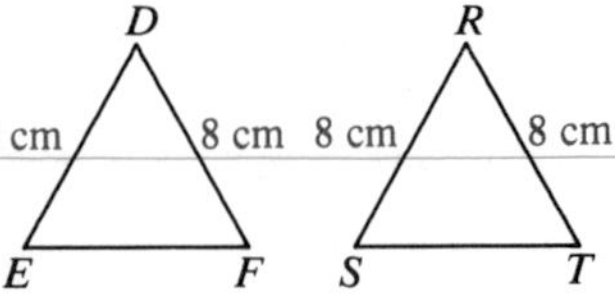

Given the two congruent angles, name two segments that must be congruent.

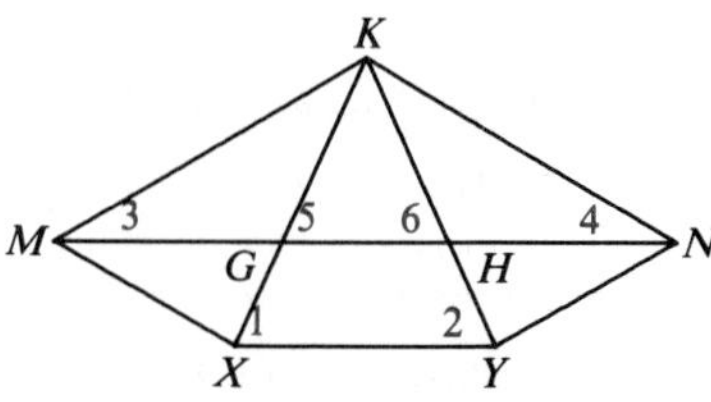

5. $\angle 1 \cong \angle 2$ **$\overline{KX}, \overline{KY}$**
6. $\angle 3 \cong \angle 4$ **$\overline{KM}, \overline{KN}$**
7. $\angle 5 \cong \angle 6$ **$\overline{KG}, \overline{KH}$**
8. Is the statement "$\overline{MK} \cong \overline{NK}$ if and only if $\angle 3 \cong \angle 4$" true or false? **True**
9. Explain how Corollary 1 follows from Theorem 4-1.
10. Explain how Corollary 2 follows from Corollary 1.
11. Explain how Corollary 3 follows from Theorem 4-1.
12. Explain how the Corollary follows from Theorem 4-2.

Proof Note

A proof of Theorem 4-2 is by no means as simple as that of Theorem 4-1. The difficulty lies in the fact that $\overline{AD}$ is the only side that can be used, but $\overline{AD}$ is not included between $\angle BAD$ and $\angle B$. Before the ASA Postulate can be used, you need to show that $\angle BDA \cong \angle CDA$. To do this use the following corollary: If two angles of one triangle are congruent to two angles of another triangle, then the third angles are congruent.

Additional Answers Classroom Exercises

9. $\triangle ABC$ is equilateral. $\overline{AB} \cong \overline{AC}$, so $\angle B \cong \angle C$. $\overline{AB} \cong \overline{BC}$, so $\angle A \cong \angle C$. Then $\angle A \cong \angle B \cong \angle C$.
10. $m\angle A = m\angle B = m\angle C$ and $m\angle A + m\angle B + m\angle C = 180$. Then $3 \cdot m\angle A = 180$ and $m\angle A = 60$. Similarly, $m\angle B = m\angle C = 60$.
11. Use the diagram for Theorem 4-1. Since $\triangle BAD \cong \triangle CAD$, $\angle BDA \cong \angle CDA$. If 2 lines form $\cong$ adjacent $\angle$s, the lines are $\perp$. $\overline{BD} \cong \overline{CD}$, so D is the midpoint of $\overline{BC}$.
12. $\triangle ABC$ is equiangular. $\angle A \cong \angle B$, so $\overline{BC} \cong \overline{AC}$. $\angle A \cong \angle C$, so $\overline{BC} \cong \overline{AB}$. Then $\overline{AB} \cong \overline{BC} \cong \overline{AC}$.

Written Exercises

Find the value of x.

A **1.** **80**

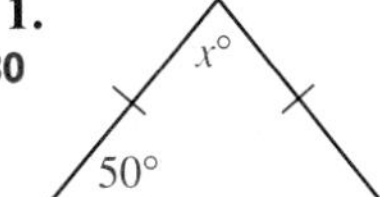

2. **45**

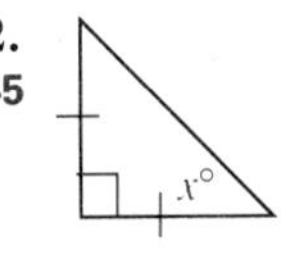

3. **53**

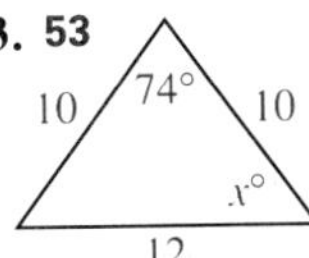

4. **11**

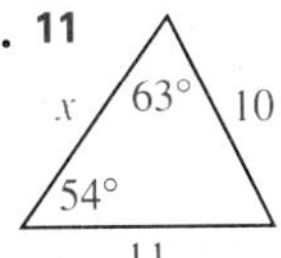

5. **5**

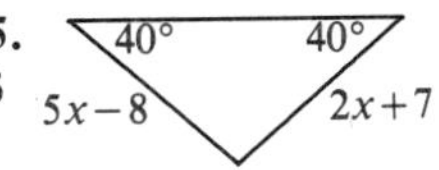

6. **6**

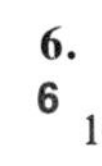
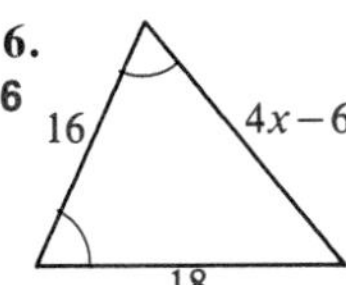

7. **41**

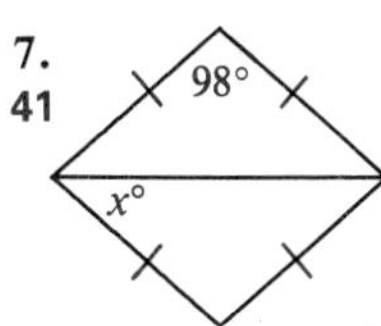

8. **30**

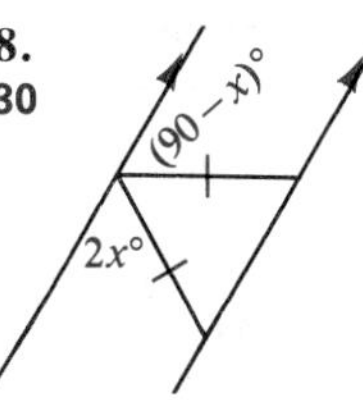

For each exercise place the statements in an appropriate order for a proof. (There may be more than one correct order.) **Answers may vary.**

9. Given: $\overline{RS} \cong \overline{RT}$
Prove: $\angle 3 \cong \angle 4$ **c, d, b, a**
(a) $\angle 3 \cong \angle 4$
(b) $\angle 3 \cong \angle 1$; $\angle 2 \cong \angle 4$
(c) $\overline{RS} \cong \overline{RT}$
(d) $\angle 1 \cong \angle 2$

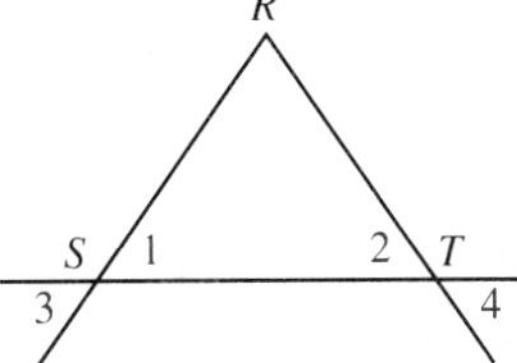

10. Given: $\overline{BD} \parallel \overline{CE}$; $\angle 5 \cong \angle 6$
Prove: $\overline{AC} \cong \overline{AE}$ **a, c, d, e, b**
(a) $\overline{BD} \parallel \overline{CE}$
(b) $\overline{AC} \cong \overline{AE}$
(c) $\angle 5 \cong \angle C$; $\angle 6 \cong \angle E$
(d) $\angle 5 \cong \angle 6$
(e) $\angle C \cong \angle E$

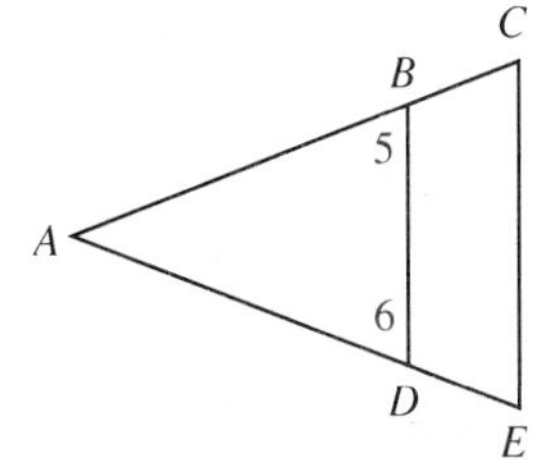

Write proofs in two-column form.

11. Theorem 4-1

12. Theorem 4-2

13. Given: M is the midpoint of $\overline{JK}$; $\angle 1 \cong \angle 2$
Prove: $\overline{JG} \cong \overline{MK}$

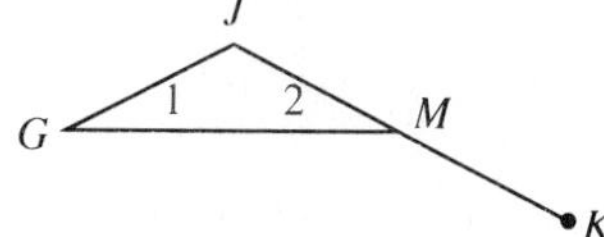

14. Given: $\overline{XY} \cong \overline{XZ}$
Prove: $\angle 3 \cong \angle 5$

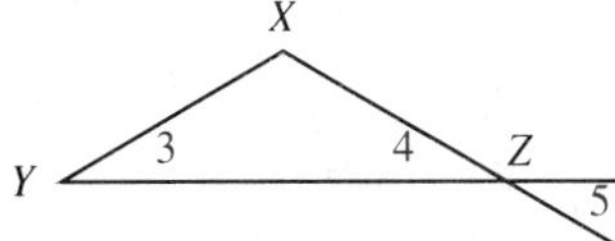

Guided Practice

Find the value of x.

1. 75

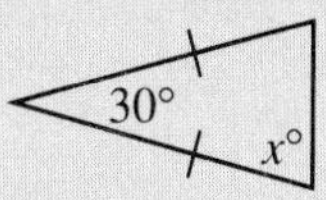

2. 9

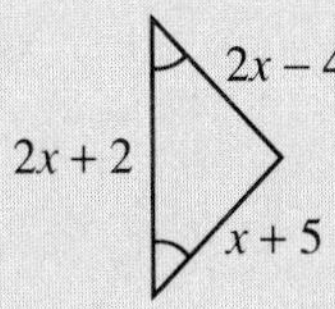

3. 42

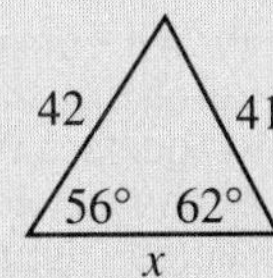

4. Place the statements in an appropriate order for a proof.

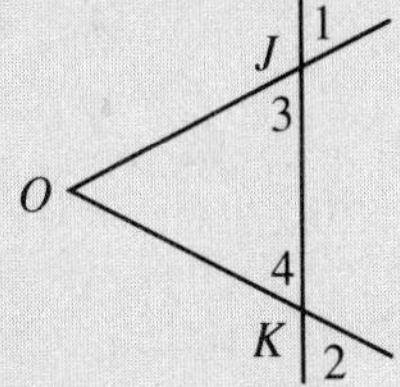

Given: $\angle 1 \cong \angle 2$
Prove: $\overline{OK} \cong \overline{OJ}$
(a) $\angle 3 \cong \angle 4$
(b) $\angle 2 \cong \angle 4$; $\angle 3 \cong \angle 1$
(c) $\overline{OK} \cong \overline{OJ}$
(d) $\angle 1 \cong \angle 2$
Answers may vary.
d, b, a, c

B **15.** Given: $\overline{PQ} \cong \overline{PR}$; $\overline{TR} \cong \overline{TS}$
Which one(s) of the following *must* be true?
(1) $\overline{ST} \parallel \overline{QP}$ (2) $\overline{ST} \cong \overline{QP}$ (3) $\angle T \cong \angle P$

16. Given: $\angle S \cong \angle T$; $\overline{ST} \parallel \overline{QP}$
Which one(s) of the following *must* be true?
(1) $\angle P \cong \angle Q$ (2) $PR = QR$
(3) R is the midpoint of $\overline{PT}$.

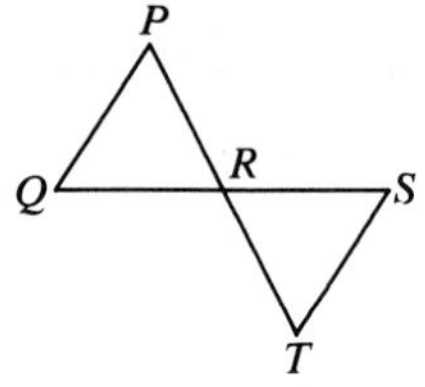

Write proofs in two-column form.

17. Given: $\overline{XY} \cong \overline{XZ}$; $\overline{OY} \cong \overline{OZ}$
Prove: $m\angle 1 = m\angle 4$

18. Given: $\overline{XY} \cong \overline{XZ}$;
$\overrightarrow{YO}$ bisects $\angle XYZ$;
$\overrightarrow{ZO}$ bisects $\angle XZY$.
Prove: $\overline{YO} \cong \overline{ZO}$

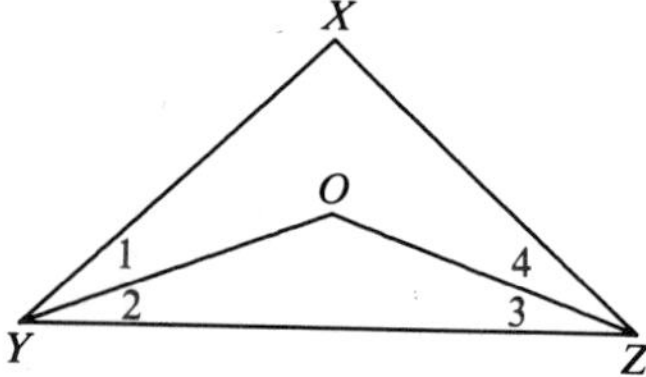

19. Given: $\overline{AB} \cong \overline{AC}$; $\overline{AL}$ and $\overline{AM}$ trisect $\angle BAC$.
(This means $\angle 1 \cong \angle 2 \cong \angle 3$.)
Prove: $\overline{AL} \cong \overline{AM}$

20. Given: $\angle 4 \cong \angle 7$; $\angle 1 \cong \angle 3$
Prove: $\triangle ABC$ is isosceles.

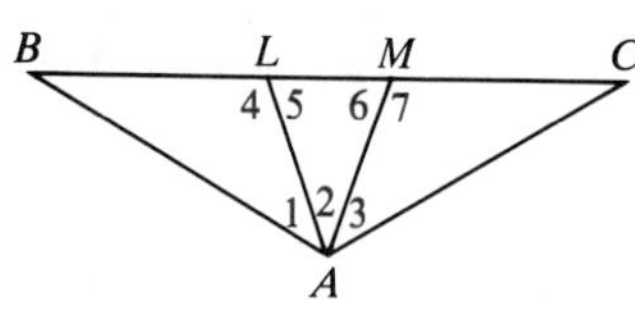

21. Given: $\overline{OP} \cong \overline{OQ}$; $\angle 3 \cong \angle 4$
Prove: $\angle 5 \cong \angle 6$

22. Given: $\overline{PO} \cong \overline{QO}$; $\overline{RO} \cong \overline{SO}$

$m\angle 2 = 40$
$m\angle 7 = 100$
$m\angle 5 = 40$
$m\angle 6 = 40$

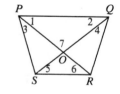

a. If you are also given that $m\angle 1 = 40$, find the measures of $\angle 2$, $\angle 7$, $\angle 5$, and $\angle 6$. Then decide whether $\overline{PQ}$ must be parallel to $\overline{SR}$. **Yes**

b. Repeat part (a), but use $m\angle 1 = k$.

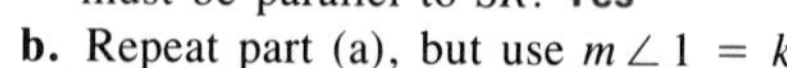

$m\angle 2 = m\angle 5 = m\angle 6 = k$, $m\angle 7 = 180 - 2k$; yes

23. Complete.
a. If $m\angle 1 = 20$, then $m\angle 3 =$ __?__, **40**
$m\angle 4 =$ __?__, and $m\angle 5 =$ __?__. **40, 60**
b. If $m\angle 1 = x$, then $m\angle 3 =$ __?__, **2x**
$m\angle 4 =$ __?__, and $m\angle 5 =$ __?__.
2x **3x**

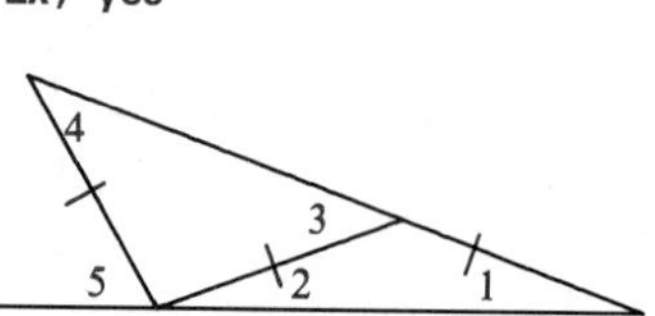

24. **a.** If $m\angle 1 = 35$, find $m\angle ABC$. **90**
b. If $m\angle 1 = k$, find $m\angle ABC$. **90**

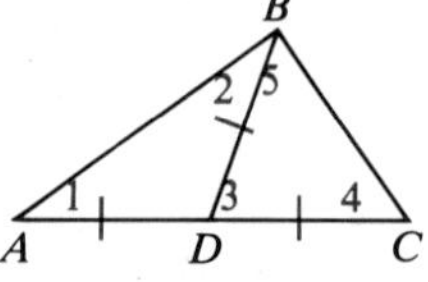

25. **a.** If $m\angle 1 = 23$, find $m\angle 7$. **90**
b. If $m\angle 1 = k$, find $m\angle 7$. **90**

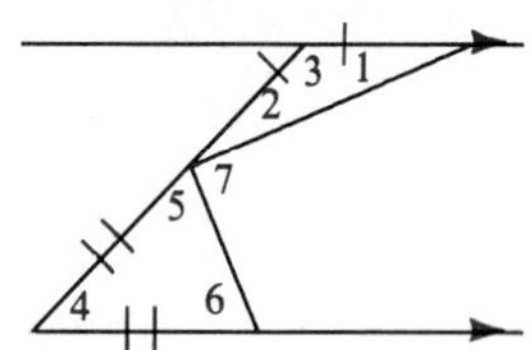

Exercise Note

Ex. 19 is worth some discussion. Point out the word *trisect* and the fact that the trisector of the vertex angle of an isosceles triangle does not trisect the base. For a deductive proof of this, see Ex. 28 on page 273.

Using a Computer

Have students use a program to draw the diagram for Ex. 24 and discover the relationship between $\angle 1$ and $\angle ABC$. Encourage them to experiment with several values of $m\angle 1$.

26. Draw an isosceles $\triangle ABC$ whose vertex angle, $\angle A$, has measure 80.

a. Draw $\overrightarrow{AX}$, the bisector of an exterior angle at A. Is $\overrightarrow{AX} \parallel \overline{BC}$? Explain. **Yes**

b. Would your answer change if the measure of $\angle A$ changed? **No**

Find the values of *x* and *y*.

27. In equiangular $\triangle ABC$, $AB = 4x - y$, $BC = 2x + 3y$, and $AC = 7$. $\boldsymbol{x = 2, y = 1}$

28. In equilateral $\triangle DEF$, $m\angle D = x + y$ and $m\angle E = 2x - y$. $\boldsymbol{x = 40, y = 20}$

29. In $\triangle JKL$, $\overline{JK} \cong \overline{KL}$, $m\angle J = 2x - y$, $m\angle K = 2x + 2y$, and $m\angle L = x + 2y$. $\boldsymbol{x = 30, y = 10}$

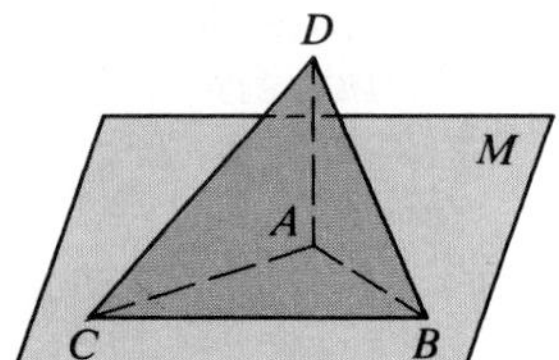

30. Given: $\triangle ABC$ in plane M, D not in plane M;
$\angle ACB \cong \angle ABC$; $\angle DCB \cong \angle DBC$

Name a pair of congruent triangles. $\boldsymbol{\triangle DAC \cong \triangle DAB}$

Prove that your answer is correct.

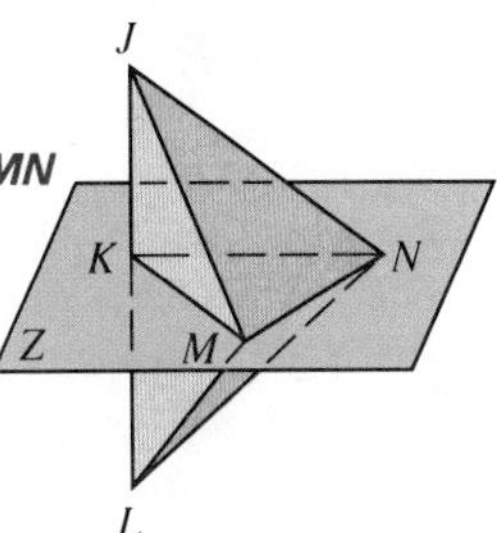

31. Given: $\overline{JL} \perp$ plane Z;
$\triangle KMN$ is isosceles, with $\overline{KM} \cong \overline{KN}$.

a. Prove that two other triangles are isosceles. $\boldsymbol{\triangle JMN, \triangle LMN}$

b. Must these two isosceles triangles be congruent? Explain. **No. They are $\cong$ if and only if $\overline{KJ} \cong \overline{KL}$.**

32. Draw an isosceles triangle and then join the midpoints of its sides to form another triangle. What can you deduce about this second triangle? Explain. **It is isosceles.**

33. *ABCDE* is a regular pentagon and *DEFG* is a square. Find the measures of $\angle EAF$, $\angle AFD$, and $\angle DAF$.

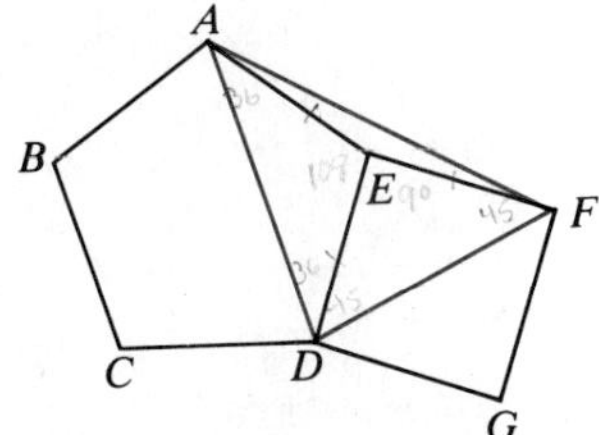

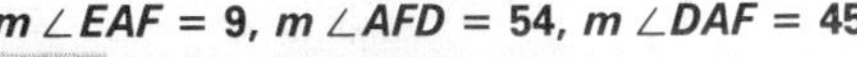

$\boldsymbol{m\angle EAF = 9, m\angle AFD = 54, m\angle DAF = 45}$

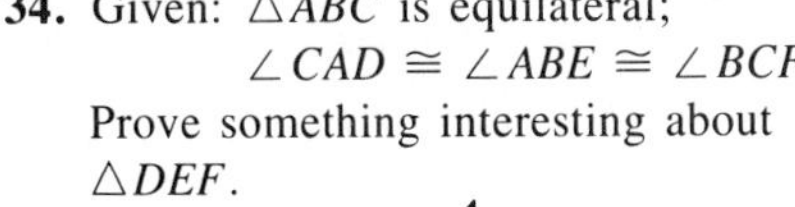

34. Given: $\triangle ABC$ is equilateral;
$\angle CAD \cong \angle ABE \cong \angle BCF$

Prove something interesting about $\triangle DEF$.

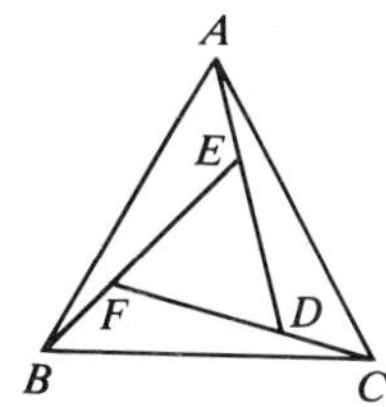

$\boldsymbol{\triangle DEF}$ **is equilateral.**

Challenge

The figure shown at the right can be dissected into three congruent pieces, as shown by the dashed lines. Can you dissect the figure into **(a)** two congruent pieces? **(b)** four congruent pieces?

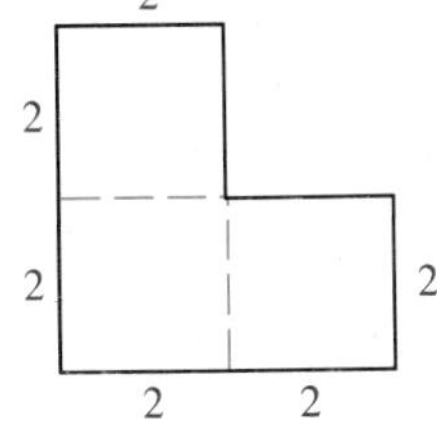

Additional Answers Written Exercises

26.a. Yes; $m\angle B = m\angle C = \frac{1}{2}(180 - 80) = 50$ (The sum of the meas. of the $\angle$s of a $\triangle$ is 180.) $m\angle XAC = \frac{1}{2}(50 + 50) = 50$ (The meas. of an ext. $\angle$ equals the sum of the meas. of the 2 remote int. $\angle$s.) Thus, $\overrightarrow{AX} \parallel \overline{BC}$ (If 2 lines are cut by a trans. and alt. int. $\angle$s are $\cong$, then the lines are $\parallel$.)

Using a Computer

Exs. 26, 32–34 can be done effectively using a program. To construct the figures for Exs. 33 and 34 will be a challenge, but the answers then follow easily.

Teaching Suggestions, pp. T90–T91

Objectives
Presenting the Lesson
Extension

Supplementary Materials

Practice Master 19
Test 15
Resource Book, pp. 20, 123
Study Guide, pp. 51–54
Computer Activity 10

Lesson Focus

This lesson presents two additional methods of proving triangles congruent, namely AAS and HL. There are now five ways to prove two triangles congruent.

Suggested Assignments

Minimum
Day 1: 143–144/1–4
Day 2: 144/5–7, 9–12
Day 3: 144–145/13, 15, 16
146/Self-Test 2

Average
Day 1: 143–144/1, 3, 5, 8, 10
S 139/29, 31
Day 2: 144–145/11, 13, 15, 16, 18, 19, 21
146/Self-Test 2

Maximum
Day 1: 144/3–9, 13
S 139/33, 34
Day 2: 144–145/10–22 even

4-5 *Other Methods of Proving Triangles Congruent*

The SSS, SAS, and ASA Postulates give us three methods of proving triangles congruent. In this section we will develop two other methods.

Theorem 4-3 *AAS Theorem*

If two angles and a non-included side of one triangle are congruent to the corresponding parts of another triangle, then the triangles are congruent.

Given: $\triangle ABC$ and $\triangle DEF$; $\angle B \cong \angle E$; $\angle C \cong \angle F$; $\overline{AC} \cong \overline{DF}$
Prove: $\triangle ABC \cong \triangle DEF$

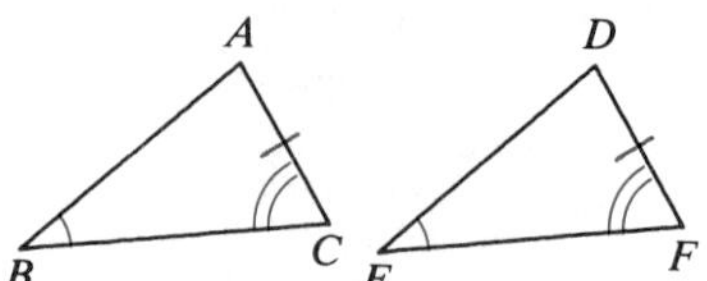

Plan for Proof: You can prove the triangles congruent if you can apply one of the SSS, SAS, or ASA Postulates. You can use the ASA Postulate if you first show that $\angle A \cong \angle D$. To do that, use the fact that the other two angles of $\triangle ABC$ are congruent to the other two angles of $\triangle DEF$.

Do you see overlapping triangles in the photograph? Sometimes you want to prove that certain overlapping triangles are congruent. For example, suppose you have the following problem:

Given: $\overline{GJ} \cong \overline{GK}$; $\angle H \cong \angle I$
Prove: $\triangle GHJ \cong \triangle GIK$

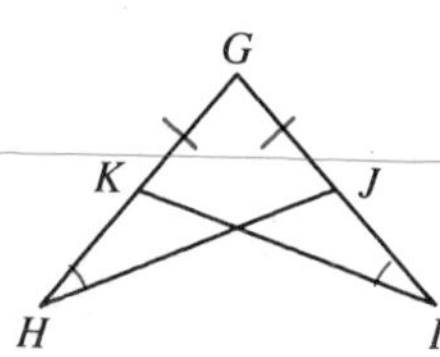

You may find it helps you visualize the congruence if you redraw the two triangles, as shown below. Now you can see that since $\angle G$ is common to both triangles, the triangles must be congruent by the AAS Theorem.

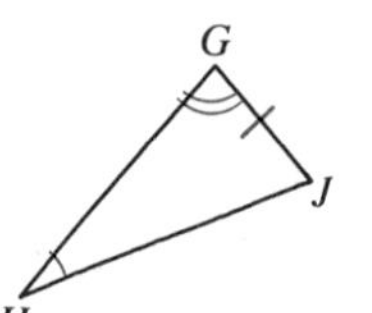

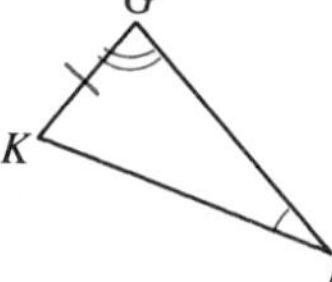

Our final method of proving triangles congruent applies only to right triangles. In a right triangle the side opposite the right angle is called the **hypotenuse** (hyp.). The other two sides are called **legs.**

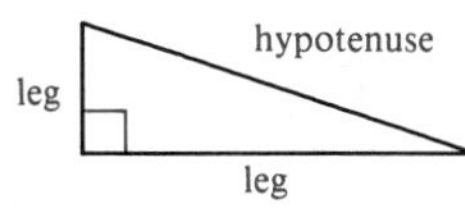

A proof in two-column form for the next theorem would be too long and involved. The proof shown below is written instead in *paragraph form*, which emphasizes the *key steps* in the proof. You will learn to write paragraph proofs in the next section.

Theorem 4-4 *HL Theorem*

If the hypotenuse and a leg of one right triangle are congruent to the corresponding parts of another right triangle, then the triangles are congruent.

Given: $\triangle ABC$ and $\triangle DEF$;
$\angle C$ and $\angle F$ are right $\angle$s;
$\overline{AB} \cong \overline{DE}$ (hypotenuses);
$\overline{BC} \cong \overline{EF}$ (legs)

Prove: $\triangle ABC \cong \triangle DEF$

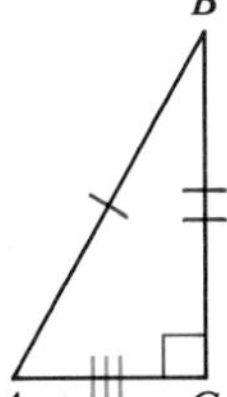

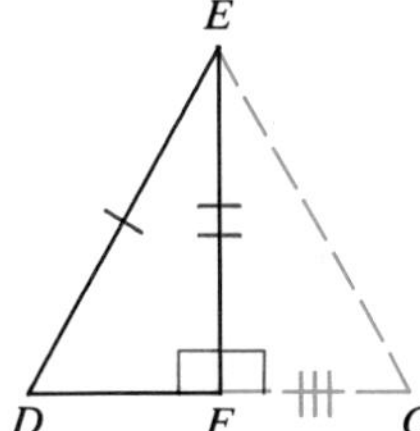

Proof:

By the Ruler Postulate there is a point G on the ray opposite to $\overrightarrow{FD}$ such that $\overline{FG} \cong \overline{CA}$. Draw $\overline{GE}$. Because $\angle DFE$ is a right angle, $\angle GFE$ is also a right angle. $\triangle ABC \cong \triangle GEF$ by the SAS Postulate. Then $\overline{AB} \cong \overline{GE}$. Since $\overline{DE} \cong \overline{AB}$, we have $\overline{DE} \cong \overline{GE}$. In isosceles $\triangle DEG$, $\angle G \cong \angle D$. Since $\triangle ABC \cong \triangle GEF$, $\angle A \cong \angle G$. Then $\angle A \cong \angle D$. Finally, $\triangle ABC \cong \triangle DEF$ by the AAS Theorem.

Recall from Exercise 22 on page 121 and Exercise 11 on page 124 that AAA and SSA correspondences do not guarantee congruent triangles. We can now summarize the methods available for proving triangles congruent.

Summary of Ways to Prove Two Triangles Congruent

All triangles:	SSS	SAS	ASA	AAS
Right triangles:	HL			

Which of these methods are postulates and which are theorems?

Using a Model

A physical demonstration of Theorem 4-4 will make its meaning clear to most students. Begin with two sticks of equal length (about 60 cm). They will be called short sticks in what follows. Have one student hold a short stick so that it is flat against the wall, has one end on the floor, and is perpendicular to the floor. Have a second student hold a meter stick against the wall with one end at the top end of the short stick. Now rotate the meter stick until it reaches the floor. Point out the triangle: meter stick, short stick, segment on floor. Let two other students, working alongside the first two, repeat the experiment. The class will see congruent triangles.

Teaching Note

To reinforce the summary of ways to prove two triangles congruent, have students draw on the chalkboard convincing diagrams showing the methods that work (SSS, SAS, ASA, AAS, HL) and some methods that do not work (AAA, SSA).

Additional Answers

Postulates: SSS, SAS, ASA
Theorems: AAS, HL

Chalkboard Examples

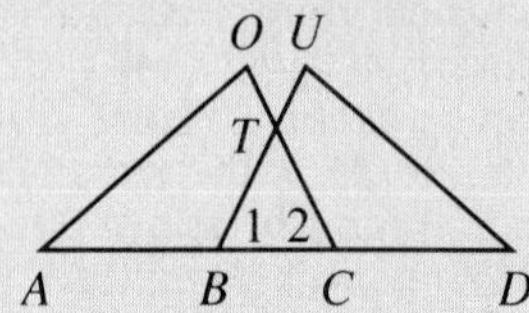

Given: $\angle A \cong \angle D$; $\angle O \cong \angle U$; $\overline{AO} \cong \overline{DU}$

Prove: $\overline{TB} \cong \overline{TC}$

1. Write a Plan for Proof. Answers will vary. We can show $\overline{TB} \cong \overline{TC}$ if we can apply the converse of the Isosceles Triangle Theorem. We can apply that converse if we first show that $\angle 1 \cong \angle 2$. We will have this congruence if we can prove $\triangle AOC \cong \triangle DUB$.
2. List the key steps of a proof. $\triangle AOC \cong \triangle DUB$; $\angle 1 \cong \angle 2$ (ASA Post.; Corr. parts of $\cong$ ▵s are $\cong$.) $\overline{TB} \cong \overline{TC}$ (If 2 angles of a $\triangle$ are $\cong$, the sides opp. those ∠s are $\cong$.)
3. Write a proof in paragraph form. From what is given we have $\triangle AOC \cong \triangle DUB$. Then $\angle 1 \cong \angle 2$. Finally, $\overline{TB} \cong \overline{TC}$ by the converse of the Isosceles Triangle Theorem.

Classroom Exercises

State which congruence method(s) can be used to prove the triangles congruent. If no method applies, say *none*.

1. 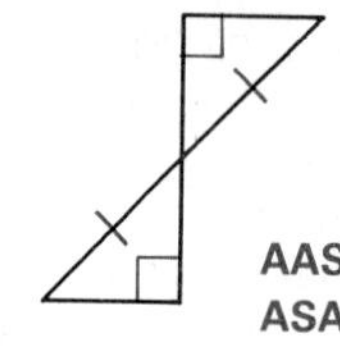 **AAS ASA**

2. **AAS HL** 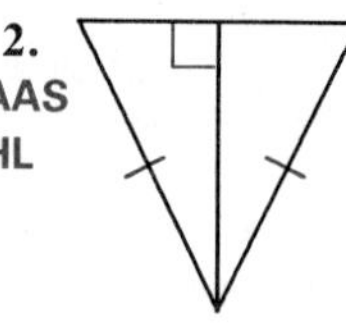

3. **ASA** 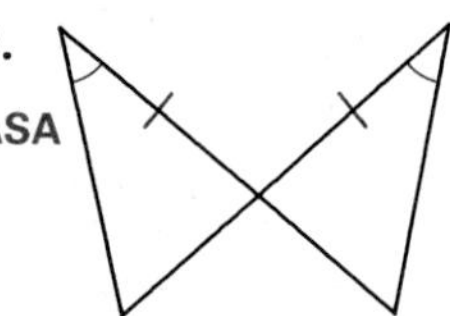

4. 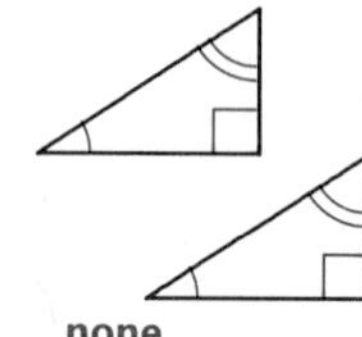 **none**

5. **SAS SSS** 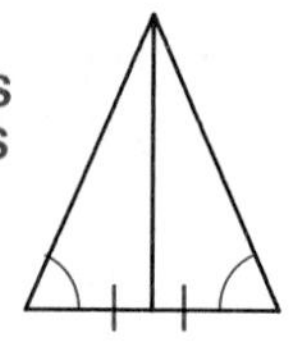

6. **HL** 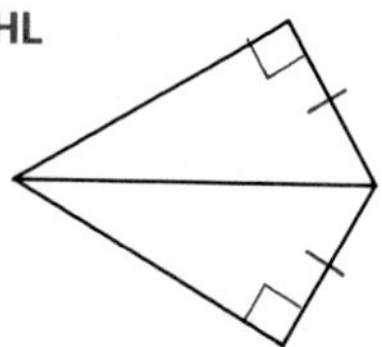

7. 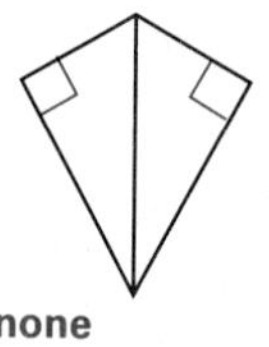 **none**

8.  **ASA SAS HL AAS**

9. 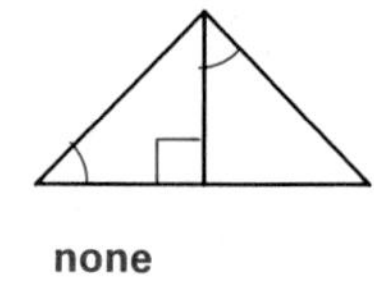 **none**

For each diagram, name a pair of overlapping triangles. Tell whether the triangles are congruent by the SSS, SAS, ASA, AAS, or HL method.

10. Given: $\overline{AB} \cong \overline{DC}$; $\overline{AC} \cong \overline{DB}$

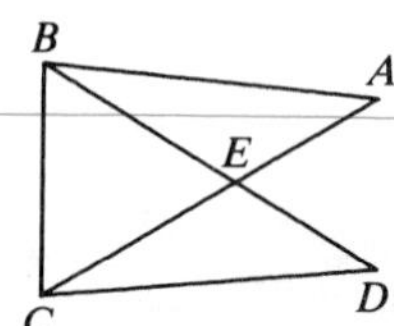

$\triangle ABC \cong \triangle DCB$ by SSS

11. Given: $\angle 2 \cong \angle 3$; $\angle 1 \cong \angle 4$

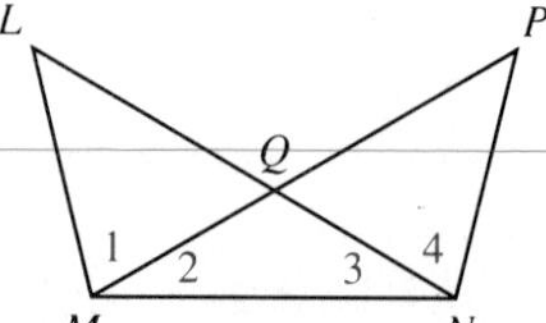

$\triangle LMN \cong \triangle PNM$ by ASA

12. Given: $\overline{WU} \cong \overline{ZV}$; $WX = YZ$; $\angle U$ and $\angle V$ are rt. ∠s.

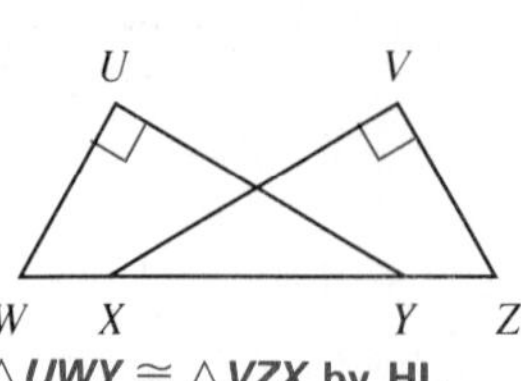

$\triangle UWY \cong \triangle VZX$ by HL

13. Given: $\angle ABC \cong \angle ACB$; $\overline{AE} \perp \overline{EC}$; $\overline{AD} \perp \overline{DB}$

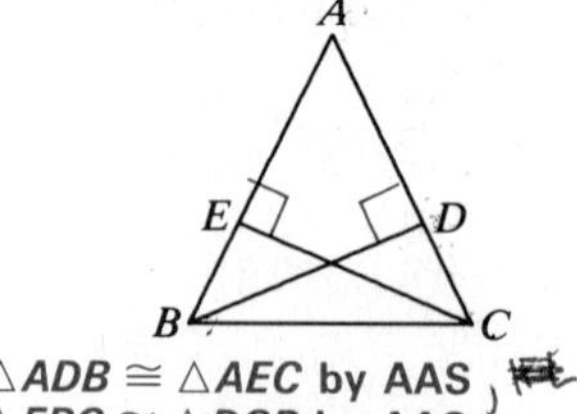

$\triangle ADB \cong \triangle AEC$ by AAS, $\triangle EBC \cong \triangle DCB$ by AAS

14. To prove that right triangles are congruent, some geometry books also use the methods stated below. For each method, draw two right triangles that appear to be congruent. Mark the given information on your triangles. Use your marks to determine which of our methods (SSS, SAS, ASA, AAS, or HL) could be used instead of each method listed.

a. Leg-Leg Method (LL) If two legs of one right triangle are congruent to the two legs of another right triangle, then the triangles are congruent. **SAS**

b. Hypotenuse-Acute Angle Method (HA) If the hypotenuse and an acute angle of one right triangle are congruent to the hypotenuse and an acute angle of another right triangle, then the triangles are congruent. **AAS**

c. Leg-Acute Angle Method (LA) If a leg and an acute angle of one right triangle are congruent to the corresponding parts in another right triangle, then the triangles are congruent. **AAS or ASA**

Written Exercises

A **1.** Supply the missing statements and reasons.

Given: $\angle W$ and $\angle Y$ are rt. $\angle$s; $\overline{WX} \cong \overline{YX}$

Prove: $\overline{WZ} \cong \overline{YZ}$

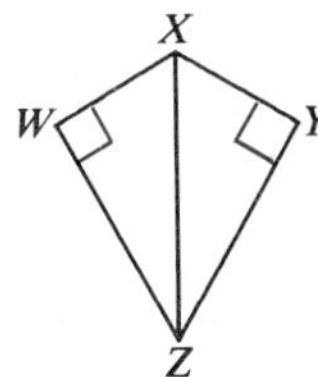

Proof:

Statements	Reasons
1. $\angle W$ and $\angle Y$ are rt. $\angle$s.	1. ? **Given**
2. $\triangle XWZ$ and $\triangle XYZ$ are rt. $\triangle$s.	2. ? **Def. of rt. $\triangle$**
3. $\overline{WX} \cong \overline{YX}$	3. ? **Given**
4. ? $\overline{XZ} \cong \overline{XZ}$	4. Reflexive Prop.
5. $\triangle XWZ \cong$? $\triangle XYZ$	5. ? **HL**
6. ? $\overline{WZ} \cong \overline{YZ}$	6. ? **Corr. parts of $\cong$ $\triangle$s are $\cong$.**

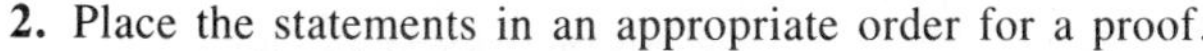

2. Place the statements in an appropriate order for a proof.

Given: $\overline{KL} \perp \overline{LA}$; $\overline{KJ} \perp \overline{JA}$; $\overrightarrow{AK}$ bisects $\angle LAJ$.

Prove: $\overline{LK} \cong \overline{JK}$

(a) $\overline{KL} \perp \overline{LA}$; $\overline{KJ} \perp \overline{JA}$
(b) $\angle 1 \cong \angle 2$
(c) $\overrightarrow{AK}$ bisects $\angle LAJ$.
(d) $m\angle L = 90$; $m\angle J = 90$
(e) $\overline{LK} \cong \overline{JK}$
(f) $\angle L \cong \angle J$
(g) $\triangle LKA \cong \triangle JKA$
(h) $\overline{KA} \cong \overline{KA}$

Answers may vary. a, d, f, c, b, h, g, e

Problem Solving

After discussing Ex. 14, ask students to draw a counterexample to the following statement: If a leg and an acute angle of one right triangle are congruent to a leg and an acute angle of another right triangle, then the triangles are congruent.
One possible answer is the following:

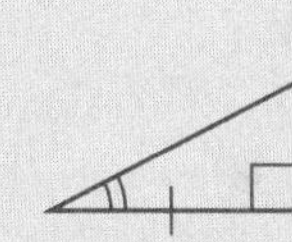

Have students compare the above statement with the one in Ex. 14(c).

Guided Practice

1. Supply the missing statements and reasons.

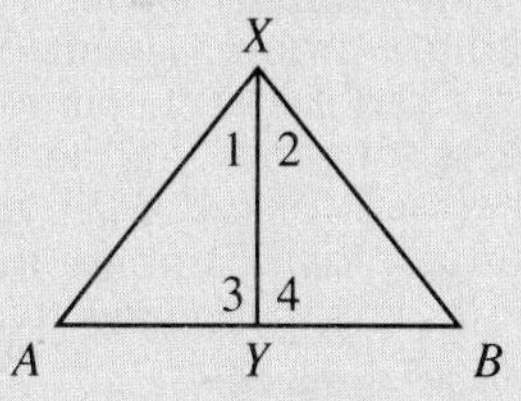

Given: $\overline{XY} \perp \overline{AB}$; $\overline{XA} \cong \overline{XB}$
Prove: $\angle 1 \cong \angle 2$
Proof:
1. $\overline{XY} \perp \overline{AB}$ (Given)
2. $\angle 3$ and $\angle 4$ are rt. $\angle$s. (Def. of $\perp$ lines)
3. $\triangle AYX$ and $\triangle BYX$ are rt. $\triangle$s. (Def. of rt. $\triangle$s)
4. $\overline{XY} \cong \overline{XY}$ (Reflexive Prop.)
5. $\overline{XA} \cong \overline{XB}$ (Given)
6. $\triangle AYX \cong \triangle BYX$ (HL Theorem)
7. $\angle 1 \cong \angle 2$ (Corr. parts of $\cong$ $\triangle$s are $\cong$.)

(continued)

2. Place the statements in an appropriate order for a proof.

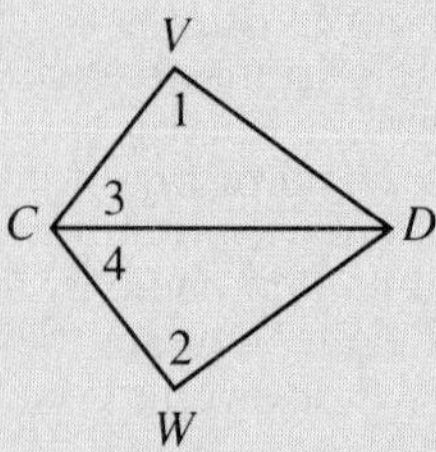

Given: $\angle 1 \cong \angle 2$;
$\overline{CD}$ bisects $\angle VCW$.
Prove: $\overline{DV} \cong \overline{DW}$

(a) $\overline{CD}$ bisects $\angle VCW$.
(b) $\overline{DV} \cong \overline{DW}$
(c) $\angle 3 \cong \angle 4$
(d) $\triangle CVD \cong \triangle CWD$
(e) $\angle 1 \cong \angle 2$
(f) $\overline{CD} \cong \overline{CD}$

Answers may vary.
e, a, c, f, d, b

Group Activity

Ex. 9 is a good one for students to discuss. You can divide the class into groups of four students each. Within a group, two students can write the statements for proof (a), the other two for proof (b). All four can then compare the two proofs, supplying reasons as they go.

Using a Computer

Exs. 10 and 16–19 are suited to the use of a construction program.
For Ex. 14, have students draw the figure using a construction program, look for pairs of congruent triangles, and verify their congruence by measurement.

Write proofs in two-column form.

3. Given: $\overline{EF} \perp \overline{EG}$; $\overline{HG} \perp \overline{EG}$;
$\overline{EH} \cong \overline{GF}$
Prove: $\angle H \cong \angle F$

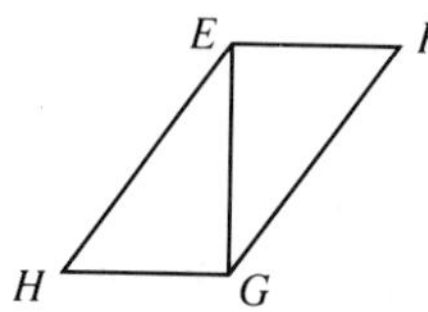

4. Given: $\overline{RT} \cong \overline{AS}$;
$\overline{RS} \cong \overline{AT}$
Prove: $\angle TSA \cong \angle STR$

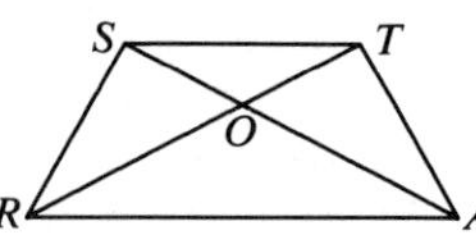

Use the information given in each exercise to name the method (SSS, SAS, ASA, AAS, or HL) you could use to prove $\triangle AOB \cong \triangle AOC$. You need not write the proofs.

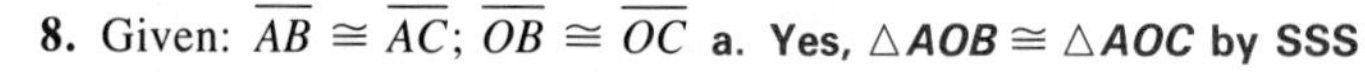

5. Given: $\overline{AO} \perp$ plane M; $\overline{BO} \cong \overline{CO}$ **SAS**

6. Given: $\overline{AO} \perp$ plane M; $\angle B \cong \angle C$ **AAS**

7. Given: $\overline{AO} \perp$ plane M; $\overline{AB} \cong \overline{AC}$ **HL**

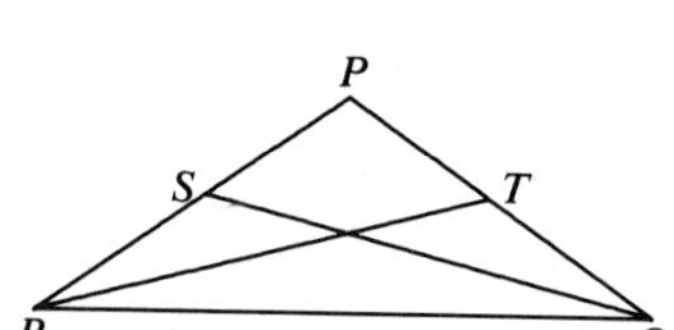

B **8.** Given: $\overline{AB} \cong \overline{AC}$; $\overline{OB} \cong \overline{OC}$ **a. Yes, $\triangle AOB \cong \triangle AOC$ by SSS**

a. Is it possible to prove that $\angle AOB \cong \angle AOC$?

b. Is it possible to prove that $\angle AOB$ and $\angle AOC$ are right angles? **No**

9. In many proofs you may find that different methods can be used. You may not know in advance which method will be better. There are *two* possible pairs of overlapping triangles that could be used in this proof. To compare the two methods, write a two-column proof for each plan.

Given: $\overline{PR} \cong \overline{PQ}$; $\overline{SR} \cong \overline{TQ}$
Prove: $\overline{QS} \cong \overline{RT}$

a. Plan for Proof: Show that $\triangle RQS \cong \triangle QRT$ by SAS.

b. Plan for Proof: Show that $\triangle PQS \cong \triangle PRT$ by SAS.

10. a. Draw an isosceles $\triangle RST$ with $\overline{RT} \cong \overline{ST}$. Let M be the midpoint of $\overline{ST}$ and N be the midpoint of $\overline{RT}$. Draw $\overline{RM}$ and $\overline{SN}$ and label their common point O. Now draw $\overline{NM}$. **Check students' drawings.**

b. Name four *pairs* of congruent triangles.
$\triangle TRM \cong \triangle TSN$; $\triangle MNR \cong \triangle NMS$; $\triangle NRS \cong \triangle MSR$; $\triangle ONR \cong \triangle OMS$

Tell which pairs of congruent parts and what method (SSS, SAS, ASA, AAS, or HL) you would use to prove the triangles are congruent.

11. Given: $\angle 1 \cong \angle 2$; $\angle 3 \cong \angle 4$; $\overline{QR} \cong \overline{TS}$
$\triangle QPR \cong \triangle TPS$ by what method?

12. Given: $\angle 3 \cong \angle 4$; $\angle 5 \cong \angle 6$
$\triangle PQX \cong \triangle PTY$ by what method?

13. Given: $\angle 3 \cong \angle 4$; $\angle 5 \cong \angle 6$ **$\angle 3 \cong \angle 4$, $\overline{PQ} \cong \overline{PT}$,**
$\triangle QPY \cong \triangle TPX$ by what method? **$\angle 6 \cong \angle 5$; AAS**

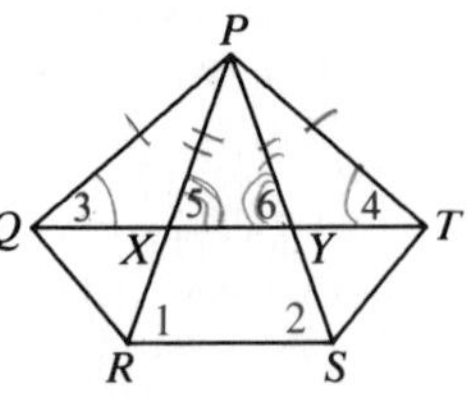

11. $\overline{PR} \cong \overline{PS}$, $\overline{PQ} \cong \overline{PT}$, $\overline{QR} \cong \overline{TS}$; SSS
12. $\angle 3 \cong \angle 4$, $\angle QXP \cong \angle TYP$, $\overline{PQ} \cong \overline{PT}$; AAS

Write proofs in two-column form.

14. Given: $\angle R \cong \angle T$; $\overline{RS} \parallel \overline{QT}$
Prove: $\overline{RS} \cong \overline{TQ}$
(*Hint*: What auxiliary line can you draw to form congruent triangles?) $\overline{QS}$

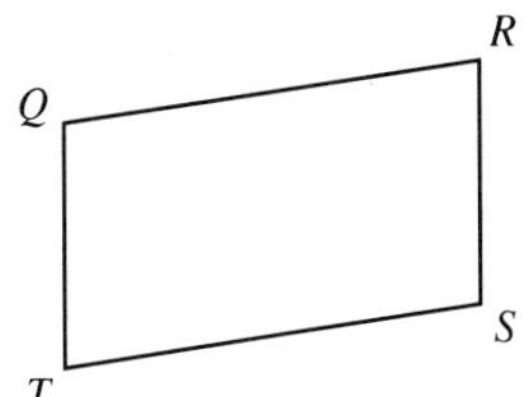

15. Given: $\angle 1 \cong \angle 2 \cong \angle 3$; $\overline{EN} \cong \overline{DG}$
Prove: $\angle 4 \cong \angle 5$

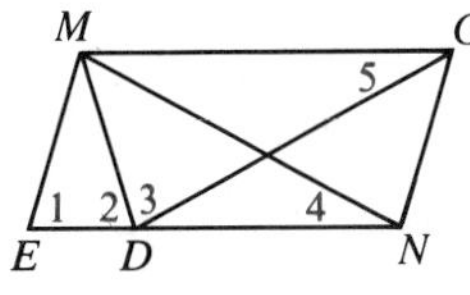

For Exercises 16–19 draw and label a diagram. List, in terms of the diagram, what is given and what is to be proved. Then write a two-column proof.

16. In two congruent triangles, if segments are drawn from two corresponding vertices perpendicular to the opposite sides, then those segments are congruent.

17. If segments are drawn from the endpoints of the base of an isosceles triangle perpendicular to the opposite legs, then those segments are congruent.

18. If $\angle A$ and $\angle B$ are the base angles of isosceles $\triangle ABC$, and the bisector of $\angle A$ meets $\overline{BC}$ at X and the bisector of $\angle B$ meets $\overline{AC}$ at Y, then $\overline{AX} \cong \overline{BY}$.

19. If segments are drawn from the midpoints of the legs of an isosceles triangle perpendicular to the base, then those segments are congruent.

20. Write a detailed plan for proof.
Given: $\overline{FL} \cong \overline{AK}$;
$\overline{SF} \cong \overline{SK}$;
M is the midpoint of $\overline{SF}$;
N is the midpoint of $\overline{SK}$.
Prove: $\overline{AM} \cong \overline{LN}$

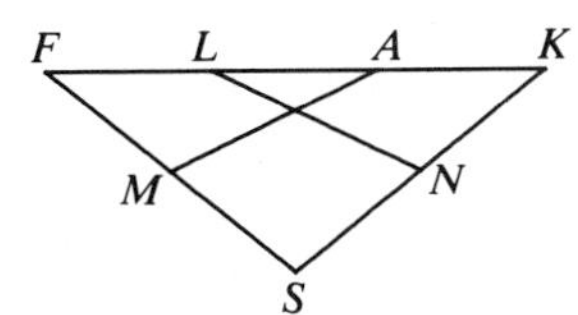

Write proofs in two-column form. Use the facts that the sides of a square are all congruent and that the angles of a square are all right angles.

C **21.** The diagram shows three squares and an equilateral triangle.
Prove: $\overline{AE} \cong \overline{FC} \cong \overline{ND}$

22. Use the results of Exercise 21 to prove that $\triangle FAN$ is equilateral.

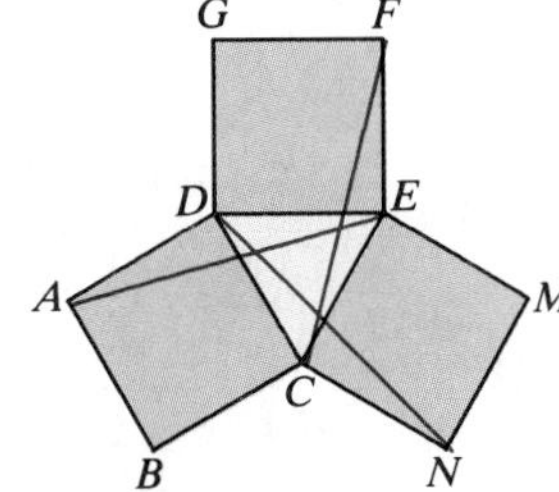

Quick Quiz

Find the value of x.

1. 50

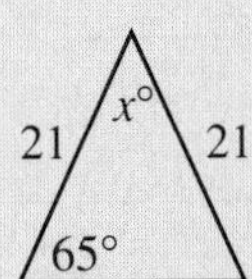

2. 4

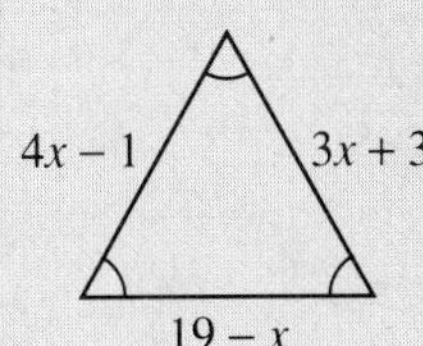

3. 50

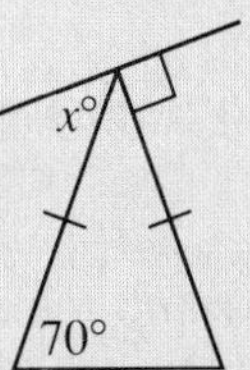

Write a two-column proof.

4.

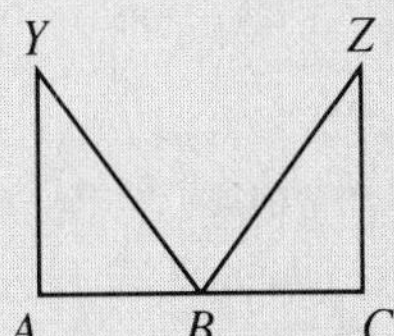

Given: $\overline{YA} \perp \overline{AC}$; $\overline{ZC} \perp \overline{AC}$; B is the midpoint of $\overline{AC}$; $\overline{YA} \cong \overline{ZC}$
Prove: $\angle ABY \cong \angle CBZ$

1. $\overline{YA} \perp \overline{AC}$; $\overline{ZC} \perp \overline{AC}$ (Given)
2. $\angle A \cong \angle C$ (Def. of $\perp$ lines)
3. B is the midpoint of $\overline{AC}$. (Given)
4. $\overline{AB} \cong \overline{CB}$ (Def. of midpoint)
5. $\overline{YB} \cong \overline{ZC}$ (Given)
6. $\triangle ABY \cong \triangle CBZ$ (SAS)
7. $\angle ABY \cong \angle CBZ$ (Corr. parts of $\cong$ ⚠ are $\cong$.)

(continued)

Self-Test 2

Find the value of x.

1. 70

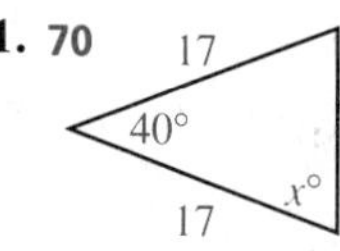

2. 7

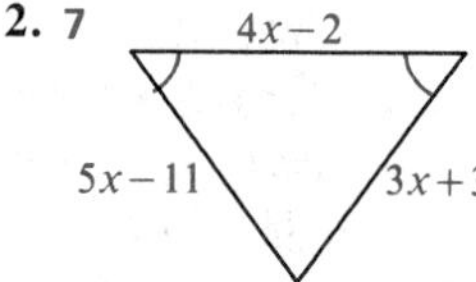

3. 30

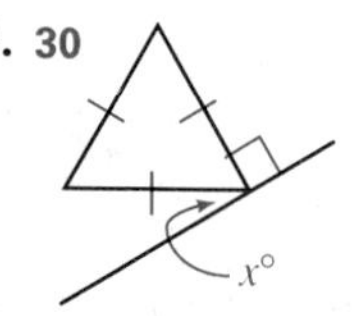

4. Given: $\overline{AB} \cong \overline{AC}$; $\overline{BN} \perp \overline{AC}$; $\overline{CM} \perp \overline{AB}$
Explain how you could prove that $\triangle ABN \cong \triangle ACM$.

5. Given: $\overline{MB} \cong \overline{NC}$; $\overline{BN} \perp \overline{AC}$; $\overline{CM} \perp \overline{AB}$
Prove: $\overline{CM} \cong \overline{BN}$

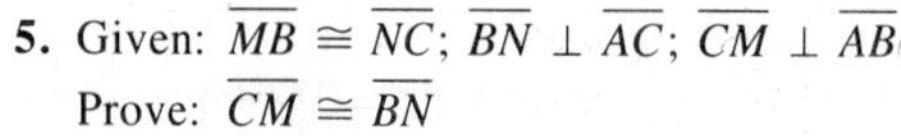

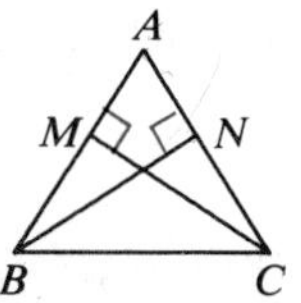

4. Since $\overline{BN} \perp \overline{AC}$ and $\overline{CM} \perp \overline{AB}$, $\angle ANB$ and $\angle AMC$ are rt. ∠s and are ≅. $\angle A \cong \angle A$ and $\overline{AB} \cong \overline{AC}$ (Given), so $\triangle ABN \cong \triangle ACM$ by AAS.

More about Proof in Geometry

Objectives

1. Prove two triangles congruent by first proving two other triangles congruent.
2. Apply the definitions of the median and the altitude of a triangle and the perpendicular bisector of a segment.
3. State and apply the theorem about a point on the perpendicular bisector of a segment, and the converse.
4. State and apply the theorem about a point on the bisector of an angle, and the converse.

4-6 *Using More than One Pair of Congruent Triangles*

Sometimes two triangles that you want to prove congruent have common parts with two *other* triangles that you can easily prove congruent. You may then be able to use corresponding parts of these other triangles to prove the original triangles congruent.

5.

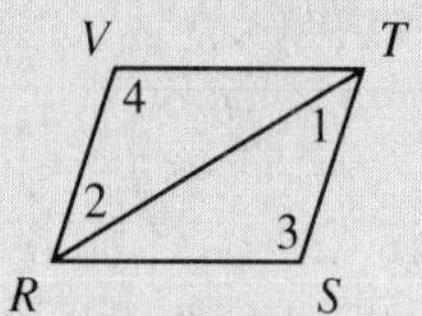

Given: $\angle 1 \cong \angle 2$; $\angle 3 \cong \angle 4$
Explain how you could prove $\triangle RST \cong \triangle TVR$.
Answers will vary. Using what is given, and the common side $\overline{RT}$, apply the AAS Theorem.

Teaching Suggestions,
p. T91

Objective
Presenting the Lesson
Problem Solving

Communication Skills,
p. T91

Supplementary Materials

Practice Master 20
Study Guide, pp. 55–56

Lesson Focus

The purpose of this lesson is to extend students' understanding and skill in writing proofs by using more than one pair of congruent triangles.

Suggested Assignments

Minimum
Day 1: 148–149/1–5
Day 2: 149–150/6–9, 11, 12
S 145/14
151/Mixed Review 1–11

Example

Given: $\angle 1 \cong \angle 2$; $\angle 5 \cong \angle 6$
Prove: $\overline{AC} \perp \overline{BD}$

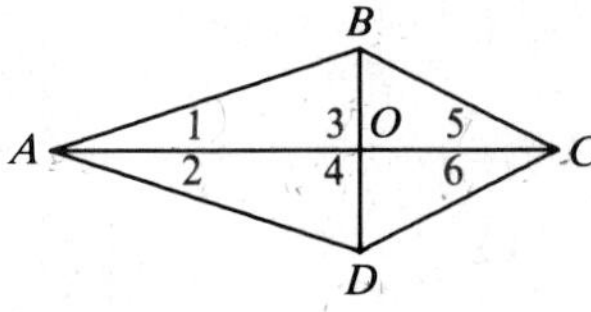

Plan for Proof: It may be helpful here to *reason backward* from what you want to prove. You can show $\overline{AC} \perp \overline{BD}$ if you can show that $\angle 3 \cong \angle 4$. You can prove $\angle 3 \cong \angle 4$ if you can prove that the angles are corresponding parts of congruent triangles. To prove $\triangle ABO \cong \triangle ADO$, you need $\overline{AB} \cong \overline{AD}$. You can prove this congruence by proving that $\triangle ABC \cong \triangle ADC$. You should prove this congruence first.

Proof:

Statements	Reasons
1. $\angle 1 \cong \angle 2$; $\angle 5 \cong \angle 6$	1. Given
2. $\overline{AC} \cong \overline{AC}$	2. Reflexive Property
3. $\triangle ABC \cong \triangle ADC$	3. ASA Postulate
4. $\overline{AB} \cong \overline{AD}$	4. Corr. parts of $\cong$ ⨻ are $\cong$.
5. $\overline{AO} \cong \overline{AO}$	5. Reflexive Property
6. $\triangle ABO \cong \triangle ADO$	6. SAS Postulate (Steps 1, 4, and 5)
7. $\angle 3 \cong \angle 4$	7. Corr. parts of $\cong$ ⨻ are $\cong$.
8. $\overline{AC} \perp \overline{BD}$	8. If two lines form $\cong$ adj. ⦣s, then the lines are $\perp$.

If you were to outline this two-column proof, you might pick out the following *key steps*.

Key steps of proof:

1. $\triangle ABC \cong \triangle ADC$ (ASA Postulate)
2. $\overline{AB} \cong \overline{AD}$ (Corr. parts of $\cong$ ⨻ are $\cong$.)
3. $\triangle ABO \cong \triangle ADO$ (SAS Postulate)
4. $\angle 3 \cong \angle 4$ (Corr. parts of $\cong$ ⨻ are $\cong$.)
5. $\overline{AC} \perp \overline{BD}$ (If two lines form $\cong$ adj. ⦣s, then the lines are $\perp$.)

In mathematics a proof is often given in paragraph form rather than in two-column form. A *paragraph proof* usually focuses on the key ideas and omits details that the writer thinks will be clear to the reader. The following paragraph proof might be given for the example above.

Paragraph proof:

$\triangle ABC \cong \triangle ADC$ by the ASA Postulate. Therefore, corresponding parts $\overline{AB}$ and $\overline{AD}$ are congruent. $\overline{AB}$ and $\overline{AD}$ are also corresponding parts of $\triangle ABO$ and $\triangle ADO$, which can now be proved congruent by the SAS Postulate. So corresponding parts $\angle 3$ and $\angle 4$ are congruent, and $\overline{AC} \perp \overline{BD}$.

Average
Day 1: 148–150/1, 3, 5, 6, 8, 10
Day 2: 150–151/12–16
151/Mixed Review 1–11
Maximum
Day 1: 149/3–8
S 145/19, 21
Day 2: 150–151/9–16

Chalkboard Examples

1. Given: $\angle 1 \cong \angle 2$; $\angle 3 \cong \angle 4$
Prove: $\overline{TU} \cong \overline{TW}$

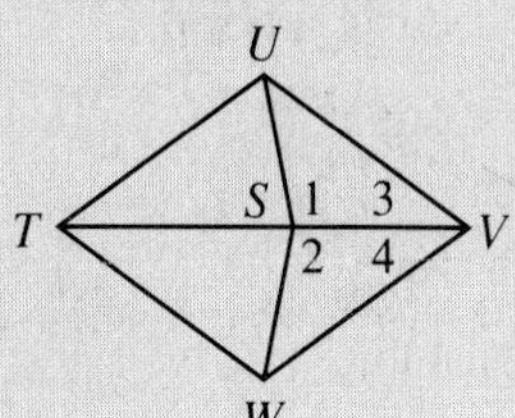

1. $\angle 1 \cong \angle 2$; $\angle 3 \cong \angle 4$ (Given)
2. $\overline{SV} \cong \overline{SV}$ (Refl. Prop.)
3. $\triangle USV \cong \triangle WSV$ (ASA)
4. $\overline{UV} \cong \overline{WV}$ (Corr. parts of $\cong$ ⨻ are $\cong$.)
5. $\overline{TV} \cong \overline{TV}$ (Refl. Prop.)
6. $\triangle TUV \cong \triangle TWV$ (SAS)
7. $\overline{TU} \cong \overline{TW}$ (Corr. parts of $\cong$ ⨻ are $\cong$.)

2. Given: $\angle 1 \cong \angle 2$; $\angle 3 \cong \angle 4$
Prove: $\angle TUV \cong \angle TWV$

1.–6. (Use steps in Ex. 1.)
7. $\angle TUV \cong \angle TWV$ (Corr. parts of $\cong$ ⨻ are $\cong$.)

Guided Practice

1. Supply a reason for each key step of the proof that $\overline{AB} \cong \overline{CD}$.

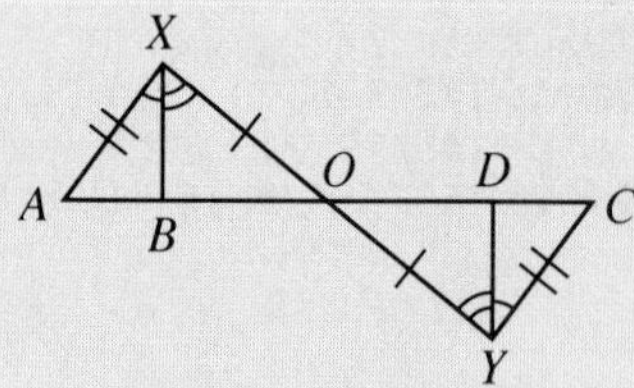

Key Steps of Proof:
(a) $\triangle BOX \cong \triangle DOY$ ASA
(b) $\overline{BX} \cong \overline{DY}$ CPCT
(c) $\triangle ABX \cong \triangle CDY$ SAS
(d) $\overline{AB} \cong \overline{CD}$ CPCT

2. Write a paragraph proof.

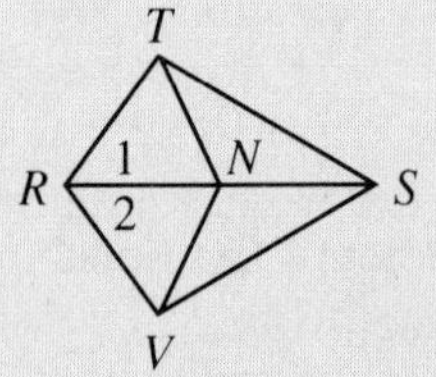

Given: $\overline{RT} \cong \overline{RV}$; $\overline{NT} \cong \overline{NV}$
Prove: $\overline{TS} \cong \overline{VS}$
Answers will vary. From $\triangle RTN \cong \triangle RVN$ by SSS, we have $\angle 1 \cong \angle 2$. Then $\triangle RTS \cong \triangle RVS$ by the SAS Post. and $\overline{TS} \cong \overline{VS}$ (CPCT).

Classroom Exercises

Note: CPCT is used for "corr. parts of $\cong$ ⚠ are $\cong$."

In Exercises 1–3 you are given a diagram that is marked with given information. Give the reason for each key step of the proof.

1. Prove: $\overline{AS} \cong \overline{DT}$
Key steps of proof:
a. $\triangle ABC \cong \triangle DEF$ SAS
b. $\angle C \cong \angle F$ CPCT
c. $\triangle ACS \cong \triangle DFT$ SAS
d. $\overline{AS} \cong \overline{DT}$ CPCT

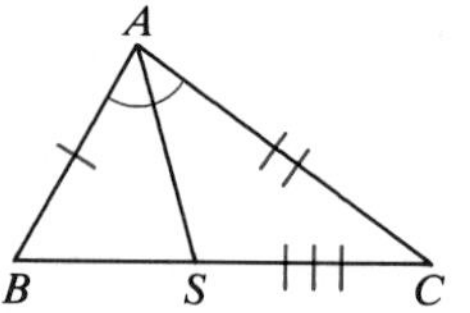

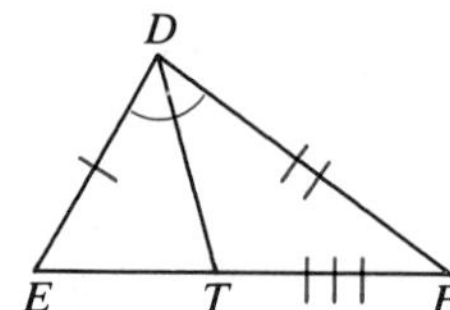

2. Prove: $\overline{AX} \cong \overline{AY}$
Key steps of proof:
a. $\triangle PAL \cong \triangle KAN$ SAS
b. $\angle L \cong \angle N$ CPCT
c. $\triangle LAX \cong \triangle NAY$ ASA
d. $\overline{AX} \cong \overline{AY}$ CPCT

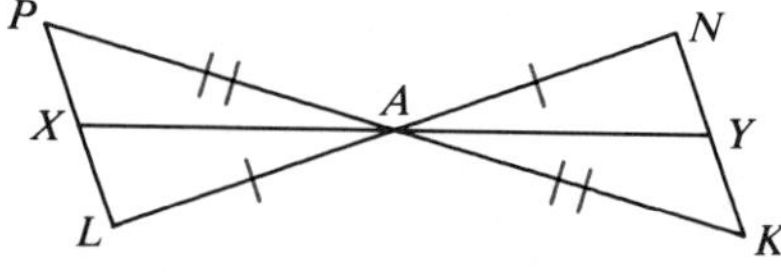

3. Prove: $\angle 3 \cong \angle 4$
Key steps of proof:
a. $\triangle LOB \cong \triangle JOB$ SSS
b. $\angle 1 \cong \angle 2$ CPCT
c. $\triangle LBA \cong \triangle JBA$ SAS
d. $\angle 3 \cong \angle 4$ CPCT

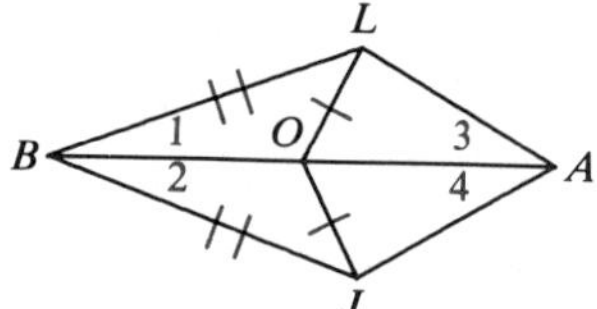

4. Suggest a plan for proving that $\angle D \cong \angle F$.
$\triangle CPE \cong \triangle GQE$ by AAS, so $\overline{CP} \cong \overline{GQ}$ (CPCT). Then $\triangle CDP \cong \triangle GFQ$ by HL, and $\angle D \cong \angle F$ (CPCT).

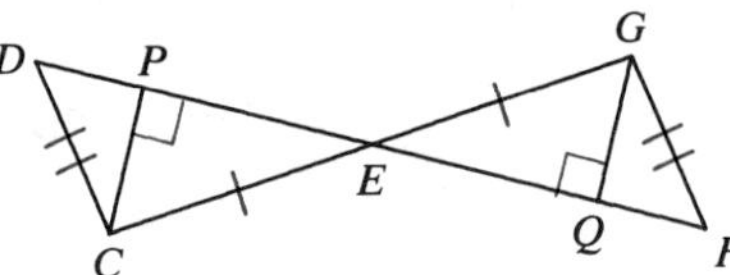

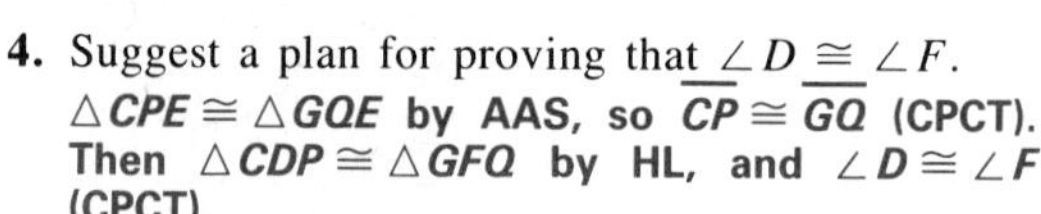

Written Exercises

In Exercises 1–6 you are given a diagram that is marked with given information. Give the reason for each key step of the proof.

A

1. Prove: $\overline{NE} \cong \overline{OS}$
Key steps of proof:
a. $\triangle RNX \cong \triangle LOY$ SSS
b. $\angle X \cong \angle Y$ CPCT
c. $\triangle NEX \cong \triangle OSY$ SAS
d. $\overline{NE} \cong \overline{OS}$ CPCT

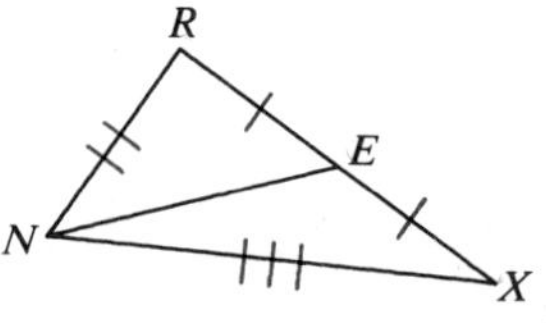

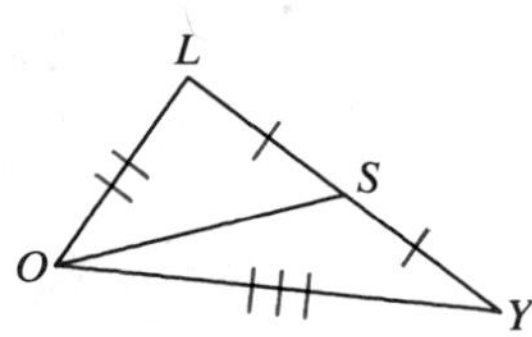

2. Prove: $\overline{BE} \cong \overline{DF}$
Key steps of proof:
a. $\triangle ABC \cong \triangle CDA$ SSS
b. $\angle 1 \cong \angle 2$ CPCT
c. $\triangle ABE \cong \triangle CDF$ AAS
d. $\overline{BE} \cong \overline{DF}$ CPCT

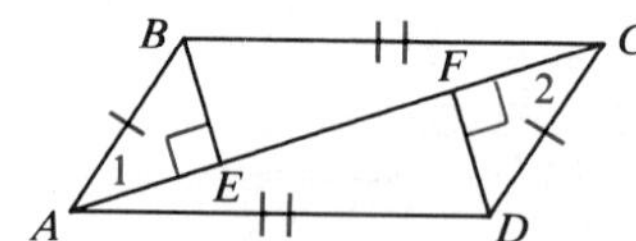

3. Prove: $\angle G \cong \angle T$
Key steps of proof:
a. $\triangle RAJ \cong \triangle NAK$ **AAS**
b. $\overline{RJ} \cong \overline{NK}$ **CPCT**
c. $\triangle GRJ \cong \triangle TNK$ **SAS**
d. $\angle G \cong \angle T$ **CPCT**

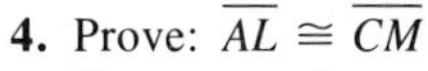

4. Prove: $\overline{AL} \cong \overline{CM}$
Key steps of proof:
a. $\triangle ABD \cong \triangle CDB$ **SAS**
b. $\overline{AD} \cong \overline{CB}$; $\angle 1 \cong \angle 2$ **CPCT**
c. $\triangle ADL \cong \triangle CBM$ **ASA**
d. $\overline{AL} \cong \overline{CM}$ **CPCT**

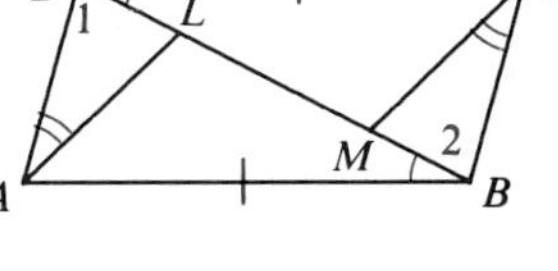

5. Prove: $\overline{DX} \cong \overline{EX}$
Key steps of proof:
a. $\triangle POD \cong \triangle POE$ **SAS**
b. $\overline{PD} \cong \overline{PE}$ **CPCT**
c. $\triangle PDX \cong \triangle PEX$ **HL**
d. $\overline{DX} \cong \overline{EX}$ **CPCT**

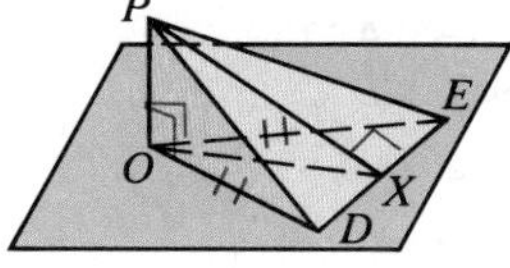

6. Prove: $\angle CBA \cong \angle DBA$ **a. If 2 ∠s of a △ are ≅, then the sides opp. those ∠s are ≅.**
Key steps of proof:
a. $\overline{OC} \cong \overline{OD}$
b. $\triangle CAO \cong \triangle DAO$ **SSS**
c. $\angle CAO \cong \angle DAO$ **CPCT**
d. $\triangle CAB \cong \triangle DAB$ **SAS**
e. $\angle CBA \cong \angle DBA$ **CPCT**

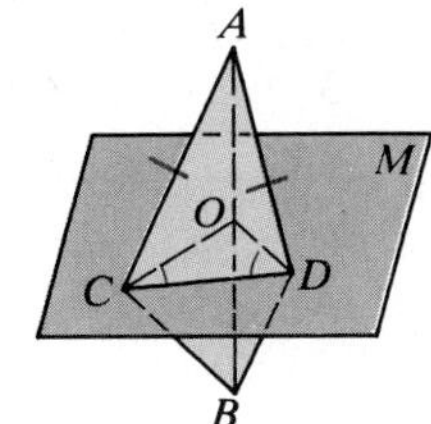

B **7.** Given: $\overline{LF} \cong \overline{KF}$; $\overline{LA} \cong \overline{KA}$
Prove: $\overline{LJ} \cong \overline{KJ}$
a. List the key steps of a proof.
b. Write a proof in two-column form.

a. (1) $\triangle FLA \cong \triangle FKA$ (SSS)
(2) $\angle 1 \cong \angle 2$ (CPCT)
(3) $\triangle FLJ \cong \triangle FKJ$ (SAS)
(4) $\overline{LJ} \cong \overline{KJ}$ (CPCT)

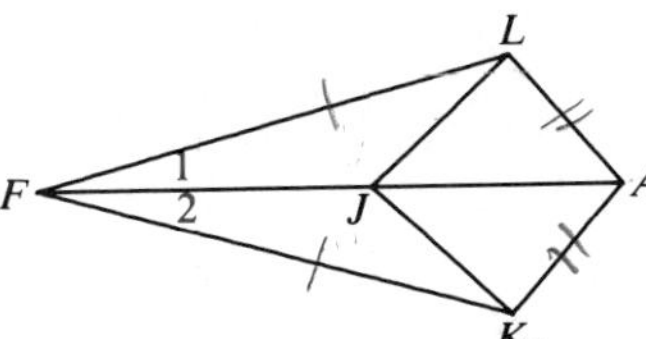

8. Given: $\overline{PR}$ bisects $\angle SPT$ and $\angle SRT$.
Prove: $\overline{PR}$ bisects $\angle SQT$.
a. List the key steps of a proof.
b. Write a proof in paragraph form.

a. (1) $\triangle PSR \cong \triangle PTR$ (ASA)
(2) $\overline{SR} \cong \overline{TR}$ (CPCT)
(3) $\triangle SRQ \cong \triangle TRQ$ (SAS)
(4) $\angle 3 \cong \angle 4$ (CPCT)
(5) $\overline{PR}$ bisects $\angle SQT$ (Def. of ∠ bisector)

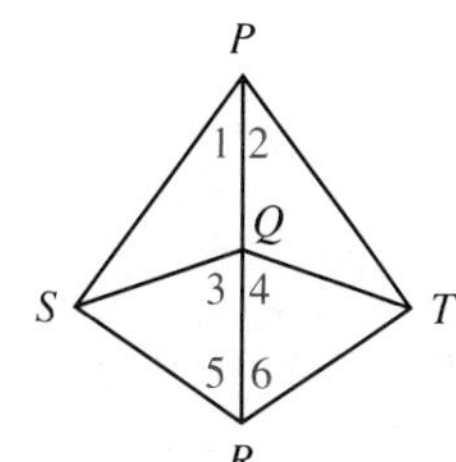

Write proofs in the form specified by your teacher (two-column form, paragraph form, or a list of key steps).

9. Given: $\triangle RST \cong \triangle XYZ$;
$\overrightarrow{SK}$ bisects $\angle RST$;
$\overrightarrow{YL}$ bisects $\angle XYZ$.
Prove: $\overline{SK} \cong \overline{YL}$

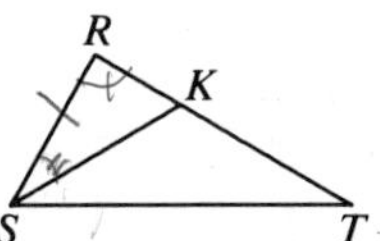

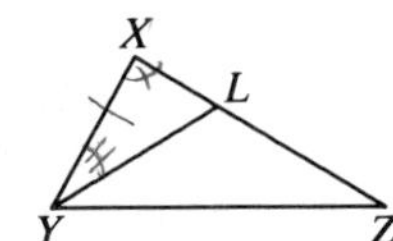

10. Given: Congruent parts as marked in the diagram.
Prove: $\angle B \cong \angle F$
(*Hint*: First draw two auxiliary lines.) **$\overline{AC}$, $\overline{AE}$**

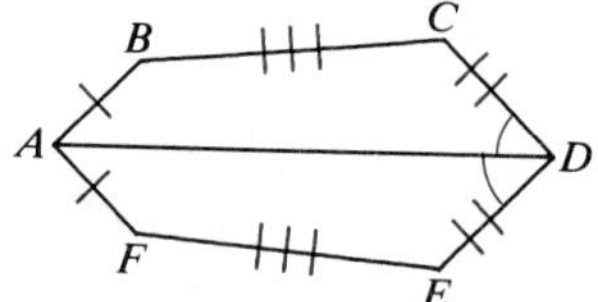

11. Given: $\overline{DE} \cong \overline{FG}$; $\overline{GD} \cong \overline{EF}$;
$\angle HDE$ and $\angle KFG$ are rt. $\angle$s.
Prove: $\overline{DH} \cong \overline{FK}$

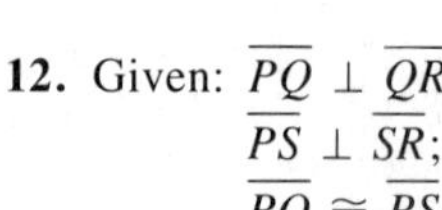

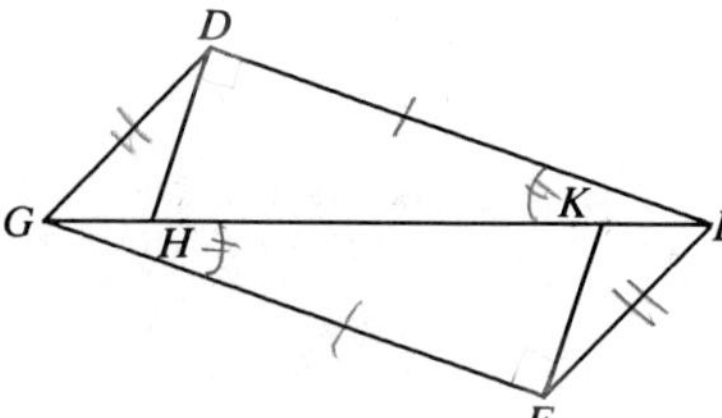

12. Given: $\overline{PQ} \perp \overline{QR}$;
$\overline{PS} \perp \overline{SR}$;
$\overline{PQ} \cong \overline{PS}$
Prove: O is the midpoint of $\overline{QS}$.

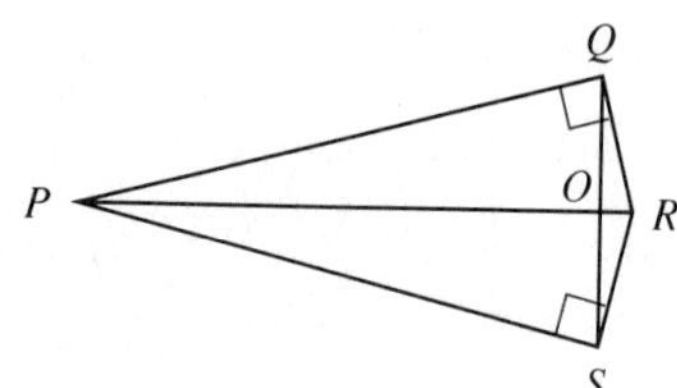

13. Draw two line segments, $\overline{KL}$ and $\overline{MN}$, that bisect each other at O. Mark a point P on $\overline{KN}$ and let Q be the point where $\overrightarrow{PO}$ intersects $\overline{ML}$. Prove that O is the midpoint of $\overline{PQ}$. (First state what is given and what is to be proved.)

Using a Computer

For Ex. 14, have students draw the figure using a construction program, look for pairs of congruent triangles, and verify their congruence by measurement.

14. This figure is like the one that Euclid used to prove that the base angles of an isosceles triangle are congruent (our Theorem 4-1). Write a paragraph proof following the key steps shown below.

Given: $\overline{AB} \cong \overline{AC}$;
$\overline{AB}$ and $\overline{AC}$ are extended so $\overline{BD} \cong \overline{CE}$.
Prove: $\angle ABC \cong \angle ACB$

Key steps of proof:
1. $\triangle DAC \cong \triangle EAB$
2. $\triangle DBC \cong \triangle ECB$
3. $\angle DBC \cong \angle ECB$
4. $\angle ABC \cong \angle ACB$

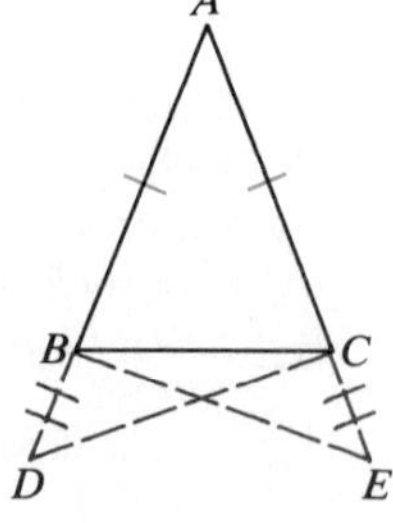

C **15.** Given: $\overline{AM} \cong \overline{MB}$; $\overline{AD} \cong \overline{BC}$;
$\angle MDC \cong \angle MCD$
Prove: $\overline{AC} \cong \overline{BD}$

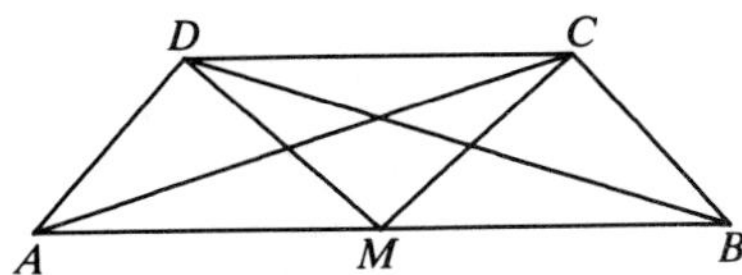

16. Given: $\angle 1 \cong \angle 2$;
$\angle 3 \cong \angle 4$;
$\angle 5 \cong \angle 6$
Prove: $\overline{BC} \cong \overline{ED}$

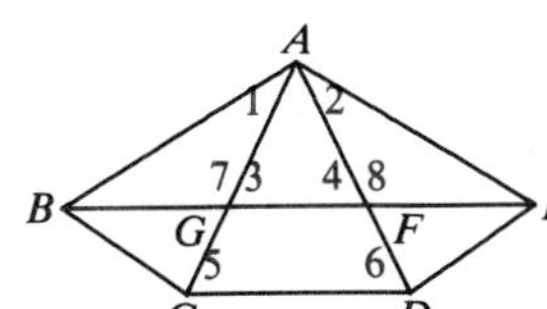

17. A, B, C, and D are noncoplanar. $\triangle ABC$, $\triangle ACD$, and $\triangle ABD$ are equilateral. X and Y are midpoints of $\overline{AC}$ and $\overline{AD}$. Z is a point on $\overline{AB}$. What kind of triangle is $\triangle XYZ$? Explain. **isosceles; $\overline{AX} \cong \overline{AY}$, $\overline{AZ} \cong \overline{AZ}$, and $\angle XAZ \cong \angle YAZ$, so $\triangle XAZ \cong \triangle YAZ$ by SAS. Then $\overline{XZ} \cong \overline{YZ}$ (CPCT) and $\triangle XYZ$ is isosceles.**

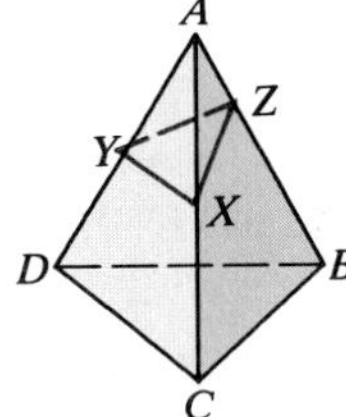

Mixed Review Exercises

1. Write the Isosceles Triangle Theorem (Theorem 4-1) and its converse (Theorem 4-2) as a single biconditional statement. **Two sides of a △ are ≅ if and only if the ∠s opposite those sides are ≅.**

Complete each statement with the word *always*, *sometimes*, or *never*.

2. Two isosceles triangles with congruent bases are _?_ congruent. **sometimes**
3. Two isosceles triangles with congruent vertex angles are _?_ congruent. **sometimes**
4. Two equilateral triangles with congruent bases are _?_ congruent. **always**

Draw a diagram for each of the following. Check students' drawings.

5. **a.** M is between A and B.
   b. M is the midpoint of $\overline{AB}$.
6. **a.** $\overline{XY}$ bisects $\overline{CD}$.
   b. $\overrightarrow{XY}$ bisects $\angle CXD$.
7. **a.** acute scalene $\triangle JKL$
   b. obtuse scalene $\triangle JKL$
8. **a.** acute isosceles $\triangle XYZ$
   b. obtuse isosceles $\triangle XYZ$
9. **a.** right scalene $\triangle RST$
   b. right isosceles $\triangle RST$
10. **a.** equilateral $\triangle EFG$
    b. equiangular $\triangle EFG$

11. Write a proof in two-column form.
    Given: $\overline{BE} \cong \overline{CD}$; $\overline{BD} \cong \overline{CE}$
    Prove: $\triangle ABC$ is isosceles.

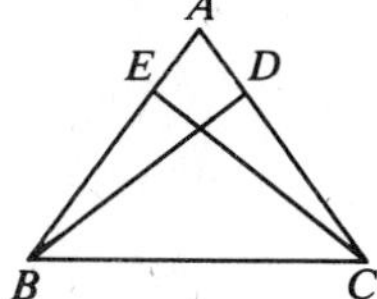

Teaching Suggestions,
pp. T91–T92

Objectives
Presenting the Lesson
Making Connections
Using Technology
Extension

Supplementary Materials

Practice Master 21
Test 16
Resource Book, pp. 21, 124
Study Guide, pp. 57–58

Lesson Focus

This lesson introduces and uses in proofs three different line segments associated with any triangle.

Suggested Assignments

Minimum
Day 1: 156/1–9
Day 2: 156/10–14
Day 3: 159/Self-Test 3
162/Chapter Test, 1–17 odd

Average
Day 1: 156–157/1–14, 18
Day 2: 159/Self-Test 3
162/Chapter Test, 1–18

Maximum
Day 1: 156–158/6–13, 15, 19, 23, 25
Day 2: 158/26–28
162–163/Chapter Test

You may wish to introduce Constructions 10 and 11 on pages 393–394 after covering this lesson.

4-7 *Medians, Altitudes, and Perpendicular Bisectors*

A **median** of a triangle is a segment from a vertex to the midpoint of the opposite side. The three medians of $\triangle ABC$ are shown below in red.

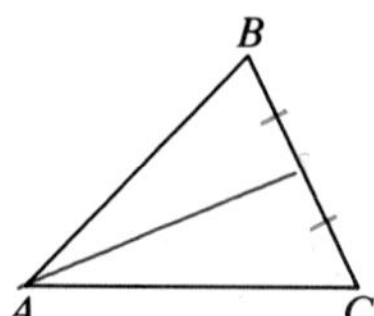

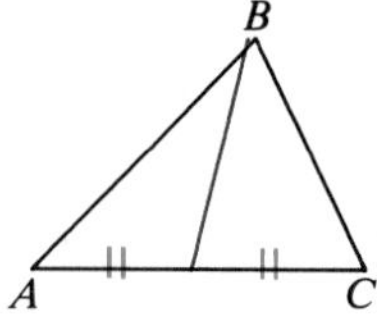

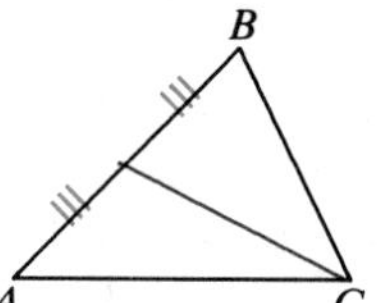

An **altitude** of a triangle is the perpendicular segment from a vertex to the line that contains the opposite side. In an acute triangle, the three altitudes are all inside the triangle.

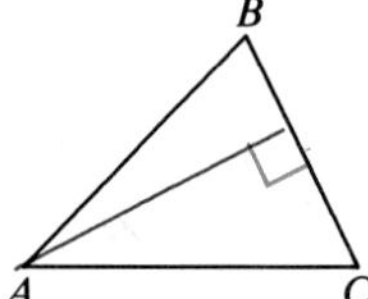

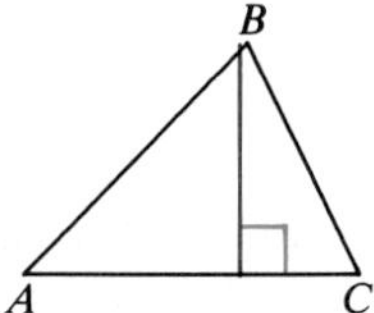

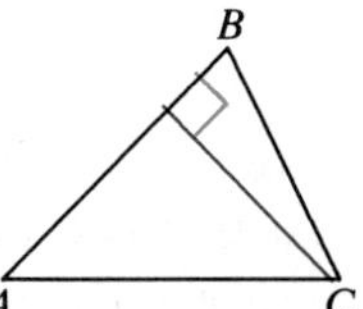

In a right triangle, two of the altitudes are parts of the triangle. They are the legs of the right triangle. The third altitude is inside the triangle.

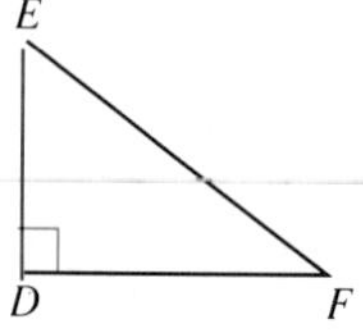

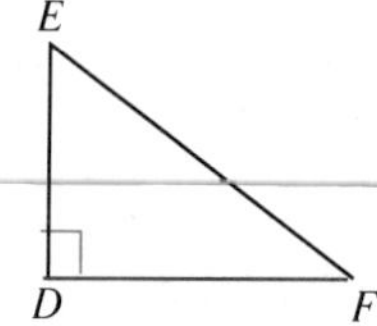

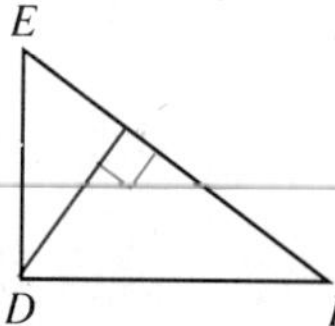

In an obtuse triangle, two of the altitudes are outside the triangle. For obtuse $\triangle KLN$, $\overline{LH}$ is the altitude from L, and $\overline{NI}$ is the altitude from N.

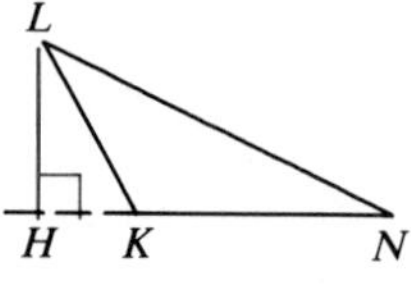

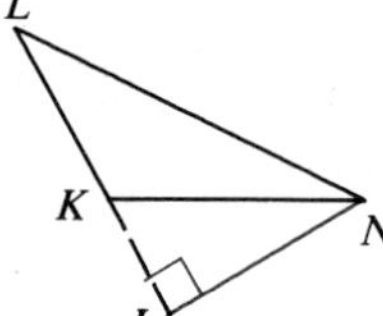

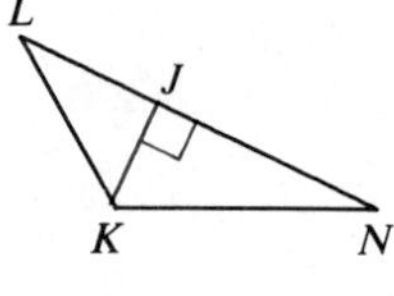

A **perpendicular bisector** of a segment is a line (or ray or segment) that is perpendicular to the segment at its midpoint. In the figure at the right, line l is a perpendicular bisector of $\overline{JK}$.

In a given plane, there is exactly one line perpendicular to a segment at its midpoint. We speak of *the* perpendicular bisector of a segment in such a case.

Proofs of the following theorems are left as Exercises 14 and 15.

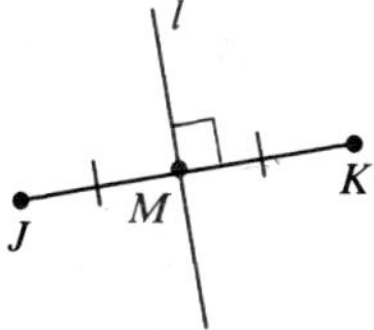

Theorem 4-5

If a point lies on the perpendicular bisector of a segment, then the point is equidistant from the endpoints of the segment.

Given: Line l is the perpendicular bisector of $\overline{BC}$; A is on l.

Prove: $AB = AC$

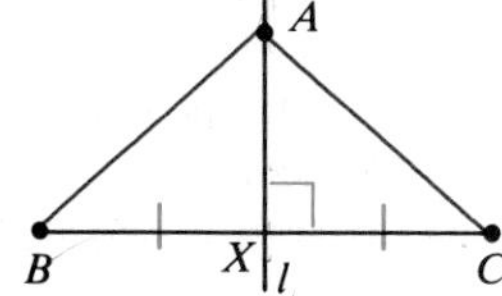

Theorem 4-6

If a point is equidistant from the endpoints of a segment, then the point lies on the perpendicular bisector of the segment.

Given: $AB = AC$

Prove: A is on the perpendicular bisector of $\overline{BC}$.

A
1 2
B X C

Plan for Proof: The perpendicular bisector of $\overline{BC}$ must contain the midpoint of $\overline{BC}$ and be perpendicular to $\overline{BC}$. Draw an auxiliary line containing A that has one of these properties and prove that it has the other property as well. For example, first draw a segment from A to the midpoint X of $\overline{BC}$. You can show that $\overline{AX} \perp \overline{BC}$ if you can show that $\angle 1 \cong \angle 2$. Since these angles are corresponding parts of two triangles, first show that $\triangle AXB \cong \triangle AXC$.

In the proof of Theorem 4-6 other auxiliary lines could have been chosen instead. For example, we can draw the altitude to $\overline{BC}$ from A, meeting $\overline{BC}$ at a point Y as shown in the diagram at the right. Here, since $\overline{AY} \perp \overline{BC}$ we need to prove that $\overline{YB} \cong \overline{YC}$. Either method can be used to prove Theorem 4-6.

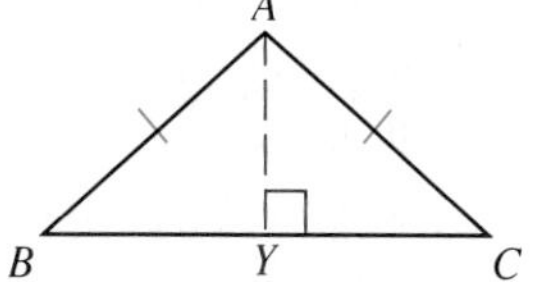

Communication Skills

The text has already defined both *perpendicular* and *bisector.* You can help students learn to think as they listen if you will simply pause for a second between the word *perpendicular* and the word *bisector* when you use the two-word phrase.

Thinking Skills

When discussing Theorem 4-6, hold up a long stick and ask students to complete the sentence: If a point is equidistant from the ends of the stick, then the point ______. A good answer is: lies in the plane that is perpendicular to the stick at its midpoint. If a student states Theorem 4-6 as the answer, ask him or her to work in space, not in a plane.

Making Connections

You can mention the fact that two lessons of Chapter 10 will concentrate on problems illustrated by the one discussed above in Thinking Skills.

Chalkboard Examples

Fill in the blank with *always*, *sometimes*, or *never*.

1. An altitude is always perpendicular to the opposite side.
2. A median is sometimes perpendicular to the opposite side.
3. An altitude is sometimes an angle bisector.
4. An angle bisector is sometimes perpendicular to the opposite side.
5. A perpendicular bisector of a segment is always equidistant from the endpoints of the segment.
6. Suppose $\overrightarrow{OG}$ bisects $\angle TOY$. What can you deduce if you also know that:
   a. Point J lies on $\overrightarrow{OG}$? The distance from J to $\overrightarrow{OT}$ equals the distance from J to $\overrightarrow{OY}$.
   b. A point K is such that the distance from K to $\overrightarrow{OT}$ is 13 cm and the distance from K to $\overrightarrow{OY}$ is 13 cm? K lies on $\overrightarrow{OG}$.

Communication Skills

Ask students if they remembered the meaning of the word *biconditional* (introduced on page 34). Students who do not should look at the two parts of the word, *bi* and *conditional*.

Example Suppose you know that line l is the perpendicular bisector of $\overline{RS}$. What can you deduce if you also know that

a. P lies on l?
b. there is a point Q such that $QR = 7$ and $QS = 7$?

Solution
a. $PR = PS$ (Theorem 4-5)
b. Q lies on l. (Theorem 4-6)

The **distance from a point to a line** (or plane) is defined to be the length of the perpendicular segment from the point to the line (or plane). Since $\overline{RS} \perp t$, RS is the distance from R to line t.

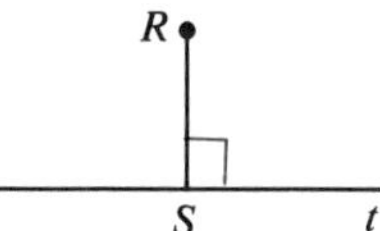

In Exercises 16 and 17 you will prove the following theorems, which are similar to Theorems 4-5 and 4-6.

Theorem 4-7

If a point lies on the bisector of an angle, then the point is equidistant from the sides of the angle.

Given: $\overrightarrow{BZ}$ bisects $\angle ABC$; P lies on $\overrightarrow{BZ}$; $\overline{PX} \perp \overrightarrow{BA}$; $\overline{PY} \perp \overrightarrow{BC}$

Prove: $PX = PY$

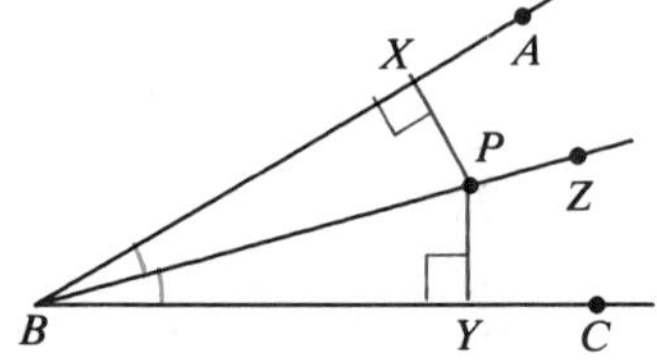

Theorem 4-8

If a point is equidistant from the sides of an angle, then the point lies on the bisector of the angle.

Given: $\overline{PX} \perp \overrightarrow{BA}$; $\overline{PY} \perp \overrightarrow{BC}$; $PX = PY$

Prove: $\overrightarrow{BP}$ bisects $\angle ABC$.

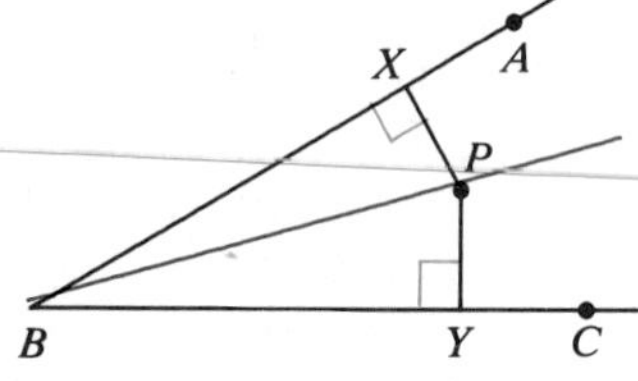

Theorem 4-5 and its converse, Theorem 4-6, can be combined into a single biconditional statement. The same is true for Theorems 4-7 and 4-8.

> A point is on the perpendicular bisector of a segment if and only if it is equidistant from the endpoints of the segment.
>
> A point is on the bisector of an angle if and only if it is equidistant from the sides of the angle.

Classroom Exercises

Complete.

1. If K is the midpoint of $\overline{ST}$, then $\overline{RK}$ is called a(n) _?_ of $\triangle RST$. **median**
2. If $\overline{RK} \perp \overline{ST}$, then $\overline{RK}$ is called a(n) _?_ of $\triangle RST$. **altitude**
3. If K is the midpoint of $\overline{ST}$ and $\overline{RK} \perp \overline{ST}$, then $\overline{RK}$ is called a(n) _?_ of $\overline{ST}$. **⊥ bisector**
4. If $\overline{RK}$ is both an altitude and a median of $\triangle RST$, then:
   a. $\triangle RSK \cong \triangle RTK$ by _?_. **4. a. SAS** **b.** $\triangle RST$ is a(n) _?_ triangle. **isosceles**
5. If R is on the perpendicular bisector of $\overline{ST}$, then R is equidistant from _?_ and _?_. Thus _?_ = _?_. ***S*** ***T*** ***RS*** ***RT***

S K T R

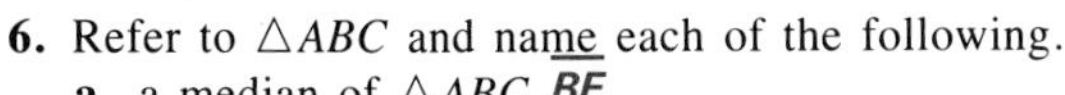

6. Refer to $\triangle ABC$ and name each of the following.
   a. a median of $\triangle ABC$ $\overline{BE}$
   b. an altitude of $\triangle ABC$ $\overline{AD}$
   c. a bisector of an angle of $\triangle ABC$ $\overrightarrow{CF}$

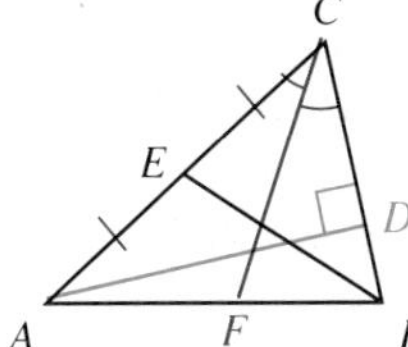

7. Draw $\overline{XY}$. Label its midpoint Q.
   a. Select a point P equidistant from X and Y. Draw $\overline{PX}$, $\overline{PY}$, and $\overline{PQ}$.
   b. What postulate justifies the statement $\triangle PQX \cong \triangle PQY$? **SSS**
   c. What reason justifies the statement $\angle PQX \cong \angle PQY$? **Corr. parts of ≅ ⩓ are ≅.**
   d. What reason justifies the statement $\overleftrightarrow{PQ} \perp \overline{XY}$? **If 2 lines form ≅ adj. ∠s, then the lines are ⊥.**
   e. What name for $\overleftrightarrow{PQ}$ best describes the relationship between $\overleftrightarrow{PQ}$ and $\overline{XY}$? **⊥ bisector**
8. Given: $\triangle DEF$ is isosceles with $DF = EF$;
   $\overline{FX}$ bisects $\angle DFE$.
   a. Would the median drawn from F to $\overline{DE}$ be the same segment as $\overline{FX}$? **Yes**
   b. Would the altitude drawn from F to $\overline{DE}$ be the same segment as $\overline{FX}$? **Yes**

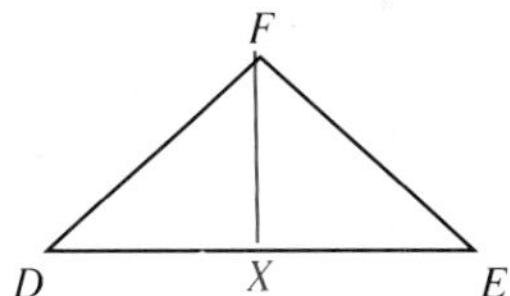

9. What kind of triangle has three angle bisectors that are also altitudes and medians? **equilateral**
10. Given: $\overrightarrow{NO}$ bisects $\angle N$.
    What can you conclude from each of the following additional statements?
    a. P lies on $\overrightarrow{NO}$. ***P* is equidistant from the sides of ∠*N*.**
    b. The distance from a point Q to each side of $\angle N$ is 13. ***Q* lies on $\overrightarrow{NO}$.**
11. Plane M is the *perpendicular bisecting plane* of $\overline{AB}$ at O (that is, M is the plane that is perpendicular to $\overline{AB}$ at its midpoint, O). Points C and D also lie in plane M. List three pairs of congruent triangles and tell which congruence method can be used to prove each pair congruent.

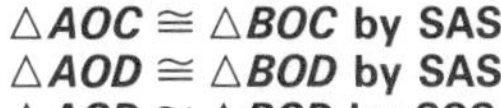

△*AOC* ≅ △*BOC* by SAS
△*AOD* ≅ △*BOD* by SAS
△*ACD* ≅ △*BCD* by SSS

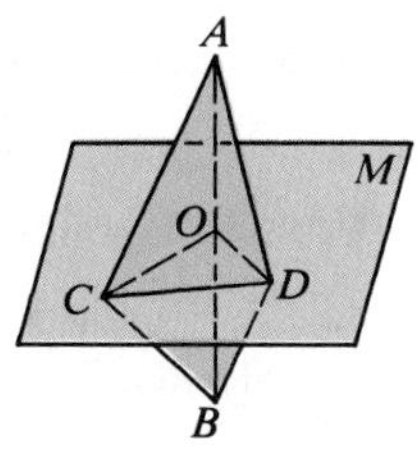

Using a Computer

Exs. 1–5 can be done using a construction program. For a related Experiment, see page T92.

Guided Practice

1. Draw an equilateral $\triangle DEF$. Draw the bisector of $\angle D$, the altitude from D, and the median from D. Are these three segments different? No
2. Draw an isosceles, but not equilateral, triangle. Draw the perpendicular bisectors of the three sides. How many of those perpendicular bisectors contain a vertex of the triangle? One

For Exs. 3 and 4, complete.

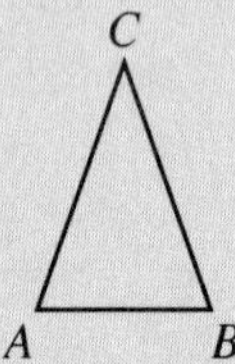

3. If Z lies on the bisector of $\angle CAB$, then Z is equidistant from $\overrightarrow{AC}$ and $\overrightarrow{AB}$.
4. If P is equidistant from $\overline{CA}$ and $\overline{CB}$, then P lies on the bisector of $\angle C$.
5. Given $\triangle RST$ and a point K, it is known that $KR = 5$, $KS = 5$, and K lies on the bisector of $\angle RTS$. Can $\triangle RST$ be:
   a. an equilateral triangle? Yes
   b. an isosceles, not equilateral, triangle? Yes
   c. an acute scalene triangle? No
   d. a right triangle? Yes
6. Given: Point P lies between points R and S; line l is the perpendicular bisector of $\overline{RP}$; line k is the perpendicular bisector of $\overline{PS}$. Describe the relationship between l and k. $l \parallel k$

Written Exercises 1.–6. Check students' drawings.

A

1. **a.** Draw a large scalene triangle ABC. Carefully draw the bisector of $\angle A$, the altitude from A, and the median from A. These three should all be different.
   b. Draw a large isosceles triangle ABC with vertex angle A. Carefully draw the bisector of $\angle A$, the altitude from A, and the median from A. Are these three different? **No**
2. Draw a large obtuse triangle. Then draw its three altitudes in color.
3. Draw a right triangle. Then draw its three altitudes in color.
4. Draw a large acute scalene triangle. Then draw the perpendicular bisectors of its three sides.

5. Draw a large scalene right triangle. Then draw the perpendicular bisectors of its three sides and tell whether they appear to meet in a point. If so, where is this point? **Yes; at the midpoint of the hypotenuse**
6. Cut out any large triangle. Fold the two sides of one angle of the triangle together to form the angle bisector. Use the same method to form the bisectors of the other two angles. What do you notice? **They intersect at a point.**

Complete each statement.

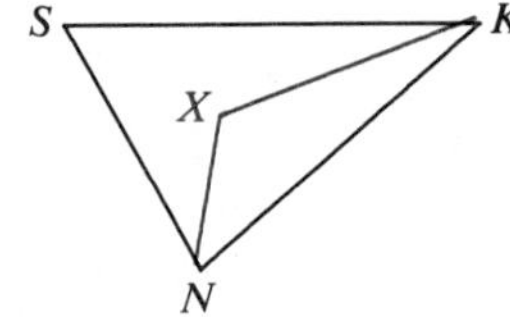

7. If X is on the bisector of $\angle SKN$, then X is equidistant from _?_ and _?_. $\overrightarrow{KS}$, $\overrightarrow{KN}$
8. If X is on the bisector of $\angle SNK$, then X is equidistant from _?_ and _?_. $\overrightarrow{NS}$, $\overrightarrow{NK}$
9. If X is equidistant from $\overline{SK}$ and $\overline{SN}$, then X lies on the _?_. **bisector of $\angle S$**

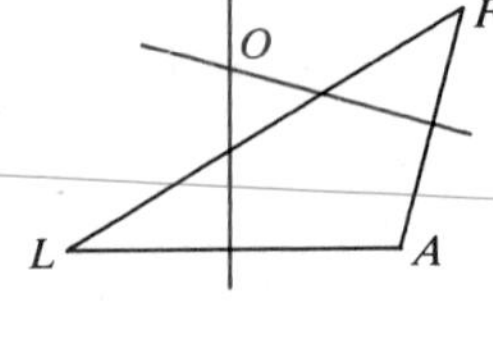

10. If O is on the perpendicular bisector of $\overline{LA}$, then O is equidistant from _?_ and _?_. **L, A**

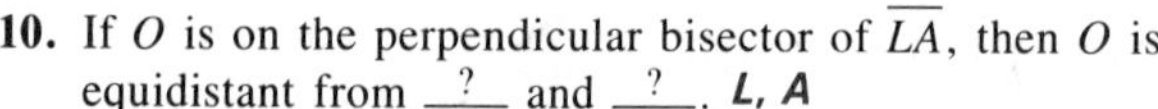

11. If O is on the perpendicular bisector of $\overline{AF}$, then O is equidistant from _?_ and _?_. **A, F**
12. If O is equidistant from L and F, then O lies on the _?_. **$\perp$ bisector of $\overline{LF}$**
13. Given: P is on the perpendicular bisector of $\overline{AB}$;
    P is on the perpendicular bisector of $\overline{BC}$.
    Prove: $PA = PC$

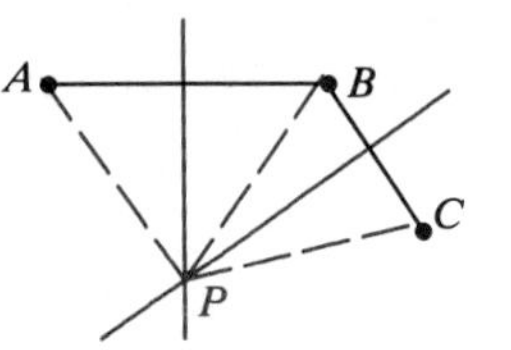

Use the diagrams on pages 153 and 154 to prove the following theorems.

B

14. Theorem 4-5
15. Theorem 4-6
16. Theorem 4-7
17. Theorem 4-8

18. Given: S is equidistant from E and D;
V is equidistant from E and D.
Prove: $\overleftrightarrow{SV}$ is the perpendicular bisector of $\overline{ED}$.

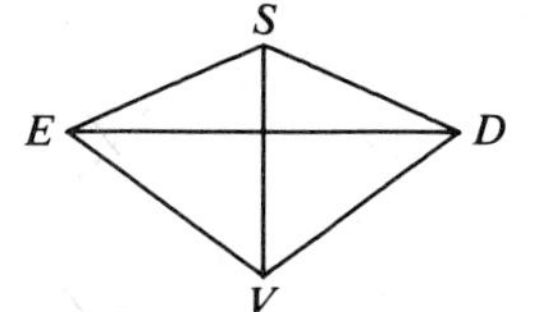

19. a. A town wants to build a beach house on the lake front equidistant from the recreation center and the school. Copy the diagram and show the point B where the beach house should be located.

b. The town also wants to build a boat-launching site that is equidistant from Elm Road and Main Street. Find the point L where it should be built.

c. On your diagram, locate the spot F for a flagpole that is to be the same distance from the recreation center, the school, and the courthouse.

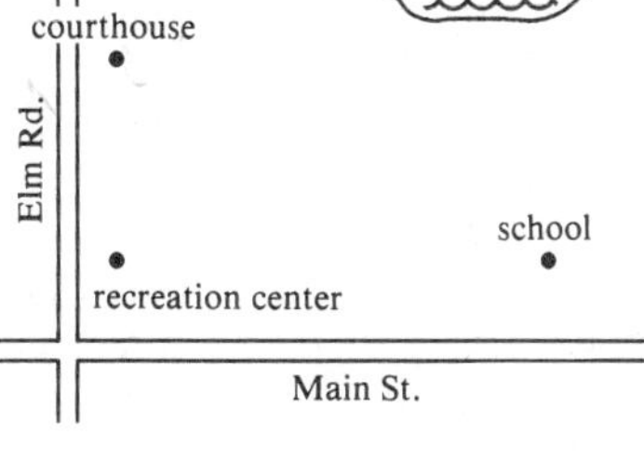

20. Given: $\triangle LMN \cong \triangle RST$;
$\overline{LX}$ and $\overline{RY}$ are altitudes.
Prove: $\overline{LX} \cong \overline{RY}$

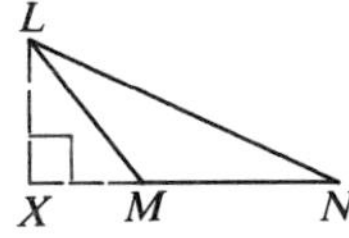

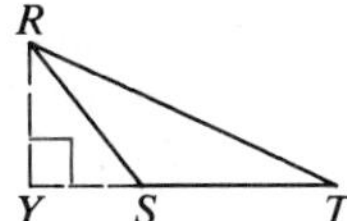

21. a. Given: $\overline{AB} \cong \overline{AC}$; $\overline{BD} \perp \overline{AC}$; $\overline{CE} \perp \overline{AB}$
Prove: $\overline{BD} \cong \overline{CE}$

b. The result you proved in part (a) can be stated as a theorem about certain altitudes. State this theorem in your own words. **The altitudes drawn to the legs of an isosceles triangle are congruent.**

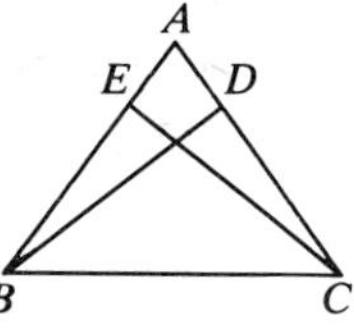

22. Prove that the medians drawn to the legs of an isosceles triangle are congruent. Write the proof in two-column form.

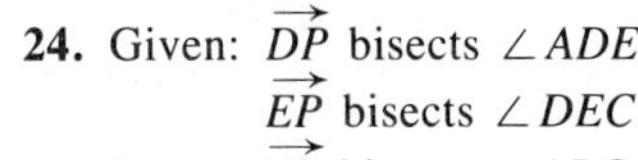

For Exercises 23–27 write proofs in paragraph form. (*Hint*: You can use theorems from this section to write fairly short proofs for Exercises 23 and 24.)

23. Given: $\overleftrightarrow{SR}$ is the $\perp$ bisector of $\overline{QT}$;
$\overleftrightarrow{QR}$ is the $\perp$ bisector of $\overline{SP}$.
Prove: $PQ = TS$

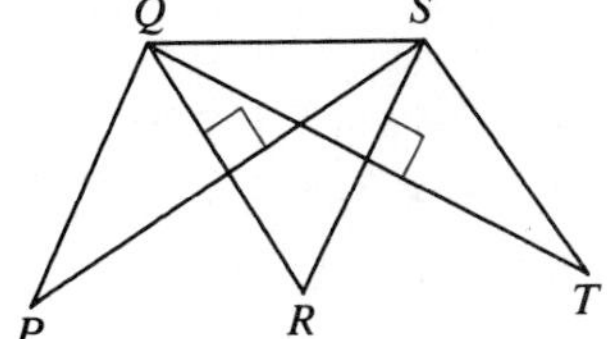

24. Given: $\overrightarrow{DP}$ bisects $\angle ADE$;
$\overrightarrow{EP}$ bisects $\angle DEC$.
Prove: $\overrightarrow{BP}$ bisects $\angle ABC$.

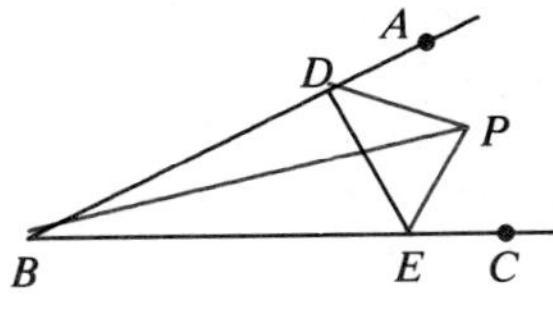

Exercise Note

In Ex. 19, we assume that land is a plane, even though, in actuality, it is the surface of a sphere. You may wish to discuss this with your students.

The town in Ex. 19 can find a spot for its flagpole. But explain why another town can run into trouble if it tries to follow the same criteria for locating the pole.

25. Given: Plane M is the perpendicular bisecting plane of $\overline{AB}$. (That is, $\overline{AB} \perp$ plane M and O is the midpoint of $\overline{AB}$.)
    Prove: **a.** $\overline{AD} \cong \overline{BD}$
    b. $\overline{AC} \cong \overline{BC}$
    c. $\angle CAD \cong \angle CBD$

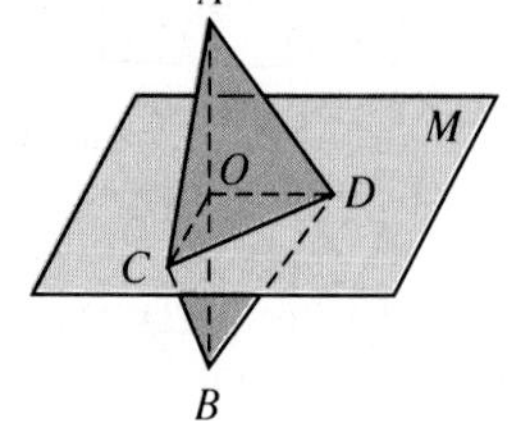

C 26. Given: $m\angle RTS = 90$; $\overleftrightarrow{MN}$ is the $\perp$ bisector of $\overline{TS}$.
    Prove: $\overline{TM}$ is a median.

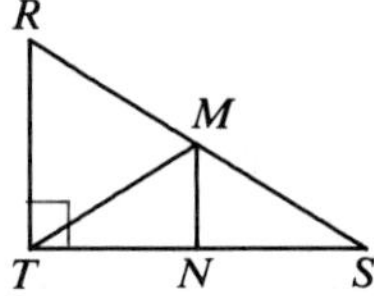

27. Given: $\overline{EH}$ and $\overline{FJ}$ are medians of scalene $\triangle EFG$; P is on $\overrightarrow{EH}$ such that $\overline{EH} \cong \overline{HP}$; Q is on $\overrightarrow{FJ}$ such that $\overline{FJ} \cong \overline{JQ}$.
    Prove: **a.** $\overline{GQ} \cong \overline{GP}$
    b. $\overline{GQ}$ and $\overline{GP}$ are both parallel to $\overline{EF}$.
    c. P, G, and Q are collinear.

Write paragraph proofs. (In this book a star designates an exercise that is unusually difficult.)

★ 28. Given: $\overline{AE} \parallel \overline{BD}$; $\overline{BC} \parallel \overline{AD}$; $\overline{AE} \cong \overline{BC}$; $\overline{AD} \cong \overline{BD}$
    Prove: **a.** $\overline{AC} \cong \overline{BE}$
    b. $\overline{EC} \parallel \overline{AB}$

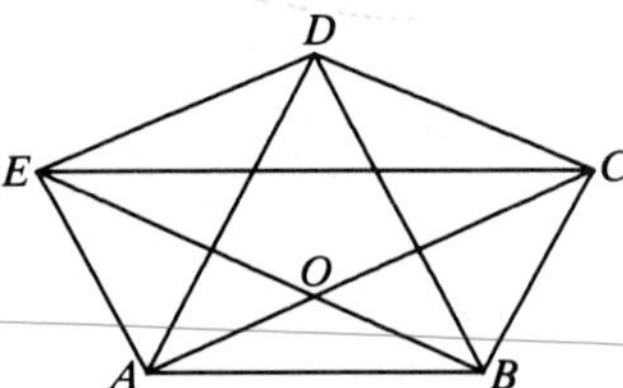

★ 29. Given: $\overleftrightarrow{AM}$ is the $\perp$ bis. of $\overline{BC}$; $\overline{AE} \perp \overline{BD}$; $\overline{AF} \perp \overline{DF}$; $\angle 1 \cong \angle 2$
    Prove: $\overline{BE} \cong \overline{CF}$

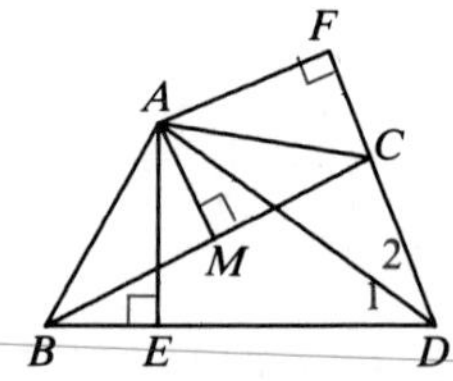

Using a Computer

These exercises extend the topics of this lesson by posing some interesting problems to pursue using a construction program.

Explorations

These exploratory exercises can be done using a computer with a program that draws and measures geometric figures.

Decide if the following statements are true or false. If you think the statement is true, give a convincing argument to support your belief. If you think the statement is false, make a sketch and give all the measurements of the triangle that you find as your counterexample. For each false statement, also discover if there are types of triangles for which the statement is true.

1. An angle bisector bisects the side opposite the bisected angle.
2. A median bisects the angle at the vertex from which it is drawn.

1., 2. False; true for vertex ∠ of isosceles △

3. The length of a median is equal to half of the length of the side it bisects.
   False; true from rt. ∠ vertex in rt. △

Self-Test 3

1. Suppose you wish to prove $\triangle AFE \cong \triangle BFD$. If you have already proved $\triangle ABE \cong \triangle BAD$, what corresponding parts from this second pair of congruent triangles would you use to prove the first pair of triangles congruent? **$\overline{EA} \cong \overline{DB}$ and $\angle AEB \cong \angle BDA$**

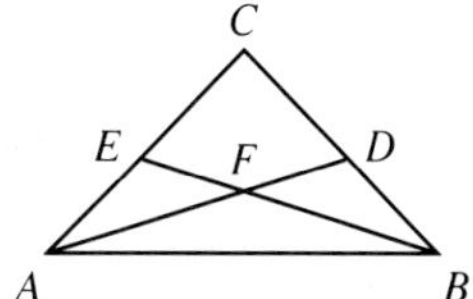

2. Given: $\triangle MPQ \cong \triangle PMN$; $\overline{MS} \cong \overline{PR}$
   Prove: $\triangle MSN \cong \triangle PRQ$

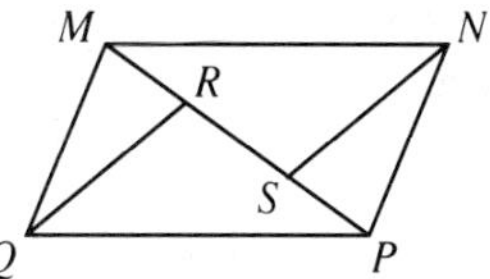

3. In $\triangle JKL$ name each of the following.
   a. an altitude **$\overline{LJ}$ or $\overline{KJ}$** **b.** a median **$\overline{KZ}$**
4. Note that $ZL = ZJ$. Can you deduce that $\overrightarrow{KZ}$ bisects $\angle LKJ$? **No**

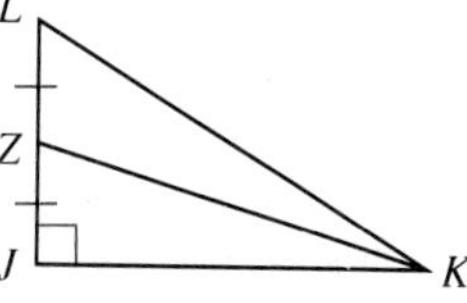

5. $\overrightarrow{UV}$ bisects $\angle WUX$. Write the theorem that justifies the statement that V is equidistant from $\overrightarrow{UW}$ and $\overrightarrow{UX}$. **Thm. 4-7**
6. In $\triangle ABC$, $AB = 7$ and $BC = 7$. Write the theorem that allows you to conclude that B is on the perpendicular bisector of $\overline{AC}$. **Thm. 4-6**

Chapter Summary

1. Congruent figures have the same size and shape. Two triangles are congruent if their corresponding sides and angles are congruent.
2. We have five ways to prove two triangles congruent:
   SSS SAS ASA AAS HL (rt. △s)
3. A common way to prove that two segments or two angles are congruent is to show that they are corresponding parts of congruent triangles.
4. A line and plane are perpendicular if and only if they intersect and the line is perpendicular to all lines in the plane that pass through the point of intersection.
5. If two sides of a triangle are congruent, then the angles opposite those sides are congruent. An equilateral triangle is also equiangular, with three 60° angles.

Quick Quiz

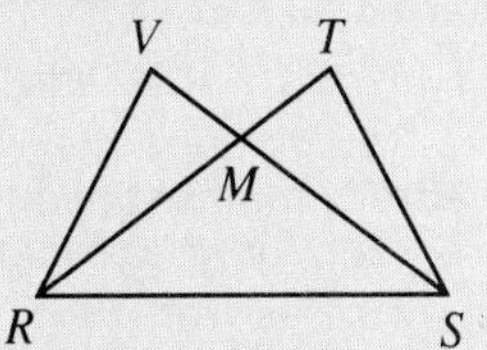

1. Suppose you are given $\triangle VMR \cong \triangle TMS$. Your goal is to show $\triangle VRS \cong \triangle TSR$. What corresponding parts of the first pair of triangles might help you achieve your goal?
   $\angle V$ and $\angle T$; $\overline{VR}$ and $\overline{TS}$; $\overline{VM}$ and $\overline{TM}$; $\overline{RM}$ and $\overline{SM}$
2.

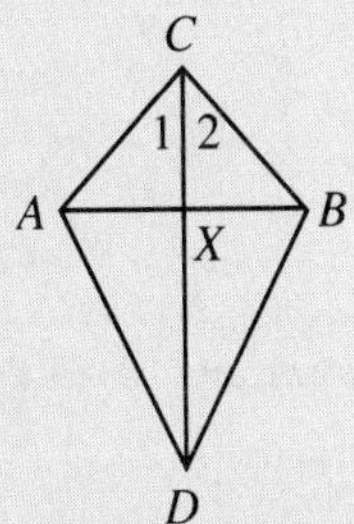

Given: $\triangle ACD \cong \triangle BCD$
Prove: $\triangle ACX \cong \triangle BCX$
1. $\triangle ACD \cong \triangle BCD$ (Given)
2. $\angle 1 \cong \angle 2$ and $\overline{AC} \cong \overline{BC}$ (CPCT)
3. $\overline{CX} \cong \overline{CX}$ (Refl. Prop.)
4. $\triangle ACX \cong \triangle BCX$ (SAS)

For Exs. 3 and 4, use the drawing below.

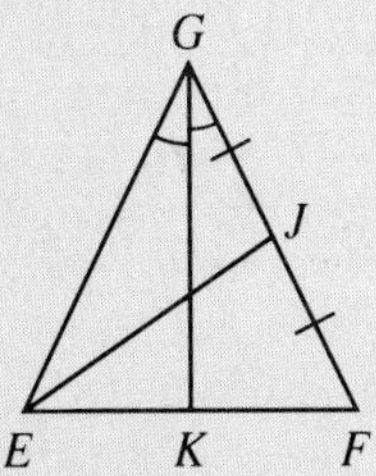

3. Name the following.
   a. an angle bisector $\overrightarrow{GK}$ or $\overline{GK}$
   b. a median $\overline{EJ}$

(continued)

6. If two angles of a triangle are congruent, then the sides opposite those angles are congruent. An equiangular triangle is also equilateral.
7. Sometimes you can prove one pair of triangles congruent and then use corresponding parts from those triangles to prove that another pair of triangles are congruent.
8. Proofs in geometry are commonly written in two-column form, as a list of key steps, or in paragraph form.
9. Every triangle has three medians and three altitudes.
10. The perpendicular bisector of a segment is the line that is perpendicular to the segment at its midpoint.
11. A point lies on the perpendicular bisector of a segment if and only if the point is equidistant from the endpoints of the segment.
12. A point lies on the bisector of an angle if and only if the point is equidistant from the sides of the angle.

Chapter Review

The two triangles shown are congruent. Complete.

1. $\triangle STW \cong$ _?_ **$\triangle QPR$**
2. $\triangle PQR \cong$ _?_ **$\triangle TSW$** 4–1
3. $\angle R \cong$ _?_ **$\angle W$**
4. _?_ $= RP$ **WT**

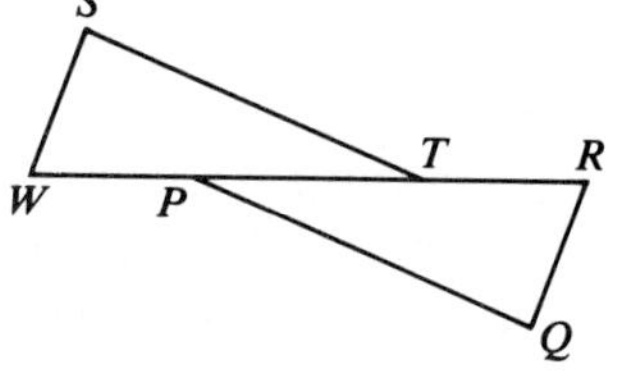

Can you deduce from the given information that $\triangle RXY \cong \triangle SXY$? If so, what postulate can you use?

5. Given: $\overline{RX} \cong \overline{SX}$; $\overline{RY} \cong \overline{SY}$ **Yes; SSS** 4–2
6. Given: $\overline{RY} \cong \overline{SY}$; $\angle R \cong \angle S$ **No**
7. Given: $\overline{XY}$ bisects $\angle RXS$ and $\angle RYS$. **Yes; ASA**
8. Given: $\angle RXY \cong \angle SXY$; $\overline{RX} \cong \overline{SX}$ **Yes; SAS**

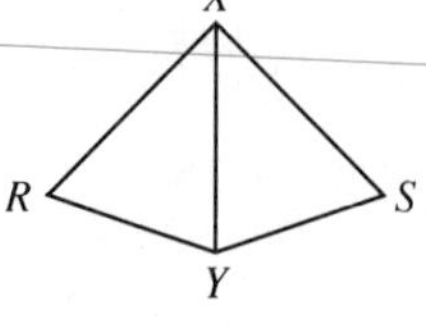

Write proofs in two-column form.

9. Given: $\overline{JM} \cong \overline{LM}$; $\overline{JK} \cong \overline{LK}$ 4–3
   Prove: $\angle MJK \cong \angle MLK$
10. Given: $\angle JMK \cong \angle LMK$; $\overline{MK} \perp$ plane P
    Prove: $\overline{JK} \cong \overline{LK}$

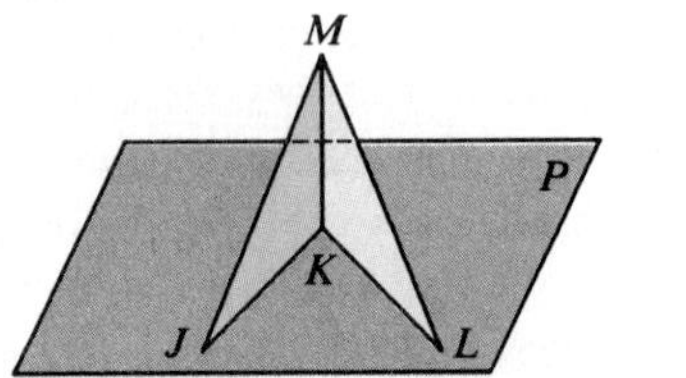

4. Note that $\angle EGK \cong \angle FGK$. Can you conclude that $\overline{EK} \cong \overline{KF}$? No

5. $\overrightarrow{BT}$ bisects $\angle ABC$ and V lies on $\overrightarrow{BT}$. State the theorem that justifies the assertion: V is as far from $\overrightarrow{BA}$ as from $\overrightarrow{BC}$.
If a point lies on the bisector of an angle, then the point is equidistant from the sides of the angle.

6. Line l is the perpendicular bisector of $\overline{YZ}$, and G is so placed that $GY = GZ$. State the theorem that justifies the assertion: G lies on l.
If a point is equidistant from the ends of a segment, then the point lies on the perpendicular bisector of the segment.

Supplementary Materials

Practice Master 22

Test 17

Resource Book, pp. 22–23, 125

Complete.

11. If $\angle 3 \cong \angle 4$, then which segments must be congruent? **$\overline{ER}$, $\overline{EV}$** 4–4

12. If $\triangle REV$ is an equiangular triangle, then $\triangle REV$ is also a(n) __?__ triangle. **equilateral**

13. If $\overline{ES} \cong \overline{ET}$, $m\angle 1 = 75$, and $m\angle 2 = 3x$, then $x =$ __?__. **25**

14. If $\angle 1 \cong \angle 2$, $ES = 3y + 5$, and $ET = 25 - y$, then $y =$ __?__. **5**

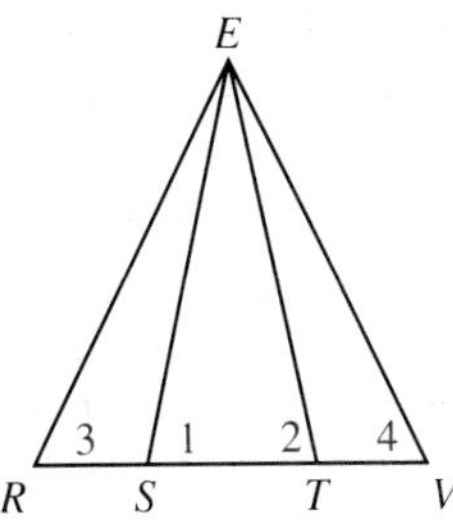

Write proofs in two-column form.

15. Given: $\overline{GH} \perp \overline{HJ}$; $\overline{KJ} \perp \overline{HJ}$; $\angle G \cong \angle K$ 4–5
Prove: $\triangle GHJ \cong \triangle KJH$

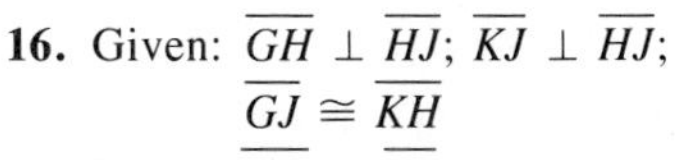

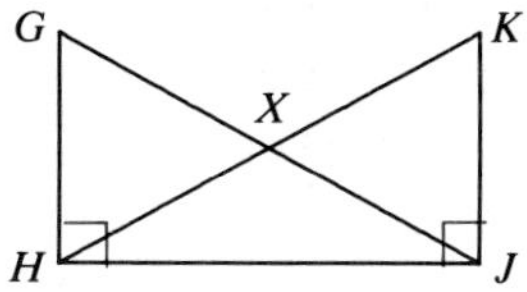

16. Given: $\overline{GH} \perp \overline{HJ}$; $\overline{KJ} \perp \overline{HJ}$; $\overline{GJ} \cong \overline{KH}$
Prove: $\overline{GH} \cong \overline{KJ}$

17. Give the reason for each key step of the proof. 4–6
Given: $\overline{AX} \cong \overline{CY}$; $\angle A \cong \angle C$; $\overline{BX} \perp \overline{AD}$; $\overline{DY} \perp \overline{BC}$
Prove: $\overline{AD} \parallel \overline{BC}$

1. $\triangle ABX \cong \triangle CDY$ **ASA**
2. $\overline{BX} \cong \overline{DY}$ **Corr. parts of ≅ ▵ are ≅.**
3. $\triangle BDX \cong \triangle DBY$ **HL**
4. $\angle 1 \cong \angle 2$ **Corr. parts of ≅ ▵ are ≅.**
5. $\overline{AD} \parallel \overline{BC}$ **If 2 lines are cut by a trans. and alt. int. ∠s are ≅, then the lines are ∥.**

18. Refer to $\triangle DEF$ and name each of the following: 4–7

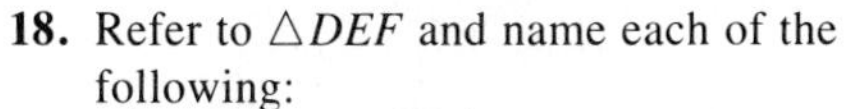

a. an altitude **$\overline{DG}$**
b. a median **$\overline{FH}$**
c. the perpendicular bisector of a side of the triangle **$\overline{KJ}$**

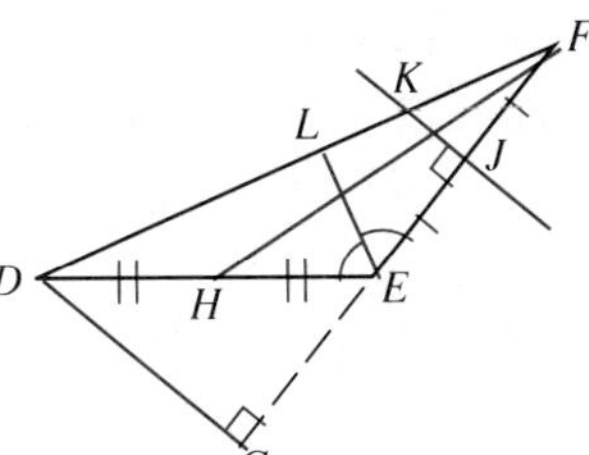

19. Point G lies on the perpendicular bisector of $\overline{EF}$. Write the theorem that justifies the statement that $GE = GF$. **Thm. 4-5**

20. $\triangle ABC$ and $\triangle ABD$ are congruent right triangles with common hypotenuse $\overline{AB}$. Write the theorem that allows you to conclude that point B lies on the bisector of $\angle DAC$. **Thm. 4-8**

Teaching References

Alternate Test, p. T15

Chapter Test

Complete.

1. If $\triangle BAD \cong \triangle TOP$, then $\overline{DB} \cong$ __?__ and $\triangle PTO \cong$ __?__. **$\overline{PT}$, $\triangle DBA$**
2. $\triangle EFG$ is isosceles, with $m\angle G = 94$. The legs are sides __?__ and __?__. $m\angle E =$ __?__ (numerical answer). **$\overline{GE}$, $\overline{GF}$; 43**
3. You want to prove $\triangle ABC \cong \triangle XYZ$. You have shown $\overline{AB} \cong \overline{XY}$ and $\overline{AC} \cong \overline{XZ}$. To prove the triangles congruent by SAS you must show that __?__ $\cong$ __?__. To prove the triangles congruent by SSS you must show that __?__ $\cong$ __?__. **$\angle A$, $\angle X$; $\overline{BC}$, $\overline{YZ}$**
4. A method that can be used to prove right triangles congruent, but cannot be used with other types of triangles, is the __?__ method. **HL**
5. $\triangle CAP$ and $\triangle TAP$ are equilateral and coplanar. $\overline{AP}$ is a common side of the two triangles. $m\angle CAT =$ __?__ (numerical answer). **120**
6. A segment from a vertex of a triangle to the midpoint of the opposite side is called a(n) __?__ of the triangle. **median**
7. A point lies on the bisector of an angle if and only if it is equidistant from __?__. **the sides of the angle**
8. If in $\triangle ABC$ $m\angle A = 50$, $m\angle C = 80$, $AC = 7x + 8$, and $BC = 38 - 3x$, then $x =$ __?__. **3**

Can two triangles be proved congruent? If so, by which method, SSS, SAS, ASA, AAS, or HL?

9. 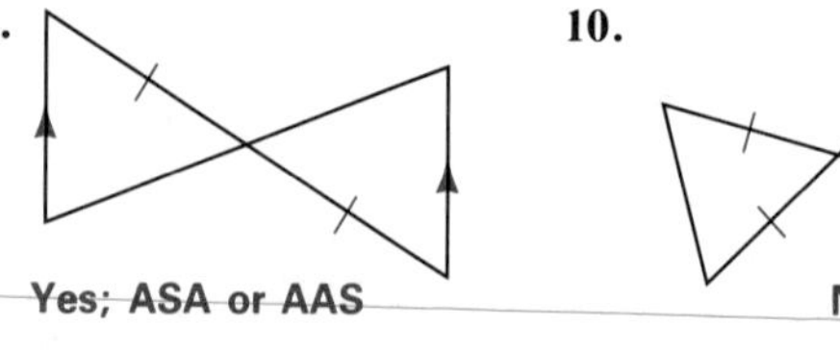
Yes; ASA or AAS

10. 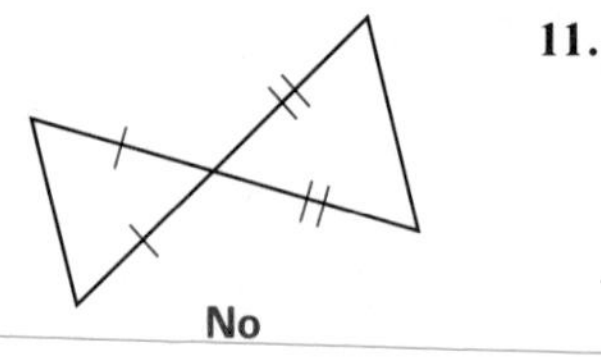
No

11. 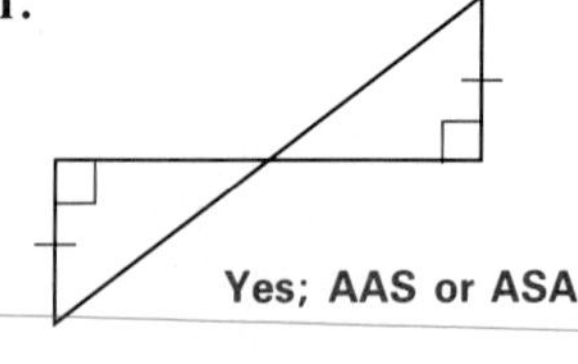
Yes; AAS or ASA

12. 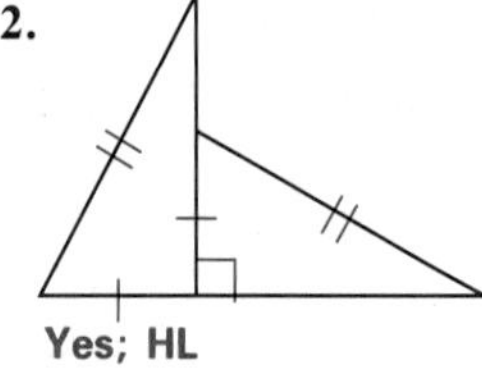
Yes; HL

13. 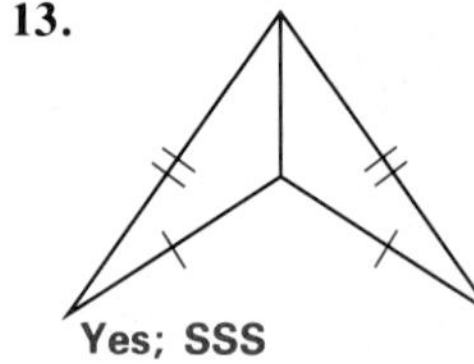
Yes; SSS

14. 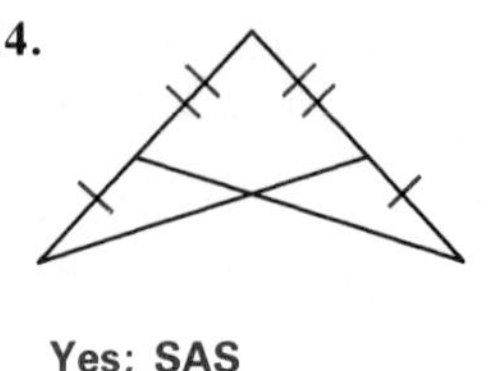
Yes; SAS

$\overline{WX}$ and $\overline{YZ}$ are perpendicular bisectors of each other.

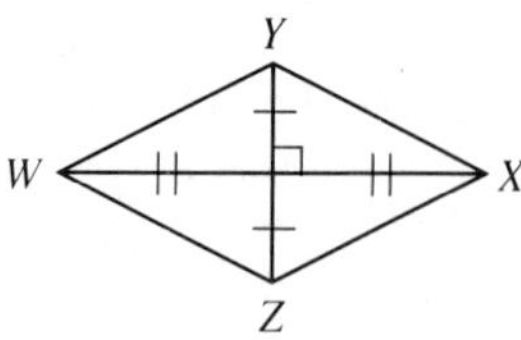

15. W is equidistant from __?__ and __?__. **Y, Z**
16. Z is equidistant from __?__ and __?__. **W, X**
17. Name four isosceles triangles.
18. How many pairs of congruent triangles are shown in the diagram? **8**

17. $\triangle YWX$, $\triangle ZWX$, $\triangle WYZ$, $\triangle XYZ$

19. Given: $\angle 1 \cong \angle 2$; $\angle PQR \cong \angle SRQ$
Prove: $\overline{PR} \cong \overline{SQ}$

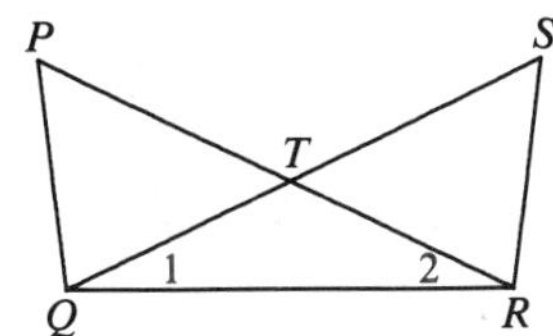

20. Given: $\angle 1 \cong \angle 2$; $\angle 3 \cong \angle 4$
Prove: $\triangle ZXY$ is isosceles.

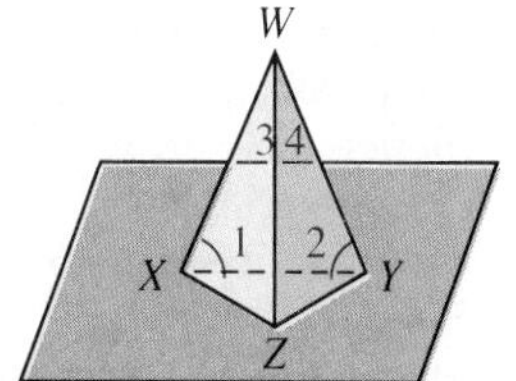

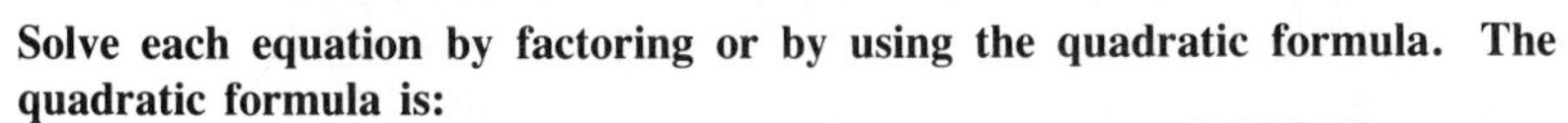

Algebra Review: *Quadratic Equations*

Solve each equation by factoring or by using the quadratic formula. The quadratic formula is:

$$\textbf{If } ax^2 + bx + c = 0, \textbf{ with } a \neq 0, \textbf{ then } x = \frac{-b \pm \sqrt{b^2 - 4ac}}{2a}.$$

Example $3x^2 + 14x + 8 = 0$

Solution 1 *By factoring*

$$3x^2 + 14x + 8 = 0$$
$$(3x + 2)(x + 4) = 0$$
$$3x + 2 = 0 \quad \text{or} \quad x + 4 = 0$$
$$x = -\frac{2}{3} \quad \text{or} \quad x = -4$$

Solution 2 *By quadratic formula*

$$3x^2 + 14x + 8 = 0 \qquad a = 3,\ b = 14,\ c = 8$$
$$x = \frac{-b \pm \sqrt{b^2 - 4ac}}{2a} = \frac{-14 \pm \sqrt{14^2 - 4(3)(8)}}{2(3)}$$
$$x = \frac{-14 \pm \sqrt{196 - 96}}{6} = \frac{-14 \pm 10}{6}$$
$$x = -\frac{2}{3} \quad \text{or} \quad x = -4$$

1. $x^2 + 5x - 6 = 0$ **−6, 1**
2. $n^2 - 6n + 8 = 0$ **2, 4**
3. $y^2 - 7y - 18 = 0$ **−2, 9**
4. $x^2 + 8x = 0$ **0, −8**
5. $y^2 = 13y$ **0, 13**
6. $2z^2 + 7z = 0$ **−3.5, 0**
7. $n^2 - 144 = 25$ **−13, 13**
8. $50x^2 = 200$ **−2, 2**
9. $50x^2 = 2$ **−0.2, 0.2**
10. $49z^2 = 1$ **$-\frac{1}{7}, \frac{1}{7}$**
11. $y^2 - 6y + 9 = 0$ **3**
12. $x^2 - 7x + 12 = 0$ **3, 4**
13. $y^2 + 8y + 12 = 0$
14. $t^2 + 5t = 24$ **−8, 3**
15. $v^2 + 25 = 10v$ **5**
16. $x^2 = 3x + 4$ **−1, 4**
17. $t^2 - t = 20$ **−4, 5**
18. $y^2 = 20y - 36$ **2, 18**
19. $3x^2 + 3x = 4$
20. $15 + 4y^2 = 17y$
21. $x^2 + 5x + 2 = 0$
22. $x^2 + 2x - 1 = 0$
23. $x^2 - 5x + 3 = 0$
24. $x^2 + 3x - 2 = 0$
25. $(y - 5)^2 = 16$ **1, 9**
26. $z^2 = 4(2z - 3)$ **2, 6**
27. $x(x + 5) = 14$ **−7, 2**

13. −6, −2 **20. 1.25, 3**

In Exercises 28–33 x represents the length of a segment. When a value of x doesn't make sense as a length, eliminate that value of x.

28. $x(x - 50) = 0$ **50**
29. $x^2 - 400 = 0$ **20**
30. $x^2 - 17x + 72 = 0$ **8, 9**
31. $2x^2 + x - 3 = 0$ **1**
32. $2x^2 - 7x - 4 = 0$ **4**
33. $6x^2 = 5x + 6$ **1.5**

Using a Calculator

Students can use a calculator to compute the $\sqrt{b^2 - 4ac}$ portion of the quadratic formula. They can also use a calculator to check their solutions.

Additional Answers Algebra Review

19. $\frac{-3 \pm \sqrt{57}}{6}$

21. $\frac{-5 \pm \sqrt{17}}{2}$

22. $-1 \pm \sqrt{2}$

23. $\frac{5 \pm \sqrt{13}}{2}$

24. $\frac{-3 \pm \sqrt{17}}{2}$

Supplementary Materials

Practice Masters 23, 24
Resource Book, p. 193

Preparing for College Entrance Exams

Strategy For Success

Some college entrance exam questions ask you to decide if several statements are true based on given information (see Exercises 3 and 8). In these exercises, check each statement separately and then choose the answer with the correct combination of true statements.

Indicate the best answer by writing the appropriate letter.

A **1.** The measures of the angles of a triangle are $2x + 10$, $3x$, and $8x - 25$. The triangle is:
(A) obtuse **(B)** right **(C)** acute **(D)** equilateral **(E)** isosceles

C **2.** A regular polygon has an interior angle of measure 120. How many vertices does the polygon have?
(A) 3 **(B)** 5 **(C)** 6 **(D)** 9 **(E)** 12

D **3.** Plane M is parallel to plane N. Line l lies in M and line k lies in N. Which of the following statement(s) are possible?
(I) Lines l and k are parallel. (II) Lines l and k intersect.
(III) Lines l and k are skew.
(A) I only **(B)** II only **(C)** III only
(D) I and III only **(E)** I, II, and III

C **4.** Given: $\overline{BE}$ bisects $\overline{AD}$. To prove that the triangles are congruent by the AAS method, you must show that:
(A) $\angle A \cong \angle E$ **(B)** $\angle A \cong \angle D$ **(C)** $\angle B \cong \angle E$
(D) $\angle B \cong \angle D$ **(E)** $\overline{AD}$ bisects $\overline{BE}$.

A B C E D

B **5.** Given: $\triangle RGA$ and $\triangle PMC$ with $\overline{RG} \cong \overline{PM}$, $\overline{RA} \cong \overline{PC}$, and $\angle R \cong \angle P$. Which method could be used to prove that $\triangle RGA \cong \triangle PMC$?
(A) SSS **(B)** SAS **(C)** HL **(D)** ASA
(E) There is not enough information for a proof.

C **6.** Predict the next number in the sequence, 2, 6, 12, 20, 30, 42, _?_.
(A) 52 **(B)** 54 **(C)** 56 **(D)** 58 **(E)** 60

E **7.** In $\triangle JKL$, $\overline{KL} \cong \overline{JL}$, $m\angle K = 2x - 36$, and $m\angle L = x + 2$. Find $m\angle J$.
(A) 56 **(B)** 52 **(C)** 53 **(D)** 55 **(E)** 64

D **8.** In $\triangle RST$, $\overleftrightarrow{SU}$ is the perpendicular bisector of $\overline{RT}$ and U lies on $\overline{RT}$. Which statement(s) must be true?
(I) $\triangle RST$ is equilateral. (II) $\triangle RSU \cong \triangle TSU$
(III) $\overrightarrow{SU}$ is the bisector of $\angle RST$.
(A) I only **(B)** II only **(C)** III only
(D) II and III only **(E)** I, II, and III

B **9.** Given: $\triangle SUN \cong \triangle TAN$. You can conclude that:
(A) $\angle S \cong \angle A$ **(B)** $\overline{SN} \cong \overline{TN}$ **(C)** $\angle T \cong \angle U$
(D) $\overline{SU} \cong \overline{TN}$ **(E)** $\overline{UN} \cong \overline{TA}$

Cumulative Review: Chapters 1–4

Complete each sentence with the most appropriate word, phrase, or value.

A 1. If S is between R and T, then $RS + ST = RT$ by the _?_. **Segment Add. Post.**

2. If two parallel planes are cut by a third plane, then the lines of intersection are _?_. **parallel**

3. $\overrightarrow{BD}$ bisects $\angle ABC$, $m\angle ABC = 5x - 4$, and $m\angle CBD = 2x + 10$. $\angle ABC$ is a(n) _?_ angle. **obtuse**

4. If two intersecting lines form congruent adjacent angles, then the lines are _?_. **perpendicular**

5. If $\angle 1$ and $\angle 2$ are complements and $m\angle 1 = 74$, then $m\angle 2 =$ _?_. **16**

6. Given the conditional "If $x = 9$, then $3x = 27$," its converse is _?_. **If $3x = 27$, then $x = 9$.**

7. If the measure of each interior angle of a polygon is 144, then the polygon has _?_ sides. **10**

8. In quadrilateral $EFGH$, $\overline{EF} \parallel \overline{HG}$, $m\angle E = y + 10$, $m\angle F = 2y - 40$, and $m\angle H = 2y - 31$. $m\angle G =$ _?_ (numerical answer) **86**

9. If a diagonal of an equilateral quadrilateral is drawn, the two triangles formed can be proved congruent by the _?_ method. **SSS**

Find the measure of each numbered angle.

10. 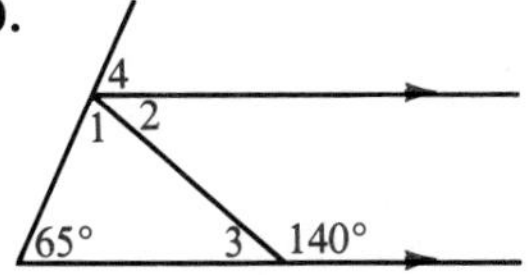

$m\angle 1 = 75$
$m\angle 2 = 40$
$m\angle 3 = 40$
$m\angle 4 = 65$

11. 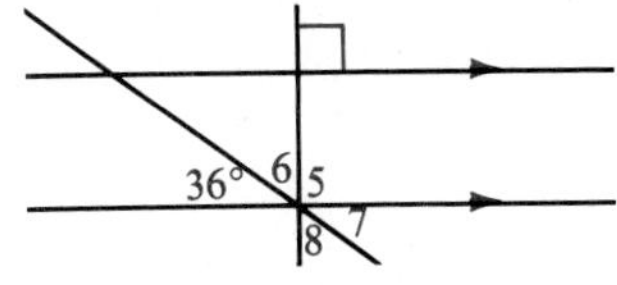

$m\angle 5 = 90$
$m\angle 6 = 54$
$m\angle 7 = 36$
$m\angle 8 = 54$

Could the given information be used to prove that two lines are parallel? If so, which lines?

12. $m\angle 8 + m\angle 9 = 180$ **Yes; $c \parallel d$**

13. $\angle 1 \cong \angle 4$ **No**

14. $m\angle 2 = m\angle 6$ **Yes; $a \parallel b$**

15. $\angle 8$ and $\angle 5$ are rt. $\angle$s. **Yes; $a \parallel b$**

	a			b	
1	2		3	4	c
8	7		6	5	
9	10		11	12	d
16	15		14	13	

B 16. Given: $\overline{MN} \cong \overline{MP}$; $\angle NMO \cong \angle PMO$
Prove: $\overleftrightarrow{MO}$ is the $\perp$ bisector of $\overline{NP}$.

17. Given: $\overline{MO} \perp \overline{NP}$; $\overline{NO} \cong \overline{PO}$
Prove: $\overline{MN} \cong \overline{MP}$

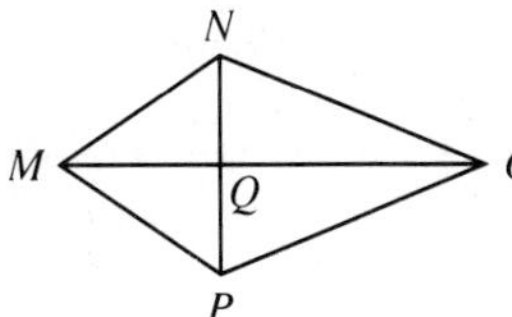

18. Write a paragraph proof: If $\overline{AX}$ is both a median and an altitude of $\triangle ABC$, then $\triangle ABC$ is isosceles.

5 Quadrilaterals

Objectives

5-1 Apply the definition of a parallelogram and the theorems about properties of a parallelogram.

5-2 Prove that certain quadrilaterals are parallelograms.

5-3 Apply theorems about parallel lines.

Apply the midpoint theorems for triangles.

5-4 Apply the definitions and identify the special properties of a rectangle, a rhombus, and a square.

Determine when a parallelogram is a rectangle, rhombus, or square.

5-5 Apply the definitions and identify the properties of a trapezoid and an isosceles trapezoid.

Assignment Guide

See page T40 for information about the Assignment Guide.

Day	Minimum Course	Average Course	Maximum Course
1	**5-1** 169/1–13	**5-1** 169/2–16 even	**5-1** 169–170/3, 6, 9, 12, 15, 16, 19–27 odd
2	**5-1** 170/17, 19, 20, 22–26 even	**5-1** 170/17–31 odd	**5-1** 170–171/20–38 even
3	**5-2** 174/1–7, 9	**5-2** 174–175/3–5, 9, 10, 12, 15, 19, 22	**5-2** 174–176/9, 11, 13, 15, 17, 18, 21, 24
4	**5-2** 174–175/8, 10, 11, 14, 19	**5-3** 180/2–14 even **S** 175/18, 20	**5-3** 180–181/5–19 odd **S** 176/25
5	**5-3** 180/1–11	**5-3** 181/16–22 even 182/Self-Test 1	**5-3** 181–182/20–25
6	**5-3** 180–181/12, 13–21 odd 182/Self-Test 1	**5-4** 187–188/1–11, 14, 17, 20–23	**5-4** 187–188/1–10, 14, 17, 28, 30, 34 **S** 181/18
7	**5-4** 187/1–13 **S** 181/20	**5-4** 188/24–34 even 189/Mixed Review 1–9	**5-4** 188–189/32, 33, 36, 37, 40–42
8	**5-4** 187–188/14, 17, 18, 20–22 189/Mixed Review 1–9	**5-5** 192–193/1, 3, 6, 7, 9, 11, 12, 14, 16	**5-5** 192–193/4, 8, 11, 12, 16, 17, 19, 20, 25
9	**5-5** 192–193/1–11	**5-5** 193/15, 17–19, 21–25, 27 195/Self-Test 2 199/Chapter Test Test, p. T16	**5-5** 193–194/21–29, 32, 33 199/Chapter Test Test, page T16
10	**5-5** 193/13, 14, 16, 17, 21–23 195/Self-Test 2 199/Chapter Test Test, p. T16		

Supplementary Materials Guide

For Use after Lesson	Practice Masters	Tests	Study Guide (Reteaching)	Resource Book: Tests	Resource Book: Practice Exercises	Resource Book: Mixed Review (MR) Prep. for College Entrance Exams (Col) Enrichment (E) Computer (C)	Computer Activities
5-1			pp. 59–60				
5-2	Sheet 25		pp. 61–62				
5-3	Sheet 26	Test 18	pp. 63–64	pp. 24–25	p. 126		
5-4	Sheet 27		pp. 65–66				
5-5	Sheet 28	Test 19	pp. 67–68	pp. 26–27	p. 127		Activity 11
Chapter 5	Sheet 29	Test 20		pp. 28–29	p. 128	p. 194 (Col) pp. 211–215 (E) p. 242 (C)	
Chapters 4–5		Test 21		pp. 30–32	p. 129		
Chapters 1–5						pp. 175–176 (MR)	

Overhead Visuals

Guided Discovery Visuals (lettered) and Teaching Visuals (numbered) available for Chapter 5.

Lessons	Visual	Title
5-1, 5-2, 5-3	10	Five Ways to Prove That a Quadrilateral Is a Parallelogram
5-4, 5-5	11	Properties of Special Quadrilaterals

Software Guide

Houghton Mifflin software for Chapter 5

Geometry Grapher (Apple or IBM)

Use with	Booklet
p. 177 (Theorem 5-9)	Classroom Demonstration, p. 14
p. 176 (Explorations)	
p. 189 (Explorations)	
p. 195 (Explorations)	

Test Generator (Apple or IBM): 75 test items

Other software appropriate for Chapter 5

Geometric Supposer (Apple): Triangles, Quadrilaterals

GeoDraw (IBM)

Guide to Integrated Curriculum

Teachers wishing to integrate coordinate and transformational geometry throughout the course can use the following lessons after Chapter 5. See pages T56–T57 and 657 for more information.

Handbook: Quadrilaterals, pp. 660–662
14-1 Cl. Ex. 1–10; Wr. Ex. 1–23
14-2 Cl. Ex. 1–20; Wr. Ex. 1–20, 23–40
14-3 Cl. Ex. 1–8; Wr. Ex. 1–17, 19, 22, 23
14-4 Cl. Ex. 1–15; Wr. Ex. 1–30, 32–37

Strategies for Teaching

Exploring Properties of Quadrilaterals

When to Use

Before Lesson 5-1

Overview

With this activity students discover many properties of parallelograms and rhombuses before discussing Theorems 5-1 through 5-7, 5-13, and 5-14.

Materials

Four different colored pencils or pens, scissors

Description of Activity

Guide students through the exploration by using the following activities and questions.

1. Draw a scalene triangle on the upper half of a sheet of paper. Fold the paper in half and cut out the triangle, thereby producing two congruent triangles. Color the three pairs of corresponding sides of the triangles three different colors. Then color each pair of corresponding angles of the two triangles in the color of the opposite sides. Finally, draw the median to the longest side of each triangle and color it a fourth color. Place the two triangles together so the longest sides coincide as shown. (The dark segments are the medians.)

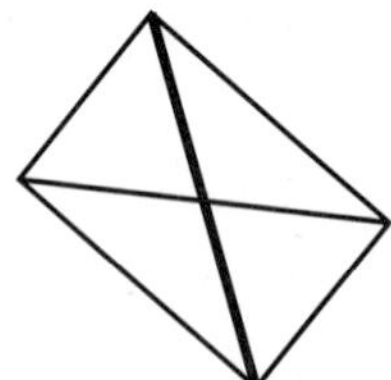

Label the vertices of the quadrilateral *A*, *B*, *C*, *D* and the midpoint of the longest side of the triangle as *M*.

a. What type of quadrilateral is *ABCD?* Give a reason for your answer. parallelogram

b. On your figure, mark all pairs of congruent segments and congruent angles. Then make a list of them.

c. Make as many conjectures about the properties of *ABCD* as you can.

2. Repeat Activity 1 with a different type of triangle. Draw an isosceles triangle on the upper half of a sheet of paper and then cut out the two congruent triangles. Color the corresponding congruent sides and angles in appropriate colors. (You will need one less color. Since the triangle is isosceles, the same color should be used for the two pairs of congruent sides and angles.) Draw the altitude to the base of each triangle and color it a third color. Place the two triangles together as before so the bases coincide. Label the vertices of the quadrilateral *X*, *Y*, *Z*, *W* and the base of the altitude as *H*.

a. What type of quadrilateral is *XYZW*? Give a reason for your answer. rhombus

b. Make as many conjectures about the properties of *XYZW* as you can.

Commentary

- This activity is best done in small groups. Assign a recorder for each group. The recorder should make a list of the group's conjectures and report them to the entire class.
- **1.** *ABCD* can be proven to be a parallelogram using alternate interior angles. With the use of the various colors, one can see that the opposite sides and angles of a quadrilateral are congruent. Since *M* is the midpoint of the longest side of each triangle, it is also apparent that the diagonals bisect each other. Since any two adjacent angles of the

parallelogram contain angles of all three colors, some students may also note that these angles are the same as in the original triangle, which makes their sum 180 degrees; hence they are supplementary.

- **2.** Again, with the use of the various colors, the additional facts that the diagonals of a rhombus are perpendicular and that they bisect the pairs of opposite angles are apparent.

Variations and Extensions

- You can follow up these activities by asking what type of triangle is needed to obtain a rectangle and a square. Students can then discover the properties of these special quadrilaterals.
- Students can do this activity with a geometric drawing program such as *Geometry Grapher* by drawing the triangle and then copying it or rotating it to the desired position to form the quadrilateral. Measurements can then be made and the data recorded.

References to Strategies

PE: Pupil's Edition **TE:** Teacher's Edition **RB:** Resource Book

Problem Solving Strategies

PE: 172 (Strategies for proof)
TE: T95, 189 (Draw a diagram)

Applications

PE: 173 (Exs. 12, 13, Parallel rulers, pliers), 174 (Ex. 7, Ironing board), 196 (Rhombuses)
TE: T94

Nonroutine Problems

PE: 168 (Exs. 15, 17, 18), 170 (Exs. 17, 18), 171 (Exs. 33–36), 173 (Exs. 10–13), 174 (Exs. 7, 8), 179 (Exs. 1, 9), 186 (Exs. 1–4, 11), 188 (Exs. 20–23, 36–39), 189 (Exs. 40–42), 193 (Exs. 19–26, 28, 29), 194 (Exs. 33–36, Challenge), 662 (Ex. 12)
TE: T95, T96
RB: 211–215

Communication

PE: 179 (Ex. 1)
TE: T93, T96, 191
RB: 262, 263 (Van Hiele activities)

Thinking Skills

PE: 186–187 (Classification)
TE: 171 (Make conjectures), 186 (Generalize), 193 (Generalize)
RB: 213–214

Explorations

PE: 176, 189, 195
TE: 165c

Connections

PE: 171 (Benjamin Banneker), 175 (Exs. 19–22, Algebra), 660–662 (Coordinate geometry)
TE: 175 (Reference to Ch. 5)

Using Technology

PE: 176, 183, 185, 189, 195
TE: T92–T93, T94, T95, 171, 175, 176, 178, 181, 183, 185, 188, 189, 193, 194, 195
RB: 242
Using Geometry Grapher: 14
Computer Activities: 25–26

Using Manipulatives/Models

PE: 173 (Exs. 12, 13), 179 (Ex. 1)
TE: T92, T94, T95, 177
RB: 211–212, 215
Overhead Visuals: 10, 11

Cooperative Learning

TE: T93, T94, 168, 171

Teaching Resources

For use in implementing the teaching strategies referenced on the previous page.

Application
Resource Book, p. 211

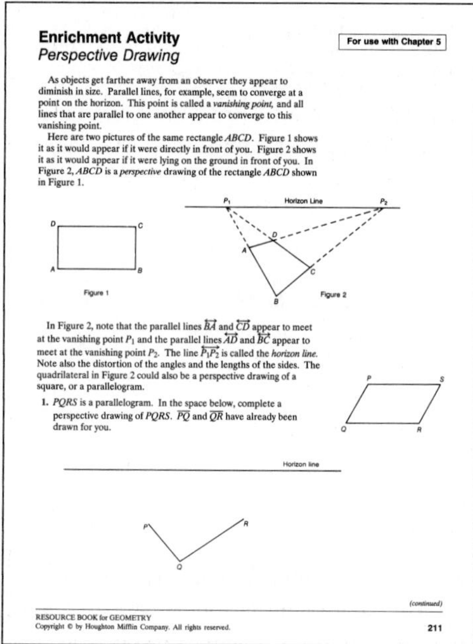

Enrichment Activity
Perspective Drawing

For use with Chapter 5

As objects get farther away from an observer they appear to diminish in size. Parallel lines, for example, seem to converge at a point on the horizon. This point is called a *vanishing point,* and all lines that are parallel to one another appear to converge to this vanishing point.

Here are two pictures of the same rectangle *ABCD*. Figure 1 shows it as it would appear if it were directly in front of you. Figure 2 shows it as it would appear if it were lying on the ground in front of you. In Figure 2, *ABCD* is a *perspective* drawing of the rectangle *ABCD* shown in Figure 1.

In Figure 2, note that the parallel lines $\overleftrightarrow{BA}$ and $\overleftrightarrow{CD}$ appear to meet at the vanishing point P_1 and the parallel lines $\overleftrightarrow{AD}$ and $\overleftrightarrow{BC}$ appear to meet at the vanishing point P_2. The line $\overleftrightarrow{P_1P_2}$ is called the *horizon line.* Note also the distortion of the angles and the lengths of the sides. The quadrilateral in Figure 2 could also be a perspective drawing of a square, or a parallelogram.

1. *PQRS* is a parallelogram. In the space below, complete a perspective drawing of *PQRS*. $\overline{PQ}$ and $\overline{QR}$ have already been drawn for you.

(continued)

RESOURCE BOOK for GEOMETRY

211

Application
Resource Book, p. 212

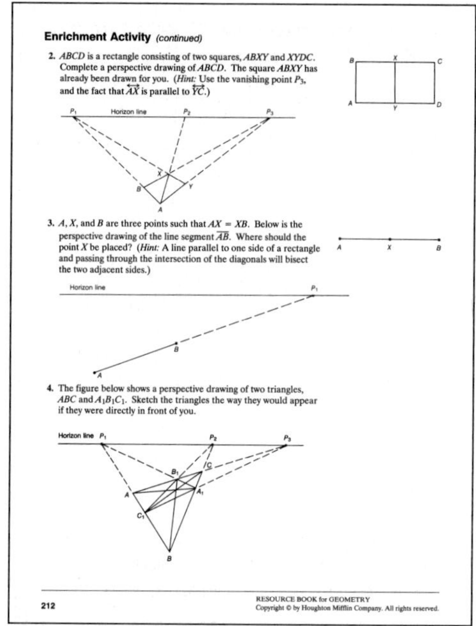

Enrichment Activity *(continued)*

2. *ABCD* is a rectangle consisting of two squares, *ABXY* and *XYDC*. Complete a perspective drawing of *ABCD*. The square *ABXY* has already been drawn for you. (*Hint:* Use the vanishing point P_3, and the fact that $\overleftrightarrow{AX}$ is parallel to $\overleftrightarrow{YC}$.)

3. *A*, *X*, and *B* are three points such that $AX = XB$. Below is the perspective drawing of the line segment $\overline{AB}$. Where should the point *X* be placed? (*Hint:* A line parallel to one side of a rectangle and passing through the intersection of the diagonals will bisect the two adjacent sides.)

4. The figure below shows a perspective drawing of two triangles, *ABC* and $A_1B_1C_1$. Sketch the triangles the way they would appear if they were directly in front of you.

212
RESOURCE BOOK for GEOMETRY

Thinking Skills
Resource Book, p. 213

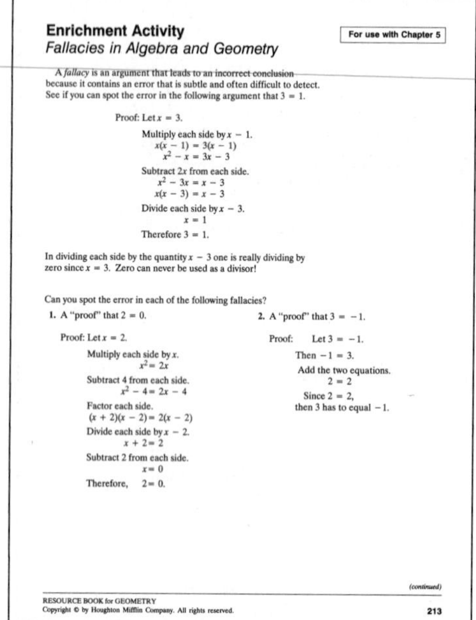

Enrichment Activity
Fallacies in Algebra and Geometry

For use with Chapter 5

A *fallacy* is an argument that leads to an incorrect conclusion because it contains an error that is subtle and often difficult to detect. See if you can spot the error in the following argument that $3 = 1$.

Proof: Let $x = 3$.

Multiply each side by $x - 1$.
$x(x - 1) = 3(x - 1)$
$x^2 - x = 3x - 3$

Subtract $2x$ from each side.
$x^2 - 3x = x - 3$
$x(x - 3) = x - 3$

Divide each side by $x - 3$.
$x = 1$

Therefore $3 = 1$.

In dividing each side by the quantity $x - 3$ one is really dividing by zero since $x = 3$. Zero can never be used as a divisor!

Can you spot the error in each of the following fallacies?

1. A "proof" that $2 = 0$.

Proof: Let $x = 2$.

Multiply each side by x.
$x^2 = 2x$

Subtract 4 from each side.
$x^2 - 4 = 2x - 4$

Factor each side.
$(x + 2)(x - 2) = 2(x - 2)$

Divide each side by $x - 2$.
$x + 2 = 2$

Subtract 2 from each side.
$x = 0$

Therefore, $2 = 0$.

2. A "proof" that $3 = -1$.

Proof: Let $3 = -1$.

Then $-1 = 3$.

Add the two equations.
$2 = 2$

Since $2 = 2$,
then 3 has to equal -1.

(continued)

RESOURCE BOOK for GEOMETRY

213

Problem Solving
Resource Book, p. 215

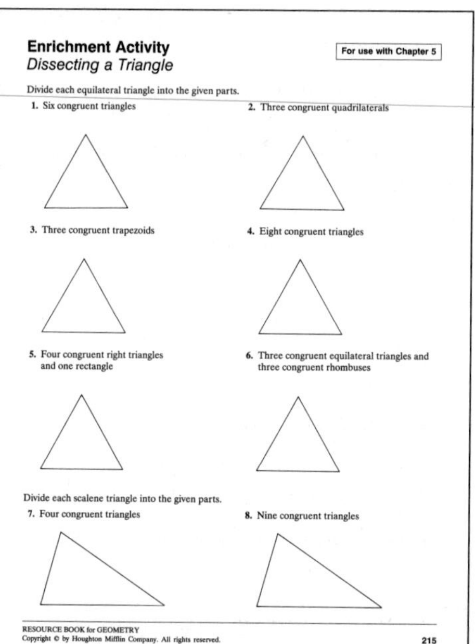

Enrichment Activity
Dissecting a Triangle

For use with Chapter 5

Divide each equilateral triangle into the given parts.

1. Six congruent triangles
2. Three congruent quadrilaterals
3. Three congruent trapezoids
4. Eight congruent triangles
5. Four congruent right triangles and one rectangle
6. Three congruent equilateral triangles and three congruent rhombuses

Divide each scalene triangle into the given parts.

7. Four congruent triangles
8. Nine congruent triangles

RESOURCE BOOK for GEOMETRY

215

Thinking Skills
Resource Book, p. 262

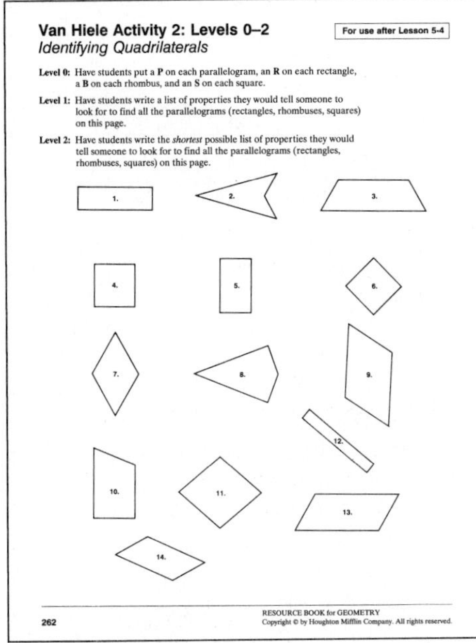

Van Hiele Activity 2: Levels 0–2
Identifying Quadrilaterals

For use after Lesson 5-4

Level 0: Have students put a **P** on each parallelogram, an **R** on each rectangle, a **B** on each rhombus, and an **S** on each square.

Level 1: Have students write a list of properties they would tell someone to look for to find all the parallelograms (rectangles, rhombuses, squares) on this page.

Level 2: Have students write the *shortest* possible list of properties they would tell someone to look for to find all the parallelograms (rectangles, rhombuses, squares) on this page.

262

RESOURCE BOOK for GEOMETRY

Cooperative Learning
Resource Book, p. 263

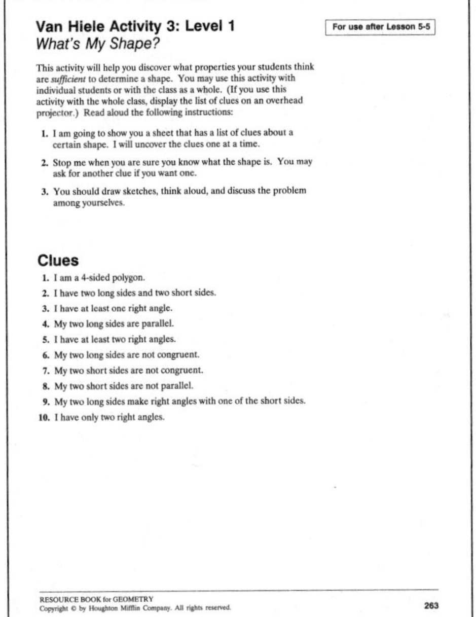

Van Hiele Activity 3: Level 1
What's My Shape?

For use after Lesson 5-5

This activity will help you discover what properties your students think are *sufficient* to determine a shape. You may use this activity with individual students or with the class as a whole. (If you use this activity with the whole class, display the list of clues on an overhead projector.) Read aloud the following instructions:

1. I am going to show you a sheet that has a list of clues about a certain shape. I will uncover the clues one at a time.
2. Stop me when you are sure you know what the shape is. You may ask for another clue if you want one.
3. You should draw sketches, think aloud, and discuss the problem among yourselves.

Clues

1. I am a 4-sided polygon.
2. I have two long sides and two short sides.
3. I have at least one right angle.
4. My two long sides are parallel.
5. I have at least two right angles.
6. My two long sides are not congruent.
7. My two short sides are not congruent.
8. My two short sides are not parallel.
9. My two long sides make right angles with one of the short sides.
10. I have only two right angles.

RESOURCE BOOK for GEOMETRY

263

Using Technology
Resource Book, p. 242

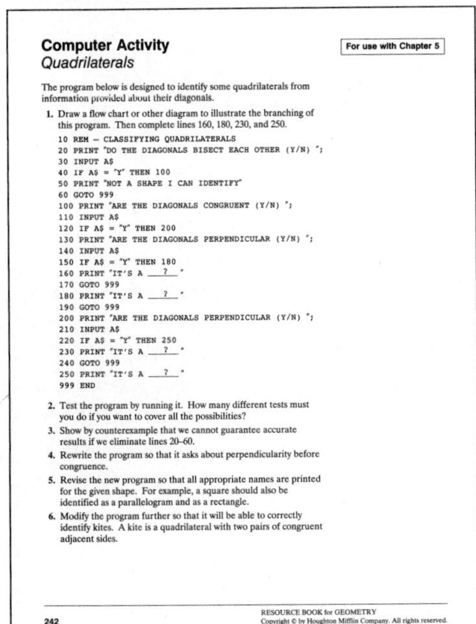

Computer Activity
Quadrilaterals

For use with Chapter 5

The program below is designed to identify some quadrilaterals from information provided about their diagonals.

1. Draw a flow chart or other diagram to illustrate the branching of this program. Then complete lines 160, 180, 230, and 250.

```
10 REM - CLASSIFYING QUADRILATERALS
20 PRINT "DO THE DIAGONALS BISECT EACH OTHER (Y/N) ";
30 INPUT A$
40 IF A$ = "Y" THEN 100
50 PRINT "NOT A SHAPE I CAN IDENTIFY"
60 GOTO 999
100 PRINT "ARE THE DIAGONALS CONGRUENT (Y/N) ";
110 INPUT A$
120 IF A$ = "Y" THEN 200
130 PRINT "ARE THE DIAGONALS PERPENDICULAR (Y/N) ";
140 INPUT A$
150 IF A$ = "Y" THEN 180
160 PRINT "IT'S A __?__"
170 GOTO 999
180 PRINT "IT'S A __?__"
190 GOTO 999
200 PRINT "ARE THE DIAGONALS PERPENDICULAR (Y/N) ";
210 INPUT A$
220 IF A$ = "Y" THEN 250
230 PRINT "IT'S A __?__"
240 GOTO 999
250 PRINT "IT'S A __?__"
999 END
```

2. Test the program by running it. How many different tests must you do if you want to cover all the possibilities?
3. Show by counterexample that we cannot guarantee accurate results if we eliminate lines 20–60.
4. Rewrite the program so that it asks about perpendicularity before congruence.
5. Revise the new program so that all appropriate names are printed for the given shape. For example, a square should also be identified as a parallelogram and as a rectangle.
6. Modify the program further so that it will be able to correctly identify kites. A kite is a quadrilateral with two pairs of congruent adjacent sides.

242

RESOURCE BOOK for GEOMETRY

Using Models
Teaching Visual 10

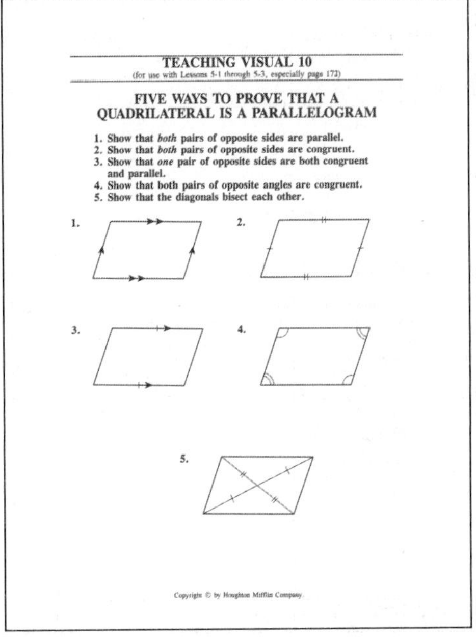

TEACHING VISUAL 10

(for use with Lessons 5-1 through 5-3, especially page 172)

FIVE WAYS TO PROVE THAT A QUADRILATERAL IS A PARALLELOGRAM

1. Show that *both* pairs of opposite sides are parallel.
2. Show that *both* pairs of opposite sides are congruent.
3. Show that *one* pair of opposite sides are both congruent and parallel.
4. Show that both pairs of opposite angles are congruent.
5. Show that the diagonals bisect each other.

Teaching References

Lesson Commentary, pp. T92–T96

Assignment Guide, pp. T44–T45

Software Guide, p. T73

Alternate Test, p. T16

Supplementary Materials

Practice Masters 25–29

Tests 18–21

Resource Book
- Tests, pp. 24–32
- Practice, pp. 126–129
- Mixed Review, pp. 175–176
- Preparing for College Entrance Exams, p. 194
- Enrichment Activities, pp. 211–215
- Computer Activity, p. 242
- van Hiele Activities, pp. 261–263

Study Guide, pp. 59–68

Overhead Visuals 10, 11

Computer Activity
- 11 Median of a Trapezoid

Handbook for Integrating Coordinate and Transformational Geometry

Quadrilaterals, pp. 660–662

Cultural Note

The words *obtuse* and *acute* both come from Latin. The Latin verb *obtundere* means *to dull or blunt. Acuēre* means *to sharpen.* Another term in geometry that comes from Latin is *perpendicular.* The Latin word *perpendiculum* refers to a plumb line. *Pendere* is a Latin verb meaning *to hang.*

5 QUADRILATERALS

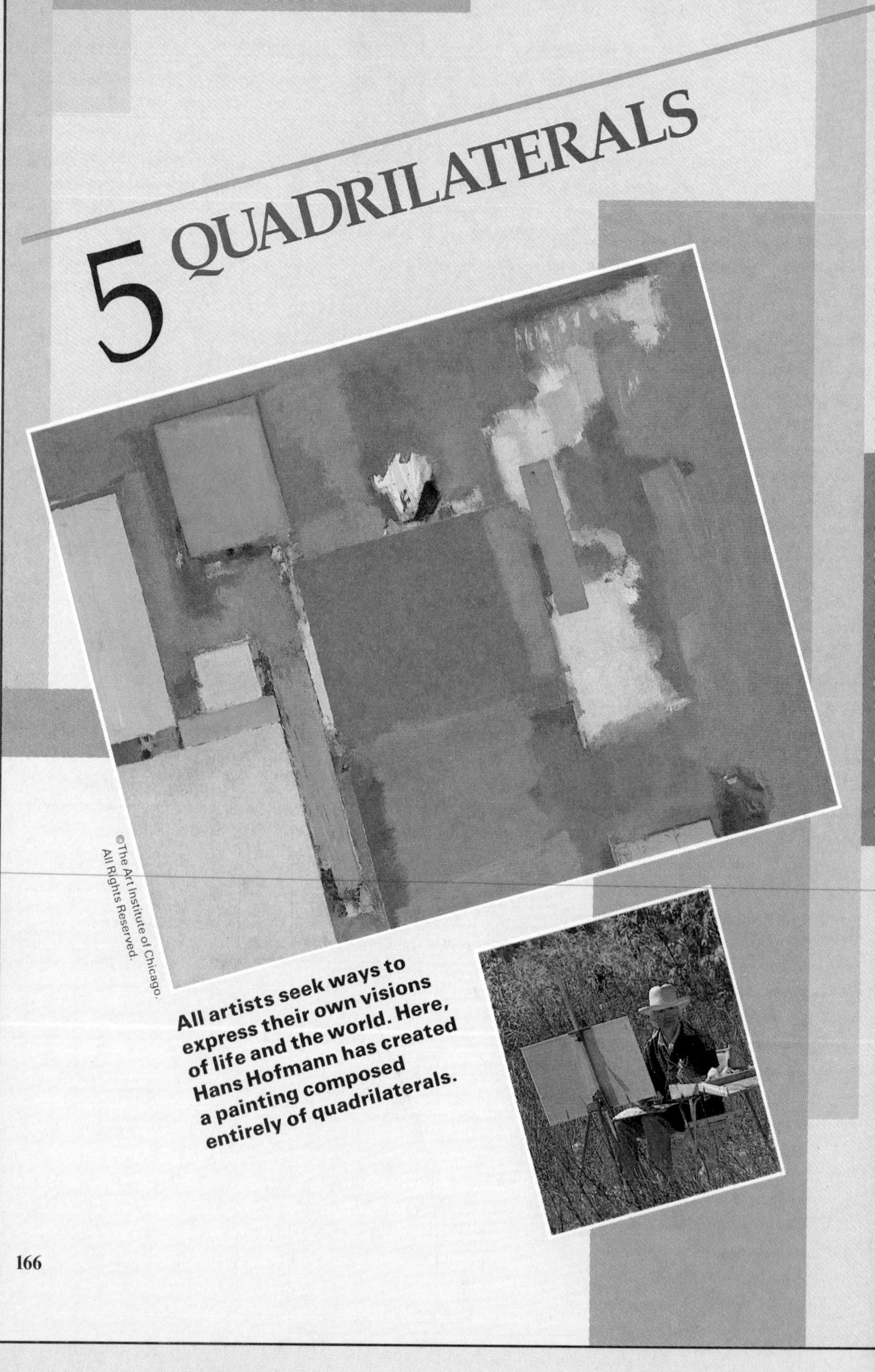

All artists seek ways to express their own visions of life and the world. Here, Hans Hofmann has created a painting composed entirely of quadrilaterals.

166

Parallelograms

Objectives

1. Apply the definition of a parallelogram and the theorems about properties of a parallelogram.
2. Prove that certain quadrilaterals are parallelograms.
3. Apply theorems about parallel lines and the segment that joins the midpoints of two sides of a triangle.

5-1 *Properties of Parallelograms*

A **parallelogram** (▱) is a quadrilateral with both pairs of opposite sides parallel. The following theorems state some properties common to all parallelograms. Your proofs of these theorems (Written Exercises 13–15) will be based on what you have learned about parallel lines and congruent triangles.

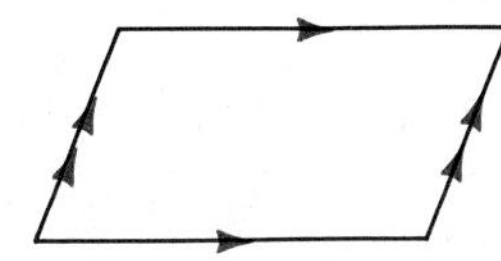

Theorem 5-1

Opposite sides of a parallelogram are congruent.

Given: ▱$EFGH$

Prove: $\overline{EF} \cong \overline{HG}$; $\overline{FG} \cong \overline{EH}$

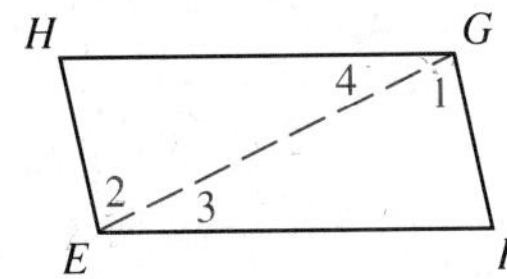

Plan for Proof: Draw $\overline{EG}$ to form triangles with corresponding sides $\overline{EF}$ and $\overline{HG}$, $\overline{FG}$ and $\overline{EH}$. Use the pairs of alternate interior angles $\angle 1$ and $\angle 2$, $\angle 3$ and $\angle 4$, to prove the triangles congruent by ASA.

Theorem 5-2

Opposite angles of a parallelogram are congruent.

Theorem 5-3

Diagonals of a parallelogram bisect each other.

Given: ▱$QRST$ with diagonals $\overline{QS}$ and $\overline{TR}$

Prove: $\overline{QS}$ and $\overline{TR}$ bisect each other.

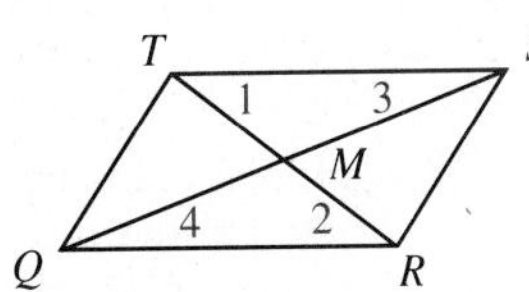

Plan for Proof: You can prove that $\overline{QM} \cong \overline{MS}$ and $\overline{RM} \cong \overline{MT}$ by showing that they are corresponding parts of congruent triangles. Since $\overline{QR} \cong \overline{TS}$ by Theorem 5-1, you can show that $\triangle QMR \cong \triangle SMT$ by ASA.

Teaching Suggestions,
pp. T92–T93

Objective
Presenting the Lesson
Using Technology
Extension

Communication Skills,
p. T93

Cooperative Learning,
p. T93

Exploring Activity, p. 165c

Supplementary Materials

Resource Book, p. 261
Study Guide, pp. 59–60

Lesson Focus

Parallelograms have many interesting properties that are developed in this lesson. Students can discover the properties by working with drawings of parallelograms, a ruler, and a protractor. Then theorems can be proved to show that the properties are true for all parallelograms.

Suggested Assignments

Minimum
Day 1: 169/1–13
Day 2: 170/17, 19, 20, 22–26 even

Average
Day 1: 169/2–16 even
Day 2: 170/17–31 odd

Maximum
Day 1: 169–170/3, 6, 9, 12, 15, 16, 19–27 odd
Day 2: 170–171/20–38 even

Chalkboard Examples

Classify each statement as true or false.

1. Every parallelogram is a quadrilateral. T
2. Every quadrilateral is a parallelogram. F
3. All angles of a parallelogram are congruent. F
4. All sides of a parallelogram are congruent. F
5. In ▱*RSTU*, $\overline{RS} \parallel \overline{TU}$. T
6. In ▱*ABCD*, if $m\angle A = 50$, then $m\angle C = 130$. F
7. In ▱*XWYZ*, $\overline{XY} \cong \overline{WZ}$. F
8. In ▱*ABCD*, $\overline{AC}$ and $\overline{BD}$ bisect each other. T

Group Activity

You may wish to form groups of three or four students to go over Exs. 9–14. Each member of the group should take turns reading the problems and naming the principal definition or theorem that justifies the given statement. Other group members should be encouraged to offer suggestions, corrections, and alternatives. Then have each group draw a new parallelogram and write as many true statements about it as they can.

Additional Answers Classroom Exercises

16.a. If a quad. is a ▱, then its opp. sides are ≅.

b. If a quad. is a ▱, then its opp. ∠s are ≅.

c. If a quad. is a ▱, then its diag. bisect each other.

Classroom Exercises

1. a. $\overline{GR} \parallel \overline{MA}$ **b.** $\overline{GM} \parallel \overline{RA}$ } **If 2 ∥ lines are cut by a trans., s-s int. ∠s are supplementary.**

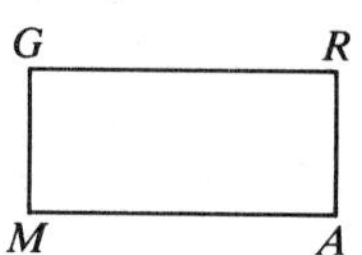

1. Quad. *GRAM* is a parallelogram.
   a. Why is $\angle G$ supplementary to $\angle M$?
   b. Why is $\angle M$ supplementary to $\angle A$?
   c. Complete: Consecutive angles of a parallelogram are __?__, while opposite angles are __?__. **supplementary, ≅**

2. Suppose that $\angle M$ is a right angle. What can you deduce about angles *G*, *R*, and *A*? **They are also right ∠s.**

In Exercises 3–5 quad. *ABCD* is a parallelogram. Find the values of *x*, *y*, and *z*.

3.

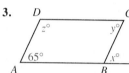

$x = 65$, $y = 65$, $z = 115$

4.

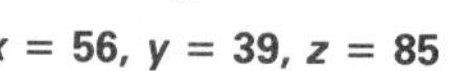
$x = 56$, $y = 39$, $z = 85$

5.

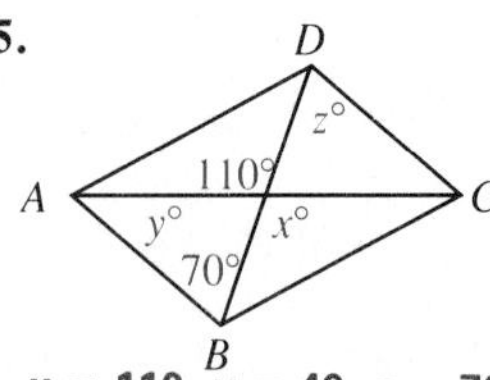

$x = 110$, $y = 40$, $z = 70$

Must quad. *EFGH* be a parallelogram? Can it be a parallelogram? Explain.

6.

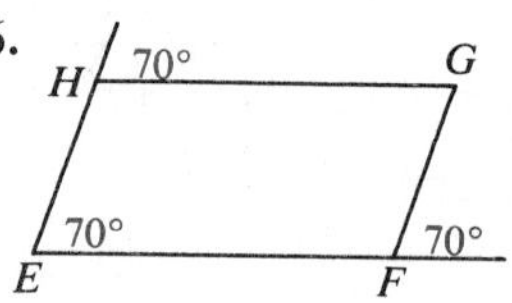

Yes; $\overline{HG} \parallel \overline{EF}$ and $\overline{HE} \parallel \overline{GF}$ since corr. ∠s are ≅.

7.

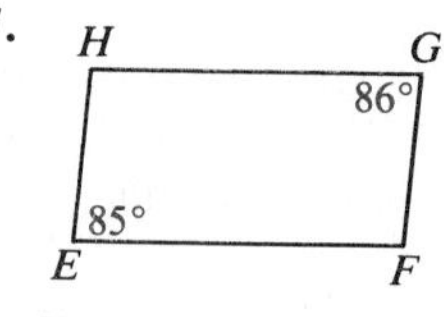

No; no; $\angle E \not\cong \angle G$

8.

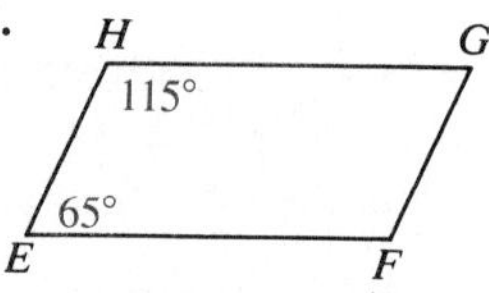

No; yes; you only know that $\overline{HG} \parallel \overline{EF}$.

Quad. *ABCD* is a parallelogram. Name the principal theorem or definition that justifies the statement.

9. $\overline{AD} \parallel \overline{BC}$ **Def. of ▱**

10. $\angle ADX \cong \angle CBX$

11. $m\angle ABC = m\angle CDA$

12. $\overline{AD} \cong \overline{BC}$

13. $AX = \frac{1}{2}AC$

14. $DX = BX$

13., 14. Diag. of a ▱ bisect each other.

15. Draw a quadrilateral that isn't a parallelogram but does have two 60° angles opposite each other.

16. State each theorem in if-then form. (Begin "If a quadrilateral is a ....")
   a. Theorem 5-1 **b.** Theorem 5-2 **c.** Theorem 5-3

17. a. Draw any two segments, $\overline{AC}$ and $\overline{BD}$, that bisect each other at *O*. What appears to be true of quad. *ABCD*? ***ABCD* is a ▱.**
   b. This exercise investigates the converse of what theorem? **Diagonals of a ▱ bisect each other.**

18. Draw two segments that are both parallel and congruent. Connect their endpoints to form a quadrilateral. What appears to be true of the quadrilateral? **It is a ▱.**

10. If 2 ∥ lines are cut by a trans., alt. int. ∠s are ≅.
11. Opp. ∠s of a ▱ are ≅. 12. Opp. sides of a ▱ are ≅.

Written Exercises

Exercises 1–4 refer to ▱*CREW*. $\overline{CR}, \overline{CE}$

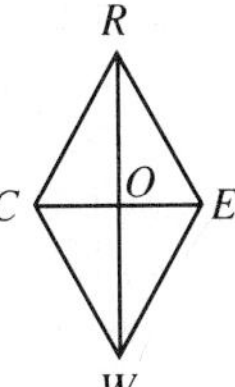

A 1. If $OE = 4$ and $WE = 8$, name two segments congruent to $\overline{WE}$.

2. If $\overline{WR} \perp \overline{CE}$, name all angles congruent to $\angle RCE$.

3. If $\overline{WR} \perp \overline{CE}$, name all segments congruent to $\overline{WE}$. $\overline{ER}, \overline{RC}, \overline{CW}$

4. If $RE = EW$, name all angles congruent to $\angle ERW$.

2. $\angle REC$, $\angle WCE$, $\angle WEC$ 4. $\angle CRW$, $\angle CWR$, $\angle EWR$

In Exercises 5–10 quad. *PQRS* is a parallelogram. Find the values of *a*, *b*, *x*, and *y*.

5. 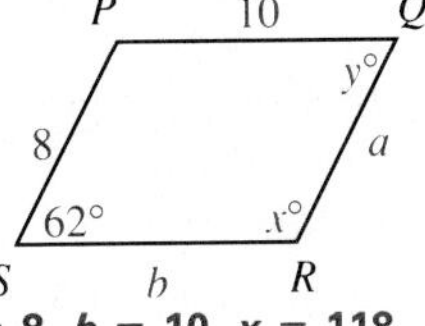

$a = 8, b = 10, x = 118, y = 62$

6. 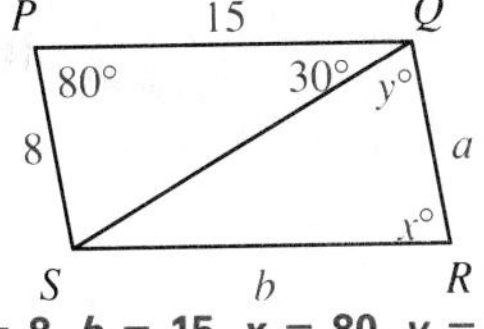

$a = 8, b = 15, x = 80, y = 70$

7. 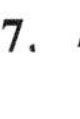 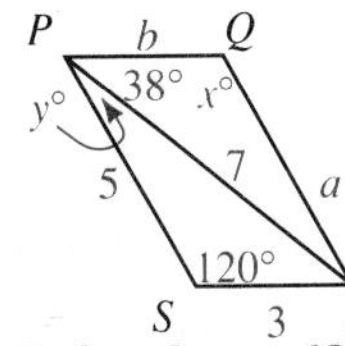

$a = 5, b = 3, x = 120, y = 22$

8. 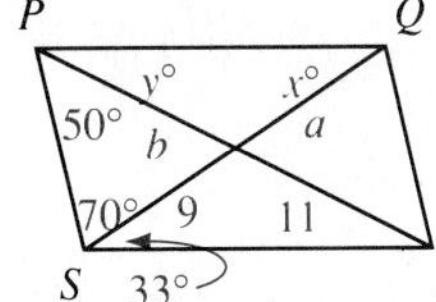

$a = 9, b = 11, x = 33, y = 27$

9. 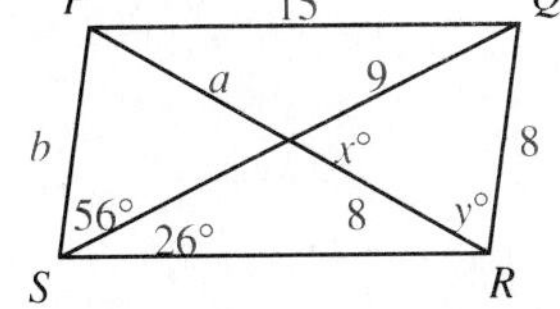

$a = 8, b = 8, x = 56, y = 68$

10. 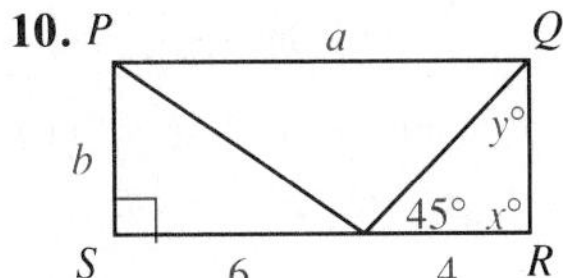

$a = 10, b = 4, x = 90, y = 45$

11. Find the perimeter of ▱*RISK* if $RI = 17$ and $IS = 13$. **60**

12. The perimeter of ▱*STOP* is 54 cm, and $\overline{ST}$ is 1 cm longer than $\overline{SP}$. Find *ST* and *SP*. **$ST = 14$, $SP = 13$**

13. Prove Theorem 5-1.

14. Prove Theorem 5-2. (Draw and label a diagram. List what is given and what is to be proved.)

15. Prove Theorem 5-3.

16. Given: *ABCX* is a ▱;
DXFE is a ▱.
Prove: $\angle B \cong \angle E$

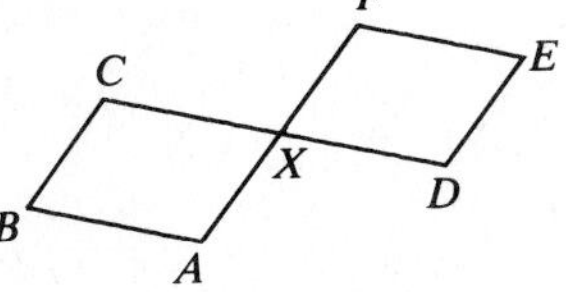

Guided Practice

Exs. 1–3 below refer to ▱*ABCD.*

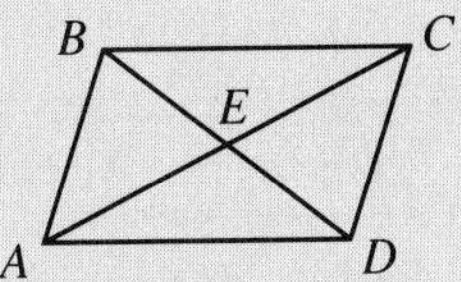

1. Name all pairs of parallel lines.
$\overleftrightarrow{AB}$ and $\overleftrightarrow{DC}$; $\overleftrightarrow{BC}$ and $\overleftrightarrow{AD}$
2. Name all pairs of congruent angles.
$\angle BAD$ and $\angle DCB$; $\angle ABC$ and $\angle CDA$; $\angle BEA$ and $\angle DEC$; $\angle BEC$ and $\angle DEA$; $\angle CBD$ and $\angle ADB$; $\angle ABD$ and $\angle CDB$; $\angle BCA$ and $\angle DAC$; $\angle BAC$ and $\angle DCA$
3. Name all pairs of congruent segments.
$\overline{AB}$ and $\overline{CD}$; $\overline{BC}$ and $\overline{DA}$; $\overline{BE}$ and $\overline{ED}$; $\overline{AE}$ and $\overline{EC}$

In Exs. 4 and 5, quad. *RSTU* is a parallelogram. Find the values of *x*, *y*, *a*, and *b*.

4. 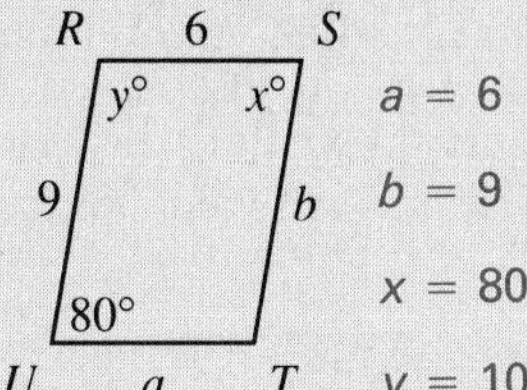

$a = 6$
$b = 9$
$x = 80$
$y = 100$

5. 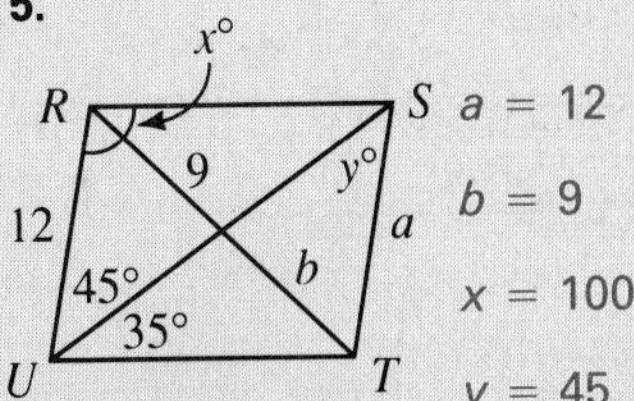

$a = 12$
$b = 9$
$x = 100$
$y = 45$

6. Find the perimeter of ▱*PINE* if $PI = 12$ and $IN = 8$. 40

(continued)

7. Given: $ABCD$ is a ▱;
$CEFG$ is a ▱.
Prove: $\angle A \cong \angle F$

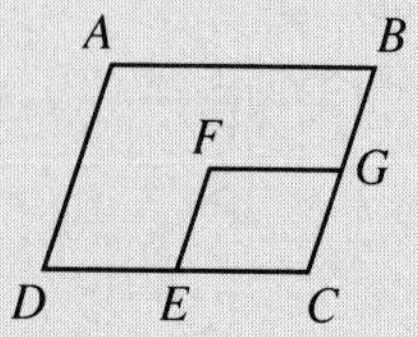

1. $ABCD$ is a ▱; $CEFG$ is a ▱. (Given)
2. $\angle A \cong \angle C$; $\angle C \cong \angle F$ (Opp. ∠s of a ▱ are ≅.)
3. $\angle A \cong \angle F$ (Transitive Prop.)

8. Three coordinates of ▱$XWYZ$ are given. Plot the points and find the coordinates of the fourth vertex. $X(4, 3)$, $W(1, -1)$, $Y(-5, -1)$, $Z(?, ?)$
$Z(-2, 3)$

Each figure in Exs. 9–11 is a parallelogram with its diagonals drawn. Find the values of x and y.

9. $x = 2$, $y = 3$

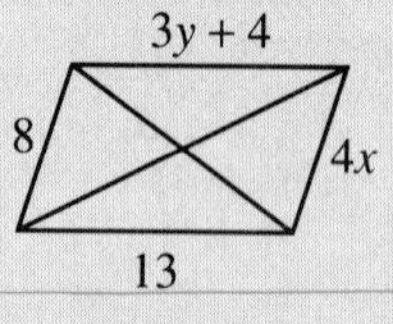

10. $x = 5$, $y = 6$

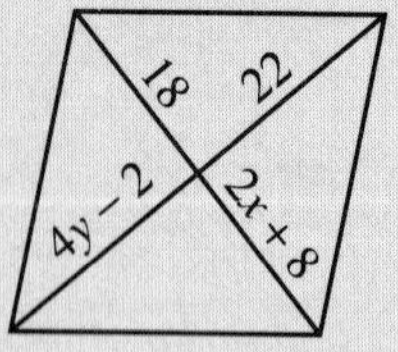

11. $x = 5$, $y = 10$

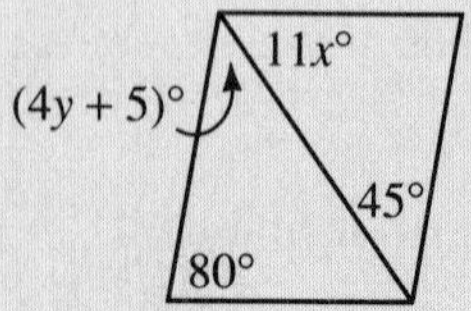

The coordinates of three vertices of ▱$ABCD$ are given. Plot the points and find the coordinates of the fourth vertex.

17. $A(1, 0)$, $B(5, 0)$, $C(7, 2)$, $D(\underline{\ ?\ }, \underline{\ ?\ })$ **3, 2**

18. $A(3, 2)$, $B(8, 2)$, $C(\underline{\ ?\ }, \underline{\ ?\ })$, $D(0, 5)$ **5, 5**

Each figure in Exercises 19–24 is a parallelogram with its diagonals drawn. Find the values of x and y.

19.

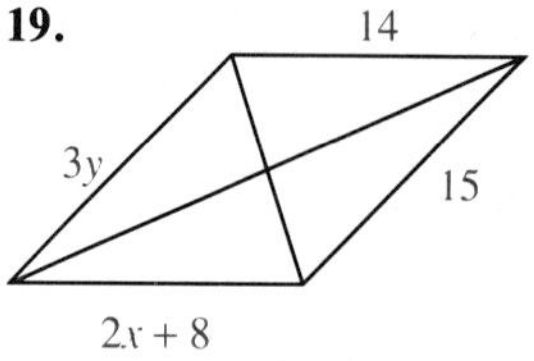

$x = 3$, $y = 5$

20.

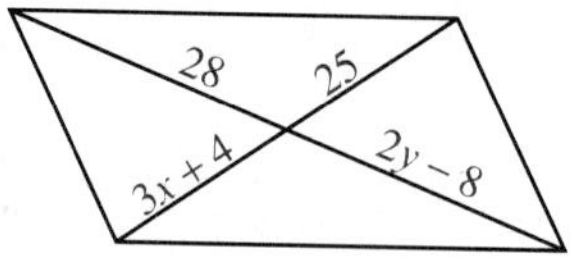

$x = 7$, $y = 18$

21.

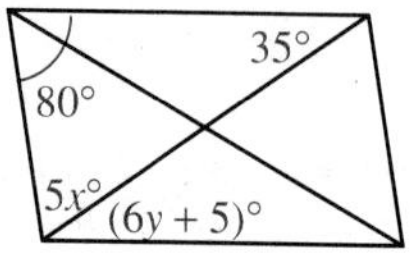

$x = 13$, $y = 5$

B **22.**

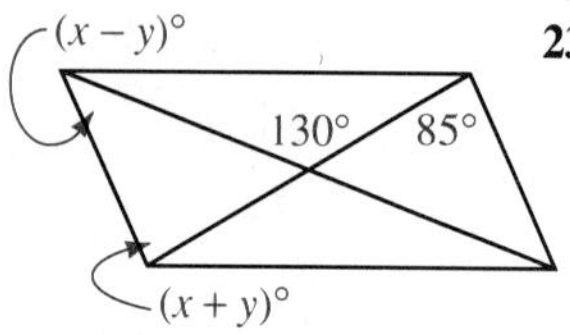

$x = 65$, $y = 20$

23.

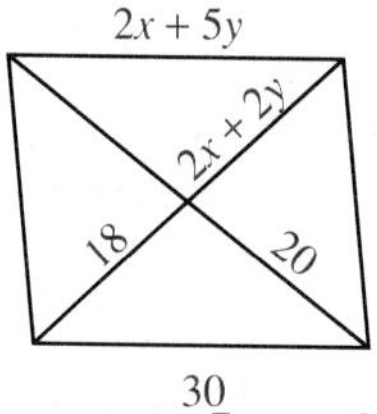

$x = 5$, $y = 4$

24.

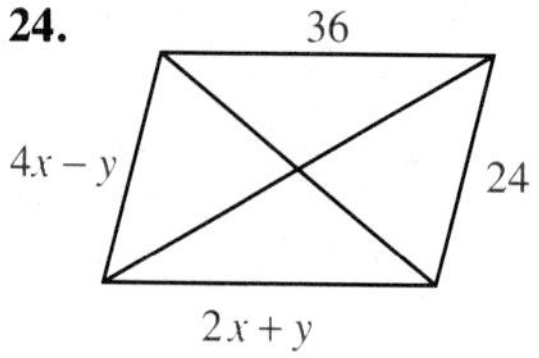

$x = 10$, $y = 16$

Quad. *DECK* is a parallelogram. Complete.

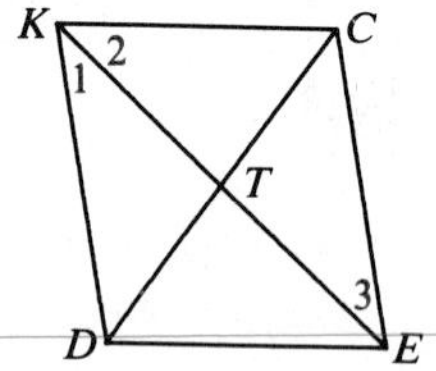

25. If $KT = 2x + y$, $DT = x + 2y$, $TE = 12$, and $TC = 9$, then $x = \underline{\ ?\ }$ and $y = \underline{\ ?\ }$. **5, 2**

26. If $DE = x + y$, $EC = 12$, $CK = 2x - y$, and $KD = 3x - 2y$, then $x = \underline{\ ?\ }$, $y = \underline{\ ?\ }$, and the perimeter of ▱$DECK = \underline{\ ?\ }$. **6, 3, 42**

27. If $m\angle 1 = 3x$, $m\angle 2 = 4x$, and $m\angle 3 = x^2 - 70$, then $x = \underline{\ ?\ }$ and $m\angle CED = \underline{\ ?\ }$ (numerical answers). **10, 70**

28. If $m\angle 1 = 42$, $m\angle 2 = x^2$, and $m\angle CED = 13x$, then $m\angle 2 = \underline{\ ?\ }$ or $m\angle 2 = \underline{\ ?\ }$ (numerical answers). **36, 49**

29. Given: ▱$PQRS$; $\overline{PJ} \cong \overline{RK}$
Prove: $\overline{SJ} \cong \overline{QK}$

30. Given: ▱$JQKS$; $\overline{PJ} \cong \overline{RK}$
Prove: $\angle P \cong \angle R$

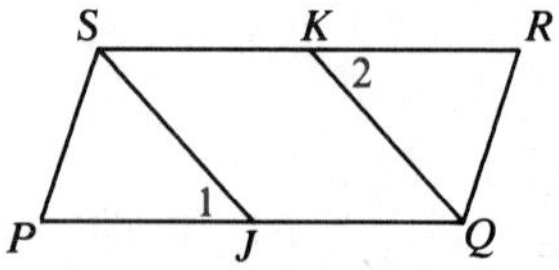

31. Given: $ABCD$ is a ▱; $\overline{CD} \cong \overline{CE}$
Prove: $\angle A \cong \angle E$

32. Given: $ABCD$ is a ▱; $\angle A \cong \angle E$
Prove: $\overline{AB} \cong \overline{CE}$

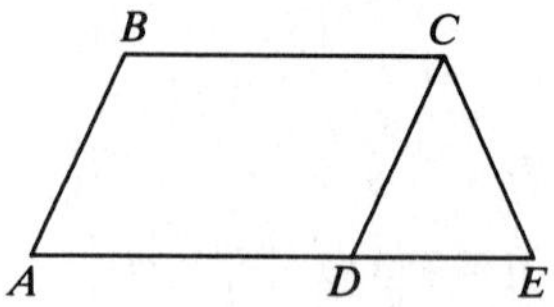

Find something interesting to prove. Then prove it. **Answers may vary.**

33. Given: ▱$ABCD$; $\angle 1 \cong \angle 2$

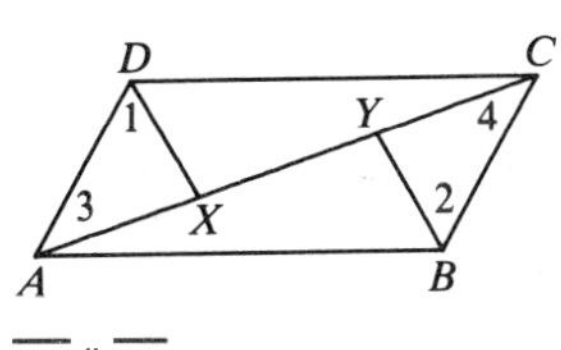

$\overline{DX} \parallel \overline{BY}$

34. Given: ▱$EFIH$; ▱$EGJH$; $\angle 1 \cong \angle 2$

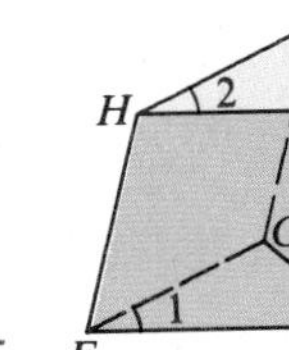

$\triangle JHI \cong \triangle GEF$

The coordinates of three vertices of a parallelogram are given. Find all the possibilities you can for the coordinates of the fourth vertex.

C **35.** (3, 4), (9, 4), (6, 8)
(6, 0); (0, 8); (12, 8)

36. (−1, 0), (2, −2), (2, 2)
(5, 0); (−1, −4); (−1, 4)

37. a. Given: Plane $P \parallel$ plane Q; $j \parallel k$
Prove: $AX = BY$

b. State a theorem about parallel planes and lines that you proved in part (a). **If ∥ planes intersect ∥ lines, then they cut off ≅ segments.**

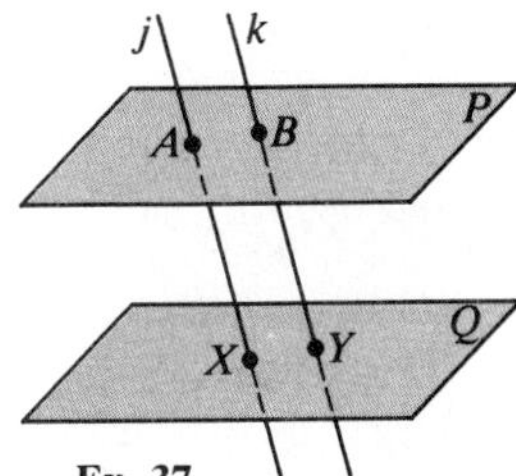

Ex. 37

38. Prove: If a segment whose endpoints lie on opposite sides of a parallelogram passes through the midpoint of a diagonal, that segment is bisected by the diagonal.

★ **39.** Write a paragraph proof: The sum of the lengths of the segments drawn from any point in the base of an isosceles triangle perpendicular to the legs is equal to the length of the altitude drawn to one leg.

Biographical Note *Benjamin Banneker*

Benjamin Banneker (1731–1806) was a noted American scholar, largely self-taught, who became both a surveyor and an astronomer. As a surveyor, Banneker was a member of the commission that defined the boundary line and laid out the streets of the District of Columbia. As an astronomer, he accurately predicted a solar eclipse in 1789. From 1791 until his death he published almanacs containing information on astronomy, tide tables, and also such diverse subjects as insect life and medicinal products. Banneker's almanacs included ideas that were far ahead of their time, for example, the formation of a Department of the Interior and an organization like the United Nations.

Thinking Skills

Students are asked to form their own conclusions in Exs. 33 and 34. These can be used as a basis for class discussion.

Group Activity

You may want to form groups of three or four students to discuss the various conclusions reached in Exs. 33 and 34, and to create similar problems. Each student in the group can be responsible for making up a problem and then forming conclusions, which should be explained to the group and defended with reasons. Other members of the group can analyze the conclusions to see if they are logical.

Using a Computer

For Ex. 39, have students draw the diagram using a program. The construction is a good exercise even if the proof is not assigned.

Teaching Suggestions, pp. T93–T94

Objective
Presenting the Lesson
Extension

Cooperative Learning, p. T94

Supplementary Materials

Practice Master 25
Study Guide, pp. 61–62

Lesson Focus

There are five ways to prove that a quadrilateral is a parallelogram. Four theorems are presented in this lesson that can be used to show that a quadrilateral is a parallelogram.

Suggested Assignments

Minimum
Day 1: 174/1–6, 7, 9
Day 2: 174–175/8, 10, 11, 14, 19

Average
174–175/3–5, 9, 10, 12, 15, 19, 22

Maximum
174–176/9, 11, 13, 15, 17, 18, 21, 24

Proof Note

You may want to emphasize the use of congruent triangles in proving Theorems 5-5, 5-6, and 5-7.

5-2 *Ways to Prove that Quadrilaterals Are Parallelograms*

If both pairs of opposite sides of a quadrilateral are parallel, then by definition the quadrilateral is a parallelogram. The following theorems will give you additional ways to prove that a quadrilateral is a parallelogram.

Theorem 5-4

If both pairs of opposite sides of a quadrilateral are congruent, then the quadrilateral is a parallelogram.

Given: $\overline{TS} \cong \overline{QR}$; $\overline{TQ} \cong \overline{SR}$

Prove: Quad. $QRST$ is a ▱.

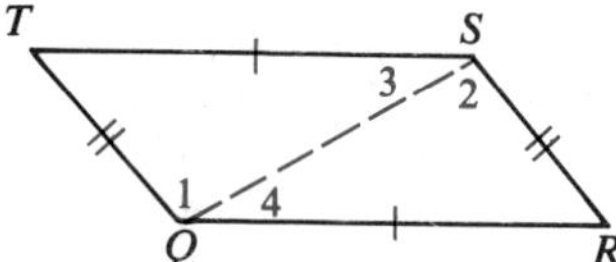

Plan for Proof: Draw $\overline{QS}$ and prove that $\triangle TSQ \cong \triangle RQS$. Then $\angle 1 \cong \angle 2$ and $\angle 3 \cong \angle 4$, and opposite sides are parallel.

Theorem 5-5

If one pair of opposite sides of a quadrilateral are both congruent and parallel, then the quadrilateral is a parallelogram.

Theorem 5-6

If both pairs of opposite angles of a quadrilateral are congruent, then the quadrilateral is a parallelogram.

Theorem 5-7

If the diagonals of a quadrilateral bisect each other, then the quadrilateral is a parallelogram.

Five Ways to Prove that a Quadrilateral Is a Parallelogram

1. Show that *both* pairs of opposite sides are parallel.
2. Show that *both* pairs of opposite sides are congruent.
3. Show that *one* pair of opposite sides are both congruent and parallel.
4. Show that both pairs of opposite angles are congruent.
5. Show that the diagonals bisect each other.

Classroom Exercises

Study the markings on each figure and decide whether *ABCD must* be a parallelogram. If the answer is *yes*, state the definition or theorem that applies.

1. Yes

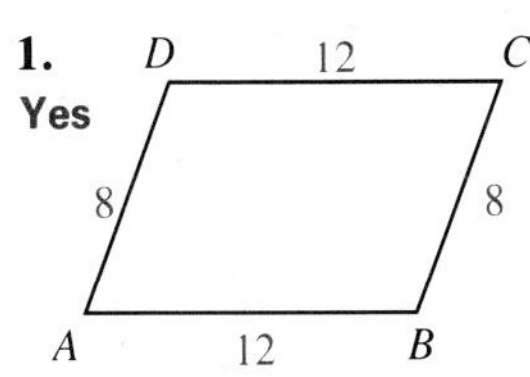

2. Yes

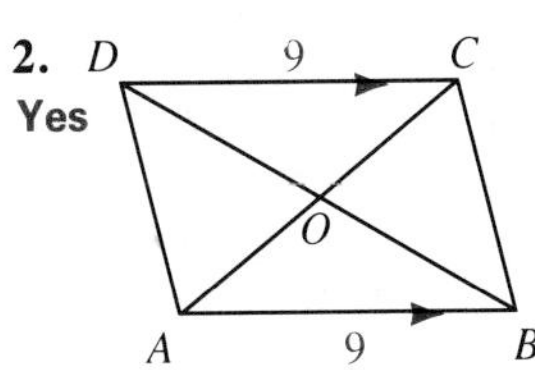

3. No

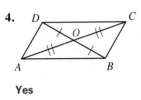

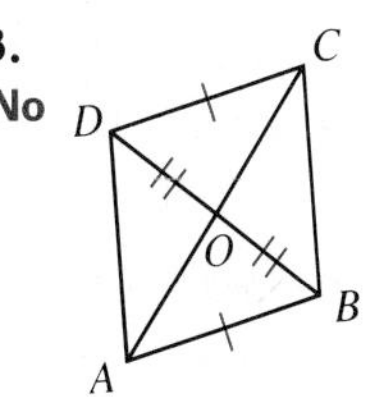

4. Yes

D C O A B

5. No

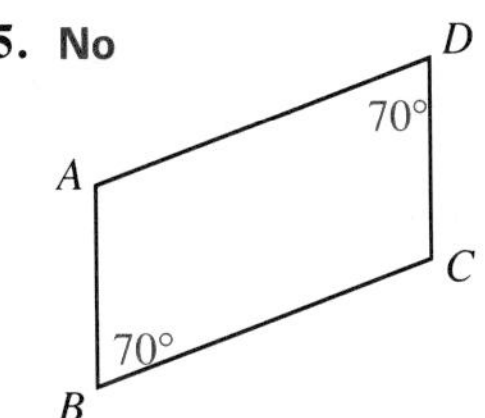

6. Yes

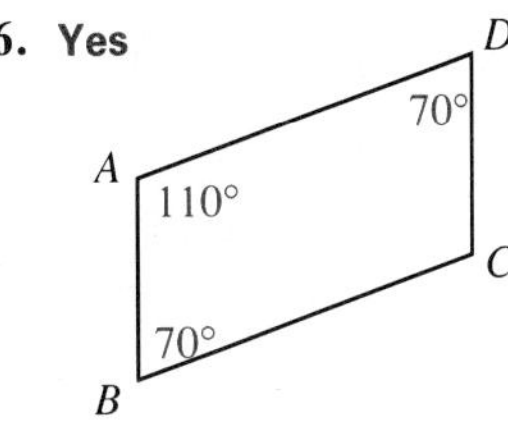

7. Yes

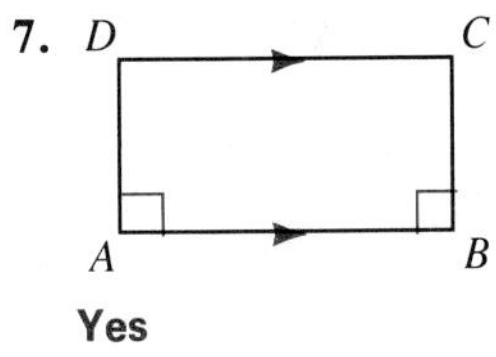

8. No

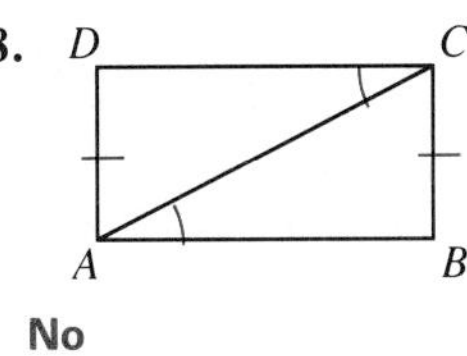

9. Yes

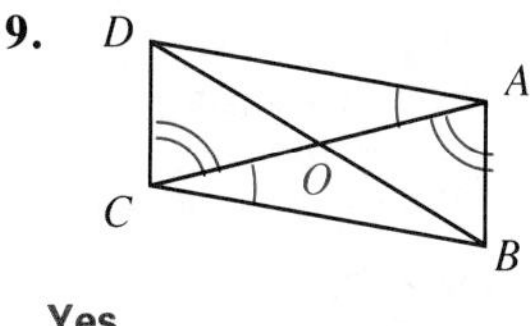

10. Draw a quadrilateral that has two pairs of congruent sides but that is *not* a parallelogram.

11. Draw a quadrilateral that is *not* a parallelogram but that has one pair of congruent sides and one pair of parallel sides.

12. *Parallel rulers*, used to draw parallel lines, are constructed so that $EF = HG$ and $HE = GF$. Since there are hinges at points E, F, G, and H, you can vary the distance between $\overleftrightarrow{HG}$ and $\overleftrightarrow{EF}$. Explain why $\overleftrightarrow{HG}$ and $\overleftrightarrow{EF}$ are always parallel.

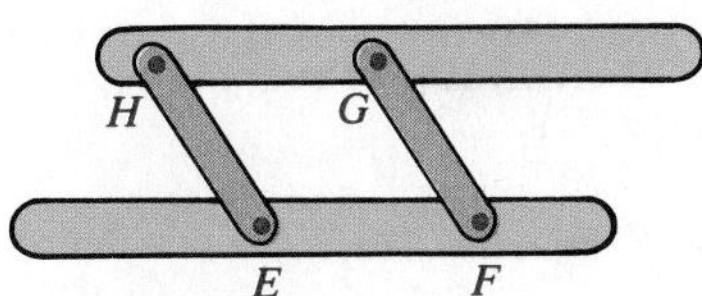

Since $EF = HG$ and $HE = GF$, $EFGH$ is a ▱ and $\overleftrightarrow{HG} \parallel \overleftrightarrow{EF}$.

13. The pliers shown are made in such a way that the jaws are always parallel. Explain.

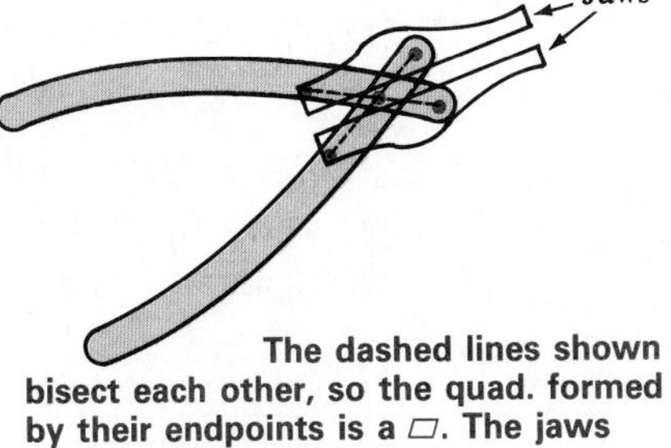

The dashed lines shown bisect each other, so the quad. formed by their endpoints is a ▱. The jaws are ∥ to 2 opp. sides of the ▱.

Additional Answers
Classroom Exercises

1. If both pairs of opp. sides of a quad. are ≅, then the quad. is a ▱.
2. If one pair of opp. sides of a quad. are both ≅ and ∥, then the quad. is a ▱.
4. If the diag. of a quad. bisect each other, then the quad. is a ▱.
6. Two possible answers: Def. of ▱ or If both pairs of opp. ∠s of a quad. are ≅, then the quad. is a ▱.
7. Def. of ▱ (A ▱ is a quad. with both pairs of opp. sides ∥.)
9. Def. of ▱ (A ▱ is a quad. with both pairs of opp. sides ∥.)

Chalkboard Examples

Complete with *always*, *sometimes*, or *never*.

1. The diagonals of a quadrilateral sometimes bisect each other.
2. If the measures of two angles of a quadrilateral are equal, then the quadrilateral is sometimes a parallelogram.
3. If one pair of opposite sides of a quadrilateral is congruent and parallel, then the quadrilateral is always a parallelogram.
4. If both pairs of opposite sides of a quadrilateral are congruent, then the quadrilateral is always a parallelogram.
5. To prove a quadrilateral is a parallelogram, it is never enough to show that one pair of opposite sides is parallel.

Guided Practice

State the principal definition or theorem that enables you to deduce, from the information given, that quad. *ABCD* is a parallelogram.

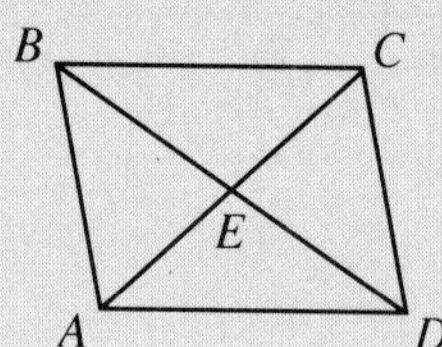

1. $BE = ED$; $CE = EA$
   If the diagonals of a quad. bisect each other, then the quad. is a ▱.
2. $\angle BAD \cong \angle DCB$; $\angle ADC \cong \angle CBA$
   If both pairs of opposite angles of a quad. are congruent, then the quad. is a ▱.
3. $\overline{BC} \parallel \overline{AD}$; $\overline{AB} \parallel \overline{DC}$
   Def. of ▱ (A ▱ is a quad. with both pairs of opp. sides ∥.)
4. $\overline{BC} \cong \overline{AD}$; $\overline{AB} \cong \overline{DC}$
   If both pairs of opposite sides of a quad. are congruent, then the quad. is a ▱.
5. $\overline{BC} \parallel \overline{AD}$; $\overline{BC} \cong \overline{AD}$
   If one pair of opposite sides of a quad. are both congruent and parallel, then the quad. is a ▱.

Written Exercises

State the principal definition or theorem that enables you to deduce, from the information given, that quad. *SACK* is a parallelogram.

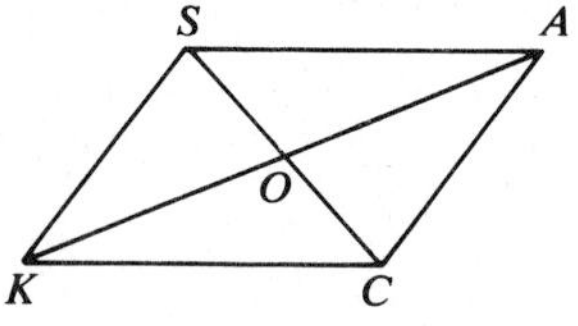

A

1. $\overline{SA} \parallel \overline{KC}$; $\overline{SK} \parallel \overline{AC}$ **Def. of ▱**
2. $\overline{SA} \cong \overline{KC}$; $\overline{SK} \cong \overline{AC}$ **Thm. 5-4**
3. $\overline{SA} \cong \overline{KC}$; $\overline{SA} \parallel \overline{KC}$ **Thm. 5-5**
4. $SO = \frac{1}{2}SC$; $KO = \frac{1}{2}KA$ **Thm. 5-7**
5. $\angle SKC \cong \angle CAS$; $\angle KCA \cong \angle ASK$ **Thm. 5-6**
6. Suppose you know that $\triangle SOK \cong \triangle COA$. Explain how you could prove that quad. *SACK* is a parallelogram. **Answers may vary.**
7. The legs of this ironing board are built so that $BO = AO = RO = DO$. What theorem guarantees that the board is parallel to the floor ($\overline{AR} \parallel \overline{BD}$)? **Thm. 5-7**
   The diag. of quad. *ABDR* bisect each other, so *ABDR* is a ▱ and $\overline{AR} \parallel \overline{BD}$.

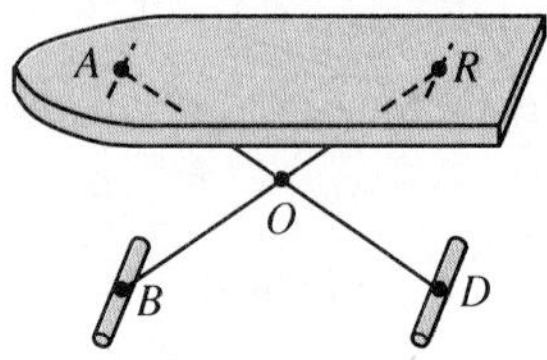

8. The quadrilaterals numbered 1, 2, 3, 4, and 5 are parallelograms. If you wanted to show that quadrilateral 6 is also a parallelogram, which of the five methods listed on page 172 would be easiest to use? **Show that one pair of opp. sides are both ≅ and ∥.**

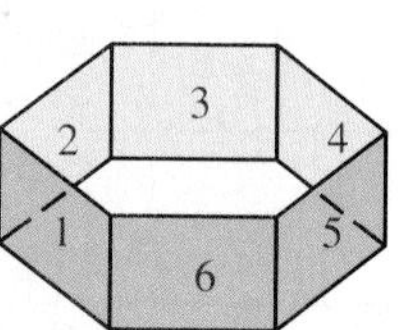

9. What theorem in this section is the converse of each theorem?
   a. Theorem 5-1 **Thm. 5-4** **b.** Theorem 5-2 **Thm. 5-6** **c.** Theorem 5-3 **Thm. 5-7**
10. Give the reasons for each step in the following proof of Theorem 5-6.
    Given: $m\angle A = m\angle C = x$;
    $m\angle B = m\angle D = y$
    Prove: *ABCD* is a ▱.

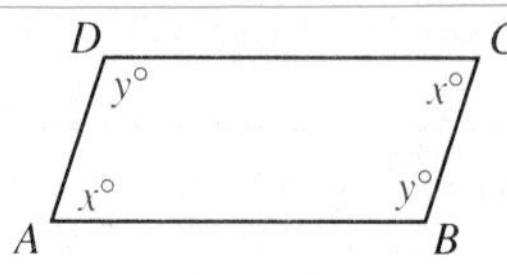

Proof:

Statements	Reasons
1. $m\angle A = m\angle C = x$; $m\angle B = m\angle D = y$	1. ___?___ **Given**
2. $2x + 2y = 360$	2. ___?___ **The sum of the meas. of the ∠s of a quad. is 360.**
3. $x + y = 180$	3. ___?___ **Div. Prop. of =**
4. $\overline{AB} \parallel \overline{DC}$ and $\overline{AD} \parallel \overline{BC}$	4. ___?___ **Thm. 3-6**
5. *ABCD* is a ▱.	5. ___?___ **Def. of ▱**

Draw and label a diagram. List what is given and what is to be proved. Then write a two-column proof of the theorem.

B **11.** Theorem 5-4 **12.** Theorem 5-5 **13.** Theorem 5-7

For Exercises 14–18 write paragraph proofs.

14. Given: ▱$ABCD$; M and N are the midpoints of $\overline{AB}$ and $\overline{DC}$.
Prove: $AMCN$ is a ▱.

15. Given: ▱$ABCD$; $\overline{AN}$ bisects $\angle DAB$; $\overline{CM}$ bisects $\angle BCD$.
Prove: $AMCN$ is a ▱.

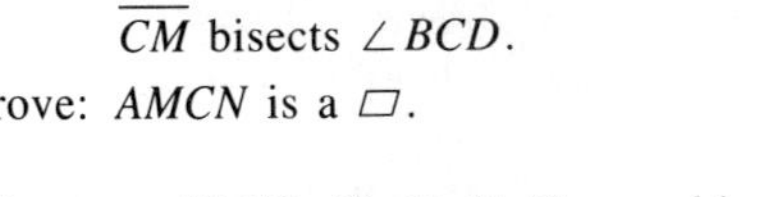

16. Given: ▱$ABCD$; W, X, Y, Z are midpoints of $\overline{AO}$, $\overline{BO}$, $\overline{CO}$, and $\overline{DO}$.
Prove: $WXYZ$ is a ▱.

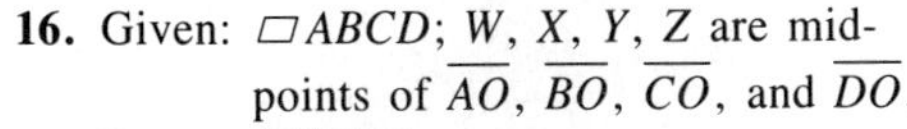

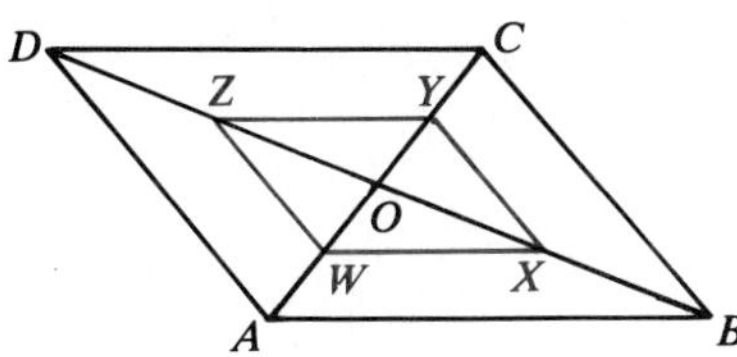

17. Given: ▱$ABCD$; $DE = BF$
Prove: $AFCE$ is a ▱.

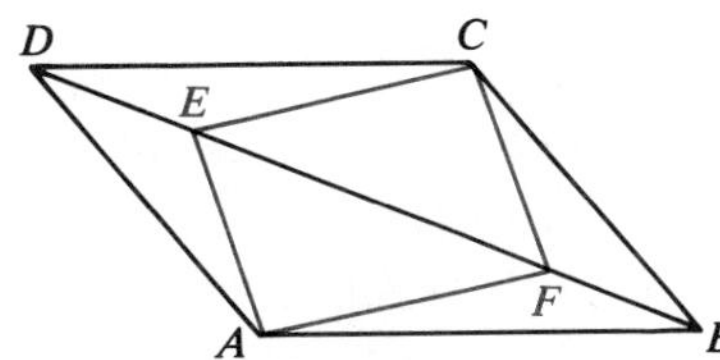

18. Given: ▱$KGLJ$; $FK = HL$
Prove: $FGHJ$ is a ▱.

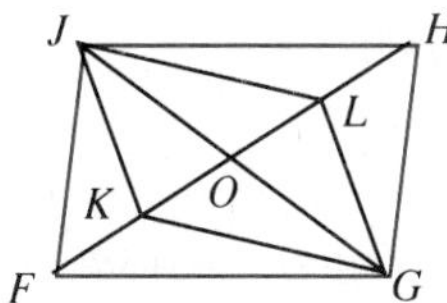

What values must x and y have to make the quadrilateral a parallelogram?

19.

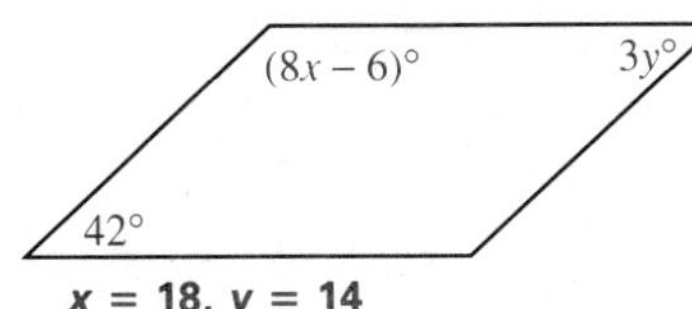

x = 18, y = 14

20.

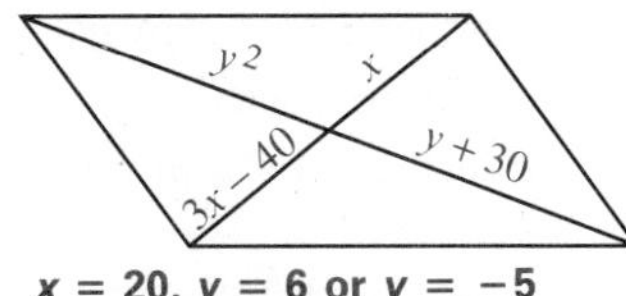

x = 20, y = 6 or y = –5

21.

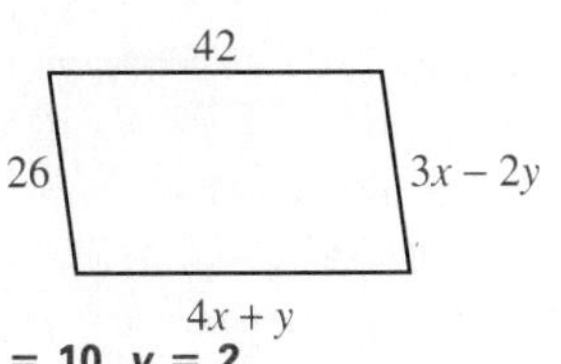

x = 10, y = 2

22.

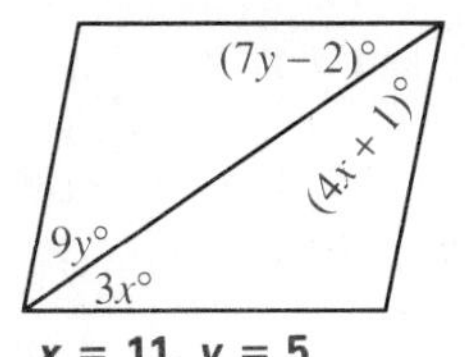

x = 11, y = 5

Using a Computer

For Exs. 14–18, have students draw the given figures using a construction program. They can verify by measurement the result to be proved. Their constructions will bring out the importance of the givens and spark ideas for the proofs.

Making Connections

Ex. 16 can also be proved in Lesson 5-3 after students have studied Theorem 5-11. It is a good learning experience to review previous exercises by reproving them with different theorems.

Exercise Note

Exs. 19–22 use algebraic skills to review the different ways to prove that a quadrilateral is a parallelogram.

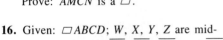

Using a Computer

In Ex. 23 the diagram can be drawn and the proof verified using a construction program.

23. Given: ▱$ABCD$;
$\overline{DE} \perp \overline{AC}$; $\overline{BF} \perp \overline{AC}$
Prove: $DEBF$ is a ▱.

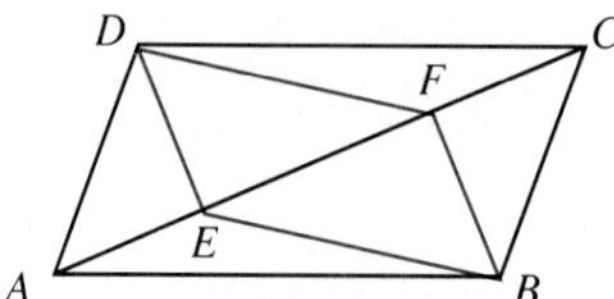

24. Given: Plane $X \parallel$ plane Y;
$\overline{LM} \cong \overline{ON}$
Prove: $LMNO$ is a ▱.

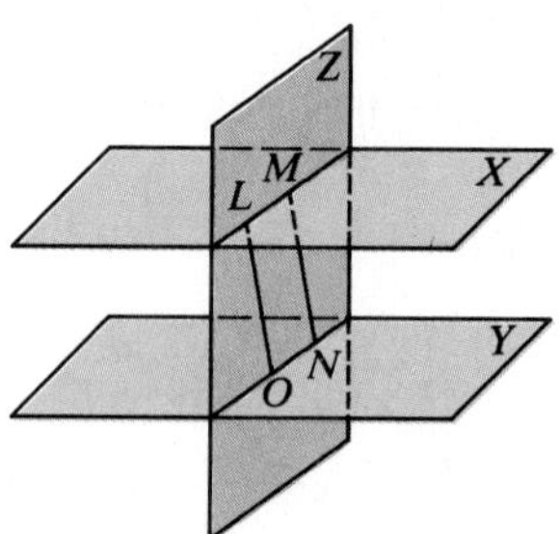

C **25.** Write a paragraph proof.
Given: ▱$ABCD$; ▱$BEDF$
Prove: $AECF$ is a ▱.
(*Hint:* A short proof is possible if certain auxiliary segments are drawn.)

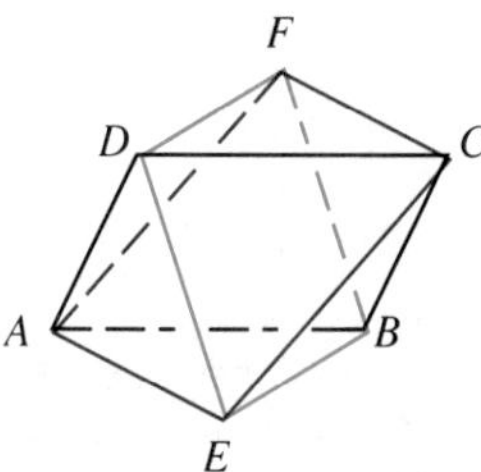

Using a Computer

These exploratory exercises provide an introduction to the contents of Lesson 5-3. As an extension, students can explore the same relationships when D is *any* point on $\overline{AB}$ rather than the midpoint. This will help pave the way for work with similar triangles in Chapter 7.

Explorations

These exploratory exercises can be done using a computer with a program that draws and measures geometric figures.

Draw any $\triangle ABC$. Label the midpoint of $\overline{AB}$ as D. Draw a segment through D parallel to $\overline{BC}$ that intersects $\overline{AC}$ at E. Measure AE and EC. What do you notice?
$AE = EC$

Draw any $\triangle ABC$. Label the midpoints of $\overline{AB}$ and $\overline{AC}$ as D and E, respectively. Draw $\overline{DE}$. Measure $\angle AED$ and $\angle ACB$. What do you notice? What is true of $\overline{DE}$ and $\overline{BC}$? Measure DE and BC. What do you notice? **$\angle AED \cong \angle ACB$; $\overline{DE} \parallel \overline{BC}$**

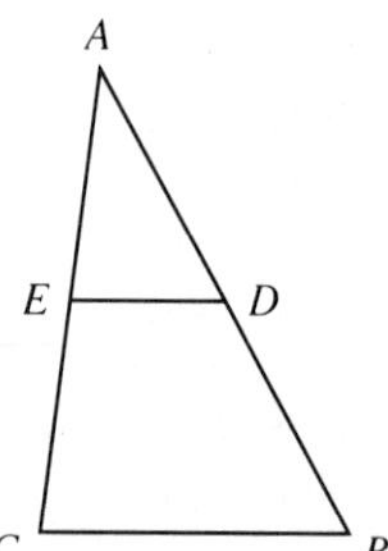

Write an equation that relates DE and BC. Repeat the drawing and measurements until you are sure of your equation. **$DE = \frac{1}{2}BC$**

5-3 *Theorems Involving Parallel Lines*

In this section we will prove four useful theorems about parallel lines. The first theorem uses the definition of the distance from a point to a line. (See page 154.)

Theorem 5-8

If two lines are parallel, then all points on one line are equidistant from the other line.

Given: $l \parallel m$; A and B are any points on l;
$\overline{AC} \perp m$; $\overline{BD} \perp m$

Prove: $AC = BD$

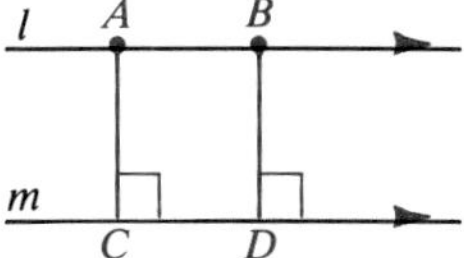

Proof:

Since $\overline{AB}$ and $\overline{CD}$ are contained in parallel lines, $\overline{AB} \parallel \overline{CD}$. Since $\overline{AC}$ and $\overline{BD}$ are coplanar and are both perpendicular to m, they are parallel. Thus $ABDC$ is a parallelogram, by the definition of a parallelogram. Since opposite sides $\overline{AC}$ and $\overline{BD}$ are congruent, $AC = BD$.

Theorem 5-9

If three parallel lines cut off congruent segments on one transversal, then they cut off congruent segments on every transversal.

Given: $\overleftrightarrow{AX} \parallel \overleftrightarrow{BY} \parallel \overleftrightarrow{CZ}$;
$\overline{AB} \cong \overline{BC}$

Prove: $\overline{XY} \cong \overline{YZ}$

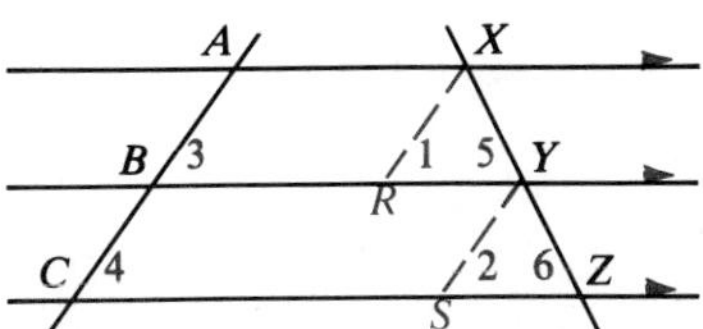

Proof:

Through X and Y draw lines parallel to $\overleftrightarrow{AC}$, intersecting $\overleftrightarrow{BY}$ at R and $\overleftrightarrow{CZ}$ at S, as shown. Then $AXRB$ and $BYSC$ are parallelograms, by the definition of a parallelogram. Since the opposite sides of a parallelogram are congruent, $\overline{XR} \cong \overline{AB}$ and $\overline{BC} \cong \overline{YS}$. It is given that $\overline{AB} \cong \overline{BC}$, so using the Transitive Property twice gives $\overline{XR} \cong \overline{YS}$. Parallel lines are cut by transversals to form the following pairs of congruent corresponding angles:

$\angle 1 \cong \angle 3$ $\quad \angle 3 \cong \angle 4$ $\quad \angle 4 \cong \angle 2$ $\quad \angle 5 \cong \angle 6$

Then $\angle 1 \cong \angle 2$ (Transitive Property), and $\triangle XYR \cong \triangle YZS$ by AAS. Since $\overline{XY}$ and $\overline{YZ}$ are corresponding parts of these triangles, $\overline{XY} \cong \overline{YZ}$.

Teaching Suggestions,
p. T94

Objectives
Presenting the Lesson
Using Technology
Applications

Supplementary Materials

Practice Master 26
Test 18
Resource Book, pp. 24–25, 126
Study Guide, pp. 63–64

Lesson Focus

Parallel lines are used by engineers and architects in designing and constructing products and buildings. This lesson presents four theorems that state useful facts about parallel lines.

Suggested Assignments

Minimum
Day 1: 180/1–11
Day 2: 180–181/12, 13–21 odd
182/Self-Test 1

Average
Day 1: 180/2–14 even
S 175/18, 20
Day 2: 181/16–22 even
182/Self-Test 1

Maximum
Day 1: 180–181/5–19 odd
S 176/25
Day 2: 181–182/20–25

Using a Model

Students can use a piece of notebook paper and Theorem 5-9 to divide a segment into a number of congruent parts. See Classroom Ex. 1 on page 179.

Chalkboard Examples

1. Given: R, S, and T are midpoints of the sides of $\triangle ABC$.

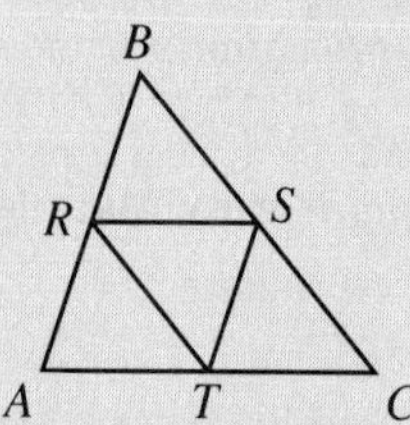

Complete the table.

	AB	BC	AC	ST	RT	RS
a.	12	14	18	6	7	9
b.	20	15	22	10	7.5	11
c.	10	18	15.6	5	9	7.8

2. Given: $\overleftrightarrow{AR} \parallel \overleftrightarrow{BS} \parallel \overleftrightarrow{CT}$; $\overline{RS} \cong \overline{ST}$

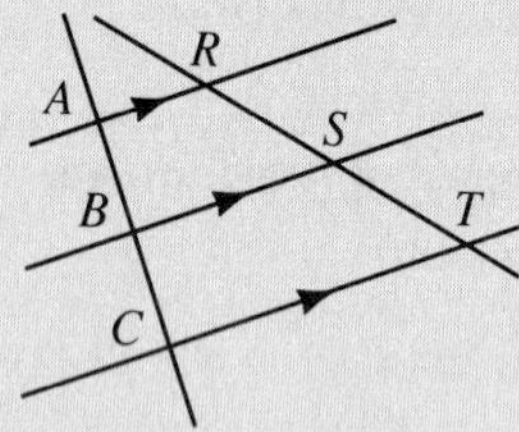

Complete.

a. If $RS = 12$, then $ST =$ 12.

b. If $AB = 8$, then $BC =$ 8.

c. If $AC = 20$, then $AB =$ 10.

d. If $AC = 10x$, then $BC =$ 5x.

Using a Computer

See page T94 for a related experiment that uses the diagram of Theorem 5-11 to explore nested triangles and limits.

Theorem 5-10

A line that contains the midpoint of one side of a triangle and is parallel to another side passes through the midpoint of the third side.

Given: M is the midpoint of $\overline{AB}$; $\overleftrightarrow{MN} \parallel \overline{BC}$

Prove: N is the midpoint of $\overline{AC}$.

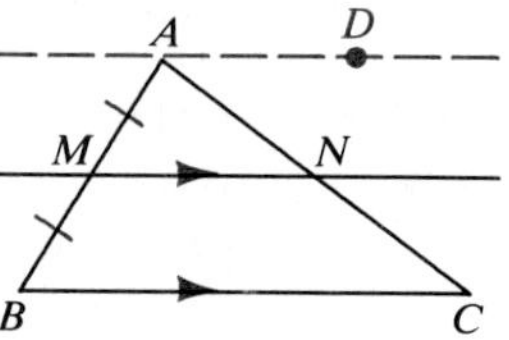

Proof:

Let $\overleftrightarrow{AD}$ be the line through A parallel to $\overleftrightarrow{MN}$. Then $\overleftrightarrow{AD}$, $\overleftrightarrow{MN}$, and $\overleftrightarrow{BC}$ are three parallel lines that cut off congruent segments on transversal $\overleftrightarrow{AB}$. By Theorem 5-9 they also cut off congruent segments on $\overleftrightarrow{AC}$. Thus $\overline{AN} \cong \overline{NC}$ and N is the midpoint of $\overline{AC}$.

The next theorem has two parts, the first of which is closely related to Theorem 5-10.

Theorem 5-11

The segment that joins the midpoints of two sides of a triangle
(1) is parallel to the third side;
(2) is half as long as the third side.

Given: M is the midpoint of $\overline{AB}$; N is the midpoint of $\overline{AC}$.

Prove: (1) $\overline{MN} \parallel \overline{BC}$
(2) $MN = \frac{1}{2}BC$

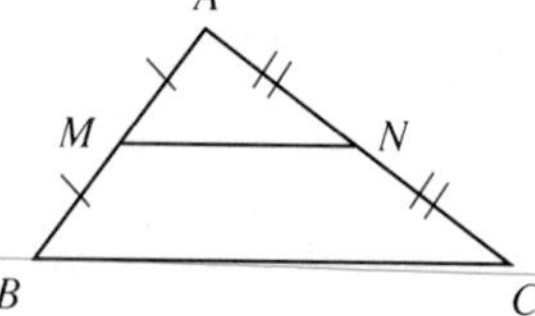

Proof of (1):

There is exactly one line through M parallel to $\overline{BC}$. By Theorem 5-10 that line passes through N, the midpoint of $\overline{AC}$. Thus $\overline{MN} \parallel \overline{BC}$.

Proof of (2):

Let L be the midpoint of $\overline{BC}$, and draw $\overline{NL}$. By part (1), $\overline{MN} \parallel \overline{BC}$ and also $\overline{NL} \parallel \overline{AB}$. Thus quad. $MNLB$ is a parallelogram. Since its opposite sides are congruent, $MN = BL$. Since L is the midpoint of $\overline{BC}$, $BL = \frac{1}{2}BC$. Therefore $MN = \frac{1}{2}BC$.

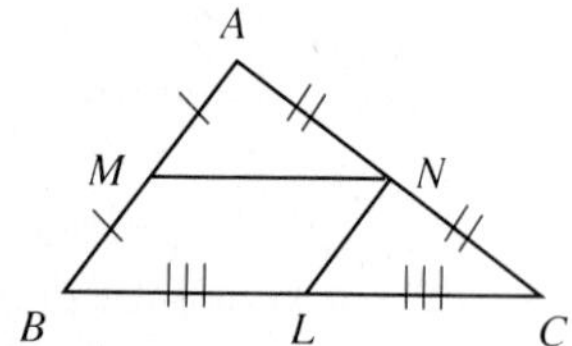

Example P, Q, and R are midpoints of the sides of $\triangle DEF$.

a. What kind of figure is $DPQR$?

b. What is the perimeter of $DPQR$?

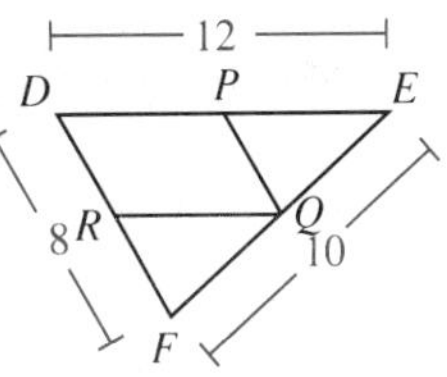

Solution **a.** Since $\overline{RQ} \parallel \overline{DE}$ and $\overline{PQ} \parallel \overline{DF}$, quad. $DPQR$ is a parallelogram.

b. $RQ = \frac{1}{2}DE = DP = 6$ and $PQ = \frac{1}{2}DF = DR = 4$. Thus the perimeter of $DPQR$ is $6 + 4 + 6 + 4$, or 20.

Classroom Exercises

1. You can use a sheet of lined notebook paper to divide a segment into a number of congruent parts. Here a piece of cardboard with edge $\overline{AB}$ is placed so that $\overline{AB}$ is separated into five congruent parts. Explain why this works. **The lines on the paper are ∥, and they cut off ≅ seg. on a trans. (vert. paper edge). So they cut off ≅ seg. on trans. $\overline{AB}$ (Thm. 5-9).**

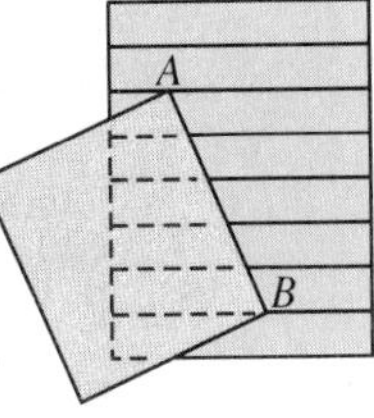

***M*, *N*, and *T* are the midpoints of the sides of $\triangle XYZ$.**

2. If $XZ = 10$, then $MN = \underline{\ ?\ }$. **5**

3. If $TN = 7$, then $XY = \underline{\ ?\ }$. **14**

4. If $ZN = 8$, then $TM = \underline{\ ?\ }$. **8**

5. If $XY = k$, then $TN = \underline{\ ?\ }$. $\frac{1}{2}k$

6. Suppose $XY = 10$, $YZ = 14$, and $XZ = 8$. What are the lengths of the three sides of

a. $\triangle TNZ$? **5, 7, 4** **b.** $\triangle MYN$? **5, 7, 4**

c. $\triangle XMT$? **5, 7, 4** **d.** $\triangle NTM$? **5, 7, 4**

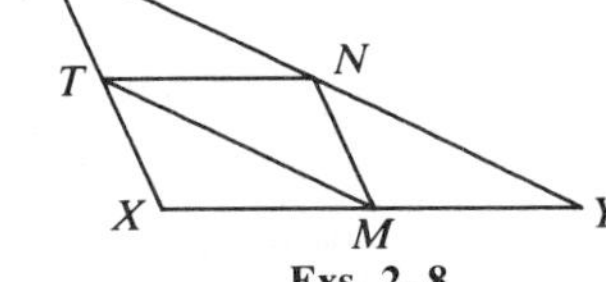

Exs. 2–8

7. State a theorem suggested by Exercise 6. **The seg. joining the midpts. of the sides of a △ divide the △ into 4 ≅ △s.**

8. How many parallelograms are in the diagram? **3**

9. What result of this section do the railings suggest? **Thm. 5-8**

Guided Practice

1. Given: Points X, Y, and Z are the midpoints of $\overline{AB}$, $\overline{BC}$, and $\overline{AC}$.

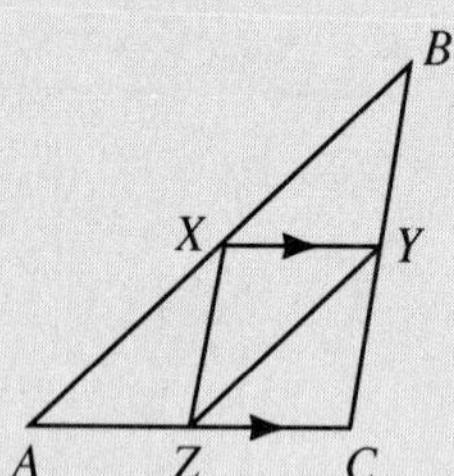

Complete.

a. If $AC = 24$, then XY = 12.

b. If $AB = k$, then $YZ = \frac{k}{2}$.

c. If $XZ = 2k + 3$, then BC = $4k + 6$.

d. If $AB = 9$, $BC = 8$, $AC = 6$, then the perimeter of $\triangle XYZ = \frac{23}{2}$.

e. If the perimeter of $\triangle XYZ = 24$, then the perimeter of $\triangle ABC$ = 48.

f. Name all the congruent triangles. $\triangle AZX \cong \triangle ZCY \cong \triangle XYB \cong \triangle YXZ$

2. Name all points that must be midpoints of the sides of $\triangle ABC$. *M, L*

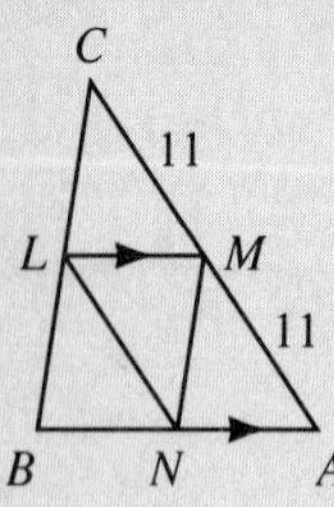

Written Exercises

Points A, B, E, and F are the midpoints of $\overline{XC}$, $\overline{XD}$, $\overline{YC}$, and $\overline{YD}$. Complete.

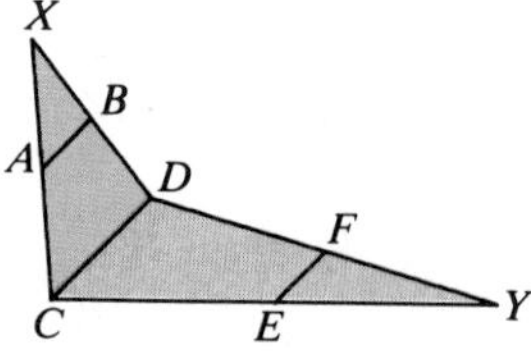

A

1. If $CD = 24$, then AB = ? and EF = ?. **12, 12**
2. If $AB = k$, then CD = ? and EF = ?. **2k, k**
3. If $AB = 5x - 8$ and $EF = 3x$, then x = ?. **4**
4. If $CD = 8x$ and $AB = 3x + 2$, then x = ?. **2**

5. Given: L, M, and N are midpoints of the sides of $\triangle TKO$. Find the perimeter of each figure.
   a. $\triangle TKO$ **40**   b. $\triangle LMK$ **20**
   c. ▱$TNML$ **26**   d. quad. $LNOK$ **34**

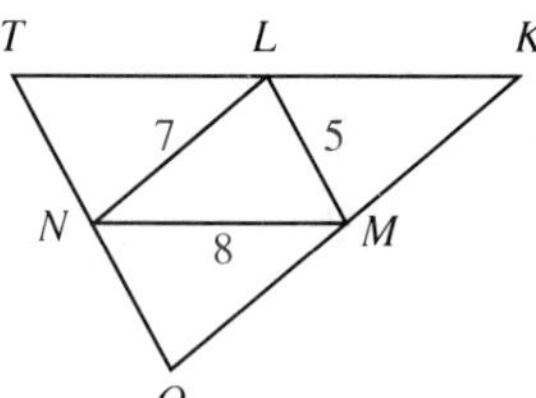

6. a. Name all triangles congruent to $\triangle TNL$. **$\triangle NOM$, $\triangle LMK$, $\triangle MLN$**
   b. Suppose you are told that the area of $\triangle NLM$ is 17.32 cm². What is the area of $\triangle TKO$? **69.28 cm²**

Name all the points shown that *must* be midpoints of the sides of the large triangle.

7. ***D, E***

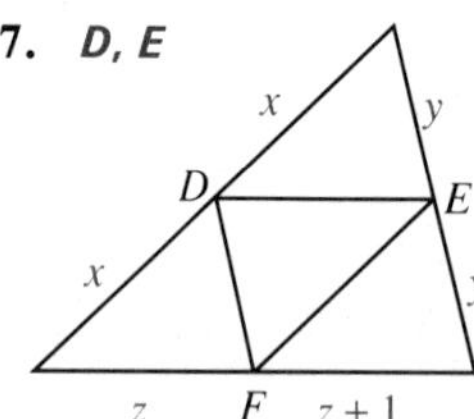

8. ***D, E***

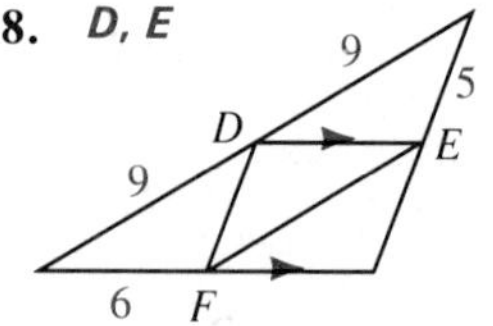

9. ***D, F***

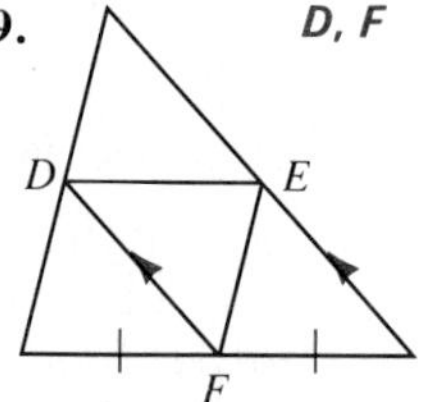

$\overleftrightarrow{AE}$, $\overleftrightarrow{BF}$, $\overleftrightarrow{CG}$, and $\overleftrightarrow{DH}$ are parallel, with $EF = FG = GH$. Complete.

10. If $AB = 5$, then AD = ?. **15**
11. If $AC = 12$, then CD = ?. **6**
12. If $AB = 5x$ and $BC = 2x + 12$, then x = ?. **4**
13. If $AC = 22 - x$ and $BD = 3x - 22$, then x = ?. **11**

B

14. If $AB = 15$, $BC = 2x - y$, and $CD = x + y$, then x = ? and y = ?. **10, 5**
15. If $AB = 12$, $BC = 2x + 3y$, and $BD = 8x$, then x = ? and y = ?. **3, 2**

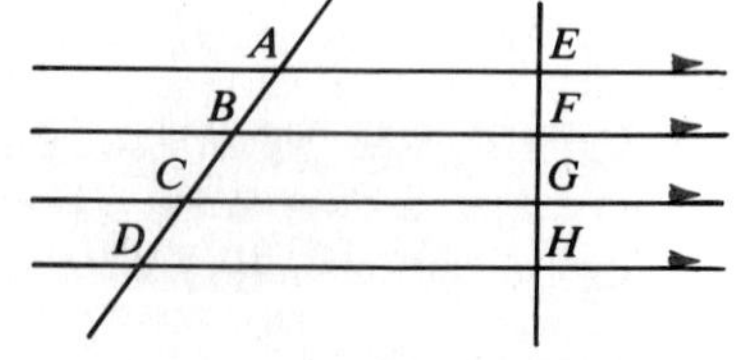

Exs. 10–15

In Exercises 16–17 a segment joins the midpoints of two sides of a triangle. Find the values of x and y.

16.

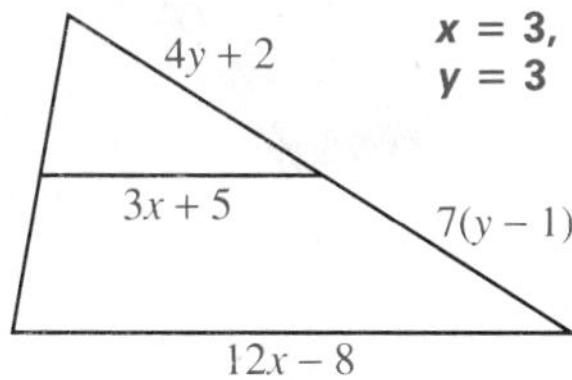

x = 3, y = 3

17.

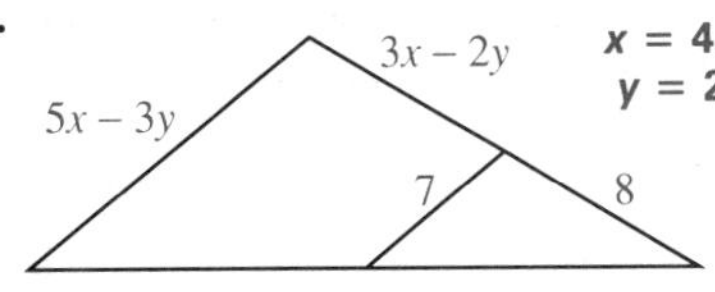

x = 4, y = 2

18. Given: A is the midpoint of $\overline{OX}$; $\overline{AB} \parallel \overline{XY}$; $\overline{BC} \parallel \overline{YZ}$

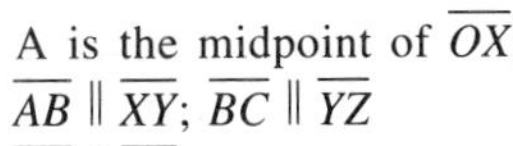

Prove: $\overline{AC} \parallel \overline{XZ}$

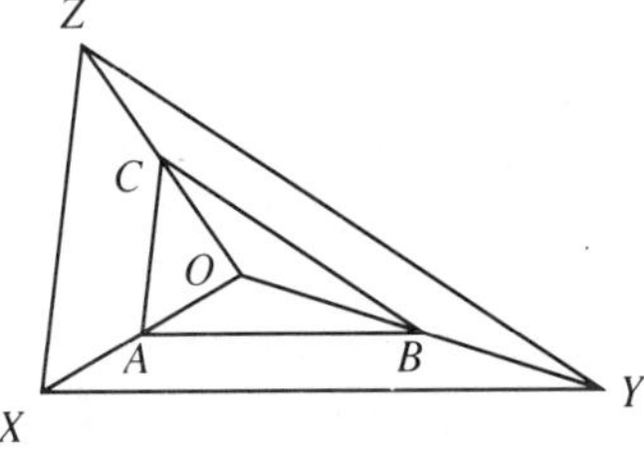

19. Given: $\square ABCD$; $\overline{BE} \parallel \overline{MD}$; M is the midpoint of $\overline{AB}$.

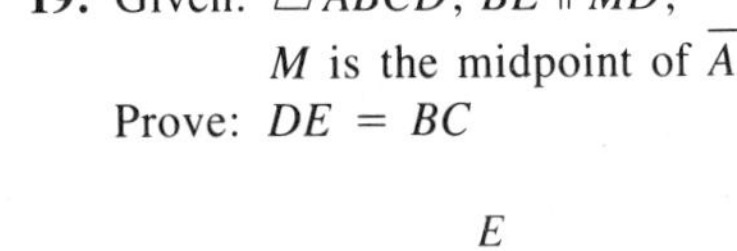

Prove: $DE = BC$

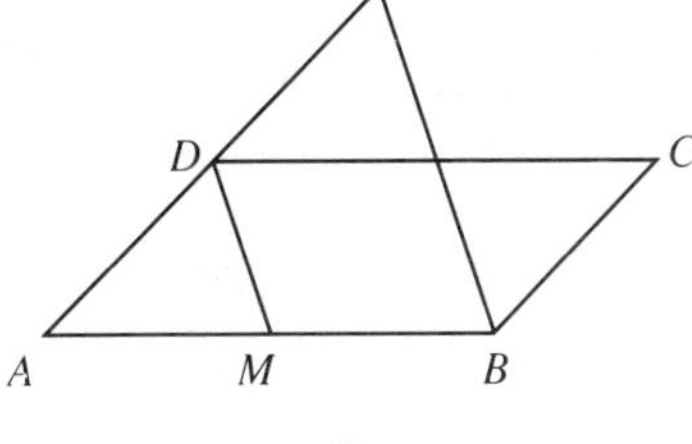

20. Given: $\overline{PQ}$, $\overline{RS}$, and $\overline{TU}$ are each perpendicular to $\overleftrightarrow{UQ}$; R is the midpoint of $\overline{PT}$.
Prove: R is equidistant from U and Q.

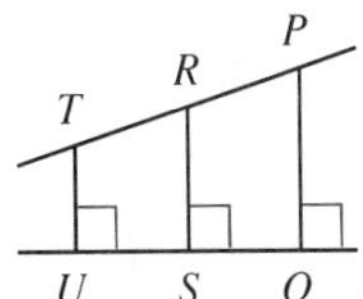

21. $EFGH$ is a parallelogram whose diagonals intersect at P. M is the midpoint of $\overline{FG}$. Prove that $MP = \frac{1}{2}EF$.

22. A *skew quadrilateral SKEW* is shown. M, N, O, and P are the midpoints of $\overline{SK}$, $\overline{KE}$, $\overline{WE}$, and $\overline{SW}$. Explain why $PMNO$ is a parallelogram.

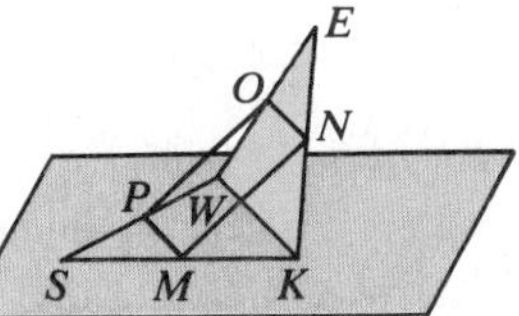

23. Draw $\triangle ABC$ and label the midpoints of $\overline{AB}$, $\overline{AC}$, and $\overline{BC}$ as X, Y, and Z, respectively. Let P be the midpoint of $\overline{BZ}$ and Q be the midpoint of $\overline{CZ}$. Prove that $PX = QY$.

24. Draw $\triangle ABC$ and let D be the midpoint of $\overline{AB}$. Let E be the midpoint of $\overline{CD}$. Let F be the intersection of $\overrightarrow{AE}$ and $\overline{BC}$. Draw $\overline{DG}$ parallel to $\overline{EF}$ meeting $\overline{BC}$ at G. Prove that $BG = GF = FC$.

3. Given: $AB = BC = CD$

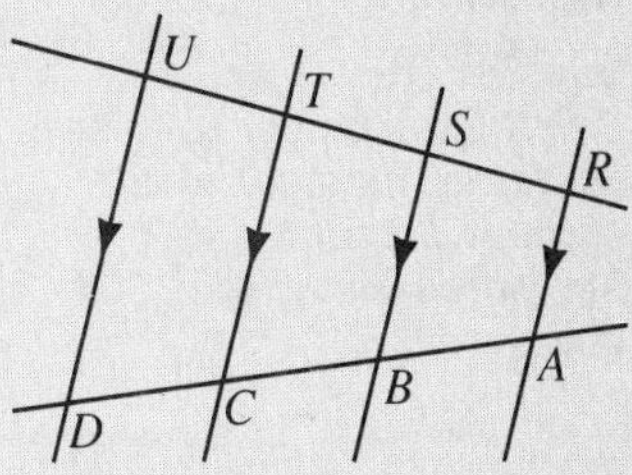

Complete.

a. If $RS = 6$, then $SU = \underline{12}$.

b. If $RT = 6x + 2$ and $TU = 10$, then $x = \underline{3}$.

Additional Answers
Written Exercises

22. By Thm. 5-11, $\overline{ON} \parallel \overline{WK}$ and $\overline{PM} \parallel \overline{WK}$. So $\overline{ON} \parallel \overline{PM}$ (2 lines $\parallel$ to a third line are $\parallel$ to each other). Also by Thm. 5-11, $ON = \frac{1}{2}WK$ and $PM = \frac{1}{2}WK$. So $ON = PM$ and $\overline{ON} \cong \overline{PM}$. Since $\overline{ON}$ and $\overline{PM}$ are both $\parallel$ and $\cong$, $PMNO$ is a $\square$ (Thm. 5-5).

Using a Computer

Exs. 23 and 24 can be done using a construction program. As a challenge, have students draw the diagrams without knowing what is to be proved. They can then hypothesize on the result to be proved.

Assessment

Use Self-Test 1 and the Quick Quiz below to assess students' mastery of the content presented in the first three lessons of this chapter.

Quick Quiz

The diagonals of ▱*DECK* intersect at *Q*. Tell whether each statement *must be*, *may be*, or *cannot* be true.

1. $\angle EDK \cong \angle KCE$ must be
2. $DE = 12$ and $EC = 13$ may be
3. $\overline{CK} \parallel \overline{DK}$ cannot be
4. $\overline{DQ} \cong \overline{QC}$ must be
5. List 5 possible ways to prove that quad. *DECK* is a ▱.
(1) Show $\overline{DK} \parallel \overline{EC}$ and $\overline{ED} \parallel \overline{CK}$. (2) Show $\overline{DE} \cong \overline{KC}$ and $\overline{DK} \cong \overline{EC}$. (3) Show $\overline{DK} \parallel \overline{EC}$ and $\overline{DK} \cong \overline{EC}$ or show $\overline{DE} \parallel \overline{KC}$ and $\overline{DE} \cong \overline{KC}$. (4) Show $\angle E \cong \angle K$ and $\angle D \cong \angle C$. (5) Show $\overline{DC}$ and $\overline{EK}$ bisect each other.
6.

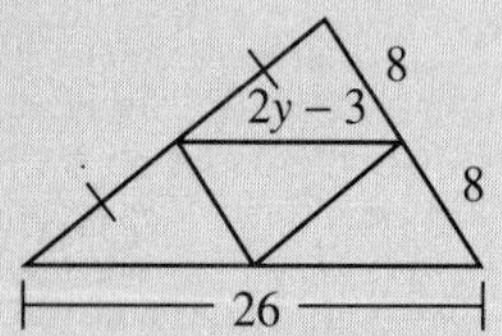

a. State a theorem that allows you to conclude that $2y - 3 = 13$.
The segment joining the midpoints of two sides of a triangle is half as long as the third side.

b. Find the value of *y*. 8

C **25.** Given: Parallel planes *P*, *Q*, and *R* cutting transversals $\overleftrightarrow{AC}$ and $\overleftrightarrow{DF}$; $AB = BC$
Prove: $DE = EF$
(*Hint:* You can't assume that $\overleftrightarrow{AC}$ and $\overleftrightarrow{DF}$ are coplanar. Draw $\overline{AF}$, cutting plane *Q* at *X*. Using the plane of $\overline{AC}$ and $\overline{AF}$, apply Theorems 3-1 and 5-10. Then use the plane of $\overline{AF}$ and $\overline{FD}$.)

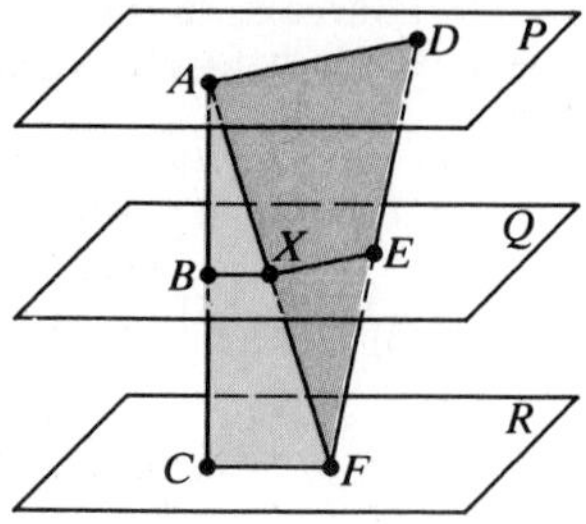

Self-Test 1

The diagonals of ▱*ABCD* intersect at *Z*. Tell whether each statement *must be*, *may be*, or *cannot be* true. **1. may be 3. must be**

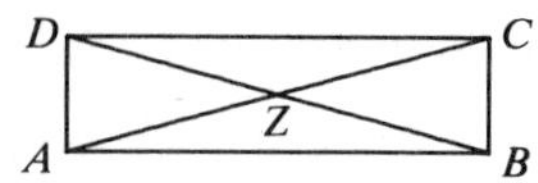

1. $\overline{AC} \cong \overline{BD}$
2. $\overline{DZ} \cong \overline{BZ}$ **must be**
3. $\overline{AD} \parallel \overline{BC}$
4. $m\angle DAB = 85$ and $m\angle BCD = 95$ **cannot be**
5. List five ways to prove that quad. *ABCD* is a parallelogram. **See page 172.**

6. a. State a theorem that allows you to conclude that $3x - 7 = 11$.
b. Find the values of *x* and *y*. **x = 6, y = 19**
a. If 3 ∥ lines cut off ≅ segments on one trans., they cut off ≅ seg. on every trans.

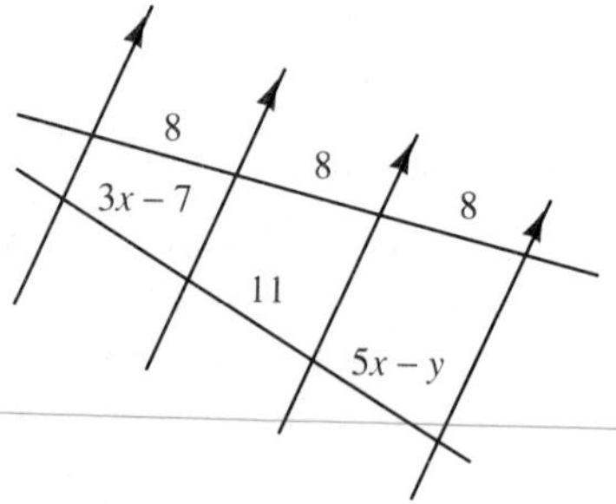

7. Given: ▱*ABCD*;
M is the midpoint of $\overline{AB}$.
Prove: $MO = \frac{1}{2}AD$

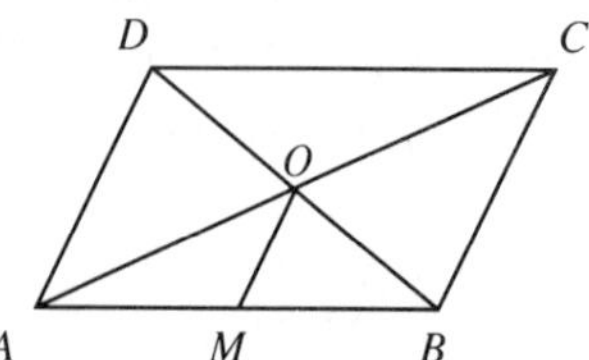

8. Given: ▱*PQRS*;
$\overline{PX}$ bisects $\angle QPR$;
$\overline{RY}$ bisects $\angle SRP$.
Prove: *RYPX* is a ▱.

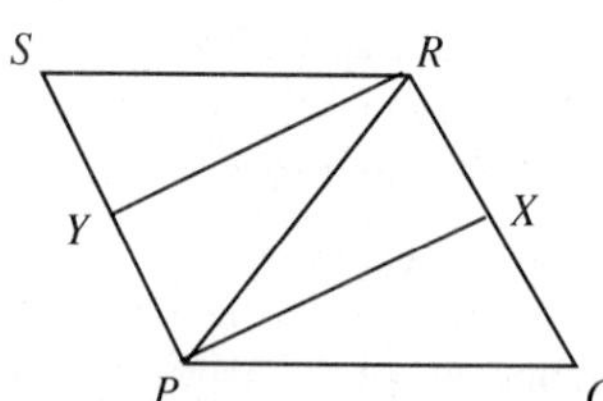

♦ Computer Key-In

The BASIC computer program below will calculate the lengths of sides and diagonals of a quadrilateral. (Line 200 uses the distance formula, which you will study in Chapter 13.) Do the exercises to see what you can discover before studying special quadrilaterals in the next two sections.

```
10 DIM X(4), Y(4), A$(4)
15 A$(1) = "A":A$(2) = "B":A$(3) = "C":A$(4) = "D"
20 FOR I = 1 TO 4
30 PRINT "VERTEX ";A$(I);" ";
40 INPUT X(I), Y(I)
50 NEXT I
60 PRINT "SIDES"
70 FOR I = 1 TO 4
80 LET J = I + 1 - 4 * INT(I/4)
90 GOSUB 200
95 NEXT I
100 PRINT "DIAGONALS"
110 LET I = 1:LET J = 3
120 GOSUB 200
130 LET I = 2:LET J = 4
140 GOSUB 200
150 END
200 LET D = SQR((X(I)-X(J)) ↑ 2 + (Y(I)-Y(J)) ↑ 2)
210 LET D = INT(100 * D + .5)/100
220 PRINT A$(I);A$(J);" = ";D
230 RETURN
```

Exercises

Plot the given points and draw quad. *ABCD* and its diagonals. Also RUN the program above, inputting the given coordinates for the vertices. Then tell which of the following statements are true for quad. *ABCD*.

I. Quad. *ABCD* is a parallelogram.
II. Both pairs of opposite sides are congruent.
III. All sides are congruent.
IV. The diagonals are congruent.
V. The diagonals are perpendicular.
VI. The sides form four right angles.

1. a. $A(1, 1)$, $B(3, 4)$, $C(10, 4)$, $D(8, 1)$
b. $A(0, -3)$, $B(-4, -1)$, $C(-2, 1)$, $D(2, -1)$
2. a. $A(1, 2)$, $B(-3, -1)$, $C(-7, 2)$, $D(-3, 5)$
b. $A(1, 1)$, $B(3, -3)$, $C(-1, -1)$, $D(-3, 3)$
3. a. $A(4, -1)$, $B(-2, -1)$, $C(-2, 2)$, $D(4, 2)$
b. $A(-5, 0)$, $B(-3, 4)$, $C(5, 0)$, $D(3, -4)$
4. a. $A(2, 2)$, $B(2, -2)$, $C(-2, -2)$, $D(-2, 2)$
b. $A(0, 3)$, $B(3, 0)$, $C(0, -3)$, $D(-3, 0)$
5. a. $A(-7, 0)$, $B(-4, 4)$, $C(-1, 4)$, $D(-1, 0)$
b. $A(4, 6)$, $B(10, 3)$, $C(4, -3)$, $D(1, 3)$
6. a. $A(0, 0)$, $B(2, 4)$, $C(4, 0)$, $D(2, -2)$
b. $A(6, 0)$, $B(3, -5)$, $C(-4, 0)$, $D(3, 5)$

1. a, b. I, II
2. a, b. I, II, III, V
3. a, b. I, II, IV, VI
4. a, b. I, II, III, IV, V, VI
5. a. None b. IV, V
6. a. V b. IV, V

7. Given: *LOPR* is a ▱; $\triangle LRM \cong \triangle POQ$.
Prove: *MOQR* is a ▱.

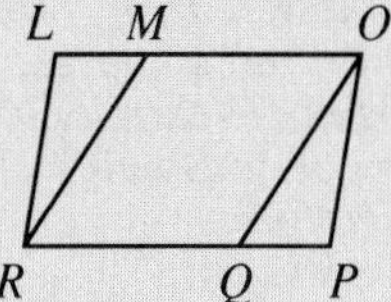

1. *LOPR* is a ▱; $\triangle LRM \cong \triangle POQ$ (Given)
2. $\overline{RM} \cong \overline{OQ}$; $\overline{LM} \cong \overline{PQ}$ (Corr. parts of ≅ ▵ are ≅.)
3. $\overline{LO} \cong \overline{PR}$ and $LO = PR$ (Opp. sides of a ▱ are ≅; Def. of ≅)
4. $LO = LM + MO$; $PR = PQ + QR$ (Segment Add. Post.)
5. $MO = QR$ and $\overline{MO} \cong \overline{QR}$ (Substitution, Steps 2–4; Def. of ≅)
6. *MOQR* is a ▱. (If both pairs of opp. sides of a quad. are ≅, the quad. is a ▱.)

Using a Computer

In these exercises, students draw and discover properties of parallelograms, rectangles, rhombuses, squares, trapezoids, and kites before formally learning about them in the next two lessons. The exercises are also useful when done using graph paper only (without a computer).

Special Quadrilaterals

Objectives

1. Apply the definitions and identify the special properties of a rectangle, a rhombus, and a square.
2. Determine when a parallelogram is a rectangle, rhombus, or square.
3. Apply the definitions and identify the properties of a trapezoid and an isosceles trapezoid.

5-4 *Special Parallelograms*

In this section you will study the properties of special parallelograms: *rectangles*, *rhombuses*, and *squares*.

A **rectangle** is a quadrilateral with four right angles. Therefore, every rectangle is a parallelogram. (Why?) **Both pairs of opp. ∠s are ≅.**

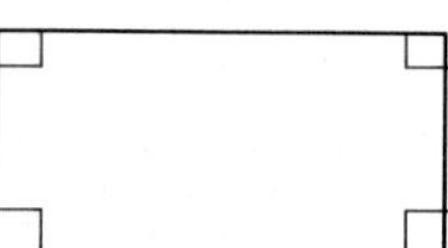

Rectangle

A **rhombus** is a quadrilateral with four congruent sides. Therefore, every rhombus is a parallelogram. (Why?) **Both pairs of opp. sides are ≅.**

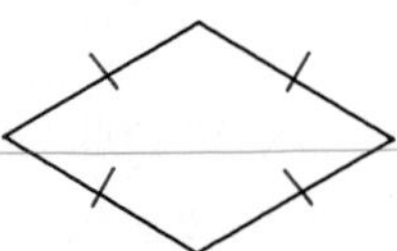

Rhombus

A **square** is a quadrilateral with four right angles and four congruent sides. Therefore, every square is a rectangle, a rhombus, and a parallelogram. (Why?) **Four right angles; four ≅ sides; both pairs of opp. ∠s (and sides) are ≅.**

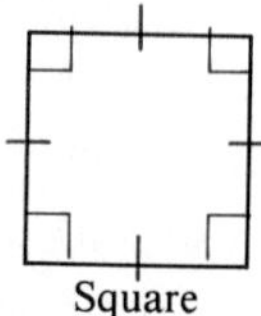

Square

Since rectangles, rhombuses, and squares are parallelograms, they have all the properties of parallelograms. They also have the special properties given in the theorems on the next page. Proofs of these theorems are left as exercises.

Teaching Suggestions, pp. T94–T95

Objectives
Presenting the Lesson
Using Technology
Problem Solving
Reinforcement
Enrichment

Supplementary Materials

Practice Master 27
Resource Book, p. 262
Study Guide, pp. 65–66

Lesson Focus

Rectangles, rhombuses, and squares are special parallelograms. This lesson studies the properties of these three kinds of parallelograms.

Suggested Assignments

Minimum
Day 1: 187/1–13
S 181/20
Day 2: 187–188/14, 17, 18, 20–22
189/Mixed Review 1–9

Average
Day 1: 187–188/1–11, 14, 17, 20–23
Day 2: 188/24–34 even
189/Mixed Review 1–9

Maximum
Day 1: 187–188/1–10, 14, 17, 28, 30, 34
S 181/18
Day 2: 188–189/32, 33, 36, 37, 40–42

Theorem 5-12

The diagonals of a rectangle are congruent.

Theorem 5-13

The diagonals of a rhombus are perpendicular.

Theorem 5-14

Each diagonal of a rhombus bisects two angles of the rhombus.

Example Given: *ABCD* is a rhombus.
What can you conclude?

Solution *ABCD* is a parallelogram, with all the properties of a parallelogram. Also:
By Theorem 5-13, $\overline{AC} \perp \overline{BD}$.
By Theorem 5-14, $\overline{AC}$ bisects $\angle DAB$ and $\angle BCD$;
$\overline{BD}$ bisects $\angle ABC$ and $\angle ADC$.

The properties of rectangles lead to the following interesting conclusion about any right triangle.

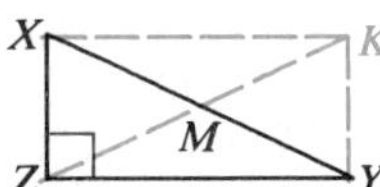

Begin with rt. $\triangle XYZ$.

1. Draw lines to form rectangle *XZYK*. (How?) **$\overline{XK} \parallel \overline{ZY}$, $\overline{XZ} \parallel \overline{KY}$**
2. Draw $\overline{ZK}$. $ZK = XY$ (Why?) **Diag. of a rectangle are ≅.**
3. $\overline{ZK}$ and $\overline{XY}$ bisect each other. (Why?) **Diag. of a ▱ bisect each other.**
4. $MX = MY = MZ = MK$, by (2) and (3).

Since $MX = MY = MZ$, we have shown the following.

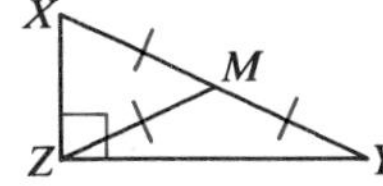

Theorem 5-15

The midpoint of the hypotenuse of a right triangle is equidistant from the three vertices.

Proofs of the next two theorems will be discussed as Classroom Exercises.

Theorem 5-16

If an angle of a parallelogram is a right angle, then the parallelogram is a rectangle.

Theorem 5-17

If two consecutive sides of a parallelogram are congruent, then the parallelogram is a rhombus.

Chalkboard Examples

Quad. *ABCD* is a rhombus.

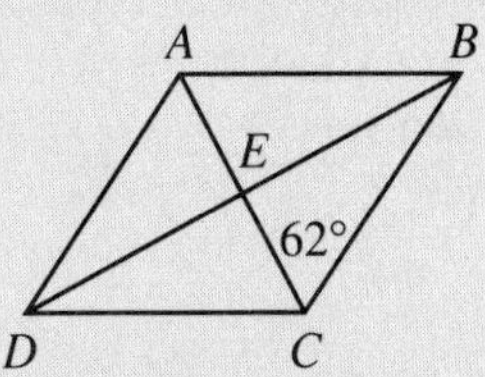

Find the measure of each angle.

1. $\angle ACD$ 62
2. $\angle DEC$ 90
3. $\angle EDC$ 28
4. $\angle ABC$ 56

Quad. *MNOP* is a rectangle.

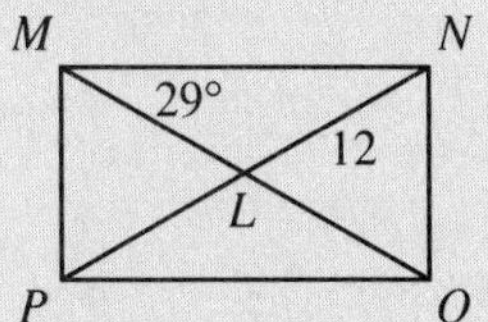

Complete.

5. $m\angle PON = \underline{90}$
6. $m\angle PMO = \underline{61}$
7. $PL = \underline{12}$
8. $MO = \underline{24}$

$\triangle ABC$ is a right $\triangle$; *M* is the midpoint of $\overline{AB}$.

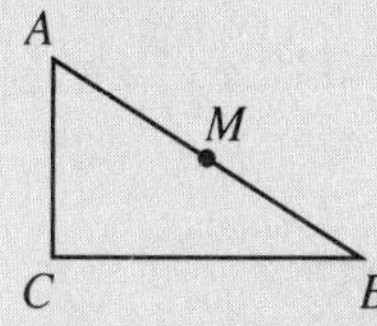

9. If $AM = 7$, then $MB = \underline{7}$, $AB = \underline{14}$, and $CM = \underline{7}$.
10. If $AB = x$, then $AM = \underline{\frac{x}{2}}$, $MB = \underline{\frac{x}{2}}$, and $MC = \underline{\frac{x}{2}}$.

Using a Computer

Theorem 5-15 can be verified easily using a construction program.

Classroom Exercises

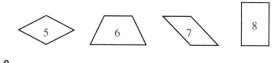

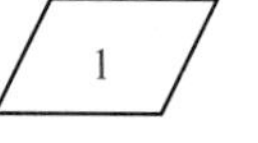

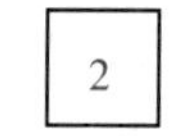

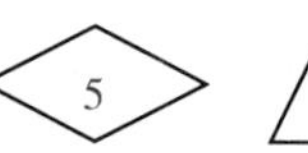

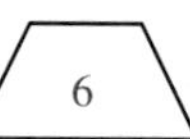

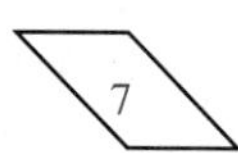

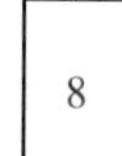

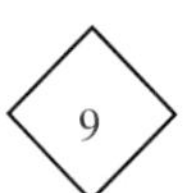

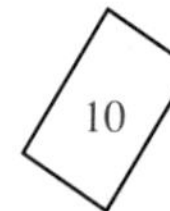

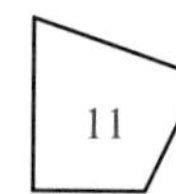

1. Name each figure shown that appears to be: **1. a. 1, 2, 4, 5, 7, 8, 9, 10, 12**
   a. a parallelogram
   b. a rectangle **2, 4, 8, 9, 10**
   c. a rhombus **2, 5, 9, 12**
   d. a square **2, 9**
2. Name each figure that is *both* a rectangle *and* a rhombus. **2, 9**
3. Name each figure that is a rectangle but not a square. **4, 8, 10**
4. Name each figure that is a rhombus but not a square. **5, 12**
5. When you know that one angle of a parallelogram is a right angle, you can prove that the parallelogram is a rectangle. Draw a diagram and explain.
6. When you know that two consecutive sides of a parallelogram are congruent, you can prove that the parallelogram is a rhombus. Draw a diagram and explain.
7. Given: Rhombus *EFGH*
   a. *F*, being equidistant from *E* and *G*, must lie on the _?_ of $\overline{EG}$. **⊥ bisector**
   b. *H*, being equidistant from *E* and *G*, must lie on the _?_ of $\overline{EG}$. **⊥ bisector**
   c. From (a) and (b) you can deduce that $\overline{FH}$ is the _?_ of $\overline{EG}$. **⊥ bisector**
   d. State the theorem of this section that you have just proved. **The diagonals of a rhombus are ⊥.**

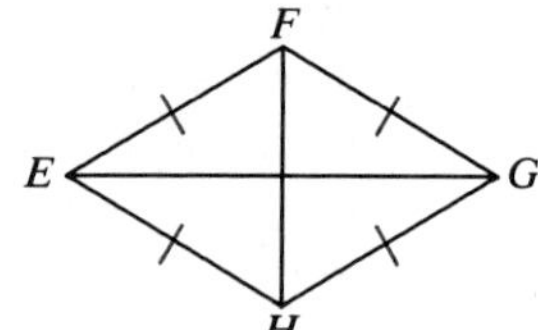

∠*KAP* is a right angle, and $\overline{AM}$ is a median. Complete.

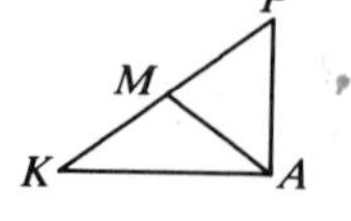

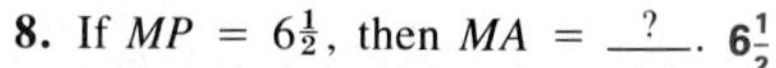

8. If $MP = 6\frac{1}{2}$, then MA = _?_. **$6\frac{1}{2}$**
9. If $MA = t$, then KP = _?_. **2t**
10. If $m\angle K = 40$, then $m\angle KAM$ = _?_. **40**
11. In the diagrams below, the red figures are formed by joining the midpoints of the sides of the quadrilaterals.
    a. What seems to be the common property of the red figures? **They are parallelograms.**
    b. Describe how you would prove your answer to part (a).

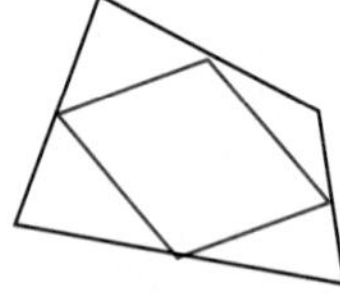
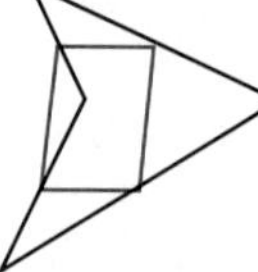

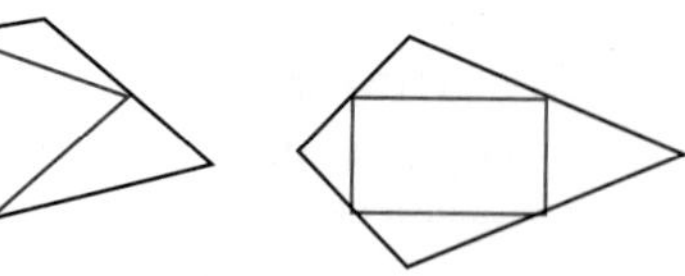

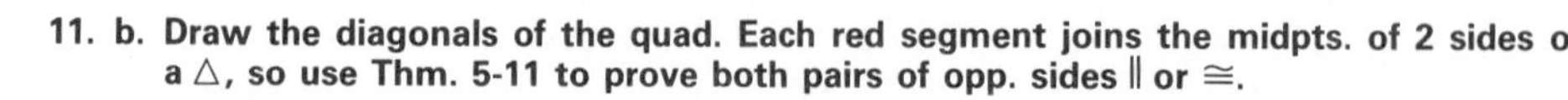
11. b. Draw the diagonals of the quad. Each red segment joins the midpts. of 2 sides of a △, so use Thm. 5-11 to prove both pairs of opp. sides ∥ or ≅.

Additional Answers
Classroom Exercises

5.

O I A E

Since *AOIE* is a ▱, ∠*I* ≅ ∠*A*. So $m\angle I = 90$. Since $\overline{OI} \parallel \overline{AE}$, $m\angle O + m\angle A = 180$. So $m\angle O = 90$ and $m\angle E = 90$. Then *AOIE* is a rectangle.

6.

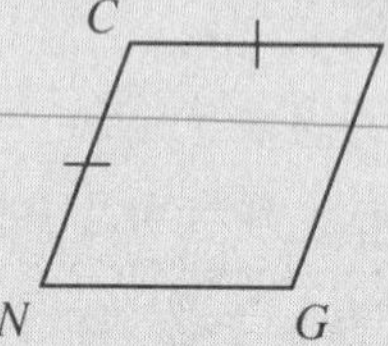

Since *CTGN* is a ▱, $\overline{CT} \cong \overline{NG}$ and $\overline{CN} \cong \overline{TG}$. Then $\overline{CT} \cong \overline{NG} \cong \overline{CN} \cong \overline{TG}$ and *CTGN* is a rhombus.

Thinking Skills

Ex. 11 asks students to generalize about the special quadrilateral formed by connecting consecutive midpoints of the sides of convex or nonconvex quadrilaterals.

Written Exercises

Copy the chart. Then place check marks in the appropriate spaces.

	Property	Parallelogram	Rectangle	Rhombus	Square
A 1.	Opp. sides are ∥.	✓	✓	✓	✓
2.	Opp. sides are ≅.	✓	✓	✓	✓
3.	Opp. ∠s are ≅.	✓	✓	✓	✓
4.	A diag. forms two ≅ △s.	✓	✓	✓	✓
5.	Diags. bisect each other.	✓	✓	✓	✓
6.	Diags. are ≅.		✓		✓
7.	Diags. are ⊥.			✓	✓
8.	A diag. bisects two ∠s.			✓	✓
9.	All ∠s are rt. ∠s.		✓		✓
10.	All sides are ≅.			✓	✓

Quad. *SLTM* is a rhombus.

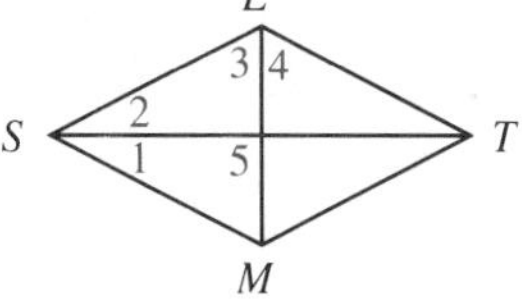

11. If $m\angle 1 = 25$, find the measures of $\angle 2$, $\angle 3$, $\angle 4$, and $\angle 5$. **25, 65, 65, 90**

12. If $m\angle 1 = 3x + 8$ and $m\angle 2 = 11x - 24$, find the value of x. **4**

13. If $m\angle 1 = 3x + 1$ and $m\angle 3 = 7x - 11$, find the value of x. **10**

Quad. *FLAT* is a rectangle.

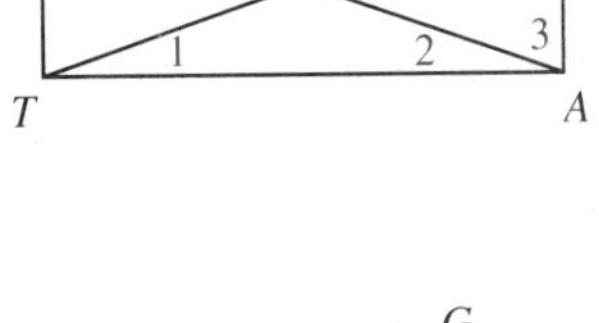

14. If $m\angle 1 = 18$, find the measures of $\angle 2$, $\angle 3$, and $\angle 4$. **18, 72, 72**

15. If $FA = 27$, find LO. **$13\frac{1}{2}$**

16. If $TO = 4y + 7$ and $FA = 30$, find the value of y. **2**

$\overline{GM}$ is a median of right △*IRG*.

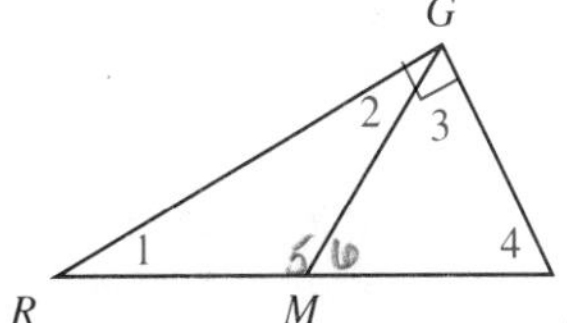

17. If $m\angle 1 = 32$, find the measures of $\angle 2$, $\angle 3$, and $\angle 4$. **32, 58, 58**

18. If $m\angle 4 = 7x - 3$ and $m\angle 3 = 6(x + 1)$, find the value of x. **9**

19. If $GM = 2y + 3$ and $RI = 12 - 8y$, find the value of y. **$\frac{1}{2}$**

Exercise Note

Instruct students to duplicate and complete the chart in Exs. 1–10. Since the chart compiles and categorizes the properties of different types of parallelograms, it is an excellent reference aid that will help students learn the properties associated with each special type of quadrilateral.

Guided Practice

Complete with *always*, *sometimes*, or *never.*

1. A square is always a rhombus.
2. The diagonals of a parallelogram sometimes bisect the angles of the parallelogram.
3. A quadrilateral with one pair of sides congruent and one pair parallel is sometimes a parallelogram.
4. The diagonals of a rhombus are sometimes congruent.
5. A rectangle sometimes has consecutive sides congruent.
6. A rectangle sometimes has perpendicular diagonals.
7. The diagonals of a rhombus always bisect each other.
8. The diagonals of a parallelogram are sometimes perpendicular bisectors of each other.

(continued)

Quad. *MORE* is a square.

9. If $ME = 7x - 3$ and $MO = 6x$, find the value of x. 3

10. If $MT = 4x$ and $TE = 3x + 2$, find OE. 16

$\overline{XW}$ is a median of right $\triangle ZYX$.

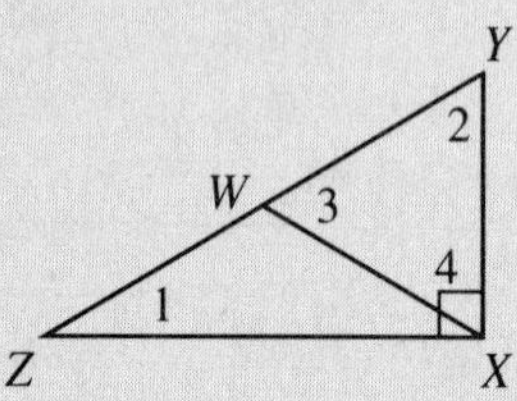

11. If $m\angle 2 = m\angle 3$, find $m\angle 1$. 30

12. If $YW = 3x - 2$ and $WZ = x + 8$, find YZ. 26

13. If $m\angle 1 = 40$, find $m\angle 2$, $m\angle 3$, and $m\angle 4$. 50, 80, 50

14. The coordinates of three vertices of a rectangle are $A(-3, 2)$, $B(4, 2)$, and $C(4, -2)$. Plot the points and find the coordinates of the fourth vertex. $(-3, -2)$ Is the rectangle a square? No

Using a Computer

Exs. 36 and 37 can be explored by using a construction program.

The coordinates of three vertices of a rectangle are given. Plot the points and find the coordinates of the fourth vertex. Is the rectangle a square?

20. $O(0, 0)$, $P(0, 5)$, $Q(\underline{?}, \underline{?})$, $R(2, 0)$ **21.** $A(2, 1)$, $B(4, 1)$, $C(4, 5)$, $D(\underline{?}, \underline{?})$

22. $O(0, 0)$, $E(4, 0)$, $F(4, 3)$, $G(\underline{?}, \underline{?})$ **23.** $H(1, 3)$, $I(4, 3)$, $J(\underline{?}, \underline{?})$, $K(1, 6)$

20. 2, 5; no 21. 2, 5; no 22. 0, 3; no 23. 4, 6; yes

$\overline{RA}$ is an altitude of $\triangle SAT$. P and Q are midpoints of $\overline{SA}$ and $\overline{TA}$. $SR = 9$, $RT = 16$, $QT = 10$, and $PR = 7.5$.

B **24.** Find RQ. **10** **25.** Find SA. **15**

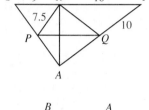

26. Find the perimeter of $\triangle PQR$. **30**

27. Find the perimeter of $\triangle SAT$. **60**

28. Given: $\square ABZY$; $\overline{ZY} \cong \overline{BX}$; $\angle 1 \cong \angle 2$
Prove: $ABZY$ is a rhombus.

29. Given: $\square ABZY$; $\overline{AY} \cong \overline{BX}$
Prove: $\angle 1 \cong \angle 2$ and $\angle 1 \cong \angle 3$

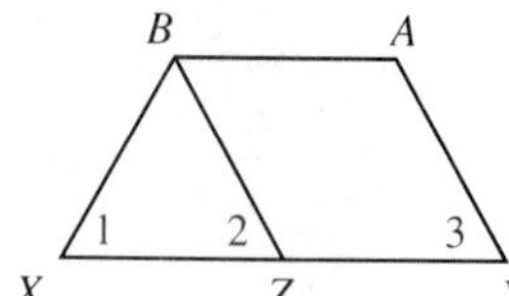

30. Given: Rectangle $QRST$; $\square RKST$
Prove: $\triangle QSK$ is isosceles.

31. Given: Rectangle $QRST$; $\square RKST$; $\square JQST$
Prove: $\overline{JT} \cong \overline{KS}$

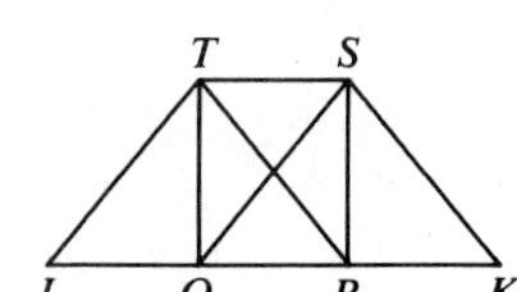

32. Prove Theorem 5-12.

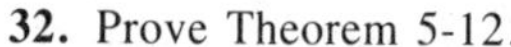

33. Prove Theorem 5-14 for one diagonal of the rhombus. (Note that a proof for the other would be similar, step-by-step.)

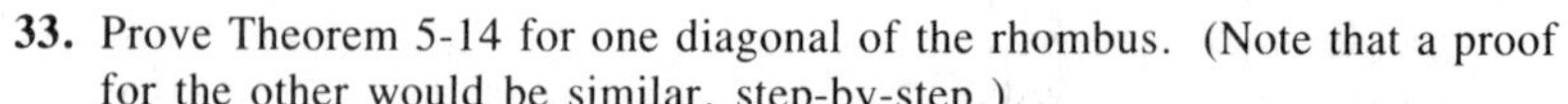

34. Prove: If the diagonals of a parallelogram are perpendicular, then the parallelogram is a rhombus.

35. Prove: If the diagonals of a parallelogram are congruent, then the parallelogram is a rectangle.

36. a. The bisectors of the angles of $\square ABCD$ intersect to form quad. $WXYZ$. What special kind of quadrilateral is $WXYZ$? **rectangle**

b. Prove your answer to part (a).

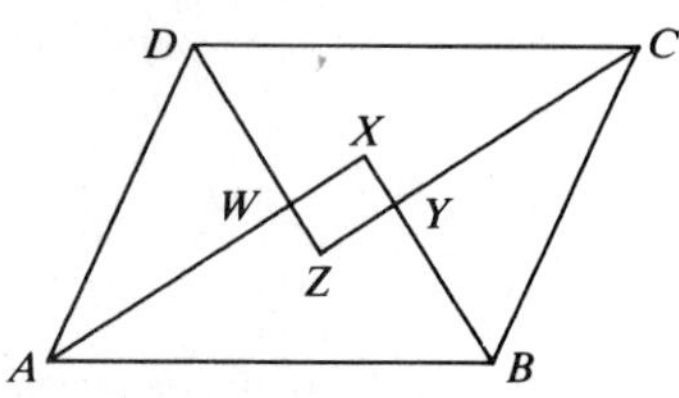

37. Draw a rectangle and bisect its angles. The bisectors intersect to form what special kind of quadrilateral? **square**

The coordinates of three vertices of a rhombus are given, not necessarily in order. Plot the points and find the coordinates of the fourth vertex. Measure the sides to check your answer.

38. $O(0, 0)$, $L(5, 0)$, $D(4, 3)$, $V(\underline{?}, \underline{?})$ **9, 3** **39.** $O(0, 0)$, $S(0, 10)$, $E(6, 18)$, $W(\underline{?}, \underline{?})$ **6, 8**

C **40. a.** Suppose that two sides of a quadrilateral are parallel and that one diagonal bisects an angle. Does that quadrilateral have to be special in other ways? If so, write a proof. If not, draw a convincing diagram. **Yes, it must have 2 ≅ consecutive sides.**

b. Repeat part (a) with these conditions: Suppose that two sides are parallel and that one diagonal bisects two angles of the quadrilateral. **Yes, a rhombus**

41. Draw a regular pentagon *ABCDE*. Let *X* be the intersection of $\overline{AC}$ and $\overline{BD}$. What special kind of quadrilateral is *AXDE*? Write a paragraph proof. **rhombus**

42. Given: Rectangle *RSTW*; equilateral △ *YWT* and *STZ*
What is true of $\triangle RYZ$? **It is equilateral.**
Write a paragraph proof.

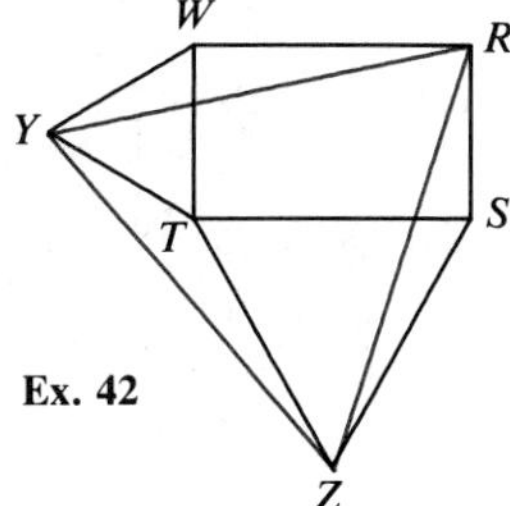

Ex. 42

Explorations

These exploratory exercises can be done using a computer with a program that draws and measures geometric figures.

As you will learn in the next section, a *trapezoid* is a quadrilateral with exactly one pair of parallel sides. Draw trapezoid *ABCD* with $\overline{BA} \parallel \overline{CD}$. Label the midpoints of $\overline{AD}$ and $\overline{BC}$ as *E* and *F* respectively, and draw $\overline{FE}$. Measure $\angle BFE$ and $\angle BCD$. What is true of $\overline{CD}$ and $\overline{FE}$? What postulate or theorem tells you this? **$\overline{CD} \parallel \overline{FE}$**
What is true of $\overline{FE}$ and $\overline{BA}$? Why? **$\overline{FE} \parallel \overline{BA}$**
Measure the lengths of $\overline{BA}$, $\overline{CD}$, and $\overline{FE}$. What do you notice?
Write an equation that relates *BA*, *CD*, and *FE*. Repeat the drawing and measurements until you are sure of your equation. **$FE = \frac{1}{2}(BA + CD)$**

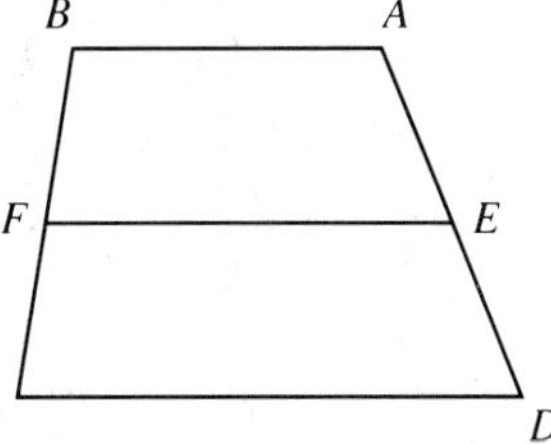

Mixed Review Exercises

Find the average of the given numbers. (The *average* is the sum of the numbers divided by the number of numbers.)

1. 17, 9 **13** **2.** 15, 25 **20** **3.** 18, 2, 13 **11** **4.** 7, 8, 5, 15, 10 **9**
5. 7.9, 8.5 **8.2** **6.** 4, −7 **−1.5** **7.** −3, 4, −7, 10 **1** **8.** 1.7, 2.6, 9.1, 0.4 **3.45**

9. The numbers given are the coordinates of the endpoints of a segment on a number line. Find the coordinate of the midpoint by taking the average.
a. 12, 34 **23** **b.** −3, 7 **2** **c.** 17, −9 **4** **d.** −5, −7 **−6**

Problem Solving

Many students will draw a variety of diagrams to help them answer Ex. 40. Students should be encouraged to do so, while being careful to make the diagrams as general as possible.

Using a Computer

This Exploration provides a good introduction to trapezoids.

Using a Calculator

Calculating averages is done quickly with a calculator. Some calculators have data features that allow students to input numbers in sequence and get the average using a single button.

Teaching Suggestions, pp. T95–T96

Objective
Presenting the Lesson
Using Technology
Problem Solving
Extension
Enrichment

Communication Skills, p. T96

Supplementary Materials

Practice Master 28
Test 19
Resource Book, pp. 26–27, 127, 263
Study Guide, pp. 67–68
Computer Activity 11

Lesson Focus

Trapezoids are useful in constructing bridges, as the photograph in the book shows. This lesson proves two theorems about the properties of trapezoids.

Suggested Assignments

Minimum
Day 1: 192–193/1–11
Day 2: 193/13, 14, 16, 17, 21–23
195/Self-Test 2
199/Chapter Test

Average
Day 1: 192–193/1, 3, 6, 7, 9, 11, 12, 14, 16
Day 2: 193/15, 17–19, 21–25, 27
195/Self-Test 2
199/Chapter Test

Maximum
Day 1: 192–193/4, 8, 11, 12, 16, 17, 19, 20, 25
Day 2: 193–194/21–29, 32, 33
199/Chapter Test

5-5 *Trapezoids*

A quadrilateral with exactly one pair of parallel sides is called a **trapezoid**. The parallel sides are called the **bases**. The other sides are **legs**.

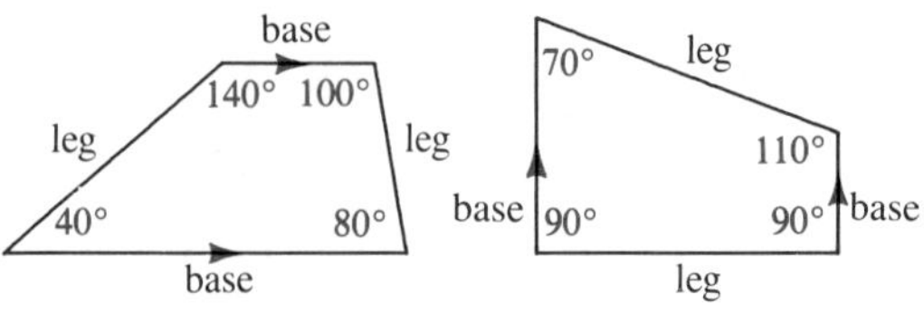

Trapezoids

A trapezoid with congruent legs is called an **isosceles trapezoid**. If you fold any isosceles trapezoid so that the legs coincide, you will find that both pairs of *base angles* are congruent.

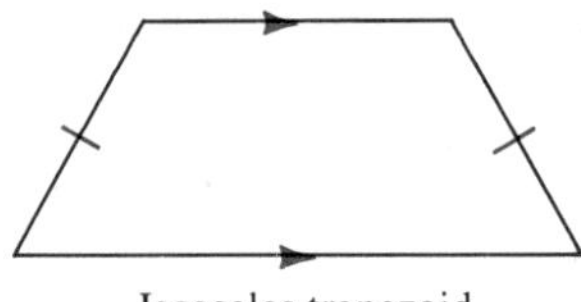
Isosceles trapezoid

A trapezoidal shape can be seen in the photograph. Is it isosceles?

Theorem 5-18

Base angles of an isosceles trapezoid are congruent.

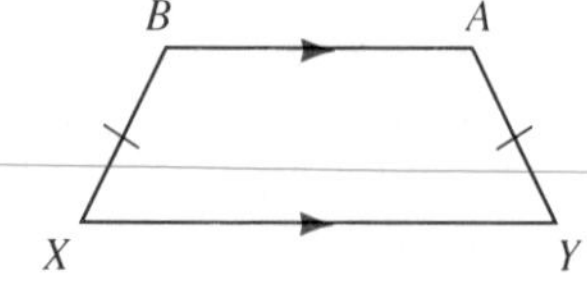

Given: Trapezoid $ABXY$ with $\overline{BX} \cong \overline{AY}$

Prove: $\angle X \cong \angle Y$; $\angle B \cong \angle A$

Plan for Proof: Note that the diagram does not contain any parallelograms or congruent triangles that might be used. To obtain such figures, you could draw auxiliary lines. You could use either diagram below to prove the theorem.

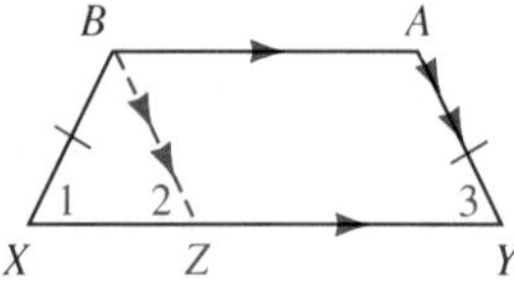

Draw $\overline{BZ} \parallel \overline{AY}$ so that $ABZY$ is a ▱.

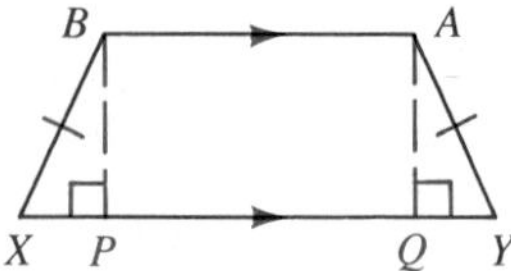

Draw $\overline{BP} \perp \overline{XY}$ and $\overline{AQ} \perp \overline{XY}$. Since $\overline{BA} \parallel \overline{XY}$, $BP = AQ$ by Theorem 5-8.

The **median** of a trapezoid is the segment that joins the midpoints of the legs. Note the difference between the median of a trapezoid and a median of a triangle.

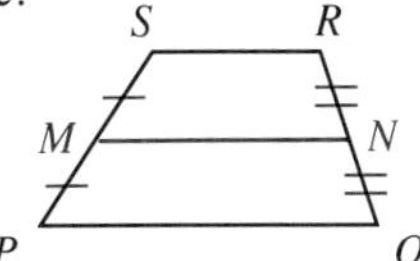

$\overline{MN}$ is *the* median of trapezoid $PQRS$.

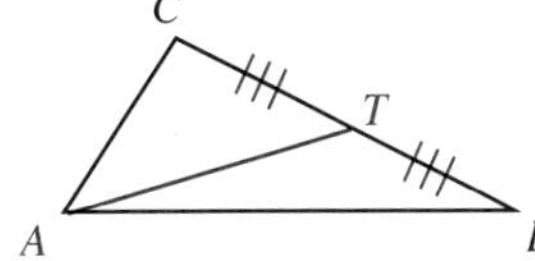

$\overline{AT}$ is *a* median of $\triangle ABC$.

Theorem 5-19

The median of a trapezoid

(1) is parallel to the bases;

(2) has a length equal to the average of the base lengths.

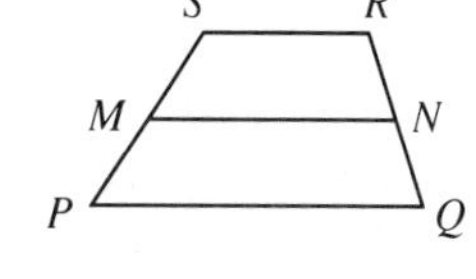

Given: Trapezoid $PQRS$ with median $\overline{MN}$

Prove: (1) $\overline{MN} \parallel \overline{PQ}$ and $\overline{MN} \parallel \overline{SR}$ (2) $MN = \frac{1}{2}(PQ + SR)$

Plan for Proof: Again it is necessary to introduce auxiliary lines, and again there is more than one way to do this. Although any of the diagrams below could be used to prove the theorem, the proof below uses the second diagram.

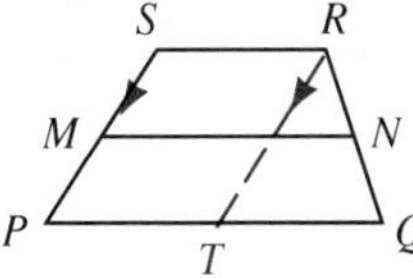

Draw $\overline{RT} \parallel \overline{SP}$.

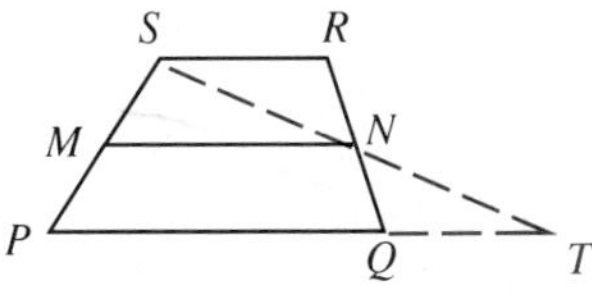

Draw $\overrightarrow{SN}$ intersecting $\overrightarrow{PQ}$ at T.

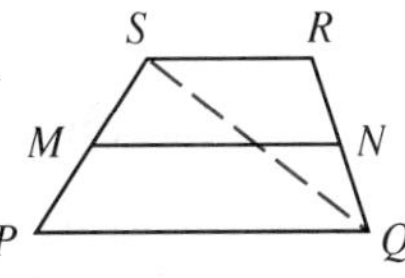

Draw $\overline{SQ}$.

Proof:

Extend $\overline{SN}$ to intersect $\overrightarrow{PQ}$ at T. $\triangle TNQ \cong \triangle SNR$ by ASA. Then $SN = NT$ and N is the midpoint of $\overline{ST}$. Using Theorem 5-11 and $\triangle PST$, (1) $\overline{MN} \parallel \overline{PQ}$ (and also $\overline{MN} \parallel \overline{SR}$), and (2) $MN = \frac{1}{2}PT = \frac{1}{2}(PQ + QT) = \frac{1}{2}(PQ + SR)$, since $\overline{QT} \cong \overline{SR}$.

Example A trapezoid and its median are shown. Find the value of x.

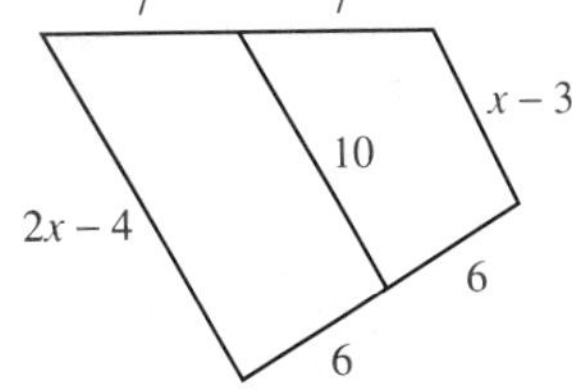

Solution

$$10 = \tfrac{1}{2}[(2x - 4) + (x - 3)]$$
$$20 = (2x - 4) + (x - 3)$$
$$20 = 3x - 7$$
$$27 = 3x$$
$$9 = x$$

Communication Skills

Students may need to review the use of auxiliary lines before proving Theorems 5-18 and 5-19. Other concepts used in these proofs include parallel lines, midpoints, and congruent triangles.

Chalkboard Examples

In trapezoid $ABCD$, $\overline{EF}$ is a median.

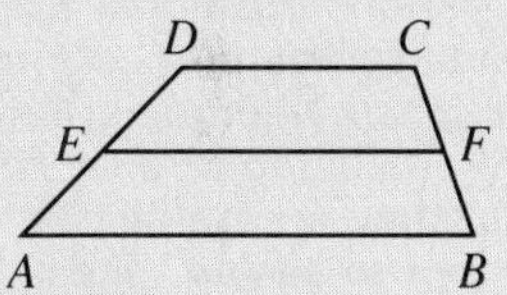

Complete.

1. $AB = 25$, $DC = 13$, $EF =$ 19
2. $AE = 11$, $FB = 8$, $AD =$ 22, $BC =$ 16
3. $AB = 29$, $EF = 24$, $DC =$ 19
4. $AB = 7y + 6$, $EF = 5y - 3$, $DC = y - 5$, $y =$ 3.5

In $\triangle KLM$, $\overline{HJ}$, $\overline{JI}$, and $\overline{IH}$ are the segments joining the midpoints of the sides.

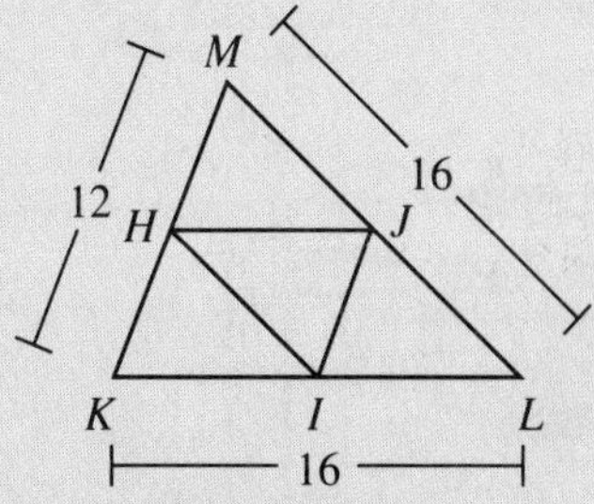

5. Name the three trapezoids in the figure. *KHJL, LIHM, MJIK*
6. Name an isosceles trapezoid and find its perimeter. *MJIK*, 34

Additional Answers
Classroom Exercises

9. Not possible; if both bases were both ≅ and ∥, the trapezoid would be a ▱.
10. Not possible; 2 of the ∠s must be supp., and 2 supp. ∠s cannot both be acute.

Exercise Note

Note that in Written Exs. 1–9, trapezoids are shown in various positions. Students sometimes become confused when diagrams are presented in a position that they are not accustomed to seeing. These exercises can help students learn to apply appropriate formulas to diagrams in nonstandard positions.

Guided Practice

Each diagram shows a trapezoid and its median. Find the value of *x*.

1. 21

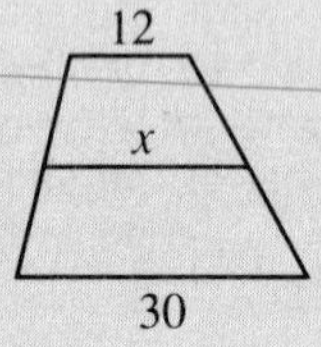

2. 29

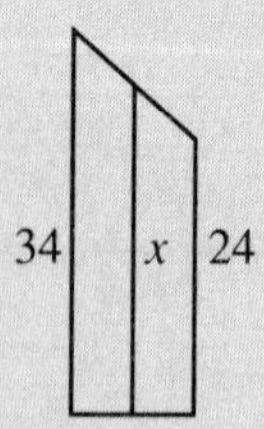

3. Quad. *TUNE* is an isosceles trapezoid with $m\angle T = 62$. Find $m\angle U$, $m\angle N$, and $m\angle E$.
118, 118, 62

Classroom Exercises **1.** $\overline{XZ} \parallel \overline{AB}$ **(Thm. 5-11) and** $\overline{AX} \nparallel \overline{BZ}$

***X*, *Y*, and *Z* are midpoints of the sides of isosceles △*ABC*.**

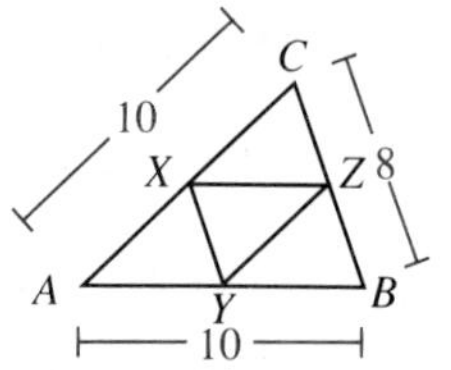

1. Explain why *XZBA* is a trapezoid.
2. Name two trapezoids other than *XZBA*. ***ACZY, XYBC***
3. Name an isosceles trapezoid and find its perimeter. ***XYBC*, 22**

Find the length of the median of each trapezoid.

4. **11**

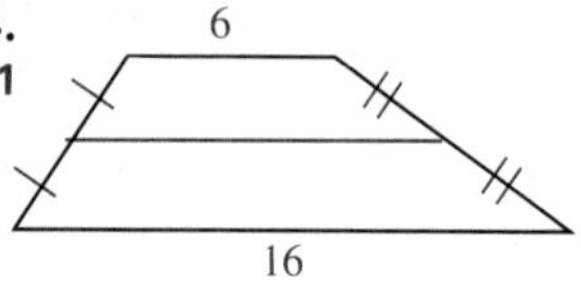

5. **7.5**

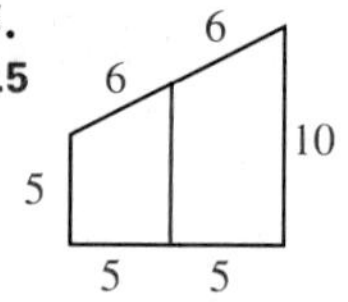

6. **11**

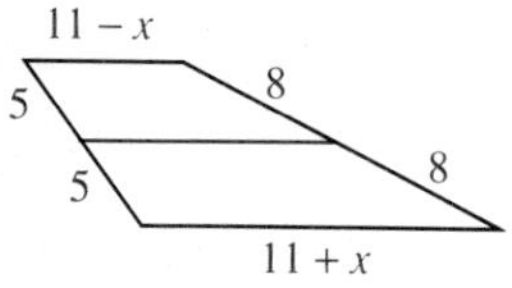

Draw the trapezoid described. If such a trapezoid cannot be drawn, explain why not.

7. with two right angles
8. with both bases shorter than the legs
9. with congruent bases
10. with three acute angles
11. Draw a quadrilateral such that exactly three sides are congruent and two pairs of angles are congruent.

Written Exercises

Each diagram shows a trapezoid and its median. Find the value of *x*.

A

1. **12**

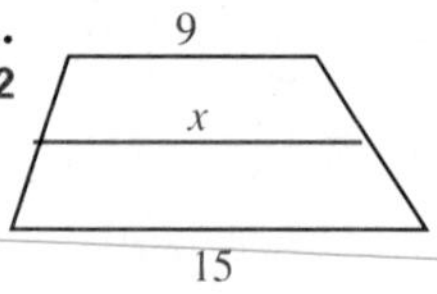

2. **19**

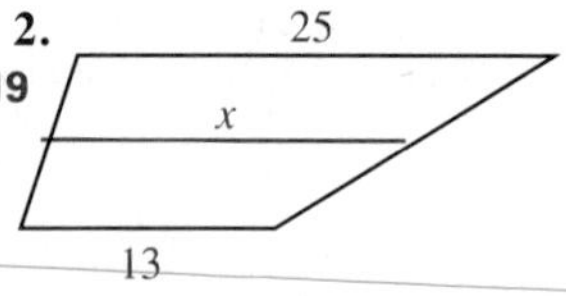

3. **15**

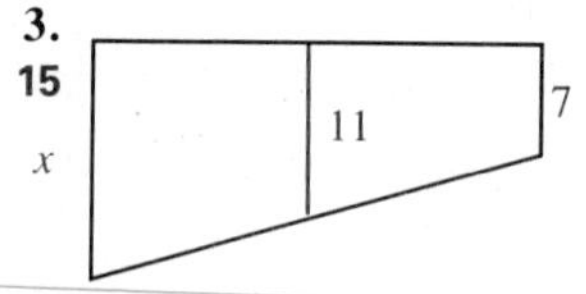

4. **5**

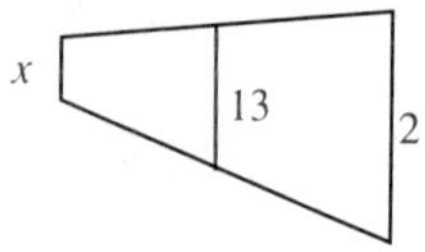

5. **9**

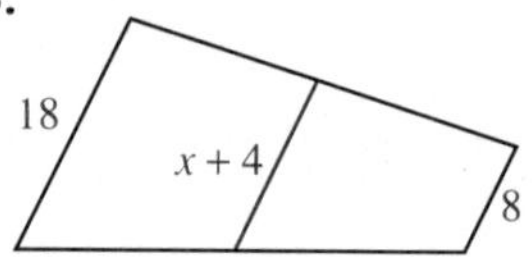

6. **5**

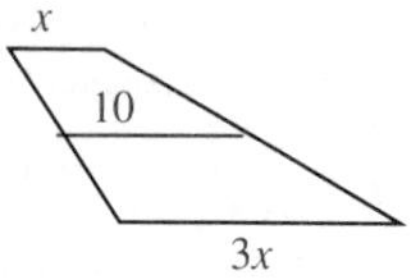

7. **4**

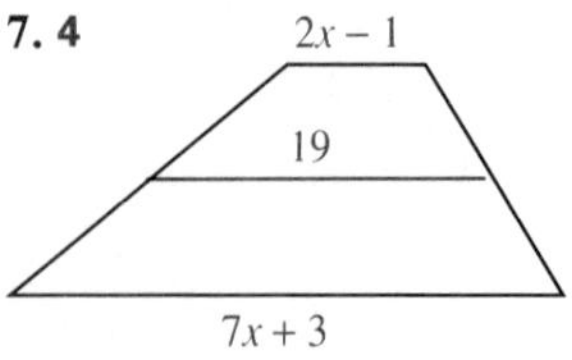

8. **5**

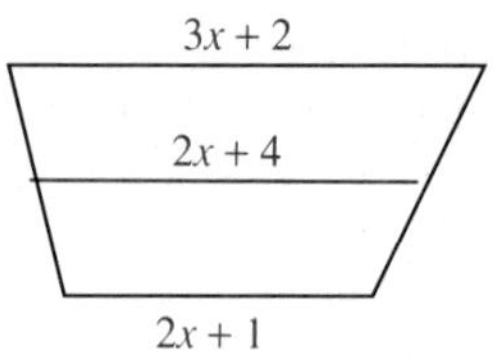

9. **6**

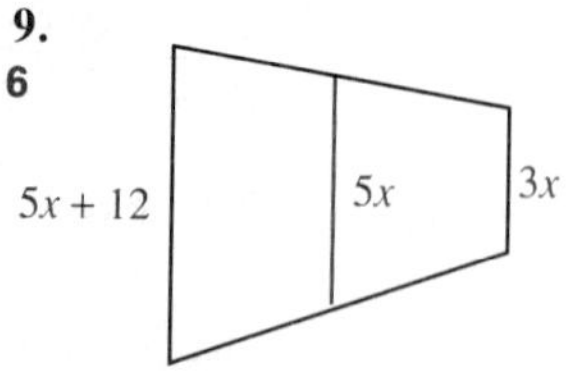

10. One angle of an isosceles trapezoid has measure 57. Find the measures of the other angles. **57, 123, 123**

11. Two congruent angles of an isosceles trapezoid have measures $3x + 10$ and $5x - 10$. Find the value of x and then give the measures of all angles of the trapezoid. **$x = 10$; 40, 40, 140, 140**

In Exercises 12–20, $TA = AB = BC$ and $TD = DE = EF$.

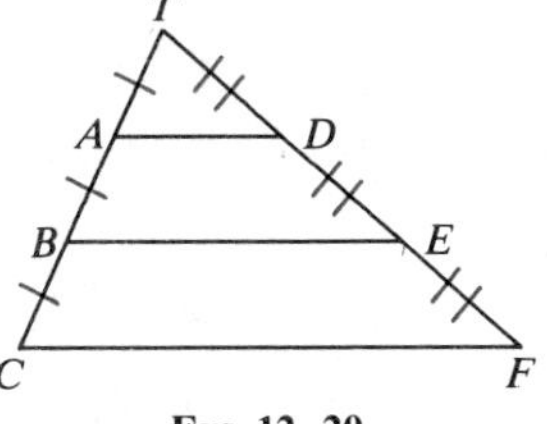

Exs. 12–20

12. Write an equation that relates AD and BE. (*Hint:* Think of $\triangle TBE$.) **$AD = \frac{1}{2}BE$**

13. Write an equation that relates AD, BE, and CF. (*Hint:* Think of trapezoid $CFDA$.) **$BE = \frac{1}{2}(AD + CF)$**

14. If $AD = 7$, then $BE =$ ___?___ and $CF =$ ___?___. **14, 21**

15. If $BE = 26$, then $AD =$ ___?___ and $CF =$ ___?___. **13, 39**

16. If $AD = x$ and $BE = x + 6$, then $x =$ ___?___ and $CF =$ ___?___ (numerical answers). **6, 18**

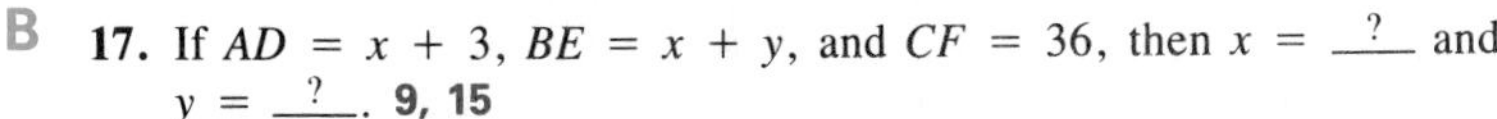

B **17.** If $AD = x + 3$, $BE = x + y$, and $CF = 36$, then $x =$ ___?___ and $y =$ ___?___. **9, 15**

18. If $AD = x + y$, $BE = 20$, and $CF = 4x - y$, then $CF =$ ___?___ (numerical answer). **30**

19. Tony makes up a problem for the figure, setting $AD = 5$ and $CF = 17$. Katie says, "You can't do that." Explain. **$CF = 3 \cdot AD$, but $17 \neq 3 \cdot 5$**

20. Mike makes up a problem for the figure, setting $AD = 2x + 1$, $BE = 4x + 2$, and $CF = 6x + 3$ and asking for the value of x. Katie says, "Anybody can do that problem." Explain. **Since $BE = 2 \cdot AD$ and $CF = 3 \cdot AD$, any $x > -\frac{1}{2}$ is a solution.**

Draw a quadrilateral of the type named. Join, in order, the midpoints of the sides. What special kind of quadrilateral do you appear to get?

21. rhombus **rectangle** **22.** rectangle **rhombus** **23.** isosceles trapezoid **rhombus**

24. non-isosceles trapezoid **▱** **25.** quadrilateral with no congruent sides **▱**

26. Carefully draw an isosceles trapezoid and measure its diagonals. What do you discover? Write a proof of your discovery. **The diagonals are ≅.**

27. Prove Theorem 5-18.

A *kite* is a quadrilateral that has two pairs of congruent sides, but opposite sides are not congruent.

28. Draw a convex kite. Discover, state, and prove whatever you can about the diagonals and angles of a kite.

29. a. Draw a convex kite. Join, in order, the midpoints of the sides. What special kind of quadrilateral do you appear to get? **rectangle**

b. Repeat part (a), but draw a nonconvex kite. **rectangle**

4. Name four trapezoids in the figure. *TRAP, XZAP, TRZX, XYQP*

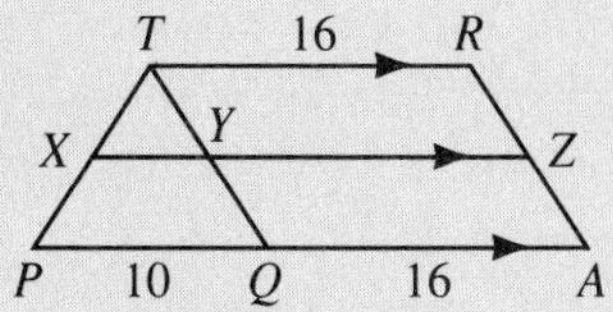

5. If $\overline{XZ}$ is a median of trap. *TRAP*, then $XZ = \underline{21}$ and $XY = \underline{5}$.

Thinking Skills

Exs. 21–25 ask students to generalize about the special type of quadrilateral formed by joining the midpoints of the sides of a quadrilateral. They should draw different size shapes for each problem and use inductive reasoning to make the generalization.

Using a Computer

Exs. 21–26 and 28–29 can be done effectively using a construction program.

Exercise Note

Ex. 28 gives each student the opportunity to make a conjecture and then try to prove it. You may want to discuss the important role of making conjectures in the learning process.

***ABCD* is a trapezoid with median $\overline{MN}$.**

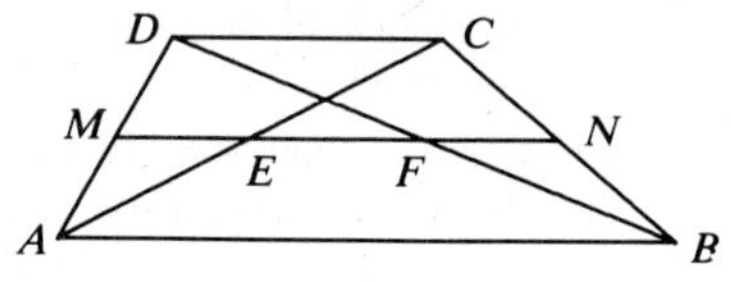

3, 3, 5

30. If $DC = 6$ and $AB = 16$, find ME, FN, and EF.

31. Prove that $EF = \frac{1}{2}(AB - DC)$.

32. If $DC = 3x$, $AB = 2x^2$, and $EF = 7$, find the value of x. **3.5**

C **33.** $\overline{VE}$ and $\overline{FG}$ are congruent. J, K, L, and M are the midpoints of $\overline{EF}$, $\overline{VF}$, $\overline{VG}$, and $\overline{EG}$. What name best describes $JKLM$? Explain. **Rhombus; $KJ = \frac{1}{2}VE = LM$ (Thm. 5-11) and $\overline{KJ} \parallel \overline{VE}$ and $\overline{LM} \parallel \overline{VE}$ so $\overline{KJ} \parallel \overline{LM}$. Since $\overline{KJ}$ and $\overline{LM}$ are both $\cong$ and $\parallel$, $JKLM$ is a $\square$. Also, $KJ = \frac{1}{2}VE = \frac{1}{2}FG = KL$ so $JKLM$ is a rhombus.**

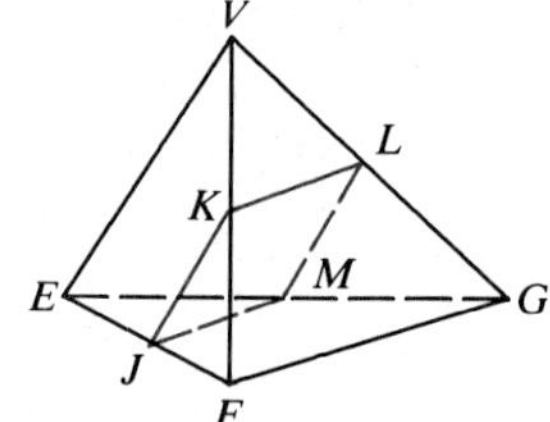

Using a Computer

Exs. 34–36 can be explored by using a construction program.

34. When the midpoints of the sides of quad. $ABCD$ are joined, rectangle $PQRS$ is formed.

a. Draw other quadrilaterals $ABCD$ with this property.

b. What must be true of quad. $ABCD$ if $PQRS$ is to be a rectangle? **The diagonals must be $\perp$.**

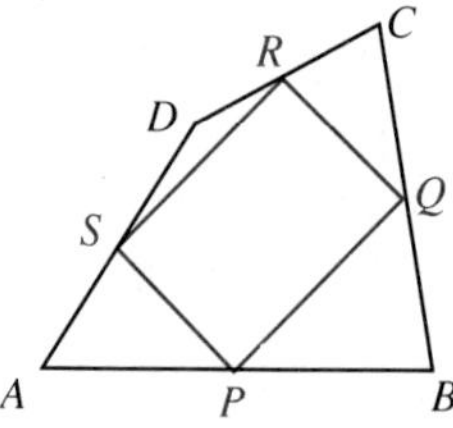

35. When the midpoints of the quad. $ABCD$ are joined, rhombus $PQRS$ is formed.

a. Draw other quadrilaterals $ABCD$ with this property.

b. What must be true of quad. $ABCD$ if $PQRS$ is to be a rhombus? **The diagonals must be $\cong$.**

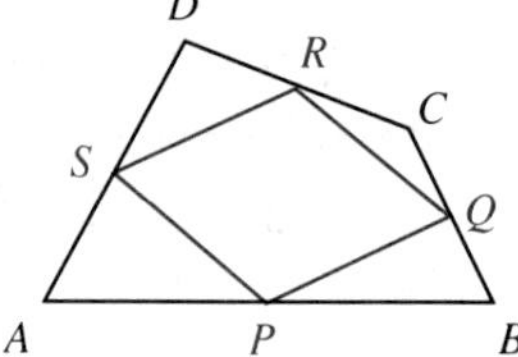

36. P, Q, R, and S are the midpoints of the sides of quad. $ABCD$. In this diagram $\overline{PR}$ and $\overline{SQ}$ have the same midpoint, point O. If you think this will be the case for *any* quad. $ABCD$, prove it. If not, tell what other information you need to know about quad. $ABCD$ before you can conclude that $\overline{PR}$ and $\overline{SQ}$ have the same midpoint. **O is the midpt. of $\overline{PR}$ and $\overline{SQ}$ for any quad. $ABCD$.**

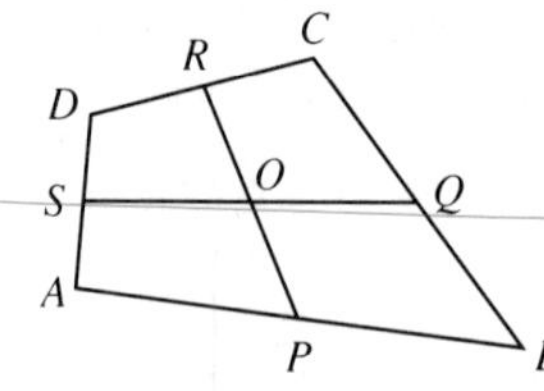

Challenge

The three-dimensional figure shown has six congruent edges. Draw four such figures. On your diagrams show how a plane can intersect the figure to form **(a)** a triangle with three congruent sides, **(b)** a triangle with sides not all congruent, **(c)** a rectangle, and **(d)** an isosceles trapezoid.

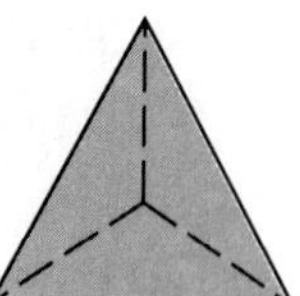

Explorations

These exploratory exercises can be done using a computer with a program that draws and measures geometric figures.

Draw any $\triangle ABC$. Label the midpoint of $\overline{AB}$ as D, of $\overline{AC}$ as E, and of $\overline{BC}$ as F.

Form a quadrilateral ($ABFE$, $BCED$, or $CADF$) by using two midpoints and two vertices.

What kind of quadrilateral is each of $ABFE$, $BCED$, and $CADF$? How do you know? **trapezoid**

Form a quadrilateral ($ADFE$, $BFED$, or $CEDF$) by using three midpoints and a vertex.

What kind of quadrilateral is each of $ADFE$, $BFED$, and $CEDF$? How do you know? **parallelogram**

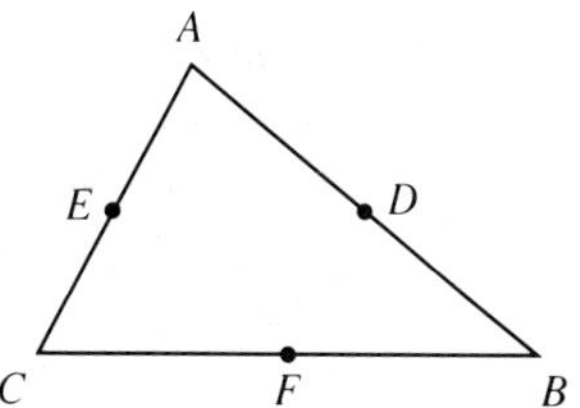

Self-Test 2

Quad. *WXYZ* must be a special figure to meet the conditions stated. Write the best name for that special quadrilateral.

1. $\overline{WX} \cong \overline{YZ}$ and $\overline{WX} \parallel \overline{YZ}$ ▱
2. $\overline{WX} \parallel \overline{YZ}$ and $\overline{WX} \ncong \overline{YZ}$ **trapezoid**
3. $\overline{WX} \cong \overline{YZ}$, $\overline{XY} \cong \overline{ZW}$, and diag. $\overline{WY} \cong$ diag. $\overline{XZ}$ **rectangle**
4. Diagonals $\overline{WY}$ and $\overline{XZ}$ are congruent and are perpendicular bisectors of each other. **square**
5. An isosceles trapezoid has sides of lengths 5, 8, 5, and 14. Find the length of the median. **11**
6. M is the midpoint of hypotenuse $\overline{AB}$. Find AM and $m\angle ACM$. **17, 67**

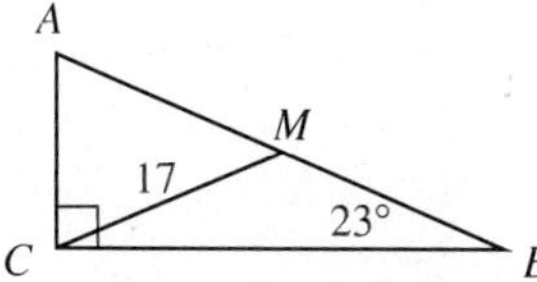

7. Given: $\angle 1 \cong \angle 2 \cong \angle 3 \cong \angle 4$
   Prove: $EFGH$ is a rhombus.

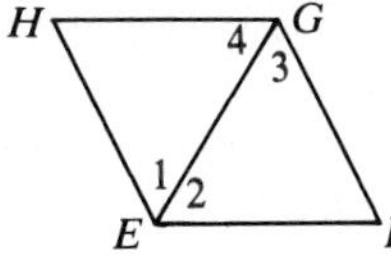

8. $PQRS$ is a ▱.
   a. If X is the midpoint of $\overline{PQ}$ and Y is the midpoint of $\overline{SR}$, what special kind of quadrilateral is $XQRY$? ▱
   b. Prove your answer to part (a).
   c. Draw a line through O intersecting $\overline{PQ}$ at J and $\overline{SR}$ at K. If J and K are not midpoints, what special kind of quadrilateral is $JQRK$? **trapezoid**

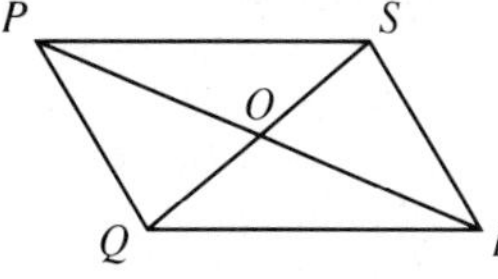

Using a Computer

This Exploration reinforces topics learned in Chapter 5.

Quick Quiz

Give the best name for special quad. $ABCD$ if it satisfies the conditions stated.

1. $\overline{AB} \parallel \overline{DC}$ and $\overline{AB} \perp \overline{AD}$ trapezoid
2. $\overline{AB} \cong \overline{DC}$, $\overline{AD} \cong \overline{BC}$, and $\overline{AB} \cong \overline{BC}$ rhombus
3. $\overline{AC} \cong \overline{BD}$, and $\overline{AC}$ and $\overline{BD}$ are $\perp$ bis. of each other. square
4. $\overline{AB} \parallel \overline{DC}$, $\overline{BC} \perp \overline{AB}$, and $\overline{AD} \perp \overline{AB}$ rectangle
5. An isosceles trapezoid has sides of length 7, 12, 7, and 22. Find the length of the median. 17
6. U is the midpoint of $\overline{RT}$. Find RU and $m\angle UST$. 11, 30

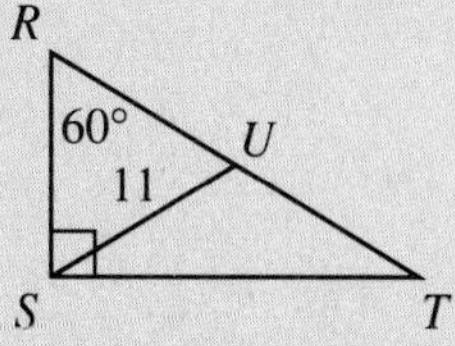

7. Given: Trapezoid $RSTU$ with median $\overline{VW}$

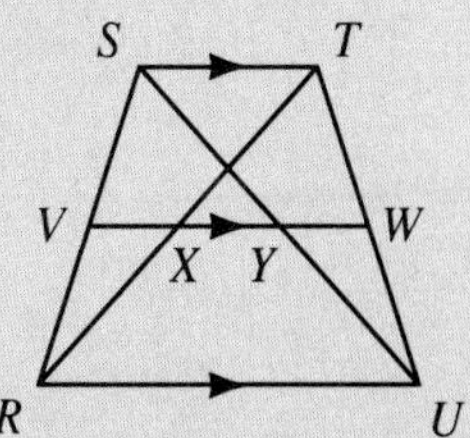

   a. If $ST = 10$ and $RU = 18$, find VX, XY, and YW. 5, 4, 5
   b. What is the relationship between VX and YW? They are =.

(continued)

c. Prove your answer to part (b). *VX* and *YW* both equal $\frac{1}{2}ST$.

Application Rhombuses

Many objects that need to change in size or shape are built in the shape of a rhombus. What makes this shape so useful is that if you keep the lengths of the sides the same, opposite sides remain parallel as you change the measures of the angles. A rhombus also has the property that as you change the measures of the angles, the vertices slide along the lines that contain the diagonals and the diagonals remain perpendicular. Two applications of this property are illustrated in the photographs below.

A rhombic shape can be used to support weight when the height of the object changes but the load must remain balanced. To use the jack shown above, you turn a crank. This brings the two hinges on the horizontal diagonal closer together and forces the hinges on the vertical diagonal farther apart, which lifts the car. Could a jack be in the shape of a parallelogram that is not a rhombus? Would a jack in the shape of a kite work?

The folding elevator gate shown at the right changes in width, but the vertical bars remain vertical. Some types of fireplace tongs can extend and retract in a similar way. Electric trains sometimes use rhombic arrangements to maintain contact with overhead wires even when the distance between the top of the coach and the wire changes. Can you think of other objects that use this property?

Additional Answers Application

No, a jack could not be in the shape of a ▱ that is not a rhombus since the diagonals are not ⊥.

Yes, a jack in the shape of a kite would work since the diagonals of a kite are ⊥.

Other objects: retractable children's gate, hanging mug rack.

Chapter Summary

1. A parallelogram has these properties:
   a. Opposite sides are parallel.
   b. Opposite sides are congruent.
   c. Opposite angles are congruent.
   d. Diagonals bisect each other.
2. The chart on page 172 lists five ways to prove that a quadrilateral is a parallelogram.
3. If two lines are parallel, then all points on one line are equidistant from the other line.
4. If three parallel lines cut off congruent segments on one transversal, then they cut off congruent segments on every transversal.
5. A line that contains the midpoint of one side of a triangle and is parallel to another side bisects the third side.
6. The segment that joins the midpoints of two sides of a triangle is parallel to the third side and has a length equal to half the length of the third side.
7. The midpoint of the hypotenuse of a right triangle is equidistant from all three vertices.
8. Rectangles, rhombuses, and squares are parallelograms with additional properties. Trapezoids and kites are not parallelograms, but are special quadrilaterals with additional properties.
9. The median of a trapezoid is parallel to the bases and has a length equal to half the sum of the lengths of the bases.

Chapter Review

In parallelogram *EFGH*, $m\angle EFG = 70$.

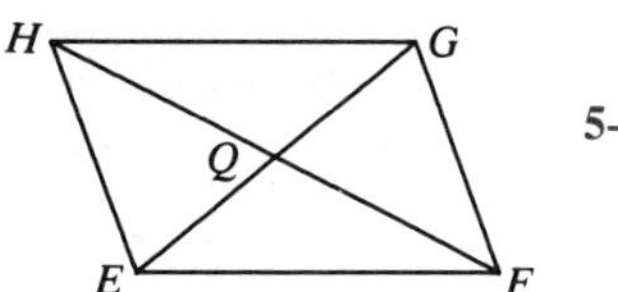

1. $m\angle HEF = \underline{\ ?\ }$ **110** 5–1
2. If $m\angle EFH = 32$, then $m\angle EHF = \underline{\ ?\ }$. **38**
3. If $HQ = 14$, then $HF = \underline{\ ?\ }$. **28**
4. If $EH = 8x - 7$ and $FG = 5x + 11$, then $x = \underline{\ ?\ }$. **6**

In each exercise you could prove that quad. *SANG* is a parallelogram if one more fact, in addition to those stated, were given. State that fact.

5. $GN = 9$; $NA = 5$; $SA = 9$ **$GS = 5$ or $\overline{SA} \parallel \overline{GN}$** 5–2
6. $\angle ASG \cong \angle GNA$ **$\angle SAN \cong \angle SGN$**
7. $\overline{SZ} \cong \overline{NZ}$ **$\overline{AZ} \cong \overline{GZ}$**
8. $\overline{SA} \parallel \overline{GN}$; $SA = 17$
   $GN = 17$

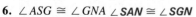

Supplementary Materials

Practice Master 29

Test 20

Resource Book, pp. 28–29, 128

State the principal theorem that justifies the statement about the diagram. 5–3

9. If $\overline{DE} \parallel \overline{BC}$, then D is the midpoint of $\overline{AB}$.
10. If D is the midpoint of $\overline{AB}$, then $\overline{DE} \parallel \overline{BC}$.
11. If D is the midpoint of $\overline{AB}$, then $DE = 6$.

9. Thm. 5-10
10. Thm. 5-11 (1)
11. Thm. 5-11 (2)

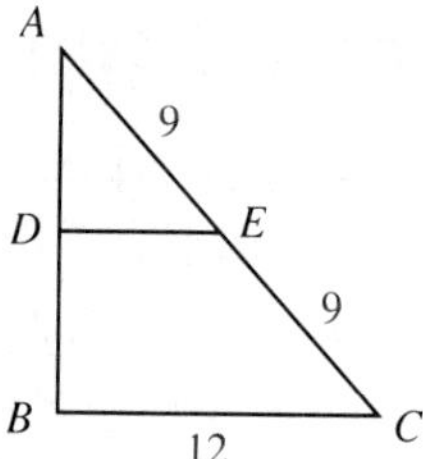

12. Given: $\square CDEF$; S and T are the midpoints of $\overline{EF}$ and $\overline{ED}$.
    Prove: $\overline{SR} \cong \overline{FD}$

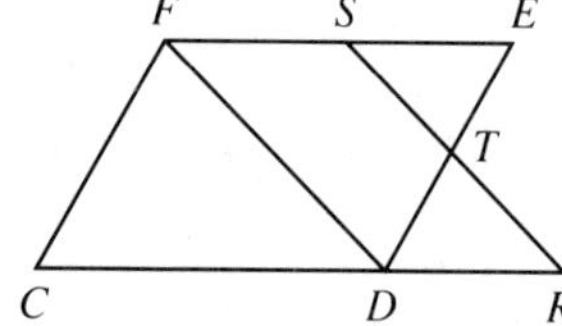

Give the most descriptive name for quad. *MNOP*. 5–4

13. $\overline{MN} \cong \overline{PO}$; $\overline{MN} \parallel \overline{PO}$ **parallelogram**
14. $\overline{MN} \parallel \overline{PO}$; $\overline{NO} \parallel \overline{MP}$; $\overline{MO} \perp \overline{NP}$ **rhombus**
15. $\angle M \cong \angle N \cong \angle O \cong \angle P$ **rectangle**
16. *MNOP* is a rectangle with $MN = NO$. **square**

17. Given: *ABCD* is a rhombus; $DE = BF$
    Prove: *AECF* is a rhombus.

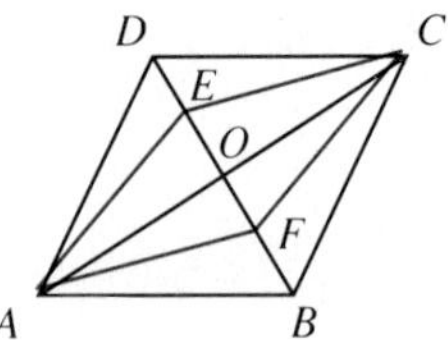

Draw and label a diagram. List, in terms of the diagram, what is given and what is to be proved. Then write a proof.

18. $\overline{PX}$ and $\overline{QY}$ are altitudes of acute $\triangle PQR$, and Z is the midpoint of $\overline{PQ}$. Prove that $\triangle XYZ$ is isosceles.

$\overline{MN}$ is the median of trapezoid *ZOID*. **$\overline{ZO}$, $\overline{DI}$** 5–5

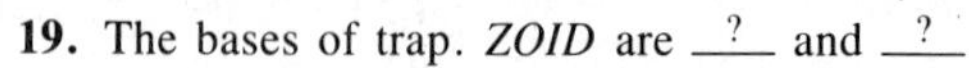

19. The bases of trap. *ZOID* are __?__ and __?__.
20. If $ZO = 8$ and $MN = 11$, then $DI =$ __?__. **14**
21. If $ZO = 8$, then $TN =$ __?__. **4**
22. If trap. *ZOID* is isosceles and $m\angle D = 80$, then $m\angle O =$ __?__. **100**

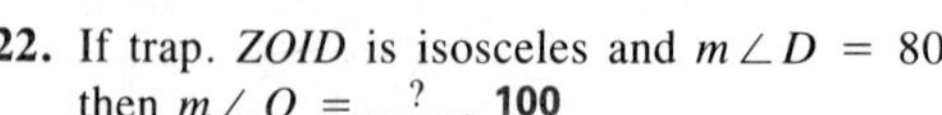

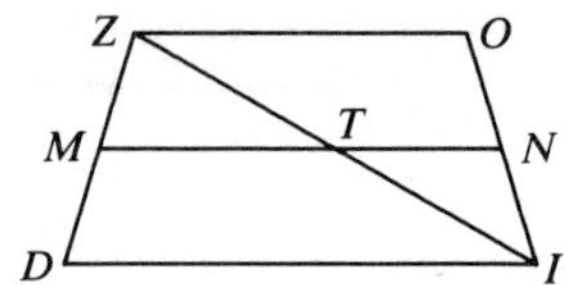

Chapter Test

Complete each statement with the word *always*, *sometimes*, or *never*.

1. A square is ___?___ a rectangle. **always**
2. A rectangle is ___?___ a rhombus. **sometimes**
3. A rhombus is ___?___ a square. **sometimes**
4. A rhombus is ___?___ a parallelogram. **always**
5. A trapezoid ___?___ has three congruent sides. **sometimes**
6. The diagonals of a trapezoid ___?___ bisect each other. **never**
7. The diagonals of a rectangle are ___?___ congruent. **always**
8. The diagonals of a parallelogram ___?___ bisect the angles. **sometimes**

Trapezoid *ABCD* has median $\overline{MN}$.

9. If $DC = 42$ and $MN = 35$, then $AB =$ ___?___. **28**
10. If $FC = 9$, then $EN =$ ___?___. **$4\frac{1}{2}$**
11. If $AB = 5j + 7k$ and $DC = 9j - 3k$, then $MN =$ ___?___. **$7j + 2k$**

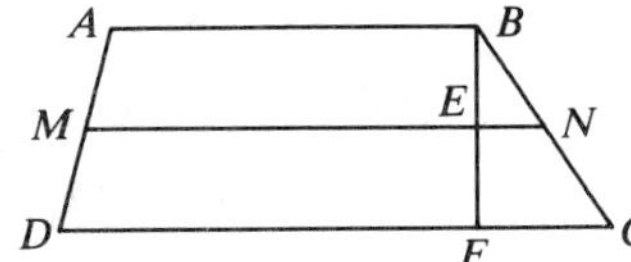

Can you deduce from the given information that quad. *ABCD* is a parallelogram? If so, what theorem can you use?

12. $\angle ADC \cong \angle CBA$ and $\angle BAD \cong \angle DCB$
13. $\overline{AD} \parallel \overline{BC}$ and $\overline{AD} \cong \overline{BC}$
14. $AT = CT$ and $DT = \frac{1}{2}DB$
15. $\overline{AB}$, $\overline{BC}$, $\overline{CD}$, and $\overline{DA}$ are all congruent.

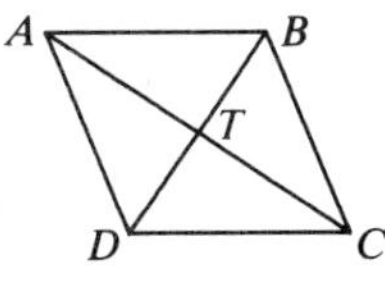

16. $\overline{RE}$ is an altitude of $\triangle RST$. Find MN, NE, and RT.

$MN = 14$, $NE = 15$, $RT = 26$

17. $l \parallel m \parallel n$ Find the values of x, y, and z.

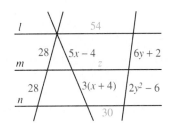

$x = 8$, $y = 4$, $z = 42$

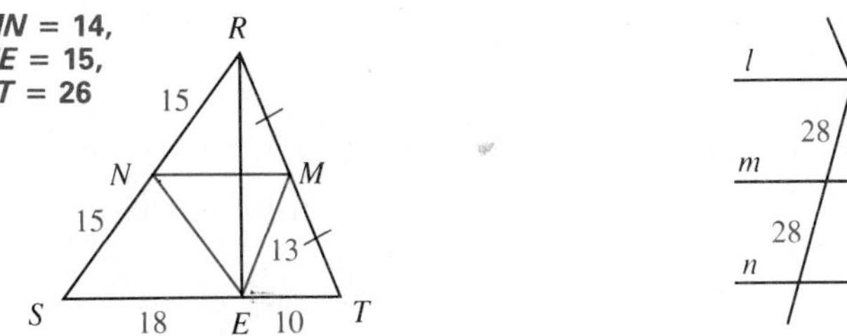

18. Given: ▱*PQRS*; $PA = RB$
Prove: $AS = BQ$

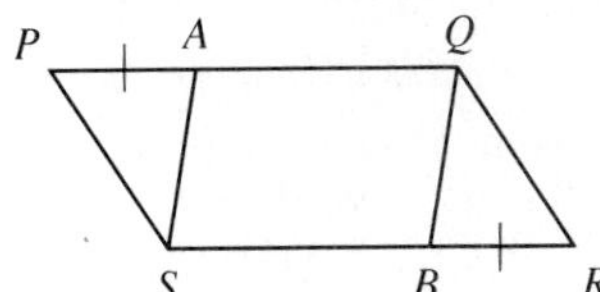

19. Given: $\overline{PR} \parallel \overline{VO}$; $\overline{RO} \parallel \overline{PV}$; $\overline{PR} \cong \overline{RO}$
Prove: $\angle 1$ and $\angle 2$ are complementary.

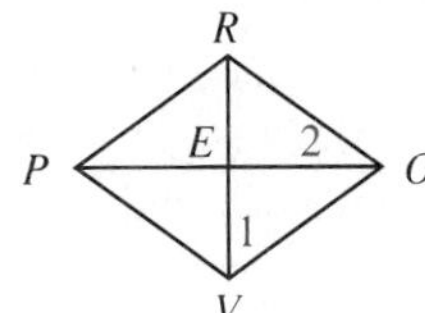

Teaching References

Alternate Test, p. T16

Additional Answers Chapter Test

12. Yes; if both pairs of opp. ∠s of a quad. are ≅, then the quad. is a ▱.
13. Yes; if one pair of opp. sides of a quad. are both ∥ and ≅, then the quad. is a ▱.
14. Yes; if the diag. of a quad. bisect each other, then the quad. is a ▱.
15. Yes; if both pairs of opp. sides of a quad. are ≅, then the quad. is a ▱.

Supplementary Materials

Test 21

Resource Book, pp. 30–32, 129, 175–176, 194

Cumulative Review: Chapters 1–5

A 1. Given two parallel lines n and k, how many planes contain n and k? **one**

2. a. Is it possible for two lines to be neither intersecting nor parallel? If so, what are the lines called? **Yes; skew**

   b. Repeat part (a), replacing *lines* with *planes*. **No**

3. Write the converse of the statement: If you are a member of the skiing club, then you enjoy winter weather. **If you enjoy winter weather, then you are a member of the skiing club.**

4. On a number line, point A has a coordinate -5 and B has a coordinate 3. Find the coordinate of the midpoint of $\overline{AB}$. **-1**

5. Name the property that justifies the statement: If $\angle 1 \cong \angle 2$ and $\angle 2 \cong \angle 3$, then $\angle 1 \cong \angle 3$. **Transitive Prop.**

In Exercises 6–10, complete each statement about the diagram. Then state the definition, postulate, or theorem that justifies your answer.

6. $m\angle 1 + m\angle 2 + m\angle 3 =$ __?__ **180**

7. $m\angle 1 + m\angle 4 =$ __?__ **180**

8. $m\angle 1 + m\angle 2 = m\angle$ __?__ **5**

9. If $\overleftrightarrow{EC} \parallel \overleftrightarrow{BD}$, then $\angle 7 \cong$ __?__. **$\angle 1$**

10. If $\angle 2 \cong \angle 3$, then $\overline{EC} \cong$ __?__. **$\overline{EB}$**

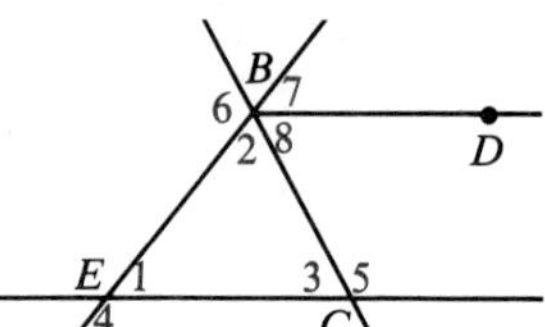

Complete each statement.

11. The median to the base of an isosceles triangle __?__ the vertex angle and is __?__ to the base. **bisects, ⊥**

12. a. If a point lies on the perpendicular bisector of $\overline{AB}$, then the point is equidistant from __?__. ***A* and *B***

    b. If a point lies on the bisector of $\angle RST$, then the point is equidistant from __?__. **$\overrightarrow{SR}$ and $\overrightarrow{ST}$**

13. Suppose $\triangle ART \cong \triangle DEB$.

    a. $\triangle EBD \cong$ __?__ **$\triangle RTA$** b. $\overline{AT} \cong$ __?__ **$\overline{DB}$** c. $m\angle R =$ __?__ **$m\angle E$**

14. If a regular polygon has 40 sides, the measure of each interior angle is __?__. **171**

15. When two parallel lines are cut by a transversal, a pair of corresponding angles have measures $2x + 50$ and $3x$. The measures of the angles are __?__ and __?__. **150, 150**

B 16. In $\triangle SUN$, $\angle S \cong \angle N$. Given that $SU = 2x + 7$, $UN = 4x - 1$, and $SN = 3x + 4$, find the numerical length of each side. **15, 15, 16**

17. M and N are the midpoints of the legs of trapezoid $EFGH$. If bases $\overline{EF}$ and $\overline{HG}$ have lengths $2r + s$ and $4r - 3s$, express the length of $\overline{MN}$ in terms of r and s. **$3r - s$**

Additional Answers Cumulative Review

6. The sum of the meas. of the ∆s of a △ is 180.
7. Angle Add. Post.
8. The meas. of an ext. ∠ of a △ equals the sum of the meas. of the 2 remote int. ∆s.
9. If 2 ∥ lines are cut by a trans., then corr. ∆s are ≅.
10. If 2 ∆s of a △ are ≅, then the sides opp. those ∆s are ≅.

Given: *ABCD* is a parallelogram;
$\overline{AD} \cong \overline{AC}$; $\overline{AE} \cong \overline{EC}$
$\angle ADF \cong \angle CDF$; $m\angle DAC = 36$
Complete each statement about the diagram.

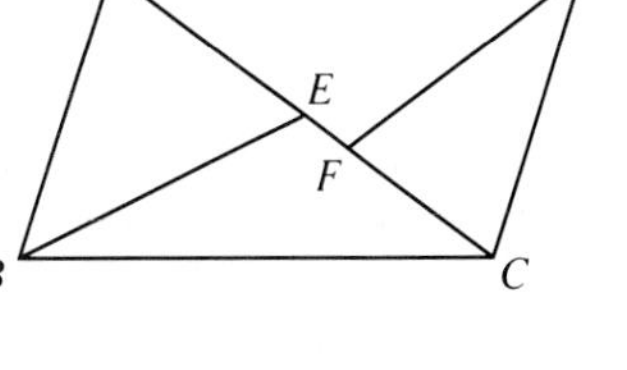

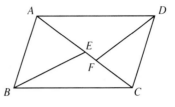

18. $\overline{AE} \cong \overline{EC}$, so $\overline{BE}$ is a(n) __?__ of $\triangle ABC$. **median**

19. $\angle ADF \cong \angle CDF$, so $\overline{DF}$ is a(n) __?__ of $\angle ADC$. **bisector**

20. $\triangle ADC$ is a(n) __?__ triangle. **isosceles**

21. $m\angle DAC = 36$, so $m\angle ADC =$ __?__ and $m\angle ADF =$ __?__. **72, 36**

22. $\triangle ADF$ is a(n) __?__ triangle. **isosceles**

23. $\angle ADC \cong \angle$ __?__ $\cong \angle$ __?__ $\cong \angle$ __?__ $\cong \angle$ __?__. ***ABC, BAC, ACD, CFD***

In the diagram, $m\angle VOZ = 90$.
$\overline{OW}$ is an altitude of $\triangle VOZ$.
$\overline{OX}$ bisects $\angle VOZ$.
$\overline{OY}$ is a median of $\triangle VOZ$.
Find the measures of the four numbered angles.

24. $m\angle Z = 30$
$m\angle 1 = m\angle 4 = 30$, $m\angle 2 = m\angle 3 = 15$

25. $m\angle Z = k$
$m\angle 1 = m\angle 4 = k$, $m\angle 2 = m\angle 3 = 45 - k$

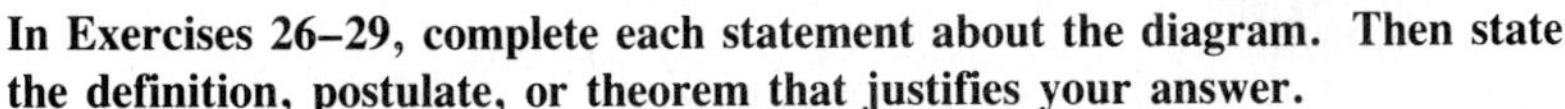

In Exercises 26–29, complete each statement about the diagram. Then state the definition, postulate, or theorem that justifies your answer.

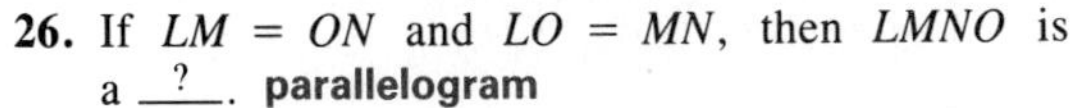

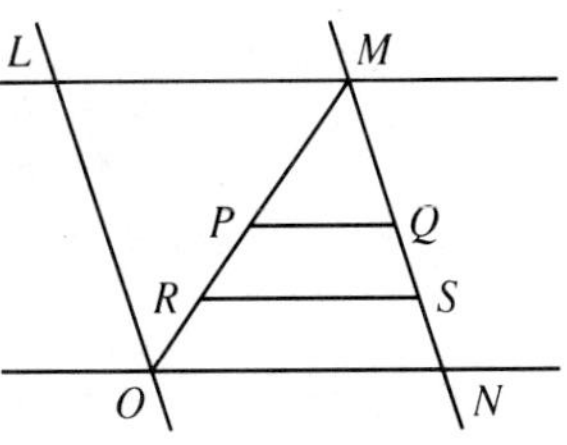

26. If $LM = ON$ and $LO = MN$, then *LMNO* is a __?__. **parallelogram**

27. If *LMNO* is a rhombus, then $\angle LOM \cong$ __?__ $\cong$ __?__ $\cong$ __?__. ***∠NOM, ∠LMO, ∠NMO***

28. If $MP = PO$ and $\overline{PQ} \parallel \overline{ON}$, then Q is the __?__ of __?__. **midpoint, *MN***

29. If $\overline{PQ} \parallel \overline{ON}$, $PR = RO$ and $QS = SN$, then $RS = \frac{1}{2}$(__?__ + __?__). ***PQ, ON***

30. Given: $WP = ZP$; $PY = PX$
Prove: $\angle WXY \cong \angle ZYX$

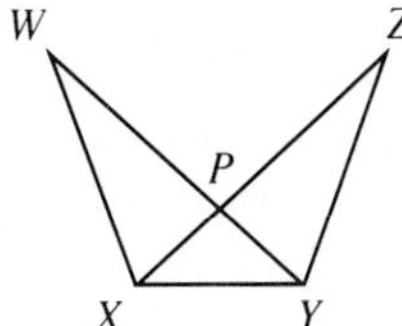

31. Given: $\overline{AD} \cong \overline{BC}$; $\overline{AD} \parallel \overline{BC}$
Prove: $\overline{EF} \cong \overline{FG}$

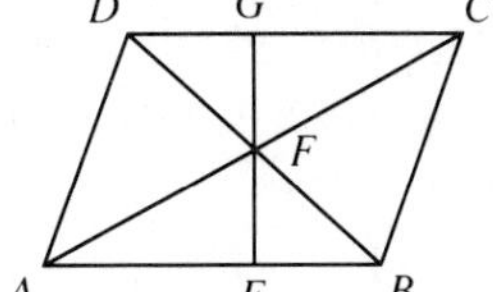

Additional Answers Cumulative Review

26. If both pairs of opp. sides of a quad. are ≅, then the quad. is a ▱.

27. Each diag. of a rhombus bisects two ∠s of the rhombus.

28. A line that contains the midpt. of one side of a △ and is ∥ to another side passes through the midpt. of the third side.

29. The median of a trapezoid has a length equal to the average of the base lengths.

6 Inequalities in Geometry

Objectives

6-1 Apply properties of inequality to positive numbers, lengths of segments, and measures of angles.

State and use the Exterior Angle Inequality Theorem.

6-2 State the contrapositive and inverse of an if-then statement.

Understand the relationship between logically equivalent statements.

Draw correct conclusions from given statements.

6-3 Write indirect proofs in paragraph form.

6-4 State and apply the inequality theorems and corollaries for one triangle.

6-5 State and apply the inequality theorems for two triangles.

Assignment Guide

See page T40 for information about the Assignment Guide.

Day	Minimum Course	Average Course	Maximum Course
1	**6-1** 206–207/1–6, 8	**6-1** 206–207/1–9	**6-1** 206–207/1–13 odd
2	**6-2** 210–211/2, 4, 6–8 S 206/7	**6-2** 210–211/3–9, 11 S 207/10	**6-2** 210–211/3, 5–8, 10, 12, 15
3	**6-2** 210–211/3, 5, 9, 11, 13 212/Mixed Review 1–9	**6-2** 211–212/12, 13, 15, 16, 18, 19 212/Mixed Review 1–9	**6-2** 211–212/11, 13, 16, 17, 20–22
4	**6-3** 216/1–8	**6-3** 216/1–10	**6-3** 216–217/2, 4–6, 9, 10, 13 S 212/18, 19
5	**6-3** 216–217/9–13 218/Self-Test 1	**6-3** 217/11, 13, 15–18 218/Self-Test 1	**6-3** 217/11, 15–20
6	**6-4** 222/1–9	**6-4** 222–223/1, 4–7, 10, 13, 16, 19	**6-4** 222–223/4, 9, 12, 13, 15–17, 19, 21, 23
7	**6-4** 222–223/10–16	**6-5** 231/1–8 S 223/14, 17	**6-5** 231–232/1–15 odd S 223/20, 22
8	**6-5** 231/1–8 S 223/17	**6-5** 232/9–13 233/Self-Test 2	**6-5** 236–237/Chapter Test Test, page T17
9	**6-5** 232/9–12 233/Self-Test 2	**6-5** 236–237/Chapter Test Test, page T17	
10	**6-5** 236–237/Chapter Test Test, page T17		

Supplementary Materials Guide

For Use after Lesson	Practice Masters	Tests	Study Guide (Reteaching)	Resource Book: Tests	Resource Book: Practice Exercises	Resource Book: Prep. for College Entrance Exams (Col) Enrichment (E)	Computer Activities
6-1			pp. 69–70				
6-2	Sheet 30		pp. 71–72				
6-3	Sheet 31	Test 22	pp. 73–74	p. 33	p. 130		
6-4	Sheet 32		pp. 75–76				Activity 12
6-5	Sheet 33	Test 23	pp. 77–78	p. 34	p. 131		
Chapter 6	Sheet 34	Test 24		pp. 35–36	p. 132	p. 195 (Col) p. 216 (E)	
Chapters 5–6	Sheets 35, 36						

Overhead Visuals

Guided Discovery Visuals (lettered) and Teaching Visuals (numbered) available for Chapter 6.

Lessons	Visual	Title
6-1, 6-2, 6-3	12	Summary of Related If-Then Statements
6-4, 6-5	13	The "Hinge" Theorems

Software Guide

Houghton Mifflin software for Chapter 6

Geometry Grapher (Apple or IBM)

Use with	Booklet
p. 219 (Theorem 6-2)	Classroom Demonstration, p. 15

Test Generator (Apple or IBM): 75 test items

Other software appropriate for Chapter 6

Geometric Supposer (Apple): Triangles

GeoDraw (IBM)

Guide to Integrated Curriculum

Teachers wishing to integrate coordinate and transformational geometry throughout the course can use the following lessons after Chapter 6. See pages T56–T57 and 657 for more information.

Handbook: Minimal Paths, pp. 662–664

Exploring Indirect Proof

When to Use

Before or with Lesson 6-3

Overview

In this activity students explore indirect proof by considering the number of acute angles of triangles and quadrilaterals.

Description of Activity

Guide students through the exploration by using the following activities and questions. Encourage students to draw many diagrams.

1. How many acute angles can a triangle have? three

- **a.** Can you draw a triangle that has three acute angles? If you can, draw one. If you can't, try to explain why you can't. Can the acute angles be congruent? yes; yes
- **b.** Can you draw a triangle that has exactly two acute angles? If you can, draw one. If you can't, try to explain why you can't. Can the acute angles be congruent? yes; yes
- **c.** Can you draw a triangle that has exactly one acute angle? If you can, draw one. If you can't, try to explain why you can't. no

2. How many acute angles can a convex quadrilateral have? three

- **a.** Can you draw a convex quadrilateral that has exactly one acute angle? If you can, draw one. If you can't, try to explain why you can't. yes
- **b.** Can you draw a convex quadrilateral that has exactly two acute angles? If you can, draw one. If you can't, try to explain why you can't. Can the acute angles be congruent? yes; yes
- **c.** Can you draw a convex quadrilateral that has exactly three acute angles? If you can, draw one. If you can't, try to explain why you can't. Can the acute angles be congruent? yes; yes
- **d.** Can you draw a convex quadrilateral that has four acute angles? If you can, draw one. If you can't, try to explain why you can't. no

3. Repeat Activity 2 for the five cases of a convex pentagon. **a.** yes **b.** yes; yes **c.** yes; yes **d.** no **e.** no

Commentary

- This activity can be used with a large group or small groups where students compare their drawings and try to explain, in their own words, why **1c, 2d, 3d,** and **3e** are impossible. Care must be taken that students do not "pick up" any incorrect ideas about indirect proof in their small groups.
- If necessary, remind the students of the definition of convex before beginning **2** and **3.**
- **1.** Part **c** could lead into the format for an indirect proof given on page 214. Temporarily assume there is a triangle, $\triangle ABC$, with exactly one acute angle, $\angle A$. Then its other two angles, $\angle B$ and $\angle C$, must be right or obtuse. Thus $m\angle B + m\angle C \geq 90 + 90 = 180$. But this contradicts the fact that $m\angle A + m\angle B + m\angle C = 180$. Therefore the temporary assumption must be false and no triangle can have exactly one acute angle.
- **2.** Some students may think part **c** is impossible because they are thinking of parallelograms whose opposite angles are congruent. A kite is a good example. Part **d** is impossible since the sum of the angles of a convex quadrilateral is 360.

• **3.** Some students may conjecture that there could be four acute angles in a convex pentagon since there could be two in a triangle and three in a quadrilateral. If there were four acute angles in a pentagon, their sum would be less than 360, meaning the fifth angle must exceed $540 - 360 = 180$—a contradiction. If there were five acute angles, their sum would be less than 450, but the sum must be $(n - 2)180 = 540$.

Variations and Extensions

Try the activity for convex n-gons with $n = 6, 7, 8, \ldots$. Most students will not expect to find that there can be at most three acute angles in a convex n-gon.

References to Strategies

PE: Pupil's Edition **TE:** Teacher's Edition **RB:** Resource Book

Problem Solving Strategies

PE: 207 (Generalize from examples), 217 (Challenge, make a deductive argument), 224, 226 (Mathematical model)
TE: 207 (Solve a simpler problem)

Applications

PE: 202 (Crystallography), 213 (Cartographer), 224 (Find the shortest path)
TE: T97

Nonroutine Problems

PE: 207 (Challenge), 217 (Challenge), 221 (Ex. 13), 223 (Exs. 20, 23), 225 (Application), 230 (Exs. 9, 10), 231 (Exs. 1, 2), 232 (Exs. 12, 15), 233–234 (Non-Euclidean geometry), 663–664 (Exs. 1–5)
TE: T98, T99, T100
RB: 216

Communication

PE: 208–209 (Venn diagrams)
TE: T98, T99, 209

Thinking Skills

PE: 208–209 (Logical equivalence), 214–215 (Indirect proof, proof by contrapositive)
TE: 209 (Recognize invalid arguments), 215 (Logic), 221 (Interpret and analyze diagrams), 228

Explorations

PE: 225
TE: 201c

Connections

PE: 203–233 (Inequalities), 213 (Cartography), 233–234 (Non-Euclidean geometry, Bolyai, Gauss, Riemann), 237 (Fractions), 662–664 (Coordinate and transformational geometry)
TE: T97, T98–T99, T100, 224 (Transformations), 229 (Converses)

Using Technology

PE: 225, 226–227
TE: T99–T100, 220, 225, 226
Using Geometry Grapher: 15
Computer Activities: 27–28

Using Manipulatives/Models

PE: 207 (Challenge), 224, 226, 228, 234
TE: T96, T99, 221
RB: 216
Overhead Visuals: 12, 13

Cooperative Learning

TE: T97, 217

Teaching Resources

For use in implementing the teaching strategies referenced on the previous page.

Communication/Thinking Skills
***Resource Book*, p. 204**

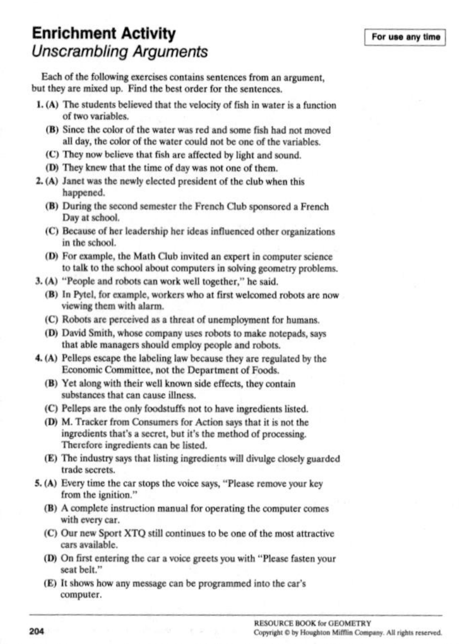

Enrichment Activity
Unscrambling Arguments

For use any time

Each of the following exercises contains sentences from an argument, but they are mixed up. Find the best order for the sentences.

1. (A) The students believed that the velocity of fish in water is a function of two variables.
   (B) Since the color of the water was red and some fish had not moved all day, the color of the water could not be one of the variables.
   (C) They now believe that fish are affected by light and sound.
   (D) They knew that the time of day was not one of them.
2. (A) Janet was the newly elected president of the club when this happened.
   (B) During the second semester the French Club sponsored a French Day at school.
   (C) Because of her leadership her ideas influenced other organizations in the school.
   (D) For example, the Math Club invited an expert in computer science to talk to the school about computers in solving geometry problems.
3. (A) "People and robots can work well together," he said.
   (B) In Pytel, for example, workers who at first welcomed robots are now viewing them with alarm.
   (C) Robots are perceived as a threat of unemployment for humans.
   (D) David Smith, whose company uses robots to make notepads, says that able managers should employ people and robots.
4. (A) Pelleps escape the labeling law because they are regulated by the Economic Committee, not the Department of Foods.
   (B) Yet along with their well known side effects, they contain substances that can cause illness.
   (C) Pelleps are the only foodstuffs not to have ingredients listed.
   (D) M. Tracker from Consumers for Action says that it is not the ingredients that's a secret, but it's the method of processing. Therefore ingredients can be listed.
   (E) The industry says that listing ingredients will divulge closely guarded trade secrets.
5. (A) Every time the car stops the voice says, "Please remove your key from the ignition."
   (B) A complete instruction manual for operating the computer comes with every car.
   (C) Our new Sport XTQ still continues to be one of the most attractive cars available.
   (D) On first entering the car a voice greets you with "Please fasten your seat belt."
   (E) It shows how any message can be programmed into the car's computer.

204 RESOURCE BOOK for GEOMETRY

Using Models
***Resource Book*, p. 216**

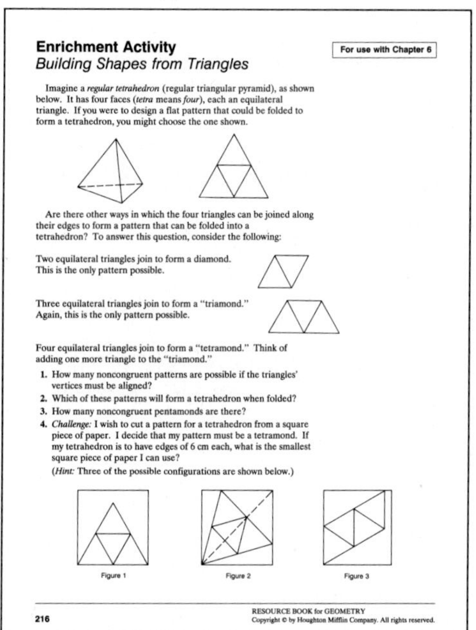

Enrichment Activity
Building Shapes from Triangles

For use with Chapter 6

Imagine a *regular tetrahedron* (regular triangular pyramid), as shown below. It has four faces (*tetra* means *four*), each an equilateral triangle. If you were to design a flat pattern that could be folded to form a tetrahedron, you might choose the one shown.

Are there other ways in which the four triangles can be joined along their edges to form a pattern that can be folded into a tetrahedron? To answer this question, consider the following:

Two equilateral triangles join to form a diamond. This is the only pattern possible.

Three equilateral triangles join to form a "triamond." Again, this is the only pattern possible.

Four equilateral triangles join to form a "tetramond." Think of adding one more triangle to the "triamond."

1. How many noncongruent patterns are possible if the triangles' vertices must be aligned?
2. Which of these patterns will form a tetrahedron when folded?
3. How many noncongruent pentamonds are there?
4. *Challenge:* I wish to cut a pattern for a tetrahedron from a square piece of paper. I decide that my pattern must be a tetramond. If my tetrahedron is to have edges of 6 cm each, what is the smallest square piece of paper I can use?
   (*Hint:* Three of the possible configurations are shown below.)

Figure 1 Figure 2 Figure 3

216 RESOURCE BOOK for GEOMETRY

Communication/Thinking Skills
***Study Guide*, p. 73**

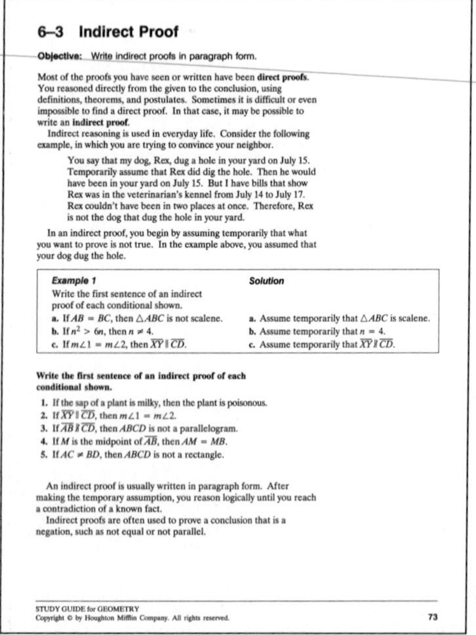

6–3 Indirect Proof

Objective: Write indirect proofs in paragraph form.

Most of the proofs you have seen or written have been **direct proofs.** You reasoned directly from the given to the conclusion, using definitions, theorems, and postulates. Sometimes it is difficult or even impossible to find a direct proof. In that case, it may be possible to write an **indirect proof.**

Indirect reasoning is used in everyday life. Consider the following example, in which you are trying to convince your neighbor.

> You say that my dog, Rex, dug a hole in your yard on July 15. Temporarily assume that Rex did dig the hole. Then he would have been in your yard on July 15. But I have bills that show Rex was in the veterinarian's kennel from July 14 to July 17. Rex couldn't have been in two places at once. Therefore, Rex is not the dog that dug the hole in your yard.

In an indirect proof, you begin by assuming temporarily that what you want to prove is not true. In the example above, you assumed that your dog dug the hole.

Example 1 Write the first sentence of an indirect proof of each conditional shown.	*Solution*
a. If $AB = BC$, then $\triangle ABC$ is not scalene.	a. Assume temporarily that $\triangle ABC$ is scalene.
b. If $n^2 > 6n$, then $n \neq 4$.	b. Assume temporarily that $n = 4$.
c. If $m\angle 1 = m\angle 2$, then $\overline{XY} \parallel \overline{CD}$.	c. Assume temporarily that $\overline{XY} \nparallel \overline{CD}$.

Write the first sentence of an indirect proof of each conditional shown.

1. If the sap of a plant is milky, then the plant is poisonous.
2. If $\overline{XY} \parallel \overline{CD}$, then $m\angle 1 = m\angle 2$.
3. If $\overline{AB} \nparallel \overline{CD}$, then $ABCD$ is not a parallelogram.
4. If M is the midpoint of $\overline{AB}$, then $AM = MB$.
5. If $AC \neq BD$, then $ABCD$ is not a rectangle.

An indirect proof is usually written in paragraph form. After making the temporary assumption, you reason logically until you reach a contradiction of a known fact.

Indirect proofs are often used to prove a conclusion that is a negation, such as not equal or not parallel.

STUDY GUIDE for GEOMETRY
 73

Communication/Thinking Skills
***Study Guide*, p. 74**

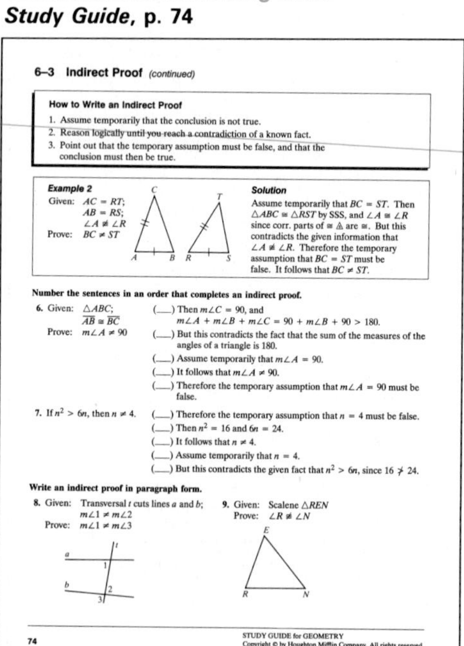

6–3 Indirect Proof *(continued)*

How to Write an Indirect Proof
1. Assume temporarily that the conclusion is not true.
2. Reason logically until you reach a contradiction of a known fact.
3. Point out that the temporary assumption must be false, and that the conclusion must then be true.

Example 2
Given: $AC = RT$; $AB = RS$; $\angle A \ncong \angle R$
Prove: $BC \neq ST$

Solution
Assume temporarily that $BC = ST$. Then $\triangle ABC \cong \triangle RST$ by SSS, and $\angle A \cong \angle R$ since corr. parts of $\cong$ △ are $\cong$. But this contradicts the given information that $\angle A \ncong \angle R$. Therefore the temporary assumption that $BC = ST$ must be false. It follows that $BC \neq ST$.

Number the sentences in an order that completes an indirect proof.

6. Given: $\triangle ABC$; $\overline{AB} \cong \overline{BC}$
   Prove: $m\angle A \neq 90$
   (___) Then $m\angle C = 90$, and $m\angle A + m\angle B + m\angle C = 90 + m\angle B + 90 > 180$.
   (___) But this contradicts the fact that the sum of the measures of the angles of a triangle is 180.
   (___) Assume temporarily that $m\angle A = 90$.
   (___) It follows that $m\angle A \neq 90$.
   (___) Therefore the temporary assumption that $m\angle A = 90$ must be false.
7. If $n^2 > 6n$, then $n \neq 4$.
   (___) Therefore the temporary assumption that $n = 4$ must be false.
   (___) Then $n^2 = 16$ and $6n = 24$.
   (___) It follows that $n \neq 4$.
   (___) Assume temporarily that $n = 4$.
   (___) But this contradicts the given fact that $n^2 > 6n$, since $16 \ngtr 24$.

Write an indirect proof in paragraph form.

8. Given: Transversal t cuts lines a and b; $m\angle 1 \neq m\angle 2$
   Prove: $m\angle 1 \neq m\angle 3$
9. Given: Scalene $\triangle REN$
   Prove: $\angle R \ncong \angle N$

74 STUDY GUIDE for GEOMETRY

Exploration/Using Technology
Computer Activities, p. 27

ACTIVITY 12. ***Triangle Inequality*** (for use with Lesson 6-4)

Directions: Write all answers in the spaces provided.

PROBLEM

Given the lengths of three segments, determine whether or not they would form a triangle.

PROGRAM

```
10  PRINT "ENTER THE LENGTHS OF THE SEGMENTS"
20  PRINT "SEPARATED BY A COMMA"
30  INPUT D,E,F
40  IF D + E < = F THEN 90
50  IF D + F < = E THEN 90
60  IF E + F < = D THEN 90
70  PRINT "THESE SEGMENTS COULD FORM A TRIANGLE"
80  GOTO 100
90  PRINT "THESE SEGMENTS COULD NOT FORM A TRIANGLE"
100 END
```

PROGRAM CHECK

Type in the program. After the question mark enter 5, 6, 7. The computer should print

THESE SEGMENTS COULD FORM A TRIANGLE

USING THE PROGRAM

Given the lengths of three segments, use the program to determine whether or not they would form a triangle. If they form a triangle, describe it. (For example, 5, 6, and 7 are the sides of a *scalene acute* triangle.)

	Triangle? (yes or no)	*Kind of triangle*
1. 1, 2, 3	______	______________
2. 1, 1, 1	______	______________
3. 8, 2, 5	______	______________
4. 8, 8, 0.001	______	______________
5. 15, 8, 9	______	______________
6. 7, 15, 15.001	______	______________

(continued)

Exploration/Using Technology
Computer Activities, p. 28

(Activity 12 continued)

ANALYSIS

The program uses the Triangle Inequality theorem in order to decide whether or not a triangle would be formed. The theorem says that the sum of the lengths of any two sides of a triangle is greater than the length of the third side. In lines 40, 50, and 60 two sides are added and compared with the third side. If the sum is less than or equal to the remaining side, then the program is sent to line 90, which prints that a triangle could not be formed. If the sum is greater than the third side in all three lines, then line 70 is executed.

EXTENSION

An extension of the Triangle Inequality theorem is a problem of the following type:

If the lengths of two sides of a triangle are 5 and 8, the length of the third side must be greater than ____, and it must be less than ____.

In order to use the computer to answer this question you must enter a new program.

```
10 PRINT "WHAT ARE THE TWO KNOWN LENGTHS";
20 INPUT A,B
30 LET G = ABS(A - B)
40 LET L = A + B
50 PRINT "THE THIRD SIDE MUST BE > ";G;" AND < ";L
60 END
```

Use this program to answer the following questions.

1. The lengths of two sides of a triangle are 7 and 13. Between what two numbers does the length of the third side lie? __________

2. The lengths of two sides of a triangle are 1 and 23. Between what two numbers does the length of the third side lie? __________

3. The lengths of two sides of a triangle are 8 and 8. Between what two numbers does the length of the third side lie? __________

CHALLENGE

Change the program above to find the answer to the following type of problem:

The lengths of three sides of a quadrilateral are 4, 7, and 10. Between what two numbers does the length of the fourth side lie? *Hint:* Make sure you subtract the smaller numbers from the larger.

Communication/Thinking Skills
Teaching Visual 12

TEACHING VISUAL 12
(for use with Lessons 6-1 through 6-3, especially page 209)

SUMMARY OF RELATED IF-THEN STATEMENTS

Statement: If p, then q.
Contrapositive: If not q, then not p.

A statement and its contrapositive are logically equivalent.

Converse: If q, then p.
Inverse: If not p, then not q.

The converse and inverse of a statement are logically equivalent.

A statement is *not* logically equivalent to its converse or to its inverse.

DRAWING CONCLUSIONS FROM IF-THEN STATEMENTS

	Model 1	Example 1
Given:	If p, then q;	If $ABCD$ is a square, then $\overline{AC}$ bisects $\overline{BD}$.
Given:	p	$ABCD$ is a square.
Conclusion:	q	$\overline{AC}$ bisects $\overline{BD}$.
	Model 2	**Example 2**
Given:	If p, then q;	If $ABCD$ is a square, then $\overline{AC}$ bisects $\overline{BD}$.
Given:	not q	$\overline{AC}$ does not bisect $\overline{BD}$.
Conclusion:	not p	$ABCD$ is not a square.
	Model 3	**Example 3**
Given:	If p, then q;	If $ABCD$ is a square, then $\overline{AC}$ bisects $\overline{BD}$.
Given:	q	$\overline{AC}$ bisects $\overline{BD}$.
Conclusion:	None	$ABCD$ might be a square, or it might not.
	Model 4	**Example 4**
Given:	If p, then q;	If $ABCD$ is a square, then $\overline{AC}$ bisects $\overline{BD}$.
Given:	not p	$ABCD$ is not a square.
Conclusion:	None	$\overline{AC}$ might bisect $\overline{BD}$, or it might not.

Using Models
Teaching Visual 13

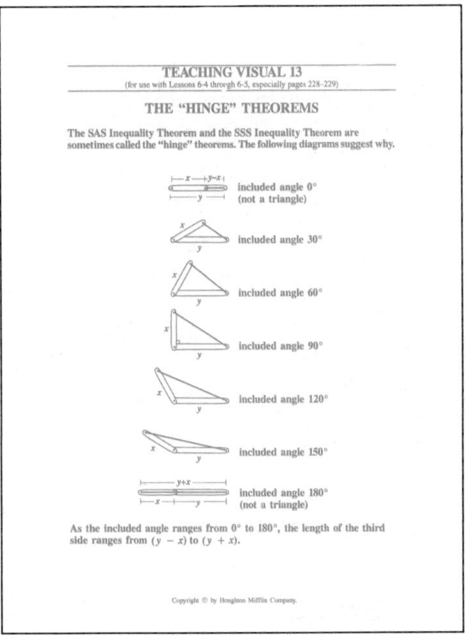

TEACHING VISUAL 13
(for use with Lessons 6-4 through 6-5, especially pages 228–229)

THE "HINGE" THEOREMS

The SAS Inequality Theorem and the SSS Inequality Theorem are sometimes called the "hinge" theorems. The following diagrams suggest why.

As the included angle ranges from 0° to 180°, the length of the third side ranges from $(y - x)$ to $(y + x)$.

Teaching References

Lesson Commentary, pp. T96–T100

Assignment Guide, pp. T44–T46

Software Guide, p. T73

Alternate Test, p. T17

Supplementary Materials

Practice Masters 30–36

Tests 22–24

Resource Book
- Tests, pp. 33–36
- Practice, pp. 130–132
- Preparing for College Entrance Exams, p. 195
- Enrichment Activity, p. 216

Study Guide, pp. 69–78

Overhead Visuals 12, 13

Computer Activity
- 12 Triangle Inequality

Handbook for Integrating Coordinate and Transformational Geometry

Minimal Paths, pp. 662–664

Cultural Note

The Roman writer Pliny the Elder (23–79 A.D.) described the mineral beryl as being cut into hexagonal prisms by craftsmen. He was unaware that the shapes of beryl and all crystals occur naturally.

6 INEQUALITIES IN GEOMETRY

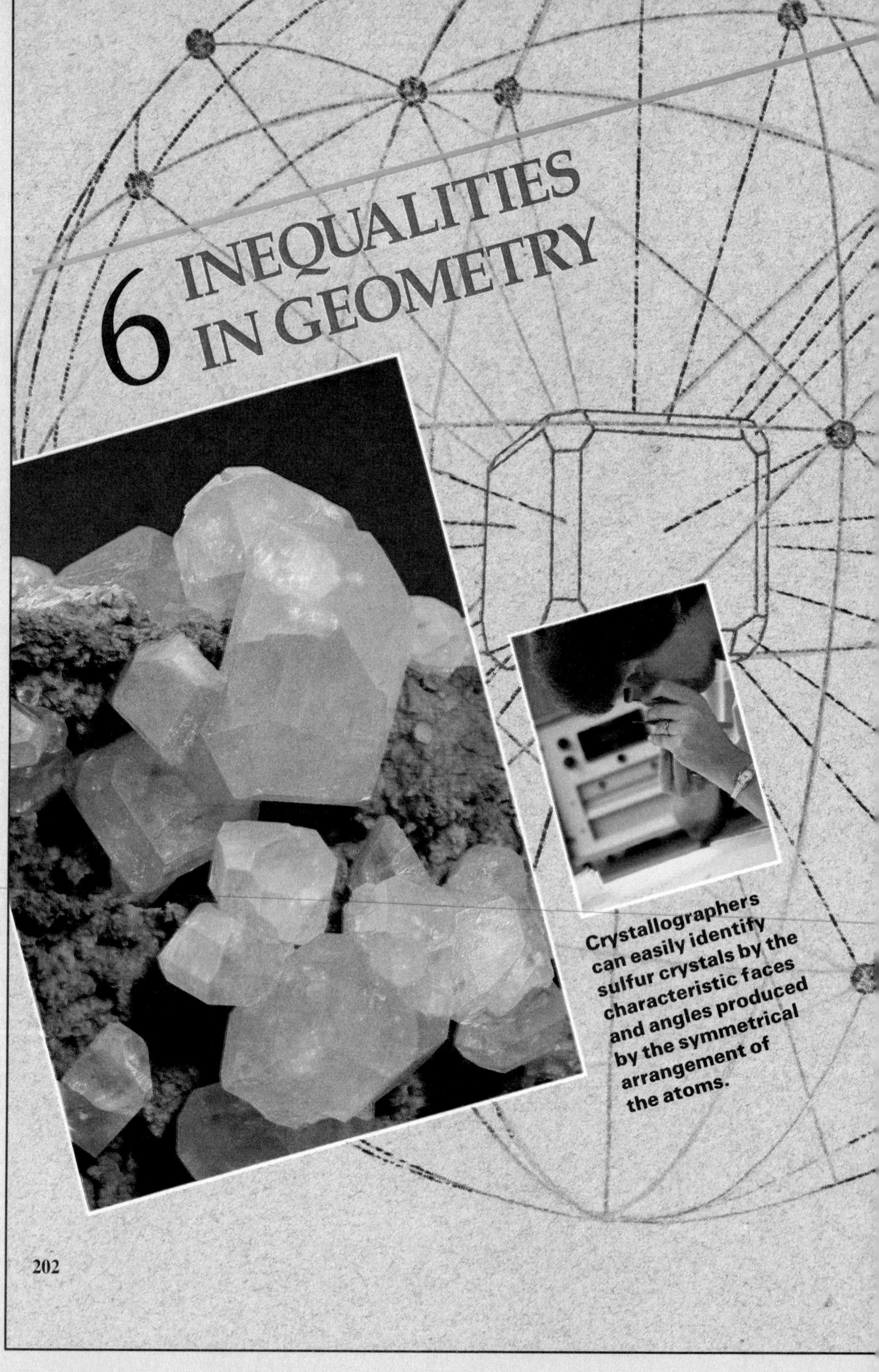

Crystallographers can easily identify sulfur crystals by the characteristic faces and angles produced by the symmetrical arrangement of the atoms.

Inequalities and Indirect Proof

Objectives

1. Apply properties of inequality to positive numbers, lengths of segments, and measures of angles.
2. State the contrapositive and inverse of an if-then statement.
3. Understand the relationship between logically equivalent statements.
4. Draw correct conclusions from given statements.
5. Write indirect proofs in paragraph form.

Teaching Suggestions,
pp. T96–T97

Objectives
Presenting the Lesson
Making Connections
Extension

Cooperative Learning,
p. T97

Supplementary Materials

Study Guide, pp. 69–70

Lesson Focus

Today's lesson uses the properties of inequality from algebra to study segment lengths and angle measures that are not equal.

Suggested Assignments

Minimum
206–207/1–6, 8

Average
206–207/1–9

Maximum
206–207/1–13 odd

6-1 *Inequalities*

Our geometry up until now has emphasized congruent segments and angles, and the triangles and polygons they form. To deal with segments whose lengths are equal and angles whose measures are equal, you have used properties of equality taken from algebra. They are stated on page 37. In this chapter you will work with segments having unequal lengths and angles having unequal measures. You will use properties of inequality taken from algebra.

Example 1 Complete each conclusion by inserting one of the symbols $<$, $=$, or $>$.

a. Given: $AC > AB$; $AB > BC$
Conclusion: AC __?__ BC

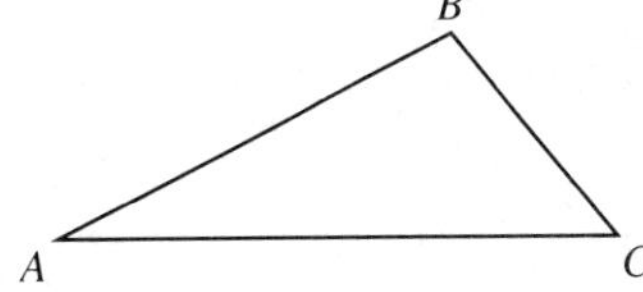

b. Given: $m\angle BAC + m\angle CAD = m\angle BAD$
Conclusion: $m\angle BAD$ __?__ $m\angle BAC$;
$m\angle BAD$ __?__ $m\angle CAD$

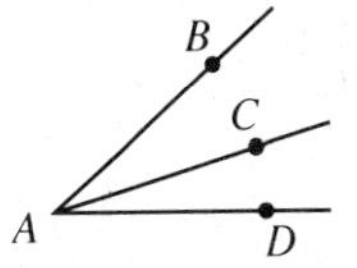

Solution **a.** $AC > BC$ (Equivalently, $BC < AC$.)

b. $m\angle BAD > m\angle BAC$ (Equivalently, $m\angle BAC < m\angle BAD$.)
$m\angle BAD > m\angle CAD$ (Equivalently, $m\angle CAD < m\angle BAD$.)

The properties of inequality you will use most often in geometry are stated on the following page. When you use any one of them in a proof, you can write as your reason *A Prop. of Ineq.* Can you see which properties were used in Example 1?

Chalkboard Examples

Complete with $<$, $=$, or $>$.

1. Given: $RS < ST$; $ST < RT$
   Conclusion: $RS \underline{<} RT$

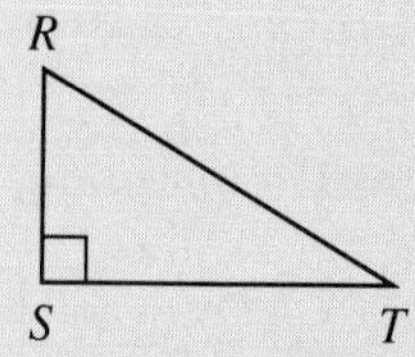

2. Given: $m\angle PQU = m\angle PQT + m\angle TQU$
   Conclusion: $m\angle PQU \underline{>} m\angle TQU$; $m\angle PQU \underline{>} m\angle PQT$

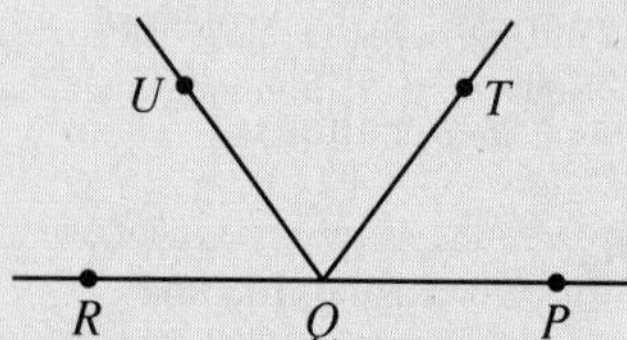

Classify each conditional as true or false.

3. If $XY = YZ + 5$, then $XY > YZ$. T
4. If $m\angle A = m\angle B + m\angle C$, then $m\angle B > m\angle C$. F
5. If $m\angle H = m\angle J + m\angle K$, then $m\angle K > m\angle H$. F
6. If $10 = y + 2$, then $y > 10$. F

Write a two-column proof.

7. Given: $m\angle R = m\angle TUS$
   Prove: $m\angle TUR > m\angle R$

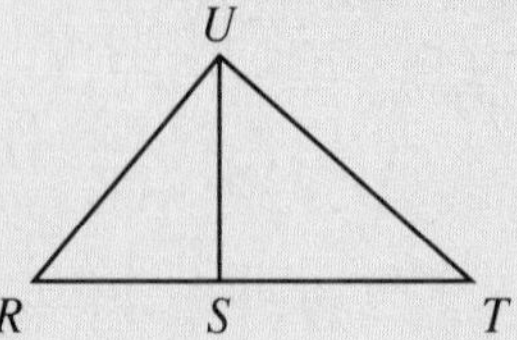

1. $m\angle R = m\angle TUS$ (Given)
2. $m\angle TUR = m\angle TUS + m\angle SUR$ (Angle Add. Post.)

Properties of Inequality

If $a > b$ and $c \geq d$, then $a + c > b + d$.

If $a > b$ and $c > 0$, then $ac > bc$ and $\frac{a}{c} > \frac{b}{c}$.

If $a > b$ and $c < 0$, then $ac < bc$ and $\frac{a}{c} < \frac{b}{c}$.

If $a > b$ and $b > c$, then $a > c$.
If $a = b + c$ and $c > 0$, then $a > b$.

Example 2

Given: $AC > BC$; $CE > CD$

Prove: $AE > BD$

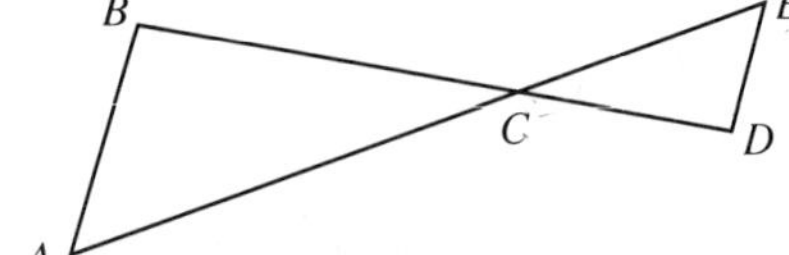

Proof:

Statements	Reasons
1. $AC > BC$; $CE > CD$	1. Given
2. $AC + CE > BC + CD$	2. A Prop. of Ineq.
3. $AC + CE = AE$; $BC + CD = BD$	3. Segment Addition Postulate
4. $AE > BD$	4. Substitution Prop.

Example 3

Given: $\angle 1$ is an exterior angle of $\triangle DEF$.

Prove: $m\angle 1 > m\angle D$;
$m\angle 1 > m\angle E$

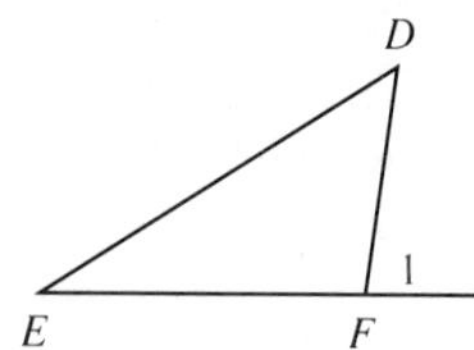

Proof:

Statements	Reasons
1. $m\angle 1 = m\angle D + m\angle E$	1. The measure of an ext. $\angle$ of a $\triangle$ equals the sum of the measures of the two remote int. $\angle$s.
2. $m\angle 1 > m\angle D$; $m\angle 1 > m\angle E$	2. A Prop. of Ineq.

Example 3 above proves the following theorem.

Theorem 6-1 *The Exterior Angle Inequality Theorem*

The measure of an exterior angle of a triangle is greater than the measure of either remote interior angle.

Classroom Exercises

Classify each conditional as true or false.

1. If $3a > 9$, then $a > 27$. **False**

2. If $4b > 20$, then $b > 5$. **True**

3. If $x > 4$, then $x + 1 > 5$. **True**

4. If $x + 1 > 5$, then $x > 4$. **True**

5. If $c - 5 > 45$, then $c > 48$. **True**

6. If $a + b = n$ and $c > b$, then $a + c > n$. **True**

7. If $y > 18$, then $y > 20$. **False**

8. If $y > 20$, then $y > 18$. **True**

9. If $a > 5$ and $5 > b$, then $a > b$. **True**

10. If $d > e$ and $f > e$, then $d > f$. **False**

11. If $g > h$ and $j = h$, then $g > j$. **True**

12. If $p = q + 6$, then $p > q$. **True**

13. If $c > d$ and $e = f$, then $c + e = d + f$. **False**

14. If $g > h$ and $i > j$, then $g + h > i + j$. **False**

15. If $k > l$ and $m > n$, then $k + m > l + n$. **True**

16. If $a > b$, then $100 - a > 100 - b$. **False**

Complete each statement by writing <, =, or >.

17.

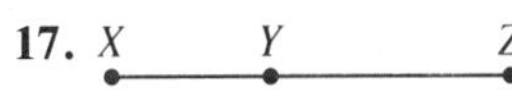

a. XZ __?__ $XY + YZ$ =
b. XZ __?__ XY >
c. XZ __?__ YZ >

18.

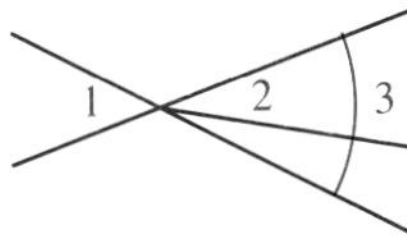

a. $m\angle 1$ __?__ $m\angle 3$ =
b. $m\angle 2$ __?__ $m\angle 3$ <
c. $m\angle 1$ __?__ $m\angle 2$ >

19.

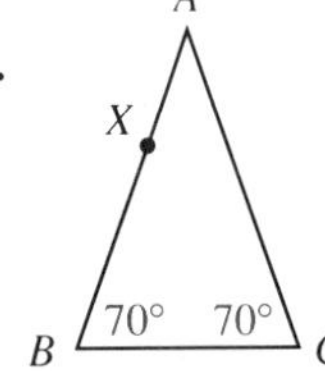

a. AB __?__ AC =
b. AB __?__ $AX + XB$ =
c. AB __?__ XB >
d. AC __?__ XB >

20. Supply reasons to complete the proof.

Given: $m\angle 2 > m\angle 1$

Prove: $m\angle 2 > m\angle 4$

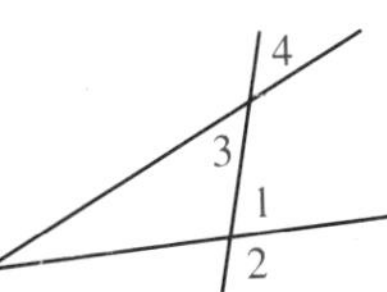

Proof:

Statements	Reasons
1. $m\angle 2 > m\angle 1$	1. __?__ **Given**
2. $m\angle 1 > m\angle 3$	2. __?__ **Ext. ∠ Ineq. Thm.**
3. $m\angle 2 > m\angle 3$	3. __?__ **A Prop. of Ineq.**
4. $\angle 3 \cong \angle 4$, or $m\angle 3 = m\angle 4$	4. __?__ **Vert. ∠s are ≅.**
5. $m\angle 2 > m\angle 4$	5. __?__ **Substitution Prop.**

3. $m\angle TUR = m\angle R + m\angle SUR$ (Substitution Prop.)
4. $m\angle TUR > m\angle R$ (A Prop. of Ineq.)

8. Given: $\angle 1$ is an exterior angle of $\triangle ACD$; $m\angle B > m\angle 1$
Prove: $m\angle B > m\angle C$

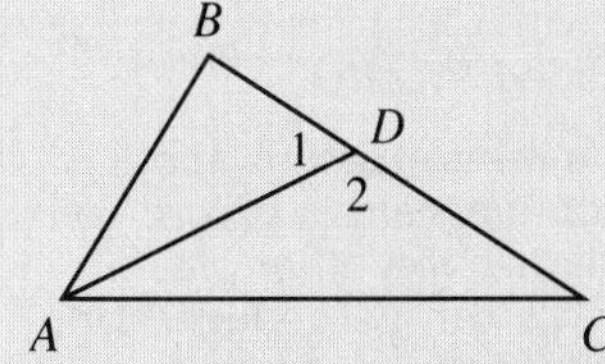

1. $\angle 1$ is an exterior angle of $\triangle ACD$; $m\angle B > m\angle 1$ (Given)
2. $m\angle 1 > m\angle C$ (Ext. ∠ Ineq. Thm.)
3. $m\angle B > m\angle C$ (A Prop. of Ineq.)

Teaching Note

To help students understand Theorem 6-1, emphasize that if an angle is equal to the sum of two angles, then it must be greater than either one of them.

Exercise Note

Students having difficulty with Exs. 1–16 should substitute numbers for the variables before classifying the conditionals as true or false.

Written Exercises

Some information about the diagram is given. Tell whether the other statements can be deduced from what is given. (Write *yes* or *no*.)

A

1. Given: Point Y lies between points X and Z.
   - a. $XY = \frac{1}{2}XZ$ **No**
   - b. $XZ = XY + YZ$ **Yes**
   - c. $XZ > XY$ **Yes**
   - d. $YZ > XY$ **No**
   - e. $XZ > YZ$ **Yes**
   - f. $XZ > 2XY$ **No**

X Y Z

2. Given: Point B lies in the interior of $\angle AOC$.
   - a. $m\angle 1 = m\angle 2$ **No**
   - b. $m\angle AOC = m\angle 1 + m\angle 2$ **Yes**
   - c. $m\angle AOC > m\angle 1$ **Yes**
   - d. $m\angle AOC > m\angle 2$ **Yes**
   - e. $m\angle 1 > m\angle 2$ **No**
   - f. $m\angle AOC > 90$ **No**

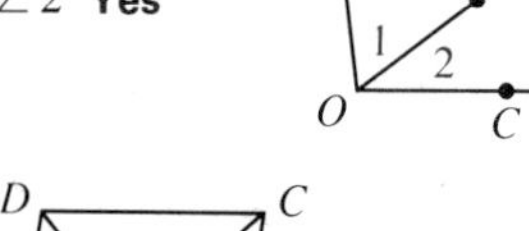

3. Given: $\square ABCD$; $AC > BD$
   - a. $AB > AD$ **No**
   - b. $AM > MC$ **No**
   - c. $DM = MB$ **Yes**
   - d. $AM > MB$ **Yes**

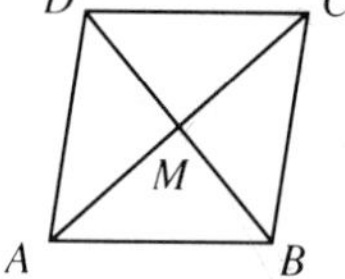

4. Given: $m\angle RVS = m\angle RSV = 65$
   - a. $RT > RS$ **Yes**
   - b. $RT > RV$ **Yes**
   - c. $RS > ST$ **No**
   - d. $VT < RS$ **No**

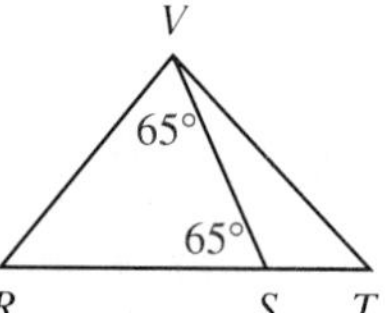

5. When some people are given that $j > k$ and $l > m$, they carelessly conclude that $j + k > l + m$. Find values for j, k, l, and m that show this conclusion is false. **$j = 2$, $k = 1$, $l = 4$, $m = 3$**

Write the reasons that justify the statements.

6.

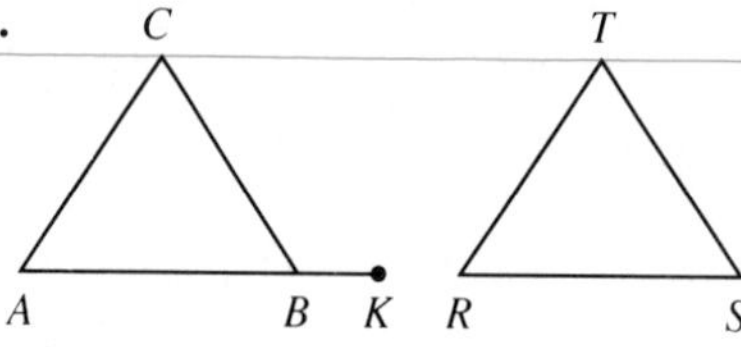

Given: $\triangle ABC \cong \triangle RST$
Prove: $AK > RS$

Statements of proof:

1. $\triangle ABC \cong \triangle RST$ **Given**
2. $\overline{AB} \cong \overline{RS}$, or $AB = RS$
3. $AK = AB + BK$ **Segment Add. Post.**
4. $AK > AB$ **A Prop. of Ineq.**
5. $AK > RS$ **Substitution Prop.**

2. Corr. parts of ≅ ▲ are ≅.

7.

D G Z F E H

Given: $\overleftrightarrow{DE}$, $\overleftrightarrow{FG}$ and $\overrightarrow{ZH}$ contain point Z.
Prove: $m\angle DZH > m\angle GZE$

Statements of proof:

1. $\angle DZF \cong \angle GZE$, **Vert. ▲ are ≅.** or $m\angle DZF = m\angle GZE$
2. $m\angle DZH = m\angle DZF + m\angle FZH$
3. $m\angle DZH > m\angle DZF$ **A Prop. of Ineq.**
4. $m\angle DZH > m\angle GZE$ **Substitution Prop.**

2. Angle Add. Post.

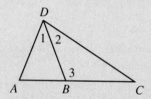

Guided Practice

Some information about each diagram is given. Tell whether the other statements can be deduced from what is given. Write *yes* or *no*.

1. Given: $\triangle ADC$; point B is between points A and C.

D 1 2 3 A B C

   - a. $m\angle 1 = m\angle 2$ no
   - b. $m\angle ADC = m\angle 1 + m\angle 2$ yes
   - c. $m\angle A + m\angle 1 = m\angle 3$ yes
   - d. $m\angle 3 > m\angle 1$ yes
   - e. $m\angle 3 > m\angle 2$ no
   - f. $m\angle A < m\angle ADC$ no

2. Given: $\square ABCD$

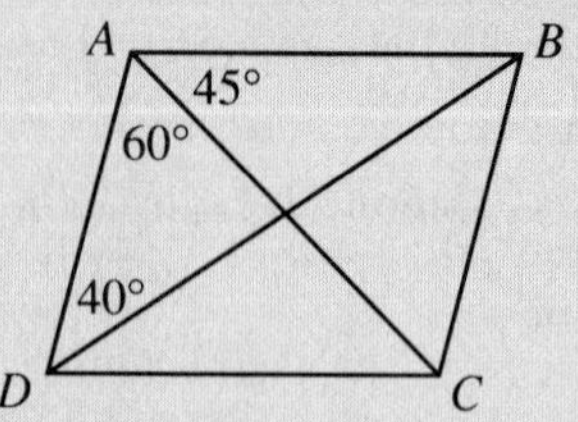

   - a. $m\angle BDC = m\angle ABD$ yes
   - b. $m\angle ADB < m\angle ACB$ yes
   - c. $m\angle DAB = m\angle BCA + m\angle ACD$ yes

Write proofs in two-column form.

B **8.** Given: $KL > NL$; $LM > LP$
Prove: $KM > NP$

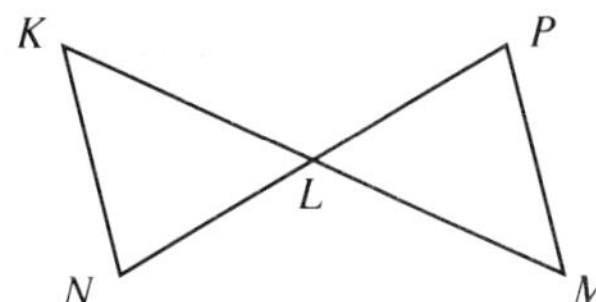

9. Given: $m\angle ROS > m\angle TOV$
Prove: $m\angle ROT > m\angle SOV$

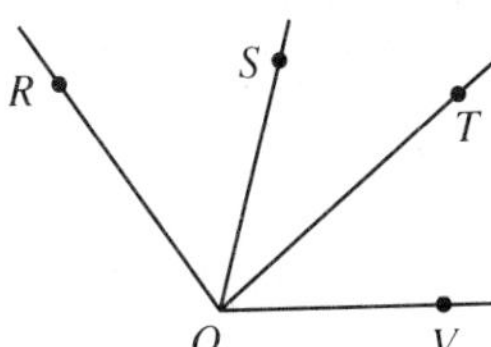

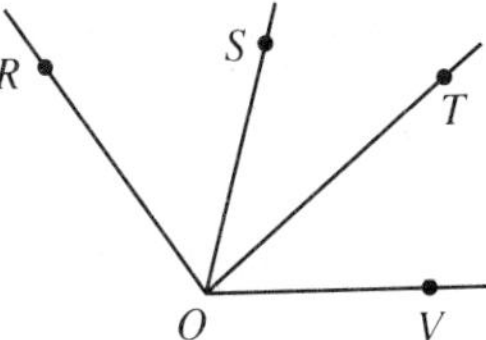

10. Given: $\overline{VY} \perp \overline{YZ}$
Prove: $\angle VXZ$ is an obtuse angle.

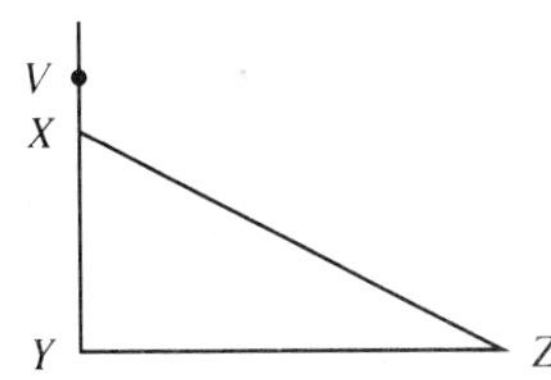

11. Given: The diagram
Prove: $m\angle 1 > m\angle 4$

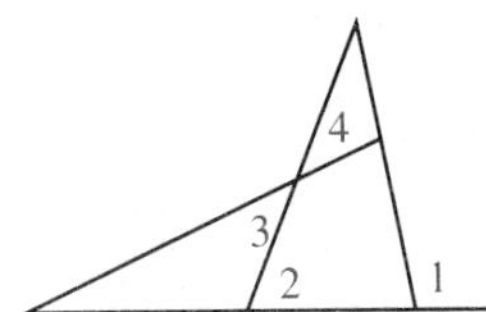

12. Given: $\overline{QR}$ and $\overline{ST}$ bisect each other.
Prove: $m\angle XRT > m\angle S$

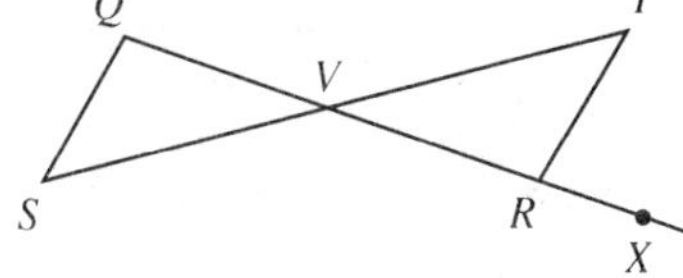

C **13.** Given: Point K lies inside $\triangle ABC$.
Prove: $m\angle K > m\angle C$

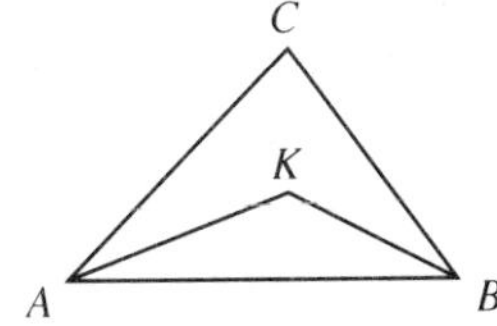

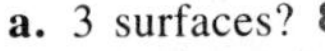

Challenge

A cube with sides n cm long is painted on all faces. It is then cut into cubes with sides 1 cm long. If $n = 4$, as the diagram at the right illustrates, how many of these smaller cubes will have paint on

a. 3 surfaces? **8** **b.** 2 surfaces? **24**
c. 1 surface? **24** **d.** 0 surfaces? **8**

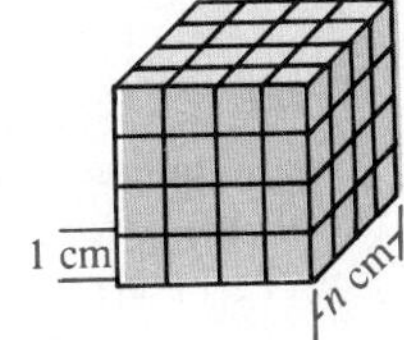

Answer the questions for any positive integer n.
a. 8 b. $12(n - 2)$ c. $6(n - 2)^2$ d. $(n - 2)^3$

3. Write the reasons that justify the statements.
Given: $\overline{CO} \perp \overline{AB}$; point D is in the interior of $\angle COB$.
Prove: $m\angle DOB < m\angle COA$

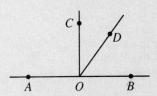

1. D is in the interior of $\angle COB$; $\overline{CO} \perp \overline{AB}$ (Given)
2. $m\angle COB = m\angle COA$ (If 2 lines are ⊥, then they form ≅ adj. ∠s.)
3. $m\angle COD + m\angle DOB = m\angle COB$ (Angle Add. Post.)
4. $m\angle DOB < m\angle COB$ (A Prop. of Ineq.)
5. $m\angle DOB < m\angle COA$ (Substitution Prop.)

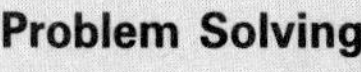

Problem Solving

A strategy that can be used for the Challenge is to solve similar but simpler problems. Suggest that students solve the cube for $n = 2$ and $n = 3$, and then look for a pattern in the numbers.

Teaching Suggestions,
pp. T97–T98

Objectives
Presenting the Lesson
Making Connections
Reinforcement
Extension
Enrichment

Communication Skills,
p. T98

Supplementary Materials

Practice Master 30

Study Guide, pp. 71–72

Lesson Focus

In geometry and other branches of mathematics, statements can be made in different ways. Some of these different ways of writing a statement have the same meaning. This lesson discusses how various if-then statements are related.

Suggested Assignments

Minimum
Day 1: 210–211/2, 4, 6–8
S 206/7
Day 2: 210–211/3, 5, 9, 11, 13
212/Mixed Review 1–9

Average
Day 1: 210–211/3–8, 9, 11
S 207/10
Day 2: 211–212/12, 13, 15, 16, 18, 19
212/Mixed Review 1–9

Maximum
Day 1: 210–211/3, 5–8, 10, 12, 15
Day 2: 211–212/11, 13, 16, 17, 20–22

6-2 *Inverses and Contrapositives*

You have already studied the converse of an if-then statement. Now we consider two other related conditionals called the *inverse* and the *contrapositive*.

Statement:	If p, then q.
Inverse:	If not p, then not q.
Contrapositive:	If not q, then not p.

Example Write (**a**) the inverse and (**b**) the contrapositive of the true conditional: If two lines are not coplanar, then they do not intersect.

Solution **a.** Inverse: If two lines are coplanar, then they intersect. (False)
b. Contrapositive: If two lines intersect, then they are coplanar. (True)

As you can see, the inverse of a true conditional is *not* necessarily true.

You can use a **Venn diagram** to represent a conditional. Since any point inside circle p is also inside circle q, this diagram represents "If p, then q." Similarly, if a point is *not* inside circle q, then it *can't* be inside circle p. Therefore, the same diagram also represents "If not q, then not p." Since the same diagram represents both a conditional and its contrapositive, these statements are either both true or both false. They are called **logically equivalent** statements.

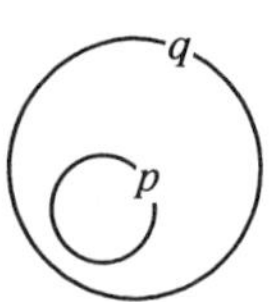

Since a conditional and its contrapositive are logically equivalent, you may prove a conditional by proving its contrapositive. Sometimes this is easier, as you will see in Written Exercises 21 and 22.

The Venn diagram at the right represents both the converse "If q, then p" and the inverse "If not p, then not q." Therefore, the converse and the inverse of a conditional are also logically equivalent statements.

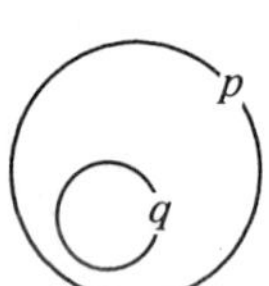

Summary of Related If-Then Statements

Given statement:	If p, then q.
Contrapositive:	If not q, then not p.
Converse:	If q, then p.
Inverse:	If not p, then not q.

A statement and its contrapositive are logically equivalent.
A statement is *not* logically equivalent to its converse or to its inverse.

Using a Venn diagram to illustrate a conditional statement can also help you determine whether an argument leads to a valid conclusion.

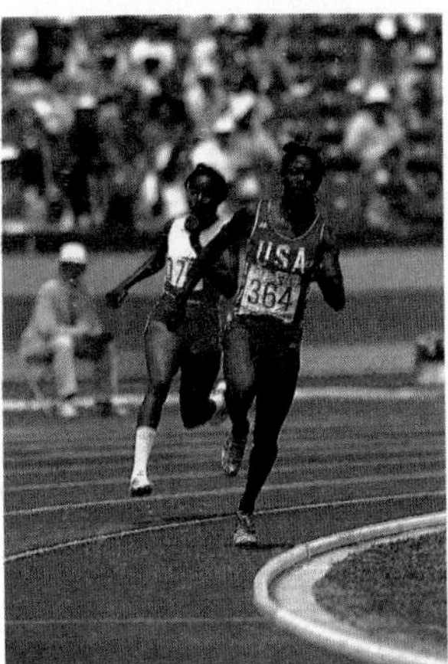

Suppose this conditional is true:

All runners are athletes.
(If a person is a runner, then that person is an athlete.)

What can you conclude from each additional statement?

1. Leroy is a runner.
2. Lucia is not an athlete.
3. Linda is an athlete.
4. Larry is not a runner.

The conditional is paired with the four different statements as shown below.

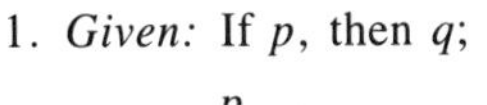

1. *Given:* If p, then q;	All runners are athletes.	
p	Leroy is a runner.	
Conclusion: q	Leroy is an athlete.	

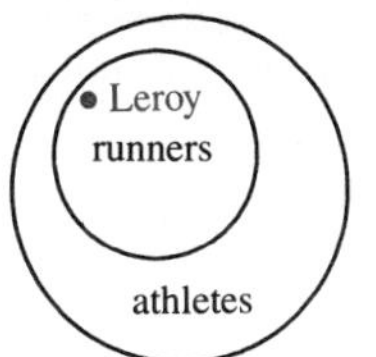

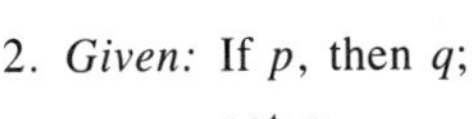

2. *Given:* If p, then q;	All runners are athletes.	
not q	Lucia is not an athlete.	
Conclusion: not p	Lucia is not a runner.	

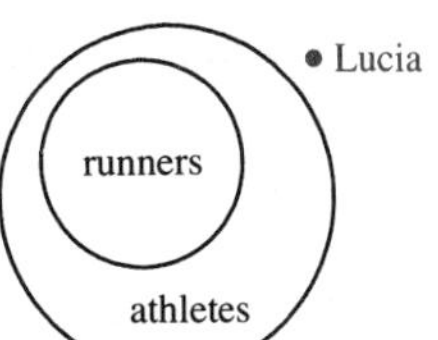

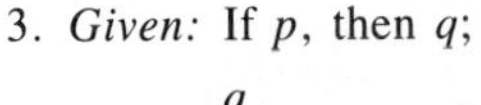

3. *Given:* If p, then q;	All runners are athletes.	
q	Linda is an athlete.	
No conclusion follows.	Linda might be a runner or she might not be.	

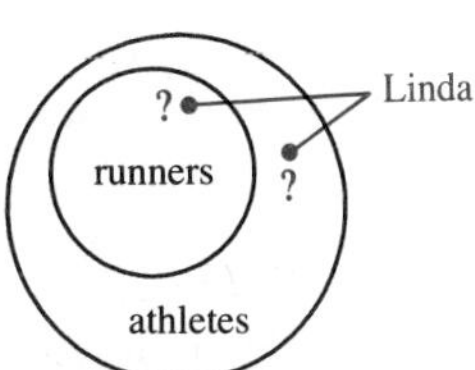

4. *Given:* If p, then q;	All runners are athletes.	
not p	Larry is not a runner.	
No conclusion follows.	Larry might be an athlete or he might not be.	

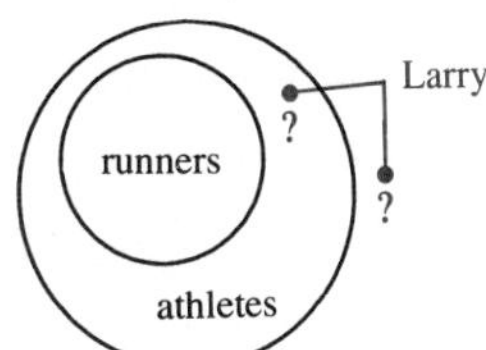

Chalkboard Examples

Write (a) the inverse and (b) the contrapositive of each true conditional.

1. If a parallelogram is a square, then it is a rectangle.
   (a) If a parallelogram is not a square, then it is not a rectangle.
   (b) If a parallelogram is not a rectangle, then it is not a square.

2. If it is snowing, then the game is canceled.
   (a) If it is not snowing, then the game is not canceled.
   (b) If the game is not canceled, then it is not snowing.

3. If $2x + 1 > 15$, then $x > 7$.
   (a) If $2x + 1 \leq 15$, then $x \leq 7$.
   (b) If $x \leq 7$, then $2x + 1 \leq 15$.

Communication Skills

The symbols "p" and "q" are used in statements 1–4 to help students see the groups of statements as inference patterns which can be applied to other groups of statements. You might want to emphasize that if the Given fits the pattern, the Conclusion must follow, according to the rules of logic.

Thinking Skills

Students should observe in problem 3 that there is more than one position for Linda in the Venn diagram, and that the positions are contradictory. This makes the argument invalid. Encourage students to think of their own examples of invalid arguments.

Classroom Exercises

1. b. If I can ride a horse, then you can play baseball.

1. State the contrapositive of each statement.
   a. If I can sing, then you can dance. **If you can't dance, then I can't sing.**
   b. If you can't play baseball, then I can't ride a horse.
   c. If $x = 4$, then $x^2 - 5 = 11$. **If $x^2 - 5 \neq 11$, then $x \neq 4$.**
   d. If $y < 3$, then $y \neq 4$. **If $y = 4$, then $y \geq 3$.**
   e. If a polygon is a triangle, then the sum of the measures of its angles is 180. **If the sum of the meas. of △s of a polygon is not 180, then the polygon is not a △.**
2. State the inverse of each statement in Exercise 1.
3. A certain conditional is true. Must its converse be true? Must its inverse be true? Must its contrapositive be true? **No; no; yes**
4. A certain conditional is false. Must its converse be false? Must its inverse be false? Must its contrapositive be false? **No; no; yes**

Classify each conditional as true or false. Then state its inverse and contrapositive, and classify each of these as true or false.

5. If a triangle is equilateral, then it is equiangular.
6. If $\angle A$ is acute, then $m\angle A \neq 100$.
7. If a triangle is not isosceles, then it is not equilateral.
8. If two planes do not intersect, then they are parallel.

Express each statement in if-then form.

9. All squares are rhombuses.
10. No trapezoids are equiangular.
11. All marathoners have stamina.
12. Suppose "All marathoners have stamina" is a true conditional. What, if anything, can you conclude from each additional statement? If no conclusion is possible, say so.
    a. Nick is a marathoner.
    b. Heidi has stamina.
    c. Mimi does not have stamina.
    d. Arlo is not a marathoner.

Written Exercises

2. a. If this is not blue, then those are not red and white.
b. If those are not red and white, then this is not blue.

Write (a) the contrapositive and (b) the inverse of each statement.

A
1. If $n = 17$, then $4n = 68$. **a. If $4n \neq 68$, then $n \neq 17$. b. If $n \neq 17$, then $4n \neq 68$.**
2. If those are red and white, then this is blue.
3. If x is not even, then $x + 1$ is not odd. **a. If $x + 1$ is odd, then x is even. b. If x is even, then $x + 1$ is odd.**
4. If Abby is not here, then she is not well.
   a. If Abby is well, then she is here. b. If Abby is here, then she is well.

Additional Answers
Classroom Exercises

2. a. If I can't sing, then you can't dance.
   b. If you can play baseball, then I can ride a horse.
   c. If $x \neq 4$, then $x^2 - 5 \neq 11$.
   d. If $y \geq 3$, then $y = 4$.
   e. If a polygon is not a triangle, then the sum of the measures of its angles is not 180.
5. True;
   Inverse: If a triangle is not equilateral, then it is not equiangular. (true);
   Contrapositive: If a triangle is not equiangular, then it is not equilateral. (true)
6. True;
   Inverse: If $\angle A$ is not acute, then $m\angle A = 100$. (false);
   Contrapositive: If $m\angle A = 100$, then $\angle A$ is not acute. (true)
7. True;
   Inverse: If a triangle is isosceles, then it is equilateral. (false);
   Contrapositive: If a triangle is equilateral, then it is isosceles. (true)
8. True;
   Inverse: If two planes intersect, then they are not parallel. (true);
   Contrapositive: If two planes are not parallel, then they intersect. (true)
9. If a polygon is a square, then it is a rhombus.
10. If a polygon is a trapezoid, then it is not equiangular.
11. If you are a marathoner, then you have stamina.

For each statement in Exercises 5–10 copy and complete a table like the one shown below.

	If ?, then ?.	True/False
Statement	?	?
Contrapositive	?	?
Converse	?	?
Inverse	?	?

5. If I live in Los Angeles, then I live in California. **True; true; false; false**

6. If ∠1 and ∠2 are vertical angles, then $m\angle 1 = m\angle 2$. **True; true; false; false**

7. If $AM = MB$, then M is the midpoint of $\overline{AB}$. **False; false; true; true**

8. If a triangle is scalene, then it has no congruent sides. **True; true; true; true**

B **9.** If $-2n < 6$, then $n > -3$. **True; true; true; true**

10. If $x^2 > 1$, then $x > 1$. **False; false; true; true**

Reword the given statement in if-then form and illustrate it with a Venn diagram. What can you conclude by using the given statement together with each additional statement? If no conclusion is possible, say so.

11. Given: All senators are at least 30 years old. **If you are a senator, then you are at least 30 years old.**
  a. Jose Avila is 48 years old. **No conclusion**
  b. Rebecca Castelloe is a senator. **She is at least 30 years old.**
  c. Constance Brown is not a senator. **No conclusion**
  d. Ling Chen is 29 years old. **He is not a senator.**

12. Given: Math teachers assign hours of homework. **If you are a math teacher, then you assign hours of homework.**
  a. Bridget Sullivan is a math teacher. **She assigns hours of homework.**
  b. August Campos assigns hours of homework. **No conclusion**
  c. Andrew Byrnes assigns no homework at all. **He is not a math teacher.**
  d. Jason Babler is not a math teacher. **No conclusion**

What can you conclude by using the given statement together with each additional statement? If no conclusion is possible, say so.

13. Given: If it is not raining, then I am happy.
  a. I am not happy. **It is raining.**
  b. It is not raining. **I am happy.**
  c. I am overjoyed. **No conclusion**
  d. It is raining. **No conclusion**

14. Given: All my students love geometry.
  a. Stu is my student. **a. Stu loves geometry.**
  b. Luis loves geometry. **No conclusion**
  c. Stella is not my student. **No concl.**
  d. George does not love geometry. **He is not my student.**

15. Given: If two angles are vertical angles, then they are congruent.
  a. $\angle 1 \cong \angle 2$ **No conclusion**
  b. $m\angle ABC \neq m\angle DBF$ **∠ABC and ∠DBF are not vert. ⁄s.**
  c. ∠3 and ∠4 are adjacent angles. **No conclusion**
  d. $\overline{RS}$ and $\overline{TU}$ intersect at V. **∠RVU ≅ ∠SVT, ∠RVT ≅ ∠SVU**

---

12. a. Nick has stamina.
b. No conclusion
c. Mimi is not a marathoner.
d. No conclusion

Guided Practice

Write (a) the inverse and (b) the contrapositive of each statement.

1. If $x - 3 = -8$, then $x = -5$.
(a) If $x - 3 \neq -8$, then $x \neq -5$.
(b) If $x \neq -5$, then $x - 3 \neq -8$.

2. If Amy rides her bicycle, then she feels happy.
(a) If Amy doesn't ride her bicycle, then she doesn't feel happy.
(b) If Amy doesn't feel happy, then she doesn't ride her bicycle.

Additional Answers Written Exercises

5. Statement: If I live in L.A., then I live in California. (true); Contrapositive: If I don't live in California, then I don't live in L.A. (true); Converse: If I live in California, then I live in L.A. (false); Inverse: If I don't live in L.A., then I don't live in California. (false)

6. Statement: If ∠1 and ∠2 are vert. ⁄s, then $m\angle 1 = m\angle 2$. (true); Contrapositive: If $m\angle 1 \neq m\angle 2$, then ∠1 and ∠2 are not vert. ⁄s. (true); Converse: If $m\angle 1 = m\angle 2$, then ∠1 and ∠2 are vert. ⁄s. (false); Inverse: If ∠1 and ∠2 are not vert. ⁄s, then $m\angle 1 \neq m\angle 2$. (false)

(continued)

7. Statement: If $AM = MB$, then M is the midpoint of $\overline{AB}$. (false); Contrapositive: If M is not the midpoint of $\overline{AB}$, then $AM \neq MB$. (false); Converse: If M is the midpoint of $\overline{AB}$, then $AM = MB$. (true); Inverse: If $AM \neq MB$, then M is not the midpoint of $\overline{AB}$. (true)

8. Statement: If a triangle is scalene, then it has no congruent sides. (true); Contrapositive: If a triangle has congruent sides, then it is not scalene. (true); Converse: If a triangle has no congruent sides, then it is scalene. (true); Inverse: If a triangle is not scalene, then it has congruent sides. (true)

9. Statement: If $-2n < 6$, then $n > -3$. (true); Contrapositive: If $n \leq -3$, then $-2n \geq 6$. (true); Converse: If $n > -3$, then $-2n < 6$. (true); Inverse: If $-2n \geq 6$, then $n \leq -3$. (true)

10. Statement: If $x^2 > 1$, then $x > 1$. (false); Contrapositive: If $x \leq 1$, then $x^2 \leq 1$. (false); Converse: If $x > 1$, then $x^2 > 1$. (true); Inverse: If $x^2 \leq 1$, then $x \leq 1$. (true)

What can you conclude by using the given statement together with each additional statement? If no conclusion is possible, say so.

16. Given: The diagonals of a rhombus are perpendicular.
    a. *JKLM* is a rhombus. **$\overline{JL} \perp \overline{KM}$**
    b. In quad. *DIME*, $\overline{DM} \perp \overline{IE}$. **No conclusion**
    c. *STUV* is not a rhombus. **No concl.**
    d. In quad. *NOPQ*, $\overline{NP} \not\perp \overline{OQ}$. ***NOPQ* is not a rhombus.**

17. Given: The diagonals of a rectangle are congruent.
    a. *PQRS* is a rectangle. **Diag. are ≅.**
    b. In quad. *ABCD*, $AC = BD$. **No conclusion**
    c. *WXYZ* is not a rectangle. **No concl.**
    d. In quad. *STAR*, $SA > TR$. ***STAR* is not a rectangle.**

18. Given: Every square is a rhombus.
    a. *ABCD* is a rhombus. **No concl.**
    b. In quad. *LAST*, $LA \neq LT$. **b. *LAST* is not a rhombus or a square.**
    c. *PQRS* is a square. ***PQRS* is a rhombus.**
    d. *GHIJ* is not a square. **No conclusion**

C 19. What simpler name can be used for the converse of the inverse of a conditional? **contrapositive**

20. Write the contrapositive of the converse of the inverse of the conditional: If *r*, then *s*. **If *r*, then *s*.**

Prove each of the following statements by proving its contrapositive. Begin by writing what is given and what is to be proved.

21. If $m\angle A + m\angle B \neq 180$, then $m\angle D + m\angle C \neq 180$.

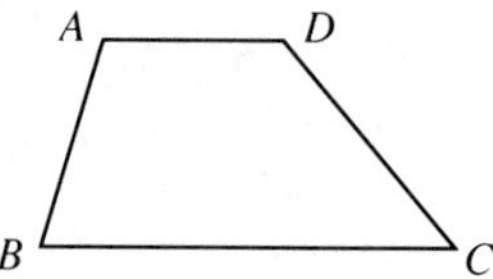

22. If n^2 is not a multiple of 3, then n is not a multiple of 3.

Mixed Review Exercises

Complete each statement with the word *always*, *sometimes*, or *never*.

1. Two lines that do not intersect are __?__ parallel. **sometimes**
2. Two lines parallel to the same plane __?__ intersect. **sometimes**
3. The diagonals of a parallelogram __?__ bisect each other. **always**
4. An acute triangle is __?__ a right triangle. **never**
5. Two lines parallel to a third line are __?__ parallel. **always**
6. A square is __?__ a rectangle. **always**
7. An altitude of a triangle is __?__ a median. **sometimes**

8. Find the measures of ∠1, ∠2, ∠3, and ∠4 in the figure shown.

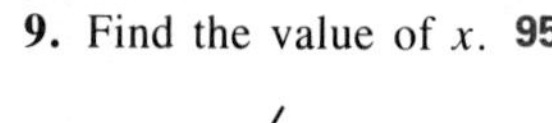

9. Find the value of *x*. **95**

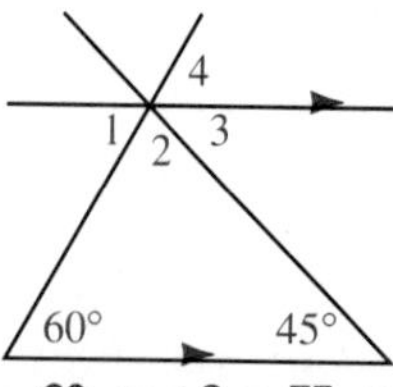

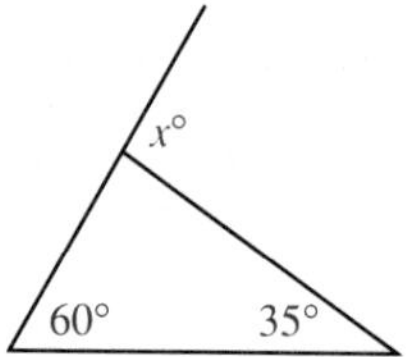

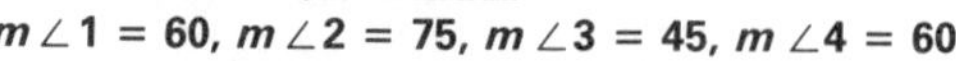

$m\angle 1 = 60$, $m\angle 2 = 75$, $m\angle 3 = 45$, $m\angle 4 = 60$

Career

Cartographer

When you think of a map, do you think of a piece of paper with colored areas and lines? Surprisingly, some maps now consist of thousands, or even millions, of numbers stored on computer tapes. Obviously *cartography*, or map-making, is changing.

Several technical advances have led to changes in mapping. Space satellites carrying scanners produce extremely detailed images of the entire world at regular intervals. Besides conventional photographs, these scanners also record images using infrared and other wavelengths beyond the range of visible light. After processing by computer, such images provide many more kinds of information than the traditional political boundaries and topographic features of conventional maps. For example, they can map soil types and land use, distinguishing among farm fields, forests, and urban areas. In fact, they can even differentiate a corn field from a soybean field, or a freshly plowed field from a field with a mature crop.

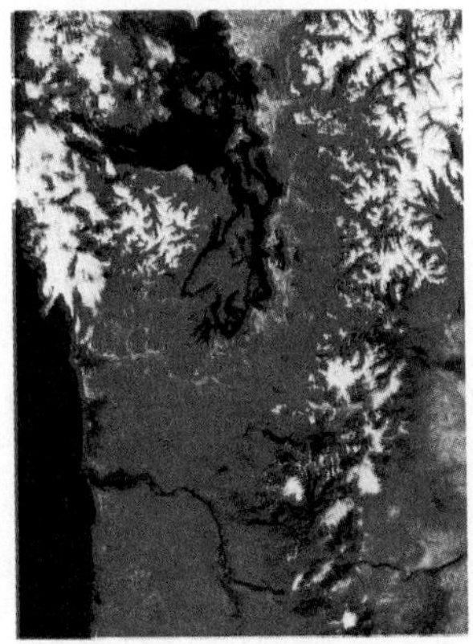

In the false-color map shown below of Oregon and Washington, vegetation appears as red, dry regions are blue, water is black, and snow on the Cascade Mountains and the Olympic Mountains is white.

Both new images and conventional map data are being digitized, that is, converted to numerical codes and stored on computer tape. As new images are received, changes in physical features are coded and recorded. Map users can thus be provided with maps that are constantly being revised and kept up to date.

Teaching Suggestions,
pp. T98–T99

Objective
Presenting the Lesson
Making Connections
Extension
Enrichment

Communication Skills,
p. T99

Exploring Activity, p. 201c

Supplementary Materials

Practice Master 31
Test 22
Resource Book, pp. 33, 130
Study Guide, pp. 73–74

Lesson Focus

This lesson discusses the important method of indirect proof. Not only is indirect proof used in mathematics to prove theorems, but also it is used by people to reason about everyday events in their lives.

Suggested Assignments

Minimum
Day 1: 216/1–8
Day 2: 216–217/9–13
218/Self-Test 1

Average
Day 1: 216/1–10
Day 2: 217/11, 13, 15–18
218/Self-Test 1

Maximum
Day 1: 216–217/2, 4–6, 9, 10, 13
S 212/18, 19
Day 2: 217/11, 15–20

6-3 *Indirect Proof*

Until now, the proofs you have written have been *direct* proofs. Sometimes it is difficult or even impossible to find a direct proof. In that case it may be possible to reason *indirectly*. Indirect reasoning is commonplace in everyday life. Suppose, for example, that after walking home, Sue enters the house carrying a dry umbrella. You can conclude that it is not raining outside. Why? Because if it were raining, then her umbrella would be wet. The umbrella is not wet. Therefore, it is not raining.

In an **indirect proof** you begin by assuming temporarily that the desired conclusion is not true. Then you reason logically until you reach a contradiction of the hypothesis or some other known fact. Because you've reached a contradiction, you know that the temporary assumption is impossible and therefore the desired conclusion must be true.

The procedure for writing an indirect proof is summarized below. Notice how these steps are applied in the examples of indirect proof that follow.

How to Write an Indirect Proof

1. Assume temporarily that the conclusion is not true.
2. Reason logically until you reach a contradiction of a known fact.
3. Point out that the temporary assumption must be false, and that the conclusion must then be true.

Example 1

Given: n is an integer and n^2 is even.

Prove: n is even.

Proof:

Assume temporarily that n is not even. Then n is odd, and

$$\begin{aligned} n^2 &= n \times n \\ &= \text{odd} \times \text{odd} = \text{odd}. \end{aligned}$$

But this contradicts the given information that n^2 is even. Therefore the temporary assumption that n is not even must be false. It follows that n is even.

Example 2

Prove that the bases of a trapezoid have unequal lengths.

Given: Trap. $PQRS$ with bases $\overline{PQ}$ and $\overline{SR}$

Prove: $PQ \neq SR$

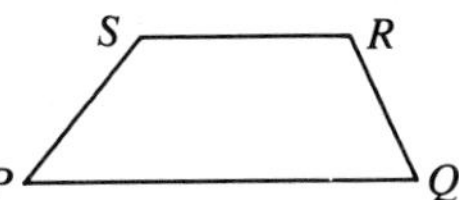

Proof:

Assume temporarily that $PQ = SR$. We know that $\overline{PQ} \parallel \overline{SR}$ by the definition of a trapezoid. Since quadrilateral $PQRS$ has two sides that are both congruent and parallel, it must be a parallelogram, and $\overline{PS}$ must be parallel to $\overline{QR}$. But this contradicts the fact that, by definition, trapezoid $PQRS$ can have only one pair of parallel sides. The temporary assumption that $PQ = SR$ must be false. It follows that $PQ \neq SR$.

Can you see how proving a statement by proving its contrapositive is related to *indirect proof*? If you want to prove the statement "If p, then q," you could prove the contrapositive "If not q, then not p." Or you could write an indirect proof—assume that q is false and show that this assumption implies that p is false.

Classroom Exercises

1. An indirect proof is to be used to prove the following:

   If $AB = AC$, then $\triangle ABD \cong \triangle ACD$.

   Which one of the following is the correct way to begin? **b**
   a. Assume temporarily that $AB \neq AC$.
   b. Assume temporarily that $\triangle ABD \ncong \triangle ACD$.

What is the first sentence of an indirect proof of the statement shown?

2. $\triangle ABC$ is equilateral.
3. Doug is a Canadian.
4. $a \geq b$
5. Kim isn't a violinist.
6. $m\angle X > m\angle Y$
7. $\overline{CX}$ isn't a median of $\triangle ABC$.

8. Planning to write an indirect proof that $\angle A$ is an obtuse angle, Becky began by saying "Assume temporarily that $\angle A$ is an acute angle." What has Becky overlooked? **$\angle A$ may be a right angle.**
9. Wishing to prove that l and m are skew lines, John began an indirect proof by supposing that l and m are intersecting lines. What possibility has John overlooked? **l and m may be $\parallel$.**

Thinking Skills

Students should be careful not to assume the Given is not true, a common error. Logically, if the Given is not true, no conclusions can be reached. Encourage students to think about and discuss what conclusions can be made in Example 2 if the Given is not true.

Chalkboard Examples

Write an indirect proof in paragraph form.

1. Given: $m\angle X \neq m\angle Y$
   Prove: $\angle X$ and $\angle Y$ are not both right angles.
   Suppose $\angle X$ and $\angle Y$ are rt. ∠s. Then $m\angle X = 90$, $m\angle Y = 90$, and $m\angle X = m\angle Y$. This contradicts $m\angle X \neq m\angle Y$ (Given). The assumption is false; $\angle X$ and $\angle Y$ are not both rt. ∠s.
2. Given: $2r + 3 \neq 17$
   Prove: $r \neq 7$
   Suppose $r = 7$. Then $2r + 3 = 2(7) + 3 = 17$. This contradicts $2r + 3 \neq 17$ (Given). The assumption is false; $r \neq 7$.

Additional Answers Classroom Exercises

2. Assume temporarily that $\triangle ABC$ is not equilateral.
3. Assume temporarily that Doug isn't a Canadian.
4. Assume temporarily that $a < b$.
5. Assume temporarily that Kim is a violinist.
6. Assume temporarily that $m\angle X \leq m\angle Y$.
7. Assume temporarily that $\overline{CX}$ is a median of $\triangle ABC$.

10. Arrange sentences (a)–(e) in an order that completes an indirect proof of the following statement: In a plane, two lines perpendicular to a third line are parallel to each other.

Given: Lines a, b, and t lie in a plane;
$a \perp t$; $b \perp t$

Prove: $a \parallel b$

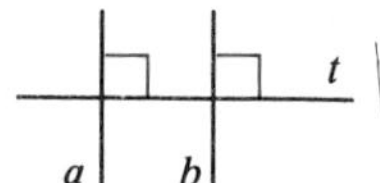

d, a, e, b, c

(a) Then a intersects b in some point Z.
(b) But this contradicts the theorem which says that there is exactly one line perpendicular to a given line through a point outside the line.
(c) It is false that a is not parallel to b, and it follows that $a \parallel b$.
(d) Assume temporarily that a is not parallel to b.
(e) Then there are two lines through Z and perpendicular to t.

Written Exercises

Suppose someone plans to write an indirect proof of each conditional. Write a correct first sentence of the indirect proof.

A 1. If $m\angle A = 50$, then $m\angle B = 40$. **Assume temp. that $m\angle B \neq 40$.**

2. If $\overline{DF} \not\cong \overline{RT}$, then $\overline{DE} \not\cong \overline{RS}$. **Assume temp. that $\overline{DE} \cong \overline{RS}$.**

3. If $a \neq b$, then $a - b \neq 0$. **Assume temp. that $a - b = 0$.**

4. If $x^2 \neq y^2$, then $x \neq y$. **Assume temp. that $x = y$.**

5. If $\overline{EF} \not\cong \overline{GH}$, then $\overleftrightarrow{EF}$ and $\overleftrightarrow{GH}$ aren't parallel. **Assume temp. that $\overleftrightarrow{EF} \parallel \overleftrightarrow{GH}$.**

Write an indirect proof in paragraph form.

6. Given: People wearing coats are shivering as they come to the door.
Prove: It's cold outside.

7. Given: $\triangle XYZ$; $m\angle X = 100$
Prove: $\angle Y$ is not a rt. $\angle$.

8. Given: n is an integer and n^2 is odd.
Prove: n is odd.

9. Given: Transversal t cuts lines a and b;
$m\angle 1 \neq m\angle 2$
Prove: $a \nparallel b$

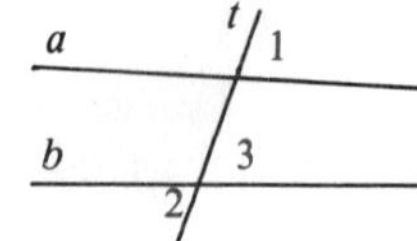

10. Given: $\overline{OJ} \cong \overline{OK}$; $\overline{JE} \not\cong \overline{KE}$
Prove: $\overrightarrow{OE}$ doesn't bisect $\angle JOK$.

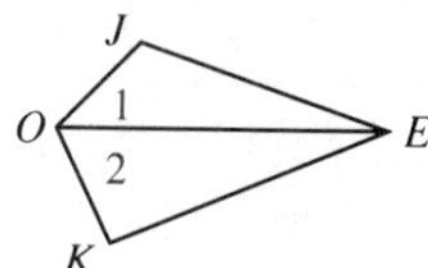

Guided Practice

Suppose someone plans to write an indirect proof of each conditional. Write a correct first sentence of the indirect proof.

1. If $AB = 12$, then $AC = 8$.
Assume $AC \neq 8$.

2. If $\angle Y \not\cong \angle B$, then $\overline{XZ} \not\cong \overline{AC}$. Assume $\overline{XZ} \cong \overline{AC}$.

3. If $a > b$ and $x > y$, then $a + x > b + y$.
Assume $a + x \leq b + y$.

4. If $m\angle C \not\cong m\angle D$, then $\angle C$ and $\angle D$ are not right angles. Assume $\angle C$ and $\angle D$ are right angles.

Write an indirect proof in paragraph form.

5. Given: Tim drove 105 miles to his friend's house in $1\frac{1}{2}$ hours.
Prove: Tim exceeded the 55 mph speed limit while driving.
Assume temporarily that Tim did not exceed the 55 mph speed limit while driving. Then the minimum driving time for 105 miles would be 105/55, or about 2 hours. But this contradicts the given information that it took him $1\frac{1}{2}$ hours to reach his friend's house. Therefore, the assumption is false. Tim exceeded the 55 mph speed limit while driving.

6. Given: ▱$XYZW$; $m\angle X = 80$
Prove: ▱$XYZW$ is not a rectangle.
Assume temporarily that ▱$XYZW$ is a rectangle. Then ▱$XYZW$ has four right angles. But this contradicts the given information that $\angle X$ measures 80. Therefore, the assumption is false. ▱$XYZW$ is not a rectangle.

B **11.** Given: $\overleftrightarrow{AB} \nparallel \overleftrightarrow{CD}$
Prove: Planes P and Q intersect.

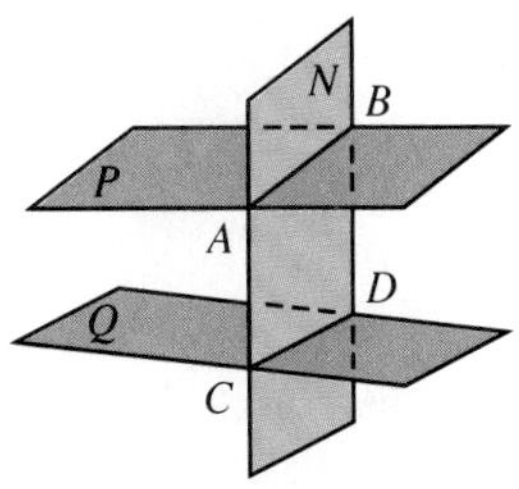

12. Given: $\triangle RVT$ and SVT are equilateral; $\triangle RVS$ is not equilateral.
Prove: $\triangle RST$ is not equilateral.

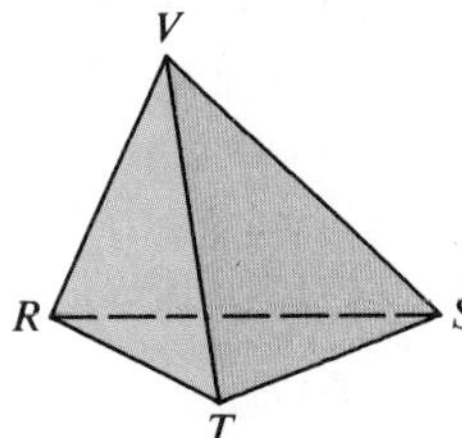

13. Given: quad. $EFGH$ in which $m\angle EFG = 93$; $m\angle FGH = 20$; $m\angle GHE = 147$; $m\angle HEF = 34$
Prove: $EFGH$ is not a convex quadrilateral.

14. Given: $AT = BT = 5$; $CT = 4$
Prove: $\angle ACB$ is not a rt. $\angle$.

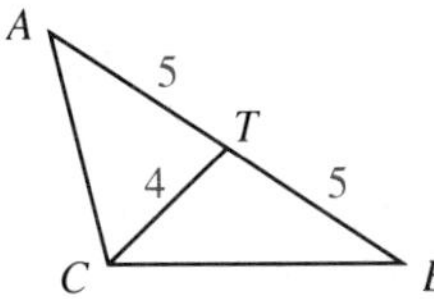

15. Given: Coplanar lines l, k, n; n intersects l in P; $l \parallel k$
Prove: n intersects k.

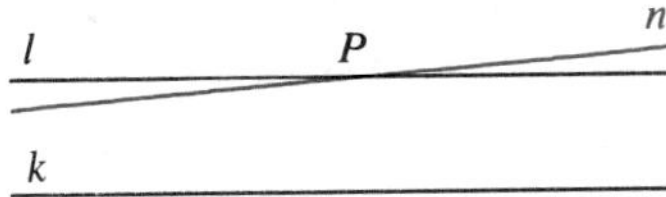

16. Prove that if two angles of a triangle are not congruent, then the sides opposite those angles are not congruent.

17. Prove that there is no regular polygon with an interior angle whose measure is 155.

18. Prove that the diagonals of a trapezoid do not bisect each other.

C **19.** Prove that if two lines are perpendicular to the same plane, then the lines do not intersect.

20. Given: Points R, S, T, and W; $\overleftrightarrow{RS}$ and $\overleftrightarrow{TW}$ are skew.
Prove: $\overleftrightarrow{RT}$ and $\overleftrightarrow{SW}$ are skew.

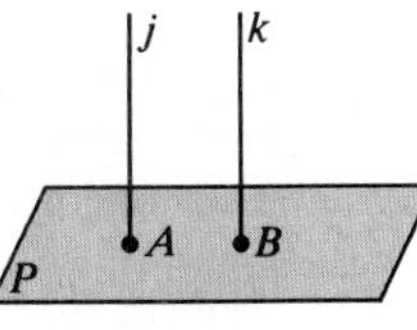

Ex. 19

Challenge

One of four children ate the last piece of lasagna. When questioned they responded as follows:

Joan: I didn't eat it. Ken: Leo ate it.
Leo: Martha ate it. Martha: Leo is lying.

If only one of the four children lied, who ate the last piece? **Leo**

Group Activity

Paragraph proofs can be worded differently by students and thus lend themselves to discussion. It might be helpful for students to form groups of three or four to go over the Written Exercises on pages 216 and 217. Students should read and discuss each other's proofs and should pay special attention to any missing parts. The entire class can then discuss any problems that are still confusing.

Exercise Note

Encourage students to draw and label diagrams and to identify the Given and Prove in Exs. 16–19.

Assessment

You might want to test students' understanding of indirect proof in an informal way. Ask students to form groups of three or four (perhaps the same groups as in the Group Activity above) and present each group with a problem involving indirect proof. Give partial credit for correctly (1) phrasing the initial assumption; (2) making deductions; (3) arriving at a contradiction; and (4) writing a convincing argument.

Quick Quiz

Classify each conditional as true or false.

1. If $a \le b$, then $b \ge a$. T
2. If $r = s$ and $s < t$, then $r < t$. T
3. If $m > n$ and $n < r$, then $m > r$. F
4. Given: If you live in Denver, then you live in Colorado.
   a. Write the inverse of the statement above. Is it true or false? If you do not live in Denver, then you do not live in Colorado. (false)
   b. Write the contrapositive of the statement. Is it true or false? If you do not live in Colorado, then you do not live in Denver. (true)
5. Choose the letter of the statement that is logically equivalent to "If you will stay, then Kim will go." D
   A. If you won't stay, then Kim will go.
   B. If Kim won't go, then you will stay.
   C. If you won't stay, then Kim won't go.
   D. If Kim won't go, then you won't stay.
6. Given: All squares are rectangles.
   What can you conclude from each additional statement? If no conclusion is possible, write *no conclusion.*
   a. *RSTU* is not a rectangle. *RSTU* is not a square.
   b. *ABCD* is not a square. no conclusion
   c. *HIJK* is a rectangle. no conclusion

Self-Test 1

Classify each conditional as true or false.

1. If $j > k$, then $k < j$. **True**
2. If $a > b$ and $b = c$, then $a > c$. **True**
3. If $r > t$ and $s > t$, then $r > s$. **False**
4. If $\angle BCD$ is an exterior angle of $\triangle ABC$, then $m\angle BCD > m\angle A + m\angle B$. **False**

Use the conditional: If $\triangle ABC$ is acute, then $m\angle C \neq 90$.

5. Write the inverse of the statement. Is it true or false? **If $\triangle ABC$ is not acute, then $m\angle C = 90$. False**
6. Write the contrapositive of the statement. Is it true or false? **If $m\angle C = 90$, then $\triangle ABC$ is not acute. True**
7. Write the letter paired with the statement that is logically equivalent to "If Dan can't go, then Valerie can go." **C**
   A. If Valerie can go, then Dan can't go. B. If Dan can go, then Valerie can't go.
   C. If Valerie can't go, then Dan can go. D. If Dan can go, then Valerie can go.
8. Given: All rhombuses are parallelograms.
   What can you conclude from each additional statement? If no conclusion is possible, write *no conclusion.* **a. *ABCD* is not a rhombus.**
   a. *ABCD* is not a parallelogram. b. *QRST* is not a rhombus. **No conclusion**
   c. *MNOP* is a parallelogram. **No concl.** d. *GHIJ* is a rhombus. ***GHIJ* is a ▱.**
9. Suppose you plan to write an indirect proof of the statement: If $AB = 7$, then $AC = 14$. Write a correct first sentence of the indirect proof. **Assume temp. that $AC \neq 14$.**
10. Write the letters (a)–(d) in an order that completes an indirect proof of the statement: Through a point outside a line, there is at most one line perpendicular to the given line.

    Given: Point P not on line k
    Prove: There is at most one line through P perpendicular to k. **d, b, a, c**

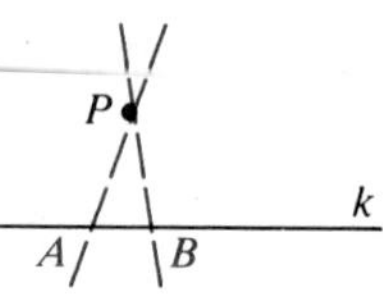

    (a) But this contradicts Corollary 3 of Theorem 3-11: In a triangle, there can be at most one right angle or obtuse angle.
    (b) Then $\angle PAB$ and $\angle PBA$ are right angles, and $\triangle PAB$ has two right angles.
    (c) Thus our temporary assumption is false, and there is at most one line through P perpendicular to k.
    (d) Assume temporarily that there are two lines through P perpendicular to k at A and B.

Inequalities in Triangles

Objectives

1. State and apply the inequality theorems and corollaries for one triangle.
2. State and apply the inequality theorems for two triangles.

6-4 *Inequalities for One Triangle*

From the information given in the diagram at the left below you can deduce that $\angle C \cong \angle B$.

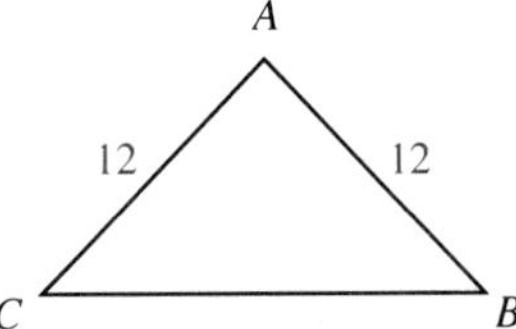

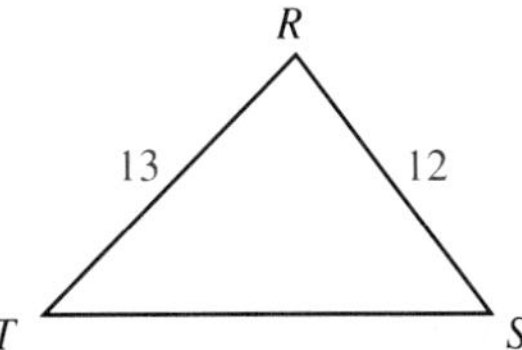

Using the information in the diagram at the right you could write an indirect proof showing that $m\angle S \neq m\angle T$. The following theorem enables you to reach an even stronger conclusion, the conclusion that $m\angle S > m\angle T$.

Theorem 6-2

If one side of a triangle is longer than a second side, then the angle opposite the first side is larger than the angle opposite the second side.

Given: $\triangle RST$; $RT > RS$

Prove: $m\angle RST > m\angle T$

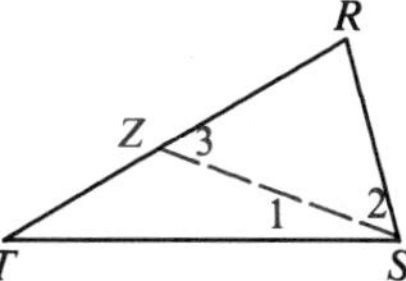

Proof:

By the Ruler Postulate there is a point Z on $\overline{RT}$ such that $RZ = RS$. Draw $\overline{SZ}$.
In isosceles $\triangle RZS$, $m\angle 3 = m\angle 2$.
Because $m\angle RST = m\angle 1 + m\angle 2$, you have $m\angle RST > m\angle 2$.
Substitution of $m\angle 3$ for $m\angle 2$ yields $m\angle RST > m\angle 3$.
Because $\angle 3$ is an ext. $\angle$ of $\triangle ZST$, you have $m\angle 3 > m\angle T$.
From $m\angle RST > m\angle 3$ and $m\angle 3 > m\angle T$, you get $m\angle RST > m\angle T$.

Teaching Suggestions,
pp. T99–T100

Objective
Presenting the Lesson
Using Technology
Making Connections
Extension

Supplementary Materials

Practice Master 32
Study Guide, pp. 75–76
Computer Activity 12

Lesson Focus

Inequalities are first studied in algebra, but they play a role in geometry also. This lesson develops the Triangle Inequality theorem, which involves an important relationship among the sides of any triangle.

Suggested Assignments

Minimum
Day 1: 222/1–9
Day 2: 222–223/10–16

Average
222–223/1, 4–7, 10, 13, 16, 19

Maximum
222–223/4, 9, 12, 13, 15–17, 19, 21, 23

Teaching Note

As you discuss Theorem 6-2, remind your students of the contrapositive of Theorem 4-2 on page 136: If the sides opposite two angles of a triangle are not congruent, then the two angles are not congruent. Point out that Theorem 6-2 adds the information that the angles will be noncongruent *in the same order* as the lengths of the sides.

Chalkboard Examples

1. Name the largest angle and the smallest angle of the triangle. $\angle I$; $\angle J$

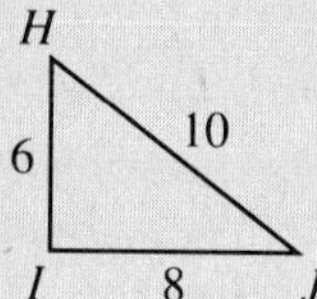

2. Name the longest side and the shortest side of the triangle. $\overline{RT}$; $\overline{RS}$

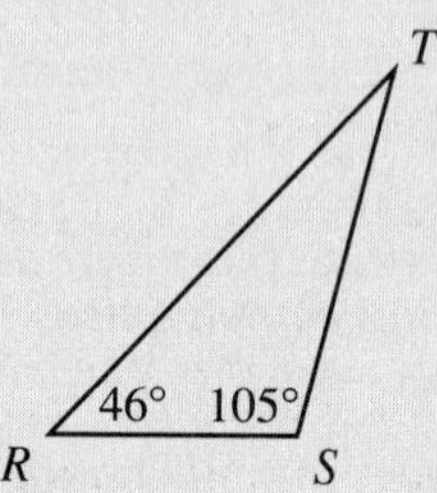

3. Complete with <, =, or >.
   Given: $\triangle ABC$ is a right triangle with $m\angle C = 90$.
   Conclusions:
   $m\angle C > m\angle A$;
   $m\angle C = m\angle A + m\angle B$;
   $AC < AB$
4. The lengths of two sides of a triangle are 8 and 13. Then, the length of the third side must be greater than 5 but less than 21.
5. Is it possible for a triangle to have sides with the lengths as indicated?
   a. 6, 8, 10 yes
   b. 3, 4, 8 no ($3 + 4 \not> 8$)
   c. 2.5, 4.1, 5.0 yes
   d. 4, 6, 2 no ($4 + 2 \not> 6$)
   e. 6, 6, 5 yes

Using a Computer

See page T99 for three experiments involving the theorems in this lesson.

Theorem 6-3

If one angle of a triangle is larger than a second angle, then the side opposite the first angle is longer than the side opposite the second angle.

Given: $\triangle RST$; $m\angle S > m\angle T$

Prove: $RT > RS$

R
T S

Proof:

Assume temporarily that $RT \not> RS$. Then either $RT = RS$ or $RT < RS$.

Case 1: If $RT = RS$, then $m\angle S = m\angle T$.

Case 2: If $RT < RS$, then $m\angle S < m\angle T$ by Theorem 6-2.

In either case there is a contradiction of the given fact that $m\angle S > m\angle T$. The assumption that $RT \not> RS$ must be false. It follows that $RT > RS$.

Corollary 1

The perpendicular segment from a point to a line is the shortest segment from the point to the line.

Corollary 2

The perpendicular segment from a point to a plane is the shortest segment from the point to the plane.

See Classroom Exercises 18 and 19 for proofs of the corollaries.

Theorem 6-4 *The Triangle Inequality*

The sum of the lengths of any two sides of a triangle is greater than the length of the third side.

Given: $\triangle ABC$

Prove: (1) $AB + BC > AC$
(2) $AB + AC > BC$
(3) $AC + BC > AB$

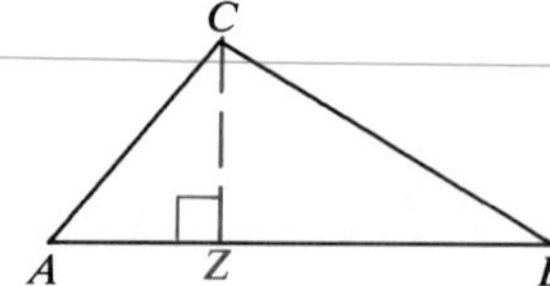

Proof:

One of the sides, say $\overline{AB}$, is the longest side. (Or $\overline{AB}$ is at least as long as each of the other sides.) Then (1) and (2) are true. To prove (3), draw a line, $\overleftrightarrow{CZ}$, through C and perpendicular to $\overleftrightarrow{AB}$. (Through a point outside a line, there is exactly one line perpendicular to the given line.) By Corollary 1 of Theorem 6-3, $\overline{AZ}$ is the shortest segment from A to $\overline{CZ}$. Also, $\overline{BZ}$ is the shortest segment from B to $\overline{CZ}$. Therefore $AC > AZ$ and $BC > ZB$.

$AC + BC > AZ + ZB$ (Why?) **A Prop. of Ineq.**

$AC + BC > AB$ (Why?) **Substitution ($AZ + ZB = AB$)**

Example The lengths of two sides of a triangle are 3 and 5. The length of the third side must be greater than _?_, but less than _?_.

Solution Let x be the length of the third side.

$$x + 3 > 5 \qquad 3 + 5 > x \qquad x + 5 > 3$$
$$x > 2 \qquad 8 > x \qquad x > -2$$

The length of the third side must be greater than 2 but less than 8.

Note that the inequality $x + 5 > 3$ did not give us any useful information. Since $5 > 3$, the sum of 5 and *any* positive number is greater than 3.

Classroom Exercises

Name the largest angle and the smallest angle of the triangle.

1. 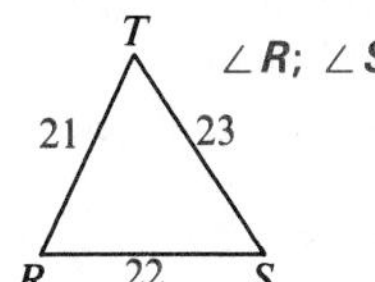

∠R; ∠S

2. 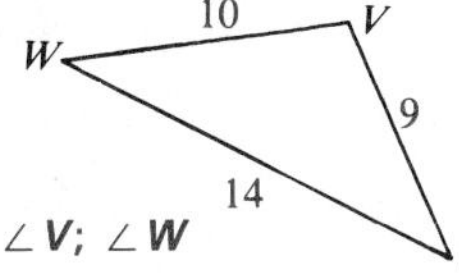

∠V; ∠W

3. 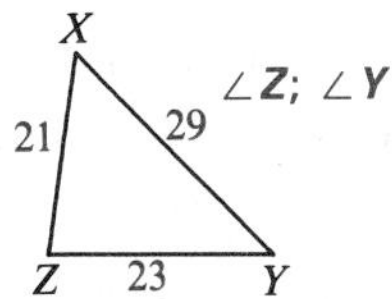

∠Z; ∠Y

Name the longest side and the shortest side of the triangle.

4. 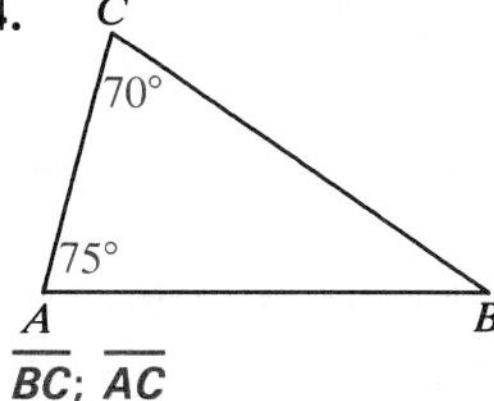

$\overline{BC}$; $\overline{AC}$

5. 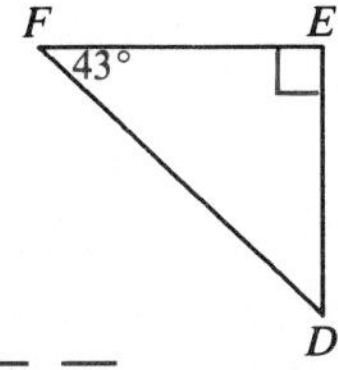

$\overline{DF}$; $\overline{DE}$

6. 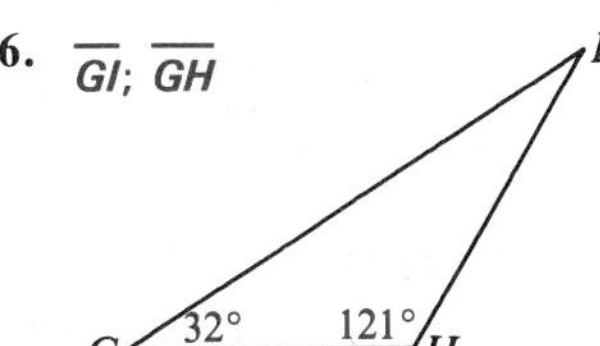

$\overline{GI}$; $\overline{GH}$

Is it possible for a triangle to have sides with the lengths indicated?

7. 10, 9, 8 **Yes** **8.** 6, 6, 20 **No** **9.** 7, 7, 14.1 **No**

10. 16, 11, 5 **No** **11.** 0.6, 0.5, 1 **Yes** **12.** 18, 18, 0.06 **Yes**

13. An isosceles triangle is to have a base that is 20 cm long. Draw a diagram to show the following.

a. The legs can be very long. **Make the base ∠s close to 90°.**

b. Although the legs must be more than 10 cm long, each length can be very close to 10 cm. **Make the base ∠s close to 0°.**

14. The base of an isosceles triangle has length 12. What can you say about the length of a leg? **It must be greater than 6.**

15. Two sides of a parallelogram have lengths 10 and 12. What can you say about the lengths of the diagonals? **They must each be between 2 and 22.**

16. Two sides of a triangle have lengths 15 and 20. The length of the third side can be any number between _?_ and _?_. **5, 35**

Using a Model

Students can demonstrate Theorem 6-4 (The Triangle Inequality) by experimenting with different combinations of three sticks of various lengths. If the three lengths can be the lengths of the sides of a triangle, a triangle can be formed. If the lengths are not correct, no polygon can be formed with the three sticks.

Thinking Skills

These exercises require students to interpret and analyze pictorial information. Students need to understand the information given by the diagrams and then apply their knowledge of theorems, definitions, and postulates to find the solutions. Exercises of this type help students develop their ability to apply theorems and properties in a variety of situations.

17. Suppose you know only that the length of one side of a rectangle is 100. What can you say about the length of a diagonal? **It must be > 100.**

18. Use the diagram below to explain how Corollary 1 follows from Theorem 6-3. **A △ can have at most one right or obtuse ∠. Then $m\angle A > m\angle B$ and by Thm. 6-3, $PB > PA$.**

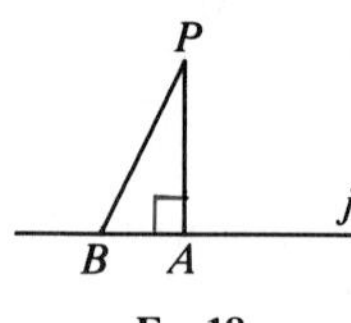

Ex. 18

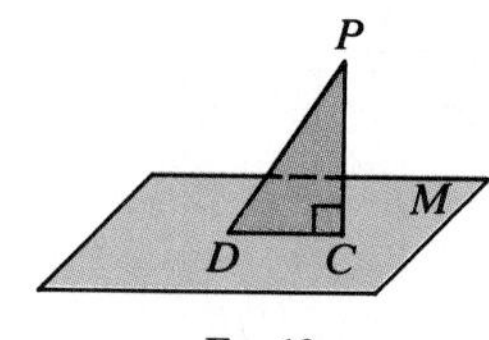

Ex. 19

19. A △ can have at most one right or obtuse ∠. Then $m\angle C > m\angle D$ and by Thm. 6-3, $PD > PC$.

19. Use the diagram, in which $\overline{PC} \perp$ plane M, to explain how Corollary 2 follows from Theorem 6-3 or from Corollary 1.

20. Which is the largest angle of a right triangle? Which is the longest side of a right triangle? Explain. **The largest ∠ is the right ∠. (The sum of the other 2 ∠s is 90, so they must both be < 90.) The longest side is the hypotenuse. (Thm. 6-3)**

Written Exercises

The lengths of two sides of a triangle are given. Write the numbers that best complete the statement: The length of the third side must be greater than __?__, but less than __?__.

A
1. 6, 9 **3, 15**
2. 15, 13 **2, 28**
3. 100, 100 **0, 200**
4. $7n$, $10n$ **$3n$, $17n$**
5. a, b (where $a > b$) **$a - b$, $a + b$**
6. k, $k + 5$ **5, $2k + 5$**

In Exercises 7–9 the diagrams are not drawn to scale. If each diagram were drawn to scale, which numbered angle would be the largest?

7. **∠2**

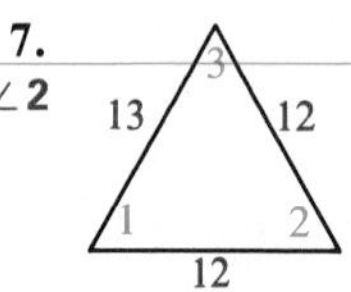

8. **∠1**

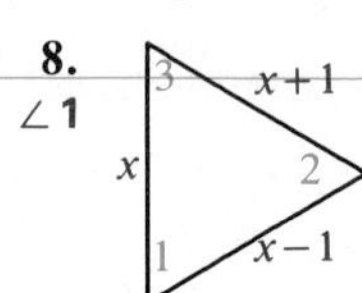

9. **∠3**

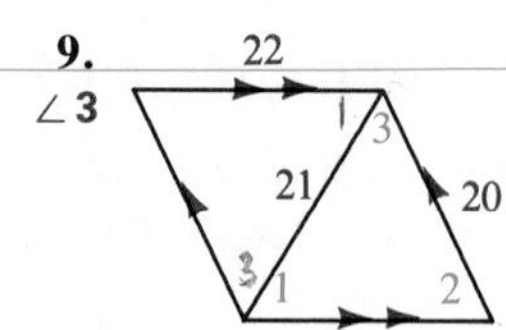

In Exercises 10–14 the diagrams are not drawn to scale. If each diagram were drawn to scale, which segment shown would be the longest?

10. **$\overline{DF}$**

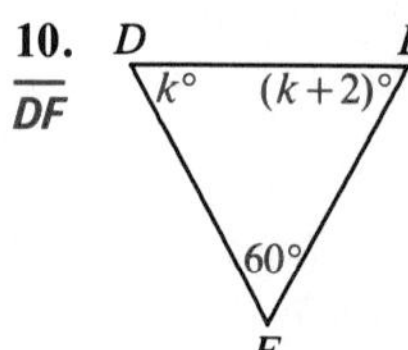

11. **$\overline{WT}$**

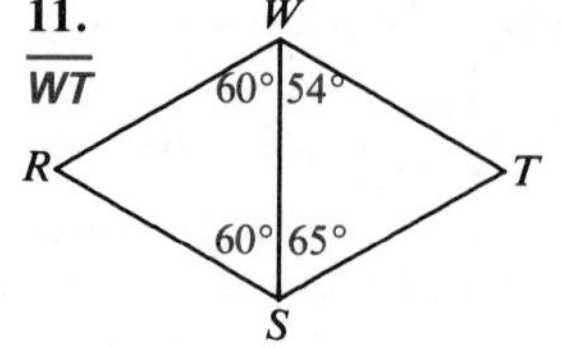

12. **$\overline{OA}$**

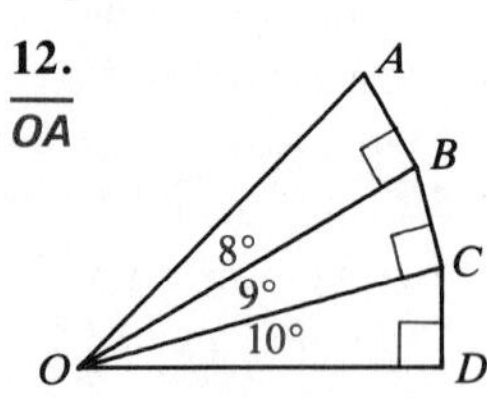

Guided Practice

1. The lengths of two sides of a triangle are given. Write the numbers that best complete the statement: The length of the third side must be greater than __?__ but less than __?__.
   a. 10, 12 2, 22
   b. 25, 25 0, 50
   c. $5x$, $7x$ $2x$, $12x$
   d. y, $y + 2$ 2, $2y + 2$

2. The following diagram is not drawn to scale. If it were drawn to scale, which of the angles would be the largest? ∠A

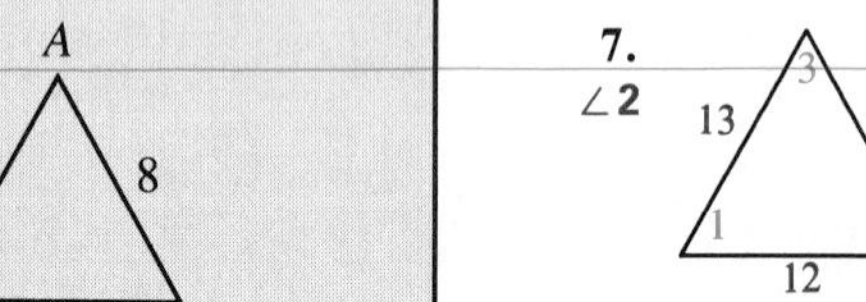

3. The following diagram is not drawn to scale. If it were drawn to scale, which segment would be the longest of those shown? $\overline{AB}$

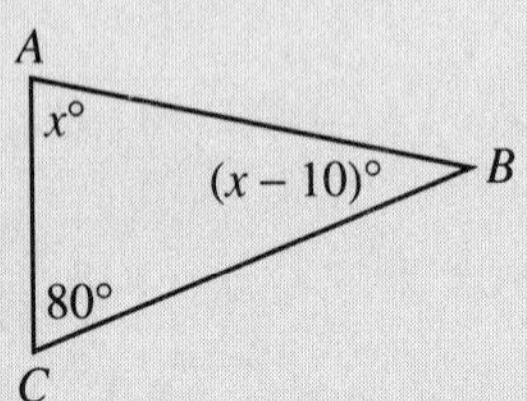

B **13.** $\overline{WY}$

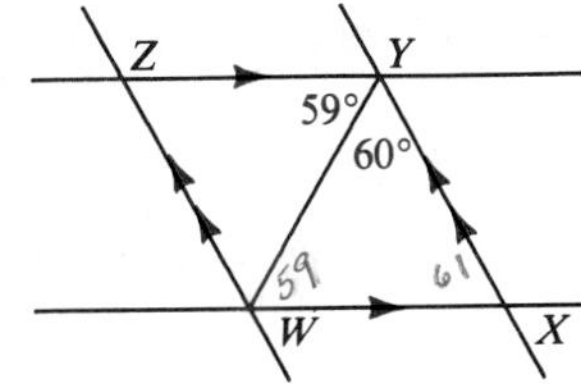

14. $\overline{VB}$

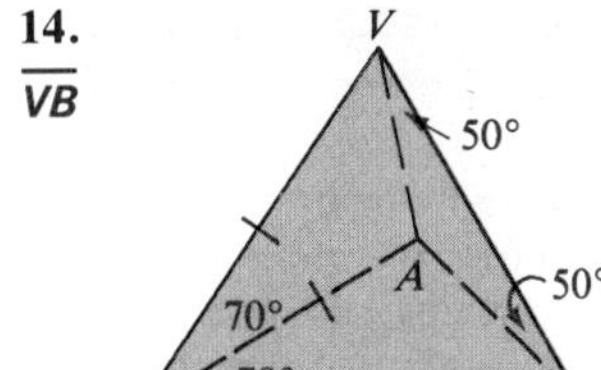

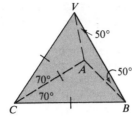

15. Use the lengths a, b, c, d, and e to complete:
___?___ > ___?___ > ___?___ > ___?___ > ___?___

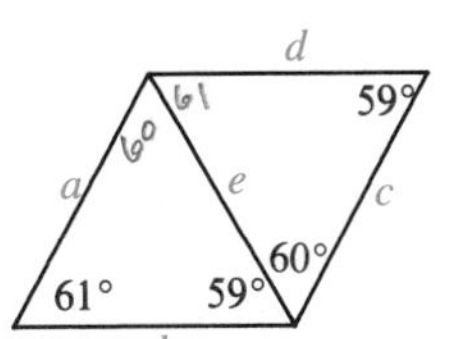

$c > d > e \geq b > a$

16. Use $m\angle 1$, $m\angle 2$, and $m\angle 3$ to complete:
___?___ > ___?___ > ___?___

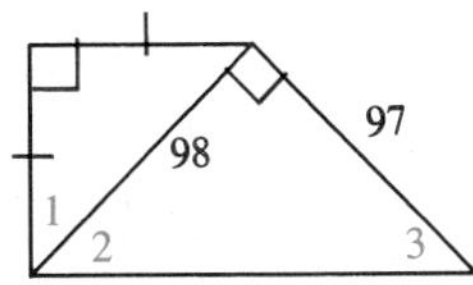

$m\angle 3 > m\angle 1 > m\angle 2$

17. The diagram is not drawn to scale. Use $m\angle 1$, $m\angle 2$, $m\angle X$, $m\angle Y$, and $m\angle XZY$ to complete:
___?___ > ___?___ > ___?___ > ___?___ > ___?___
$m\angle 2 > m\angle X > m\angle XZY > m\angle Y > m\angle 1$

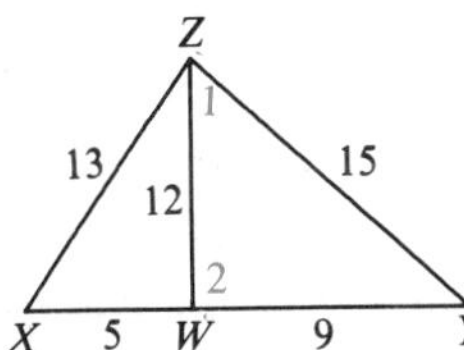

18. Given: Quad. $ABCD$
Prove: $AB + BC + CD + DA > 2(AC)$

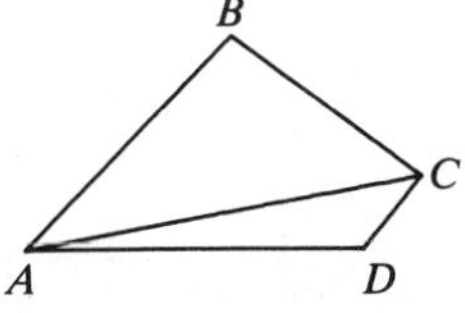

19. Given: ▱$EFGH$; $EF > FG$
Prove: $m\angle 1 > m\angle 2$

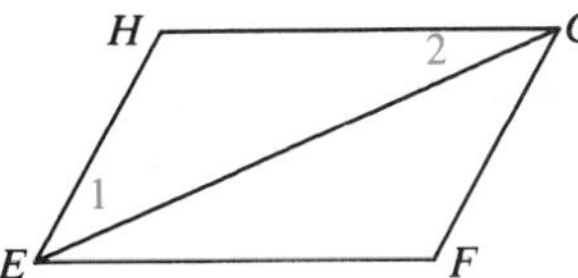

The perim. of a quad. > the sum of the lengths of the diag.

C **20.** Discover, state, and prove a theorem that compares the perimeter of a quadrilateral with the sum of the lengths of the diagonals.

21. Prove that the sum of the lengths of the medians of a triangle is greater than half the perimeter.

22. If you replace "medians" with "altitudes" in Exercise 21, can you prove the resulting statement? Explain. **No; consider △ ABC with $m\angle A = 170$.**

In Exercises 23 and 24, begin your proofs by drawing auxiliary lines.

23. Discover, state, and prove a theorem that compares the length of the longest side of a quadrilateral with the sum of the lengths of the other three sides. **The length of the longest side of a quad. is < the sum of the lengths of the other 3 sides.**

24. Prove: If P is any point inside $\triangle XYZ$, then $ZX + ZY > PX + PY$.

Exercise Note

For Exs. 23 and 24, remind students about the use of auxiliary lines in proofs.

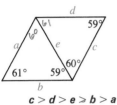

Application — Finding the Shortest Path

The owners of pipeline l plan to construct a pumping station at a point S on line l in order to pipe oil to two major customers, located at A and B. To minimize the cost of constructing lines from S to A and B, they wish to locate S along l so that the distance $SA + SB$ is as small as possible.

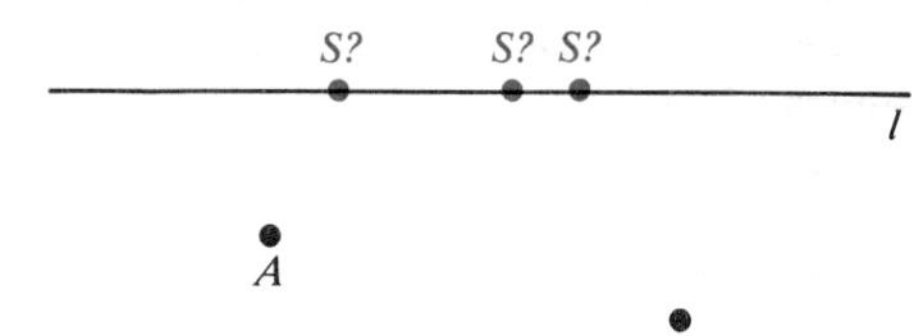

The construction engineer uses the following method to locate S:

1. Draw a line through B perpendicular to l, intersecting l at point P.
2. On this perpendicular, locate point C so that $PC = PB$.
3. Draw $\overline{AC}$.
4. Locate S at the intersection of $\overline{AC}$ and l.

Figure 1

Making Connections

In transformational geometry, point C is known as the reflection image of point B. A composition of reflections can be used to find the path of a billiard ball or a golf ball, a topic studied in Chapter 14.

Figure 2 shows the path of the new pipelines through the pumping station located at S, and an alternative path going through a different point, X, on l. You can use Theorem 6-4 (the Triangle Inequality) to show that if X is any point on l other than S, then $AX + XB > AS + SB$. So any alternative path is longer than the path through S.

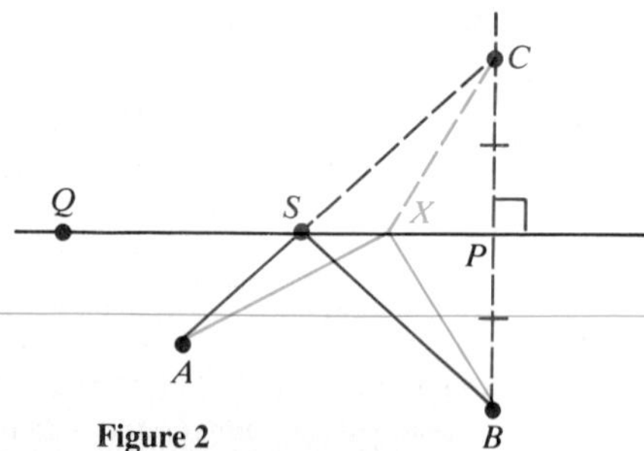

Figure 2

Exercises

Exercises 1 and 2 refer to Figure 2 on the preceding page.

1. Supply the reason for each key step of the proof that the method given for finding S yields the shortest total length for the pipelines serving A and B.

1. l is the perpendicular bisector of $\overline{BC}$. **Def. of ⊥ bisector**
2. $SC = SB$ **If a pt. lies on the ⊥ bis. of a seg., it is equid. from the endpts. of the seg.**
3. $AS + SC = AC$ **Segment Add. Post.**
4. $AS + SB = AC$ **Substitution Prop.**
5. $XC = XB$ **See 2. (above)**
6. $AX + XC > AC$ **△ Ineq. Thm.**
7. $AX + XB > AS + SB$ **Substitution Prop.**

2. This method for finding S is sometimes called a *solution by reflection*, since it involves *reflecting* point B in line l. (See Chapter 14 for more on reflections.) Show that $\overline{AS}$ and $\overline{SB}$, like reflected paths of light, make congruent angles with l. That is, prove that $\angle QSA \cong \angle PSB$. (*Hint*: Draw your own diagram, omitting the part of Figure 2 shown in blue.)

Explorations

These exploratory exercises can be done using a computer with a program that draws and measures geometric figures.

Draw several *pairs* of triangles, varying the size of just one side or just one angle. Make charts like the ones below to record your data. Record the lengths of the sides and measures of the angles you give, as well as the measurements you get. Do as many pairs as you need to help you recognize a pattern.

Enter the lengths of all three sides (SSS).

pair 1	
$AB =$ $BC =$ $AC =$	same $AB =$ same $BC =$ longer $AC =$
$m\angle ABC =$	$m\angle ABC =$

What happened to the angle opposite the side you made longer? **It got larger.**

Enter the lengths of two sides and the included angle (SAS).

pair 1	
$AB =$ $\angle BAC =$ $AC =$	same $AB =$ larger $\angle BAC =$ same $AC =$
$BC =$	$BC =$

What happened to the side opposite the angle you made larger? **It got longer.**

Using a Computer

These exercises explore the inequality theorems of the next lesson.

Using a Computer

This Computer Key-In features an interesting problem using random numbers and probability theory. It shows how computer simulation can be used to solve a geometric problem. Even if you do not assign the exercises, you may wish to discuss the program with students because it provides an interesting application of Theorem 6-4.

♦ Computer Key-In

If you break a stick into three pieces, what is the probability that you can join the pieces end-to-end to form a triangle?

It's easy to see that if the sum of the lengths of any two of the pieces is less than or equal to that of the third, a triangle can't be formed. This is the Triangle Inequality (Theorem 6-4).

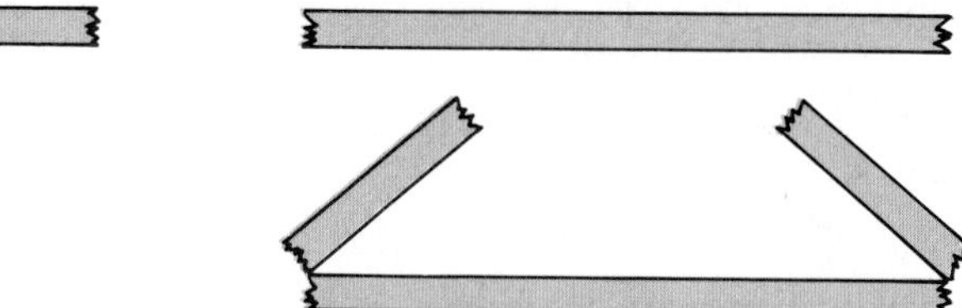

By an experiment, your class can estimate the probability that three pieces of broken stick will form a triangle. Suppose everyone in your class has a stick 1 unit long and breaks it into three pieces. If there are thirty people in your class and eight people are able to form a triangle with their pieces, we estimate that the probability of forming a triangle is about $\frac{8}{30}$, or $\frac{4}{15}$.

Of course, this experiment is not very practical. You can get much better results by having a computer simulate the breaking of many, many sticks, as in the program in BASIC on the next page.

Computer simulations are useful whenever large numbers of operations need to be done in a short period of time. In this problem, for example, an accurate probability depends on using a large number of sticks. Computer simulations have been used when a real experiment would be costly or dangerous; aeronautics companies use real-time flight simulators on the ground to train pilots. Simulations are also applied to investigate statistical data where many variables determine the outcome, as in the analysis and prediction of weather patterns. In the stick-triangle problem, using the computer has another advantage—a computer can break very small pieces that a human couldn't, so the probability figure will be theoretically more accurate, if less "realistic."

In lines 30 and 40 of the following program, you tell the computer how many sticks you want to break. Each stick is 1 unit long, and the computer breaks each stick by choosing two random numbers x and y between 0 and 1. These numbers divide the stick into three lengths r, s, and t.

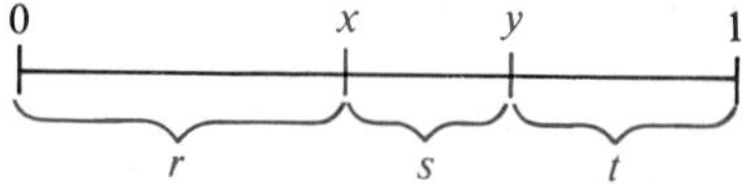

The computer then keeps count of the number of sticks (N) which form a triangle when broken.

Notice that RND is used in lines 70 and 80. Since usage of RND varies, check this with the manual for your computer and make any necessary changes. The computer print-outs shown in this text use capital letters. The x, y, r, s, and t used in the discussion above appear as X, Y, R, S, T.

```
10  PRINT "SIMULATION--BREAKING STICKS TO MAKE TRIANGLES"
20  PRINT
30  PRINT "HOW MANY STICKS DO YOU WANT TO BREAK";
40  INPUT D
50  LET N = 0
60  FOR I = 1 TO D
70  LET X = RND (1)
80  LET Y = RND (1)
90  IF X > = Y THEN 70
100  LET R = X
110  LET S = Y - R
120  LET T = 1 - R - S
130  IF R + S < = T THEN 170
140  IF S + T < = R THEN 170
150  IF R + T < = S THEN 170
160  LET N = N + 1
170  NEXT I
180  LET P = N/D
190  PRINT
200  PRINT "THE EXPERIMENTAL PROBABILITY THAT"
210  PRINT "A BROKEN STICK CAN FORM A TRIANGLE IS ";P
220  END
```

Line Number	Explanation
60–120	These lines simulate the breaking of each stick. When I = 10, for example, the computer is "breaking" the tenth stick.
130–150	Here the computer uses the Triangle Inequality to check whether the pieces of the broken stick can form a triangle. If not, the computer goes on to the next stick (line 170) and the value of N is not affected.
160	If the broken stick has survived the tests of steps 130–150, then the pieces can form a triangle and the value of N is increased by 1.
170	Lines 60–170 form a loop that is repeated D times. After I = D, the probability P is calculated and printed (lines 180–210).

Exercises

1. Pick any two numbers x and y between 0 and 1 with $x < y$. With paper and pencil, carry out the instructions in lines 100 through 150 of the program to see how the computer finds r, s, and t and tests to see whether the values can be the lengths of the sides of a triangle.

2. If you use a language other than BASIC, write a similar program for your computer.

3. Run the program several times for large values of D, say 100, 400, 800, and compare your results with those of some classmates. Does the probability that the pieces of a broken stick form a triangle appear to be less than or greater than $\frac{1}{2}$? **Less than $\frac{1}{2}$**

Teaching Suggestions, p. T100

Objective
Presenting the Lesson
Extension

Supplementary Materials

Practice Master 33
Test 23
Resource Book, pp. 34, 131
Study Guide, pp. 77–78

Lesson Focus

This lesson presents two inequality theorems for triangles. The theorems are not difficult to understand but are somewhat difficult to prove.

Suggested Assignments

Minimum
Day 1: 231/1–8
S 223/17
Day 2: 232/9–12
233/Self-Test 2
Day 3: 236–237/Chapter Test

Average
Day 1: 231/1–8
S 223/14, 17
Day 2: 232/9–13
233/Self-Test 2
Day 3: 236–237/Chapter Test

Maximum
Day 1: 231–232/1–15 odd
S 223/20, 22
Day 2: 236–237/Chapter Test

Thinking Skills

Theorems 6-5 and 6-6 are often referred to as "hinge theorems." Ask students to explain why.

6-5 *Inequalities for Two Triangles*

Begin with two matched pairs of sticks joined loosely at B and E. Open them so that $m\angle B > m\angle E$ and you find that $AC > DF$. Conversely, if you open them so that $AC > DF$, you see that $m\angle B > m\angle E$. Two theorems are suggested by these examples. The first theorem is surprisingly difficult to prove. The second theorem has an indirect proof.

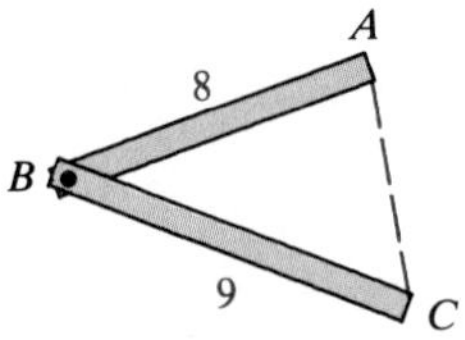

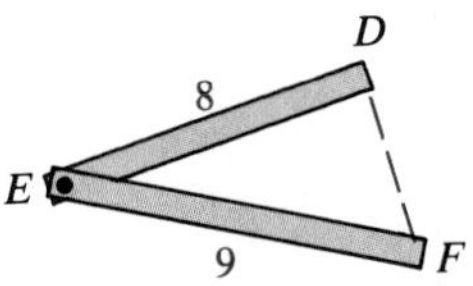

Theorem 6-5 *SAS Inequality Theorem*

If two sides of one triangle are congruent to two sides of another triangle, but the included angle of the first triangle is larger than the included angle of the second, then the third side of the first triangle is longer than the third side of the second triangle.

Given: $\overline{BA} \cong \overline{ED}$; $\overline{BC} \cong \overline{EF}$;
$m\angle B > m\angle E$

Prove: $AC > DF$

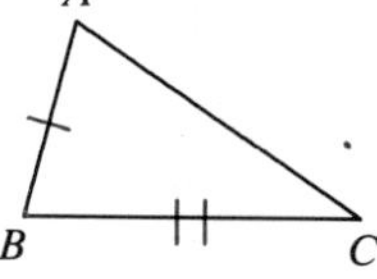

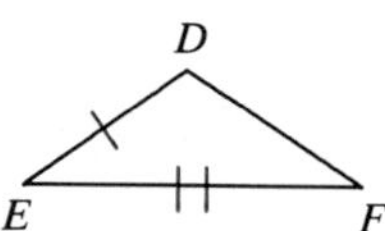

Proof:

Draw $\overrightarrow{BZ}$ so that $m\angle ZBC = m\angle E$. On $\overrightarrow{BZ}$ take point X so that $BX = ED$.
Then either X is on $\overline{AC}$ or X is not on $\overline{AC}$.
In both cases $\triangle XBC \cong \triangle DEF$ by SAS, and $XC = DF$.

Case 1: X is on $\overline{AC}$.
$AC > XC$ (Seg. Add. Post. and a Prop. of Ineq.)
$AC > DF$ (Substitution Property, using the equation in red above)

Case 2: X is not on $\overline{AC}$.
Draw the bisector of $\angle ABX$, intersecting $\overline{AC}$ at Y.
Draw $\overline{XY}$ and $\overline{XC}$.
$BA = ED = BX$
Since $\triangle ABY \cong \triangle XBY$ (SAS), $AY = XY$.
$XY + YC > XC$ (Why?) **The △ Ineq.**
$AY + YC > XC$ (Why?), or $AC > XC$
$AC > DF$ (Substitution Property)
Substitution Prop.

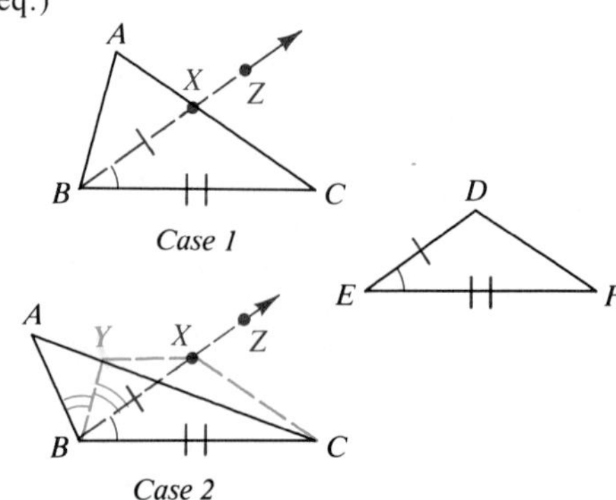

Theorem 6-6 *SSS Inequality Theorem*

If two sides of one triangle are congruent to two sides of another triangle, but the third side of the first triangle is longer than the third side of the second, then the included angle of the first triangle is larger than the included angle of the second.

Given: $\overline{BA} \cong \overline{ED}$; $\overline{BC} \cong \overline{EF}$;
$AC > DF$

Prove: $m\angle B > m\angle E$

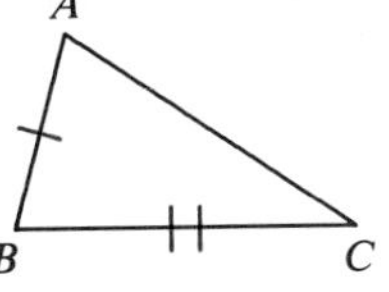

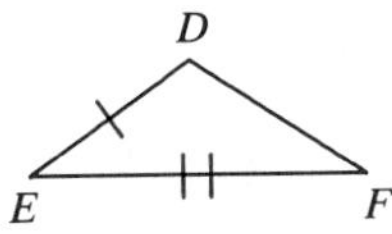

Proof:

Assume temporarily that $m\angle B \not> m\angle E$.
Then either $m\angle B = m\angle E$ or $m\angle B < m\angle E$.

Case 1: If $m\angle B = m\angle E$, then $\triangle ABC \cong \triangle DEF$ by the SAS Postulate, and $AC = DF$.

Case 2: If $m\angle B < m\angle E$, then $AC < DF$ by the SAS Inequality Theorem.

In both cases there is a contradiction of the given fact that $AC > DF$. What was temporarily assumed to be true, that $m\angle B \not> m\angle E$, must be false. It follows that $m\angle B > m\angle E$.

Example 1 Given: $\overline{RS} \cong \overline{RT}$; $m\angle 1 > m\angle 2$
What can you deduce?

Solution In the two triangles you have $\overline{RV} \cong \overline{RV}$ as well as $\overline{RS} \cong \overline{RT}$. Since $m\angle 1 > m\angle 2$, you can apply the SAS Inequality Theorem to get $SV > TV$.

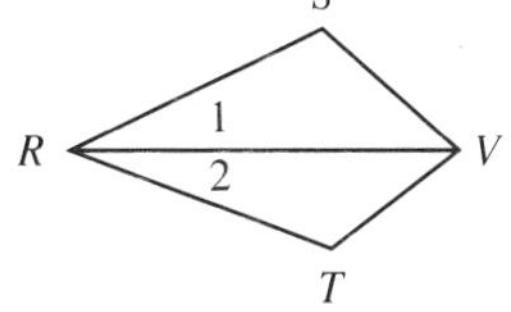

Example 2 Given: $\overline{EF} \cong \overline{EG}$; $DF > DG$
What can you deduce?

Solution $\overline{DE}$ and $\overline{EF}$ of $\triangle DEF$ are congruent to $\overline{DE}$ and $\overline{EG}$ of $\triangle DEG$. Since $DF > DG$, you can apply the SSS Inequality Theorem to get $m\angle DEF > m\angle DEG$.

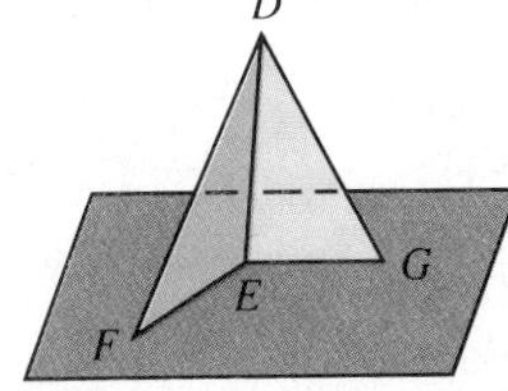

Making Connections

Converses of theorems are important in mathematics because they may also be true. The converse of Theorem 6-5 is also true (Theorem 6-6). You may want to review converses, introduced on page 33.

Chalkboard Examples

1. Given: D is the midpoint of $\overline{AC}$; $m\angle 1 < m\angle 2$
What can you deduce?

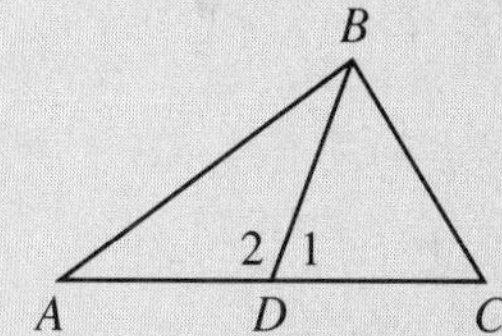

In the two triangles, you have $\overline{BD} \cong \overline{BD}$ (Reflexive) as well as $\overline{AD} \cong \overline{CD}$ (Definition of midpoint). Since $m\angle 1 < m\angle 2$, you can apply the SAS Inequality Theorem to get $BC < AB$.

2. Write a two-column proof.
Given: $\overline{BC} \cong \overline{DC}$;
$AB > AD$
Prove: $m\angle 1 > m\angle 2$

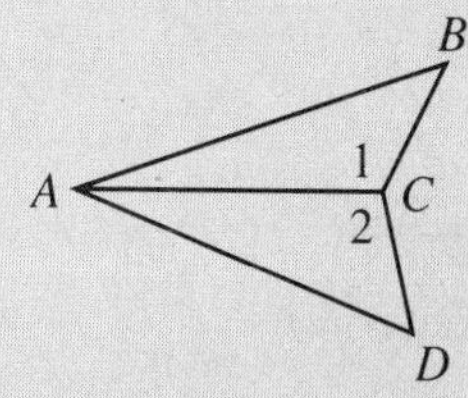

1. $\overline{BC} \cong \overline{DC}$; $AB > AD$ (Given)
2. $\overline{AC} \cong \overline{AC}$ (Refl. Prop.)
3. $m\angle 1 > m\angle 2$ (SSS Ineq. Thm.)

Classroom Exercises

What can you deduce? Name the theorem that supports your answer.

1.

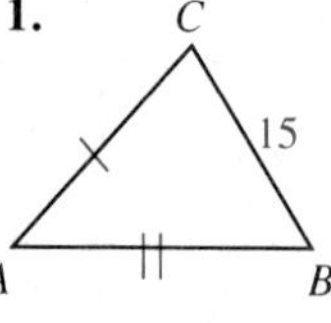

F 14 D E

***m∠CAB > m∠FDE*; SSS Ineq.**

2.

L 40° J K

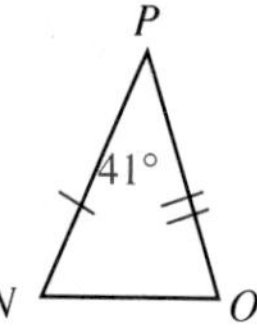

***NO > JK*; SAS Ineq.**

3. $m\angle 1 > m\angle 2$

T 1 2 R V S

***RT > TS*; SAS Ineq.**

4. ∠1 is a rt. ∠; ∠2 is an obtuse ∠.

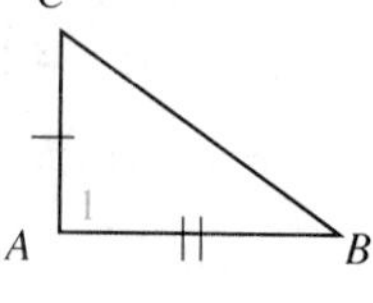

F 2 D E

***EF > BC*; SAS Ineq.**

5.

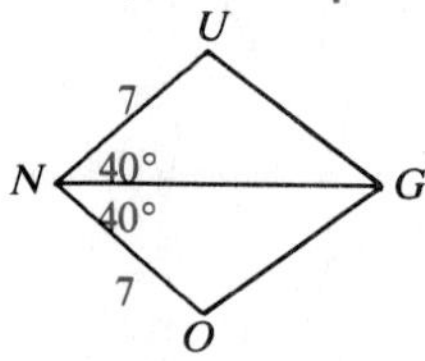

△*UNG* ≅ △*ONG*; SAS

6.

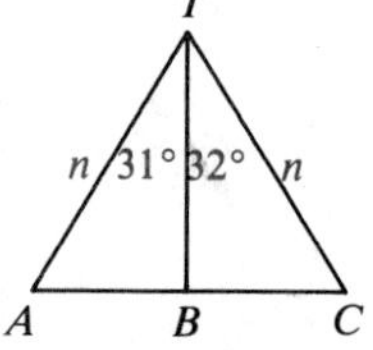

***BC > AB*; SAS Ineq.**

7.

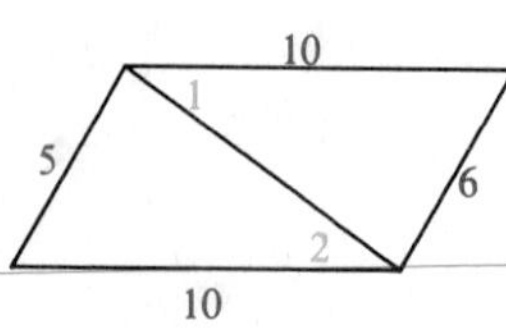

***m∠1 > m∠2*; SSS Ineq.**

8.

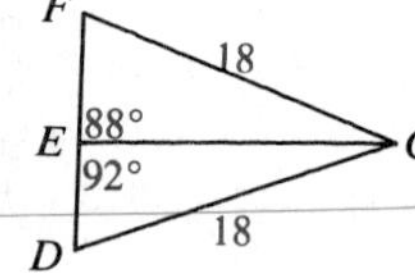

***EF > ED*; SAS Ineq.**

You will need a centimeter ruler and a protractor for Exercises 9 and 10.

9. a. Draw an isosceles triangle with legs 7 cm long and a vertex angle of 120°. Measure the length of the base of the triangle. **about 12.1 cm**

b. If you keep the legs at 7 cm in length but halve the measure of the vertex angle to 60°, what happens to the length of the base? What kind of triangle is this new triangle? What is the length of the third side? **equilateral; 7 cm**

10. a. Draw a right triangle with legs of 6 cm and 8 cm. Measure the length of the hypotenuse. **10 cm**

b. If you keep the 6 cm and 8 cm sides the same lengths but halve the measure of the included angle to 45°, what happens to the length of the third side? Test your answer by drawing the new triangle. **about 5.6 cm**

Written Exercises

What can you deduce? Name the theorem that supports your answer.

A

1. Given: $\overline{AM}$ is a median of $\triangle ABC$; $AB > AC$

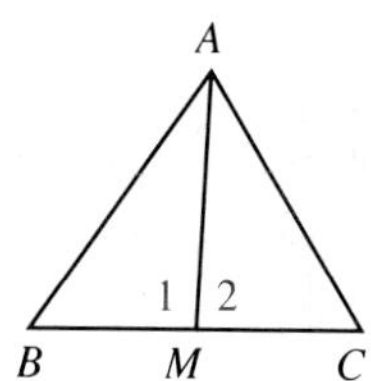

$m\angle 1 > m\angle 2$; **SSS Ineq.**

2. Given: $\square RSTV$; $m\angle TSR > m\angle VRS$

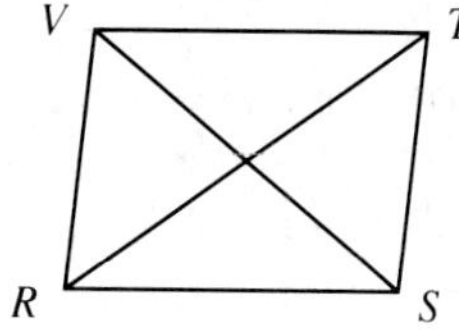

$TR > VS$; **SAS Ineq.**

Complete the statements by writing $<$, $=$, or $>$.

3. XY __?__ XZ; $>$
XW __?__ 12 $>$

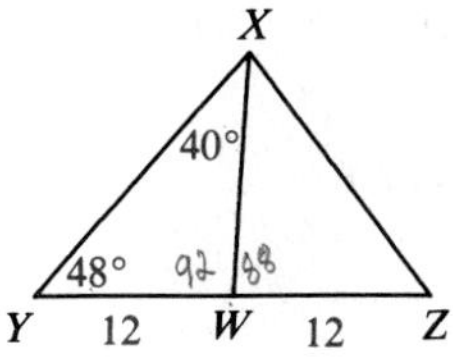

4. AD __?__ CE $<$

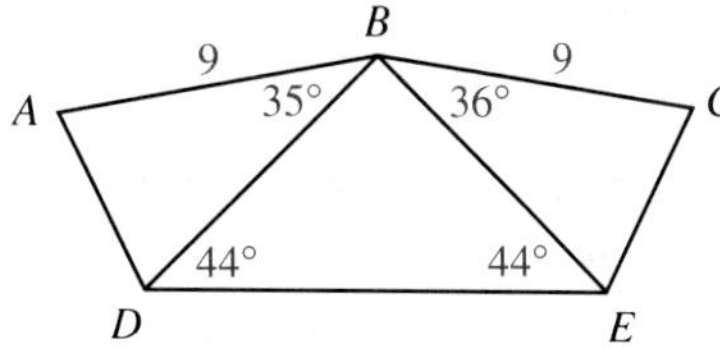

5. $m\angle 1$ __?__ $m\angle 2$; $<$
$m\angle 3$ __?__ $m\angle 4$ $>$

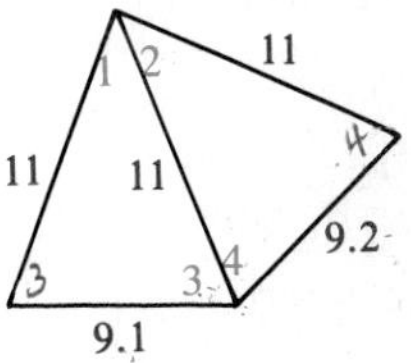

6. $m\angle 5$ __?__ $m\angle 6$ $<$

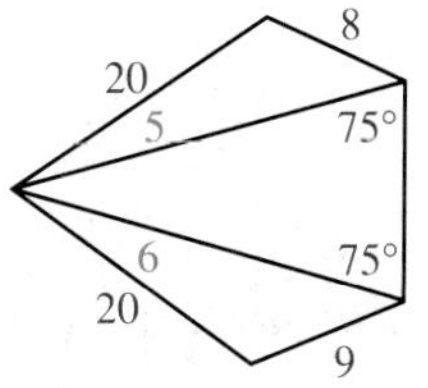

7. a __?__ b $<$

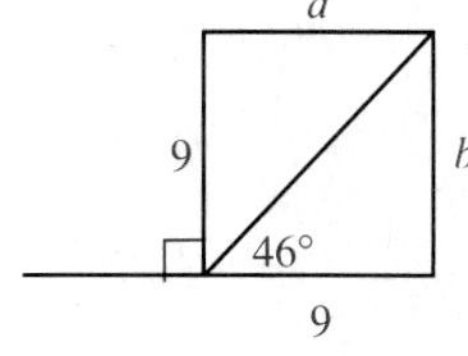

8. c __?__ 10 $<$

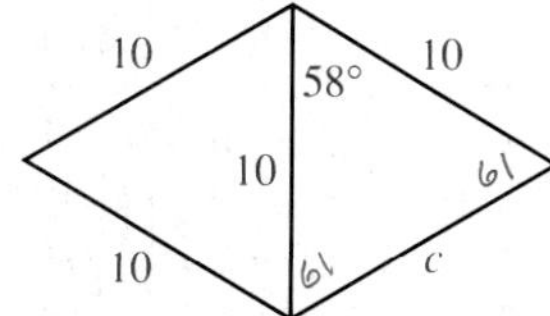

Guided Practice

1. What can you deduce? Name the theorem that supports your answer.
Given: $\overline{XZ} \cong \overline{YZ}$;
$m\angle 3 > m\angle 4$
$\overline{XW} > \overline{WY}$ (SAS Ineq. Thm.)

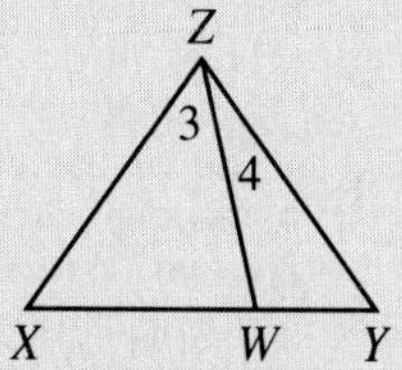

Complete with $<$, $=$, or $>$.

2. $m\angle 1 \geq m\angle 2$

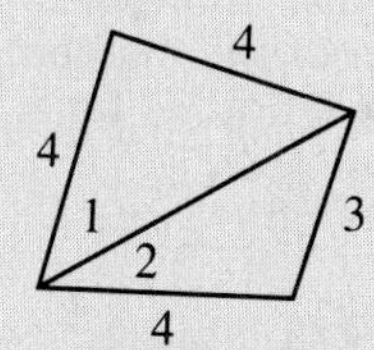

3. $m\angle SRT \leq m\angle URV$

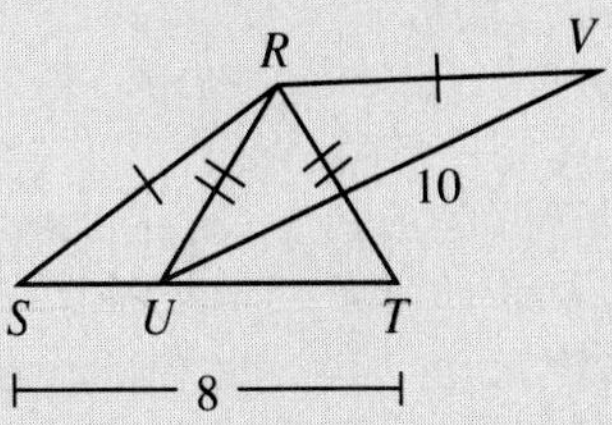

Cultural Note

Students reading about non-Euclidean geometries on pages 233–234 may be interested to learn about the impact that Euclidean geometry has had upon mathematics. Euclid's *Elements*, which dates from around 300 B.C., is essentially a geometry textbook and has served as such until modern times. It is one of the most widely translated and published books ever. Little is known about Euclid himself. Like many other scholars of his time, he lived in Alexandria, Egypt. His greatest achievement in the *Elements* is his clear and logical organization of the mathematical knowledge of his time.

Complete the statements by writing <, =, or >.

B 9. $m\angle 1$ _?_ $m\angle 2$ **>**

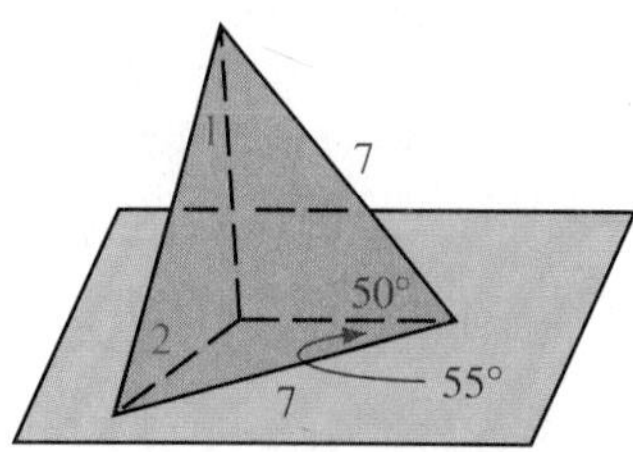

10. $SR = ST$; $VX = VT$
$m\angle RSV$ _?_ $m\angle TSV$ **>**

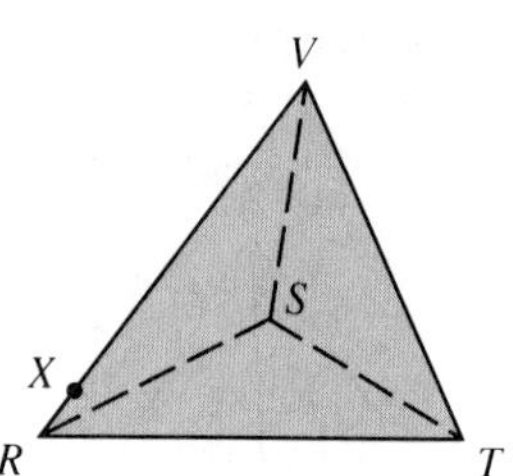

Write proofs in two-column form.

11. Given: $\overline{TU} \cong \overline{US} \cong \overline{SV}$
Prove: $ST > SV$

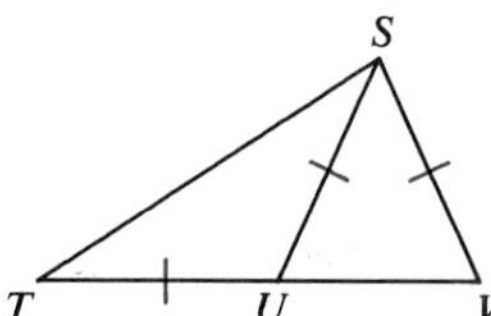

12. Given: Plane P bisects $\overline{XZ}$ at Y;
$WZ > WX$
Discover and prove something about the figure. **$\overline{XZ}$ is not ⊥ to plane P**

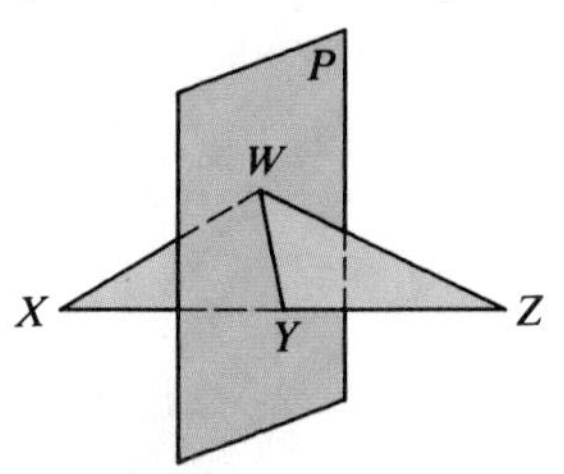

C 13. Given: $\overline{PA} \cong \overline{PC} \cong \overline{QC} \cong \overline{QB}$
Prove: $m\angle PCA < m\angle QCB$

14. Given: $\overline{DE} \perp$ plane M; $EK > EJ$
Prove: $DK > DJ$
(*Hint*: On $\overline{EK}$, take Z so that $EZ = EJ$.)

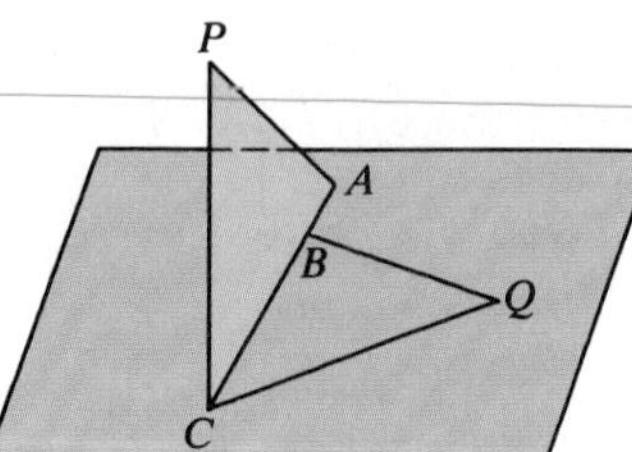

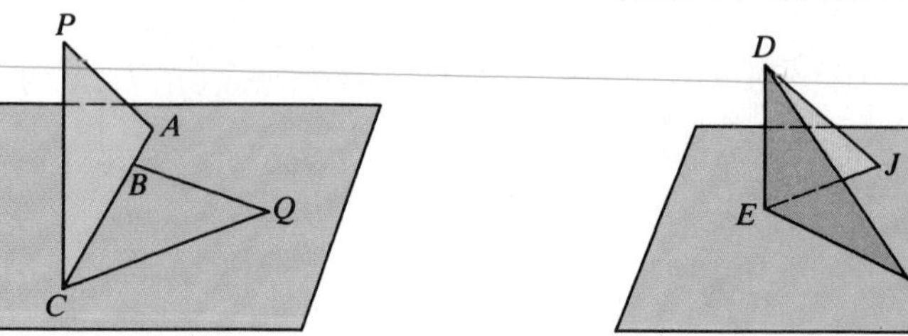

15. In the three-dimensional figure shown, all the edges *except* $\overline{VC}$ are congruent. What can you say about the measures of the largest angles of the twelve angles in the figure

a. if $\overline{VC}$ is longer than the other edges?

b. if $\overline{VC}$ is shorter than the other edges?

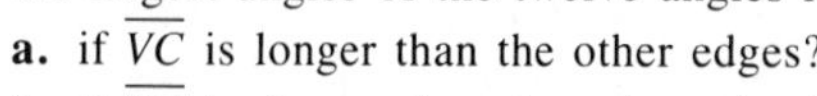

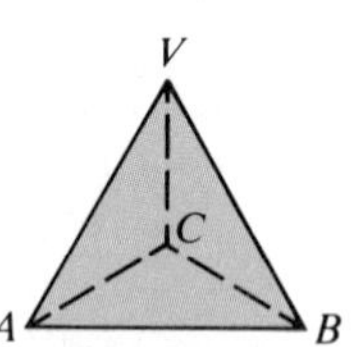

a. $\angle VBC$ and $\angle VAC$ are the largest ∠s, each measuring > 60, but < 120.
b. $\angle BVC$, $\angle BCV$, $\angle AVC$, and $\angle ACV$ are the largest ∠s, each measuring > 60, but < 90.

Self-Test 2

1. In $\triangle XYZ$, $m\angle X = 50$, $m\angle Y = 60$, and $m\angle Z = 70$. Name the longest side of the triangle. $\overline{XY}$
2. In $\triangle DOM$, $\angle O$ is a right angle and $m\angle D > m\angle M$. Which side of $\triangle DOM$ is the shortest side? $\overline{OD}$

Complete each statement by writing <, =, or >.

3. If $ER > EN$, then $m\angle R$ _?_ $m\angle N$. <
4. If $\overline{AG} \cong \overline{ER}$, $\overline{AP} \cong \overline{EN}$, and $\angle A \cong \angle E$, then GP _?_ RN. =
5. If $\overline{GA} \cong \overline{RE}$, $\overline{GP} \cong \overline{RN}$, and $AP > EN$, then $m\angle G$ _?_ $m\angle R$. >

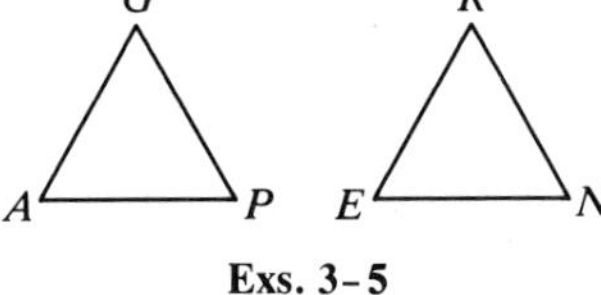

Exs. 3–5

6. The lengths of the sides of a triangle are 5, 6, and x. Then x must be greater than _?_ and less than _?_. 1, 11

The longer diagonal of ▱*QRST* is $\overline{QS}$. Tell whether each statement *must be*, *may be*, or *cannot be* true.

7. $\angle R$ is an acute angle. cannot be
8. $QS > RS$ must be
9. $RS > RT$ may be

Extra — *Non-Euclidean Geometries*

When you develop a geometry, you have some choice as to which statements you are going to postulate and which you are going to prove. For example, consider these two statements:

(A) If two parallel lines are cut by a transversal, then corresponding angles are congruent.

(B) Through a point outside a line, there is exactly one line parallel to the given line.

In this book, statement (A) is Postulate 10 and statement (B) is Theorem 3-8. In some books, statement (B) is a postulate (commonly called Euclid's *Parallel Postulate*) and statement (A) is a theorem. In still other developments, both of these statements are proved on the basis of some third statement chosen as a postulate.

A geometry that provides for a unique parallel to a line through a point not on the line is called *Euclidean*, so this text is a Euclidean geometry book. In the nineteenth century, it was discovered that geometries exist in which the Parallel Postulate is *not true*. Such geometries are called *non-Euclidean*. The statements at the top of the next page show the key differences between Euclidean geometry and two types of non-Euclidean geometry.

Quick Quiz

1. In $\triangle ABC$, $m\angle A = 40$, $m\angle B = 80$, and $m\angle C = 60$. Name the longest side of the triangle. $\overline{AC}$
2. In $\triangle XYZ$, $m\angle X > m\angle Z$ and $m\angle Y = 90$. Which side of $\triangle XYZ$ is the longest? $\overline{XZ}$

Complete with <, =, or >.

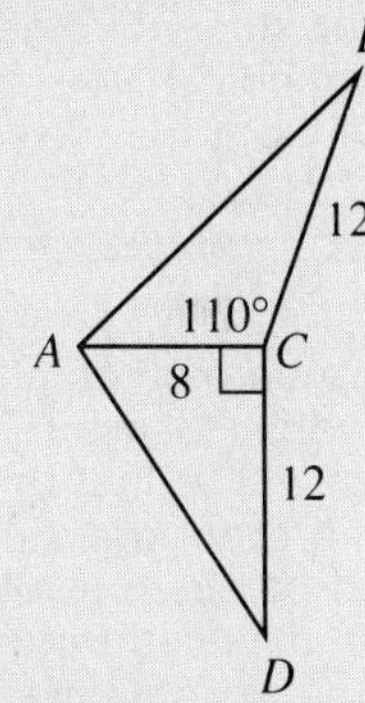

3. $m\angle CAD$ $\underline{>}$ $m\angle D$
4. $\overline{AD}$ $\underline{<}$ $\overline{AB}$
5. $m\angle B$ $\underline{<}$ $m\angle BAC$
6. The lengths of the sides of a triangle are 3.2, 4.5, and x. The value of x must be greater than $\underline{1.3}$ and less than $\underline{7.7}$.
7. Write the lengths a, b, c, d, and e in order from the smallest to largest. c, b, e, a, d

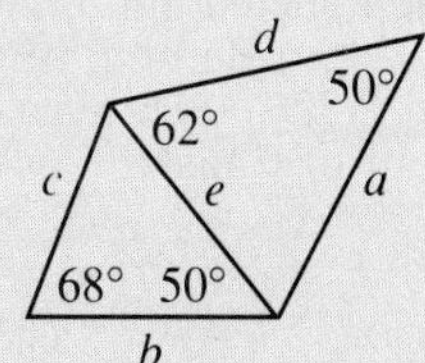

Euclidean geometry	Through a point outside a line, there is *exactly one* line parallel to the given line.
Hyperbolic geometry	Through a point outside a line, there is *more than one* line parallel to the given line. (This geometry was discovered by Bolyai, Lobachevsky, and Gauss.)
Elliptic geometry	Through a point outside a line, there is *no* line parallel to the given line. (This geometry was discovered by Riemann and is used by ship and airplane navigators.)

To see a model of a no-parallel geometry, visualize the surface of a sphere. Think of a line as being a great circle of the sphere, that is, the intersection of the sphere and a plane that passes through the center of the sphere. On the sphere, through a point outside a line, there is no line parallel to the given line. All lines, as defined, intersect. In the figure, for example, X is a point not on the red great circle. A line has been drawn through X, namely the great circle shown in blue. You can see that the two lines intersect in *two* points, A and B.

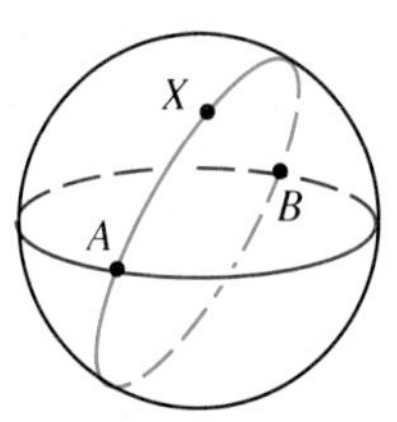

To see how statement (B) follows from our postulates, notice that Postulates 10 and 11 play a crucial role in the following proof. In fact, without such assumptions about parallels there couldn't be a proof. Before the discovery of non-Euclidean geometries people didn't know that this was the case and tried, without success, to find a proof that was independent of any assumption about parallels.

Given: Point P outside line k.

Prove: (1) There is a line through P parallel to k.
(2) There is only one line through P parallel to k.

Key steps of proof of (1):

1. Draw a line through P and some point Q on k. (Postulates 5 and 6)
2. Draw line l so that $\angle 2$ and $\angle 1$ are corresponding angles and $m\angle 2 = m\angle 1$. (Protractor Postulate)
3. $l \parallel k$, so there is a line through P parallel to k. (Postulate 11)

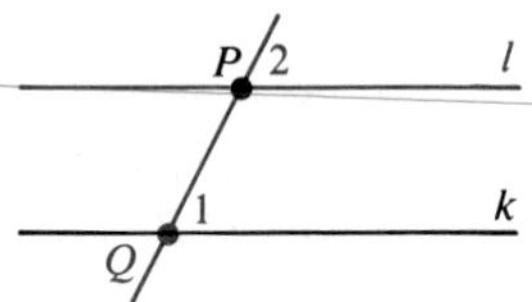

Indirect proof of (2):

Assume temporarily that there are at least two lines, x and y, through P parallel to k. Draw a line through P and some point R on k. $\angle 4 \cong \angle 3$ and $\angle 5 \cong \angle 3$ by Postulate 10, so $\angle 5 \cong \angle 4$. But since x and y are different lines we also have $m\angle 5 > m\angle 4$. This is impossible, so our assumption must be false, and it follows that there is only one line through P parallel to k.

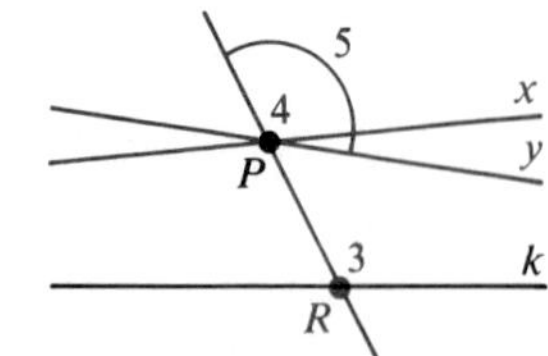

Teaching Note

At this point in the course, students may not have a clear idea of what constitutes a geometry. Since this Extra on "Non-Euclidean Geometries" provides particularly interesting and useful information on the existence of other geometries and the Parallel Postulate, you may wish to cover it in class with your students. See also the Biographical Note on page 304.

Cultural Note

The German mathematician Carl Friedrich Gauss (1777–1855) set out at first to provide solid proof that Euclid's so-called parallel postulate could be deduced from Euclid's other axioms. He eventually became convinced that it was impossible to do so, and began to work on a non-Euclidean geometry. The Hungarian mathematician Jànos Bolyai (1802–1860) and the Russian mathematician Nikolai Lobachevsky (1793–1856) made contemporary but independent explorations of non-Euclidean geometry. (For more on Lobachevsky, see page 304.) The German mathematician and philosopher Georg Bernhard Riemann (1826–1866) was a student of Gauss.

Chapter Summary

1. The properties of inequality most often used are stated on page 204.
2. The measure of an exterior angle of a triangle is greater than the measure of either remote interior angle. (The Exterior Angle Inequality Theorem)
3. The summary on page 208 gives the relationship between an if-then statement, its converse, its inverse, and its contrapositive. An if-then statement and its contrapositive are logically equivalent.
4. You begin an indirect proof by assuming temporarily that what you wish to prove true is *not* true. If this temporary assumption leads to a contradiction of a known fact, then your temporary assumption must be false and what you wish to prove true must be true.
5. In $\triangle RST$, if $RT > RS$, then $m\angle S > m\angle T$. Conversely, if $m\angle S > m\angle T$, then $RT > RS$.
6. The perpendicular segment from a point to a line (or plane) is the shortest segment from the point to the line (or plane).
7. The sum of the lengths of any two sides of a triangle is greater than the length of the third side. (The Triangle Inequality)
8. You can use the SAS Inequality and SSS Inequality Theorems to compare the lengths of sides and measures of angles in two triangles.

Supplementary Materials

Practice Master 34

Test 24

Resource Book, pp. 35–36, 132

Chapter Review

Complete each statement by writing <, =, or >.

1. $m\angle 1$ _?_ $m\angle 5$ > **6–1**
2. $m\angle 1$ _?_ $m\angle 2$ >
3. $m\angle 3$ _?_ $m\angle 4$ =
4. $m\angle 5$ _?_ $m\angle 2$ =
5. If $a > b$, $c < b$, and $d = c$, then a _?_ d. >

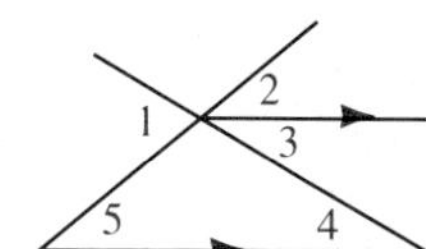

Given: All registered voters must be at least 18 years old.
What, if anything, can you conclude from each additional statement?

6. Eric is 19 years old. **No concl.**
7. Bonnie is not registered to vote. **No concl.** **6–2**
8. Will is 15 years old. **Will is not a registered voter.**
9. Barbara is a registered voter. **Barbara is at least 18 years old.**

10. Write the letters (a)–(d) in an order that completes an indirect proof of the statement: If $n^2 + 6 = 32$, then $n \neq 5$. **c, d, a, b** 6–3
(a) But this contradicts the fact that $n^2 + 6 = 32$.
(b) Our temporary assumption must be false, and it follows that $n \neq 5$.
(c) Assume temporarily that $n = 5$.
(d) Then $n^2 + 6 = 31$.

11. In $\triangle TOP$, if $OT > OP$, then $m\angle P >$ __?__. **$m\angle T$** 6–4

12. In $\triangle RED$, if $m\angle D < m\angle E$, then $RD >$ __?__. **RE**

13. Points X and Y are in plane M. If $\overline{PX} \perp$ plane M, then PX __?__ PY. $<$

14. Two sides of a triangle have lengths 6 and 8. The length of the third side must be greater than __?__ and less than __?__. **2, 14**

Complete each statement by writing $<$, $=$, or $>$.

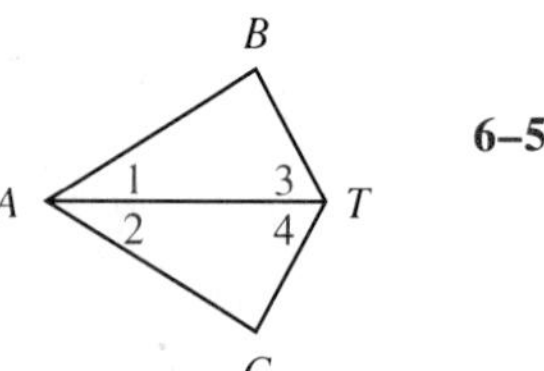

15. If $\overline{AB} \cong \overline{AC}$ and $m\angle 1 > m\angle 2$, then BT __?__ CT. $>$ 6–5

16. If $\overline{TB} \cong \overline{TC}$ and $AB < AC$, then $m\angle 3$ __?__ $m\angle 4$. $<$

17. If $\angle 1 \cong \angle 2$ and $\angle 3 \cong \angle 4$, then AB __?__ AC. $=$

18. If $\overline{TB} \cong \overline{TC}$ and $m\angle 3 > m\angle 4$, then AB __?__ AC. $>$

Teaching References

Alternate Test, p. T17

Chapter Test

5. a. If point P is not on $\overline{AB}$, then $AB \leq AP$.
b. If $AB \leq AP$, then point P is not on $\overline{AB}$.

Complete each statement by writing $<$, $=$, or $>$.

1. If $x > y$ and $y = z$, then x __?__ z. $>$

2. If $a > b$, and $c < b$, then c __?__ a. $<$

3. If $s = t + 4$, then s __?__ t. $>$

4. If $e + 5 = f + 4$, then e __?__ f. $<$

5. Write (a) the inverse and (b) the contrapositive of "If point P is on $\overline{AB}$, then $AB > AP$." **See above.**

6. Pair each statement below with the given statement above and tell what conclusion, *if any*, must follow.
a. P is not on $\overline{AB}$. **b.** P is on $\overline{AB}$. **c.** $AB \leq AP$ **d.** $AB > AP$

6. a. No concl.
b. $AB > AP$
c. P is not on $\overline{AB}$.
d. No concl.

7. If the lengths of the sides of a triangle are x, 15, and 21, then x must be greater than __?__ and less than __?__. **6, 36**

In Exercises 8–10 the diagrams are not drawn to scale. If each diagram were drawn accurately, which segment shown would be the shortest?

8. **$\overline{BC}$**

C
A 57° 62° B

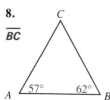

9. **$\overline{DG}$**

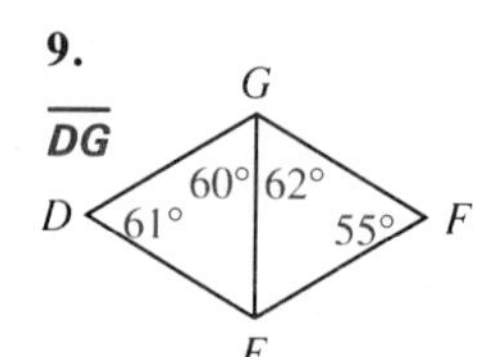

10. **$\overline{JK}$**

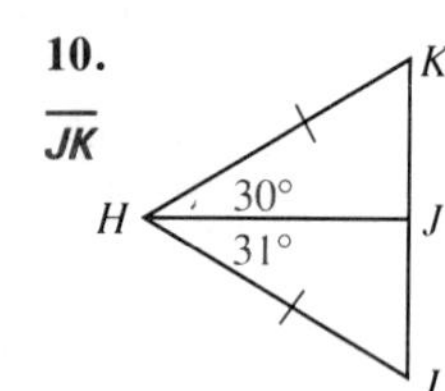

11. If $VE > VO$, then $m\angle$ __?__ $> m\angle$ __?__. **VOE** **VEO**

12. If $m\angle UEO > m\angle UOE$, then __?__ $>$ __?__. **UO, UE**

13. If $\overline{VE} \cong \overline{VO}$ and $m\angle UVE > m\angle UVO$, then __?__ $>$ __?__. **UE, UO**

14. If $m\angle EVU = 60$, $\overline{OE} \cong \overline{OU}$, and $m\angle VOE > m\angle VOU$, then the largest angle of $\triangle UVE$ is $\angle$__?__. **VUE**

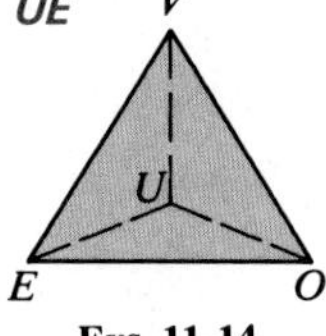

Exs. 11–14

15. Write an indirect proof.
Given: Trap. $ABCD$ with $\overline{AB} \parallel \overline{DC}$
Prove: $\angle C$ and $\angle D$ are not both right angles.

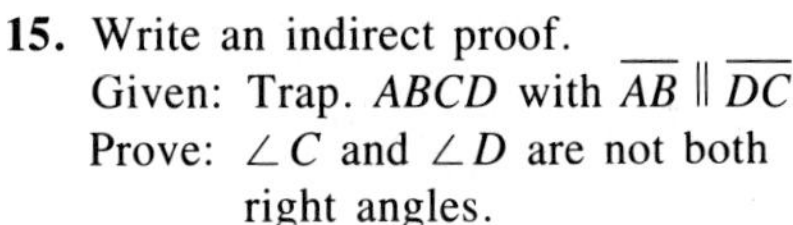

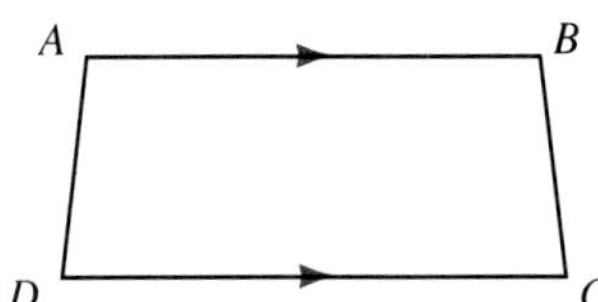

16. Given: $XS > YS$; $\overline{RX} \cong \overline{TY}$; S is the midpoint of $\overline{RT}$.
Prove: $m\angle R > m\angle T$

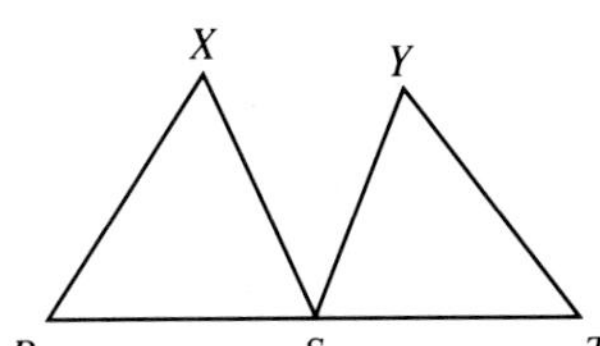

Algebra Review: *Fractions*

Simplify the following fractions.

Example **a.** $\dfrac{8w}{2}$ **b.** $\dfrac{5t - 10}{15}$ **c.** $\dfrac{x + 6}{36 - x^2}$

Solution **a.** $4w$ **b.** $\dfrac{5(t - 2)}{15} = \dfrac{t - 2}{3}$ **c.** $\dfrac{x + 6}{(6 - x)(6 + x)} = \dfrac{1}{6 - x}$

10. $a + 2$ **11. $3x - 2y$**

1. $\dfrac{14}{70}$ **$\frac{1}{5}$** **2.** $\dfrac{75}{15}$ **5** **3.** $\dfrac{18a}{36}$ **$\frac{a}{2}$** **4.** $\dfrac{3x}{x}$ **3**

5. $\dfrac{x}{3x}$ **$\frac{1}{3}$** **6.** $\dfrac{5bc}{10b^2}$ **$\frac{c}{2b}$** **7.** $\dfrac{-8y^3}{2y}$ **$-4y^2$** **8.** $\dfrac{-18r^3t}{12rt}$ **$\frac{-3r^2}{2}$**

9. $\dfrac{3ab^2}{6bc}$ **$\frac{ab}{2c}$** **10.** $\dfrac{6a + 12}{6}$ **11.** $\dfrac{9x - 6y}{3}$ **12.** $\dfrac{33ab - 22b}{11b}$ **$3a - 2$**

13. $\dfrac{x + 2}{3x + 6}$ **$\frac{1}{3}$** **14.** $\dfrac{2c - 2d}{2c + 2d}$ **$\frac{c - d}{c + d}$** **15.** $\dfrac{t^2 - 1}{t - 1}$ **$t + 1$** **16.** $\dfrac{5a + 5b}{a^2 - b^2}$ **$\frac{5}{a - b}$**

17. $\dfrac{b^2 - 25}{b^2 - 12b + 35}$ **$\frac{b + 5}{b - 7}$** **18.** $\dfrac{a^2 + 8a + 16}{a^2 - 16}$ **$\frac{a + 4}{a - 4}$** **19.** $\dfrac{3x^2 - 6x - 24}{3x^2 + 2x - 8}$ **$\frac{3(x - 4)}{3x - 4}$**

Supplementary Materials

Practice Masters 35, 36
Resource Book, p. 195

Preparing for College Entrance Exams

Strategy for Success

You may find it helpful to sketch figures or do calculations in your test booklet. Be careful not to make extra marks on your answer sheet.

Indicate the best answer by writing the appropriate letter.

A **1.** The diagonals of quadrilateral *MNOP* intersect at *X*. Which statement guarantees that *MNOP* is a rectangle?
(A) $MX = NX = OX = PX$ **(B)** $\angle PMN \cong \angle MNO \cong \angle NOP$
(C) $MO = NP$ **(D)** $\overline{MO} \perp \overline{NP}$ **(E)** $\overline{MN} \perp \overline{MP}$

A **2.** Which statement does *not* guarantee that quadrilateral *WXYZ* is a parallelogram?
(A) $\overline{WX} \cong \overline{YZ}$; $\overline{XY} \parallel \overline{WZ}$ **(B)** $\angle W \cong \angle Y$; $\angle X \cong \angle Z$
(C) $\overline{WX} \cong \overline{YZ}$; $\overline{XY} \cong \overline{WZ}$ **(D)** $\overline{XY} \parallel \overline{WZ}$; $\overline{WX} \parallel \overline{ZY}$
(E) $\overline{XY} \cong \overline{WZ}$; $\overline{XY} \parallel \overline{WZ}$

B **3.** In $\triangle ABC$, if $AB = BC$ and $AC > BC$, then:
(A) $AB < AC - BC$ **(B)** $m\angle B > m\angle C$ **(C)** $m\angle B < m\angle A$
(D) $m\angle B = 60$ **(E)** $m\angle B = m\angle A$

B **4.** Which statement is not always true for every rhombus *ABCD*?
(A) $AB = BC$ **(B)** $AC = BD$ **(C)** $\angle B \cong \angle D$
(D) $\overline{AC} \perp \overline{BD}$ **(E)** $\angle ABD \cong \angle CBD$

B **5.** Given: $m\angle 3 > m\angle 4$
Compare: $x = m\angle 1 + m\angle 4$ and
$y = m\angle 2 + m\angle 3$
(A) $x > y$ **(B)** $y > x$ **(C)** $x = y$
(D) No comparison possible with information given

E **6.** Given: Trapezoid *LMNO*; $\overleftrightarrow{MN} \parallel \overleftrightarrow{LO}$; $\overline{LO}$ is twice as long as $\overline{MN}$. How long is the median of the trapezoid?

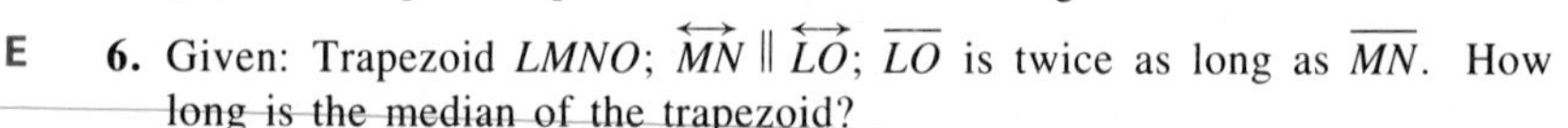

(A) $\frac{4}{3}LO$ **(B)** $\frac{3}{2}LO$ **(C)** $\frac{2}{3}MN$ **(D)** $\frac{3}{4}MN$ **(E)** $\frac{3}{2}MN$

E **7.** Quad. *CAKE* is a rectangle. Find *CK*.
(A) 2 **(B)** 3 **(C)** 4 **(D)** 6 **(E)** 8

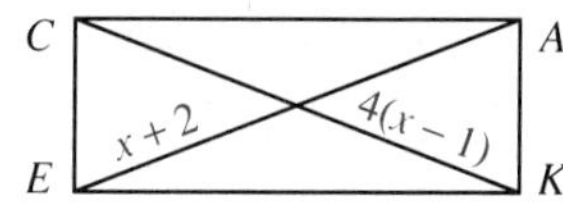

C **8.** Which of the following statement(s) are true?
(I) If $a > b$, then $ax > bx$ for all numbers x.
(II) If $ax > bx$ for some number x, then $a > b$.
(III) If $a > b$, then for some number x, $ax < bx$.
(A) I only **(B)** II only **(C)** III only **(D)** all of the above
(E) none of the above

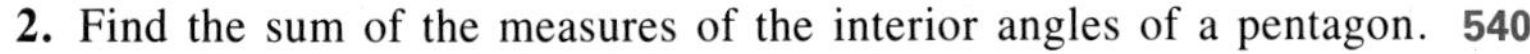

Cumulative Review: Chapters 1–6

A

1. An angle and its complement have the measures $x + 38$ and $2x - 5$. Find the measure of the angle. **57**

2. Find the sum of the measures of the interior angles of a pentagon. **540**

3. Can the given information be used to prove the triangles congruent? If so, which congruence postulate or theorem would you use?

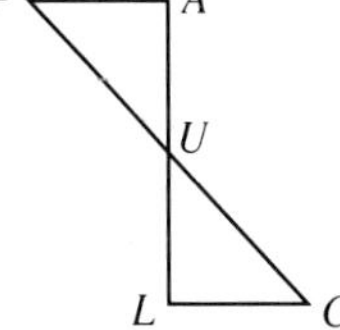

a. Given: $\overline{PC}$ and $\overline{AL}$ bisect each other. **Yes; SAS**

b. Given: $\angle P \cong \angle C$; U is the midpoint of $\overline{PC}$. **Yes; ASA**

c. Given: $\overline{PA} \parallel \overline{LC}$ **No**

d. Given: $\overline{PA} \perp \overline{AL}$; $\overline{LC} \perp \overline{AL}$; $\overline{PU} \cong \overline{UC}$ **Yes; AAS**

4. Tell whether the statement is *always*, *sometimes*, or *never* true for a parallelogram $ABCD$ with diagonals that intersect at P.

a. $AB = BC$ **S** **b.** $\overline{AC} \perp \overline{BD}$ **S** **c.** $\angle A$ and $\angle B$ are complementary $\angle$s. **N**

d. $\angle ADB \cong \angle CBD$ **A** **e.** $\overline{AP} \cong \overline{PC}$ **A** **f.** $\triangle ABC \cong \triangle CDA$ **A**

5. In $\triangle XYZ$, $m\angle X = 64$ and $m\angle Y = 54$. Name **(a)** the longest and **(b)** the shortest side of $\triangle XYZ$. **a.** $\overline{YZ}$ **b.** $\overline{XZ}$

6. a. Which segment is longer: $\overline{RS}$ or $\overline{JK}$? $\overline{RS}$

b. Name the theorem that supports your answer. **SAS Ineq. Thm.**

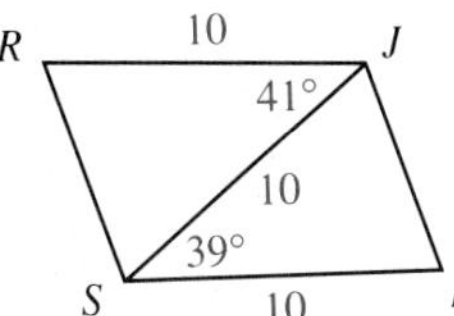

B

7. The difference between the measures of two supplementary angles is 38. Find the measure of each angle. **109, 71**

8. The lengths of the sides of a triangle are z, $z + 3$, and $z + 6$. What can you conclude about the value of z? $z > 3$

9. Write an indirect proof of the following statement: If $PQRS$ is a quadrilateral, then $\angle Q$, $\angle R$, and $\angle S$ are not all 120°.

10. Given: $m\angle B > m\angle A$; $m\angle E > m\angle D$
Prove: $AD > BE$

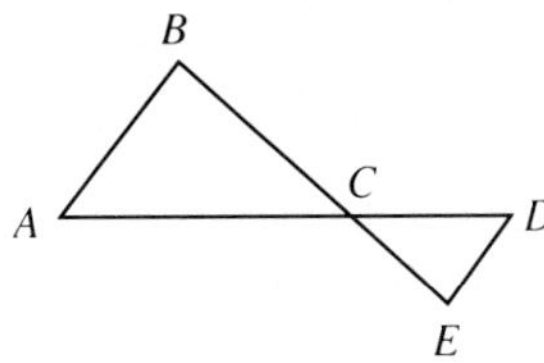

11. Given: $\overline{DC} \parallel \overline{AB}$; $\overline{CE} \perp \overline{AB}$; $\overline{AF} \perp \overline{AB}$
Prove: $AECF$ is a rectangle.

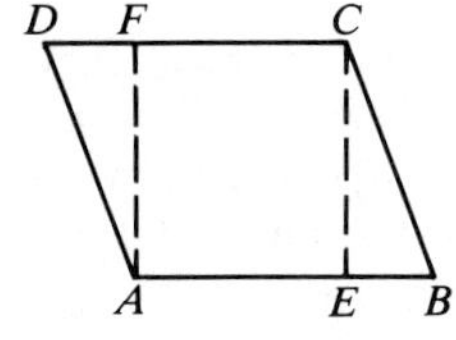

7 Similar Polygons

Objectives

7-1 Express a ratio in simplest form.

7-2 Solve for an unknown term in a given proportion.

Express a given proportion in an equivalent form.

7-3 State and apply the properties of similar polygons.

7-4 Use the AA Similarity Postulate to prove triangles similar.

Use similar triangles to deduce information about segments or angles.

7-5 Use the SAS Similarity Theorem and the SSS Similarity Theorem to prove triangles similar.

7-6 Apply the Triangle Proportionality Theorem and its corollary.

State and apply the Triangle Angle-Bisector Theorem.

Assignment Guide

See page T40 for information about the Assignment Guide.

Day	Minimum Course	Average Course	Maximum Course
1	**7-1** 243–244/1–20	**7-1** 243–244/1–35 odd	**7-1** 243–244/5, 10, 14, 15, 20, 25, 28, 30, 33, 35, 36
2	**7-1** 244/21–31	**7-2** 247/2–8 even, 11, 12, 16, 20 **S** 244/34, 36	**7-2** 247–248/4, 8, 12, 15, 20, 25, 30, 35, 37, 40 **S** 244/34
3	**7-2** 247/1–8, 9–15 odd **S** 244/32, 33	**7-2** 247–248/21–29 odd, 32, 33, 35–37	**7-3** 250–251/5, 10, 12, 15, 19, 21, 23, 25, 26 **S** 248/41, 43
4	**7-2** 247/16–20 even, 21–27 odd, 29	**7-3** 250–251/1–12, 13–19 odd, 21–24	**7-3** 251/20, 24, 27, 29, 31–37 odd
5	**7-3** 250–251/1–12, 14–20 even	**7-3** 251/25, 26, 29, 31 252/Self-Test 1	**7-4** 257–259/5, 9, 14, 15, 20, 21, 24, 27, 29, 31
6	**7-3** 251/21–25 252/Self-Test 1	**7-4** 257–259/5–15 odd, 16–24 even	**7-5** 266–267/5, 10, 14, 16, 17, 20, 22, 23 **S** 260/33
7	**7-4** 257–258/1–16	**7-5** 266–267/1–15 odd **S** 259/25–31 odd	**7-6** 272–273/6, 11, 12, 15, 20, 21, 25, 27, 31 **S** 267/18
8	**7-4** 258–259/18–20, 23, 24	**7-5** 266–267/14–22 even 268/Mixed Review 1, 2	**7-6** 273/29, 30, 32, 33 **S** 267/19, 21
9	**7-5** 266/1–10 **S** 258/17 268/Mixed Review 1, 2	**7-6** 272–273/2–6 even, 7–15 odd, 16–18 **S** 267/22	**7-6** 279/Chapter Test Test, page T18
10	**7-6** 272/1–8 **S** 266/11, 13	**7-6** 273/19, 20, 22, 25, 27, 29, 30 274/Self-Test 2	

11	**7-6** 272–273/10–20 even	**7-6** 279/Chapter Test Test, page T18	
12	**7-6** 273/21, 24, 25 274/Self-Test 2		
13	**7-6** 279/Chapter Test Test, page T18		

Supplementary Materials Guide

				Resource Book			
For Use after Lesson	**Practice Masters**	**Tests**	**Study Guide (Reteaching)**	**Tests**	**Practice Exercises**	**Mixed Review (MR) Prep. for College Entrance Exams (Col) Enrichment (E) Computer (C)**	**Computer Activities**
7-1			pp. 79–80				Activity 13
7-2	Sheet 37		pp. 81–82				
7-3	Sheet 38	Test 25	pp. 83–84	p. 37	p. 133		
7-4	Sheet 39		pp. 85–86				Activity 14
7-5	Sheet 40	Test 26	pp. 87–88	p. 38	p. 134		
7-6	Sheet 41	Test 27	pp. 89–90	p. 39	p. 135		
Chapter 7	Sheet 42	Test 28		pp. 40–41	p. 136	p. 196 (Col) p. 217 (E) p. 243 (C)	
Chapters 6–7		Test 29		pp. 42–44	p. 137		
Chapters 1–7		Test 30		pp. 45–49	pp. 138–139	pp. 177–179 (MR)	

Overhead Visuals

Guided Discovery Visuals (lettered) and Teaching Visuals (numbered) available for Chapter 7.

Lessons	Visual	Title
7-4, 7-5	E	Similar Polygons in Space
7-6	N	Which Method is Easier?
7-1, 7-2, 7-3	14	Similar Polygons
7-4, 7-5, 7-6	15	Proportions in Triangles

Software Guide

Houghton Mifflin software for Chapter 7

Geometry Grapher (Apple or IBM)

Use with	**Booklet**
p. 270 (Theorem 7–4)	Classroom Demonstration, p. 15
p. 268 (Explorations)	

Test Generator (Apple or IBM): 90 test items

Other software appropriate for Chapter 7

Geometric Supposer (Apple): Triangles

GeoDraw (IBM)

Spreadsheets

Guide to Integrated Curriculum

Teachers wishing to integrate coordinate and transformational geometry throughout the course can use the following lessons after Chapter 7. See pages T56–T57 and 657 for more information.

14-5 Cl. Ex. 1–12, 14–17; Wr. Ex. 1–21, 25–28
Handbook: Dilations and Similarity, pp. 664–665

Guide to Distribution of Constructions

The text teaches constructions in Chapter 10. Teachers wishing to distribute work with constructions throughout the first nine chapters can use this guide.

Introduce after	Constructions	Pages
Lesson 7-6	12, 13	396, 397

Strategies for Teaching

Exploring Similar Polygons

When to Use

With or after Lesson 7-3

Overview

In this activity students build larger figures similar to a given figure by using copies of the given figure. Building such figures, called ''reptiles'' (short for repeated tiles) reinforces the ideas that similar figures have congruent angles and proportional sides. The activity also reinforces visualization skills.

Materials

Graph paper, scissors

Description of Activity

An equilateral triangle is an example of a reptile of order 4 since it takes 4 copies of the original triangle to form a larger, similar triangle. It is also a reptile of order 9 as shown below.

order 1

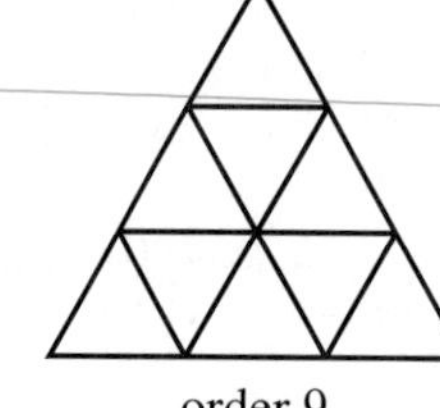

order 4

order 9

1. Which of the following polygons are reptiles of order 4? First make four copies of each polygon. Using them, build a larger polygon similar to the original one or explain why you think it is impossible to do so.

a.

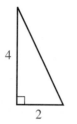

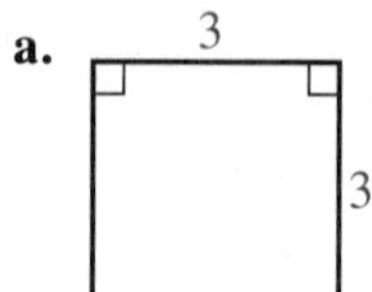

b.

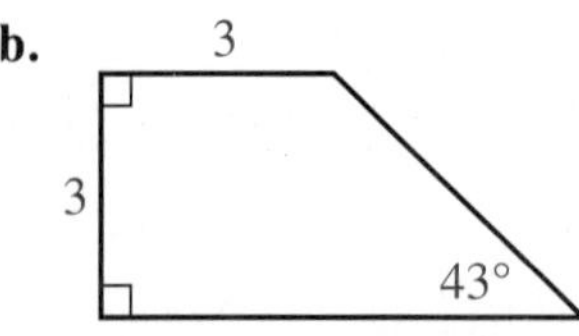

c.

4
2

d.

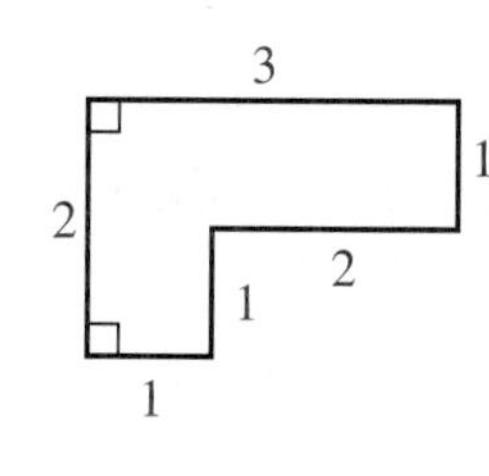

e.

2
1
1
1
1
1
1
2

f.

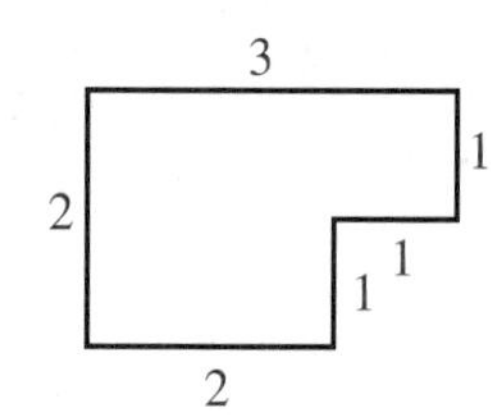

2. What is the next order of a reptile for the right triangle in **1c**? five

3. For which of the following types of polygons can you find reptiles of order 4? In each case, give a counterexample or a convincing argument.

a. triangle yes **b.** rectangle yes
c. parallelogram yes **d.** trapezoid yes

Commentary

- **1e** cannot be done, and the others are shown below.

b.

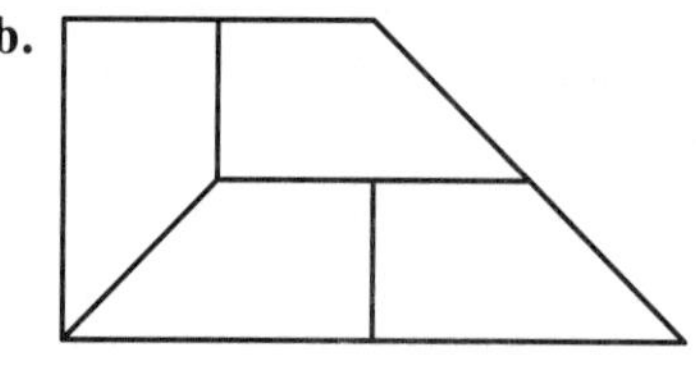

c.

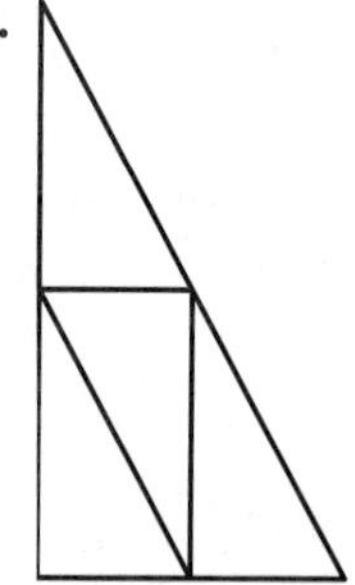

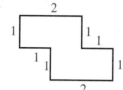

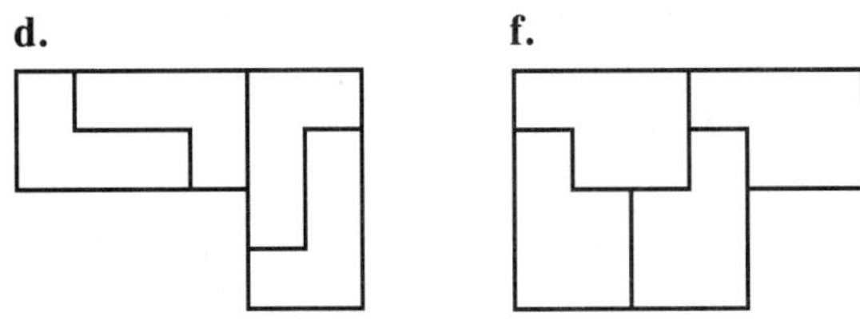

Variations and Extensions

- Have students draw their answers on square grid paper, instead of cutting and building.
- Have students draw the larger polygon and then see how to decompose it into four pieces, each similar to the original figure.

References to Strategies

PE: Pupil's Edition **TE:** Teacher's Edition **RB:** Resource Book

Problem Solving Strategies

PE: 256 (Strategies for proof), 258 (Exs. 16, 17, Mathematical model), 260 (Challenge, Draw a diagram), 280 (Challenge, Use auxiliary lines), 274 (Challenge, Deductive argument)
TE: T104, T105, 252 (Understand conditions), 273 (Make conjectures)

Applications

PE: 240 (Cartography), 248 (Scale drawing), 253 (Art and architecture), 256–259 (Estimating distances), 260 (Ex. 35, Lens law), 261 (Fibonacci sequence), 262 (Scale drawings), 265 (Ex. 9, Pantograph), 273 (Estimating distance)
TE: T101, T103, 257
RB: 217

Nonroutine Problems

PE: 243 (Ex. 6), 244 (Ex. 33), 251 (Exs. 32, 33), 252 (Exs. 35–37), 258 (Ex. 20), 259 (Ex. 32), 260 (Challenge), 262 (Application), 265 (Ex. 9), 271 (Ex. 8), 273 (Exs. 27, 29, 30), 274 (Challenge), 275–276 (Topology), 280 (Challenge), 665 (Ex. 8)
TE: T105
RB: 217

Communication

PE: 248, 262 (Scale drawings)
TE: T102, T104, 251

Thinking Skills

TE: 243 (Generalize), 250 (Recall properties and definitions)

Explorations

PE: 254, 268
TE: 239c

Connections

PE: 241–248 (Ratio and proportion), 261 (Fibonacci sequence), 273 (Ceva), 280 (Algebra review), 664–665 (Transformational geometry)
TE: T101, T103, T104, T105, 244, 257 (Algebra)

Using Technology

PE: 253, 254, 261, 268
TE: T101, T102, T103, T105, 242, 244, 247, 249, 253, 254, 255, 261, 264, 268, 273
RB: 243
Using Geometry Grapher: 15
Computer Activities: 29–34

Using Manipulatives/Models

PE: 248, 250 (Exs. 16, 17), 258 (Ex. 20), 262, 265 (Ex. 9)
TE: T102, T103, T105
Overhead Visuals: E, N, 14, 15

Cooperative Learning

TE: T103, T104, 251, 257, 259, 267

Teaching Resources

For use in implementing the teaching strategies referenced on the previous page.

Application
Resource Book, p. 217

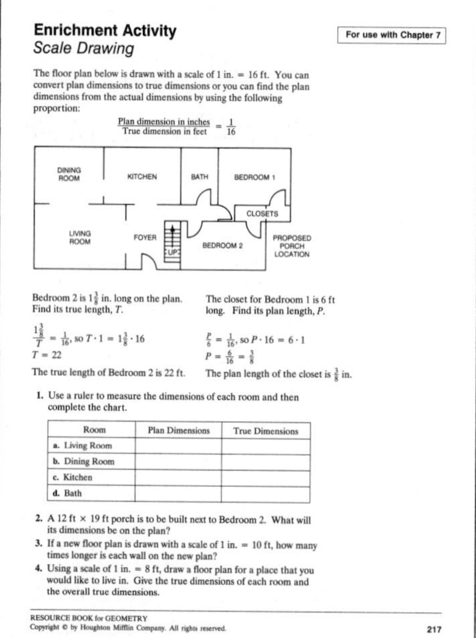

Enrichment Activity
Scale Drawing

For use with Chapter 7

The floor plan below is drawn with a scale of 1 in. = 16 ft. You can convert plan dimensions to true dimensions or you can find the plan dimensions from the actual dimensions by using the following proportion:

$$\frac{\text{Plan dimension in inches}}{\text{True dimension in feet}} = \frac{1}{16}$$

Bedroom 2 is $1\frac{3}{8}$ in. long on the plan. Find its true length, T.

$\frac{1\frac{3}{8}}{T} = \frac{1}{16}$, so $T \cdot 1 = 1\frac{3}{8} \cdot 16$

$T = 22$

The true length of Bedroom 2 is 22 ft.

The closet for Bedroom 1 is 6 ft long. Find its plan length, P.

$\frac{P}{6} = \frac{1}{16}$, so $P \cdot 16 = 6 \cdot 1$

$P = \frac{6}{16} = \frac{3}{8}$

The plan length of the closet is $\frac{3}{8}$ in.

1. Use a ruler to measure the dimensions of each room and then complete the chart.

Room	Plan Dimensions	True Dimensions
a. Living Room		
b. Dining Room		
c. Kitchen		
d. Bath		

2. A 12 ft × 19 ft porch is to be built next to Bedroom 2. What will its dimensions be on the plan?
3. If a new floor plan is drawn with a scale of 1 in. = 10 ft, how many times longer is each wall on the new plan?
4. Using a scale of 1 in. = 8 ft, draw a floor plan for a place that you would like to live in. Give the true dimensions of each room and the overall true dimensions.

RESOURCE BOOK for GEOMETRY

217

Using Technology
Resource Book, p. 243

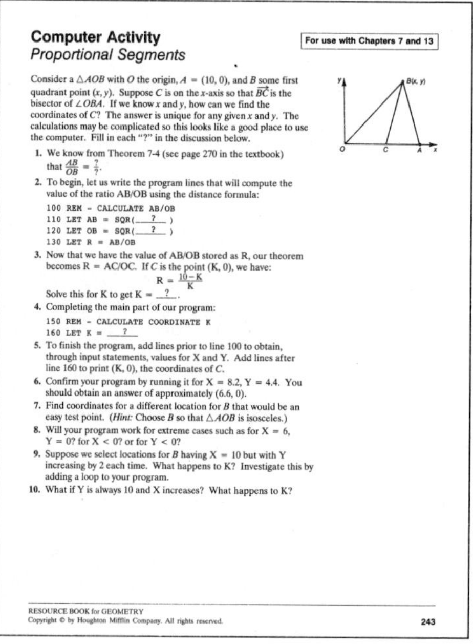

Computer Activity
Proportional Segments

For use with Chapters 7 and 13

Consider a $\triangle AOB$ with O the origin, $A = (10, 0)$, and B some first quadrant point (x, y). Suppose C is on the x-axis so that $\overrightarrow{BC}$ is the bisector of $\angle OBA$. If we know x and y, how can we find the coordinates of C? The answer is unique for any given x and y. The calculations may be complicated so this looks like a good place to use the computer. Fill in each "?" in the discussion below.

1. We know from Theorem 7-4 (see page 270 in the textbook) that $\frac{AB}{OB} = \frac{?}{?}$.
2. To begin, let us write the program lines that will compute the value of the ratio AB/OB using the distance formula:

```
100 REM - CALCULATE AB/OB
110 LET AB = SQR(___?___)
120 LET OB = SQR(___?___)
130 LET R = AB/OB
```

3. Now that we have the value of AB/OB stored as R, our theorem becomes R = AC/OC. If C is the point (K, 0), we have:

$$R = \frac{10 - K}{K}$$

Solve this for K to get K = __?__.

4. Completing the main part of our program:

```
150 REM - CALCULATE COORDINATE K
160 LET K = ___?___
```

5. To finish the program, add lines prior to line 100 to obtain, through input statements, values for X and Y. Add lines after line 160 to print (K, 0), the coordinates of C.
6. Confirm your program by running it for X = 8.2, Y = 4.4. You should obtain an answer of approximately (6.6, 0).
7. Find coordinates for a different location for B that would be an easy test point. (*Hint:* Choose B so that $\triangle AOB$ is isosceles.)
8. Will your program work for extreme cases such as for X = 6, Y = 0? for X < 0? or for Y < 0?
9. Suppose we select locations for B having X = 10 but with Y increasing by 2 each time. What happens to K? Investigate this by adding a loop to your program.
10. What if Y is always 10 and X increases? What happens to K?

RESOURCE BOOK for GEOMETRY

243

Using Technology
Computer Activities, p. 32

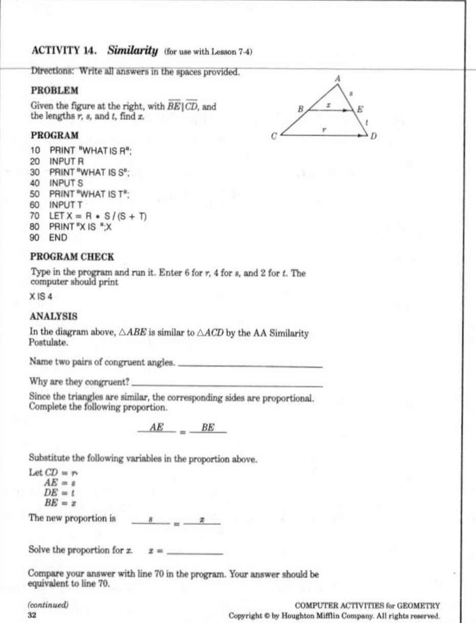

ACTIVITY 14. ***Similarity*** (for use with Lesson 7-4)

Directions: Write all answers in the spaces provided.

PROBLEM

Given the figure at the right, with $\overline{BE} \parallel \overline{CD}$, and the lengths r, s, and t, find x.

PROGRAM

```
10  PRINT "WHAT IS R";
20  INPUT R
30  PRINT "WHAT IS S";
40  INPUT S
50  PRINT "WHAT IS T";
60  INPUT T
70  LET X = R * S / (S + T)
80  PRINT "X IS ";X
90  END
```

PROGRAM CHECK

Type in the program and run it. Enter 6 for r, 4 for s, and 2 for t. The computer should print

X IS 4

ANALYSIS

In the diagram above, $\triangle ABE$ is similar to $\triangle ACD$ by the AA Similarity Postulate.

Name two pairs of congruent angles. ______________________

Why are they congruent? ______________________

Since the triangles are similar, the corresponding sides are proportional. Complete the following proportion.

$$\frac{AE}{\quad} = \frac{BE}{\quad}$$

Substitute the following variables in the proportion above.

Let $CD = r$
$AE = s$
$DE = t$
$BE = x$

The new proportion is $\frac{s}{\quad} = \frac{x}{\quad}$

Solve the proportion for x. $x =$ __________

Compare your answer with line 70 in the program. Your answer should be equivalent to line 70.

(continued)
32
COMPUTER ACTIVITIES for GEOMETRY

Using Technology
Computer Activities, p. 33

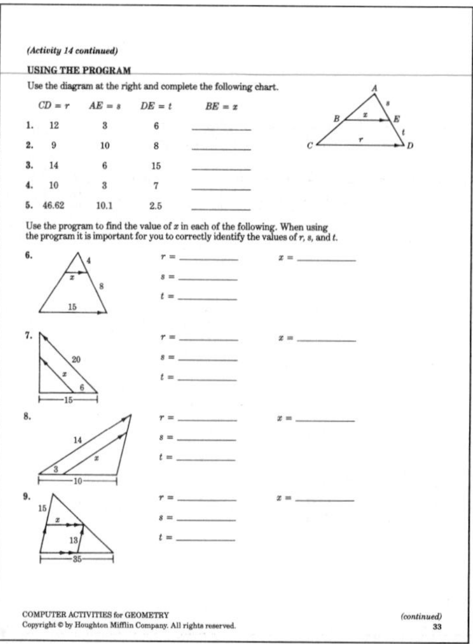

(Activity 14 continued)

USING THE PROGRAM

Use the diagram at the right and complete the following chart.

	$CD = r$	$AE = s$	$DE = t$	$BE = x$
1.	12	3	6	______
2.	9	10	8	______
3.	14	6	15	______
4.	10	3	7	______
5.	46.62	10.1	2.5	______

Use the program to find the value of x in each of the following. When using the program it is important for you to correctly identify the values of r, s, and t.

6. $r =$ ______ $s =$ ______ $t =$ ______ $x =$ ______

7. $r =$ ______ $s =$ ______ $t =$ ______ $x =$ ______

8. $r =$ ______ $s =$ ______ $t =$ ______ $x =$ ______

9. $r =$ ______ $s =$ ______ $t =$ ______ $x =$ ______

COMPUTER ACTIVITIES for GEOMETRY

(continued)
33

Using Models
Teaching Visual 14

TEACHING VISUAL 14
(for use with Lessons 7-1 through 7-3, especially page 249)

SIMILAR POLYGONS

When drawing similar polygons, arrange them so that corresponding sides in the two figures are parallel.

In similar figures, corresponding angles are congruent, and corresponding sides are in proportion.

In the diagram above, $\overline{BA}$ corresponds to $\overline{FE}$, and $\overline{AD}$ corresponds to $\overline{EH}$. Also, $\angle BAD$ corresponds to $\angle FEH$.

The following ratios are all equal:

$$\frac{AB}{EF} = \frac{BC}{FG} = \frac{CD}{GH} = \frac{DA}{HE} = \frac{AC}{EG} = \frac{BD}{FH} = \text{scale factor}$$

Furthermore, the following proportions are true:

$$\frac{AB}{BC} = \frac{EF}{FG} \qquad \frac{AB}{CD} = \frac{EF}{GH} \qquad \frac{AC}{AD} = \frac{EG}{EH}$$

Using Models
Teaching Visual 15

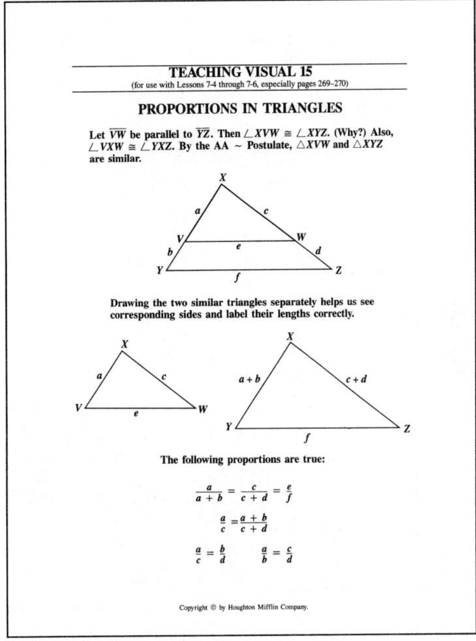

TEACHING VISUAL 15
(for use with Lessons 7-4 through 7-6, especially pages 269–270)

PROPORTIONS IN TRIANGLES

Let $\overline{VW}$ be parallel to $\overline{YZ}$. Then $\angle XVW \cong \angle XYZ$. (Why?) Also, $\angle VXW \cong \angle YXZ$. By the AA ~ Postulate, $\triangle XVW$ and $\triangle XYZ$ are similar.

Drawing the two similar triangles separately helps us see corresponding sides and label their lengths correctly.

The following proportions are true:

$$\frac{a}{a+b} = \frac{c}{c+d} = \frac{e}{f}$$

$$\frac{a}{c} = \frac{a+b}{c+d}$$

$$\frac{a}{c} = \frac{b}{d} \qquad \frac{a}{b} = \frac{c}{d}$$

Using Models
Guided Discovery Visual E, Sheets 1 and 2

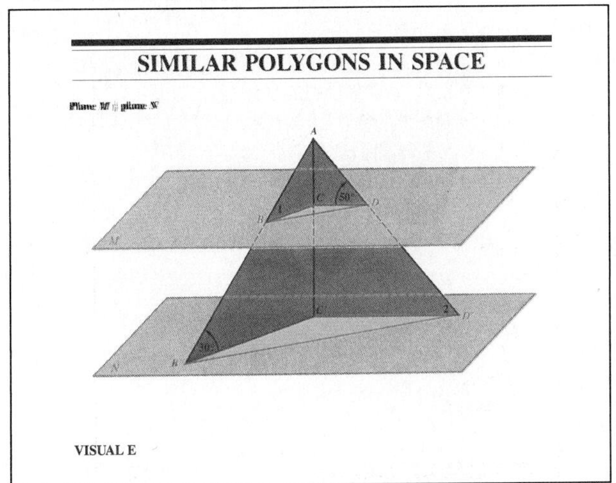

Problem Solving
Guided Discovery Visual N, Sheet 1

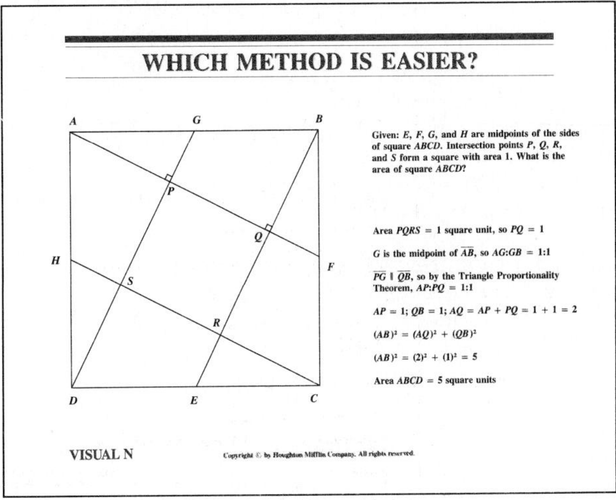

WHICH METHOD IS EASIER?
A
G
B
P
Q
H
F
S
R
D
E
C
Given: E, F, G, and H are midpoints of the sides of square ABCD. Intersection points P, Q, R, and S form a square with area 1. What is the area of square ABCD?
Area PQRS = 1 square unit, so PQ = 1
G is the midpoint of AB, so AG:GB = 1:1
PG ∥ QB, so by the Triangle Proportionality Theorem, AP:PQ = 1:1
AP = 1; QB = 1; AQ = AP + PQ = 1 + 1 = 2
(AB)² = (AQ)² + (QB)²
(AB)² = (2)² + (1)² = 5
Area ABCD = 5 square units
VISUAL N
Copyright © by Houghton Mifflin Company. All rights reserved.

Teaching References

Lesson Commentary, pp. T100–T106

Assignment Guide, pp. T45–T46

Software Guide, p. T73

Alternate Test, p. T18

Supplementary Materials

Practice Masters 37–42

Tests 25–30

Resource Book
- Tests, pp. 37–49
- Practice, pp. 133–139
- Mixed Review, pp. 177–179
- Preparing for College Entrance Exams, p. 196
- Enrichment Activity, p. 217
- Computer Activity, p. 243

Study Guide, pp. 79–90

Overhead Visuals E, N, 14, 15

Computer Activities
- 13 Ratio
- 14 Similarity

Handbook for Integrating Coordinate and Transformational Geometry

Dilations and Similarity, pp. 664–665

Cultural Note

In 1973, archaeologists working in China discovered several maps dating from around the 2nd century B.C. One of the maps shows great accuracy of scale for an area of land that has a complicated topography. To achieve such accuracy, the ancient cartographers must have used indirect measurement to survey the land.

7 SIMILAR POLYGONS

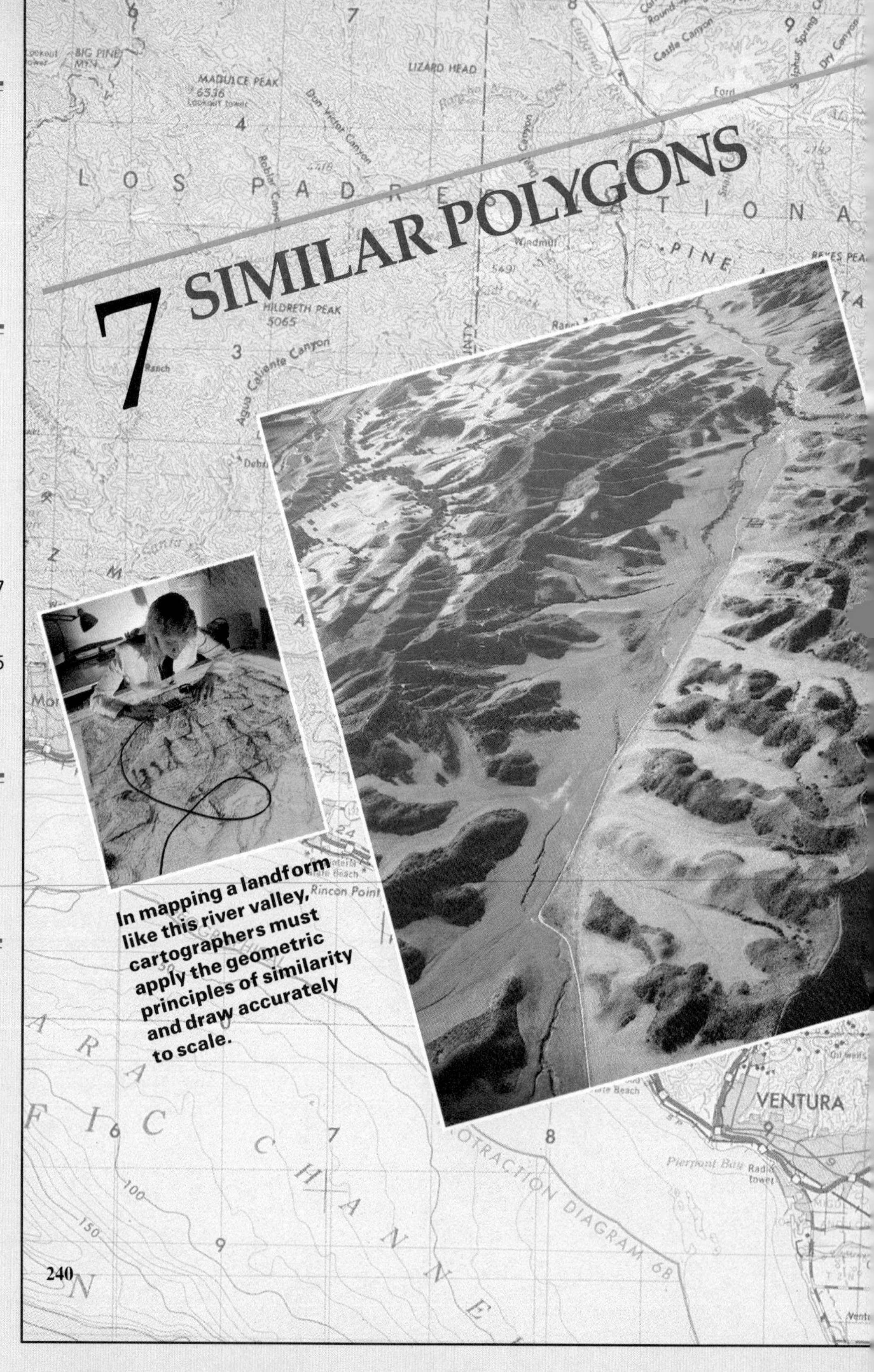

In mapping a landform like this river valley, cartographers must apply the geometric principles of similarity and draw accurately to scale.

240

Ratio, Proportion, and Similarity

Objectives

1. Express a ratio in simplest form.
2. Solve for an unknown term in a given proportion.
3. Express a given proportion in an equivalent form.
4. State and apply the properties of similar polygons.

7-1 *Ratio and Proportion*

The **ratio** of one number to another is the quotient when the first number is divided by the second. This quotient is usually expressed in *simplest form*.

$$\text{The ratio of 8 to 12 is } \frac{8}{12}, \text{ or } \frac{2}{3}.$$

$$\text{If } y \neq 0, \text{ the ratio of } x \text{ to } y \text{ is } \frac{x}{y}.$$

Since we cannot divide by zero, a ratio $\frac{r}{s}$ is defined only if $s \neq 0$. When an expression such as $\frac{r}{s}$ appears in this book, you may assume that $s \neq 0$.

Example 1 **a.** Find the ratio of OI to ZD.

b. Find the ratio of the measure of the smallest angle of the trapezoid to that of the largest angle.

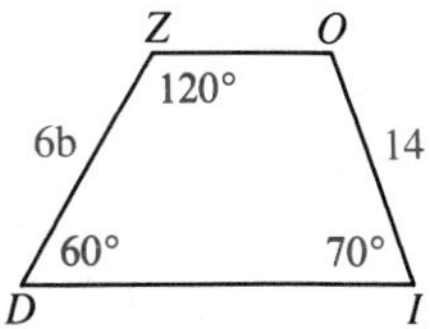

Solution **a.** $\frac{OI}{ZD} = \frac{14}{6b} = \frac{7}{3b}$

The ratio of OI to ZD is 7 to $3b$.

b. $\angle O$ has measure $180 - 70$, or 110. Thus $\angle D$ is the smallest angle and $\angle Z$ is the largest angle.

$$\frac{m\angle D}{m\angle Z} = \frac{60}{120} = \frac{1}{2}$$

The ratio of the measure of the smallest angle of the trapezoid to that of the largest angle is 1 to 2.

Ratios can be used to compare two numbers. To find the ratio of the lengths of two segments, the segments must be measured in terms of the same unit.

Teaching Suggestions, p. T101

Objective
Presenting the Lesson
Using Technology
Applications
Making Connections
Reinforcement

Supplementary Materials

Study Guide, pp. 79–80
Computer Activity 13

Lesson Focus

This lesson reviews the ideas of ratio and proportion in preparation for the study of the geometric concept of similarity. Similar figures have the same shape but not necessarily the same size.

Suggested Assignments

Minimum
Day 1: 243–244/1–20
Day 2: 244/21–31

Average
243–244/1–35 odd

Maximum
243–244/5, 10, 14, 15, 20, 25, 28, 30, 33, 35, 36

Chalkboard Examples

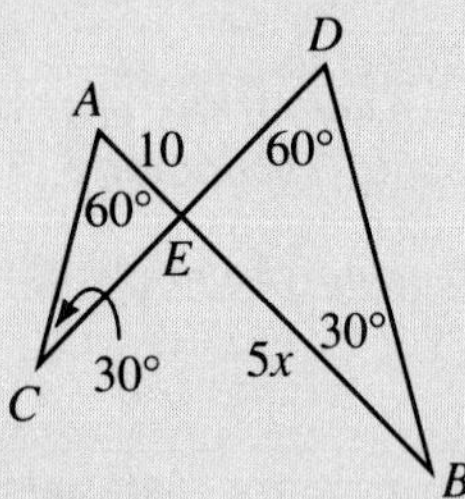

1. a. Find the ratio of AE to BE. 2:x
   b. Find the ratio of the largest angle of $\triangle ACE$ to the smallest angle of $\triangle DBE$. 3:1
2. A rectangular field has a length of one kilometer and a width of 300 meters. Find the ratio of the length to the width. 10:3
3. A telephone pole 7 meters tall snaps into two parts during a wind storm. The ratio of the two parts is 3 to 2. Find the length of each part. 4.2 m, 2.8 m

Teaching Note

In Example 3, stress that the answer is the *measure* of each angle and not the value for x. Point out also that although ratios must be in the same units, proportions do not have to be.

Using a Computer

See page T101 for an experiment involving ratio and proportion.

Example 2 A poster is 1 m long and 52 cm wide. Find the ratio of the width to the length.

Solution *Method 1*

Use centimeters.

1 m = 100 cm

$$\frac{\text{width}}{\text{length}} = \frac{52}{100} = \frac{13}{25}$$

Method 2

Use meters.

52 cm = 0.52 m

$$\frac{\text{width}}{\text{length}} = \frac{0.52}{1} = \frac{52}{100} = \frac{13}{25}$$

Example 2 shows that the ratio of two quantities is not affected by the unit chosen.

Sometimes the ratio of a to b is written in the form $a:b$. This form can also be used to compare three or more numbers. The statement that three numbers are in the ratio $c:d:e$ (read "c to d to e") means:

(1) The ratio of the first two numbers is $c:d$.
(2) The ratio of the last two numbers is $d:e$.
(3) The ratio of the first and last numbers is $c:e$.

Example 3 The measures of the three angles of a triangle are in the ratio 2:2:5. Find the measure of each angle.

Solution Let $2x$, $2x$, and $5x$ represent the measures.

$$2x + 2x + 5x = 180$$
$$9x = 180$$
$$x = 20$$

Then $2x = 40$ and $5x = 100$.

The measures of the angles are 40, 40, and 100.

A **proportion** is an equation stating that two ratios are equal. For example,

$$\frac{a}{b} = \frac{c}{d} \quad \text{and} \quad a:b = c:d$$

are equivalent forms of the same proportion. Either form can be read "a is to b as c is to d." The number a is called the first *term* of the proportion. The numbers b, c, and d are the second, third, and fourth terms, respectively.

When three or more ratios are equal, you can write an *extended proportion:*

$$\frac{a}{b} = \frac{c}{d} = \frac{e}{f}$$

Classroom Exercises

Express the ratio in simplest form.

1. $\frac{12}{20}$ $\frac{3}{5}$ 2. $\frac{3p}{5p}$ $\frac{3}{5}$ 3. $\frac{4n}{n^2}$ $\frac{4}{n}$ 4. $\frac{n^2}{4n}$ $\frac{n}{4}$

5. Is the ratio $a:b$ always, sometimes, or never equal to the ratio $b:a$? Explain. **Sometimes; the ratios are equal when $|a| = |b|$.**
6. An office copy machine can make a reduction to 90%, thus making the copy slightly smaller than the original. What is the ratio of the length of a line of text in the original to the length of a copy of that line? **10:9**
7. Barbara is making oatmeal for breakfast. The instructions say to use 3 cups of water with 2 cups of oatmeal.
   a. What is the ratio of water to oatmeal? $\frac{3}{2}$
   b. If Barbara uses 6 cups of water, how much oatmeal does she need? **4 cups**

Express the ratio in simplest form.

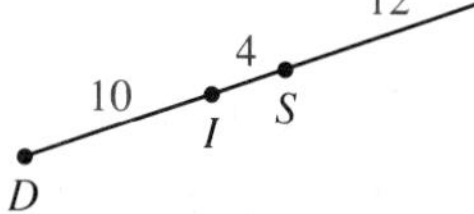

8. $DI:IS$ **5:2** 9. $ST:DI$ **6:5** 10. $IT:DT$ **8:13**
11. $DI:IT$ **5:8** 12. $IT:DS$ **8:7** 13. $IS:DI:IT$ **2:5:8**
14. What is the ratio of 750 mL to 1.5 L? **1:2**
15. Can you find the ratio of 2 L to 4 km? Explain. **No; there is no common unit.**
16. The ratio of the lengths of two segments is 4:3 when they are measured in centimeters. What is their ratio when they are measured in inches? **4:3**
17. Three numbers aren't known, but the ratio of the numbers is 1:2:5. Is it possible that the numbers are 1, 2, and 5? 10, 20, and 50? 3, 6, and 20? x, $2x$, and $5x$? **Yes, Yes, No, Yes**
18. What is the second term of the proportion $\frac{a}{b} = \frac{x}{y}$? ***b***

Written Exercises

***ABCD* is a parallelogram. Find the value of each ratio.**

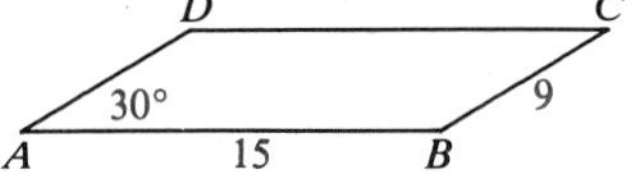

A 1. $AB:BC$ **5:3** 2. $AB:CD$ **1:1**
3. $m\angle C:m\angle D$ **1:5** 4. $m\angle B:m\angle C$ **5:1**
5. AD:perimeter of $ABCD$ **3:16**

In Exercises 6–14, $x = 12$, $y = 10$, and $z = 24$. Write each ratio in simplest form.

6. x to y **6 to 5** 7. z to x **2 to 1** 8. $x + y$ to z **11 to 12**
9. $\frac{x}{x + z}$ $\frac{1}{3}$ 10. $\frac{x + y}{z + y}$ $\frac{11}{17}$ 11. $\frac{y + z}{x - y}$ $\frac{17}{1}$
12. $x:y:z$ **6:5:12** 13. $z:x:y$ **12:6:5** 14. $x:(x + y):(y + z)$ **6:11:17**

Thinking Skills

Classroom Ex. 17 helps students understand the concept of a ratio and how to think about finding sets of equivalent ratios. Substitute other variable names for x, such as a, b, c, and y, to help students generalize their view of the role of the variable in this exercise.

Guided Practice

ABCD is a parallelogram. Find the value of each ratio.

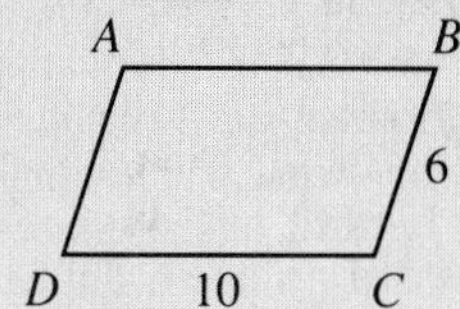

1. $AB:BC$ 5:3
2. $BC:AD$ 1:1
3. $m\angle A:m\angle C$ 1:1
4. AB:perimeter of $ABCD$ 5:16

In Exs. 5–7, $x = 2$ and $y = 3$. Write each ratio in simplest form.

5. x to y 2 to 3
6. $6x^2$ to $12xy$ 1 to 3
7. $\frac{y - x}{x}$ $\frac{1}{2}$

Write each algebraic ratio in simplest form.

8. $\frac{6a^2}{12abc}$ $\frac{a}{2bc}$
9. $\frac{2(a - b)}{3a - 3b}$ $\frac{2}{3}$

Exercises 15–20 refer to a triangle. Express the ratio of the height to the base in simplest form.

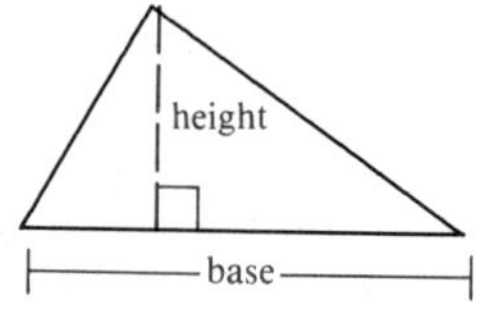

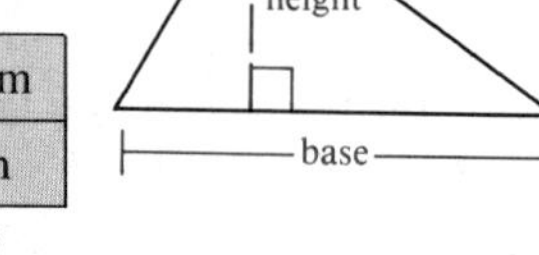

	15.	16.	17.	18.	19.	20.
height	5 km	1 m	0.6 km	1 m	8 cm	40 mm
base	45 km	0.6 m	0.8 km	85 cm	50 mm	0.2 m
	1:9	**5:3**	**3:4**	**20:17**	**8:5**	**1:5**

Making Connections

Exs. 21–23 provide more practice with algebraic ratios. In earlier courses in mathematics, students worked primarily with arithmetic ratios. These types of exercises help students to expand their understanding of the meaning of ratio.

Write the algebraic ratio in simplest form.

21. $\frac{3a}{4ab}$ **$\frac{3}{4b}$** **22.** $\frac{2cd}{5c^2}$ **$\frac{2d}{5c}$** **23.** $\frac{3(x+4)}{a(x+4)}$ **$\frac{3}{a}$**

In Exercises 24–29 find the measure of each angle.

B **24.** The ratio of the measures of two complementary angles is 4:5. **40, 50**

25. The ratio of the measures of two supplementary angles is 11:4. **132, 48**

26. The measures of the angles of a triangle are in the ratio 3:4:5. **45, 60, 75**

27. The measures of the acute angles of a right triangle are in the ratio 5:7. **37.5, 52.5**

28. The measures of the angles of an isosceles triangle are in the ratio 3:3:2. **67.5, 67.5, 45**

29. The measures of the angles of a hexagon are in the ratio 4:5:5:8:9:9. **72, 90, 90, 144, 162, 162**

30. The perimeter of a triangle is 132 cm and the lengths of its sides are in the ratio 8:11:14. Find the length of each side. **32 cm, 44 cm, 56 cm**

31. The measures of the consecutive angles of a quadrilateral are in the ratio 5:7:11:13. Find the measure of each angle, draw a quadrilateral that satisfies the requirements, and explain why two sides must be parallel. **50, 70, 110, 130; 2 s.-s. int. ∠s are supp.**

Using a Calculator

Ex. 33 is a good problem to solve by using a calculator, since batting averages are expressed as decimals to the nearest thousandth.

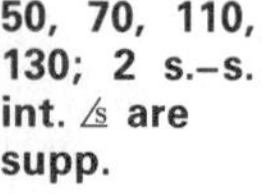

32. What is the ratio of the measure of an interior angle to the measure of an exterior angle in a regular hexagon? A regular decagon? A regular n-gon? **2:1, 4:1, $(n-2):2$**

33. A team's best hitter has a lifetime batting average of .320. He has been at bat 325 times.

a. How many hits has he made? **104**

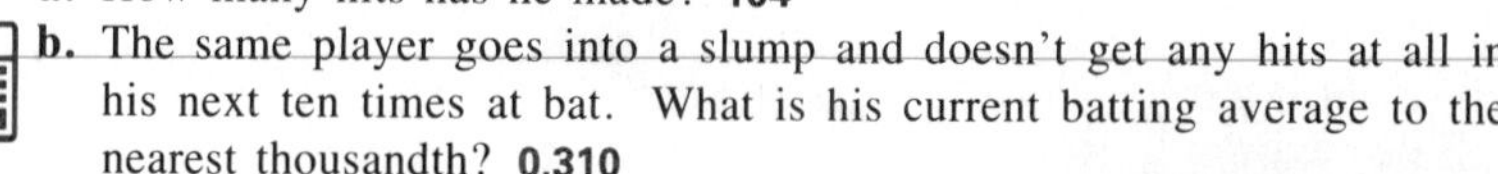

b. The same player goes into a slump and doesn't get any hits at all in his next ten times at bat. What is his current batting average to the nearest thousandth? **0.310**

C **34.** A basketball player has made 24 points out of 30 free throws. She hopes to make all her next free throws until her free-throw percentage is 85 or better. How many consecutive free throws will she have to make? **10**

35. Points B and C lie on $\overline{AD}$. Find AC if $\frac{AB}{BD} = \frac{3}{4}$, $\frac{AC}{CD} = \frac{5}{6}$, and $BD = 66$. **52.5**

36. Find the ratio of x to y: $\frac{4}{y} + \frac{3}{x} = 44$
5:8 $\frac{12}{y} - \frac{2}{x} = 44$

7-2 *Properties of Proportions*

The first and last terms of a proportion are called the *extremes*. The middle terms are the *means*. In the proportions below, the extremes are shown in red. The means are shown in black.

$$a:b = c:d \qquad 6:9 = 2:3 \qquad \frac{6}{9} = \frac{2}{3}$$

Notice that $6 \cdot 3 = 9 \cdot 2$. This illustrates a property of all proportions, called the *means-extremes* property of proportions:

The product of the extremes equals the product of the means.

$\frac{a}{b} = \frac{c}{d}$ is *equivalent* to $ad = bc$.

The two equations are equivalent because we can change either of them into the other by multiplying (or dividing) each side by bd. Try this yourself.

It is often necessary to replace one proportion by an equivalent proportion. When you do so in a proof, you can use the reason "A property of proportions." The following properties will be justified in the exercises.

Properties of Proportions

1. $\frac{a}{b} = \frac{c}{d}$ is equivalent to:

a. $ad = bc$ **b.** $\frac{a}{c} = \frac{b}{d}$ **c.** $\frac{b}{a} = \frac{d}{c}$ **d.** $\frac{a+b}{b} = \frac{c+d}{d}$

2. If $\frac{a}{b} = \frac{c}{d} = \frac{e}{f} = \cdots$, then $\frac{a+c+e+\cdots}{b+d+f+\cdots} = \frac{a}{b} = \cdots$. (perimeters)

Example Use the proportion $\frac{x}{y} = \frac{5}{2}$ to complete each statement.

a. $5y = \underline{\ ?\ }$ **b.** $\frac{x+y}{y} = \frac{?}{?}$

c. $\frac{2}{5} = \frac{?}{?}$ **d.** $\frac{x}{5} = \frac{?}{?}$

Solution **a.** $5y = 2x$ **b.** $\frac{x+y}{y} = \frac{7}{2}$

c. $\frac{2}{5} = \frac{y}{x}$ **d.** $\frac{x}{5} = \frac{y}{2}$

Teaching Suggestions,
pp. T101–T102

Objectives
Presenting the Lesson

Communication Skills,
p. T102

Supplementary Materials

Practice Master 37
Study Guide, pp. 81–82

Lesson Focus

This lesson introduces equivalent proportions. In the study of similar polygons, students rewrite proportions as equivalent proportions.

Suggested Assignments

Minimum
Day 1: 247/1–8, 9–15 odd
S 244/32, 33
Day 2: 247/16–20 even, 21–27 odd, 29

Average
Day 1: 247/2–8 even, 11, 12, 16, 20
S 244/34, 36
Day 2: 247–248/21–29 odd, 32, 33, 35–37

Maximum
247–248/4, 8, 12, 15, 20, 25, 30, 35, 37, 40
S 244/34

Teaching Note

For some students, you may wish to derive the equivalent proportions. Property 2 can be shown by following the suggestions given in Exs. 41 and 42 on page 248. Many students can remember the properties if names are attached to them. Ask students to suggest names for each property of proportions.

Chalkboard Examples

Use the proportion $\frac{a}{b} = \frac{3}{5}$ to complete each statement.

1. $5a = \underline{3b}$
2. $\frac{5}{b} = \frac{3}{\underline{a}}$
3. $\frac{a+b}{b} = \frac{3+5}{\underline{5}}$
4. $\frac{5}{3} = \frac{b}{\underline{a}}$

Exercise Note

In Ex. 8, point out to students that multiple answers are possible. In Ex. 11, students use the means-extremes property to solve a proportion. Written Exs. 9–20 on the next page provide additional practice in solving proportions.

Guided Practice

1. If $\frac{x}{7} = \frac{4}{2}$, then $2x = \underline{28}$.
2. If $2x = 3y$, then $\frac{2}{3} = \frac{y}{\underline{x}}$.
3. If $\frac{x}{7} = \frac{4}{2}$, then $\frac{x+7}{7} = \frac{6}{\underline{2}}$.
4. If $\frac{x}{3} = \frac{y-2}{2}$, then $\frac{x+3}{3} = \frac{y}{\underline{2}}$.

Classroom Exercises

1. If $\frac{e}{f} = \frac{g}{h}$, which equation is correct?

   a. $ef = gh$ (b.) $eh = fg$ c. $eg = fh$

2. Which proportions are equivalent to $\frac{x}{12} = \frac{3}{4}$?

   (a.) $\frac{x}{3} = \frac{12}{4}$ b. $\frac{x}{4} = \frac{12}{3}$ (c.) $\frac{12}{x} = \frac{4}{3}$ (d.) $\frac{x+12}{12} = \frac{7}{4}$

Complete the statement.

3. If $\frac{a}{b} = \frac{2}{3}$, then $3a = \underline{\ ?\ }$. **2b**
4. If $\frac{c}{d} = \frac{4}{7}$, then $\frac{d}{c} = \frac{?}{?}$. $\frac{7}{4}$
5. If $\frac{e}{f} = \frac{5}{9}$, then $\frac{e}{5} = \frac{?}{?}$. $\frac{f}{9}$
6. If $\frac{g}{h} = \frac{j}{8}$, then $\frac{j}{g} = \frac{?}{?}$. $\frac{8}{h}$
7. If $\frac{k}{m} = \frac{2}{3}$, then $\frac{k+m}{m} = \frac{?}{?}$. $\frac{5}{3}$
8. If $\frac{n}{p} = \frac{q}{r} = \frac{7}{9}$, then $\frac{n+q+7}{p+r+9} = \frac{?}{?}$. $\frac{n}{p}$ **or** $\frac{q}{r}$ **or** $\frac{7}{9}$
9. a. Apply the means-extremes property of proportions to the proportion $\frac{e}{f} = \frac{g}{5}$ and you get $5e = \underline{\ ?\ }$. ***fg***

   b. Apply the property to the proportion $\frac{5}{f} = \frac{g}{e}$ and you get $\underline{\ ?\ } = \underline{\ ?\ }$. $5e = fg$

   c. Are the proportions $\frac{e}{f} = \frac{g}{5}$ and $\frac{5}{f} = \frac{g}{e}$ equivalent? Why? **Yes; the product of the means equals the product of the extremes.**
10. Explain an easy way to show that the proportions $\frac{x}{7} = \frac{2}{3}$ and $\frac{x}{2} = \frac{3}{7}$ are not equivalent. **Use the means-extremes property.**
11. Apply the means-extremes property to $\frac{x}{10} = \frac{4}{5}$ and you get $5x = \underline{\ ?\ }$ **40** and $x = \underline{\ ?\ }$. **8**
12. If $\frac{4}{y} = \frac{7}{9}$, then $\underset{\mathbf{7y}}{\underline{\ ?\ }} = \underset{\mathbf{36}}{\underline{\ ?\ }}$ and $y = \underline{\ ?\ }$. $\frac{36}{7}$

What can you conclude from the given information?

13. $\frac{b}{a} = \frac{t}{x}$ and $\frac{a}{b} = \frac{x}{p}$ $t = p$
14. $\frac{2}{5} = \frac{y}{k}$ and $\frac{2}{z} = \frac{5}{k}$ $y = z$
15. Apply the means-extremes property to $\frac{a}{b} = \frac{c}{d}$ and also to $\frac{a}{c} = \frac{b}{d}$. (Note that you have justified Property 1(b) on page 245 by showing that each proportion is equivalent to the same equation.) $ad = bc, ad = cb$
16. Explain why $\frac{a}{b} = \frac{c}{d}$ and $\frac{b}{a} = \frac{d}{c}$ are equivalent. (This justifies Property 1(c) on page 245.) **Apply the means-extremes property to both;** $ad = bc, bc = ad$

Written Exercises

Complete each statement.

A **1.** If $\frac{x}{3} = \frac{2}{5}$, then $5x =$ _?_. **6**

2. If $\frac{4}{x} = \frac{2}{7}$, then $2x =$ _?_. **28**

3. If $a:3 = 7:4$, then $4a =$ _?_. **21**

4. If $4:t = 8:9$, then $8t =$ _?_. **36**

5. If $\frac{a}{4} = \frac{b}{7}$, then $\frac{a}{b} = \frac{?}{?}$. $\mathbf{\frac{4}{7}}$

6. If $\frac{x}{y} = \frac{3}{8}$, then $\frac{y}{x} = \frac{?}{?}$. $\mathbf{\frac{8}{3}}$

7. If $\frac{x}{2} = \frac{y}{3}$, then $\frac{x+2}{2} =$ _?_. $\mathbf{\frac{y+3}{3}}$

8. If $\frac{a}{b} = \frac{5-x}{x}$, then $\frac{a+b}{b} =$ _?_. $\mathbf{\frac{5}{x}}$

Find the value of *x*.

9. $\frac{x}{4} = \frac{3}{5}$ $\mathbf{2\frac{2}{5}}$

10. $\frac{4}{x} = \frac{2}{5}$ **10**

11. $\frac{2}{5} = \frac{3x}{7}$ $\mathbf{\frac{14}{15}}$

12. $\frac{8}{x} = \frac{2}{5}$ **20**

13. $\frac{x+5}{4} = \frac{1}{2}$ **−3**

14. $\frac{x+3}{2} = \frac{4}{3}$ $\mathbf{-\frac{1}{3}}$

15. $\frac{x+2}{x+3} = \frac{4}{5}$ **2**

16. $\frac{2x+1}{4x-1} = \frac{2}{3}$ $\mathbf{2\frac{1}{2}}$

17. $\frac{x+3}{2} = \frac{2x-1}{3}$ **11**

18. $\frac{x+4}{x-4} = \frac{6}{5}$ **44**

19. $\frac{7}{6x-4} = \frac{9}{4x+6}$ **3**

20. $\frac{3x+5}{3} = \frac{18x+5}{7}$ $\mathbf{\frac{20}{33}}$

For the figure shown, it is given that $\frac{KR}{RT} = \frac{KS}{SU}$. Copy and complete the table.

	KR	*RT*	*KT*	*KS*	*SU*	*KU*
21.	12	9	? **21**	16	? **12**	? **28**
22.	8	? **2**	10	12	? **3**	? **15**
23.	16	? **8**	? **24**	? **20**	10	30
24.	? **6**	2	? **8**	9	? **3**	12
B **25.**	? **8**	? **4**	12	10	5	? **15**
26.	12	4	? **16**	? **15**	? **5**	20
27.	? **27**	9	36	? **36**	? **12**	48
28.	? **20**	? **10**	30	28	? **14**	42

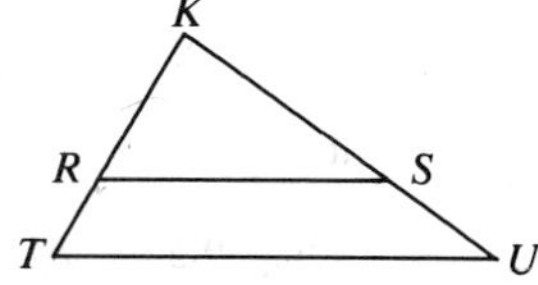

(*Hint for Ex. 25*: Let $KR = x$, then $RT = 12 - x$.)

29. Show that the proportions $\frac{a+b}{b} = \frac{c+d}{d}$ and $\frac{a}{b} = \frac{c}{d}$ are equivalent. (Note that this exercise justifies property 1(d) on page 245.)

30. Given the proportions $\frac{x+y}{y} = \frac{r}{s}$ and $\frac{x-y}{x+y} = \frac{s}{y}$, what can you conclude? $\mathbf{x - y = r}$

In the figure, $\frac{AD}{DB} = \frac{CE}{EB}$.

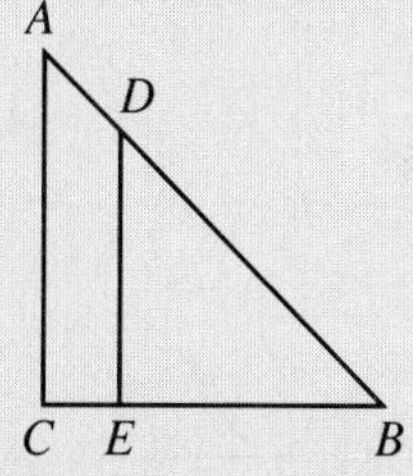

5. If $CE = 2$, $EB = 6$, and $AD = 3$, then $DB = \underline{9}$.

6. If $AB = 10$, $DB = 8$, and $CB = 7.5$, then $EB = \underline{6}$.

Using a Calculator

Students may want to use a calculator for Exs. 21–28. For example, in Ex. 21 the proportion $\frac{12}{9} = \frac{16}{SU}$ is solved on a calculator by inputting: $9 \times 16 \div 12 =$.

Additional Answers Written Exercises

29. By the means-extremes property, $\frac{a+b}{b} = \frac{c+d}{d}$ is equivalent to $ad + bd = bc + bd$ and $\frac{a}{b} = \frac{c}{d}$ is equivalent to $ad = bc$. But $ad + bd = bc + bd$ is also equivalent to $ad = bc$.

(continued)

31. By the means-extremes property, $\frac{a-b}{a+b} = \frac{c-d}{c+d}$ is equivalent to $(a-b)(c+d) = (a+b)(c-d)$; $ac - bc + ad - bd = ac + bc - ad - bd$; $2ad = 2bc$; $ad = bc$. But $ad = bc$ is equivalent to $\frac{a}{b} = \frac{c}{d}$.

32. By the means-extremes property, $\frac{a+c}{b+d} = \frac{a-c}{b-d}$ is equivalent to $(a+c)(b-d) = (b+d)(a-c)$; $ab + bc - ad - cd = ab + ad - bc - cd$; $-2ad = -2bc$; $ad = bc$. But $ad = bc$ is equivalent to $\frac{a}{b} = \frac{c}{d}$.

41. Let $\frac{a}{b} = r$. Then $a = br$, $c = dr$, and $e = fr$. Then $\frac{a+c+e}{b+d+f} = \frac{br+dr+fr}{b+d+f} = \frac{r(b+d+f)}{b+d+f} = r = \frac{a}{b}$

Teaching Suggestions, pp. T102–T103

Objective
Presenting the Lesson
Using Technology
Making Connections

Cooperative Learning, p. T103

Exploring Activity, p. 239c

Supplementary Materials

Practice Master 38; Test 25
Resource Book, pp. 37, 133
Study Guide, pp. 83–84
Overhead Visual 5

Show that the given proportions are equivalent.

31. $\frac{a-b}{a+b} = \frac{c-d}{c+d}$ and $\frac{a}{b} = \frac{c}{d}$

32. $\frac{a+c}{b+d} = \frac{a-c}{b-d}$ and $\frac{a}{b} = \frac{c}{d}$

Find the value of x.

33. $\frac{x}{x+5} = \frac{x-4}{x}$ **20**

34. $\frac{x-2}{x} = \frac{x}{x+3}$ **6**

35. $\frac{x+1}{x-2} = \frac{x+5}{x-6}$ **$\frac{1}{2}$**

C 36. $\frac{x-1}{x-2} = \frac{x+4}{x+2}$ **6**

37. $\frac{x(x+5)}{4x+4} = \frac{9}{5}$ **4 or $-\frac{9}{5}$**

38. $\frac{x-1}{x+2} = \frac{10}{3x-2}$ **6 or −1**

Find the values of x and y.

39. $\frac{y}{x-9} = \frac{4}{7}$ **x = 16**
$\frac{x+y}{x-y} = \frac{5}{3}$ **y = 4**

40. $\frac{x-3}{4} = \frac{y+2}{2}$ **x = 11**
$\frac{x+y-1}{6} = \frac{x-y+1}{5}$ **y = 2**

41. Prove: If $\frac{a}{b} = \frac{c}{d} = \frac{e}{f}$, then $\frac{a+c+e}{b+d+f} = \frac{a}{b}$. (*Hint*: Let $\frac{a}{b} = r$. Then $a = br$, $c = dr$, and $e = \underline{\ ?\ }$.) ***fr***

42. Explain how to extend the proof of Exercise 41 to justify Property 2 on page 245.

43. If $\frac{4a-9b}{4a} = \frac{a-2b}{b}$, find the numerical value of the ratio $a:b$. **3:2**

7-3 *Similar Polygons*

When you draw a diagram of a soccer field, you don't need an enormous piece of paper. You use a convenient sheet and draw *to scale*. That is, you show the right shape, but in a convenient size. Two figures, such as those below, that have the same shape are called *similar*.

Two polygons are **similar** if their vertices can be paired so that:

(1) Corresponding angles are congruent.
(2) Corresponding sides are in proportion. (Their lengths have the same ratio.)

When you refer to similar polygons, their corresponding vertices must be listed in the same order. If polygon $PQRST$ is similar to polygon $VWXYZ$, you write polygon $PQRST \sim$ polygon $VWXYZ$.

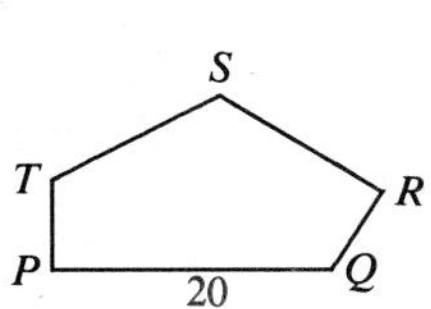

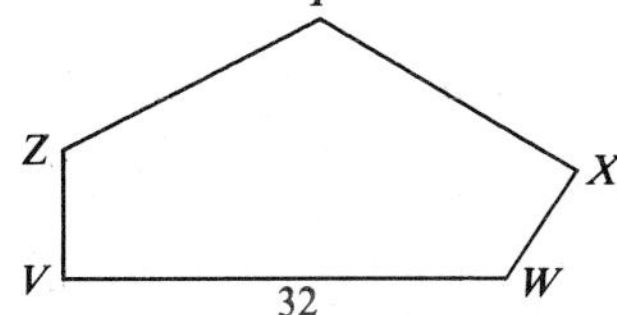

From the definition of similar polygons, we have:

(1) $\angle P \cong \angle V \quad \angle Q \cong \angle W \quad \angle R \cong \angle X \quad \angle S \cong \angle Y \quad \angle T \cong \angle Z$

(2) $\frac{PQ}{VW} = \frac{QR}{WX} = \frac{RS}{XY} = \frac{ST}{YZ} = \frac{TP}{ZV}$

Similarity has some of the same properties as equality and congruence (page 37). Similarity is reflexive, symmetric, and transitive.

If two polygons are similar, then the ratio of the lengths of two corresponding sides is called the **scale factor** of the similarity. The scale factor of pentagon $PQRST$ to pentagon $VWXYZ$ is $\frac{PQ}{VW} = \frac{20}{32} = \frac{5}{8}$.

The example that follows shows one convenient way to label corresponding vertices: A and A' (read A prime), B and B', and so on.

Example Quad. $ABCD \sim$ quad. $A'B'C'D'$. Find:

a. their scale factor
b. the values of x, y, and z
c. the perimeters of the two quadrilaterals
d. the ratio of the perimeters

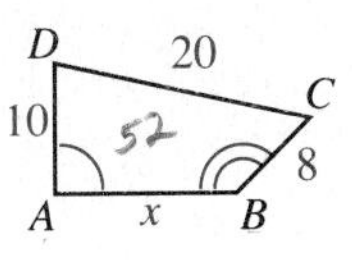

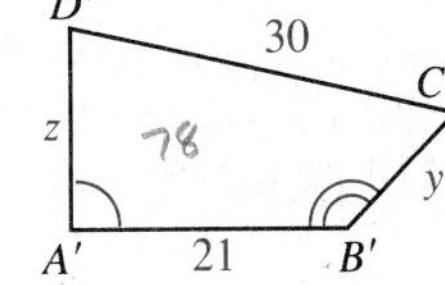

Solution **a.** The scale factor is $\frac{DC}{D'C'} = \frac{20}{30} = \frac{2}{3}$.

b. $\frac{DC}{D'C'} = \frac{AB}{A'B'}$ $\qquad$ $\frac{DC}{D'C'} = \frac{BC}{B'C'}$ $\qquad$ $\frac{DC}{D'C'} = \frac{AD}{A'D'}$

$\frac{2}{3} = \frac{x}{21}$ $\qquad$ $\frac{2}{3} = \frac{8}{y}$ $\qquad$ $\frac{2}{3} = \frac{10}{z}$

$x = 14$ $\qquad$ $y = 12$ $\qquad$ $z = 15$

c. The perimeter of quad. $ABCD$ is $10 + 20 + 8 + 14 = 52$.
The perimeter of quad. $A'B'C'D'$ is $15 + 30 + 12 + 21 = 78$.

d. The ratio of the perimeters is $\frac{52}{78}$, or $\frac{2}{3}$.

If you compare the ratio of the perimeters with the scale factor of the similarity, you discover they are the same. This property will be discussed further in Exercise 23 on page 251 and in Theorem 11-7.

Lesson Focus

This lesson introduces one of the major topics in geometry, the study of similar figures. Congruent figures have the same size and shape. Similar figures have the same shape.

Suggested Assignments

Minimum
Day 1: 250–251/1–12, 14–20 even
Day 2: 251/21–25
252/Self-Test 1

Average
Day 1: 250–251/1–12, 13–19 odd, 21–24
Day 2: 251/25, 26, 29, 31
252/Self-Test 1

Maximum
Day 1: 250–251/5, 10, 12, 15, 19, 21, 23, 25, 26
S 248/41, 43
Day 2: 251/20, 24, 27, 29, 31–37 odd

Teaching Note

Point out to students that the ratio of perimeters in Example (d) is an application of Property 2 on page 245. The use of this property also will help students with Ex. 23 on page 251.

Using a Computer

See page T102 for an experiment involving scale factor and similar polygons.

Classroom Exercises

Are the quadrilaterals similar? If they aren't, tell why not.

1. *ABCD* and *EFGH* **No, corr. sides aren't in proportion.**
2. *ABCD* and *JKLM* **Yes**
3. *ABCD* and *NOPQ* **No, corr. $\angle$s aren't $\cong$.**
4. *JKLM* and *NOPQ* **No, corr. $\angle$s aren't $\cong$.**

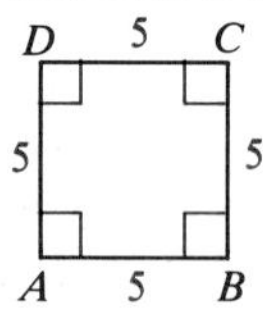

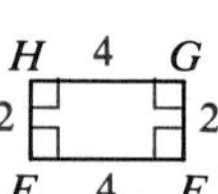

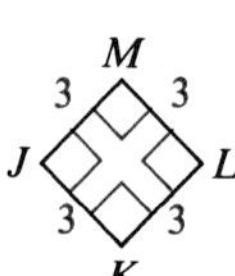

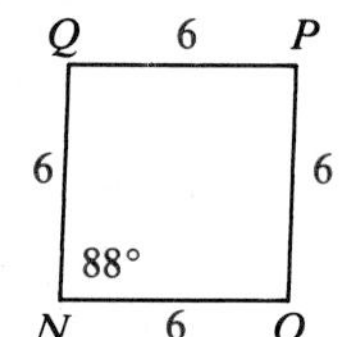

5. If the corresponding angles of two polygons are congruent, must the polygons be similar? **No**
6. If the corresponding sides of two polygons are in proportion, must the polygons be similar? **No**
7. Two polygons are similar. Do they have to be congruent? **No**
8. Two polygons are congruent. Do they have to be similar? **Yes**
9. Are all regular pentagons similar? **Yes**
10. Quad. *JUDY* ~ quad. *J'U'D'Y'*. Complete.
    a. $m\angle Y'$ = ___?___ and $m\angle D$ = ___?___. **70, 90**
    b. The scale factor of quad. *JUDY* to quad. *J'U'D'Y'* is ___?___. **4:3**
    c. Find *DU*, *Y'J'*, and *J'U'*. **8, 21, 9*t***
    d. The ratio of the perimeters is ___?___. **4:3**
    e. Explain why it is not true that quad. *DUJY* ~ quad. *Y'J'U'D'*. **Corr. $\angle$s are not $\cong$.**

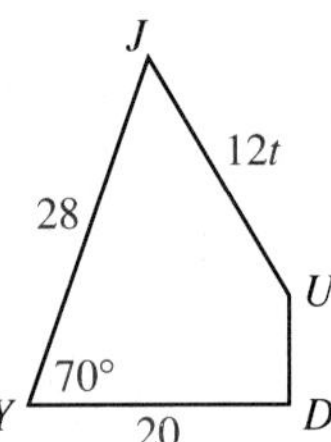

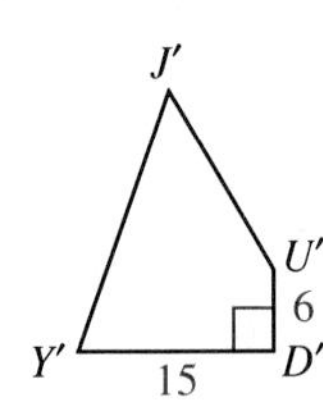

Written Exercises

Tell whether the two polygons are *always*, *sometimes*, or *never* similar.

A

1. Two equilateral triangles **always**
2. Two right triangles **sometimes**
3. Two isosceles triangles **sometimes**
4. Two scalene triangles **sometimes**
5. Two squares **always**
6. Two rectangles **sometimes**
7. Two rhombuses **sometimes**
8. Two isosceles trapezoids **sometimes**
9. Two regular hexagons **always**
10. Two regular polygons **sometimes**
11. A right triangle and an acute triangle **never**
12. An isosceles triangle and a scalene triangle **never**
13. A right triangle and a scalene triangle **sometimes**
14. An equilateral triangle and an equiangular triangle **always**

Chalkboard Exercises

1. Quad. *ABCD* ~ quad. *A'B'C'D'*.

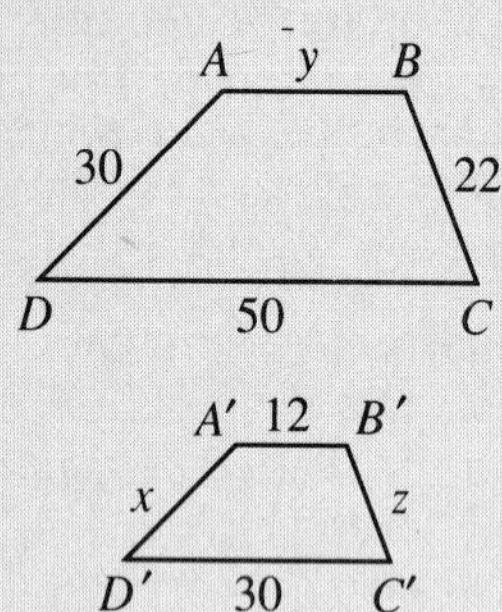

Find:
a. their scale factor 5:3
b. the values of *x*, *y*, and *z* 18, 20, 13.2
c. the ratio of the perimeters 5:3

2. Quad. *EFGH* ~ quad. *E'F'G'H'*.

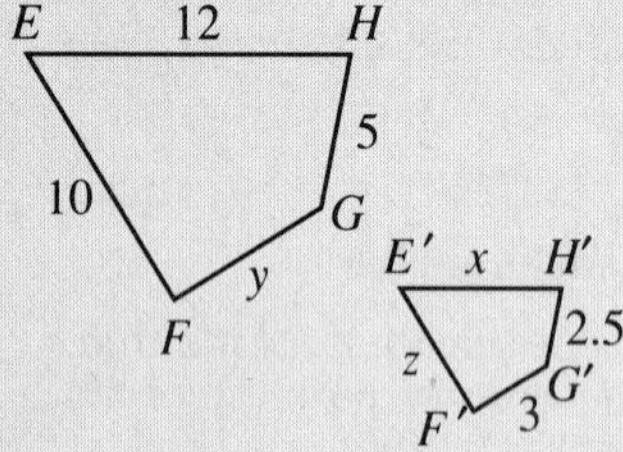

Find:
a. their scale factor 2:1
b. the values of *x*, *y*, and *z* 6, 6, 5
c. the ratio of the perimeters 2:1

Thinking Skills

Written Exs. 1–14 require students to think carefully about the properties of the figures used and the definition of similar polygons. Encourage them to draw diagrams. Ask students to explain their answers so you can evaluate their understanding of the exercises.

In Exercises 15-23 quad. *TUNE* ~ quad. *T'U'N'E'*.

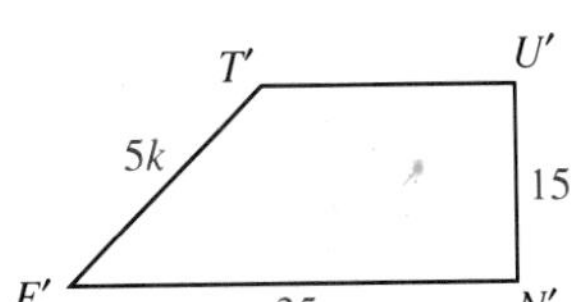

15. What is the scale factor of quad. *TUNE* to quad. *T'U'N'E'*? **4:5**

16. What special kind of quadrilateral must quad. *T'U'N'E'* be? Explain. **Trapezoid; $\overline{T'U'} \parallel \overline{E'N'}$**

17. Find $m\angle T'$. **135** **18.** Find $m\angle E'$. **45**

19. Find *UN*. **12** **20.** Find *T'U'*. **20**

21. Find *TE*. **4k** **22.** Find the ratio of the perimeters. **4:5**

B **23.** What property of proportions on page 245 would you use to show that the ratio of the perimeters is equal to the ratio of the lengths of any two corresponding sides? **Property 2**

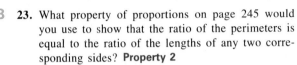

Two similar polygons are shown. Find the values of *x*, *y*, and *z*.

24.

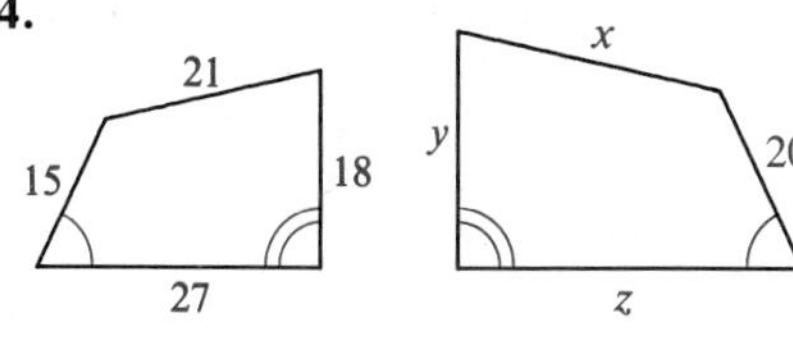

x = 28, y = 24, z = 36

25.

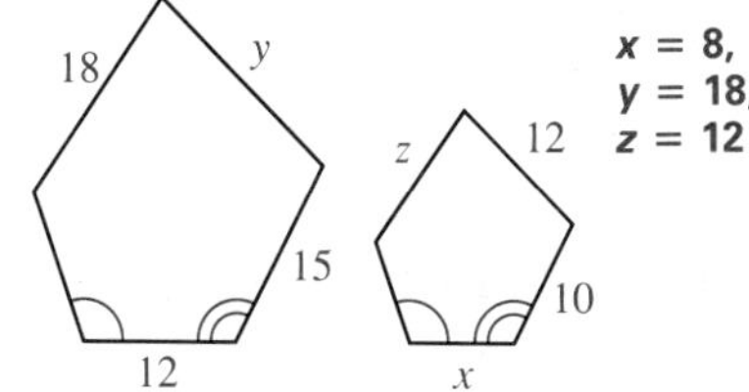

x = 8, y = 18, z = 12

26.

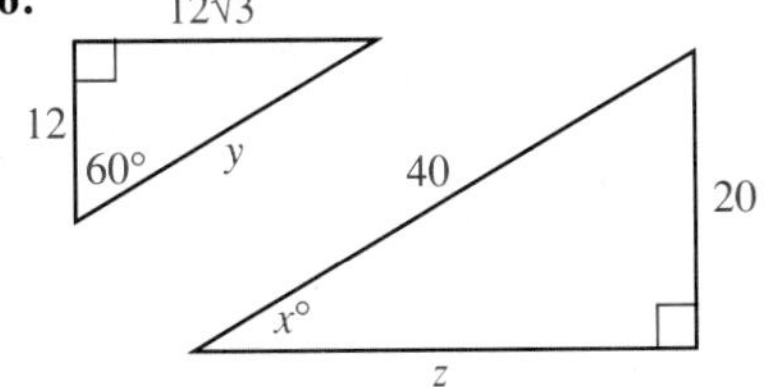

x = 30, y = 24, z = 20√3

27.

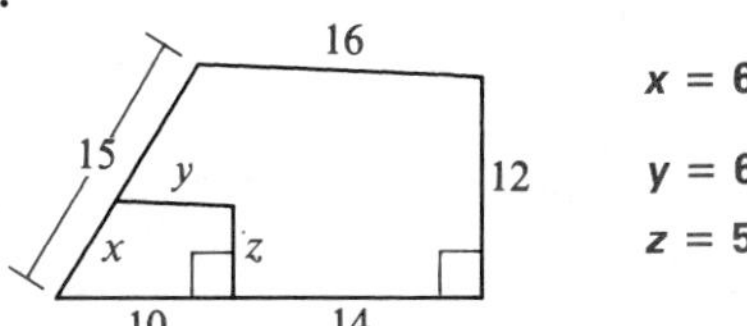

$x = 6\frac{1}{4}$, $y = 6\frac{2}{3}$, $z = 5$

28. Draw two equilateral hexagons that are clearly not similar.

29. Draw two equiangular hexagons that are clearly not similar.

30. If $\triangle ABC \sim \triangle DEF$, express *AB* in terms of other lengths. (There are two possible answers.) **See below.**

31. Explain how you can tell at once that quadrilateral *RSWX* is not similar to quadrilateral *RSYZ*. **See below.**

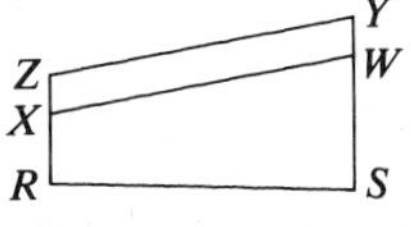

Plot the given points on graph paper. Draw quadrilateral *ABCD* and $\overline{A'B'}$. Locate points *C'* and *D'* so that *A'B'C'D'* is similar to *ABCD*.

32. *A*(0, 0), *B*(4, 0), *C*(2, 4), *D*(0, 2), *A'*(−10, −2), *B'*(−2, −2)

33. *A*(0, 0), *B*(4, 0), *C*(2, 4), *D*(0, 2), *A'*(7, 2), *B'*(7, 0)

30. $\frac{BC \cdot DE}{EF}$ **or** $\frac{AC \cdot DE}{DF}$ **31.** ***RS* = *RS*, but *ZR* > *XR*, so** $\frac{RS}{RS} = 1 \neq \frac{ZR}{XR}$.

Communication Skills

The use of the term *scale factor* might confuse some students because they are used to thinking of a factor as a whole number, as in "2 is a factor of 4 and 6." Stress that a scale factor in geometry is a *ratio.*

Guided Practice

1. Quad. *ABCD* ~ quad. *EFGH.*

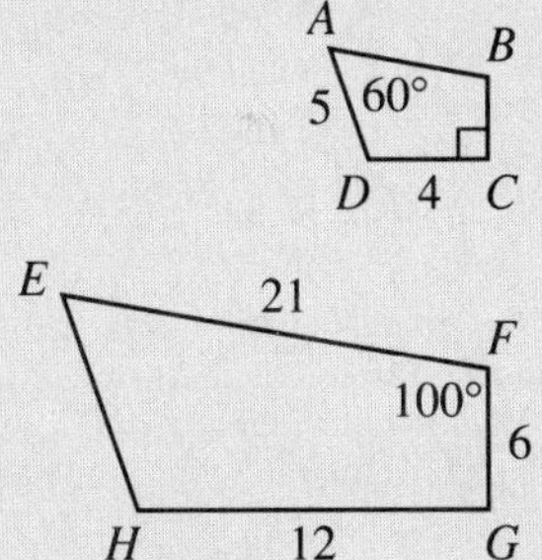

Complete.

a. $m\angle E$ = 60
b. $m\angle G$ = 90
c. $m\angle B$ = 100
d. If $m\angle D$ = 110, then $m\angle H$ = 110.
e. The scale factor is 1:3.
f. *EH* = 15
g. *BC* = 2
h. *AB* = 7

Group Activity

Exs. 28–29 and 32–33 can be used for a small group activity. All students can participate in the drawing activities. Have a volunteer from each group draw at least one solution for Exs. 28 and 29 on the chalkboard.

Problem Solving

You may wish to assign the following problem to capable students.

Given: $\triangle ABC \sim \triangle DEF$;
$AB = DF = 18$;
$BC = DE = 27$

Although five parts (three angles and two sides) of one triangle are congruent to five parts of the other, the triangles are not congruent. Find AC and EF.
12; 40.5

Quick Quiz

Express in simplest form.

1. 4:24 1:6
2. 45 cm to 1 m 9 to 20
3. $\frac{2x^2y}{4y}$ $\frac{x^2}{2}$

Solve for x.

4. $\frac{x}{3} = \frac{12}{9}$ 4
5. $\frac{x+3}{4} = \frac{9}{8}$ $\frac{3}{2}$
6. $\frac{4+x}{5} = \frac{x-2}{2}$ 6

Tell whether the equation is equivalent to the proportion $\frac{x}{y} = \frac{3}{4}$.

7. $3y = 4x$ Yes
8. $3x = 4y$ No
9. $\frac{x+y}{y} = \frac{7}{4}$ Yes

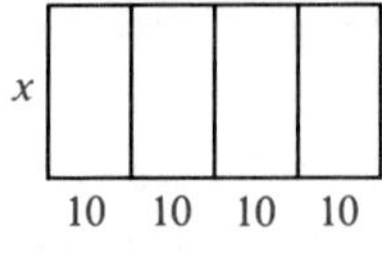

34. The card shown was cut into four congruent pieces with each piece similar to the original. Find the value of x. **$x = 20$**

35. Quad. *WHAT* is a figure such that $WHAT \sim HATW$. Find the measure of each angle. What special kind of figure must the quadrilateral be? **90; square**

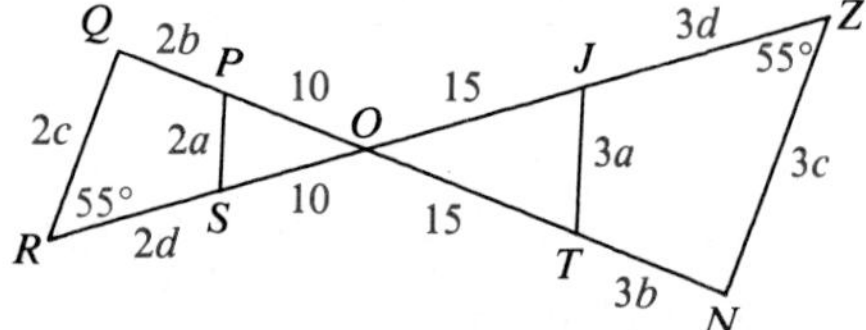

C **36.** What can you deduce from the diagram shown at the right? Explain. **Answers may vary. For example, $\overline{PS} \parallel \overline{JT}$, $\overline{RQ} \parallel \overline{NZ}$, or $PQRS \sim TNZJ$.**

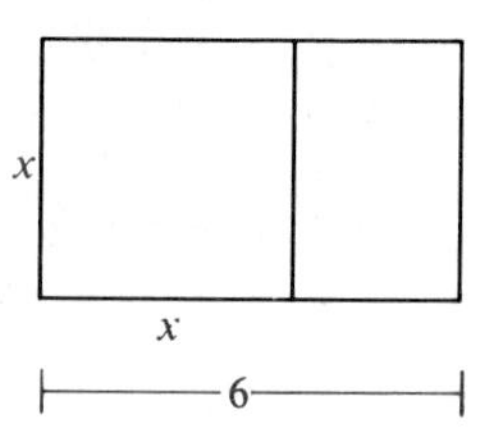

37. The large rectangle shown is a *golden rectangle*. This means that when a square is cut off, the rectangle that remains is similar to the original rectangle.

a. How wide is the original rectangle? **$-3 + 3\sqrt{5}$**

b. The ratio of length to width in a golden rectangle is called the *golden ratio*. Write the golden ratio in simplified radical form. Then use a calculator to find an approximation to the nearest hundredth **$\frac{1+\sqrt{5}}{2}$; 1.62**

Self-Test 1

Express the ratio in simplest form.

1. 9:15 **3:5**
2. 60 cm to 2 m **3 to 10**
3. $\frac{4ab}{6b^2}$ **$\frac{2a}{3b}$**

Solve for x.

4. $\frac{x}{8} = \frac{9}{12}$ **6**
5. $\frac{x-2}{2} = \frac{x+6}{4}$ **10**
6. $\frac{x}{5-x} = \frac{12}{8}$ **3**

Tell whether the equation is equivalent to the proportion $\frac{a}{b} = \frac{5}{7}$.

7. $\frac{a}{7} = \frac{b}{5}$ **No**
8. $7a = 5b$ **Yes**
9. $\frac{a+b}{b} = \frac{12}{7}$ **Yes**

10. If $\triangle ABC \sim \triangle RST$, $m\angle A = 45$, and $m\angle C = 60$, then $m\angle R = \underline{\ ?\ }$ **45**, $m\angle T = \underline{\ ?\ }$ **60**, and $m\angle S = \underline{\ ?\ }$ **75**.

The quadrilaterals shown are similar.

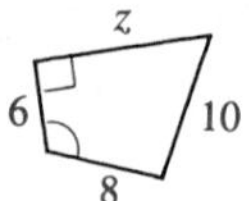

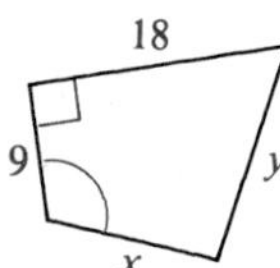

11. The scale factor of the smaller quadrilateral to the larger quadrilateral is $\underline{\ ?\ }$. **2:3**
12. $x = \underline{\ ?\ }$ **12**
13. $y = \underline{\ ?\ }$ **15**
14. $z = \underline{\ ?\ }$ **12**
15. The measures of the angles of a hexagon are in the ratio 5:5:5:6:7:8. Find the measures. **100, 100, 100, 120, 140, 160**

♦ Calculator Key-In

Before the pediment on top of the Parthenon in Athens was destroyed, the front of the building fit almost exactly into a golden rectangle. In a **golden rectangle,** the length l and width w satisfy the equation $\frac{l}{w} = \frac{l + w}{l}$. The ratio $\frac{l}{w}$ is called the **golden ratio.**

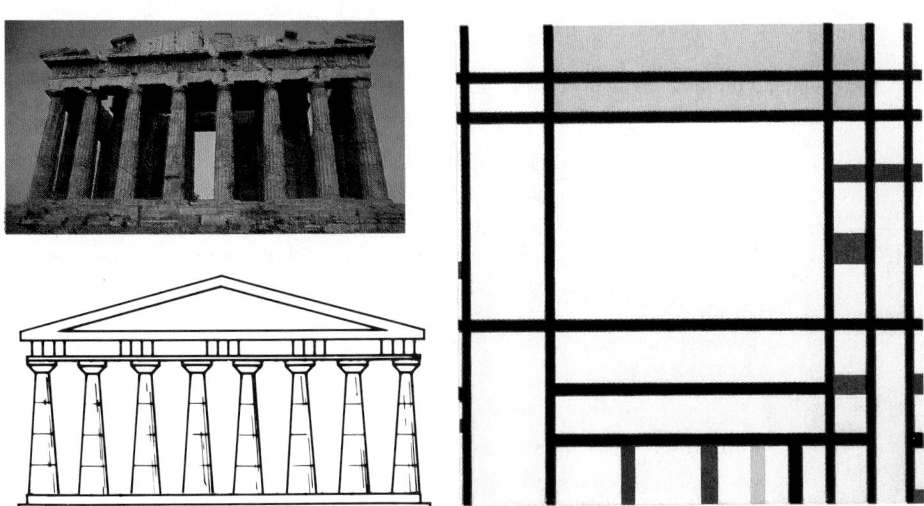

Over the centuries, artists and architects have found the golden rectangle to be especially pleasing to the eye. How many golden rectangles can you find in the painting by Piet Mondrian (1872–1944) that is shown?

Exercises

$\frac{AD}{AC} \approx 1.62$, $\frac{AC}{AB} \approx 1.62$, $\frac{AB}{BC} \approx 1.62$

1. A regular pentagon is shown. It happens to be true that $\frac{AD}{AC}$, $\frac{AC}{AB}$, and $\frac{AB}{BC}$ all equal the golden ratio. Measure the appropriate lengths to the nearest millimeter and compute the ratios with a calculator.

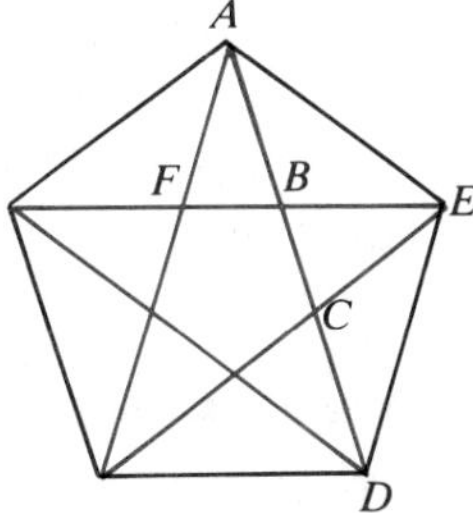

2. From the equation $\frac{l}{w} = \frac{l + w}{l}$ it can be shown that the numerical value of $\frac{l}{w}$ is $\frac{1 + \sqrt{5}}{2}$. Express the value of $\frac{l}{w}$, the golden ratio, as a decimal. **$\approx$ 1.618**

For Exs. 10–12, $\triangle LMN \sim \triangle PQR$.

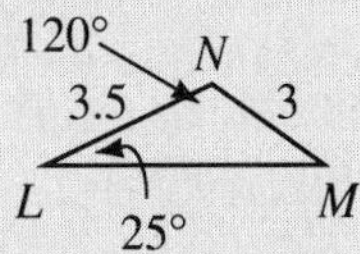

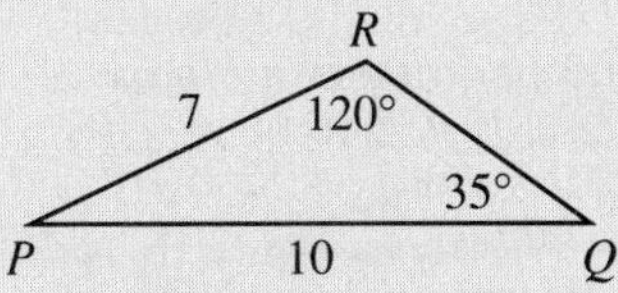

10. The scale factor of $\triangle LNM$ to $\triangle PRQ$ is $\underline{\frac{1}{2}}$.
11. $RQ = \underline{6}$
12. $LM = \underline{5}$
13. The measures of the angles of a pentagon are in the ratio 5:7:8:4:3. Find the measure of each angle.
    100, 140, 160, 80, 60

Using a Calculator

Have students use a calculator to compute the golden ratio and its reciprocal. Explain how to use the $1/x$ (or x^{-1}) key for the reciprocal. Ask them to discover and prove a relationship between the golden ratio and its reciprocal.

Using a Computer

These exercises explore the properties of similar triangles. Point out that once $\triangle ABC \sim \triangle DEF$ and $AB:DE = r$, then the ratios of the medians, altitudes, and perimeters are also equal to r. See page T102 for a related experiment.

Teaching Suggestions, pp. T103–T104

Objectives
Presenting the Lesson
Using Technology
Applications

Communication Skills, p. T104

Supplementary Materials

Practice Master 39
Study Guide, pp. 85–86
Overhead Visual E
Computer Activity 14

Lesson Focus

The focus of this lesson is a postulate for establishing when two triangles are similar. The postulate states that two triangles are similar whenever two pairs of angles are congruent.

Suggested Assignments

Minimum
Day 1: 257–258/1–16
Day 2: 258–259/18–20, 23, 24

Average
257–259/5–15 odd, 16–24 even

Maximum
257–259/5, 9, 14, 15, 20, 21, 24, 27, 29, 31

Explorations

These exploratory exercises can be done using a computer with a program that draws and measures geometric figures.

Draw any triangle and a median of the triangle. Measure and record the lengths of the sides and the median, the measures of the angles, and the perimeter of the triangle.

Change the scale of your triangle. Remeasure and record the lengths of the sides and the median, the measures of the angles, and the perimeter of the triangle.

Compare the measurements of the corresponding angles of the two triangles. What do you notice? **Corr. ∠s are ≅.**

Divide the length of each side of the original triangle by the length of the corresponding side of the second triangle. What do you notice? **Ratios are equal.**

What do you know about the two triangles? **The triangles are similar.**

Divide the length of the median of the original triangle by the length of the median of the second triangle. What do you notice? **Ratio of the medians = ratio of corr. sides.**

Divide the perimeter of the original triangle by the perimeter of the second triangle. What do you notice?
Ratio of the perimeters = ratio of corr. sides.

Working with Similar Triangles

Objectives

1. Use the AA Similarity Postulate, the SAS Similarity Theorem, and the SSS Similarity Theorem to prove triangles similar.
2. Use similar triangles to deduce information about segments or angles.
3. Apply the Triangle Proportionality Theorem and its corollary.
4. State and apply the Triangle Angle-Bisector Theorem.

7-4 *A Postulate for Similar Triangles*

You can always prove that two triangles are similar by showing that they satisfy the definition of similar polygons. However, there are simpler methods. The following experiment suggests the first of these methods: Two triangles are similar whenever two pairs of angles are congruent.

1. Draw any two segments $\overline{AB}$ and $\overline{A'B'}$.
2. Draw any angle at A and a congruent angle at A'. Draw any angle at B and a congruent angle at B'. Label points C and C' as shown. $\angle ACB \cong \angle A'C'B'$. (Why?)
3. Measure each pair of corresponding sides and compute an approximate decimal value for the ratio of their lengths:

$$\frac{AB}{A'B'} \qquad \frac{BC}{B'C'} \qquad \frac{AC}{A'C'}$$

4. Are the ratios computed in Step 3 approximately the same?

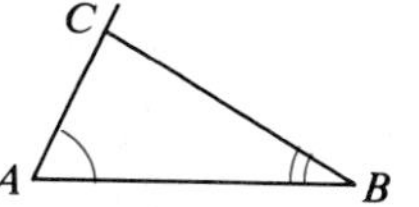

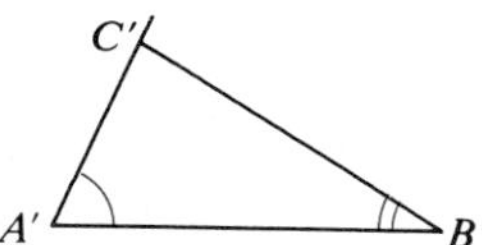

If you worked carefully, your answer in Step 4 was *yes*. Corresponding angles of the two triangles are congruent and corresponding sides are in proportion. By the definition of similar polygons, $\triangle ABC \sim \triangle A'B'C'$.

Whenever you draw two triangles with two angles of one triangle congruent to two angles of the other, you will find that the third angles are also congruent and that corresponding sides are in proportion.

Postulate 15 *AA Similarity Postulate*

If two angles of one triangle are congruent to two angles of another triangle, then the triangles are similar.

Example

Given: $\angle H$ and $\angle F$ are rt. ∠s.

Prove: $HK \cdot GO = FG \cdot KO$

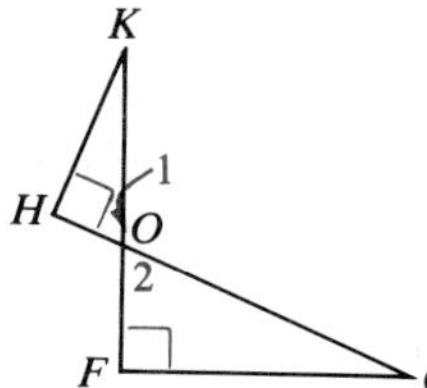

Plan for Proof: You can prove that $HK \cdot GO = FG \cdot KO$ if you show that $\frac{HK}{FG} = \frac{KO}{GO}$. You can get this proportion if you show that $\triangle HKO \sim \triangle FGO$.

Proof:

Statements	Reasons
1. $\angle 1 \cong \angle 2$	1. Vertical ∠s are ≅.
2. $\angle H$ and $\angle F$ are rt. ∠s.	2. Given
3. $m\angle H = 90 = m\angle F$	3. Def. of a rt. ∠
4. $\angle H \cong \angle F$	4. Def. of ≅ ∠s
5. $\triangle HKO \sim \triangle FGO$	5. AA Similarity Postulate
6. $\frac{HK}{FG} = \frac{KO}{GO}$	6. Corr. sides of ~ △s are in proportion.
7. $HK \cdot GO = FG \cdot KO$	7. A property of proportions

Chalkboard Examples

1. Given: $\overline{AC} \parallel \overline{BD}$
Prove: $\triangle AOC \sim \triangle BOD$

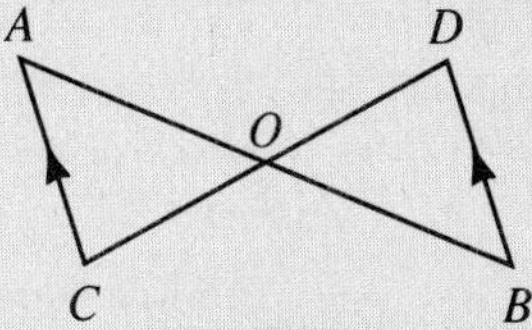

1. $\overline{AC} \parallel \overline{BD}$ (Given)
2. $\angle A \cong \angle B$; $\angle C \cong \angle D$ (If 2 ∥ lines are cut by a trans., alt. int. ∠s are ≅.)
3. $\triangle AOC \sim \triangle BOD$ (AA ~ Post.)

2. Given: $\overline{AB} \perp \overline{BF}$; $\overline{RH} \perp \overline{AF}$; $\angle 1 \cong \angle 2$
Prove: $HR \cdot BF = BA \cdot HA$

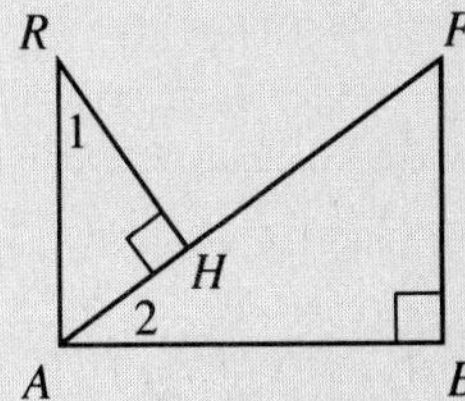

1. $\overline{AB} \perp \overline{BF}$; $\overline{RH} \perp \overline{AF}$; $\angle 1 \cong \angle 2$ (Given)
2. $\angle RHA \cong \angle FBA$ (Def. of ⊥ Lines)
3. $\triangle RHA \sim \triangle ABF$ (AA ~ Post.)
4. $\frac{HA}{BF} = \frac{HR}{BA}$ (Corr. sides of ~ △s are in prop.)
5. $HR \cdot BF = BA \cdot HA$ (Means-ext. prop.)

Using a Computer

The AA Similarity Postulate can be demonstrated easily using a construction program. See page T103.

Guided Practice

Tell whether the triangles are similar or not similar.

1. Similar

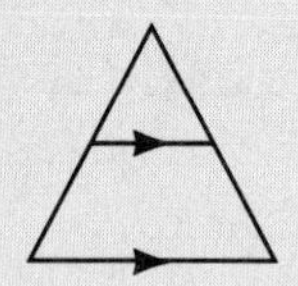

2. Similar

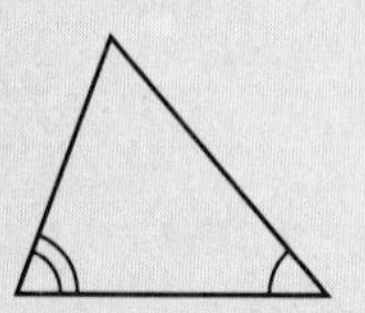

3. Similar

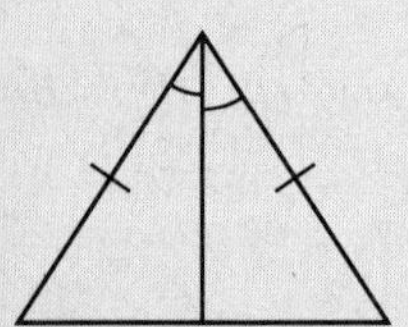

4. Similar

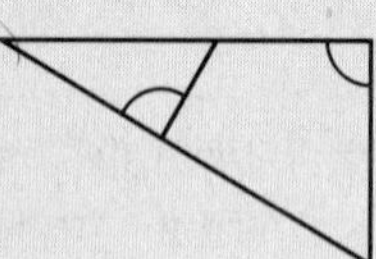

Find the value of x.

5. $\frac{5}{3}$

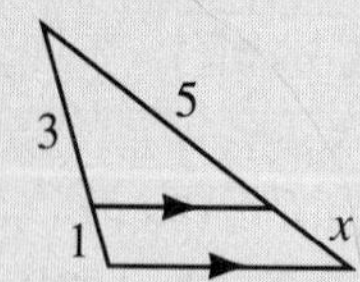

6.

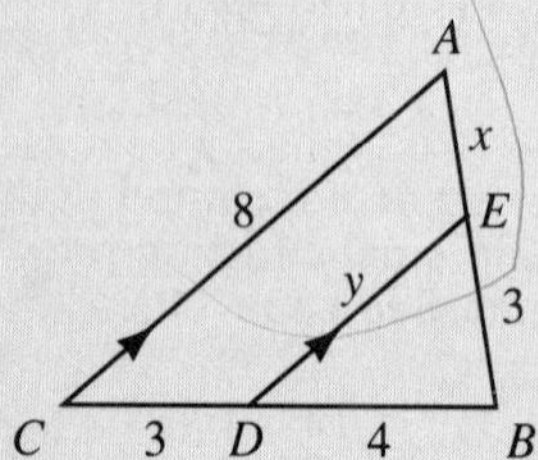

The example shows one way to prove that the product of the lengths of two segments is equal to the product of the lengths of two other segments. You prove that two triangles are similar, write a proportion, and then apply the means-extremes property of proportions.

Classroom Exercises

In Exercises 1–8 $\triangle ABC \sim \triangle DEF$. Tell whether each statement must be true.

1. $\triangle BAC \sim \triangle EFD$ **No**
2. If $m\angle D = 45$, then $m\angle A = 45$. **Yes**
3. If $m\angle B = 70$, then $m\angle F = 70$. **No**
4. $AB:DE = EF:BC$ **No**
5. $AC:DF = AB:DE$ **Yes**

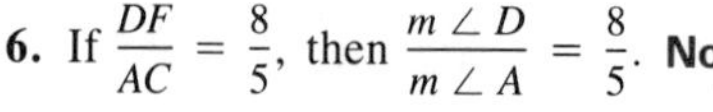

6. If $\frac{DF}{AC} = \frac{8}{5}$, then $\frac{m\angle D}{m\angle A} = \frac{8}{5}$. **No**

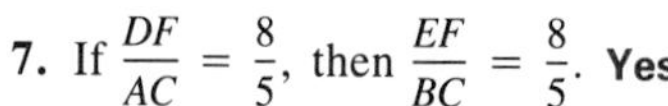

7. If $\frac{DF}{AC} = \frac{8}{5}$, then $\frac{EF}{BC} = \frac{8}{5}$. **Yes**

8. If the scale factor of $\triangle ABC$ to $\triangle DEF$ is 5 to 8, then the scale factor of $\triangle DEF$ to $\triangle ABC$ is 8 to 5. **Yes**

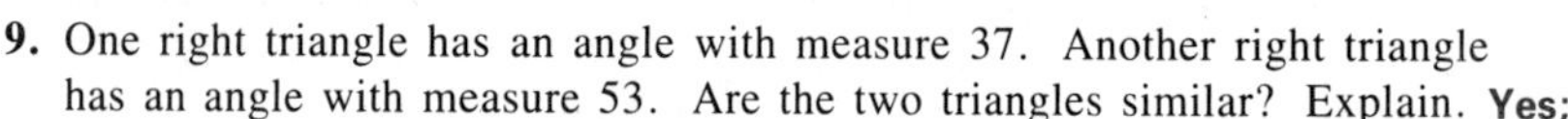

9. One right triangle has an angle with measure 37. Another right triangle has an angle with measure 53. Are the two triangles similar? Explain. **Yes; AA ~ Post.**
10. Name all pairs of congruent angles in the figure. ***∠JIK and ∠JHL, ∠JKI and ∠JLH***
11. Complete.
    a. $\triangle IKJ \sim$ _?_ ***△HLJ***
    b. $\frac{?}{x} = \frac{9}{24}$ and $x =$ _?_ **12; 32**
    c. $\frac{9}{24} = \frac{6}{?}$ and $y =$ _?_ ***y* + 6; 10**

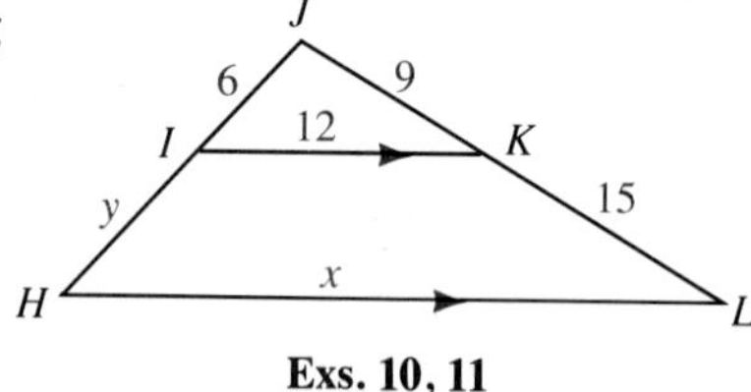

Exs. 10, 11

12. Suppose you want to show $AB \cdot YZ = CD \cdot WX$. What are some proportions that are equivalent to that equation? $\frac{AB}{CD} = \frac{WX}{YZ}$; $\frac{YZ}{CD} = \frac{WX}{AB}$
13. Cecelia wanted to find the height of a certain tree for a report in her biology class. Her method used shadows as shown in the diagram. She measured the shadow of the tree and found it was 5 m long. She measured her shadow and found it was 0.8 m long.
    a. △_?_ ~ △_?_ ***SCH, STR***
    b. Complete: $\frac{SC}{?} = \frac{CH}{?}$ ***ST, TR***
    c. If Cecelia is 1.6 m tall, about how tall is the tree? **about 10 m**

(Not to scale)

Written Exercises

Tell whether the triangles are similar or not similar. If you can't reach a conclusion, write *no conclusion is possible*.

A **1.** **Similar**

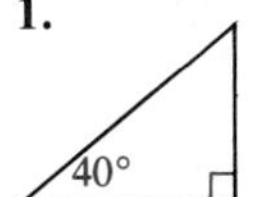
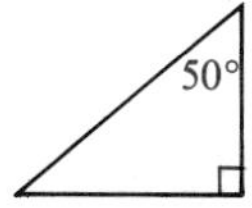

2. **Similar**

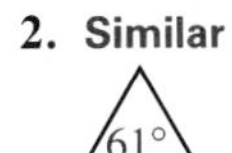
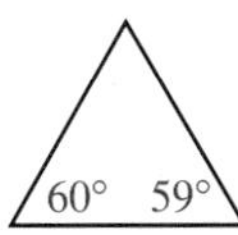

3. **Similar**

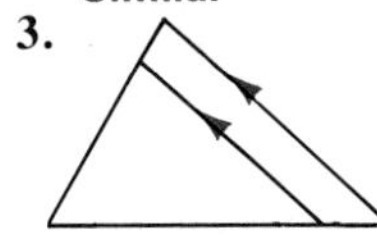

4. **Similar**

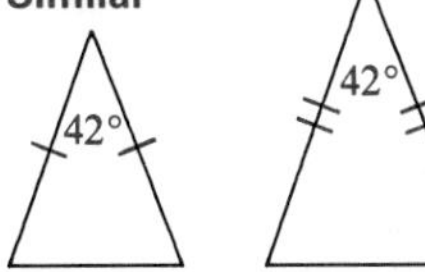

5. **No conclusion**

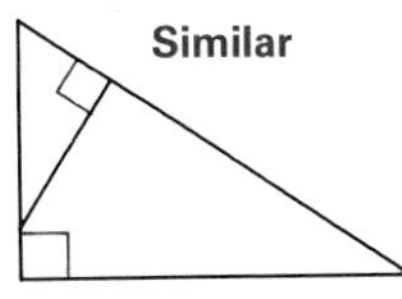

6. **Similar**

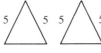

7. **Similar**

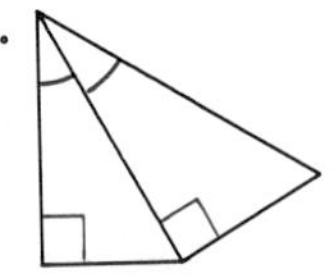

8. **Similar**

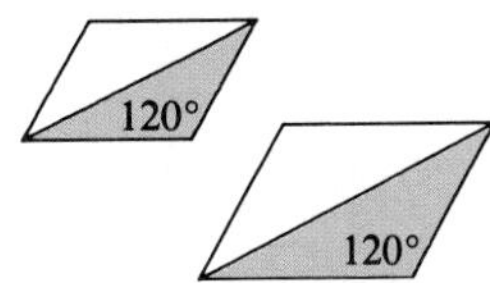

Trapezoid given

9. **No conclusion**

Parallelograms given

10. Complete.

a. $\triangle JKN \sim$ __?__ **$\triangle MLN$**

b. $\frac{JK}{?} = \frac{JN}{?} = \frac{KN}{?}$ **ML, MN, LN**

c. $\frac{15}{?} = \frac{18}{?}$ and $\frac{15}{?} = \frac{12}{?}$ **20, x, 20, y**

d. $x =$ __?__ **24** and $y =$ __?__ **16**

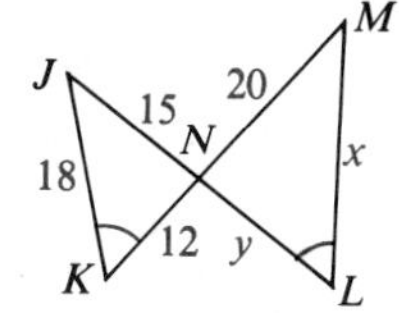

Find the values of x and y.

11.

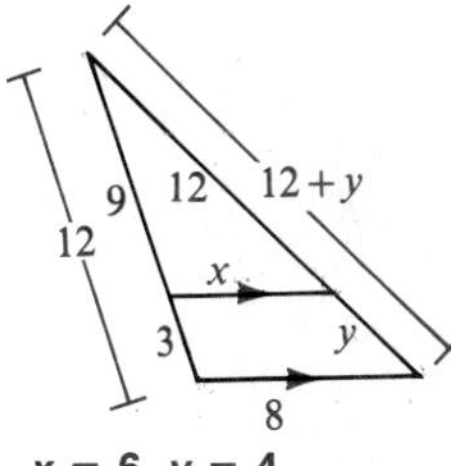

$x = 6$, $y = 4$

12.

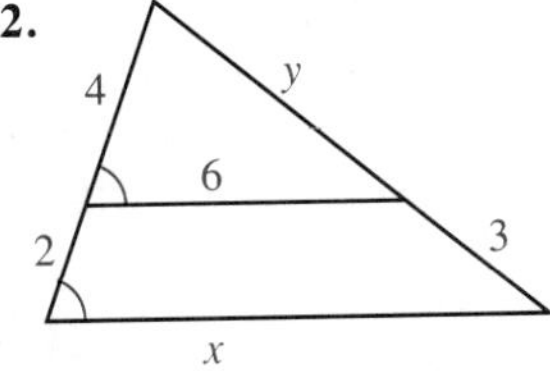

$x = 9$, $y = 6$

13.

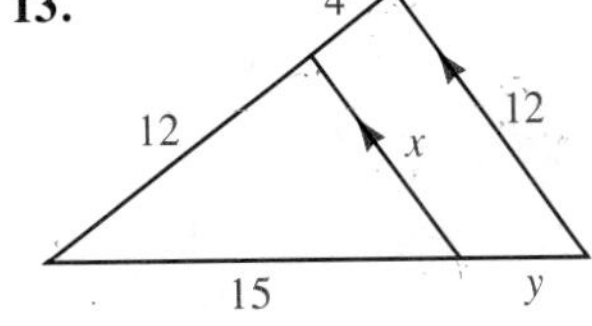

$x = 9$, $y = 5$

B **14. a.** Name two triangles that are similar to $\triangle ABC$. **$\triangle ACD$, $\triangle CBD$**

b. Find the values of x and y. **$x = 15$, $y = 9$**

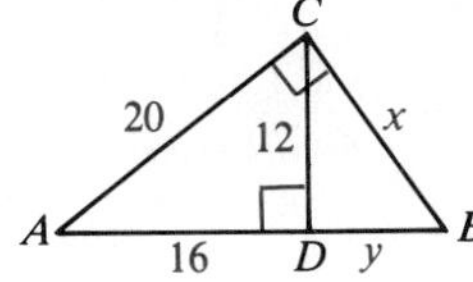

15. If $IV = 36$ m, $VE = 20$ m, and $EB = 15$ m, find the width, RI, of the river. **27 m**

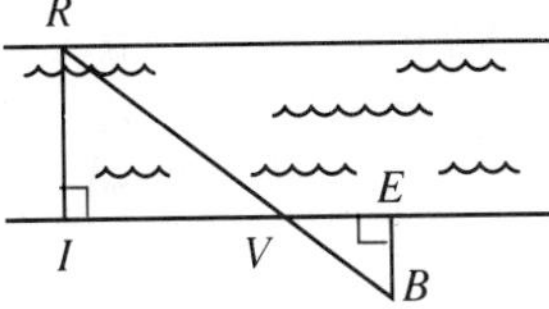

a. $\triangle ABC \sim$ $\underline{\triangle EBD}$

b. $y = \frac{32}{7}$

c. $\frac{BE}{BA} = \frac{BD}{BC}$, so $x = \frac{9}{4}$.

Group Activity

Classroom Ex. 13 and Written Ex. 16 can be used as a field trip activity on a sunny day. Select groups of two to four students and have each group measure the height of a tall tree, pole, or building.

Assessment

When reviewing the answers to Exs. 1–9, ask students to explain their answers. Verbal explanations by students as to why the triangles are similar or not similar will enable you to assess informally their understanding of the definition of similarity and the AA Similarity Postulate.

Making Connections

Exs. 11–14 reinforce the connections of algebra and geometry and the importance of students having good algebraic skills in learning geometry.

Application

Students will find the application of similar triangles to solving real-world problems interesting. Exs. 15–17 and 20 provide an opportunity for students to work on some applications.

16. To estimate the height of a pole, a basketball player exactly 2 m tall stood so that the ends of his shadow and the shadow of the pole coincided. He found that $\overline{DE}$ and $\overline{DF}$ measured 1.6 m and 4.4 m, respectively. About how tall was the pole? **About 5.5 m**

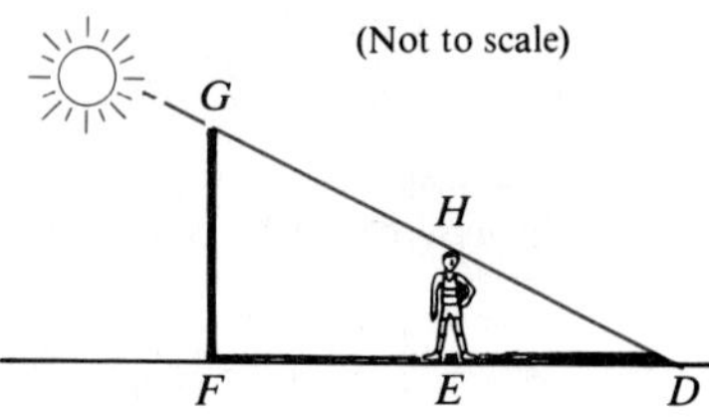

17. The diagram, *not* drawn to scale, shows a film being projected on a screen. $LF = 6$ cm and $LS = 24$ m. The screen image is 2.2 m tall. How tall is the film image? **0.55 cm**

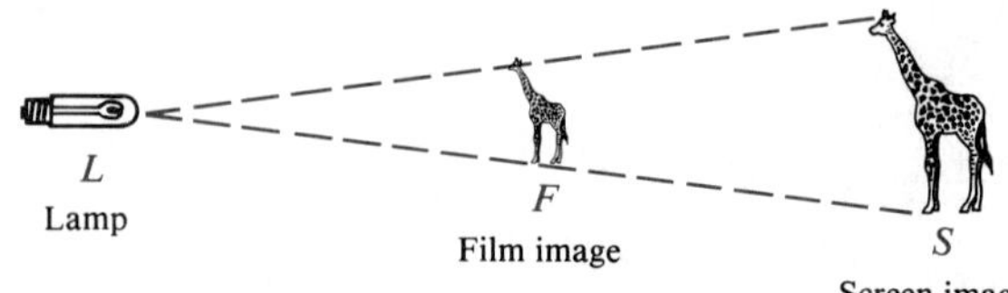

In Exercises 18 and 19 *ABCD* is a parallelogram. Find the values of *x* and *y*.

18. **$x = 9$, $y = 5.4$**

19.

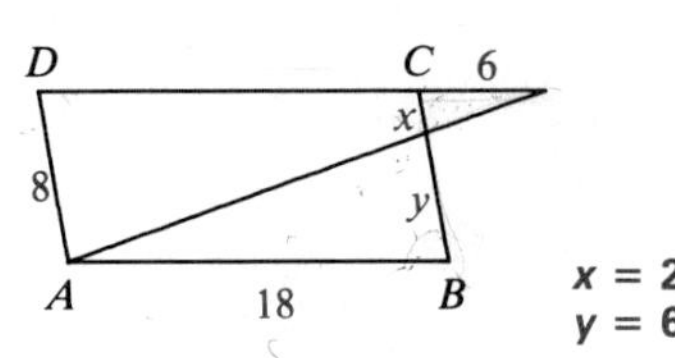

$x = 2$, $y = 6$

20. You can estimate the height of a flagpole by placing a mirror on level ground so that you see the top of the flagpole in it. The girl shown is 172 cm tall. Her eyes are about 12 cm from the top of her head. By measurement, AM is about 120 cm and $A'M$ is about 4.5 m. From physics it is known that $\angle 1 \cong \angle 2$. Explain why the triangles are similar and find the approximate height of the pole. **About 6 m**

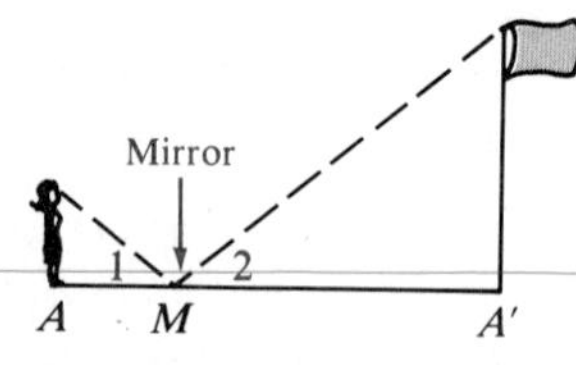

21. Given: $\overline{EF} \parallel \overline{RS}$

Prove: **a.** $\triangle FXE \sim \triangle SXR$

b. $\frac{FX}{SX} = \frac{EF}{RS}$

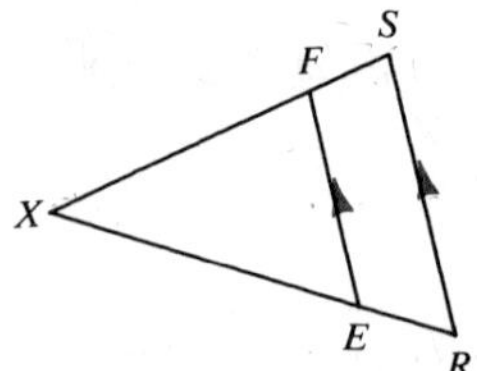

22. Given: $\angle 1 \cong \angle 2$

Prove: **a.** $\triangle JIG \sim \triangle JZY$

b. $\frac{JG}{JY} = \frac{GI}{YZ}$

Cultural Note

The earliest surviving Chinese book on mathematics and astronomy dates from around the 2nd century B.C. Along with presenting a theorem equivalent to the Pythagorean theorem, it describes how to use similar right triangles in surveying heights, depths, and distances.

Additional Answers Written Exercises

20. The girl and the flagpole are both ⊥ to the ground so $\angle A \cong \angle A'$ and the △ are ~ by the AA Similarity Post. Let h = height of pole in cm; $\frac{160}{h} = \frac{120}{450}$; $120h = 72{,}000$; $h = 600$; 600 cm or 6 m.

23. Given: $\angle B \cong \angle C$
Prove: $NM \cdot CM = LM \cdot BM$

24. Given: $\overline{BN} \parallel \overline{LC}$
Prove: $BN \cdot LM = CL \cdot NM$

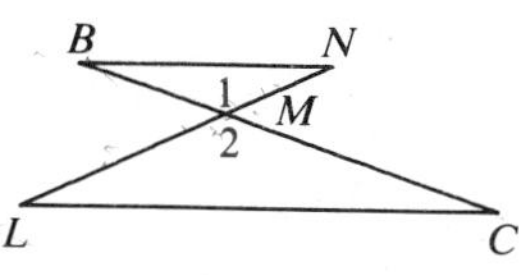

25. Given: $\triangle ABC \sim \triangle XYZ$;
$\overline{AD}$ and $\overline{XW}$ are altitudes.
Prove: $\frac{AD}{XW} = \frac{AB}{XY}$

26. Given: $\triangle PQR \sim \triangle GHI$;
$\overrightarrow{PS}$ and $\overrightarrow{GJ}$ are angle bisectors.
Prove: $\frac{PS}{GJ} = \frac{PQ}{GH}$

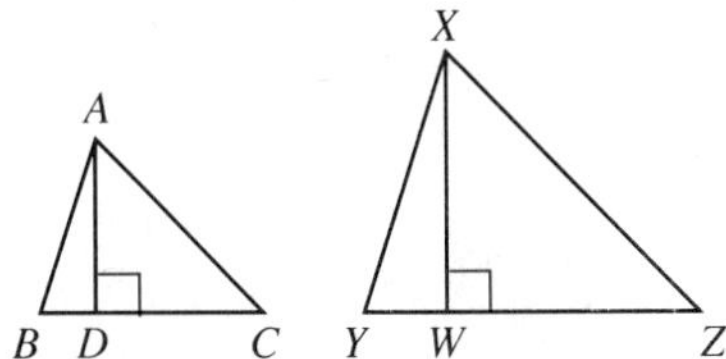

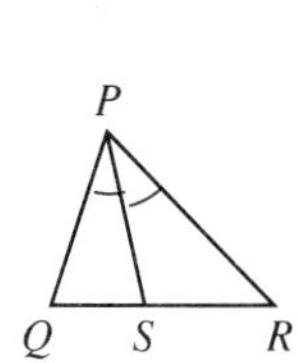

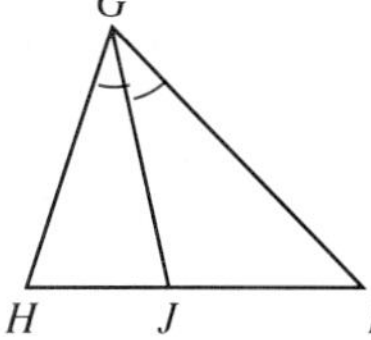

27. Given: $\overline{AH} \perp \overline{EH}$; $\overline{AD} \perp \overline{DG}$
Prove: $AE \cdot DG = AG \cdot HE$

28. Given: $\overline{QT} \parallel \overline{RS}$
Prove: $\frac{QU}{RV} = \frac{UT}{VS}$

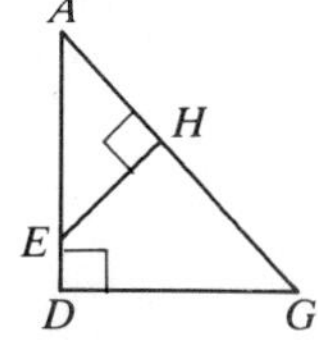

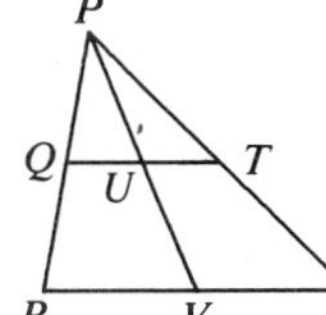

29. Given: $\angle 1 \cong \angle 2$
Prove: $(AB)^2 = AD \cdot AC$

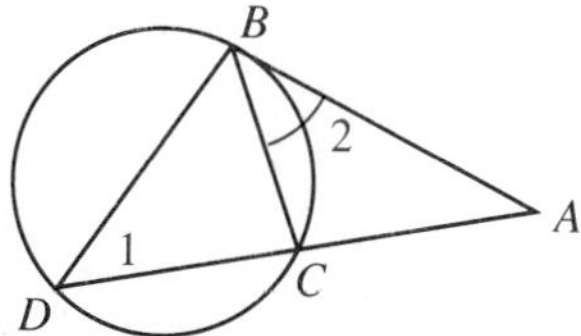

In the diagram for Exercises 30 and 31, the plane of $\triangle A'B'C'$ is parallel to the plane of $\triangle ABC$.

30. $VA' = 15$ and $A'A = 20$
a. If $VC' = 18$, then $VC =$ __?__. **42**
b. If $VB = 49$, then $BB' =$ __?__. **28**
c. If $A'B' = 24$, then $AB =$ __?__. **56**

31. If $VA' = 10$, $VA = 25$, $AB = 20$, $BC = 14$, and $AC = 16$, find the perimeter of $\triangle A'B'C'$. **20**

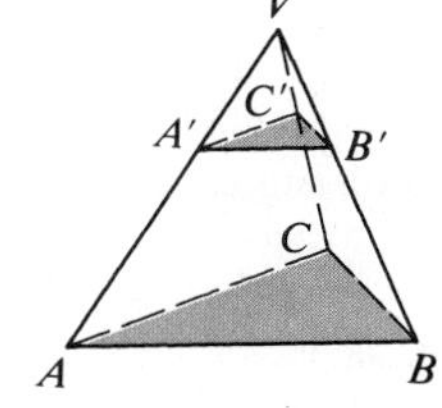

C **32.** Two vertical poles have heights 6 ft and 12 ft. A rope is stretched from the top of each pole to the bottom of the other. How far above the ground do the ropes cross? (*Hint*: The lengths y and z do not affect the answer.) **4 ft**

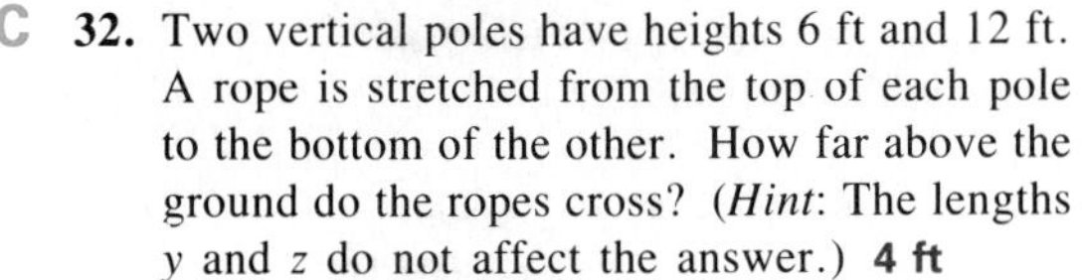

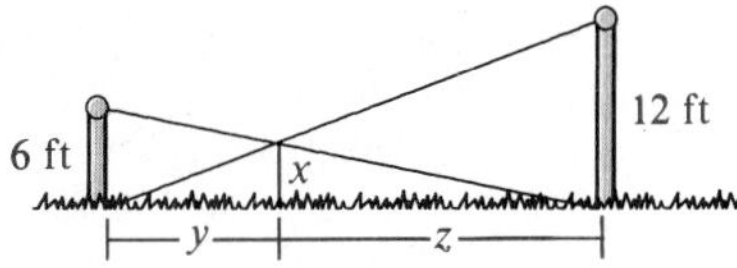

Group Activity

You may wish to use some of the proof exercises on this page for group activities. Suggest that some students in the group provide the Statements and others the Reasons. Completed proofs can be written on the chalkboard or on overhead projector sheets for class review and discussion.

In Exercises 33 and 34 write a paragraph proof for anything you are asked to prove.

33. Given: Regular pentagon *ABCDE*

a. Make a large copy of the diagram.

b. Write the angle measures on your diagram.

c. Prove that $\frac{DA}{DK} = \frac{DK}{AK}$.

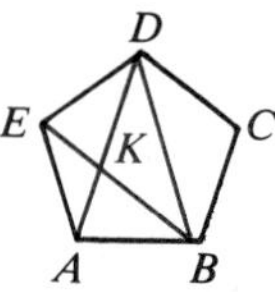

★ **34.** *ABCD* is a square.

a. Find the distance from *H* to each side of the square.

b. Find *BF*, *FC*, *CG*, *DE*, *EA*, *EH*, and *HF*.

a. Draw lines from *H* that are ⊥ to each side.
***HW* = *HX* = 8, *HY* = 6, *HZ* = 10**

b. *BF* = 0.5, *FC* = 15.5, *CG* = 4, *DE* = 3.5, *EA* = 12.5, *EH* = 7.5, *HF* = 12.5

★ **35.** Related to any doubly convex lens there is a focal distance *OF*. Physicists have determined experimentally that a vertical lens, a vertical object $\overline{JT}$ (with $\overline{JO}$ horizontal), a vertical image $\overline{IM}$, and a focus *F* are related as shown in the diagram. Once the relationship is known, geometry can be used to establish a lens law:

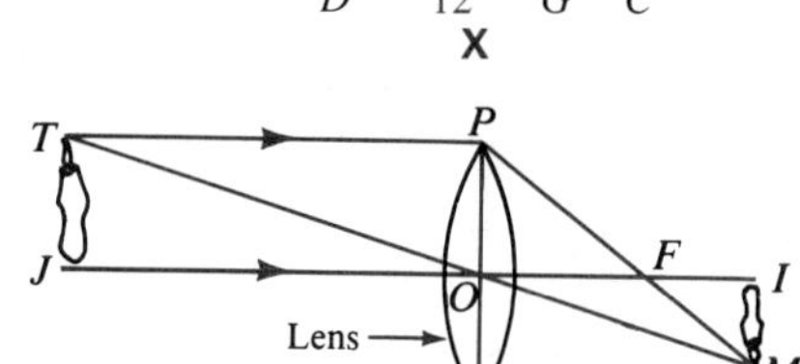

$$\frac{1}{\text{object distance}} + \frac{1}{\text{image distance}} = \frac{1}{\text{focal distance}}$$

a. Prove that $\frac{1}{OJ} + \frac{1}{OI} = \frac{1}{OF}$.

b. Show algebraically that $OF = \frac{OJ \cdot OI}{OJ + OI}$.

Challenges

1. Explain how to pass a plane through a cube so that the intersection is:

a. an equilateral triangle

b. a trapezoid

c. a pentagon

d. a hexagon

2. The six edges of the three-dimensional figure are congruent. Each of the four corners is cut off by a plane that passes through the midpoints of the three edges that intersect at that corner. For example, corner A is cut off by plane *MNT*. Describe the three-dimensional figure that remains.

It is a 3-D figure with 8 faces that are ≅ equilateral ⚠s (a reg. octahedron).

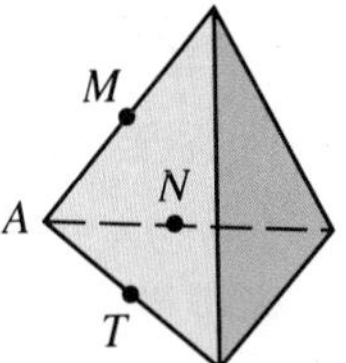

♦ Computer Key-In

The sequence 1, 1, 2, 3, 5, 8, 13, 21, . . . is called a *Fibonacci sequence* after its discoverer, Leonardo Fibonacci, a thirteenth century mathematician. The first two terms are 1 and 1. You then add two consecutive terms to get the next term.

$$\begin{matrix}\text{1st} \\ \text{term}\end{matrix} + \begin{matrix}\text{2nd} \\ \text{term}\end{matrix} = \begin{matrix}\text{3rd} \\ \text{term}\end{matrix} \qquad \begin{matrix}\text{2nd} \\ \text{term}\end{matrix} + \begin{matrix}\text{3rd} \\ \text{term}\end{matrix} = \begin{matrix}\text{4th} \\ \text{term}\end{matrix} \qquad \begin{matrix}\text{3rd} \\ \text{term}\end{matrix} + \begin{matrix}\text{4th} \\ \text{term}\end{matrix} = \begin{matrix}\text{5th} \\ \text{term}\end{matrix}$$

The following computer program computes the first twenty-five terms of the Fibonacci sequence shown above and finds the ratio of any term to its preceding term. For example, we want to look at the ratios

$$\frac{1}{1} = 1, \frac{2}{1} = 2, \frac{3}{2} = 1.5, \frac{5}{3} \approx 1.66667, \text{ and so on.}$$

```
10  PRINT "TERM NO.", "TERM", "RATIO"
20  LET A = 1
30  LET B = 1
40  PRINT "1",A,"-"
50  FOR N = 2 TO 25
60    LET D = B/A
70    LET E = 10000 * D
80    LET F = INT(E)
90    LET G = F/10000
100   PRINT N,B,G
110   LET C = B + A
120   LET A = B
130   LET B = C
140 NEXT N
150 END
```

Exercises

Type the program into your computer and use it in Exercises 1–4.

1. RUN the given computer program. As the terms become larger, what happens to the values of the ratios? **The values approach 1.618.**
2. Suppose another sequence is formed by choosing starting numbers different from 1 and 1. For example, suppose the sequence is 3, 11, 14, 25, 39, . . . , where the pattern for creating the terms of the sequence is still the same. Change lines 20 and 30 to:

```
20  LET A = 3
30  LET B = 11
```

RUN the modified program. What happens to the values of the ratios as the terms become larger and larger? **They approach 1.618.**

3. Modify the program again so that another pair of starting numbers is used and the first thirty terms are computed. RUN the program. What can you conclude from the results? **The values of the ratios always approach 1.618.**
4. Compare this ratio to the golden ratio calculated in Exercise 2 on page 253. Do you see a connection? **The value approaches the golden ratio, $\frac{1+\sqrt{5}}{2}$.**

Using a Computer

Students can use a spreadsheet as well as the program at the left to calculate the first twenty-five terms of the Fibonacci sequence.

Application

Scale Drawings

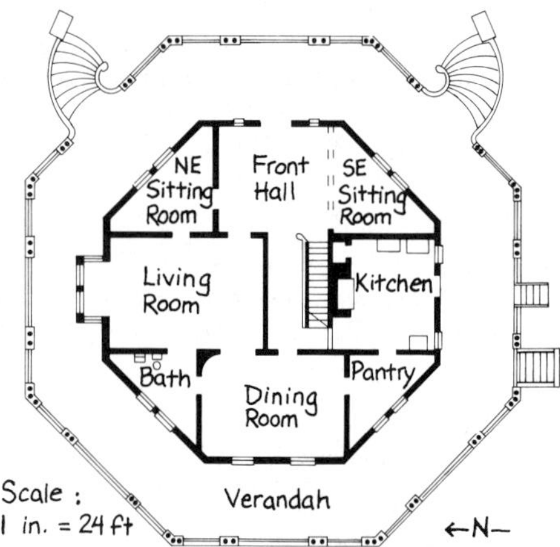

This "octagon house" was built in Irvington, New York, in 1860. The plan shows the rooms on the first floor. The scale on this *scale drawing* tells you that a length of 1 in. on the plan represents a true length of 24 ft.

$$\frac{\text{Plan length in inches}}{\text{True length in feet}} = \frac{1}{24}$$

The following examples show how you can use this formula to find actual dimensions of the house from the plan or to convert dimensions of full-sized objects to plan size.

The verandah measures $\frac{3}{8}$ in. wide on the plan. Find its true width, T.

$\frac{\frac{3}{8}}{T} = \frac{1}{24}$, so $1 \cdot T = \frac{3}{8} \cdot 24$

$T = 9$ The real verandah is 9 ft wide.

A sofa is 6 ft long. Find its plan length, P.

$\frac{P}{6} = \frac{1}{24}$, so $24 \cdot P = 6 \cdot 1$

$P = \frac{1}{4}$ The plan length is $\frac{1}{4}$ in.

Exercises

1. Find the true length and width of the dining room. **18 ft, 12 ft**
2. A rug measures 9 ft by $7\frac{1}{2}$ ft. What would its dimensions be on the floor plan? Would it fit in the northeast sitting room? **$\frac{3}{8}$ in. by $\frac{5}{16}$ in.; No**
3. If a new floor plan is drawn with a scale of 1 in. = 10 ft, how many times longer is each line segment on the new plan than the corresponding segment on the plan shown? **2.4**
4. Suppose that on the architect's drawings each side of the verandah (the outer octagon) measured 12 in. What was the scale of these drawings? **1 in. = 2 ft**

7-5 *Theorems for Similar Triangles*

You can prove two triangles similar by using the definition of similar polygons or by using the AA Postulate. Of course, in practice you would always use the AA Postulate instead of the definition. (Why?) Two additional methods are established in the theorems below. The proofs involve proportions, congruence, and similarity.

Theorem 7-1 *SAS Similarity Theorem*

If an angle of one triangle is congruent to an angle of another triangle and the sides including those angles are in proportion, then the triangles are similar.

Given: $\angle A \cong \angle D$; $\frac{AB}{DE} = \frac{AC}{DF}$

Prove: $\triangle ABC \sim \triangle DEF$

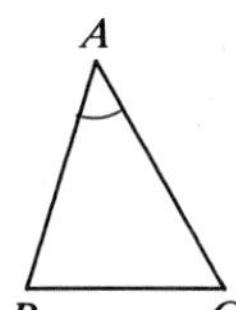

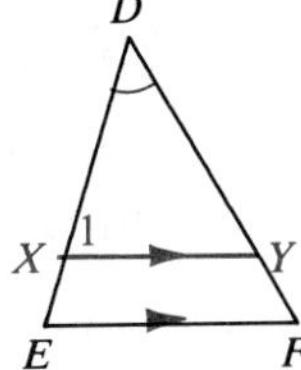

Plan for Proof: Take X on $\overline{DE}$ so that $DX = AB$. Draw a line through X parallel to $\overleftrightarrow{EF}$. Then $\triangle DEF \sim \triangle DXY$ and $\frac{DX}{DE} = \frac{DY}{DF}$. Since $\frac{AB}{DE} = \frac{AC}{DF}$ and $DX = AB$, you can deduce that $DY = AC$. Thus $\triangle ABC \cong \triangle DXY$ by SAS. Therefore, $\triangle ABC \sim \triangle DXY$, and $\triangle ABC \sim \triangle DEF$ by the Transitive Property of Similarity.

Theorem 7-2 *SSS Similarity Theorem*

If the sides of two triangles are in proportion, then the triangles are similar.

Given: $\frac{AB}{DE} = \frac{BC}{EF} = \frac{AC}{DF}$

Prove: $\triangle ABC \sim \triangle DEF$

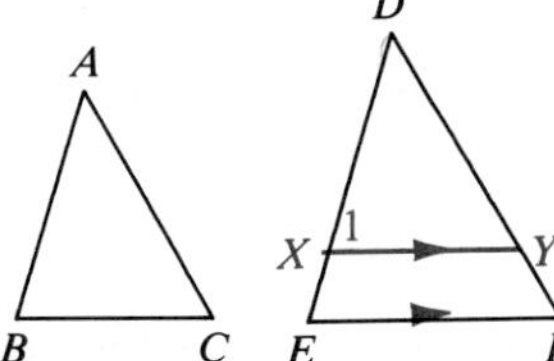

Plan for Proof: Take X on $\overline{DE}$ so that $DX = AB$. Draw a line through X parallel to $\overleftrightarrow{EF}$. Then $\triangle DEF \sim \triangle DXY$ and $\frac{DX}{DE} = \frac{XY}{EF} = \frac{DY}{DF}$. With the given proportion and $DX = AB$, you can deduce that $AC = DY$ and $BC = XY$. Thus $\triangle ABC \cong \triangle DXY$ by SSS. Therefore, $\triangle ABC \sim \triangle DXY$, and $\triangle ABC \sim \triangle DEF$ by the Transitive Property of Similarity.

Teaching Suggestions,
p. T104

Objective
Presenting the Lesson
Making Connections
Problem Solving

Cooperative Learning,
p. T104

Supplementary Materials

Practice Master 40
Test 26
Resource Book, pp. 38, 134
Study Guide, pp. 87–88
Overhead Visual E

Lesson Focus

Two theorems for showing that two triangles are similar are presented in this lesson. These theorems, along with the definition of similarity and the AA Similarity Postulate, provide four ways to prove that two triangles are similar.

Suggested Assignments

Minimum
266/1–10
S 258/17
268/Mixed Review 1, 2

Average
Day 1: 266–267/1–15 odd
S 259/25–31 odd
Day 2: 266–267/14–22 even
268/Mixed Review 1, 2

Maximum
266–267/5, 10, 14, 16, 17, 20, 22, 23
S 260/33

Using a Computer

Have students demonstrate the SAS and SSS Similarity Theorems by using a construction program.

Chalkboard Examples

1. The measures of the sides of $\triangle ABC$ are 4, 5, and 7, and the measures of the sides of $\triangle XYZ$ are 16, 20, and 28. Are the two triangles similar? Yes
2. In $\triangle ABC$, $AB = 2$, $AC = 5$, and $BC = 6$. In $\triangle XYZ$, $XY = 2.5$, $YZ = 2$, and $XZ = 3$. Is $\triangle ABC \sim \triangle XYZ$? No
3. 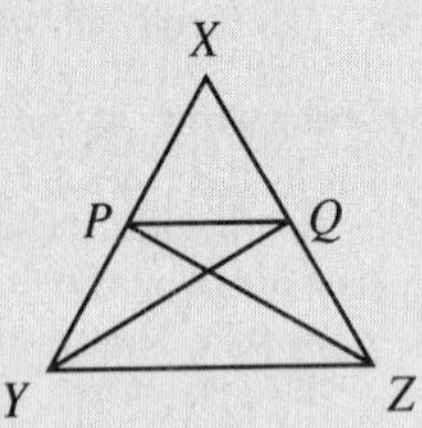

   If $\triangle XYQ \sim \triangle XZP$, does it follow that $\triangle XPQ \sim \triangle XZY$? Yes

Guided Practice

Name similar triangles and give the postulate or theorem that justifies your answer.

1. $\triangle ADE \sim \triangle ABC$ by AA $\sim$ Post.

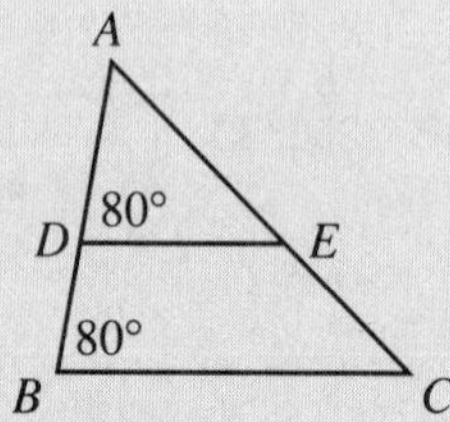

To prove two polygons similar, you might need to compare the corresponding sides. As shown in the example below, a useful technique is to compare the longest sides, the shortest sides, and so on.

Example Can the information given in each part be used to prove $\triangle RST \sim \triangle WZT$? If so, how?

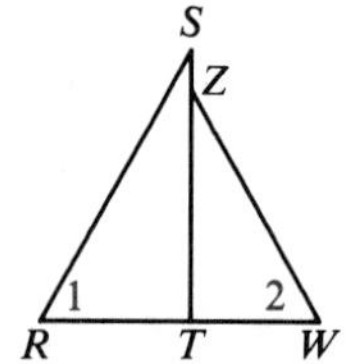

a. $RS = 18$, $ST = 15$, $RT = 10$, $WT = 6$, $ZT = 9$, $WZ = 10.8$

b. $\angle 1 \cong \angle 2$, $\dfrac{WZ}{RS} = \dfrac{TZ}{TS}$

c. $\overline{ST} \perp \overline{RW}$, $ST = 32$, $SZ = 8$, $RT = 20$, $WT = 15$

Solution

a. Comparing the longest sides, $\dfrac{RS}{WZ} = \dfrac{18}{10.8} = \dfrac{5}{3}$.

Comparing the shortest sides, $\dfrac{RT}{WT} = \dfrac{10}{6} = \dfrac{5}{3}$.

Comparing the remaining sides, $\dfrac{ST}{ZT} = \dfrac{15}{9} = \dfrac{5}{3}$.

Thus, $\dfrac{RS}{WZ} = \dfrac{RT}{WT} = \dfrac{ST}{ZT}$.

$\triangle RST \sim \triangle WZT$ by the SSS Similarity Theorem.

b. Notice that $\angle 1$ and $\angle 2$ are not the angles included by the sides that are in proportion. Therefore, the triangles cannot be proved similar.

c. Comparing the shorter legs, $\dfrac{RT}{WT} = \dfrac{20}{15} = \dfrac{4}{3}$.

Comparing the other legs, $\dfrac{ST}{ZT} = \dfrac{32}{32 - 8} = \dfrac{32}{24} = \dfrac{4}{3}$.

$\dfrac{RT}{WT} = \dfrac{ST}{ZT}$ and $\angle RTS \cong \angle WTS$.

$\triangle RST \sim \triangle WZT$ by the SAS Similarity Theorem.

The perimeters of similar polygons are in the same ratio as the corresponding sides. By using similar triangles, you can prove that corresponding segments such as diagonals of similar polygons also have this ratio. (See Exercises 25 and 26, page 259 and Exercises 17 and 18, page 267.)

Classroom Exercises

Can the two triangles shown be proved similar? If so, state the similarity and tell which similarity postulate or theorem you would use.

1. 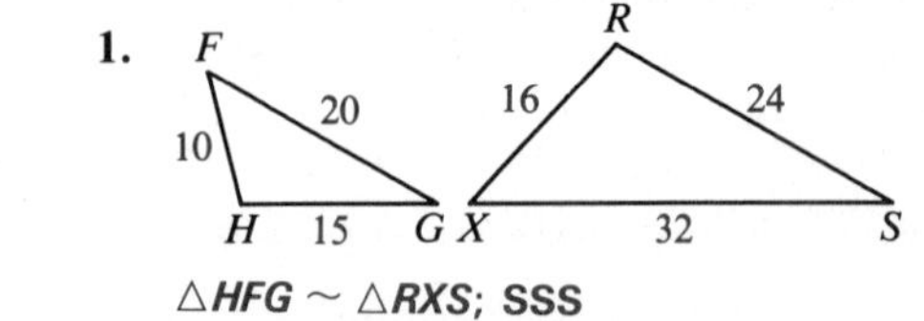

   $\triangle HFG \sim \triangle RXS$; SSS

2. 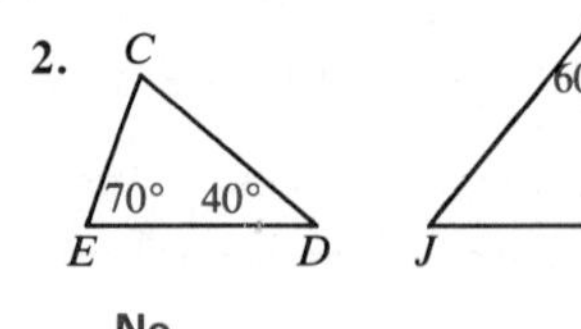

   No

3.

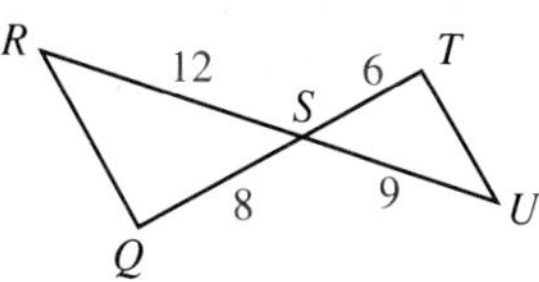

△RQS ~ △UTS; SAS

4.

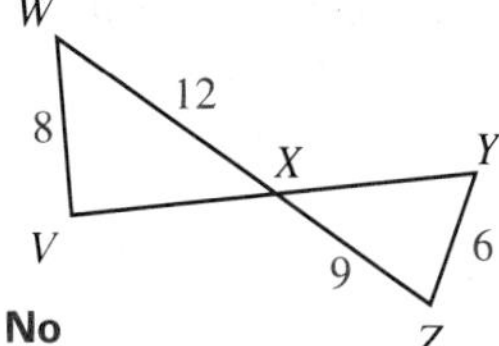

No

5.

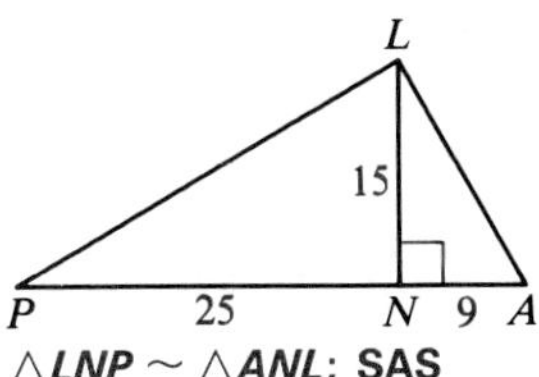

△LNP ~ △ANL; SAS

6.

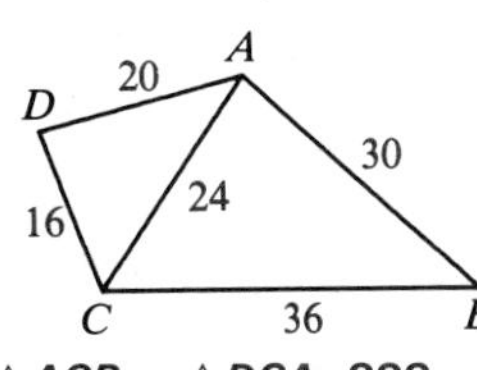

△ACB ~ △DCA; SSS

7. Suppose you want to prove that △*RST* ~ △*XYZ* by the SSS Similarity Theorem. State the extended proportion you would need to prove first. $\frac{RS}{XY} = \frac{RT}{XZ} = \frac{ST}{YZ}$

8. Suppose you want to prove that △*RST* ~ △*XYZ* by the SAS Similarity Theorem. If you know that ∠*R* ≅ ∠*X*, what else do you need to prove? $\frac{RS}{XY} = \frac{RT}{XZ}$

9. A *pantograph* is a tool for enlarging or reducing maps and drawings. Four bars are pinned together at *A*, *B*, *C*, and *D* so that *ABCD* is a parallelogram and points *P*, *D*, and *E* lie on a line. Point *P* is fixed to the drawing board. To enlarge a figure, the artist inserts a stylus at *D*, a pen or pencil at *E*, and guides the stylus so that it traces the original. As *D* moves, the angles of the parallelogram change, but *P*, *D*, and *E* remain collinear. Suppose *PA* is 3 units and *AB* is 7 units.

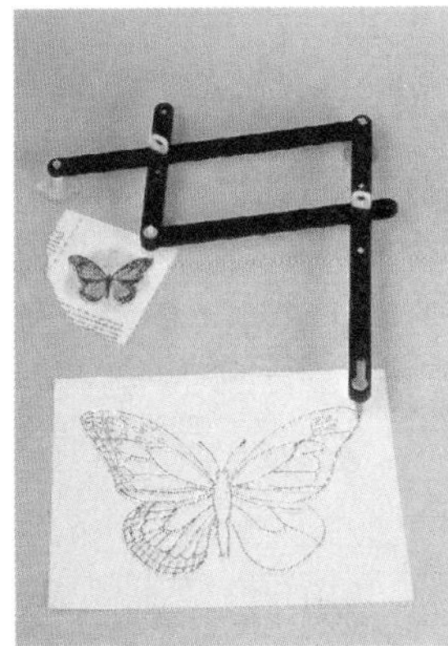

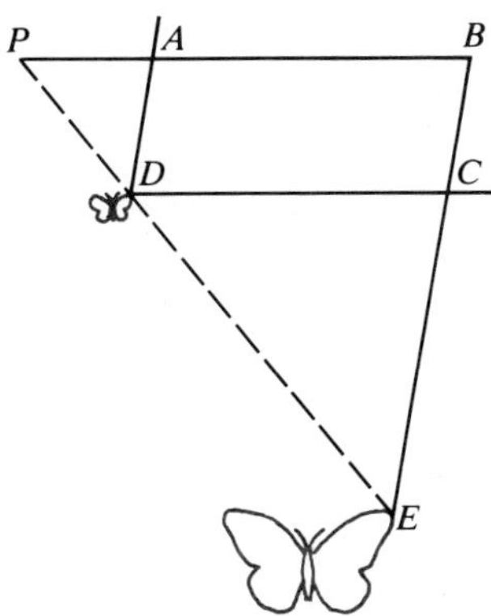

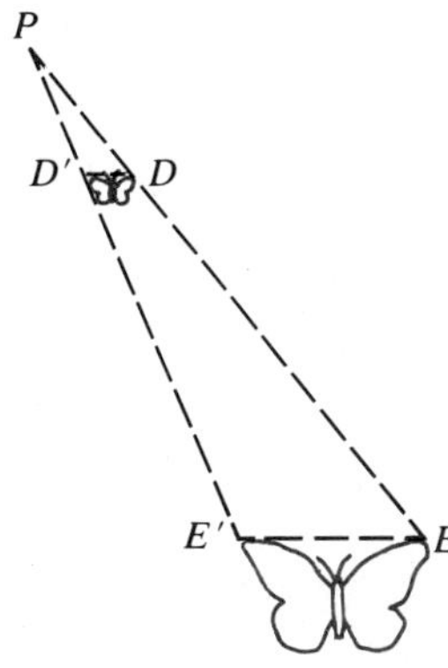

a. Explain why △*PBE* ~ △*PAD*. **$\overline{AD} \parallel \overline{BC}$ so ∠PAD ≅ ∠B and ∠ADP ≅ ∠E; △PBE ~ △PAD (AA)**

b. What is the ratio of *PB* to *PA*? **10:3**

c. What is the ratio of *PE* to *PD*? **10:3**

d. What is the ratio of the butterfly's wingspan, *E′E*, in the enlargement to its wingspan, *D′D*, in the original? **10:3**

2. △*CDE* ~ △*CAB* by SAS

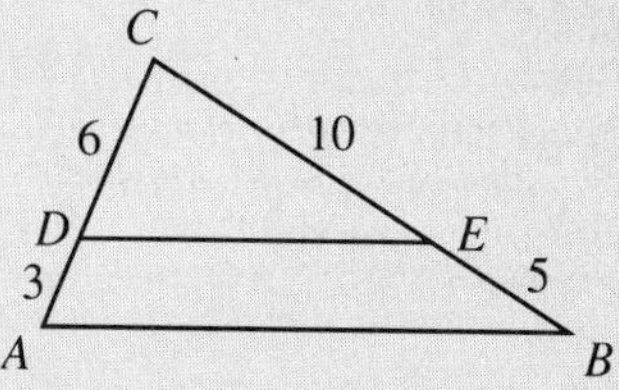

3. △*KLM* ~ △*KON* by SSS

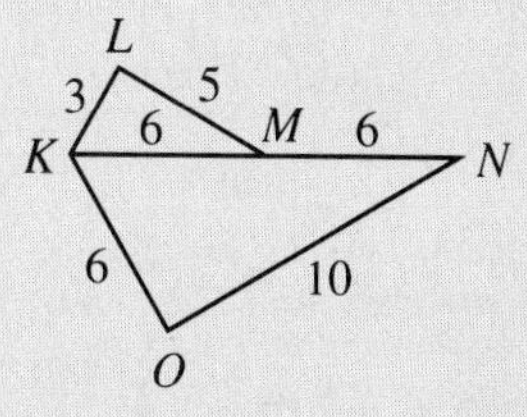

4. If △*ABC* ~ △*DEF*, does $\overline{AB}$ correspond to $\overline{DE}$? Yes
Does $\overline{BC}$ correspond to $\overline{EF}$? Yes
Does $\overline{AC}$ correspond to $\overline{DF}$? Yes

5. Given: ∠*B* ≅ ∠*DEC*
Prove: △*ABC* ~ △*DEC*

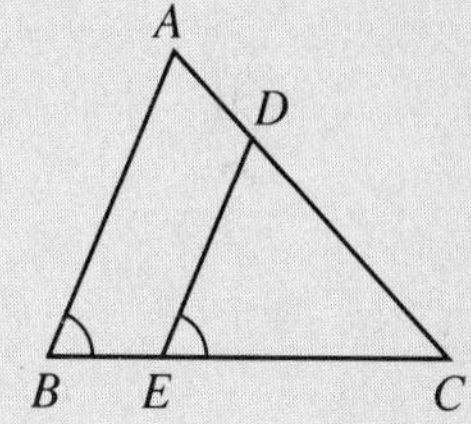

1. ∠*B* ≅ ∠*DEC* (Given)
2. ∠*C* ≅ ∠*C* (Reflexive)
3. △*ABC* ~ △*DEC* (AA ~ Post.)

Teaching Note

Remind students that they need to match corresponding vertices when naming similar triangles.

Written Exercises

1. $\triangle BAC \sim \triangle EDC$, SAS 2. $\triangle CAB \sim \triangle JTH$, AA

Name two similar triangles. What postulate or theorem justifies your answer?

A

1.

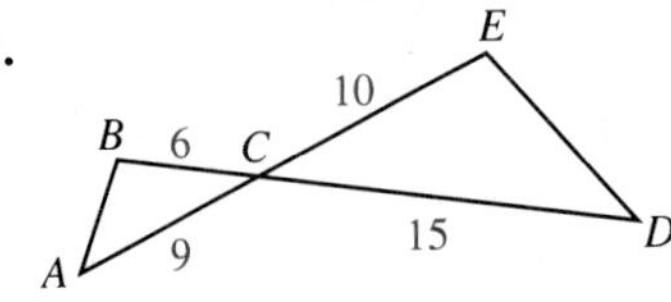

2.

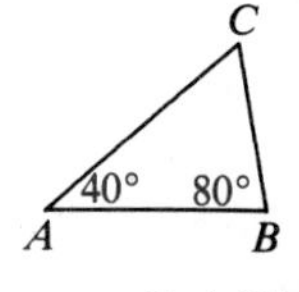

3.

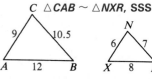

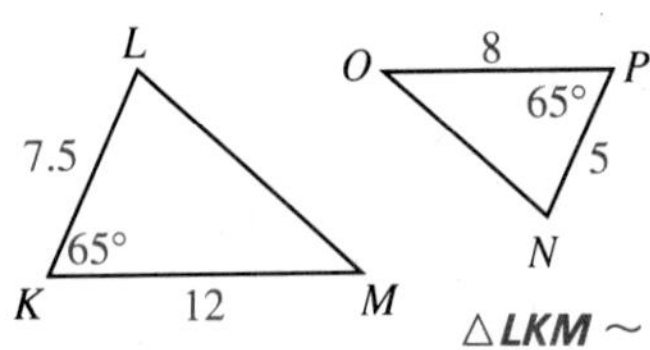

$\triangle LKM \sim \triangle NPO$, SAS

4. $\triangle CAB \sim \triangle NXR$, SSS

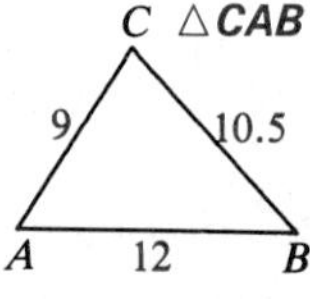

5.

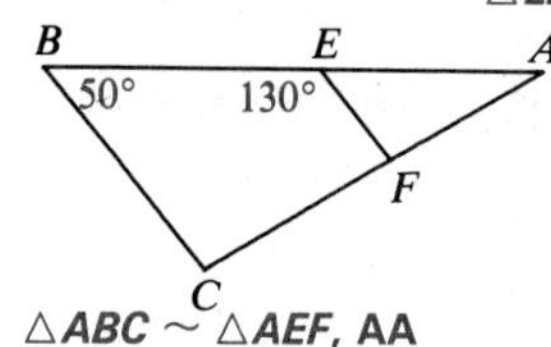

$\triangle ABC \sim \triangle AEF$, AA

6. $\triangle SRA \sim \triangle CBA$, SAS

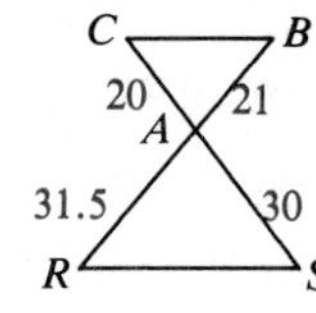

One triangle has vertices *A*, *B*, and *C*. Another has vertices *T*, *R*, and *I*. Are the two triangles similar? If so, state the similarity and the scale factor.

	AB	*BC*	*AC*	*TR*	*RI*	*TI*	
7.	6	8	10	9	12	15	$\triangle ABC \sim \triangle TRI$, 2:3
8.	6	8	10	12	22	16	No
9.	6	8	10	20	25	15	$\triangle ABC \sim \triangle ITR$, 2:5
10.	6	8	10	10	7.5	12.5	$\triangle ABC \sim \triangle IRT$, 4:5

11. Given: $\frac{DE}{GH} = \frac{DF}{GI} = \frac{EF}{HI}$

Prove: $\angle E \cong \angle H$

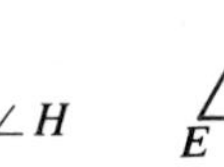

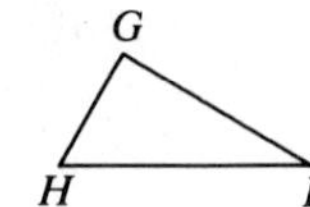

12. Given: $\frac{DE}{GH} = \frac{EF}{HI}$; $\angle E \cong \angle H$

Prove: $\frac{EF}{HI} = \frac{DF}{GI}$

B

13. Given: $\frac{VW}{VX} = \frac{VZ}{VY}$

Prove: $\overline{WZ} \parallel \overline{XY}$

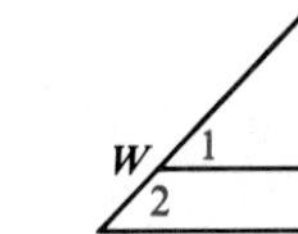

14. Given: $\frac{VW}{VY} = \frac{VZ}{VX}$

Which one(s) of the following *must* be true?

(1) $\triangle VWZ \sim \triangle VXY$ (2) $\overline{WZ} \parallel \overline{XY}$ (3) $\angle 1 \cong \angle Y$

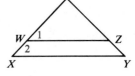

15. Given: $\frac{JL}{NL} = \frac{KL}{ML}$

Prove: $\angle J \cong \angle N$

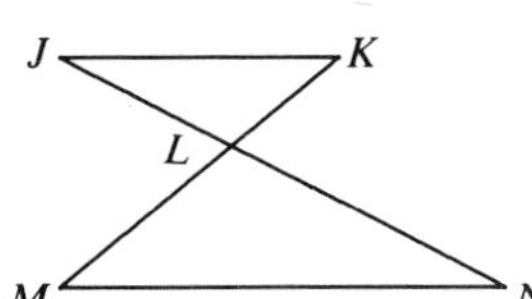

16. Given: $\frac{AB}{SR} = \frac{BC}{RA} = \frac{CA}{AS}$

Prove: $\overline{BC} \parallel \overline{AR}$

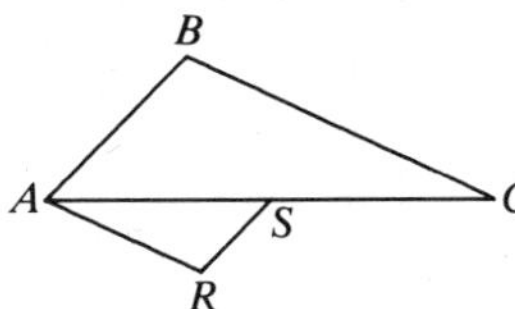

Draw and label a diagram. List, in terms of the diagram, what is given and what is to be proved. Then write a proof.

17. If two triangles are similar, then the lengths of corresponding medians are in the same ratio as the lengths of corresponding sides.

18. If two quadrilaterals are similar, then the lengths of corresponding diagonals are in the same ratio as the lengths of corresponding sides.

19. If the vertex angle of one isosceles triangle is congruent to the vertex angle of another isosceles triangle, then the triangles are similar.

20. The faces of a cube are congruent squares. The cube shown is cut by plane $ABCD$. $VA = VB$ and $VW = 4 \cdot VA$. Find, in terms of AB, the length of the median of trap. $ABCD$.

$\frac{5}{2} \cdot AB$

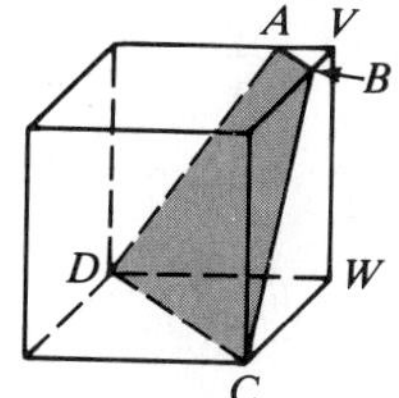

21. Given: $OR' = 2 \cdot OR$; $OS' = 2 \cdot OS$; $OT' = 2 \cdot OT$

Prove: $\triangle RST \sim \triangle R'S'T'$

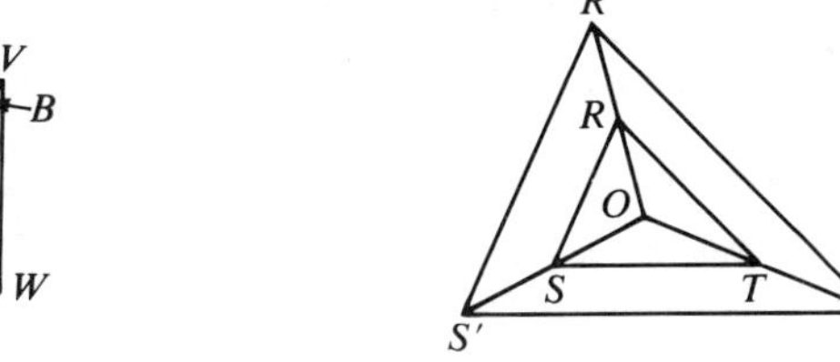

22. Prove Theorem 5-11 on page 178: The segment that joins the midpoints of two sides of a triangle is parallel to the third side and is half as long as the third side.

Given: M is the midpoint of $\overline{AB}$; N is the midpoint of $\overline{AC}$.

Prove: $\overline{MN} \parallel \overline{BC}$; $MN = \frac{1}{2}BC$

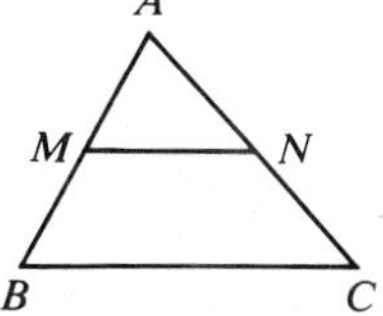

C 23. Given: ▱ $WXYZ$

Prove: $\triangle ATB \sim \triangle A'TB'$

(*Hint:* Show that $\frac{AT}{A'T}$ and $\frac{BT}{B'T}$ both equal $\frac{TW}{TY}$.)

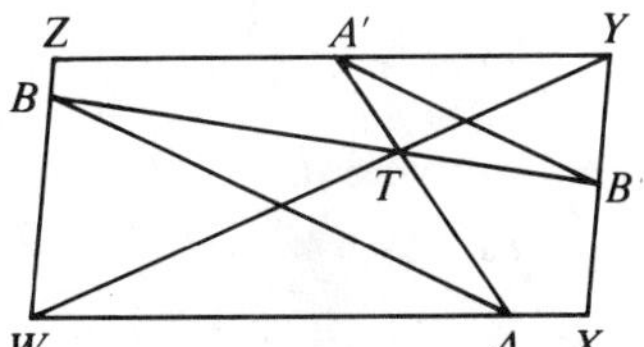

Group Activity

Exs. 17–19 may be used for a group activity. As the groups are working, you can observe their progress and lend assistance as needed. When students are having difficulty, asking questions rather than giving answers will encourage them to think for themselves.

Exercise Note

You may wish to postpone Ex. 22 until the next lesson, considering it then as a special case of Theorem 7-3.

Using a Computer

This Exploration demonstrates Theorems 7-3 and 7-4 of the next lesson.

Explorations

These exploratory exercises can be done using a computer with a program that draws and measures geometric figures.

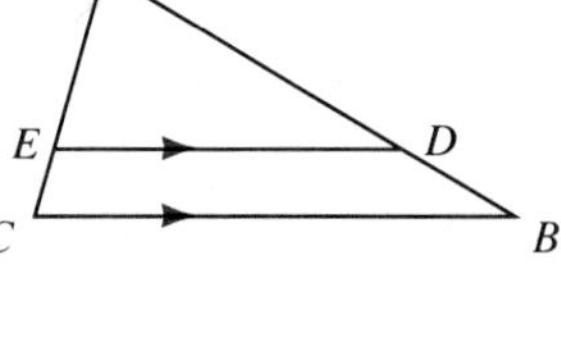

1. Draw any triangle ABC. Choose a point D on $\overline{AB}$. Draw a line through D parallel to $\overline{BC}$ and intersecting $\overline{AC}$ at point E.

   What do you know about $\triangle ABC$ and $\triangle ADE$? **$\triangle ABC \sim \triangle ADE$**

   What do you know about $\frac{AE}{AC}$ and $\frac{AD}{AB}$? **$\frac{AE}{AC} = \frac{AD}{AB}$**

   Calculate $\frac{AE}{EC}$ and $\frac{AD}{DB}$. What do you notice? **$\frac{AE}{EC} = \frac{AD}{DB}$**

   Calculate $\frac{EC}{AC}$ and $\frac{DB}{AB}$. What do you notice? **$\frac{EC}{AC} = \frac{DB}{AB}$**

   Repeat on other triangles. What do you notice? **The ratios are equal.**

2. Draw any triangle ABC. Draw the bisector of $\angle A$ intersecting $\overline{CB}$ at point D.

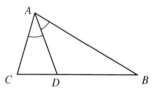

   Measure and record the four lengths: AB, AC, BD, DC.

   Calculate $\frac{BD}{DC}$ and $\frac{AB}{AC}$. What do you notice? **$\frac{BD}{DC} = \frac{AB}{AC}$**

   Repeat on other triangles. What do you notice? **$\frac{BD}{DC} = \frac{AB}{AC}$ for any triangle.**

Mixed Review Exercises

Complete.

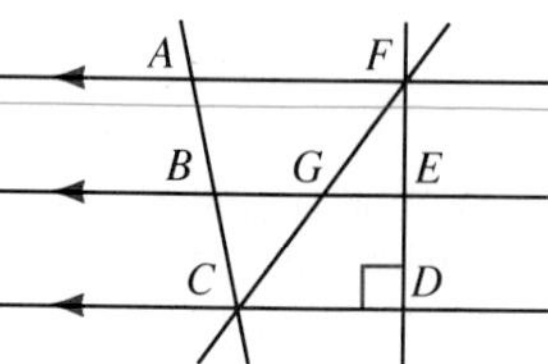

1. Given: $\overline{AF} \parallel \overline{BE} \parallel \overline{CD}$; $\overline{AB} \cong \overline{BC}$
   a. $\overline{GF} \cong$ _?_ and $\overline{ED} \cong$ _?_. **$\overline{GC}$; $\overline{EF}$**
   b. If $AB = 9$, then $AC =$ _?_. **18**
   c. If $FG = 3x + 2$ and $GC = 7x - 10$, then $x =$ _?_. **3**
   d. $m\angle FEG =$ _?_ **90**

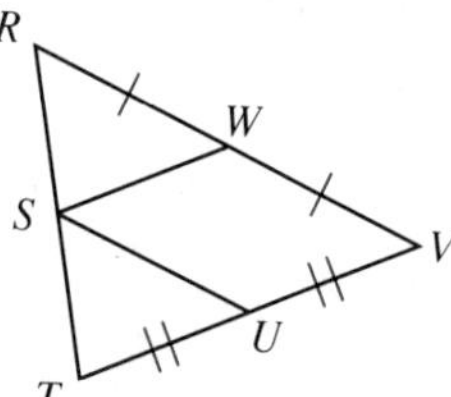

2. Given: W and U are the midpoints of $\overline{RV}$ and $\overline{VT}$; $\overline{SW} \parallel \overline{VT}$ **midpoint**
   a. S is the _?_ of $\overline{RT}$ and $\overline{SU} \parallel$ _?_. **$\overline{RV}$**
   b. If $TV = 12x + 4$ and $SW = 3x + 8$, then $x =$ _?_. **2**
   c. If $RW = 4y + 1$ and $SU = 9y - 19$, then $y =$ _?_. **4**

7-6 *Proportional Lengths*

Points L and M lie on $\overline{AB}$ and $\overline{CD}$, respectively. If $\frac{AL}{LB} = \frac{CM}{MD}$, we say that $\overline{AB}$ and $\overline{CD}$ are **divided proportionally.**

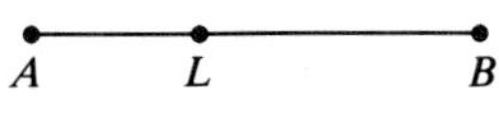

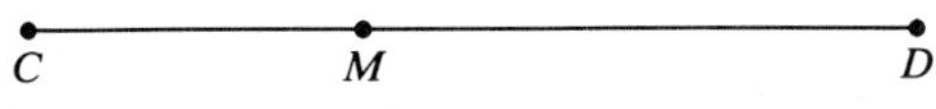

Theorem 7-3 *Triangle Proportionality Theorem*

If a line parallel to one side of a triangle intersects the other two sides, then it divides those sides proportionally.

Given: $\triangle RST$; $\overleftrightarrow{PQ} \parallel \overline{RS}$

Prove: $\frac{RP}{PT} = \frac{SQ}{QT}$

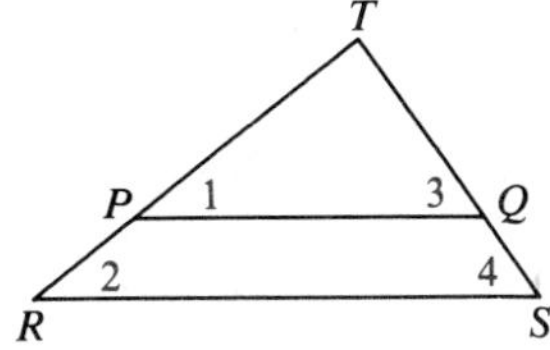

Proof:

Statements	Reasons
1. $\overleftrightarrow{PQ} \parallel \overline{RS}$	1. ? **Given**
2. $\angle 1 \cong \angle 2$; $\angle 3 \cong \angle 4$	2. ? **If 2 ∥ lines are cut by a trans., then corr. ∠s are ≅.**
3. $\triangle RST \sim \triangle PQT$	3. ? **AA ~ Post.**
4. $\frac{RT}{PT} = \frac{ST}{QT}$	4. Corr. sides of ~ △s are in proportion.
5. $RT = RP + PT$; $ST = SQ + QT$	5. ? **Segment Add. Post.**
6. $\frac{RP + PT}{PT} = \frac{SQ + QT}{QT}$	6. ? **Substitution Property**
7. $\frac{RP}{PT} = \frac{SQ}{QT}$	7. A property of proportions (Property 1(d), page 245.)

We will use the Triangle Proportionality Theorem to justify any proportion equivalent to $\frac{RP}{PT} = \frac{SQ}{QT}$. For the diagram at the right, some of the proportions that may be justified by the Triangle Proportionality Theorem include:

$$\frac{a}{j} = \frac{c}{k} \qquad \frac{a}{c} = \frac{j}{k} \qquad \frac{b}{j} = \frac{d}{k}$$

$$\frac{a}{b} = \frac{c}{d} \qquad \frac{a}{c} = \frac{b}{d} \qquad \frac{b}{d} = \frac{j}{k}$$

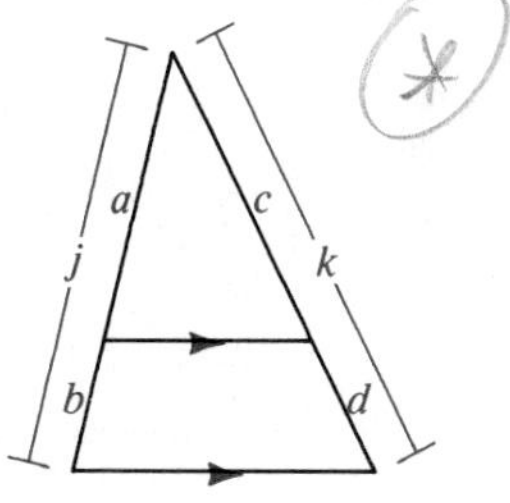

Teaching Suggestions,
pp. T104–T106

Objectives
Presenting the Lesson
Making Connections
Problem Solving
Extension
Using Technology

Supplementary Materials

Practice Master 41
Test 27
Resource Book, pp. 39, 135
Study Guide, pp. 89–90
Overhead Visual N

Lesson Focus

The focus of this lesson is on how the sides of a triangle can be divided into proportional segments. Two theorems that establish the conditions are developed.

Suggested Assignments

Minimum
Day 1: 272/1–8
S 266/11, 13
Day 2: 272–273/10–20 even
Day 3: 273/21, 24, 25
274/Self-Test 2
Day 4: 279/Chapter Test

Average
Day 1: 272–273/2–6 even, 7–15 odd, 16–18
S 267/22
Day 2: 273/19, 20, 22, 25, 27, 29, 30
274/Self-Test 2
Day 3: 279/Chapter Test

Maximum
Day 1: 272–273/6, 11, 12, 15, 20, 21, 25, 27, 31
S 267/18
Day 2: 273/29, 30, 32, 33
S 267/19, 21
Day 3: 279/Chapter Test

You may wish to introduce Constructions 12 and 13 on pages 396–397 after covering this lesson.

Chalkboard Examples

1. 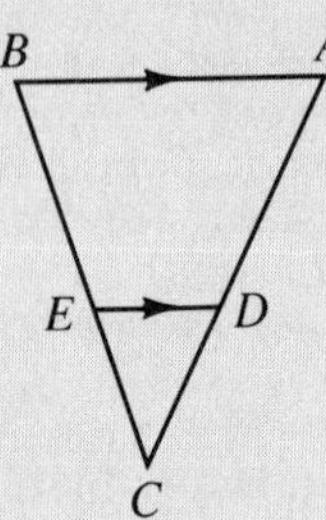

a. $\frac{CD}{DA} = \frac{CE}{EB}$
b. If $CD = 3$, $DA = 6$, and $DE = 3.5$, then $AB = \underline{10.5}$.
c. If $CB = 12$, $EB = 8$, and $CD = 6$, then $DA = \underline{12}$.

2. 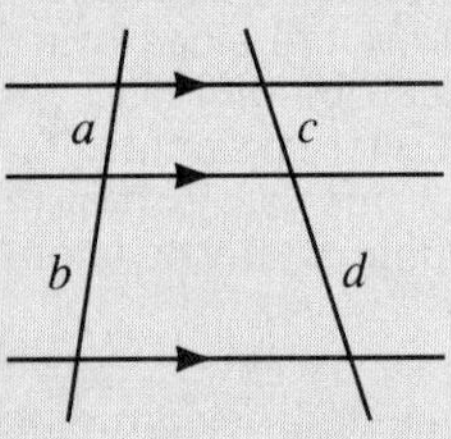

a. If $a = 2$, $b = 3$, and $c = 5$, then $d = \underline{7.5}$.
b. If $a = 4$, $b = 8$, $c = 5$, then $c + d = \underline{15}$.

Guided Practice

1. True or false?

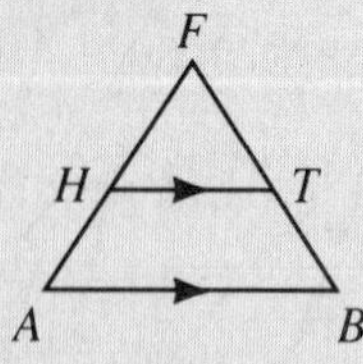

a. $\frac{FA}{HA} = \frac{FB}{TB}$ T
b. $\frac{FT}{FH} = \frac{FB}{FA}$ T
c. $\frac{FH}{FT} = \frac{HA}{TB}$ T
d. $\frac{FA}{FH} = \frac{FT}{TB}$ F

Example Find the numerical value.

a. $\frac{TN}{NR}$ **b.** $\frac{TR}{NR}$ **c.** $\frac{RN}{RT}$

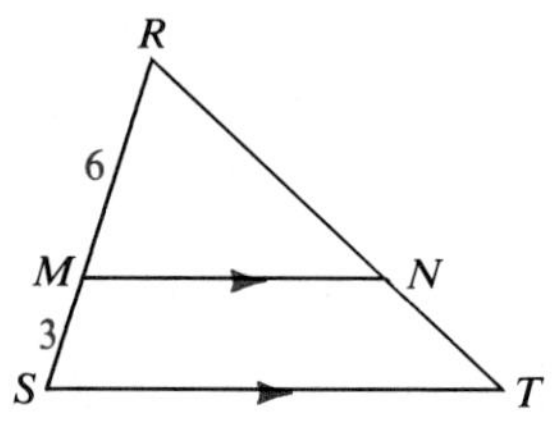

Solution

a. $\frac{TN}{NR} = \frac{SM}{MR} = \frac{3}{6} = \frac{1}{2}$

b. $\frac{TR}{NR} = \frac{SR}{MR} = \frac{9}{6} = \frac{3}{2}$

c. $\frac{RN}{RT} = \frac{RM}{RS} = \frac{6}{9} = \frac{2}{3}$

Compare the following corollary with Theorem 5-9 on page 177.

Corollary

If three parallel lines intersect two transversals, then they divide the transversals proportionally.

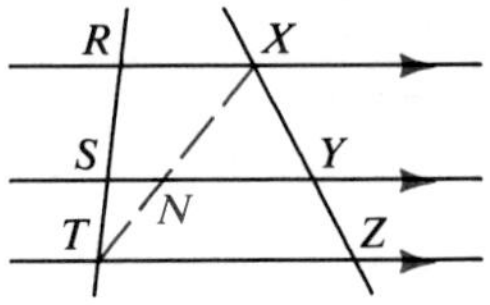

Given: $\overleftrightarrow{RX} \parallel \overleftrightarrow{SY} \parallel \overleftrightarrow{TZ}$

Prove: $\frac{RS}{ST} = \frac{XY}{YZ}$

Plan for Proof: Draw $\overline{TX}$, intersecting $\overleftrightarrow{SY}$ at N. Note that $\overleftrightarrow{SY}$ is parallel to one side of $\triangle RTX$, and also to one side of $\triangle TXZ$. You can apply the Triangle Proportionality Theorem to both of these triangles. Use those proportions to show $\frac{RS}{ST} = \frac{XY}{YZ}$.

Theorem 7-4 *Triangle Angle-Bisector Theorem*

If a ray bisects an angle of a triangle, then it divides the opposite side into segments proportional to the other two sides.

Given: $\triangle DEF$; $\overrightarrow{DG}$ bisects $\angle FDE$.

Prove: $\frac{GF}{GE} = \frac{DF}{DE}$

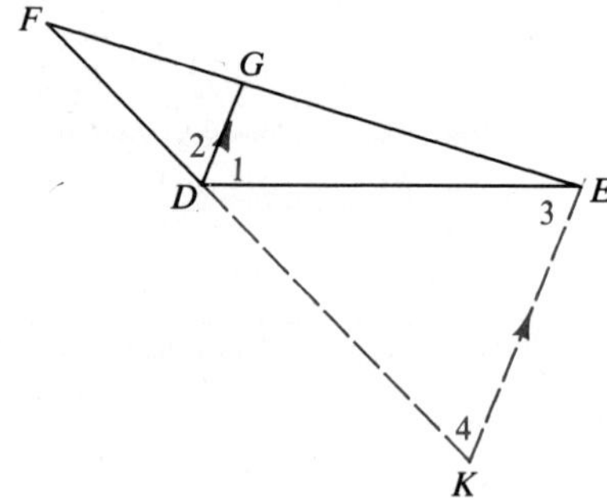

Plan for Proof: Draw a line through E parallel to $\overrightarrow{DG}$ and intersecting $\overrightarrow{FD}$ at K. Apply the Triangle Proportionality Theorem to $\triangle FKE$. $\triangle DEK$ is isosceles with $DK = DE$. Substitute this into your proportion to complete the proof.

Classroom Exercises

1. Answers may vary; $\frac{u}{w} = \frac{x}{z}, \frac{u}{v} = \frac{x}{y}, \frac{u}{x} = \frac{w}{z}$, etc.

1. The two segments are divided proportionally. State several correct proportions.

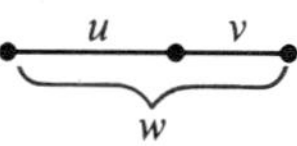

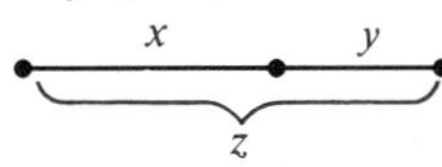

2. Complete the proportions stated informally below.

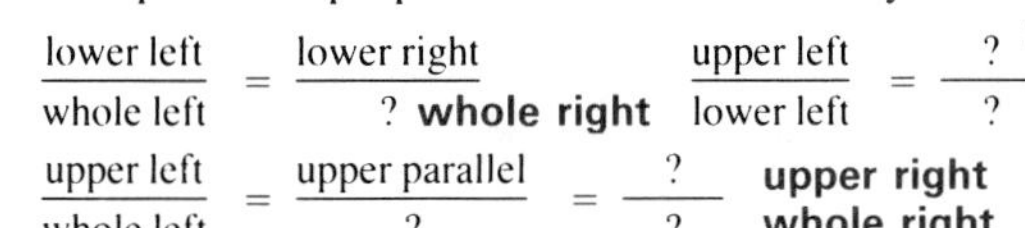

$\frac{\text{lower left}}{\text{whole left}} = \frac{\text{lower right}}{?}$ **whole right** $\qquad \frac{\text{upper left}}{\text{lower left}} = \frac{?}{?}$ **upper right / lower right**

$\frac{\text{upper left}}{\text{whole left}} = \frac{\text{upper parallel}}{?} = \frac{?}{?}$ **upper right / whole right**

lower parallel

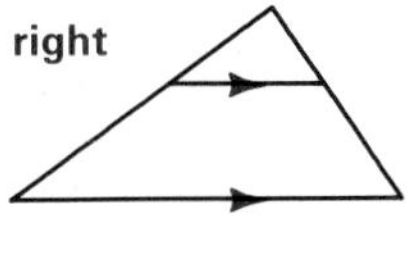

State a proportion for each diagram.

3.

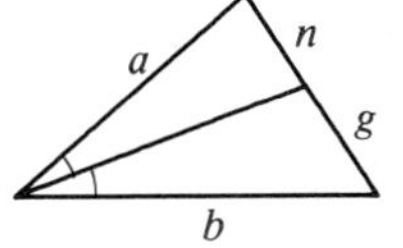

$\frac{n}{g} = \frac{a}{b}$

4.

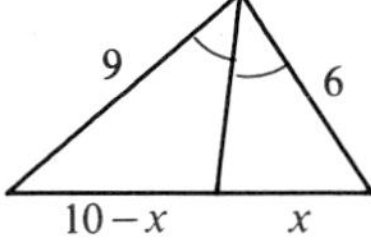

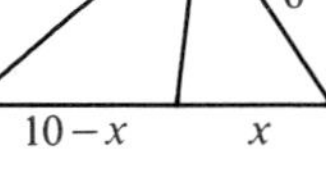

$\frac{10 - x}{x} = \frac{9}{6}$

5.

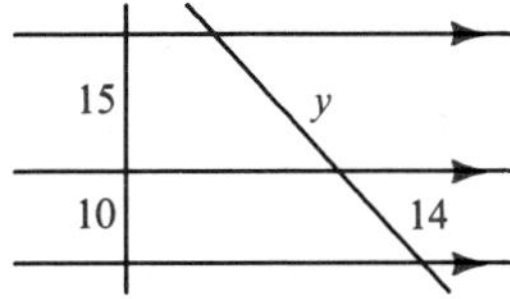

$\frac{y}{14} = \frac{15}{10}$

6. Suppose you want to find the length of the upper left segment in the diagram at the right. Three methods are suggested below. Complete each solution.

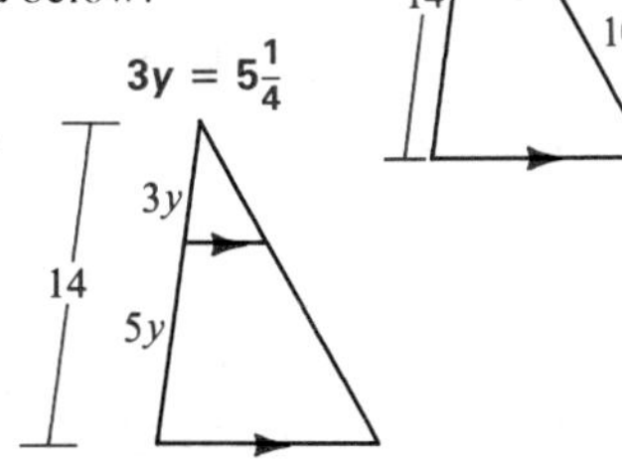

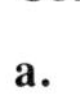

a. $x = 5\frac{1}{4}$

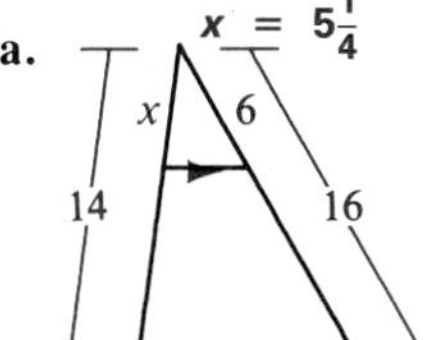

b. $x = 5\frac{1}{4}$

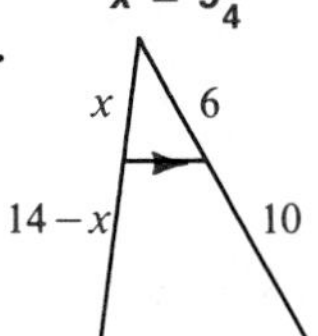

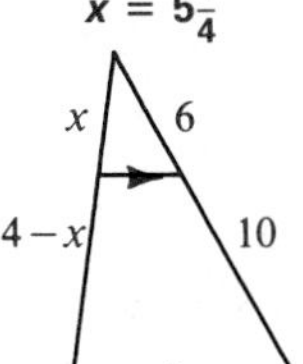

c. $3y = 5\frac{1}{4}$

Since 6 and 10 are in the ratio 3:5, so are the lengths of the parts of the unknown side.

7. Explain why the expressions $3y$ and $5y$ can be used in Exercise 6(c).

8. The converse of the corollary of the Triangle Proportionality Theorem is: If three lines divide two transversals proportionally, then the lines are parallel. Is the converse true? (*Hint:* Can you draw a diagram with lengths like those shown below, but in which lines *r*, *s*, and *t* are not parallel?) **The converse is not true.**

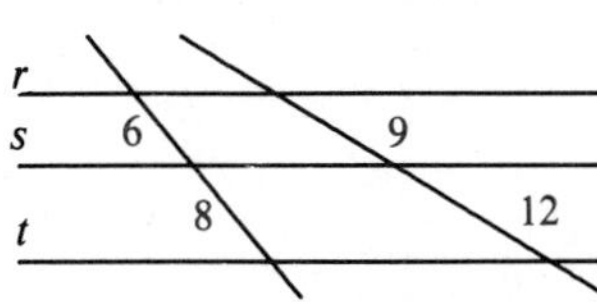

Ex. 8

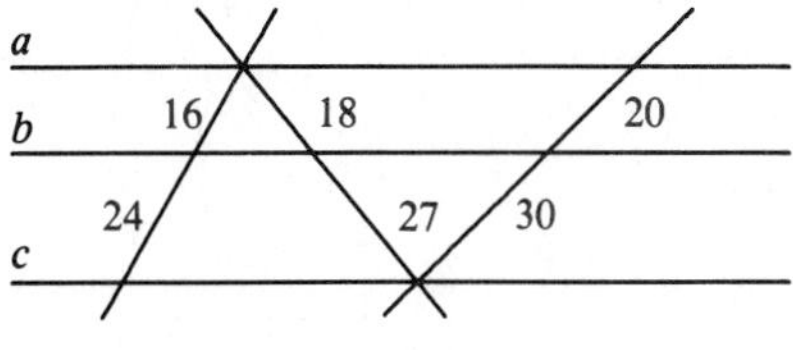

Ex. 9

9. Must lines *a*, *b*, and *c* shown above be parallel? Explain. **Yes; each pair of transversals form 2 ~ △s. Thus corr. ∠s are ≅ and the lines are ∥.**

e. $\frac{FH}{AB} = \frac{AH}{FT}$ F

f. $\frac{FA}{FB} = \frac{AH}{TB}$ T

2. True or false?

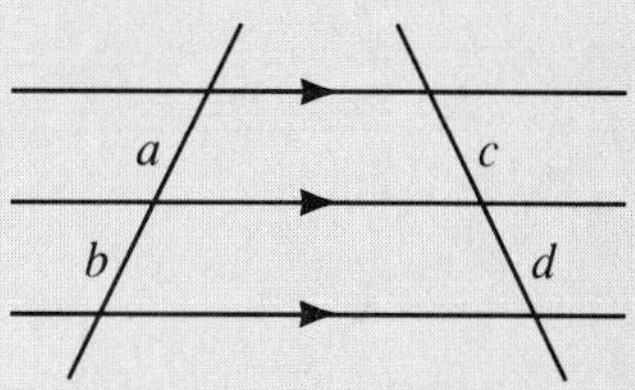

a. $\frac{a}{b} = \frac{c}{d}$ T

b. $\frac{a}{c} = \frac{c}{d}$ F

c. $\frac{a}{d} = \frac{c}{b}$ F

d. $\frac{b}{c} = \frac{a}{d}$ F

Find the value of x.

3. 30

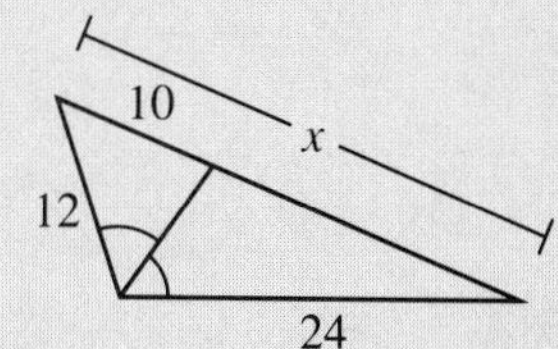

4. 4

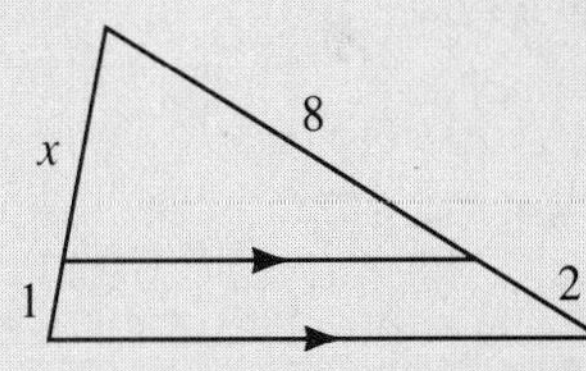

5. $\frac{45}{7}$

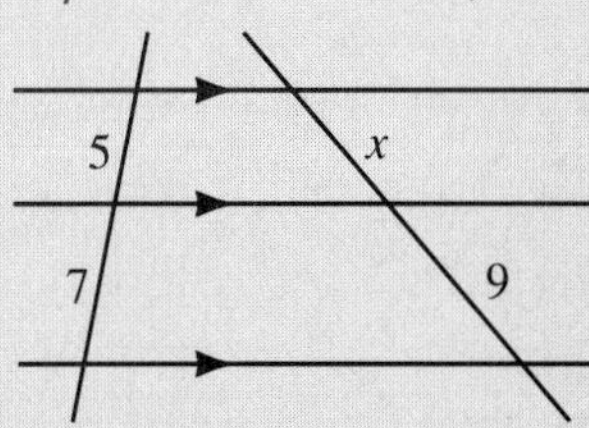

Written Exercises

A **1.** Tell whether the proportion is correct.

a. $\frac{r}{s} = \frac{a}{b}$ **No** **b.** $\frac{j}{a} = \frac{s}{r}$ **Yes** **c.** $\frac{a}{b} = \frac{n}{t}$ **Yes**

d. $\frac{t}{k} = \frac{a}{j}$ **No** **e.** $\frac{r}{s} = \frac{n}{k}$ **Yes** **f.** $\frac{b}{j} = \frac{t}{k}$ **Yes**

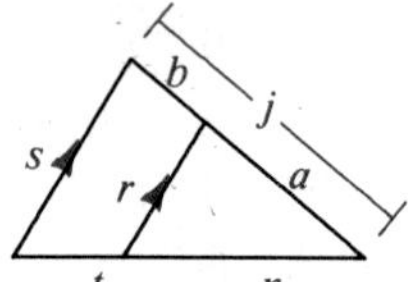

2. Tell whether the proportion is correct.

a. $\frac{d}{f} = \frac{g}{e}$ **No** **b.** $\frac{f}{g} = \frac{e}{d}$ **No**

c. $\frac{g}{f} = \frac{e}{d}$ **Yes** **d.** $\frac{d}{f} = \frac{e}{g}$ **Yes**

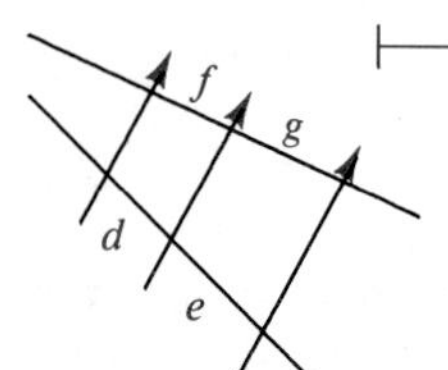

Find the value of x.

3. **7.5**

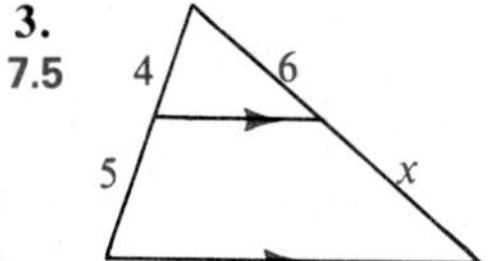

4. **35**

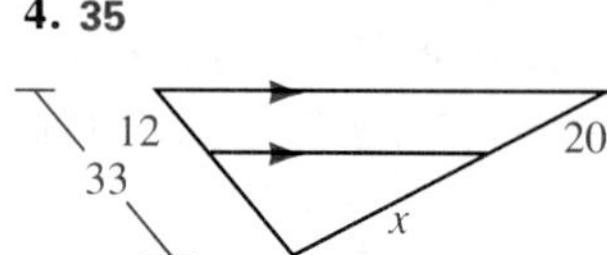

5. **26**

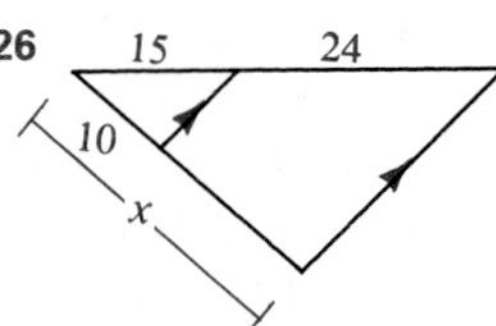

6. **12**

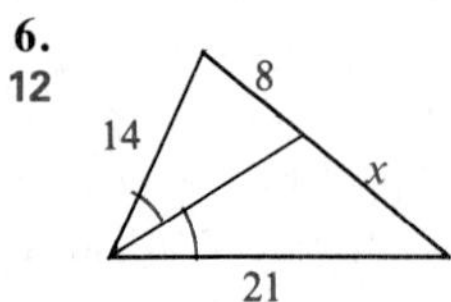

7. **18**

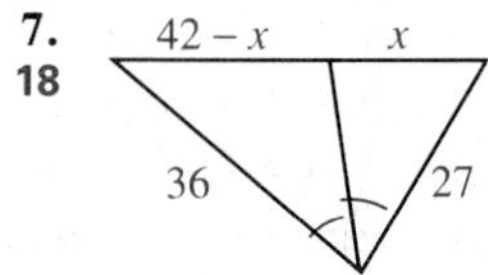

8. **30**

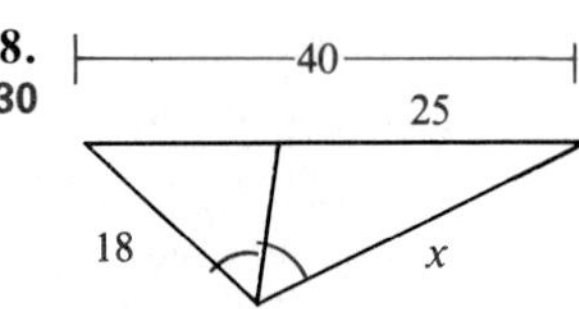

9. **14.5**

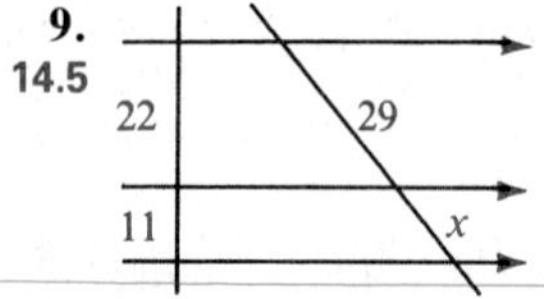

10. **8**

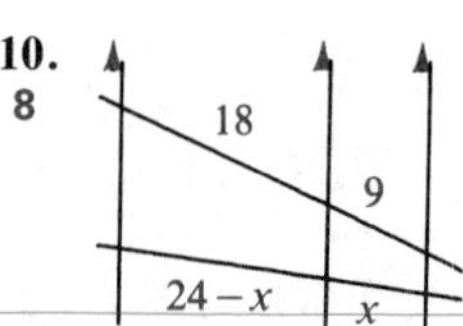

11. **4**

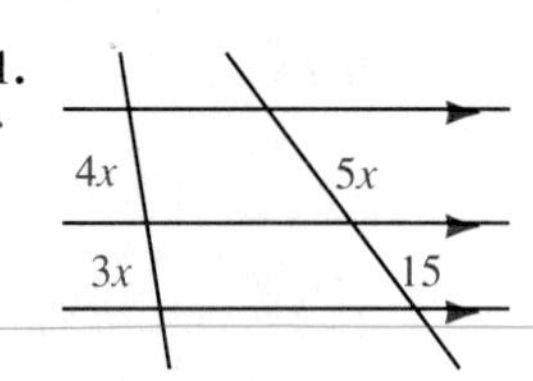

Copy the table and fill in as many spaces *as possible*. It may help to draw a new sketch for each exercise and label lengths as you find them. **Note: It is not possible to determine the lengths circled in Exs. 13, 14, 17.**

	AR	*RT*	*AT*	*AN*	*NP*	*AP*	*RN*	*TP*
B **12.**	6	4	? **10**	9	? **6**	? **15**	? **9**	15
13.	(?)	(?)	(?)	? **10**	6	16	(?)	(?)
14.	18	? **6**	? **24**	(?)	(?)	(?)	30	40
15.	12	? **8**	20	? **18**	? **12**	30	15	? **25**
16.	? **9**	18	? **27**	? **13**	26	? **39**	12	36
17.	? **8**	8	16	6	? **6**	? **12**	(?)	(?)

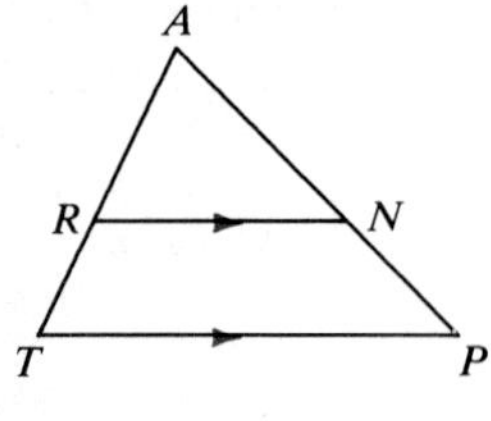

18. Prove the corollary of the Triangle Proportionality Theorem.

19. Prove the Triangle Angle-Bisector Theorem.

Complete.

20. $AD = 21$, $DC = 14$, $AC = 25$, $AB = \underline{\ ?\ }$ **15**

21. $AC = 60$, $CD = 30$, $AD = 50$, $BC = \underline{\ ?\ }$ **22.5**

22. $AB = 27$, $BC = x$, $CD = \frac{4}{3}x$, $AD = x$, $AC = \underline{\ ?\ }$ **63**

23. $AB = 2x - 12$, $BC = x$, $CD = x + 5$, $AD = 2x - 4$, $AC = \underline{\ ?\ }$ **78**

24. Three lots with parallel side boundaries extend from the avenue to the boulevard as shown. Find, to the nearest tenth of a meter, the frontages of the lots on Martin Luther King Avenue. **53.3 m, 40 m, 46.7 m**

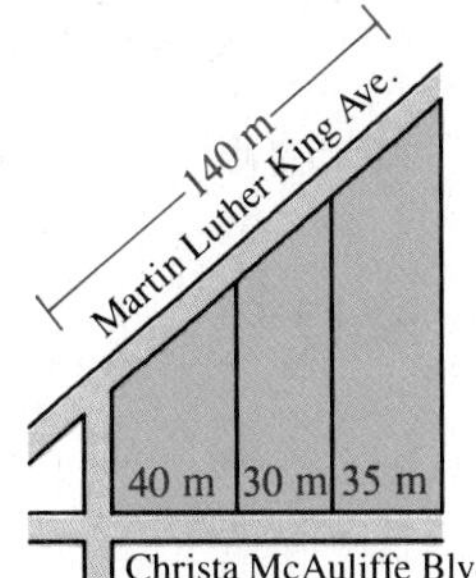

Ex. 24

25. The lengths of the sides of $\triangle ABC$ are $BC = 12$, $CA = 13$, and $AB = 14$. If M is the midpoint of $\overline{CA}$, and P is the point where $\overline{CA}$ is cut by the bisector of $\angle B$, find MP. **0.5**

26. Prove: If a line bisects both an angle of a triangle and the opposite side, then the triangle is isosceles.

C **27.** Discover and prove a theorem about planes and transversals suggested by the corollary of the Triangle Proportionality Theorem.

28. Prove that there cannot be a triangle in which the trisectors of an angle also trisect the opposite side.

29. Can there exist a $\triangle ROS$ in which the trisectors of $\angle O$ intersect $\overline{RS}$ at D and E, with $RD = 1$, $DE = 2$, and $ES = 4$? Explain.

30. Angle E of $\triangle ZEN$ is obtuse. The bisector of $\angle E$ intersects $\overline{ZN}$ at X. J and K lie on $\overline{ZE}$ and $\overline{NE}$ with $ZJ = ZX$ and $NK = NX$. Discover and prove something about quadrilateral $ZNKJ$.

★ **31.** In $\triangle ABC$, $AB = 8$, $BC = 6$, and $AC = 12$. Each of the three segments drawn through point K has length x and is parallel to a side of the triangle. Find the value of x. $x = 5\frac{1}{3}$

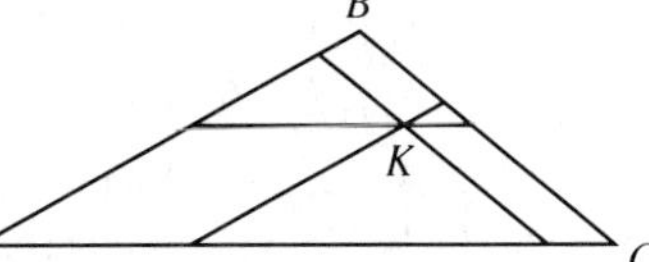

★ **32.** In $\triangle RST$, U lies on $\overline{TS}$ with $TU:US = 2:3$. M is the midpoint of $\overline{RU}$. $\overrightarrow{TM}$ intersects $\overline{RS}$ in V. Find the ratio $RV:RS$. **2:7**

★ **33.** Prove *Ceva's Theorem:* If P is any point inside $\triangle ABC$, then $\frac{AX}{XB} \cdot \frac{BY}{YC} \cdot \frac{CZ}{ZA} = 1$.

(*Hint:* Draw lines parallel to $\overline{CX}$ through A and B. Apply the Triangle Proportionality Theorem to $\triangle ABM$. Show that $\triangle APN \sim \triangle MPB$, $\triangle BYM \sim \triangle CYP$, and $\triangle CZP \sim \triangle AZN$.)

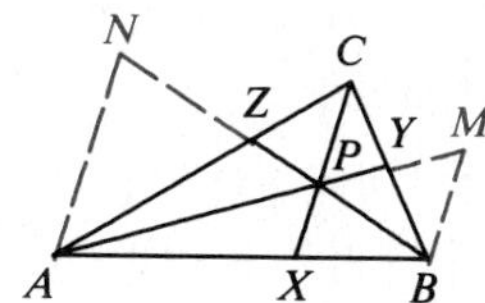

Problem Solving

Exs. 27–33 provide many opportunities for capable students to exercise their problem-solving skills. Encourage students to be flexible, using an experimental approach when trying to discover and prove something new. Students should make conjectures first and then try to prove or disprove their conjectures.

Using a Computer

See page T105 for two experiments that extend the topics of Chapter 7.

Cultural Note

Ceva's theorem is named after the Italian mathematician Giovanni Ceva (ca. 1647–1736). Ceva described the theorem in a work published in 1678.

Quick Quiz

State the postulate or theorem you can use to prove that two triangles are similar.

1. AA

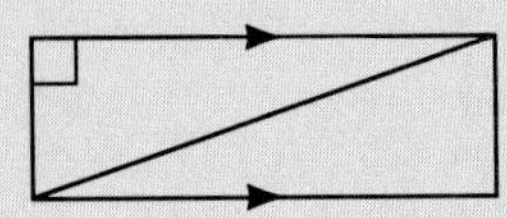

2. SSS

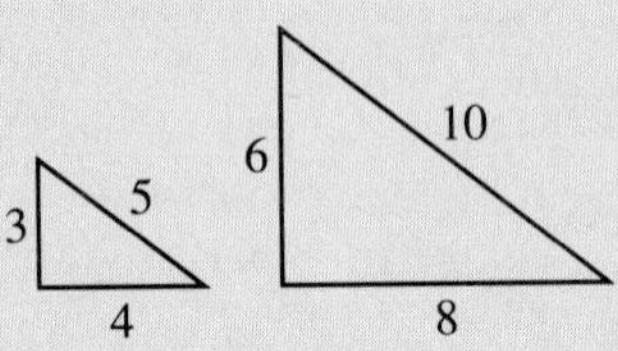

3. SAS

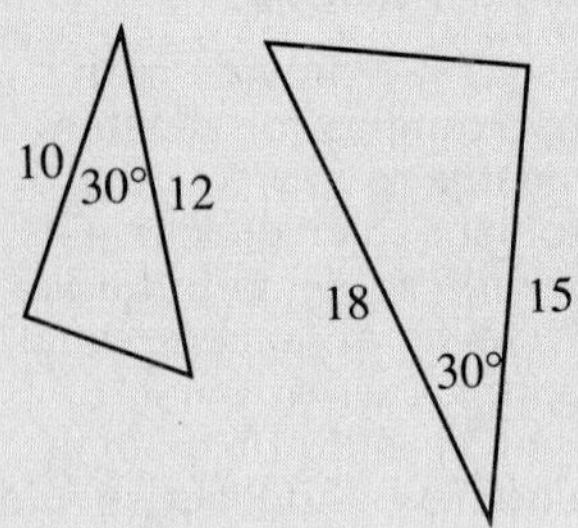

Complete.

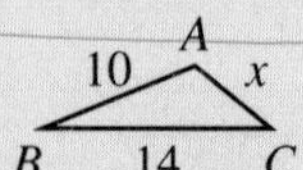

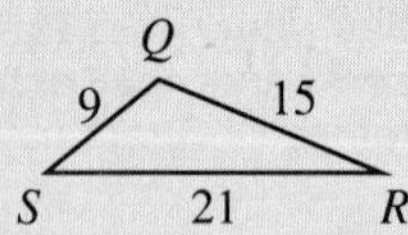

4. $\triangle ABC \sim \underline{\triangle QRS}$
5. $\frac{AB}{QR} = \frac{10}{15}$
6. $\frac{AB}{QR} = \frac{x}{9} = \frac{14}{21}$
7. $x = \underline{6}$

Self-Test 2

State the postulate or theorem you can use to prove that two triangles are similar.

1. **SSS**

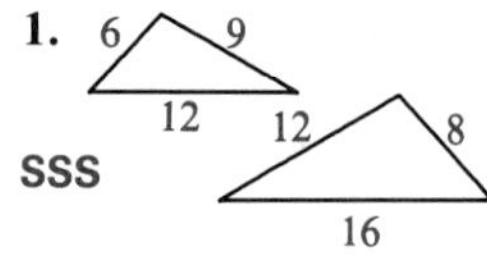

2. **AA**

3. **SAS**

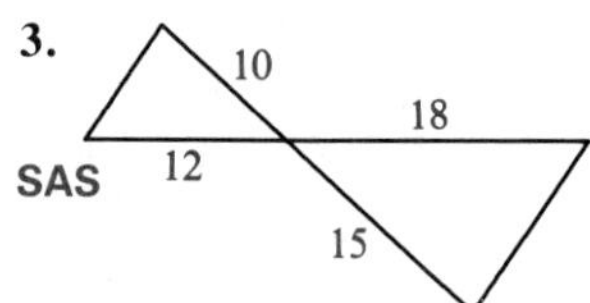

4. Complete.

a. $\triangle ABC \sim \underline{\quad ? \quad}$ **△EDC**

b. $\frac{AB}{?} = \frac{AC}{?} = \frac{BC}{?}$ **ED EC DC**

c. $\frac{15}{?} = \frac{21}{?}$, **10; x** and $x = \underline{\quad ? \quad}$ **14**

d. $\frac{15}{?} = \frac{?}{12}$, **10; y** and $y = \underline{\quad ? \quad}$ **18**

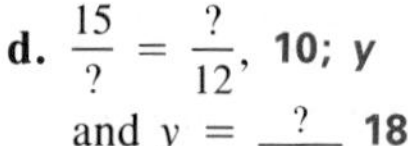

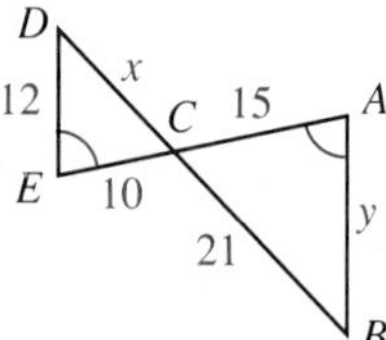

In the figure, it is given that $\overline{RS} \parallel \overline{TQ}$. Complete each proportion.

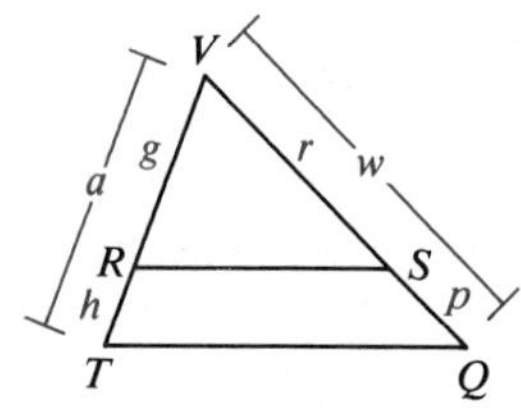

5. $\frac{g}{h} = \frac{?}{p}$ ***r***

6. $\frac{a}{h} = \frac{w}{?}$ ***p***

7. $\frac{r}{g} = \frac{p}{?}$ ***h***

8. $\frac{h}{p} = \frac{?}{w}$ ***a***

Find the value of *x*.

9. **12**

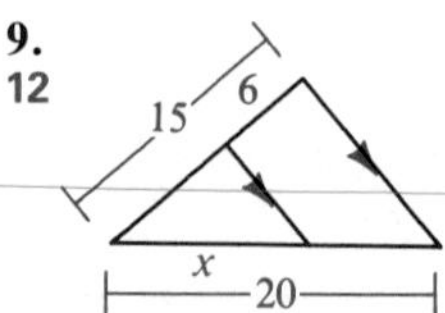

10. **14**

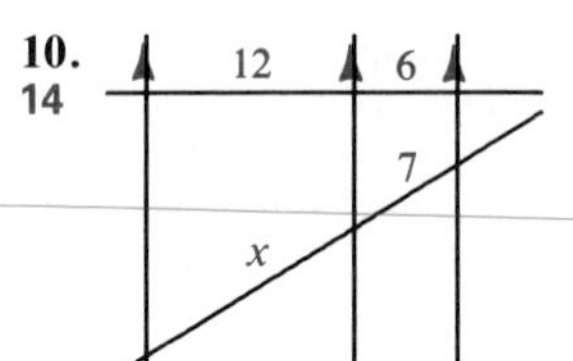

11. $6\frac{2}{3}$

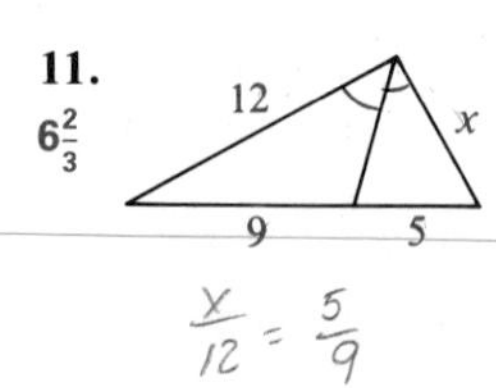

Challenge

Given: $\overline{FD} \parallel \overline{AC}$; $\overline{BD} \parallel \overline{AE}$; $\overline{FB} \parallel \overline{EC}$

Show that B, D, and F are midpoints of $\overline{AC}$, $\overline{CE}$, and $\overline{EA}$.

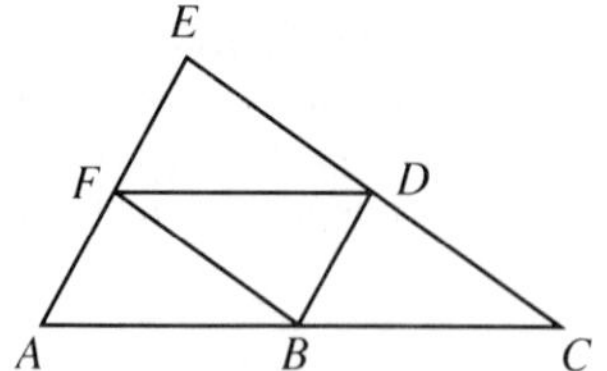

Extra

Topology

In the geometry we have been studying, our interest has been in congruent figures and similar figures, that is, figures with the same size and shape or at least the same shape. If we were studying the branch of geometry called *topology*, we would be interested in properties of figures that are even more basic than size and shape. For example, imagine taking a rubber band and stretching it into all kinds of figures.

These figures have different sizes and shapes, but they still have something in common: Each one can be turned into any of the others by stretching and bending the rubber band. In topology figures are classified according to this kind of family resemblance. Figures that can be stretched, bent, or molded into the same shape without cutting or puncturing belong to the same family and are called *topologically equivalent*. Thus circles, squares, and triangles are equivalent. Likewise the straight line segment and wiggly curves below are equivalent.

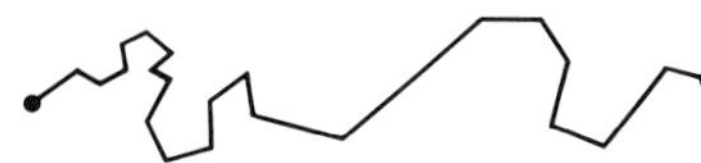

Notice that to make one of the figures above out of the rubber band you would have to cut the band, so these two-ended curves are not equivalent to the closed curves in the first illustration.

Suppose that in the plane figures below, the lines are joined where they cross. Then these figures belong to a third family. They are equivalent to each other but not to any of the figures above.

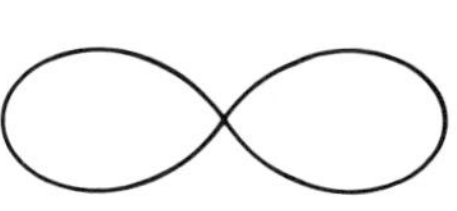
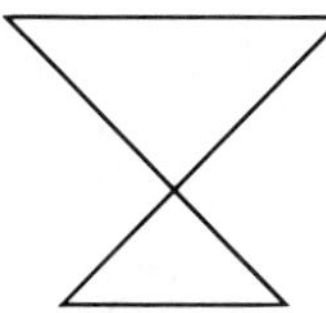
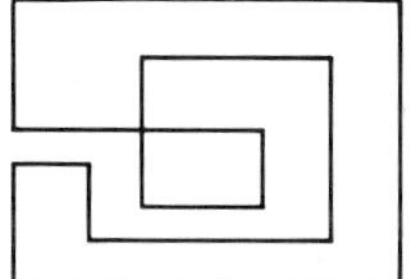

One of the goals of topology is to identify and describe the different families of equivalent figures. A person who studies topology (called a *topologist*) is interested in classifying solid figures as well as figures in a plane. For example, a topologist considers an orange, a teaspoon, and a brick equivalent to each other.

Complete each proportion.

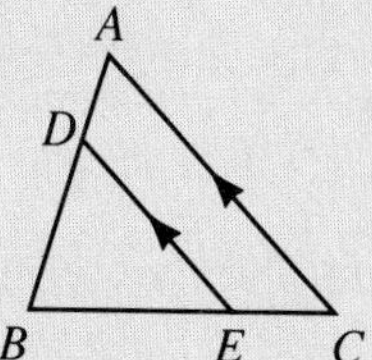

8. $\frac{AD}{DB} = \frac{CE}{EB}$

9. $\frac{BE}{BD} = \frac{BC}{BA}$

10. $\frac{BD}{BA} = \frac{BE}{BC}$

Find the value of x.

11. $2\frac{2}{7}$

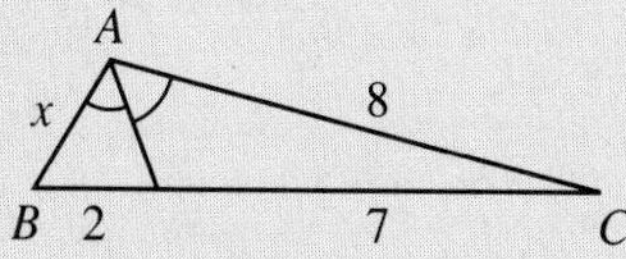

12. 10

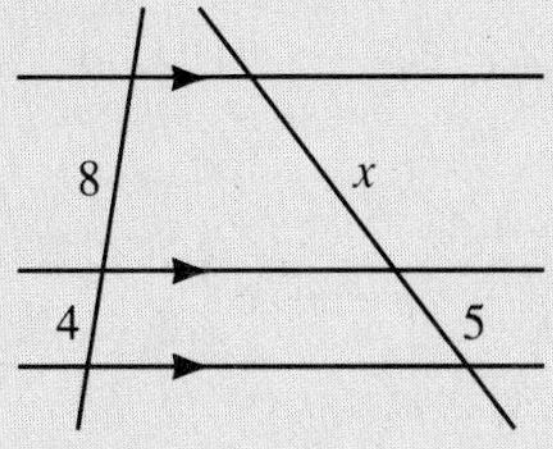

Additional Answers
Challenge

$\overline{FB} \parallel \overline{EC}$ so $\frac{FE}{AF} = \frac{BC}{AB}$ ($\triangle$ Prop. Thm.) $\overline{BD} \parallel \overline{AE}$ so $\frac{BC}{AB} = \frac{CD}{DE}$. Then $\frac{FE}{AF} = \frac{CD}{DE}$. $\overline{FD} \parallel \overline{AC}$ so $\frac{FE}{AF} = \frac{DE}{CD}$; $\frac{CD}{DE} = \frac{DE}{CD}$ (Subst.). $(CD)^2 = (DE)^2$, $CD = DE$; D is the midpt. of $\overline{CE}$. B and F can be shown to be the midpts. of $\overline{AC}$ and $\overline{EA}$, respectively.

Orange

Teaspoon

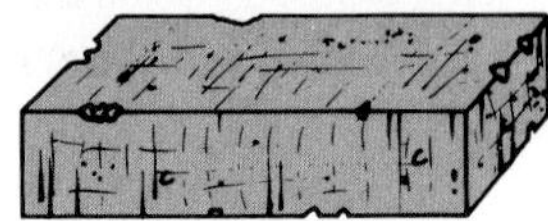

Brick

In fact, a doughnut is topologically equivalent to a coffee cup. (See the diagrams below.) For this reason, a topologist has been humorously described as a mathematician who can't tell the difference between a doughnut and a coffee cup!

Think of the objects as made of modeling clay.

Push thumb into clay to make room for coffee.

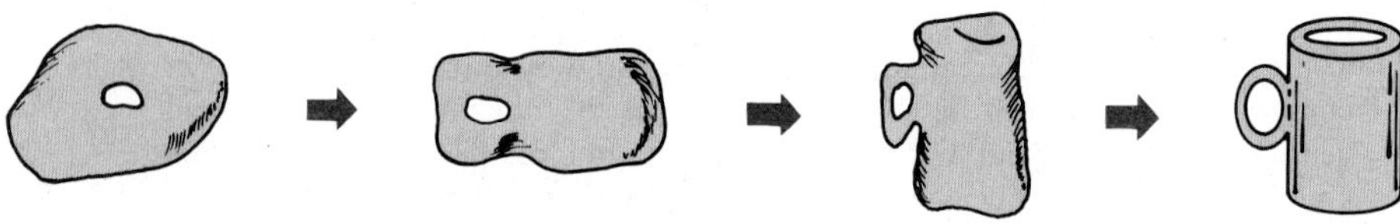

Exercises

In each exercise tell which figure is *not* topologically equivalent to the rest. Exercises 1 and 2 show plane figures.

1. **a.**  **b.**  **(c.)**  **d.** 

2. **a.** 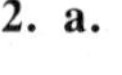 **b.**  **c.**  **(d.)**  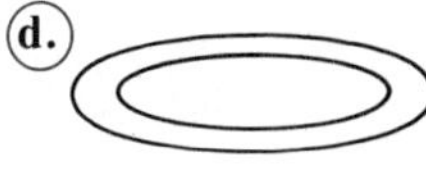

3. **a.** solid ball **(b.)** hollow ball **c.** crayon **d.** comb
4. **(a.)** saucer **b.** house key **c.** coffee cup **d.** wedding ring
5. **a.** hammer **b.** screwdriver **c.** thimble **(d.)** sewing needle
6. Group the block numbers shown into three groups such that the numbers in each group are topologically equivalent to each other. **{1, 2, 3, 5, 7}, {0, 4, 6, 9}, {8}**

7. Make a series of drawings showing that the items in each pair are topologically equivalent to each other. **Check students' drawings.**
   a. a drinking glass and a dollar bill **b.** a tack and a paper clip

Chapter Summary

1. The ratio of a to b is the quotient $\frac{a}{b}$ (b cannot be 0). The ratio $\frac{a}{b}$ can also be written $a:b$.
2. A proportion is an equation, such as $\frac{a}{b} = \frac{c}{d}$, stating that two ratios are equal.
3. The properties of proportions (see page 245) are used to change proportions into equivalent equations. For example, the product of the extremes equals the product of the means.
4. Similar figures have the same shape. Two polygons are similar if and only if corresponding angles are congruent and corresponding sides are in proportion.
5. Ways to prove two triangles similar:
   AA Similarity Postulate   SAS Similarity Theorem   SSS Similarity Theorem
6. Ways to show that segments are proportional:
   a. Corresponding sides of similar polygons are in proportion.
   b. If a line is parallel to one side of a triangle and intersects the other two sides, then it divides those sides proportionally.
   c. If three parallel lines intersect two transversals, they divide the transversals proportionally.
   d. If a ray bisects an angle of a triangle, then it divides the opposite side into segments proportional to the other two sides.

Chapter Review

Write the ratio in simplest form.

1. 15:25 **3:5** **2.** 6:12:9 **2:4:3** **3.** $\frac{16xy}{24x^2}$ $\frac{2y}{3x}$ 7–1

4. The measures of the angles of a triangle are in the ratio 4:4:7. Find the three measures. **48, 48, and 84**

Is the equation equivalent to the proportion $\frac{30 - x}{x} = \frac{8}{7}$?

5. $7x = 8(30 - x)$ **No** **6.** $\frac{x}{30 - x} = \frac{7}{8}$ **Yes** 7–2

7. $8x = 210 - 7x$ **Yes** **8.** $\frac{30}{x} = \frac{15}{7}$ **Yes**

Supplementary Materials

Practice Master 42

Test 28

Resource Book, pp. 40–41, 136

9. If $\triangle ABC \sim \triangle NJT$, then $\angle B \cong$ _?_. $\angle J$ 7–3

10. If quad. $DEFG \sim$ quad. $PQRS$, then $\frac{FG}{RS} = \frac{GD}{?}$. SP

11. $\triangle ABC \sim \triangle JET$, and the scale factor of $\triangle ABC$ to $\triangle JET$ is $\frac{5}{3}$.

a. If $BC = 20$, then $ET =$ _?_. **12**

b. If the perimeter of $\triangle JET$ is 30, then the perimeter of $\triangle ABC$ is _?_. **50**

12. The quadrilaterals are similar. Find the values of x and y.
x = 9
y = 13.5

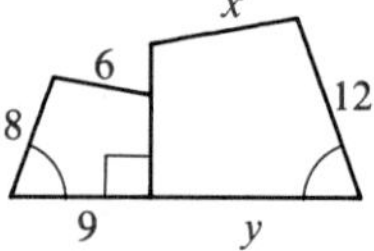

13. a. $\triangle RTS \sim$ _?_ **△UVH** 7–4

b. What postulate or theorem justifies the statement in part (a)? **AA Similarity Post.**

14. $\frac{RT}{?} = \frac{TS}{?} = \frac{RS}{?}$ **UV, VH, UH**

15. Suppose you wanted to prove

$$RS \cdot UV = RT \cdot UH.$$

You would first use similar triangles to show that $\frac{RS}{?} = \frac{?}{?}$.  $\frac{RT}{UV}$
UH

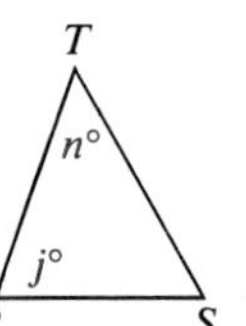
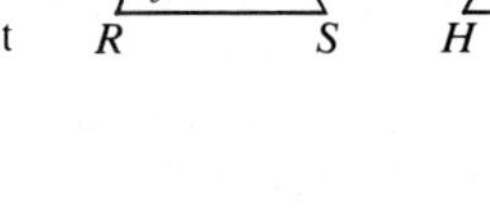

Can the two triangles be proved similar? If so, state the similarity and the postulate or theorem you would use. If not, write *no*.

16. $\angle A \cong \angle D$

△NCD ~ △NBA, AA

17. $\angle B \cong \angle D$
△NCD ~ △NAB, AA 7–5

18. $CN = 16$, $ND = 14$, $BN = 7$, $AN = 8$
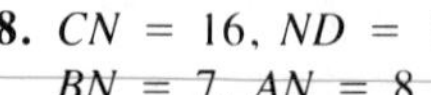
△NCD ~ △NAB, SAS

19. $AN = 7$, $AB = 13$, $DN = 14$, $DC = 26$ **No**

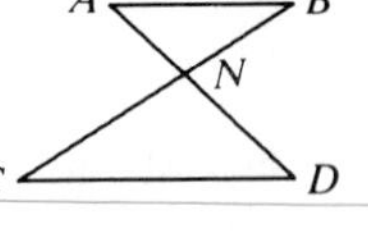

Exs. 16–19

20.

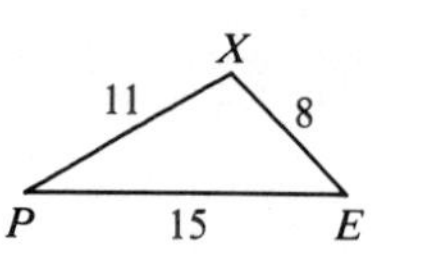

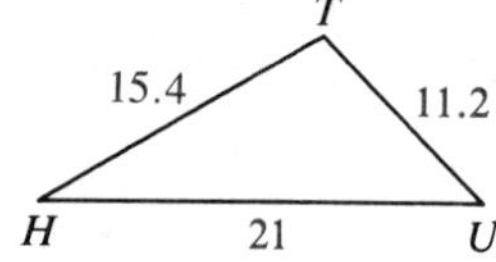

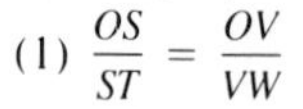
△PXE ~ △HTU, SSS

21. Which proportion is *incorrect*? 7–6

(1) $\frac{OS}{ST} = \frac{OV}{VW}$ **(2)** $\frac{SV}{TW} = \frac{OS}{ST}$ (3) $\frac{OT}{OW} = \frac{OS}{OV}$

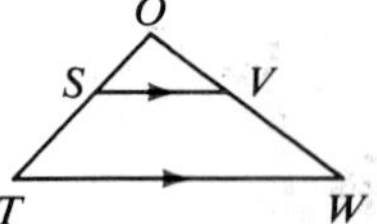

22. If $OS = 8$, $ST = 12$, and $OV = 10$, then $OW =$ _?_. **25**

23. If $OS = 8$, $ST = 12$, and $OW = 24$, then $VW =$ _?_. **14.4**

24. In $\triangle ABC$, the bisector of $\angle B$ meets $\overline{AC}$ at K. $AB = 18$, $BC = 24$, and $AC = 28$. Find AK. **12**

Chapter Test

1. Two sides of a rectangle have the lengths 20 and 32. Find, in simplest form, the ratio of:
   a. the length of the shorter side to the length of the longer side **5:8**
   b. the perimeter to the length of the longer side **13:4**

2. If quad. $ABCD \sim$ quad. $THUS$, then:
   a. $\angle U \cong$ _?_ **∠C**
   b. $\frac{BC}{HU} = \frac{AD}{?}$ **TS**

3. If $x:y:z = 4:6:9$ and $z = 45$, then $x =$ _?_ **20** and $y =$ _?_ **30**.

4. If $\frac{8}{9} = \frac{x}{15}$, then $x =$ _?_. **$13\frac{1}{3}$**

5. If $\frac{a}{b} = \frac{c}{10}$, then $\frac{a+b}{?} = \frac{?}{10}$. **b; c + 10**

6. What postulate or theorem justifies the statement $\triangle AVB \sim \triangle NVK$? **AA Similarity Post.**

7. $\frac{AB}{NK} = \frac{VA}{?}$ **VN**

8. $\angle VBA \cong$ _?_ **∠NKV**

9. The scale factor of $\triangle AVB$ to $\triangle NVK$ is $\frac{5}{8}$. If $VA = 2.5$ and $VB = 1.7$, then $VN =$ _?_. **4**

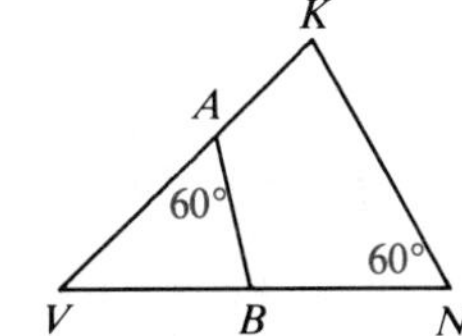

10. If $PR = 10$, $RS = 6$, and $PT = 15$, then $TU =$ _?_. **9**
11. If $PT = 32$, $PU = 48$, and $RS = 10$, then $PR =$ _?_. **20**
12. If $PR = 14$, $RS = 7$, and $RT = 26$, then $SU =$ _?_. **39**

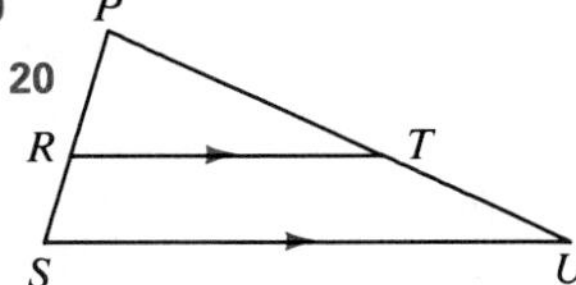

In $\triangle GEB$, the bisector of $\angle E$ meets $\overline{GB}$ at K.

13. If $GK = 5$, $KB = 8$, and $GE = 7$, then $EB =$ _?_. **11.2**
14. If $GE = 14$, $EB = 21$, and $GB = 30$, then $GK =$ _?_. **12**

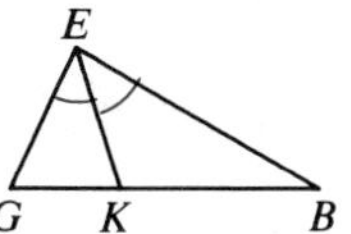

15. Given: $\overleftrightarrow{DE} \parallel \overleftrightarrow{FG} \parallel \overleftrightarrow{HJ}$
    Prove: $DF \cdot GJ = FH \cdot EG$

D E
F G
H J

16. Given: $BX = 6$; $AX = 8$; $CX = 9$; $DX = 12$
    Prove: $\overline{AB} \parallel \overline{CD}$

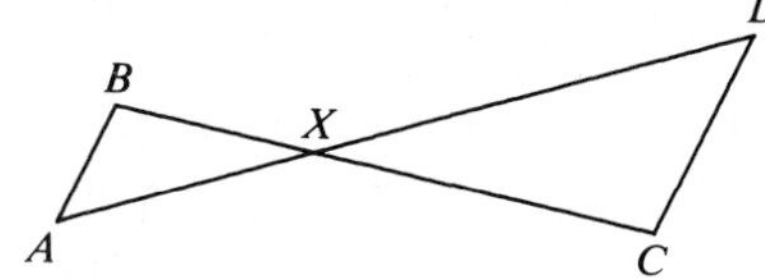

Teaching References

Alternate Test, p. T18

Supplementary Materials

Tests 29, 30

Resource Book, pp. 42–49, 137–139, 177–179, 196

Algebra Review: *Radical Expressions*

The symbol $\sqrt{\ }$ always indicates the positive square root of a number. The *radical* $\sqrt{64}$ can be *simplified*.

Simplify.

Example 1 a. $\sqrt{56}$ b. $\sqrt{\frac{16}{3}}$ c. $(3\sqrt{7})^2$

Solution

a. $\sqrt{56} = \sqrt{4 \cdot 14} = \sqrt{4} \cdot \sqrt{14} = 2\sqrt{14}$

b. $\sqrt{\frac{16}{3}} = \frac{\sqrt{16}}{\sqrt{3}} = \frac{4}{\sqrt{3}} \cdot \frac{\sqrt{3}}{\sqrt{3}} = \frac{4\sqrt{3}}{3}$

c. $(3\sqrt{7})^2 = 3\sqrt{7} \cdot 3\sqrt{7} = 3 \cdot 3 \cdot \sqrt{7} \cdot \sqrt{7} = 9 \cdot 7 = 63$

10. $\mathbf{\frac{5\sqrt{30}}{12}}$

15. 162

$10\sqrt{3}$

1. $\sqrt{36}$ **6**
2. $\sqrt{81}$ **9**
3. $\sqrt{24}$ **$2\sqrt{6}$**
4. $\sqrt{98}$ **$7\sqrt{2}$**
5. $\sqrt{300}$
6. $\sqrt{\frac{1}{4}}$ **$\frac{1}{2}$**
7. $\frac{\sqrt{5}}{\sqrt{3}}$ **$\frac{\sqrt{15}}{3}$**
8. $\sqrt{\frac{80}{25}}$ **$\frac{4\sqrt{5}}{5}$**
9. $\frac{2\sqrt{3}}{\sqrt{12}}$ **1**
10. $\sqrt{\frac{250}{48}}$
11. $\sqrt{13^2}$ **13**
12. $(\sqrt{17})^2$ **17**
13. $(2\sqrt{3})^2$ **12**
14. $(3\sqrt{8})^2$ **72**
15. $(9\sqrt{2})^2$
16. $5\sqrt{18}$ **$15\sqrt{2}$**
17. $4\sqrt{27}$ **$12\sqrt{3}$**
18. $6\sqrt{24}$ **$12\sqrt{6}$**
19. $5\sqrt{8}$ **$10\sqrt{2}$**
20. $9\sqrt{40}$ **$18\sqrt{10}$**

Solve for *x*. Assume *x* represents a positive number.

Example 2 $2^2 + x^2 = 4^2$

Solution

$$4 + x^2 = 16$$
$$x^2 = 12$$
$$x = \sqrt{12}$$
$$x = 2\sqrt{3}$$

Example 3 $x^2 + (3\sqrt{2})^2 = 9^2$

Solution

$$x^2 + 18 = 81$$
$$x^2 = 63$$
$$x = \sqrt{63}$$
$$x = 3\sqrt{7}$$

21. $3^2 + 4^2 = x^2$ **5**
22. $x^2 + 4^2 = 5^2$ **3**
23. $5^2 + x^2 = 13^2$ **12**
24. $x^2 + 3^2 = 4^2$ **$\sqrt{7}$**
25. $4^2 + 7^2 = x^2$ **$\sqrt{65}$**
26. $x^2 + 5^2 = 10^2$ **$5\sqrt{3}$**
27. $1^2 + x^2 = 3^2$ **$2\sqrt{2}$**
28. $x^2 + 5^2 = (5\sqrt{2})^2$ **5**
29. $(x)^2 + (7\sqrt{3})^2 = (2x)^2$ **7**

Challenge

Given regular hexagon *ABCDEF*, with center *O* and sides of length 12. Let *G* be the midpoint of $\overline{BC}$. Let *H* be the midpoint of $\overline{DE}$. $\overline{AH}$ intersects $\overline{EB}$ at *J* and $\overline{FG}$ intersects $\overline{EB}$ at *K*.

Find *JK*. **8**

(*Hint*: Draw auxiliary lines $\overline{HG}$ and $\overline{DA}$.)

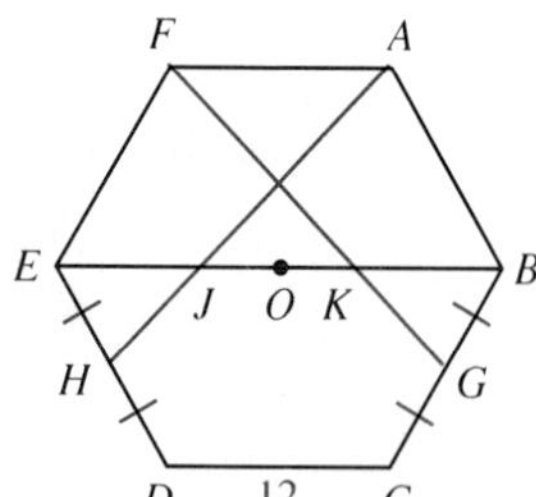

Cumulative Review: Chapters 1–7

True-False Exercises

Write T or F to indicate your answer.

A **1.** If $AX = XB$, then X must be the midpoint of $\overline{AB}$. F

2. Definitions may be used to justify statements in a proof. T

3. If a line and a plane are parallel, then the line is parallel to every line in the plane. F

4. When two parallel lines are cut by a transversal, any two angles formed are either congruent or supplementary. T

5. If the sides of one triangle are congruent to the corresponding sides of another triangle, then the corresponding angles must also be congruent. T

6. Every isosceles trapezoid contains two pairs of congruent angles. T

B **7.** If a quadrilateral has two pairs of supplementary angles, then it must be a parallelogram. F

8. If the diagonals of a quadrilateral bisect each other and are congruent, then the quadrilateral must be a square. F

9. In $\triangle PQR$, $m\angle P = m\angle R = 50$. If T lies on $\overline{PR}$ and $m\angle PQT = 42$, then $PT < TR$. F

10. In quad. $WXYZ$, if $WX = XY = 25$, $YZ = 20$, $ZW = 16$, and $WY = 20$, then $\overline{WY}$ divides the quadrilateral into two similar triangles. T

11. Two equiangular hexagons are always similar. F

Multiple-Choice Exercises

Indicate the best answer by writing the appropriate letter.

A **1.** Which pair of angles must be congruent?

a. $\angle 1$ and $\angle 4$ **b.** $\angle 2$ and $\angle 3$ **c.** $\angle 2$ and $\angle 4$ **(d.)** $\angle 4$ and $\angle 5$ **e.** $\angle 2$ and $\angle 8$

2. If a, b, c, and d are coplanar lines such that $a \perp b$, $c \perp d$, and $b \parallel c$, then:

a. $a \perp d$ **b.** $b \parallel d$ **(c.)** $a \parallel d$ **d.** $a \parallel c$ **e.** none of these

3. If $\triangle ABC \cong \triangle NDH$, then it is also true that:

a. $\angle B \cong \angle H$ **b.** $\angle A \cong \angle H$ **c.** $\overline{AB} \cong \overline{HD}$ **(d.)** $\overline{CA} \cong \overline{HN}$ **e.** $\triangle CBA \cong \triangle DHN$

B **4.** If $PQRS$ is a parallelogram, which of the following *must* be true?

a. $PQ = QR$ **(b.)** $PQ = RS$ **c.** $PR = QS$ **d.** $\overline{PR} \perp \overline{QS}$ **e.** $\angle Q \cong \angle R$

5. Which of the following can be the lengths of the sides of a triangle?

a. 3, 7, 10 **b.** 3, 7, 11 **(c.)** 0.5, 7, 7 **d.** $\frac{1}{2}, \frac{1}{4}, \frac{1}{5}$ **e.** 1, 3, 5

Always-Sometimes-Never Exercises

Write A, S, or N to indicate your choice.

A 1. If a conditional is false, then its converse is _?_ false. **S**

2. Two vertical angles are _?_ adjacent. **N**

3. An angle _?_ has a complement. **S**

4. Two parallel lines are _?_ coplanar. **A**

5. Two perpendicular lines are _?_ both parallel to a third line. **N**

6. A scalene triangle is _?_ equiangular. **N**

7. A regular polygon is _?_ equilateral. **A**

8. A rectangle is _?_ a rhombus. **S**

9. If $\overline{RS} \cong \overline{MN}$, $\overline{ST} \cong \overline{NO}$, and $\angle R \cong \angle M$, then $\triangle RST$ and $\triangle MNO$ are _?_ congruent. **S**

10. The HL method is _?_ appropriate for proving that two acute triangles are congruent. **N**

11. If $AX = BX$, $AY = BY$, and points A, B, X, and Y are coplanar, then $\overline{AB}$ and $\overline{XY}$ are _?_ perpendicular. **A**

B 12. The diagonals of a trapezoid are _?_ perpendicular. **S**

13. If a line parallel to one side of a triangle intersects the other two sides, then the triangle formed is _?_ similar to the given triangle. **A**

14. If $\triangle JKL \cong \triangle NET$ and $\overline{NE} \perp \overline{ET}$, then it is _?_ true that $LJ < TE$. **N**

15. If $AB + BC > AC$, then A, B, and C are _?_ collinear points. **S**

16. A triangle with sides of length $x - 1$, x, and x is _?_ an obtuse triangle. **N**

Completion Exercises

Complete each statement in the best way.

A 1. If $\overrightarrow{YW}$ bisects $\angle XYZ$ and $m\angle WYX = 60$, then $m\angle XYZ =$ _?_. **120**

2. The acute angles of a right triangle are _?_. **complementary**

3. A supplement of an acute angle is a(n) _?_ angle. **obtuse**

4. Adjacent angles formed by _?_ lines are congruent. **perpendicular**

5. The measure of each interior angle of a regular pentagon is _?_. **108**

6. In $\triangle ABC$ and $\triangle DEF$, $\angle A \cong \angle D$ and $\angle B \cong \angle E$. $\triangle ABC$ and $\triangle DEF$ must be _?_. **similar**

B 7. When the midpoints of the sides of a rhombus are joined in order, the resulting quadrilateral is best described as a _?_. **rectangle**

8. If $\frac{r}{s} = \frac{t}{u}$, then $\frac{r+s}{t+u} = \frac{?}{?}$. $\mathbf{\frac{s}{u}}$

9. The ratio of the measures of the acute angles of a right triangle is 3:2. The measure of the smaller acute angle is _?_. **36**

Algebraic Exercises

In Exercises 1–9 find the value of x.

A **1.** On a number line, R and S have coordinates -8 and x, and the midpoint of $\overline{RS}$ has coordinate -1. **6**

2. Two vertical angles have measures $x^2 + 18x$ and $x^2 + 54$. **3**

3. The measures of the angles of a quadrilateral are x, $x + 4$, $x + 8$, and $x + 12$. **84**

4. The lengths of the legs of an isosceles triangle are $7x - 13$ and $2x + 17$. **6**

5. Consecutive angles of a parallelogram have measures $6x$ and $2x + 20$. **20**

6. A trapezoid has bases of length x and $x + 8$ and a median of length 15. **11**

7. $\frac{3x - 1}{4x + 2} = \frac{2}{3}$ **7** **8.** $\frac{5}{8} = \frac{x - 1}{6}$ **$4\frac{3}{4}$** **9.** $\frac{x}{x + 4} = \frac{x + 3}{x + 9}$ **6**

B **10.** The measure of a supplement of an angle is 8 more than three times the measure of a complement. Find the measure of the angle. **49**

11. In a regular polygon, the ratio of the measure of an exterior angle to the measure of an interior angle is 2:13. How many sides does the polygon have? **15**

12. The sides of a parallelogram have lengths 12 cm and 15 cm. Find the lengths of the sides of a similar parallelogram with perimeter 90 cm. **20 cm, 25 cm**

13. A triangle with perimeter 64 cm has sides with lengths in the ratio 4:5:7. Find the length of each side. **16 cm, 20 cm, 28 cm**

14. In $\triangle XYZ$, $XY = YZ$. Find the measure of $\angle Z$ if $m\angle X : m\angle Y = 5:2$. **75**

15. In the diagram, $\overline{AB} \parallel \overline{DC}$ and $\overline{AD} \parallel \overline{GC}$. Find the values of x and y. **$x = 6$, $y = 3.5$**

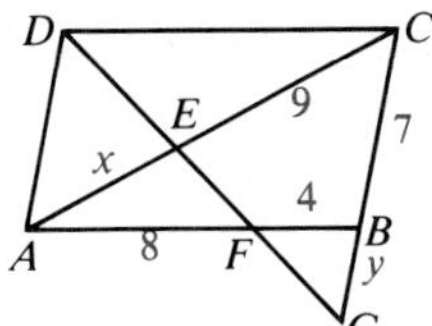

Proof Exercises

A **1.** Given: $\overline{SU} \cong \overline{SV}$; $\angle 1 \cong \angle 2$
Prove: $\overline{UQ} \cong \overline{VQ}$

2. Given: $\overrightarrow{QS}$ bisects $\angle RQT$; $\angle R \cong \angle T$
Prove: $\overrightarrow{SQ}$ bisects $\angle RST$.

B **3.** Given: $\triangle QRU \cong \triangle QTV$; $\overline{US} \cong \overline{VS}$
Prove: $\triangle QRS \cong \triangle QTS$

4. Given: $\overline{QS}$ bisects $\angle UQV$ and $\angle USV$; $\angle R \cong \angle T$
Prove: $\overline{RQ} \cong \overline{TQ}$

5. Given: $\overline{EF} \parallel \overline{JK}$; $\overline{JK} \parallel \overline{HI}$
Prove: $\triangle EFG \sim \triangle IHG$

6. Given: $\frac{JG}{HG} = \frac{KG}{IG}$, $\angle 1 \cong \angle 2$
Prove: $\overline{EF} \parallel \overline{HI}$

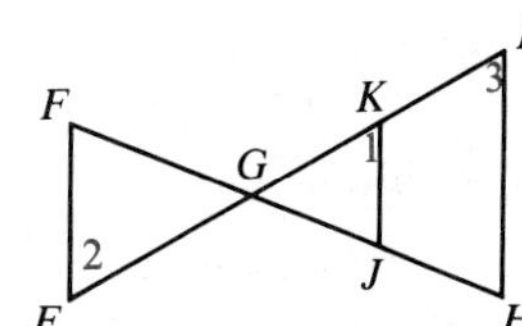

8 Right Triangles

Objectives

8-1 Determine the geometric mean between two numbers.

State and apply the relationships that exist when the altitude is drawn to the hypotenuse of a right triangle.

8-2 State and apply the Pythagorean Theorem.

8-3 State and apply the converse of the Pythagorean Theorem and related theorems about obtuse and acute angles.

8-4 Determine the lengths of two sides of a 45°-45°-90° or a 30°-60°-90° triangle when the length of the third side is known.

8-5 Define the tangent ratio for an acute angle.

Solve right triangle problems by using the tangent ratio.

8-6 Define the sine and cosine ratios for an acute angle.

Solve right triangle problems by using the sine and cosine ratios.

8-7 Solve right triangle problems by correct selection and use of the tangent, sine, and cosine ratios.

Assignment Guide

See page T40 for information about the Assignment Guide.

Day	Minimum Course	Average Course	Maximum Course
1	**8-1** 288/1–21	**8-1** 288–289/1–29 odd, 22–36 even, 40, 41	**8-1** 288–289/3, 8, 11, 15, 16, 19, 22, 25–43 odd
2	**8-1** 288–289/22–33	**8-2** 292/2–16 even, 17–20 **S** 289/42	**8-2** 292–293/5, 8, 10, 16, 19, 21–24, 26, 31
3	**8-2** 292/1–8, 9–15 odd	**8-2** 292–293/21, 22, 24, 25, 28, 33–36 294/Mixed Review 1–7	**8-2** 293–294/27, 28, 33–38
4	**8-2** 292/10–16 even, 17–22, 24 294/Mixed Review 1–7	**8-3** 297/1–7, 10, 12, 13	**8-3** 297/1–15 odd **S** 294/39
5	**8-3** 297/1–9 odd	**8-3** 297–298/11, 14–20	**8-3** 297–298/12–20 even, 21, 22
6	**8-3** 297/2–12 even, 13, 15	**8-4** 302/2–14 even, 15, 16, 18, 19, 21, 22	**8-4** 302/5–7, 11–13, 17–20 **S** 297/19
7	**8-4** 302/1–16 **S** 297/14, 16	**8-4** 302–303/20, 23, 25, 28, 31 304/Self-Test 1	**8-4** 302–303/21–23, 25, 27–30, 32, 35, 38
8	**8-4** 302/17–24 304/Self-Test 1	**8-5** 308/1–6, 9, 10, 12 **S** 303/30	**8-5** 308/1–15
9	**8-5** 308/1–9	**8-5** 308–309/7, 8, 11, 13–15, 17, 19, 25	**8-5** 308–310/16–30 even
10	**8-5** 308/10–18	**8-6** 314–315/1–10, 12–14	**8-6** 314–315/2–10 even, 11–14 **S** 309/25, 27
11	**8-6** 314/1–9 **S** 309/19, 20	**8-6** 315–316/11, 15–25 odd	**8-6** 315–316/16–26 even

12	**8-6** 315/10–17	**8-7** 318–319/1–6	**8-7** 318–319/1–9 **S** 316/21, 25
13	**8-6** 316/18–24 even	**8-7** 319/7–12	**8-7** 319–320/10–14
14	**8-7** 318–319/1–6 **S** 316/19	**8-7** 320/13, 14 320/Self-Test 2	**8-7** 324–325/Chapter Test Test, page T19
15	**8-7** 319/7–12	**8-7** 324–325/Chapter Test Test, page T19	
16	**8-7** 320/Self-Test 2 324–325/Chapter Test 1–12		
17	**8-7** 325/Chapter Test 13–27 Test, page T19		

Supplementary Materials Guide

For Use after Lesson	Practice Masters	Tests	Study Guide (Reteaching)	Resource Book: Tests	Resource Book: Practice Exercises	Resource Book: College Entrance (Col) Enrichment (E) Computer (C)	Computer Activities
8-1			pp. 91–92				Activity 15
8-2	Sheet 43	Test 31	pp. 93–94	p. 50	p. 140		Activity 16
8-3			pp. 95–96				
8-4	Sheet 44	Test 32	pp. 97–98	p. 51	p. 141		
8-5			pp. 99–100, 105				
8-6	Sheet 45		pp. 101–102, 106				Activity 17
8-7	Sheet 46	Test 33	pp. 103–104	p. 52	p. 142		Activity 18
Chapter 8	Sheet 47	Test 34		pp. 53–54	p. 143	p. 197 (Col) pp. 218–219 (E) pp. 244–249 (C)	
Chapters 7–8	Sheets 48, 49						

Overhead Visuals

Guided Discovery Visuals (lettered) and Teaching Visuals (numbered) available for Chapter 8.

Lessons	Visual	Title
8-2	F	Diagonals of Prisms
8-2	N	Which Method is Easier?
8-1, 8-2, 8-3, 8-4	16	Right Triangle Summary
8-5, 8-6, 8-7	17	Trigonometry Summary

Guide to Distribution of Constructions

The text teaches constructions in Chapter 10. Teachers wishing to distribute work with constructions throughout the first nine chapters can use this guide.

Introduce after	Construction	Page
Lesson 8-1	14	397

Software Guide

Houghton Mifflin software for Chapter 8

Geometry Grapher (Apple or IBM)
Use with
pp. 298, 310 (Explorations)

Test Generator (Apple or IBM): 105 test items

Other software appropriate for Chapter 8

Geometric Supposer (Apple): Triangles, Quadrilaterals
GeoDraw (IBM)
Spreadsheets

Guide to Integrated Curriculum

Teachers wishing to integrate coordinate and transformational geometry throughout the course can use the following lessons after Chapter 8. See pages T56–T57 and 657 for more information.

Handbook: Right Triangles, pp. 665–667

Strategies for Teaching

Exploring Pythagorean Dissections

When to Use

With or after Lesson 8-2 (Activity 1)
After Lesson 8-5 (Activity 2)

Overview

The first activity is a visual "proof" of the Pythagorean Theorem. The second activity is a paradox that can be explained using the Pythagorean Theorem, among other possible ways.

Materials

Scissors, ruler

Description of Activity

1. a. On a piece of paper, draw square *ABCD* and a smaller square *DEFG* adjacent to it as shown.

b. Locate point *P* on $\overline{AD}$ so that $AP = DG$.

c. Draw $\overline{PB}$ and $\overline{PF}$.

d. Cut out the figure and cut along $\overline{PB}$ and $\overline{PF}$, forming three pieces.

e. Arrange the three pieces into one square.

f. How does this activity suggest a proof of the Pythagorean Theorem? Prove that the figure formed is a square.

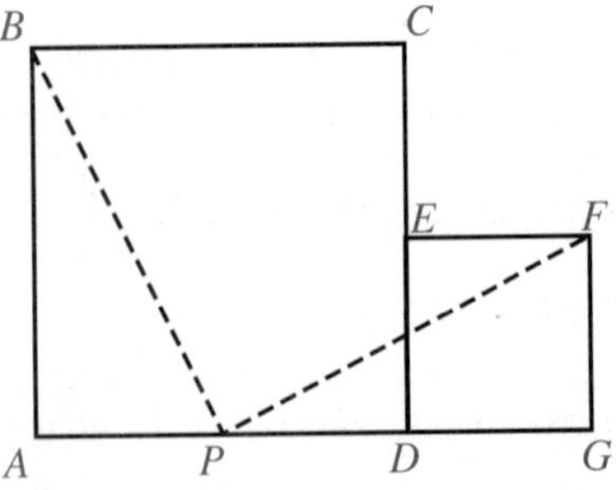

2. Cut up an 8-by-8 square into four pieces as shown. Assemble the pieces into an isosceles triangle.

a. Find the area of the square. 64

b. Find the area of the triangle. 65

c. Explain the discrepancy between the areas you found in parts **a** and **b.**

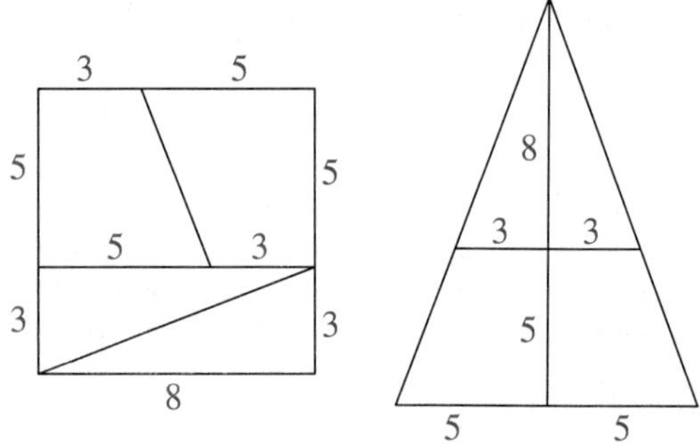

Commentary

• **1.** The dissection proof of the Pythagorean Theorem is due to H. Perigal (1873). Let $DG = a$, $AD = b$, and $BP = c$. Then the area of square *DEFG* is a^2, and the area of square *ABCD* is b^2. Rearranging the pieces forms one square with length *c*; its area is then c^2. Since the pieces were not altered, only rearranged, $a^2 + b^2 = c^2$. To prove that the figure formed is a square, use the diagram below.

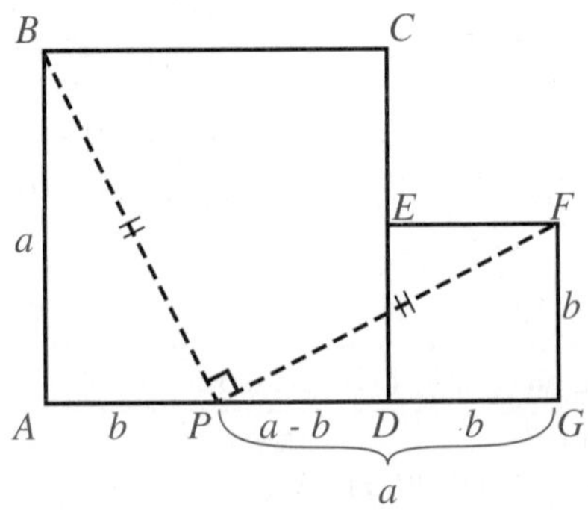

Proof: $\triangle ABP \cong \triangle GPF$; thus $BP = PF$. Also, $m\angle ABP + m\angle BPA = 90$, and since $\angle ABP \cong \angle GPF$, $m\angle BPA + m\angle GPF = 90$. So $m\angle BPF = 90$. After moving the pieces, the side opposite $\overline{BP}$ is the same as $\overline{BP}$, and the side opposite $\overline{PF}$ is the same as $\overline{PF}$. Thus with four sides of equal length, and a right angle, the figure must be a square.

- **2. c.** Use the Pythagorean Theorem to show that $AD + DB \neq AB$; thus the triangle cannot exist as pictured. Or find the area of $\triangle ADF$, which is 24, and the area of trapezoid $BDFC$, which is 40, giving 64, not 65.

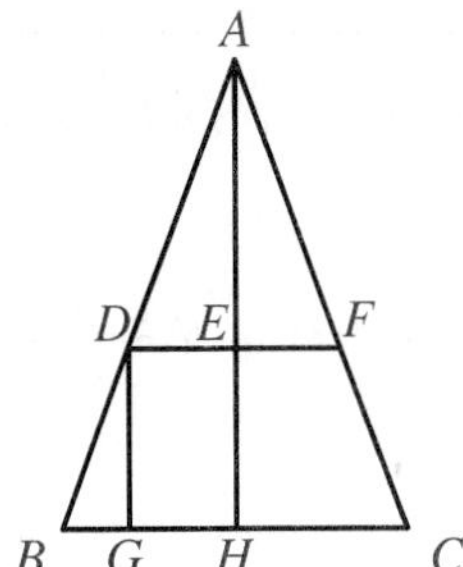

References to Strategies

PE: Pupil's Edition **TE:** Teacher's Edition **RB:** Resource Book

Problem Solving Strategies

PE: 285, 317 (Choose a method of solution), 294 (Challenge, Draw a diagram), 298 (Ex. 22, Mathematical model), 316 (Challenge, Change your point of view), 319 (Ex. 9, Mathematical model)
TE: T110, 319 (Accept reasonable estimates)

Applications

PE: 284 (Sail design), 298 (Ex. 22, Scissors truss), 303 (Ex. 38, Wrench), 309 (Exs. 19, 20, Road grade), 310 (Exs. 29, 30, Estimating distance), 315, 317–320 (Estimating distance using trigonometry), 321 (Passive solar design)
TE: T108, T109, T110

Nonroutine Problems

PE: 291 (Ex. 1), 294 (Challenge), 297 (Exs. 16, 17), 298 (Ex. 22), 301 (Ex. 12), 303 (Exs. 32–34), 307 (Exs. 10, 11), 309 (Ex. 25), 313 (Ex. 11), 314 (Exs. 12, 14, 15), 316 (Challenge), 318 (Ex. 7), 321–322 (Application), 666 (Ex. 9)
TE: T106, T110
RB: 218–219

Communication

PE: 319–320
TE: T107, T109, T111, 306

Explorations

PE: 298, 310
TE: 283c

Connections

PE: 287 (Radicals), 290 (Ex. 45, Algebra), 299 (Euclid), 304 (Nikolai Lobachevsky), 317–320 (Trigonometry), 665–667 (Coordinate and transformational geometry)
TE: T106, T107, T108, T110, 290

Using Technology

PE: 298, 299, 310
TE: T106, 285, 294, 297, 298, 299, 302, 306, 310, 313
RB: 244–249
Computer Activities: 35–44

Using Manipulatives/Models

PE: 294 (Challenge), 298 (Ex. 22), 319 (Ex. 9), 666 (Ex. 9)
TE: T106, T107, T108
RB: 218–219
Overhead Visuals: F, N, 16, 17

Cooperative Learning

TE: T107, T109, 297

Teaching Resources

For use in implementing the teaching strategies referenced on the previous page.

Using Manipulatives
Resource Book, p. 218

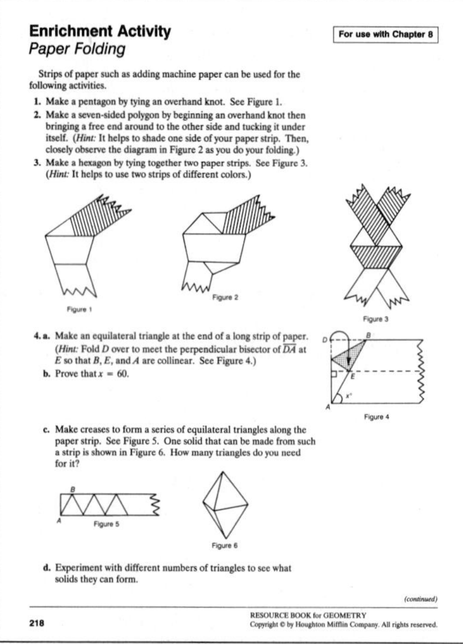

Enrichment Activity
Paper Folding

For use with Chapter 8

Strips of paper such as adding machine paper can be used for the following activities.

1. Make a pentagon by tying an overhand knot. See Figure 1.
2. Make a seven-sided polygon by beginning an overhand knot then bringing a free end around to the other side and tucking it under itself. (*Hint:* It helps to shade one side of your paper strip. Then, closely observe the diagram in Figure 2 as you do your folding.)
3. Make a hexagon by tying together two paper strips. See Figure 3. (*Hint:* It helps to use two strips of different colors.)

Figure 1 Figure 2 Figure 3

4. a. Make an equilateral triangle at the end of a long strip of paper. (*Hint:* Fold D over to meet the perpendicular bisector of $\overline{DA}$ at E so that B, E, and A are collinear. See Figure 4.)
   b. Prove that $x = 60$.

Figure 4

   c. Make creases to form a series of equilateral triangles along the paper strip. See Figure 5. One solid that can be made from such a strip is shown in Figure 6. How many triangles do you need for it?

Figure 5 Figure 6

   d. Experiment with different numbers of triangles to see what solids they can form.

(continued)

218 RESOURCE BOOK for GEOMETRY

Using Manipulatives
Resource Book, p. 219

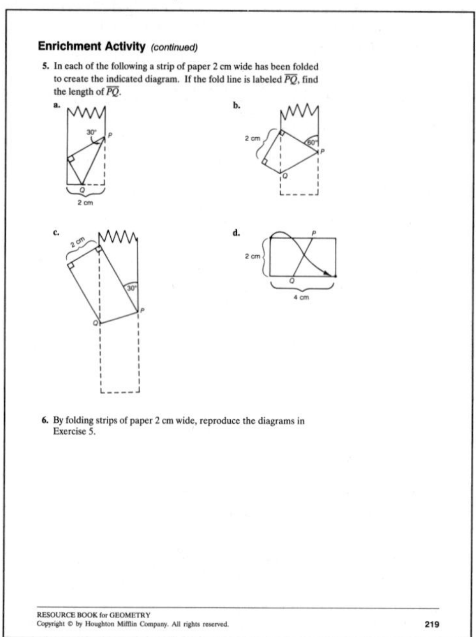

Enrichment Activity *(continued)*

5. In each of the following a strip of paper 2 cm wide has been folded to create the indicated diagram. If the fold line is labeled $\overline{PQ}$, find the length of $\overline{PQ}$.

6. By folding strips of paper 2 cm wide, reproduce the diagrams in Exercise 5.

RESOURCE BOOK for GEOMETRY

219

Using Technology
Resource Book, p. 244

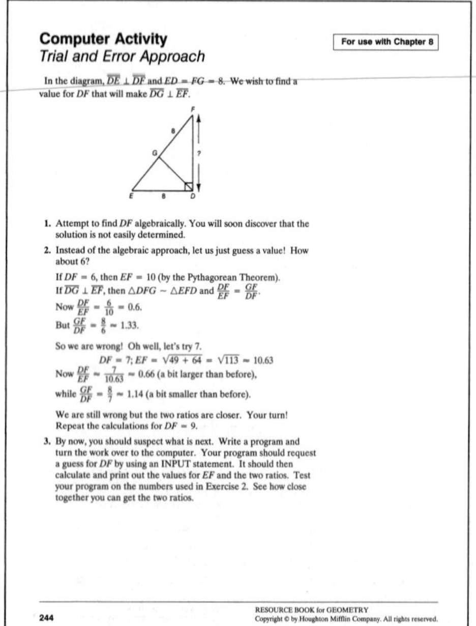

Computer Activity
Trial and Error Approach

For use with Chapter 8

In the diagram, $\overline{DE} \perp \overline{DF}$ and $ED = FG = 8$. We wish to find a value for DF that will make $\overline{DG} \perp \overline{EF}$.

1. Attempt to find DF algebraically. You will soon discover that the solution is not easily determined.
2. Instead of the algebraic approach, let us just guess a value! How about 6?

   If $DF = 6$, then $EF = 10$ (by the Pythagorean Theorem).
   If $\overline{DG} \perp \overline{EF}$, then $\triangle DFG \sim \triangle EFD$ and $\frac{DF}{EF} = \frac{GF}{DF}$.
   Now $\frac{DF}{EF} = \frac{6}{10} = 0.6$.
   But $\frac{GF}{DF} = \frac{8}{6} \approx 1.33$.

   So we are wrong! Oh well, let's try 7.
   $$DF = 7;\ EF = \sqrt{49 + 64} = \sqrt{113} \approx 10.63$$
   Now $\frac{DF}{EF} \approx \frac{7}{10.63} \approx 0.66$ (a bit larger than before),
   while $\frac{GF}{DF} = \frac{8}{7} \approx 1.14$ (a bit smaller than before).

   We are still wrong but the two ratios are closer. Your turn! Repeat the calculations for $DF = 9$.
3. By now, you should suspect what is next. Write a program and turn the work over to the computer. Your program should request a guess for DF by using an INPUT statement. It should then calculate and print out the values for EF and the two ratios. Test your program on the numbers used in Exercise 2. See how close together you can get the two ratios.

244 RESOURCE BOOK for GEOMETRY

Using Technology
Resource Book, p. 245

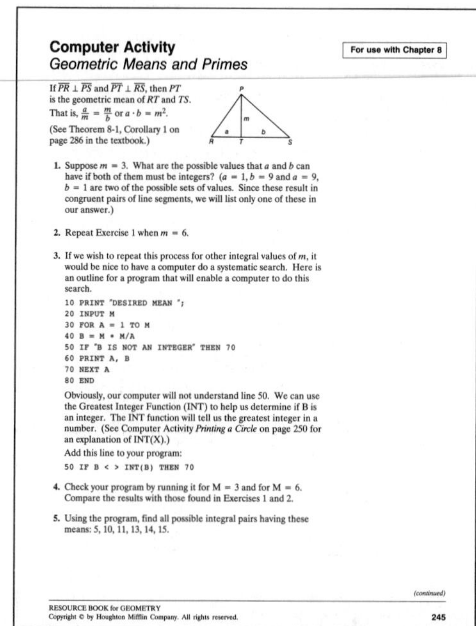

Computer Activity
Geometric Means and Primes

For use with Chapter 8

If $\overline{PR} \perp \overline{PS}$ and $\overline{PT} \perp \overline{RS}$, then PT is the geometric mean of RT and TS. That is, $\frac{a}{m} = \frac{m}{b}$ or $a \cdot b = m^2$.
(See Theorem 8-1, Corollary 1 on page 286 in the textbook.)

1. Suppose $m = 3$. What are the possible values that a and b can have if both of them must be integers? ($a = 1, b = 9$ and $a = 9$, $b = 1$ are two of the possible sets of values. Since these result in congruent pairs of line segments, we will list only one of these in our answer.)
2. Repeat Exercise 1 when $m = 6$.
3. If we wish to repeat this process for other integral values of m, it would be nice to have a computer do a systematic search. Here is an outline for a program that will enable a computer to do this search.

```
10 PRINT "DESIRED MEAN ";
20 INPUT M
30 FOR A = 1 TO M
40 B = M * M/A
50 IF "B IS NOT AN INTEGER" THEN 70
60 PRINT A, B
70 NEXT A
80 END
```

   Obviously, our computer will not understand line 50. We can use the Greatest Integer Function (INT) to help us determine if B is an integer. The INT function will tell us the greatest integer in a number. (See Computer Activity *Printing a Circle* on page 250 for an explanation of INT(X).)
   Add this line to your program:

```
50 IF B < > INT(B) THEN 70
```

4. Check your program by running it for M = 3 and for M = 6. Compare the results with those found in Exercises 1 and 2.
5. Using the program, find all possible integral pairs having these means: 5, 10, 11, 13, 14, 15.

(continued)

RESOURCE BOOK for GEOMETRY

245

Using Technology
Resource Book, p. 247

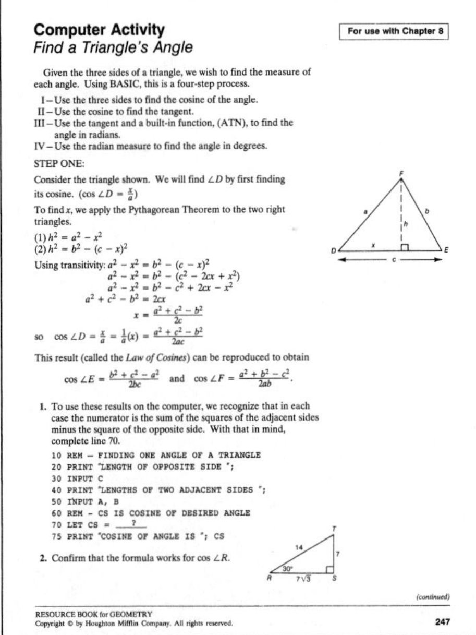

Computer Activity

Find a Triangle's Angle

For use with Chapter 8

Given the three sides of a triangle, we wish to find the measure of each angle. Using BASIC, this is a four-step process.

I – Use the three sides to find the cosine of the angle.
II – Use the cosine to find the tangent.
III – Use the tangent and a built-in function, (ATN), to find the angle in radians.
IV – Use the radian measure to find the angle in degrees.

STEP ONE:

Consider the triangle shown. We will find $\angle D$ by first finding its cosine. $(\cos \angle D = \frac{x}{a})$

To find x, we apply the Pythagorean Theorem to the two right triangles.

(1) $h^2 = a^2 - x^2$
(2) $h^2 = b^2 - (c - x)^2$

Using transitivity:

$$\begin{aligned} a^2 - x^2 &= b^2 - (c - x)^2 \\ a^2 - x^2 &= b^2 - (c^2 - 2cx + x^2) \\ a^2 - x^2 &= b^2 - c^2 + 2cx - x^2 \\ a^2 + c^2 - b^2 &= 2cx \\ x &= \frac{a^2 + c^2 - b^2}{2c} \end{aligned}$$

so $\cos \angle D = \frac{x}{a} = \frac{1}{a}(x) = \frac{a^2 + c^2 - b^2}{2ac}$

This result (called the *Law of Cosines*) can be reproduced to obtain

$$\cos \angle E = \frac{b^2 + c^2 - a^2}{2bc} \quad \text{and} \quad \cos \angle F = \frac{a^2 + b^2 - c^2}{2ab}.$$

1. To use these results on the computer, we recognize that in each case the numerator is the sum of the squares of the adjacent sides minus the square of the opposite side. With that in mind, complete line 70.

```
10 REM – FINDING ONE ANGLE OF A TRIANGLE
20 PRINT "LENGTH OF OPPOSITE SIDE ";
30 INPUT C
40 PRINT "LENGTHS OF TWO ADJACENT SIDES ";
50 INPUT A, B
60 REM - CS IS COSINE OF DESIRED ANGLE
70 LET CS = ___?___
75 PRINT "COSINE OF ANGLE IS "; CS
```

2. Confirm that the formula works for $\cos \angle R$.

(continued)

RESOURCE BOOK for GEOMETRY
Copyright © by Houghton Mifflin Company. All rights reserved. 247

Problem Solving
Study Guide, p. 106

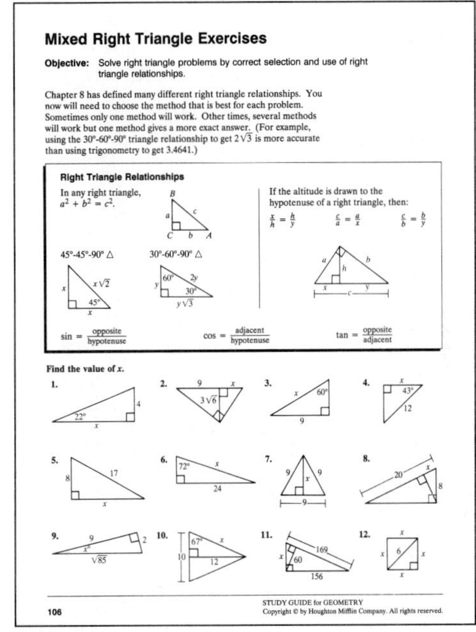

Mixed Right Triangle Exercises

Objective: Solve right triangle problems by correct selection and use of right triangle relationships.

Chapter 8 has defined many different right triangle relationships. You now will need to choose the method that is best for each problem. Sometimes only one method will work. Other times, several methods will work but one method gives a more exact answer. (For example, using the 30°-60°-90° triangle relationship to get $2\sqrt{3}$ is more accurate than using trigonometry to get 3.4641.)

Right Triangle Relationships

In any right triangle, $a^2 + b^2 = c^2$.

45°-45°-90° △ 30°-60°-90° △

If the altitude is drawn to the hypotenuse of a right triangle, then:

$\frac{x}{h} = \frac{h}{y}$ $\frac{c}{a} = \frac{a}{x}$ $\frac{c}{b} = \frac{b}{y}$

$\sin = \frac{\text{opposite}}{\text{hypotenuse}}$ $\cos = \frac{\text{adjacent}}{\text{hypotenuse}}$ $\tan = \frac{\text{opposite}}{\text{adjacent}}$

Find the value of x.

1. 2. 3. 4. 5. 6. 7. 8. 9. 10. 11. 12.

106 STUDY GUIDE for GEOMETRY
Copyright © by Houghton Mifflin Company. All rights reserved.

Application
Study Guide, p. 103

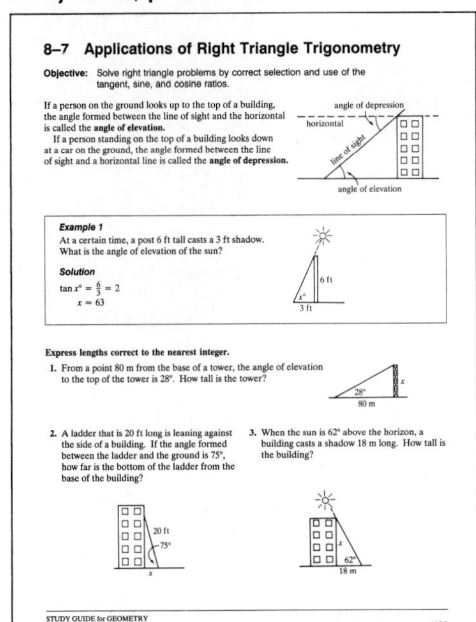

8–7 Applications of Right Triangle Trigonometry

Objective: Solve right triangle problems by correct selection and use of the tangent, sine, and cosine ratios.

If a person on the ground looks up to the top of a building, the angle formed between the line of sight and the horizontal is called the **angle of elevation.**

If a person standing on the top of a building looks down at a car on the ground, the angle formed between the line of sight and a horizontal line is called the **angle of depression.**

Example 1

At a certain time, a post 6 ft tall casts a 3 ft shadow. What is the angle of elevation of the sun?

Solution

$\tan x° = \frac{6}{3} = 2$
$x \approx 63$

Express lengths correct to the nearest integer.

1. From a point 80 m from the base of a tower, the angle of elevation to the top of the tower is 28°. How tall is the tower?

2. A ladder that is 20 ft long is leaning against the side of a building. If the angle formed between the ladder and the ground is 75°, how far is the bottom of the ladder from the base of the building?

3. When the sun is 62° above the horizon, a building casts a shadow 18 m long. How tall is the building?

STUDY GUIDE for GEOMETRY
Copyright © by Houghton Mifflin Company. All rights reserved. 103

Application
Study Guide, p. 104

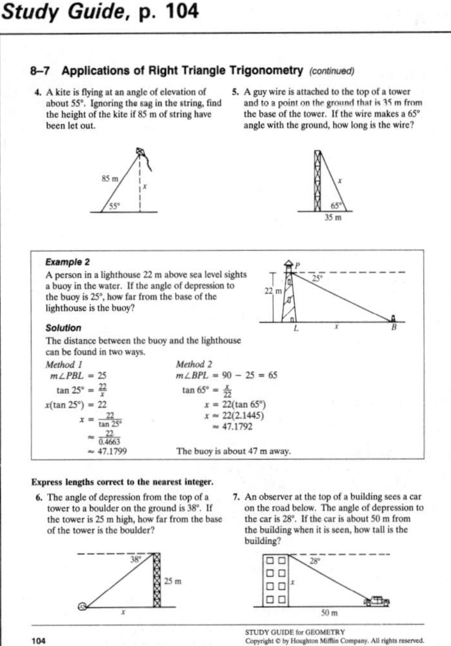

8–7 Applications of Right Triangle Trigonometry *(continued)*

4. A kite is flying at an angle of elevation of about 55°. Ignoring the sag in the string, find the height of the kite if 85 m of string have been let out.

5. A guy wire is attached to the top of a tower and to a point on the ground that is 35 m from the base of the tower. If the wire makes a 65° angle with the ground, how long is the wire?

Example 2

A person in a lighthouse 22 m above sea level sights a buoy in the water. If the angle of depression to the buoy is 25°, how far from the base of the lighthouse is the buoy?

Solution

The distance between the buoy and the lighthouse can be found in two ways.

Method 1

$m\angle PBL = 25$
$\tan 25° = \frac{22}{x}$
$x(\tan 25°) = 22$
$x = \frac{22}{\tan 25°}$
$\approx \frac{22}{0.4663}$
≈ 47.1799

Method 2

$m\angle BPL = 90 - 25 = 65$
$\tan 65° = \frac{x}{22}$
$x = 22(\tan 65°)$
$x \approx 22(2.1445)$
≈ 47.1792

The buoy is about 47 m away.

Express lengths correct to the nearest integer.

6. The angle of depression from the top of a tower to a boulder on the ground is 38°. If the tower is 25 m high, how far from the base of the tower is the boulder?

7. An observer at the top of a building sees a car on the road below. The angle of depression to the car is 28°. If the car is about 50 m from the building when it is seen, how tall is the building?

104 STUDY GUIDE for GEOMETRY
Copyright © by Houghton Mifflin Company. All rights reserved.

Teaching References

Lesson Commentary, pp. T106–T111
Assignment Guide, pp. T45–T47
Software Guide, p. T73
Alternate Test, p. T19

Supplementary Materials

Practice Masters 43–49
Tests 31–34
Resource Book
- Tests, pp. 50–54
- Practice, pp. 140–143
- Preparing for College Entrance Exams, p. 197
- Enrichment Activity, pp. 218–219
- Computer Activities, pp. 244–249

Study Guide, pp. 91–106
Overhead Visuals F, N, 16, 17
Computer Activities
- 15 Similar Right Triangles and Geometric Means
- 16 Pythagorean Theorem
- 17 Using Factorials to Approximate Sine
- 18 Solving Right Triangles

Handbook for Integrating Coordinate and Transformational Geometry

Right Triangles, pp. 665–667

Cultural Note

The triangular shaped sail was developed in the shipbuilding towns on the Mediterranean. The best quality sails, made of cotton or linen canvas, came from Marseilles and Genoa.

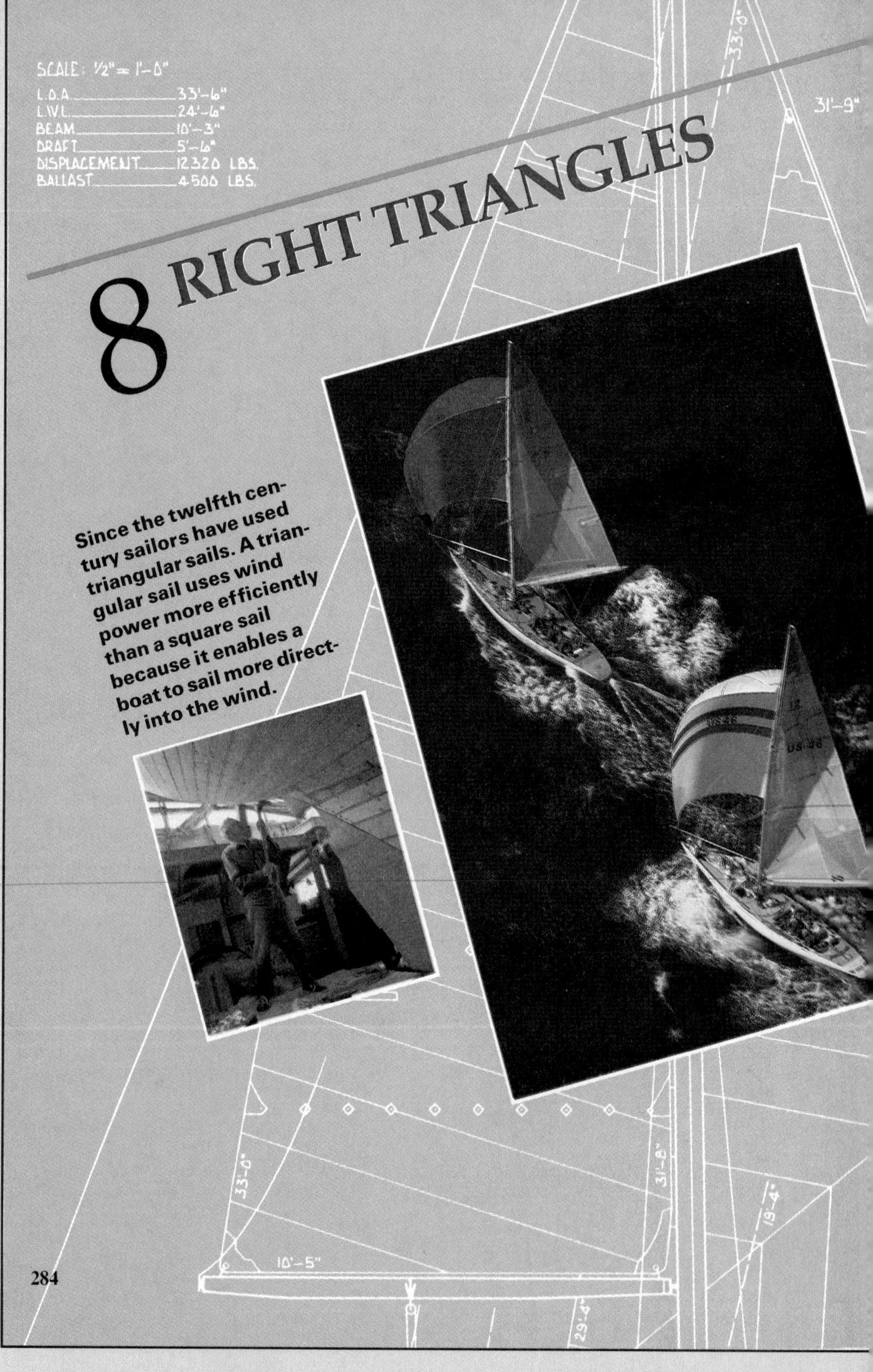

8 RIGHT TRIANGLES

Since the twelfth century sailors have used triangular sails. A triangular sail uses wind power more efficiently than a square sail because it enables a boat to sail more directly into the wind.

Right Triangles

Objectives

1. Determine the geometric mean between two numbers.
2. State and apply the relationships that exist when the altitude is drawn to the hypotenuse of a right triangle.
3. State and apply the Pythagorean Theorem.
4. State and apply the converse of the Pythagorean Theorem and related theorems about obtuse and acute triangles.
5. Determine the lengths of two sides of a 45°-45°-90° or a 30°-60°-90° triangle when the length of the third side is known.

8-1 *Similarity in Right Triangles*

Recall that in the proportion $\frac{a}{x} = \frac{y}{b}$, the terms shown in red are called the *means*. If a, b, and x are positive numbers and $\frac{a}{x} = \frac{x}{b}$, then x is called the **geometric mean** between a and b. If you solve this proportion for x, you will find that $x = \sqrt{ab}$, a positive number. (The other solution, $x = -\sqrt{ab}$, is discarded because x is defined to be positive.)

Example 1 Find the geometric mean between 5 and 11.

Solution 1 Solve the proportion $\frac{5}{x} = \frac{x}{11}$: $x^2 = 5 \cdot 11$; $x = \sqrt{55}$.

Solution 2 Use the equation $x = \sqrt{ab} = \sqrt{5 \cdot 11} = \sqrt{55}$.

Theorem 8-1

If the altitude is drawn to the hypotenuse of a right triangle, then the two triangles formed are similar to the original triangle and to each other.

Given: $\triangle ABC$ with rt. $\angle ACB$;
altitude $\overline{CN}$

Prove: $\triangle ACB \sim \triangle ANC \sim \triangle CNB$

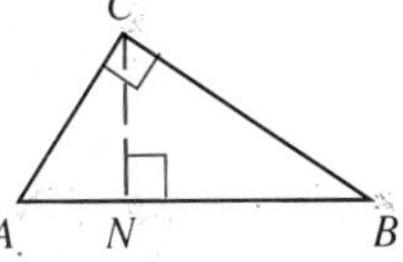

Plan for Proof: Begin by redrawing the three triangles you want to prove similar. Mark off congruent angles and apply the AA Similarity Postulate.

Teaching Suggestions,
pp. T106–T107

Objectives
Presenting the Lesson
Using Technology
Making Connections
Enrichment

Communication Skills,
p. T107

Supplementary Materials

Study Guide, pp. 91–92
Computer Activity 15

Lesson Focus

Right triangles have many interesting properties. This lesson begins the study of the properties of right triangles. Algebraic skills with radicals are reviewed and are used throughout the chapter.

Suggested Assignments

Minimum
Day 1: 288/1–21
Day 2: 288–289/22–33

Average
288–289/1–29 odd, 22–36 even, 40, 41

Maximum
288–289/3, 8, 11, 15, 16, 19, 22, 25, 27, 29, 31, 33, 37–43 odd

You may wish to introduce Construction 14 on page 397 after covering this lesson.

Using a Computer

Students can discover Theorem 8-1 with a construction program. See the experiment on page T106.

The proof of Theorem 8-1 is left as Exercise 40. The altitude to the hypotenuse divides the hypotenuse into two segments. Corollaries 1 and 2 of Theorem 8-1 deal with geometric means and the lengths of these segments.

For simplicity in stating these corollaries, the words *segment*, *side*, *leg*, and *hypotenuse* are used to refer to the *length* of a segment rather than the segment itself. We will use this convention throughout the book when the context makes this meaning clear.

Corollary 1

When the altitude is drawn to the hypotenuse of a right triangle, the length of the altitude is the geometric mean between the segments of the hypotenuse.

Given: $\triangle ABC$ with rt. $\angle ACB$; altitude $\overline{CN}$

Prove: $\frac{AN}{CN} = \frac{CN}{BN}$

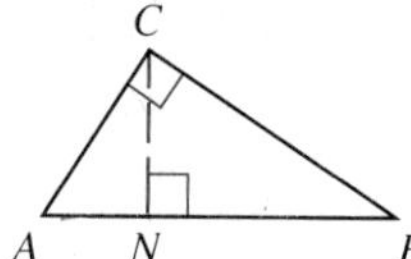

Proof:

By Theorem 8-1, $\triangle ANC \sim \triangle CNB$. Because corresponding sides of similar triangles are in proportion, $\frac{AN}{CN} = \frac{CN}{BN}$.

Corollary 2

When the altitude is drawn to the hypotenuse of a right triangle, each leg is the geometric mean between the hypotenuse and the segment of the hypotenuse that is adjacent to that leg.

Given: $\triangle ABC$ with rt. $\angle ACB$; altitude $\overline{CN}$

Prove: (1) $\frac{AB}{AC} = \frac{AC}{AN}$ and (2) $\frac{AB}{BC} = \frac{BC}{BN}$

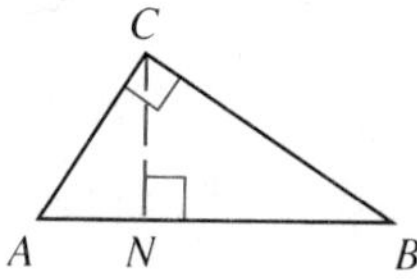

Proof of (1):

By Theorem 8-1, $\triangle ACB \sim \triangle ANC$. Because corresponding sides of similar triangles are in proportion, $\frac{AB}{AC} = \frac{AC}{AN}$. The proof of (2) is very similar.

Example 2 Use the diagram to find the values of h, a, and b.

Solution First determine what parts of the "big" triangle are labeled h, a, and b:

h is the altitude to the hypotenuse,
a is a leg, and b is a leg.

By Corollary 1, $\frac{3}{h} = \frac{h}{7}$ and $h = \sqrt{21}$.

By Corollary 2, $\frac{10}{a} = \frac{a}{3}$ and $a = \sqrt{30}$.

By Corollary 2, $\frac{10}{b} = \frac{b}{7}$ and $b = \sqrt{70}$.

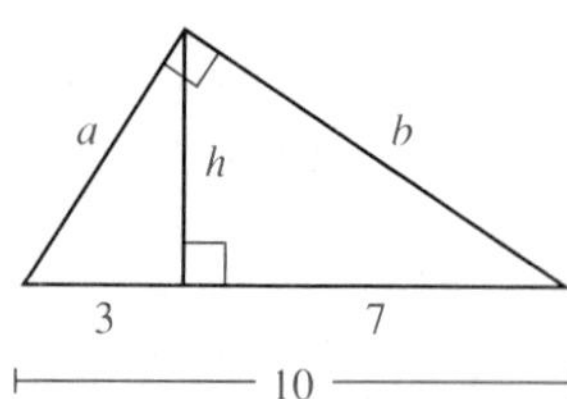

Chalkboard Examples

1. If $JR = 16$ and $EJ = 9$, find HJ, RE, RH, and HE.
12, 25, 20, 15

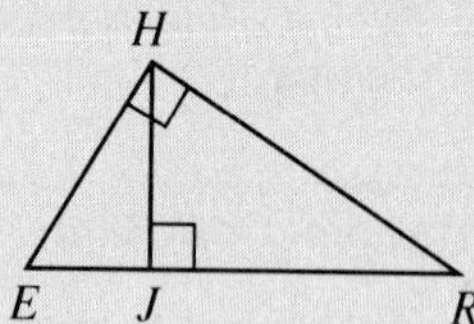

2. If $JR = 4$ and $JH = 2$, find EJ, RE, RH, and HE.
1, 5, $2\sqrt{5}$, $\sqrt{5}$

Teaching Note

Instead of having students memorize Corollaries 1 and 2 of Theorem 8-1, you may prefer to have them use the principles of similarity. To illustrate how this can be done, consider Example 2. To find h directly from Theorem 8-1 and without explicit use of the corollaries, students may reason that the two small triangles are similar, so that the ratio of the short leg to the long leg is constant.

$$\frac{\text{short leg}}{\text{long leg}} = \frac{3}{h} = \frac{h}{7}$$

Likewise, to find a, observe that the short leg to hypotenuse ratio is constant in the similar triangles.

$$\frac{\text{short leg}}{\text{hypotenuse}} = \frac{3}{a} = \frac{a}{10}$$

Of course, these properties are exactly what the corollaries give, but many teachers have found that when students rely on the theorem, instead of trying to remember specific corollaries, they usually retain the concepts longer.

Working with geometric means may involve working with radicals. Radicals should always be written in **simplest form.** This means writing them so that

1. No perfect square factor other than 1 is under the radical sign.
2. No fraction is under the radical sign.
3. No fraction has a radical in its denominator.

Example 3 Simplify: **a.** $5\sqrt{18}$ **b.** $\sqrt{\frac{3}{2}}$ **c.** $\frac{15}{\sqrt{5}}$

Solution **a.** Since $18 = 9 \cdot 2$, there is a perfect square factor, 9, under the radical sign.

$$5\sqrt{18} = 5 \cdot \sqrt{9 \cdot 2} = 5 \cdot \sqrt{9} \cdot \sqrt{2} = 5 \cdot 3 \cdot \sqrt{2} = 15\sqrt{2}$$

b. There is a fraction, $\frac{3}{2}$, under the radical sign.

$$\sqrt{\frac{3}{2}} = \sqrt{\frac{3}{2} \cdot \frac{2}{2}} = \sqrt{\frac{6}{4}} = \frac{\sqrt{6}}{\sqrt{4}} = \frac{\sqrt{6}}{2}$$

c. There is a radical in the denominator of the fraction.

$$\frac{15}{\sqrt{5}} = \frac{15}{\sqrt{5}} \cdot \frac{\sqrt{5}}{\sqrt{5}} = \frac{15\sqrt{5}}{5} = 3\sqrt{5}$$

Example 4 Find the values of w, x, y, and z.

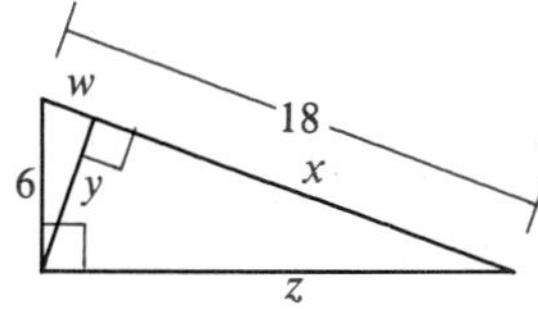

Solution

$\frac{18}{6} = \frac{6}{w}$ (Cor. 2)
$18w = 36$
$w = 2$

Then $x = 18 - 2 = 16$.

$\frac{16}{y} = \frac{y}{2}$ (Cor. 1)
$y^2 = 16 \cdot 2$
$y = \sqrt{16 \cdot 2}$
$y = \sqrt{16} \cdot \sqrt{2}$
$y = 4\sqrt{2}$

$\frac{18}{z} = \frac{z}{16}$ (Cor. 2)
$z^2 = 16 \cdot 18$
$z = \sqrt{16 \cdot 18}$
$z = \sqrt{16 \cdot 9 \cdot 2}$
$z = 4 \cdot 3 \cdot \sqrt{2} = 12\sqrt{2}$

Classroom Exercises

Use the diagram to complete each statement.

1. If $m\angle R = 30$, then $m\angle RSU =$ __?__, **60**
   $m\angle TSU =$ __?__, and $m\angle T =$ __?__. **30, 60**
2. If $m\angle R = k$, then $m\angle RSU =$ __?__, ***90 − k***
   $m\angle TSU =$ __?__, and $m\angle T =$ __?__. ***k, 90 − k***
3. $\triangle RST \sim \triangle$ __?__ $\sim \triangle$ __?__ ***RUS, SUT***
4. $\triangle RSU \sim \triangle$ __?__ $\sim \triangle$ __?__ ***RTS, STU***

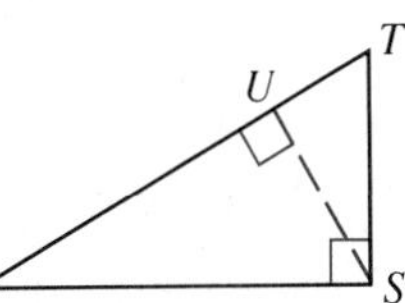

Exs. 1–4

Teaching Note

A thorough review of simplifying radicals will be necessary for most students. The examples given should be worked in class before any exercises are assigned.

Chalkboard Examples

Simplify each expression.

1. $\sqrt{75}$ $5\sqrt{3}$
2. $\sqrt{\frac{2}{5}}$ $\frac{\sqrt{10}}{5}$
3. $2\sqrt{48}$ $8\sqrt{3}$
4. $\sqrt{16} \cdot \sqrt{4}$ 8

Assessment

Having students demonstrate their work at the chalkboard for Classroom Exs. 5–14 and Written Exs. 1–15 will provide a good indication of their skills in simplifying radicals.

Guided Practice

Simplify.

1. $3\sqrt{50}$ $15\sqrt{2}$
2. $\sqrt{7} \cdot \sqrt{14}$ $7\sqrt{2}$
3. $\frac{12}{\sqrt{3}}$ $4\sqrt{3}$
4. $\frac{8}{2\sqrt{2}}$ $2\sqrt{2}$
5. $\sqrt{45} \cdot \sqrt{5}$ 15
6. $\sqrt{\frac{3}{4}}$ $\frac{\sqrt{3}}{2}$

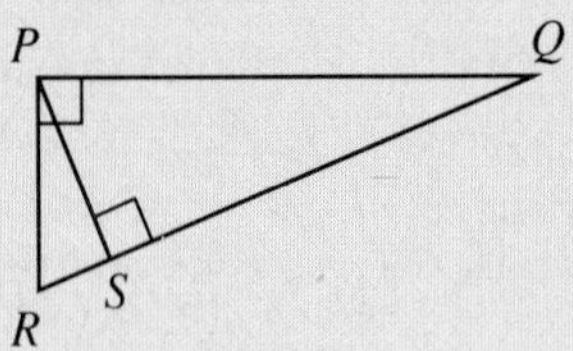

7. If $RS = 2$ and $SQ = 8$, find PS. 4
8. If $RP = 10$ and $RS = 5$, find SQ. 15
9. If $RS = 4$ and $PS = 6$, find SQ. 9

Simplify.

5. $\sqrt{50}$ **$5\sqrt{2}$**
6. $3\sqrt{8}$ **$6\sqrt{2}$**
7. $\sqrt{225}$ **15**
8. $7\sqrt{63}$ **$21\sqrt{7}$**
9. $\sqrt{288}$ **$12\sqrt{2}$**
10. $\sqrt{\frac{3}{4}}$ **$\frac{\sqrt{3}}{2}$**
11. $\sqrt{\frac{1}{5}}$ **$\frac{\sqrt{5}}{5}$**
12. $\frac{\sqrt{5}}{\sqrt{2}}$ **$\frac{\sqrt{10}}{2}$**
13. $\sqrt{\frac{5}{2}}$ **$\frac{\sqrt{10}}{2}$**
14. $\frac{3}{4}\sqrt{\frac{28}{3}}$ **$\frac{\sqrt{21}}{2}$**

15. Give the geometric mean between:
    a. 2 and 3 **$\sqrt{6}$** b. 2 and 6 **$2\sqrt{3}$** c. 4 and 25 **10**

Study the diagram. Then complete each statement.

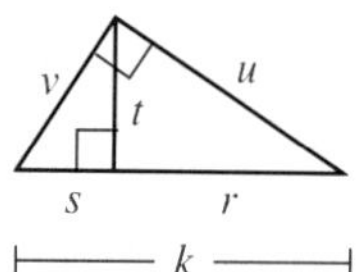

16. a. t is the geometric mean between _?_ and _?_. ***s, r***
    b. u is the geometric mean between _?_ and _?_. ***k, r***
    c. v is the geometric mean between _?_ and _?_. ***k, s***

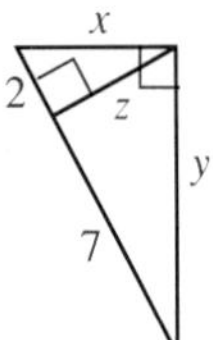

17. a. z is the geometric mean between _?_ and _?_. **2, 7**
    Thus z = _?_. **$\sqrt{14}$**
    b. x is the geometric mean between _?_ and _?_. **9, 2**
    Thus x = _?_. **$3\sqrt{2}$**
    c. y is the geometric mean between _?_ and _?_. **9, 7**
    Thus y = _?_. **$3\sqrt{7}$**

Written Exercises

Simplify.

A

1. $\sqrt{12}$ **$2\sqrt{3}$**
2. $\sqrt{72}$ **$6\sqrt{2}$**
3. $\sqrt{45}$ **$3\sqrt{5}$**
4. $\sqrt{75}$ **$5\sqrt{3}$**
5. $\sqrt{800}$ **$20\sqrt{2}$**
6. $\sqrt{54}$ **$3\sqrt{6}$**
7. $9\sqrt{40}$ **$18\sqrt{10}$**
8. $4\sqrt{28}$ **$8\sqrt{7}$**
9. $\sqrt{30} \cdot \sqrt{6}$ **$6\sqrt{5}$**
10. $\sqrt{5} \cdot \sqrt{35}$ **$5\sqrt{7}$**
11. $\sqrt{\frac{3}{7}}$ **$\frac{\sqrt{21}}{7}$**
12. $\sqrt{\frac{9}{5}}$ **$\frac{3\sqrt{5}}{5}$**
13. $\frac{18}{\sqrt{3}}$ **$6\sqrt{3}$**
14. $\frac{24}{3\sqrt{2}}$ **$4\sqrt{2}$**
15. $\frac{\sqrt{15}}{3\sqrt{45}}$ **$\frac{\sqrt{3}}{9}$**

Find the geometric mean between the two numbers.

16. 2 and 18 **6**
17. 3 and 27 **9**
18. 49 and 25 **35**
19. 1 and 1000 **$10\sqrt{10}$**
20. 16 and 24 **$8\sqrt{6}$**
21. 22 and 55 **$11\sqrt{10}$**

Exercises 22–30 refer to the figure at the right.

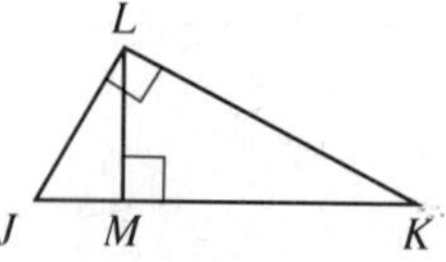

22. If $LM = 4$ and $MK = 8$, find JM. **2**
23. If $LM = 6$ and $JM = 4$, find MK. **9**
24. If $JM = 3$ and $MK = 6$, find LM. **$3\sqrt{2}$**
25. If $JM = 4$ and $JK = 9$, find LK. **$3\sqrt{5}$**
26. If $JM = 3$ and $MK = 9$, find LJ. **6**

B

27. If $JM = 3$ and $JL = 6$, find MK. **9**
28. If $JL = 9$ and $JM = 6$, find MK. **7.5**
29. If $LK = 3\sqrt{6}$ and $MK = 6$, find JM. **3**
30. If $LK = 7$ and $MK = 6$, find JM. **$2\frac{1}{6}$**

Find the values of *x*, *y*, and *z*.

31.

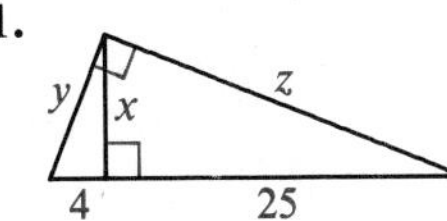

$x = 10$, $y = 2\sqrt{29}$, $z = 5\sqrt{29}$

32.

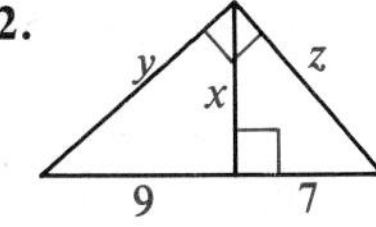

$x = 3\sqrt{7}$, $y = 12$, $z = 4\sqrt{7}$

33.

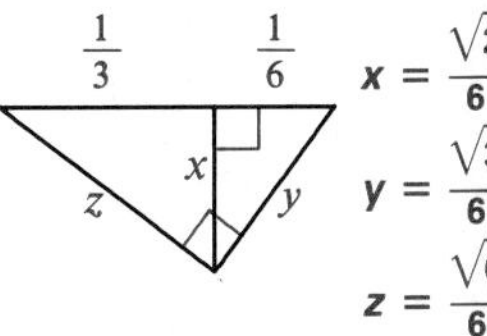

$x = \frac{\sqrt{2}}{6}$

$y = \frac{\sqrt{3}}{6}$

$z = \frac{\sqrt{6}}{6}$

34.

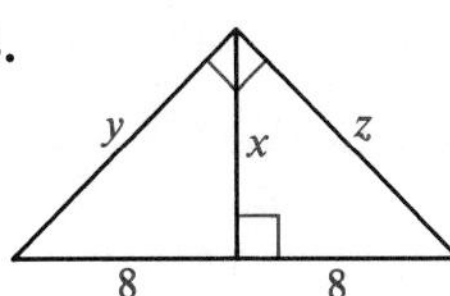

$x = 8$, $y = 8\sqrt{2}$, $z = 8\sqrt{2}$

35.

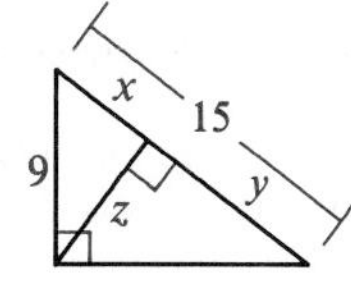

$x = 5.4$, $y = 9.6$, $z = 7.2$

36.

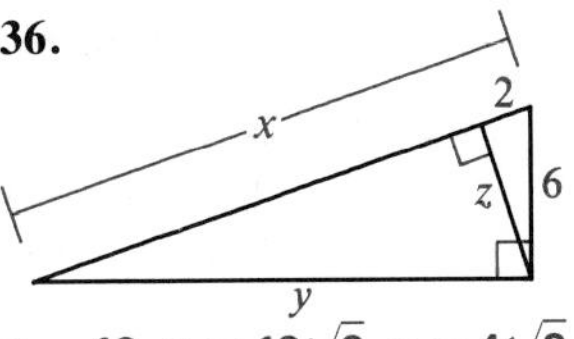

$x = 18$, $y = 12\sqrt{2}$, $z = 4\sqrt{2}$

37.

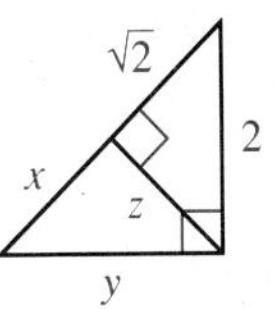

$x = \sqrt{2}$, $y = 2$, $z = \sqrt{2}$

38.

x, y, x + 7, 12, z

$x = 9$, $y = 15$, $z = 20$

39.

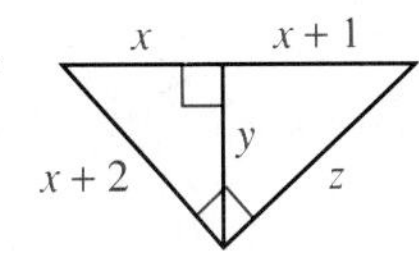

$x = 4$, $y = 2\sqrt{5}$, $z = 3\sqrt{5}$

40. Prove Theorem 8-1.

41. a. Refer to the figure at the right, and use Corollary 2 to complete:
$a^2 = \underline{\ ?\ }$ **cd** and $b^2 = \underline{\ ?\ }$ **ce**

b. Add the equations in part (a), factor the sum on the right, and show that $a^2 + b^2 = c^2$.

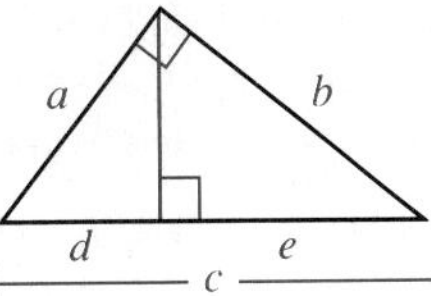

C 42. Prove: In a right triangle, the product of the hypotenuse and the length of the altitude drawn to the hypotenuse equals the product of the two legs.

43. Given: *PQRS* is a rectangle;
PS is the geometric mean between *ST* and *TR*.
Prove: $\angle PTQ$ is a right angle.

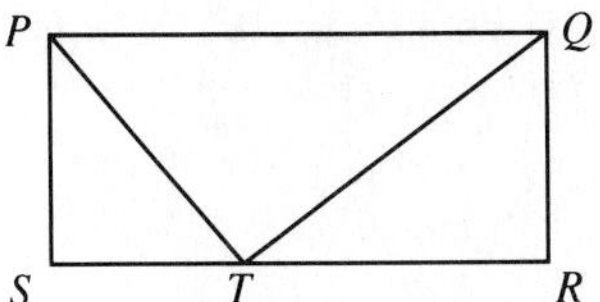

44. Given: *PQRS* is a rectangle;
$\angle A$ is a right angle.
Prove: $BS \cdot RC = PS \cdot QR = (PS)^2$

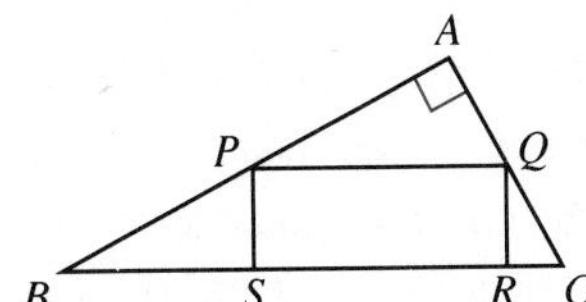

Exercise Note

Be sure to assign Ex. 41 in anticipation of proving the Pythagorean Theorem in the next lesson.

Additional Answers Written Exercises

41.b. $a^2 + b^2 = cd + ce$
$= c(d + e)$
$= c(c)$
$= c^2$

Making Connections

Ex. 45 makes a nice connection between algebra and geometry. Although it is labeled as a C exercise, it is not inaccessible.

Teaching Suggestions, p. T107

Objective
Presenting the Lesson
Making Connections
Enrichment

Cooperative Learning, p. T107

Exploring Activity, p. 283c

Supplementary Materials

Practice Master 43
Test 31
Resource Book, pp. 50, 140
Study Guide, pp. 93–94
Overhead Visuals F, N
Computer Activity 16

Lesson Focus

This lesson states and proves the Pythagorean Theorem, which is used extensively throughout mathematics to solve problems.

Suggested Assignments

Minimum
Day 1: 292/1–8, 9–15 odd
Day 2: 292/10–16 even, 17–22, 24
294/Mixed Review 1–7

45. The *arithmetic mean* between two numbers r and s is defined to be $\frac{r+s}{2}$.

a. $\overline{CM}$ is the median and $\overline{CH}$ is the altitude to the hypotenuse of right $\triangle ABC$. Show that CM is the arithmetic mean between AH and BH, and that CH is the geometric mean between AH and BH. Then use the diagram to show that the arithmetic mean is greater than the geometric mean.

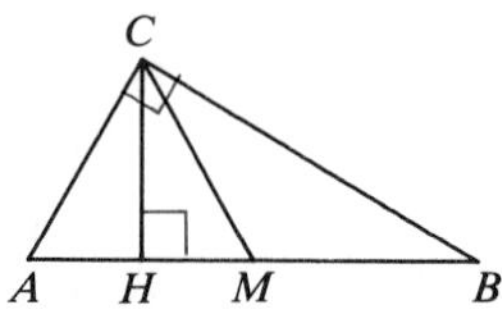

b. Show algebraically that the arithmetic mean between two different numbers r and s is greater than the geometric mean. (*Hint*: The geometric mean is $\sqrt{rs}$. Work backward from $\frac{r+s}{2} > \sqrt{rs}$ to $(r-s)^2 > 0$ and then reverse the steps.)

8-2 *The Pythagorean Theorem*

One of the best known and most useful theorems in all of mathematics is the *Pythagorean Theorem*. It is believed that Pythagoras, a Greek mathematician and philosopher, proved this theorem about twenty-five hundred years ago. Many different proofs exist, including one by President Garfield (Exercise 32, page 438) and the proof suggested by the Challenge on page 294.

Theorem 8-2 *Pythagorean Theorem*

In a right triangle, the square of the hypotenuse is equal to the sum of the squares of the legs.

Given: $\triangle ABC$; $\angle ACB$ is a rt. $\angle$.
Prove: $c^2 = a^2 + b^2$

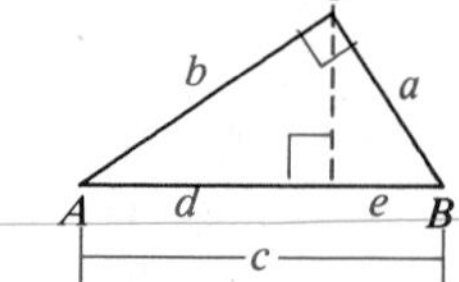

Proof:

Statements	Reasons
1. Draw a perpendicular from C to $\overline{AB}$.	1. Through a point outside a line, there is exactly one line __?__. **⊥ to the given line**
2. $\frac{c}{a} = \frac{a}{e}$; $\frac{c}{b} = \frac{b}{d}$	2. When the altitude is drawn to the hypotenuse of a rt. $\triangle$, each leg is the geometric mean between __?__. **See below.**
3. $ce = a^2$; $cd = b^2$	3. A property of proportions
4. $ce + cd = a^2 + b^2$	4. Addition Property of =
5. $c(e + d) = a^2 + b^2$	5. Distributive Property
6. $c^2 = a^2 + b^2$	6. Substitution Property

the hyp. and the seg. of the hyp. that is adjacent to that leg

Example Find the value of x. Remember that the length of a segment must be a positive number.

a.

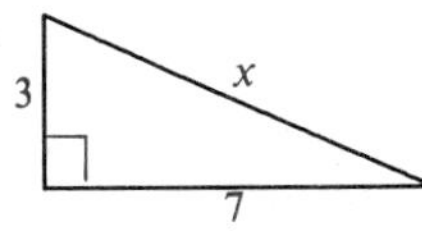

b.

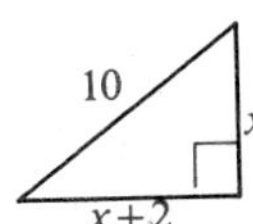

Solution

a.
$$x^2 = 7^2 + 3^2$$
$$x^2 = 49 + 9$$
$$x^2 = 58$$
$$x = \sqrt{58}$$

b.
$$x^2 + (x + 2)^2 = 10^2$$
$$x^2 + x^2 + 4x + 4 = 100$$
$$2x^2 + 4x - 96 = 0$$
$$x^2 + 2x - 48 = 0$$
$$(x + 8)(x - 6) = 0$$
$$\cancel{x = -8};\ x = 6$$

Classroom Exercises

1. The early Greeks thought of the Pythagorean Theorem in this form: *The area of the square on the hypotenuse of a right triangle equals the sum of the areas of the squares on the legs.* Draw a diagram to illustrate that interpretation.

2. Which equations are correct for the right triangle shown?
   a. $r^2 = s^2 + t^2$ **b.** $s^2 = r^2 + t^2$ **(c.)** $s^2 + r^2 = t^2$
   (d.) $s^2 = t^2 - r^2$ **e.** $t = r + s$ **f.** $t^2 = (r + s)^2$

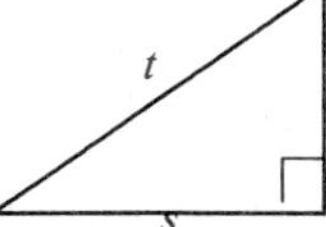

Complete each simplification.

3. $(\sqrt{3})^2 = \sqrt{3} \cdot \underline{\ ?\ } = \underline{\ ?\ }$ **$\sqrt{3}$**; **3**

4. $(3\sqrt{11})^2 = \underline{\ ?\ } \cdot \underline{\ ?\ } = 9 \cdot \underline{\ ?\ } = \underline{\ ?\ }$ **3^2**; **$(\sqrt{11})^2$**; **11**; **99**

Simplify each expression.

5. $(\sqrt{5})^2$ **5**
6. $(2\sqrt{7})^2$ **28**
7. $(7\sqrt{2})^2$ **98**
8. $(2n)^2$ **$4n^2$**
9. $\left(\frac{3}{\sqrt{5}}\right)^2$ **$\frac{9}{5}$**
10. $\left(\frac{\sqrt{2}}{2}\right)^2$ **$\frac{1}{2}$**
11. $\left(\frac{n}{\sqrt{3}}\right)^2$ **$\frac{n^2}{3}$**
12. $\left(\frac{2}{3}\sqrt{6}\right)^2$ **$\frac{8}{3}$**

State an equation you could use to find the value of x. Then find the value of x in simplest radical form.

13.

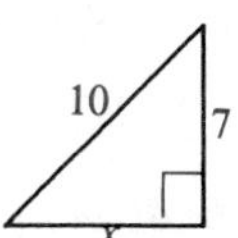

$x^2 = 10^2 - 7^2$
$x = \sqrt{51}$

14.

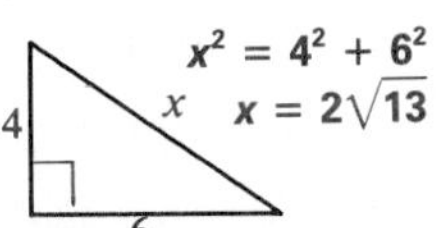

$x^2 = 4^2 + 6^2$
$x = 2\sqrt{13}$

15.

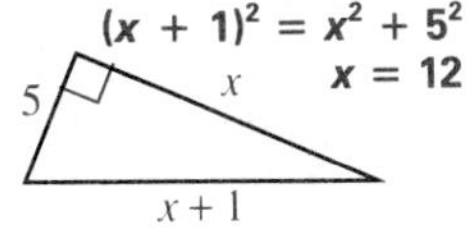

$(x + 1)^2 = x^2 + 5^2$
$x = 12$

16.

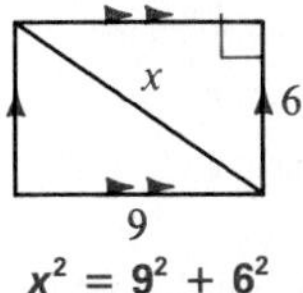

$x^2 = 9^2 + 6^2$
$x = 3\sqrt{13}$

17.

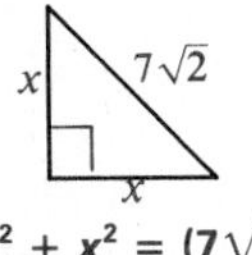

$x^2 + x^2 = (7\sqrt{2})^2$
$x = 7$

18.

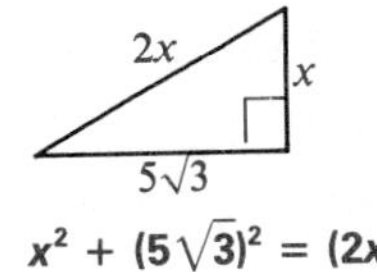

$x^2 + (5\sqrt{3})^2 = (2x)^2$
$x = 5$

Average
Day 1: 292/2–16 even, 17–20
S 289/42
Day 2: 292–293/21, 22, 24, 25, 28, 33–36
294/Mixed Review 1–7

Maximum
Day 1: 292–293/5, 8, 10, 16, 19, 21–24, 26, 31
Day 2: 293–294/27, 28, 33–38

Chalkboard Examples

Find the value of y.

1. $5\sqrt{5}$

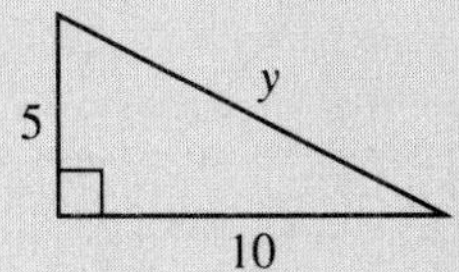

2. 13

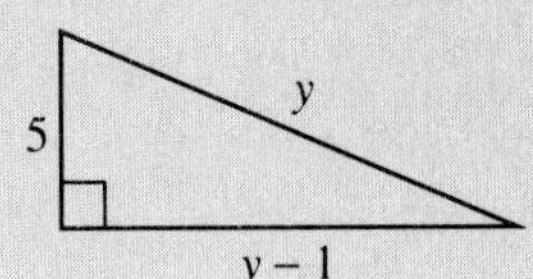

Guided Practice

Find the value of each variable.

1. $\sqrt{13}$

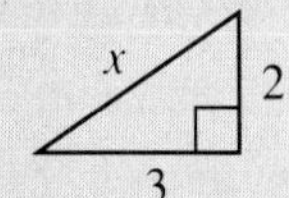

2. $2\sqrt{5}$

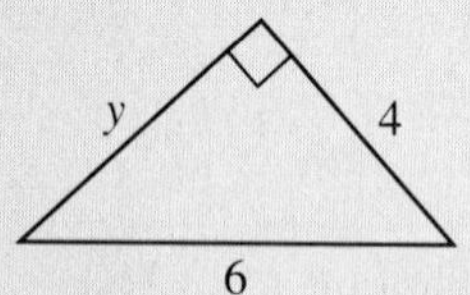

3. $2\sqrt{2}$

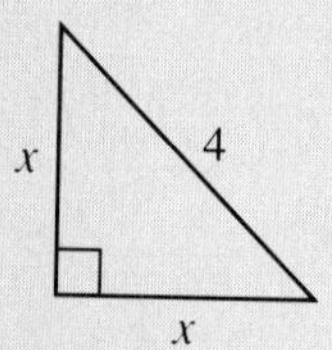

4. Find the length of a diagonal of a rectangle with length 8 and width 4

4. $4\sqrt{5}$

Written Exercises

Find the value of x.

A

1. 5

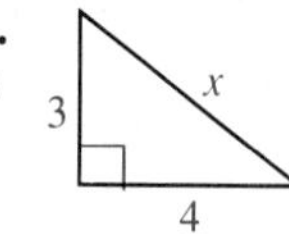

2. 13

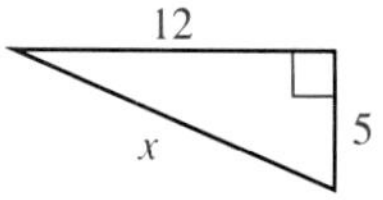

12
5
x

3. 8

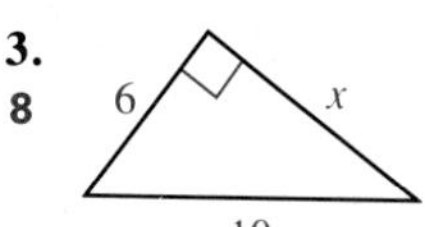

4. $2\sqrt{10}$

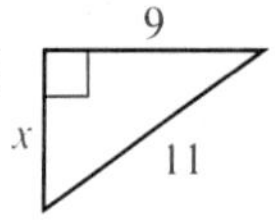

9
x
11

5. $10\sqrt{3}$

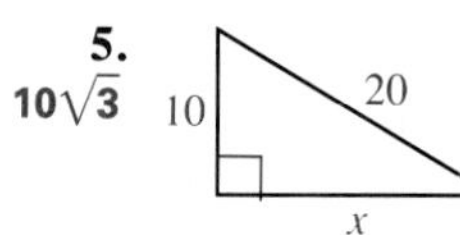

6. $4\sqrt{5}$

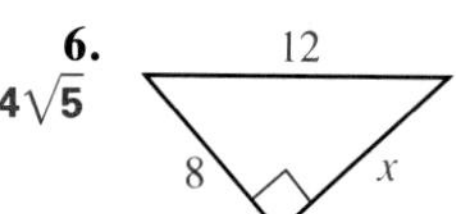

7. 8

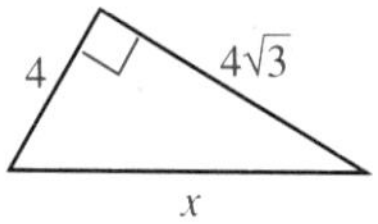

4
$4\sqrt{3}$
x

8. 6

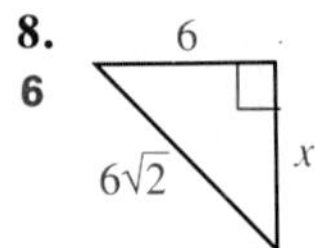

9. 25

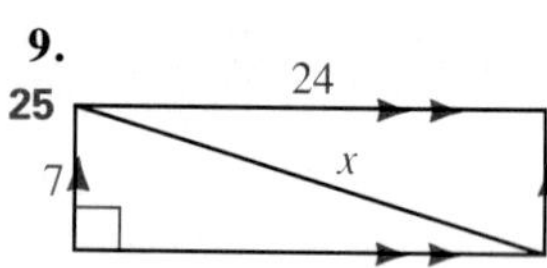

10. 9

12
15
x

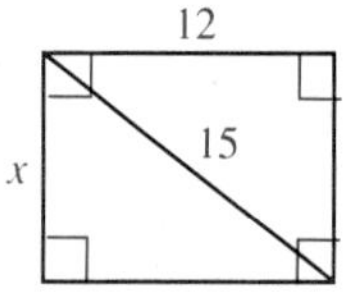

11. $8\sqrt{2}$

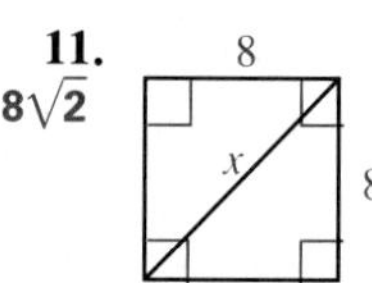

12. 6

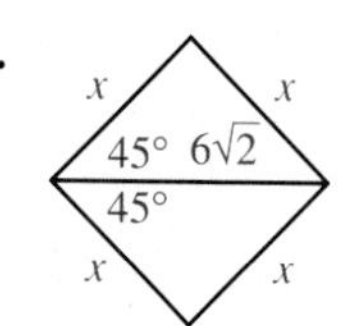

13. A rectangle has length 2.4 and width 1.8. Find the length of a diagonal. **3**

14. A rectangle has a diagonal of 2 and length of $\sqrt{3}$. Find its width. **1**

15. Find the length of a diagonal of a square with perimeter 16. **$4\sqrt{2}$**

16. Find the length of a side of a square with a diagonal of length 12. **$6\sqrt{2}$**

17. The diagonals of a rhombus have lengths 16 and 30. Find the perimeter of the rhombus. **68**

18. The perimeter of a rhombus is 40 cm, and one diagonal is 12 cm long. How long is the other diagonal? **16 cm**

Find the value of x.

B

19. 3

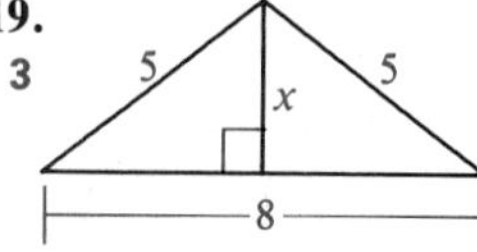

20. 8

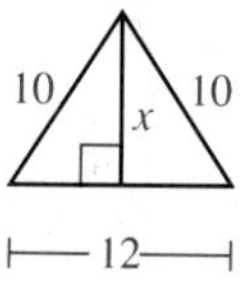

10
x
10
12

21. $3\sqrt{5}$

6
6
x
x

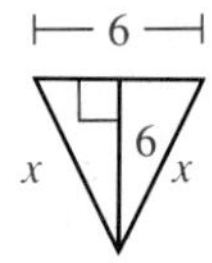

Find the value of *x*.

22. **$4\sqrt{7}$**

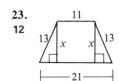

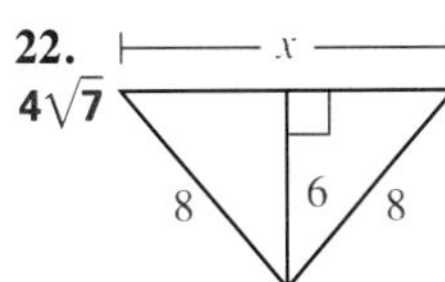

23. **12**

24. **28**

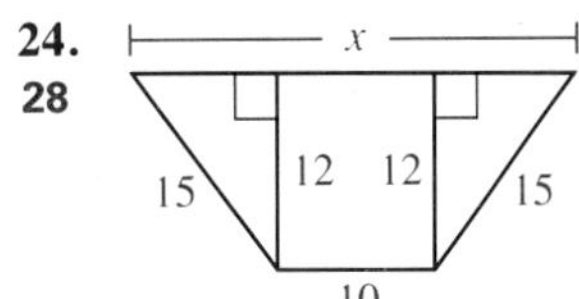

25. **10**

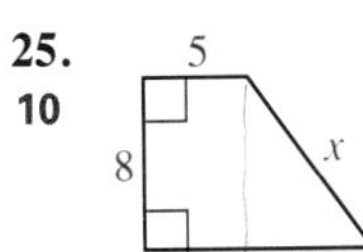

26. **$8\sqrt{2}$**

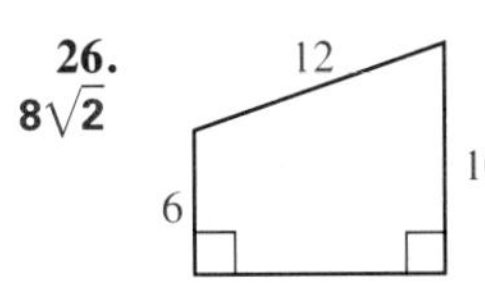

27. **17**

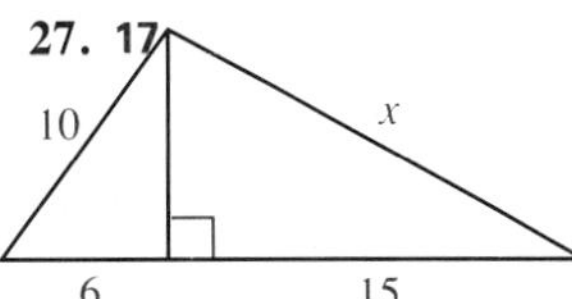

28. **$2\frac{1}{7}$**

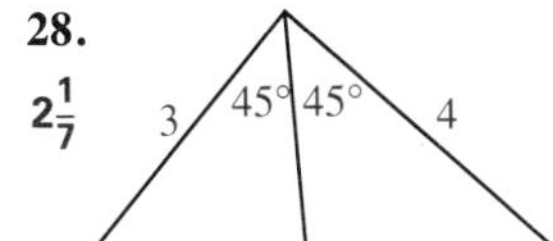

(*Hint*: Use the Angle-Bisector Theorem, p. 270.)

29. **20**

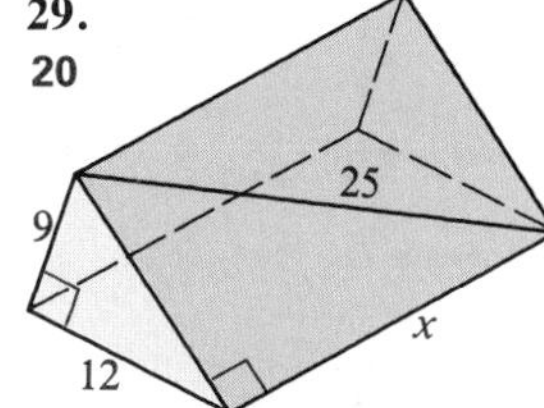

30. **$3\sqrt{29}$**

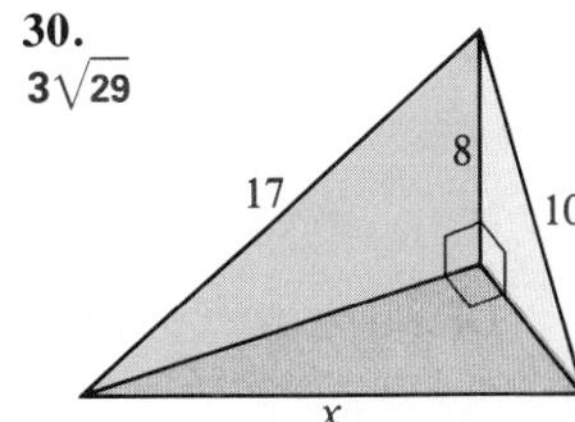

31. A right triangle has legs of 6 and 8. Find the lengths of:
a. the median to the hypotenuse **5** **b.** the altitude to the hypotenuse. **4.8**

32. A rectangle is 2 cm longer than it is wide. The diagonal of the rectangle is 10 cm long. Find the perimeter of the rectangle. **28 cm**

In Exercises 33–36 the dimensions of a rectangular box are given. Sketch the box and find the length of a diagonal of the box.

Example Dimensions 6, 4, 3

Solution

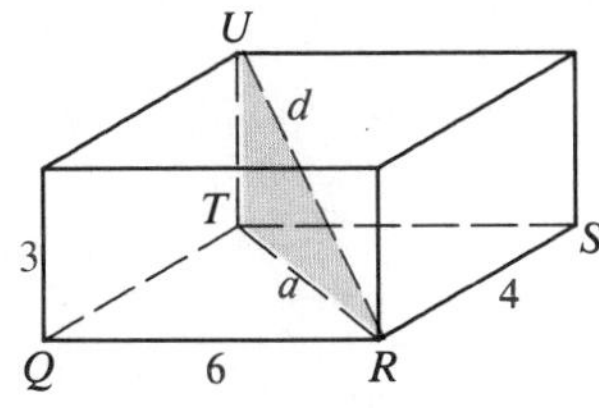

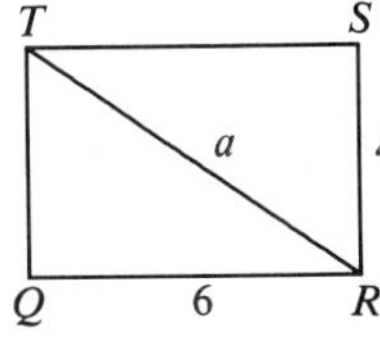

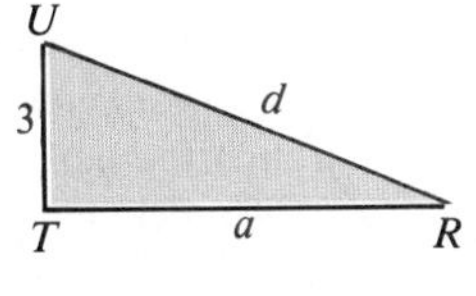

$a^2 = 6^2 + 4^2$
$a^2 = 36 + 16$
$a^2 = 52$

$d^2 = a^2 + 3^2$
$d^2 = 52 + 9$
$d^2 = 61$
$d = \sqrt{61}$

33. 12, 4, 3 **13** **34.** 5, 5, 2 **$3\sqrt{6}$** **35.** *e*, *e*, *e* **$e\sqrt{3}$** **36.** *l*, *w*, *h* **$\sqrt{l^2 + w^2 + h^2}$**

Cultural Note

Pythagoras was born around 572 B.C. on the island of Samos. Like many other scholars, he studied mathematics in Alexandria, Egypt.

Other ancient civilizations knew of the Pythagorean relationship. For example, a Chinese theorem stating the same principle was described in a book dating from around the 2nd century B.C. Recent translation of an ancient clay tablet shows that the Pythagorean relationship was known to the Babylonians 1000 years before the time of Pythagoras. There is also evidence that the 3, 4, 5 triangle relationship was known to the Egyptian builders of the pyramids.

Exercise Note

Ex. 35 leads to the formula for the length of a diagonal of a cube. ($d = \sqrt{3} \cdot e$, where e = edge of cube.) Ex. 36 leads to the formula for the length of a diagonal of a rectangular solid. ($d^2 = l^2 + w^2 + h^2$; $d = \sqrt{l^2 + w^2 + h^2}$)

Find the value of h.

C **37.** **12**

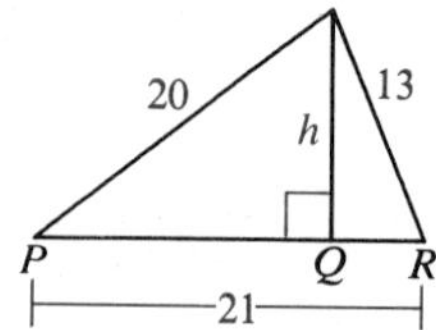

(*Hint*: Let $PQ = x$; $QR = 21 - x$.)

38. **24**

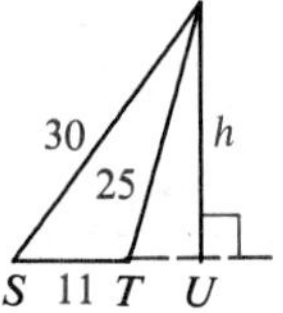

(*Hint*: Let $TU = x$; $SU = x + 11$.)

39. O is the *center* of square $ABCD$ (the point of intersection of the diagonals) and $\overline{VO}$ is perpendicular to the plane of the square. Find OE, the distance from O to the plane of $\triangle VBC$. **12**

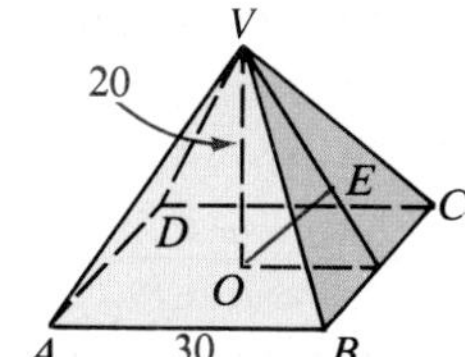

Mixed Review Exercises

Given: $\triangle ABC$. Complete.

1. If $m\angle A > m\angle B$, then $BC >$ __?__. ***AC***
2. If $AB > BC$, then $m\angle C$ __?__ $m\angle$ __?__. **>**, ***A***
3. $AB + BC$ __?__ AC **>**
4. If $\angle C$ is a right angle, then __?__ is the longest side. $\overline{AB}$
5. If $AB = AC$, then $\angle$ __?__ $\cong \angle$ __?__. ***B, C***
6. If $\angle A \cong \angle C$, then $BC =$ __?__. ***AB***
7. If $\angle C$ is a right angle and X is the midpoint of the hypotenuse, then $AX =$ __?__ $=$ __?__. ***BX, CX***

Using a Computer

Have students use a program to construct the figure in the Challenge. Their construction may give a hint for the proof.

Challenge

Start with a right triangle. Build a square on each side. Locate the center of the square drawn on the longer leg. Through the center, draw a parallel to the hypotenuse and a perpendicular to the hypotenuse.

Cut out the pieces numbered 1–5. Can you arrange the five pieces to cover exactly the square built on the hypotenuse? (This suggests another proof of the Pythagorean Theorem.) **Yes; answers may vary.**

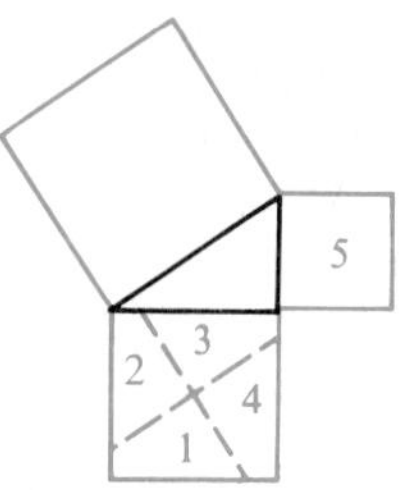

8-3 *The Converse of the Pythagorean Theorem*

We have seen that the converse of a theorem is not necessarily true. However, the converse of the Pythagorean Theorem *is* true. It is stated below as Theorem 8-3.

Theorem 8-3

If the square of one side of a triangle is equal to the sum of the squares of the other two sides, then the triangle is a right triangle.

Given: $\triangle ABC$ with $c^2 = a^2 + b^2$

Prove: $\triangle ABC$ is a right triangle.

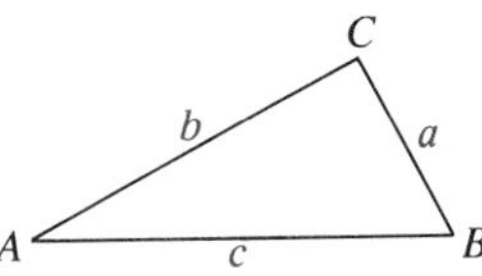

Key steps of proof:

1. Draw rt. $\triangle EFG$ with legs a and b.
2. $d^2 = a^2 + b^2$ (Pythagorean Theorem)
3. $c^2 = a^2 + b^2$ (Given)
4. $c = d$ (Substitution)
5. $\triangle ABC \cong \triangle EFG$ (SSS Postulate)
6. $\angle C$ is a rt. $\angle$. (Corr. parts of $\cong$ ⚠ are $\cong$.)
7. $\triangle ABC$ is a rt. $\triangle$. (Def. of a rt. $\triangle$)

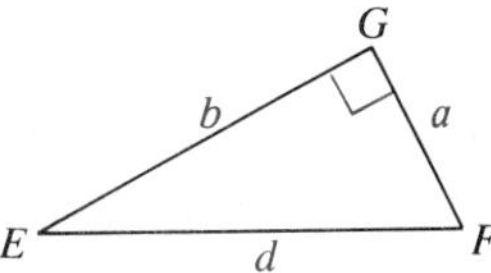

A triangle with sides 3 units, 4 units, and 5 units long is called a 3-4-5 triangle. The numbers 3, 4, and 5 satisfy the equation $a^2 + b^2 = c^2$, so we can apply Theorem 8-3 to conclude that a 3-4-5 triangle is a right triangle. The side lengths shown in the table all satisfy the equation $a^2 + b^2 = c^2$, so the triangles formed are right triangles.

Some Common Right Triangle Lengths

3, 4, 5	5, 12, 13	8, 15, 17	7, 24, 25
6, 8, 10	10, 24, 26		
9, 12, 15			
12, 16, 20			
15, 20, 25			

Theorem 8-3 is restated on the next page, along with Theorems 8-4 and 8-5. If you know the lengths of the sides of a triangle, you can use these theorems to determine whether the triangle is right, acute, or obtuse. In each theorem, *c is the length of the longest side* of $\triangle ABC$. Exercises 20 and 19 ask you to state Theorems 8-4 and 8-5 more formally and then prove them.

Teaching Suggestions,
pp. T107–T108

Objective
Presenting the Lesson
Applications
Making Connections
Reinforcement

Supplementary Materials

Study Guide, pp. 95–96

Lesson Focus

The purpose of this lesson is to state and prove the converse of the Pythagorean Theorem. The converse tells when a triangle is a right triangle.

Suggested Assignments

Minimum
Day 1: 297/1–9 odd
Day 2: 297/2–12 even, 13, 15

Average
Day 1: 297/1–7, 10, 12, 13
Day 2: 297–298/11, 14–20

Maximum
Day 1: 297/1–15 odd
S 294/39
Day 2: 297–298/12–18 even, 20–22

Teaching Note

When you discuss the table of common right triangle lengths, ask students what they notice about the triples in the first column. They should reach the conclusion that any triangle whose sides are in the ratio 3:4:5 is a right triangle. Students will find it useful to memorize the first row of lengths shown in red in the table.

Chalkboard Examples

The sides of a triangle have the lengths given. Is the triangle acute, right, or obtuse?

1. 20, 21, 29 right
2. 20, 21, 30 obtuse
3. 20, 21, 28 acute
4. 5, 6, 8 obtuse

Teaching Note

When discussing Exs. 1–6, you may need to review the conditions necessary to form a triangle (Theorem 6-4). From this, students can develop a test to determine when a triangle cannot be formed: longest side $\geq$ the sum of the two shorter sides.

Theorem 8-3

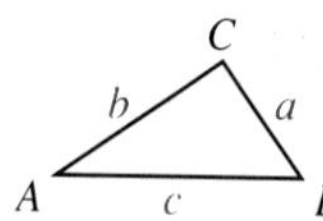

If $c^2 = a^2 + b^2$, then $m\angle C = 90$, and $\triangle ABC$ is right.

Theorem 8-4

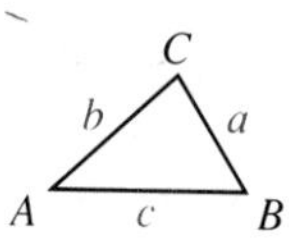

If $c^2 < a^2 + b^2$, then $m\angle C < 90$, and $\triangle ABC$ is acute.

Theorem 8-5

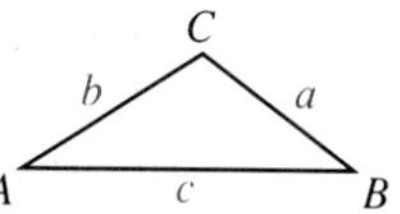

If $c^2 > a^2 + b^2$, then $m\angle C > 90$, and $\triangle ABC$ is obtuse.

Example A triangle has sides of the given lengths. Is it acute, right, or obtuse?
a. 9, 40, 41 **b.** 6, 7, 8 **c.** 7, 8, 11

Solution

a. $41^2 \overset{?}{=} 9^2 + 40^2$
$1681 \overset{?}{=} 81 + 1600$
$1681 = 1681$
The triangle is right.

b. $8^2 \overset{?}{=} 6^2 + 7^2$
$64 \overset{?}{=} 36 + 49$
$64 < 85$
The triangle is acute.

c. $11^2 \overset{?}{=} 7^2 + 8^2$
$121 \overset{?}{=} 49 + 64$
$121 > 113$
The triangle is obtuse.

Classroom Exercises

If a triangle is formed with sides having the lengths given, is it acute, right, or obtuse? If a triangle can't be formed, say *not possible*.

1. 6, 8, 10 **right**
2. 4, 6, 8 **obtuse**
3. 1, 4, 6 **not possible**
4. 8, 10, 12 **acute**
5. $\sqrt{7}, \sqrt{7}, \sqrt{14}$ **right**
6. $4, 4\sqrt{3}, 8$ **right**

7. Specify all values of x that make the statement true.
a. $\angle 1$ is a right angle. **$x = 10$**
b. $\angle 1$ is an acute angle. **$2 < x < 10$**
c. $\angle 1$ is an obtuse angle. **$10 < x < 14$**
d. The triangle is isosceles. **$x = 8$ or $x = 6$**
e. No triangle is possible. **$x \leq 2$ or $x \geq 14$**

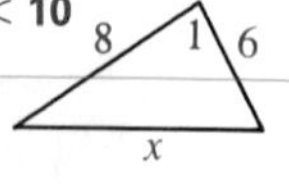

Exercises 8–10 refer to the figures below.

8. Explain why x must equal 5. **8. Since $10^2 = 8^2 + 6^2$, $\triangle ABC$ is a rt. $\triangle$. The midpt. of the hyp. of a rt. $\triangle$ is equidistant from the vertices.**

9. Explain why $\angle D$ must be a right angle. **$n = \sqrt{3^2 - 2^2} = \sqrt{5}$, $(\sqrt{5})^2 = (\sqrt{3})^2 + (\sqrt{2})^2$**

10. Explain why $\angle P$ must be a right angle. **See below.**

C
8
6
x
A 5 K 5 B

Ex. 8

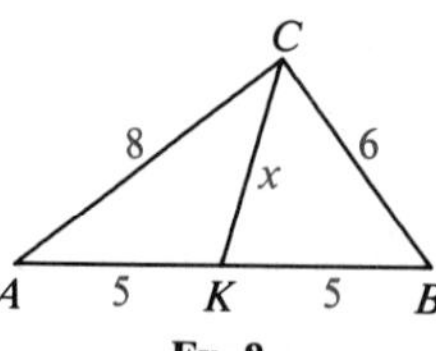

Ex. 9

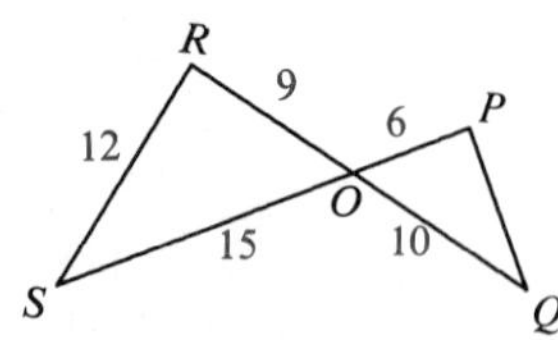

Ex. 10

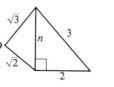

10. $\triangle ROS \sim \triangle POQ$ (SAS $\sim$ Thm.) and since $15^2 = 9^2 + 12^2$, $\angle R$ is a rt. $\angle$. Then $\angle P$ is a rt. $\angle$. (Corr. $\angle$s of $\sim$ $\triangle$s are $\cong$.)

Written Exercises

Tell whether a triangle with sides of the given lengths is acute, right, or obtuse.

A

1. 11, 11, 15 **acute**
2. 9, 9, 13 **obtuse**
3. 8, $8\sqrt{3}$, 16 **right**
4. 6, 6, $6\sqrt{2}$ **right**
5. 8, 14, 17 **obtuse**
6. 0.6, 0.8, 1 **right**
7. **a.** 0.5, 1.2, 1.3 **right** **b.** $5n$, $12n$, $13n$ where $n > 0$ **right**
8. **a.** 33, 44, 55 **right** **b.** $3n$, $4n$, $5n$ where $n > 0$ **right**

9. Given: $\angle UTS$ is a rt. $\angle$.
Show that $\triangle RST$ must be a rt. $\triangle$.
$(ST)^2 = 13^2 - 12^2 = 25$
$(ST)^2 = (RS)^2 + (RT)^2 = 25$

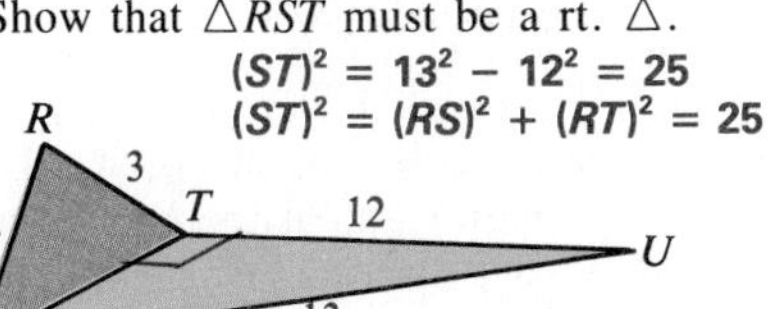

By the converse of the Pythagorean Thm., $\triangle TRS$ is a rt. $\triangle$.

10. Given: $\overline{AC} \perp$ plane P
Show that $\triangle BCD$ must be obtuse.
$(BC)^2 = 36$
$(BD)^2 = 121 > (BC)^2 + (CD)^2$

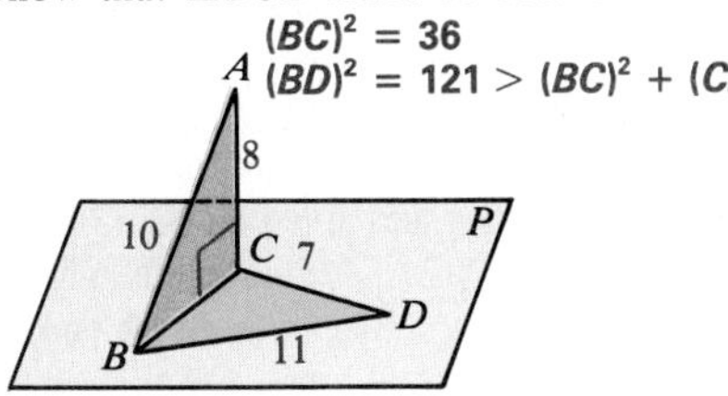

Use the information to decide if $\triangle ABC$ is acute, right, or obtuse.

B

11. $AC = 13$, $BC = 15$, $CD = 12$ **acute**
12. $AC = 10$, $BC = 17$, $CD = 8$ **obtuse**
13. $AC = 13$, $BC = \sqrt{34}$, $CD = 3$ **obtuse**
14. $AD = 2$, $DB = 8$, $CD = 4$ **right**

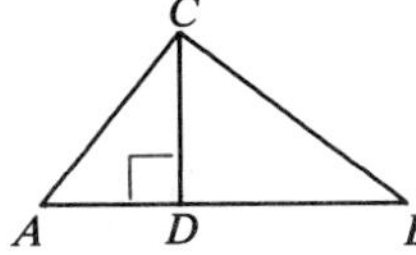

15. The sides of a triangle have lengths x, $x + 4$, and 20. Specify those values of x for which the triangle is acute with longest side 20. **$12 < x \leq 16$**
16. Sketch $\square EFGH$ with $EF = 13$, $EG = 24$, and $FH = 10$. What special kind of parallelogram is $EFGH$? Explain. **rhombus**
17. Sketch $\square RSTU$, with diagonals intersecting at M. $RS = 9$, $\overline{ST} = 20$, and $RM = 11$. Which segment is longer, $\overline{SM}$ or $\overline{RM}$? Explain. **$\overline{RM}$**
18. If x and y are positive numbers with $x > y$, show that a triangle with sides of lengths $2xy$, $x^2 - y^2$, and $x^2 + y^2$ is always a right triangle.
19. **a.** Complete this statement of Theorem 8-5:
If the square of the longest side of a triangle __?__.
b. Prove Theorem 8-5.
Given: $\triangle RST$; $l^2 > j^2 + k^2$
Prove: $\triangle RST$ is an obtuse triangle.
(*Hint*: Start by drawing right $\triangle UVW$ with legs j and k. Compare lengths l and n.)

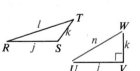

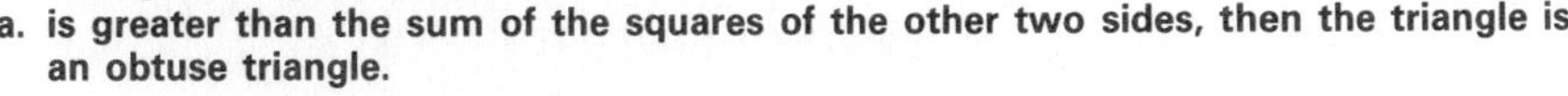

a. is greater than the sum of the squares of the other two sides, then the triangle is an obtuse triangle.

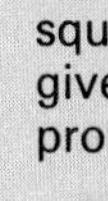

Using a Calculator

The x^2 key on a calculator can make problems involving the Pythagorean Theorem quicker to solve. For Exs. 1–8, encourage students to use a calculator to square each length. This will give them more time for problem solving.

Guided Practice

Classify each triangle with sides of the given lengths as acute, right, or obtuse.

1. 5, 12, 14 obtuse
2. 6, 7, 8 acute
3. $\sqrt{3}$, $\sqrt{4}$, $\sqrt{5}$ acute
4. 1, 3, $\sqrt{10}$ right

Additional Answers Written Exercises

18. $(2xy)^2 + (x^2 - y^2)^2 = 4x^2y^2 + x^4 - 2x^2y^2 + y^4 = x^4 + 2x^2y^2 + y^4 = (x^2 + y^2)^2$

Group Activity

You may wish to use Exs. 19 and 20 for a group learning activity. As the groups work on the proofs, move around the room observing their progress. Provide assistance, if necessary, by asking questions rather than giving direct answers.

20. a. Complete this statement of Theorem 8-4:
If the square of the longest side of a triangle __?__.

b. Prove Theorem 8-4.

Given: $\triangle RST$; $\overline{RT}$ is the longest side; $l^2 < j^2 + k^2$
Prove: $\triangle RST$ is an acute triangle.
(*Hint*: Start by drawing right $\triangle UVW$ with legs j and k. Compare lengths l and n.)

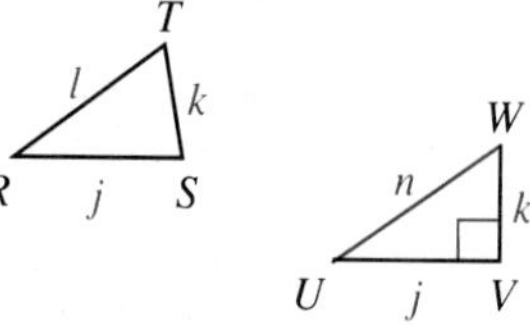

a. is less than the sum of the squares of the other two sides, then the triangle is an acute triangle.

C **21.** Given: $\overline{CN} \perp \overline{AB}$;
h is the geometric mean between d and e.
Prove: $\triangle ABC$ is a right triangle.

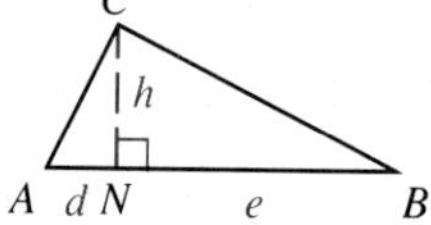

22. A frame in the shape of the simple *scissors truss* shown at the right below can be used to support a peaked roof. The weight of the roof compresses some parts of the frame (green), while other parts are in tension (blue). A frame made with s segments joined at j points is stable if $s \geq 2j - 3$. In the truss shown, 9 segments connect 6 points. Verify that the truss is stable. Then find the values of x and y.

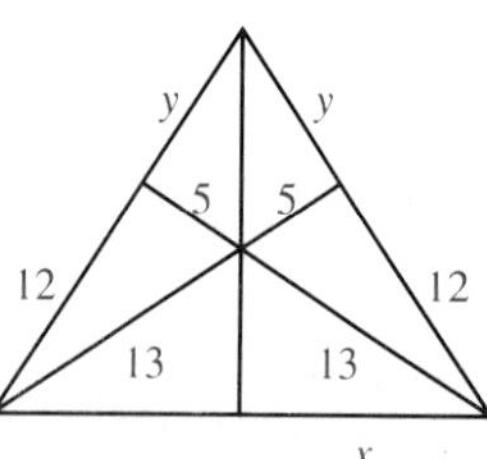

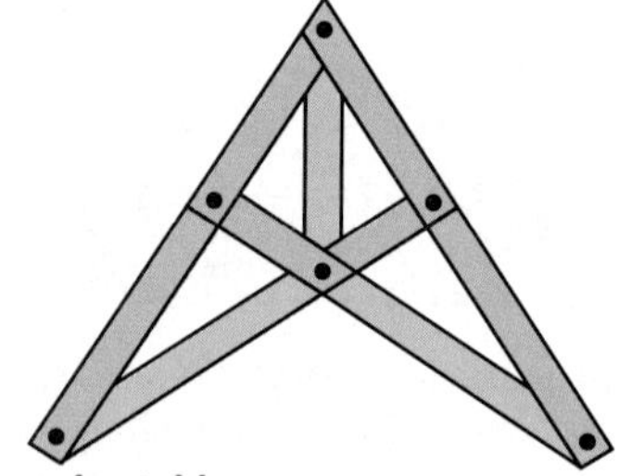

$s = 9$, $j = 6$; $9 = 2(6) - 3$, so the truss is stable.
$x = 3\sqrt{13}$, $y = 7.5$

Using a Computer

This Exploration extends your students' work on triangles to quadrilaterals. It can be used as the basis for some interesting projects.

Explorations

These exploratory exercises can be done using a computer with a program that draws and measures geometric figures.

The sides of a quadrilateral have lengths a, b, c, and d. The diagonals have lengths e and f. For what kinds of quadrilaterals does

$$a^2 + b^2 + c^2 + d^2 = e^2 + f^2?$$

Draw various quadrilaterals including a parallelogram, rectangle, rhombus, trapezoid, and a random quadrilateral.

parallelogram, rectangle, rhombus, square

♦ Computer Key-In

Suppose a, b, and c are positive integers such that $a^2 + b^2 = c^2$. Then the converse of the Pythagorean Theorem guarantees that a, b, and c are the lengths of the sides of a right triangle. Because of this, any such triple of integers is called a **Pythagorean triple.**

For example, 3, 4, 5 is a Pythagorean triple since $3^2 + 4^2 = 5^2$. Another triple is 6, 8, 10, since $6^2 + 8^2 = 10^2$. The triple 3, 4, 5 is called a *primitive* Pythagorean triple because no factor (other than 1) is common to all three integers. The triple 6, 8, 10 is *not* a primitive triple.

The following program in BASIC lists some Pythagorean triples.

```
10  FOR X = 2 TO 7
20    FOR Y = 1 TO X - 1
30      LET A = 2 * X * Y
40      LET B = X * X - Y * Y
50      LET C = X * X + Y * Y
60      PRINT A;",";B;",";C
70    NEXT Y
80  NEXT X
90  END
```

2. $(2xy)^2 + (x^2 - y^2)^2$
$= 4x^2y^2 + x^4 - 2x^2y^2 + y^4$
$= x^4 + 2x^2y^2 + y^4$
$= (x^2 + y^2)^2$

3b. $(2n + 1)^2 + (2n^2 + 2n)^2$
$= 4n^2 + 4n + 1 + 4n^4 + 8n^3 + 4n^2$
$= 4n^4 + 8n^3 + 8n^2 + 4n + 1$
$= (2n^2 + 2n + 1)^2$

Exercises

1. Type and RUN the program. (If your computer uses a language other than BASIC, write and RUN a similar program.) What Pythagorean triples did it list? Which of these are primitive Pythagorean triples?

2. The program above uses a method for finding Pythagorean triples that was developed by Euclid around 320 B.C. His method can be stated as follows:

If x and y are positive integers with $y < x$, then $a = 2xy$, $b = x^2 - y^2$, and $c = x^2 + y^2$ is a Pythagorean triple.

To verify that Euclid's method is correct, show that the equation below is true. **See above.**

$$(2xy)^2 + (x^2 - y^2)^2 = (x^2 + y^2)^2$$

3. Look at the primitive Pythagorean triples found in Exercise 1. List those triples that have an odd number as their lowest value. Do you notice a pattern in some of these triples?

Another method for finding Pythagorean triples begins with an odd number. If n is any positive integer, $2n + 1$ is an odd number. A triple is given by: $a = 2n + 1$, $b = 2n^2 + 2n$, $c = (2n^2 + 2n) + 1$.
For example, when $n = 3$, the triple is

$$2(3) + 1 = 7, \quad 2(3^2) + 2(3) = 24, \quad 24 + 1 = 25.$$

a. Use the formula to find another primitive triple with 33 as its lowest value. (*Hint*: $n = 16$) **33, 544, 545**

b. Use the Pythagorean Theorem to verify the method described. **See above.**

Using a Computer

This Computer Key-In explores Pythagorean triples, triples of integers that satisfy the Pythagorean Theorem. It also gives students an introduction to number theory.

You could introduce the material by using the first two paragraphs and then doing Ex. 2 *before* explaining and/or running the given program. Ex. 2 is essentially the same as Written Ex. 18, which could be assigned as homework before this Computer Key-In is discussed.

Teaching Suggestions, pp. T108–T109

Objective
Presenting the Lesson
Applications
Reinforcement
Enrichment

Cooperative Learning, p. T109

Supplementary Materials

Practice Master 44
Test 32
Resource Book, pp. 51, 141
Study Guide, pp. 97–98

Lesson Focus

There are two types of right triangles that occur very frequently in solving problems. This lesson studies these two types of triangles, which are named by the size of their angles: the 45°-45°-90° triangle, and the 30°-60°-90° triangle.

Suggested Assignments

Minimum
Day 1: 302/1–16
S 297/14, 16
Day 2: 302/17–24
304/Self-Test 1

Average
Day 1: 302/2–14 even, 15, 16, 18, 19, 21, 22
Day 2: 302–303/20, 23, 25, 28, 31
304/Self-Test 1

Maximum
Day 1: 302/5–7, 11–13, 17–20
S 297/19
Day 2: 302–303/21–23, 25, 27–30, 32, 35, 38

8-4 *Special Right Triangles*

An isosceles right triangle is also called a 45°-45°-90° triangle, because the measures of the angles are 45, 45, and 90.

Theorem 8-6 *45°-45°-90° Theorem*

In a 45°-45°-90° triangle, the hypotenuse is $\sqrt{2}$ times as long as a leg.

Given: A 45°-45°-90° triangle

Prove: hypotenuse $= \sqrt{2} \cdot$ leg

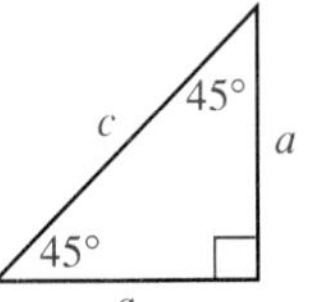

Plan for Proof: Let the sides of the given triangle be a, a, and c. Apply the Pythagorean Theorem and solve for c in terms of a.

Example 1 Find the value of x.

a.

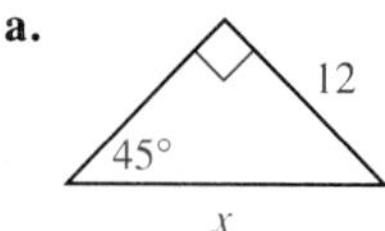

b.

Solution

a. $\text{hyp} = \sqrt{2} \cdot \text{leg}$
$x = \sqrt{2} \cdot 12$
$x = 12\sqrt{2}$

b. $\text{hyp} = \sqrt{2} \cdot \text{leg}$
$8 = \sqrt{2} \cdot x$
$x = \dfrac{8}{\sqrt{2}} = \dfrac{8}{\sqrt{2}} \cdot \dfrac{\sqrt{2}}{\sqrt{2}} = \dfrac{8\sqrt{2}}{2}$
$x = 4\sqrt{2}$

Another special right triangle has acute angles measuring 30 and 60.

Theorem 8-7 *30°-60°-90° Theorem*

In a 30°-60°-90° triangle, the hypotenuse is twice as long as the shorter leg, and the longer leg is $\sqrt{3}$ times as long as the shorter leg.

Given: $\triangle ABC$, a 30°-60°-90° triangle

Prove: hypotenuse $= 2 \cdot$ shorter leg
longer leg $= \sqrt{3} \cdot$ shorter leg

Plan for Proof: Build onto $\triangle ABC$ as shown. $\triangle ADC \cong \triangle ABC$, so $\triangle ABD$ is equiangular and equilateral with $c = 2a$. Since $\triangle ABC$ is a right triangle, $a^2 + b^2 = c^2$. By substitution, $a^2 + b^2 = 4a^2$, so $b^2 = 3a^2$ and $b = a\sqrt{3}$.

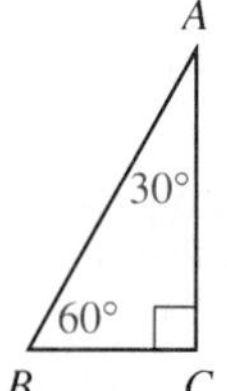

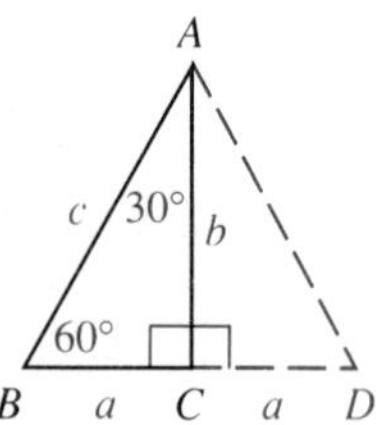

Example 2 Find the values of x and y.

a.

b.

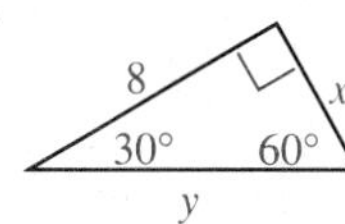

Solution

a. hyp. $= 2 \cdot$ shorter leg

$x = 2 \cdot 6$

$x = 12$

longer leg $= \sqrt{3} \cdot$ shorter leg

$y = 6\sqrt{3}$

b. longer leg $= \sqrt{3} \cdot$ shorter leg

$8 = \sqrt{3} \cdot x$

$x = \frac{8}{\sqrt{3}} = \frac{8\sqrt{3}}{3}$

hyp. $= 2 \cdot$ shorter leg

$y = 2 \cdot \frac{8\sqrt{3}}{3} = \frac{16\sqrt{3}}{3}$

Classroom Exercises

Find the value of x.

1. **$6\sqrt{2}$**

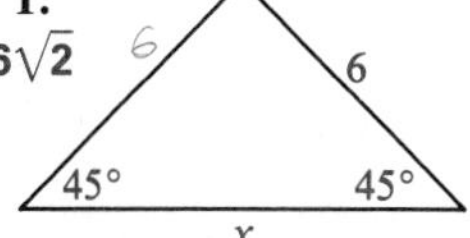

2. **10**

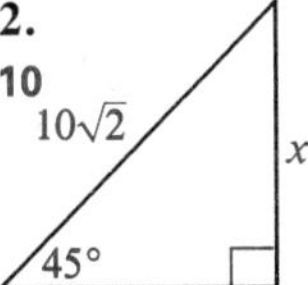

3. **$6\sqrt{2}$**

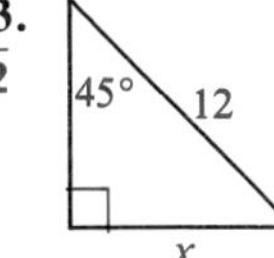

4. **10**

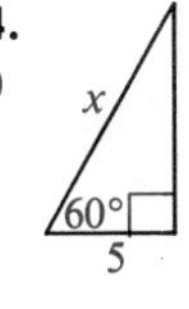

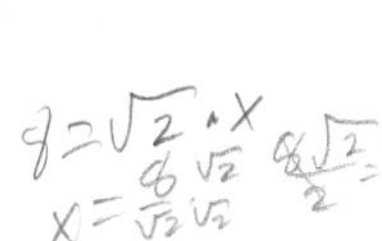

5. **6.5**

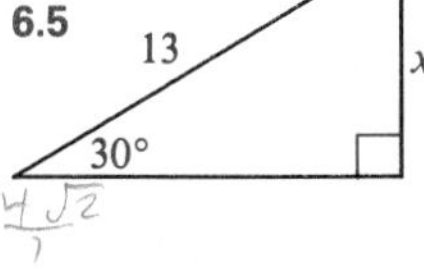

6. **$3\sqrt{3}$**

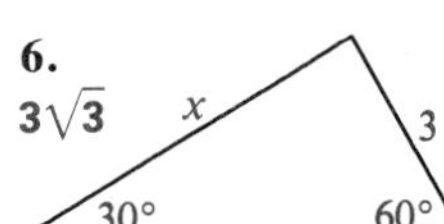

7. **$4\sqrt{2}$**

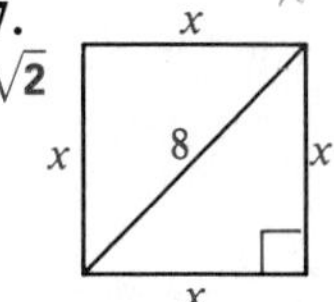

8. **$10\sqrt{3}$**

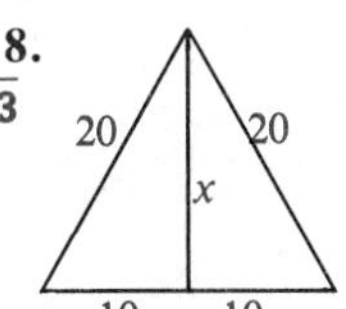

9. **$9\sqrt{2}$**

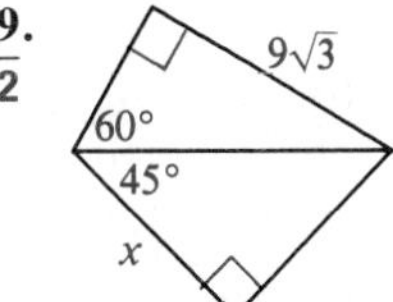

10. In regular hexagon $ABCDEF$, $AB = 8$. Find AD and AC. **$AD = 16$** **$AC = 8\sqrt{3}$**

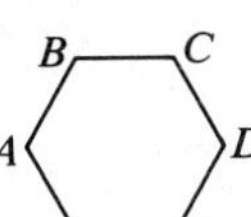

11. Express PQ, PS, and QR in terms of a. **$PQ = 2a$** **$PS = a\sqrt{3}$** **$QR = a\sqrt{2}$**

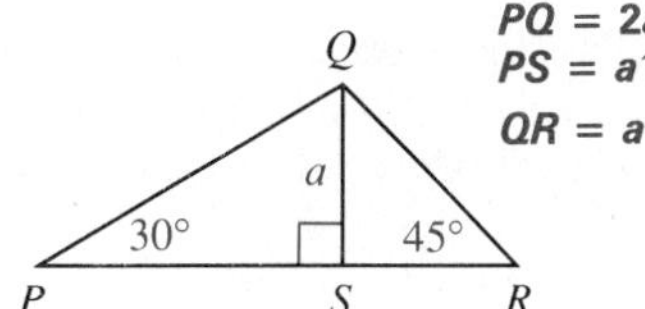

12. If the measures of the angles of a triangle are in the ratio 1:2:3, are the lengths of the sides in the same ratio? Explain. **No. In a 30°-60°-90° △, the sides are in the ratio $1{:}\sqrt{3}{:}2$.**

Chalkboard Examples

1. Find the value of x.
$3\sqrt{2}$

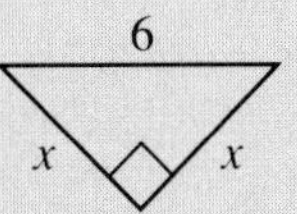

2. Find the values of x and y.
$x = 5\sqrt{3}$, $y = 10$

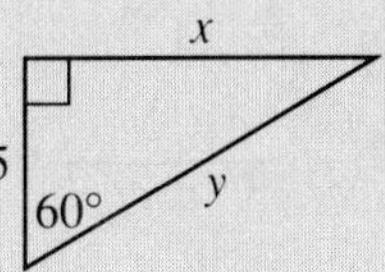

Guided Practice

Complete.

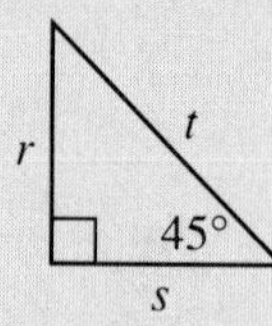

1. If $r = 6$, $t = \underline{6\sqrt{2}}$.
2. If $s = 2\sqrt{5}$, $t = \underline{2\sqrt{10}}$.
3. If $t = \sqrt{2}$, $r = \underline{1}$.
4. If $t = 10$, $s = \underline{5\sqrt{2}}$.

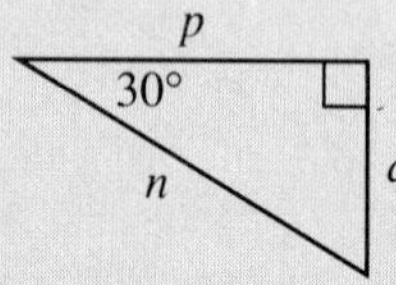

5. If $q = 8$, $p = \underline{8\sqrt{3}}$ and $n = \underline{16}$.
6. If $n = 20$, $q = \underline{10}$ and $p = \underline{10\sqrt{3}}$.
7. If $p = 4\sqrt{3}$, $q = \underline{4}$ and $n = \underline{8}$.
8. If $p = 9$, $q = \underline{3\sqrt{3}}$ and $n = \underline{6\sqrt{3}}$.
9. A diagonal of a square has length 6. What is the perimeter of the square? $12\sqrt{2}$

Using a Computer

Ex. 27 can be extended using a construction program. The points *A*, *B*, *C*, *D*, and *E* lie on a spiral. Have students draw this spiral and calculate its length ($AB + BC + CD + DE$). Then ask them to draw a spiral in which each added segment has length 1. They can then write a description of how to do this construction.

Written Exercises

Copy and complete the tables.

A

	1.	2.	3.	4.	5.	6.	7.	8.
a	4	?	$\sqrt{5}$	?	?	?	?	?
b	?	$\frac{2}{3}$	?	?	?	?	$4\sqrt{2}$	?
c	?	?	?	$3\sqrt{2}$	6	$\sqrt{14}$	?	5

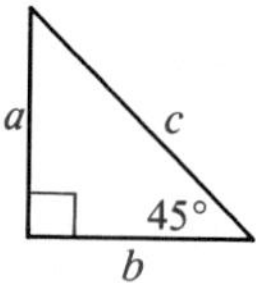

	9.	10.	11.	12.	13.	14.	15.	16.
d	7	$\frac{1}{4}$	?	?	?	?	?	?
e	?	?	$5\sqrt{3}$	6	?	?	3	?
f	?	?	?	?	10	13	?	$6\sqrt{3}$

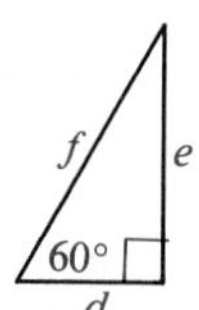

17. Find the length of a diagonal of a square whose perimeter is 48. **$12\sqrt{2}$**
18. A diagonal of a square has length 8. What is the perimeter of the square? **$16\sqrt{2}$**
19. An altitude of an equilateral triangle has length $6\sqrt{3}$. What is the perimeter of the triangle? **36**
20. Find the altitude of an equilateral triangle if each side is 10 units long. **$5\sqrt{3}$**

Find the values of *x* and *y* in each diagram.

B

21.

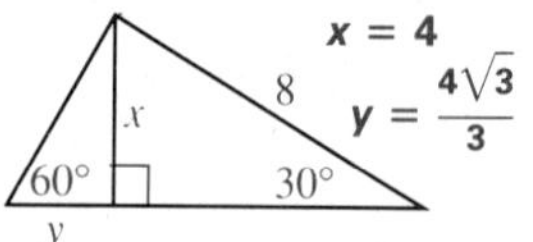

$x = 4$, $y = \frac{4\sqrt{3}}{3}$

22.

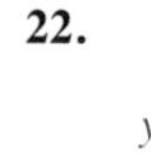
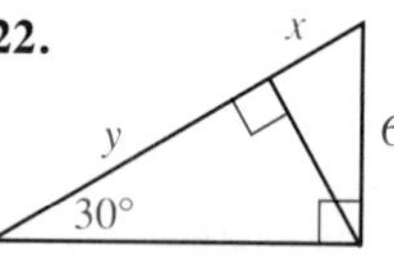

$x = 3$, $y = 9$

23.

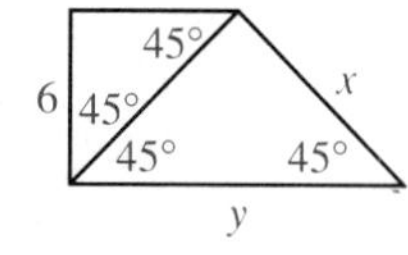

$x = 6\sqrt{2}$, $y = 12$

24.

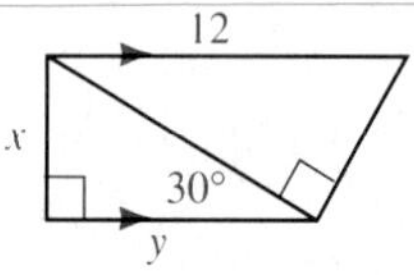

$x = 3\sqrt{3}$, $y = 9$

25.

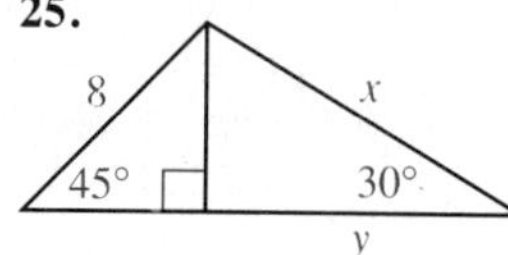

$x = 8\sqrt{2}$, $y = 4\sqrt{6}$

26.

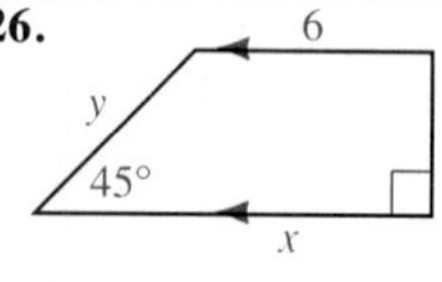

$x = 10$, $y = 4\sqrt{2}$

27. The diagram shows four 45°-45°-90° triangles. If $OA = 1$, find OB, OC, OD, and OE.
$OB = \sqrt{2}$, $OC = 2$, $OD = 2\sqrt{2}$, $OE = 4$

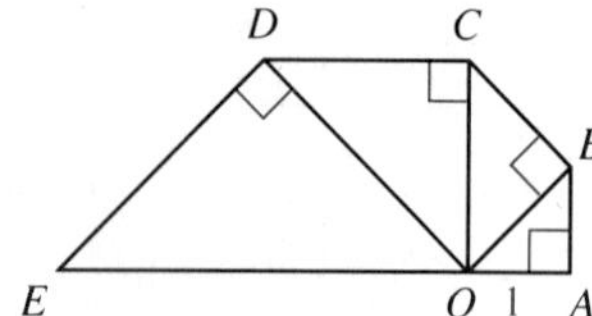

28. The diagonals of a rectangle are 8 units long and intersect at a 60° angle. Find the dimensions of the rectangle. **length = $4\sqrt{3}$, width = 4**

29. The perimeter of a rhombus is 64 and one of its angles has measure 120. Find the lengths of the diagonals. **16, $16\sqrt{3}$**

30. Prove Theorem 8-6.

31. Explain why any triangle having sides in the ratio $1:\sqrt{3}:2$ must be a 30°-60°-90° triangle.

Find the lengths of as many segments as possible.

32.

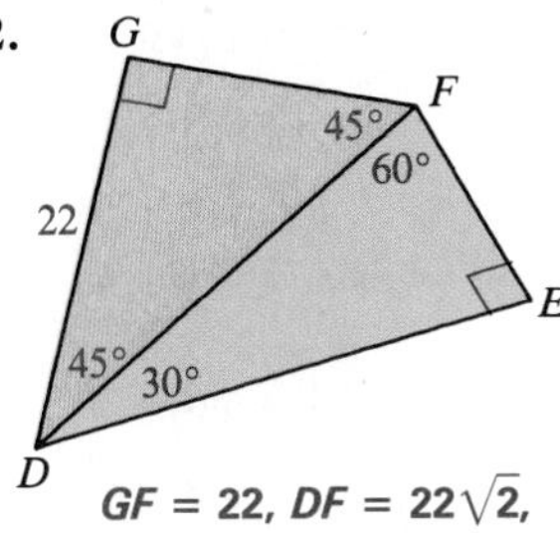

$GF = 22$, $DF = 22\sqrt{2}$, $FE = 11\sqrt{2}$, $DE = 11\sqrt{6}$

33.

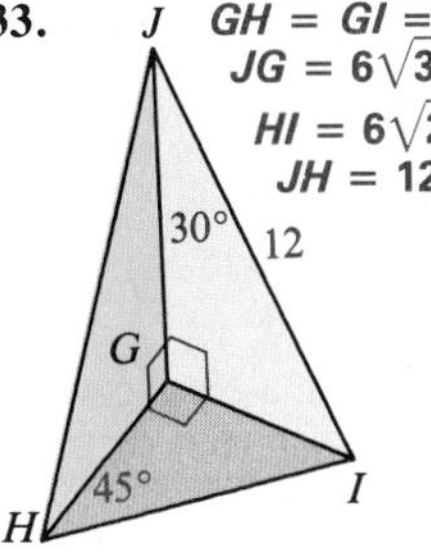

$GH = GI = 6$, $JG = 6\sqrt{3}$, $HI = 6\sqrt{2}$, $JH = 12$

34.

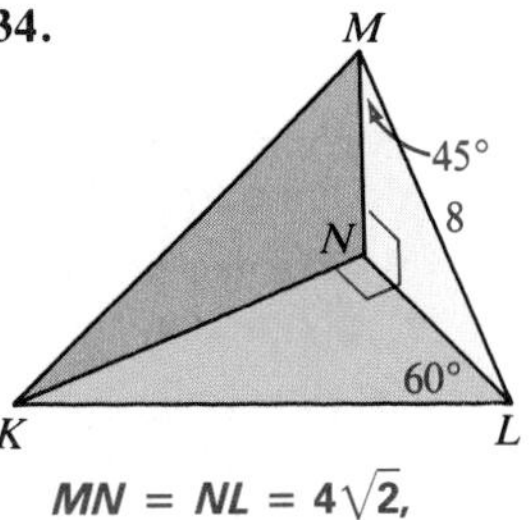

$MN = NL = 4\sqrt{2}$, $KL = 8\sqrt{2}$, $KN = 4\sqrt{6}$

C **35.** In quadrilateral $QRST$, $m\angle R = 60$, $m\angle T = 90$, $QR = RS$, $ST = 8$, and $TQ = 8$.

a. How long is the longer diagonal of the quadrilateral? **$4\sqrt{2} + 4\sqrt{6}$**

b. Find the ratio of RT to QS. **$(1 + \sqrt{3}):2$**

36. Find the perimeter of the triangle. **$8 + 12\sqrt{2} + 4\sqrt{6}$**

37. Find the length of the median of the trapezoid in terms of j. **$\frac{3j + j\sqrt{3}}{4}$**

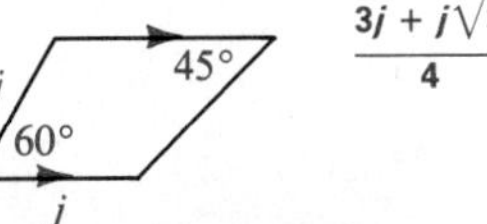

38. If the wrench just fits the hexagonal nut, what is the value of x? **$\sqrt{3}$ cm**

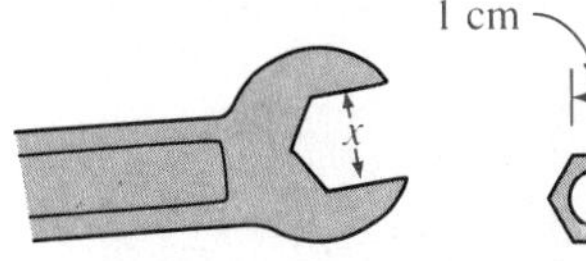

★ **39.** The six edges of the solid shown are 8 units long. A and B are midpoints of two edges as shown. Find AB. **$4\sqrt{2}$**

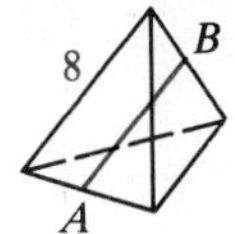

Exercise Note

In Ex. 34, $m\angle MNK$ may not be 90, so MK cannot be found.

Additional Answers Written Exercises

1. $b = 4$, $c = 4\sqrt{2}$
2. $a = \frac{2}{3}$, $c = \frac{2\sqrt{2}}{3}$
3. $b = \sqrt{5}$, $c = \sqrt{10}$
4. $a = 3$, $b = 3$
5. $a = 3\sqrt{2}$, $b = 3\sqrt{2}$
6. $a = \sqrt{7}$, $b = \sqrt{7}$
7. $a = 4\sqrt{2}$, $c = 8$
8. $a = \frac{5\sqrt{2}}{2}$, $b = \frac{5\sqrt{2}}{2}$
9. $e = 7\sqrt{3}$, $f = 14$
10. $e = \frac{\sqrt{3}}{4}$, $f = \frac{1}{2}$
11. $d = 5$, $f = 10$
12. $d = 2\sqrt{3}$, $f = 4\sqrt{3}$
13. $d = 5$, $e = 5\sqrt{3}$
14. $d = \frac{13}{2}$, $e = \frac{13\sqrt{3}}{2}$
15. $d = \sqrt{3}$, $f = 2\sqrt{3}$
16. $d = 3\sqrt{3}$, $e = 9$

Quick Quiz

1. Find the geometric mean between 5 and 30. $5\sqrt{6}$

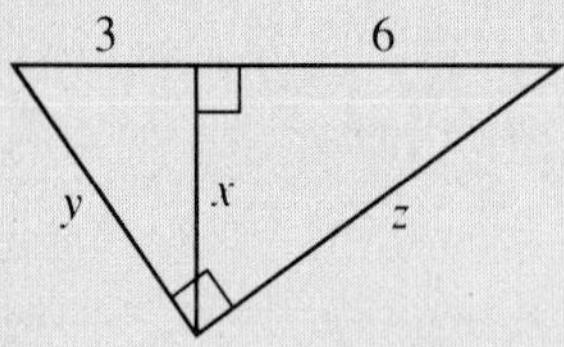

2. Use the diagram above.
   a. $x = \underline{3\sqrt{2}}$
   b. $y = \underline{3\sqrt{3}}$
   c. $z = \underline{3\sqrt{6}}$

The sides of a triangle are given. Is the triangle acute, right, or obtuse?

3. 3, 6, 7 obtuse
4. 50, 120, 130 right
5. 8, 10, 13 obtuse
6. A rectangle has length 6 and width 2. How long is each diagonal? $2\sqrt{10}$
7. Find the perimeter of a square if each diagonal is 8 cm long. $16\sqrt{2}$ cm
8. The perimeter of an equilateral triangle is 30 cm. Find the length of an altitude. $5\sqrt{3}$ cm
9. An isosceles triangle has sides 10, 10, and 12. How long is the altitude to the base? 8

Self-Test 1

1. Find the geometric mean between 3 and 15. $3\sqrt{5}$
2. The diagram shows the altitude drawn to the hypotenuse of a right triangle.
   a. $x =$ __?__ 4
   b. $y =$ __?__ $2\sqrt{5}$
   c. $z =$ __?__ $4\sqrt{5}$

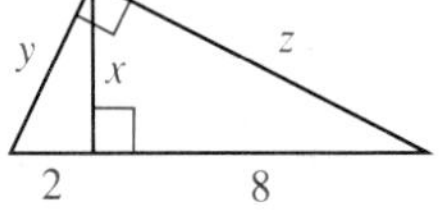

3. The sides of a triangle are given. Is the triangle acute, right, or obtuse?
   a. 11, 60, 61 **right** b. 7, 9, 11 **acute** c. 0.2, 0.3, 0.4 **obtuse**
4. A rectangle has length 8 and width 4. Find the lengths of the diagonals. $4\sqrt{5}$
5. Find the perimeter of a square that has diagonals 10 cm long. $20\sqrt{2}$ **cm**
6. The sides of an equilateral triangle are 12 cm long. Find the length of an altitude of the triangle. $6\sqrt{3}$ **cm**
7. How long is the altitude to the base of an isosceles triangle if the sides of the triangle are 13, 13, and 10? **12**

Biographical Note *Nikolai Lobachevsky*

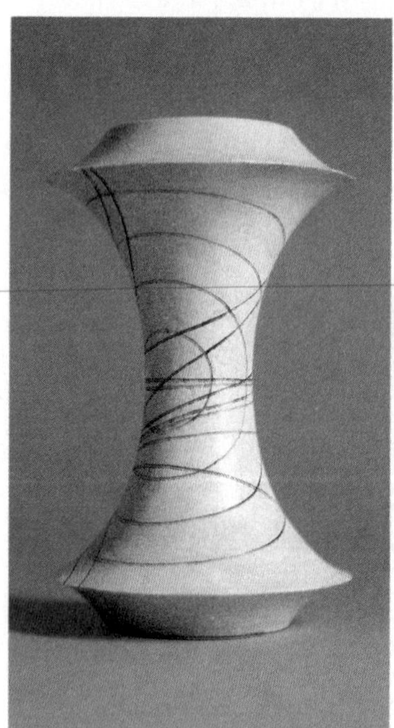

Lobachevsky (1793–1856) was a Russian mathematician who brought a new insight to the study of geometry. He realized that Euclidean geometry is only one geometry, and that other geometric systems are possible.

A modern restatement of Euclid's fifth postulate, often called the Parallel Postulate, is "Through a point outside a line, there is exactly one line parallel to the given line." It is this postulate that defines *Euclidean* geometry. For 2000 years, mathematicians tried to prove this fifth postulate from the other four.

Lobachevsky tried a different approach. He created a geometric system where Euclid's first four postulates were the same but the fifth was changed to allow *more than one* parallel through a given point. The antique model at the left shows such a system. Other geometric systems based on a different fifth postulate followed. (See Extra: Non-Euclidean Geometries, page 233.)

Although Lobachevsky thought our universe was Euclidean, some physicists have decided the universe may be better described by Lobachevsky's system. Even so, over small regions Euclidean geometry is accurate. Similarly, although the surface of the Earth is a sphere, we treat small areas of it as flat.

Trigonometry

Objectives

1. Define the tangent, sine, and cosine ratios for an acute angle.
2. Solve right triangle problems by correct selection and use of the tangent, sine, and cosine ratios.

8-5 *The Tangent Ratio*

The word trigonometry comes from Greek words that mean "triangle measurement." In this book our study will be limited to the trigonometry of right triangles. In the right triangle shown, one acute angle is marked. The leg opposite this angle and the leg adjacent to this angle are labeled.

The following ratio of the lengths of the legs is called the *tangent ratio*.

tangent of $\angle A = \dfrac{\text{leg opposite } \angle A}{\text{leg adjacent to } \angle A}$

In abbreviated form: $\tan A = \dfrac{\text{opposite}}{\text{adjacent}}$

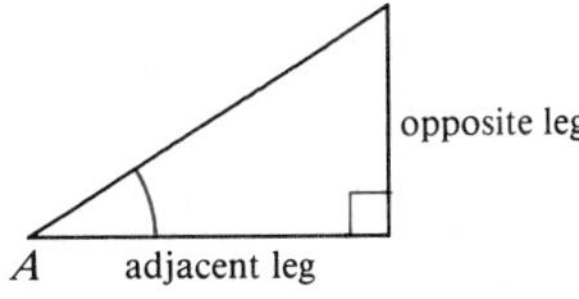

Example 1 Find tan X and tan Y.

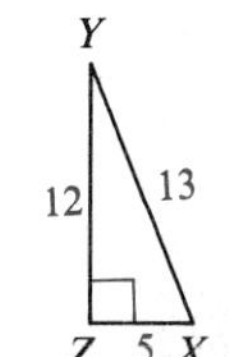

Solution $\tan X = \dfrac{\text{leg opposite } \angle X}{\text{leg adjacent to } \angle X} = \dfrac{12}{5}$

$\tan Y = \dfrac{\text{leg opposite } \angle Y}{\text{leg adjacent to } \angle Y} = \dfrac{5}{12}$

In the right triangles shown below, $m\angle A = m\angle R$. Then by the AA Similarity Postulate, the triangles are similar. We can write these proportions:

$\dfrac{a}{r} = \dfrac{b}{s}$ (Why?)

$\dfrac{a}{b} = \dfrac{r}{s}$ (A property of proportions)

$\tan A = \tan R$ (Def. of tangent ratio)

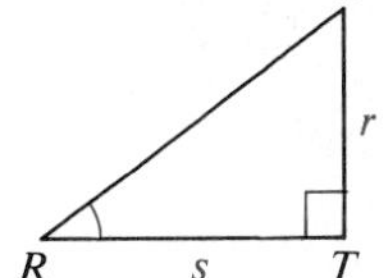

We have shown that if $m\angle A = m\angle R$, then $\tan A = \tan R$. Thus, we have shown that the value of the tangent of an angle depends only on the size of the angle, not on the size of the right triangle. It is also true that if $\tan A = \tan R$ for acute angles A and R, then $m\angle A = m\angle R$.

Teaching Suggestions, p. T109
Objectives
Presenting the Lesson

Communication Skills, p. T109

Exploring Activity, p. 283c

Supplementary Materials

Study Guide, pp. 99–100, 105

Lesson Focus

The purpose of this lesson is to introduce a very important ratio that is formed by using the lengths of the two legs of a right triangle. The study of this ratio is part of a branch of mathematics called trigonometry.

Suggested Assignments

Minimum
Day 1: 308/1–9
Day 2: 308/10–18

Average
Day 1: 308/1–6, 9, 10, 12
S 303/30
Day 2: 308–309/7, 8, 11, 13–15, 17, 19, 25

Maximum
Day 1: 308/1–15
Day 2: 308–310/16–30 even

Chalkboard Examples

Find tan *A*, tan *B*, $m\angle A$, and $m\angle B$.

1. $\frac{2}{7}, \frac{7}{2}, \approx 16, \approx 74$

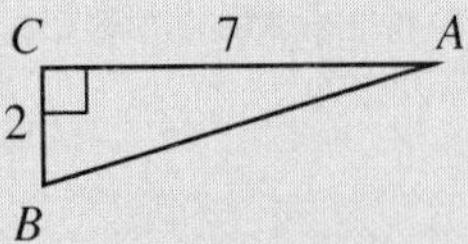

2. $\frac{8}{15}, \frac{15}{8}, \approx 28, \approx 62$

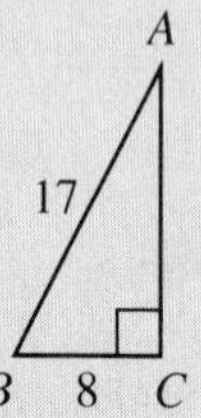

3. Find the value of *x* to the nearest tenth. 8.9

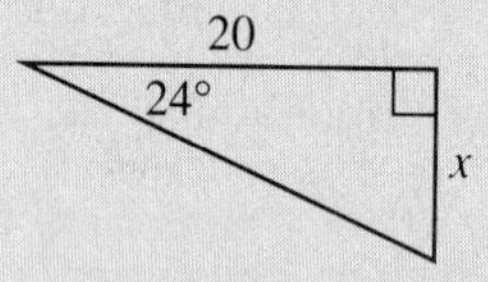

Communication Skills

Make sure students read the symbol $\approx$ correctly as *is approximately equal to.*

Using a Calculator

Explain to students how to use the tangent and inverse tangent functions of a scientific calculator. For Ex. 7(a)–(c) use tan, and for Ex. 7(d)–(f) use inverse tan. Point out to students that they should be calculating in degrees, not radians.

Since the tangent of an angle depends only on the measure of the angle, we can write tan 10°, for example, to stand for the tangent of any angle with a degree measure of 10. The table on page 311 lists the values of the tangents of some angles with measures between 0 and 90. Most of the values are approximations, rounded to four decimal places. Suppose you want the approximate value of tan 33°. Locate 33° in the angle column. Go across to the tangent column. Read .6494. You write tan 33° $\approx$ 0.6494, where the symbol $\approx$ means "is approximately equal to." You can also use a scientific calculator to find tan 33° $\approx$ 0.649407593. Your calculator may give more or fewer decimal places than the nine that are shown.

Example 2 Find the value of *y* to the nearest tenth.

Solution

$$\tan 56° = \frac{y}{32}$$
$$y = 32(\tan 56°)$$
$$y \approx 32(1.4826)$$
$$y \approx 47.4432, \text{ or } 47.4$$

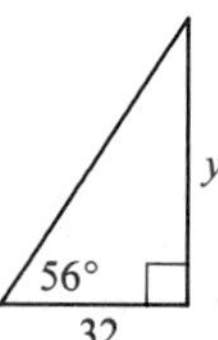

You can find the approximate degree measure of an angle with a given tangent by reading the table from the tangent column across to the angle column, or by using the inverse tangent key(s) of a calculator.

Example 3 The grade of a road is the ratio of its rise to its run and is usually given as a decimal or percent. Find the angle that the road makes with the horizontal if its grade is 4% ($\frac{4}{100}$ or 0.04).

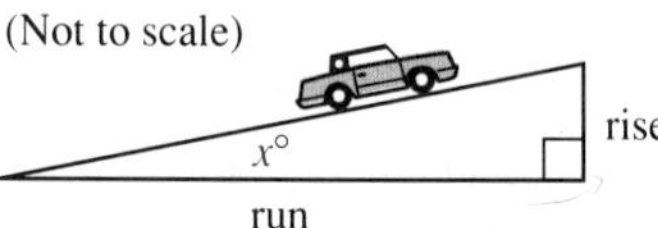

Solution

$$\tan x° = 0.0400$$
$$x° \approx 2°$$

$$\text{grade} = \frac{\text{rise}}{\text{run}}$$

If you use the table on page 311, notice that 0.0400 falls between two values in the tangent column: tan 2° $\approx$ 0.0349 and tan 3° $\approx$ 0.0524. Since 0.0349 is closer to 0.0400, we use 2° as an approximate value for *x*°.

Classroom Exercises

In Exercises 1–3 express tan *R* as a ratio.

1. $\frac{3}{8}$

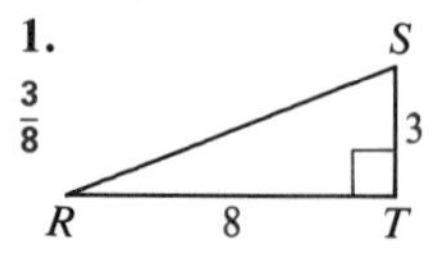

2. $\frac{13}{19}$

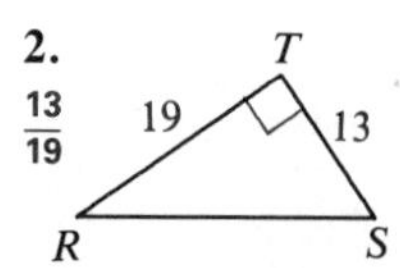

3. $\frac{15}{8}$

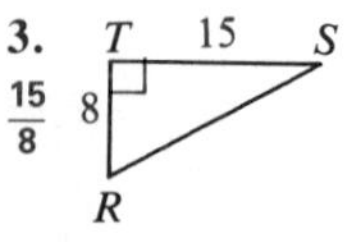

4–6. Express tan *S* as a ratio for each triangle above. $\frac{8}{3}; \frac{19}{13}; \frac{8}{15}$

7. Use the table on page 311 to complete the statements.
   a. tan 24° $\approx$ _?_ **0.4452**
   b. tan 41° $\approx$ _?_ **0.8693**
   c. tan 88° $\approx$ _?_ **28.6363**
   d. tan _?_ $\approx$ 2.4751 **68°**
   e. tan _?_ $\approx$ 0.3057 **17°**
   f. tan _?_ $\approx$ 0.8098 **39°**

8. Three 45°-45°-90° triangles are shown below.

a. In each triangle, express tan 45° in simplified form. **1**

b. See the entry for tan 45° on page 311. Is the entry exact? **Yes**

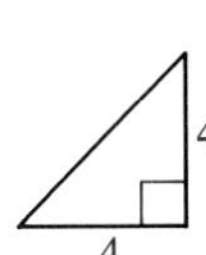

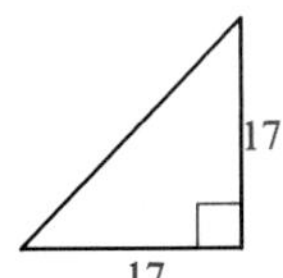

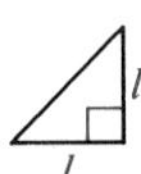

9. Three 30°-60°-90° triangles are shown below.

a. In each triangle, express tan 60° in simplified radical form. $\sqrt{3}$

b. Use $\sqrt{3} \approx 1.732051$ to find an approximate value for tan 60°. **1.7321**

c. Is the entry for tan 60° on page 311 exact? Is it correct to four decimal places? **No; yes**

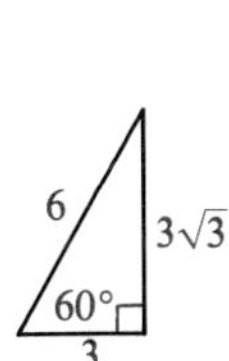

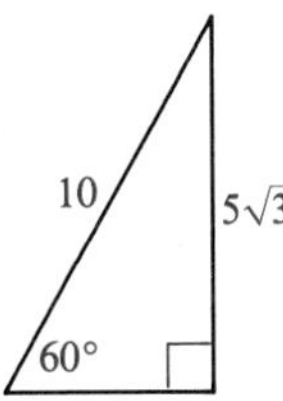

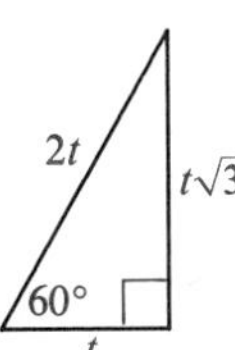

10. Notice that the tangent values increase rapidly toward the end of the table on page 311. Explain how you know that there is some angle with a tangent value equal to 1,000,000. Is there any upper limit to tangent values? **See below.**

11. Two ways to find the value of x are started below.

Using tan 40°:

$$\tan 40° = \frac{27}{x}$$

$$0.8391 \approx \frac{27}{x}$$

Using tan 50°:

$$\tan 50° = \frac{x}{27}$$

$$1.1918 \approx \frac{x}{27}$$

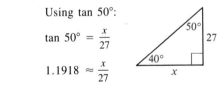

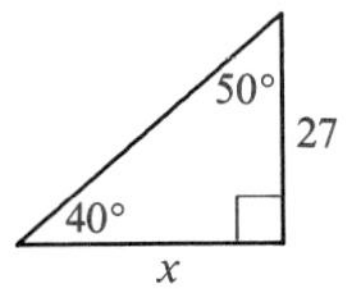

Which of the following statements are correct?

a. $x \approx 27 \cdot 0.8391$

(b.) $x \approx 27 \cdot 1.1918$

(c.) $x \approx \frac{27}{0.8391}$

d. $x \approx \frac{27}{1.1918}$

Which correct statement is easier to use for computing if you are *not* using a calculator for the arithmetic? **b**

10. You can draw a rt. △ with legs 1,000,000 and 1; the tangent of one of the acute ∠s is $\frac{1,000,000}{1} = 1,000,000$.
There is no upper limit to tangent values.

Teaching Note

Explain to students how to use the table on page 311. Also let students know your preference for their using the table or a calculator in assigned exercises.

Teaching Note

Ex. 10 helps students discover that the tangent values increase rapidly without a limit as the angle measure approaches 90. While students are examining the tangent values from the table, use the following discussion to aid their understanding of this concept. Draw several right triangles with the same adjacent leg on the chalkboard.

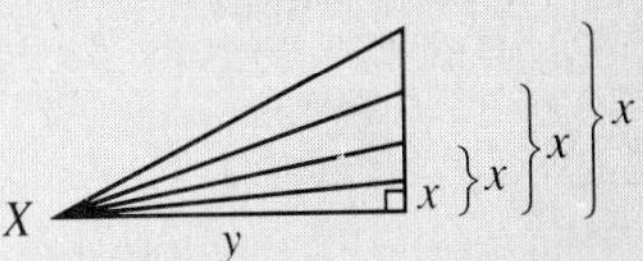

Keeping side y fixed, side x increases as ∠X becomes larger and larger. In fact, as the measure of ∠X gets closer and closer to 90°, side x becomes larger and larger without bound. Therefore, since the ratio $\frac{x}{y}$ has an increasingly large numerator and a constant denominator, tan X will become large without bound.

Guided Practice

Find the value of x to the nearest tenth.

1. 7.0

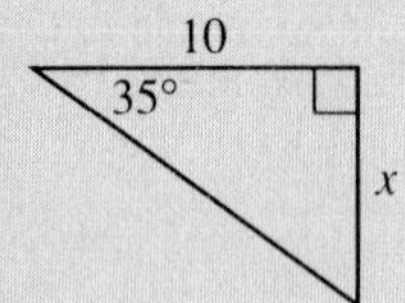

2. 78.1

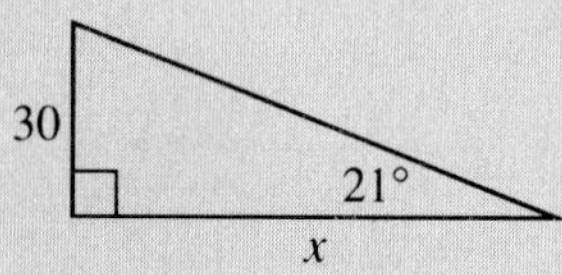

Find $y°$ correct to the nearest degree.

3. 58°

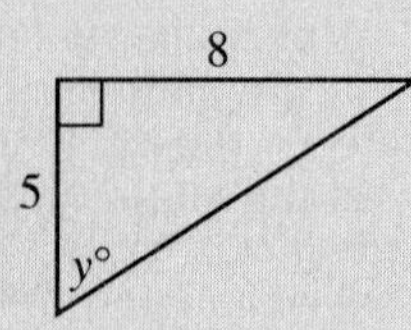

4. 37°

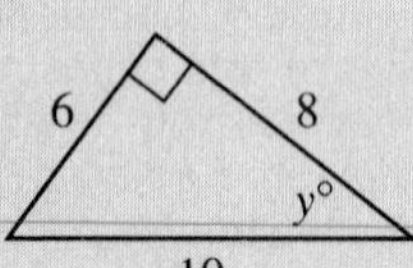

Written Exercises

Find the value of x to the nearest tenth. Use a calculator or the table on page 311.

A

1. 13.7

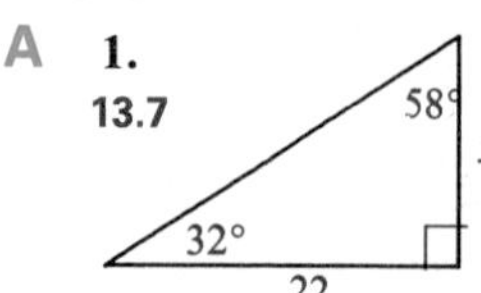

2. 23.6

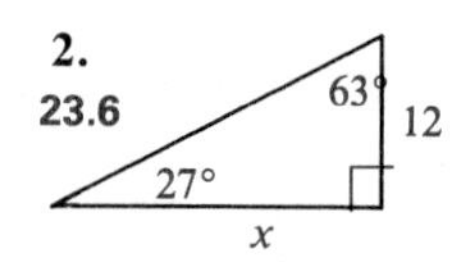

3. 48.3

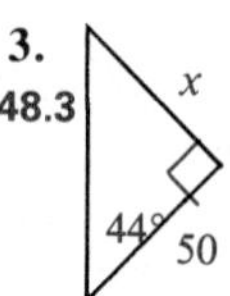

4. 1.4

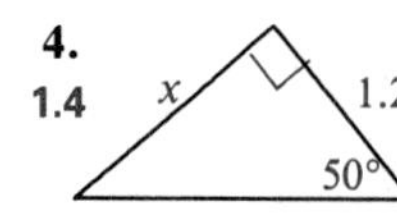

5. 55.4

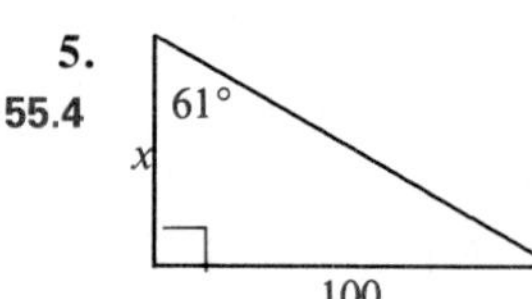

6. 3.3

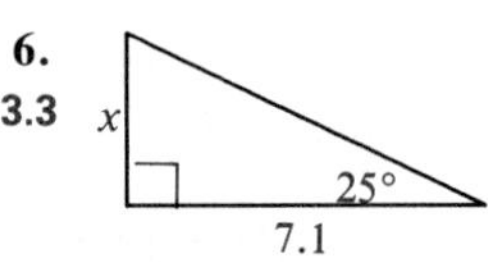

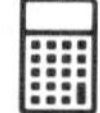

Find $y°$ correct to the nearest degree.

7. 57°

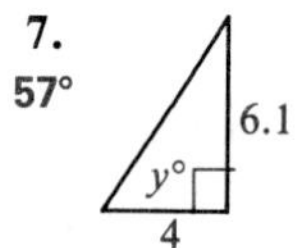

8. 28°

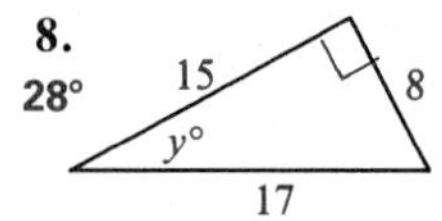

9. 27°

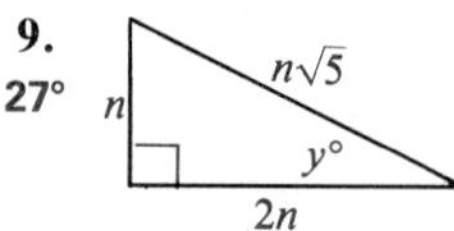

10. 37°

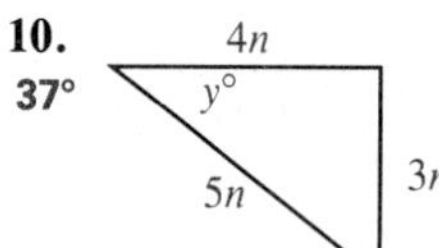

11. 31°

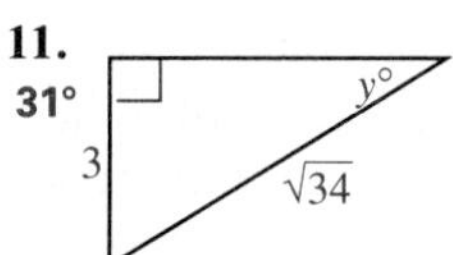

12. 56°

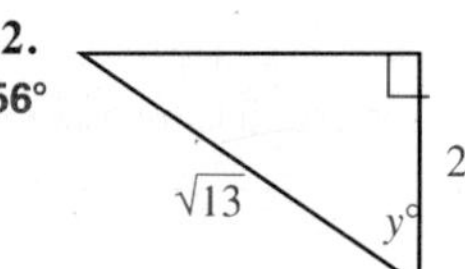

Find w, then z, correct to the nearest integer. Answers may vary slightly.

B

13.

$w = 60$
$z \approx 54$

14.

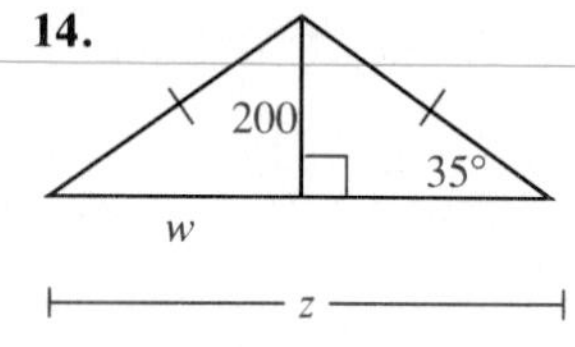

$w \approx 286$, $z \approx 571$

15.

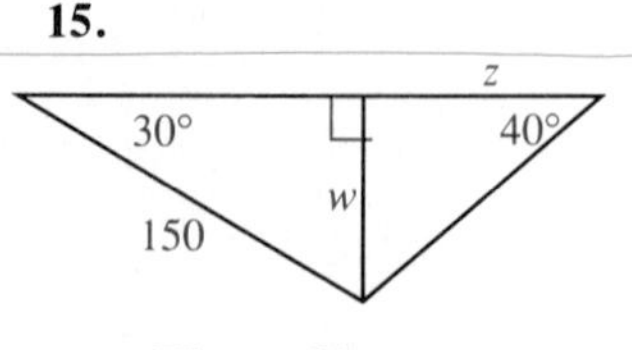

$w = 75$, $z \approx 89$

16.

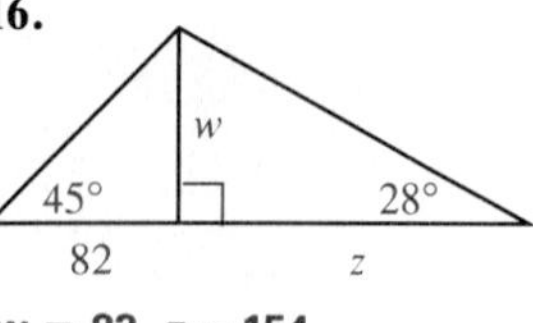

$w = 82$, $z \approx 154$

17.

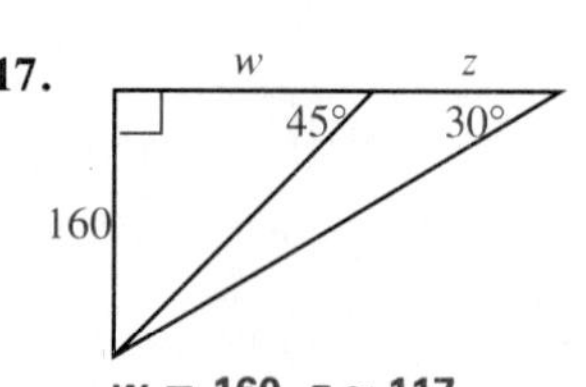

$w = 160$, $z \approx 117$

18.

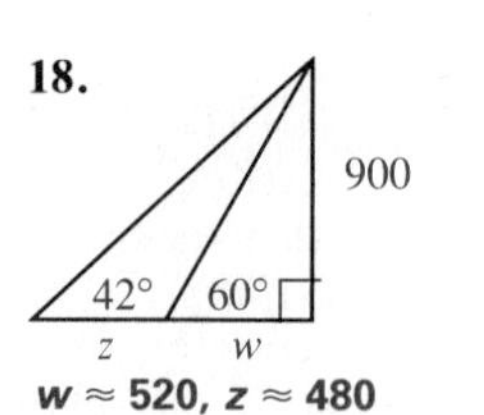

$w \approx 520$, $z \approx 480$

19. The grade of a road is 7%. What angle does the road make with the horizontal? **about 4°**

20. A road climbs at an 8° angle with the horizontal. What is the grade of the road? **about 14%**

21. The base of an isosceles triangle is 70 cm long. The altitude to the base is 75 cm long. Find, to the nearest degree, the base angles of the triangle. **65°**

22. A rhombus has diagonals of length 4 and 10. Find the angles of the rhombus to the nearest degree. **44°, 136°**

23. The shorter diagonal of a rhombus with a 70° angle is 122 cm long. How long, to the nearest centimeter, is the longer diagonal? **174 cm**

24. A rectangle is 80 cm long and 20 cm wide. Find, to the nearest degree, the acute angle formed at the intersection of the diagonals. **28°**

25. A natural question to consider is the following:

Does $\tan A + \tan B = \tan (A + B)$?

Try substituting 35° for A and 25° for B.

a. $\tan 35° + \tan 25° \approx$ _?_ + _?_ = _?_ **0.7002, 0.4663, 1.1665**
b. $\tan (35° + 25°) = \tan$ _?_° $\approx$ _?_ **60°, 1.7321**
c. What is your answer to the general question raised in this exercise, *yes* or *no*? **No**
d. Do you think $\tan A - \tan B = \tan (A - B)$? Explain. **No**

26. **a.** Given: $\triangle PQR$; $\angle R$ is a right angle.
Prove: $\tan P \cdot \tan Q = 1$

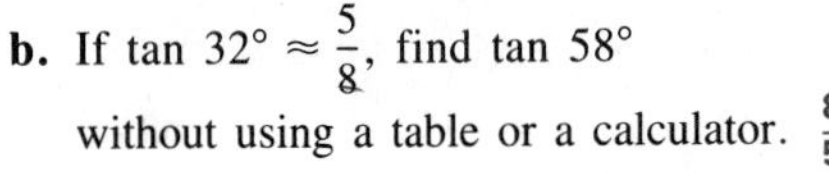

b. If $\tan 32° \approx \frac{5}{8}$, find $\tan 58°$ without using a table or a calculator. $\mathbf{\frac{8}{5}}$

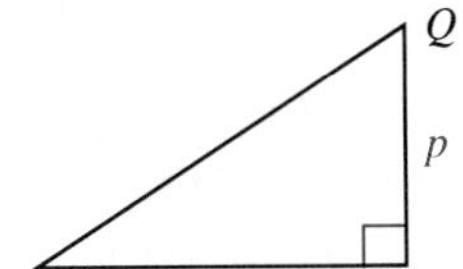

27. A rectangular box has length 4, width 3, and height 2.
a. Find BD. **5**
b. Find $\angle GBD$ to the nearest degree. **22°**

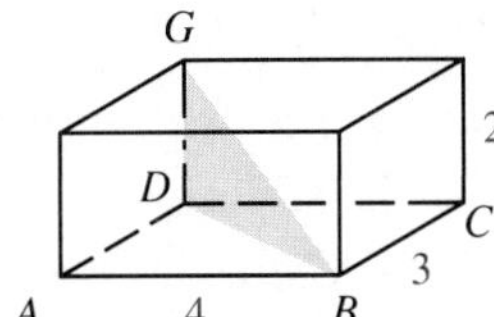

C **28.** If the figure is a cube, find $\angle TQS$ to the nearest degree. **35°**

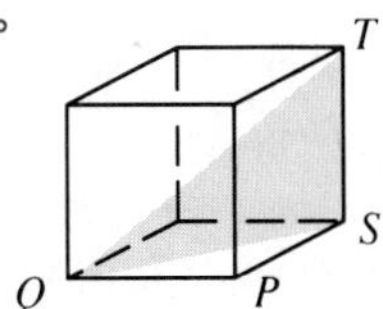

29. A person at window W, 40 ft above street level, sights points on a building directly across the street. H is chosen so that $\overline{WH}$ is horizontal. T is directly above H, and B is directly below. By measurement, $m\angle TWH = 61$ and $m\angle BWH = 37$. How far above street level is T? **about 136 ft**

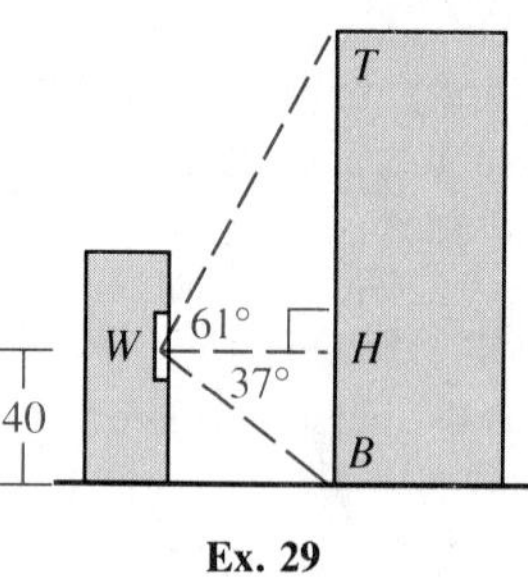

Ex. 29

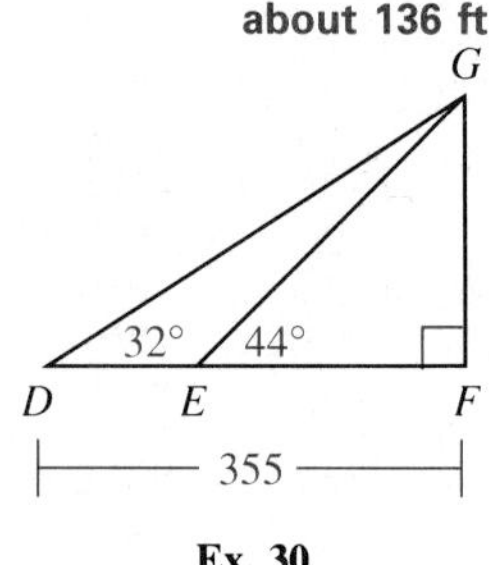

Ex. 30

30. Use the figure to find EF to the nearest integer. **230**

Using a Computer

This Exploration introduces sine and cosine ratios and explores their properties.

Explorations

These exploratory exercises can be done using a computer with a program that draws and measures geometric figures.

As you will learn in the next section, two other trigonometric ratios are the *sine* and *cosine*. If $\triangle ABC$ has a right angle at B, then:

$$\sin A = \frac{\text{leg opposite } \angle A}{\text{hypotenuse}} = \frac{BC}{AC}$$

$$\cos A = \frac{\text{leg adjacent to } \angle A}{\text{hypotenuse}} = \frac{AB}{AC}$$

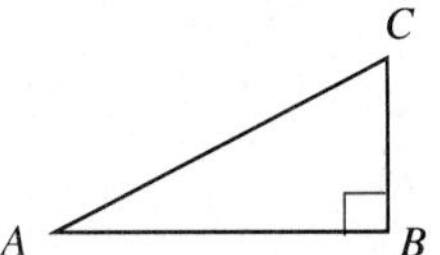

Using ASA, draw nine right triangles using nine values for $m\angle A$: 10, 20, 30, 40, 45, 50, 60, 70, and 80. Keep $m\angle B = 90$.

Compute and record sin A, cos A, and tan A for each measure of $\angle A$. What do you notice?

If you change the length of $\overline{AB}$ but keep the measures of $\angle A$ and $\angle B$ the same, do the sine, cosine, and tangent of $\angle A$ change?

Complete.

1. $\cos x° = \sin x°$ when $x =$ __?__ **45**
2. $\cos (90 - x)° = \sin$ __?__ ***x***
3. $\sin (90 - x)° = \cos$ __?__ ***x***
4. $\tan x° \cdot \tan (90 - x)° =$ __?__ **1**
5. For acute angles, what trigonometric ratios have values between 0 and 1? **sine and cosine**
6. What trigonometric ratio can have values greater than 1? **tangent**

Table of Trigonometric Ratios

Angle	Sine	Cosine	Tangent	Angle	Sine	Cosine	Tangent
1°	.0175	.9998	.0175	**46°**	.7193	.6947	1.0355
2°	.0349	.9994	.0349	**47°**	.7314	.6820	1.0724
3°	.0523	.9986	.0524	**48°**	.7431	.6691	1.1106
4°	.0698	.9976	.0699	**49°**	.7547	.6561	1.1504
5°	.0872	.9962	.0875	**50°**	.7660	.6428	1.1918
6°	.1045	.9945	.1051	**51°**	.7771	.6293	1.2349
7°	.1219	.9925	.1228	**52°**	.7880	.6157	1.2799
8°	.1392	.9903	.1405	**53°**	.7986	.6018	1.3270
9°	.1564	.9877	.1584	**54°**	.8090	.5878	1.3764
10°	.1736	.9848	.1763	**55°**	.8192	.5736	1.4281
11°	.1908	.9816	.1944	**56°**	.8290	.5592	1.4826
12°	.2079	.9781	.2126	**57°**	.8387	.5446	1.5399
13°	.2250	.9744	.2309	**58°**	.8480	.5299	1.6003
14°	.2419	.9703	.2493	**59°**	.8572	.5150	1.6643
15°	.2588	.9659	.2679	**60°**	.8660	.5000	1.7321
16°	.2756	.9613	.2867	**61°**	.8746	.4848	1.8040
17°	.2924	.9563	.3057	**62°**	.8829	.4695	1.8807
18°	.3090	.9511	.3249	**63°**	.8910	.4540	1.9626
19°	.3256	.9455	.3443	**64°**	.8988	.4384	2.0503
20°	.3420	.9397	.3640	**65°**	.9063	.4226	2.1445
21°	.3584	.9336	.3839	**66°**	.9135	.4067	2.2460
22°	.3746	.9272	.4040	**67°**	.9205	.3907	2.3559
23°	.3907	.9205	.4245	**68°**	.9272	.3746	2.4751
24°	.4067	.9135	.4452	**69°**	.9336	.3584	2.6051
25°	.4226	.9063	.4663	**70°**	.9397	.3420	2.7475
26°	.4384	.8988	.4877	**71°**	.9455	.3256	2.9042
27°	.4540	.8910	.5095	**72°**	.9511	.3090	3.0777
28°	.4695	.8829	.5317	**73°**	.9563	.2924	3.2709
29°	.4848	.8746	.5543	**74°**	.9613	.2756	3.4874
30°	.5000	.8660	.5774	**75°**	.9659	.2588	3.7321
31°	.5150	.8572	.6009	**76°**	.9703	.2419	4.0108
32°	.5299	.8480	.6249	**77°**	.9744	.2250	4.3315
33°	.5446	.8387	.6494	**78°**	.9781	.2079	4.7046
34°	.5592	.8290	.6745	**79°**	.9816	.1908	5.1446
35°	.5736	.8192	.7002	**80°**	.9848	.1736	5.6713
36°	.5878	.8090	.7265	**81°**	.9877	.1564	6.3138
37°	.6018	.7986	.7536	**82°**	.9903	.1392	7.1154
38°	.6157	.7880	.7813	**83°**	.9925	.1219	8.1443
39°	.6293	.7771	.8098	**84°**	.9945	.1045	9.5144
40°	.6428	.7660	.8391	**85°**	.9962	.0872	11.4301
41°	.6561	.7547	.8693	**86°**	.9976	.0698	14.3007
42°	.6691	.7431	.9004	**87°**	.9986	.0523	19.0811
43°	.6820	.7314	.9325	**88°**	.9994	.0349	28.6363
44°	.6947	.7193	.9657	**89°**	.9998	.0175	57.2900
45°	.7071	.7071	1.0000				

Teaching Suggestions,
pp. T109–T110

Objectives
Presenting the Lesson
Problem Solving

Supplementary Materials

Practice Master 45

Study Guide, pp. 101–102, 106

Computer Activity 17

Lesson Focus

This lesson introduces two additional trigonometric ratios for right triangles, namely the sine and cosine ratios. These two ratios are used to solve problems involving right triangles.

Suggested Assignments

Minimum
Day 1: 314/1–9
S 309/19, 20
Day 2: 315/10–17
Day 3: 316/18–24 even

Average
Day 1: 314–315/1–10, 12–14
Day 2: 315–316/11, 15–25 odd

Maximum
Day 1: 314–315/2–10 even, 11–14
S 309/25, 27
Day 2: 315–316/16–26 even

Teaching Note

Provide plenty of practice with the definitions of sine, cosine, and tangent ratios. Draw right triangles in various positions on the chalkboard, label them, and ask students to state the three trigonometric ratios for each acute angle.

8-6 *The Sine and Cosine Ratios*

Suppose you want to find the legs, x and y, in the triangle at the right. You can't easily find these values using the tangent ratio because the only side you know is the hypotenuse. The ratios that relate the legs to the hypotenuse are the *sine* and *cosine*.

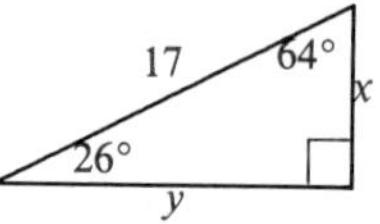

sine of $\angle A = \dfrac{\text{leg opposite } \angle A}{\text{hypotenuse}}$

cosine of $\angle A = \dfrac{\text{leg adjacent to } \angle A}{\text{hypotenuse}}$

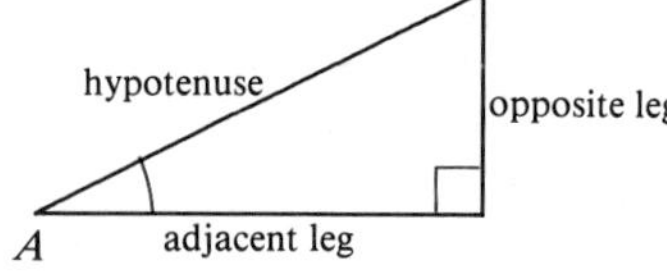

We now have three useful trigonometric ratios, given below in abbreviated form:

$$\tan A = \frac{\text{opposite}}{\text{adjacent}}$$

$$\sin A = \frac{\text{opposite}}{\text{hypotenuse}}$$

$$\cos A = \frac{\text{adjacent}}{\text{hypotenuse}}$$

Example 1 Find the values of x and y to the nearest integer.

Solution

$\sin 67° = \dfrac{x}{120}$
$x = 120 \cdot \sin 67°$
$x \approx 120(0.9205)$
$x \approx 110.46$, or 110

$\cos 67° = \dfrac{y}{120}$
$y = 120 \cdot \cos 67°$
$y \approx 120(0.3907)$
$y \approx 46.884$, or 47

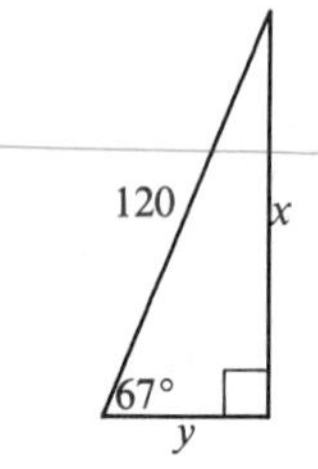

Example 2 Find the value of n to the nearest integer.

Solution

$\sin n° = \dfrac{22}{40}$
$\sin n° = 0.5500$
$n \approx 33$

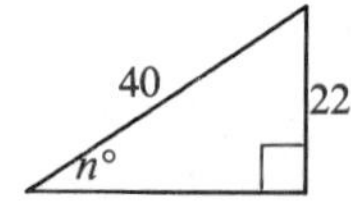

Example 3 An isosceles triangle has sides 8, 8, and 6. Find the lengths of its three altitudes.

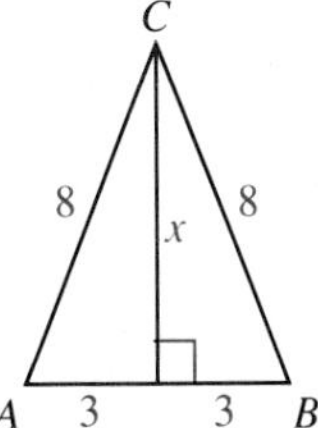

Solution The altitude to the base can be found using the Pythagorean Theorem.

$x^2 = 8^2 - 3^2 = 55$
$x = \sqrt{55} \approx 7.4$

Notice that $\cos B = \frac{3}{8}$ (so $m\angle B \approx 68$), and that the altitudes from A and B are congruent. (Why?)
To find the length of the altitudes from A and B, use

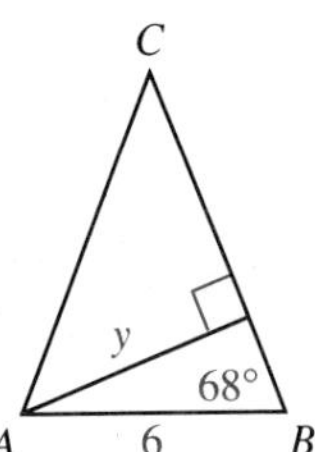

$\sin B \approx \sin 68° \approx \frac{y}{6}.$

$y \approx 6 \cdot \sin 68°$
$y \approx 5.6$

Classroom Exercises

1. $\frac{8}{17}, \frac{15}{17}, \frac{8}{15}$ **2.** $\frac{7}{25}, \frac{24}{25}, \frac{7}{24}$ **3.** $\frac{a}{c}, \frac{b}{c}, \frac{a}{b}$

In Exercises 1–3 express sin *A*, cos *A*, and tan *A* as fractions.

1.

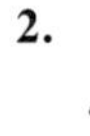

2.

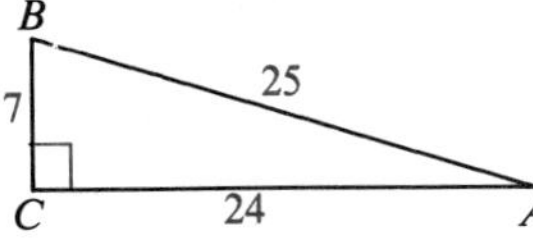

3.

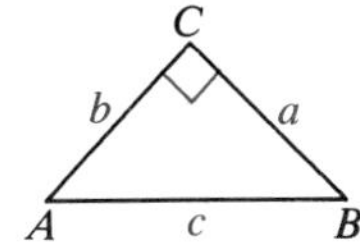

4–6. Using the triangles in Exercises 1–3, express sin B, cos B, and tan B as fractions. **See below.**

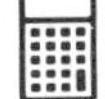

7. Use the table on page 311 or a scientific calculator to complete the statements.

a. $\sin 24° \approx$ _?_ **0.4067** **b.** $\cos 57° \approx$ _?_ **0.5446** **c.** $\sin 87° \approx$ _?_ **0.9986**
d. cos _?_ ≈ 0.9659 **15°** **e.** sin _?_ ≈ 0.1045 **6°** **f.** cos _?_ ≈ 0.1500 **81°**

State two different equations you could use to find the value of *x*.

8. $\sin 41° = \frac{x}{100}$ $\cos 49° = \frac{x}{100}$

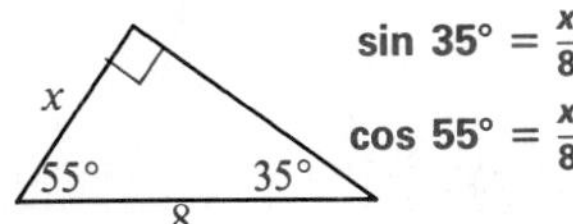

9. $\sin 35° = \frac{x}{8}$ $\cos 55° = \frac{x}{8}$

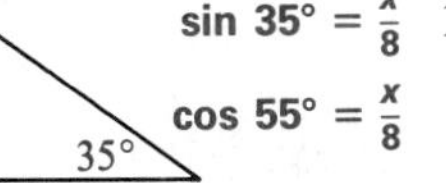

10. $\sin 50° = \frac{x}{12}$ $\cos 40° = \frac{x}{12}$

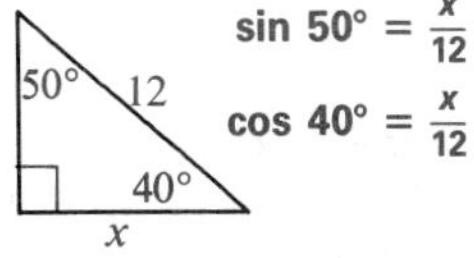

11. The word *cosine* is related to the phrase "complement's sine." Explain the relationship by using the diagram to express the cosine of $\angle A$ and the sine of its complement, $\angle B$. **$\cos A = \frac{b}{c}$, $\sin B = \frac{b}{c}$, $\cos A = \sin B$**

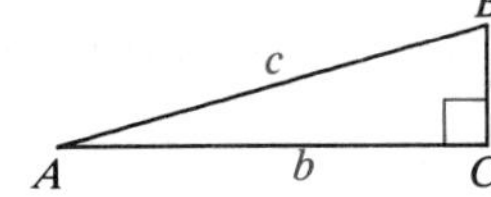

4. $\frac{15}{17}, \frac{8}{17}, \frac{15}{8}$ **5.** $\frac{24}{25}, \frac{7}{25}, \frac{24}{7}$ **6.** $\frac{b}{c}, \frac{a}{c}, \frac{b}{a}$

Chalkboard Examples

1. Find the values of x and y to the nearest integer. $x = 470$, $y = 883$

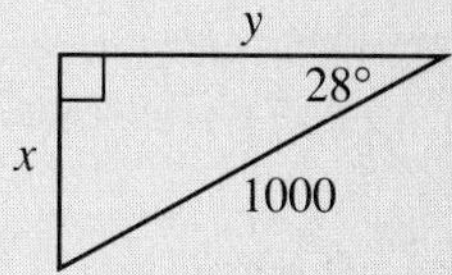

2. Find $x°$ correct to the nearest degree. 37°

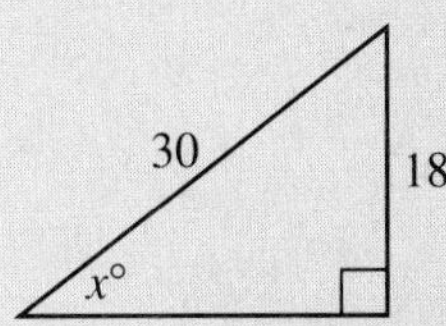

3.

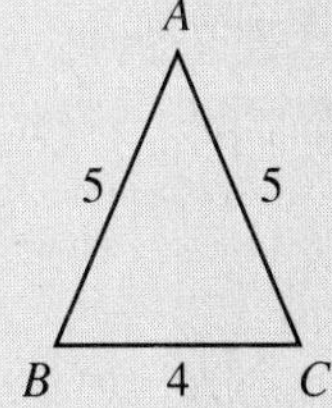

a. Find the measures of the three angles of $\triangle ABC$.
$m\angle A \approx 48$; $m\angle B \approx 66$; $m\angle C \approx 66$

b. Find the lengths of the three altitudes of $\triangle ABC$.
Altitude from $A = \sqrt{21} \approx 4.6$; altitudes from B and $C \approx 3.7$

Using a Calculator

Explain how to calculate sine, cosine, and their inverses using a scientific calculator. For Ex. 7(a)–(c) use sin or cos, and for Ex. 7(d)–(f) use inverses. Remind students to calculate in degrees, not radians.

12. The table on page 311 lists 0.5000 as the value of sin 30°. This value is exact. Explain why. **See below.**

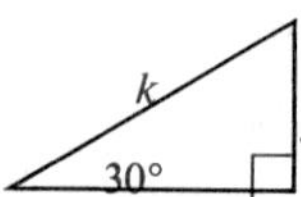

13. Suppose sin $n° = \frac{5}{13}$. Find cos $n°$ and tan $n°$ without using a table or calculator.

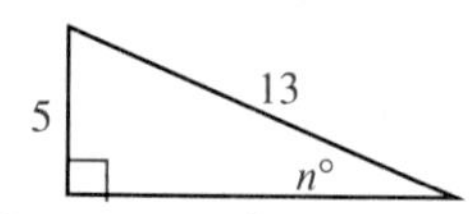

cos $n° = \frac{12}{13}$, tan $n° = \frac{5}{12}$

14. According to the table on page 311, sin 1° and tan 1° are both approximately 0.0175. Which is actually larger? How do you know? **See below.**

15. a. Using the definition of sine, explain why the sine of an acute angle is always less than one. **Hyp. is always the longest side, so $\frac{\text{opp.}}{\text{hyp.}} < 1$.**
b. Is the cosine of an acute angle always less than one? **Yes**

12. By the 30°-60°-90° △ Thm., $k = 2j$; sin 30° $= \frac{j}{k} = \frac{j}{2j} = \frac{1}{2}$.

14. Tan 1° is larger. In any rt. △, the hyp. is always the longest side, so $\frac{\text{opp.}}{\text{hyp.}} < \frac{\text{opp.}}{\text{adj.}}$.

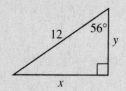

Written Exercises

In these exercises, use a scientific calculator or the table on page 311. Find lengths correct to the nearest integer and angles to the nearest degree. **Answers may vary slightly.**

In Exercises 1–12 find the values of the variables.

A

1. 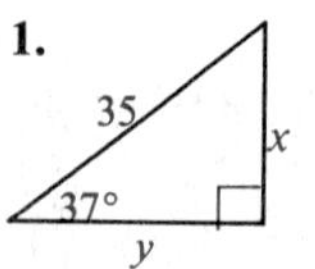

$x \approx 21$, $y \approx 28$

2. 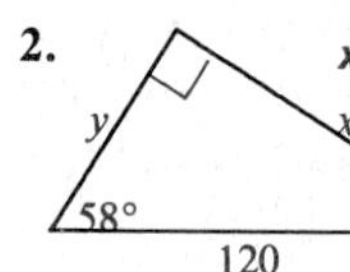

$x \approx 102$, $y \approx 64$

3. 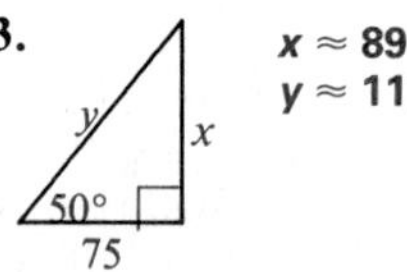

$x \approx 89$, $y \approx 117$

4. 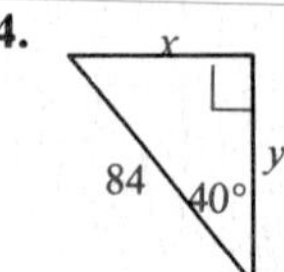

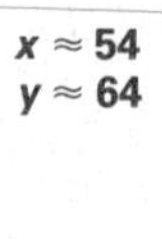
$x \approx 54$, $y \approx 64$

5. 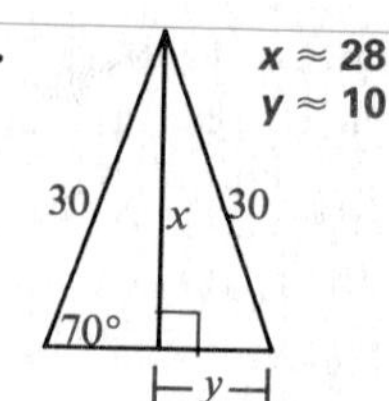

$x \approx 28$, $y \approx 10$

6. 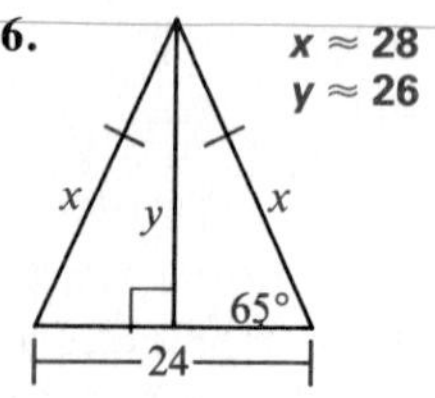

$x \approx 28$, $y \approx 26$

7. 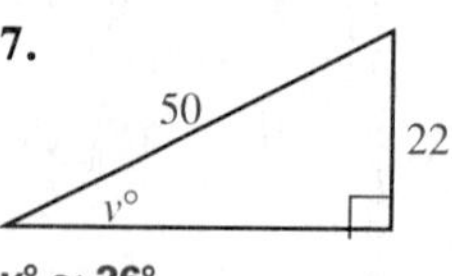

$v° \approx 26°$

8. 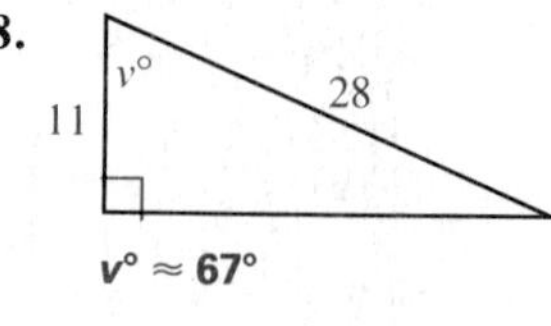

$v° \approx 67°$

9. 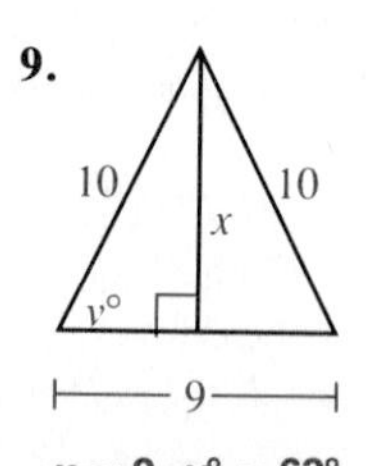

$x \approx 9$, $v° \approx 63°$

Guided Practice

Find the value of each variable.

1. $x \approx 9.9$, $y \approx 6.7$

2. $a \approx 8.5$, $b \approx 18.1$

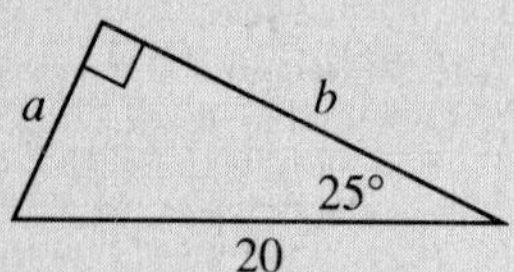

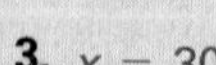

3. $x = 30$

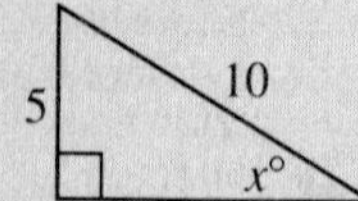

10.

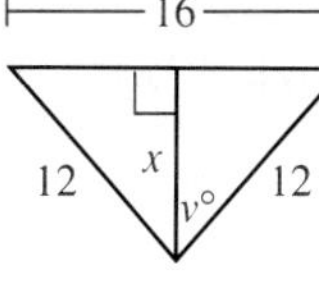

$x \approx 9$, $v° \approx 42°$

11.

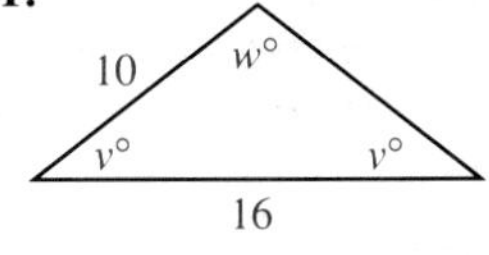

$v° \approx 37°$, $w° \approx 106°$

12.

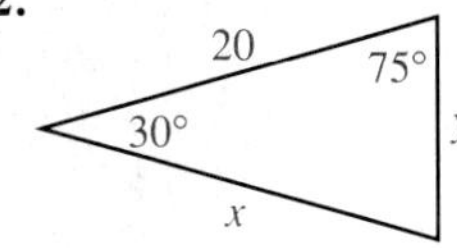

$x = 20$, $y \approx 10$

13. a. Use the Pythagorean Theorem to find the value of x in radical form. **$\sqrt{115}$**

b. Use trigonometry to find the values of y, then x. **$y \approx 40$ $x \approx 10.7$**

c. Are the values of x from parts (a) and (b) in reasonable agreement? **Yes; $\sqrt{115} \approx 10.7$**

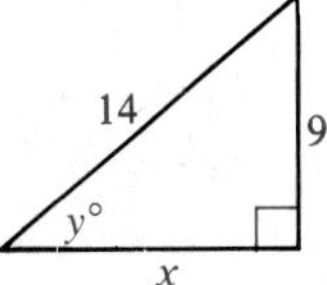

B **14.** A guy wire is attached to the top of a 75 m tower and meets the ground at a 65° angle. How long is the wire? **about 83 m**

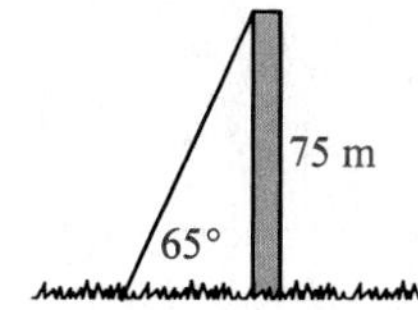

15. To find the distance from point A on the shore of a lake to point B on an island in the lake, surveyors locate point P with $m\angle PAB = 65$ and $m\angle APB = 25$. By measurement, $PA = 352$ m. Find AB. **about 149 m**

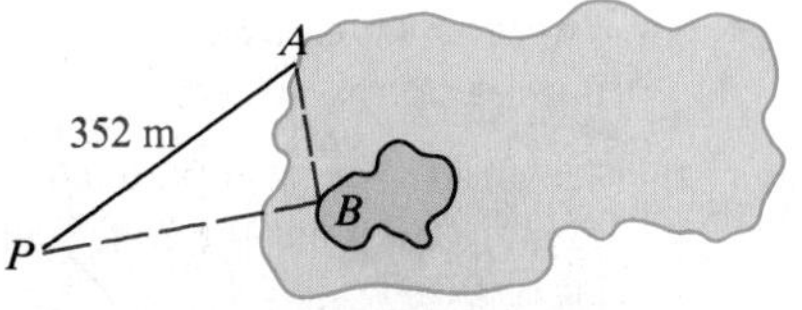

16. A certain jet is capable of a steady 20° climb. How much altitude does the jet gain when it moves 1 km through the air? Answer to the nearest 50 m. **350 m**

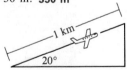

17. A 6 m ladder reaches higher up a wall when placed at a 70° angle than when placed at a 60° angle. How much higher, to the nearest tenth of a meter? **0.4 m**

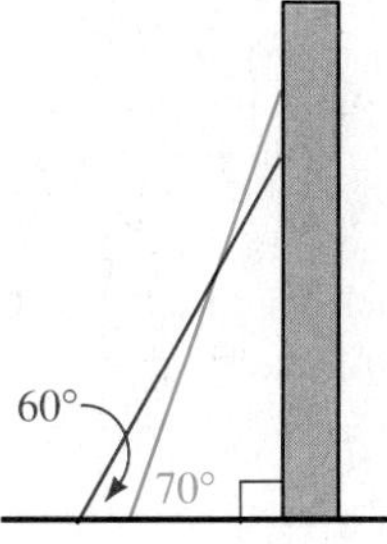

18. In $\triangle ABC$, $AB = AC = 13$ and $BC = 10$.
a. Find the length of the altitude from A. **12**
b. Find the measures of the three angles of $\triangle ABC$. **$m\angle B = m\angle C \approx 67$, $m\angle A \approx 46$**
c. Find the length of the altitude from C. **≈ 9**

19. In $\triangle ABC$, $m\angle B = m\angle C = 72$ and $BC = 10$.
a. Find AB and AC. **$AB = AC \approx 16$**
b. Find the length of the bisector of $\angle A$ to $\overline{BC}$. **≈ 15**

20. In $\triangle PAL$, $m\angle A = 90$, $m\angle L = 24$ and median $\overline{AM}$ is 6 cm long. Find PA. **about 5 cm**

21. The diagonals of rectangle $ABCD$ are 18 cm long and intersect in a 34° angle. Find the length and width of the rectangle. **length $\approx$ 17 cm, width $\approx$ 5 cm**

22. Points A, B, and C are three consecutive vertices of a regular decagon whose sides are 16 cm long. How long is diagonal $\overline{AC}$? **about 30 cm**

23. Points A, B, C, and D are consecutive vertices of a regular decagon with sides 20 cm long. $\overrightarrow{AB}$ and $\overrightarrow{DC}$ are drawn and intersect at X. Find BX. **about 12 cm**

For Exercises 24–26 write proofs in paragraph form.

C **24.** Prove that in any triangle with acute angles A and B, $\frac{a}{\sin A} = \frac{b}{\sin B}$. (*Hint*: Draw a perpendicular from the third vertex to $\overline{AB}$. Label it p.)

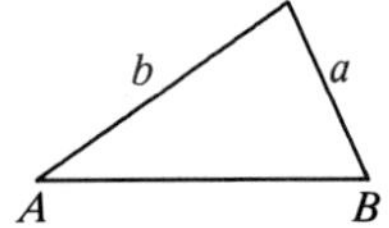

25. Prove: If R is any acute angle, $(\sin R)^2 + (\cos R)^2 = 1$. (*Hint*: From any point on one side of $\angle R$, draw a perpendicular to the other side.)

26. A rectangular card is 10 cm wide. The card is folded so that the vertex D falls at point D' on $\overline{AB}$ as shown. Crease $\overline{CE}$ with length k makes an $n°$ angle with $\overline{CD}$. Prove: $k = \frac{10}{\sin (2n)° \cos n°}$

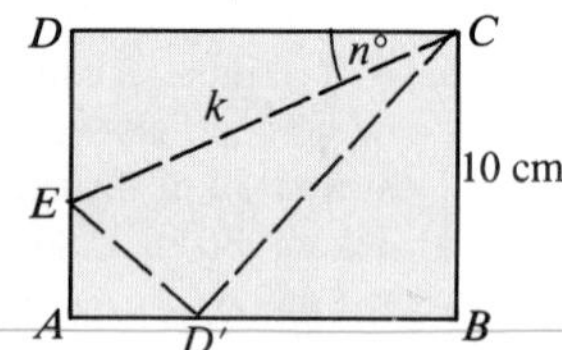

Challenge

The two blocks of wood have the same size and shape. It is possible to cut a hole in one block in such a way that you can pass the other block completely through the hole. How?

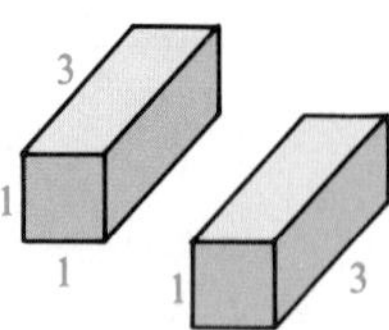

Teaching Note

When discussing the example on page 317, point out to students why the angle of elevation is congruent to the angle of depression. Both angles are formed with respect to a horizontal line. The two horizontal lines are parallel, and the line of sight serves as a transversal. The angle of elevation and the angle of depression, being alternate interior angles, are congruent.

8-7 *Applications of Right Triangle Trigonometry*

Suppose an operator at the top of a lighthouse sights a sailboat on a line that makes a 2° angle with a horizontal line. The angle between the horizontal and the line of sight is called an **angle of depression.** At the same time, a person in the boat must look 2° above the horizontal to see the tip of the lighthouse. This is an **angle of elevation.**

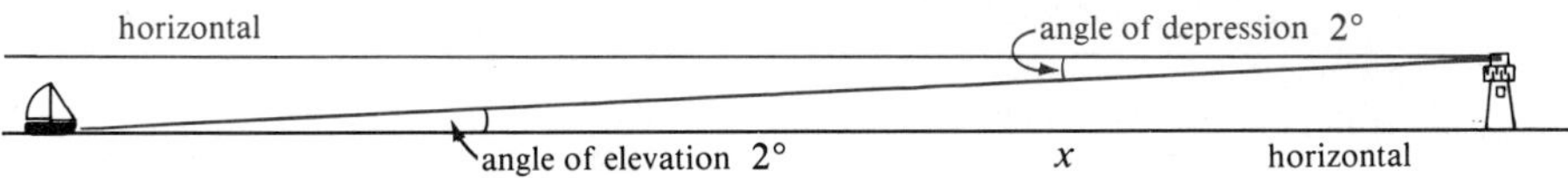

If the top of the lighthouse is 25 m above sea level, the distance x between the boat and the base of the lighthouse can be found in these two ways:

Method 1

$$\tan 2° = \frac{25}{x}$$
$$x = \frac{25}{\tan 2°}$$
$$x \approx \frac{25}{0.0349}$$
$$x \approx 716.3$$

Method 2

$$\tan 88° = \frac{x}{25}$$
$$x = 25(\tan 88°)$$
$$x \approx 25(28.6363)$$
$$x \approx 715.9$$

Because the tangent values in the table are approximations, the two methods give slightly different answers. In practice, the angle measurement will not be exact, and the boat may be moving. In a case like this we cannot claim high accuracy for our answer. A good answer would be: The boat is roughly 700 m from the lighthouse.

Classroom Exercises

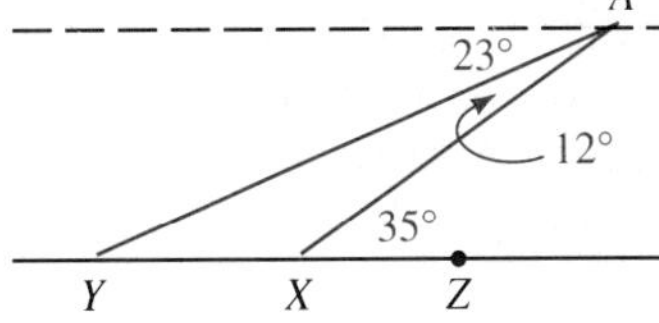

1. Two people at points X and Y sight an airplane at A.
   a. What is the angle of elevation from X to A? **35°**
   b. What is the angle of depression from A to X? **35°**
   c. What is the angle of depression from A to Y? **23°**
   d. What is the angle of elevation from Y to A? **23°**
   e. Is the measure of the angle of elevation from Z to A greater or less than 35? **greater than 35**

Teaching Suggestions, pp. T110–T111

Objective
Presenting the Lesson
Making Connections
Applications
Enrichment

Communication Skills, p. T111

Supplementary Materials

Practice Master 46
Test 33
Resource Book, pp. 52, 142
Study Guide, pp. 103–104
Computer Activity 18

Lesson Focus

The purpose of this lesson is to use trigonometry to solve problems involving right triangles.

Suggested Assignments

Minimum
Day 1: 318–319/1–6
S 316/19
Day 2: 319/7–12
Day 3: 320/Self-Test 2
324–325/Chapter Test 1–12
Day 4: 325/Chapter Test 13–27

Average
Day 1: 318–319/1–6
Day 2: 319/7–12
Day 3: 320/13, 14
320/Self-Test 2
Day 4: 324–325/Chapter Test

Maximum
Day 1: 318–319/1–9
S 316/21, 25
Day 2: 319–320/10–14
Day 3: 324–325/Chapter Test

Chalkboard Example

1. Draw a diagram showing a person who is 1.5 m tall standing 20 m from the base of a building. Also show that the person sights the top of the building with an angle of elevation of 58°. Find the height of the building. ≈ 33.5 m

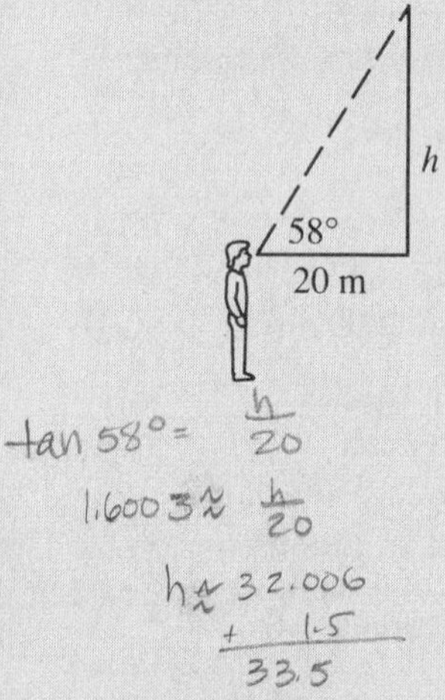

Guided Practice

1. When the sun's angle of elevation is 38°, a building casts a shadow of 45 m. How high is the building? ≈ 35 m
2. From the top of a lighthouse 20 m high, a sailboat is sighted having an angle of depression of 4°. How far from the lighthouse is the boat? ≈ 286 m

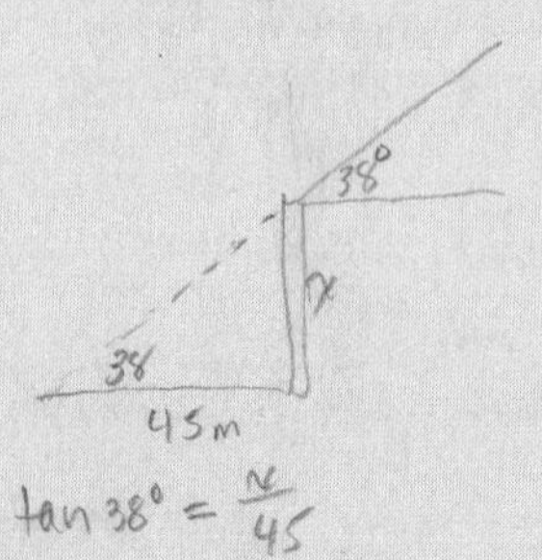

The lines shown are horizontal and vertical lines except for $\overleftrightarrow{HT}$ and $\overleftrightarrow{HG}$. Give the number of the angle and its special name when:

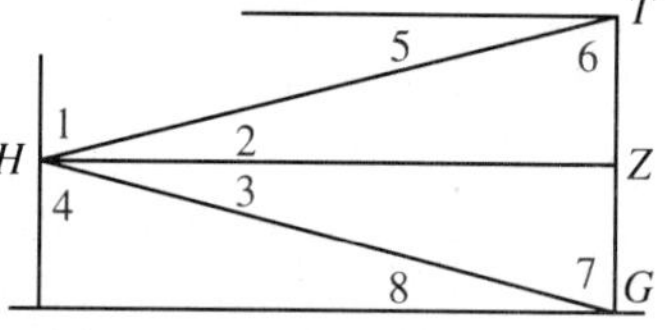

2. A person at H sights T. **∠2, ∠ of elev.**
3. A person at H sights G. **∠3, ∠ of depr.**
4. A person at T sights H. **∠5, ∠ of depr.**
5. A person at G sights H. **∠8, ∠ of elev.**

6. A driveway has a 15% grade.
   a. What is the angle of elevation of the driveway? **≈ 9°**
   b. If the driveway is 12 m long, about how much does it rise? **about 1.8 m**

7. A toboggan travels from point A at the top of the hill to point B at the bottom. Because the steepness of the hill varies, the angle of depression from A to B is only an approximate measure of the hill's steepness. We can, however, think of this angle of depression as representing the average steepness.
   a. If the toboggan travels 130 m from A to B and the vertical descent AC is 50 m, what is the approximate angle of depression? **≈ 23°**
   b. Why is your answer approximate? **130 m is an estimate of AB.**

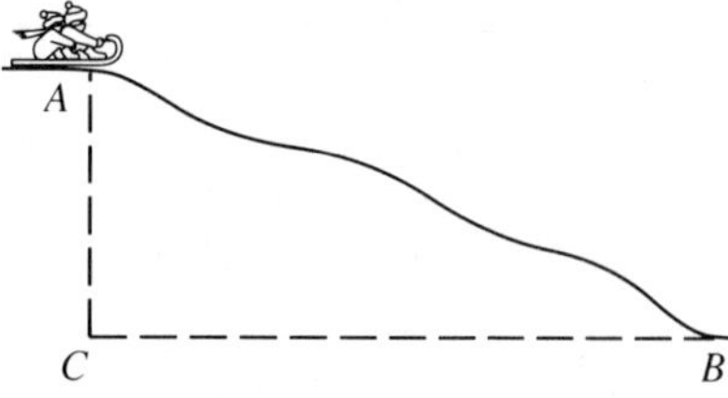

Written Exercises

Express lengths correct to the nearest integer and angles correct to the nearest degree. Use a calculator or the table on page 311.

A

1. When the sun's angle of elevation is 57°, a building casts a shadow 21 m long. How high is the building? **about 32 m**

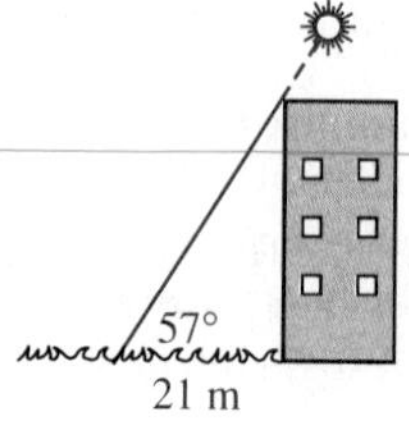

2. At a certain time, a vertical pole 3 m tall casts a 4 m shadow. What is the angle of elevation of the sun? **≈ 37°**

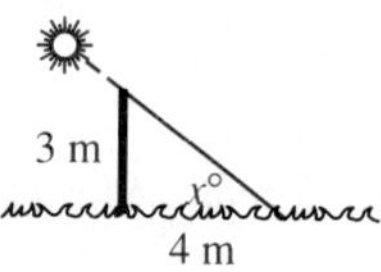

In Exercises 3–8 first draw a diagram.

3. A kite is flying at an angle of elevation of about 40°. All 80 m of string have been let out. Ignoring the sag in the string, find the height of the kite to the nearest 10 m. **about 50 m**

4. An advertising blimp hovers over a stadium at an altitude of 125 m. The pilot sights a tennis court at an 8° angle of depression. Find the ground distance in a straight line between the stadium and the tennis court. (*Note*: In an exercise like this one, an answer saying *about . . . hundred meters* is sensible.) **about 900 m**

5. An observer located 3 km from a rocket launch site sees a rocket at an angle of elevation of 38°. How high is the rocket at that moment? **about 2.3 km**

6. To land, an airplane will approach an airport at a 3° angle of depression. If the plane is flying at 30,000 ft, find the ground distance from the airport to the point directly below the plane when the pilot begins descending. Give your answer to the nearest 10,000 feet. **about 570,000 ft**

B **7.** Martha is 180 cm tall and her daughter Heidi is just 90 cm tall. Who casts the longer shadow, Martha when the sun is 70° above the horizon, or Heidi when the sun is 35° above the horizon? How much longer? **Heidi, ≈ 63 cm longer**

8. Two buildings on opposite sides of a street are 40 m apart. From the top of the taller building, which is 185 m high, the angle of depression to the top of the shorter building is 13°. Find the height of the shorter building. **≈ 176 m**

9. Scientists can estimate the depth of craters on the moon by studying the lengths of their shadows in the craters. Shadows' lengths can be estimated by measuring them on photographs. Find the depth of a crater if the shadow is estimated to be 400 m long and the angle of elevation of the sun is 48°. **about 440 m**

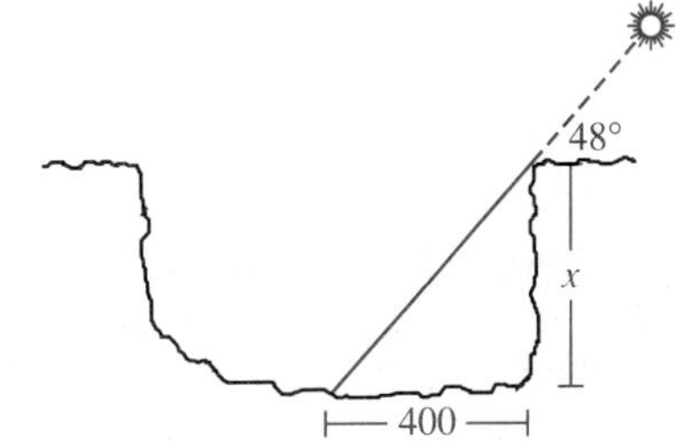

10. A road has a 10% grade.

a. What is the angle of elevation of the road? **≈ 6°**

b. If the road is 2 km long, how much does it rise? **≈ 0.2 km, or 200 m**

11. A road 1.6 km long rises 400 m. What is the angle of elevation of the road? **≈ 14°**

12. The force of gravity pulling an object down a hill is its weight multiplied by the sine of the angle of elevation of the hill.

a. With how many pounds of force is gravity pulling on a 3000 lb car on a hill with a 3° angle of elevation? **about 160 lb**

b. Could you push against the car and keep it from rolling down the hill? **Answers will vary.**

Problem Solving

The word problems given in the Written Exercises provide good applications of trigonometry. Many students will want to use calculators for this lesson. Since the number of decimal places for the answers will vary, you need to make clear to students how much rounding is expected. In the textbook, we assume given lengths and angle measures are exact; however, in actuality physical measurements always have some error. To allow for this error, answers might be rounded to only one or two significant digits. Such rounding is suggested, for example, in Ex. 4.

13. A soccer goal is 24 ft wide. Point A is 40 ft in front of the center of the goal. Point B is 40 ft in front of the right goal post.

a. Which angle is larger, $\angle A$ or $\angle B$? **∠A**

b. From which point would you have a better chance of kicking the ball into the goal? Why?
A; a player at A has a wider angle over which to aim at the goal.

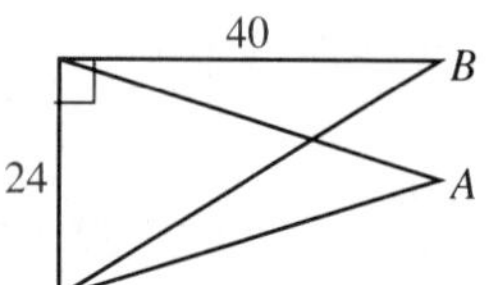

C 14. From the stage of a theater, the angle of elevation of the first balcony is 19°. The angle of elevation of the second balcony, 6.3 m directly above the first, is 29°. How high above stage level is the first balcony? (*Hint*: Use tan 19° and tan 29° to write two equations involving x and d. Solve for d, then find x.)

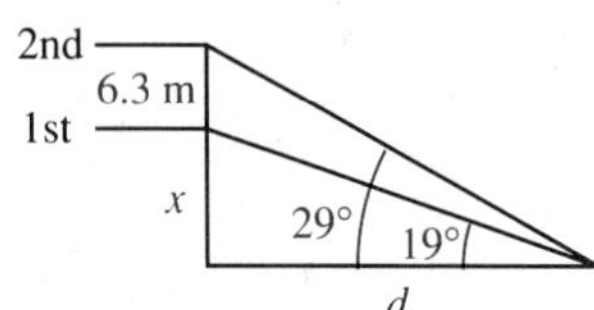

$\tan 19° = \frac{x}{d}$

$\tan 29° = \frac{x + 6.3}{d}$

$d = \frac{x}{\tan 19°} = \frac{x + 6.3}{\tan 29°}$

$x \approx 10.3$ **m**

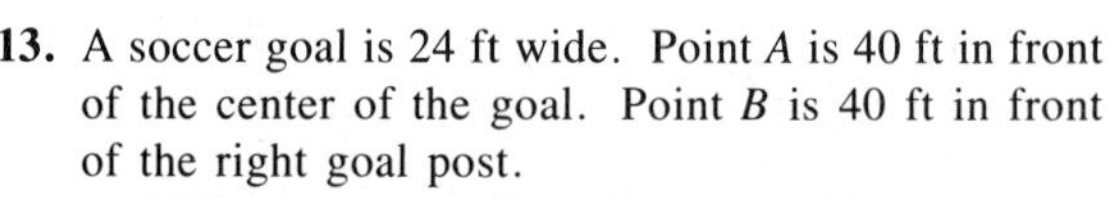

Self-Test 2

Exercises 1–5 refer to the diagram at the right.

1. $\tan E = \underline{\ ?\ }$ $\frac{7}{24}$ **2.** $\cos E = \underline{\ ?\ }$ $\frac{24}{25}$

3. $\sin E = \underline{\ ?\ }$ $\frac{7}{25}$ **4.** $\tan D = \underline{\ ?\ }$ $\frac{24}{7}$

5. To the nearest integer, $m\angle D = \underline{\ ?\ }$. **74**

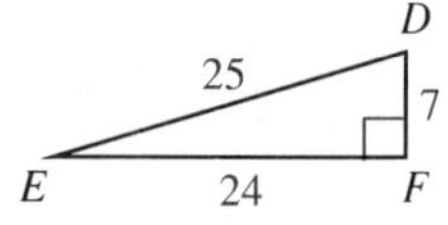

Find the value of x to the nearest integer. Answers may vary slightly.

6. **74**

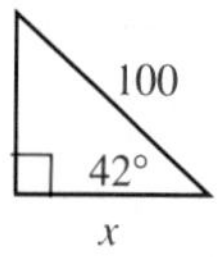

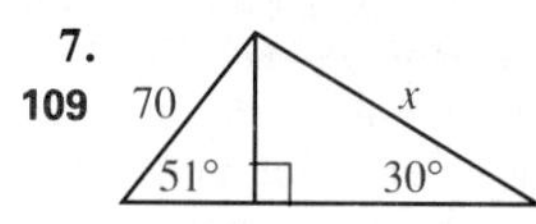

7. **109**

8. **113**

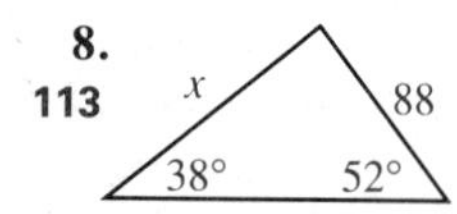

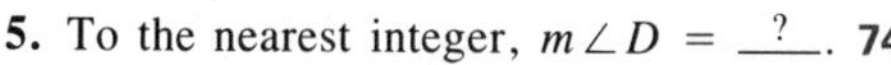

9. From a point on the ground 100 m from the foot of a cliff, the angle of elevation of the top of the cliff is 24°. How high is the cliff? **about 45 m**

Quick Quiz

Refer to the diagram and complete each statement.

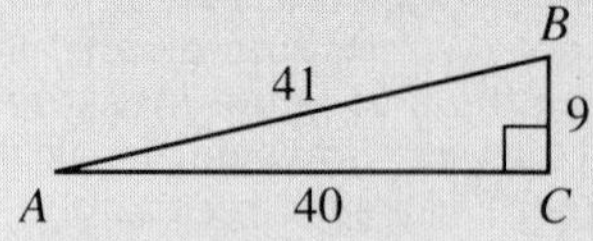

1. $\tan A = \frac{9}{40}$

2. $\tan B = \frac{40}{9}$

3. $\sin A = \frac{9}{41}$

4. $\cos B = \frac{9}{41}$

5. $m\angle A \approx 13$

Find the value of x to the nearest integer.

6. 15

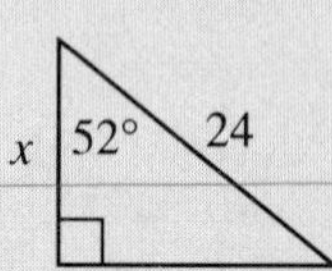

7. 143

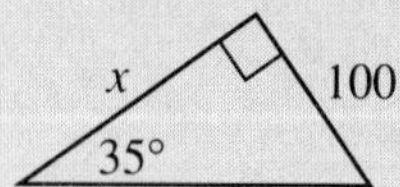

8. 83

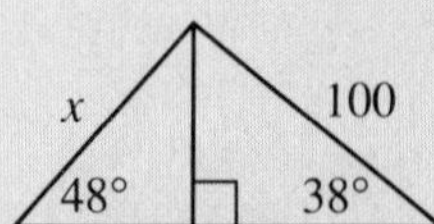

9. A building 25 m tall casts a shadow 17 m long. Find the angle of elevation of the sun. 56°

Application — *Passive Solar Design*

Passive solar homes are designed to let the sun heat the house during the winter but to prevent the sun from heating the house during the summer. Because the Earth's axis is not perpendicular to the *ecliptic* (the plane of the Earth's orbit around the sun), the sun is lower in the sky in the winter than it is in the summer.

From the latitude of the homesite the architect can determine the elevation angle of the sun (the angle at which a person has to look up from the horizontal to see the sun at noon) during the winter and during the summer. The architect can then design an overhang for windows that will let sunlight in the windows during the winter, but will shade the windows during the summer.

The Earth's axis makes an angle of $23\frac{1}{2}°$ with a perpendicular to the ecliptic plane. So for places in the northern hemisphere between the Tropic of Cancer and the Arctic Circle, the angle of elevation of the sun at noon on the longest day of the year, at the summer solstice, is 90° − the latitude + $23\frac{1}{2}°$. Its angle of elevation at noon on the shortest day, at the winter solstice, is 90° − the latitude − $23\frac{1}{2}°$. For example, in Terre Haute, Indiana, at latitude $39\frac{1}{2}°$ north, the angle of elevation of the sun at noon on the longest day is 74° ($90 - 39\frac{1}{2} + 23\frac{1}{2} = 74$), and at noon on the shortest day it is 27° ($90 - 39\frac{1}{2} - 23\frac{1}{2} = 27$).

Exercises

Find the angle of elevation of the sun at noon on the longest day and at noon on the shortest day in the following cities. The approximate north latitudes are in parentheses.

1. Seattle, Washington ($47\frac{1}{2}°$) **66°, 19°**

2. Chicago, Illinois (42°) **$71\frac{1}{2}°$, $24\frac{1}{2}°$**

3. Houston, Texas (30°) **$83\frac{1}{2}°$, $36\frac{1}{2}°$**

4. Los Angeles, California (34°) **$79\frac{1}{2}°$, $32\frac{1}{2}°$**

5. Nome, Alaska ($64\frac{1}{2}°$) **49°, 2°**

6. Miami, Florida (26°) **$87\frac{1}{2}°$, $40\frac{1}{2}°$**

7. For a city south of the Tropic of Cancer, such as San Juan, Puerto Rico (18°N), the formula gives a summer solstice angle greater than 90°. What does this mean? **See below.**

8. For a place north of the Arctic Circle, such as Prudhoe Bay, Alaska (70°N), the formula gives a negative value for the angle of elevation of the sun at noon at the winter solstice. What does this mean? **The sun doesn't rise at all (i.e., it is never seen above the horizon).**

7. The sun is more than 90° from the southern horizon and is therefore less than 90° from the northern horizon.

9. An architect is designing a passive solar house to be located in Terre Haute, Indiana. The diagram shows a cross-section of a wall that will face south. How long must the overhang x be to shade the entire window at noon at the summer solstice? **about 2 ft**

10. If the overhang has the length found in Exercise 9, how much of the window will be in the sun at noon at the winter solstice? **the entire window**

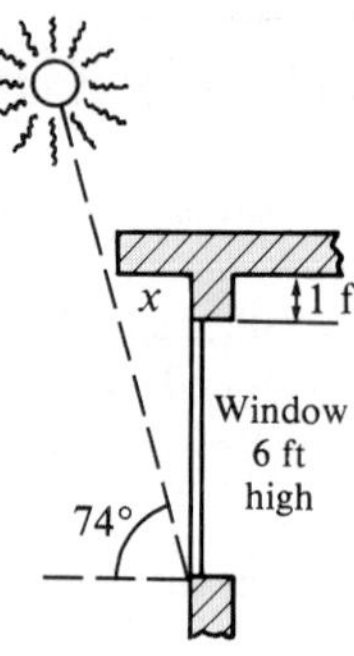

Chapter Summary

1. When $\frac{a}{x} = \frac{x}{b}$, x is the geometric mean between a and b.

2. A right triangle is shown with the altitude drawn to the hypotenuse.

a. The two triangles formed are similar to the original triangle and to each other.

$$\frac{x}{h} = \frac{h}{y} \qquad \frac{c}{b} = \frac{b}{x} \qquad \frac{c}{a} = \frac{a}{y}$$

b. Pythagorean Theorem: $c^2 = a^2 + b^2$

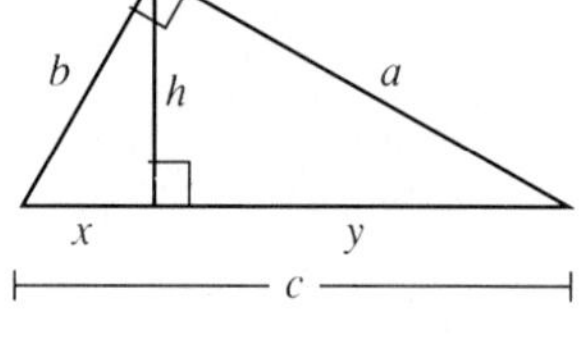

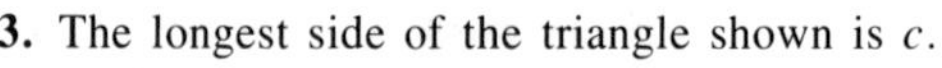

3. The longest side of the triangle shown is c.

If $c^2 = a^2 + b^2$, then the triangle is a right triangle.
If $c^2 > a^2 + b^2$, then the triangle is obtuse.
If $c^2 < a^2 + b^2$, then the triangle is acute.

4. The sides of a 45°-45°-90° triangle and the sides of a 30°-60°-90° triangle are related as shown.

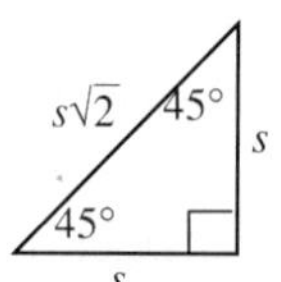

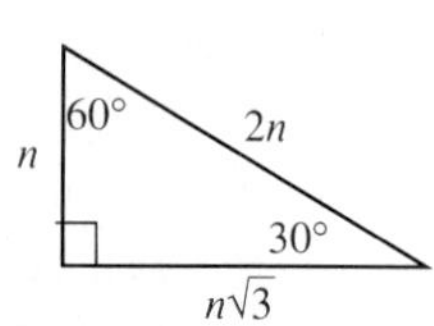

5. In the right triangle shown:

$$\tan A = \frac{a}{b} \qquad \sin A = \frac{a}{c} \qquad \cos A = \frac{b}{c}$$

The tangent, sine, and cosine ratios are useful in solving problems involving right triangles.

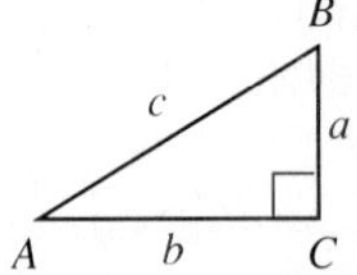

Supplementary Materials

Practice Master 47

Test 34

Resource Book, pp. 53–54, 143

Chapter Review

1. Find the geometric mean between 12 and 3. **6** 8–1

2. $x =$ _?_ **$5\sqrt{2}$**

3. $y =$ _?_ **$5\sqrt{6}$**

4. $z =$ _?_ **$5\sqrt{3}$**

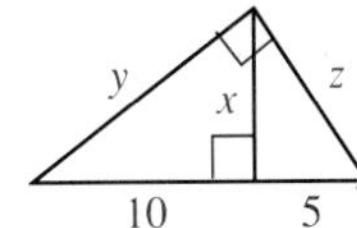

5. The legs of a right triangle are 3 and 6. Find the length of the hypotenuse. **$3\sqrt{5}$** 8–2

6. A rectangle has sides 10 and 8. Find the length of a diagonal. **$2\sqrt{41}$**

7. The diagonal of a square has length 14. Find the length of a side. **$7\sqrt{2}$**

8. The legs of an isosceles triangle are 10 units long and the altitude to the base is 8 units long. Find the length of the base. **12**

Tell whether a triangle formed with sides having the lengths named is acute, right, or obtuse. If a triangle can't be formed, write *not possible*.

9. 4, 5, 6 **acute** **10.** 8, 8, 17 **not possible** 8–3

11. 11, 60, 61 **right** **12.** $2\sqrt{3}$, $3\sqrt{2}$, 6 **obtuse**

Find the value of *x*. 8–4

13. **$5\sqrt{3}$**

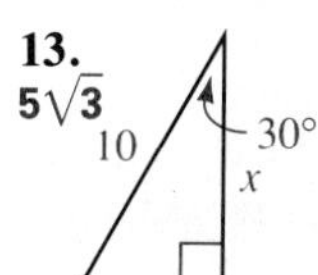

14. **$7\sqrt{2}$**

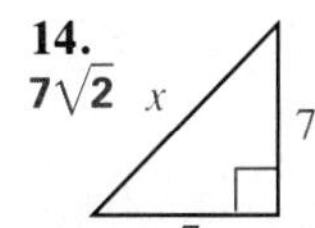

15. **16**

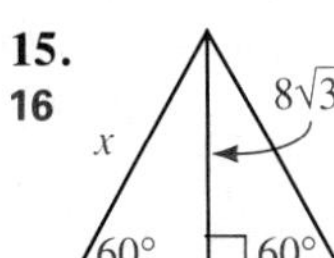

16. The legs of an isosceles right triangle have length 12. Find the lengths of the hypotenuse and the altitude to the hypotenuse. **$12\sqrt{2}$; $6\sqrt{2}$**

Complete. Find angle measures and lengths correct to the nearest integer. Use a calculator or the table on page 311 if needed.

17. 8–5

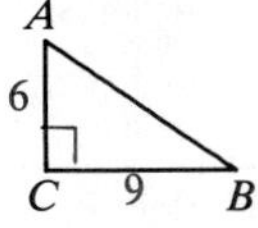

a. $\tan A =$ _?_ **1.5**

b. $\tan B =$ _?_ **$\frac{2}{3}$**

c. $m\angle B \approx$ _?_ **34**

18.

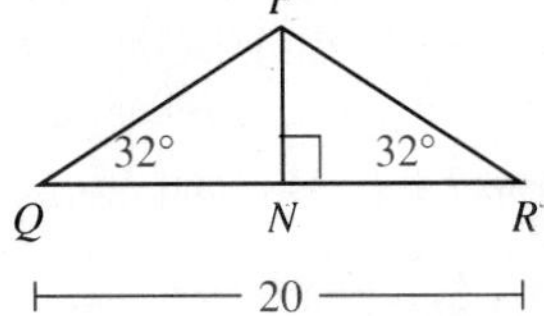

a. $QN =$ _?_ **10**

b. $PN \approx$ _?_ **6**

Complete. Find angle measures and lengths correct to the nearest integer. Use a calculator or the table on page 311 if needed.

19. 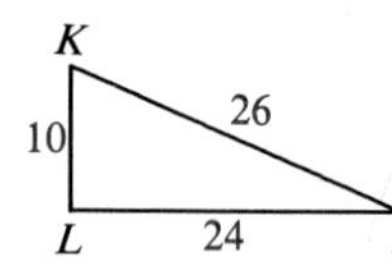

a. cos J = ___?___ **$\frac{12}{13}$**

b. sin K = ___?___ **$\frac{12}{13}$**

c. $m\angle K \approx$ ___?___ **67**

20. 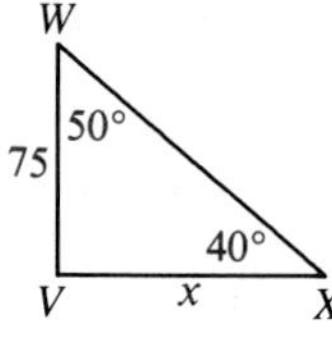 8–6

a. $WX \approx$ ___?___ **117**

b. $VX \approx$ ___?___ **89**

Find the values of *x* and *y* correct to the nearest integer.

21. **57** 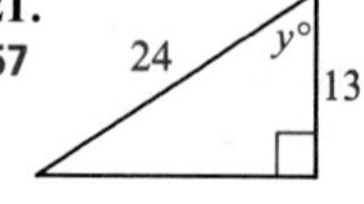

22. **26** 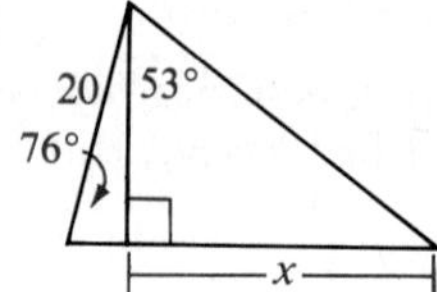

23. **23** 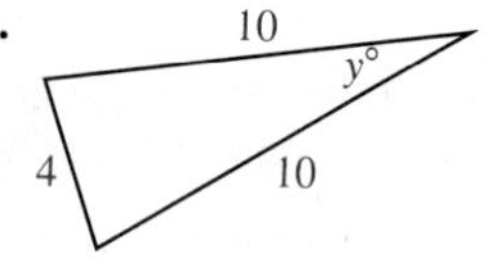

24. Lee, on the ground, looks up at Chong Ye in a hot air balloon at a 35° angle of elevation. If Lee and Chong Ye are 500 ft apart, about how far off the ground is Chong Ye? **about 290 ft** 8–7

Teaching References

Alternate Test, p. T19

Chapter Test

Find the geometric mean between the numbers.

1. 5 and 20 **10** **2.** 6 and 8 **$4\sqrt{3}$**

In the diagram, $\angle DNF$ is a right angle and $\overline{NE} \perp \overline{DF}$.

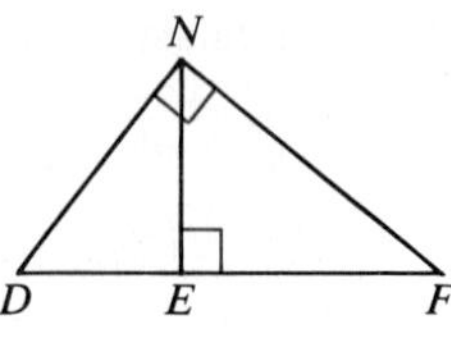

3. $\triangle DNF \sim \triangle$ ___?___, and $\triangle DNF \sim \triangle$ ___?___. ***DEN, NEF***

4. NE is the geometric mean between ___?___ and ___?___. ***DE, EF***

5. NF is the geometric mean between ___?___ and ___?___. ***DF, EF***

6. If $DE = 10$ and $EF = 15$, then ND = ___?___. **$5\sqrt{10}$**

Find the values of *x* and *y*.

7. 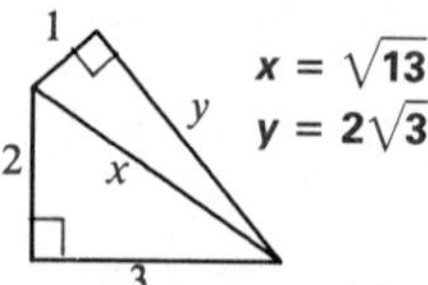

$x = \sqrt{13}$
$y = 2\sqrt{3}$

8. 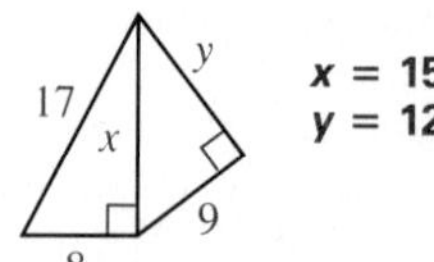

$x = 15$
$y = 12$

Tell whether a triangle formed with sides having the lengths named is acute, right, or obtuse. If a triangle can't be formed, write *not possible*.

9. 3, 4, 8 **not possible**

10. 11, 12, 13 **acute**

11. 7, 7, 10 **obtuse**

12. $\frac{3}{5}, \frac{4}{5}, 1$ **right**

Find the value of x.

13. **$11\sqrt{2}$**

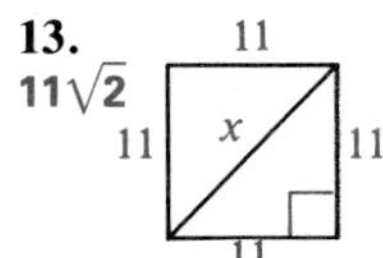

14. **9**

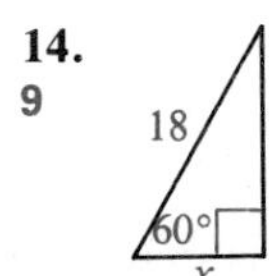

15. **14**

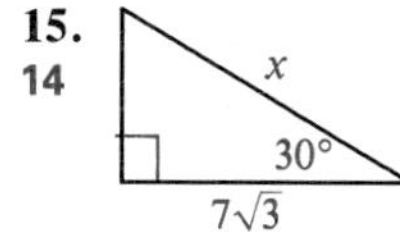

16. **$\sqrt{3}$**

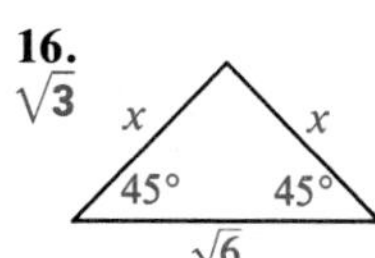

17. **24**

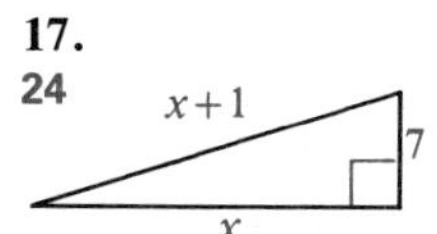

18. **6**

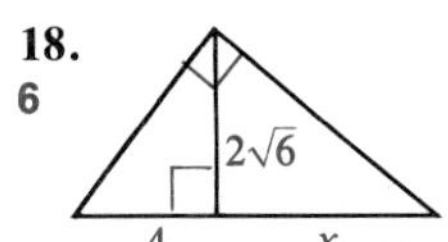

Find lengths correct to the nearest integer and angles correct to the nearest degree.

19. **21**

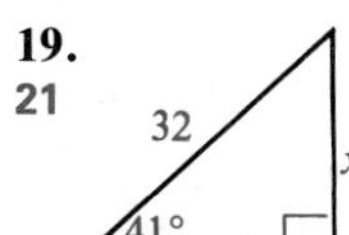

20. **31**

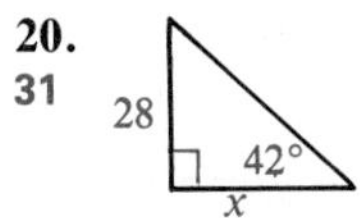

21. **28**

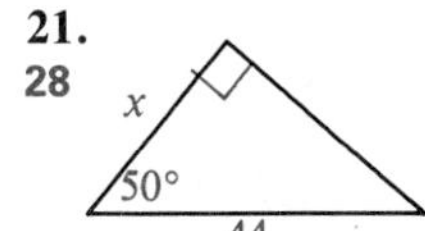

22. **37°**

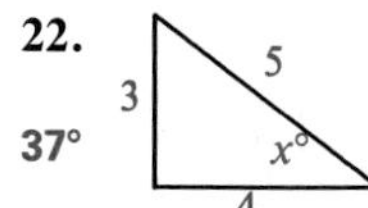

23. **32°**

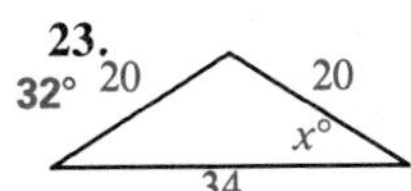

24. **31**

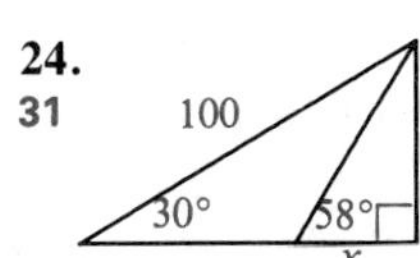

25. The sides of a rhombus are 4 units long and one diagonal has length 4. How long is the other diagonal? **$4\sqrt{3}$**

26. In the diagram, $\angle RTS$ is a right angle; $\overline{RT}$, $\overline{RS}$, $\overline{VT}$ and $\overline{VS}$ have the lengths shown.
What is the measure of $\angle V$? Explain. **90 See below.**

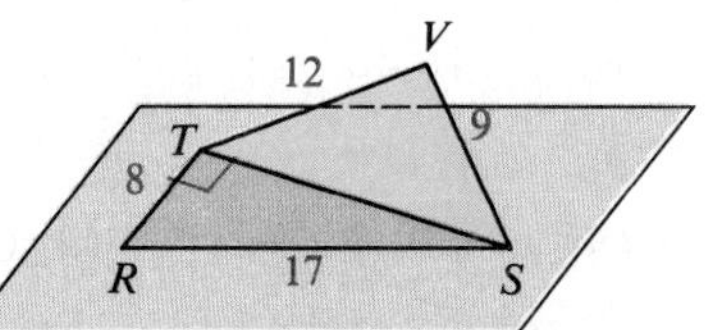

27. From the top of a lighthouse 18 m high, the angle of depression to sight a boat is 4°. What is the distance between the boat and the base of the lighthouse? **about 260 m**

26. **$TS = 15$. Because $15^2 = 12^2 + 9^2$, $\triangle TVS$ is a rt. $\triangle$. The largest $\angle$ of a $\triangle$ is opp. the longest side, so $\angle V$ is a rt. $\angle$.**

Supplementary Materials

Practice Masters 48, 49

Resource Book, p. 197

Preparing for College Entrance Exams

Strategy for Success

Problems in college entrance exams often involve right triangles. One thing you can do in preparing for the exams is to learn the common right-triangle lengths listed on page 295. These Pythagorean triples are often used on tests where calculators are not allowed. Also, keep in mind that if a, b, and c are the lengths of the sides of a right triangle, then for any $k > 0$, ak, bk, and ck are also lengths of sides of a right triangle.

Indicate the best answer by writing the appropriate letter.

A **1.** In $\triangle ABC$, $m\angle A : m\angle B : m\angle C = 2:5:5$. $m\angle B =$
(A) 75 **(B)** 60 **(C)** 30 **(D)** 40 **(E)** 100

C **2.** The proportion $\frac{t}{z} = \frac{m}{k}$ is *not* equivalent to:
(A) $\frac{t - z}{z} = \frac{m - k}{k}$ **(B)** $\frac{k}{z} = \frac{m}{t}$ **(C)** $\frac{t}{m} = \frac{k}{z}$ **(D)** $tk = mz$ **(E)** $\frac{z}{t} = \frac{k}{m}$

B **3.** If $\triangle ABC \sim \triangle DEF$, which statement is not necessarily true?
(A) $\angle C \cong \angle F$ **(B)** $\overline{BC} \cong \overline{EF}$ **(C)** $\frac{AB}{BC} = \frac{DE}{EF}$
(D) $m\angle A + m\angle E = m\angle B + m\angle D$ **(E)** $AC \cdot DE = DF \cdot AB$

C **4.** If $ZY = 2x + 9$, $ZM = 10$, $ZN = x + 3$, and $MW = x$, then $x =$
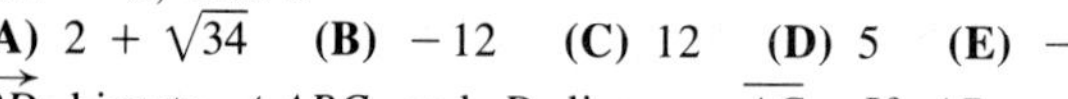
(A) $2 + \sqrt{34}$ **(B)** -12 **(C)** 12 **(D)** 5 **(E)** -5

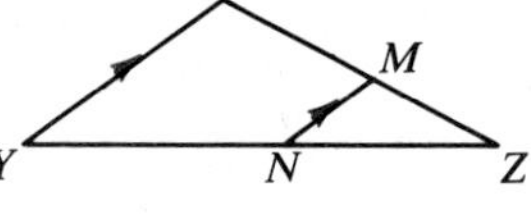

E **5.** $\overrightarrow{BD}$ bisects $\angle ABC$ and D lies on $\overline{AC}$. If $AB = 6$, $BC = 14$, and $AC = 14$, find AD.
(A) 6 **(B)** 8.4 **(C)** 9.8 **(D)** 7 **(E)** 4.2

A **6.** Find the geometric mean of $2x$ and $2y$.
(A) $2\sqrt{xy}$ **(B)** $\sqrt{2xy}$ **(C)** $2\sqrt{x + y}$ **(D)** $\sqrt{2(x + y)}$ **(E)** $4xy$

C **7.** If $XY = 8$, $YZ = 40$, and $XZ = 41$, then:
(A) $\triangle XYZ$ is acute **(B)** $\triangle XYZ$ is right **(C)** $\triangle XYZ$ is obtuse
(D) $m\angle Y < m\angle Z$ **(E)** no $\triangle XYZ$ is possible

A **8.** A rhombus contains a 120° angle. Find the ratio of the length of the longer diagonal to the length of the shorter diagonal.
(A) $\sqrt{3}:1$ **(B)** $\sqrt{3}:3$ **(C)** $\sqrt{2}:1$ **(D)** $\sqrt{2}:2$ **(E)** cannot be determined

B **9.** $k =$
(A) $j \sin A$ **(B)** $j \tan A$ **(C)** $\frac{l}{\sin A}$
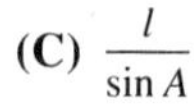
(D) $l \cos A$ **(E)** $l \tan A$

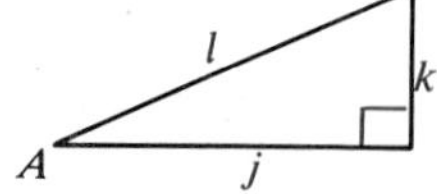

C **10.** The legs of an isosceles triangle have length 4 and the base angles have measure 65. If $\sin 65° \approx 0.91$, $\cos 65° \approx 0.42$, and $\tan 65° \approx 2.14$, then the approximate length of the base of the triangle is:
(A) 1.7 **(B)** 1.9 **(C)** 3.4 **(D)** 3.6 **(E)** 4.4

Cumulative Review: Chapters 1–8

In Exercises 1–8, complete each statement.

A **1.** If S is between R and T, then $RS + ST = RT$ by the __?__. **Segment Add. Post.**

2. A statement that is accepted without proof is called a __?__. **postulate**

3. A statement that can be proved easily by using a theorem is called a __?__. **corollary**

4. To write an indirect proof, you assume temporarily that the __?__ is not true. **conclusion**

5. A conditional and its __?__ are always logically equivalent. **contrapositive**

6. The sides of an obtuse triangle have lengths x, $2x + 2$, and $2x + 3$. __?__ $< x <$ __?__. **1, 5**

7. In an isosceles right triangle, the ratio of the length of a leg to the length of the hypotenuse is __?__. **1:$\sqrt{2}$**

8. If $\sin B = \frac{8}{17}$, then $\cos B =$ __?__. **$\frac{15}{17}$**

9. Given: A triangle is equiangular only if it is isosceles.

a. Write an if-then statement that is logically equivalent to the given conditional. **If a triangle is equiangular, then it is isosceles.**

b. State the converse. Sketch a diagram to disprove the converse. **If a △ is isos., then it is equiangular.**

10. Use inductive reasoning to guess the next two numbers in the sequence:

1, 2, 6, 15, 31, 56, . . . **92, 141**

11. When two parallel lines are cut by a transversal, two corresponding angles have measures x^2 and $6x$. Find the measure of each angle. **36**

B **12.** In $\triangle XYZ$, $m\angle X : m\angle Y : m\angle Z = 3:3:4$.

a. Is $\triangle XYZ$ scalene, isosceles, or equilateral? **isos.**

b. Is $\triangle XYZ$ acute, right, or obtuse? **acute**

c. Name the longest side of $\triangle XYZ$. **$\overline{XY}$**

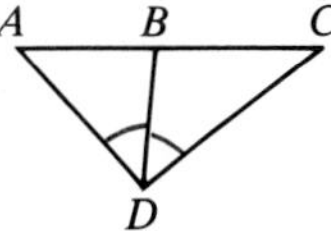

13. If $AB = x - 5$, $BC = x - 2$, $CD = x + 4$, and $DA = x$, find the value of x. **20**

14. The diagonals of a rhombus have lengths 18 and 24. Find the length of one side. **15**

15. Write a paragraph proof: If $\overline{AX}$ is a median and an altitude of $\triangle ABC$, then $\triangle ABC$ is isosceles.

16. Given: $NPQRST$ is a regular hexagon.
Prove: $NPRS$ is a rectangle.
(Begin by drawing a diagram.)

17. Given: $\angle WXY \cong \angle XZY$
Prove: $(XY)^2 = WY \cdot ZY$

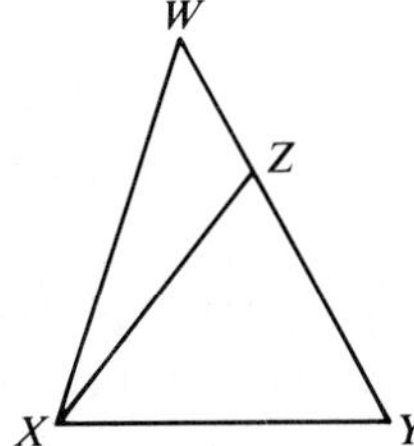

9 Circles

Objectives

9-1 Define a circle, a sphere, and terms related to them.

Recognize inscribed polygons and circumscribed circles.

9-2 Apply theorems that relate tangents and radii.

Recognize circumscribed polygons and inscribed circles.

9-3 Define and apply properties of arcs and central angles.

9-4 Apply theorems about the chords of a circle.

9-5 Solve problems and prove statements involving inscribed angles.

Solve problems and prove statements involving angles formed by chords, secants, and tangents.

9-6 Solve problems and prove statements involving angles formed by chords, secants, and tangents.

9-7 Solve problems involving lengths of chords, secant segments, and tangent segments.

Assignment Guide

See page T40 for information about the Assignment Guide.

Day	Minimum Course	Average Course	Maximum Course
1	**9-1** 330–331/1–12	**9-1** 330–331/1–12, 13–17 odd	**9-1** 330–331/1–11 odd, 12–20 even
2	**9-2** 335–336/1–8	**9-1** 330–331/18–20	**9-2** 335–336/5–15 odd
3	**9-2** 336/9–12 337/Mixed Review 1–3	**9-2** 335–336/5–11 **S** 331/14, 16	**9-2** 337/17–23
4	**9-3** 341–342/1–10	**9-2** 336–337/12–20 even 337/Mixed Review 1–3	**9-3** 341–343/2–12 even, 13–21 odd, 22 **S** 337/16
5	**9-3** 342/11–16	**9-3** 341–342/1–9 odd, 10, 12	**9-4** 347/1–7 odd, 8, 10, 14 **S** 342–343/16, 23
6	**9-4** 347/1–9	**9-3** 342–343/13–21	**9-4** 347–348/11, 13, 15, 16–26 even
7	**9-4** 347/10–15 349/Self-Test 1	**9-4** 347/2–8 even, 9–15 odd	**9-5** 354–355/1–9 odd, 10, 12, 13 **S** 348/23, 25
8	**9-5** 354/1–9	**9-4** 348/16–22 even 349/Self-Test 1	**9-5** 355–356/14, 15, 19–21, 25, 27
9	**9-5** 354–355/10–13 357/Mixed Review 1–6	**9-5** 354/1–12	**9-6** 359–360/2–20 even, 21, 22
10	**9-6** 359/1–14 **S** 355/16	**9-5** 355/13–15, 19–23 357/Mixed Review 1–6	**9-6** 360/23, 25–30
11	**9-6** 360/15–23	**9-6** 359–360/1–17	**9-7** 364–365/1–10, 12, 13
12	**9-6** 360/24–30	**9-6** 360/18–21, 22–30 even	**9-7** 365–366/11, 15–27
13	**9-7** 364/1–9	**9-7** 364–365/1–11, 13, 15	**9-7** 371/Chapter Test Test, page T20

14	9-7 365/10, 11, 13–18	9-7 365–366/16–21 367/Self-Test 2	
15	9-7 367/Self-Test 2	9-7 371/Chapter Test Test, page T20	
16	9-7 371/Chapter Test Test, page T20		

Supplementary Materials Guide

For Use after Lesson	Practice Masters	Tests	Study Guide (Reteaching)	Resource Book			Computer Activities
				Tests	Practice Exercises	Prep. for College Entrance Exams (Col) Enrichment (E) Computer (C)	
9-1			pp. 107–108				
9-2	Sheet 50		pp. 109–110				
9-3			pp. 111–112				
9-4	Sheet 51	Test 35	pp. 113–114	pp. 55–56	p. 144		Activity 19
9-5	Sheet 52		pp. 115–116				
9-6	Sheet 53		pp. 117–118				
9-7	Sheet 54	Test 36	pp. 119–120	pp. 57–58	p. 145		Activity 20
Chapter 9	Sheet 55	Test 37		pp. 59–60	p. 146	p. 198 (Col) pp. 220–221 (E) pp. 250–253 (C)	

Overhead Visuals

Guided Discovery Visuals (lettered) and Teaching Visuals (numbered) available for Chapter 9.

Lessons	Visual	Title
9-1	D	Segments and Angles in Space Figures
9-7	G	The Pythagorean Theorem: Alternate Proofs
9-1, 9-2, 9-3, 9-4	18	Circle Terms
9-5, 9-6, 9-7	19	Angles and Secants with Circles

Software Guide

Houghton Mifflin software for Chapter 9

Geometry Grapher (Apple or IBM)

Use with	Booklet
p. 362 (Theorem 9-11)	Class Demonstration, p. 16
p. 338 (Explorations)	
p. 361 (Explorations)	

Test Generator (Apple or IBM): 105 test items

Other software appropriate for Chapter 9

Geometric Supposer (Apple): Quadrilaterals, Circles

GeoDraw (IBM)

Guide to Integrated Curriculum

Teachers wishing to integrate coordinate and transformational geometry throughout the course can use the following lessons after Chapter 9. See pages T56–T57 and 657 for more information.

13-1 Cl. Ex. 11, 12; Wr. Ex. 17–26, 34–40, 45
Handbook: Circles, pp. 667–669

Guide to Distribution of Constructions

The text teaches constructions in Chapter 10. Teachers wishing to distribute work with constructions throughout the first nine chapters can use this guide.

Introduce after	Constructions	Page
Lesson 9-2	8	392
Lesson 9-5	9	393

Strategies for Teaching

Exploring Angles and Arcs

When to Use

Before Lesson 9-6

Overview

This activity motivates Theorems 9-9 and 9-10 and suggests proof strategies.

Materials

Cardboard, scissors, string

Description of Activity

Cut out a large cardboard rectangle and a cardboard circle. Make two small cuts on each long side of the rectangle near the corners. Attach two pieces of string to the cardboard in the shape of a big "X" by slipping the ends of the string through the cuts. Draw an angle the same measure as one of the acute angles formed by the pieces of string on the rectangle as an inscribed angle of the circle.

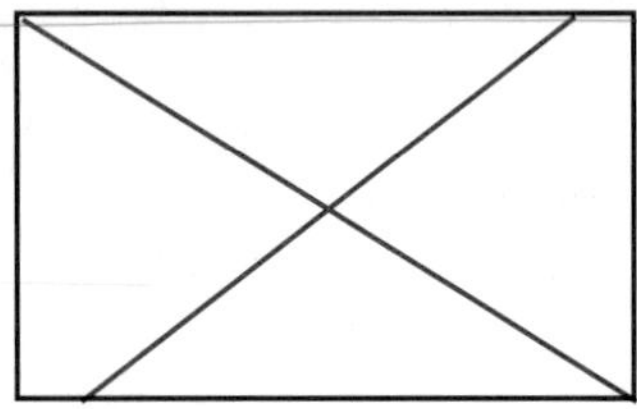

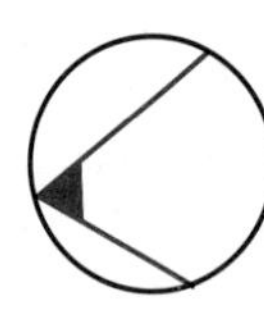

1. Place the circle so that $\overline{AB} \parallel n$ and P is inside the circle.

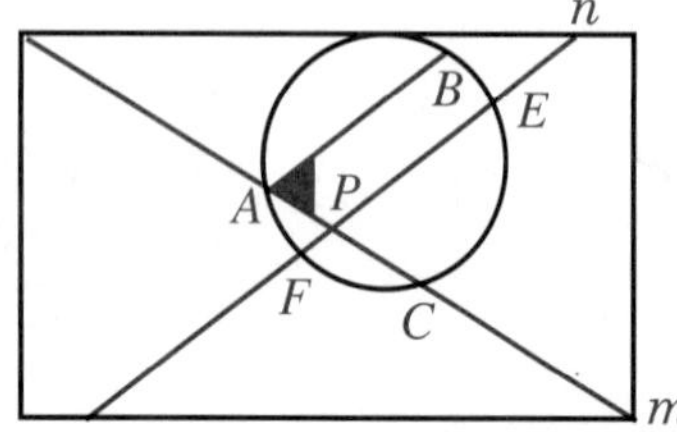

a. $m\angle BAC = \frac{1}{2}m\ \widehat{?}$ BEC

b. $m\angle EPC = m\angle ?$ so $m\angle EPC = \frac{1}{2}m\ \widehat{?}$ BAC, BEC

c. $m\widehat{BEC} = m\widehat{BE} + m\ \widehat{?}$ EC

d. $m\widehat{BE} = m\ \widehat{?}$ AF

e. Make a conjecture about the measure of $\angle EPC$ formed by chords $\overline{AC}$ and $\overline{EF}$.

$m\angle EPC = \frac{1}{2}(m\widehat{EC} + m\widehat{AF})$

2. Place the circle so that $\overline{AB} \parallel n$ and P is outside the circle.

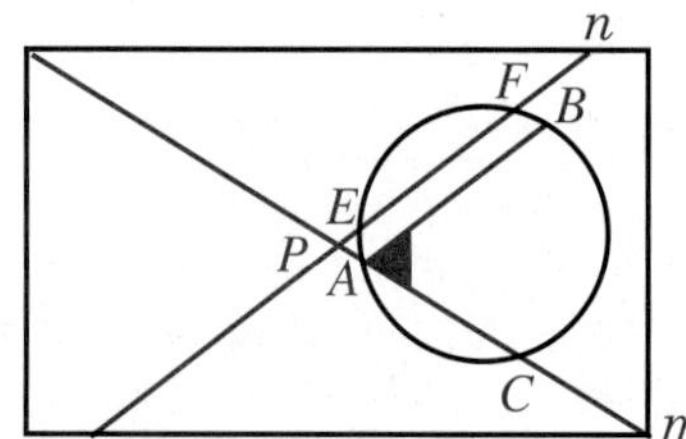

a. $m\angle BAC = \frac{1}{2}m\ \widehat{?}$ BC

b. $m\angle FPC = m\angle ?$ so $m\angle FPC = \frac{1}{2}m\ \widehat{?}$ BAC, BC

c. $m\widehat{BC} = m\widehat{FBC} - m\ \widehat{?}$ FB

d. $m\widehat{FB} = m\ \widehat{?}$ AE

e. Make a conjecture about the measure of $\angle FPC$ formed by secants $\overline{AC}$ and $\overline{EF}$.

$m\angle FPC = (\frac{1}{2})(m\widehat{FBC} - m\widehat{AE})$

3. Hypothesize about the theorem suggested by each figure, and plan a proof.

a.

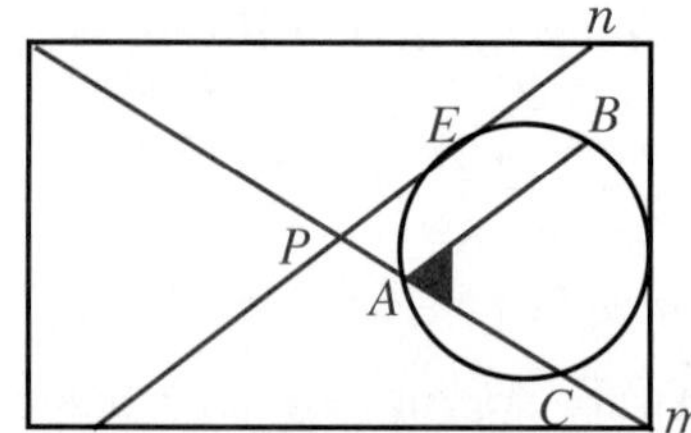

$m\angle EPC = (\frac{1}{2})(m\widehat{EBC} - m\widehat{AE})$

b.

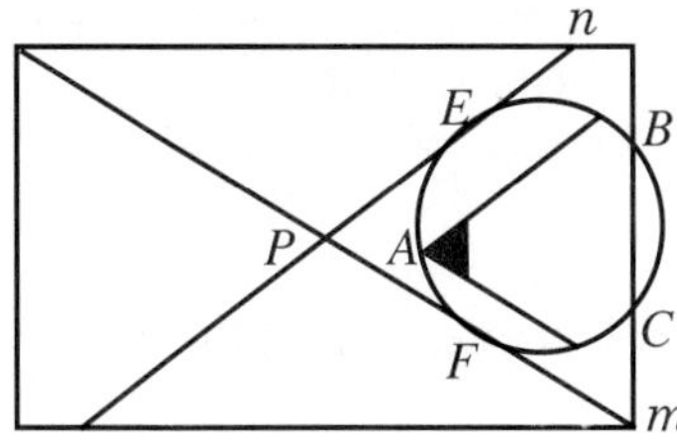

$m\angle EPF = (\frac{1}{2})(m\widehat{EBF} - m\widehat{EF})$

Commentary

- This exploratory activity can be done either in small groups or as a class, using transparencies for the rectangle and the circle.
- Key to understanding the proof steps in each activity is recalling that parallel lines cut off congruent arcs. To review this, see Exercise 10 on page 354. The proofs of **3** are similar to those for **1** and **2.**
- These activities explore theorems of Lesson 9-6: **1.** (Thm. 9-9) **2.** (Thm. 9-10, Case I) **3. a.** (Thm. 9-10, Case III) **3. b.** (Thm. 9-10, Case II).

References to Strategies

PE: Pupil's Edition **TE:** Teacher's Edition **RB:** Resource Book

Problem Solving Strategies

PE: 332 (Mathematical model), 367–368 (Mathematical model)
TE: 356 (Be persistent)
RB: 220–221 (Apply a formula)

Applications

PE: 328 (Wheels), 340 (Arctic circle), 342 (Exs. 17–20, Latitude), 343 (Exs. 23, 24, Satellite communication), 367–368 (Distance to the horizon)
TE: 329, 339, 345

Nonroutine Problems

PE: 330 (Exs. 1–3), 331 (Exs. 16, 20), 332 (Networks), 335 (Ex. 5), 336 (Exs. 7–9, 12, 13), 337 (Ex. 19), 342 (Exs. 12, 13, 17–20), 343 (Exs. 22–24), 353 (Ex. 14), 360 (Ex. 30), 361 (Exs. 31, 32), 366 (Ex. 21), 368 (Application), 668 (Exs. 7–9)
TE: T111, T113
RB: 220–221

Communication

TE: T112, T113, 348

Thinking Skills

TE: 347 (Extend an idea)

Explorations

PE: 338, 361
TE: 327c

Connections

PE: 332 (Euler), 338 (Maria Agnesi), 356 (Ptolemy), 667–669 (Coordinate and transformational geometry)
TE: T112, 337, 350, 351 (Reference to Ch. 3), 355

Using Technology

PE: 338, 361
TE: T112, T115, 330, 336, 338, 340, 342, 343, 344, 355, 361, 367, 368
RB: 250–253
Using Geometry Grapher: 16
Computer Activities: 45–49

Using Manipulatives/Models

PE: 332–333, 367–368
TE: T111, T113, 350
Overhead Visuals: D, G, 18, 19

Cooperative Learning

TE: T112, T113, T115, T116, 348

Teaching Resources

For use in implementing the teaching strategies referenced on the previous page.

Application/Using Technology
Resource Book, p. 252

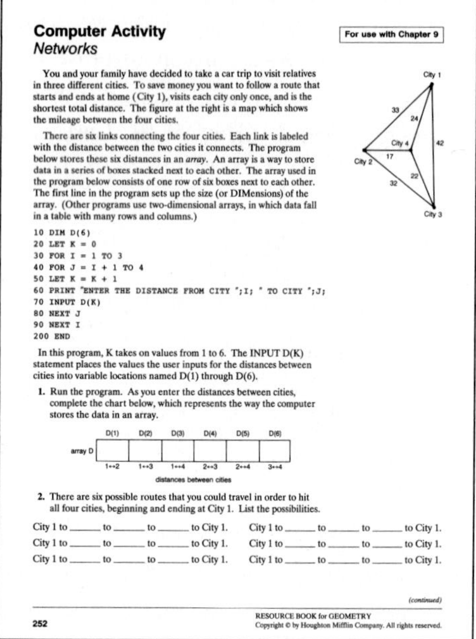

Computer Activity
Networks

For use with Chapter 9

You and your family have decided to take a car trip to visit relatives in three different cities. To save money you want to follow a route that starts and ends at home (City 1), visits each city only once, and is the shortest total distance. The figure at the right is a map which shows the mileage between the four cities.

There are six links connecting the four cities. Each link is labeled with the distance between the two cities it connects. The program below stores these six distances in an *array*. An array is a way to store data in a series of boxes stacked next to each other. The array used in the program below consists of one row of six boxes next to each other. The first line in the program sets up the size (or DIMensions) of the array. (Other programs use two-dimensional arrays, in which data fall in a table with many rows and columns.)

```
10 DIM D(6)
20 LET K = 0
30 FOR I = 1 TO 3
40 FOR J = I + 1 TO 4
50 LET K = K + 1
60 PRINT "ENTER THE DISTANCE FROM CITY ";I; " TO CITY ";J;
70 INPUT D(K)
80 NEXT J
90 NEXT I
200 END
```

In this program, K takes on values from 1 to 6. The INPUT D(K) statement places the values the user inputs for the distances between cities into variable locations named D(1) through D(6).

1. Run the program. As you enter the distances between cities, complete the chart below, which represents the way the computer stores the data in an array.

	D(1)	D(2)	D(3)	D(4)	D(5)	D(6)
array D						
	1↔2	1↔3	1↔4	2↔3	2↔4	3↔4

distances between cities

2. There are six possible routes that you could travel in order to hit all four cities, beginning and ending at City 1. List the possibilities.

City 1 to _____ to _____ to _____ to City 1. City 1 to _____ to _____ to _____ to City 1.
City 1 to _____ to _____ to _____ to City 1. City 1 to _____ to _____ to _____ to City 1.
City 1 to _____ to _____ to _____ to City 1. City 1 to _____ to _____ to _____ to City 1.

(continued)

252 RESOURCE BOOK for GEOMETRY

Application/Using Technology
Resource Book, p. 253

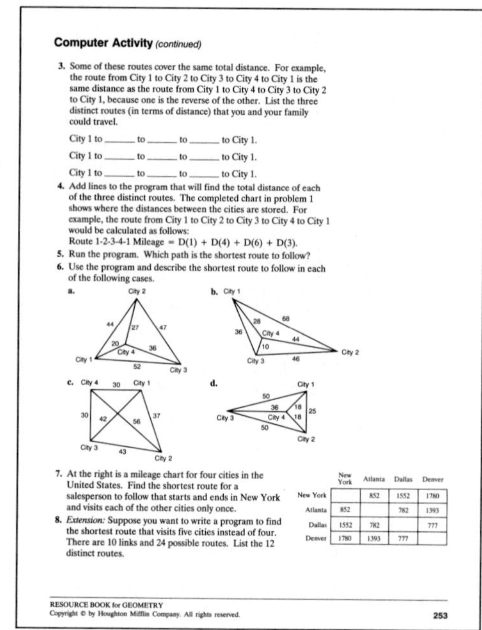

Computer Activity *(continued)*

3. Some of these routes cover the same total distance. For example, the route from City 1 to City 2 to City 3 to City 4 to City 1 is the same distance as the route from City 1 to City 4 to City 3 to City 2 to City 1, because one is the reverse of the other. List the three distinct routes (in terms of distance) that you and your family could travel.

City 1 to _____ to _____ to _____ to City 1.
City 1 to _____ to _____ to _____ to City 1.
City 1 to _____ to _____ to _____ to City 1.

4. Add lines to the program that will find the total distance of each of the three distinct routes. The completed chart in problem 1 shows where the distances between the cities are stored. For example, the route from City 1 to City 2 to City 3 to City 4 to City 1 would be calculated as follows:
Route 1-2-3-4-1 Mileage = D(1) + D(4) + D(6) + D(3).
5. Run the program. Which path is the shortest route to follow?
6. Use the program and describe the shortest route to follow in each of the following cases.

a. b. c. d.

7. At the right is a mileage chart for four cities in the United States. Find the shortest route for a salesperson to follow that starts and ends in New York and visits each of the other cities only once.
8. *Extension:* Suppose you want to write a program to find the shortest route that visits five cities instead of four. There are 10 links and 24 possible routes. List the 12 distinct routes.

	New York	Atlanta	Dallas	Denver
New York		852	1552	1780
Atlanta	852		782	1393
Dallas	1552	782		777
Denver	1780	1393	777	

RESOURCE BOOK for GEOMETRY
 253

Communication
Study Guide, p. 107

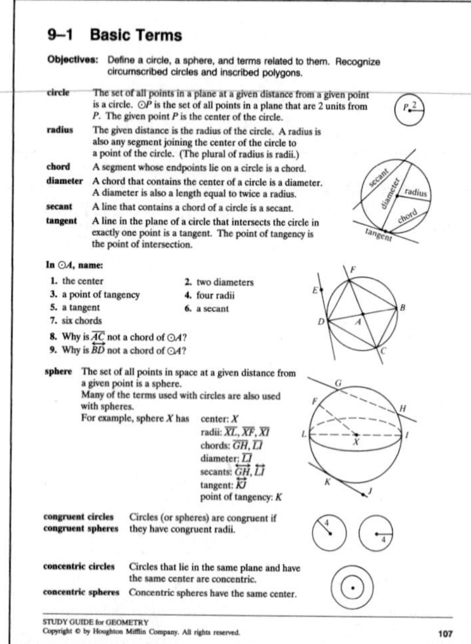

9–1 Basic Terms

Objectives: Define a circle, a sphere, and terms related to them. Recognize circumscribed circles and inscribed polygons.

circle The set of all points in a plane at a given distance from a given point is a circle. ⊙P is the set of all points in a plane that are 2 units from P. The given point P is the center of the circle.

radius The given distance is the radius of the circle. A radius is also any segment joining the center of the circle to a point of the circle. (The plural of radius is radii.)

chord A segment whose endpoints lie on a circle is a chord.

diameter A chord that contains the center of a circle is a diameter. A diameter is also a length equal to twice a radius.

secant A line that contains a chord of a circle is a secant.

tangent A line in the plane of a circle that intersects the circle in exactly one point is a tangent. The point of tangency is the point of intersection.

In ⊙A, name:

1. the center
2. two diameters
3. a point of tangency
4. four radii
5. a tangent
6. a secant
7. six chords
8. Why is $\overline{AC}$ not a chord of ⊙A?
9. Why is $\overleftrightarrow{BD}$ not a chord of ⊙A?

sphere The set of all points in space at a given distance from a given point is a sphere. Many of the terms used with circles are also used with spheres.
For example, sphere X has center: X
radii: $\overline{XL}, \overline{XF}, \overline{XI}$
chords: $\overline{GH}, \overline{LI}$
diameter: $\overline{LI}$
secants: $\overleftrightarrow{GH}, \overleftrightarrow{LI}$
tangent: $\overleftrightarrow{KJ}$
point of tangency: K

congruent circles / congruent spheres Circles (or spheres) are congruent if they have congruent radii.

concentric circles Circles that lie in the same plane and have the same center are concentric.

concentric spheres Concentric spheres have the same center.

STUDY GUIDE for GEOMETRY
 107

Communication
Study Guide, p. 108

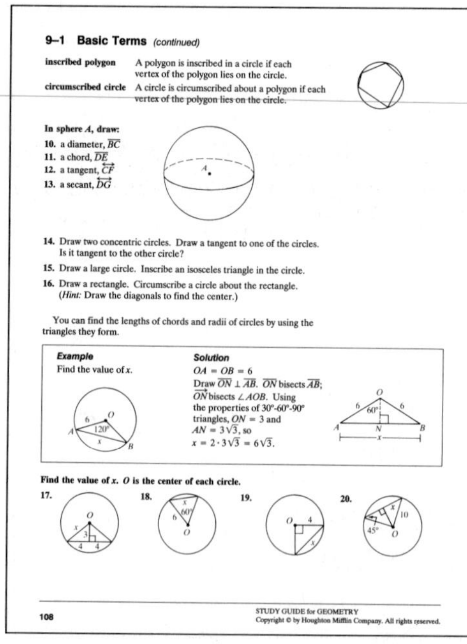

9–1 Basic Terms *(continued)*

inscribed polygon A polygon is inscribed in a circle if each vertex of the polygon lies on the circle.

circumscribed circle A circle is circumscribed about a polygon if each vertex of the polygon lies on the circle.

In sphere A, draw:

10. a diameter, $\overline{BC}$
11. a chord, $\overline{DE}$
12. a tangent, $\overleftrightarrow{CF}$
13. a secant, $\overleftrightarrow{DG}$
14. Draw two concentric circles. Draw a tangent to one of the circles. Is it tangent to the other circle?
15. Draw a large circle. Inscribe an isosceles triangle in the circle.
16. Draw a rectangle. Circumscribe a circle about the rectangle. (*Hint:* Draw the diagonals to find the center.)

You can find the lengths of chords and radii of circles by using the triangles they form.

Example
Find the value of x.

Solution
$OA = OB = 6$
Draw $\overline{ON} \perp \overline{AB}$. $\overline{ON}$ bisects $\overline{AB}$; $\overrightarrow{ON}$ bisects $\angle AOB$. Using the properties of 30°-60°-90° triangles, $ON = 3$ and $AN = 3\sqrt{3}$, so $x = 2 \cdot 3\sqrt{3} = 6\sqrt{3}$.

Find the value of x. O is the center of each circle.

17. 18. 19. 20.

108 STUDY GUIDE for GEOMETRY

Problem Solving

Resource Book, p. 220

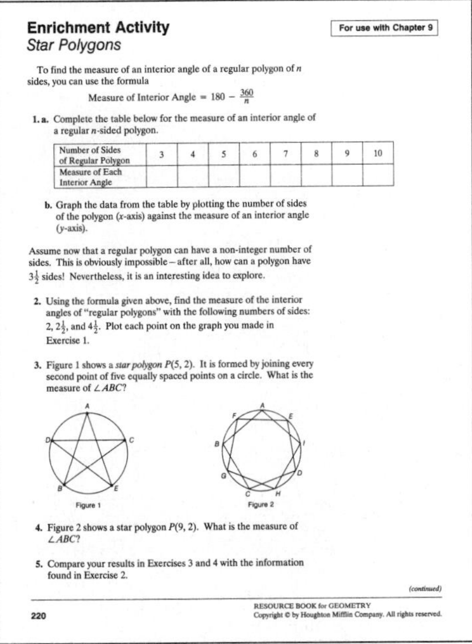

Enrichment Activity
Star Polygons

For use with Chapter 9

To find the measure of an interior angle of a regular polygon of n sides, you can use the formula

$$\text{Measure of Interior Angle} = 180 - \frac{360}{n}$$

1. a. Complete the table below for the measure of an interior angle of a regular n-sided polygon.

Number of Sides of Regular Polygon	3	4	5	6	7	8	9	10
Measure of Each Interior Angle								

b. Graph the data from the table by plotting the number of sides of the polygon (x-axis) against the measure of an interior angle (y-axis).

Assume now that a regular polygon can have a non-integer number of sides. This is obviously impossible – after all, how can a polygon have $3\frac{1}{2}$ sides! Nevertheless, it is an interesting idea to explore.

2. Using the formula given above, find the measure of the interior angles of "regular polygons" with the following numbers of sides: 2, $2\frac{1}{2}$, and $4\frac{1}{2}$. Plot each point on the graph you made in Exercise 1.

3. Figure 1 shows a *star polygon* $P(5, 2)$. It is formed by joining every second point of five equally spaced points on a circle. What is the measure of $\angle ABC$?

Figure 1

Figure 2

4. Figure 2 shows a star polygon $P(9, 2)$. What is the measure of $\angle ABC$?

5. Compare your results in Exercises 3 and 4 with the information found in Exercise 2.

(continued)

220

RESOURCE BOOK for GEOMETRY

Using Models

Teaching Visual 18

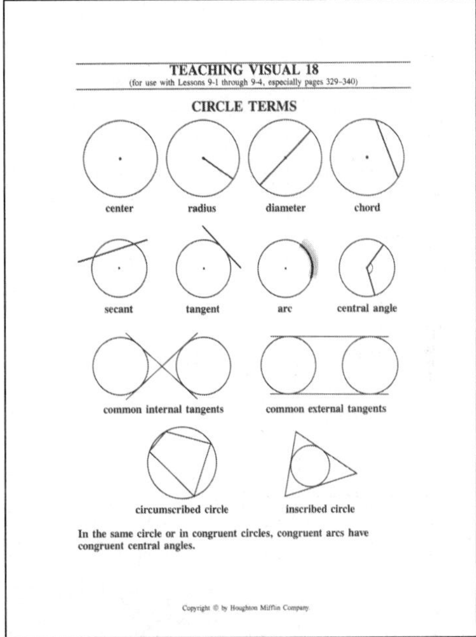

Connection

Guided Discovery Visual G, Sheet 1

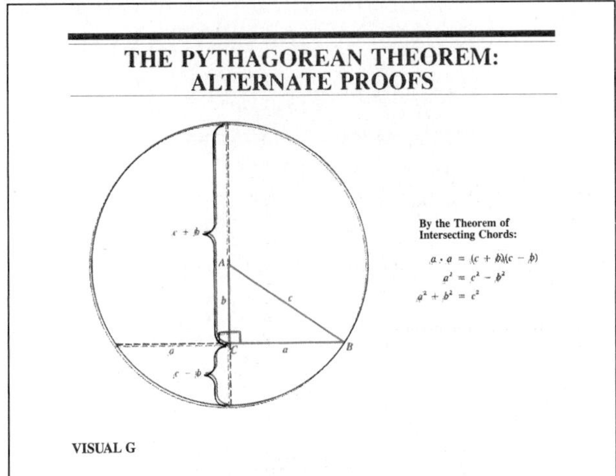

Connection

Guided Discovery Visual G, Sheet 2

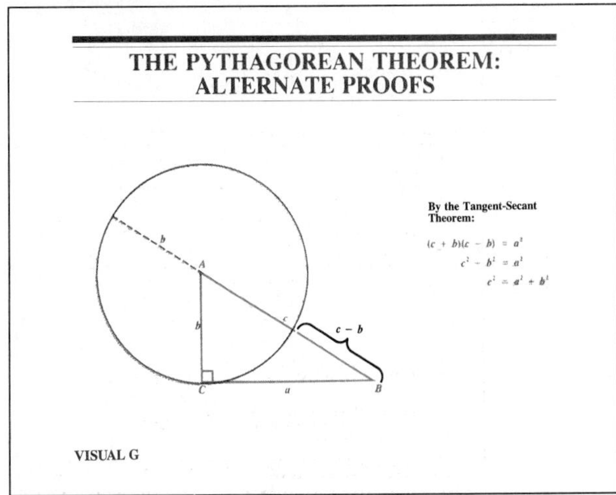

Teaching References

Lesson Commentary, pp. T111–T116

Assignment Guide, pp. T46–T48

Software Guide, p. T73

Alternate Test, p. T20

Supplementary Materials

Practice Masters 50–55

Tests 35–37

Resource Book
- Tests, pp. 55–60
- Practice, pp. 144–146
- Preparing for College Entrance Exams, p. 198
- Enrichment Activity, pp. 220–221
- Computer Activities, pp. 250–253

Study Guide, pp. 107–120

Overhead Visuals D, G, 18, 19

Computer Activities
- 19 Chords and the Pythagorean Theorem
- 20 The Power of a Point

Handbook for Integrating Coordinate and Transformational Geometry

Circles, pp. 667–669

Cultural Note

The practice of dividing a circle into 360° was begun by Babylonian astronomers and mathematicians over 2000 years ago. The Babylonians were also aware that an angle inscribed in a semicircle is a right angle.

9 CIRCLES

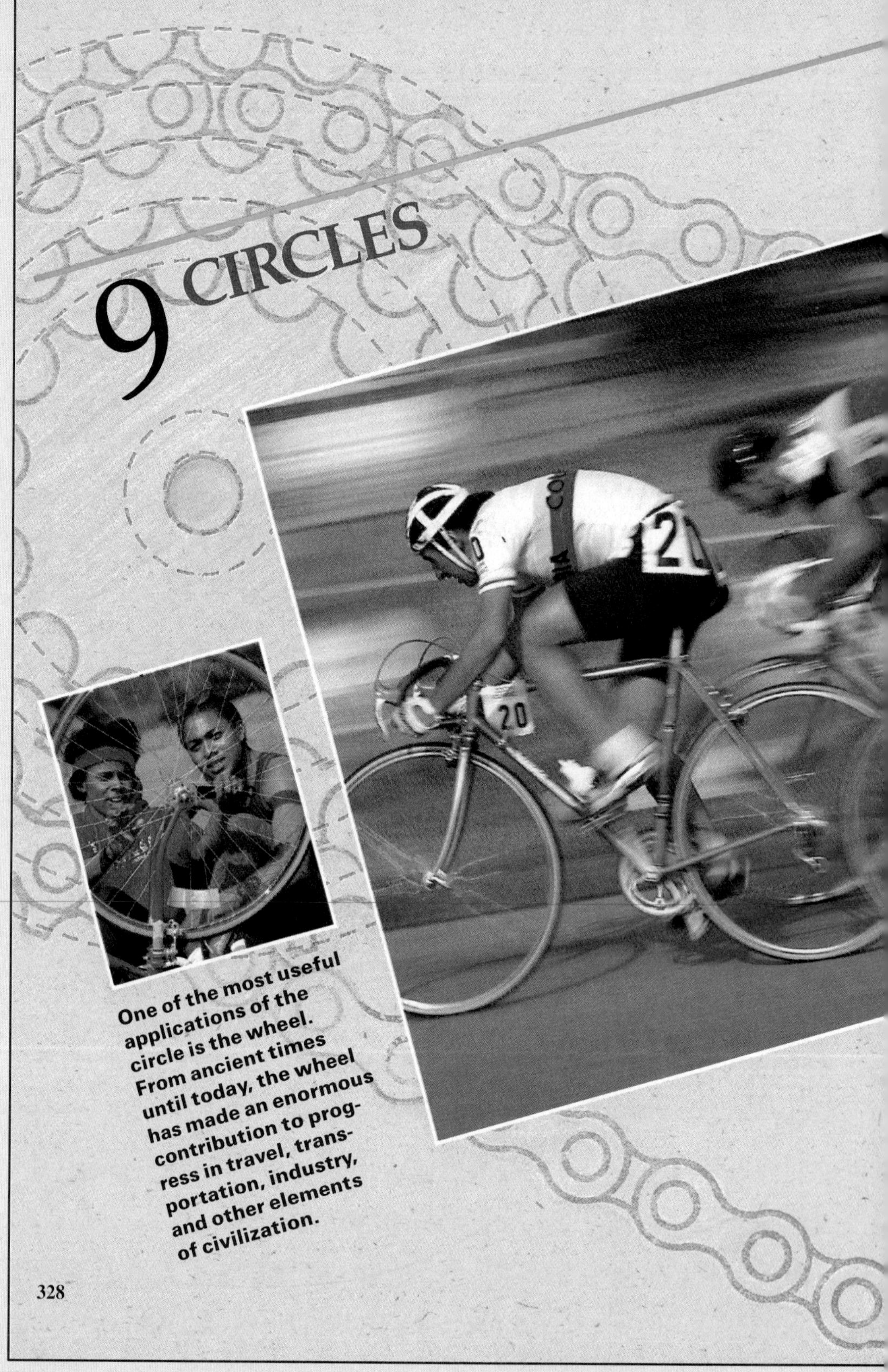

One of the most useful applications of the circle is the wheel. From ancient times until today, the wheel has made an enormous contribution to progress in travel, transportation, industry, and other elements of civilization.

Tangents, Arcs, and Chords

Objectives

1. Define a circle, a sphere, and terms related to them.
2. Recognize circumscribed and inscribed polygons and circles.
3. Apply theorems that relate tangents and radii.
4. Define and apply properties of arcs and central angles.
5. Apply theorems about the chords of a circle.

9-1 *Basic Terms*

A **circle** is the set of points in a plane at a given distance from a given point in that plane. The given point is the **center** of the circle and the given *distance* is *the* **radius.** Any *segment* that joins the center to a point of the circle is called *a* radius. All radii of a circle are congruent. The rim of the Ferris wheel shown is a circle with center O ($\odot O$) and radius 10.

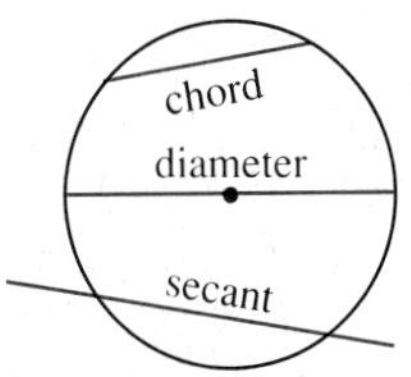

A **chord** is a segment whose endpoints lie on a circle. A **secant** is a line that contains a chord. A **diameter** is a chord that contains the center of a circle. (Like the word *radius*, the word *diameter* can refer to *the* length of a segment or to *a* segment.)

A **tangent** is a line in the plane of a circle that intersects the circle in exactly one point, called the **point of tangency.** The *tangent ray* $\overrightarrow{PA}$ and *tangent segment* $\overline{PA}$ are often called tangents.

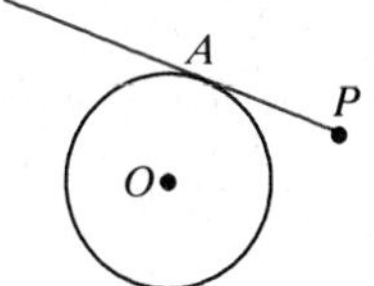

$\overleftrightarrow{AP}$ is tangent to $\odot O$.
$\odot O$ is tangent to $\overleftrightarrow{AP}$.
A is the point of tangency.

A **sphere** with center O and radius r is the set of all points in space at a distance r from point O. Many of the terms used with spheres are the same as those used with circles.

$\overline{OA}$, $\overline{OB}$, and $\overline{OD}$ are radii.
$\overline{BD}$ is a diameter.
$\overline{BC}$ is a chord.
$\overleftrightarrow{BC}$ is a secant.
$\overleftrightarrow{AT}$ is a tangent.
$\overline{AT}$ is a tangent segment.

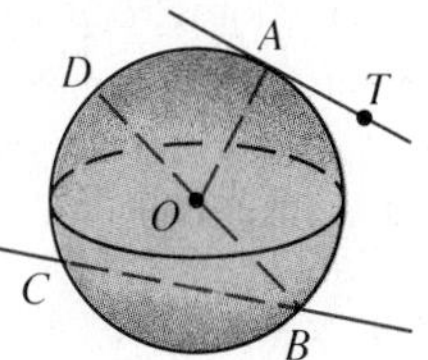

Teaching Suggestions, pp. T111–T112
Objectives
Presenting the Lesson
Extension
Using Technology

Communication Skills, p. T112

Supplementary Materials
Study Guide, pp. 107–108
Overhead Visual D

Lesson Focus
Circles and spheres are very common geometric figures. This lesson defines a circle and a sphere and introduces the terms related to them.

Suggested Assignments
Minimum
330–331/1–12
Average
Day 1: 330–331/1–12, 13–17 odd
Day 2: 330–331/18–20
Maximum
330–331/1–11 odd, 12–20 even

Application
Circular and spherical shapes can be seen frequently in nature, in architecture, and in physical objects. You can use tree rings, spherical fruit, circular sports arenas, domed towers, bicycle tires, globes or other examples to motivate the discussion about the properties of circles and spheres.

Chalkboard Examples

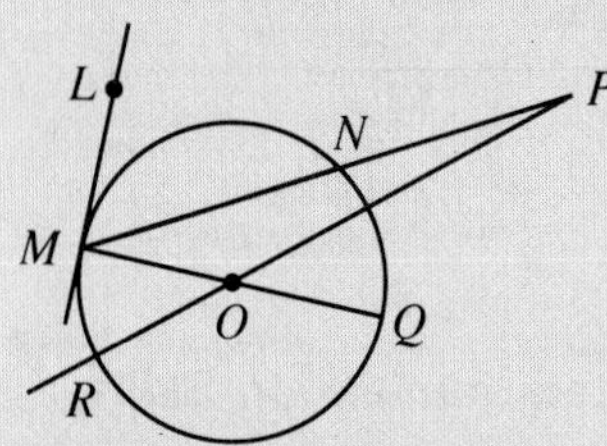

Point O is the center of the circle. Name each figure.

1. $\overline{OM}$ radius
2. $\overline{MN}$ chord
3. $\overleftrightarrow{MN}$ secant
4. $\overline{MQ}$ diameter, chord
5. $\overline{ML}$ tangent segment
6. $\overleftrightarrow{ML}$ tangent
7. Point M point of tangency

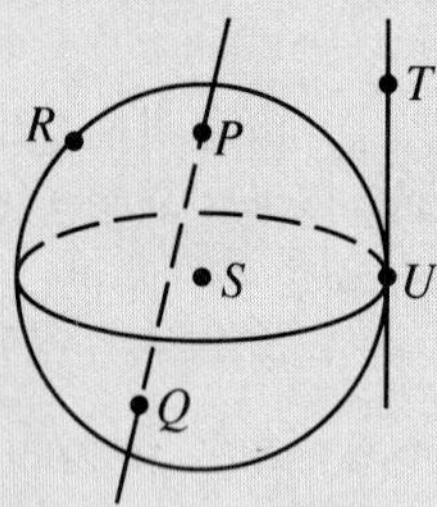

8. Name a tangent to sphere S. $\overleftrightarrow{TU}$
9. Name a secant and a chord of the sphere. $\overleftrightarrow{PQ}$; $\overline{PQ}$
10. Name two radii of the sphere (not drawn). $\overline{SU}, \overline{SP}, \overline{SQ}, \overline{SR}$

Using a Computer

The following Written Exercises can be done effectively using a construction program: 1–3, 12–18, 20.

Congruent circles (or **spheres**) are circles (or spheres) that have congruent radii.

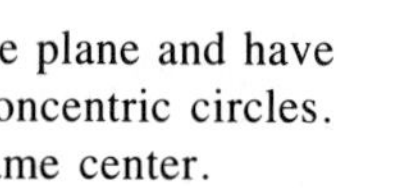

Concentric circles are circles that lie in the same plane and have the same center. The rings of the target illustrate concentric circles. **Concentric spheres** are spheres that have the same center.

A polygon is **inscribed in a circle** and the circle is **circumscribed about the polygon** when each vertex of the polygon lies on the circle.

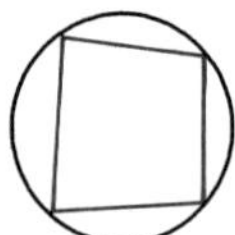

Inscribed polygons

Circumscribed circles

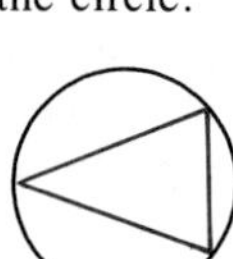

Classroom Exercises

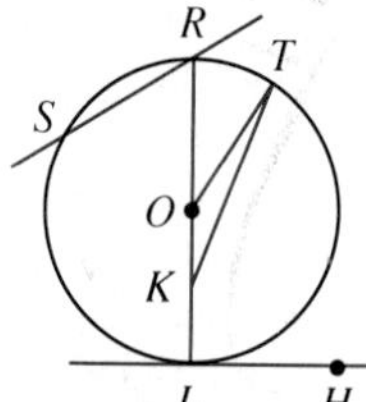

1. Name three radii of $\odot O$. $\overline{OT}, \overline{OR}, \overline{OL}$
2. Name a diameter. $\overline{RL}$
3. Consider $\overline{RS}$ and $\overleftrightarrow{RS}$. Which is a chord and which is a secant? **$\overline{RS}$ is a chord; $\overleftrightarrow{RS}$ is a secant.**
4. Why is $\overline{TK}$ not a chord? **K is not on $\odot O$.**
5. Name a tangent to $\odot O$. $\overleftrightarrow{LH}$
6. What name is given to point L? **point of tangency**
7. Name a line tangent to sphere Q. $\overleftrightarrow{EF}$
8. Name a secant of the sphere and a chord of the sphere. $\overleftrightarrow{AB}, \overline{AB}$
9. Name 4 radii. (None are drawn in the diagram.) $\overline{QA}, \overline{QB}, \overline{QC}, \overline{QF}$
10. What is the diameter of a circle with radius 8? 5.2? $4\sqrt{3}$? j?
11. What is the radius of a sphere with diameter 14? 13? 5.6? $6n$?

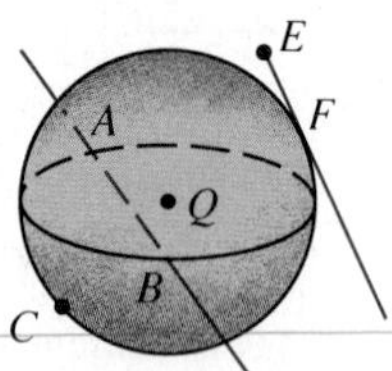

10. 16; 10.4; $8\sqrt{3}$; $2j$ 11. 7; 6.5; 2.8; $3n$

Written Exercises

A

1. Draw a circle and several parallel chords. What do you think is true of the midpoints of all such chords? **The midpoints lie on a diameter ⊥ to the given chords.**
2. Draw a circle with center O and a line $\overleftrightarrow{TS}$ tangent to $\odot O$ at T. Draw $\overline{OT}$, and use a protractor to find $m\angle OTS$. **90**

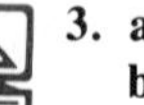

3. **a.** Draw a right triangle inscribed in a circle.
   b. What do you know about the midpoint of the hypotenuse? **It is equidist. from the 3 vertices.**
   c. Where is the center of the circle? **at the midpoint of the hypotenuse**
   d. If the legs of the right triangle are 6 and 8, find the radius of the circle. **5**

4. Plane Z passes through the center of sphere Q. **All radii of a sphere are ≅.**
   a. Explain why $QR = QS = QT$.
   b. Explain why the intersection of the plane and the sphere is a circle. (The intersection of a sphere with any plane passing through the center of the sphere is called a **great circle** of the sphere.)

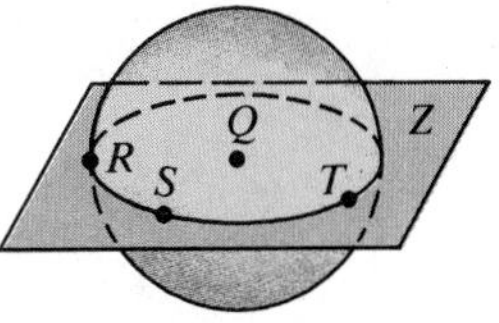

5. The radii of two concentric circles are 15 cm and 7 cm. A diameter $\overline{AB}$ of the larger circle intersects the smaller circle at C and D. Find two possible values for AC. **8, 22**

For each exercise draw a circle and inscribe the polygon in the circle.

6. A rectangle
7. A trapezoid
8. An obtuse triangle
9. A parallelogram
10. An acute isosceles triangle
11. A quadrilateral $PQRS$, with $\overline{PR}$ a diameter

For each exercise draw ⊙O with radius 12. Then draw radii $\overline{OA}$ and $\overline{OB}$ to form an angle with the measure named. Find the length of $\overline{AB}$.

B 12. $m\angle AOB = 90$ **$12\sqrt{2}$**
13. $m\angle AOB = 180$ **24**
14. $m\angle AOB = 60$ **12**
15. $m\angle AOB = 120$ **$12\sqrt{3}$**

16. Draw two points A and B and several circles that pass through A and B. Locate the centers of these circles. On the basis of your experiment, complete the following statement:
The centers of all circles passing through A and B lie on __?__. **the ⊥ bis. of $\overline{AB}$**
Write an argument to support your statement.

17. ⊙Q and ⊙R are congruent circles that intersect at C and D. $\overline{CD}$ is called the *common chord* of the circles.
   a. What kind of quadrilateral is $QDRC$? Why?
   b. $\overline{CD}$ must be the perpendicular bisector of $\overline{QR}$. Why?
   c. If $QC = 17$ and $QR = 30$, find CD. **16**

18. Draw two congruent circles with radii 6 each passing through the center of the other. Find the length of their common chord. **$6\sqrt{3}$**

C 19. ⊙P and ⊙Q have radii 5 and 7 and $PQ = 6$. Find the length of the common chord $\overline{AB}$. (*Hint*: $APBQ$ is a kite and $\overline{PQ}$ is the perpendicular bisector of $\overline{AB}$. See Exercise 28, page 193. Let N be the intersection of $\overline{PQ}$ and $\overline{AB}$, and let $PN = x$ and $AN = y$. Write two equations in terms of x and y.) **$4\sqrt{6}$**

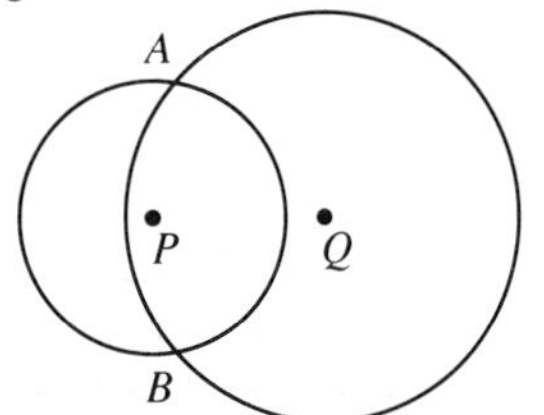

20. Draw a diagram similar to the one shown, but much larger. Carefully draw the perpendicular bisectors of $\overline{AB}$ and $\overline{BC}$.
   a. The perpendicular bisectors intersect in a point. Where does that point appear to be? **the center of the circle**
   b. Write an argument that justifies your answer to part (a).
   The ⊥ bis. int. at a pt. equidistant from *A*, *B*, and *C*, by def. the ctr. of a ⊙ on which *A*, *B*, and *C* lie.

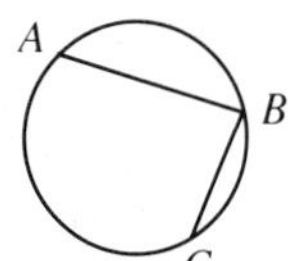

Guided Practice

1. Draw two tangent segments to a circle from the same point outside the circle. What do you think is true about the lengths of the segments? They are equal.
2. Draw a circle with center O and radius $\overline{OA}$. Draw $\overline{AT}$ perpendicular to $\overline{OA}$. What kind of segment is $\overline{AT}$? tangent
3. Describe the ways in which a plane can intersect a sphere.
in a single point or in a circle
4. Draw a sphere and several parallel planes intersecting the sphere. What are the resulting figures?
circles
5. Is it possible to inscribe in a circle a nonrectangular parallelogram? no a nonisosceles trapezoid? no a nonregular pentagon? yes
6. Name great circles on the globe. (See Written Ex. 4.)
equator, longitudinal lines

Additional Answers Written Exercises

4.b. The pts. in the intersection lie in a plane and are equidistant from Q; by def., the intersection is a ⊙.

16. The centers are the set of all points equidistant from A and B.

17.a. rhombus; ⊙Q ≅ ⊙R, so $\overline{QC}$, $\overline{QD}$, $\overline{RC}$, and $\overline{RD}$ are ≅.
b. The diagonals of a rhombus are ⊥ bisectors of each other.

Extra Networks

The Pregel River flows through the old city of Koenigsberg, now Kaliningrad. Once, seven bridges joined the shores and the two islands in the river as shown in the diagram at the left below. A popular problem of that time was to try to walk across all seven bridges without crossing any bridge more than once. Can you find a way to do it?

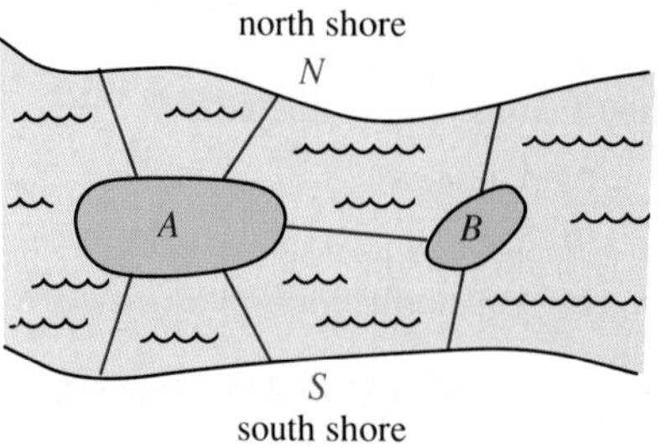

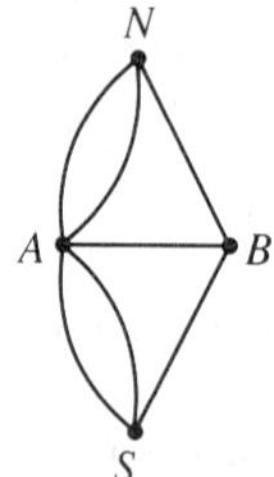

Mathematician Leonard Euler analyzed this problem using a diagram called a *network*, shown at the right above. He represented each land mass by a point (called a vertex) and each bridge by an arc. He then classified each vertex with an odd number of arcs coming from it as *odd* and each vertex with an even number of arcs as *even*. From here Euler discovered which networks can be traced without backtracking, that is, without drawing over an arc twice.

Exercises

Find the number of odd and even vertices in each network. Imagine traveling each network to see if it can be traced without backtracking.

1. 4 odd, 1 even: cannot be traced

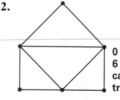

2. 0 odd, 6 even: can be traced

3.

2 odd, 6 even: can be traced

The number of odd vertices will tell you whether or not a network can be traced without backtracking. Do you see how? If not, read on.

4. Suppose that a given network can be traced without backtracking.
   a. Consider a vertex that is neither the start nor end of a journey through this network. Is such a vertex odd or even? **even**
   b. Now consider the two vertices at the start and finish of a journey through this network. Can both of these vertices be odd? even? **Yes; yes**
   c. Can just one of the start and finish vertices be odd? **No**

5. Tell why it is impossible to walk across the seven bridges of Koenigsberg without crossing any bridge more than once.
There are more than 2 odd vertices.

9-2 *Tangents*

In Written Exercise 2 on page 330 you had the chance to preview the next theorem about tangents and radii.

Theorem 9-1

If a line is tangent to a circle, then the line is perpendicular to the radius drawn to the point of tangency.

Given: m is tangent to $\odot O$ at T.

Prove: $\overline{OT} \perp m$

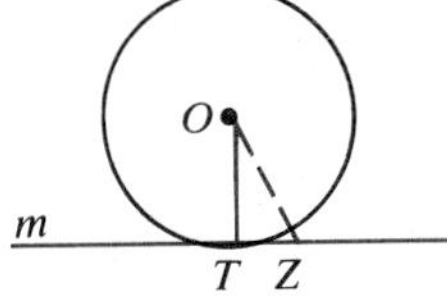

Proof:

Assume temporarily that $\overline{OT}$ is not perpendicular to m. Then the perpendicular segment from O to m intersects m in some other point Z. Draw $\overline{OZ}$. By Corollary 1, page 220, the perpendicular segment from O to m is the shortest segment from O to m, so $OZ < OT$. Because tangent m intersects $\odot O$ only in point T, Z lies outside $\odot O$, and $OZ > OT$. The statements $OZ < OT$ and $OZ > OT$ are contradictory. Thus the temporary assumption must be false. It follows that $\overline{OT} \perp m$.

Corollary

Tangents to a circle from a point are congruent.

In the figure, $\overline{PA}$ and $\overline{PB}$ are tangent to the circle at A and B. By the corollary, $\overline{PA} \cong \overline{PB}$. For a proof, see Classroom Exercise 4.

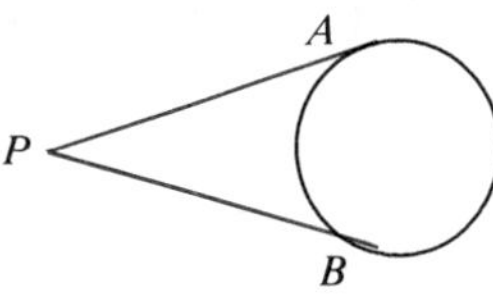

Theorem 9-2 is the converse of Theorem 9-1. Its proof is left as Exercise 22.

Theorem 9-2

If a line in the plane of a circle is perpendicular to a radius at its outer endpoint, then the line is tangent to the circle.

Given: Line l in the plane of $\odot Q$;
$l \perp$ radius $\overline{QR}$ at R

Prove: l is tangent to $\odot Q$.

Teaching Suggestions,
pp. T112–T113

Objectives
Presenting the Lesson
Making Connections

Communication Skills,
p. T112

Cooperative Learning,
pp. T112–T113

Supplementary Materials

Practice Master 50
Study Guide, pp. 109–110

Lesson Focus

The purpose of this lesson is to study the properties of lines that are tangent to a circle.

Suggested Assignments

Minimum
Day 1: 335–336/1–8
Day 2: 336/9–12
337/Mixed Review 1–3

Average
Day 1: 335–336/5–11
S 331/14, 16
Day 2: 336–337/12–20 even
337/Mixed Review 1–3

Maximum
Day 1: 335–336/5–15 odd
Day 2: 337/17–23

You may wish to introduce Construction 8 on page 392 after covering this lesson.

Chalkboard Examples

1. Draw two circles, with all their common tangents, so that the number of common tangents is (a) one, (b) two, (c) three, and (d) four. Answers will vary.

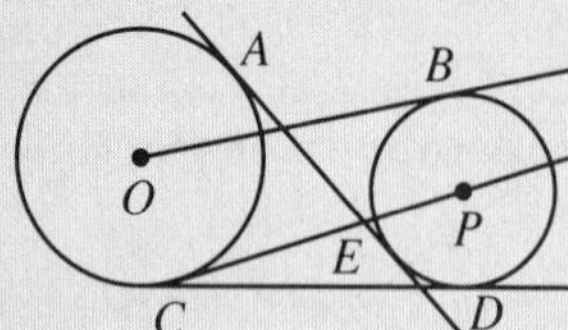

Name a line that satisfies the given description.

2. Tangent to ⊙P but not to ⊙O $\overleftrightarrow{OB}$
3. Common external tangent to ⊙O and ⊙P $\overleftrightarrow{CD}$
4. Common internal tangent to ⊙O and ⊙P $\overleftrightarrow{AE}$

In the diagram, ⊙M and ⊙N are tangent at P. $\overline{PR}$ and $\overline{SR}$ are tangents to ⊙N. ⊙N has diameter 16, $PQ = 3$, and $RQ = 12$.

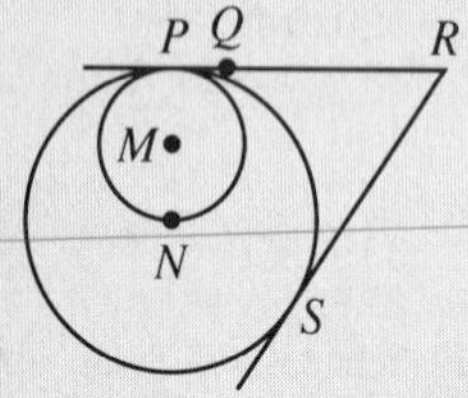

Complete.

5. $PM = \underline{4}$
6. $MQ = \underline{5}$
7. $PR = \underline{15}$
8. $SR = \underline{15}$
9. $NS = \underline{8}$
10. $NR = \underline{17}$

When each side of a polygon is tangent to a circle, the polygon is said to be **circumscribed about the circle** and the circle is **inscribed in the polygon.**

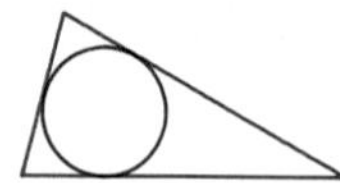

Circumscribed polygons

Inscribed circles

A line that is tangent to each of two coplanar circles is called a **common tangent.**

A common *internal* tangent intersects the segment joining the centers.

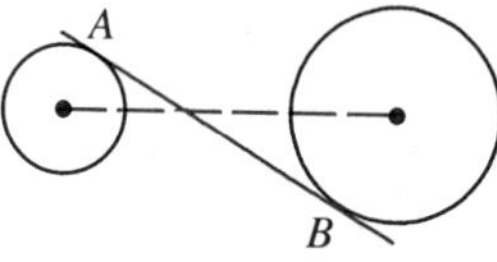

$\overleftrightarrow{AB}$ is a common internal tangent. Can you find another one that has not been drawn?

A common *external* tangent does *not* intersect the segment joining the centers.

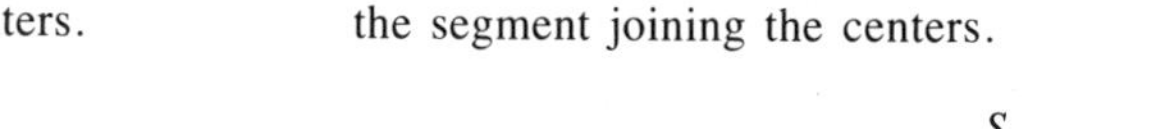

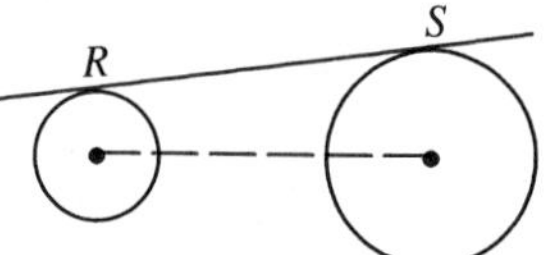

$\overleftrightarrow{RS}$ is a common external tangent. Can you find another one that has not been drawn?

A circle can be tangent to a line, but it can also be tangent to another circle. **Tangent circles** are coplanar circles that are tangent to the same line at the same point.

⊙A and ⊙B are *externally* tangent.

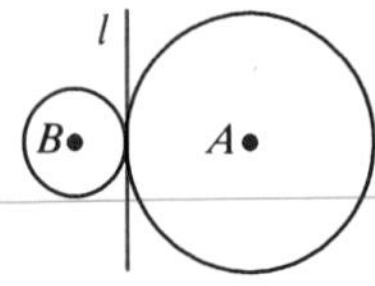

⊙C and ⊙D are *internally* tangent.

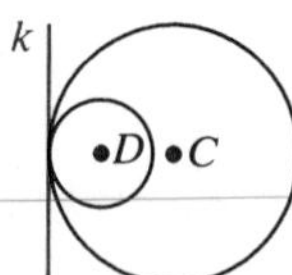

The ends of the plastic industrial pipes shown in the photograph illustrate externally tangent circles. Notice that when a circle is surrounded by tangent circles of the same radius, six of these circles fit exactly around the inner circle.

Classroom Exercises

4. By Thm. 9-1, $\angle A$ and $\angle B$ are rt. $\triangle$s. Since $\overline{OA} \cong \overline{OB}$ and $\overline{OP} \cong \overline{OP}$, $\triangle OAP \cong \triangle OBP$ (HL). Then $\overline{PA} \cong \overline{PB}$.

1. How many common external tangents can be drawn to the two circles?

a. 2

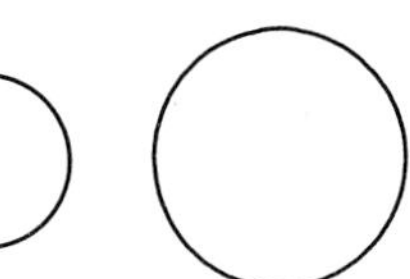

b. 2

c. 2

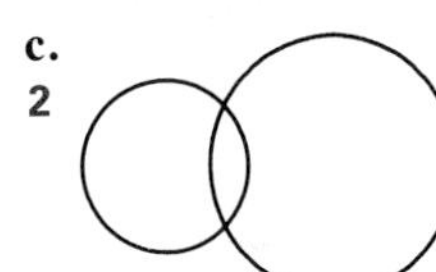

d. 2

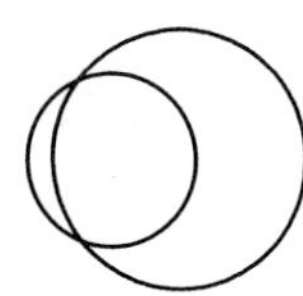

e. 1

f. 0

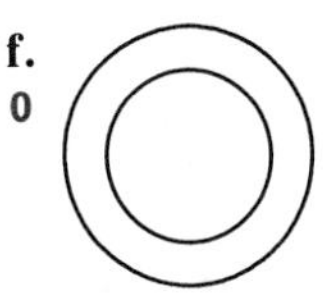

2. How many common internal tangents can be drawn to each pair of circles in Exercise 1 above? **a. 2 b. 1 c. 0 d. 0 e. 0 f. 0**
3. **a.** Which pair of circles shown above are externally tangent? **b**
   b. Which pair are internally tangent? **e**
4. Given: $\overline{PA}$ and $\overline{PB}$ are tangents to $\odot O$.
   Use the diagram at the right to explain how the corollary on page 333 follows from Theorem 9-1. **See above.**

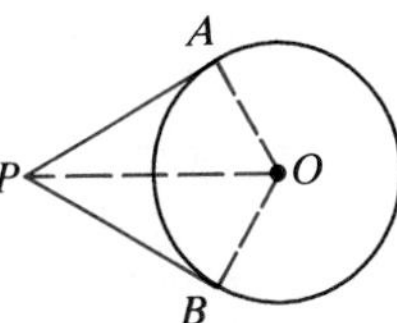

5. In the diagram, which pairs of angles are congruent? Which pairs of angles are complementary? Which pairs of angles are supplementary?

Written Exercises

$\overline{JT}$ is tangent to $\odot O$ at T. Complete.

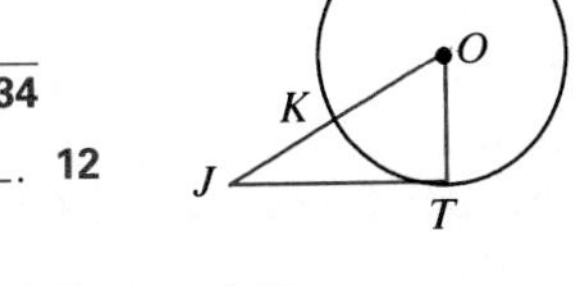

A 1. If $OT = 6$ and $JO = 10$, then $JT =$ __?__. **8**
2. If $OT = 6$ and $JT = 10$, then $JO =$ __?__. **$2\sqrt{34}$**
3. If $m\angle TOJ = 60$ and $OT = 6$, then $JO =$ __?__. **12**
4. If $JK = 9$ and $KO = 8$, then $JT =$ __?__. **15**
5. The diagram below shows tangent lines and circles. Find PD. **8.2**

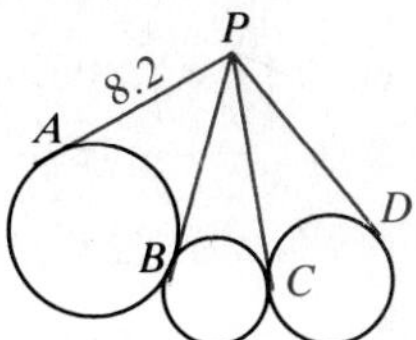

6. $\overline{RS}$ and $\overline{TU}$ are common internal tangents to the circles. If $RZ = 4.7$ and $ZU = 7.3$, find RS and TU. **$RS = TU = 12$**

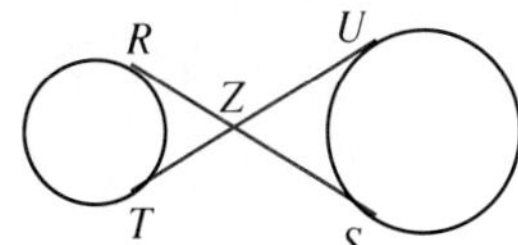

Additional Answers Classroom Exercises

5. $\angle A \cong \angle B$, $\angle OPA \cong \angle OPB$, $\angle AOP \cong \angle BOP$; comp. $\triangle$s: $\angle AOP$, $\angle APO$; $\angle BOP$, $\angle BPO$; $\angle AOP$, $\angle BPO$; $\angle BOP$, $\angle APO$ supp. $\triangle$s: $\angle A$, $\angle B$; $\angle APB$, $\angle AOB$

Guided Practice

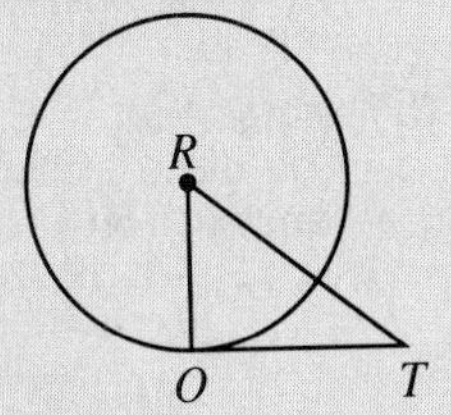

1. If $OR = 6$ and $OT = 8$, then $RT =$ __10__.
2. If $m\angle OTR = 45$, and $OT = 4$, then $RT =$ __$4\sqrt{2}$__.
3. What do you think is true about common internal tangents $\overline{RS}$ and $\overline{TU}$? Prove your conjecture. $\overline{RS} \cong \overline{TU}$; $RV = VT$, and $VU = VS$, so $RV + VS = VT + VU$.

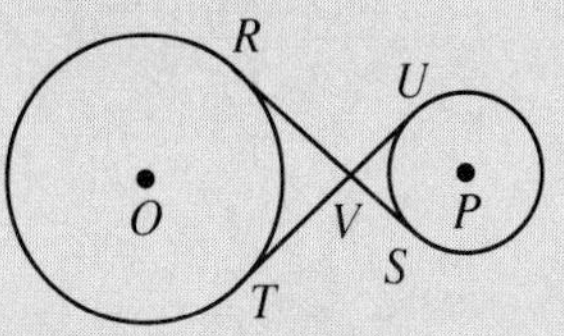

(continued)

4. Given: $\overline{BA}$ and $\overline{BC}$ are tangents to $\odot O$ from B.

a. Copy the diagram. Draw $\overline{BO}$. Use Classroom Ex. 5 to make a conclusion about $\angle ABO$ and $\angle CBO$. $\angle ABO \cong \angle CBO$

b. Draw $\overline{AC}$. Make a conjecture about the line drawn from the center of a circle to the point of intersection of two tangents. The line is the $\perp$ bis. of the chord connecting the points of tangency.

Using a Computer

The following Written Exercises can be done effectively using a construction program: 7, 9, 12, 14, 19, 20.

Additional Answers Written Exercises

9.a. $\overline{XZ} \perp \overline{OX}$, so $\overline{XZ} \parallel \overline{OY}$. Similarly, $\overline{ZY} \parallel \overline{OX}$ so $OXZY$ is a rectangle. Since 2 cons. sides of $OXZY$ are $\cong$, $OXZY$ is a square.

11. $\overline{AR} \perp \overleftrightarrow{RS}$ and $\overline{BS} \perp \overleftrightarrow{RS}$ (Thm. 9-1), so $\overline{AR} \parallel \overline{BS}$. Then $\angle A \cong \angle B$ and $\triangle ARC \sim \triangle BSC$ (AA). So, $\frac{AC}{BC} = \frac{RC}{SC}$ (Corr. sides of $\sim$ △ are in prop.)

7. a. What do you think is true of common external tangents $\overline{AB}$ and $\overline{CD}$? Prove it.

b. Will your results in part (a) be true if the circles are congruent?

7. a. $\overline{AB} \cong \overline{CD}$
b. Yes

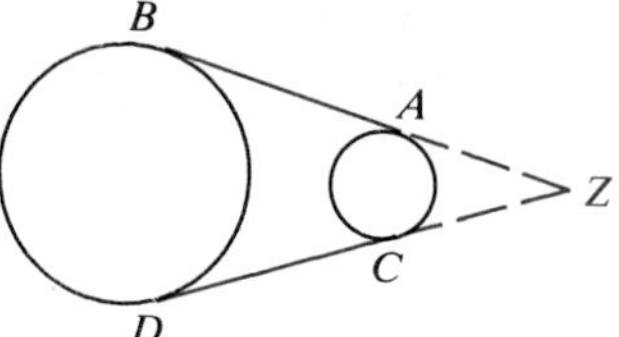

8. Given: $\overline{TR}$ and $\overline{TS}$ are tangents to $\odot O$ from T; $m\angle RTS = 36$

a. Copy the diagram. Draw $\overline{RS}$ and find $m\angle TSR$ and $m\angle TRS$. **72, 72**

b. Draw radii $\overline{OS}$ and $\overline{OR}$ and find $m\angle ORS$ and $m\angle OSR$. **18, 18**

c. Find $m\angle ROS$. **144**

d. Does your result in part (c) support one of your conclusions about angles in Classroom Exercise 5? Explain. **Yes; $\angle RTS$ and $\angle ROS$ are supp.**

9. Draw $\odot O$ with perpendicular radii $\overline{OX}$ and $\overline{OY}$. Draw tangents to the circle at X and Y.

a. If the tangents meet at Z, what kind of figure is $OXZY$? Explain. **Square**

b. If $OX = 5$, find OZ. **$5\sqrt{2}$**

10. Given: $\overline{PT}$ is tangent to $\odot O$ at T; $\overline{TS} \perp \overline{PO}$

Complete the following statements.

a. TS is the geometric mean between __?__ and __?__. **OS, SP**

b. TO is the geometric mean between __?__ and __?__. **OP, OS**

c. If $OS = 6$ and $SP = 24$, $TS =$ __?__ and $TP =$ __?__. **12, $12\sqrt{5}$**

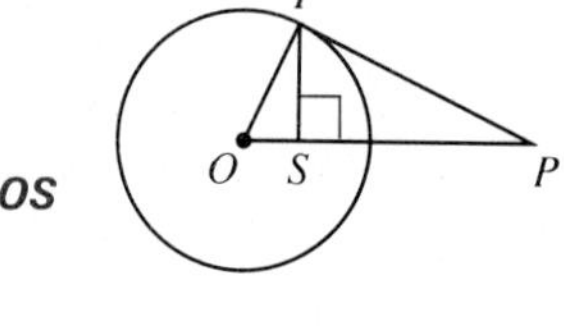

11. Given: $\overline{RS}$ is a common internal tangent to $\odot A$ and $\odot B$.

Explain why $\frac{AC}{BC} = \frac{RC}{SC}$.

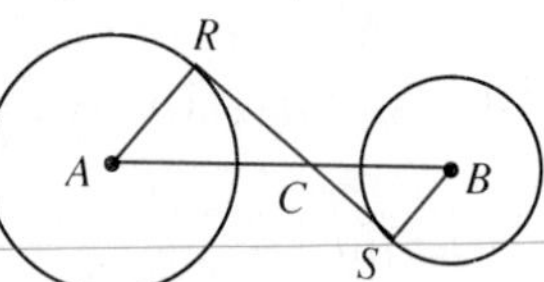

B **12.** Discover and prove a theorem about two lines tangent to a circle at the endpoints of a diameter. **Two lines tan. to a $\odot$ at the endpts. of a diam. are $\parallel$.**

13. Is there a theorem about spheres related to the theorem in Exercise 12? If so, state the theorem. **Two planes tan. to a sphere at the endpts. of a diam. are $\parallel$.**

14. Quad. $ABCD$ is circumscribed about a circle. Discover and prove a relationship between $AB + DC$ and $AD + BC$. **$AB + DC = AD + BC$**

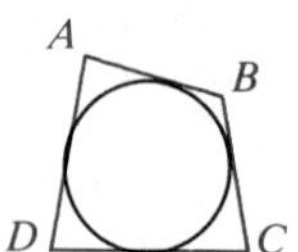

15. $\overline{PA}$, $\overline{PB}$, and $\overline{RS}$ are tangents. Explain why $PR + RS + SP = PA + PB$.

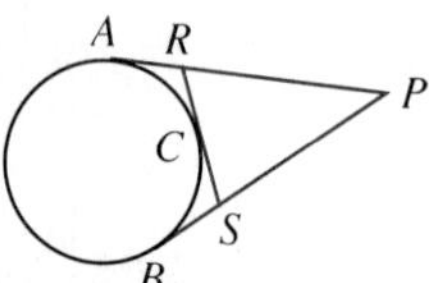

$RA = RC$ and $SB = SC$ (Corollary, p. 333), so $PR + RS + SP = PA + PB$ by subst.

16. $\overline{SR}$ is tangent to $\odot P$ and $\odot Q$. $QT = 6$; $TR = 8$; $PR = 30$. $PQ = \underline{\ ?\ }$; $PS = \underline{\ ?\ }$; $ST = \underline{\ ?\ }$. **20**; **18**; **16**

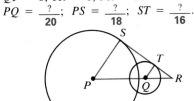

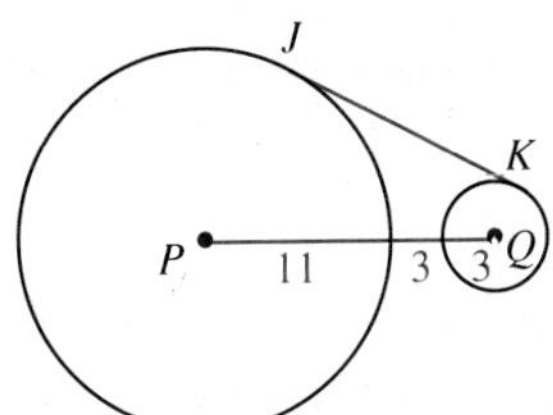

17. $\overline{JK}$ is tangent to $\odot P$ and $\odot Q$. $JK = \underline{\ ?\ }$ (*Hint*: What kind of quadrilateral is $JPQK$?) **15; trapezoid**

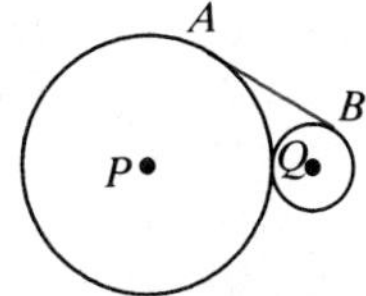

18. Circles P and Q have radii 6 and 2 and are tangent to each other. Find the length of their common external tangent $\overline{AB}$. (*Hint*: Draw $\overline{PQ}$, $\overline{PA}$, and $\overline{QB}$.) **$4\sqrt{3}$**

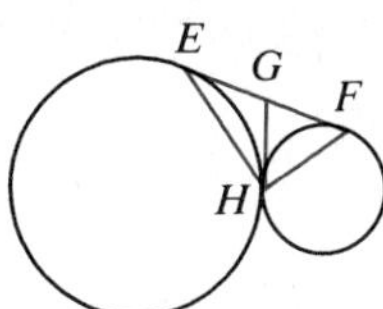

19. Given: Two tangent circles; $\overline{EF}$ is a common external tangent; $\overline{GH}$ is the common internal tangent. ***G* is the midpt. of $\overline{EF}$.**

a. Discover and prove something interesting about point G.

b. Discover and prove something interesting about $\angle EHF$. **$m\angle EHF = 90$**

20. Three circles are shown. How many circles tangent to all three of the given circles can be drawn? **8**

C **21.** Suppose the three circles represent three spheres.

a. How many planes tangent to each of the spheres can be drawn? **8**

b. How many spheres tangent to all three spheres can be drawn? **infinitely many**

22. Prove Theorem 9-2. (*Hint*: Write an indirect proof.)

23. Find the radius of the circle inscribed in the triangle. **$2\sqrt{2}$**

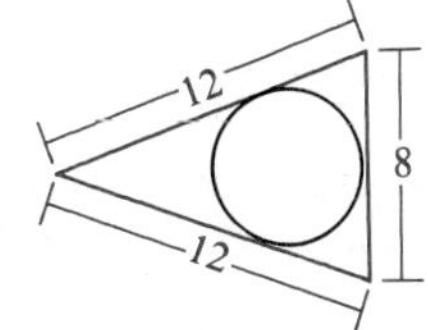

Mixed Review Exercises

Find AB. In Exercise 3, $\overline{CB}$ is tangent to $\odot A$.

1. **15**

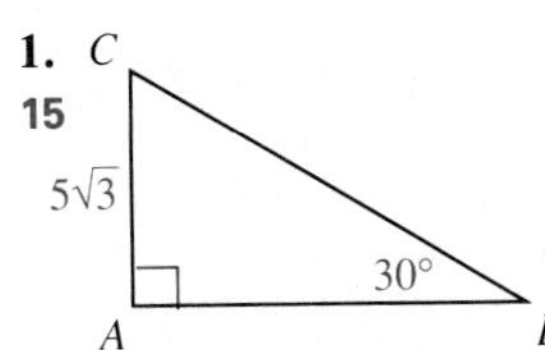

2. **$9\sqrt{2}$**

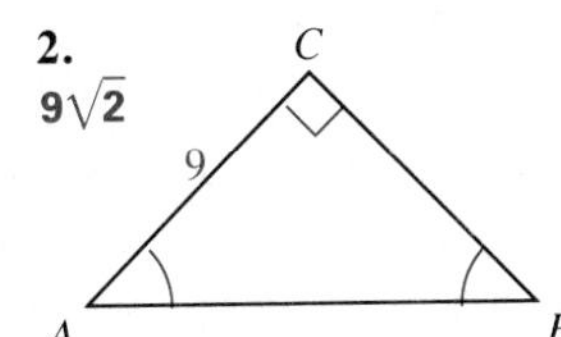

3. **$2\sqrt{7}$**

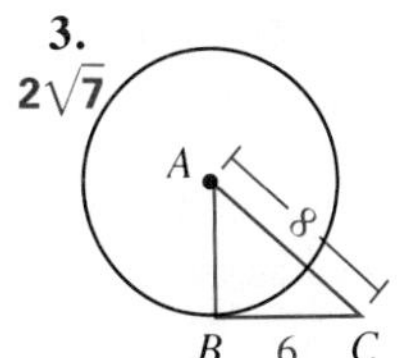

Exercise Note

Ex. 17 uses the common procedure of drawing radii to the points of tangency, in this case to form a trapezoid. A perpendicular is then drawn from Q to $\overline{JP}$, forming a rectangle. The properties of rectangles and the Pythagorean Theorem can now be used. This technique also works when the circles are tangent to each other, as in Ex. 18.

Making Connections

Ex. 23 is an excellent example of applying algebraic skills to solve a geometry problem.

Biographical Note — Maria Gaetana Agnesi

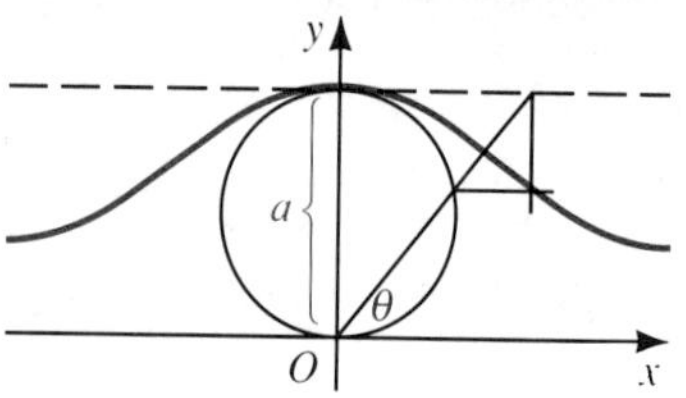

Maria Gaetana Agnesi (1718–1799) was born in Milan, Italy. A child prodigy, she had mastered seven languages by the age of thirteen. Between the ages of twenty and thirty she compiled the works of the mathematicians of her time into two volumes on calculus, called *Analytical Institutions*. This was an enormous task, since the mathematicians had originally published their results in different languages and had used a variety of methods of approach.

Agnesi's volumes were praised as clear, methodical, and comprehensive. They were translated into English and French and were widely used as textbooks. One of the most famous aspects of Agnesi's volumes was an exercise in analytic geometry and the discussion of a curve called a *versirea*, shown at the left below. The name, derived from the Latin *vertere*, "to turn," was apparently mistranslated into English texts as "witch." Thus the curve is commonly known as the "witch of Agnesi."

Due to Agnesi's scholarship, she was elected to the Bologna Academy of Sciences and in 1750 she was appointed honorary professor in mathematics at the University of Bologna, shown at the left.

Using a Computer

This Exploration leads to interesting, surprising results involving circles and quadrilaterals.

Explorations

These exploratory exercises can be done using a computer with a program that draws and measures geometric figures.

Draw parallelogram *ABCD*. Draw four circles as follows.

(1) Use *A*, *B*, and *D* to draw circle *E*.
(2) Use *A*, *D*, and *C* to draw circle *F*.
(3) Use *B*, *C*, and *D* to draw circle *G*.
(4) Use *A*, *B*, and *C* to draw circle *H*.

Connect the centers of the circles to get quad. *EFGH*.
Compare quad. *ABCD* with quad. *EFGH*. What do you notice? **$ABCD \sim FGHE$**

Repeat on other types of quadrilaterals: a rhombus, a trapezoid, a rectangle, and an isosceles trapezoid. What do you notice? **$ABCD \sim FGHE$ is true for all quads. except the rectangle and isos. trap. for which *E*, *F*, *G*, and *H* are the same point.**

9-3 *Arcs and Central Angles*

A **central angle** of a circle is an angle with its vertex at the center of the circle. In the diagrams below, $\angle YOZ$ is a central angle. An *arc* is an unbroken part of a circle. Two points Y and Z on a circle O are always the endpoints of two arcs. Y and Z and the points of $\odot O$ in the interior of $\angle YOZ$ form a **minor arc.** Y and Z and the remaining points of $\odot O$ form a **major arc.** If Y and Z are the endpoints of a diameter, then the two arcs are called **semicircles.** A minor arc is named by its endpoints: $\overset{\frown}{YZ}$ is read "arc YZ." You use three letters to name a semicircle or a major arc: $\overset{\frown}{YWZ}$ is read "arc YWZ."

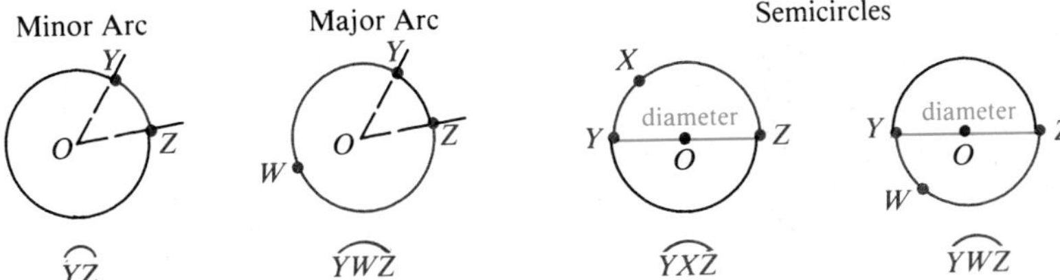

The **measure of a minor arc** is defined to be the measure of its central angle. In the diagram at the left below, $m\overset{\frown}{YZ}$ represents the measure of minor arc YZ. In the middle diagram, can you see why the **measure of a major arc** is 360 minus the measure of its minor arc? The third diagram shows that the **measure of a semicircle** is 180.

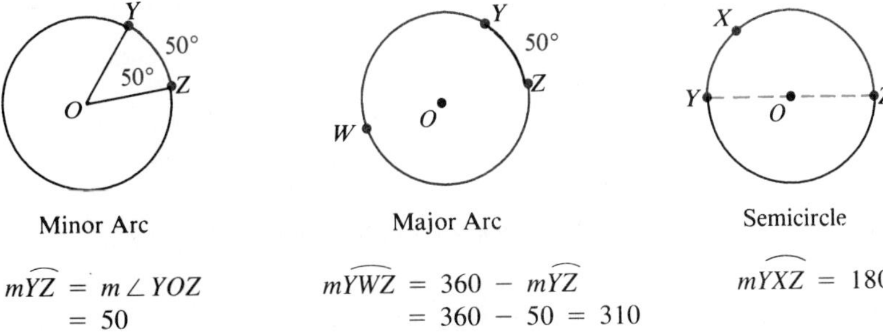

$m\overset{\frown}{YZ} = m\angle YOZ = 50$

$m\overset{\frown}{YWZ} = 360 - m\overset{\frown}{YZ} = 360 - 50 = 310$

$m\overset{\frown}{YXZ} = 180$

Adjacent arcs of a circle are arcs that have exactly one point in common. The following postulate can be used to find the measure of an arc formed by two adjacent arcs.

Postulate 16 *Arc Addition Postulate*

The measure of the arc formed by two adjacent arcs is the sum of the measures of these two arcs.

Teaching Suggestions,
p. T113

Objective
Presenting the Lesson
Extension

Communication Skills,
p. T113

Cooperative Learning,
p. T113

Supplementary Materials

Study Guide, pp. 111–112

Lesson Focus

A part of a circle is called an arc. Arcs can be associated with angles whose vertices are at the centers of circles. The purpose of this lesson is to study arcs and central angles.

Suggested Assignments

Minimum
Day 1: 341–342/1–10
Day 2: 342/11–16

Average
Day 1: 341–342/1–9 odd, 10, 12
Day 2: 342–343/13–20, 21

Maximum
341–343/2–12 even, 13–21 odd, 22
S 337/16

Application

Each angle formed by the spokes of a bicycle wheel has its vertex at the center of the wheel. You can motivate this lesson by discussing bicycle wheels and then asking students for other real-world examples of central angles.

Chalkboard Examples

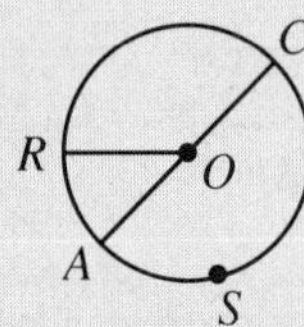

Name:

1. two minor arcs $\overset{\frown}{AR}$, $\overset{\frown}{RC}$, $\overset{\frown}{RS}$, $\overset{\frown}{AS}$, $\overset{\frown}{SC}$
2. two major arcs $\overset{\frown}{ARS}$, $\overset{\frown}{ACR}$, $\overset{\frown}{RCS}$, $\overset{\frown}{RSA}$, $\overset{\frown}{RSC}$, $\overset{\frown}{CRS}$, $\overset{\frown}{CSR}$
3. two semicircles $\overset{\frown}{ARC}$, $\overset{\frown}{ASC}$
4. an acute central angle $\angle AOR$
5. two congruent arcs $\overset{\frown}{ARC}$, $\overset{\frown}{ASC}$

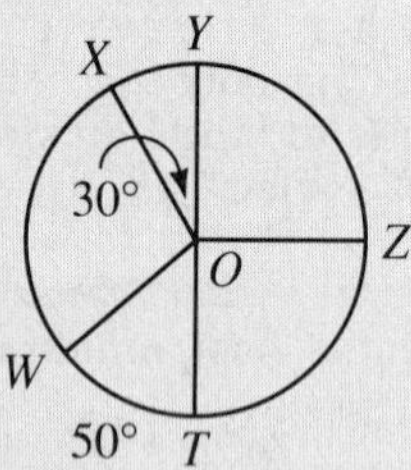

Give the measure of each angle or arc.

6. $\overset{\frown}{WX}$ 100
7. $\angle WOT$ 50
8. $\overset{\frown}{XYT}$ 210

Teaching Note

In this Example, the value of sin 23.4° was conveniently obtained using a calculator. If the Example is worked using the value of sin 23° given in the book's table as an approximation for sin 23.4°, the final result will be the same when rounded to the nearest hundred kilometers.

Applying the Arc Addition Postulate to the circle shown at the right, we have

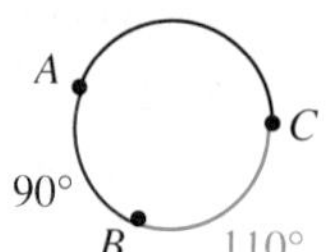

$$m\overset{\frown}{AB} + m\overset{\frown}{BC} = m\overset{\frown}{ABC}$$
$$90 + 110 = 200$$

Congruent arcs are arcs, in the same circle or in congruent circles, that have equal measures. In the diagram below, $\odot P$ and $\odot Q$ are congruent circles and $\overset{\frown}{AB} \cong \overset{\frown}{CD} \cong \overset{\frown}{EF}$. However, $\overset{\frown}{EF}$ is not congruent to $\overset{\frown}{RS}$ even though both arcs have the same degree measure, because $\odot Q$ is not congruent to $\odot O$.

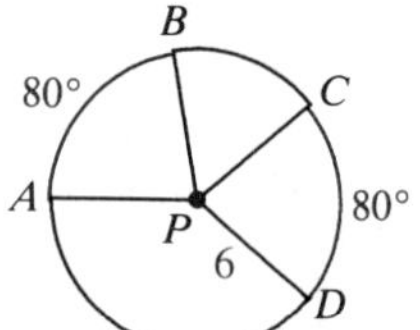

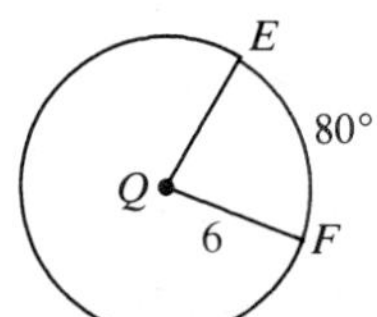

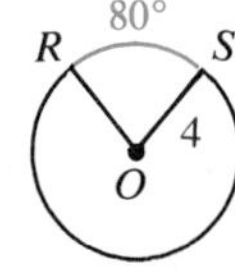

Notice that each of the congruent arcs above has an 80° central angle, so these congruent arcs have congruent central angles. The relationship between congruence of minor arcs and congruence of their central angles is stated in Theorem 9-3 below. This theorem follows immediately from the definition of congruent arcs.

Theorem 9-3

In the same circle or in congruent circles, two minor arcs are congruent if and only if their central angles are congruent.

Example The radius of the Earth is about 6400 km. The latitude of the Arctic Circle is 66.6° North. (That is, in the figure, $m\overset{\frown}{BE} = 66.6$.) Find the radius of the Arctic Circle.

Solution Let N be the North Pole and let $\overline{ON}$ intersect $\overline{AB}$ in M. Since $m\overset{\frown}{NE} = 90$, $m\overset{\frown}{NB} = 90 - 66.6 = 23.4$ and $m\angle NOB = 23.4$. Similarly, $m\angle NOA = 23.4$. Since $\triangle AOB$ is isosceles and $\overline{OM}$ bisects the vertex $\angle AOB$, (1) M is the midpoint of $\overline{AB}$ (and thus the center of the Arctic Circle) and (2) $\overline{OM} \perp \overline{AB}$. Using trigonometry in right $\triangle MOB$:

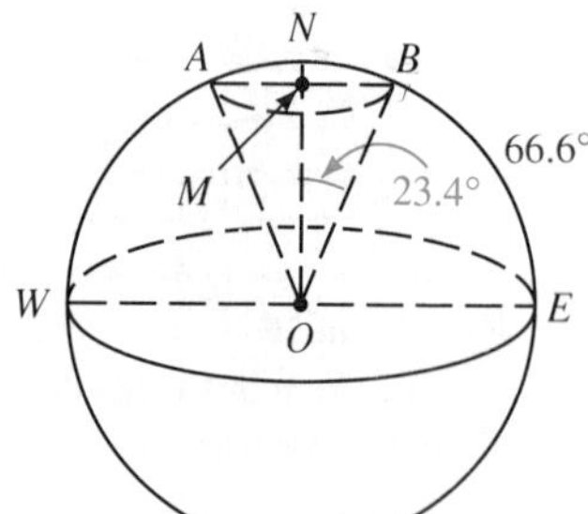

$$\sin 23.4° = \frac{MB}{OB}$$
$$MB = OB \cdot \sin 23.4°$$
$$MB \approx 6400(0.3971)$$
$$MB \approx 2500 \text{ km}$$

Classroom Exercises

1. Using the letters shown in the diagram, name:
   a. two central angles **a.** $\angle DOC$, $\angle COB$, $\angle COA$, $\angle DOB$, $\angle AOB$
   b. a semicircle $\overset{\frown}{DCA}$, $\overset{\frown}{DBA}$
   c. two minor arcs $\overset{\frown}{DC}$, $\overset{\frown}{CB}$, $\overset{\frown}{CA}$, $\overset{\frown}{DB}$, $\overset{\frown}{AB}$
   d. two major arcs $\overset{\frown}{ADC}$, $\overset{\frown}{ADB}$, $\overset{\frown}{BDC}$, $\overset{\frown}{BAD}$, $\overset{\frown}{CAD}$

In Exercises 2–7 find the measure of the arc.

2. $\overset{\frown}{AB}$ **50**
3. $\overset{\frown}{AC}$ **130**
4. $\overset{\frown}{ABD}$ **180**
5. $\overset{\frown}{BAD}$ **230**
6. $\overset{\frown}{CDA}$ **230**
7. $\overset{\frown}{CDB}$ **280**

In Exercises 8–13 find the measure of the angle or the arc named.

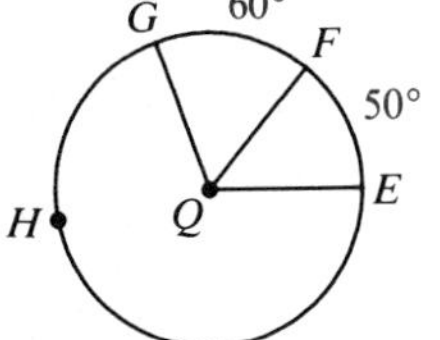

8. $\angle GQF$ **60**
9. $\angle EQF$ **50**
10. $\angle GQE$ **110**
11. $\overset{\frown}{GE}$ **110**
12. $\overset{\frown}{GHE}$ **250**
13. $\overset{\frown}{EHF}$ **310**

Written Exercises

Find the measure of central $\angle 1$.

A 1. **85**

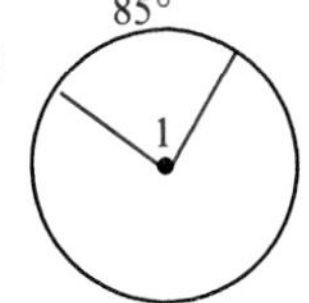

2. **80**

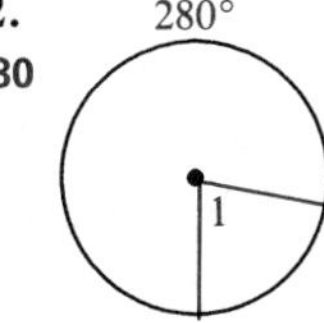

3. **150**

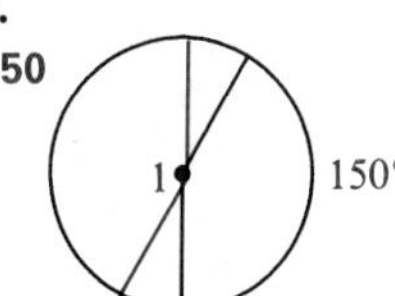

4. **50**

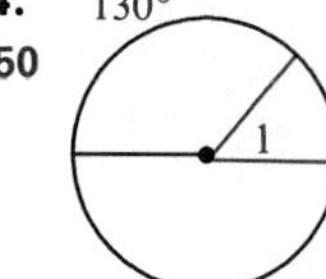

5. **52**

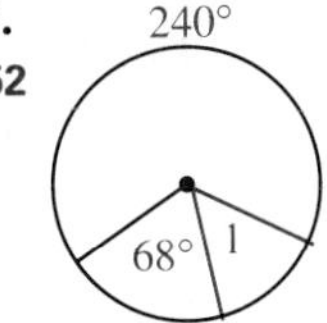

6. **55**

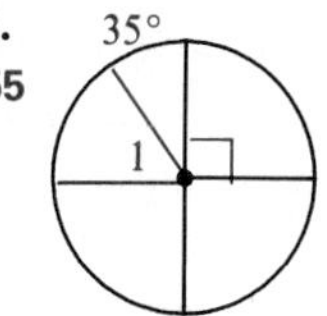

7. At 11 o'clock the hands of a clock form an angle of $\underline{\ ?\ }°$. **30**
8. The hands of a clock form a 120° angle at $\underline{\ ?\ }$ o'clock and at $\underline{\ ?\ }$ o'clock. **4, 8**
9. **a.** Draw a circle. Place points A, B, and C on it in such positions that $m\overset{\frown}{AB} + m\overset{\frown}{BC}$ does not equal $m\overset{\frown}{AC}$.
   b. Does your example in part (a) contradict Postulate 16? **No**

Exercise Note

After working Written Ex. 8, capable students may be interested in using algebra to get other possible answers besides 4 o'clock and 8 o'clock. There are twenty other possible times during a twelve-hour period. Some of these are 12:21 $\frac{9}{11}$, 12:43 $\frac{7}{11}$, 1:27 $\frac{3}{11}$, and 1:49 $\frac{1}{11}$.

Guided Practice

Find the measure of central $\angle 1$.

1. 72
2. 95

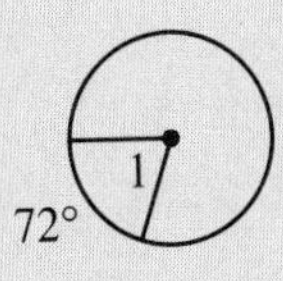

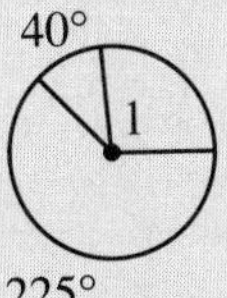

3. 150
4. 50

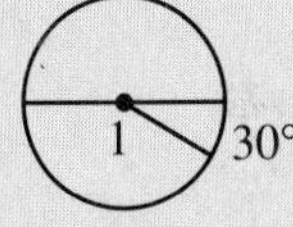

5. Find the measure of each arc.

x=26

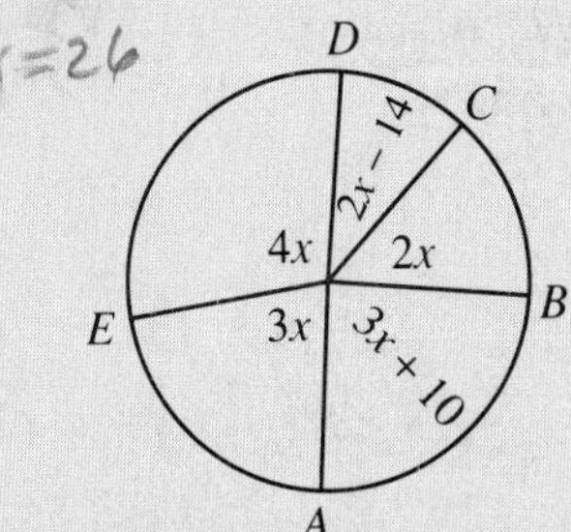

a. $\overset{\frown}{AB}$ 88 b. $\overset{\frown}{BC}$ 52
c. $\overset{\frown}{CD}$ 38 d. $\overset{\frown}{DE}$ 104
e. $\overset{\frown}{EA}$ 78

Complete the tables in Exercises 10 and 11.

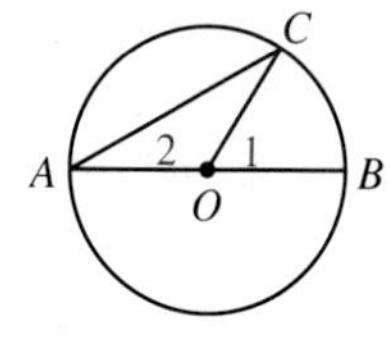

10.

$m\overparen{CB}$	60	70	? 56	? 50	? 2x
$m\angle 1$	? 60	? 70	56	? 50	? 2x
$m\angle 2$	? 30	? 35	? 28	25	x

11.

$m\overparen{CB}$	70	60	66	60	p
$m\overparen{BD}$	30	28	? 34	? 44	q
$m\angle COD$	?100	? 88	100	?104	? $p + q$
$m\angle CAD$	? 50	? 44	? 50	52	? $\frac{1}{2}(p + q)$

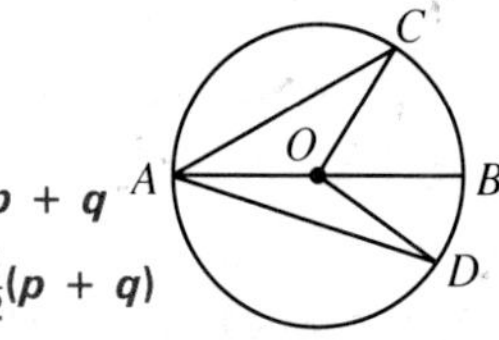

Using a Computer

Exs. 12 and 13 can be done with a construction program.

12. Use a compass to draw a large $\odot O$. Draw a central $\angle AOB$.

a. Label three other points P, Q, and R that are on $\odot O$ but not on $\overparen{AB}$. Then draw $\angle APB$, $\angle AQB$, and $\angle ARB$.

b. Use a protractor to find $m\angle AOB$, $m\angle APB$, $m\angle AQB$, and $m\angle ARB$. **$m\angle APB = m\angle AQB = m\angle ARB$**

c. What is the relationship between $m\angle APB$, $m\angle AQB$, and $m\angle ARB$? What is the relationship between $m\angle AOB$ and $m\angle APB$? **$m\angle AOB = 2m\angle APB$**

13. a. Draw three large circles and inscribe a different-shaped quadrilateral $ABCD$ in each.

b. Use a protractor to measure all the angles.

c. Compute $m\angle A + m\angle C$ and $m\angle B + m\angle D$.

d. What is the relationship between opposite angles of an inscribed quadrilateral? **The opp. ∠s of an inscribed quad. are supp.**

Exercise Note

Ex. 15 previews the concepts stated in Theorem 9-7 on page 350.

B **14.** Given: $\overline{WZ}$ is a diameter of $\odot O$; $\overline{OX} \parallel \overline{ZY}$
Prove: $\overparen{WX} \cong \overparen{XY}$
(*Hint*: Draw $\overline{OY}$.)

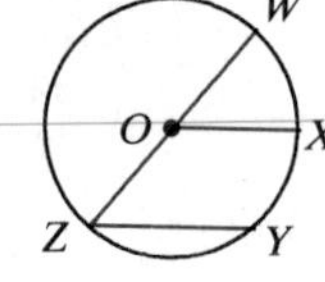

15. Given: $\overline{WZ}$ is a diameter of $\odot O$;
$m\overparen{WX} = m\overparen{XY} = n$
Prove: $m\angle Z = n$

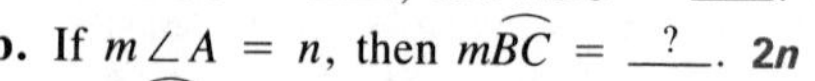

16. $\overline{AC}$ is a diameter of $\odot O$.

a. If $m\angle A = 35$, then $m\angle B =$ _?_, **35**
$m\angle BOC =$ _?_, **70** and $m\overparen{BC} =$ _?_. **70**

b. If $m\angle A = n$, then $m\overparen{BC} =$ _?_. **2n**

c. If $m\overparen{BC} = 6k$, then $m\angle A =$ _?_. **3k**

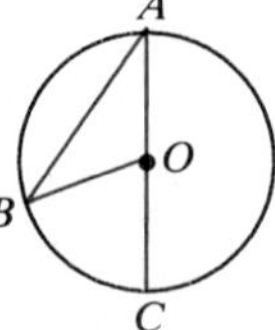

In Exercises 17–20, the latitude of a city is given. Sketch the Earth and a circle of latitude through the city. Find the radius of this circle.

17. Milwaukee, Wisconsin; 43°N
18. Columbus, Ohio; 40°N
19. Sydney, Australia; 34°S
20. Rio de Janeiro; 23°S

17. $r \approx$ **4700 km** **18.** $r \approx$ **4900 km** **19.** $r \approx$ **5300 km** **20.** $r \approx$ **5900 km**

C **21.** Given: $\odot O$ and $\odot Q$ intersect at R and S;
$m\widehat{RVS} = 60$; $m\widehat{RUS} = 120$

Prove: $\overline{OR}$ is tangent to $\odot Q$;
$\overline{QR}$ is tangent to $\odot O$.

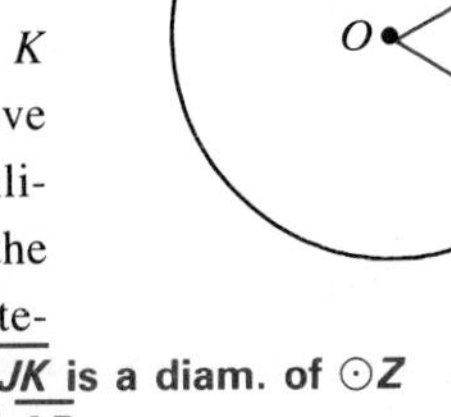

22. Given: $\overline{AB}$ is a diameter of $\odot Z$; points J and K lie on $\odot Z$ with $m\widehat{AJ} = m\widehat{BK}$. Discover and prove something about $\overline{JK}$. (*Hint*: There are two possibilities, depending on whether $\widehat{AJ}$ and $\widehat{BK}$ lie on the same side of $\overline{AB}$ or on opposite sides. So your statement will be of the *either* . . . *or* type.)

Either $\overline{JK}$ is a diam. of $\odot Z$ or $\overline{JK} \parallel \overline{AB}$.

The diagram, not drawn to scale, shows satellite S above the Earth, represented as sphere E. All lines tangent to the Earth from S touch the Earth at points on a circle with center C. Any two points on the Earth's surface on or above that circle can communicate with each other via S. X and Y are as far apart as two communication points can be. The Earth distance between X and Y equals the length of $\widehat{XTY}$, which equals $\frac{n}{360}$ · circumference of the Earth. That circumference is approximately 40,200 km and the radius of the Earth is approximately 6400 km.

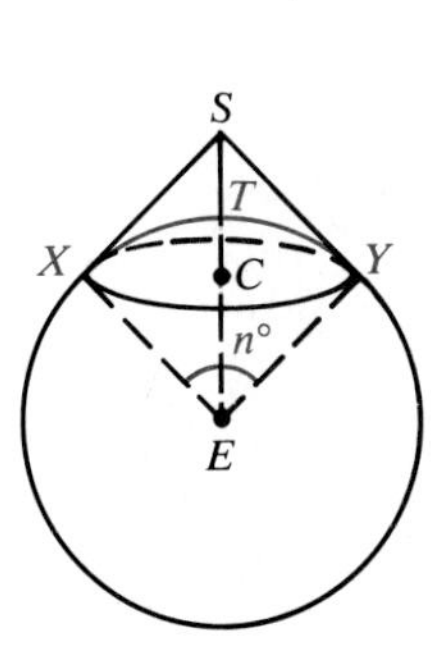

23. The photograph above shows the view from Gemini V looking north over the Gulf of California toward Los Angeles. The orbit of Gemini V ranged from 160 km to 300 km above the Earth. Take S to be 300 km above the Earth. That is, $ST = 300$ km. Find the Earth distance, rounded to the nearest 100 km, between X and Y. (*Hint*: Since you can find a value for $\cos \frac{n^\circ}{2}$ you can determine n°.) $\approx$ **3800 km**

24. Repeat Exercise 23, but with S twice as far from the Earth. Note that the distance between X and Y is not twice as great as before. $\approx$ **5300 km**

Using a Calculator

A calculator may be helpful in Exs. 23 and 24.

Teaching Suggestions,
pp. T113–T114

Objective
Presenting the Lesson
Enrichment

Supplementary Materials

Practice Master 51
Test 35
Resource Book, pp. 55–56, 144
Study Guide, pp. 113–114
Computer Activity 19

Lesson Focus

This lesson presents three theorems that state properties of chords and arcs of a circle or congruent circles.

Suggested Assignments

Minimum
Day 1: 347/1–9
Day 2: 347/10–15
349/Self-Test 1

Average
Day 1: 347/2–8 even, 9–15 odd
Day 2: 348/16–22 even
349/Self-Test 1

Maximum
Day 1: 347/1–7 odd, 8, 10, 14
S 342–343/16, 23
Day 2: 347–348/11, 13, 15, 16–26 even

Using a Computer

Theorems 9-4, 9-5, and 9-6 can all be discovered and verified using a construction program.

9-4 *Arcs and Chords*

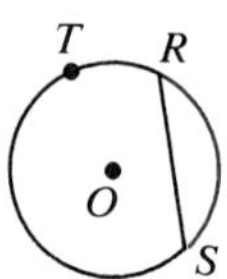

In $\odot O$ shown at the right, $\overline{RS}$ cuts off two arcs, $\overset{\frown}{RS}$ and $\overset{\frown}{RTS}$. We speak of $\overset{\frown}{RS}$, the minor arc, as being *the arc of chord* $\overline{RS}$.

Theorem 9-4

In the same circle or in congruent circles:

(1) Congruent arcs have congruent chords.

(2) Congruent chords have congruent arcs.

Here is a paragraph proof of part (1) for one circle. You will be asked to write a paragraph proof of part (2) in Written Exercise 16.

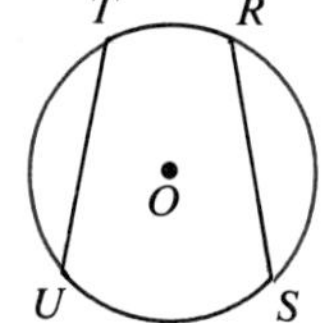

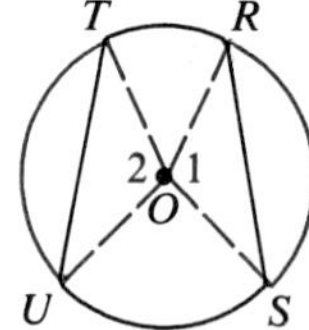

Given: $\odot O$; $\overset{\frown}{RS} \cong \overset{\frown}{TU}$

Prove: $\overline{RS} \cong \overline{TU}$

Proof:

Draw radii $\overline{OR}$, $\overline{OS}$, $\overline{OT}$, and $\overline{OU}$. $\overline{OR} \cong \overline{OT}$ and $\overline{OS} \cong \overline{OU}$ because they are all radii of the same circle. Since $\overset{\frown}{RS} \cong \overset{\frown}{TU}$, central angles 1 and 2 are congruent. Then $\triangle ROS \cong \triangle TOU$ by SAS and corresponding parts $\overline{RS}$ and $\overline{TU}$ are congruent.

A point Y is called the *midpoint* of $\overset{\frown}{XYZ}$ if $\overset{\frown}{XY} \cong \overset{\frown}{YZ}$. Any line, segment, or ray that contains Y bisects $\overset{\frown}{XYZ}$.

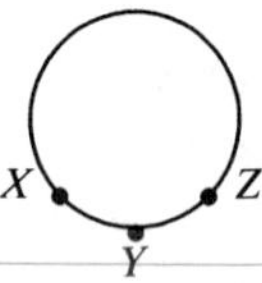

Theorem 9-5

A diameter that is perpendicular to a chord bisects the chord and its arc.

Given: $\odot O$; $\overline{CD} \perp \overline{AB}$

Prove: $\overline{AZ} \cong \overline{BZ}$; $\overset{\frown}{AD} \cong \overset{\frown}{BD}$

Plan for Proof: Draw $\overline{OA}$ and $\overline{OB}$. Then use the HL Theorem to prove that $\triangle OZA \cong \triangle OZB$. Then use corresponding parts of congruent triangles to show that $\overline{AZ} \cong \overline{BZ}$ and $\angle 1 \cong \angle 2$. Finally, apply the theorem that congruent central angles have congruent arcs.

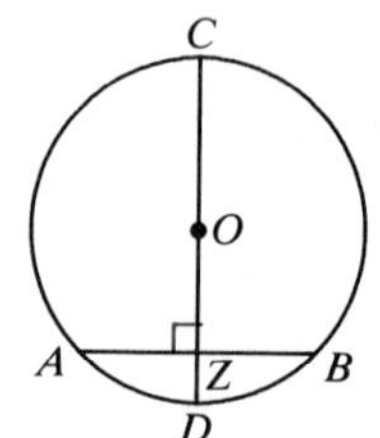

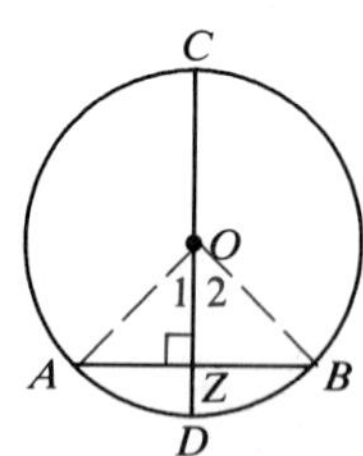

Example 1 Find the values of x and y.

Solution Diameter $\overline{CD}$ bisects chord $\overline{AB}$, so $x = 5$. (Theorem 9-5)
$\overline{AB} \cong \overline{EF}$, so $m\widehat{AB} = 86$. (Theorem 9-4)
Diameter $\overline{CD}$ bisects $\widehat{AB}$, so $y = 43$. (Theorem 9-5)

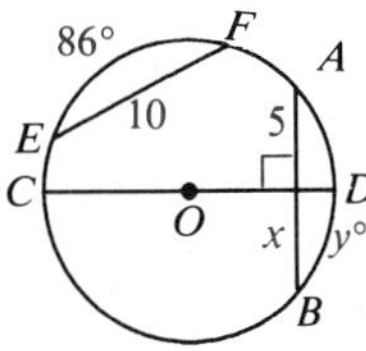

Recall (page 154) that the distance from a point to a line is the length of the perpendicular segment from the point to the line. This definition is used in the following example.

Example 2 Find the length of a chord that is a distance 5 from the center of a circle with radius 8.

Solution Draw the perpendicular segment, $\overline{OP}$, from O to $\overline{AB}$.

$$x^2 + 5^2 = 8^2$$
$$x^2 + 25 = 64$$
$$x^2 = 39$$
$$x = \sqrt{39}$$

By Theorem 9-5, $\overline{OP}$ bisects $\overline{AB}$ so $AB = 2 \cdot AP = 2x = 2\sqrt{39}$.

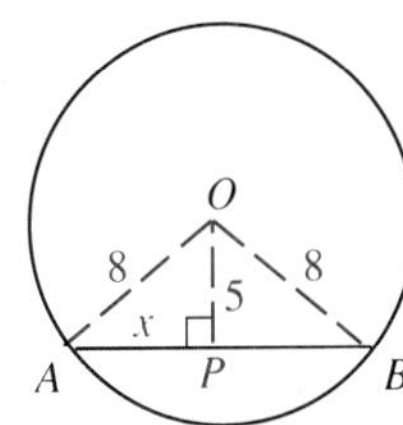

It should be clear that *all* chords in $\odot O$ above that are a distance 5 from center O will have length $2\sqrt{39}$. Thus, all such chords are congruent, as stated in part (1) of the next theorem. You will prove part (2) of the theorem as Classroom Exercise 6.

Theorem 9-6

In the same circle or in congruent circles:

(1) Chords equally distant from the center (or centers) are congruent.

(2) Congruent chords are equally distant from the center (or centers).

Example 3 Find the value of x.

Solution S is the midpoint of $\overline{RT}$, so $RT = 6$. (Theorem 9-5)
$\overline{RT} \cong \overline{UV}$, so $x = 4$. (Theorem 9-6)

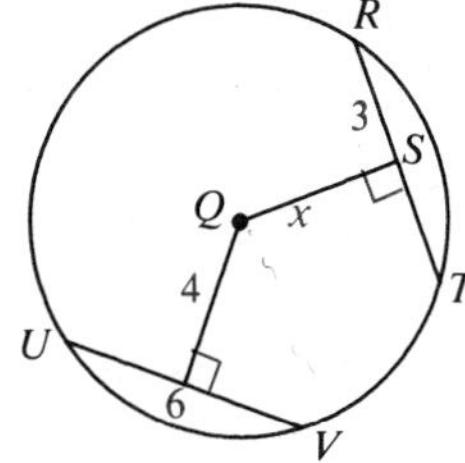

Application

Circular barbecue grills are constructed with parallel chords supported by two perpendicular chords. The perpendicular chords are an equal distance from the center and therefore are congruent.

Chalkboard Examples

1. $x = \underline{12}$, $y = \underline{12}$

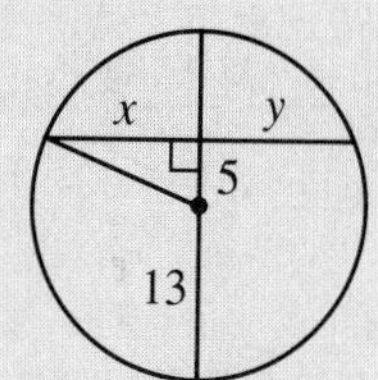

2. $x = \underline{3\sqrt{3}}$, $y = \underline{3}$, $m\widehat{AB} = \underline{120}$

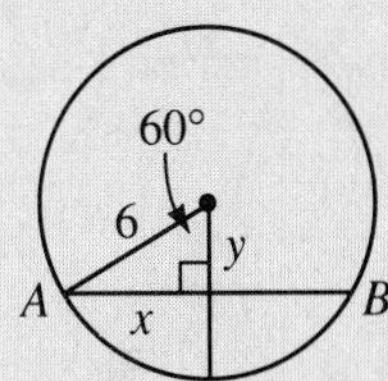

3. $x = \underline{8}$, $y = \underline{16}$

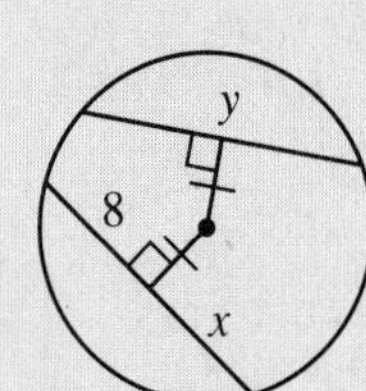

Classroom Exercises

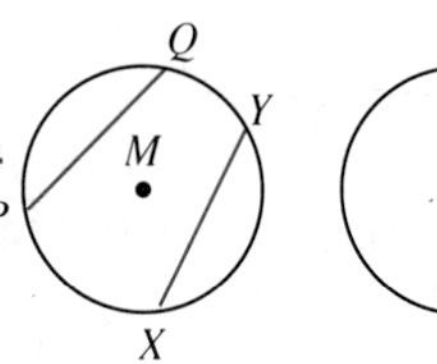

1. If $\overline{PQ} \cong \overline{XY}$, can you conclude that $\widehat{PQ} \cong \widehat{XY}$? Why or why not? **Yes; Thm. 9-4**
2. If $\overline{PQ} \cong \overline{RS}$, can you conclude that $\widehat{PQ} \cong \widehat{RS}$? Why or why not? **No; you can't assume $\odot M \cong \odot N$.**
3. Study the diagram at the right and tell what theorem justifies each statement.
   a. $LK = 8$ **Thm. 9-5**
   b. $OE = 3$ **Thm. 9-6**
   c. $\widehat{LK} \cong \widehat{GH}$ **Thm. 9-4**

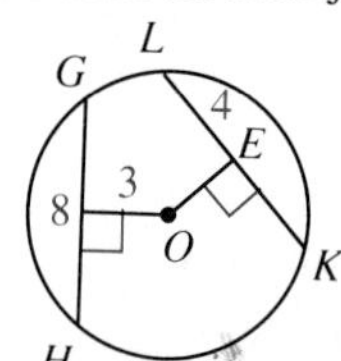

4. $AB = 16$
   $OM = 6$ **10**
   radius = __?__

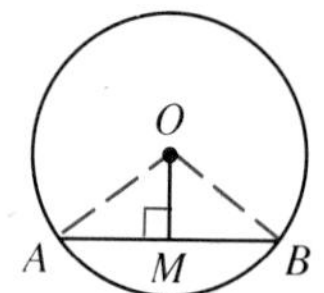

5. $PQ = 10$
   radius = 13
   OM = __?__ **12**

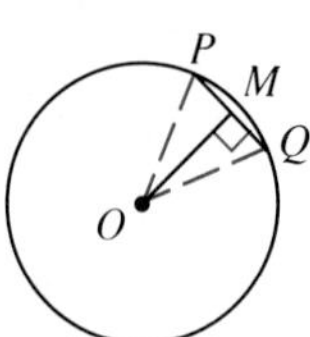

6. Supply reasons to complete a proof of Theorem 9-6, part (2), for one circle.
   Given: $\odot O$; $\overline{AB} \cong \overline{CD}$; $\overline{OY} \perp \overline{AB}$; $\overline{OZ} \perp \overline{CD}$
   Prove: $OY = OZ$

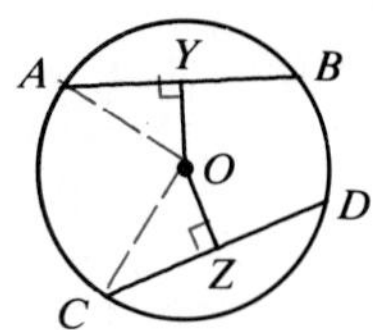

Proof:

Statements	Reasons
1. Draw radii $\overline{OA}$ and $\overline{OC}$.	1. __?__ **Through any 2 pts. there is exactly one line.**
2. $\overline{OY} \perp \overline{AB}$; $\overline{OZ} \perp \overline{CD}$	2. __?__ **Given**
3. $\overline{AB} \cong \overline{CD}$, or $AB = CD$	3. __?__ **Given**
4. $\frac{1}{2}AB = \frac{1}{2}CD$	4. __?__ **Mult. Prop. of =**
5. $AY = \frac{1}{2}AB$; $CZ = \frac{1}{2}CD$	5. __?__ **A diam. that is ⊥ to a chord bis. the chord.**
6. $AY = CZ$, or $\overline{AY} \cong \overline{CZ}$	6. __?__ **Substitution Prop.**
7. $\overline{OA} \cong \overline{OC}$	7. __?__ **All radii of a ⊙ are ≅.**
8. rt. $\triangle OYA \cong$ rt. $\triangle OZC$	8. __?__ **HL**
9. $\overline{OY} \cong \overline{OZ}$, or $OY = OZ$	9. __?__ **Corr. parts of ≅ △s are ≅.**

7. Suppose that in Theorem 9-6, the words "circle" and "circles" are replaced by "sphere" and "spheres." Is the resulting statement true? **Yes**

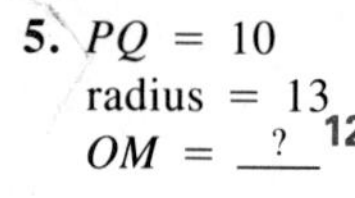

Guided Practice

In the diagrams that follow, point O is the center of the circle. Complete.

1. RT = 30, OM = 8

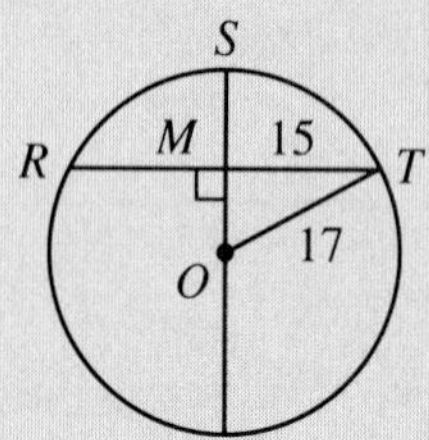

2. $m\widehat{ACB}$ = 140, $m\angle AOC$ = 70

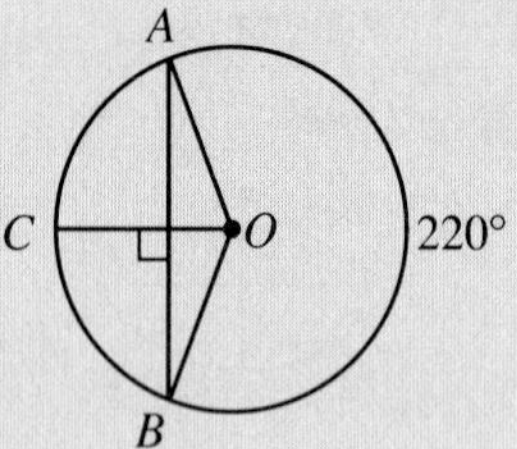

3. $m\widehat{CD}$ = 80

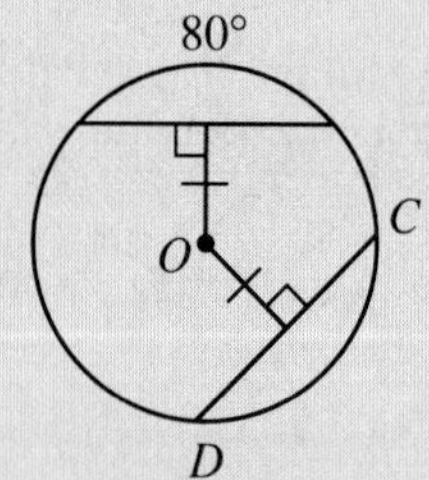

4. Draw a circle and a diameter. Then draw several chords parallel to the diameter. Which chord is the longest? diameter
5. Draw $\odot O$ with radius 12 cm and chord $\overline{RS}$ 6 cm from O. How long is the chord? $12\sqrt{3}$ cm

Written Exercises

In the diagrams that follow, *O* is the center of the circle.

A

1.

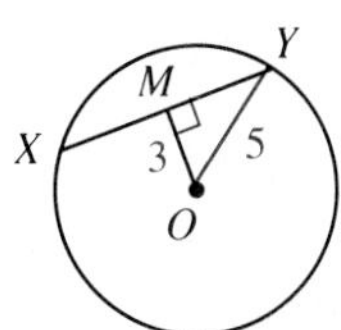

$XY = \underline{\ ?\ }$ **8**

2.

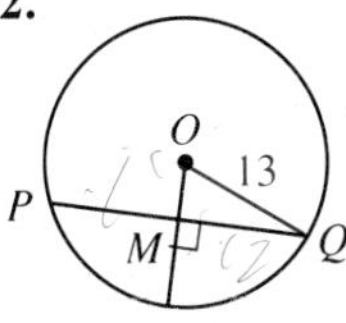

$PQ = 24$; $OM = \underline{\ ?\ }$ **5**

3.

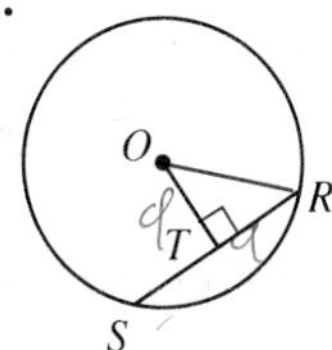

$OT = 9$; $RS = 18$
$OR = \underline{\ ?\ }$ **$9\sqrt{2}$**

4.

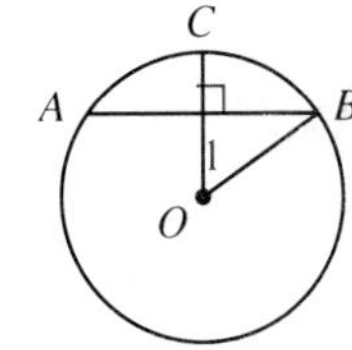

$m\widehat{ACB} = 110$;
$m\angle 1 = \underline{\ ?\ }$ **55**

5.

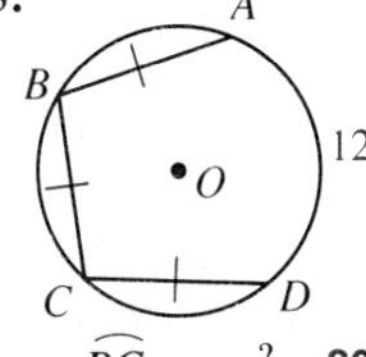

$m\widehat{BC} = \underline{\ ?\ }$ **80**

6.

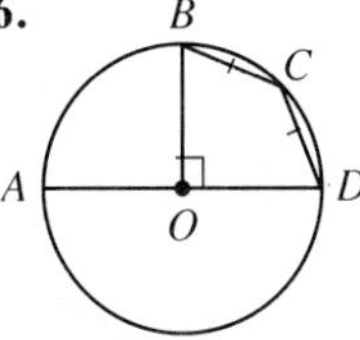

$m\widehat{CD} = \underline{\ ?\ }$ **45**

7.

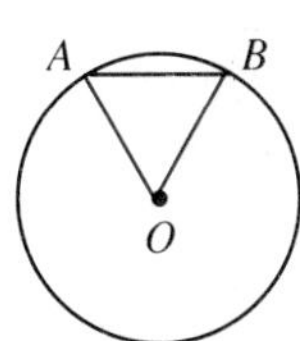

$m\angle AOB = 60$;
$AB = 24$; $OA = \underline{\ ?\ }$ **24**

8.

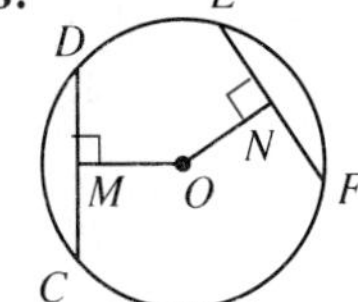

$OM = ON = 7$;
$CM = 6$; $EF = \underline{\ ?\ }$ **12**

9.

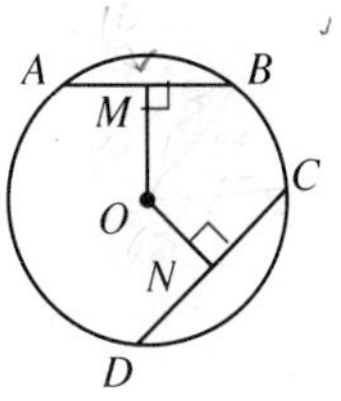

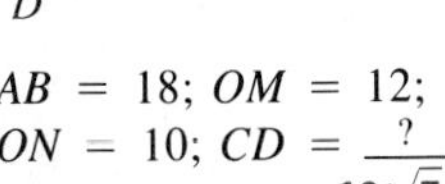

$AB = 18$; $OM = 12$;
$ON = 10$; $CD = \underline{\ ?\ }$
$10\sqrt{5}$

10. Sketch a circle with two noncongruent chords. Is the longer chord farther from the center or closer to the center than the shorter chord? **closer**

11. Sketch a circle O with radius 10 and chord $\overline{XY}$ 8 cm long. How far is the chord from O? **$2\sqrt{21}$ cm**

12. Sketch a circle Q with a chord $\overline{RS}$ that is 16 cm long and 2 cm from Q. What is the radius of $\odot Q$? **$2\sqrt{17}$ cm**

13. Sketch a circle P with radius 5 cm and chord $\overline{AB}$ that is 2 cm from P. Find the length of $\overline{AB}$. **$2\sqrt{21}$ cm**

14. Given: $\widehat{JZ} \cong \widehat{KZ}$
Prove: $\angle J \cong \angle K$

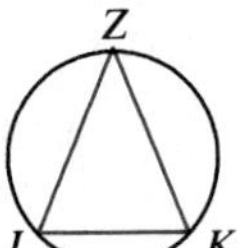

15. Prove the converse of Exercise 14.

6. Given: $\widehat{AB} \cong \widehat{DB}$
Prove: $\angle ABC \cong \angle DBC$

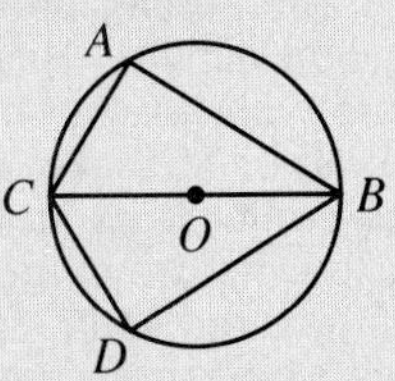

1. $\widehat{AB} \cong \widehat{DB}$ (Given)
2. $\overline{AB} \cong \overline{DB}$ (In the same $\odot$, $\cong$ arcs have $\cong$ chords.)
3. $m\widehat{AC} = 180 - m\widehat{AB}$; $m\widehat{DC} = 180 - m\widehat{DB}$ (Arc Add. Post.)
4. $m\widehat{AC} = m\widehat{DC}$ or $\widehat{AC} \cong \widehat{DC}$ (Subst., Steps 1 and 3)
5. $\overline{AC} \cong \overline{DC}$ (In the same $\odot$, $\cong$ arcs have $\cong$ chords.)
6. $\overline{CB} \cong \overline{CB}$ (Reflexive)
7. $\triangle ABC \cong \triangle DBC$ (SSS)
8. $\angle ABC \cong \angle DBC$ (Corr. parts of $\cong$ ⚠ are $\cong$.)

Thinking Skills

Ex. 10 can be expanded by using the intuitive notion of a limit. Ask students what the limiting length of a chord is as its distance from the center approaches 0.
the length of the diameter

Group Activity

Exs. 23 and 24 can be done as a group activity. Have students work in groups of three or four to make and discuss conjectures suggested by the drawing. If the conjectures seem reasonable to a group, they should try to prove them.

Additional Answers Written Exercises

23. Given 2 concentric ⊙s, if a chord of the outer ⊙ is tan. to the inner ⊙, the pt. of tangency is the midpt. of the chord.

24. If a chord of a ⊙ is ∥ to a tan. of the ⊙, the tan. bis. the arc of the chord.

Quick Quiz

1. Points *R*, *S*, and *T* lie on circle *O*.

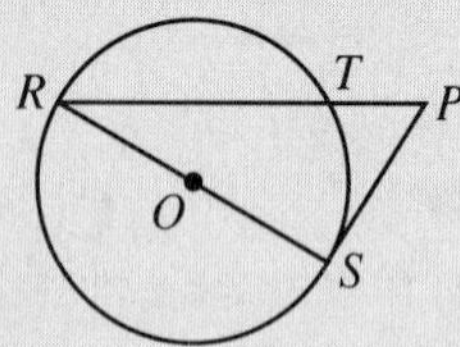

a. Name two radii of ⊙*O*. $\overline{OR}, \overline{OS}, \overline{OT}$

b. Name a diameter of ⊙*O*. $\overline{RS}$

c. Name a tangent of ⊙*O*. $\overline{PS}$

d. Name a chord and secant of ⊙*O*. $\overline{RT}$ or $\overline{RS}$, $\overleftrightarrow{RT}$ or $\overleftrightarrow{RS}$

2. Sketch each of the following.

a. Rt. △*XYZ* inscribed in ⊙*O*.

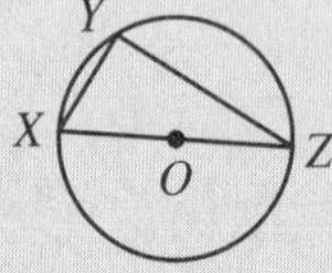

B **16.** Write a paragraph proof of part (2) of Theorem 9-4. First list what is given and what is to be proved.

17.

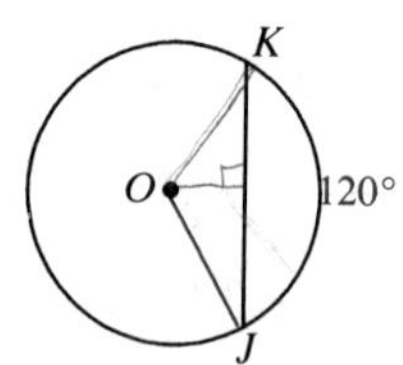

If $OJ = 10$, $JK = $ __?__. **$10\sqrt{3}$**

18.

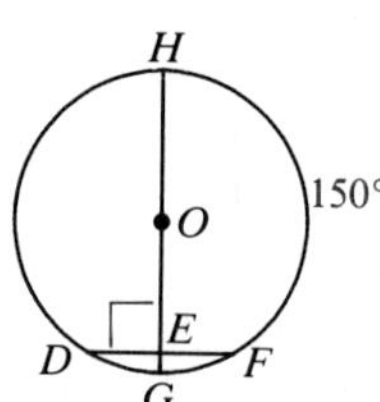

If $OE = 8\sqrt{3}$, $HG = $ __?__. **32**

19. A plane 5 cm from the center of a sphere intersects the sphere in a circle with diameter 24 cm. Find the diameter of the sphere. **26 cm**

20. A plane *P* cuts sphere *O* in a circle that has diameter 20. If the diameter of the sphere is 30, how far is the plane from *O*? **$5\sqrt{5}$**

21. Use trigonometry to find the measure of the arc cut off by a chord 12 cm long in a circle of radius 10 cm. **≈ 74**

22. In ⊙*O*, $m\overset{\frown}{RS} = 70$ and $RS = 20$. Use trigonometry to find the radius of ⊙*O*. **≈ 17.4**

State and prove a theorem suggested by the figure.

C **23.**

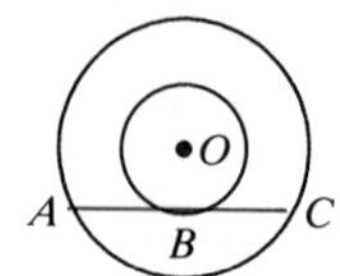

24.

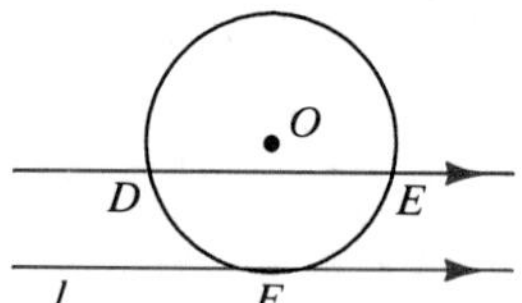

25. *A*, *B*, *C* are points on ⊙*O* such that △*ABC* is equilateral. If the radius of the circle is 6, what is the perimeter of △*ABC*? **$18\sqrt{3}$**

26. Investigate the possibility, given a circle, of drawing two chords whose lengths are in the ratio 1:2 and whose distances from the center are in the ratio 2:1. If the chords can be drawn, find the length of each in terms of the radius. If not, prove that the figure is impossible. **$\frac{2\sqrt{5}}{5}r$ and $\frac{4\sqrt{5}}{5}r$**

27. Three parallel chords of ⊙*O* are drawn as shown. Their lengths are 20, 16, and 12 cm. Find, to the nearest tenth of a centimeter, the length of chord $\overline{XY}$ (not shown). **2.8 cm**

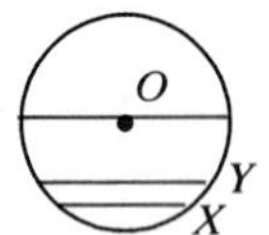

Self-Test 1

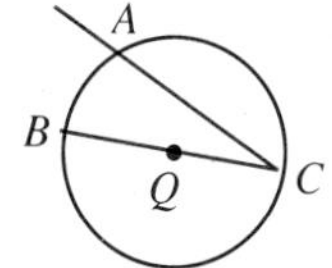

1. Points A, B, and C lie on $\odot Q$.
   a. Name two radii of $\odot Q$. **$\overline{QB}$, $\overline{QC}$**
   b. Name a diameter of $\odot Q$. **$\overline{BC}$**
   c. Name a chord and a secant of $\odot Q$. **$\overline{AC}$, $\overleftrightarrow{AC}$**
2. Sketch each of the following.
   a. $\triangle ABC$ inscribed in $\odot O$ b. Quad. $LUMX$ circumscribed about $\odot Q$
3. $\overline{NP}$ is tangent to $\odot O$ at P. If $NO = 25$ and $NP = 20$, find OP. **15**
4. A plane passes through the common center of two concentric spheres. Describe the intersection of the plane and the two spheres. **two concentric circles**
5. Find the length of a chord that is 3 cm from the center of a circle with radius 7 cm. **$4\sqrt{10}$ cm**
6. Points E, F, G, H, and J lie on $\odot O$.
   a. $m\widehat{EF} = \underline{\ ?\ }$ **50** and $m\widehat{EHF} = \underline{\ ?\ }$. **310**
   b. Suppose $\overline{JH} \cong \overline{HG}$. State the theorem that supports the conclusion that $\widehat{JH} \cong \widehat{HG}$.
   In the same $\odot$, $\cong$ chords have $\cong$ arcs.

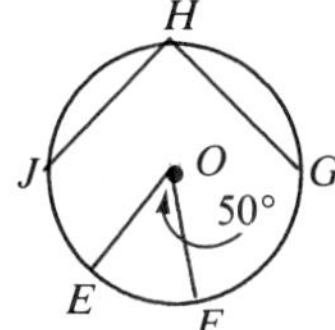

Angles and Segments

Objectives

1. Solve problems and prove statements involving inscribed angles.
2. Solve problems and prove statements involving angles formed by chords, secants, and tangents.
3. Solve problems involving lengths of chords, secant segments, and tangent segments.

9-5 *Inscribed Angles*

Angles 1 and 2 shown at the right are called *inscribed angles*. An **inscribed angle** is an angle whose vertex is on a circle and whose sides contain chords of the circle. We say that the angles at the right *intercept* the arcs shown in color. $\angle 1$ intercepts a minor arc. $\angle 2$ intercepts a major arc.

b. Trapezoid $TRAP$ circumscribed about $\odot O$.

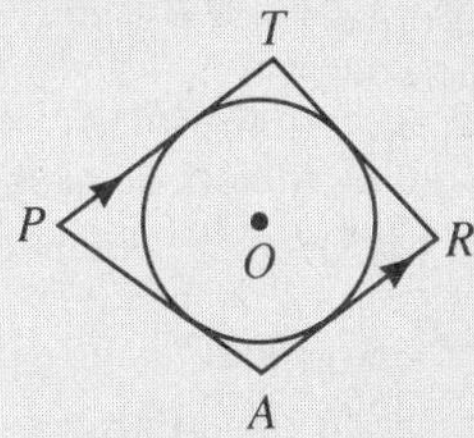

3. $\overleftrightarrow{AB}$ is tangent to $\odot O$ at A. If $AB = 10$ and $AO = 5$, find OB. $5\sqrt{5}$
4. A plane passes through the centers of two externally tangent spheres. Describe the intersection of the plane and the spheres. two externally tangent circles
5. Find the length of a chord that is 8 cm from the center of a circle with radius 17 cm. 30 cm

Teaching Suggestions, p. T114

Objectives
Presenting the Lesson
Reinforcement

Supplementary Materials

Practice Master 52
Study Guide, pp. 115–116

Lesson Focus

The purpose of this lesson is to study angles whose vertices are on a circle. The sides of these angles pass through the circle and cut off arcs. The measures of the angles are related to the measures of the arcs.

Suggested Assignments

Minimum
Day 1: 354/1–9
Day 2: 354–355/10–13
357/Mixed Review 1–6

Average
Day 1: 354/1–12
Day 2: 355/13–15, 19–23
357/Mixed Review 1–6

Maximum
Day 1: 354–355/1–9 odd, 10, 12, 13
S 348/23, 25
Day 2: 355–356/14, 15, 19–21, 25, 27

You may wish to introduce Construction 9 on page 393 after covering this lesson.

Using a Model

You can motivate Theorem 9-7 by having students measure various inscribed angles on a geoboard. The students could form the angles out of rubber bands or string and then use a protractor to measure the angles.

Making Connections

Use Theorem 9-7 as an alternate way to show that the sum of the angles of a triangle is 180° (see p. 94).

The next theorem compares the measure of an inscribed angle with the measure of its intercepted arc. Its proof requires us to consider three possible cases.

Theorem 9-7

The measure of an inscribed angle is equal to half the measure of its intercepted arc.

Given: $\angle ABC$ inscribed in $\odot O$

Prove: $m\angle ABC = \frac{1}{2}m\widehat{AC}$

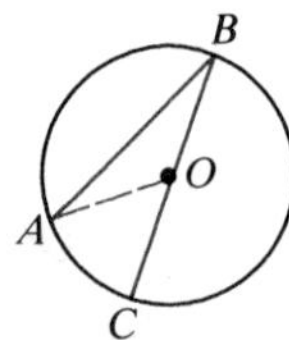

Case I:
Point O lies on $\angle ABC$.

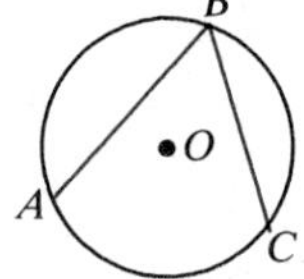

Case II:
Point O lies inside $\angle ABC$.

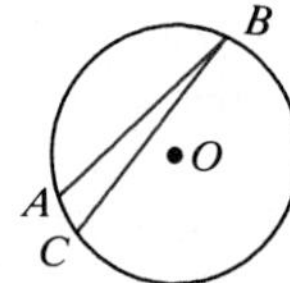

Case III:
Point O lies outside $\angle ABC$.

Key steps of proof of Case I:

1. Draw radius $\overline{OA}$ and let $m\angle ABC = x$.
2. $m\angle A = x$ (Why?) **Isosceles △ Theorem**
3. $m\angle AOC = 2x$ (Why?) **Theorem 3-12, page 95**
4. $m\widehat{AC} = 2x$ (Why?) **Def. of measure of minor arc**
5. $m\angle ABC = \frac{1}{2}m\widehat{AC}$ (Substitution Prop.)

Now that Case I has been proved, it can be used to prove Case II and Case III. An auxiliary line will be used in those proofs, which are left as Classroom Exercises 12 and 13.

Example 1 Find the values of x and y in $\odot O$.

Solution

$m\angle PTQ = \frac{1}{2}m\widehat{PQ}$, so
$x = \frac{1}{2} \cdot 40 = 20.$

$m\angle PSR = \frac{1}{2}m\widehat{PR}$, so
$50 = \frac{1}{2}(40 + y)$ and $y = 60.$

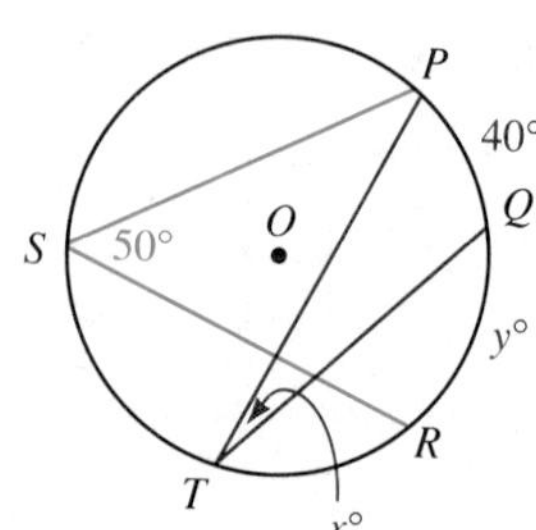

Proofs of the following three corollaries of Theorem 9-7 will be considered in Classroom Exercises 1–3.

Corollary 1

If two inscribed angles intercept the same arc, then the angles are congruent.

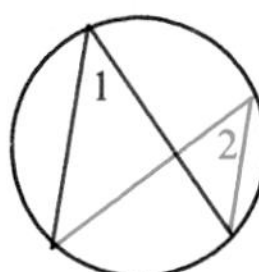

$\angle 1 \cong \angle 2$

Corollary 2

An angle inscribed in a semicircle is a right angle.

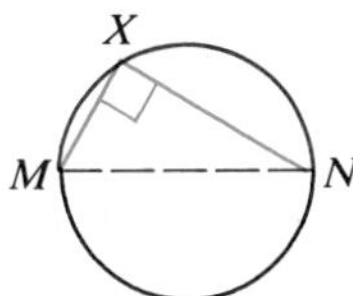

If $\overset{\frown}{MXN}$ is a semicircle, then $\angle X$ is a right angle.

Corollary 3

If a quadrilateral is inscribed in a circle, then its opposite angles are supplementary.

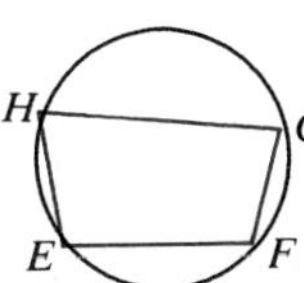

$\angle E$ is supp. to $\angle G$.
$\angle F$ is supp. to $\angle H$.

Example 2 Find the values of x, y, and z.

Solution $\angle ADB$ and $\angle ACB$ intercept the same arc, so $x = 40$. (Corollary 1)

$\angle ABC$ is inscribed in a semicircle, so $\angle ABC$ is a right angle and $y = 90$. (Corollary 2)

$ABCD$ is an inscribed quadrilateral, so $\angle BAD$ and $\angle BCD$ are supplementary. (Corollary 3)

Therefore, $z = 180 - (x + 30)$
$z = 180 - (40 + 30) = 110.$

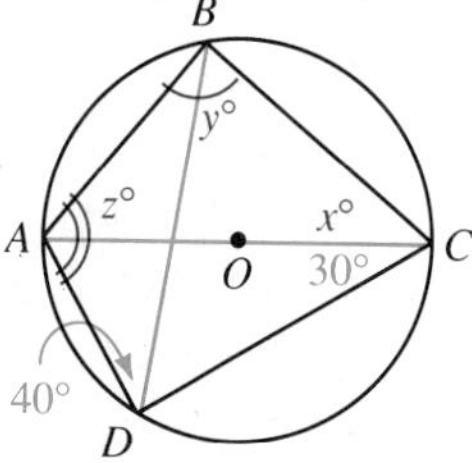

Chalkboard Examples

Find the values of x and y in $\odot O$.

1. $x = 40$, $y = 75$

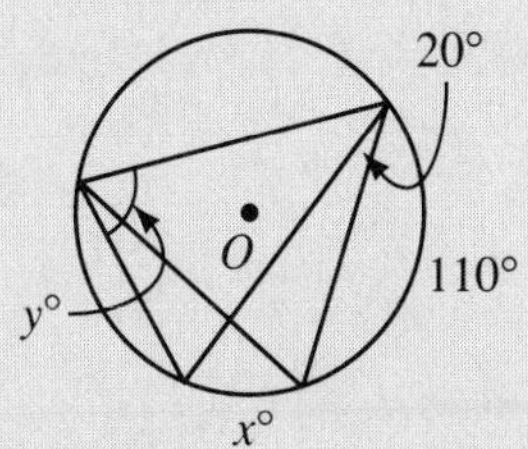

2. $x = 20$, $y = 90$

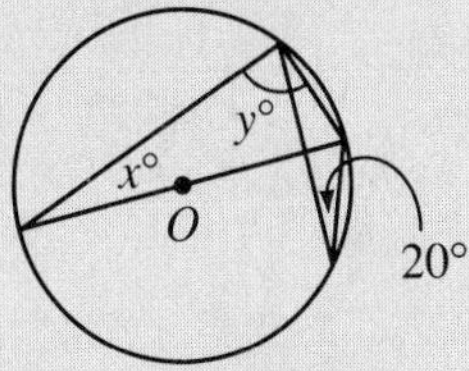

3. $x = 60$, $y = 50$

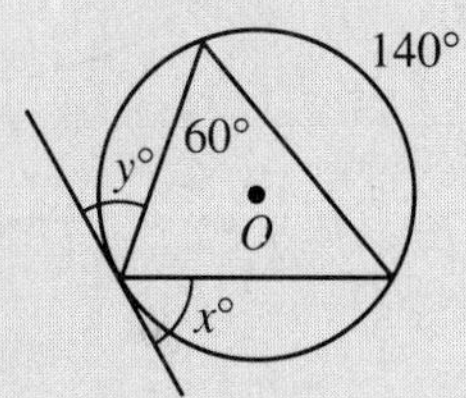

4. $x = 40$, $y = 50$

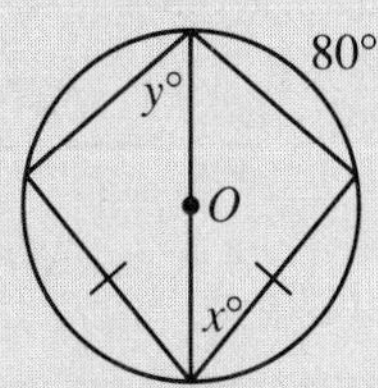

Making Connections

Corollary 3 can be used as an alternate way of showing that the sum of the measures of the angles of a convex quadrilateral is 360° (see page 102).

Study the diagrams below from left to right. Point B moves along the circle closer and closer to point T. Finally, in diagram (4), point B has merged with T, and one side of $\angle T$ has become a tangent.

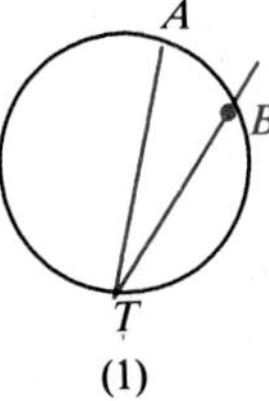

(1)

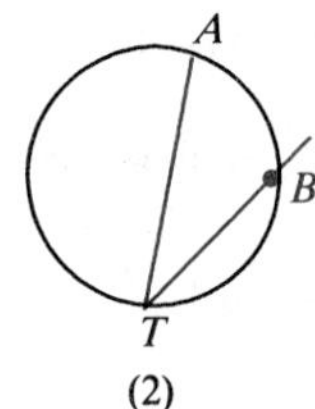

(2)

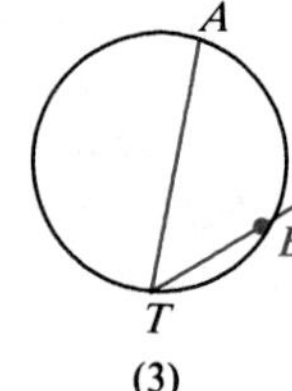

(3)

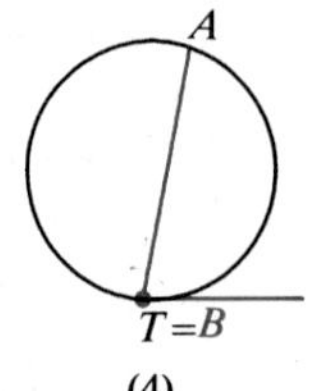

(4)

Apply Theorem 9-7 to diagrams (1), (2), and (3) and you have $m\angle T = \frac{1}{2}m\overparen{AB}$. As you might expect, this equation applies to diagram (4), too, since we say that $\angle T$ intercepts $\overparen{AB}$ in this case as well. Diagram (4) suggests Theorem 9-8. In Exercises 13–15 you will prove the three cases of the theorem.

Theorem 9-8

The measure of an angle formed by a chord and a tangent is equal to half the measure of the intercepted arc.

For example, if $\overline{PT}$ is tangent to the circle and $\overline{AT}$ is a chord, then $\angle ATP$ intercepts $\overparen{AT}$ and $m\angle ATP = \frac{1}{2}m\overparen{AT} = \frac{1}{2} \cdot 140 = 70$.

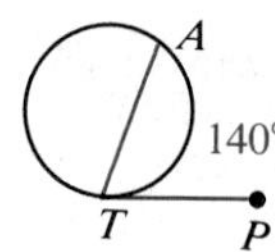

Classroom Exercises

1. Explain why Corollary 1 of Theorem 9-7 is true. That is, explain why $\angle 1 \cong \angle 2$. **Say the measure of the intercepted arc is n; then the measure of each angle is $\frac{1}{2}n$.**

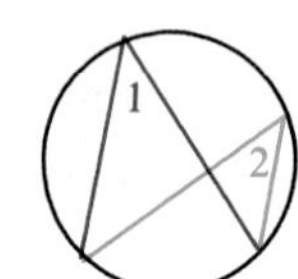

2. Explain why Corollary 2 is true. That is, explain how the fact that $\overparen{MXN}$ is a semicircle leads to a conclusion that $\angle X$ is a right angle. **$\angle X$ intercepts a semicircle, so $m\angle X = \frac{1}{2}(180) = 90$.**

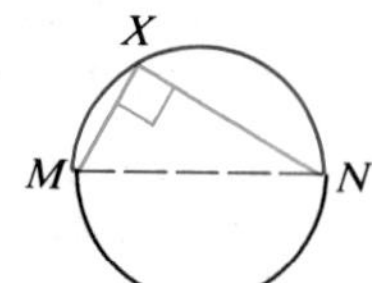

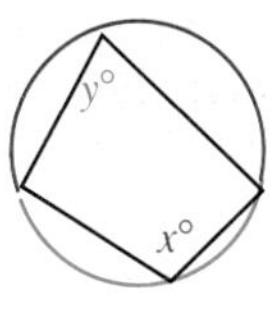

3. a. What is the sum of the measures of the red and blue arcs? **360**

b. Explain how part (a) allows you to deduce that $x + y = 180$. $x + y = \frac{1}{2}(\text{red}) + \frac{1}{2}(\text{blue}) = \frac{1}{2}(360) = 180$

c. State the corollary of Theorem 9-7 that you have just proved. **If a quad. is inscribed in a circle, then its opposite ∠s are supp.**

Tangents and chords are shown. Find the values of *x* and *y*. In Exercise 5, *O* is the center of the circle.

4.

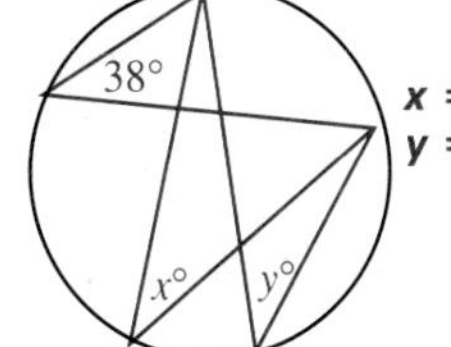

x = 38
y = 38

5.

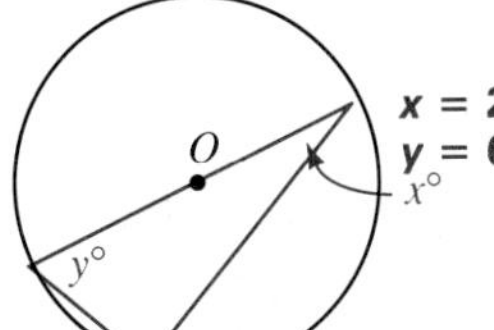

x = 25
y = 65

6.

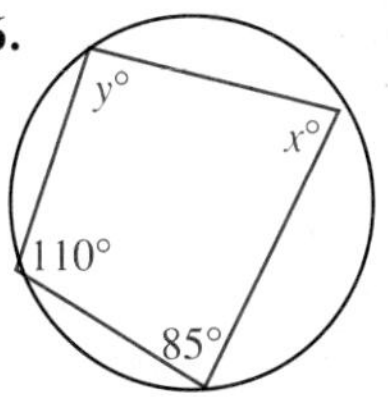

x = 70
y = 95

7.

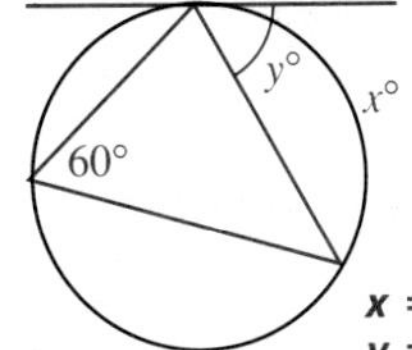

x = 120
y = 60

8.

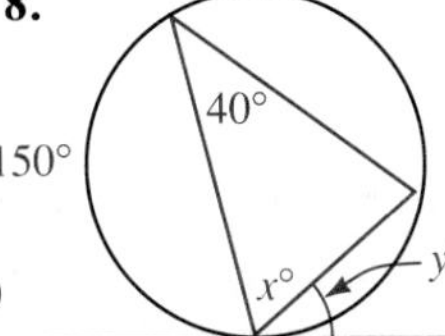

x = 65
y = 40

9.

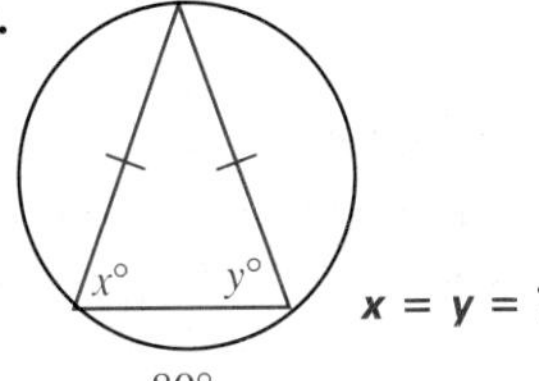

x = y = 70

10. a. State the contrapositive of Corollary 3. **If the opp. ∠s of a quad. are not supp., then the quad. cannot be inscribed in a ⊙**

b. In quadrilateral *PQRS*, $m\angle P = 100$ and $m\angle R = 90$. Is it possible to circumscribe a circle about *PQRS*? Why or why not? **No; ∠*P* and ∠*R* are opp. ∠s and are not supp.**

11. In the diagram, $m\angle AKB = m\angle CKD = n$. $m\overset{\frown}{AB} = \underline{\ ?\ }$ and $m\overset{\frown}{CD} = \underline{\ ?\ }$. State a theorem suggested by this exercise. **2*n*; 2*n*. In the same ⊙, ≅ inscr. ∠s int. ≅ arcs.**

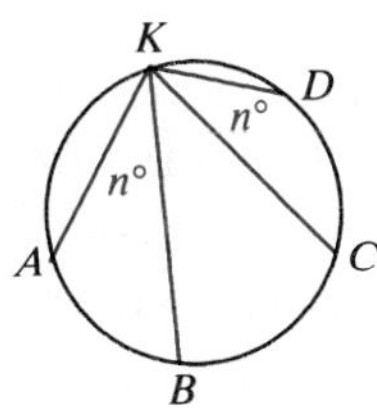

12. Outline a proof of Case II of Theorem 9-7. Use the diagram on page 350. (*Hint*: Draw the diameter from *B* and apply Case I.)

13. Repeat Exercise 12 for Case III.

14. Equilateral △*ABC* is inscribed in ⊙*O*. Tangents to the circle at *A* and *C* meet at *D*. What kind of figure is *ABCD*? **rhombus**

Exercise Note

You may need to review contrapositives before doing Ex. 10.

Additional Answers
Classroom Exercises

12. To prove Case II, first draw diameter $\overline{BD}$. Apply Case I of Theorem 9-7 twice, then use the Angle Add. Post. and the Arc Add. Post.

13. To prove Case III, follow the same procedure as outlined above.

Guided Practice

In the diagrams that follow, point O is the center of the circle. Find the values of x, y, and z.

1. $x = 160$, $y = 100$, $z = 100$

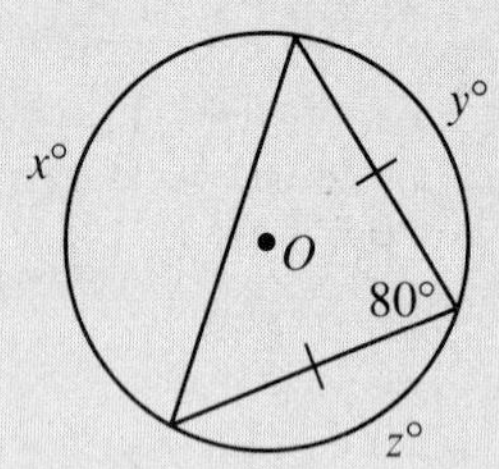

2. $x = 30$, $y = 60$, $z = 150$

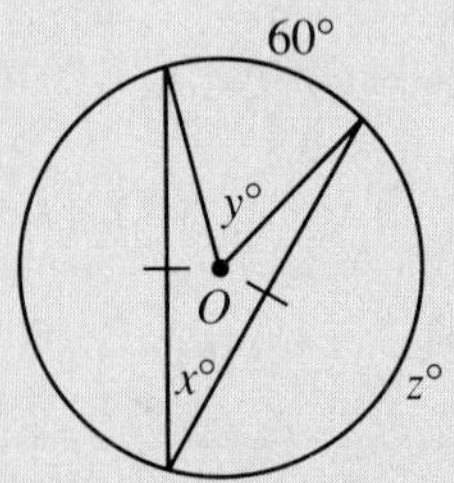

3. $x = 98$, $y = 49$, $z = 49$

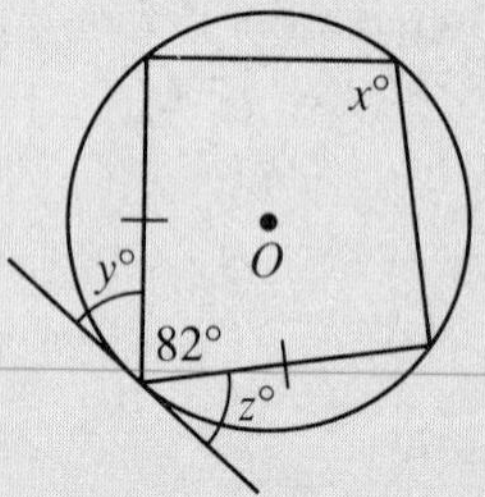

4. Given: $\odot O \cong \odot P$; $\overset{\frown}{AC} \cong \overset{\frown}{AB}$
Prove: $\triangle ABD \cong \triangle ACE$

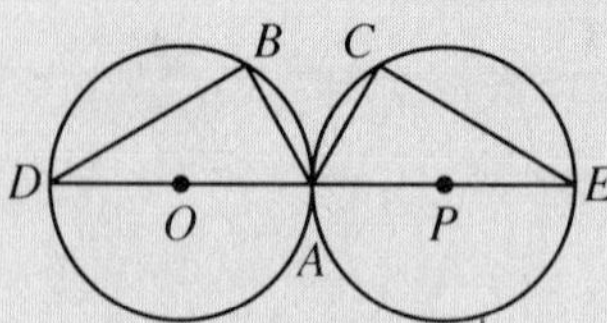

If the circles are congruent, then their diameters are congruent. $\angle B$ and $\angle C$ are inscribed right angles, making

Written Exercises

In the diagrams that follow, O is the center of the circle. In Exercises 1–9 find the values of x, y, and z.

A

1.

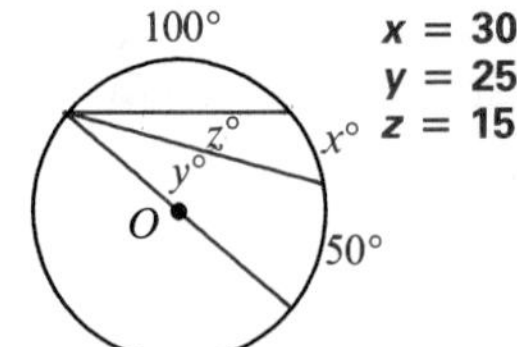

x = 30 y = 25 z = 15

2.

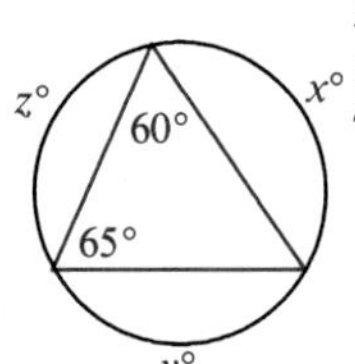

x = 130 y = 120 z = 110

3.

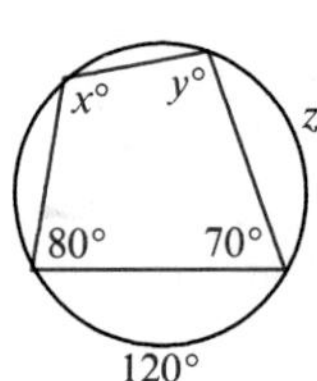

x = 110 y = 100 z = 100

4.

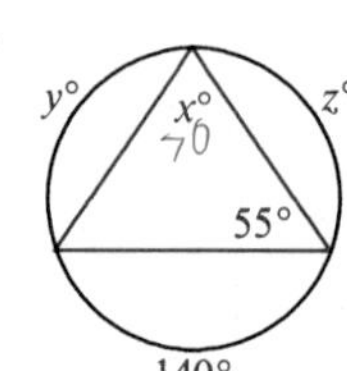

x = 70 y = 110 z = 110

5.

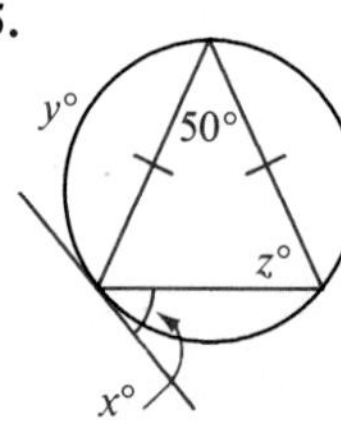

x = 50 y = 130 z = 65

6.

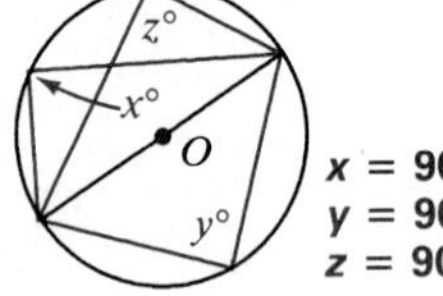

x = 90 y = 90 z = 90

7.

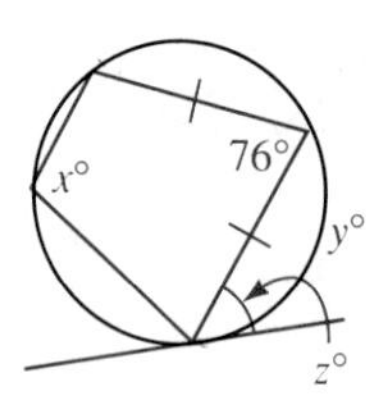

x = 104 y = 104 z = 52

8.

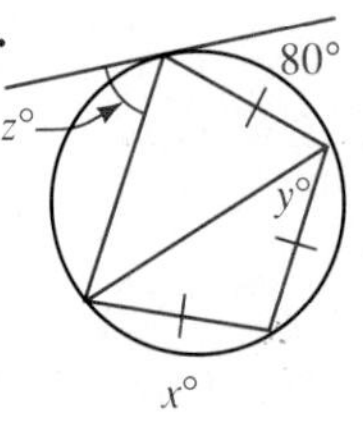

x = 80 y = 40 z = 60

9.

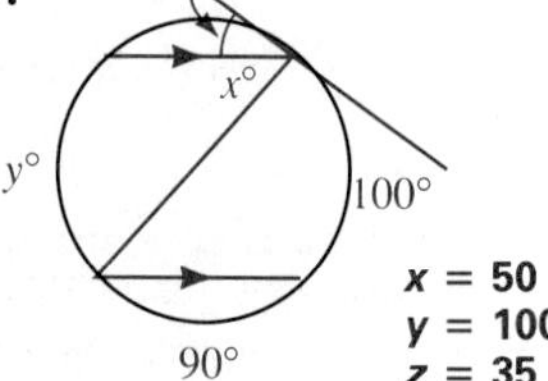

x = 50 y = 100 z = 35

10. Prove: If two chords of a circle are parallel, the two arcs between the chords are congruent.
Given: $\overline{AB} \parallel \overline{CD}$
Prove: $\overset{\frown}{AC} \cong \overset{\frown}{BD}$
(*Hint*: Draw an auxiliary line.)

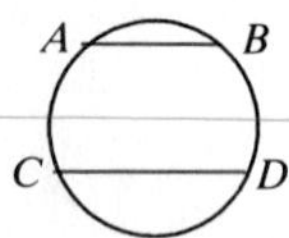

11. a. State the converse of the statement in Exercise 10. **See below.**
b. Is this converse true or false? If it is true, write a proof. If not, explain why it is false. **False; the chords may intersect.**

12. Prove: $\triangle UXZ \sim \triangle YVZ$

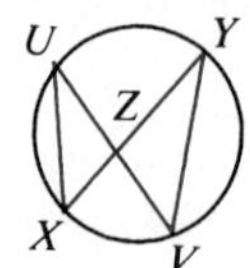

11. a. If the arcs between two chords are $\cong$, then the chords are $\parallel$.

Exercises 13–15 prove the three possible cases of Theorem 9-8. In each case you are given chord $\overline{TA}$ and tangent $\overline{TP}$ of $\odot O$.

13. Supply reasons for the key steps of the proof that $m\angle ATP = \frac{1}{2}m\widehat{ANT}$ in Case I.

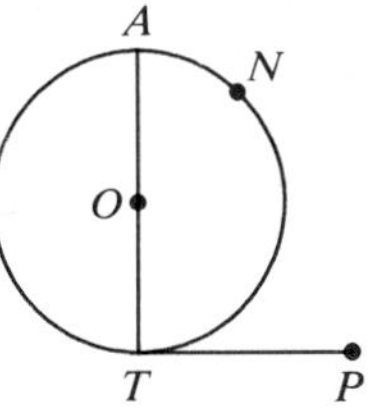

Case I: O lies on $\angle ATP$.

1. $\overline{TP} \perp \overline{TA}$ and $m\angle ATP = 90$.
2. $\widehat{ANT}$ is a semicircle and $m\widehat{ANT} = 180$.
3. $m\angle ATP = \frac{1}{2}m\widehat{ANT}$

In Case II and Case III, $\overline{AT}$ is not a diameter. You can draw diameter $\overline{TZ}$ and then use Case I, Theorem 9-7, and the Angle Addition and Arc Addition Postulates.

B **14.** Case II. O lies inside $\angle ATP$.
Prove $m\angle ATP = \frac{1}{2}m\widehat{ANT}$

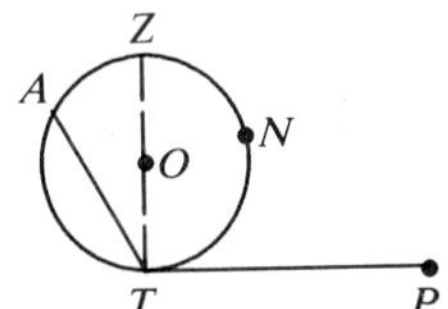

15. Case III. O lies outside $\angle ATP$.
Prove $m\angle ATP = \frac{1}{2}m\widehat{ANT}$

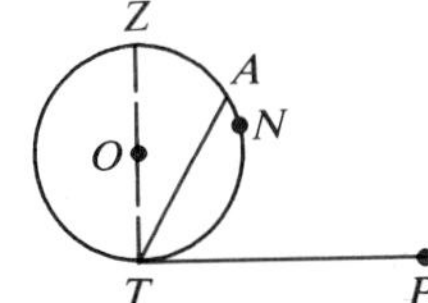

16. Prove that if one pair of opposite sides of an inscribed quadrilateral are congruent, then the other sides are parallel.

17. Draw an inscribed quadrilateral $ABCD$ and its diagonals intersecting at E. Name two pairs of similar triangles. **$\triangle ADE \sim \triangle BCE$; $\triangle EDC \sim \triangle EAB$**

18. Draw an inscribed quadrilateral $PQRS$ with shortest side $\overline{PS}$. Draw its diagonals intersecting at T. Extend $\overrightarrow{QP}$ and $\overrightarrow{RS}$ to meet at V. Name two pairs of similar triangles such that each triangle has a vertex at V. **$\triangle VPS \sim \triangle VRQ$; $\triangle VSQ \sim \triangle VPR$**

Exercises 19–21 refer to a quadrilateral $ABCD$ inscribed in a circle.

19. $m\angle A = x$, $m\angle B = 2x$, and $m\angle C = x + 20$. Find x and $m\angle D$. **$x = 80$; $m\angle D = 20$**

20. $m\angle A = x^2$, $m\angle B = 9x - 2$, and $m\angle C = 11x$. Find x and $m\angle D$. **$x = 9$; $m\angle D = 101$**

21. $m\angle D = 75$, $m\widehat{AB} = x^2$, $m\widehat{BC} = 5x$, and $m\widehat{CD} = 6x$. Find x and $m\angle A$. **$x = 10$; $m\angle A = 55$**

22. Parallelogram $ABCD$ is inscribed in $\odot O$. Find $m\angle A$. **90**

23. Equilateral $\triangle ABC$ is inscribed in a circle. P and Q are midpoints of $\widehat{BC}$ and $\widehat{CA}$, respectively. What kind of figure is quadrilateral $AQPB$? Justify your answer. **rectangle**

$\triangle ABD$ and $\triangle ACE$ right triangles. Since $\overline{AB} \cong \overline{AC}$ (Given) the triangles are congruent by HL Theorem.

Proof Note

Having students study proofs that require cases gives them practice at understanding more complex proofs. Point out to students that proof by cases is necessary when the conditions of a problem can be interpreted in different ways.

Using a Computer

Exs. 17 and 18 can be done using a construction program.

Exercise Note

Exs. 19–21 give students an opportunity to apply their algebraic skills to solving geometry problems.

Additional Answers
Written Exercises

13. 1. If a line is tan. to a $\odot$, the line is $\perp$ to the radius drawn to the pt. of tangency; def. of $\perp$ lines.
2. Def. of semicircle
3. Substitution Prop.

23. $m\widehat{AB} = m\widehat{BC} = m\widehat{CA} = 120$, $m\widehat{AQ} = m\widehat{QC} = m\widehat{BP} = m\widehat{PC} = 60$. $m\widehat{BAQ} = m\widehat{AQP} = 180$ (Arc Add. Post.), $m\angle BPQ = m\angle ABP = 90$ (the meas. of an inscr. $\angle$ = half the meas. of its int. arc). $m\angle AQP = m\angle BAQ = 90$ (Corollary 3). $AQPB$ is a rectangle.

24. The diagram at the right shows a regular polygon with 7 sides.

a. Explain why the numbered angles are all congruent. (*Hint*: You may assume that a circle can be circumscribed about any regular polygon.) **See below.**

b. Will your reasoning apply to a regular polygon with any number of sides? **Yes**

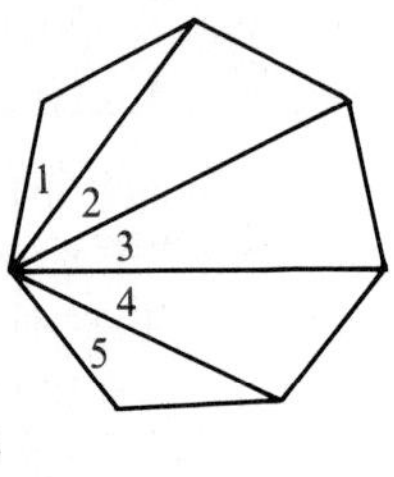

a. In the circum. ⊙, all inscribed ∠s intercept ≅ arcs.

C **25.** Given: Vertices A, B, and C of quadrilateral $ABCD$ lie on $\odot O$; $m\angle A + m\angle C = 180$; $m\angle B + m\angle D = 180$.
Prove: D lies on $\odot O$.

(*Hint*: Use an indirect proof. Assume temporarily that D is not on $\odot O$. You must then treat two cases: (1) D is inside $\odot O$, and (2) D is outside $\odot O$. In each case let X be the point where $\overrightarrow{AD}$ intersects $\odot O$ and draw $\overline{CX}$. Show that what you can conclude about $\angle AXC$ contradicts the given information.)

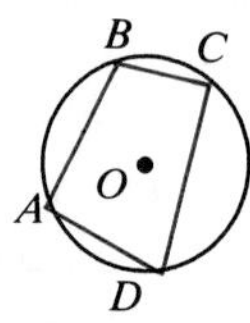

26. Given: $\overline{PQ} \parallel \overline{SR}$
Prove: $\overline{PS} \parallel \overline{QR}$

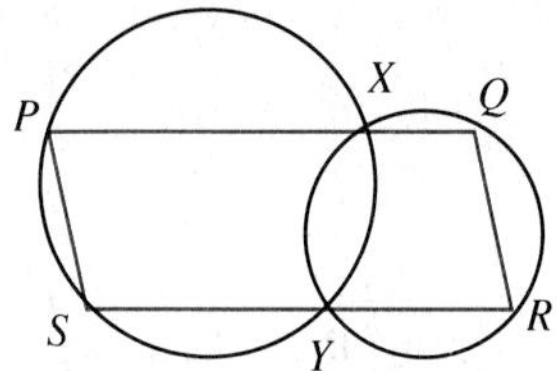

27. *Ptolemy's Theorem* states that in an inscribed quadrilateral, the sum of the products of its opposite sides is equal to the product of its diagonals. This means that for $ABCD$ shown,

$$AB \cdot CD + BC \cdot AD = AC \cdot BD.$$

Prove the theorem by choosing point Q on $\overline{AC}$ so that $\angle ADQ \cong \angle BDC$. Then show $\triangle ADQ \sim \triangle BDC$ and $\triangle ADB \sim \triangle QDC$. Use these similar triangles to show that

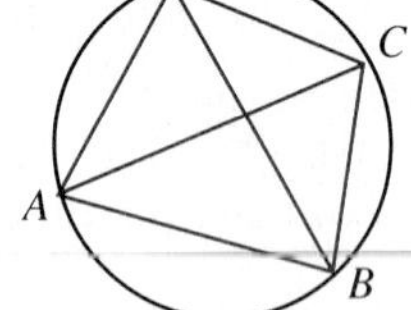

$$AQ = \frac{BC \cdot AD}{BD} \text{ and } QC = \frac{AB \cdot CD}{BD}.$$

Add these two equations and complete the proof.

28. Equilateral $\triangle ABC$ is inscribed in a circle. P is any point on $\overset{\frown}{BC}$. Prove $PA = PB + PC$. (*Hint*: Use Ptolemy's Theorem.)

★ **29.** Angle C of $\triangle ABC$ is a right angle. The sides of the triangle have the lengths shown. The smallest circle (not shown) through C that is tangent to $\overline{AB}$ intersects $\overline{AC}$ at J and $\overline{BC}$ at K. Express the distance JK in terms of a, b, and c. $\mathbf{\frac{ab}{c}}$

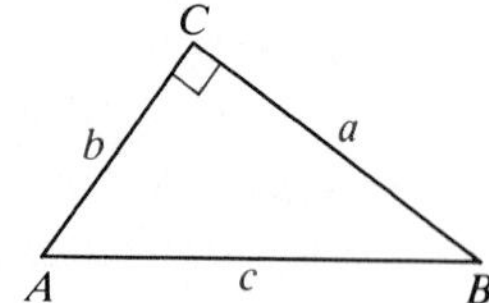

Problem Solving

Exs. 27–29 are good, challenging problems. Students need to learn that problem solving is a creative process that may take a great deal of time and effort. Encourage them to work on these exercises over a period of several days.

Exercise Note

In Ex. 27, if Ptolemy's Theorem is applied to an inscribed rectangle, the Pythagorean Theorem is obtained.

Cultural Note

Ptolemy (ca. 85–165 A.D.) was an astronomer and mathematician who lived in Alexandria, Egypt. His ideas on astronomy dominated western thought until the 15th and 16th centuries.

Mixed Review Exercises

1. Name a diameter of $\odot O$. **$\overline{LM}$**
2. Name a secant of $\odot O$. **$\overleftrightarrow{LM}$**
3. Name a tangent segment. **$\overline{NP}$**
4. If $OQ = 7$, then $LM = \underline{\ ?\ }$. **14**
5. If $m\overset{\frown}{MQ} = x$, express $m\overset{\frown}{QLM}$ in terms of x. **$360 - x$**
6. Find the geometric mean between 4 and 9. **6**

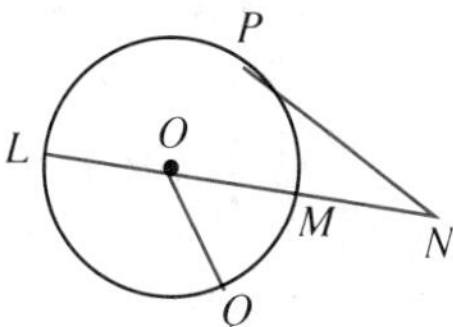

9-6 *Other Angles*

The preceding section dealt with angles that have their vertices on a circle. Theorem 9-9 deals with the angle formed by two chords that intersect inside a circle. Such an angle and its vertical angle intercept two arcs.

Theorem 9-9

The measure of an angle formed by two chords that intersect inside a circle is equal to half the sum of the measures of the intercepted arcs.

Given: Chords $\overline{AB}$ and $\overline{CD}$ intersect inside a circle.
Prove: $m\angle 1 = \frac{1}{2}(m\overset{\frown}{AC} + m\overset{\frown}{BD})$

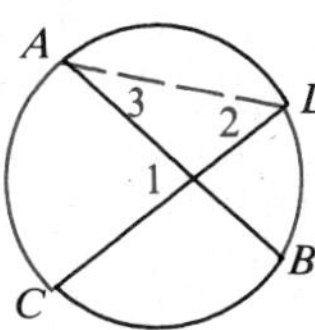

Proof:

Statements	Reasons
1. Draw chord $\overline{AD}$.	1. Through any two points there is exactly one line.
2. $m\angle 1 = m\angle 2 + m\angle 3$	2. The measure of an exterior $\angle$ of a $\triangle$ = the sum of the measures of the two remote interior $\angle$s.
3. $m\angle 2 = \frac{1}{2}m\overset{\frown}{AC}$; $m\angle 3 = \frac{1}{2}m\overset{\frown}{BD}$	3. The measure of an inscribed angle is equal to half the measure of its intercepted arc.
4. $m\angle 1 = \frac{1}{2}m\overset{\frown}{AC} + \frac{1}{2}m\overset{\frown}{BD}$ or $m\angle 1 = \frac{1}{2}(m\overset{\frown}{AC} + m\overset{\frown}{BD})$	4. Substitution (Step 3 in Step 2)

Teaching Suggestions, pp. T114–T115

Objective
Presenting the Lesson
Reinforcement

Cooperative Learning, p. T115

Exploring Activity, p. 327c

Supplementary Materials

Practice Master 53
Study Guide, pp. 117–118

Lesson Focus

This lesson studies the relationships among the arcs of a circle and the angles formed by chords, secants, and tangents.

Suggested Assignments

Minimum
Day 1: 359/1–14
S 355/16
Day 2: 360/15–23
Day 3: 360/24–30

Average
Day 1: 359–360/1–17
Day 2: 360/18–21, 22–30 even

Maximum
Day 1: 359–360/2–20 even, 21, 22
Day 2: 360/23, 25–30

Chalkboard Examples

$\overline{UT}$ is tangent to the circle.

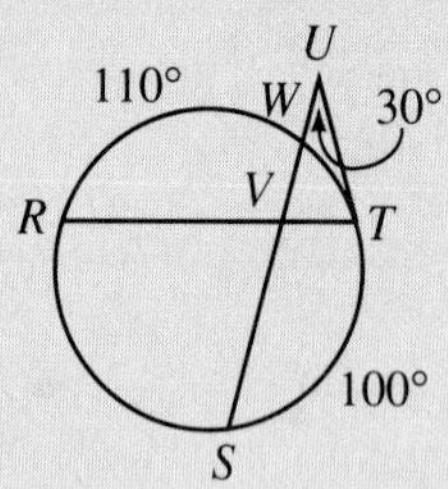

Complete.

1. $m\overset{\frown}{WT} = \underline{40}$
2. $m\angle TVS = \underline{105}$
3. $m\angle RVS = \underline{75}$
4. $m\overset{\frown}{RS} = \underline{110}$

Complete.

5. If $m\overset{\frown}{AB} = 105$, then $m\angle D = \underline{75}$.

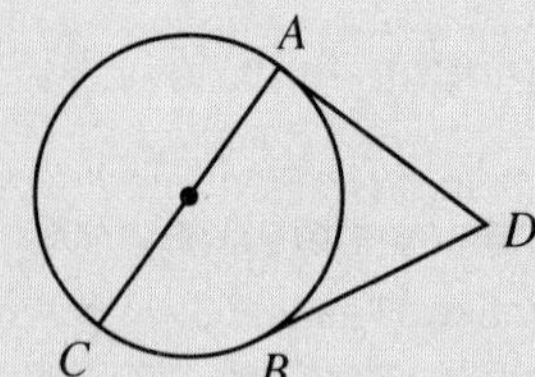

6. $m\overset{\frown}{AB} = \underline{40}$

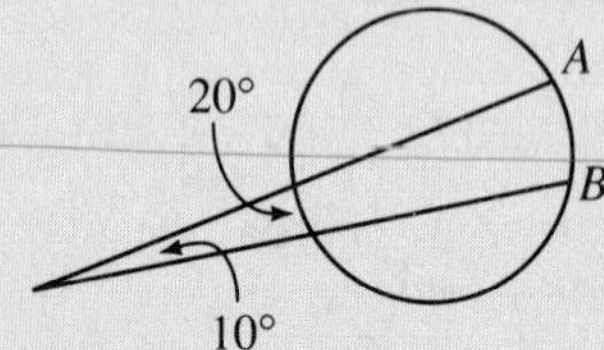

Proof Note

In discussing the proof of Case I of Theorem 9-10 (Classroom Ex. 10), you may want to point out that drawing chord $\overline{AD}$ would also provide a way to do the proof. The important idea is that this proof requires that one interior angle and one exterior angle of a triangle be associated with the given arcs of the circle.

One case of the next theorem will be proved in Classroom Exercise 10, the other two cases in Exercises 25 and 26. Notice that angles formed by two secants, two tangents, or a secant and a tangent intercept two arcs.

Theorem 9-10

The measure of an angle formed by two secants, two tangents, or a secant and a tangent drawn from a point outside a circle is equal to half the difference of the measures of the intercepted arcs.

Case I: Two secants

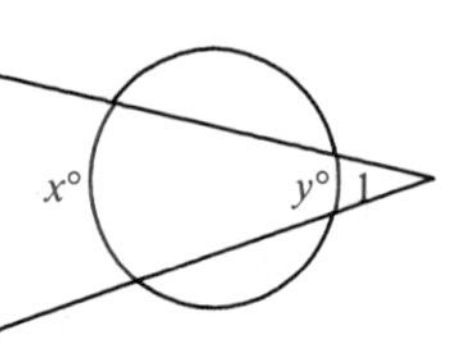

$m\angle 1 = \frac{1}{2}(x - y)$

Case II: Two tangents

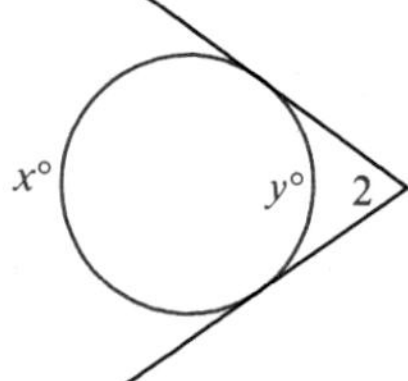

$m\angle 2 = \frac{1}{2}(x - y)$

Case III: A secant and a tangent

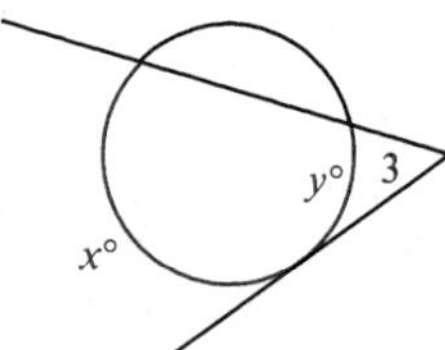

$m\angle 3 = \frac{1}{2}(x - y)$

Example 1 Find the measures of $\angle 1$ and $\angle 2$.

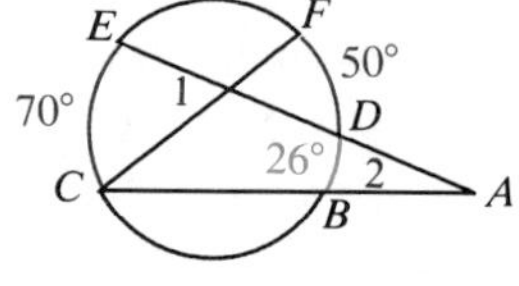

Solution

$m\angle 1 = \frac{1}{2}(m\overset{\frown}{CE} + m\overset{\frown}{FD})$ (Theorem 9-9)

$m\angle 1 = \frac{1}{2}(70 + 50) = 60$

$m\angle 2 = \frac{1}{2}(m\overset{\frown}{CE} - m\overset{\frown}{BD})$ (Theorem 9-10)

$m\angle 2 = \frac{1}{2}(70 - 26) = 22$

Example 2 $\overline{BA}$ is a tangent. Find $m\overset{\frown}{BD}$ and $m\overset{\frown}{BC}$.

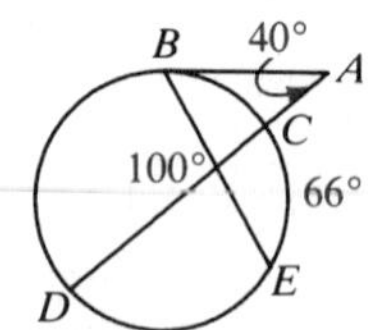

Solution

$100 = \frac{1}{2}(m\overset{\frown}{BD} + 66)$ (Theorem 9-9)

$200 = m\overset{\frown}{BD} + 66$, so $m\overset{\frown}{BD} = 134$

$40 = \frac{1}{2}(m\overset{\frown}{BD} - m\overset{\frown}{BC})$ (Theorem 9-10)

$80 = 134 - m\overset{\frown}{BC}$, so $m\overset{\frown}{BC} = 54$

Classroom Exercises

Find the measure of each numbered angle.

1.

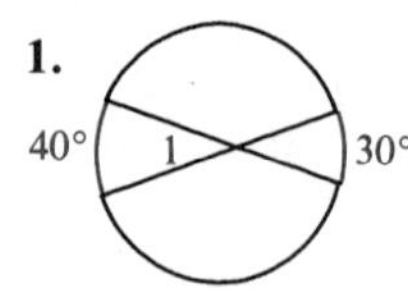

$m\angle 1 = 35$

2.

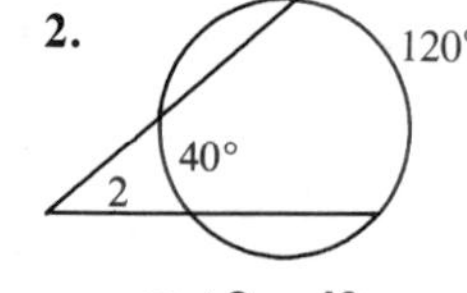

$m\angle 2 = 40$

3.

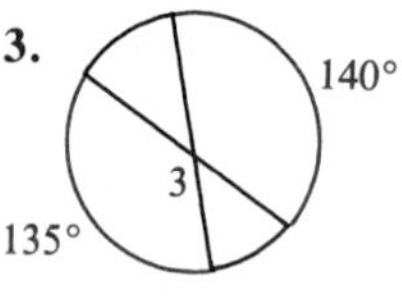

$m\angle 3 = 137.5$

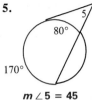

4.

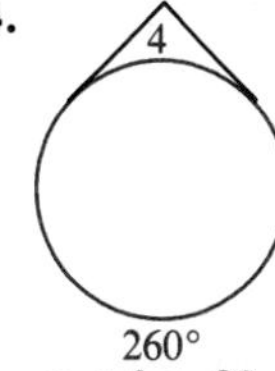

m∠4 = 80

5.

m∠5 = 45

6.

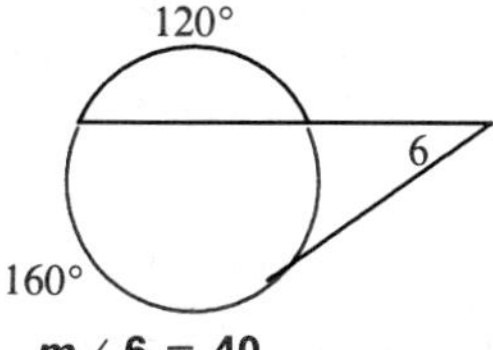

m∠6 = 40

State an equation you could use to find the value of x. Then solve for x.

7.

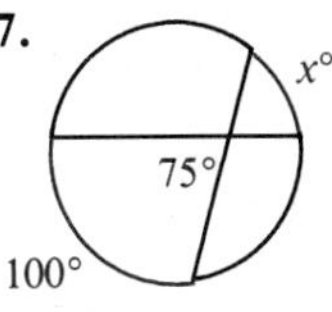

$75 = \frac{1}{2}(x + 100)$; $x = 50$

8.

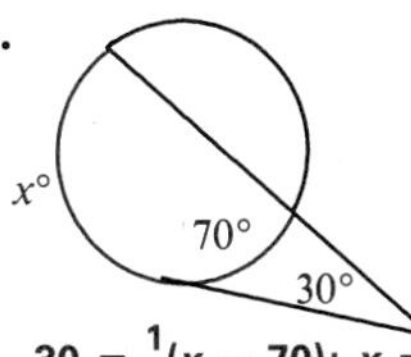

$30 = \frac{1}{2}(x - 70)$; $x = 130$

9.

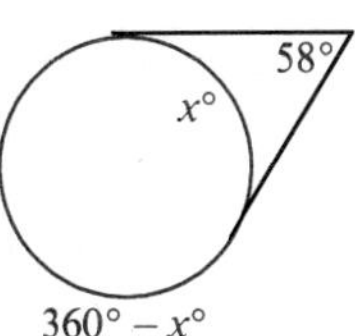

$58 = \frac{1}{2}(360 - x - x)$; $x = 122$

10. Supply reasons to complete a proof of Case I of Theorem 9-10.

Given: Secants $\overline{PA}$ and $\overline{PC}$

Prove: $m\angle 1 = \frac{1}{2}(m\overset{\frown}{AC} - m\overset{\frown}{BD})$

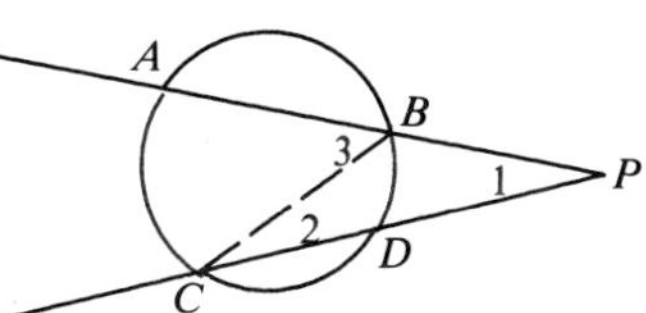

Proof:

1. Draw chord $\overline{BC}$.
2. $m\angle 1 + m\angle 2 = m\angle 3$
3. $m\angle 1 = m\angle 3 - m\angle 2$
4. $m\angle 3 = \frac{1}{2}m\overset{\frown}{AC}$; $m\angle 2 = \frac{1}{2}m\overset{\frown}{BD}$
5. $m\angle 1 = \frac{1}{2}m\overset{\frown}{AC} - \frac{1}{2}m\overset{\frown}{BD}$, or $m\angle 1 = \frac{1}{2}(m\overset{\frown}{AC} - m\overset{\frown}{BD})$

Written Exercises

A **1–10.** $\overleftrightarrow{BZ}$ is tangent to $\odot O$; $\overline{AC}$ is a diameter; $m\overset{\frown}{BC} = 90$; $m\overset{\frown}{CD} = 30$; $m\overset{\frown}{DE} = 20$. Draw your own large diagram so that you can write arc measures alongside the arcs. Find the measure of each numbered angle.

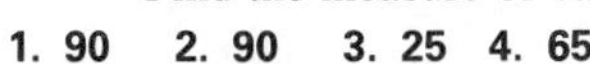

1. 90 2. 90 3. 25 4. 65
5. 55 6. 125 7. 35 8. 60
9. 90 10. 60

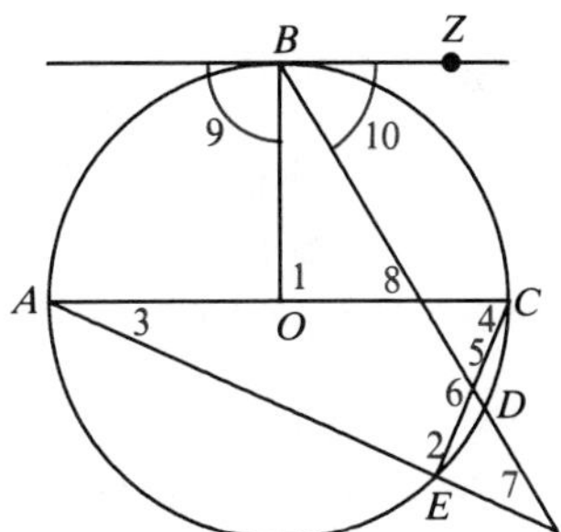

Complete.

11. If $m\overset{\frown}{RT} = 80$ and $m\overset{\frown}{US} = 40$, then $m\angle 1 =$ __?__. **60**

12. If $m\overset{\frown}{RU} = 130$ and $m\overset{\frown}{TS} = 100$, then $m\angle 1 =$ __?__. **65**

13. If $m\angle 1 = 50$ and $m\overset{\frown}{RT} = 70$, then $m\overset{\frown}{US} =$ __?__. **30**

14. If $m\angle 1 = 52$ and $m\overset{\frown}{US} = 36$, then $m\overset{\frown}{RT} =$ __?__. **68**

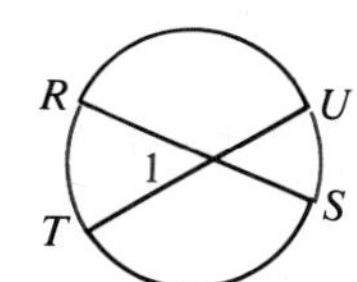

Additional Answers
Classroom Exercises

10. 1. Through any 2 pts. there is exactly one line.
2. The meas. of an ext. ∠ of a △ = sum of the meas. of the remote int. ∠s.
3. Subtr. Prop. of =
4. The meas. of an inscr. ∠ = half the meas. of its int. arc.
5. Subst. Prop.; Distrib. Prop.

Guided Practice

For Exs. 1–8, $\overleftrightarrow{AB}$ is tangent to $\odot O$; $\overline{AF}$ is a diameter; $m\overset{\frown}{AG} = 100$; $m\overset{\frown}{CE} = 30$; $m\overset{\frown}{EF} = 25$. Complete.

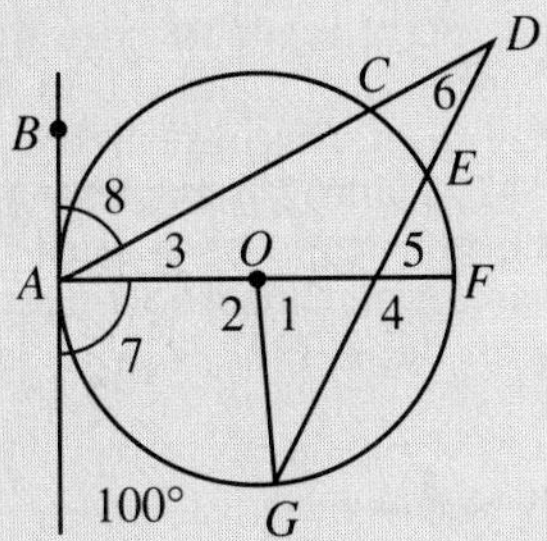

1. $m\angle 1 =$ __80__
2. $m\angle 2 =$ __100__
3. $m\angle 3 =$ __$27\frac{1}{2}$__
4. $m\angle 4 =$ __$117\frac{1}{2}$__
5. $m\angle 5 =$ __$62\frac{1}{2}$__
6. $m\angle 6 =$ __35__
7. $m\angle 7 =$ __90__
8. $m\angle 8 =$ __$62\frac{1}{2}$__

(continued)

Complete.

9. $m\overset{\frown}{RS} = \underline{65}$

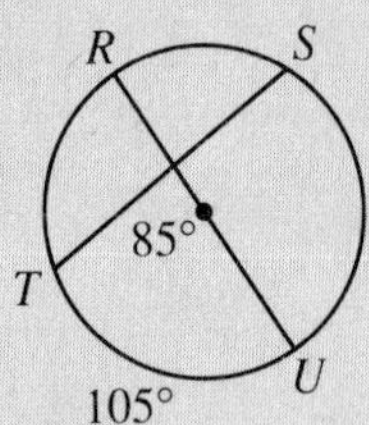

10. $m\angle S = \underline{70}$

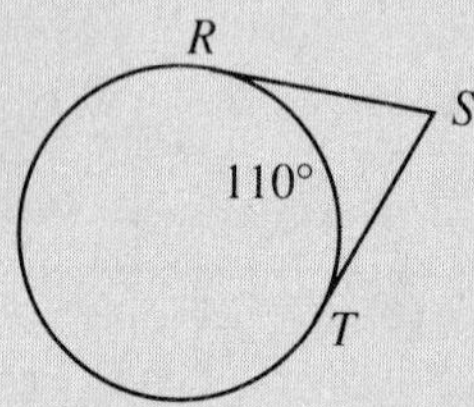

11. $m\overset{\frown}{UV} = \underline{15}$

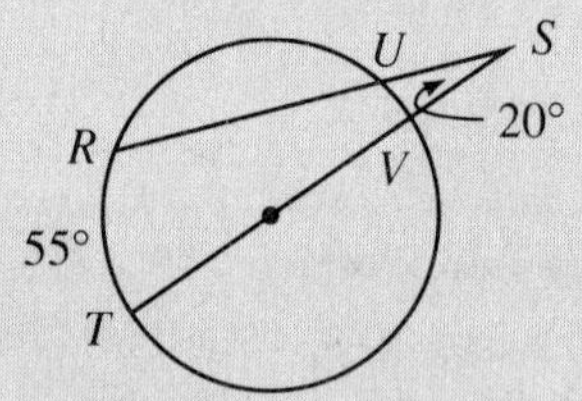

Proof Note

You might want to note that the proofs of Case II and Case III of Theorem 9-10 (Exs. 25 and 26) are essentially the same as that of Case I (see Classroom Ex. 10 on page 359).

In Exercises 15–17 $\overline{AT}$ is a tangent.

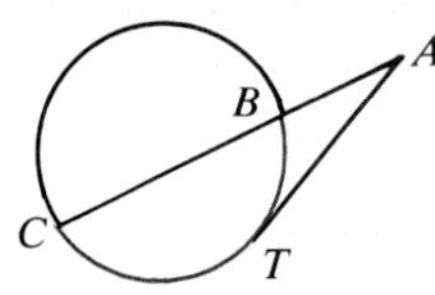

15. If $m\overset{\frown}{CT} = 110$ and $m\overset{\frown}{BT} = 50$, then $m\angle A = \underline{\ ?\ }$. **30**
16. If $m\angle A = 28$ and $m\overset{\frown}{BT} = 46$, then $m\overset{\frown}{CT} = \underline{\ ?\ }$. **102**
17. If $m\angle A = 35$ and $m\overset{\frown}{CT} = 110$, then $m\overset{\frown}{BT} = \underline{\ ?\ }$. **40**

In Exercises 18–21 $\overline{PX}$ and $\overline{PY}$ are tangents.

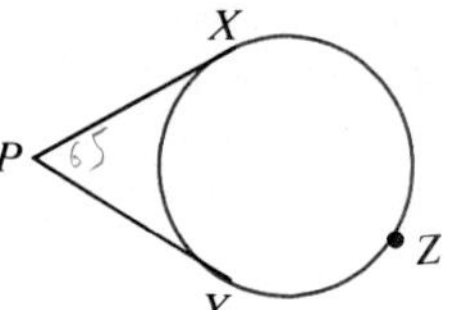

18. If $m\overset{\frown}{XZY} = 250$, then $m\angle P = \underline{\ ?\ }$. **70**
19. If $m\overset{\frown}{XY} = 90$, then $m\angle P = \underline{\ ?\ }$. **90**
20. If $m\overset{\frown}{XY} = t$, then $m\overset{\frown}{XZY} = \underline{\ ?\ }$ and **360 − t**
$m\angle P = \underline{\ ?\ }$ in terms of t. **180 − t**
21. If $m\angle P = 65$, then $m\overset{\frown}{XY} = \underline{\ ?\ }$. **115**

B 22. A secant and a tangent to a circle intersect in a 42° angle. The two arcs of the circle intercepted by the secant and tangent have measures in a 7:3 ratio. Find the measure of the third arc. **150**

23. A quadrilateral circumscribed about a circle has angles of 80°, 90°, 94°, and 96°. Find the measures of the four nonoverlapping arcs determined by the points of tangency. **100, 90, 86, 84**

24. In the inscribed quadrilateral $ABCD$, the sides $\overline{AB}$, $\overline{BC}$, and $\overline{CD}$ are congruent. $\overrightarrow{AB}$ and $\overrightarrow{DC}$ meet at a 32° angle. Find the measures of the angles of $ABCD$. **$m\angle A = m\angle D = 74$; $m\angle B = m\angle C = 106$**

25. Prove Case II of Theorem 9-10. (*Hint*: See Classroom Exercise 10. Draw a figure like the second one shown below the theorem on page 358. Label your figure, and draw the chord joining the points of tangency.)

26. Prove Case III of Theorem 9-10.

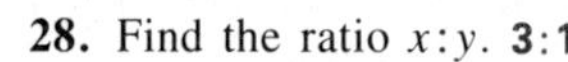

27. Write an equation involving a, b, and c. **$b - a = c$**

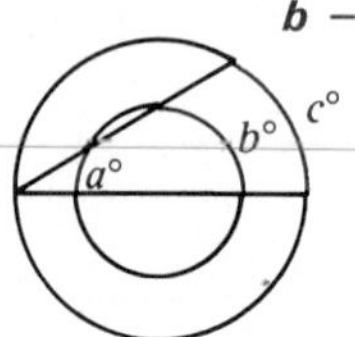

28. Find the ratio $x:y$. **3:1**

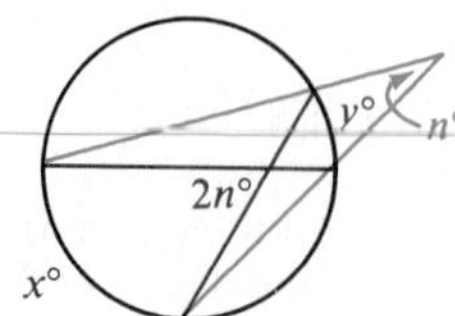

29. Isosceles $\triangle ABC$ with base $\overline{BC}$ is inscribed in a circle. P is a point on $\overset{\frown}{AC}$ and $\overrightarrow{AP}$ and $\overrightarrow{BC}$ meet at Q. Prove that $\angle ABP \cong \angle Q$.

C 30. $\overline{PT}$ is a tangent. It is known that $80 < m\overset{\frown}{RS} < m\overset{\frown}{ST} < 90$. State as much as you can about the measure of $\angle P$.
$45 < m\angle P < 60$

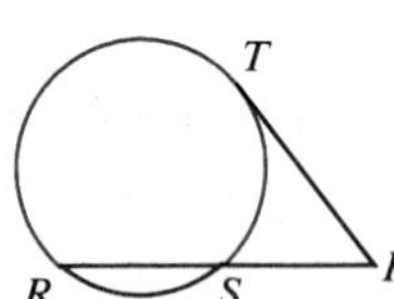

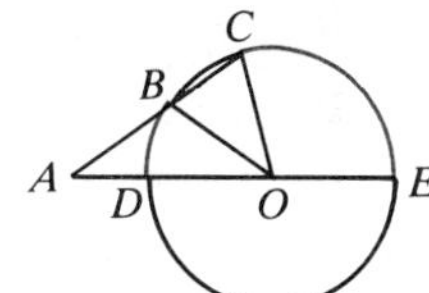

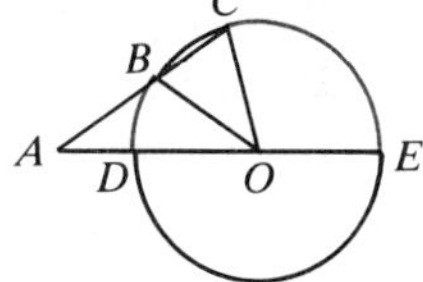

31. $\overline{AC}$ and $\overline{AE}$ are secants of $\odot O$. It is given that $\overline{AB} \cong \overline{OB}$. Discover and prove a relation between the measures of $\overset{\frown}{CE}$ and $\overset{\frown}{BD}$. $m\overset{\frown}{CE} = 3m\overset{\frown}{BD}$

32. Take any point P outside a circle. Draw a tangent segment $\overline{PT}$ and a secant $\overline{PBA}$ with A and B points on the circle. Take K on $\overline{PA}$ so that $PK = PT$. Draw $\overrightarrow{TK}$. Let the intersection of $\overrightarrow{TK}$ with the circle be point X. Discover and prove a relationship between $\overset{\frown}{AX}$ and $\overset{\frown}{XB}$. $\overset{\frown}{AX} \cong \overset{\frown}{XB}$

Explorations

These exploratory exercises can be done using a computer with a program that draws and measures geometric figures.

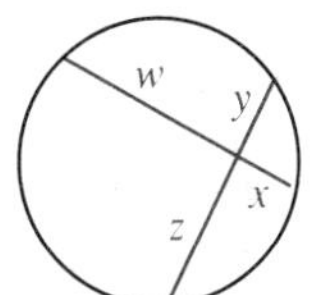

1. Draw a circle. Choose four points on the circle. Draw two intersecting chords using the points as endpoints.

   Measure the lengths of the pieces of the chords and compute the products $w \cdot x$ and $y \cdot z$. What do you notice? $w \cdot x = y \cdot z$

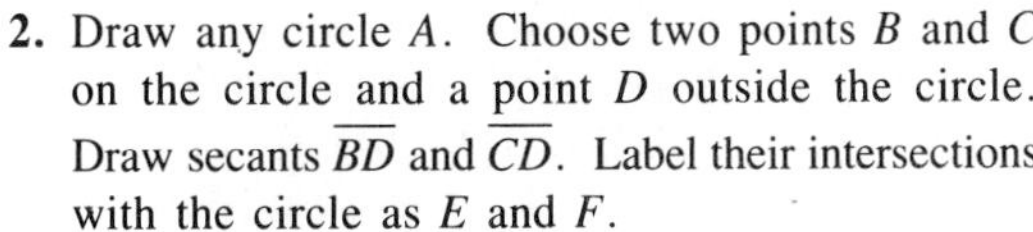

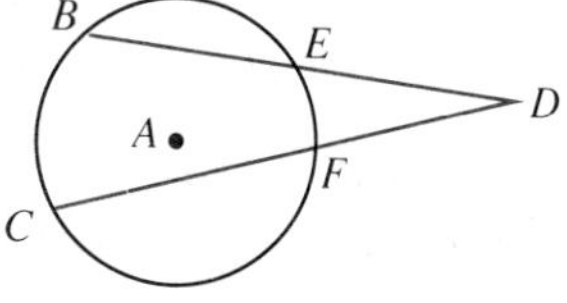

2. Draw any circle A. Choose two points B and C on the circle and a point D outside the circle. Draw secants $\overline{BD}$ and $\overline{CD}$. Label their intersections with the circle as E and F.

   Measure and compute $DE \cdot DB$ and $DF \cdot DC$. What do you notice? $DE \cdot DB = DF \cdot DC$

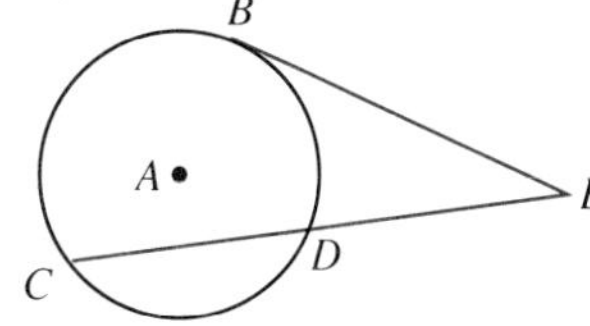

3. Draw any circle A. Choose three points B, C, and D on the circle. Draw a tangent to the circle through point B that intersects $\overleftrightarrow{CD}$ at a point E.

   Measure and compute $(BE)^2$ and $ED \cdot CE$. What do you notice? $ED \cdot CE = (BE)^2$

9-7 *Circles and Lengths of Segments*

You can use similar triangles to prove that lengths of chords, secants, and tangents are related in interesting ways.

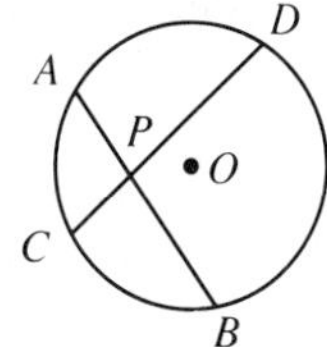

In the figure at the right, chords $\overline{AB}$ and $\overline{CD}$ intersect inside $\odot O$. $\overline{AP}$ and $\overline{PB}$ are called *the segments of chord* $\overline{AB}$. As we did with the terms "radius" and "diameter" we will use the phrase "segment of a chord" to refer to the length of a segment as well as to the segment itself.

Using a Computer

Ex. 32 can be done with a construction program.

Using a Computer

This Exploration examines the different cases mentioned in Lesson 9-6 but explores the lengths of various segments rather than the measures of angles. It provides an excellent introduction to Lesson 9-7.

Teaching Suggestions,
pp. T115–T116

Objective
Presenting the Lesson
Reinforcement
Using Technology

Cooperative Learning,
p. T116

Supplementary Materials

Practice Master 54
Test 36
Resource Book, pp. 57–58, 145
Study Guide, pp. 119–120
Overhead Visual G
Computer Activity 20

Lesson Focus

This lesson presents three theorems that state some interesting relationships involving products of parts of chords, parts of secants, and parts of tangents and secants. A part of a chord, secant, or tangent is called a segment.

Suggested Assignments

Minimum
Day 1: 364/1–9
Day 2: 365/10, 11, 13–18
Day 3: 367/Self-Test 2
Day 4: 371/Chapter Test

Average
Day 1: 364–365/1–11, 13, 15
Day 2: 365–366/16–21
367/Self-Test 2
Day 3: 371/Chapter Test

Maximum
Day 1: 364–365/1–10, 12, 13
Day 2: 365–366/11, 15–27
Day 3: 371/Chapter Test

Chalkboard Examples

Find the value of x.

1. 8

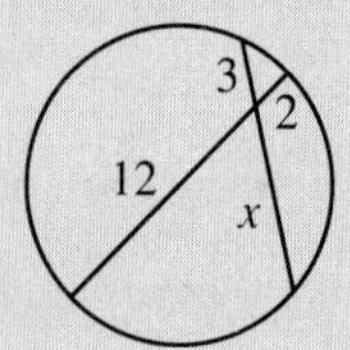

2. 12

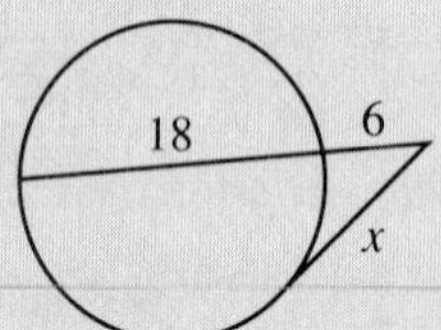

3. 2

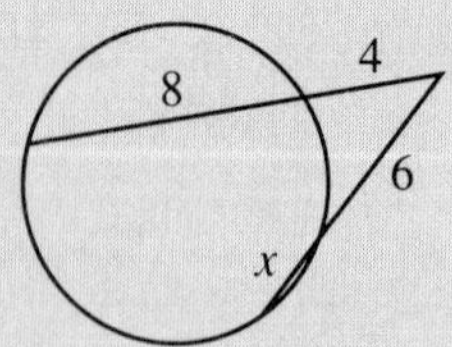

Theorem 9-11

When two chords intersect inside a circle, the product of the segments of one chord equals the product of the segments of the other chord.

Given: $\overline{AB}$ and $\overline{CD}$ intersect at P.

Prove: $r \cdot s = t \cdot u$

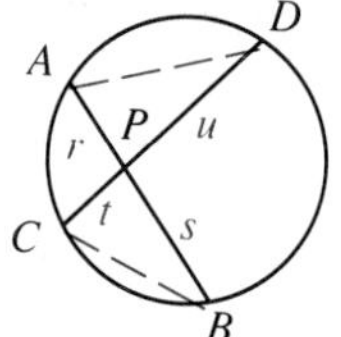

Proof:

Statements	Reasons
1. Draw chords $\overline{AD}$ and $\overline{CB}$.	1. Through any two points there is exactly one line.
2. $\angle A \cong \angle C$; $\angle D \cong \angle B$	2. If two inscribed angles intercept __?__. **the same arc, then the ∆s are ≅.**
3. $\triangle APD \sim \triangle CPB$	3. __?__ **AA ~ Post.**
4. $\frac{r}{t} = \frac{u}{s}$	4. __?__ **Corr. sides of ~ ∆s are in prop.**
5. $r \cdot s = t \cdot u$	5. A property of proportions

For a proof of the following theorem, see Classroom Exercise 7. In the diagram for the theorem, $\overline{AP}$ and $\overline{CP}$ are *secant segments*. $\overline{BP}$ and $\overline{DP}$ are exterior to the circle and are referred to as *external segments*. The terms "secant segment" and "external segment" can refer to the length of a segment as well as to the segment itself.

Theorem 9-12

When two secant segments are drawn to a circle from an external point, the product of one secant segment and its external segment equals the product of the other secant segment and its external segment.

Given: $\overline{PA}$ and $\overline{PC}$ drawn to the circle from point P

Prove: $r \cdot s = t \cdot u$

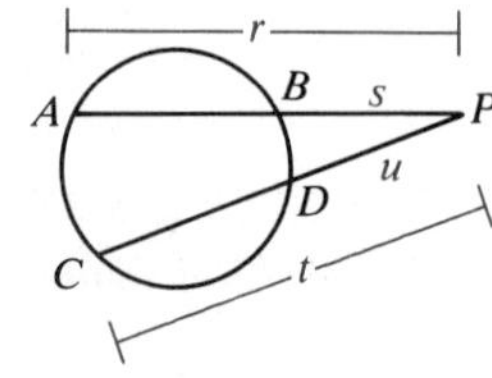

Study the diagrams at the top of the next page from left to right. As $\overline{PC}$ approaches a position of tangency, C and D move closer together until they merge. Then $\overline{PC}$ becomes a tangent, and $t = u$.

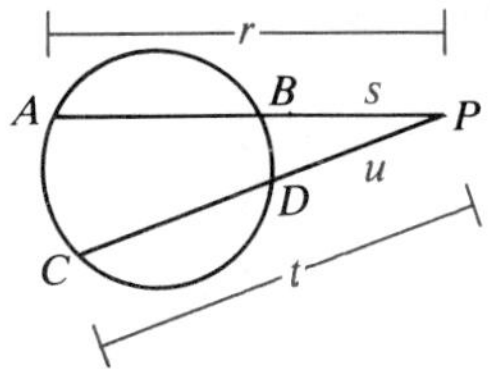

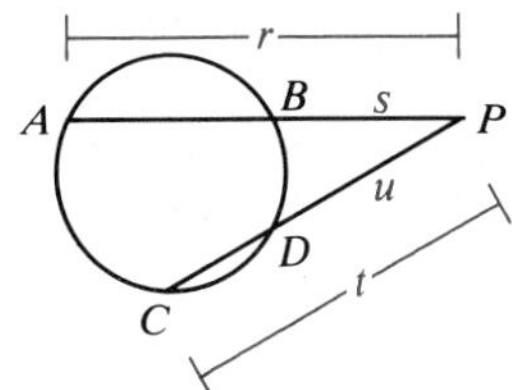

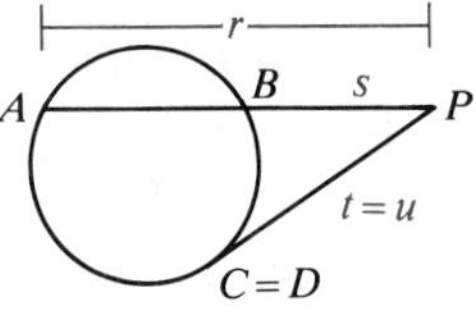

In the first two diagrams we know that $r \cdot s = t \cdot u$. In the third diagram, u and t both become equal to the length of the tangent segment, and the equation becomes $r \cdot s = t^2$. This result, stated below, will be proved more formally in Exercise 10. As with earlier terms, the term "tangent segment" can refer to the length of a segment as well as to the segment itself.

Theorem 9-13

When a secant segment and a tangent segment are drawn to a circle from an external point, the product of the secant segment and its external segment is equal to the square of the tangent segment.

Example 1 Find the value of x.

Solution $3x \cdot x = 6 \cdot 8$ (Theorem 9-11)
$3x^2 = 48$, $x^2 = 16$, and $x = 4$

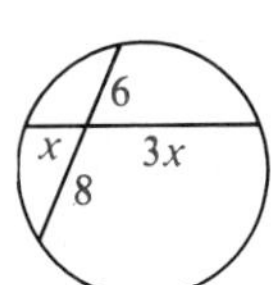

Example 2 Find the values of x and y.

Solution $4(4 + 5) = 3(3 + x)$ (Theorem 9-12)
$36 = 3(3 + x)$, $12 = 3 + x$, and $x = 9$
$4(4 + 5) = y^2$ (Theorem 9-13)
$36 = y^2$, so $y = 6$

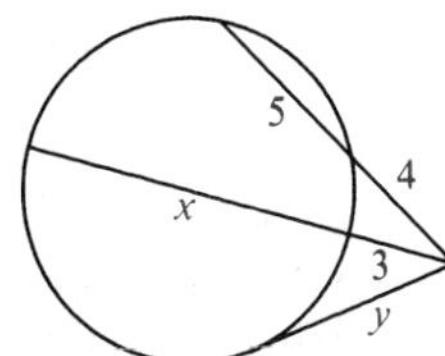

Classroom Exercises

Chords, secants, and tangents are shown. State the equation you would use to find the value of x. Then solve for x.

1.
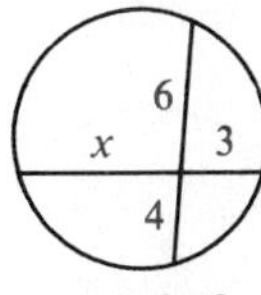

$3x = 4 \cdot 6$
$x = 8$

2.
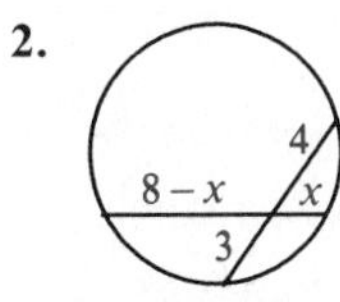

$x(8 - x) = 3 \cdot 4$
$x = 6$ or $x = 2$

3.
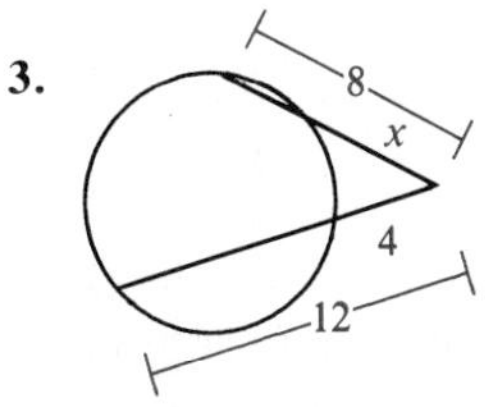

$8x = 12 \cdot 4$
$x = 6$

Teaching Note

In the discussion leading up to Theorem 9-13, students should see the theorem as a special case of Theorem 9-12. Since the limiting position of one of the secants is a tangent, the entire tangent segment is also the external segment. Therefore, in Theorem 9-12, $t \cdot u$ becomes $t \cdot t = t^2$.

Chords, secants, and tangents are shown. State the equation you would use to find the value of x. Then solve for x.

4.

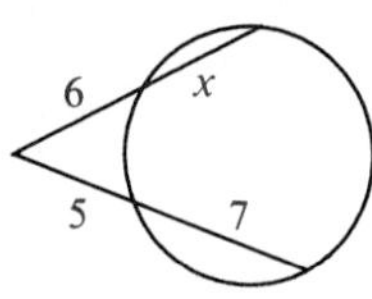

$6(x + 6) = 5 \cdot 12$; $x = 4$

5.

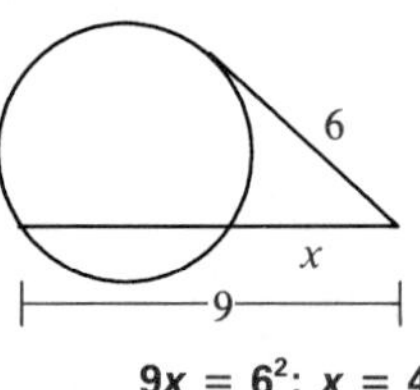

$9x = 6^2$; $x = 4$

6.

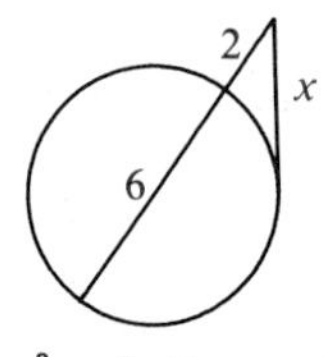

$x^2 = 8 \cdot 2$; $x = 4$

7. Supply reasons to complete the proof of Theorem 9-12.

Given: $\overline{PA}$ and $\overline{PC}$ drawn to the circle from point P

Prove: $r \cdot s = t \cdot u$

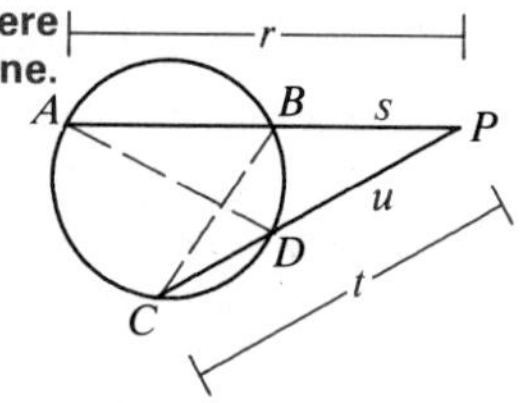

Proof:

1. Draw chords $\overline{AD}$ and $\overline{BC}$. **Through any 2 pts. there is exactly one line.**
2. $\angle A \cong \angle C$ **See below.**
3. $\angle P \cong \angle P$ **Refl. Prop.**
4. $\triangle APD \sim \triangle CPB$ **AA ~ Post.**
5. $\frac{r}{t} = \frac{u}{s}$ **Corr. sides of ~ △s are in prop.**
6. $r \cdot s = t \cdot u$ **Means-extremes Prop.**

2. If 2 inscr. ∠s int. the same arc, then the ∠s are ≅.

Written Exercises

Chords, secants, and tangents are shown. Find the value of x.

A **1.** 10

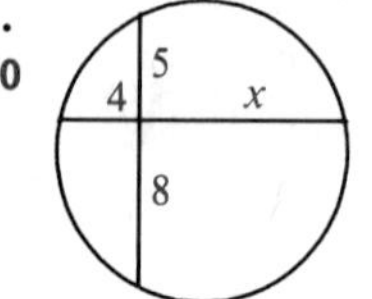

2. 12

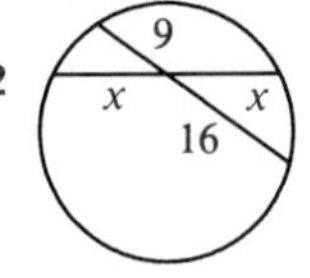

3. $\sqrt{21}$

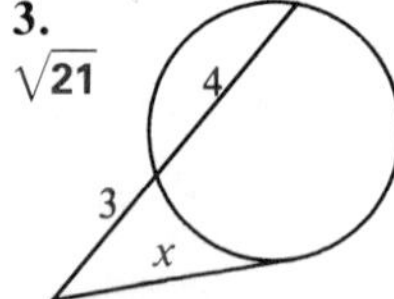

4. 2

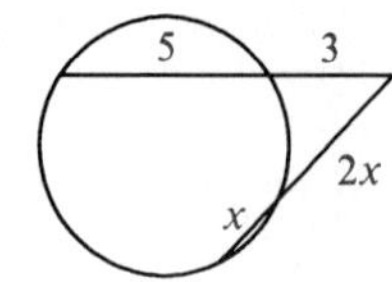

5. 6

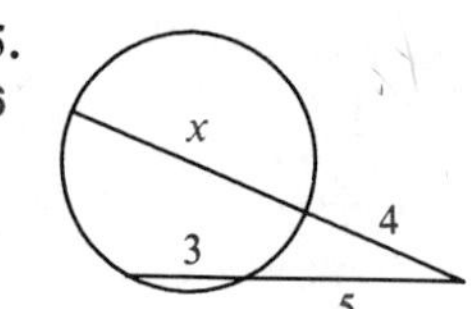

6. $3\sqrt{3}$

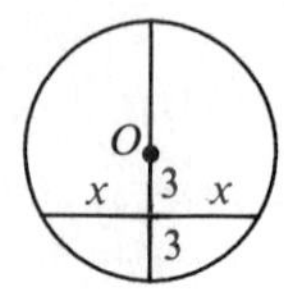

7. 8

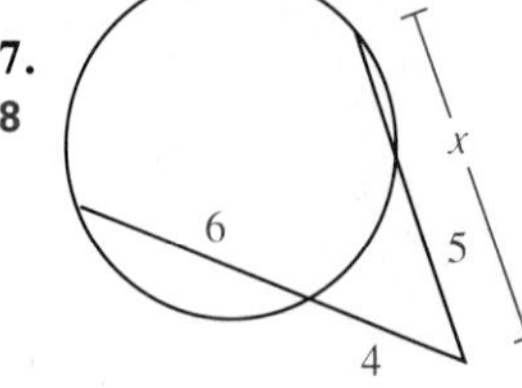

8. $2\frac{2}{3}$

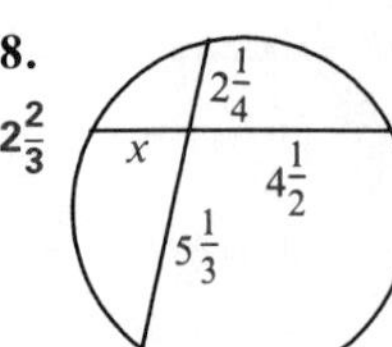

9. 5

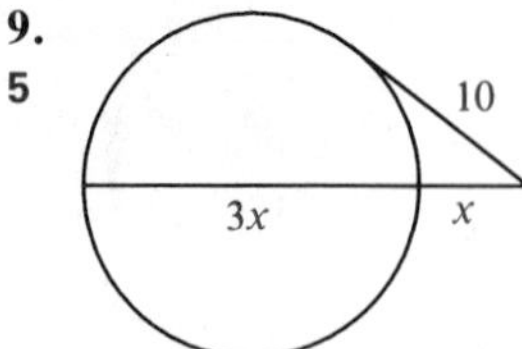

Guided Practice

Chords, secants, and tangents are as shown. Find the value of x.

1. 1.5

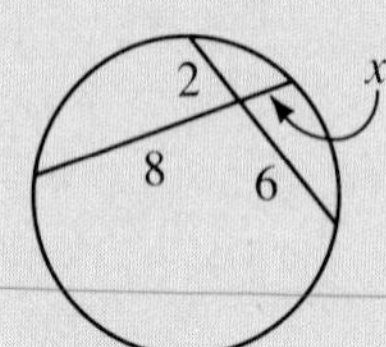

2. 13

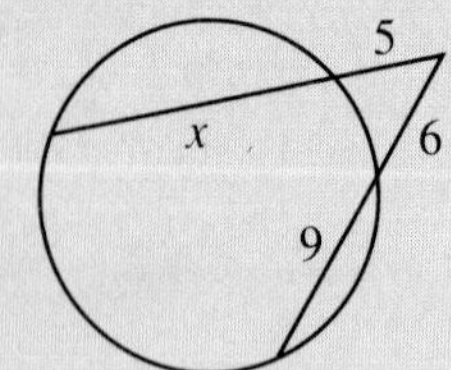

3. $4\sqrt{5}$

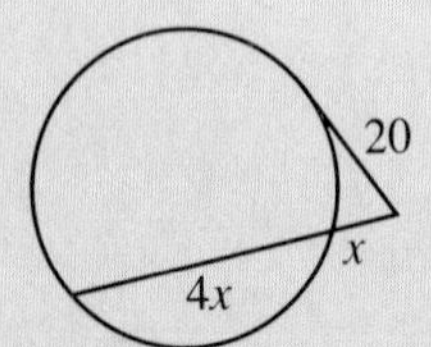

10. Write a proof of Theorem 9-13.

Given: Secant segment $\overline{PA}$ and tangent segment $\overline{PC}$ drawn to the circle from P.

Prove: $r \cdot s = t^2$

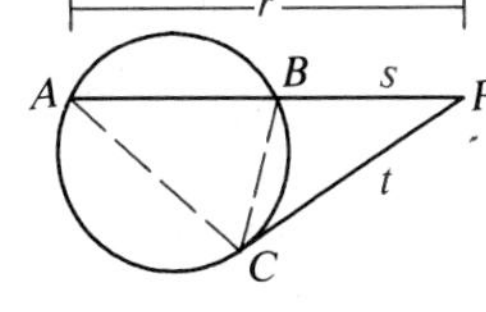

Plan for Proof: Draw chords $\overline{AC}$ and $\overline{BC}$. Show that $\angle A$ and $\angle PCB$ are congruent because they intercept the same arc. Then show that $\triangle PAC$ and $\triangle PCB$ are similar triangles and use the properties of proportions to complete the proof.

B **11.** Given: $\odot O$ and $\odot P$ are tangent to $\overline{UT}$ at T.
Prove: $UV \cdot UW = UX \cdot UY$

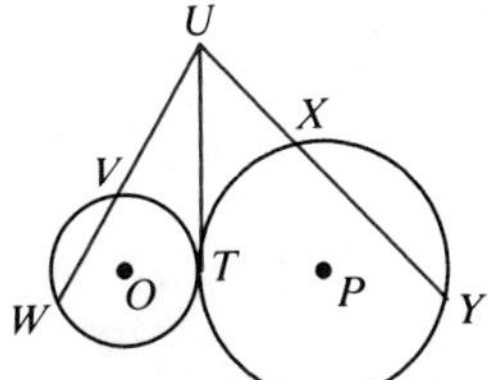

12. Given: $\overline{AB}$ is tangent to $\odot Q$;
$\overline{AC}$ is tangent to $\odot S$.
Prove: $\overline{AB} \cong \overline{AC}$

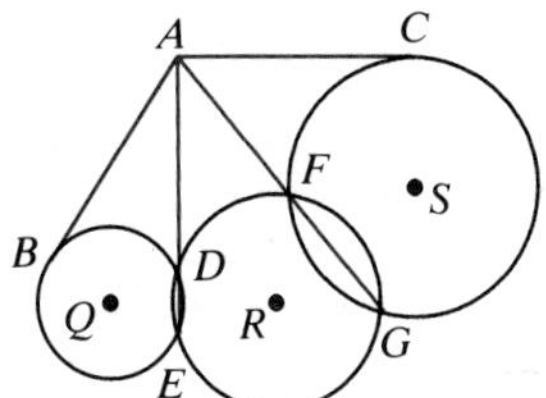

Chords $\overline{AB}$ and $\overline{CD}$ intersect at P. Find the lengths indicated.

Example $AP = 5$; $BP = 4$; $CD = 12$; $CP = \underline{\ ?\ }$

Solution Let $CP = x$. Then $DP = 12 - x$.

$x(12 - x) = 5 \cdot 4$
$12x - x^2 = 20$
$x^2 - 12x + 20 = 0$
$(x - 2)(x - 10) = 0$
$x = 2$ or $x = 10$
$CP = 2$ or 10

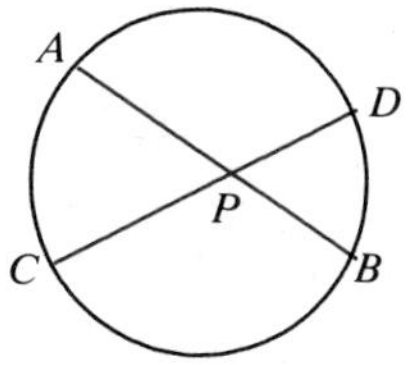

13. $AP = 6$; $BP = 8$; $CD = 16$; $DP = \underline{\ ?\ }$ **4 or 12**

14. $CD = 10$; $CP = 6$; $AB = 11$; $AP = \underline{\ ?\ }$ **3 or 8**

15. $AB = 12$; $CP = 9$; $DP = 4$; $BP = \underline{\ ?\ }$ **6**

16. $AP = 6$; $BP = 5$; $CP = 3 \cdot DP$; $DP = \underline{\ ?\ }$ $\mathbf{\sqrt{10}}$

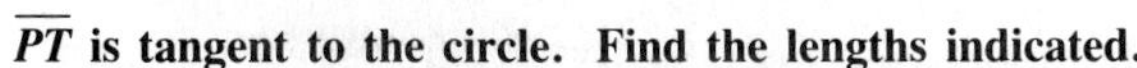

$\overline{PT}$ is tangent to the circle. Find the lengths indicated.

17. $PT = 6$; $PB = 3$; $AB = \underline{\ ?\ }$ **9**

18. $PT = 12$; $CD = 18$; $PC = \underline{\ ?\ }$ **24**

19. $PD = 5$; $CD = 7$; $AB = 11$; $PB = \underline{\ ?\ }$ **4**

20. $PB = AB = 5$; $PD = 4$; $PT = \underline{\ ?\ }$ and $PC = \underline{\ ?\ }$
$\mathbf{5\sqrt{2}}$ **12.5**

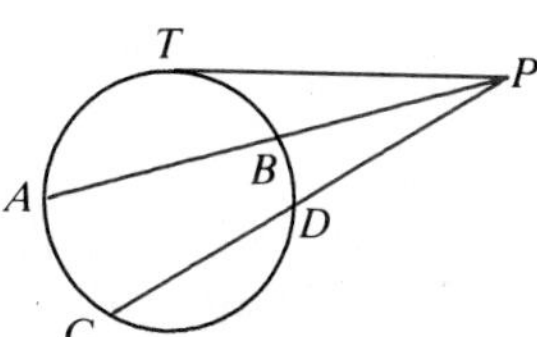

21. A secant, a radius, and a tangent of $\odot O$ are shown.
   a. Explain why $(r + h)^2 = r^2 + d^2$. **Pythagorean Thm.**
   b. Simplify the equation in part (a) to show that $d^2 = h(2r + h)$. **See below.**
   c. You have proved a special case of a theorem. What theorem is this? **Theorem 9-13**

   b. $r^2 + 2rh + h^2 = r^2 + d^2$; $d^2 = 2rh + h^2$; $d^2 = h(2r + h)$

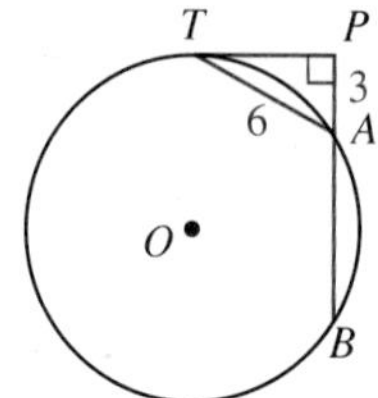

22. $\overline{PT}$ is tangent to $\odot O$. Secant $\overrightarrow{BA}$ is perpendicular to $\overline{PT}$ at P. If $TA = 6$ and $PA = 3$, find **(a)** AB, **(b)** the distance from O to $\overline{AB}$, and **(c)** the radius of $\odot O$. **6; $3\sqrt{3}$; 6**

23. A bridge over a river has the shape of a circular arc. The span of the bridge is 24 meters. (The span is the length of the chord of the arc.) The midpoint of the arc is 4 meters higher than the endpoints. What is the radius of the circle that contains this arc? **20 m**

24. A circle can be drawn through points X, Y, and Z.
   a. What is the radius of the circle? **$5\sqrt{5}$**
   b. How far is the center of the circle from point W? **$\sqrt{29}$**

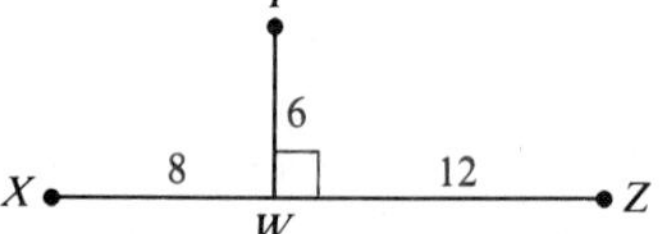

25. Draw two intersecting circles with common chord $\overline{PQ}$ and let X be any point on $\overline{PQ}$. Through X draw any chord $\overline{AB}$ of one circle. Also draw through X any chord $\overline{CD}$ of the other circle. Prove that $AX \cdot XB = CX \cdot XD$.

26. A line is tangent to two intersecting circles at P and Q. The common chord is extended to meet $\overline{PQ}$ at T. Prove that T is the midpoint of $\overline{PQ}$.

C 27. In the diagram at the left below, $\overline{PT}$ is tangent to $\odot O$ and $\overline{PN}$ intersects $\odot O$ at J. Find the radius of the circle. **$2\sqrt{10}$**

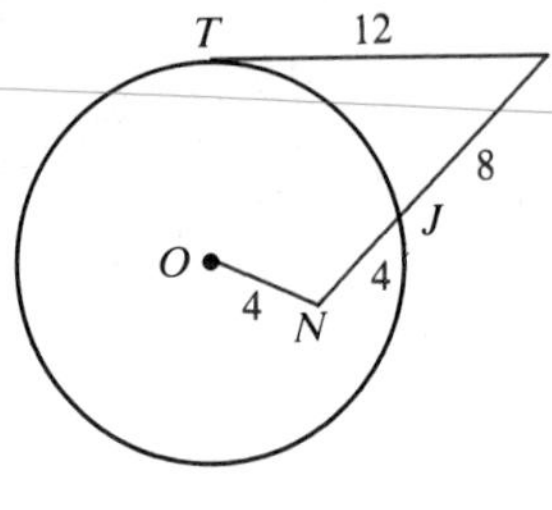

Ex. 27

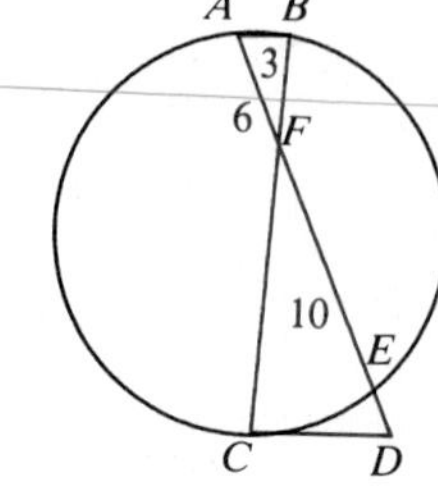

Ex. 28

★28. In the diagram at the right above, $\overline{CD}$ is a tangent, $\overset{\frown}{AC} \cong \overset{\frown}{BC}$, $AB = 3$, $AF = 6$, and $FE = 10$. Find ED. (*Hint*: Let $ED = x$ and $CD = y$. Then write two equations in x and y.) **$ED = 2$**

Quick Quiz

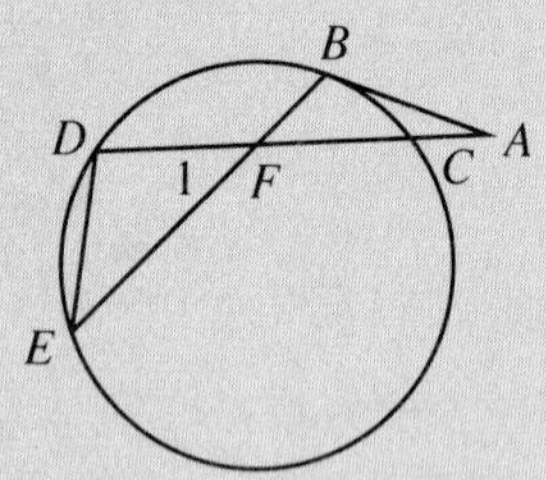

$\overline{AB}$ is tangent to the circle.

1. If $m\overset{\frown}{BC} = 32$, $m\overset{\frown}{BD} = 72$, $m\angle BAD = \underline{20}$.
2. If $DF = 8$, $CF = 6$, $BF = 4$, $EF = \underline{12}$.
3. If $m\overset{\frown}{BC} = 32$ and $m\angle 1 = 42$, $m\overset{\frown}{DE} = \underline{52}$.
4. If $m\angle E = 38$, $m\overset{\frown}{DB} = \underline{76}$.
5. Find the values of x, y, and z.
   $x = 80$, $y = 100$, $z = 80$

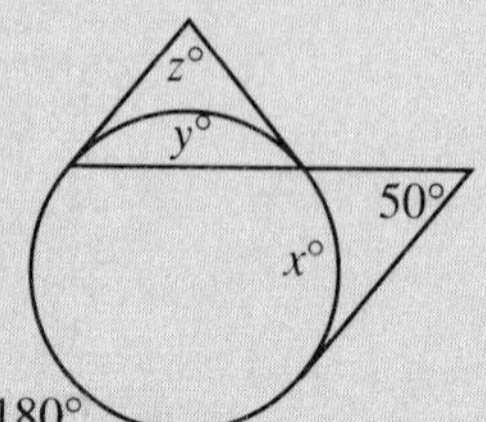

Self-Test 2

$\overleftrightarrow{MD}$ is tangent to the circle.

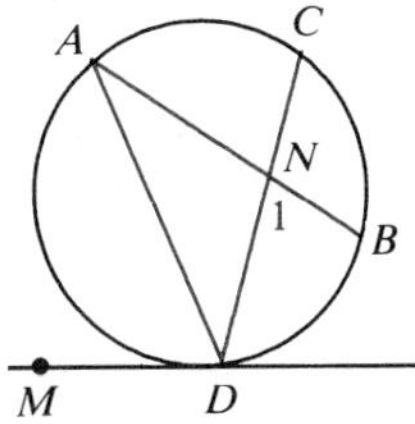

1. If $m\widehat{BD} = 80$, then $m\angle A =$ __?__. **40**
2. If $m\angle ADM = 75$, then $m\widehat{AD} =$ __?__. **150**
3. If $m\widehat{BD} = 80$ and $m\angle 1 = 81$, then $m\widehat{AC} =$ __?__. **82**
4. If $AN = 12$, $BN = 6$, and $CN = 8$, then $DN =$ __?__. **9**

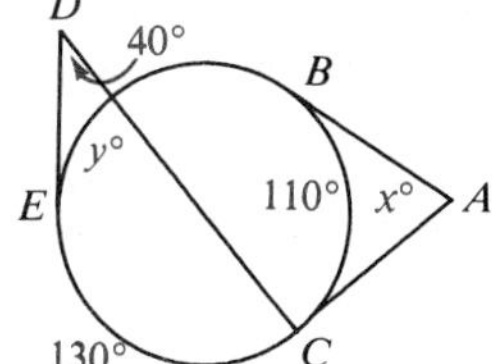

5. $\overline{AB}$, $\overline{AC}$, and $\overline{DE}$ are tangents. Find the values of x and y.
   $x = 70$, $y = 50$

$\overline{PE}$ and $\overline{PF}$ are secants and $\overline{PJ}$ is a tangent.

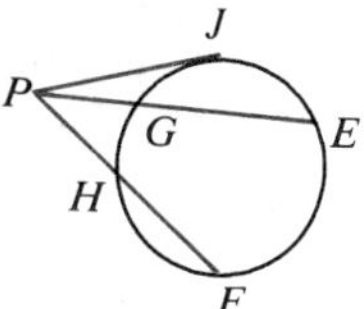

6. If $m\widehat{EF} = 100$ and $m\widehat{GH} = 30$, then $m\angle FPE =$ __?__. **35**
7. If $PG = 4$, $PE = 15$, and $PH = 6$, then $PF =$ __?__. **10**
8. If $PH = 8$ and $HF = 10$, then $PJ =$ __?__. **12**

Application — *Distance to the Horizon*

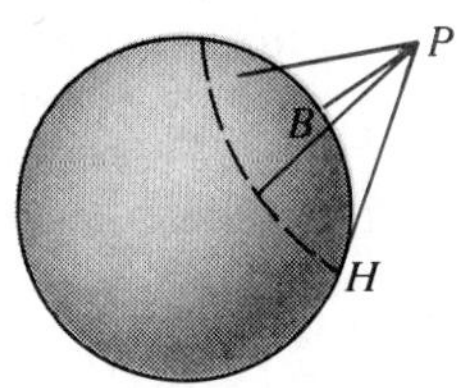

If you look out over the surface of the Earth from a position at P, directly above point B on the surface, you see the horizon wherever your line of sight is tangent to the surface of the Earth. If the surface around B is smooth (say you are on the ocean on a calm day), the horizon will be a circle, and the higher your lookout is, the farther away this horizon circle will be.

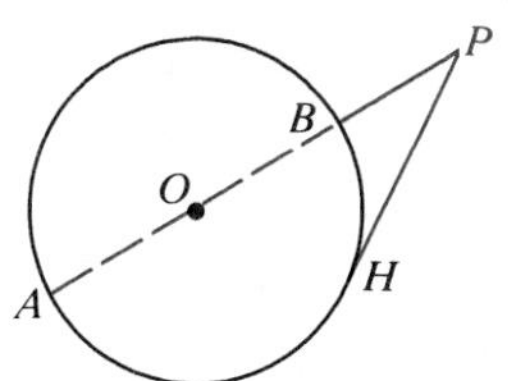

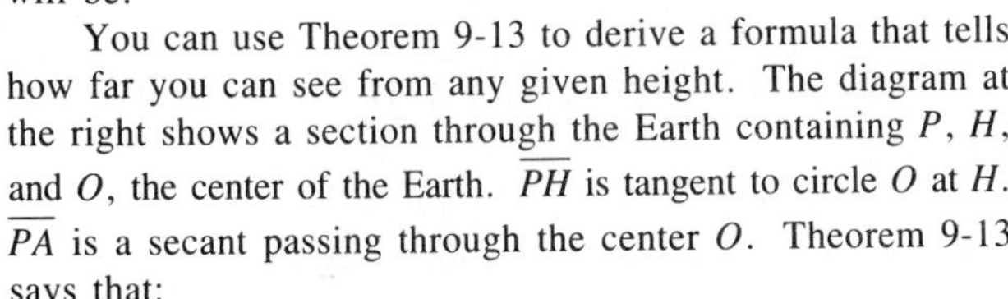

You can use Theorem 9-13 to derive a formula that tells how far you can see from any given height. The diagram at the right shows a section through the Earth containing P, H, and O, the center of the Earth. $\overline{PH}$ is tangent to circle O at H. $\overline{PA}$ is a secant passing through the center O. Theorem 9-13 says that:

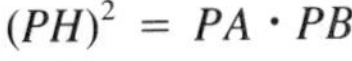

$$(PH)^2 = PA \cdot PB$$

$\overleftrightarrow{AE}$ and $\overleftrightarrow{AF}$ are secants; $\overleftrightarrow{AB}$ is a tangent.

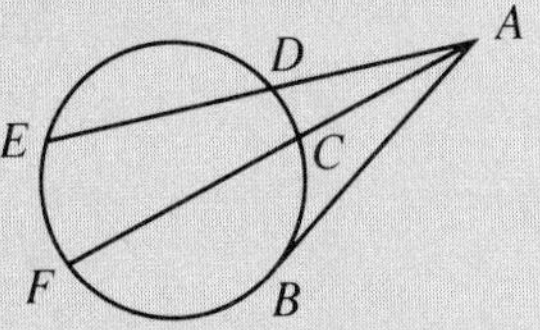

6. If $m\widehat{DC} = 40$ and $m\widehat{EF} = 70$, then $m\angle EAF =$ 15.
7. If $AC = 8$, $CF = 12$, and $AD = 10$, then $ED =$ 6.
8. If $AD = 16$ and $ED = 10$, then $AB =$ $4\sqrt{26}$.

Using a Computer

See page T115 for a project that extends this Application to computers.

In the formula $(PH)^2 = AP \cdot BP$, PH is the distance from the observer to the horizon, and BP is the observer's height above the surface of the Earth. If the height is small compared to the diameter, AB, of the Earth, then $AP \approx AB$ in the formula. Using 12,800,000 m for AB, you can rewrite the formula as:

$$(\text{distance})^2 \approx (12{,}800{,}000)(\text{height})$$

Taking square roots, you get:

$$\text{distance} \approx \sqrt{12{,}800{,}000} \cdot \sqrt{\text{height}} \approx 3600\sqrt{\text{height}}$$

So the approximate distance (in meters) to the horizon is 3600 times the square root of your height (in meters) above the surface of the Earth. If your height is less than 400 km, the error in this approximation will be less than one percent.

Using a Calculator

Use a calculator in these exercises to find distance in meters for a given height ($d = 3600\sqrt{h}$) or height in meters for a given distance ($h = d^2 \div 12{,}800{,}000$).

Exercises

In Exercises 1 and 2 give your answer to the nearest kilometer, in Exercises 3 and 5 to the nearest 10 km, and in Exercise 4 to the nearest meter.

1. If you stand on a dune with your eyes about 16 m above sea level, how far out to sea can you look? **14 km**
2. A lookout climbs high in the rigging of a sailing ship to a point 36 m above the water line. About how far away is the horizon? **22 km**
3. From a balloon floating 10 km above the ocean, how far away is the farthest point you can see on the Earth's surface? **360 km**
4. How high must a lookout be to see an object on the horizon 8 km away? **5 m**
5. You are approaching the coast of Japan in a small sailboat. The highest point on the central island of Honshu is the cone of Mount Fuji, 3776 m above sea level. Roughly how far away from the mountain will you be when you can first see the top? (Assume that the sky is clear!) **220 km**

Chapter Summary

1. Many of the terms used with circles and spheres are discussed on pages 329 and 330.
2. If a line is tangent to a circle, then the line is perpendicular to the radius drawn to the point of tangency. The converse is also true.
3. Tangents to a circle from a point are congruent.

4. In the same circle or in congruent circles:
- **a.** Congruent minor arcs have congruent central angles. Congruent central angles have congruent arcs.
- **b.** Congruent arcs have congruent chords. Congruent chords have congruent arcs.
- **c.** Chords equally distant from the center are congruent. Congruent chords are equally distant from the center.

5. A diameter that is perpendicular to a chord bisects the chord and its arc.

6. If two inscribed angles intercept the same arc, then the angles are congruent.

7. An angle inscribed in a semicircle is a right angle.

8. If a quadrilateral is inscribed in a circle, then its opposite angles are supplementary.

9. Relationships expressed by formulas:

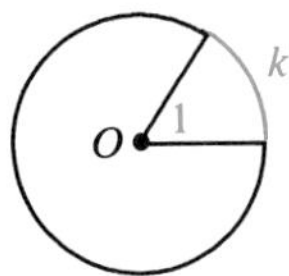

$m\angle 1 = k$

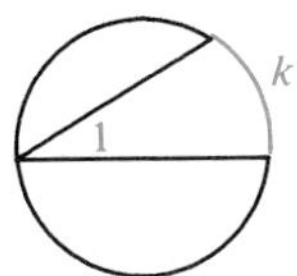

$m\angle 1 = \frac{1}{2}k$

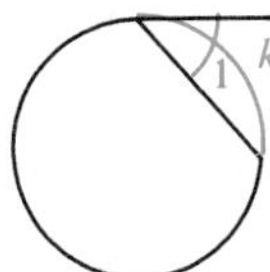

$m\angle 1 = \frac{1}{2}k$

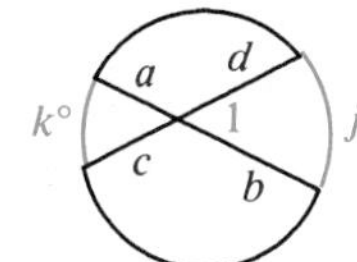

$m\angle 1 = \frac{1}{2}(k + j)$
$a \cdot b = c \cdot d$

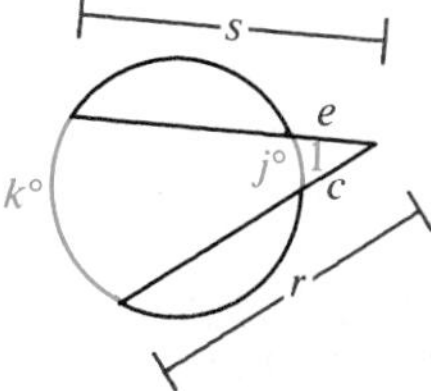

$m\angle 1 = \frac{1}{2}(k - j)$
$s \cdot e = r \cdot c$

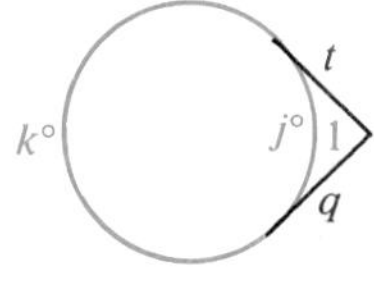

$m\angle 1 = \frac{1}{2}(k - j)$
$t = q$

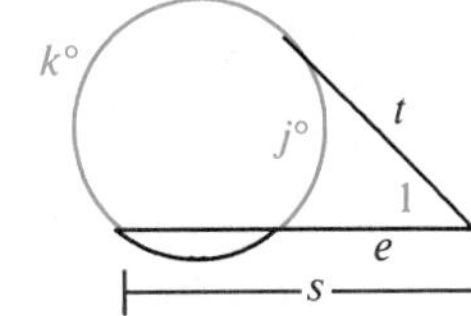

$m\angle 1 = \frac{1}{2}(k - j)$
$s \cdot e = t^2$

Chapter Review

Points *A*, *B*, and *C* lie on ⊙*O*. 9–1

1. $\overline{AC}$ is called a _?_, while $\overleftrightarrow{AC}$ is called a _?_. **chord, secant**
2. $\overline{OB}$ is called a _?_. **radius**
3. The best name for $\overline{AB}$ is _?_. **diameter**
4. $\triangle ABC$ is __**inscribed in** ?__ (inscribed in/circumscribed about) ⊙*O*.
5. $\overleftrightarrow{CD}$ intersects ⊙*O* in one point. $\overleftrightarrow{CD}$ is called a _?_. **tangent**

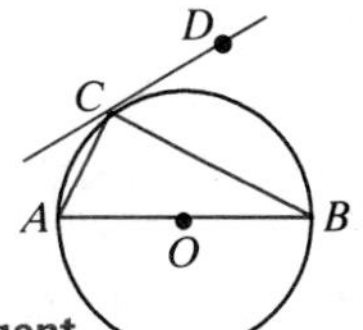

Supplementary Materials

Practice Master 55
Test 37
Resource Book, pp. 59–60, 146

Lines $\overleftrightarrow{ZX}$ and $\overleftrightarrow{ZY}$ are tangent to ⊙*P*.

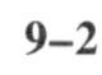

6. $\overline{PX}$, if drawn, would be ___?___ to $\overleftrightarrow{XZ}$. **⊥** 9–2
7. If the radius of ⊙*P* is 6 and $XZ = 8$, then PZ = ___?___. **10**
8. If $m\angle Z = 90$ and $XZ = 13$, then XY = ___?___. **$13\sqrt{2}$**

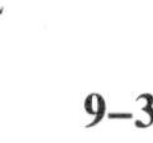

9. If $m\angle XPY = 100$, then $m\widehat{XY}$ = ___?___. **100** 9–3
10. If $m\widehat{XW} = 135$ and $m\widehat{WY} = 125$, then $m\widehat{XWY}$ = ___?___. **260**
11. If $\widehat{XW} \cong \widehat{WY}$, then $\angle XPW \cong$ ___?___. **∠*YPW***

In ⊙*X*, $m\widehat{AC}$ = 120.

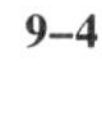

12. $m\widehat{AB}$ = ___?___ **60** 9–4
13. If $\overline{AC} \cong \overline{CD}$, then $m\widehat{CD}$ = ___?___. **120**
14. If $XE = 5$ and $AC = 24$, then the radius = ___?___. **13**

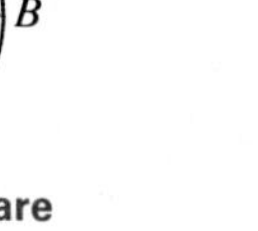

15. If $\overline{AC} \cong \overline{DC}$, state the theorem that allows you to deduce that $XE = XF$. **In the same ⊙, ≅ chords are equally dist. from the center.**

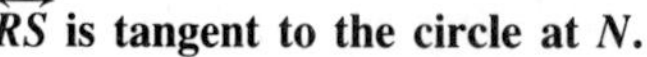

$\overleftrightarrow{RS}$ is tangent to the circle at *N*.

16. If $m\angle K = 105$, then $m\angle PNL$ = ___?___. **75** 9–5
17. If $m\widehat{PN} = 100$, then $m\angle PLN$ = ___?___ and $m\angle PNR$ = ___?___. **50** and **50**
18. If $m\angle K = 110$, then $m\widehat{PNL}$ = ___?___ and $m\widehat{PL}$ = ___?___. **220** and **140**

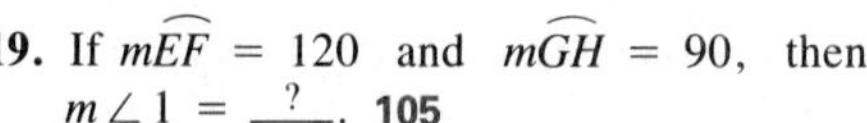

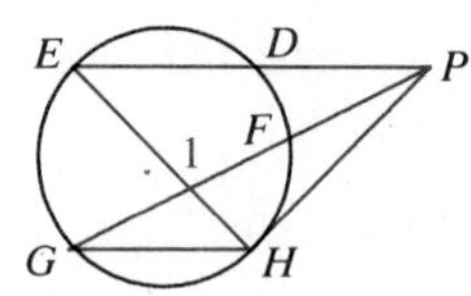
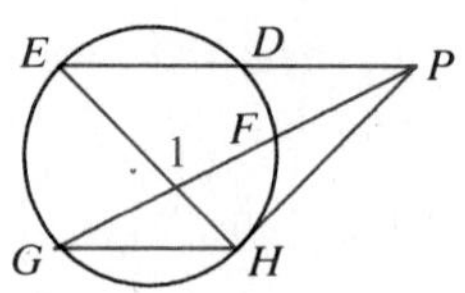

19. If $m\widehat{EF} = 120$ and $m\widehat{GH} = 90$, then $m\angle 1$ = ___?___. **105** 9–6
20. If $m\widehat{EG} = 100$ and $m\widehat{DF} = 40$, then $m\angle EPG$ = ___?___. **30**
21. If $\overline{PH}$ is a tangent, $m\widehat{GH} = 90$ and $m\angle GPH = 25$, then $m\widehat{FH}$ = ___?___. **40**

Chords, secants, and a tangent are shown. Find the value of *x*. 9–7

22. **12**

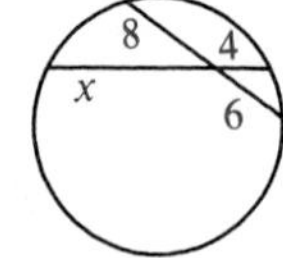

23. **9**

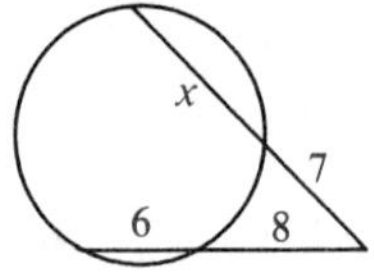

24. **$\sqrt{55}$**

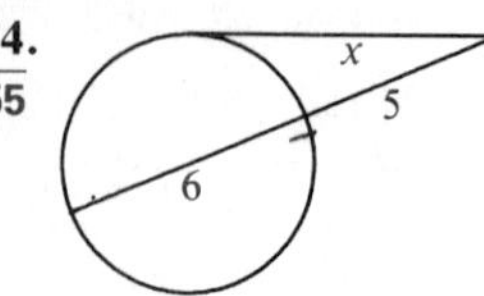

Teaching References
Alternate Test, p. T20

Chapter Test

Classify each statement as true or false.

1. Opposite angles of an inscribed quadrilateral must be congruent. **False**
2. If a chord in one circle is congruent to a chord in another circle, the arcs of these chords must have congruent central angles. **False**
3. A diameter that is perpendicular to a chord must bisect the chord. **True**
4. If a line bisects a chord, that line must pass through the center of the circle. **False**
5. If $\overrightarrow{GM}$ intersects a circle in just one point, $\overline{GM}$ must be tangent to the circle. **False**
6. It is possible to draw two circles so that no common tangents can be drawn. **True**
7. An angle inscribed in a semicircle must be a right angle. **True**
8. When one chord is farther from the center of a circle than another chord, the chord farther from the center is the longer of the two chords. **False**

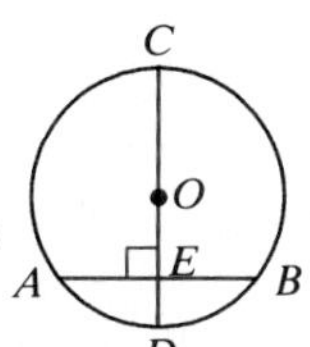

9. In $\odot O$, if $m\widehat{AB} = 100$, then $m\widehat{AC} = \underline{\ ?\ }$. **130**
10. If the radius of $\odot O$ is 17 and $AB = 30$, then $OE = \underline{\ ?\ }$. **8**

$\overline{DA}$ and $\overline{DB}$ are tangent to the circle.

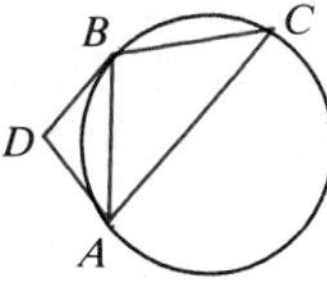

11. If $\overline{AB} \cong \overline{BC}$ and $m\widehat{BC} = 80$, then $m\angle ABC = \underline{\ ?\ }$. **100**
12. If $m\angle D = 110$, then $m\angle BCA = \underline{\ ?\ }$. **35**
13. Given: $m\widehat{BC} = m\widehat{AB}$
    Prove: $\overline{AC} \parallel \overline{DB}$

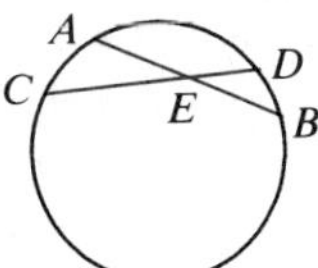

14. If $m\widehat{AC} = 40$ and $m\widehat{BD} = 28$, then $m\angle AEC = \underline{\ ?\ }$. **34**
15. If $AE = 10$, $EB = 9$, and $CE = 15$, then $ED = \underline{\ ?\ }$. **6**

$\overline{PT}$ is tangent to the circle.

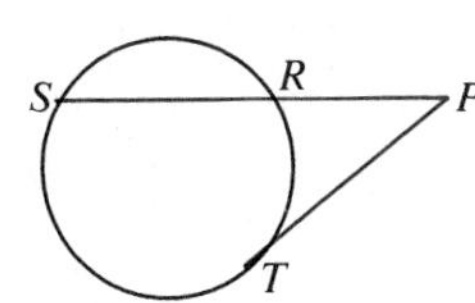

16. If $m\widehat{RS} = 120$ and $m\widehat{ST} = 160$, then $m\angle P = \underline{\ ?\ }$. **40**
17. If $PT = 12$ and $PS = 18$, then $PR = \underline{\ ?\ }$. **8**
18. Given: $\square ABCD$ is inscribed in a circle.
    Prove: $ABCD$ is a rectangle.

Supplementary Materials

Resource Book, p. 198

Cumulative Review: Chapters 1–9

A

1. If x, $x + 3$, and y are the lengths of the sides of a triangle, then $\underset{\mathbf{3}}{\underline{?}} < y < \underset{\mathbf{2x+3}}{\underline{?}}$.
2. Find the measure of an angle if the measures of a supplement and a complement of the angle have the ratio 5:2. **30**
3. Given: $\overline{MN}$ is the median of a trapezoid $WXYZ$.
   Prove: $\overline{MN}$ bisects $\overline{WY}$.

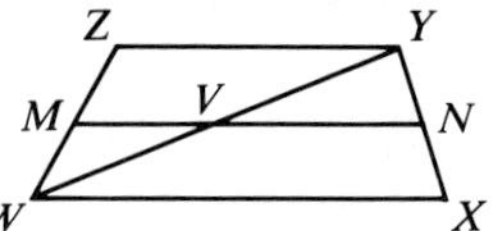

4. Prove: The diagonals of a rhombus divide the rhombus into four congruent triangles.
5. A 30°-60°-90° triangle is inscribed in a circle of radius 7. Find the length of each leg of the triangle. **7, $7\sqrt{3}$**
6. Must three parallel lines be coplanar? Draw a diagram to illustrate your answer. **No; check students' drawings.**
7. The measures of the angles of a triangle are in the ratio 1:9:10. Find the measure of each angle. **9; 81; 90**
8. If a regular polygon has 18 sides, find the measure of each interior angle and the measure of each exterior angle. **interior: 160; exterior: 20**
9. If $ABCE$ is a square and $AC = 4$, find AB. **$2\sqrt{2}$**
10. If the lengths of two sides of a right triangle are 6 and 10, find two possible lengths for the third side. **8, $2\sqrt{34}$**
11. Given: $\angle 1 \cong \angle 2$; $\angle 2 \cong \angle 3$
    Prove: $\overline{AB} \cong \overline{DC}$

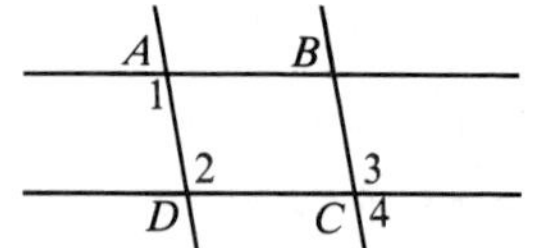

12. When the altitude to the hypotenuse of a certain right triangle is drawn, the altitude divides the hypotenuse into segments of lengths 8 and 10. Find the length of the shorter leg. **12**
13. Write **(a)** the contrapositive and **(b)** the inverse of the following statement: If quad. $ABCD$ is a parallelogram, then $\angle A \cong \angle C$.
14. If $\overrightarrow{OB}$ bisects $\angle AOC$, $m\angle AOB = 5t - 7$, and $m\angle AOC = 8t + 10$, find the numerical measure of $\angle BOC$. **53**
15. Two chords of a circle intersect inside a circle, dividing one chord into segments of length 15 and 12 and the other chord into segments of length 9 and t. Find the value of t. **20**
16. If points R and S on a number line have coordinates -11 and 3, and $\overline{RS}$ has midpoint T, find RS and ST. **$RS = 14$, $ST = 7$**

Additional Answers Cumulative Review

13.a. If $\angle A \not\cong \angle C$, then quad. $ABCD$ is not a ▱.

b. If quad. $ABCD$ is not a ▱, then $\angle A \not\cong \angle C$.

17. Complete with *outside*, *inside*, or *on*: In a right triangle, **(a)** the medians intersect _?_ the triangle, **(b)** the altitudes intersect _?_ the triangle, and **(c)** the perpendicular bisectors of the sides intersect _?_ the triangle. **a. inside b. on c. on**

18. In $\triangle RST$, the bisector of $\angle T$ meets $\overline{RS}$ at X. $RS = 15$, $ST = 27$, $TR = 18$. Find RX. **6**

19. Given: All of Bill's sisters like to dance.
    What can you conclude from each additional statement? If no conclusion is possible, write *no conclusion*.
    a. Janice is Bill's sister.
    b. Holly loves to dance.
    c. Maureen is not Bill's sister.
    d. Kim does not like to dance.

20. Suppose someone plans to write an indirect proof of the statement "In ▱$ABCD$ if $\overline{AB} \perp \overline{BC}$, then $ABCD$ is a rectangle." Write a correct first sentence of the indirect proof. **Assume temp. that *ABCD* is not a rect.**

Complete each statement with the words *always*, *sometimes*, or *never*.

21. A contrapositive of a true conditional statement is _?_ true. **always**
22. The sides of a triangle are _?_ 14 cm, 17 cm, and 31 cm long. **never**
23. In ▱$ABCD$, if $m\angle A > m\angle B$, then $\angle D$ is _?_ an acute angle. **always**
24. Two obtuse triangles are _?_ similar. **sometimes**
25. Two lines perpendicular to a third line are _?_ perpendicular to each other. **sometimes**

Complete.

26. If $\frac{7}{x} = \frac{9}{10}$, then $\frac{?}{} = \frac{?}{}$ (**7 · 10**; **9 · x**), and $x = $ _?_. **$7\frac{7}{9}$**

B 27. The sine of any acute angle must be greater than _?_ and less than _?_. **0; 1**

28. **a.** $\triangle RWZ \sim$ _?_ **△ZWS**
    b. $\frac{RW}{?} = \frac{ZR}{?} = \frac{WZ}{?}$ **ZW; SZ; WS**
    c. $RW = 15$, $ZR = 10$, and $SZ = 8$. $WZ = $ _?_ **12** and $RS = $ _?_ **$5\frac{2}{5}$**

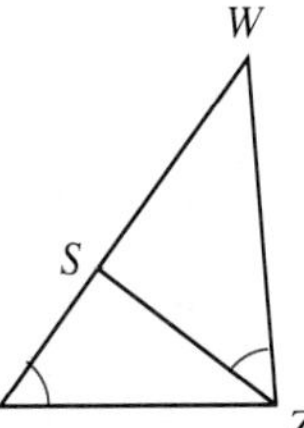

29. Given: $AB > AC$; $\overline{BD} \cong \overline{EC}$
    Prove: $BE > CD$

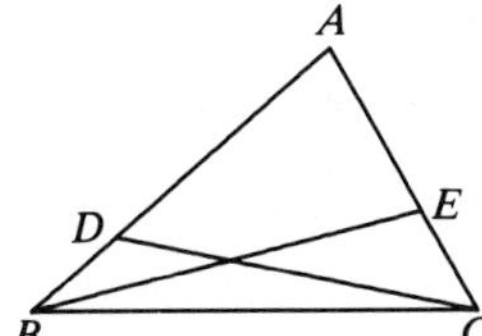

30. Given: $\frac{PR}{TR} = \frac{SR}{QR}$
    Prove: $\angle S \cong \angle Q$

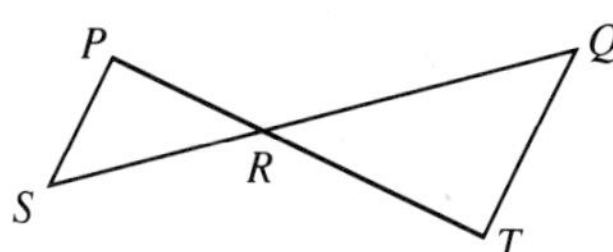

Additional Answers Cumulative Review

19.a. Janice likes to dance.
b. no conclusion
c. no conclusion
d. Kim is not Bill's sister.

10 Constructions and Loci

Objectives

10-1 Perform three basic constructions.

Use these basic constructions in original construction exercises.

10-2 Perform four basic constructions.

Use these basic constructions in original construction exercises.

10-3 State and apply theorems involving concurrent lines.

10-4 Perform four additional basic constructions.

Use the basic constructions in original construction exercises.

10-5 Perform three additional basic constructions.

Use the basic constructions in original construction exercises.

10-6 Describe the locus that satisfies a given condition.

Describe the locus that satisfies more than one given condition.

10-7 Describe the locus that satisfies a given condition.

Describe the locus that satisfies more than one given condition.

10-8 Apply the concept of locus in the solution of construction exercises.

Assignment Guide

See page T40 for information about the Assignment Guide.

Day	Minimum Course	Average Course	Maximum Course
1	**10-1** 378/1–6	**10-1** 378/1–9, 11–16	**10-1** 378/2–10 even, 11–14, 17–21
2	**10-1** 378/7–9, 11–14, 16 380/Mixed Review 1–6	**10-1** 378–379/17–21, 23 380/Mixed Review 1–6	**10-1** 378–379/22–25
3	**10-2** 383/1–8 **S** 378/15, 17	**10-2** 383–384/3, 4, 6, 7, 9–14	**10-2** 383–384/5–8, 11–16 **S** 379/26
4	**10-2** 384/9–18	**10-2** 384/15, 16, 17–23 odd, 24	**10-2** 384/17–25 odd
5	**10-3** 388/1–5	**10-3** 388–389/1–7, 10 **S** 384/25	**10-2** 384–385/18–26 even, 27
6	**10-3** 389/6, 8 390/Self-Test 1 391/Mixed Review 1–4	**10-3** 389/8, 11–14 390/Self-Test 1 391/Mixed Review 1–4	**10-3** 388–389/1–7 odd, 8, 9, 11, 13
7	**10-4** 395/1–3, 6, 9	**10-4** 395/1–3, 5, 6, 10, 11, 13, 15	**10-3** 389/10, 12, 14–16 **S** 385/28
8	**10-4** 395/5, 8, 10, 11, 14	**10-5** 399/1, 3, 5–8 **S** 395/16	**10-4** 395/5, 6, 9–11, 13, 16–18
9	**10-5** 399/1–4	**10-5** 399/9–13, 15 401/Self-Test 2	**10-5** 399/3, 6, 7, 9–11 **S** 396/19, 20
10	**10-5** 399/5–7, 9 401/Self-Test 2	**10-6** 404–405/1–19 odd	**10-5** 399/12, 14–17
11	**10-6** 404/1–8	**10-7** 407–409/1, 4, 6–10 even, 11–17 odd, 18	**10-6** 404–405/1–12, 14–20 even, 21
12	**10-6** 404/9–15	**10-8** 412–413/2, 4–7	**10-7** 408–409/5–11 odd, 14, 16–18, 20, 22

Assignment Guide (continued)

Day	Minimum Course	Average Course	Maximum Course
13	**10-7** 407–408/1–5 odd	**10-8** 413/9, 12, 15 414/Self-Test 3	**10-8** 413/6, 9, 12, 15, 16–19
14	**10-7** 408/6, 7, 9 414/Self-Test 3, 1–6	**10-8** 418/Chapter Test Test, page T21	**10-8** 418/Chapter Test Test, page T21
15	**10-7** 418/Chapter Test 1–11 Test, page T21		

Supplementary Materials Guide

For Use after Lesson	Practice Masters	Tests	Study Guide (Reteaching)	Resource Book: Tests	Resource Book: Practice Exercises	Resource Book: Mixed Review (MR) College Entrance (Col) Enrichment (E) Computer (C)	Computer Activities
10-1			pp. 121–122				
10-2	Sheet 56		pp. 123–124				
10-3	Sheet 57	Test 38	pp. 125–126	pp. 61–62	p. 147		
10-4			pp. 127–128				
10-5	Sheet 58	Test 39	pp. 129–130	pp. 63–64	p. 148		
10-6			pp. 131–132				Activity 21
10-7	Sheet 59		pp. 133–134				
10-8	Sheet 60	Test 40	pp. 135–136	p. 65	p. 149		
Chapter 10	Sheet 61	Test 41		pp. 66–69	p. 150	p. 199 (Col); p. 254 (C); pp. 222–224 (E)	
Chapters 8–10		Test 42		pp. 70–72	p. 151		
Chapters 9–10	Sheets 62, 63						
Chapters 1–10						pp. 180–182 (MR)	

Overhead Visuals

Guided Discovery Visuals (lettered) and Teaching Visuals (numbered) available for Chapter 10.

Lessons	Visual	Title
10-1, 10-2, 10-3	20	Concurrent Lines
10-4, 10-5	21	Circumscribed and Inscribed Circles
10-6, 10-7, 10-8	22	Locus

Guide to Integrated Curriculum

Teachers wishing to integrate coordinate and transformational geometry throughout the course can use the following lessons after Chapter 10. See pages T56–T57 and 657 for more information.

Handbook: Constructions, pp. 669–670

Software Guide

Houghton Mifflin software for Chapter 10

Geometry Grapher (Apple or IBM)

Use with	Booklet
p. 387 (Theorem 10-4)	Class Demonstration, p. 16
p. 385 (Explorations)	
p. 392 (Explorations)	

Test Generator (Apple or IBM): 120 test items

Other software appropriate for Chapter 10

Geometric Supposer (Apple): Triangles

GeoDraw (IBM)

Guide to Distribution of Constructions

The text teaches constructions in Chapter 10. Teachers wishing to distribute work with constructions throughout the first nine chapters can use the guide on page T51.

Strategies for Teaching

Exploring Clever Constructions

When to Use

With or after Lesson 10-2

Overview

Activity 1 offers an alternate method of "dropping perpendiculars" (Construction 6). Activity 2 can be used to motivate Theorem 10-3 on page 387. Activity 3 is related to Exercise 26 on page 384.

Materials

Straightedge and compass

Description of Activity

1. Construct a perpendicular from P to m using the following procedure.
   - **i.** Draw line m.
   - **ii.** Choose a point P above line m and points A and B on line m.
   - **iii.** Using A as the center, draw an arc with radius AP.
   - **iv.** Using B as the center, draw an arc with radius BP.
   - **v.** Draw $\overline{PQ}$ where P and Q are the points of intersection of the two arcs.

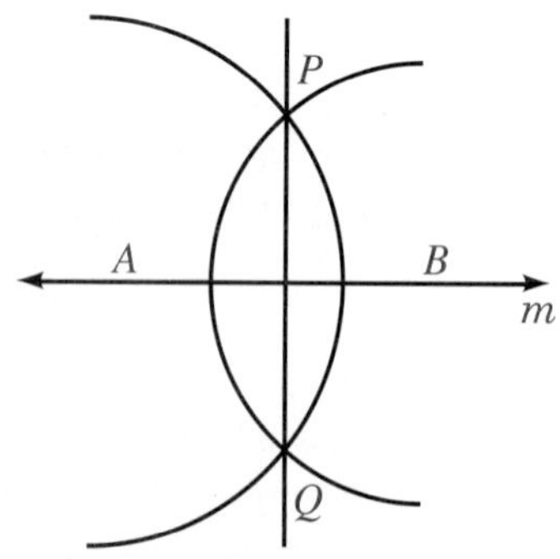

   - **a.** Will your construction still work if points A and B are on the same side of perpendicular $\overline{PQ}$? yes
   - **b.** What happens if B is chosen to be on $\overline{PQ}$?
   - **c.** Draw $\overline{PA}$, $\overline{PB}$, $\overline{QA}$, and $\overline{QB}$ on your original construction. Use this figure to prove $\overline{PQ} \perp m$.
2. Using the method in Activity **1** to create perpendiculars, draw a scalene triangle and construct its three altitudes. Then draw an isosceles triangle and construct its three altitudes. Repeat this for a right triangle and an obtuse triangle, then make a conjecture. The lines that contain the altitudes of a triangle intersect in a point.
3. Construct the bisector of the angle without placing your compass or straightedge in the inaccessible region that contains its vertex.

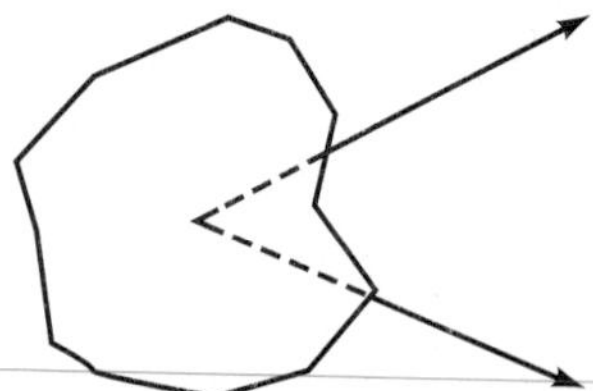

Commentary

- **1c.** You can use either of the facts that the diagonals of a kite are perpendicular or that the line determined by the two points of intersection of two circles is perpendicular to the line joining their centers, if you have proved this previously. Students may develop their own proofs in this question.
- **2.** This activity illustrates Theorem 10-3, and further shows that the point of intersection of the altitudes can be in the interior, exterior, or on the triangle, depending on the triangle's shape.

• **3.** Use perpendiculars and angle copies to construct a parallelogram using the given angle. Find the difference of the longer and shorter sides. Add half the difference to the shorter side and subtract half from the longer side to make a rhombus. One diagonal of the rhombus will bisect the given angle.

References to Strategies

PE: Pupil's Edition **TE:** Teacher's Edition **RB:** Resource Book

Problem Solving Strategies

PE: 374 (Mathematical model), 385 (Challenge, Draw a diagram)
RB: 222–224 (Draw a diagram)

Applications

PE: 374 (Air flow), 390–391 (Center of gravity), 400 (Accountant), 410 (Ex. 24, Animal study)
TE: T117

Nonroutine Problems

PE: 384 (Ex. 26), 385 (Challenge), 389 (Exs. 8–10), 391 (Application), 399 (Ex. 18), 403 (Exs. 11, 12), 410 (Ex. 24, Challenge), 414–415 (Nine-point circle), 670 (Exs. 6, 7)
TE: T119, T121
RB: 210, 222–224

Communication

TE: T117, T118, T120

Explorations

PE: 385, 392
TE: 373c
RB: 222–224

Connections

PE: 379 (Grace Hopper), 419 (Algebraic expressions), 669–670 (Transformational geometry)
TE: T116, T117, T119, T120, 377 (Reference to Ch. 4)

Using Technology

PE: 385, 392
TE: T118, T121, 375, 385, 387, 389, 392, 399, 414
RB: 254
Using Geometry Grapher: 16
Computer Activities: 50–52

Using Manipulatives/Models

PE: 375–418 (Constructions), 390–391
TE: T117, T118
RB: 210
Overhead Visuals: 20a, 20b, 20c, 21, 22

Cooperative Learning

TE: T120, 405

Teaching Resources

For use in implementing the teaching strategies referenced on the previous page.

Exploration
***Resource Book*, p. 222**

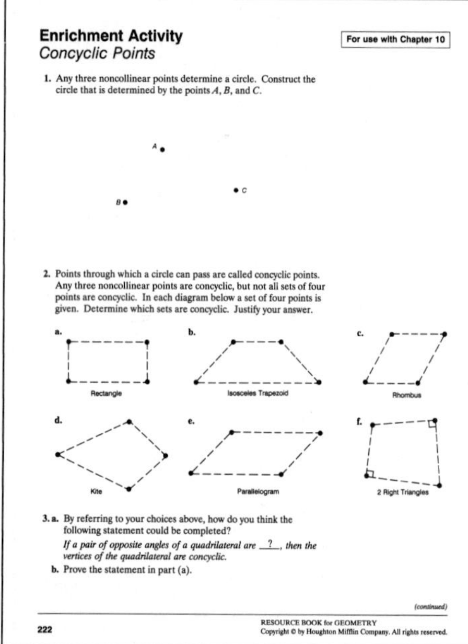

Enrichment Activity
Concyclic Points

For use with Chapter 10

1. Any three noncollinear points determine a circle. Construct the circle that is determined by the points A, B, and C.

2. Points through which a circle can pass are called concyclic points. Any three noncollinear points are concyclic, but not all sets of four points are concyclic. In each diagram below a set of four points is given. Determine which sets are concyclic. Justify your answer.

3. a. By referring to your choices above, how do you think the following statement could be completed?
If a pair of opposite angles of a quadrilateral are __?__, *then the vertices of the quadrilateral are concyclic.*
b. Prove the statement in part (a).

(continued)

Exploration
***Resource Book*, p. 223**

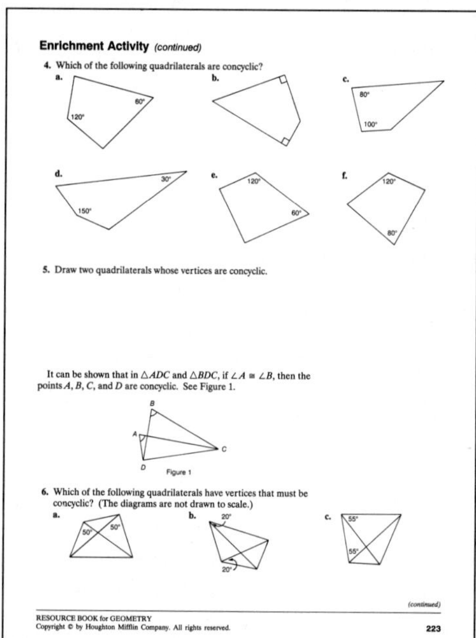

Enrichment Activity *(continued)*

4. Which of the following quadrilaterals are concyclic?

5. Draw two quadrilaterals whose vertices are concyclic.

It can be shown that in $\triangle ADC$ and $\triangle BDC$, if $\angle A \cong \angle B$, then the points A, B, C, and D are concyclic. See Figure 1.

Figure 1

6. Which of the following quadrilaterals have vertices that must be concyclic? (The diagrams are not drawn to scale.)

(continued)

Exploration
***Resource Book*, p. 224**

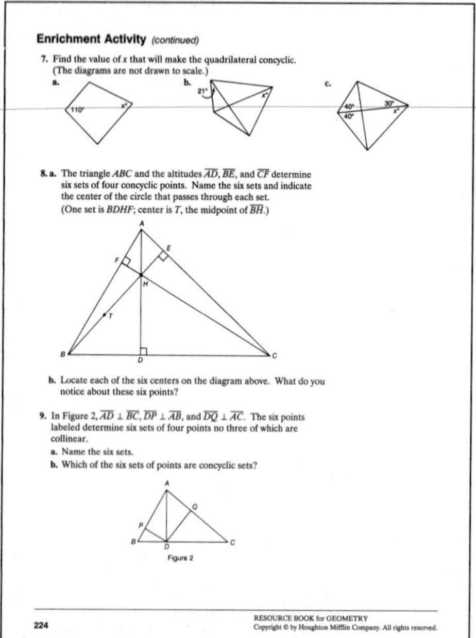

Enrichment Activity *(continued)*

7. Find the value of x that will make the quadrilateral concyclic. (The diagrams are not drawn to scale.)

8. a. The triangle ABC and the altitudes $\overline{AD}$, $\overline{BE}$, and $\overline{CF}$ determine six sets of four concyclic points. Name the six sets and indicate the center of the circle that passes through each set. (One set is $BDHF$; center is T, the midpoint of $\overline{BH}$.)

b. Locate each of the six centers on the diagram above. What do you notice about these six points?

9. In Figure 2, $\overline{AD} \perp \overline{BC}$, $\overline{DP} \perp \overline{AB}$, and $\overline{DQ} \perp \overline{AC}$. The six points labeled determine six sets of four points no three of which are collinear.
a. Name the six sets.
b. Which of the six sets of points are concyclic sets?

Figure 2

Using Manipulatives
***Resource Book*, p. 210**

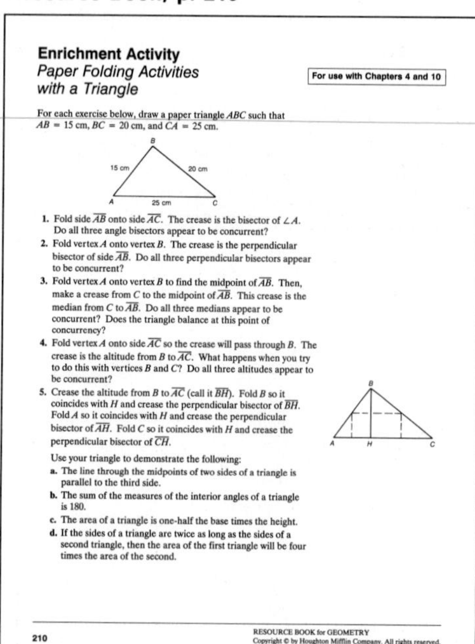

Enrichment Activity
Paper Folding Activities with a Triangle

For use with Chapters 4 and 10

For each exercise below, draw a paper triangle ABC such that $AB = 15$ cm, $BC = 20$ cm, and $CA = 25$ cm.

1. Fold side $\overline{AB}$ onto side $\overline{AC}$. The crease is the bisector of $\angle A$. Do all three angle bisectors appear to be concurrent?
2. Fold vertex A onto vertex B. The crease is the perpendicular bisector of side $\overline{AB}$. Do all three perpendicular bisectors appear to be concurrent?
3. Fold vertex A onto vertex B to find the midpoint of $\overline{AB}$. Then, make a crease from C to the midpoint of $\overline{AB}$. This crease is the median from C to $\overline{AB}$. Do all three medians appear to be concurrent? Does the triangle balance at this point of concurrency?
4. Fold vertex A onto side $\overline{AC}$ so the crease will pass through B. The crease is the altitude from B to $\overline{AC}$. What happens when you try to do this with vertices B and C? Do all three altitudes appear to be concurrent?
5. Crease the altitude from B to $\overline{AC}$ (call it $\overline{BH}$). Fold B so it coincides with H and crease the perpendicular bisector of $\overline{BH}$. Fold A so it coincides with H and crease the perpendicular bisector of $\overline{AH}$. Fold C so it coincides with H and crease the perpendicular bisector of $\overline{CH}$.

Use your triangle to demonstrate the following:
a. The line through the midpoints of two sides of a triangle is parallel to the third side.
b. The sum of the measures of the interior angles of a triangle is 180.
c. The area of a triangle is one-half the base times the height.
d. If the sides of a triangle are twice as long as the sides of a second triangle, then the area of the first triangle will be four times the area of the second.

Using Technology
Resource Book, p. 254

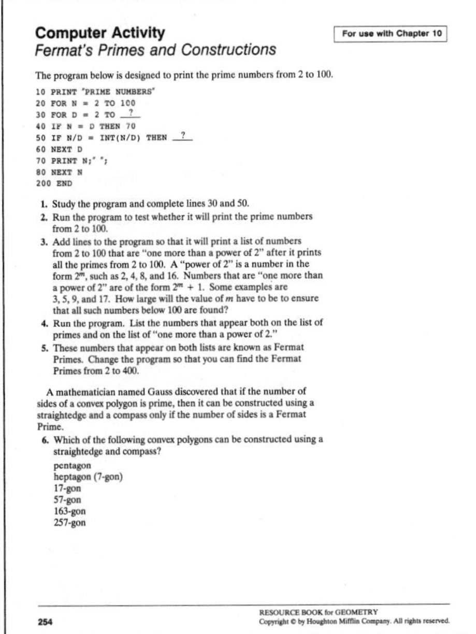

Computer Activity
Fermat's Primes and Constructions

For use with Chapter 10

The program below is designed to print the prime numbers from 2 to 100.

```
10 PRINT "PRIME NUMBERS"
20 FOR N = 2 TO 100
30 FOR D = 2 TO __?__
40 IF N = D THEN 70
50 IF N/D = INT(N/D) THEN __?__
60 NEXT D
70 PRINT N;" ";
80 NEXT N
200 END
```

1. Study the program and complete lines 30 and 50.
2. Run the program to test whether it will print the prime numbers from 2 to 100.
3. Add lines to the program so that it will print a list of numbers from 2 to 100 that are "one more than a power of 2" after it prints all the primes from 2 to 100. A "power of 2" is a number in the form 2^m, such as 2, 4, 8, and 16. Numbers that are "one more than a power of 2" are of the form $2^m + 1$. Some examples are 3, 5, 9, and 17. How large will the value of m have to be to ensure that all such numbers below 100 are found?
4. Run the program. List the numbers that appear both on the list of primes and on the list of "one more than a power of 2."
5. These numbers that appear on both lists are known as Fermat Primes. Change the program so that you can find the Fermat Primes from 2 to 400.

A mathematician named Gauss discovered that if the number of sides of a convex polygon is prime, then it can be constructed using a straightedge and a compass only if the number of sides is a Fermat Prime.

6. Which of the following convex polygons can be constructed using a straightedge and compass?
   pentagon
   heptagon (7-gon)
   17-gon
   57-gon
   163-gon
   257-gon

254 RESOURCE BOOK for GEOMETRY

Using Models
Teaching Visual 22

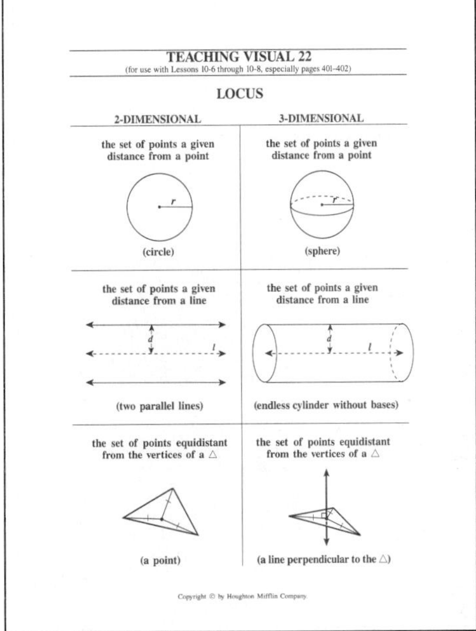

TEACHING VISUAL 22
(for use with Lessons 10-6 through 10-8, especially pages 401–402)

LOCUS

2-DIMENSIONAL	3-DIMENSIONAL
the set of points a given distance from a point (circle)	the set of points a given distance from a point (sphere)
the set of points a given distance from a line (two parallel lines)	the set of points a given distance from a line (endless cylinder without bases)
the set of points equidistant from the vertices of a △ (a point)	the set of points equidistant from the vertices of a △ (a line perpendicular to the △)

Using Manipulatives
Study Guide, p. 121

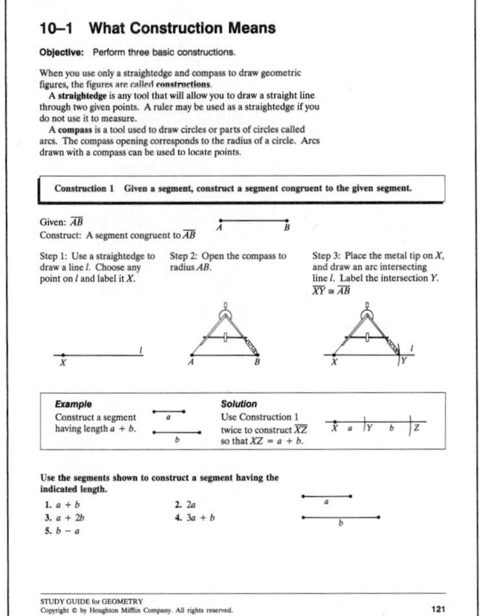

10–1 What Construction Means

Objective: Perform three basic constructions.

When you use only a straightedge and compass to draw geometric figures, the figures are called **constructions**.

A **straightedge** is any tool that will allow you to draw a straight line through two given points. A ruler may be used as a straightedge if you do not use it to measure.

A **compass** is a tool used to draw circles or parts of circles called arcs. The compass opening corresponds to the radius of a circle. Arcs drawn with a compass can be used to locate points.

Construction 1 Given a segment, construct a segment congruent to the given segment.

Given: $\overline{AB}$
Construct: A segment congruent to $\overline{AB}$

Step 1: Use a straightedge to draw a line l. Choose any point on l and label it X.

Step 2: Open the compass to radius AB.

Step 3: Place the metal tip on X, and draw an arc intersecting line l. Label the intersection Y. $\overline{XY} \cong \overline{AB}$

Example
Construct a segment having length $a + b$.

Solution
Use Construction 1 twice to construct $\overline{XZ}$ so that $XZ = a + b$.

Use the segments shown to construct a segment having the indicated length.

1. $a + b$
2. $2a$
3. $a + 2b$
4. $3a + b$
5. $b - a$

STUDY GUIDE for GEOMETRY

121

Using Manipulatives
Study Guide, p. 122

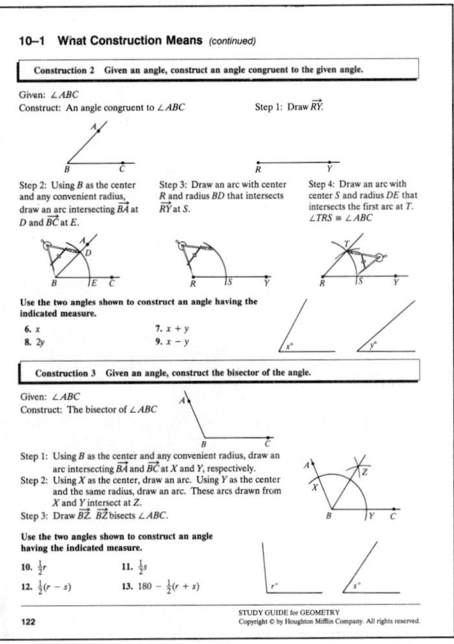

10–1 What Construction Means *(continued)*

Construction 2 Given an angle, construct an angle congruent to the given angle.

Given: $\angle ABC$
Construct: An angle congruent to $\angle ABC$

Step 1: Draw $\overrightarrow{RY}$.

Step 2: Using B as the center and any convenient radius, draw an arc intersecting $\overrightarrow{BA}$ at D and $\overrightarrow{BC}$ at E.

Step 3: Draw an arc with center R and radius BD that intersects $\overrightarrow{RY}$ at S.

Step 4: Draw an arc with center S and radius DE that intersects the first arc at T. $\angle TRS \cong \angle ABC$

Use the two angles shown to construct an angle having the indicated measure.

6. x
7. $x + y$
8. $2y$
9. $x - y$

Construction 3 Given an angle, construct the bisector of the angle.

Given: $\angle ABC$
Construct: The bisector of $\angle ABC$

Step 1: Using B as the center and any convenient radius, draw an arc intersecting $\overrightarrow{BA}$ and $\overrightarrow{BC}$ at X and Y, respectively.
Step 2: Using X as the center, draw an arc. Using Y as the center and the same radius, draw an arc. These arcs drawn from X and Y intersect at Z.
Step 3: Draw $\overrightarrow{BZ}$. $\overrightarrow{BZ}$ bisects $\angle ABC$.

Use the two angles shown to construct an angle having the indicated measure.

10. $\frac{1}{2}r$
11. $\frac{1}{2}s$
12. $\frac{1}{2}(r - s)$
13. $180 - \frac{1}{2}(r + s)$

122 STUDY GUIDE for GEOMETRY

Teaching References

Lesson Commentary, pp. T116–T121
Assignment Guide, pp. T47–T49
Software Guide, p. T73
Alternate Test, p. T21

Supplementary Materials

Practice Masters 56–63
Tests 38–42
Resource Book
- Tests, pp. 61–72
- Practice, pp. 147–151
- Mixed Rev., pp. 180–182
- Preparing for College Entrance Exams, p. 199
- Enrichment Activity, pp. 222–224
- Computer Activity, p. 254

Study Guide, pp. 121–136
Overhead Visuals 20–22
Computer Activity
- 21 Drawing Polygons

Handbook for Integrating Coordinate and Transformational Geometry

Constructions, pp. 669–670

Cultural Note

Records show that Egyptians used compasses to mark off distances or construct circles as early as the 2nd millennium B.C. Compasses were found in the ruins of Pompeii, which was destroyed by the eruption of Mount Vesuvius in 79 A.D. (For more on compasses, see *Teaching Note* on page 377.)

10 CONSTRUCTIONS AND LOCI

Engineers can test the efficiency of a car's design by observing the air currents in a wind tunnel. Strips of cloth attached to the body, as well as smoke patterns, indicate the flow of air around the car.

374

www.mathopenref.com/constructions.html

Basic Constructions

animated website has some easier methods also

Objectives

1. Perform seven basic constructions.
2. Use these basic constructions in original construction exercises.
3. State and apply theorems involving concurrent lines.

10-1 *What Construction Means*

In Chapters 1–9 we have used rulers and protractors to draw segments with certain lengths and angles with certain measures. In this chapter we will *construct* geometric figures using only two instruments, a *straightedge* and a *compass*. (You may use a ruler as a straightedge as long as you do not use the marks on the ruler.)

Using a Straightedge in Constructions

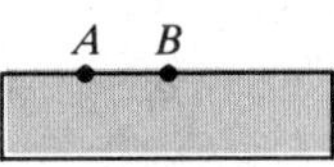

Given two points A and B, we know from Postulate 6 that there is exactly one line through A and B. We agree that we can use a straightedge to draw $\overleftrightarrow{AB}$ or parts of the line, such as $\overline{AB}$ and $\overrightarrow{AB}$.

Using a Compass in Constructions

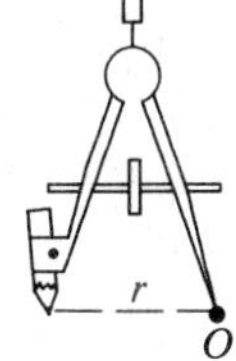

Given a point O and a length r, we know from the definition of a circle that there is exactly one circle with center O and radius r. We agree that we can use a compass to draw this circle or arcs of the circle.

Construction 1

Given a segment, construct a segment congruent to the given segment.

Given: $\overline{AB}$

Construct: A segment congruent to $\overline{AB}$

Procedure:

1. Use a straightedge to draw a line. Call it l.
2. Choose any point on l and label it X.
3. Set your compass for radius AB. Using X as center, draw an arc intersecting line l. Label the point of intersection Y.

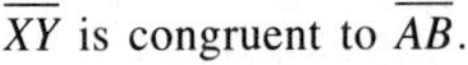

$\overline{XY}$ is congruent to $\overline{AB}$.

Justification: Since you used AB for the radius of $\odot X$, $\overline{XY} \cong \overline{AB}$.

Teaching Suggestions, pp. T116–T117

Objectives
Presenting the Lesson
Making Connections

Communication Skills, p. T117

Supplementary Materials

Study Guide, pp. 121–122

Lesson Focus

The purpose of this lesson is to learn the meaning of the term *construction* as it is used in geometry, and also to learn to perform the first three of fourteen constructions that are presented in the chapter.

Suggested Assignments

Minimum
Day 1: 378/1–6
Day 2: 378/7–9, 11–14, 16
380/Mixed Review 1–6

Average
Day 1: 378/1–9, 11–16
Day 2: 378–379/17–21, 23
380/Mixed Review 1–6

Maximum
Day 1: 378/2–10 even, 11–14, 17–20, 21
Day 2: 378–379/22–25

Using a Computer

All of the constructions in this chapter can be done using a construction program.

Chalkboard Examples

Given segments with lengths *a*, *b*, and *c*, construct segments having the indicated lengths.

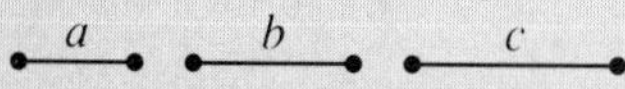

1. $3a$ Extended use of Const. 1
2. $a + c$ Draw $\overrightarrow{PQ}$. Use Const. 1 to locate point X such that $PX = a$. In like manner, locate point Q such that $XQ = c$. $\overline{PQ}$ is the required segment.
3. $2c - b$ Draw $\overrightarrow{PW}$. Use Const. 1 to locate point X such that $PX = 2c$. Locate point Q between P and X so that $XQ = b$. $\overline{PQ}$ is the required segment.
4. Construct an isosceles triangle with base length a and legs each of length b. Draw a line and mark off $AB = a$. Draw 2 arcs using A as center with radius $= b$, then B as center with radius $= b$. Locate C, the intersection of the 2 arcs. $\triangle ABC$ is the required $\triangle$.
5. Given $\angle A$ and $\angle B$, construct $\angle PQR$ so that the measure of $\angle PQR$ is $\frac{1}{2}(m\angle A + m\angle B)$. Use Const. 2 and Const. 3.

Construction 2

Given an angle, construct an angle congruent to the given angle.

Given: $\angle ABC$

Construct: An angle congruent to $\angle ABC$

Procedure:

1. Draw a ray. Label it $\overrightarrow{RY}$.
2. Using B as center and any radius, draw an arc intersecting $\overrightarrow{BA}$ and $\overrightarrow{BC}$. Label the points of intersection D and E, respectively.
3. Using R as center and the same radius as in Step 2, draw an arc intersecting $\overrightarrow{RY}$. Label the arc $\overparen{XS}$, with S the point where the arc intersects $\overrightarrow{RY}$.
4. Using S as center and a radius equal to DE, draw an arc that intersects $\overparen{XS}$ at a point Q.
5. Draw $\overrightarrow{RQ}$.

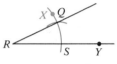

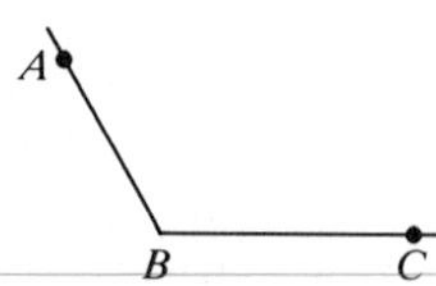

$\angle QRS$ is congruent to $\angle ABC$.

Justification: If you draw $\overline{DE}$ and $\overline{QS}$, $\triangle DBE \cong \triangle QRS$ (SSS Postulate). Then $\angle QRS \cong \angle ABC$.

Construction 3

Given an angle, construct the bisector of the angle.

Given: $\angle ABC$

Construct: The bisector of $\angle ABC$

Procedure:

1. Using B as center and any radius, draw an arc that intersects $\overrightarrow{BA}$ at X and $\overrightarrow{BC}$ at Y.
2. Using X as center and a suitable radius, draw an arc. Using Y as center and the same radius, draw an arc that intersects the arc with center X at a point Z.
3. Draw $\overrightarrow{BZ}$.

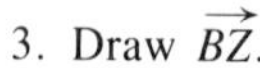

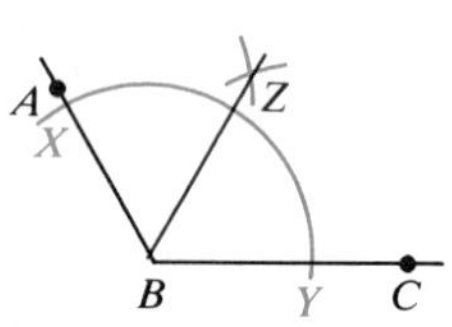

$\overrightarrow{BZ}$ bisects $\angle ABC$.

Justification: If you draw $\overline{XZ}$ and $\overline{YZ}$, $\triangle XBZ \cong \triangle YBZ$ (SSS Postulate). Then $\angle XBZ \cong \angle YBZ$ and $\overrightarrow{BZ}$ bisects $\angle ABC$.

Example Given $\angle 1$ and $\angle 2$, construct an angle whose measure is equal to $m\angle 1 + m\angle 2$.

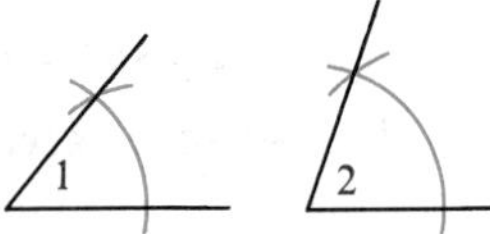

Solution First use Construction 2 to construct $\angle LON$ congruent to $\angle 1$. Then use the same method to construct $\angle MOL$ congruent to $\angle 2$ (as shown) so that $m\angle MON = m\angle 1 + m\angle 2$.

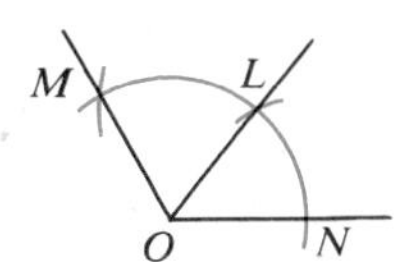

In construction exercises, you won't ordinarily have to write out the procedure and the justification. However, you should be able to supply them when asked to do so.

1. Answers may vary. Example: Const. $\overline{AB} \cong \overline{JK}$; const. $\angle CAB \cong \angle J$ and $\angle CBA \cong \angle K$.

Classroom Exercises

1. Given: $\triangle JKM$
   Explain how to construct a triangle that is congruent to $\triangle JKM$. **See above.**

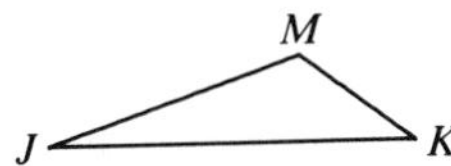

2. Draw any $\overline{AB}$.
   a. Construct $\overline{XY}$ so that $XY = AB$.
   b. Using X and Y as centers, and a radius equal to AB, draw arcs that intersect. Label the point of intersection Z.
   c. Draw $\overline{XZ}$ and $\overline{YZ}$.
   d. What kind of triangle is $\triangle XYZ$? **equilateral**
3. Explain how you could construct a 30° angle. **See below.**
4. Exercise 3 suggests that you could construct other angles with certain measures. Name some. **Answers may vary. Examples: 15°, 45°, 60°, 90°, 75°, 120°**
5. Suppose you are given the three lengths shown and are asked to construct a triangle whose sides have lengths r, s, and t. Can you do so? State the theorem from Chapter 6 that applies. **No; Triangle Inequality Thm.**

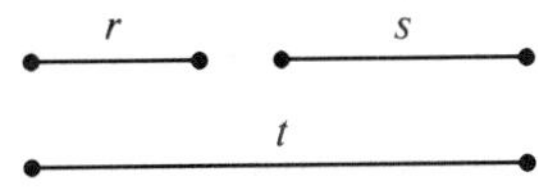

6. $\angle 1$ and $\angle 2$ are given. You see two attempts at constructing an angle whose measure is equal to $m\angle 1 + m\angle 2$. Are both constructions satisfactory? **Yes**

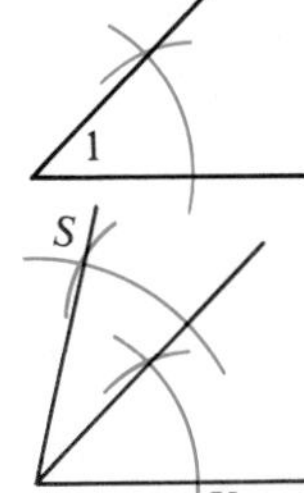

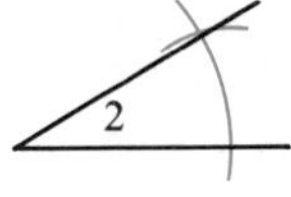

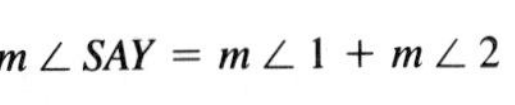

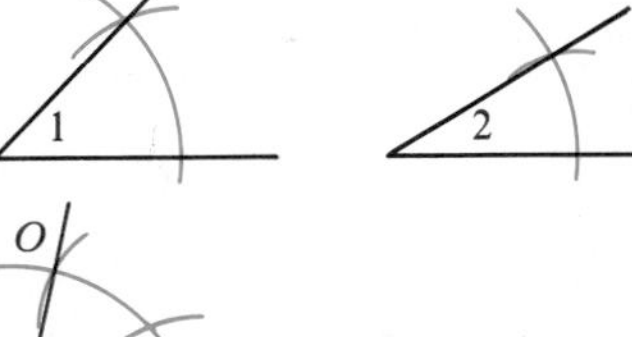

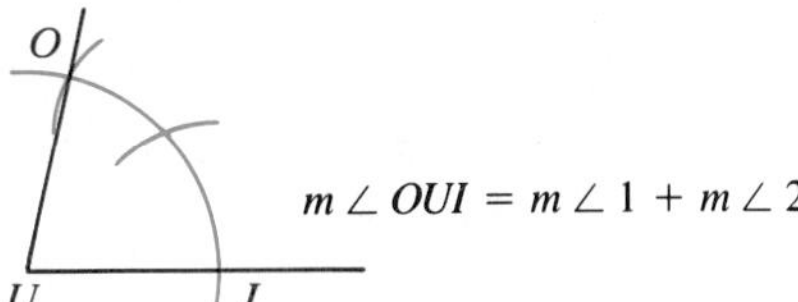

3. Construct an equilateral triangle as in Exercise 2 and bisect one of the angles.

Teaching Note

You may wish to discuss with students the difference between the modern compass and the compass used during Euclid's time. The Euclidean compass is a collapsing compass. Such a compass can only be used to draw a circle with a given center and radius. When you complete the circle and lift the compass from its position it will collapse. All constructions that are performed with a modern compass can be performed with a collapsing one. A good reference is *A Survey of Geometry* by Howard Eves.

Making Connections

Classroom Ex. 1 and Written Exs. 7–10 provide an opportunity to review the SSS, SAS, and ASA Postulates for congruent triangles. Have students construct on the chalkboard several triangles congruent to the same triangle using different methods.

Written Ex. 15 previews Theorem 10-1 that concerns the point of concurrency for angle bisectors of a triangle.

Guided Practice

Draw segments and angles roughly like those shown.

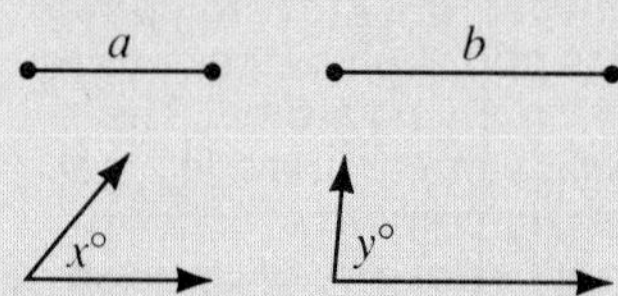

Construct segments having the indicated lengths.

1. $2a$
2. $3b + a$
3. $2a - b$

Construct angles having the indicated measures.

4. $y - x$
5. $2x$
6. $180 - x$
7. $\frac{1}{2}(x + y)$
8. Draw a triangle roughly like the one shown. Construct $\triangle XYZ$ so that the scale factor of $\triangle ABC$ to $\triangle XYZ$ is 1 to 3.

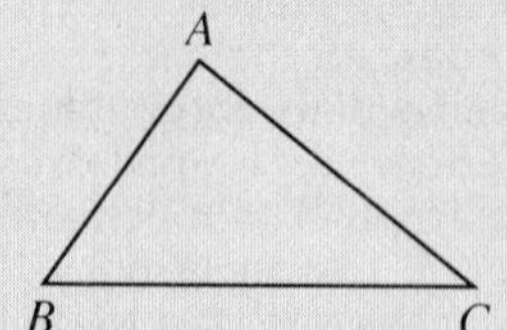

Written Exercises

On your paper, draw two segments roughly like those shown. Use these segments in Exercises 1–4 to construct a segment having the indicated length.

A

1. $a + b$ **2.** $b - a$ **3.** $3a - b$ **4.** $a + 2b$

5. Using any convenient length for a side, construct an equilateral triangle.

6. a. Construct a 30° angle. **b.** Construct a 15° angle.

7. Draw any acute $\triangle ACU$. Use a method based on the SSS Postulate to construct a triangle congruent to $\triangle ACU$.

8. Draw any obtuse $\triangle OBT$. Use the SSS method to construct a triangle congruent to $\triangle OBT$.

9. Repeat Exercise 7, but use the SAS method.

10. Repeat Exercise 8, but use the ASA method.

On your paper, draw two angles roughly like those shown. Then for Exercises 11–14 construct an angle having the indicated measure.

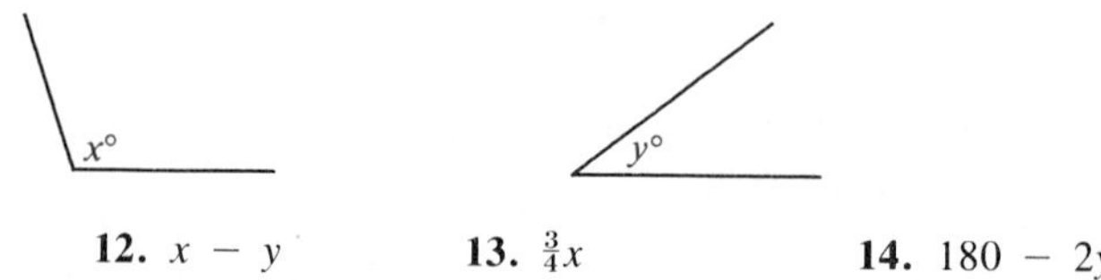

11. $x + y$ **12.** $x - y$ **13.** $\frac{3}{4}x$ **14.** $180 - 2y$

B

15. a. Draw any acute triangle. Bisect each of the three angles.
b. Draw any obtuse triangle. Bisect each of the three angles.
c. What do you notice about the points of intersection of the bisectors in parts (a) and (b)? **They are the same pt., which is equidistant from the sides of the △.**

16. Construct a six-pointed star using the following procedure.
1. Draw a ray, $\overrightarrow{AB}$. On $\overrightarrow{AB}$ mark off, in order, points C and D such that $AB = BC = CD$.
2. Construct equilateral $\triangle ADG$.
3. On $\overline{AG}$ mark off points E and F so that both AE and EF equal AB.
4. On $\overline{GD}$ mark off points H and I so that both GH and HI equal AB.
5. To complete the star, draw the three lines $\overleftrightarrow{FH}$, $\overleftrightarrow{EB}$, and $\overleftrightarrow{CI}$.

Construct an angle having the indicated measure. **17–21. Methods may vary.**

17. 120 **18.** 150 **19.** 165 **20.** 45

21. Draw any $\triangle ABC$. Construct $\triangle DEF$ so that $\triangle DEF \sim \triangle ABC$ and $DE = 2AB$.

22. Construct a $\triangle RST$ such that $RS:ST:TR = 4:6:7$.

On your paper draw figures roughly like those shown. Use them in constructing the figures described in Exercises 23–25.

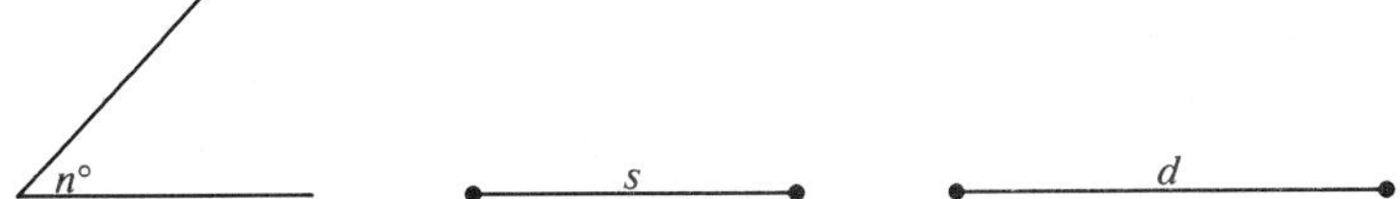

23. An isosceles triangle with a vertex angle of $n°$ and legs of length d

24. An isosceles triangle with a vertex angle of $n°$ and base of length s

C **25.** A parallelogram with an $n°$ angle, longer side of length s, and longer diagonal of length d

★ **26.** On your paper draw figures roughly like the ones shown. Then construct a triangle whose three angles are congruent to $\angle 1$, $\angle 2$, and $\angle 3$, and whose circumscribed circle has radius r.

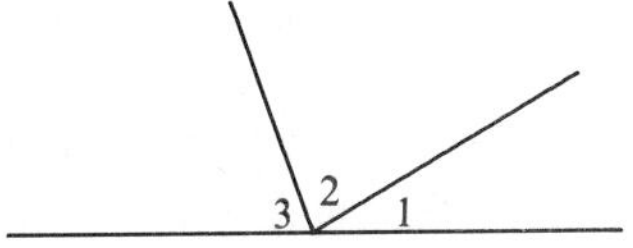

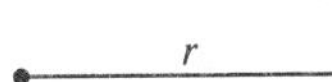

Biographical Note — *Grace Hopper*

In 1944 the Mark I, the first working computing machine, started operations at Harvard. It could do three additions per second; calculations that took six months by hand could now be done in a day. Today, computers are one *billion* times as fast, partly because software (programming) has become more efficient, but mostly because of advances in hardware (electronics) such as the development of integrated circuits and silicon chips.

Rear Adm. Grace Hopper, U.S. Navy (Ret.) worked on that first computing machine and many others since. After getting her Ph.D. in mathematics in 1934 from Yale and teaching for several years, Hopper joined the Navy in 1943 and was assigned to Harvard as a programmer of the Mark I. In 1957, her work on making programming faster and easier resulted in her language called Flowmatic, based on the novel idea of using English words in a computer language. The first machine-independent language, COBOL, was announced in 1960 and was based on her language. She continues today to promote computers and learning, saying computers are the "first tool to assist man's brain instead of his arm."

Additional Answers Written Exercises

21. Const. $DE = 2AB$. Const. $\angle D \cong \angle A$ and $DF = 2AC$. By SAS $\sim$, $\triangle DEF \sim \triangle ABC$.

22. Draw a line and with any convenient radius, r, mark off 7 $\cong$ arcs with length r. Label the pts. A, B, C, D, E, F, G, and H. Const. $\overline{ST}$ such that $\overline{ST} \cong \overline{AG}$; with centers S and T and radii $\overline{AE}$ and $\overline{AH}$, resp., draw arcs int. at R. Draw $\overline{RS}$ and $\overline{RT}$.

24. Const. $\angle A$ with measure n; bisect the supp. of $\angle A$ to const. $\angle 1$ adjacent to $\angle A$; mark off $AB = s$ with $\overrightarrow{AB}$ a side of $\angle 1$; at B, const. $\angle 2 \cong \angle 1$. Extend sides of $\angle 1$ and $\angle 2$ to intersect at C.

Exercise Note

Ex. 26 is quite challenging and can provide a good discussion topic for very capable students.

Teaching Suggestions, p. T117

Objectives
Presenting the Lesson
Making Connections
Extension

Exploring Activity, p. 373c

Supplementary Materials

Practice Master 56

Study Guide, pp. 123–124

Lesson Focus

The four constructions show how to construct perpendicular and parallel lines.

Suggested Assignments

Minimum
Day 1: 383/1–8
S 378/15, 17
Day 2: 384/9–16, 17, 18

Average
Day 1: 383–384/3, 4, 6, 7, 9–14
Day 2: 384/15, 16, 17–23 odd, 24

Maximum
Day 1: 383–384/5–8, 11–16
S 379/26
Day 2: 384/17–25 odd
Day 3: 384–385/18–26 even, 27

Chalkboard Examples

Draw a large acute △*ABC*.

1. Construct the ⊥ bisector of $\overline{BC}$. Const. 4
2. Locate the midpoint *M* of $\overline{AB}$. Const. 4
3. Given a point *P* on $\overline{BC}$, construct $\overline{XP} \perp \overline{BC}$ at *P*. Const. 5
4. Construct line *k* ⊥ to $\overline{BC}$ through point *A*, which is outside $\overline{BC}$. Const. 6

Mixed Review Exercises

Complete.

1. A median of a triangle is a segment from a vertex to the __?__ of the opposite side. **midpoint**
2. A quadrilateral with both pairs of opposite angles congruent is a __?__. **parallelogram**
3. A parallelogram with congruent diagonals is a __?__. **rectangle**
4. A parallelogram with perpendicular diagonals is a __?__. **rhombus**
5. If a side of a square has length 5 cm, then a diagonal of the square has length __?__ cm. $5\sqrt{2}$
6. The measure of each interior angle of a regular pentagon is __?__. **108**

10-2 *Perpendiculars and Parallels*

The next three constructions are based on a theorem and postulate from earlier chapters. The theorem and postulate are repeated here for your use.

(1) If a point is equidistant from the endpoints of a segment, then the point lies on the perpendicular bisector of the segment.

(2) Through any two points there is exactly one line.

Construction 4

Given a segment, construct the perpendicular bisector of the segment.

Given: $\overline{AB}$

Construct: The perpendicular bisector of $\overline{AB}$

Procedure:

1. Using any radius greater than $\frac{1}{2}AB$, draw four arcs of equal radii, two with center *A* and two with center *B*. Label the points of intersections of these arcs *X* and *Y*.
2. Draw $\overleftrightarrow{XY}$.

$\overleftrightarrow{XY}$ is the perpendicular bisector of $\overline{AB}$.

Justification: Points *X* and *Y* are equidistant from *A* and *B*. Thus $\overleftrightarrow{XY}$ is the perpendicular bisector of $\overline{AB}$.

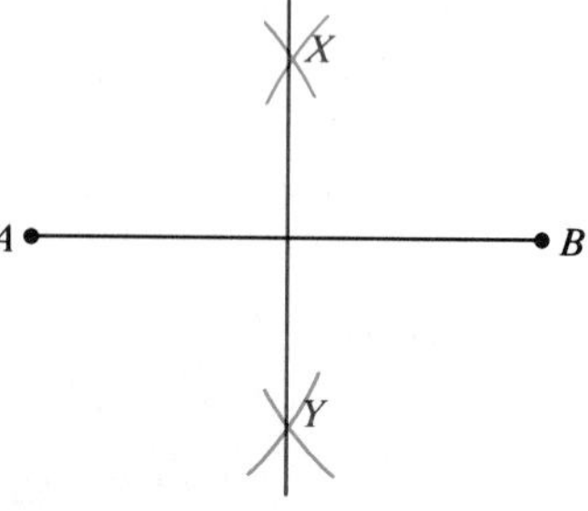

Note that you can use Construction 4 to find the midpoint of a segment.

Construction 5

Given a point on a line, construct the perpendicular to the line at the given point.

Given: Point C on line k

Construct: The perpendicular to k at C

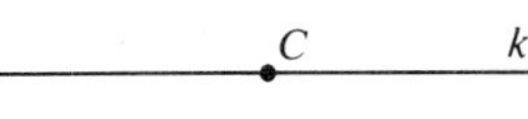

Procedure:

1. Using C as center and any radius, draw arcs intersecting k at X and Y.
2. Using X as center and a radius greater than CX, draw an arc. Using Y as center and the same radius, draw an arc intersecting the arc with center X at a point Z.
3. Draw $\overleftrightarrow{CZ}$.

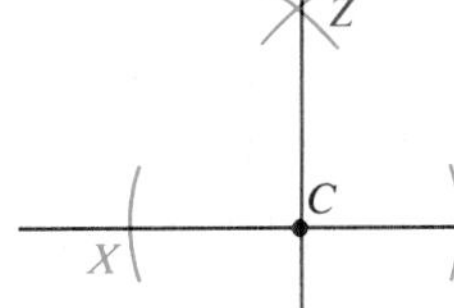

$\overleftrightarrow{CZ}$ is perpendicular to k at C.

Justification: You constructed points X and Y so that C is equidistant from X and Y. Then you constructed point Z so that Z is equidistant from X and Y. Thus $\overleftrightarrow{CZ}$ is the perpendicular bisector of $\overline{XY}$, and $\overleftrightarrow{CZ} \perp k$ at C.

Construction 6

Given a point outside a line, construct the perpendicular to the line from the given point.

Given: Point P outside line k

Construct: The perpendicular to k from P

P•

k

Procedure:

1. Using P as center, draw two arcs of equal radii that intersect k at points X and Y.
2. Using X and Y as centers and a suitable radius, draw arcs that intersect at a point Z.
3. Draw $\overleftrightarrow{PZ}$.

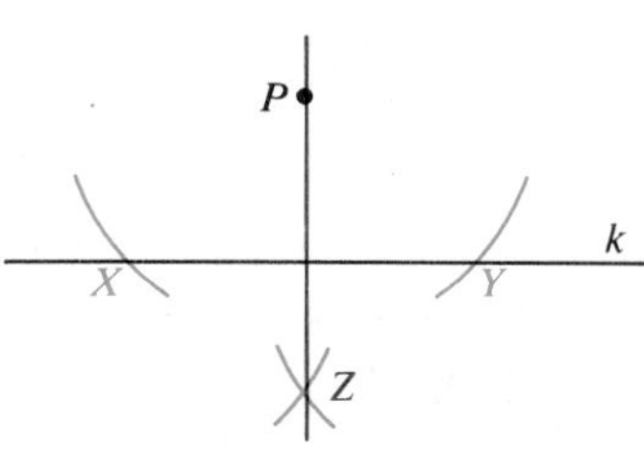

$\overleftrightarrow{PZ}$ is perpendicular to k.

Justification: Both P and Z are equidistant from X and Y. Thus $\overleftrightarrow{PZ}$ is the perpendicular bisector of $\overline{XY}$, and $\overleftrightarrow{PZ} \perp k$.

5. Construct line $f \parallel$ to $\overleftrightarrow{AB}$ through point C which is outside $\overleftrightarrow{AB}$. Const. 7

Two segments are given below. For Exs. 6–9, construct the indicated figure.

6. A segment with length $\frac{1}{2}(a + 2b)$.
Draw a line. Mark off $AB = (a + 2b)$. Const. the $\perp$ bis. of AB. Locate M the midpt. of $\overline{AB}$. $\overline{AM}$ is the required segment.

7. A segment with length c, where $4c = a$.
Draw a line. Mark off $AB = a$. Const. $\perp$ bis. of $\overline{AB}$. Locate M the midpt. of $\overline{AB}$. Const. the $\perp$ bis. of $\overline{AM}$. Locate N the midpt. of $\overline{AM}$. $\overline{AN}$ is the required segment.

8. A right triangle with legs a and b.
Draw a line. Mark off $AB = a$. At B, const. a line $\perp \overline{AB}$. On the line, mark off $BC = b$. $\triangle ABC$ is the required $\triangle$.

9. A rectangle with sides $a + b$ and $a - b$.
Draw a line. Mark off $AB = (a - b)$. At A and B, const. lines $\perp \overline{AB}$. Mark off $BC = (a + b)$ on one of the lines and $AD = (a + b)$ on the other. Quad. $ABCD$ is the required rectangle.

Construction 7

Given a point outside a line, construct the parallel to the given line through the given point.

Given: Point P outside line k

Construct: The line through P parallel to k

Procedure:

1. Let A and B be two points on line k. Draw $\overleftrightarrow{PA}$.
2. At P, construct $\angle 1$ so that $\angle 1$ and $\angle PAB$ are congruent corresponding angles. Let l be the line containing the ray you just constructed.

l is the line through P parallel to k.

Justification: If two lines are cut by a transversal and corresponding angles are congruent, then the lines are parallel. (Postulate 11)

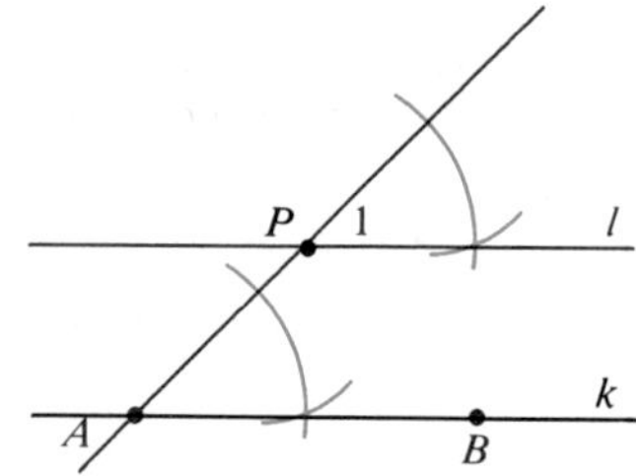

Classroom Exercises

1. Suggest an alternative procedure for Construction 7 that uses Constructions 5 and 6. **Use Const. 6 to construct $j \perp k$ through P. Then use Const. 5 to construct $l \perp j$ through P; $l \parallel k$.**

Describe how you would construct each of the following.

2. The midpoint of $\overline{BC}$ **Use Const. 4.**
3. The median of $\triangle ABC$ that contains vertex B
4. The altitude of $\triangle ABC$ that contains vertex B } **See below.**
5. The altitude of $\triangle ABC$ that contains vertex A

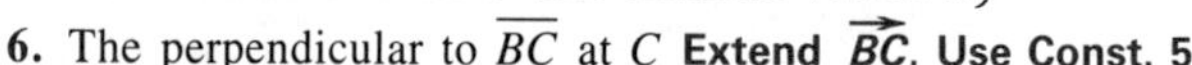

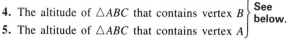

6. The perpendicular to $\overline{BC}$ at C **Extend $\overrightarrow{BC}$. Use Const. 5.**
7. A square whose sides each have length AC
8. A square whose perimeter equals AC
9. A right triangle with hypotenuse and one leg equal to AC and BC, respectively
10. A triangle whose sides are in the ratio $1:2:\sqrt{5}$

3. Use Const. 4 to locate the midpt. M of $\overline{AC}$; draw $\overline{MB}$.
4. Use Const. 6 to construct a $\perp$ to $\overline{AC}$ through B.
5. Extend $\overrightarrow{CB}$. Use Const. 6 to construct a $\perp$ to $\overleftrightarrow{BC}$ through A.

Teaching Note

In Constructions 4 and 5, no plane is given; you create one doing the construction. Constructions 6 and 7 are different in the sense that the given conditions, a line and a point outside the line, determine exactly one plane. Students' comprehension of these ideas will be helpful in discussing the locus problems presented in Lesson 10-6.

Construction 7, which concerns parallel lines, uses corresponding angles. Ask students to design a different construction using alternate interior angles or perpendicular lines.

Additional Answers Classroom Exercises

7. Const. $\overline{DE} \cong \overline{AC}$; const. $\perp$s to $\overline{DE}$ at D and E; mark off $\overline{DG} \cong \overline{AC}$ and $\overline{EF} \cong \overline{AC}$ on the $\perp$s; draw $\overline{FG}$.
8. Const. $\overline{DX} \cong \overline{AC}$; const. the $\perp$ bis. of $\overline{DX}$ to locate the midpt. Y; const. the $\perp$ bis. of $\overline{DY}$ to locate the midpt. E; proceed as in Ex. 7 above.
9. Const. $\overline{DE} \cong \overline{BC}$; const. a $\perp$ to $\overline{DE}$ at D; with center E and radius AC, draw an arc int. the $\perp$ at F. Draw $\overline{EF}$.
10. Draw $\overline{DE}$; const. a $\perp$ to $\overline{DE}$ at D; const. $\overline{DF}$ on the $\perp$ with $DF = 2DE$. Draw $\overline{EF}$.

Exercises 11–13 will analyze the following problem.

Given: Line l; points X and Y

Construct: A circle through Y and tangent to l at X

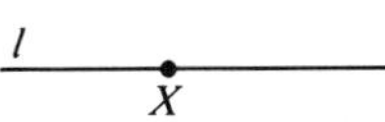

13. Use Const. 5 to const. a ⊥ to l at X; use Const. 4 to const. the ⊥ bis. of $\overline{XY}$; their intersection, O, is the ctr. of the circle; radius = OX (or OY).

If the problem had been solved, we would have a diagram something like the one shown.

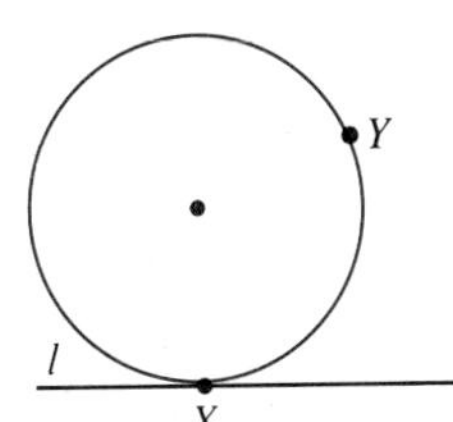

11. Where does the center of the circle lie with respect to line l and point X? **on the ⊥ to l through X**
12. Where does the center of the circle lie with respect to $\overline{XY}$? **on the ⊥ bisector of $\overline{XY}$**
13. Explain how to carry out the construction of the circle. **See above.**

Written Exercises

Draw a figure roughly like the one shown, but larger. Do the indicated construction clearly enough so that your method can be understood easily.

A

1. The perpendicular to l at P **Const. 5**

2. The perpendicular to l from S **Const. 6**

3. The perpendicular bisector of $\overline{JK}$ **Const. 4**

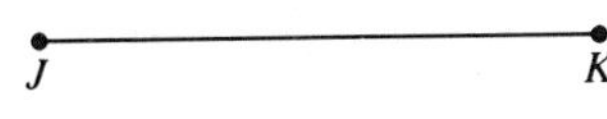

4. The parallel to l through T **Const. 7**

5. The parallel to $\overleftrightarrow{ED}$ through F **Const. 7**

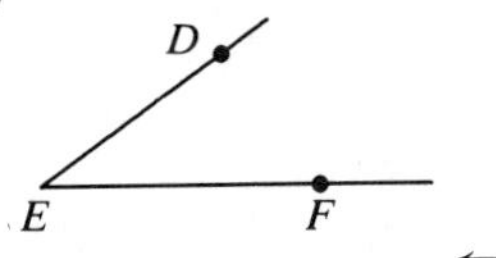

6. The perpendicular to $\overleftrightarrow{BA}$ at A **Const. 5**

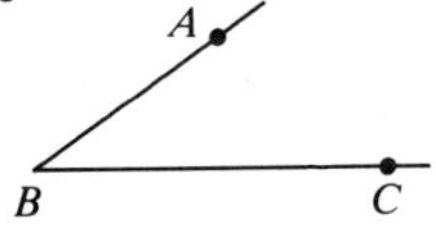

7. The perpendicular to $\overleftrightarrow{HJ}$ from G **Extend $\overrightarrow{HJ}$; Use Const. 6.**

8. A complement of $\angle KMN$

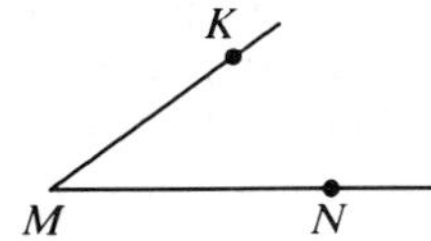

Methods may vary. Example: Draw $\overrightarrow{NM}$. Const. $\overline{PM} \perp \overline{MN}$; $\angle PMK$ is comp. to $\angle KMN$.

Teaching Note

Stress to students that drawing a sketch of the desired construction result may be helpful when doing the construction.

Guided Practice

Draw figures like the ones shown, but larger.

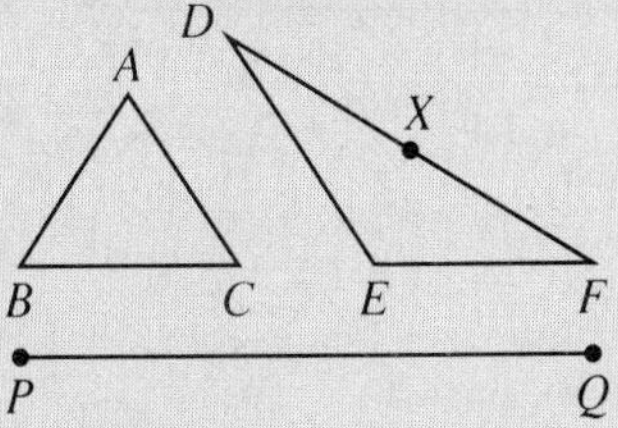

Construct the following:

1. the perpendicular to $\overline{DF}$ at X Const. 5
2. the perpendicular to $\overline{BC}$ from A Const. 6
3. the parallel to $\overleftrightarrow{DF}$ through E Const. 7
4. the perpendicular to $\overleftrightarrow{EF}$ from D Const. 6
5. the perpendicular bisector of $\overline{AC}$ Const. 4
6. the complement of $\angle ACB$ Const. a right angle then subtract $\angle ACB$ using Const. 2.
7. Construct $\overline{JK}$ having length equal to $\frac{1}{4}PQ$. Const. $\overline{JM}$ by bisecting $\overline{PQ}$. Const. $\overline{JK}$ by bisecting $\overline{JM}$.

Construct angles having the indicated measures.

8. 90 Const. 4
9. 30 Const. an equilateral △ and bisect an angle.
10. 120 Const. an equilateral △ and use one of the exterior angles.

Exercise Note

Exs. 14–16 are an important preview of the concurrency theorems in the next lesson.

Before working Exs. 23 and 24 with students, review the Pythagorean Theorem and angles inscribed in a semicircle.

Additional Answers Written Exercises

13. Use Const. 4 to locate the midpt. M of $\overline{AB}$ and the midpt. N of $\overline{AM}$. Const. $\overline{XY} \cong \overline{NB}$.

17. Const. $\triangle DAB$ with $m\angle A = n$, $AB = a$, and $AD = b$; with ctrs. D and B and radii a and b, resp., draw arcs int. at C; draw $\overline{BC}$ and $\overline{DC}$.

18. Methods may vary. Example: Const. 2 ⊥ lines int. at A; mark off $\overline{AB}$ on one line so that $AB = a$, and $\overline{AD}$ on the other line so that $AD = b$; with ctrs. D and B and radii a and b, resp., draw arcs int. at C; draw $\overline{BC}$ and $\overline{DC}$.

20. Const. $\overline{AC}$ so that $AC = a$. Const. j, the ⊥ bis. of $\overline{AC}$ int. $\overline{AC}$ at M. Const. $\overline{MB}$ and $\overline{MD}$, both on j, so that $MB = MD = \frac{1}{2}b$. Draw $ABCD$.

21. Draw a line and const. $\overline{AC}$ so that $AC = b$. Const. the ⊥ bis. of $\overline{AC}$, intersecting $\overline{AC}$ at M. Const. $\overline{MB}$ and $\overline{MD}$ on the ⊥ bis. of $\overline{AC}$ and both ≅ to $\overline{AM}$. Draw $ABCD$.

Construct an angle with the indicated measure. **9–12. Methods may vary.**

9. 45 **10.** 135

11. $22\frac{1}{2}$ **12.** 105

13. Draw a segment $\overline{AB}$. Construct a segment $\overline{XY}$ whose length equals $\frac{3}{4}AB$.

B **14. a.** Draw an acute triangle. Construct the perpendicular bisector of each side. **Const. 4**

b. Do the perpendicular bisectors intersect in one point? **Yes**

c. Repeat parts (a) and (b) using an obtuse triangle. **Const. 4; yes**

15. a. Draw an acute triangle. Construct the three altitudes.

b. Do the lines that contain the altitudes intersect in one point? **Yes**

c. Repeat parts (a) and (b) using an obtuse triangle. **Yes**

16. a. Draw a very large acute triangle. Construct the three medians.

b. Do the lines that contain the medians intersect in one point? **Yes**

c. Repeat parts (a) and (b) using an obtuse triangle. **Yes**

On your paper draw figures roughly like those shown. Use them in constructing the figures described in Exercises 17–24.

17. A parallelogram with an $n°$ angle and sides of lengths a and b

18. A rectangle with sides of lengths a and b

19. A square with perimeter $2a$

20. A rhombus with diagonals of lengths a and b

21. A square with diagonals of length b

22. A segment of length $\sqrt{a^2 + b^2}$

23. A square with diagonals of length $b\sqrt{2}$

24. A right triangle with hypotenuse of length a and one leg of length b

22. Const. 2 ⊥ lines at A; mark off $AB = a$ on one line and $AC = b$ on the other line. Draw $\overline{BC}$.

24. Const. 2 ⊥ lines at A; mark off $AB = b$ on one line; with ctr. B and radius a, draw an arc int. the other line at C. Draw $\overline{BC}$.

C **25.** Draw a segment and let its length be s. Construct a segment whose length is $s\sqrt{3}$.

26. Draw a diagram roughly like the one shown. Without laying your straightedge across any part of the lake, construct more of $\overrightarrow{RS}$.

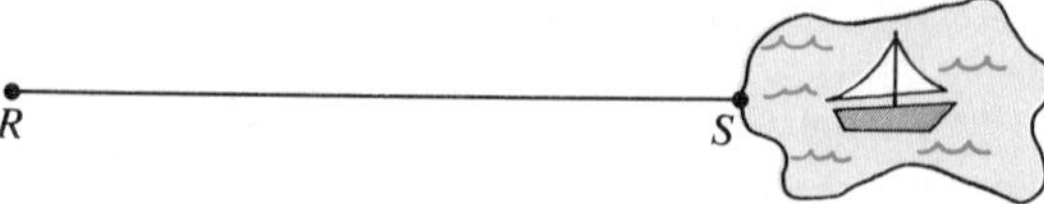

27. Draw three noncollinear points R, S, and T. Construct a triangle whose sides have R, S, and T as midpoints. (*Hint*: How is $\overline{RT}$ related to the side of the triangle that has S as its midpoint?)

28. Draw a segment and let its length be 1.

a. Construct a segment of length $\sqrt{5}$.

b. Construct a segment of length $\frac{1}{2} + \frac{\sqrt{5}}{2}$, or $\frac{1 + \sqrt{5}}{2}$.

c. Construct a *golden rectangle* (as discussed on page 253) whose sides are in the ratio $1 : \frac{1 + \sqrt{5}}{2}$.

Challenge

Given $\overline{AB}$, its midpoint M, and a point Z outside $\overline{AB}$, use only a straightedge (and *no* compass) to construct a line through Z parallel to $\overleftrightarrow{AB}$. (*Hint*: Use Ceva's Theorem, Exercise 33, page 273.)

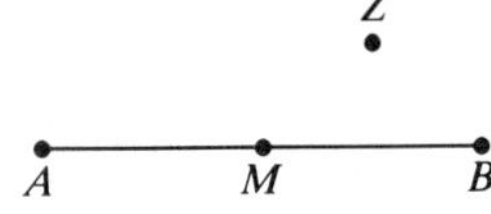

Explorations

These exploratory exercises can be done using a computer with a program that draws and measures geometric figures.

1. Draw any $\triangle ABC$. Draw the bisectors of the angles of the triangle. They should intersect in one point. Draw a perpendicular segment from this point to each of the sides. Measure the length of each perpendicular segment. What do you notice? **The three lengths are equal.**

2. a. Draw any acute $\triangle ABC$. Draw the perpendicular bisector of each side of the triangle. They should intersect in one point. Measure the distance from this point of intersection to each of the vertices of the triangle. What do you notice? **The three distances are equal.**

b. Repeat using an obtuse triangle and a right triangle. Is the same result true for these triangles as well? **Yes**

c. In a right triangle, the perpendicular bisectors of the sides intersect in what point? **the midpoint of the hypotenuse**

3. Draw any $\triangle ABC$. Draw the three medians. They should intersect in one point, as shown in the diagram at the right. Find the ratios $\frac{AG}{AD}$, $\frac{BG}{BE}$, and $\frac{CG}{CF}$. What do you notice?
$\frac{AG}{AD} = \frac{BG}{BE} = \frac{CG}{CF} = \frac{2}{3}$

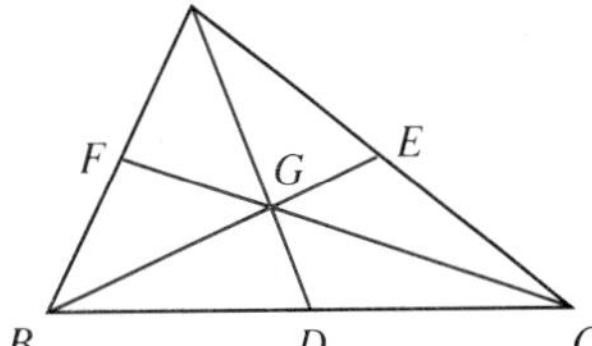

Using a Computer

These exercises explore concurrent lines and introduce the theorems of the next lesson.

Teaching Suggestions, pp. T117–T118

Objective
Presenting the Lesson
Enrichment
Using Technology

Communication Skills, p. T118

Supplementary Materials

Practice Master 57
Test 38
Resource Book, pp. 61–62, 147
Study Guide, pp. 125–126

Lesson Focus

In this lesson, special sets of lines associated with triangles are studied. The interesting fact about these lines is that the lines in each set intersect in a single point.

Suggested Assignments

Minimum
Day 1: 388/1–5
Day 2: 389/6, 8
390/Self-Test 1
391/Mixed Review 1–4

Average
Day 1: 388–389/1–7, 10
S 384/25
Day 2: 389/8, 11–14
390/Self-Test 1
391/Mixed Review 1–4

Maximum
Day 1: 388–389/1–7 odd, 8, 9, 11, 13
Day 2: 389/10, 12, 14–16
S 385/28

10-3 *Concurrent Lines*

When two or more lines intersect in one point, the lines are said to be **concurrent.** For example, as you saw in Exercise 15, page 378, the bisectors of the angles of a triangle are concurrent.

Theorem 10-1

The bisectors of the angles of a triangle intersect in a point that is equidistant from the three sides of the triangle.

Given: $\triangle ABC$; the bisectors of $\angle A$, $\angle B$, and $\angle C$

Prove: The angle bisectors intersect in a point; that point is equidistant from $\overline{AB}$, $\overline{BC}$, and $\overline{AC}$.

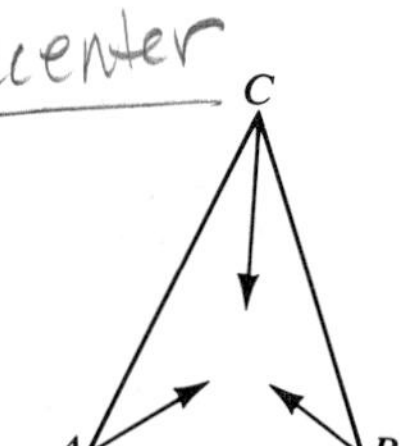

Proof:

The bisectors of $\angle A$ and $\angle B$ intersect at some point I. We will show that point I also lies on the bisector of $\angle C$ and that I is equidistant from $\overline{AB}$, $\overline{BC}$, and $\overline{AC}$.

Draw perpendiculars from I intersecting $\overline{AB}$, $\overline{BC}$, and $\overline{AC}$ at R, S, and T, respectively. Since any point on the bisector of an angle is equidistant from the sides of the angle (Theorem 4-7, page 154), $IT = IR$ and $IR = IS$. Thus $IT = IS$. Since any point equidistant from the sides of an angle is on the bisector of the angle (Theorem 4-8, page 154), I is on the bisector of $\angle C$. Since $IR = IS = IT$, point I is equidistant from $\overline{AB}$, $\overline{BC}$, and $\overline{AC}$.

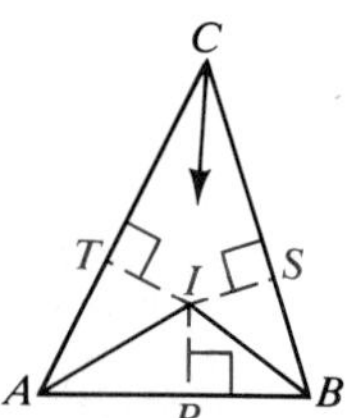

In Exercises 14–16, page 384, you discovered three other sets of concurrent lines related to triangles: the perpendicular bisectors of the sides, the lines containing the altitudes, and the medians. As you can see in the diagrams below, concurrent lines may intersect in a point outside the triangle. The intersection point may also lie on the triangle (see Classroom Exercise 4, page 388).

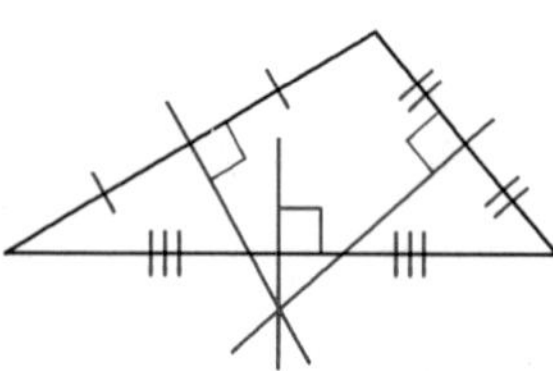

Perpendicular bisectors

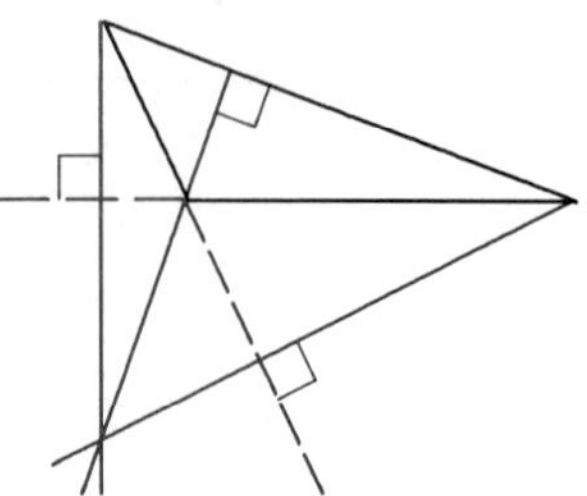

Lines containing altitudes

Theorem 10-2

The perpendicular bisectors of the sides of a triangle intersect in a point that is equidistant from the three vertices of the triangle.

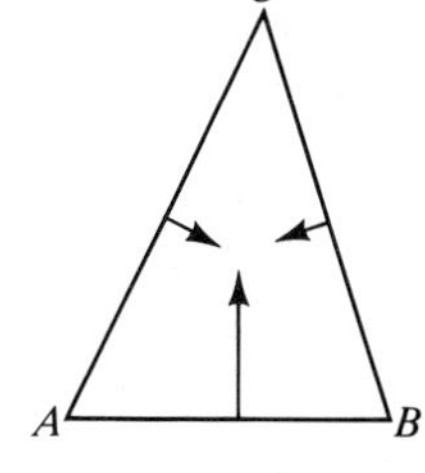

Given: $\triangle ABC$; the $\perp$ bisectors of $\overline{AB}$, $\overline{BC}$, and $\overline{AC}$

Prove: The $\perp$ bisectors intersect in a point; that point is equidistant from A, B, and C.

Proof:

The perpendicular bisectors of $\overline{AC}$ and $\overline{BC}$ intersect at some point O. We will show that point O lies on the perpendicular bisector of $\overline{AB}$ and is equidistant from A, B, and C.

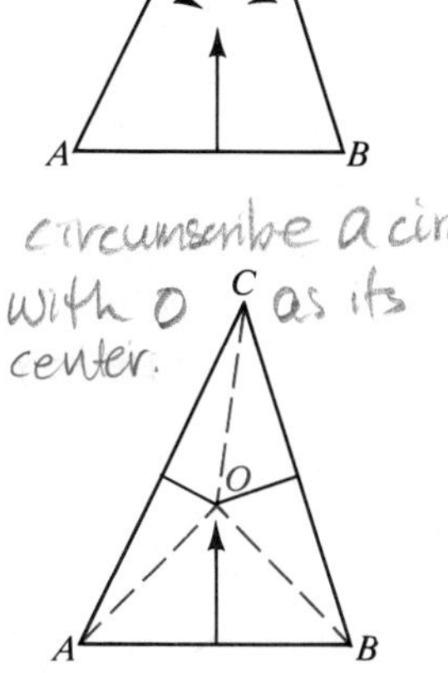

Draw $\overline{OA}$, $\overline{OB}$, and $\overline{OC}$. Since any point on the perpendicular bisector of a segment is equidistant from the endpoints of the segment (Theorem 4-5, page 153), $OA = OC$ and $OC = OB$. Thus $OA = OB$. Since any point equidistant from the endpoints of a segment lies on the perpendicular bisector of the segment (Theorem 4-6, page 153), O is on the perpendicular bisector of $\overline{AB}$. Since $OA = OB = OC$, point O is equidistant from A, B, and C.

The following theorems will be proved in Chapter 13.

Theorem 10-3

The lines that contain the altitudes of a triangle intersect in a point.

Theorem 10-4

The medians of a triangle intersect in a point that is two thirds of the distance from each vertex to the midpoint of the opposite side.

According to Theorem 10-4, if $\overline{AM}$, $\overline{BN}$, and $\overline{CO}$ are medians of $\triangle ABC$, then:

$$AX = \tfrac{2}{3}AM$$
$$XN = \tfrac{1}{3}BN$$
$$CX:XO:CO = 2:1:3$$

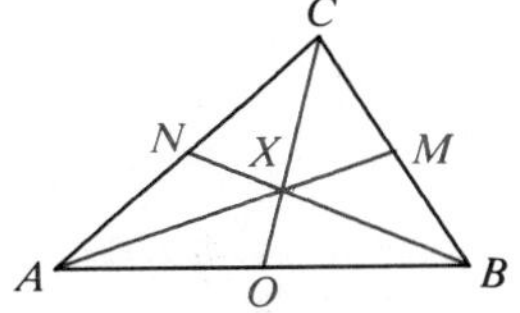

The points of intersection described in the theorems in this section are sometimes called the *incenter* (point where the angle bisectors meet), *circumcenter* (point where the perpendicular bisectors meet), *orthocenter* (point where the altitudes meet), and *centroid* (point where the medians meet).

Teaching Note

The proofs of Theorems 10-3 and 10-4 are involved and quite long when done in two-column form. For this reason, these two theorems are proved in Chapter 13 using coordinate geometry.

Chalkboard Examples

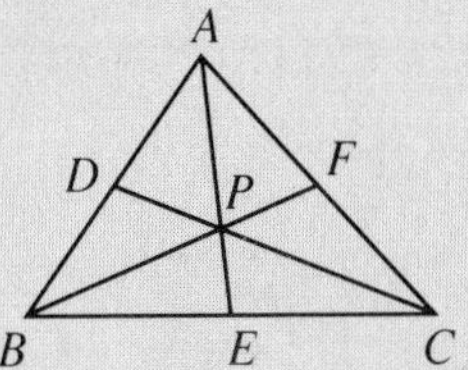

$\overline{AE}$, $\overline{BF}$, and $\overline{DC}$ are medians of $\triangle ABC$.

1. If $BF = 12$, then $PF = \underline{4}$ and $BP = \underline{8}$.
2. If $DC = 15$, then $DP = \underline{5}$ and $PC = \underline{10}$.
3. Describe the location of the incenter in an obtuse triangle. interior of $\triangle$
4. Describe the location of the orthocenter in:
   a. an acute $\triangle$. inside the $\triangle$
   b. a right $\triangle$. vertex of the right angle
   c. an obtuse $\triangle$. outside the $\triangle$
5. Can the incenter, circumcenter, and orthocenter ever be the same point? yes, in an equilateral $\triangle$

Using a Computer

See page T118 for an experiment that reveals a relationship between the incenter, circumcenter, orthocenter, and centroid.

Additional Answers Classroom Exercises

6.a. $\overline{XY} \parallel \overline{RS}$, $XY = \frac{1}{2}RS$; Thm. 5-11
b. $\overline{KJ} \parallel \overline{RS}$, $KJ = \frac{1}{2}RS$; Thm. 5-11
c. $\overline{KJ} \parallel \overline{XY}$, $KJ = XY$; 2 lines ∥ to a third line are ∥; Substitution
d. ▱; If one pair of opp. sides of a quad. are ≅ and ∥, the quad. is a ▱.
e. Diags. of a ▱ bisect each other.
f. $RX = XG = GJ = \frac{1}{3}RJ$, $RX + XG = RG = \frac{2}{3}RJ$

Guided Practice

1. Describe a triangle that satisfies the conditions.
a. The point where the ⊥ bisectors meet is outside the triangle. obtuse △
b. The point where the medians meet is on an angle bisector. isosceles △
c. The point where the altitudes meet is on the triangle. right △

2. In △*ABC*, the medians are shown. Find the values of *x*, *y*, and *z*. 6, 10, 8

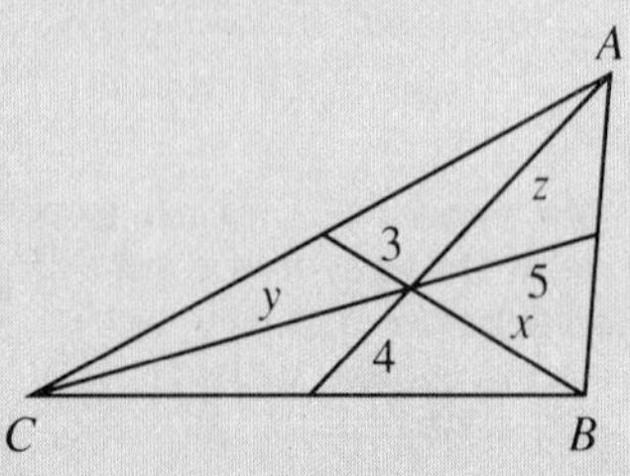

Classroom Exercises

1. Draw, if possible, a triangle in which the perpendicular bisectors of the sides intersect in a point with the location described. **Answers may vary. Examples:**
a. A point inside the triangle **acute** **b.** A point outside the triangle **obtuse**
c. A point on the triangle **right**

2. Repeat Exercise 1, but work with angle bisectors. **a. any △ b, c. not poss.**

3. Is there some kind of triangle such that the perpendicular bisector of each side is also an angle bisector, a median, and an altitude? **equilateral**

4. △*JAM* is a right triangle.

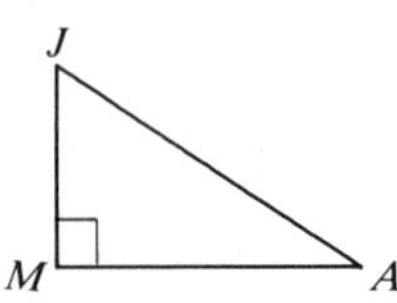

a. Is $\overline{JM}$ an altitude of △*JAM*? **Yes**
b. Name another altitude shown. $\overline{AM}$
c. In what point do the three altitudes of △*JAM* meet? ***M***
d. Where do the perpendicular bisectors of the sides of △*JAM* meet? **at the midpoint of** $\overline{JA}$
e. Does your answer to (d) agree with Theorem 10-2? **Yes**

5. The medians of △*DEF* are shown. Find the lengths indicated.

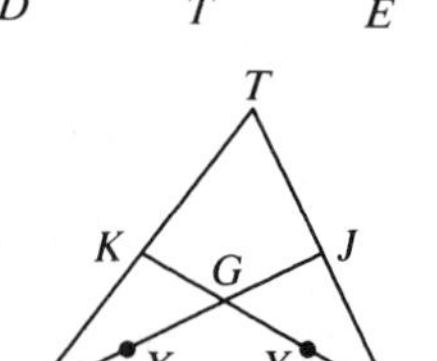

a. $EP = \underline{\ ?\ }$ **10** **b.** $PR = \underline{\ ?\ }$ **4**
c. If $FT = 9$, then $PT = \underline{\ ?\ }$ and $FP = \underline{\ ?\ }$. **3, 6**

6. Given: $\overline{RJ}$ and $\overline{SK}$ are medians of △*RST*;
X and *Y* are the midpoints of $\overline{RG}$ and $\overline{SG}$.
a. How are $\overline{XY}$ and $\overline{RS}$ related? Why?
b. How are $\overline{KJ}$ and $\overline{RS}$ related? Why?
c. How are $\overline{KJ}$ and $\overline{XY}$ related? Why?
d. What special kind of quadrilateral is *XYJK*? Why?
e. Why does $XG = GJ$?
f. Explain why $RG = \frac{2}{3}RJ$.

Written Exercises

A

1. Draw a triangle such that the lines containing the three altitudes intersect in a point with the location described. **a. any acute △**
a. A point inside the triangle **b.** A point outside the triangle **any obtuse △**
c. A point on the triangle **any right △**

Exercises 2–5 refer to the diagram in which the medians of a triangle are shown.

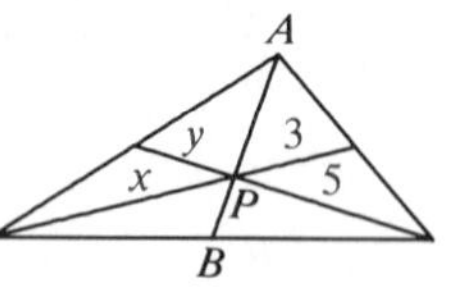

2. Find the values of *x* and *y*. $x = 6$; $y = 2\frac{1}{2}$
3. If $AB = 6$, then $BP = \underline{\ ?\ }$ and $AP = \underline{\ ?\ }$. **2, 4**
4. If $AB = 7$, then $BP = \underline{\ ?\ }$ and $AP = \underline{\ ?\ }$.
5. If $PB = 1.9$, then $AP = \underline{\ ?\ }$ and $AB = \underline{\ ?\ }$.

4. $\frac{7}{3}, \frac{14}{3}$ **5.** 3.8, 5.7

6. Use a ruler and a protractor to draw a regular pentagon. Then construct the perpendicular bisectors of the five sides. **Const. 4**

7. Draw a regular pentagon as in Exercise 6. Construct the angle bisectors. **Const. 3**

8. Draw any large $\triangle ABC$ and construct equilateral triangles on each of the sides as shown.
   a. In each of the three equilateral triangles, construct any two medians and find their point of intersection.
   b. Draw the three segments connecting these three points of intersection.
   c. What appears to be true about the triangle you drew in part (b)? **The 3 seg. form an equilateral △.**

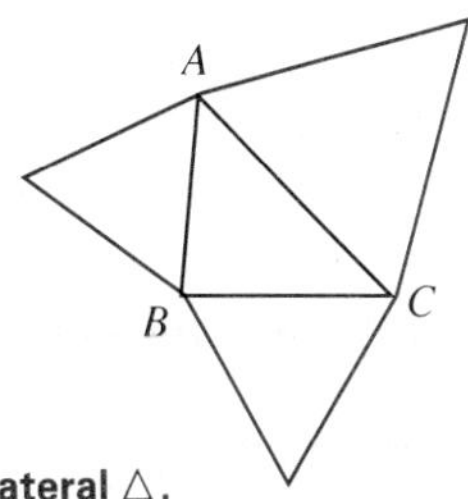

B

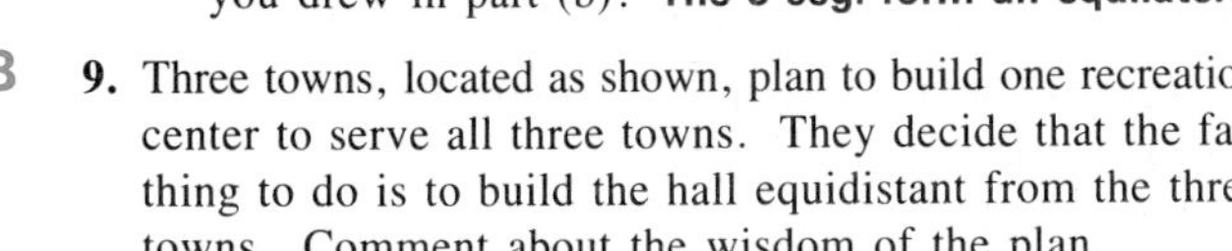

9. Three towns, located as shown, plan to build one recreation center to serve all three towns. They decide that the fair thing to do is to build the hall equidistant from the three towns. Comment about the wisdom of the plan.

•X •Y •Z

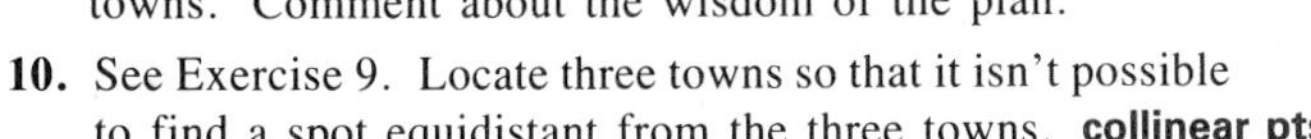

10. See Exercise 9. Locate three towns so that it isn't possible to find a spot equidistant from the three towns. **collinear pts.**

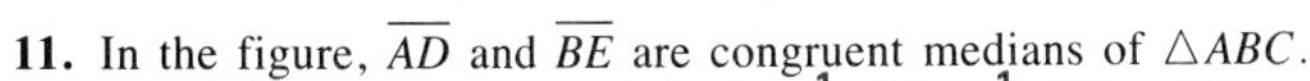

11. In the figure, $\overline{AD}$ and $\overline{BE}$ are congruent medians of $\triangle ABC$.
   a. Explain why $GD = GE$. $\boldsymbol{GD = \frac{1}{3} \cdot AD = \frac{1}{3} \cdot BE = GE}$
   b. $GA =$ __?__ **GB**
   c. Name three angles congruent to $\angle GAB$. **∠GBA, ∠GED, ∠GDE**

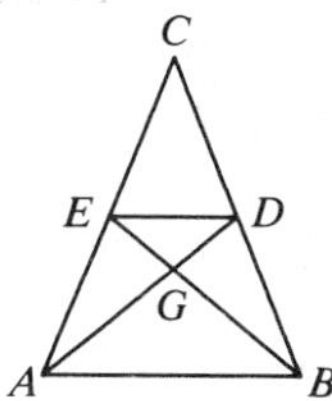

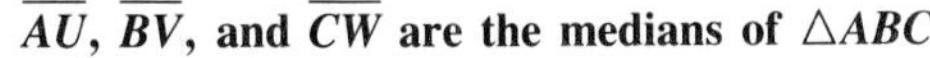

$\overline{AU}$, $\overline{BV}$, and $\overline{CW}$ are the medians of $\triangle ABC$.

12. If $AP = x^2$ and $PU = 2x$, then $x =$ __?__. **4**

13. If $BP = y^2 + 1$ and $PV = y + 2$, then $y =$ __?__ or $y =$ __?__. **3, −1**

14. If $CW = 2z^2 - 5z - 12$ and $CP = z^2 - 15$, then $z =$ __?__ and $PW =$ __?__. **7, 17**

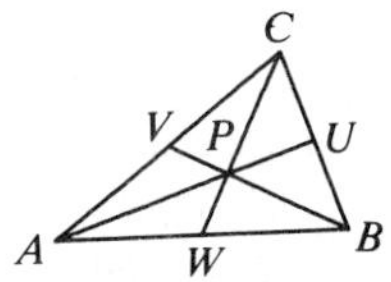

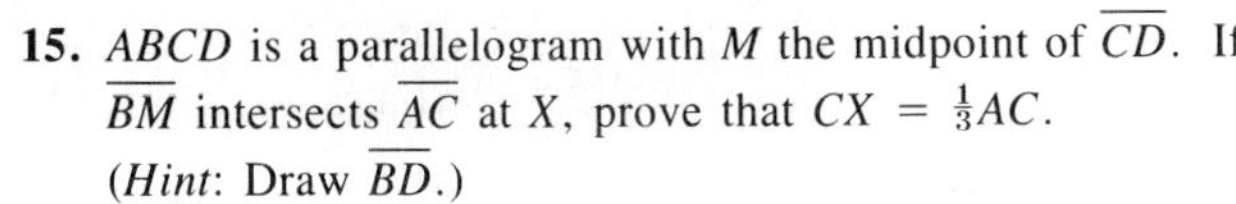

15. $ABCD$ is a parallelogram with M the midpoint of $\overline{CD}$. If $\overline{BM}$ intersects $\overline{AC}$ at X, prove that $CX = \frac{1}{3}AC$. (*Hint*: Draw $\overline{BD}$.)

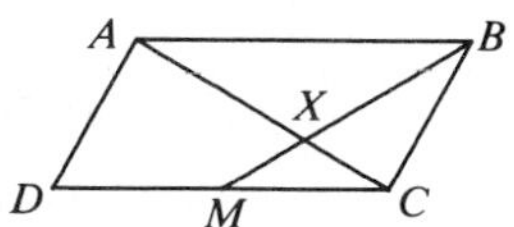

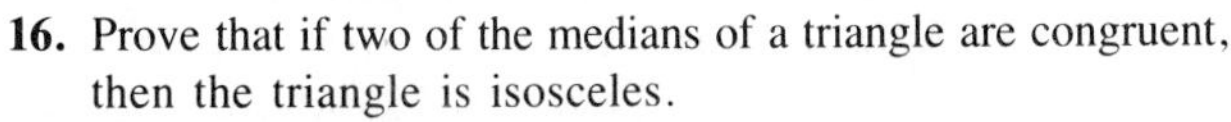

16. Prove that if two of the medians of a triangle are congruent, then the triangle is isosceles.

C

17. In the plane figure, point P is equidistant from R, S, and T. Describe the location of the following points in the plane. **a. pts. in the interior of ∠XPY**
   a. Points farther from both R and S than from T
   b. Points closer to both R and S than to T
   pts. in the int. of the ∠ vertical to ∠XPY

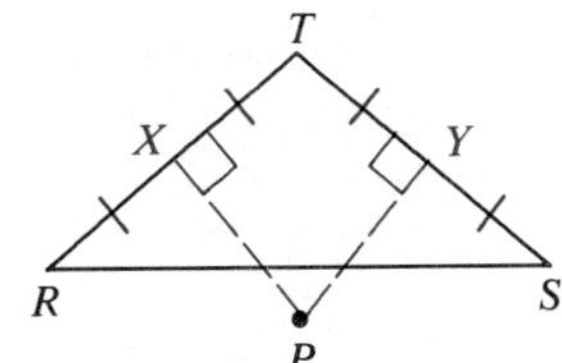

3. Draw a large acute $\triangle ABC$ and construct the point where the ⊥ bisectors meet. Const. the 3 ⊥ bisectors. Const. 4

4. Draw a large acute $\triangle ABC$ and construct the point where the altitudes meet. Const. the 3 altitudes. Const. 6

Using a Computer

Exs. 1, 6–8 can be done using a construction program.

Exercise Note

Encourage students to try Exs. 6 and 7 with nonregular pentagons. Ex. 17 provides a good opportunity to preview locus.

Additional Answers Written Exercises

9. The point of intersection of the ⊥ bis. of $\overline{XY}$, $\overline{XZ}$, and $\overline{YZ}$ is equidistant from all 3 towns. It would be wiser to build it equidistant from X and Z, near Y.

Additional Answers Self-Test 1

2. Draw $\overline{ST}$. With centers S and T, and radius ST, draw arcs int. at R. Draw $\overrightarrow{SR}$; $m\angle RST = 60$. Use Const. 3.
5. Construct $\overline{JK}$ such that $JK = 2AB$ (Const. 1). Construct lines $\perp$ to $\overline{JK}$ at J and K. Construct $\overline{JM} \cong \overline{KL} \cong \overline{AB}$. Draw $\overline{ML}$. (Other methods are possible.)

Quick Quiz

1. Draw any $\overline{AB}$ and construct the midpoint of $\overline{AB}$. Const. 4
2. Construct a 30° angle. Construct an equilateral $\triangle$ and bisect one angle.
3. Construct $\overline{AD}$, an altitude of acute $\triangle ABC$. Const. 6
4. Given point P not on $\overleftrightarrow{XY}$, construct $\overleftrightarrow{PQ} \parallel \overleftrightarrow{XY}$. Const. 7
5. Draw any $\overline{AB}$. Construct a square with each side having length AB. Draw a line and mark off $\overline{DE} \cong \overline{AB}$. Const. $\perp$s to $\overline{DE}$ at D and at E. Mark off $\overline{DC}$ on one $\perp$, $\cong$ to $\overline{AB}$, and mark off $\overline{EF}$ on the other $\perp$, $\cong$ to $\overline{AB}$. Draw $\overline{CF}$.
6. Right $\triangle ABC$, with right angle at C, has legs 10. The medians intersect at X. $CX = \frac{10\sqrt{2}}{3}$

Self-Test 1

1. Draw any $\overline{CD}$. Construct the perpendicular bisector of $\overline{CD}$. **Const. 4**
2. Construct a 60° angle, $\angle RST$, and its bisector, $\overrightarrow{SQ}$.
3. Draw a large acute $\triangle ABC$. Then construct altitude $\overline{AD}$ from vertex A. **Const. 6**
4. Draw line t and choose any point P that is not on line t. Construct $\overleftrightarrow{PQ} \parallel t$. **Const. 7**
5. Draw any $\overline{AB}$. Construct rectangle $JKLM$ so that $JK = 2AB$ and $KL = AB$.
6. Name four types of concurrent lines, rays, or segments that are associated with triangles. **lines containing the altitudes, medians, $\angle$ bis., $\perp$ bis. of the sides**
7. The perpendicular bisectors of the sides of a right triangle intersect in a point located at __?__. **the midpoint of the hypotenuse**
8. The medians of equilateral $\triangle ABC$ intersect at point X. If $\overline{AD}$ is a median and $AB = 12$, then $AX =$ __?__ and $XD =$ __?__. **$4\sqrt{3}$, $2\sqrt{3}$**

Application — *Center of Gravity*

The *center of gravity* of an object is the point where the weight of the object is focused. If you lift or support an object, you can do this most easily under its center of gravity.

A mobile is either hung or supported at its center of gravity. In planning a mobile, a sculptor must take into account the centers of gravity of the component parts.

If an object is not supported under its center of gravity, it becomes unstable. Suppose you hold a heavy bar in one hand. If you support it near the center of gravity, it will be easy to hold (Figure 1). To support it at one end requires more effort (Figure 2), since the pole tends to turn until the center of gravity is directly below the point of support (Figure 3).

The center of gravity may be inside an object or outside of it. The center of gravity of an ice cube is in the middle of the ice, but the center of gravity of an automobile tire is not in a part of the tire itself.

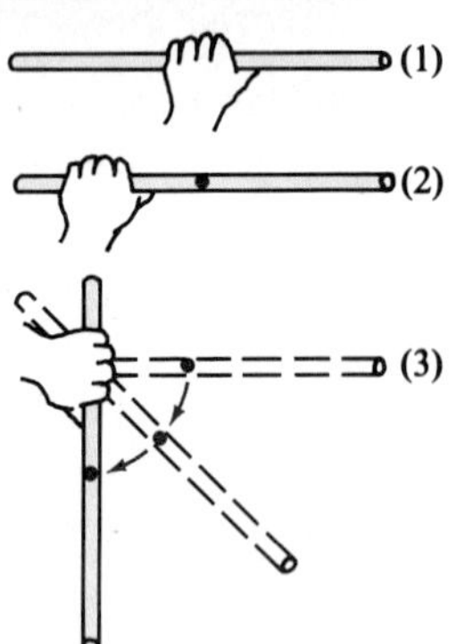

Exercises

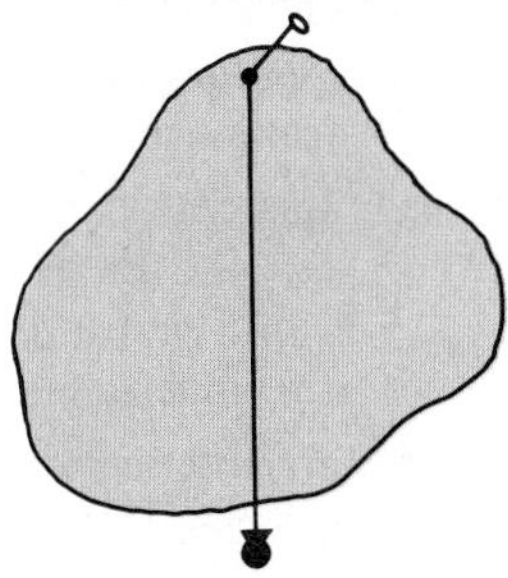

1. For this experiment, cut out a large, irregularly shaped piece of cardboard.
   a. Near the edge, poke a hole just large enough to allow the cardboard to rotate freely when pinned through the hole.
   b. Pin the cardboard through the hole to a suitable wall surface. The piece of cardboard will position itself so that its center of gravity is as low as possible. This means that it will lie on a vertical line through the point of suspension. To find this line, tie a weighted string to the pin. Then draw on the cardboard the line determined by the string.
   c. Repeat parts (a) and (b) but use a different hole. The center of gravity of the cardboard ought to lie on both of the lines you have drawn and should therefore be their point of intersection. The cardboard should balance if supported at this point.

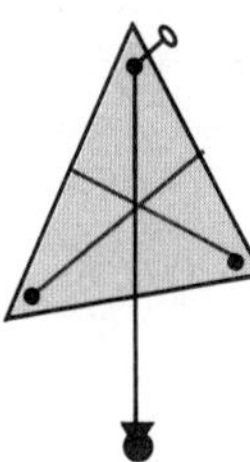

2. Cut out a piece of cardboard in the shape of a large scalene triangle.
   a. Follow the steps of Exercise 1 using three holes, one near each of the three vertices.
   b. If you worked carefully, all three lines drawn intersect in one point, the center of gravity of the cardboard. This point is also referred to as the *center of mass* or the *centroid* of the cardboard. Study the lines you have drawn and explain why in geometry the point of intersection of the medians of a triangle is called the *centroid of the triangle*. **The lines drawn are the medians of the △.**

3. Do you think that the center of gravity of a parallelogram is the point where the diagonals intersect? Use the technique of Exercise 1 to test this idea. **Yes**

Mixed Review Exercises

$\overline{AB}$ is tangent to ⊙*O* at *B*. Complete.

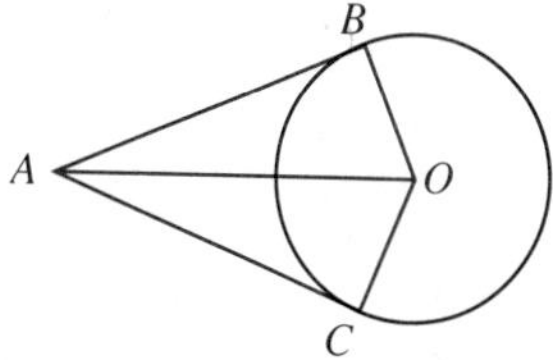

1. If the radius of ⊙*O* is 5 and $AO = 13$, then $AB =$ _?_. **12**
2. If $m\angle ACO = 90$ and $AB = 10$, then $\overline{AC}$ is _?_ to ⊙*O* at *C* and $AC =$ _?_. **tangent, 10**
3. A triangle circumscribed about a circle intersects the circle in how many points? **3**
4. Quad. *QRST* is inscribed in a circle. If $m\angle Q = 39$, find $m\angle S$. **141**

Using a Computer

In this Exploration, students construct inscribed and circumscribed circles. They find the incenter and circumcenter of a triangle. See page T118 for a related experiment.

Teaching Suggestions, pp. T118–T119

Objectives
Presenting the Lesson

Supplementary Materials

Study Guide, pp. 127–128

Lesson Focus

The purpose of this lesson is to study how to do two constructions involving tangents to circles and two others involving circles and triangles.

Suggested Assignments

Minimum
Day 1: 395/1–3, 6, 9
Day 2: 395/5, 8, 10, 11, 14

Average
395/1–3, 5, 6, 10, 11, 13, 15

Maximum
395/5, 6, 9–11, 13, 16–18

Explorations

These exploratory exercises can be done using a computer with a program that draws and measures geometric figures.

1. Inscribe a circle D inside a $\triangle ABC$. Draw $\overline{DA}$, $\overline{DB}$, and $\overline{DC}$. Compare the measures of $\angle ABD$ and $\angle ABC$, $\angle ACD$ and $\angle ACB$, $\angle BAD$ and $\angle BAC$. What do you notice? What type of lines intersect at the center of a circle inscribed in a triangle? **$m\angle ABD = \frac{1}{2}m\angle ABC$, and so on; $\angle$ bis.**
2. Circumscribe a circle D about a $\triangle ABC$. Draw perpendicular segments from D to $\overline{AB}$, $\overline{BC}$, and $\overline{CA}$, intersecting the sides at E, F, and G, respectively. Compare the lengths of $\overline{AE}$ and $\overline{AB}$, $\overline{BF}$ and $\overline{BC}$, and $\overline{CG}$ and $\overline{CA}$. What do you notice? What type of lines intersect at the center of a circle circumscribed about a triangle? **$AE = \frac{1}{2}AB$, and so on; the $\perp$ bis. of the sides**

More Constructions

Objectives

1. Perform seven additional basic constructions.
2. Use the basic constructions in original construction exercises.

10-4 *Circles*

Construction 8

Given a point on a circle, construct the tangent to the circle at the given point.

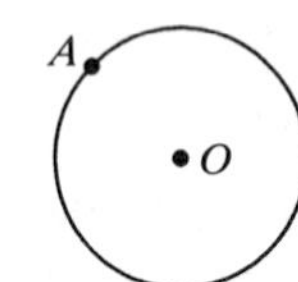

Given: Point A on $\odot O$

Construct: The tangent to $\odot O$ at A

Procedure:

1. Draw $\overrightarrow{OA}$.
2. Construct the line perpendicular to $\overrightarrow{OA}$ at A. Call it t.

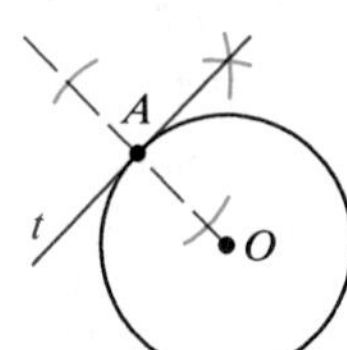

Line t is tangent to $\odot O$ at A.

Justification: Because t is perpendicular to radius $\overline{OA}$ at A, t is tangent to $\odot O$.

Construction 9

Given a point outside a circle, construct a tangent to the circle from the given point.

Given: Point P outside $\odot O$

Construct: A tangent to $\odot O$ from P

Procedure:

1. Draw $\overline{OP}$.
2. Find the midpoint M of $\overline{OP}$ by constructing the perpendicular bisector of $\overline{OP}$.
3. Using M as center and MP as radius, draw a circle that intersects $\odot O$ in a point X.
4. Draw $\overrightarrow{PX}$.

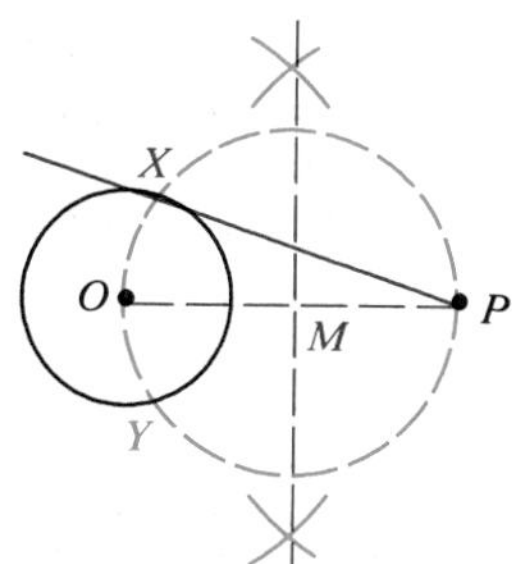

$\overrightarrow{PX}$ is tangent to $\odot O$ from P. $\overrightarrow{PY}$, not drawn, is the other tangent from P.

Justification: If you draw $\overline{OX}$, $\angle OXP$ is inscribed in a semicircle. Then $\angle OXP$ is a right angle and $\overrightarrow{PX} \perp \overline{OX}$. Because $\overrightarrow{PX}$ is perpendicular to radius $\overline{OX}$ at its outer endpoint, $\overrightarrow{PX}$ is tangent to $\odot O$.

Construction 10

Given a triangle, circumscribe a circle about the triangle.

Given: $\triangle ABC$

Construct: A circle passing through A, B, and C

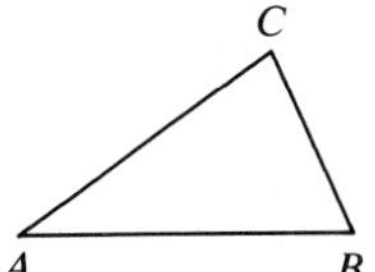

Procedure:

1. Construct the perpendicular bisectors of any two sides of $\triangle ABC$. Label the point of intersection O.
2. Using O as center and OA as radius, draw a circle.

Circle O passes through A, B, and C.

Justification: See Theorem 10-2 on page 387.

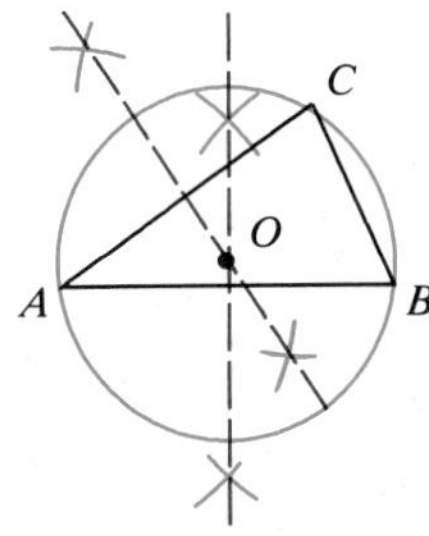

Teaching Note

When introducing Constructions 8 and 9, ask students what fact or facts about tangents might be useful in constructing tangents to circles. They should respond that a tangent to a circle is perpendicular to the radius drawn to the point of tangency.

Chalkboard Examples

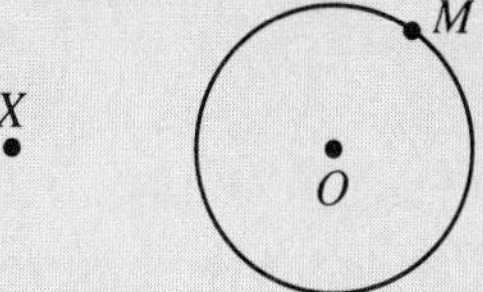

Use the given figure to do the indicated constructions.

1. a tangent line at M Const. 8
2. a pair of parallel tangents Use Const. 8 to create a tangent line at M. Extend $\overline{MO}$ to intersect the circle at P. Then use Const. 8 at point P.
3. two tangents that intersect at point X Use Const. 9 twice.
4. two perpendicular tangents, one through point M Use Const. 8 to create a line k tangent at M. Use Const. 7 to const. $\overleftrightarrow{OP} \parallel$ *to* k int. $\odot O$ at P. Use Const. 8 at P.
5. an isosceles triangle with legs tangent to $\odot O$ Use Const. 9 twice.

Construction 11

Given a triangle, inscribe a circle in the triangle.

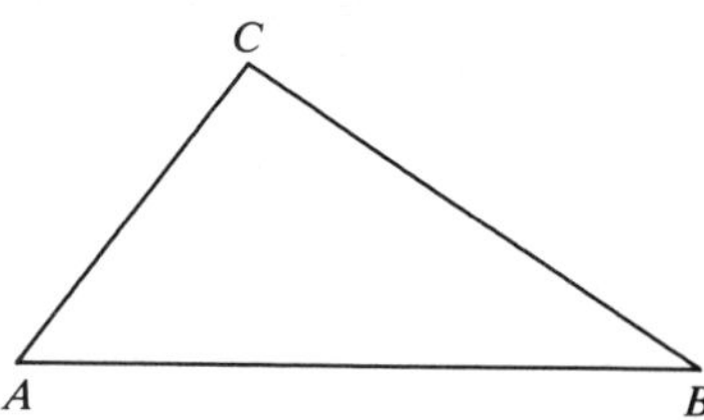

Given: $\triangle ABC$

Construct: A circle tangent to $\overline{AB}$, $\overline{BC}$, and $\overline{AC}$

Procedure:

1. Construct the bisectors of $\angle A$ and $\angle B$. Label the point of intersection I.
2. Construct a perpendicular from I to $\overline{AB}$, intersecting $\overline{AB}$ at a point R.
3. Using I as center and IR as radius, draw a circle.

Circle I is tangent to $\overline{AB}$, $\overline{BC}$, and $\overline{AC}$.

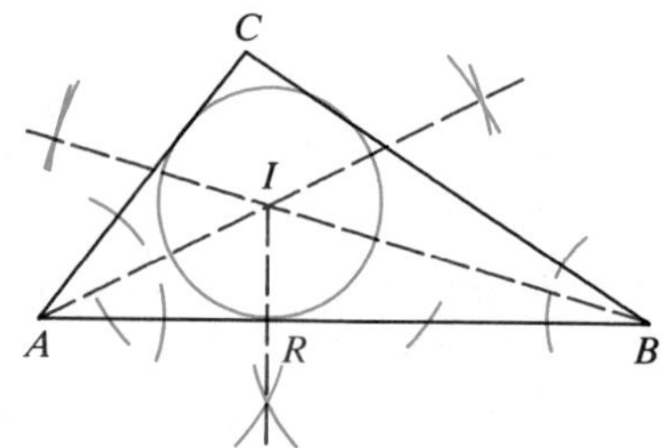

Justification: See Theorem 10-1 on page 386.

1. Const. the ⊥ bis., *k*, of $\overline{AB}$. The ctr. of the ⊙ is on *k* since the ctr. is equidistant from *A* and *B*, so *k* contains a diameter of the ⊙. *k* bisects $\overset{\frown}{AB}$.

Teaching Note

The diagram next to the proof of Theorem 10-1 (page 386) can be used to introduce Construction 11. In Construction 11, students are often tempted to estimate the radius of the inscribed circle by sight rather than by constructing a perpendicular segment to one of the sides of the triangle. Be sure students understand that estimation is not acceptable in geometric construction.

Classroom Exercises

1. Explain how to find the midpoint of $\overset{\frown}{AB}$. **See above.**

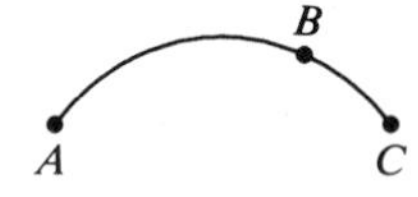

2. Explain how to construct the center of the circle containing points A, B, and C. **Const. the ⊥ bis. of 2 chords. They int. at the ctr. of the ⊙.**

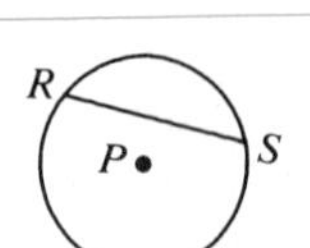

3. Explain how to find the line described.
   a. Parallel to $\overline{RS}$ and passing through P **Const. 7**
   b. Parallel to $\overline{RS}$ and tangent to $\odot P$ **See below.**

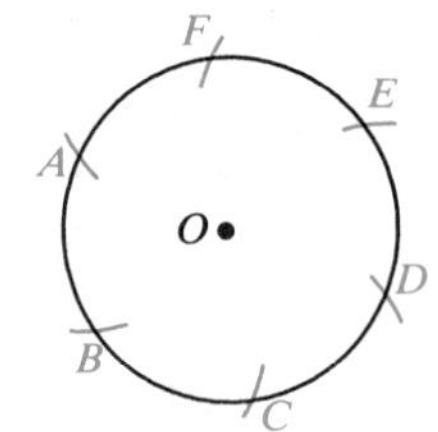

4. Here you see a common method for using just one compass setting for drawing a circle and dividing the circle into six congruent arcs. Explain how the method works.
5. Suppose a circle is given. Explain how you can use the method of Exercise 4 to inscribe an equilateral triangle in the circle.
6. Suppose the construction of Exercise 4 has been carried out. Explain how you can then inscribe a regular twelve-sided polygon in the circle. **Methods may vary.**

3. b. Const. a ⊥ to $\overline{RS}$ through *P* int. ⊙*P* at *Q*. Const. a ∥ to $\overline{RS}$ through *Q* (or a ⊥ to $\overline{PQ}$ through *Q*).

Additional Answers Classroom Exercises

4. Let r = radius; choose A on $\odot O$ and mark off an arc with center A and radius r, int. $\odot O$ at B. Continue the process. Six equilateral △ have been constructed. $\overline{AB} \cong \overline{BC}$, and so on. Since ≅ chords have ≅ arcs, the ⊙ is divided into 6 ≅ arcs.
5. Draw $\triangle AEC$; $\overset{\frown}{AE} \cong \overset{\frown}{AC} \cong \overset{\frown}{CE}$, so $\angle A \cong \angle E \cong \angle C$; hence, $\triangle AEC$ is equiangular and equilateral. Similarly, for $\triangle FBD$.
6. Const. ⊥s from the center to $\overline{AB}$, $\overline{BC}$, and so forth, int. the chords at U, V, W, X, Y, and Z. The ⊙ is divided into 12 ≅ arcs. Since ≅ arcs have ≅ chords, $AUBVCWDXEYFZ$ is a reg. 12-sided polygon.

7. A student intends to inscribe a circle in $\triangle RST$. The center I has been found as shown. How should the student find the radius needed?

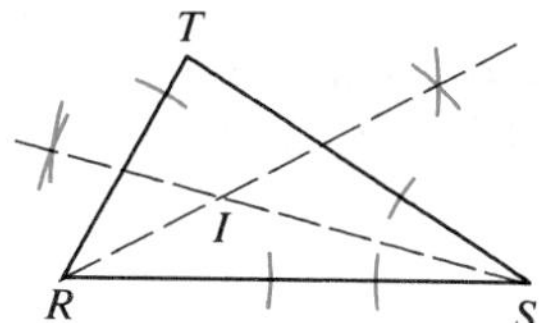
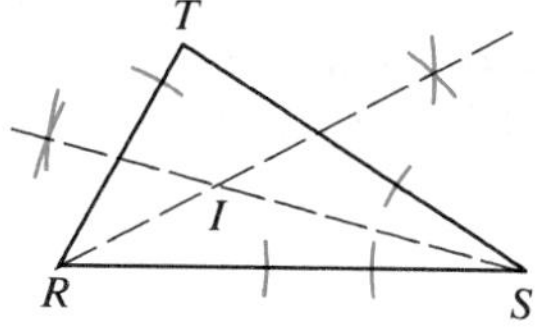

Written Exercises

In Exercises 1 and 2 draw a diagram similar to the one shown, but larger.

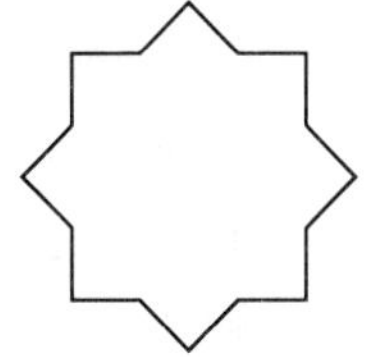

A 1. Construct a tangent at A. **Const. 8**

2. Construct two tangents from P. **Const. 9**

3. Draw a large acute triangle. Construct the circumscribed circle. **Const. 10**

4. Construct a large right triangle. Construct the circumscribed circle. **Const. 10**

5. Draw a large obtuse triangle. Construct the circumscribed circle. **Const. 10**

6. Draw a large acute triangle. Construct the inscribed circle.

7. Construct a large right triangle. Construct the inscribed circle.

8. Draw a large obtuse triangle. Construct the inscribed circle.

} **Const. 11**

B 9. Draw a circle. Inscribe an equilateral triangle in the circle.

10. Draw a circle. Inscribe a square in the circle.

11. a. Draw a circle. Inscribe a regular octagon in the circle.
 b. How would you use your construction in part (a) to create an eight-pointed star as shown at the right?

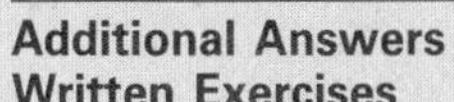

Ex. 11(b)

12. Draw a circle. Circumscribe a square about the circle.

13. Construct a square. Circumscribe a circle about the square.

14. Construct a square. Inscribe a circle in the square.

15. Draw a circle. Circumscribe an equilateral triangle about the circle.

In each of Exercises 16 and 17 begin with a diagram roughly like the one shown, but larger.

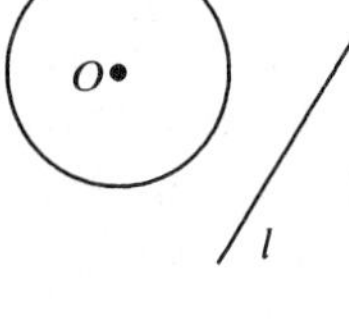

16. Construct a line that is parallel to line l and tangent to $\odot O$. **See below.**

17. Construct a line that is perpendicular to line l and tangent to $\odot O$. **Const. a ∥ to l through O, int. $\odot O$ at P. Const. a tan. to $\odot O$ at P.**

C 18. Construct three congruent circles, each tangent to the other two circles. Then construct an equilateral triangle, each side of which is tangent to two of the circles.

16. Const. a ⊥ to l through O, int. $\odot O$ at P. Const. a tan. to $\odot O$ at P.

Additional Answers Classroom Exercises

7. Const. a ⊥ from I to any one of the sides of $\triangle RST$. The length of the ⊥ is the radius of the circle.

Guided Practice

1. Construct a tangent to a circle at a point on the circle. Const. 8
2. Construct two tangents to a circle from an outside point. Const. 9
3. Draw a large scalene triangle and construct the circumscribed circle. Const. 10
4. Draw a large isosceles triangle and construct the circumscribed circle. Const. 10
5. Draw a scalene triangle and construct the inscribed circle. Const. 11

Additional Answers Written Exercises

10. Draw $\odot O$ and diam. $\overline{AC}$. Const. the ⊥ bis. of $\overline{AC}$, intersecting $\odot O$ at B and D. Draw $\overline{AB}$, $\overline{BC}$, $\overline{CD}$, $\overline{AD}$.

12. Draw $\odot O$ and diam. $\overline{AC}$. Const. the ⊥ bis. of $\overline{AC}$ intersecting $\odot O$ at B and D. Const. tans. to $\odot O$ at A, B, C, and D intersecting at E, F, G, and H.

14. Draw the diags. of the square, intersecting at O. Const. the ⊥ bis. of one side of the square, intersecting the side at M. Draw the ⊙ with center O, radius $\overline{OM}$.

Exercise Note

Encourage students to make sketches before they attempt solutions to Exs. 19–21.

Teaching Suggestions,
p. T119

Objectives
Presenting the Lesson
Making Connections
Extension

Supplementary Materials

Practice Master 58

Test 39

Resource Book, pp. 63–64, 148

Study Guide, pp. 129–130

Lesson Focus

In this lesson, three constructions are developed that involve working with line segments. These are the last three constructions presented in the chapter.

Suggested Assignments

Minimum
Day 1: 399/1–4
Day 2: 399/5, 6, 7, 9
401/Self-Test 2

Average
Day 1: 399/1, 3, 5–8
S 395/16
Day 2: 399/9–13, 15
401/Self-Test 2

Maximum
Day 1: 399/3, 6, 7, 9–11
S 396/19, 20
Day 2: 399/12, 14–17

In Exercises 19–21 begin with two circles P and Q such that $\odot P$ and $\odot Q$ do not intersect and Q is not inside $\odot P$. Let the radii of $\odot P$ and $\odot Q$ be p and q respectively, with $p > q$.

19. Construct a circle, with radius equal to PQ, that is tangent to $\odot P$ and $\odot Q$.

20. Construct a common external tangent to $\odot P$ and $\odot Q$. One method is suggested below.

1. Draw a circle with center P and radius $p - q$.
2. Construct a tangent to this circle from Q, and call the point of tangency Z.
3. Draw $\overrightarrow{PZ}$. $\overrightarrow{PZ}$ intersects $\odot P$ in a point X.
4. With center X and radius ZQ, draw an arc that intersects $\odot Q$ in a point Y.
5. Draw $\overleftrightarrow{XY}$.

As a justification for this construction, you could begin by drawing $\overline{QY}$. Then show that $XZQY$ is a rectangle. The rest of the justification is easy.

21. Construct a common internal tangent to $\odot P$ and $\odot Q$. (*Hint*: Draw a circle with center P and radius $p + q$.)

10-5 *Special Segments*

Construction 12

Given a segment, divide the segment into a given number of congruent parts. (3 shown)

Given: $\overline{AB}$

Construct: Points X and Y on $\overline{AB}$ so that $AX = XY = YB$

A • ——— • B

Procedure:

1. Choose any point Z not on $\overleftrightarrow{AB}$. Draw $\overrightarrow{AZ}$.
2. Using any radius, start with A as center and mark off R, S, and T so that $AR = RS = ST$.
3. Draw $\overline{TB}$.
4. At R and S construct lines parallel to $\overline{TB}$, intersecting $\overline{AB}$ in X and Y.

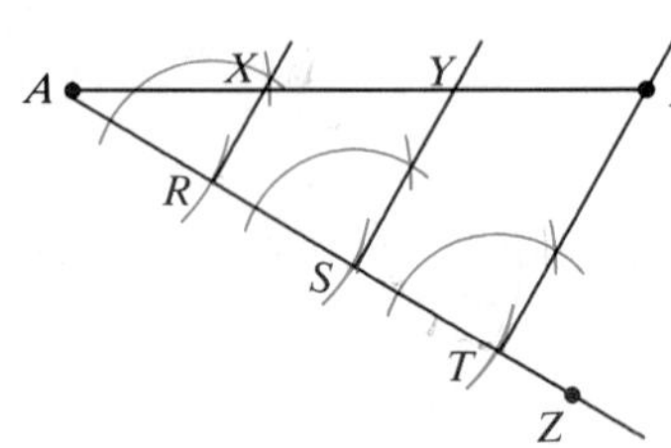

$\overline{AX}$, $\overline{XY}$, and $\overline{YB}$ are congruent parts of $\overline{AB}$.

Justification: Since the parallel lines you constructed cut off congruent segments on transversal $\overleftrightarrow{AZ}$, they cut off congruent segments on transversal $\overleftrightarrow{AB}$. (It may help you to think of the parallel to $\overline{TB}$ through A.)

Construction 13

Given three segments, construct a fourth segment so that the four segments are in proportion.

Given: Segments with lengths a, b, and c

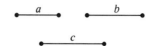

Construct: A segment of length x such that $\frac{a}{b} = \frac{c}{x}$

Procedure:

1. Draw an $\angle HIJ$.
2. On $\overrightarrow{IJ}$, mark off $IR = a$ and $RS = b$.
3. On $\overrightarrow{IH}$, mark off $IT = c$.
4. Draw $\overline{RT}$.
5. At S, construct a parallel to $\overline{RT}$, intersecting $\overrightarrow{IH}$ in a point U.

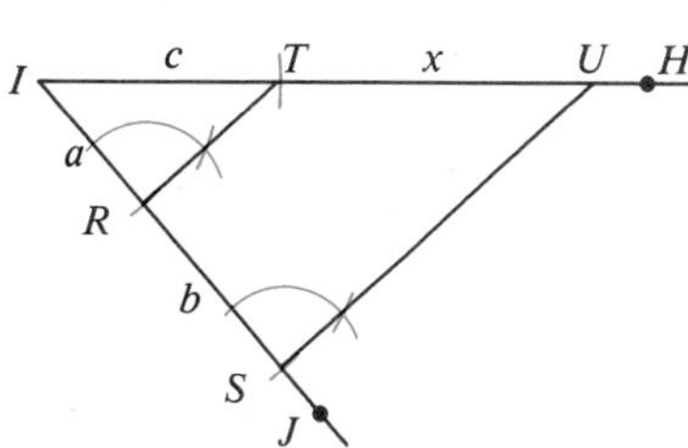

$\overline{TU}$ has length x such that $\frac{a}{b} = \frac{c}{x}$.

Justification: Because $\overline{RT}$ is parallel to side $\overline{SU}$ of $\triangle SIU$, $\overline{RT}$ divides the other two sides of the triangle proportionally. Therefore, $\frac{a}{b} = \frac{c}{x}$.

Construction 14

Given two segments, construct their geometric mean.

Given: Segments with lengths a and b

Construct: A segment of length x such that $\frac{a}{x} = \frac{x}{b}$ (or $x = \sqrt{ab}$)

Procedure:

1. Draw a line and mark off $RS = a$ and $ST = b$.
2. Locate the midpoint O of $\overline{RT}$ by constructing the perpendicular bisector of $\overline{RT}$.
3. Using O as center draw a semicircle with a radius equal to OR.
4. At S, construct a perpendicular to $\overline{RT}$. The perpendicular intersects the semicircle at a point Z.

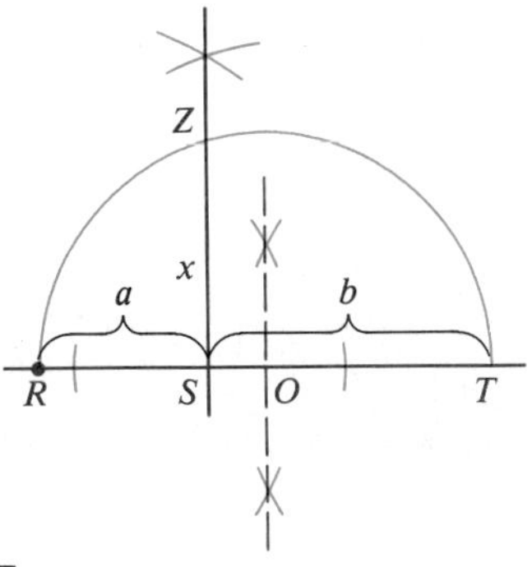

ZS, or x, is the geometric mean between a and b.

Justification: $\widehat{RZT}$ is a semicircle. If you draw $\overline{RZ}$ and $\overline{ZT}$, then $\triangle RZT$ is a right triangle. Since $\overline{ZS}$ is the altitude to the hypotenuse of rt. $\triangle RZT$, $\frac{a}{x} = \frac{x}{b}$.

Chalkboard Examples

1. Construct two segments, one 4 units in length and the other 9 units in length. Construct the geometric mean between the two segments and measure its length. Then use algebra to show that the measure is 6.

   Const. 14; $\frac{4}{x} = \frac{x}{9}$
   $x^2 = 36$
   $x = 6$

2. Complete each step to do the construction. Steps (a)–(f) make up one construction.
   a. Divide a segment $\overline{PQ}$ into 8 equal lengths using Const. 12.
   b. Locate point M on $\overline{PQ}$ so that $PM = 3$ and $MQ = 5$.
   c. Construct a ray $\overrightarrow{PR}$ with segment $\overline{PR} = 6$. Const. 1
   d. Draw $\overline{MR}$.
   e. Construct a line parallel to $\overline{MR}$ through Q intersecting $\overleftrightarrow{PR}$ at N. Const. 7
   f. Measure $\overline{RN}$ and show, using algebra, that $RN = 10$.

   $\frac{3}{5} = \frac{6}{x}$
   $3x = 30$
   $x = 10$

Teaching Note

In Construction 14, draw $\overline{RZ}$ and $\overline{ZT}$. $\triangle RZT$ is a right triangle. Since $\overline{ZS}$ is the altitude, it is the geometric mean between a and b, the segments of the hypotenuse.

Classroom Exercises

1. Given a segment, tell how to construct an equilateral triangle whose perimeter equals the length of the given segment.

Draw three segments and label their lengths *a*, *b*, and *c*.

2. Construct a segment of length x such that $\frac{c}{a} = \frac{b}{x}$. **Const. 13**
3. Describe how to construct a segment of length x such that $x = \sqrt{2ab}$.
4. Describe how to construct a segment of length x such that $x = \sqrt{5ab}$. **See below.** (answers to 3 and 4)
5. Describe how to construct a segment of length x such that $x = \sqrt{4ab}$.

Exercises 6–11 will analyze the following problem.

Given: Line t; points A and B

Construct: A circle through A and B and tangent to t

3. Const. a seg. with length 2*a* (or 2*b*); then use Const. 14.
4. Const. a seg. with length 5*a* (or 5*b*); then use Const. 14.

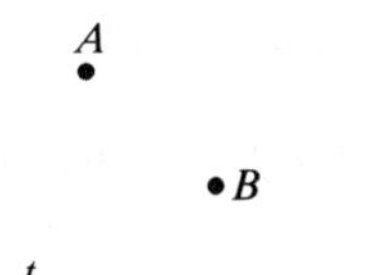

If the problem had been solved, we would have a diagram something like the one shown.

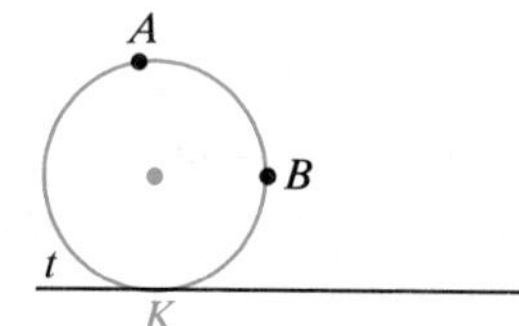

6. Where does the center of the circle lie with respect to $\overline{AB}$? **on the ⊥ bis. of $\overline{AB}$**
7. Where does the center of the circle lie with respect to line t and K, the point of tangency? **on the ⊥ to *t* through *K***

8. $(JK)^2 = JB \cdot JA$

Note that we don't have point K located in the given diagram. Hunting for ideas, we draw $\overleftrightarrow{AB}$. We now have a point J, which we can locate in the given diagram.

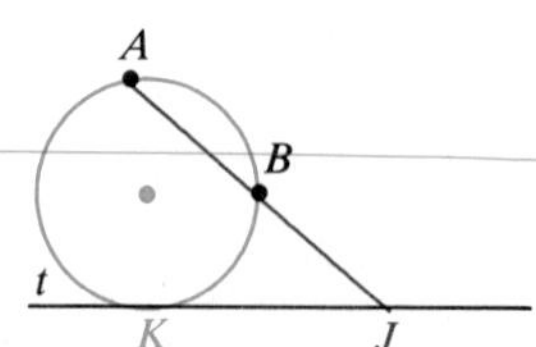

8. State an equation that relates JK to JA and JB.
9. Rewrite your equation in the form $\frac{?}{JK} = \frac{JK}{?}$. ***JB*, *JA*** **Answers may vary.**
10. What construction can we use to get the length JK? **Const. 14**

In a *separate* diagram we can mark off the lengths JA and JB on some line l and then use Construction 14 to find x such that $\frac{JA}{x} = \frac{x}{JB}$. Once we have x, which equals JK, we return to the given diagram and draw an arc to locate K.

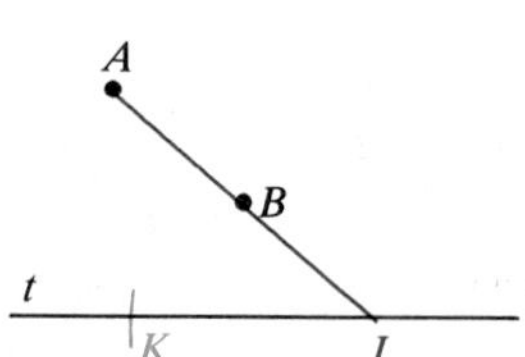

11. Explain how to complete the construction of the circle. **Const. the ⊥ bis. of $\overline{AB}$ and a ⊥ to *t* at *K*, int. at *O*. Draw ⊙*O* with radius *OA* = *OB* = *OK*.**

Assessment

Have students give verbal answers to the exercises on this page. Students' answers will indicate their degree of understanding of the ideas presented in this lesson. Encourage all students to participate in the discussion of the exercises.

Additional Answers Classroom Exercises

1. Divide the segment $\overline{AD}$ into 3 ≅ parts, $\overline{AB}$, $\overline{BC}$, and $\overline{CD}$. With centers A and B and radius $\overline{AB}$, draw arcs intersecting at E. Draw $\overline{EA}$ and $\overline{EB}$.
5. Construct segments with lengths $4a$ and b (or $4b$ and a, or $2a$ and $2b$); then use Const. 14. Or use Const. 14 to find $x = \sqrt{ab}$; then const. a segment with length $2\sqrt{ab}$.

Guided Practice

For each of Exs. 1–5, begin by drawing $\overline{PQ}$ approximately 20 cm long.

1. Divide $\overline{PQ}$ into five congruent segments. Const. 12
2. Locate point X such that $PX = \frac{2}{3}PQ$. Const. 12
3. Locate point Y so that $PY = \frac{1}{4}PQ$. Const. 12
4. Locate Z so that $ZQ = \frac{1}{4}PQ$. Const. 12
5. Divide $\overline{PQ}$ into two segments having the ratio 3:2. Const. 12

Written Exercises

3. c. Let the 5 ≅ seg. from Ex. 3(a) be $\overline{AW}$, $\overline{WX}$, $\overline{XY}$, $\overline{YZ}$, and $\overline{ZB}$. $AX:XB = 2:3$

In each of Exercises 1–4 begin by drawing $\overline{AB}$ roughly 15 cm long.

A 1. Divide $\overline{AB}$ into three congruent segments. **Const. 12**

2. a. Use Construction 12 to divide $\overline{AB}$ into four congruent segments.
   b. Use Construction 4 to divide $\overline{AB}$ into four congruent segments.

3. a. Use Construction 12 to divide $\overline{AB}$ into five congruent segments.
   b. Can Construction 4 be used to divide $\overline{AB}$ into five congruent segments? **No**
   c. Divide $\overline{AB}$ into two segments that have the ratio 2:3. **See above.**

4. Divide $\overline{AB}$ into two segments that have the ratio 3:4. **Use Const. 12 to divide $\overline{AB}$ into 7 ≅ parts, $\overline{AU}$, $\overline{UV}$, $\overline{VW}$, $\overline{WX}$, $\overline{XY}$, $\overline{YZ}$, and $\overline{ZB}$. $AW:WB = 3:4$**

On your paper draw four segments roughly as long as those shown below. Use your segments in Exercises 5–14. In each exercise construct a segment that has length x satisfying the given condition.

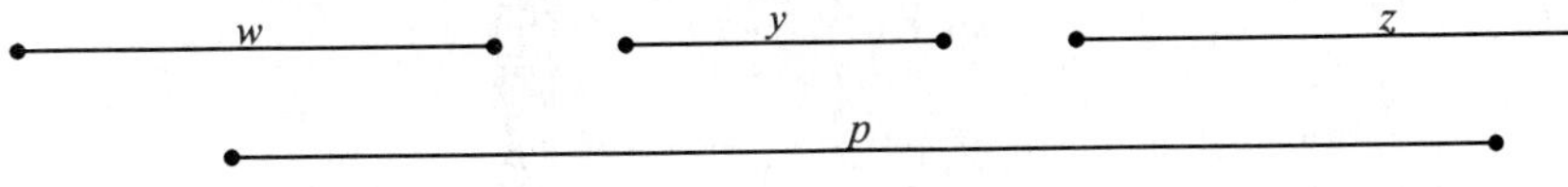

5. $\frac{y}{w} = \frac{z}{x}$ **Const. 13**

6. $\frac{w}{x} = \frac{x}{y}$ **Const. 14**

7. $x = \sqrt{yp}$ **Const. 14**

8. $3x = w + 2y$ **Const. 1, 12**

B 9. $zx = wy$ (*Hint*: First write a proportion that is equivalent to the given equation and has x as the last term.) **Const. 13**

10–13. See below.

10. $x = \frac{yp}{z}$

11. $x = \frac{1}{3}\sqrt{yp}$

12. $x = \sqrt{3wz}$

13. $x = \sqrt{6yz}$

14. Construct $\overline{AB}$, with $AB = p$. Divide $\overline{AB}$ into two parts that have the ratio $w:y$.

15. Draw a segment like the one shown and let its length be 1. Use the segment to construct a segment of length $\sqrt{15}$.

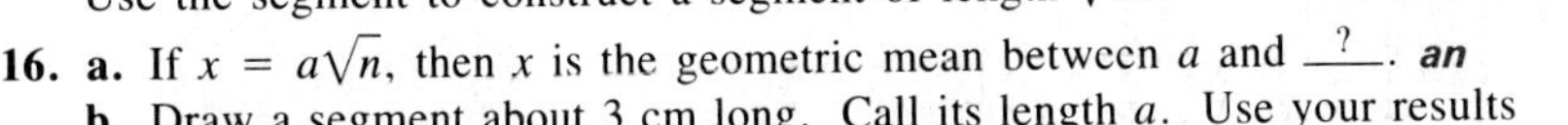

16. a. If $x = a\sqrt{n}$, then x is the geometric mean between a and __?__. ***an***
    b. Draw a segment about 3 cm long. Call its length a. Use your results from part (a) to construct a segment of length $a\sqrt{n}$ for $n = 2, 3,$ and 4.

C 17. Draw $\overline{CD}$ about 20 cm long. Construct a triangle whose perimeter is equal to CD and whose sides are in the ratio 2:2:3.

★ 18. To trisect a general angle G, a student tried this procedure:

1. Mark off $\overline{GA}$ congruent to $\overline{GB}$.
2. Draw $\overline{AB}$.
3. Divide $\overline{AB}$ into three congruent parts using Construction 12.
4. Draw $\overline{GX}$ and $\overline{GY}$.

Show that the student did not trisect $\angle G$. (*Hint*: Show that $GA > GY$. Then use an indirect proof to show that $m\angle 2 \neq m\angle 1$.)

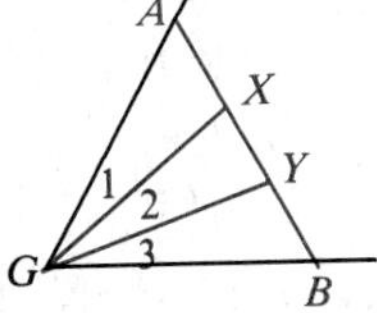

10. Const. 13 11. Const. 14, 12 12. Const. 1, 14 13. Const. 1, 14

On your paper, draw four segments having lengths as given. $a = 4$ cm, $b = 2.5$ cm, $c = 5$ cm, and $d = 10$ cm. Construct a segment with length x satisfying the given condition.

6. $\frac{a}{b} = \frac{c}{x}$ Const. 13
7. $\frac{c}{x} = \frac{x}{d}$ Const. 14
8. $x = \sqrt{ac}$ Const. 14
9. $3x = a + c - b$ Const. 1 and Const. 12

Exercise Note

Ex. 22 on page 378 and Ex. 10 on page 382 required triangles with sides in a given proportion. Ex. 17 on this page adds the requirement that the triangle have a given perimeter.

Additional Answers Written Exercises

14. Draw $\overrightarrow{AX}$ and const. $\overline{AR}$ and $\overline{RS}$ on $\overrightarrow{AX}$ so that $AR = w$ and $RS = y$. Draw $\overline{SB}$. Const. a ∥ to $\overline{SB}$ through R, intersecting $\overline{AB}$ at T. $AT:TB = w:y$.
15. Draw a line and mark off $\overline{AB}$ and $\overline{BC}$ so that $AB = 3$ and $BC = 5$. Use Const. 14.
16.b. Methods may vary. Use Const. 14 with lengths $2a$ and a; $3a$ and a; $4a$ and a.

Using a Computer

Extend Ex. 18 by having students try to construct a triangle having an angle that *can* be trisected. What type of triangle works?

Career

Accountant

An accountant is a financial expert. Accountants study and analyze a company's or an organization's overall financial dealings. They prepare many different kinds of financial reports. These include profit-and-loss statements, which summarize the company's earnings for a given period of time, and balance sheets, which state the current net worth of the company. Another important accounting function is the preparation of tax reports and statements. A company's owners or managers rely on the accountant's reports to determine whether the company is operating efficiently and profitably, and where improvements can be made.

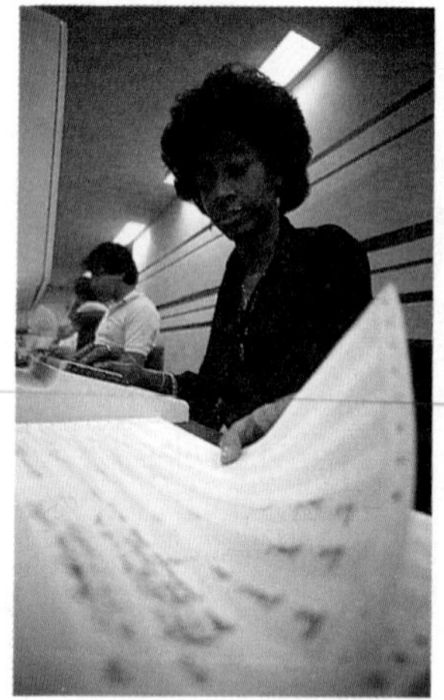

Accountants are usually college graduates with a major in accounting. They often begin work as junior accountants. After sufficient work experience they take an examination in order to become certified. Upon passing this examination, an accountant becomes a certified public accountant, or CPA. Further career advancement may lead to promotion to senior accountant, specializing in areas such as cost accounting or auditing. Advancement in a different direction may lead to a financial policy position such as that of controller or to starting an independent accounting company.

Quick Quiz

1. Draw $\odot O$, with diameter $\overline{AB}$. Construct the tangents to the circle at A and B. Const. 8
2. Draw a large 45°-45°-90° triangle. Construct the circumscribed circle. Const. the $\perp$ bis. of the hypotenuse. Draw a circle with center the midpt. of the hypotenuse and radius $= \frac{1}{2}$ the length of the hypotenuse.
3. Draw a long segment. By construction, divide the segment into three segments whose lengths are in the ratio 2:2:3. Const. 12 (divide seg. into 7 $\cong$ parts.)

Self-Test 2

3. Use Const. 12 to divide a seg. $\overline{AB}$ into 3 ≅ parts, $\overline{AX}$, $\overline{XY}$, and $\overline{YB}$. Then $AY:YB = 2:1$.

1. Draw a large ⊙O. Choose a point A that is outside ⊙O. Construct the two tangents to ⊙O from point A. **Const. 9**
2. Draw a very large obtuse triangle. Construct the inscribed circle. **Const. 11**
3. Draw a segment about half as long as the width of your paper. Then divide the segment by construction into two segments whose lengths have the ratio 2:1. **See above.**
4. Draw a large △ABC. Then construct $\overline{DE}$ such that $\frac{AB}{BC} = \frac{AC}{DE}$. **Const. 13**
5. Use △ABC drawn in Exercise 4 to construct a segment, $\overline{PQ}$, whose length is the geometric mean of AB and AC. **Const. 14**
6. You are given ⊙S and diameter $\overline{FG}$. To construct parallel tangents to ⊙S, you could construct a line that is __?__ to $\overline{FG}$ at __?__ and a line that is __?__ to $\overline{FG}$ at __?__. **⊥, *F*, ⊥, *G***
7. You are given △TRI. Describe the steps you would use to circumscribe a circle about △TRI. **Const. the ⊥ bis. of 2 sides of △*TRI*, int. at *O*. Draw a ⊙ with ctr. *O* and radius *OT*.**

Locus

Objectives

1. Describe the locus that satisfies a given condition.
2. Describe the locus that satisfies more than one given condition.
3. Apply the concept of locus in the solution of construction exercises.

10-6 *The Meaning of Locus*

A radar system is used to determine the position, or *locus*, of airplanes relative to an airport. In geometry **locus** means a figure that is the set of all points, and only those points, that satisfy one or more conditions.

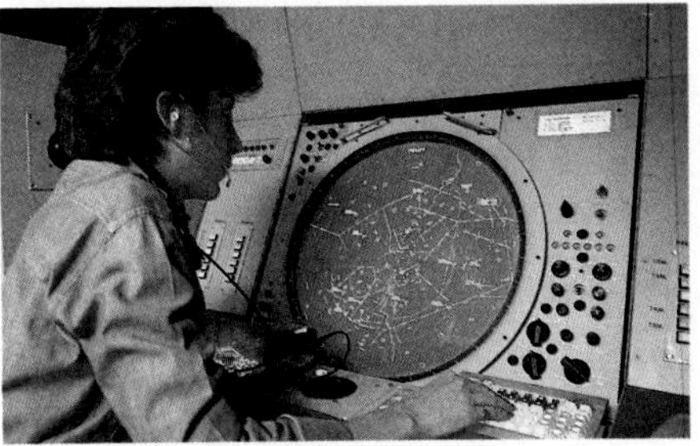

Use the given segments to construct a segment of length *x*.

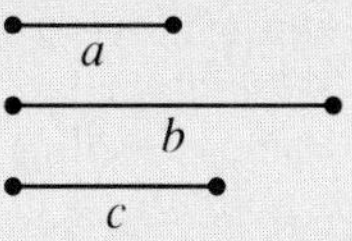

4. $\frac{c}{a} = \frac{x}{b}$ Const. 13 $\left(\frac{a}{c} = \frac{b}{x}\right)$

5. $x^2 = ac$ Const. 14 $\left(\frac{a}{x} = \frac{x}{c}\right)$

6. $2ax = 3bc$ Const. 13 $\left(\frac{2a}{3b} = \frac{c}{x}\right)$

Teaching Suggestions,
pp. T119–T120

Objectives
Presenting the Lesson
Making Connections
Reinforcement

Communication Skills,
p. T120

Supplementary Materials

Study Guide, pp. 131–132
Computer Activity 21

Lesson Focus

This lesson introduces a new idea called *locus.* A locus is a set of points that must satisfy one or more conditions.

Suggested Assignments

Minimum
Day 1: 404/1–8
Day 2: 404/9–15

Average
404–405/1–19 odd

Maximum
404–405/1–12, 14–20 even, 21

Chalkboard Examples

Describe the locus of points in a plane satisfying the given conditions.

1. the locus of points 10 cm from point *A* a ⊙ with *A* as center and radius of 10 cm
2. the locus of the center of a circle with radius 5 cm as it revolves about ⊙ *A* that has radius 2 cm and to which it is externally tangent a ⊙ with center *A* and radius 7 cm
3. the locus of all points equidistant from the vertices of a triangle the point where the ⊥ bisectors meet

Teaching Note

Students should understand that unless a locus problem restricts the solution to a plane, they should find all points *in space* that satisfy the given condition. Also emphasize that the solution to a locus problem must contain *all* points satisfying the given condition, and *only* those points.

Suppose we have a line *k* in a plane and wish to picture the locus of points in the plane that are 1 cm from *k*. Several points are shown in the first diagram below.

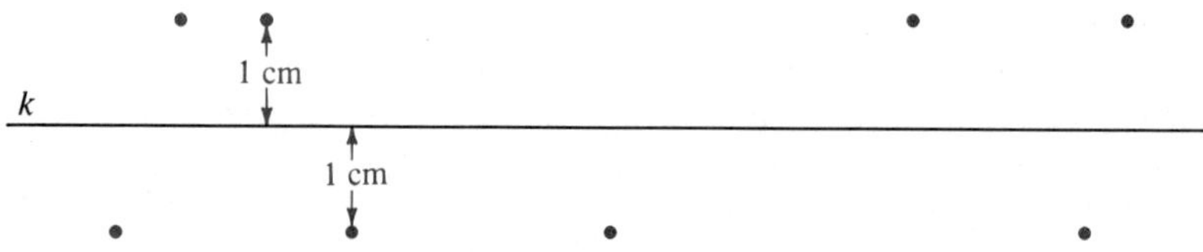

All the points satisfying the given conditions are indicated in the next diagram. You see that the required locus is a pair of lines parallel to, and 1 cm from, *k*.

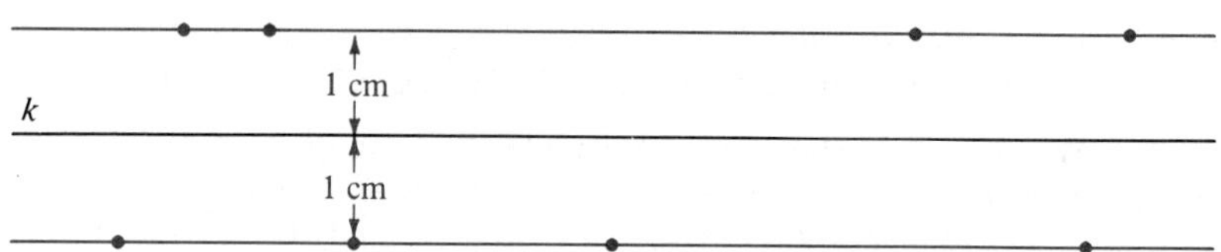

Suppose we wish to picture the locus of points 1 cm from *k* without requiring the points to be *in a plane*. The problem changes. Now you need to consider all the points in space that are 1 cm from line *k*. The required locus is a cylindrical surface with axis *k* and a 1 cm radius, as shown below. Of course, the surface will extend in both directions without end, just as line *k* does.

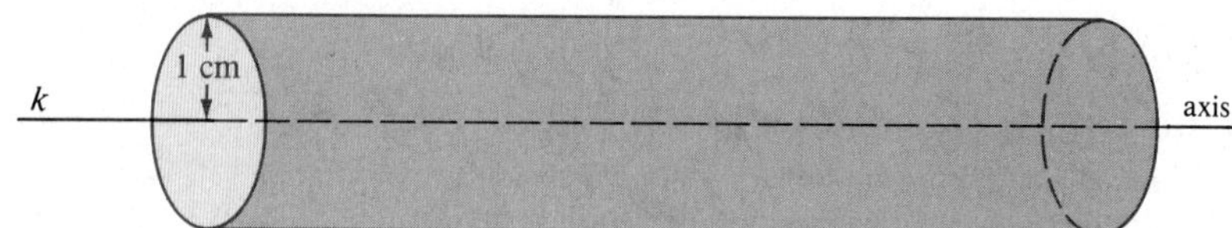

When you are solving a locus problem, always think in terms of three dimensions unless the statement of the problem restricts the locus to a plane.

Classroom Exercises

1. Draw a point *A* on the chalkboard.

a. Draw several points on the chalkboard that are 20 cm from *A*.
b. Draw all the points on the chalkboard that are 20 cm from *A*. } **Check students' drawings.**
c. Complete: The locus of all points on the chalkboard that are 20 cm from point *A* is _?_. **a circle with center *A* and radius 20 cm**
d. Remove the restriction that the points must lie in the plane of the chalkboard. Now describe the locus. **A sphere with center *A* and radius 20 cm**

2. Draw two parallel lines k and l.
   a. Draw several points that are in the plane containing k and l and are equidistant from k and l.
   b. Draw all the points that are in the plane containing k and l and are equidistant from k and l.
   c. Describe the locus of points that are in the plane of two parallel lines and equidistant from them. **a line ∥ to both lines and halfway between them**
   d. Remove the restriction that the points must lie in the plane of the two lines. Now describe the locus. **a plane ∥ to both lines and halfway between them**
3. Draw an angle.
   a. Draw several points in the plane of the angle that are equidistant from the sides of the angle.
   b. Draw all the points in the plane of the angle that are equidistant from the sides of the angle.
   c. Describe the locus of points in the plane of a given angle that are equidistant from the sides of the angle. **the bisector of the angle**
4. What is the locus of points in your classroom that are equidistant from the ceiling and floor?
5. What is the locus of points in your classroom that are 1 m from the floor?
6. Choose a point P on the floor of the classroom.
   a. What is the locus of points, on the floor, that are 1 m from P?
   b. What is the locus of points, in the room, that are 1 m from P?
7. What is the locus of points in your classroom that are equidistant from the ceiling and floor and are also equidistant from two opposite side walls?

8. What is the locus of points in your classroom that are equidistant from the front and back walls and are also equidistant from the two side walls?
9. Describe the locus of points on a football field that are equidistant from the two goal lines. **the 50-yard line**
10. Draw a circle with radius 6 cm. Use the following definition of *distance from a circle*: A point P is x cm from a circle if there is a point of the circle that is x cm from P but there is no point of the circle that is less than x cm from P.
    a. Draw all the points in the plane of the circle that are 2 cm from the circle. **b. 2 ⊙s concentric with the given ⊙ and with radii 4 cm and 8 cm**
    b. Complete: Given a circle with a 6 cm radius, the locus of all points in the plane of the circle and 2 cm from the circle is __?__.
    c. Remove the restriction that the points must lie in the plane of the circle. Now describe the locus.
11. Make up a locus problem for which the locus contains exactly one point.
12. Make up a locus problem for which the locus doesn't contain any points.

Answers may vary. (11, 12)

Additional Answers Classroom Exercises

4. The locus is the portion of a plane inside the classroom ∥ to the floor and ceiling, halfway between them.
5. The locus is the portion of a plane inside the classroom ∥ to the floor and 1 m above it.
6. a. a ⊙ with center P and radius 1 m (Part of the ⊙ may be outside the classroom.)
   b. a hemisphere with center P and radius 1 m
7. A line that is the intersection of 2 planes. One plane is ∥ and halfway between the floor and ceiling. The second plane is ∥ and halfway between the 2 side walls. The line joins the centers of the front and back walls.
8. A line that is the intersection of 2 planes. One plane is ∥ and halfway between the front and back walls. The second plane is ∥ and halfway between the 2 side walls. The line joins the centers of the floor and ceiling.
10. c. The surface of a *doughnut* with a hole 4 cm in radius and an outer radius of 8 cm (This shape is called a torus in topology.)

Written Exercises

3. 2 ∥ lines 4 cm apart with h halfway between them

Exercises 1–4 deal with figures in a plane. Draw a diagram showing the locus. Then write a description of the locus.

A

1. Given two points A and B, what is the locus of points equidistant from A and B? **the ⊥ bisector of $\overline{AB}$**
2. Given a point P, what is the locus of points 2 cm from P? **⊙P with radius 2 cm**
3. Given a line h, what is the locus of points 2 cm from h? **See above.**
4. Given ⊙O, what is the locus of the midpoints of all radii of ⊙O? **a ⊙ concentric with the given ⊙ with radius half the radius of the given ⊙**

In Exercises 5–8 begin each exercise with a square $ABCD$ that has sides 4 cm long. Draw a diagram showing the locus of points on or inside the square that satisfy the given conditions. Then write a description of the locus.

5. the segment joining the midpoints of $\overline{AD}$ and $\overline{BC}$

5. Equidistant from $\overline{AB}$ and $\overline{CD}$
6. Equidistant from points B and D **$\overline{AC}$**
7. Equidistant from $\overline{AB}$ and $\overline{BC}$ **diagonal $\overline{BD}$**
8. Equidistant from all four sides **the int. of $\overline{AC}$ and $\overline{BD}$**

Exercises 9–12 deal with figures in space.

9. Given two parallel planes, what is the locus of points equidistant from the two planes? **a plane ∥ to both planes and halfway between them**
10. Given a plane, what is the locus of points 5 cm from the plane? **See below.**
11. Given point E, what is the locus of points 3 cm from E? **a sphere with ctr. E and radius 3 cm**
12. Given points C and D, what is the locus of points equidistant from C and D? **a plane ⊥ to $\overline{CD}$ that bisects $\overline{CD}$**

Exercises 13–17 deal with figures in a plane. (*Note*: If a point in a segment or in an arc is not included in the locus, indicate the point by an open dot.)

B

13. **a.** Draw an angle HEX. Construct the locus of points equidistant from the sides of $\angle HEX$. **Use Const. 3 to bisect $\angle HEX$.**
    b. Draw two intersecting lines j and k. Construct the locus of points equidistant from j and k. **Use Const. 3 to bisect the ∠s formed by j and k; locus is 2 ⊥ lines.**
14. Draw a segment $\overline{DE}$ and a line n. Construct the locus of points whose distance from n is DE.
15. Draw a segment $\overline{AB}$. Construct the locus of points P such that $\angle APB$ is a right angle.
16. Draw a segment $\overline{CD}$. Construct the locus of points Q such that $\triangle CQD$ is isosceles with base $\overline{CD}$.
17. Draw a segment $\overline{EF}$. Construct the locus of points G such that $\triangle EFG$ is isosceles with leg $\overline{EF}$.

10. 2 ∥ planes 10 cm apart with the given plane halfway between them

---

Guided Practice

Draw a diagram and describe each of the following.

1. What is the locus of all points in a plane 10 cm from point O? a ⊙ with center O and radius 10 cm
2. What is the locus of all points in a plane 3 cm from $\overleftrightarrow{AB}$? two lines ∥ $\overleftrightarrow{AB}$ and each 3 cm from $\overleftrightarrow{AB}$
3. What is the locus of all points in a plane equidistant from the sides of an angle? a ray bisecting the angle
4. What is the locus of points equidistant from points A and B? a plane that is the ⊥ bisector of $\overline{AB}$
5. What is the locus of all points equidistant from the vertices of an equilateral triangle? a line ⊥ to the plane of the △ and passing through the point where the medians meet
6. What is the locus of all points r cm from point P? a sphere with center at P and radius r cm
7. What is the locus of all points in a plane equidistant from the sides of a triangle? the point where the angle bisectors meet

Additional Answers Written Exercises

14. Const. a pair of ∥ lines on either side of n at a distance DE from n.
16. Const. the ⊥ bis. of $\overline{CD}$ (excluding the midpt. of $\overline{CD}$).

Exercises 18–20 deal with figures in space.

18. Given a sphere, what is the locus of the midpoints of the radii of the sphere?

19. Given a square, what is the locus of points equidistant from the sides?

20. Given a scalene triangle, what is the locus of points equidistant from the vertices?

21. A ladder leans against a house. As A moves up or down on the wall, B moves along the ground. What path is followed by midpoint M? (*Hint*: Experiment with a meter stick, a wall, and the floor.)

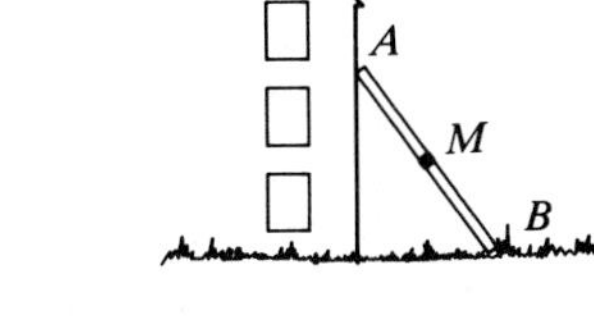

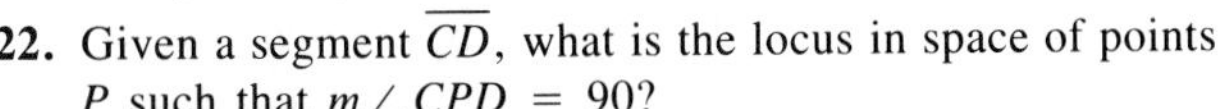

22. Given a segment $\overline{CD}$, what is the locus in space of points P such that $m\angle CPD = 90$?

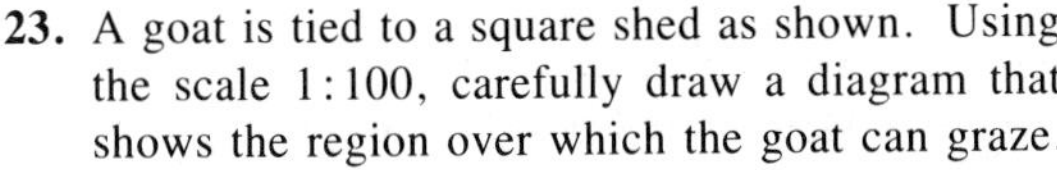

23. A goat is tied to a square shed as shown. Using the scale 1:100, carefully draw a diagram that shows the region over which the goat can graze.

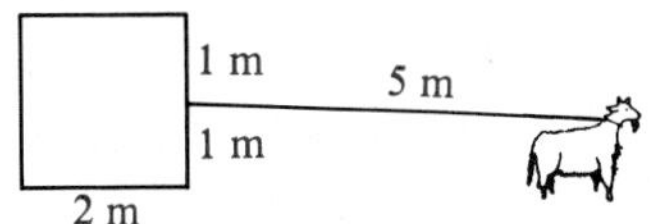

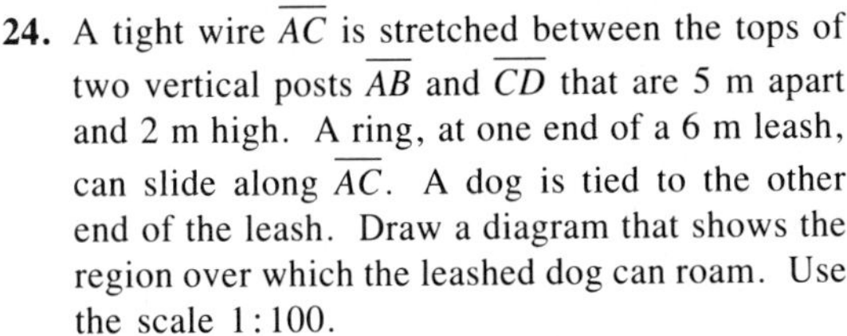

24. A tight wire $\overline{AC}$ is stretched between the tops of two vertical posts $\overline{AB}$ and $\overline{CD}$ that are 5 m apart and 2 m high. A ring, at one end of a 6 m leash, can slide along $\overline{AC}$. A dog is tied to the other end of the leash. Draw a diagram that shows the region over which the leashed dog can roam. Use the scale 1:100.

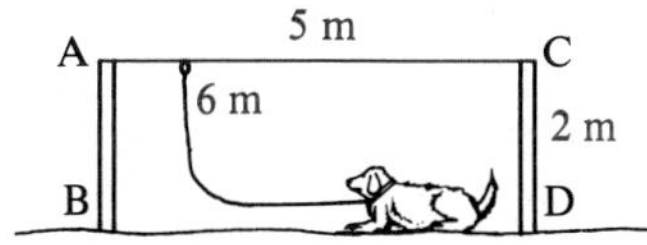

10-7 *Locus Problems*

The plural of *locus* is *loci*. The following problem involves intersections of loci.

Suppose you are given three noncollinear points, A, B, and C. In the plane of A, B, and C, what is the locus of points that are 1 cm from A and are, at the same time, equidistant from B and C?

You can analyze one part of the problem at a time.

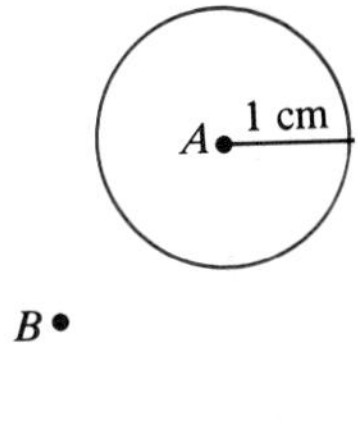

The locus of points 1 cm from A is $\odot A$ with radius 1 cm.

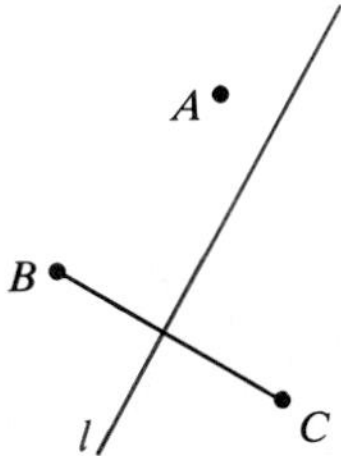

The locus of points equidistant from B and C is l, the perpendicular bisector of $\overline{BC}$.

Additional Answers Written Exercises

18. a sphere with the same center as the given sphere and radius half the radius of the given sphere

20. a line ⊥ to the plane of the △ at the intersection of the ⊥ bis. of the sides

Group Activity

Students may enjoy working together in small groups on Exs. 21–24. In this way, capable students can help others achieve solutions to these C-level problems.

Teaching Suggestions,
p. T120

Objectives
Presenting the Lesson
Making Connections

Cooperative Learning,
p. T120

Supplementary Materials

Practice Master 59

Study Guide, pp. 133–134

Lesson Focus

The locus problems in this lesson place two conditions on the points that are a solution to any problem. A solution must satisfy both conditions.

Suggested Assignments

Minimum
Day 1: 407–408/1–5 odd
Day 2: 408/6, 7, 9
414/Self-Test 3, 1–6
Day 3: 418/Chapter Test 1–11

Average
407–409/1, 4, 6–10 even, 11–17 odd, 18

Maximum
408–409/5–9 odd, 11, 14, 16–18, 20, 22

Chalkboard Examples

Draw a diagram to show a circle and a square in a plane with the given number of points of intersection. Answers may vary.

1. 1 **2.** 2 **3.** 3 **4.** 4

The locus of all points in space 3 cm from A and 5 cm from B is described below. What conclusions can you state about AB?

5. The locus contains no points.
$AB > 8$ or $AB < 2$

6. The locus is one point.
$AB = 8$ or $AB = 2$

7. The locus is a circle.
$2 < AB < 8$

Teaching Note

This lesson is more difficult than the preceding one. Be prepared to spend more time with your explanations. Colored chalk and the use of an overhead projector can help to illustrate the various loci. Encourage students to approach the exercises in this lesson in a systematic manner, establishing each locus individually and then considering the intersection.

The locus of points satisfying *both* conditions given on the previous page must lie on both circle A and line l. There are three possibilities, depending on the positions of A, B, and C, as shown below.

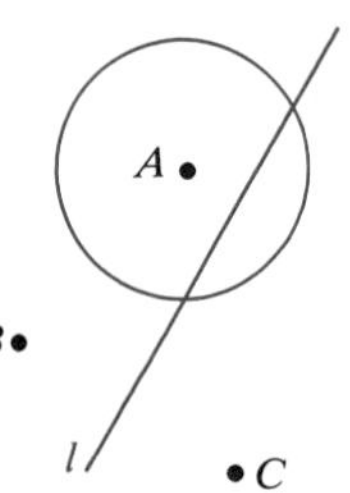

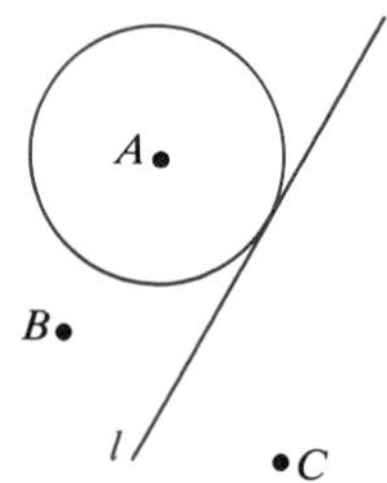

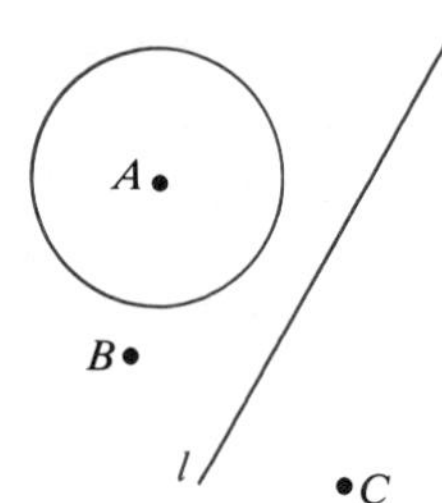

All three can be described in one sentence:

> The locus is two points, one point, or no points, depending on the intersection of the circle with center A and radius 1 cm and the line that is the perpendicular bisector of $\overline{BC}$.

The example that follows deals with the corresponding problem in three dimensions.

Example Given three noncollinear points A, B, and C, what is the locus of points 1 cm from A and equidistant from B and C?

Solution

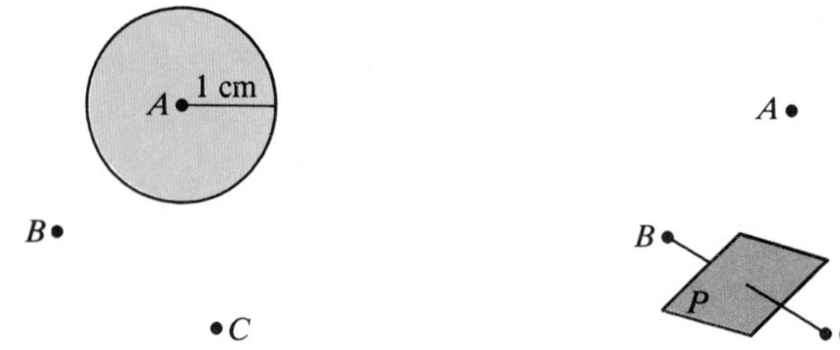

The first locus is sphere A with radius 1 cm.

The second locus is plane P, the perpendicular bisector of $\overline{BC}$.

Possibilities:

The plane might cut the sphere in a circle.
The plane might be tangent to the sphere.
The plane might not have any points in common with the sphere.

Thus, the locus is a circle, one point, or no points, depending on the intersection of the sphere with center A and radius 1 cm and the plane which is the perpendicular bisector of $\overline{BC}$.

Classroom Exercises

Exercises 1–4 refer to coplanar figures. Describe the possible intersections of the figures named.

1. A line and a circle **0, 1, or 2 pts.**
2. Two circles **0, 1, or 2 pts.**
3. Two parallel lines and a circle **0, 1, 2, 3, or 4 pts.**
4. Two perpendicular lines and a circle **0, 1, 2, 3, or 4 pts.**
5. Consider the following problem: In a plane, what is the locus of points that are equidistant from the sides of $\angle A$ and are equidistant from two points B and C?
   a. The locus of points equidistant from the sides of $\angle A$ is __?__. **the bis. of $\angle A$**
   b. The locus of points equidistant from B and C is __?__. **the $\perp$ bis. of $\overline{BC}$**
   c. Draw diagrams to show three possibilities with regard to points that satisfy both conditions (a) and (b).
   d. Describe the locus. **0 pts., 1 pt., or a ray**

Exercises 6–9 refer to figures in space. Describe the possible intersections of the figures named.

6. A line and a plane **0 pts., 1 pt., or the line**
7. A line and a sphere **0, 1, or 2 pts.**
8. Two spheres **0 pts., 1 pt., or a circle**
9. A plane and a sphere **0 pts., 1 pt., or a circle**
10. Let C be the point in the center of your classroom (*not* the center of the floor). Describe the locus of points in the room that satisfy the given conditions.
    a. 3 m from C
    b. 3 m from C and equidistant from the ceiling and the floor
    c. 3 m from C and 1 m from either the ceiling or the floor

Written Exercises

Exercises 1 and 2 refer to plane figures.

A 1. Draw a new $\odot O$ for each part. Then place two points A and B outside $\odot O$ so that the locus of points on $\odot O$ and equidistant from A and B is:
   a. 2 points **$\perp$ bis. of $\overline{AB}$ int. $\odot O$ in 2 pts.**
   b. 0 points **$\perp$ bis. of $\overline{AB}$ doesn't int. $\odot O$.**
   c. 1 point **$\perp$ bis. of $\overline{AB}$ is tangent to $\odot O$.**

2. Draw two parallel lines m and n. Then place two points R and S so that the locus of points equidistant from m and n and also equidistant from R and S is:
   a. 1 point
   b. 1 line
   c. 0 points

Additional Answers
Classroom Exercises

10.a. the portion inside the classroom of a sphere that has center C and radius 3 m
b. the portion inside the classroom of the $\odot$ that is the int. of the sphere in part (a) and the plane $\parallel$ to the floor and ceiling halfway between them
c. the portion inside the classroom of 2 $\odot$s, the intersection of the sphere in part (a) and 2 planes, each $\parallel$ to the floor, one 1 m from the floor, the other 1 m from the ceiling

Additional Answers Written Exercises

3.d. The locus is 0, 1, or 2 points, depending on the intersection of ⊙D and ⊙E.

4.d. The locus is 0, 1, 2, 3, or 4 points, depending on the intersection of ⊙A with radius 3 cm, and 2 lines ∥ to k and 1 cm from k.

Guided Practice

1. Draw a new diagram for parts (a) and (b). Place $\angle BAC$ with point A on ⊙O and points B and C outside ⊙O so that the locus of points on ⊙O and equidistant from $\overline{AB}$ and $\overline{AC}$ is:

   a. 1 point

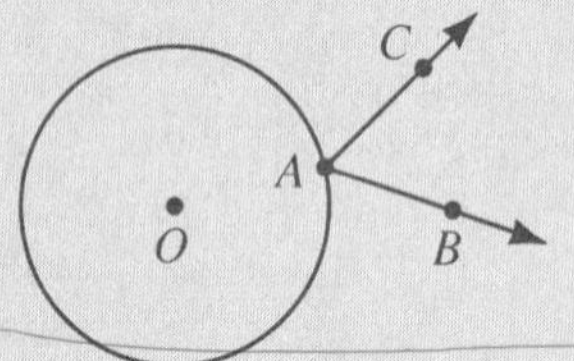

   b. 2 points

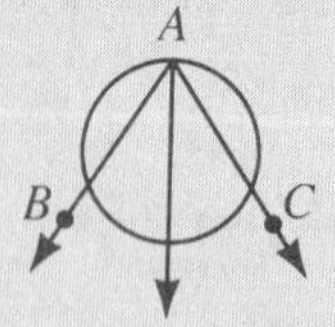

   c. Could the locus be zero points? No, because point A is always on the circle and on the locus of points equid. from $\overline{AB}$ and $\overline{AC}$ (the ∠ bisector of $\angle BAC$).

Exercises 3 and 4 refer to plane figures.

3. Consider the following problem: Given two points D and E, what is the locus of points 1 cm from D and 2 cm from E?
   a. The locus of points 1 cm from D is __?__. **a ⊙ with ctr. D and radius 1 cm**
   b. The locus of points 2 cm from E is __?__. **a ⊙ with ctr. E and radius 2 cm**
   c. Draw diagrams to show three possibilities with regard to points that satisfy both conditions (a) and (b).
   d. Give a one-sentence solution to the problem.

4. Consider the following problem: Given a point A and a line k, what is the locus of points 3 cm from A and 1 cm from k?
   a. The locus of points 3 cm from A is __?__. **a ⊙ with ctr. A and radius 3 cm**
   b. The locus of points 1 cm from k is __?__. **2 ∥ lines 2 cm apart with k halfway between them**
   c. Draw diagrams to show five possibilities with regard to points that satisfy both conditions (a) and (b).
   d. Give a one-sentence solution to the problem.

Exercises 5–10 refer to plane figures. Draw a diagram of the locus. Then write a description of the locus.

5. Point P lies on line l. What is the locus of points on l and 3 cm from P? **5. the int. of ⊙P, with radius 3 cm, and l (2 pts.)**

6. Point Q lies on line l. What is the locus of points 5 cm from Q and 3 cm from l? **the int. of ⊙Q, with radius 5 cm, and 2 lines ∥ to l and 3 cm from l (4 pts.)**

7. Points A and B are 3 cm apart. What is the locus of points 2 cm from both A and B? **the int. of ⊙A, with radius 2 cm, and ⊙B, with radius 2 cm (2 pts.)**

8. Lines j and k intersect in point P. What is the locus of points equidistant from j and k, and 2 cm from P? **See below.**

9. Given $\angle A$, what is the locus of points equidistant from the sides of $\angle A$ and 2 cm from vertex A? **See below.**

10. Given $\triangle RST$, what is the locus of points equidistant from $\overline{RS}$ and $\overline{RT}$ and also equidistant from R and S?
    the int. of the bis. of $\angle R$ and the ⊥ bis. of $\overline{RS}$ (1 pt.)

In Exercises 11–14 draw diagrams to show the possibilities with regard to points in a plane. Possibilities are given.

B 11. Given points C and D, what is the locus of points 2 cm from C and 3 cm from D? **0, 1, or 2 pts.**

12. Given point E and line k, what is the locus of points 3 cm from E and 2 cm from k? **0, 1, 2, 3, or 4 pts.**

13. Given a point A and two parallel lines j and k, what is the locus of points 30 cm from A and equidistant from j and k? **0, 1, or 2 pts.**

14. Given four points P, Q, R, and S, what is the locus of points that are equidistant from P and Q and equidistant from R and S? **0 pts., 1 pt., or a line**

8. the int. of ⊙P, with radius 2 cm, and the bis. of the ∠s formed by j and k (4 pts.)
9. the int. of ⊙A, with radius 2 cm, and the bis. of $\angle A$ (1 pt.)

Exercises 15–19 refer to figures in space. In each exercise tell what the locus is. You need not draw the locus or describe it precisely.

Example Given two parallel planes and a point A, what is the locus of points equidistant from the planes and 3 cm from A?

Solution The locus is a circle, a point, or no points.

15. Given plane Z and point B outside Z, what is the locus of points in Z that are 3 cm from B? **0 pts., 1 pt., or a circle**

16. Given plane Y and point P outside Y, what is the locus of points 2 cm from P and 2 cm from Y? **0 pts., 1 pt., or a circle**

17. Given $\overleftrightarrow{AB} \perp$ plane Q, what is the locus of points 2 cm from $\overleftrightarrow{AB}$ and 2 cm from Q? **2 circles**

18. Given square $ABCD$, what is the locus of points equidistant from the vertices of the square? **a line ⊥ to the plane of *ABCD* at the pt. of intersection of the diagonals**

19. Given point A in plane Z, what is the locus of points 5 cm from A and d cm from Z? (More than 1 possibility) **0 pts. ($d > 5$), 2 pts. ($d = 5$), 2 circles ($d < 5$)**

20. Given three points, each 2 cm from the other two, draw a diagram to show the locus of points that are in the plane of the given points and are not more than 2 cm away from any of them.

21. Points R, S, T, and W are not coplanar and no three of them are collinear.
 a. The locus of points equidistant from R and S is _?_. **the ⊥ bis. plane of $\overline{RS}$**
 b. The locus of points equidistant from R and T is _?_. **the ⊥ bis. plane of $\overline{RT}$**
 c. The loci found in parts (a) and (b) intersect in a _?_, and all points in this _?_ are equidistant from points R, S, and T. **line, line**
 d. The locus of points equidistant from R and W is _?_. **the ⊥ bis. plane of $\overline{RW}$**
 e. The intersection of the figures found in (c) and (d) is a _?_. This _?_ is equidistant from the four given points. **point; point**

C 22. Can you locate four points J, K, L, and M so that the locus of points equidistant from J, K, L, and M is named below? If the answer is *yes*, describe the location of the points J, K, L, and M.
 a. a point **Yes; *J, K, L,* and *M* are not coplanar; no 3 collinear**
 b. a line **Yes; for example, *J, K, L,* and *M* are any 4 points on a circle.**
 c. a plane **No**
 d. no points **Yes; any 3 collinear**

23. Assume that the Earth is a sphere. How many points are there on the Earth's surface that are equidistant from
 a. Houston and Toronto? **infinitely many**
 b. Houston, Toronto, and Los Angeles? **2**
 c. Houston, Toronto, Los Angeles, and Mexico City? **none**

---

2. Given two points, A and B, what is the locus of points in a plane 2 cm from A and 3 cm from B?
 a. The locus 2 cm from A is _?_. a ⊙ with center A and radius 2 cm
 b. The locus 3 cm from B is _?_. a ⊙ with center B and radius 3 cm
 c. Draw separate diagrams to show all possibilities with regard to parts (a) and (b).

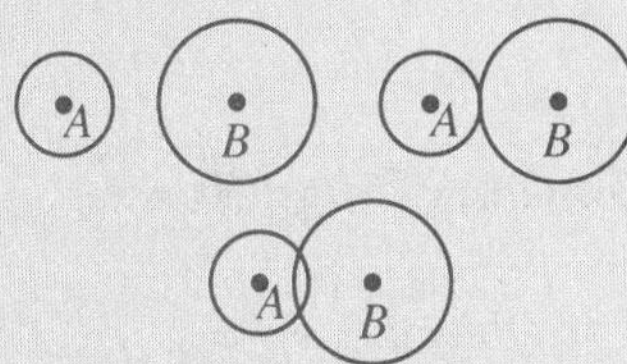

 d. Describe the locus. The locus is 0, 1, or 2 points depending on the intersection of ⊙A and ⊙B.

3. Draw a diagram and write a description of the locus. Points P and Q are 5 cm apart. What is the locus of points in:
 a. the plane of $\overleftrightarrow{PQ}$ 2 cm from P and 2 cm from Q? no points
 b. the plane of $\overleftrightarrow{PQ}$ 2 cm from P and 3 cm from Q? one point
 c. the plane of $\overleftrightarrow{PQ}$ 3 cm from P and 3 cm from Q? two points
 d. space 3 cm from P and 3 cm from Q? a circle

24. A mini-radio transmitter has been secured to a bear. Rangers D, E, and F are studying the bear's movements. Rangers D and E can receive the bear's beep at distances up to 10 km, ranger F at distances up to 15 km.

Draw a diagram showing where the bear might be at these times:

a. When all three rangers can receive the signal

b. When ranger F suddenly detects the signal after a period of time during which only rangers D and E could receive the signal

c. When ranger D is off duty, and ranger F begins to detect the signal just as ranger E loses it

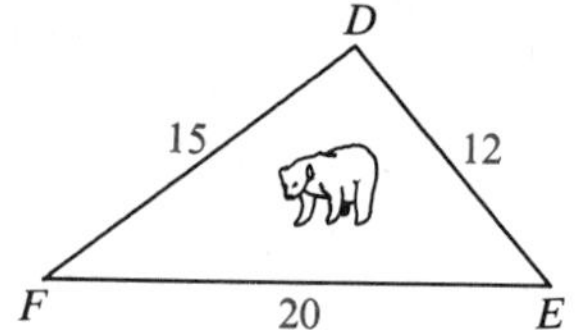

Challenge

Given $\overline{AB}$, it is possible to construct the midpoint M of $\overline{AB}$ using only a compass (and *no* straightedge). Study the diagram until you understand the procedure. Then draw $\overline{AB}$, about 10 cm long, construct its midpoint M as shown, and prove that M is the midpoint.

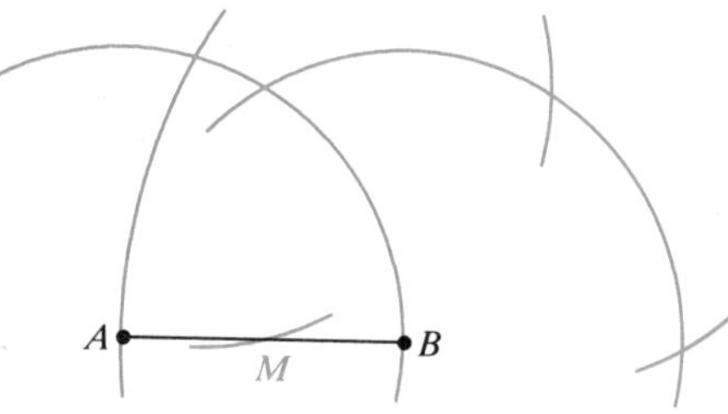

Teaching Suggestions, p. T121

Objective
Presenting the Lesson
Reinforcement
Extension
Enrichment
Using Technology

Supplementary Materials

Practice Master 60
Test 40
Resource Book, pp. 65, 149
Study Guide, pp. 135–136

Lesson Focus

The purpose of this lesson is to study construction problems by using the idea of a locus.

Suggested Assignments

Average
Day 1: 412–413/2, 4–7
Day 2: 413/9, 12, 15
414/Self-Test 3
Day 3: 418/Chapter Test

Maximum
Day 1: 413/6, 9, 12, 15, 16–19
Day 2: 418/Chapter Test

10-8 *Locus and Construction*

Sometimes the solution to a construction problem depends on finding a point that satisfies more than one condition. To locate the point, you may have to begin by constructing a locus of points satisfying *one* of the conditions.

Example Given the angle and the segments shown, construct $\triangle ABC$ with $m\angle A = n$, $AB = r$, and the altitude to $\overleftrightarrow{AB}$ having length s.

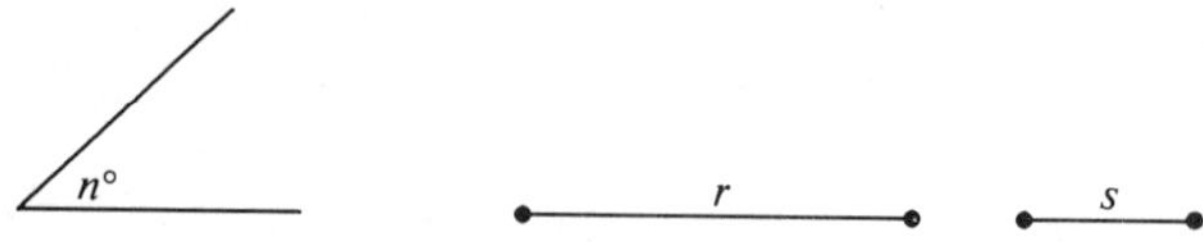

Solution It is easy to construct $\angle A$ and side $\overline{AB}$. Point C must satisfy two conditions: C must lie on $\overrightarrow{AZ}$, and C must be s units from $\overleftrightarrow{AB}$. The locus of points s units from $\overleftrightarrow{AB}$ is a pair of parallel lines. Only the upper parallel will intersect $\overrightarrow{AZ}$. We construct that parallel to $\overleftrightarrow{AB}$ as follows:

1. Construct the perpendicular to $\overleftrightarrow{AB}$ at any convenient point X.
2. Mark off s units on the perpendicular to locate point Y.
3. Construct the perpendicular to $\overrightarrow{XY}$ at Y. Call it $\overleftrightarrow{YW}$.

Note that all points on $\overleftrightarrow{YW}$ are s units from $\overleftrightarrow{AB}$. Thus the intersection of $\overleftrightarrow{YW}$ and $\overrightarrow{AZ}$ is the desired point C. To complete the solution, we simply draw $\overline{CB}$.

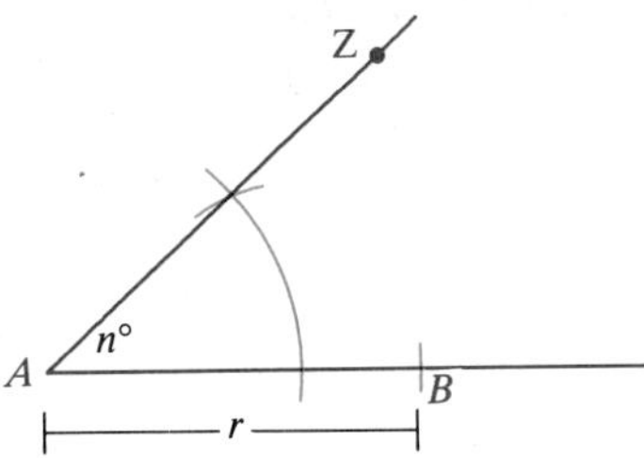

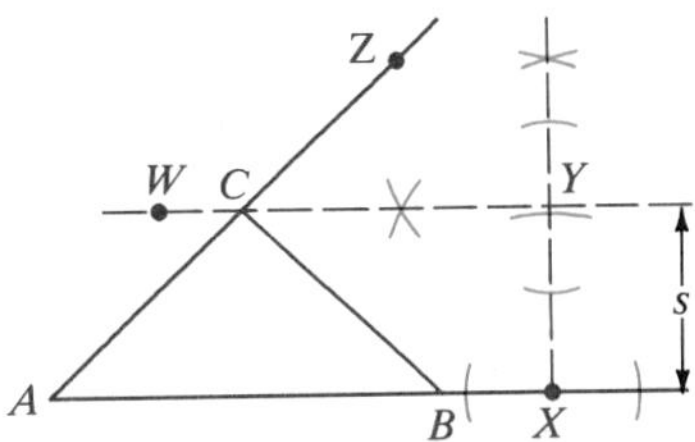

Classroom Exercises

1. The purpose of this exercise is to analyze the following construction problem:

   Given a circle and a segment with length k, inscribe in the circle an isosceles triangle RST with base $\overline{RS}$ k units long.

   a. Suppose R has been chosen. Where must S lie so that RS equals k? (In other words, what is the locus of points k units from R?) **on the ⊙ with ctr. *R* and radius *k***

   b. Now suppose $\overline{RS}$ has been drawn. Where must T lie so that $RT = ST$? (In other words, what is the locus of points equidistant from R and S?) **on the ⊥ bis. of $\overline{RS}$**

   c. Explain the steps of the construction shown.

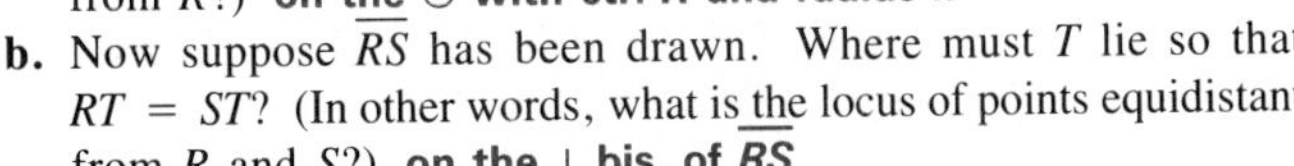

(1)

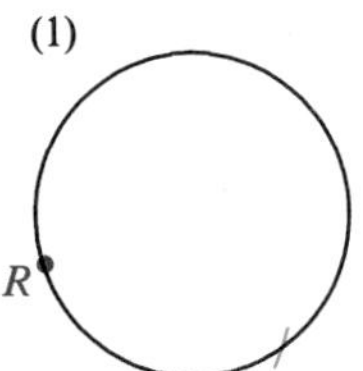

(2)

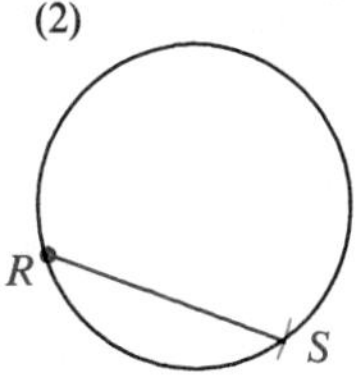

(3)

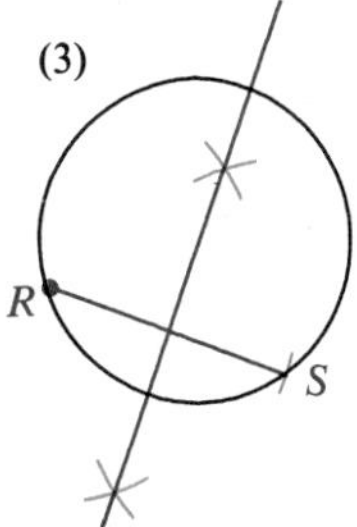

   d. Explain two different ways to finish the construction. **(1) Let *T* be one of the pts. where the ⊥ bis. of $\overline{RS}$ int. the ⊙; draw $\overline{TR}$ and $\overline{TS}$. (2) Let *T* be the other pt. of intersection.**

Chalkboard Examples

$\overline{BD} \parallel \overline{AF}$, $BF = s$, $CD = 2$, and $m\angle BAF = n$.

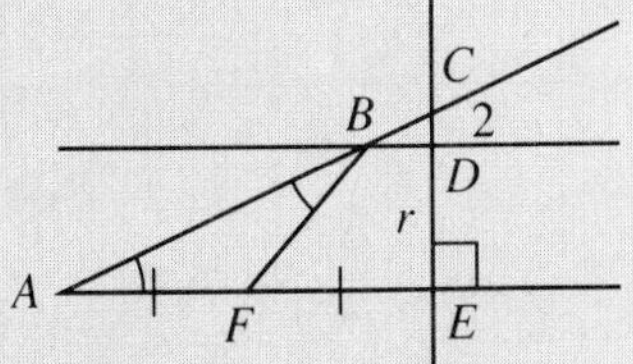

Refer to the figure above. Name a figure that satisfies the given condition.

1. all points a distance r from $\overleftrightarrow{FE}$ $\overleftrightarrow{BD}$
2. a triangle with altitude r and one median of length s $\triangle ABE$
3. a right triangle with an acute angle of n and a leg of length 2 $\triangle BCD$
4. Given a segment of length a, construct a 45°-45°-90° triangle with the altitude to the hypotenuse having length a.

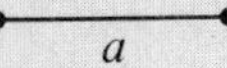

Draw a line. Mark off $AB = 2a$. Const. ⊥ bis. of $\overline{AB}$. Locate M the midpt. of $\overline{AB}$. On ⊥ bis. mark off $CM = a$. $\triangle ABC$ is the required △.

Additional Answers Classroom Exercises

1.c. (1) Choose R on the circle. With center R and radius k, draw an arc intersecting the circle. (2) Let S be the pt. where the arc intersects the circle. Draw $\overline{RS}$. (3) Const. the ⊥ bis. of $\overline{RS}$.

Additional Answers
Classroom Exercises

2. First solution: Const. $\overline{AB}$ so that $AB = s$. Const. the ⊥ bis. of $\overline{AB}$ to locate its midpt., M. Draw a semicircle with center M and radius $\overline{AM}$. Draw an arc with center A and radius r int. the semicircle at C. Draw $\overline{CA}$ and $\overline{CB}$. Since $\angle C$ is inscr. in a semicircle, $\angle C$ is a rt. ∠.
   Second solution: Draw a line and choose pt. C. Const. a ⊥ to the line at C such that $AC = r$. With center A and radius s, draw an arc int. the line at B. Draw $\overline{AB}$.

Guided Practice

Draw any $\overline{AB}$. Use the following steps to construct the locus of points P such that every $\triangle APB$ would be a right triangle with hypotenuse $\overline{AB}$.

1. Construct the perpendicular bisector of $\overline{AB}$.
2. Locate the midpoint M of $\overline{AB}$.
3. Using AM as a radius and M as the center, construct a circle that has $\overline{AB}$ as a diameter.
4. Select any point on the circle (excluding A and B) to use as point P.

2. Two different solutions, both correct, are shown for the following construction problem. Analyze the diagrams and explain the solutions.

Given segments with lengths r and s, construct $\triangle ABC$ with $m\angle C = 90$, $AC = r$, and $AB = s$.

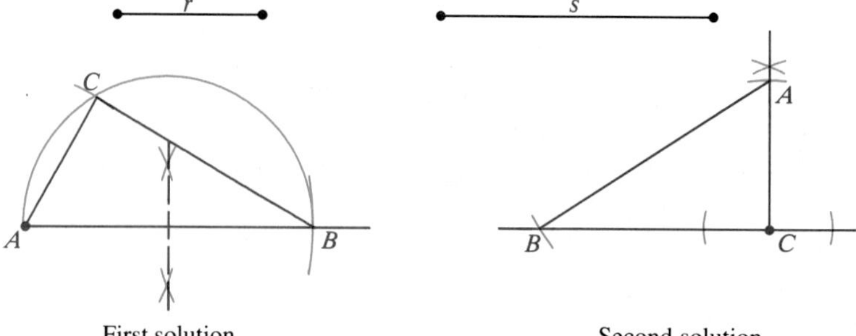

First solution   Second solution

Written Exercises

Exercises 1–4 refer to plane figures.

A **1.** Draw any $\overline{AB}$ and a segment with length h. Use the following steps to construct the locus of points P such that for every $\triangle APB$ the altitude from P to $\overleftrightarrow{AB}$ would equal h. **The locus is the 2 ∥ lines.**

a. Construct a perpendicular to $\overline{AB}$.

b. Construct two lines parallel to $\overline{AB}$, h units from $\overline{AB}$.

2. Begin each part of this exercise by drawing any $\overline{CD}$. Then construct the locus of points P that meet the given condition.

a. $\angle CDP$ is a right angle. **The locus is the ⊥ to $\overline{CD}$ at D, excluding pt. D.**

b. $\angle CPD$ is a right angle. (*Hint*: See Classroom Exercise 2.) **The locus is a ⊙ with ctr. at the midpt. of $\overline{CD}$ and radius = $\frac{1}{2}CD$, excluding pts. C and D.**

On your paper draw a segment roughly as long as the one shown. Use it in Exercises 3 and 4.

3. Draw an angle XYZ. Construct a circle, with radius a, that is tangent to the sides of $\angle XYZ$. (*Hint*: The center of the circle will be a units from the sides of $\angle XYZ$.)

4. Draw a figure roughly like the one shown. Then construct a circle, with radius a, that passes through N and is tangent to line k. (*Hint*: Construct the locus of points that would, as centers, be the correct distance from k. Also construct the locus of points that would, as centers, be the correct distance from N.)

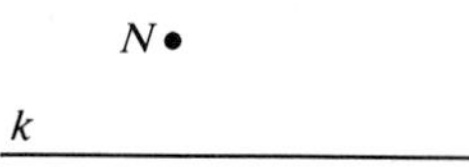

On your paper draw an angle and three segments roughly like those shown. Use them in Exercises 5–19. You may find it helpful to begin with a sketch.

5. Construct $\overline{AB}$ so that $AB = t$. Then construct the locus of all points C so that in $\triangle ABC$ the altitude from C has length r.
6. Construct $\overline{AB}$ so that $AB = t$. Then construct the locus of all points C so that in $\triangle ABC$ the median from C has length s.

B

7. Construct isosceles $\triangle ABC$ so that $AB = AC = t$ and so that the altitude from A has length s.
8. Construct an isosceles trapezoid $ABCD$ with $\overline{AB}$ the shorter base, with $AB = AD = BC = t$, and with an altitude of length r.
9. Construct $\triangle ABC$ so that $AB = t$, $AC = s$, and the median to $\overline{AB}$ has length r.
10. Construct $\triangle ABC$ so that $m\angle A = m\angle B = n$, and the altitude to $\overline{AB}$ has length s.
11. Construct $\triangle ABC$ so that $m\angle C = 90$, $m\angle A = n$, and the altitude to $\overline{AB}$ has length s.
12. Construct $\triangle ABC$ so that $AB = s$, $AC = t$, and the altitude to $\overline{AB}$ has length r.
13. Construct $\triangle ABC$ so that $AB = t$, and the median to $\overline{AB}$ and the altitude to $\overline{AB}$ have lengths s and r, respectively.
14. Construct a right triangle such that the altitude to the hypotenuse and the median to the hypotenuse have lengths r and s, respectively.
15. Construct both an acute isosceles triangle and an obtuse isosceles triangle such that each leg has length s and each altitude to a leg has length r.

C

16. Construct a square whose sides each have length $4s$. A segment of length $3s$ moves so that its endpoints are always on the sides of the square. Construct the locus of the midpoint of the moving segment.
17. Construct a right triangle such that the bisector of the right angle divides the hypotenuse into segments whose lengths are r and s.
18. Construct an isosceles right triangle such that the radius of the inscribed circle is r.
19. Construct $\overline{AB}$ so that $AB = t$. Then construct the locus of points P such that $m\angle APB = n$.

Additional Answers Written Exercises

6. The locus is a ⊙ with center M, the midpt. of $\overline{AB}$, and radius s, excluding pts. where $\overleftrightarrow{AB}$ intersects ⊙M.

8. Draw a line k. Choose D on k and const. a ⊥ to k at D. Const. $\overline{DX}$ on the ⊥ so that $DX = r$. Const. $m \parallel$ to k through X. With center D and radius t, draw an arc int. the $\parallel$ at A. Draw $\overline{AD}$. On m, construct $\overline{AB} \cong \overline{AD}$. With center B and radius t, draw an arc int. k at C with $\overline{BC} \nparallel \overline{AD}$. Draw $\overline{BC}$.

10. Const. $\angle XAY$ with measure n. Const. line $j \parallel$ to and s units from $\overrightarrow{AX}$; j intersects $\overrightarrow{AY}$ at C. With center C and radius AC, draw an arc intersecting $\overrightarrow{AX}$ at B. Draw $\overline{BC}$.

12. Const. $\overline{AB}$ of length s. Const. line j, $\parallel$ to and r units from $\overleftrightarrow{AB}$. With center A and radius t, draw an arc intersecting j at C. Draw $\overline{CA}$ and $\overline{CB}$.

14. Const. ⊙R with radius s. Draw diameter $\overline{ST}$. Const. line j, $\parallel$ to and r units from $\overleftrightarrow{ST}$. Line j intersects ⊙R at pts. Y and Z. Rt. △ SYT and SZT both satisfy the requirements.

15. Const. $\overline{AB}$ of length r. Const. line $j \perp \overline{AB}$ at B. With center A and radius s, draw an arc intercepting j at C. Draw $\overline{AC}$. Const. $\overline{CE}$ and $\overline{CD}$, both on j, so that $CE = CD = s$. $\triangle ACD$ and $\triangle ACE$ are the two △.

Additional Answers
Self-Test 3

4. the intersection of the bisector of $\angle DEF$ and a pair of rays $\parallel$ to $\overrightarrow{EF}$ and each 4 cm from $\overrightarrow{EF}$ (1 point)
5. the intersection of $\odot A$ with radius 4 cm and a line $\parallel$ to s and t halfway between them (0, 1, or 2 points)
6. Use Const. 4 to const. the $\perp$ bis. of 2 sides of $\triangle RST$. The locus is the point of intersection of the $\perp$ bisectors.

Using a Computer

To use a construction program with this Extra, see page T121.

Self-Test 3

1. the bis. of the vertical $\measuredangle$ formed by j and k (2 lines)

Describe briefly the locus of points that satisfy the conditions.

1. In the plane of two intersecting lines j and k, and equidistant from the lines
2. In space and t units from point P **the sphere with ctr. P and radius t**
3. In space and equidistant from points W and X that are 10 cm apart **the $\perp$ bis. plane of $\overline{WX}$**
4. In the plane of $\angle DEF$, equidistant from the sides of the angle, and 4 cm from $\overrightarrow{EF}$
5. In the plane of two parallel lines s and t, equidistant from s and t, and 4 cm from a particular point A in the plane (three possibilities)
6. Construct a large isosceles $\triangle RST$. Then construct the locus of points that are equidistant from the vertices of $\triangle RST$.
7. Draw a long segment, $\overline{BC}$, and an acute angle, $\angle 1$. Construct a right triangle with an acute angle congruent to $\angle 1$ and hypotenuse congruent to $\overline{BC}$. **Const. may vary. Example: Const. $\angle X \cong \angle 1$. Const. $\overline{XY} \cong \overline{BC}$ on one side of $\angle X$. Const. a line from $Y \perp$ to the other side of $\angle X$.**

Extra — *The Nine-Point Circle*

Given any $\triangle ABC$, let H be the intersection of the three altitudes. There is a circle that passes through these nine special points:

midpoints L, M, N of the three sides

points R, S, T, where the three altitudes of the triangle meet the sides

midpoints X, Y, Z of $\overline{HA}$, $\overline{HB}$, $\overline{HC}$

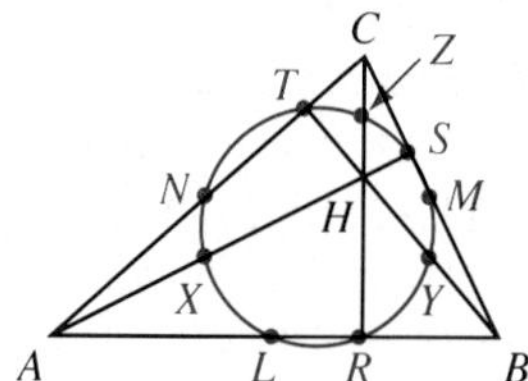

Key steps of proof:

1. $XYMN$ is a rectangle.
2. The circle circumscribed about $XYMN$ has diameters $\overline{MX}$ and $\overline{NY}$.
3. Because $\angle XSM$ and $\angle YTN$ are right angles, the circle contains points S and T as well as X, Y, M, and N.
4. $XLMZ$ is a rectangle.
5. The circle circumscribed about $XLMZ$ has diameters $\overline{MX}$ and $\overline{LZ}$.
6. Because $\angle XSM$ and $\angle ZRL$ are right angles, the circle contains points S and R as well as X, L, M, and Z.

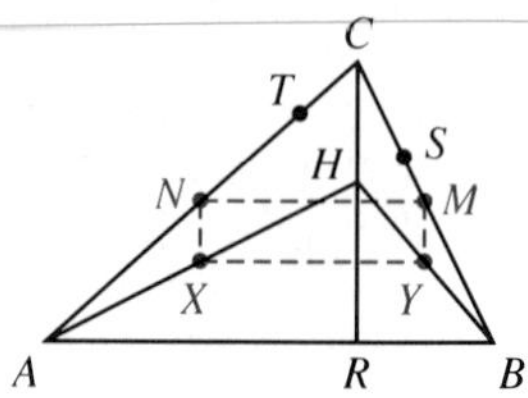

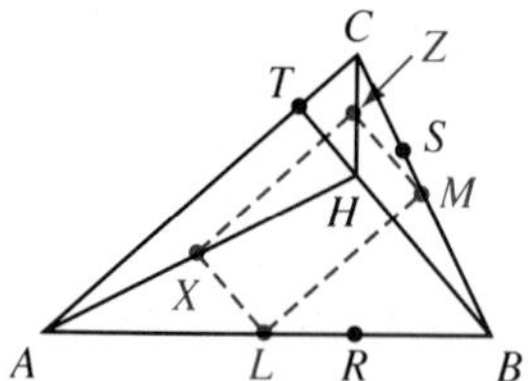

7. The circle of Steps 1–3 and the circle of Steps 4–6 must be the same circle, because $\overline{MX}$ is a diameter of both circles.
8. There is a circle that passes through the nine points, L, M, N, R, S, T, X, Y, and Z. (See Steps 3 and 6.)

One way to locate the center of the circle is to locate points X and M, then the midpoint of $\overline{XM}$.

Exercises

1. Test your mechanical skill by constructing the nine-point circle for an acute triangle. (The larger the figure, the better.)
2. Repeat Exercise 1, but use an obtuse triangle.
3. Repeat Exercise 1, but use an equilateral triangle. What happens to some of the nine points? **Some of the pts. are the same: *L* and *R*, *M* and *S*, *N* and *T*. The ⊙ has ctr. *H*.**
4. Repeat Exercise 1, but use a right triangle. How many of the nine points are at the vertex of the right angle? **3; if ∠ *C* is a rt. ∠, the legs are alt. and $S = T = Z = C$**
5. Prove that $XYMN$ is a rectangle. Use the diagram shown for Steps 1–3 of the key steps of proof. (*Hint*: Compare $\overline{NM}$ with $\overline{AB}$ and $\overline{NX}$ with $\overline{CR}$.)
6. What is the ratio of the radius of the nine-point circle to the radius of the circumscribed circle? **1:2**

Chapter Summary

1. Geometric constructions are diagrams that are drawn using only a straightedge and a compass.
2. Basic constructions:
   (1) A segment congruent to a given segment, page 375
   (2) An angle congruent to a given angle, page 376
   (3) The bisector of a given angle, page 376
   (4) The perpendicular bisector of a given segment, page 380
   (5) A line perpendicular to a given line at a given point on the line, page 381
   (6) A line perpendicular to a given line from a given point outside the line, page 381
   (7) A line parallel to a given line through a given point outside the line, page 382
   (8) A tangent to a given circle at a given point on the circle, page 392
   (9) A tangent to a given circle from a given point outside the circle, page 393
   (10) A circle circumscribed about a given triangle, page 393
   (11) A circle inscribed in a given triangle, page 394

Quick Quiz

Describe briefly the locus of points that satisfy the conditions.

1. in a plane and equidistant from the sides of an angle — the angle bisector
2. in a plane and 10 cm from point B — a ⊙ with ctr. B and radius 10 cm
3. in space and equidistant from two points — a plane that is the ⊥ bisector of the segment joining the two points
4. In a plane, given a point X and $\overline{YZ}$, the locus of points that are r units from X and equidistant from the endpoints of $\overline{YZ}$ (three possibilities). The locus could be 0 points, 1 point, or 2 points, depending upon the intersection of ⊙X with radius r and the ⊥ bis. of $\overline{YZ}$.
5. Construct a right △ROG with $\overline{RG}$ the hypotenuse. Then construct the locus of points that are equidistant from points O, G, and R. the point where the ⊥ bisectors meet: the midpt. of $\overline{RG}$
6. Construct a right △ABC, given the hypotenuse $\overline{AC}$ and leg $\overline{AB}$.

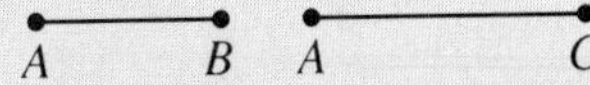

Draw a line l and choose point B. Const. a ⊥ to l at B. Locate A on the ⊥. With ctr. A and radius AC, locate C on l.

(12) Division of a given segment into any number of congruent parts, page 396

(13) A segment of length x such that $\frac{a}{b} = \frac{c}{x}$ when segments of lengths a, b, and c are given, page 397

(14) A segment whose length is the geometric mean between the lengths of two given segments, page 397

3. Every triangle has these concurrency properties:
   (1) The bisectors of the angles intersect in a point that is equidistant from the three sides of the triangle.
   (2) The perpendicular bisectors of the sides intersect in a point that is equidistant from the three vertices of the triangle.
   (3) The lines that contain the altitudes intersect in a point.
   (4) The medians intersect in a point that is two thirds of the distance from each vertex to the midpoint of the opposite side.
4. A locus is the set of all points, and only those points, that satisfy one or more conditions.
5. A locus that satisfies more than one condition is found by considering all possible intersections of the loci for the separate conditions.

Supplementary Materials

Practice Master 61

Test 41

Resource Book, pp. 66–69, 150

Chapter Review

In Exercises 1–3 draw a diagram that is similar to, but larger than, the one shown. Then do the constructions.

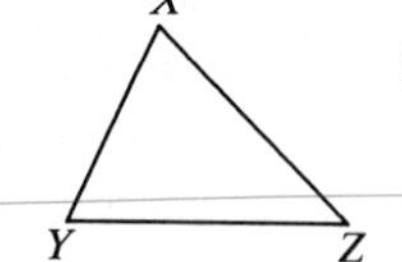

1. Draw any line m. On m construct $\overline{ST}$ such that $ST = 3XY$. 10–1
2. Construct an angle with measure equal to $m\angle X + m\angle Z$.
3. Bisect $\angle Y$. **Const. 3**

Use a diagram like the one below for Exercises 4–7.

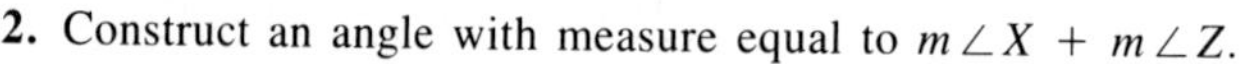

4. Construct the perpendicular bisector of $\overline{AB}$. **Const. 4** 10–2
5. Construct the perpendicular to $\overleftrightarrow{AC}$ at C. **Const. 5**
6. Construct the perpendicular to $\overleftrightarrow{AC}$ from D. **Const. 6**
7. Construct the parallel to $\overleftrightarrow{AC}$ through E. **Const. 7**

8. The __?__ of a triangle intersect in a point that is equidistant from the vertices of the triangle. **See below.** 10–3

9. The __?__ of a triangle intersect in a point that is equidistant from the sides of the triangle. **∠ bisectors**

10. If $MR = 12$, then $MP =$ __?__. **18**

11. $QR:RO =$ __?__ (numerical answer) **1:2**

8. ⊥ bisectors of the sides

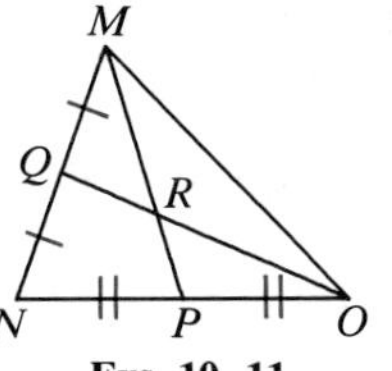

Exs. 10, 11

Draw a large ⊙*O*. Label a point *F* on ⊙*O* and a point *G* outside ⊙*O*.

12. Construct the tangent to ⊙O at F. **Const. 8** 10–4

13. Construct a tangent to ⊙O from G. **Const. 9**

14. Draw a large acute triangle. Find, by construction, the center of the circle that could be inscribed in the triangle. **See below.**

15. Draw a large obtuse triangle. Construct a circle that circumscribes the triangle. **Const. 10**

14. Const. the bis. of 2 of the ⚠s. Their int. is the ctr. of the inscribed circle.

Draw segments about as long as those shown below. In each exercise, construct a segment with the required length *t*.

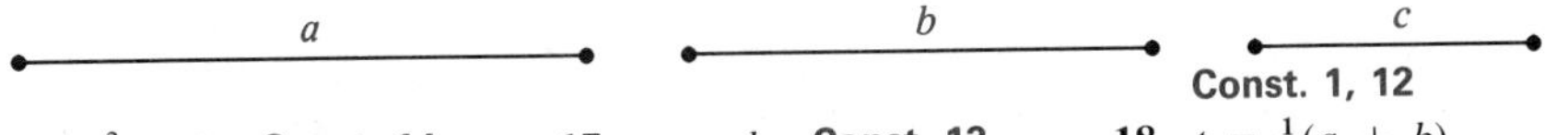

Const. 1, 12

16. $t^2 = bc$ **Const. 14** **17.** $at = bc$ **Const. 13** **18.** $t = \frac{1}{3}(a + b)$ 10–5

19. Given two parallel lines l and m, what is the locus of points in their plane and equidistant from them? **a line ∥ to *l* and *m* and halfway between them** 10–6

20. Given two points A and B, what is the locus of points, in space, equidistant from A and B? **the ⊥ bis. plane of $\overline{AB}$**

21. What is the locus of points in space equidistant from two parallel planes?

22. What is the locus of points in space that are equidistant from the vertices of equilateral $\triangle HJK$?

23. Points P and Q are 6 cm apart. What is the locus of points in a plane that are equidistant from P and Q and are 8 cm from P? Sketch the locus. 10–7

24. Point R is on line l. What is the locus in space of points that are 8 cm from l and 8 cm from R?

25. What is the locus of points in space that are 1 m from plane Q and 2 m from point Z not in Q? (There is more than one possibility.)

Use the segments with lengths *a*, *b*, and *c* that you drew for Exercises 16–18.

26. Construct an isosceles right triangle with hypotenuse of length a. 10–8

27. Construct a $\triangle RST$ with $RS = a$, $RT = c$, and the median to $\overline{RS}$ of length b.

Additional Answers Chapter Review

21. a plane ∥ to both planes and halfway between them

22. a line ⊥ to the plane of $\triangle HJK$ at the intersection of the medians (or altitudes or ∠ bisectors)

23. the intersection of the ⊥ bis. of $\overline{PQ}$ and ⊙P with radius 8 cm (2 points)

24. the intersection of the cylindrical surface with axis l and radius 8 cm, and the sphere with center R and radius 8 cm: a circle

25. 0 points, 1 point, a ⊙, a ⊙ and a point, or 2 ⊙s, depending on the intersection of 2 planes ∥ to Q and 1 m from Q and a sphere with center Z and radius 2 m.

Teaching References

Alternate Test, p. T21

Chapter Test **1–7. Methods may vary.**

Begin by drawing segments and an angle roughly like those shown.

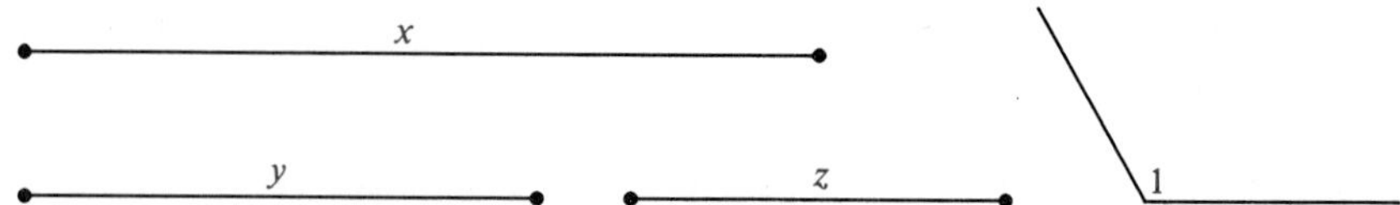

1. Construct an isosceles triangle with vertex angle congruent to ∠ 1 and legs of length z. **Const. 2, 1**
2. Construct a 30°-60°-90° triangle with shorter leg of length y.
3. Construct a segment of length $\sqrt{xy}$. **Const. 14**
4. Construct a segment of length $\frac{2}{3}(y + 2z)$. **Const. 1, 12**
5. Construct a segment of length n such that $\frac{x}{z} = \frac{y}{n}$. **Const. 13**
6. Draw a large circle and a point K not on the circle. Using K as one vertex, construct any triangle that is circumscribed about the circle. **See below.**
7. Draw a large triangle and construct the circle inscribed in the triangle. **Const. 11**
8. In a right triangle **(a)** the __?__ of the triangle intersect at a point on the hypotenuse, **(b)** the __?__ intersect at a point inside the triangle, and **(c)** the altitudes of the triangle intersect at a __?__ of the triangle. **See below.**
9. An isosceles triangle has sides of length 5, 5, and 8.
   a. What is the length of the median to the base? **3**
   b. When the three medians are drawn, the median to the base is divided into segments with lengths __?__ and __?__. **2, 1**
10. Given points R and S in plane Z, what is the locus of points **(a)** in Z and equidistant from R and S and **(b)** in space and equidistant from R and S? **See below.**
11. Given points T and U 8 units apart, what is the locus of points, in space, that are 6 units from T and 4 units from U? **See below.**
12. Draw a line l and a point A on it. Using y and z from Exercises 1–5, construct the locus of points z units from l and y units from A.

6. Use Const. 9 to const. 2 tangents to the ⊙ from *K*. Choose a pt. *P* on the major arc det. by the tangents (other than the end pts. of the arc). Use Const. 8 to const. a tangent to the ⊙ at *P*; the 3 tangents intersect to form the required △.

8. a. ⊥ bis. of the sides b. ∠ bis. or medians c. vertex

10. a. the ⊥ bis. of $\overline{RS}$ b. the ⊥ bis. plane of $\overline{RS}$

11. a ⊙ formed by the intersection of a sphere with ctr. *T*, *r* = 6, and a sphere with ctr. *U*, *r* = 4

Additional Answers Chapter Test

2. Construct $\overline{AB}$ of length y. Const. line $j \perp$ to $\overline{AB}$ at B. Draw an arc with ctr. A and radius $2y$ that intersects j at pt. C. $\triangle ABC$ is a 30°-60°-90°△.

12. Const. 2 lines, ∥ to and z units from line l. Const. ⊙A with radius y units. The locus is the intersection of the 2 lines and the circle (4 points).

Algebra Review: *Evaluating Formulas*

Evaluate each expression for the given values of the variables.

Example $\frac{1}{2}bh$ when $b = 12$ and $h = 6\sqrt{3}$ **Solution** $\frac{1}{2}(12)(6\sqrt{3}) = 36\sqrt{3}$

1. Area of a square: s^2 when $s = 1.3$ **1.69**
2. Length of hypotenuse of a right triangle: $\sqrt{a^2 + b^2}$ when $a = 15$ and $b = 20$ **25**
3. Perimeter of parallelogram: $2x + 2y$ when $x = \frac{5}{3}$ and $y = \frac{3}{2}$ $\mathbf{\frac{19}{3}}$
4. Perimeter of triangle: $a + b + c$ when $a = 11.5$, $b = 7.2$, and $c = 9.9$ **28.6**
5. Area of a rectangle: lw when $l = 2\sqrt{6}$ and $w = 3\sqrt{3}$ $\mathbf{18\sqrt{2}}$
6. Perimeter of isosceles trapezoid: $2r + s + t$ when $r = \frac{4}{7}$, $s = 1$, and $t = \frac{13}{7}$ **4**
7. πr^2 when $r = 30$ (Use 3.14 for π.) **2826**
8. lwh when $l = 8$, $w = 6\frac{1}{4}$, and $h = 3\frac{1}{2}$ **175**
9. $2(lw + wh + lh)$ when $l = 4.5$, $w = 3$, and $h = 1$ **42**
10. $\frac{x-3}{y+2}$ when $x = 3$ and $y = -4$ **0**
11. $\frac{x+5}{y-2}$ when $x = -2$ and $y = -4$ $\mathbf{-\frac{1}{2}}$
12. $mx + b$ when $x = -6$, $m = \frac{5}{2}$, and $b = -2$ **−17**
13. $6t^2$ when $t = 3$ **54**
14. $(6t)^2$ when $t = 3$ **324**
15. $\frac{1}{2}h(a + b)$ when $h = 3$, $a = 3\sqrt{2}$, and $b = 7\sqrt{2}$ $\mathbf{15\sqrt{2}}$
16. $\sqrt{(x-5)^2 + (y-3)^2}$ when $x = 1$ and $y = 0$ **5**
17. $\frac{1}{3}x^2h$ when $x = 4\sqrt{3}$ and $h = 6$ **96**
18. $2s^2 + 4sh$ when $s = \sqrt{6}$ and $h = \frac{5}{2}\sqrt{6}$ **72**

Use the given information to rewrite each expression.

Example Bh when $B = \frac{1}{2}rs$ **Solution** $Bh = (\frac{1}{2}rs)h = \frac{1}{2}rsh$

19. $c(x + y)$ when $x + y = d$ ***cd***
20. $\frac{1}{3}Bh$ when $B = \pi r^2$ $\mathbf{\frac{1}{3}\pi r^2 h}$
21. $\frac{1}{2}pl$ when $p = 2\pi r$ $\mathbf{\pi r l}$
22. $2(l + w)$ when $l = s$ and $w = s$ **4*s***
23. $4\pi r^2$ when $r = \frac{1}{2}d$ $\mathbf{\pi d^2}$
24. $n(\frac{1}{2}sa)$ when $ns = p$ $\mathbf{\frac{1}{2}pa}$

Solve each formula for the variable shown in color.

Example $y = mx + b$ **Solution** $y - b = mx$; $x = \frac{y-b}{m}$, $m \neq 0$

25. $ax + by = c$
26. $C = \pi d$ $\mathbf{d = \frac{C}{\pi}}$
27. $S = (n - 2)180$
28. $x^2 + y^2 = r^2$
29. $\frac{x}{h} = \frac{h}{y}$ $\mathbf{h = \pm\sqrt{xy}}$
30. $a^2 + b^2 = (a\sqrt{2})^2$ $\mathbf{b = \pm a}$
31. $A = \frac{1}{2}bh$ $\mathbf{h = \frac{2A}{b}, b \neq 0}$
32. $m = \frac{y+4}{x-2}$ $\mathbf{y = m(x-2) - 4}$

Additional Answers Algebra Review

25. $x = \frac{c - by}{a}$, $a \neq 0$
27. $n = \frac{S}{180} + 2$
28. $y = \pm\sqrt{r^2 - x^2}$, $r^2 - x^2 \geq 0$

Supplementary Materials

Practice Masters 62, 63

Test 42

Resource Book, pp. 70–72, 151, 180–182, 199

Preparing for College Entrance Exams

Strategy for Success

Often the answer to a question can be found by writing an equation or inequality and solving it. When a complete solution is time-consuming, you may find that the fastest way to answer the question is to test the suggested answers in your equation or inequality.

Indicate the best answer by writing the appropriate letter.

B **1.** $\overline{AB}$ and $\overline{AC}$ are tangent to $\odot O$ at B and C. If $m\widehat{BC} = x$, then $m\angle BAC =$
(A) x **(B)** $180 - x$ **(C)** $360 - x$ **(D)** $180 + x$ **(E)** $\frac{1}{2}x$

C **2.** If quadrilateral $JKLM$ is inscribed in a circle and $\angle J$ and $\angle K$ are supplementary angles, then $\angle J$:
(A) must be congruent to $\angle L$
(B) must be a right angle
(C) must be congruent to $\angle M$
(D) must be an acute angle
(E) must be supplementary to $\angle M$

E **3.** In $\odot M$, chords $\overline{RS}$ and $\overline{TU}$ intersect at X. If $RX = 15$, $XS = 18$, and $TX:XU = 3:10$, then $XU =$
(A) 3 **(B)** 9 **(C)** $20\frac{10}{13}$ **(D)** $25\frac{5}{13}$ **(E)** 30

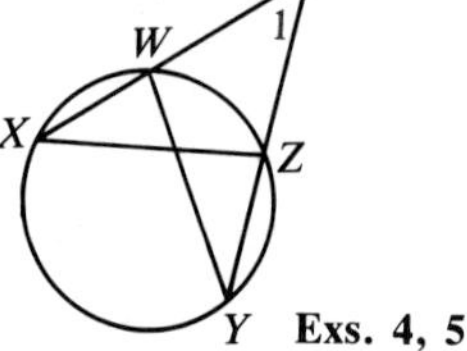

Exs. 4, 5

A **4.** If $m\widehat{XW} = 60$, $m\widehat{WZ} = 70$, and $m\widehat{ZY} = 70$, then $m\angle 1 =$
(A) 45 **(B)** 50 **(C)** 60 **(D)** 65 **(E)** 70

B **5.** If $VW = 10$, $WX = 6$, and $VZ = 8$, then $ZY =$
(A) 4.8 **(B)** 12 **(C)** 7.5 **(D)** 20 **(E)** 16

C **6.** Given $\triangle ABC$, you can find the locus of points in the plane of $\triangle ABC$ and equidistant from $\overline{AB}$, $\overline{BC}$, and $\overline{AC}$ by constructing:
(A) two medians **(B)** two altitudes **(C)** two angle bisectors
(D) the perpendicular bisectors of two sides **(E)** the circumscribed circle

A **7.** To construct a tangent to $\odot R$ from a point S outside $\odot R$, you need to construct:
(A) the perpendicular bisector of $\overline{RS}$
(B) a perpendicular to $\overline{RS}$ at the point where $\overline{RS}$ intersects $\odot R$
(C) a diameter that is perpendicular to $\overline{RS}$
(D) a perpendicular to $\overline{RS}$ through point S
(E) a 30°-60°-90° triangle with vertex S

C **8.** The locus of points 6 cm from plane P and 10 cm from a given point J *cannot* be:
(A) no points **(B)** one point **(C)** a line **(D)** a circle **(E)** two circles

E **9.** The locus of the midpoints of all 8 cm chords in a circle of radius 5 cm is:
(A) a point **(B)** a segment **(C)** a line **(D)** a ray **(E)** a circle

Cumulative Review: Chapters 1–10

Write *always, sometimes,* or *never* to complete each statement.

A

1. A quadrilateral ___?___ has four obtuse angles. **never**
2. Two isosceles right triangles with congruent hypotenuses are ___?___ congruent. **always**
3. If $\overset{\frown}{AC}$ on $\odot O$ and $\overset{\frown}{BD}$ on $\odot P$ have the same measure, then $\overset{\frown}{AC}$ is ___?___ congruent to $\overset{\frown}{BD}$. **sometimes**
4. If two consecutive sides of a parallelogram are perpendicular, then the diagonals are ___?___ perpendicular. **sometimes**
5. If the lengths of the sides of two triangles are in proportion, then the corresponding angles are ___?___ congruent. **always**
6. The tangent of an angle is ___?___ greater than 1. **sometimes**
7. A triangle with sides of length $2x$, $3x$, and $4x$, with $x > 0$, is ___?___ acute. **never**
8. Given a plane containing points A and B, the locus of points in the plane that are equidistant from A and B and are 10 cm from A is ___?___ one point. **sometimes**

Complete each statement in Exercises 9–12.

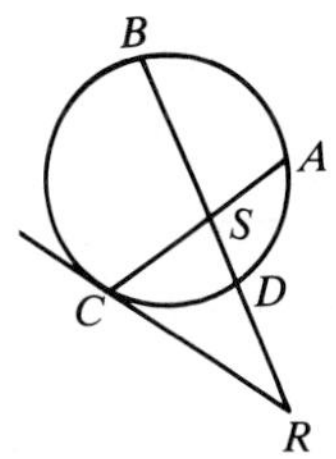

9. If $m\overset{\frown}{AB} = 80$, $m\overset{\frown}{CD} = 66$, and $m\overset{\frown}{DA} = 70$, then $m\angle ASD =$ ___?___. **107**
10. If $BS = 12$, $SD = 6$, and $AS = 8$, then $SC =$ ___?___. **9**
11. If $RD = 9$ and $DB = 16$, then $RC =$ ___?___. **15**
12. If $m\overset{\frown}{AB} = 80$, $m\overset{\frown}{CD} = 66$, and $m\overset{\frown}{DA} = 70$, then $m\angle R =$ ___?___. **39**
13. Draw a large $\triangle MNP$. Construct a $\triangle XYZ$ congruent to $\triangle MNP$.

B

14. Describe the locus of points in space that are 4 cm from plane X and 8 cm from point J. **0 pts., 1 pt., a ⊙, a pt. and a ⊙, or 2 ⊙s**
15. $\triangle DEF$ is a right triangle with hypotenuse $\overline{DF}$. $DE = 6$ and $EF = 8$.
    a. If $\overline{EX} \perp \overline{DF}$ at X, find DX. **3.6**
    b. If Y lies on $\overline{DF}$ and $\overrightarrow{EY}$ bisects $\angle DEF$, find DY. **$4\frac{2}{7}$**
16. If each interior angle of a regular polygon has measure 160, how many sides does the polygon have? **18**
17. Given: $\odot O$; $m\angle 1 = 45$
    Prove: $\triangle OPQ$ is a 45°-45°-90° $\triangle$.
18. Use the given diagram to prove that $WX \cdot YV = XV \cdot ZY$.

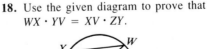

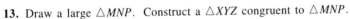

19. Draw $\overline{AB}$. Construct any rectangle with a diagonal congruent to $\overline{AB}$.

Additional Answers Cumulative Review

13. Const. $\overline{XY} \cong \overline{MN}$, $\angle X \cong \angle M$, and $\angle Y \cong \angle N$. Extend the sides of $\angle X$ and $\angle Y$ to intersect at Z. (Other methods are possible.)
19. Const. the ⊥ bis. of $\overline{AB}$ to locate M, the midpoint of $\overline{AB}$. Const. $\odot M$ with diameter $\overline{AB}$. Choose P on $\odot M$ and draw $\overrightarrow{PM}$, int. $\odot M$ at Q. Draw $APBQ$. (Other methods are possible.)

11 Areas of Plane Figures

Objectives

11-1 Understand what is meant by the area of a polygon.

Understand the area postulates.

Know and use the formula for the area of a rectangle.

11-2 Know and use the formulas for the areas of parallelograms, triangles, and rhombuses.

11-3 Know and use the formula for the area of a trapezoid.

11-4 Know and use the formula for the areas of regular polygons.

11-5 Know and use formulas for the circumferences and areas of circles that are derived from the perimeter and area formulas for regular polygons.

11-6 Know and use the formulas for arc length and the areas of sectors of a circle.

11-7 Find the ratio of the areas of two triangles.

Understand and apply the relationships between scale factors, perimeters, and areas of similar figures.

11-8 Use areas to solve problems involving geometric probability.

Assignment Guide

See page T40 for information about the Assignment Guide.

Day	Minimum Course	Average Course	Maximum Course
1	**11-1** 426/1–15 odd, 17–19	**11-1** 426/1, 3, 4, 7, 10, 12, 15, 17, 19, 21	**11-1** 426–427/11, 15, 17–19, 20–28 even, 29–31, 35, 37
2	**11-1** 426–427/2, 10, 14, 16, 20, 22, 23, 25, 28	**11-1** 426–427/18, 20, 22–26, 28, 29, 31, 33	**11-2** 431–432/10, 11, 14, 15–21 odd
3	**11-2** 431/1–9	**11-2** 431/2, 4, 5, 8, 9–11, 13–15, 17, 19	**11-2** 432–433/23–27 odd, 28, 30, 32, 33, 35, 37 **S** 427/36
4	**11-2** 431–432/10–13, 18, 19, 22, 23, 25 **S** 427/26, 29	**11-2** 432–433/21, 22–26, 28, 30, 32, 34	**11-3** 436–437/8, 10, 14, 16, 18, 21, 24, 26–28
5	**11-3** 436/1–7, 9–11	**11-3** 436–437/1, 2, 5, 10–12, 15, 17, 21, 24, 26 440/Mixed Review, 1–8	**11-4** 443–444/7, 10, 13–15, 17 **S** 437/25, 30
6	**11-3** 436–437/12–19 440/Mixed Review 1–8	**11-4** 443/1, 3, 5, 6, 10–13	**11-4** 444/18–22
7	**11-4** 443/1–12	**11-4** 443–444/14, 15, 18–22 444/Self-Test 1	**11-5** 448–450/7, 11, 12, 15, 17, 18, 20, 22–24, 26
8	**11-4** 443/13, 15 444/Self-Test 1	**11-5** 448–449/2, 5–13 odd, 16–19, 21	**11-5** 450/27, 29–34
9	**11-5** 448–449/1–8, 9–15 odd	**11-5** 449–450/23–27, 29, 30, 32	**11-6** 453–455/12, 14, 16–20, 22–26
10	**11-5** 448–449/10–16 even, 17, 18, 21	**11-6** 453–455/3, 4, 6, 10, 11, 13, 14, 16–19, 21, 22, 25	**11-7** 458–459/5, 8, 10, 13, 15, 17, 19, 20 **S** 455/27, 29

11	**11-6** 453–454/1–13 odd, 15–17	**11-7** 458–459/1–15 odd **S** 455/26	**11-7** 459–460/21–31 odd
12	**11-6** 454/18, 19, 21	**11-7** 459–460/16, 18–21, 23, 26, 30	**11-8** 463–464/2–10 even, 11–17 odd
13	**11-7** 458/1–8	**11-8** 463/1–7 odd 465/Self-Test 2 471/Chapter Test Test, page T22	**11-8** 465/Self-Test 2 471/Chapter Test Test, page T22
14	**11-7** 458–459/9–12, 14, 15, 18		
15	**11-7** 465/Self-Test 2, 1–8 471/Chapter Test 1–18 Test, page T22		

Supplementary Materials Guide

For Use after Lesson	Practice Masters	Tests	Study Guide (Reteaching)	Resource Book: Tests	Resource Book: Practice Exercises	Resource Book: College Entrance (Col) Enrichment (E) Computer (C)	Computer Activities
11-1			pp. 137–138				Activity 22
11-2	Sheet 64		pp. 139–140				
11-3	Sheet 65		pp. 141–142				
11-4	Sheet 66	Test 43	pp. 143–144	p. 73	p. 152		
11-5	Sheet 67		pp. 145–146				Activity 23
11-6	Sheet 68	Test 44	pp. 147–148	p. 74	p. 153		
11-7	Sheet 69		pp. 149–150				
11-8	Sheet 70	Test 45	pp. 151–152	p. 75	p. 154		Activity 24
Chapter 11	Sheet 71	Test 46		pp. 76–77	p. 155	p. 200 (Col); p. 255 (C); pp. 210, 225–227 (E)	

Overhead Visuals

Guided Discovery Visuals (lettered) and Teaching Visuals (numbered) available for Chapter 11.

Lessons	Visual	Title
11-3	G	The Pythagorean Theorem: Alternate Proofs
11-2, 11-3	H	Areas of Simple Polygons
11-1, 11-2, 11-3, 11-4	23	Areas of Polygons
11-5, 11-6, 11-7, 11-8	24	Area and Circumference of a Circle

Software Guide

Houghton Mifflin software for Chapter 11

Geometry Grapher (Apple or IBM)

Use with

p. 433 (Explorations)

Test Generator (Apple or IBM): 120 test items

Other software appropriate for Chapter 11

Geometric Supposer (Apple): Quadrilaterals

GeoDraw (IBM)

Spreadsheets

Guide to Integrated Curriculum

Teachers wishing to integrate coordinate and transformational geometry throughout the course can use the following lessons after Chapter 11. See pages T56–T57 and 657 for more information.

Handbook: Areas, pp. 670–672

Exploring Geometric Probability

When to Use

Before Lesson 11-8, or with Example 3 and Written Exercises 9, 10, 12, 13 of Lesson 11-8 (pp. 462–463).

Overview

In this activity students will be introduced to geometric probability by simulating a situation that can be analyzed using areas. They will also explore relationships between experimental probability and theoretical probability.

Materials

- $\frac{1}{2}$-in. and $\frac{3}{8}$-in. square grid paper
- $\frac{1}{4}$-in. (diameter) paper punch
- heavy-weight paper, such as that used to make manila folders

Description of Activity

1. Use the paper punch to make at least 20 disks from the heavy-weight paper. Make a table to record the number of "Wins" and the number of "Tosses" for each trial. For each trial, perform the following steps a minimum of 20 times.

a. Hold a disk about 12 in. above the middle of the grid paper.

b. Drop the disk on the paper. If it lands in the interior of a square (without touching or overlapping any grid lines), it is a "Win." Record the number of "Wins" in the first row.

c. Record the total number of disks used in the "Tosses" row.

d. Repeat 6 times, or as many as you like.

e. Add the numbers in the "Wins" row and the "Tosses" row. Compare the ratio of number of "Wins" to number of "Tosses" with the theoretical result from Example 3 on page 462.

f. Repeat these steps for the second size of grid paper.

2. How do the results you obtained using the $\frac{1}{2}$-in. grid differ from those using the $\frac{3}{8}$-in. grid? Why might the results be different?

3. How is the number of times the experiment is performed related to the difference between the experimental probability and the theoretical probability?

Commentary

- This activity can be done effectively in groups of 3 or 4 students. Ask one student in each group to act as recorder while others perform the experiments. You can then compile the results from all groups. Discuss why compiling the results from all of the groups will bring the experimental probability closer to the theoretical probability.
- **2.** Students should find that there are more "wins" with the $\frac{1}{2}$-in. grid paper. The grid squares are much larger in relation to the size of the disk, so the disk has more of a chance to land in a "win" position.
- **3.** The more times an experiment is performed, the closer the experimental probability will be to the theoretical probability.

Extensions and Variations

For each trial, generate 20 pairs (x, y) of random numbers, each between 0 and 1. Use a random number table, your calculator, or a computer. Find the experimental probability of each:

a. $0.75 < x + y < 1.5$ **b.** $1 < \frac{x}{y} < 2$.

Do as many trials as you wish. Then compute the theoretical probability in each case by comparing the areas of appropriately sketched regions in the coordinate plane. (The theoretical probability for **a** is $\frac{19}{32}$, or approximately 0.59, and for **b** is $\frac{1}{4}$, or 0.25.)

References to Strategies

PE: Pupil's Edition **TE:** Teacher's Edition **RB:** Resource Book

Problem Solving Strategies

PE: 425 (Choose a method of solution), 427 (Exs. 35, 36, Mathematical model), 442 (Choose a method of solution), 455 (Challenge, Deductive argument), 461–464 (Apply a formula, Mathematical model)
TE: 461 (Imagine a simulation)
RB: 225–227 (Solve a simpler problem)

Applications

PE: 422 (Furniture design), 427 (Exs. 29, 30, Painting surfaces), 427 (Ex. 35, Maximizing area), 449–450, 454–455, 462–464 (Geometric probability), 467–469 (Space shuttle landings)
TE: 423

Nonroutine Problems

PE: 425 (Ex. 15), 427 (Exs. 35, 36), 433 (Ex. 34), 436 (Ex. 7), 438 (Ex. 32), 455 (Exs. 26, 27, Challenge), 461–464 (Geometric probability), 465–466 (Congruence and area), 469 (Application), 671–672 (Exs. 1–7)
TE: T122, T126
RB: 225–227

Communication

TE: T125, T126, 450, 454

Thinking Skills

TE: 441 (Dissect a diagram), 452 (Recall definitions)
RB: 264 (Van Hiele activity)

Explorations

PE: 433
TE: 421c

Connections

PE: 434 (Heron), 451 (Archimedes, Sharpe, Vieta, Wallis), 451 (Algebraic expressions), 461–464 (Geometric probability), 670–672 (Transformational geometry)
TE: T124, 428, 434 (Trigonometry), 438 (Calculus), 446 (Limits), 671 (Infinite series)

Using Technology

PE: 428, 433, 434, 435, 438–439, 445, 451
TE: T122, T123, 433
RB: 255
Computer Activities: 53–59

Using Manipulatives/Models

PE: 427 (Exs. 35, 36), 433 (Exs. 34, 38), 461–464, 670–672
TE: T123, T125, 424, 458, 672
RB: 225, 226
Overhead Visuals: G, H, 23, 24

Cooperative Learning

TE: T124, T125, T126, 450, 454

Teaching Resources

For use in implementing the teaching strategies referenced on the previous page.

Using Models
Resource Book, p. 225

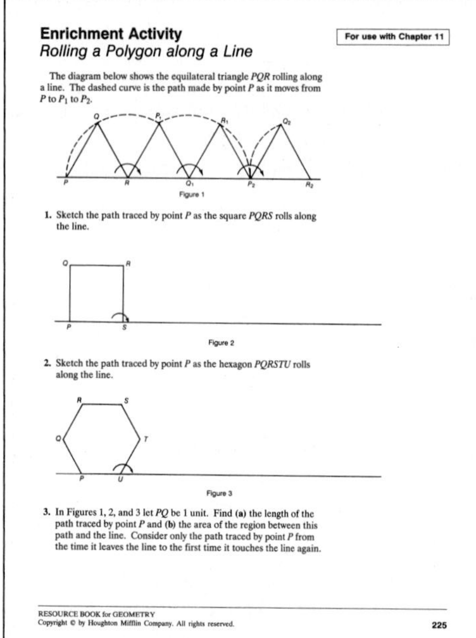

Enrichment Activity | For use with Chapter 11

Rolling a Polygon along a Line

The diagram below shows the equilateral triangle *PQR* rolling along a line. The dashed curve is the path made by point *P* as it moves from *P* to P_1 to P_2.

Figure 1

1. Sketch the path traced by point *P* as the square *PQRS* rolls along the line.

Figure 2

2. Sketch the path traced by point *P* as the hexagon *PQRSTU* rolls along the line.

Figure 3

3. In Figures 1, 2, and 3 let *PQ* be 1 unit. Find **(a)** the length of the path traced by point *P* and **(b)** the area of the region between this path and the line. Consider only the path traced by point *P* from the time it leaves the line to the first time it touches the line again.

225

Using Models
Resource Book, p. 226

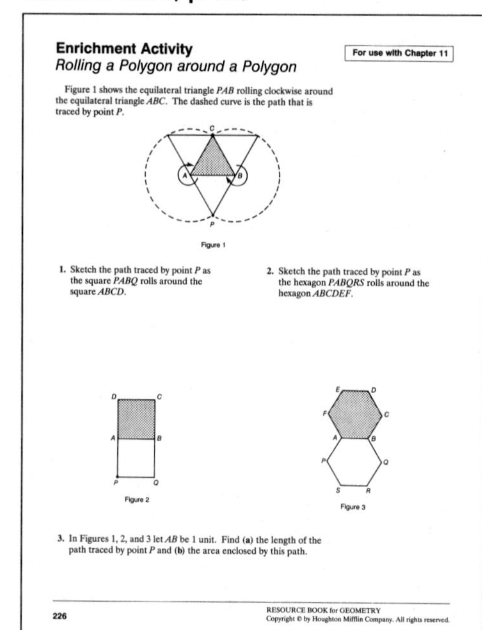

Enrichment Activity | For use with Chapter 11

Rolling a Polygon around a Polygon

Figure 1 shows the equilateral triangle *PAB* rolling clockwise around the equilateral triangle *ABC*. The dashed curve is the path that is traced by point *P*.

Figure 1

1. Sketch the path traced by point *P* as the square *PABQ* rolls around the square *ABCD*.

2. Sketch the path traced by point *P* as the hexagon *PABQRS* rolls around the hexagon *ABCDEF*.

Figure 2

Figure 3

3. In Figures 1, 2, and 3 let *AB* be 1 unit. Find **(a)** the length of the path traced by point *P* and **(b)** the area enclosed by this path.

226

Problem Solving
Resource Book, p. 227

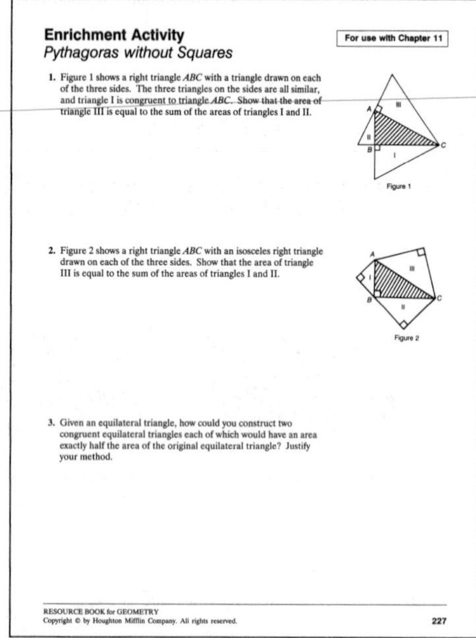

Enrichment Activity | For use with Chapter 11

Pythagoras without Squares

1. Figure 1 shows a right triangle *ABC* with a triangle drawn on each of the three sides. The three triangles on the sides are all similar, and triangle I is congruent to triangle *ABC*. Show that the area of triangle III is equal to the sum of the areas of triangles I and II.

Figure 1

2. Figure 2 shows a right triangle *ABC* with an isosceles right triangle drawn on each of the three sides. Show that the area of triangle III is equal to the sum of the areas of triangles I and II.

Figure 2

3. Given an equilateral triangle, how could you construct two congruent equilateral triangles each of which would have an area exactly half the area of the original equilateral triangle? Justify your method.

227

Thinking Skills
Resource Book, p. 264

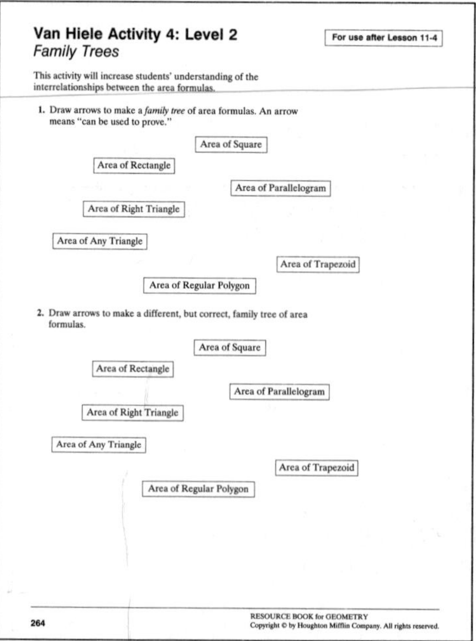

Van Hiele Activity 4: Level 2 | For use after Lesson 11-4

Family Trees

This activity will increase students' understanding of the interrelationships between the area formulas.

1. Draw arrows to make a *family tree* of area formulas. An arrow means "can be used to prove."

2. Draw arrows to make a different, but correct, family tree of area formulas.

264

Application/Connection
Study Guide, p. 151

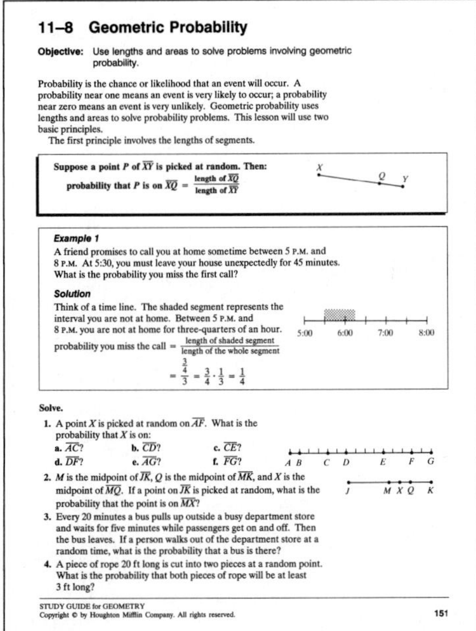

11–8 Geometric Probability

Objective: Use lengths and areas to solve problems involving geometric probability.

Probability is the chance or likelihood that an event will occur. A probability near one means an event is very likely to occur; a probability near zero means an event is very unlikely. Geometric probability uses lengths and areas to solve probability problems. This lesson will use two basic principles.

The first principle involves the lengths of segments.

Suppose a point P of $\overline{XY}$ is picked at random. Then:

probability that P is on $\overline{XQ}$ = $\frac{\text{length of } \overline{XQ}}{\text{length of } \overline{XY}}$

Example 1

A friend promises to call you at home sometime between 5 P.M. and 8 P.M. At 5:30, you must leave your house unexpectedly for 45 minutes. What is the probability you miss the first call?

Solution

Think of a time line. The shaded segment represents the interval you are not at home. Between 5 P.M. and 8 P.M. you are not at home for three-quarters of an hour.

probability you miss the call = $\frac{\text{length of shaded segment}}{\text{length of the whole segment}}$

$$= \frac{\frac{3}{4}}{3} = \frac{3}{4} \cdot \frac{1}{3} = \frac{1}{4}$$

Solve.

1. A point X is picked at random on $\overline{AF}$. What is the probability that X is on:
   a. $\overline{AC}$? **b.** $\overline{CD}$? **c.** $\overline{CE}$?
   d. $\overline{DF}$? **e.** $\overline{AG}$? **f.** $\overline{FG}$?

2. M is the midpoint of $\overline{JK}$, Q is the midpoint of $\overline{MK}$, and X is the midpoint of $\overline{MQ}$. If a point on $\overline{JK}$ is picked at random, what is the probability that the point is on $\overline{MX}$?

3. Every 20 minutes a bus pulls up outside a busy department store and waits for five minutes while passengers get on and off. Then the bus leaves. If a person walks out of the department store at a random time, what is the probability that a bus is there?
4. A piece of rope 20 ft long is cut into two pieces at a random point. What is the probability that both pieces of rope will be at least 3 ft long?

STUDY GUIDE for GEOMETRY

151

Using Models
Teaching Visual 24

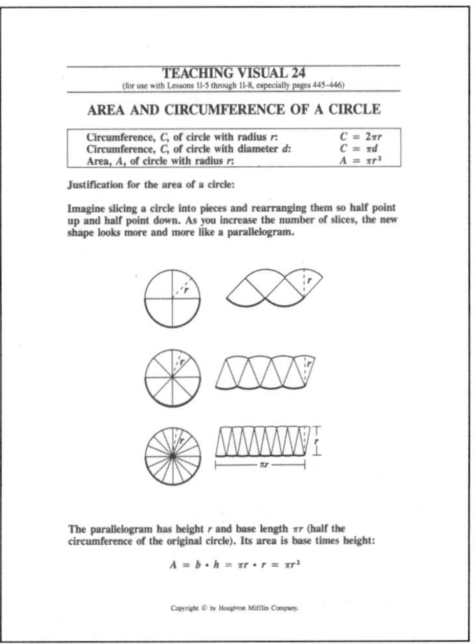

TEACHING VISUAL 24
(for use with Lessons 11-5 through 11-8, especially pages 445–446)

AREA AND CIRCUMFERENCE OF A CIRCLE

Circumference, C, of circle with radius r:	$C = 2\pi r$
Circumference, C, of circle with diameter d:	$C = \pi d$
Area, A, of circle with radius r:	$A = \pi r^2$

Justification for the area of a circle:

Imagine slicing a circle into pieces and rearranging them so half point up and half point down. As you increase the number of slices, the new shape looks more and more like a parallelogram.

The parallelogram has height r and base length πr (half the circumference of the original circle). Its area is base times height:

$$A = b \cdot h = \pi r \cdot r = \pi r^2$$

Problem Solving/Connection
Guided Discovery Visual G, Sheet 3

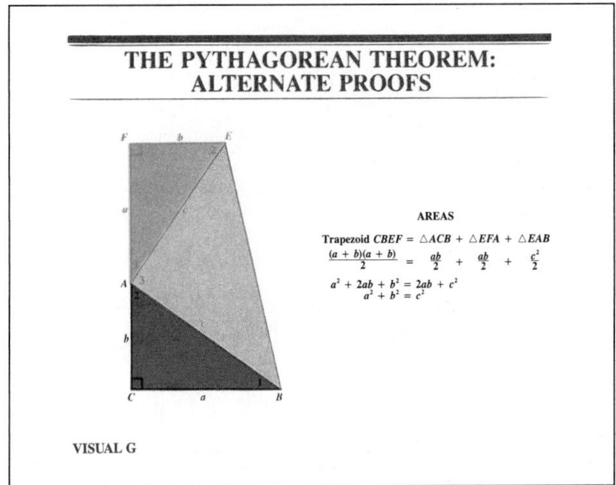

THE PYTHAGOREAN THEOREM: ALTERNATE PROOFS

AREAS

Trapezoid $CBEF$ = $\triangle ACB + \triangle EFA + \triangle EAB$

$$\frac{(a+b)(a+b)}{2} = \frac{ab}{2} + \frac{ab}{2} + \frac{c^2}{2}$$

$$a^2 + 2ab + b^2 = 2ab + c^2$$
$$a^2 + b^2 = c^2$$

VISUAL G

Using Models
Guided Discovery Visual H, Sheet 3

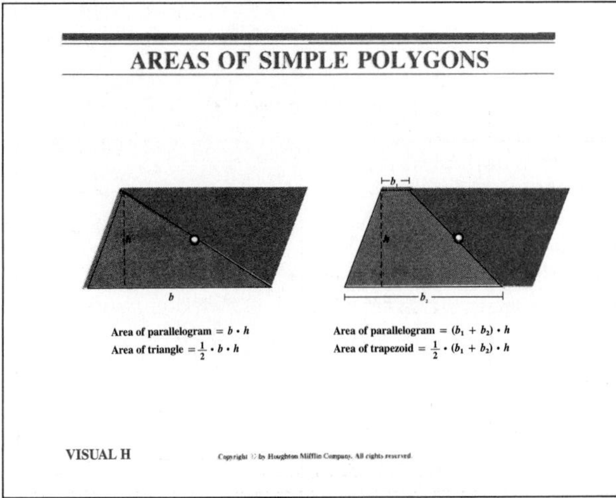

AREAS OF SIMPLE POLYGONS

Area of parallelogram = $b \cdot h$
Area of triangle = $\frac{1}{2} \cdot b \cdot h$

Area of parallelogram = $(b_1 + b_2) \cdot h$
Area of trapezoid = $\frac{1}{2} \cdot (b_1 + b_2) \cdot h$

VISUAL H

Teaching References

Lesson Commentary, pp. T122–T127
Assignment Guide, pp. T48–T50
Software Guide, p. T73
Alternate Test, p. T22

Supplementary Materials

Practice Masters 64–71
Tests 43–46
Resource Book
- Tests, pp. 73–77
- Practice, pp. 152–155
- Preparing for College Entrance Exams, p. 200
- Enrichment Activities, pp. 210, 225–227
- Computer Activity, p. 255
- van Hiele Activity, p. 264

Study Guide, pp. 137–152
Overhead Visuals G, H, 23, 24
Computer Activities
- 22 Perimeter and Area
- 23 Approximation of Pi
- 24 Geometric Probability

Handbook for Integrating Coordinate and Transformational Geometry

Areas, pp. 670–672

Cultural Note

Much of what is known about ancient Egyptian mathematics comes from two papyri that date from around 1650 and 1850 B.C. These documents indicate that the Egyptians knew how to calculate the areas of a number of plane figures.

11 AREAS OF PLANE FIGURES

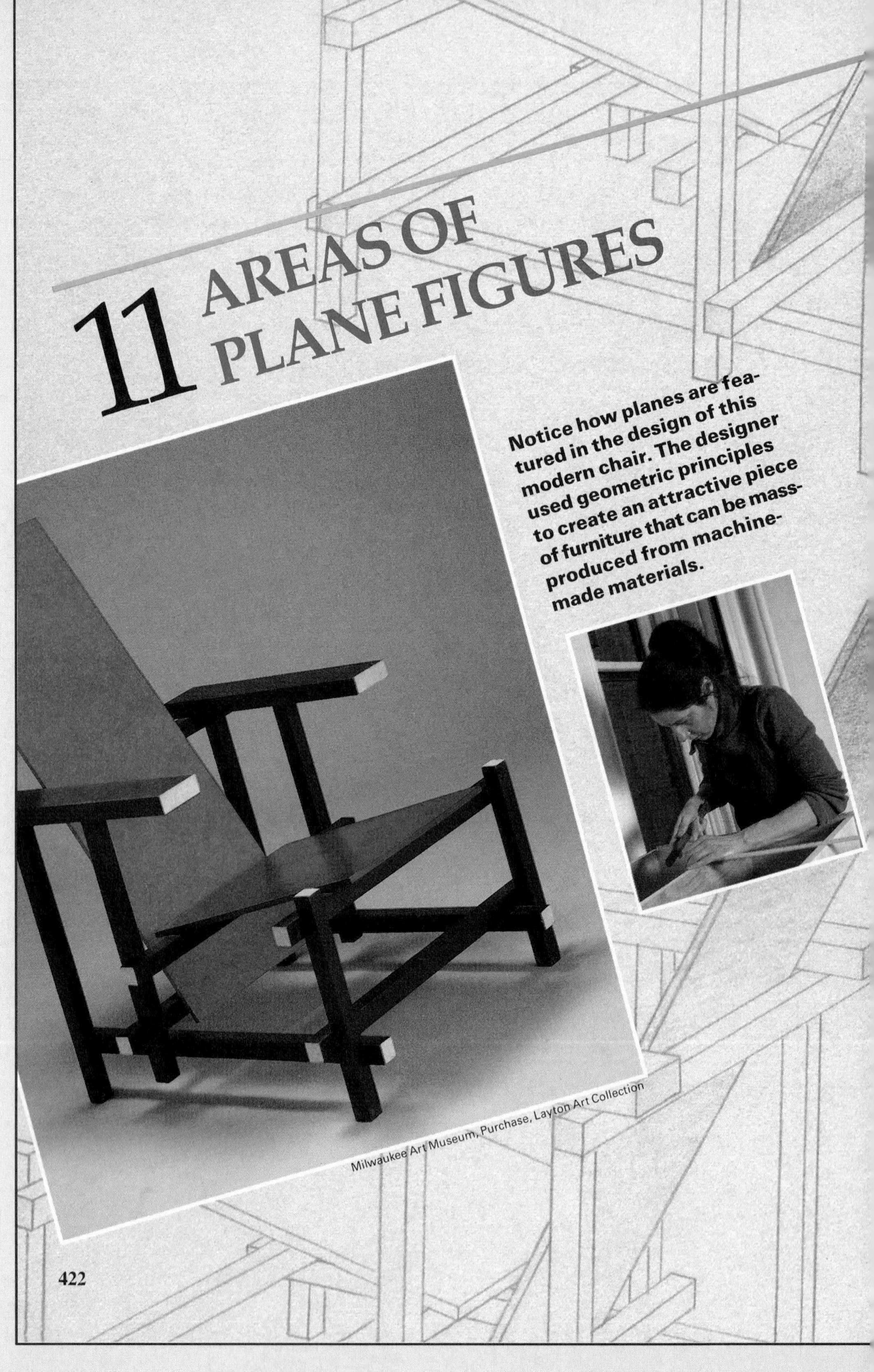

Notice how planes are featured in the design of this modern chair. The designer used geometric principles to create an attractive piece of furniture that can be mass-produced from machine-made materials.

Milwaukee Art Museum, Purchase, Layton Art Collection

Areas of Polygons

Objectives

1. Understand what is meant by the area of a polygon.
2. Understand the area postulates.
3. Know and use the formulas for the areas of rectangles, parallelograms, triangles, rhombuses, trapezoids, and regular polygons.

11-1 *Areas of Rectangles*

In everyday conversation people often refer to the *area* of a rectangle when what they really mean is the area of a rectangular region.

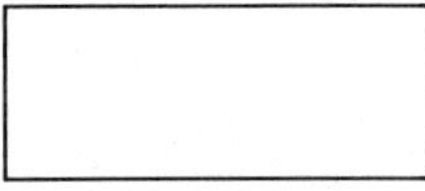
Rectangle

Rectangular region

We will continue this common practice to simplify our discussion. Thus, when we speak of the area of a triangle, we will mean the area of the triangular region that includes the triangle *and* its interior.

In Chapter 1 we accepted postulates that enable us to express the lengths of segments and the measures of angles as positive numbers. Similarly, the areas of figures are positive numbers with properties given by area postulates.

Postulate 17
The area of a square is the square of the length of a side. ($A = s^2$)

Length: 1 unit

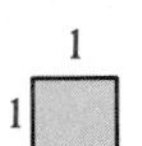

Area: 1 square unit

By counting,
Area = 9 square units

By using the formula,
Area $= 3^2 = 9$ (square units)

Postulate 18 *Area Congruence Postulate*
If two figures are congruent, then they have the same area.

Teaching Suggestions,
pp. T122–T123
Objectives
Presenting the Lesson
Using Technology
Enrichment

Supplementary Materials
Study Guide, pp. 137–138
Computer Activity 22

Lesson Focus
The concept of the area of a geometric figure is introduced in this lesson. Three postulates are stated that give basic information about the area of a square, areas of congruent figures, and the addition of areas. The formula for the area of a rectangle is proved as a theorem.

Suggested Assignments
Minimum
Day 1: 426/1–15 odd, 17–19
Day 2: 426–427/2, 10, 14, 16, 20, 22, 23, 25, 28
Average
Day 1: 426/1, 3, 4, 7, 10, 12, 15, 17, 19, 21
Day 2: 426–427/18, 20, 22–26, 28, 29, 31, 33
Maximum
426–427/11, 15, 17–19, 20–28 even, 29–31, 35, 37

Application
Ask students for examples of occupations that require the computation of area. These might include occupations like surveyor, architect, carpetlayer, and interior designer.

Proof Note

The proof of Theorem 11-1 provides an excellent example of applying algebraic skills to geometry problems.

Using a Model

Students can find the areas of polygons drawn on graph paper by counting the unit squares within the interior region of each polygon. Various rectangles drawn on graph paper may be used to arrive at the formula for the area of a rectangle inductively.

Chalkboard Examples

Classify each statement as true or false.

1. If two figures have the same area, then they must be congruent. F
2. If two figures have the same perimeter, then they must have the same area. F
3. If two figures are congruent, then they must have the same area. T
4. Every square is a rectangle. T
5. Every rectangle is a square. F
6. The base of a rectangle can be any side of the rectangle. T

Exs. 7–10 refer to rectangles. Complete the table.

	7.	8.	9.	10.
b	12 m	9 cm	$4\sqrt{3}$	$y - 2$
h	3 m	6 cm	$5\sqrt{3}$	y
A	36 m²	54 cm²	60	$y^2 - 2y$

Postulate 19 *Area Addition Postulate*

The area of a region is the sum of the areas of its non-overlapping parts.

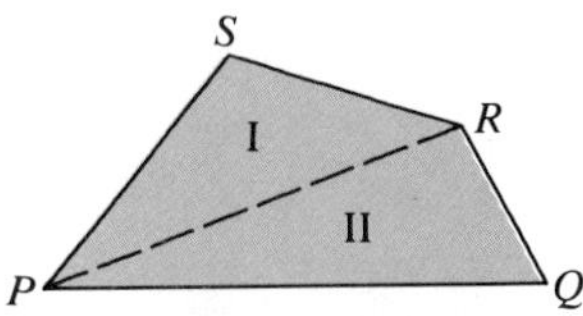

Area of $PQRS$ = Area I + Area II

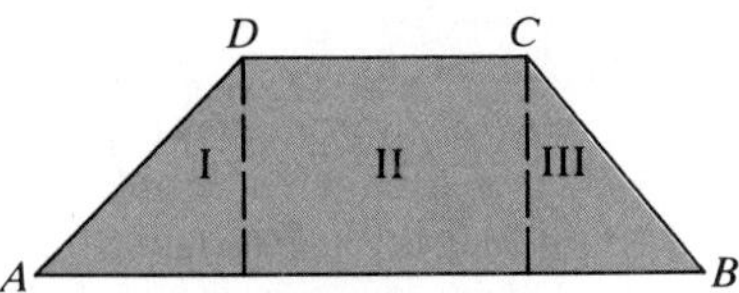

Area of $ABCD$ = Area I + Area II + Area III

Any side of a rectangle or other parallelogram can be considered to be a **base.** The length of a base will be denoted by b. In this text the term *base* will be used to refer either to the line segment or to its length. An **altitude** to a base is any segment perpendicular to the line containing the base from any point on the opposite side. The length of an altitude is called the **height** (h). All the altitudes to a particular base have the same length.

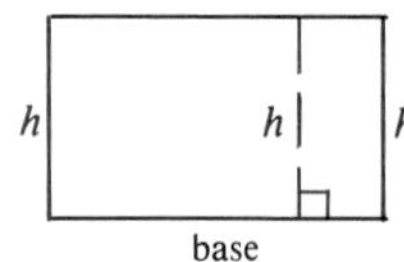

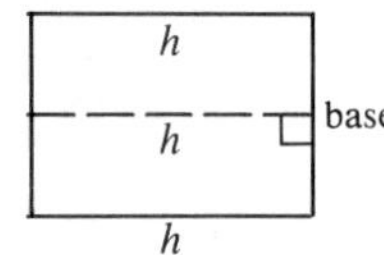

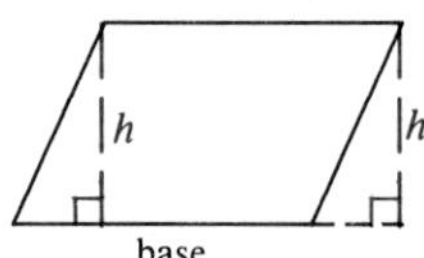

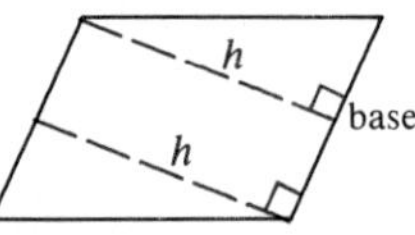

Theorem 11-1

The area of a rectangle equals the product of its base and height. ($A = bh$)

Given: A rectangle with base b and height h

Prove: $A = bh$

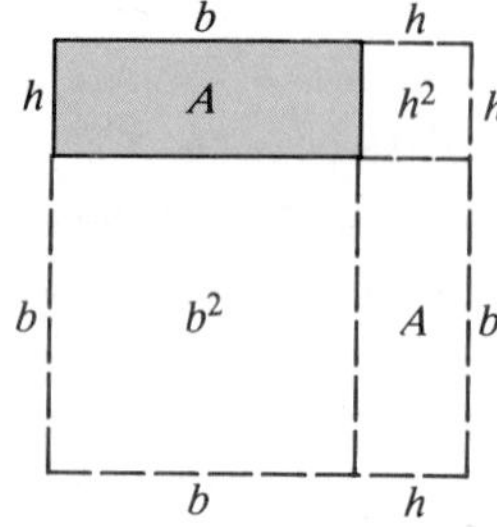

Proof:

Building onto the given shaded rectangle, we can draw a large square consisting of these non-overlapping parts:

the given rectangle with area A
a congruent rectangle with area A
a square with area b^2
a square with area h^2

Area of big square $= 2A + b^2 + h^2$	(Area Addition Postulate)
Area of big square $= (b + h)^2 = b^2 + 2bh + h^2$	($A = s^2$)
$2A + b^2 + h^2 = b^2 + 2bh + h^2$	(Substitution Prop.)
$2A = 2bh$	(Subtraction Prop. of =)
$A = bh$	(Division Prop. of =)

Areas are always measured in square units. Some common units of area are the square centimeter (cm^2) and the square meter (m^2). In part (b) of the example below, notice that the unit of length and the unit of area are understood to be "units" and "square units," respectively. It is important to remember that the implied units for length and area are different.

Example Find the area of each figure.

a. A rectangle with base 3.5 cm and height 2 cm

b.

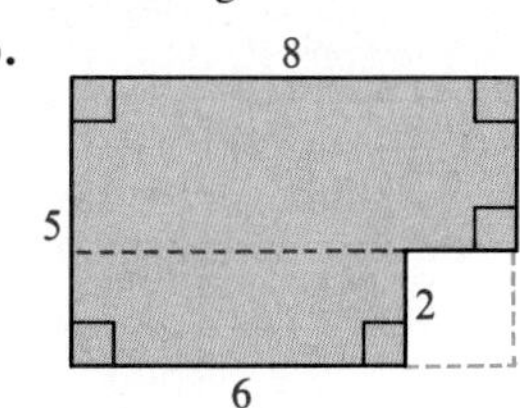

Solution **a.** $A = 3.5(2) = 7\ (cm^2)$

b. *Method 1* (see blue lines) $A = (8 \cdot 5) - (2 \cdot 2) = 40 - 4 = 36$
Method 2 (see red line) $A = (8 \cdot 3) + (6 \cdot 2) = 24 + 12 = 36$

Classroom Exercises

1. Tell what each letter represents in the formula $A = s^2$.
2. Tell what each letter represents in the formula $A = bh$.
3. Find the area and perimeter of a square with sides 5 cm long. **25 cm²; 20 cm**
4. The perimeter of a square is 28 cm. What is the area? **49 cm²**
5. The area of a square is 64 cm^2. What is the perimeter? **32 cm**

Exercises 6–13 refer to rectangles. Complete the table.

	6.	7.	8.	9.	10.	11.	12.	13.
b	8 cm	4 cm	12 m	?	$3\sqrt{2}$	$4\sqrt{2}$	$5\sqrt{3}$	$x + 3$
h	3 cm	1.2 cm	?	5 cm	2	$\sqrt{2}$	$2\sqrt{3}$	x
A	?	?	36 m^2	55 cm^2	?	?	?	?
	24 cm²	**4.8 cm²**	**3 m**	**11 cm**	**$6\sqrt{2}$**	**8**	**30**	**$x^2 + 3x$**

14. **a.** What is the converse of the Area Congruence Postulate?
    b. Is this converse true or false? Explain. **False**
15. **a.** Draw three noncongruent rectangles, each with perimeter 20 cm. Find the area of each rectangle. **Answers may vary.**
    b. Of all rectangles having perimeter 20 cm, which one do you think has the greatest area? (Give its length and width.) **5 cm × 5 cm**

Additional Answers
Classroom Exercises

1. *A:* area of a square
s: length of a side

2. *A:* area of a rectangle
b: length of a base
h: height (length of an altitude to a base)

14.a. If 2 figures have the same area, then they are ≅.

b. For example, a rectangle with length 8 cm and width 5 cm has the same area as a rectangle with length 10 cm and width 4 cm, but the two rectangles are not congruent.

15.a. Examples:
1 cm × 9 cm (9 cm²);
2 cm × 8 cm (16 cm²);
5 cm × 5 cm (25 cm²)

Written Exercises

Exercises 1–16 refer to rectangles. Complete the tables. p is the perimeter.

A

32.8 cm^2 (answer to 2) $2x^2 - 6x$ (answer to 7)

	1.	2.	3.	4.	5.	6.	7.	8.
b	12 cm	8.2 cm	16 cm	?	$3\sqrt{2}$	$\sqrt{6}$	$2x$	$4k - 1$
h	5 cm	4 cm	?	8 m	$4\sqrt{2}$	$\sqrt{2}$	$x - 3$	$k + 2$
A	?	?	80 cm^2	120 m^2	?	?	?	?

60 cm^2 5 cm 15 m 24 $2\sqrt{3}$ $4k^2 + 7k - 2$

	9.	10.	11.	12.	13.	14.	15.	16.
b	9 cm	40 cm	16 cm	$x + 5$	$a + 3$	$k + 7$	x	?
h	4 cm	?	?	x	$a - 3$	?	?	y
A	?	?	?	?	?	?	$x^2 - 3x$	$y^2 + 7y$
p	?	100 cm	42 cm	?	?	$4k + 20$	?	?

Consecutive sides of the figures are perpendicular. Find the area of each figure.

B

17. 130

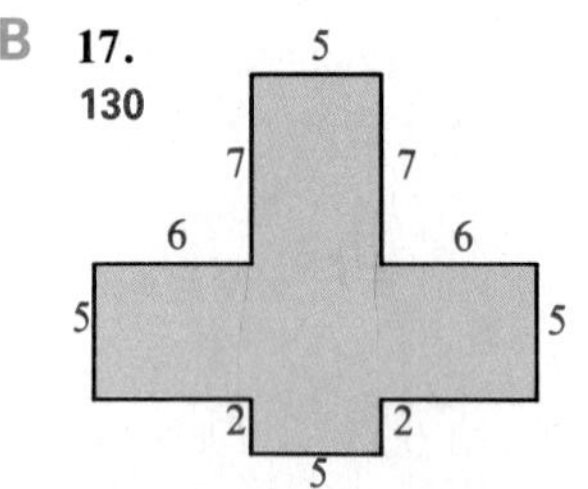

18. 56

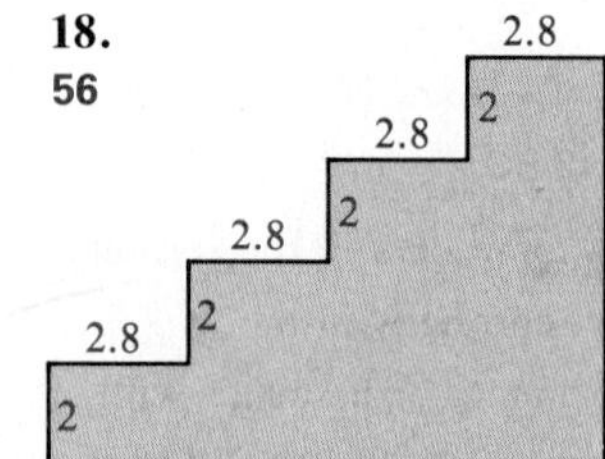

19. 48

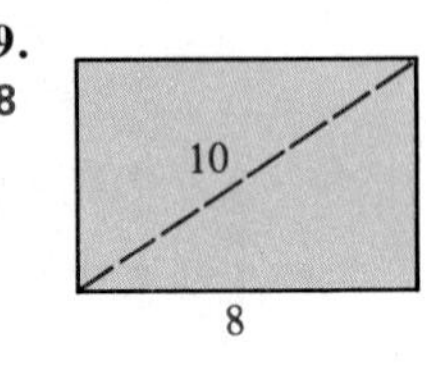

20.

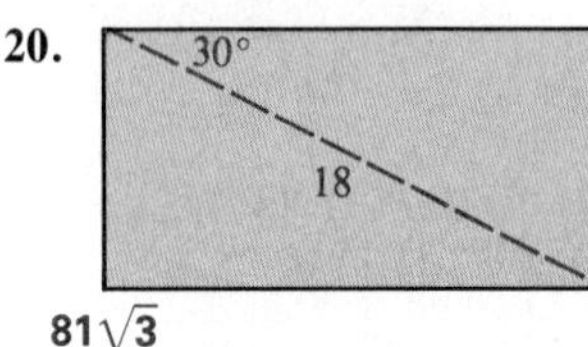

$81\sqrt{3}$

21.

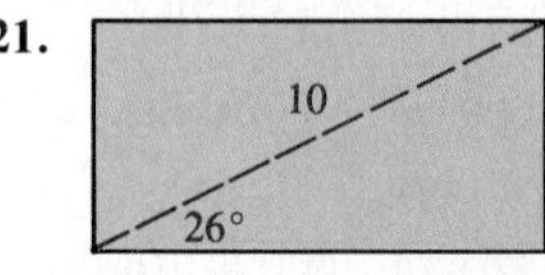

(Give answer correct to the nearest tenth.)
39.4

22. 24.5

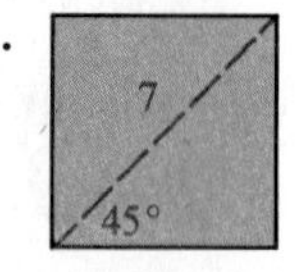

In Exercises 23 and 24 find each area in terms of the variables.

23.

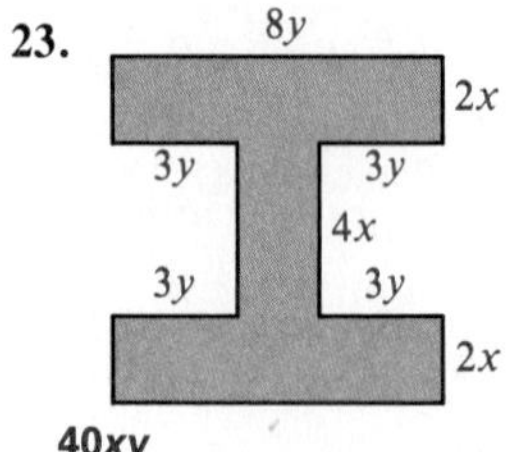

40xy

24.

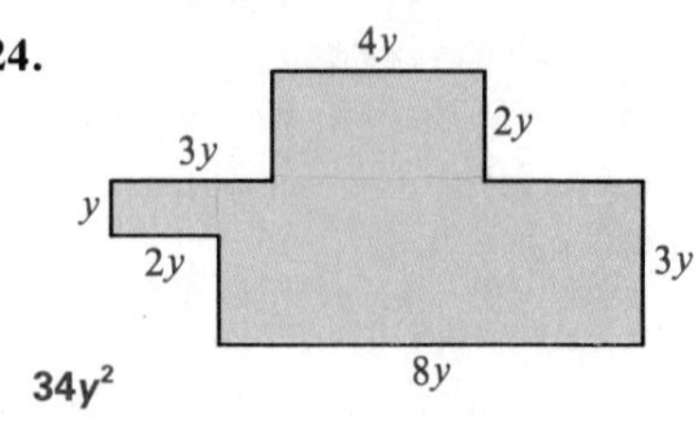

$34y^2$

Guided Practice

Exs. 1–7 refer to rectangles. Complete the tables. p is the perimeter.

	1.	2.	3.	4.
b	18 cm	7.5 cm	25 cm	$4\sqrt{2}$
h	3 cm	12 cm	6 cm	$5\sqrt{2}$
A	54 cm^2	90 cm^2	150 cm^2	40
p	42 cm	39 cm	62 cm	$18\sqrt{2}$

	5.	6.	7.
b	$4y$	$x - 2$	k
h	$3y - 1$	$2x$	$k - 4$
A	$12y^2 - 4y$	$2x^2 - 4x$	$k^2 - 4k$
p	$14y - 2$	$6x - 4$	$4k - 8$

Additional Answers Written Exercises

9. $A = 36\ cm^2$; $p = 26$ cm
10. $h = 10$ cm; $A = 400\ cm^2$
11. $h = 5$ cm; $A = 80\ cm^2$
12. $A = x^2 + 5x$; $p = 4x + 10$
13. $A = a^2 - 9$; $p = 4a$
14. $h = k + 3$; $A = k^2 + 10k + 21$
15. $h = x - 3$; $p = 4x - 6$
16. $b = y + 7$; $p = 4y + 14$

Exercise Note

When doing area problems involving irregular regions, students may have difficulty partitioning the figure into nonoverlapping regions. Ex. 18 may be done by using the distributive property to find the area of the nonoverlapping rectangles.

$$\begin{aligned}\text{Area} &= (2.8)8 + (2.8)6 + (2.8)4 + (2.8)2 \\ &= 2.8(8 + 6 + 4 + 2) \\ &= 2.8(20) \\ &= 56 \text{ square units}\end{aligned}$$

25. Find the area of a square with diagonals of length d. $\frac{d^2}{2}$

26. The length of a rectangle is 12 cm more than its width. Find the area of the rectangle if its perimeter is 100 cm. **589 cm²**

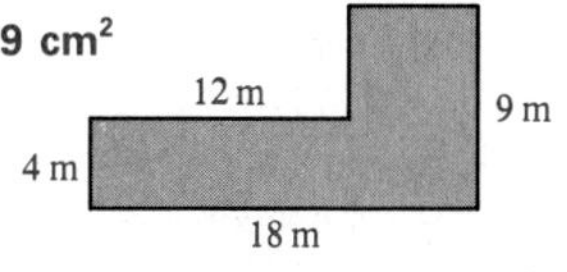

Ex. 28

27. A path 2 m wide surrounds a rectangular garden 20 m long and 12 m wide. Find the area of the path. **144 m²**

28. How much will it cost to blacktop the driveway shown if blacktopping costs \$11.00 per square meter? **\$1122**

29. A room 28 ft long and 20 ft wide has walls 8 ft high.
- **a.** What is the total wall area? **768 ft²**
- **b.** How many gallon cans of paint should be bought to paint the walls if 1 gal of paint covers 300 ft^2? **3 cans**

30. A wooden fence 6 ft high and 220 ft long is to be painted on both sides.
- **a.** What is the total area to be painted? **2640 ft²**
- **b.** A gallon of a certain type of paint will cover only 200 ft^2 of area for the first coat, but on the second coat a gallon of the same paint will cover 300 ft^2. If the fence is to be given two coats of paint, how many gallons of paint should be bought? **22 gal**

31. A rectangle having area 392 m^2 is twice as long as it is wide. Find its dimensions. **14 m × 28 m**

32. 132 cm

32. The lengths of the sides of three squares are s, $s + 1$, and $s + 2$. If their total area is 365 cm^2, find their total perimeter.

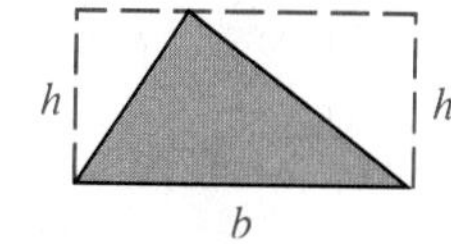

Ex. 33

33. Derive a formula for the area of the triangle shown by using the formula for the area of a rectangle.

34. The diagonals of a rectangle are 18 cm long and intersect at a 60° angle. Find the area of the rectangle. **$81\sqrt{3}$ cm²**

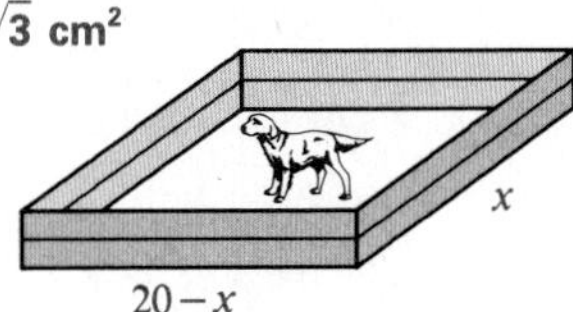

35. a. Suppose you have 40 m of fencing with which to make a rectangular pen for a dog. If one side of the rectangle is x m long, explain why the other side is $(20 - x)$ m long.
- **b.** Express the area of the pen in terms of x. $\mathbf{20x - x^2}$
- **c.** Find the area of the pen for each value of x: 0, 2, 4, 6, 8, 10, 12, 14, 16, 18, 20. Record your answers on a set of axes like the one shown.
- **d.** Give the dimensions of the pen with the greatest area. **10 m × 10 m**

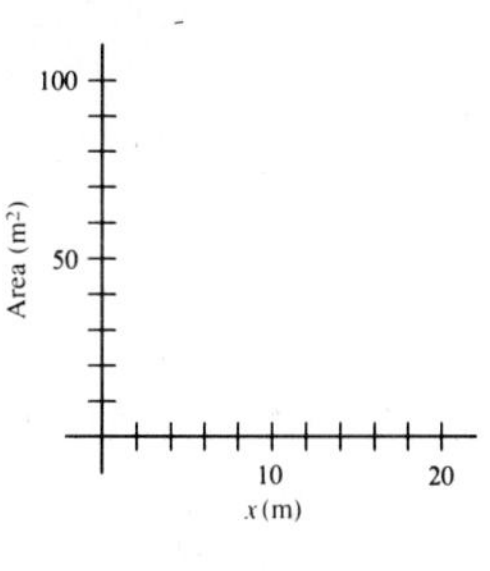

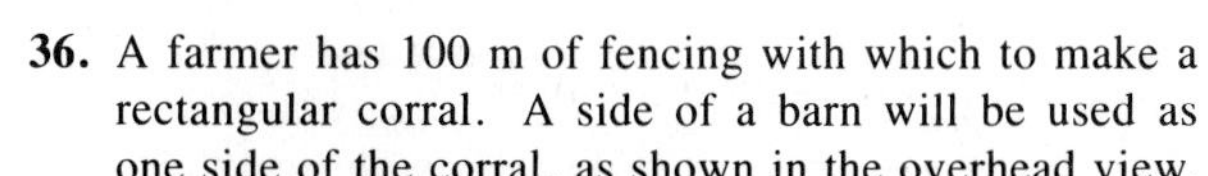

C **36.** A farmer has 100 m of fencing with which to make a rectangular corral. A side of a barn will be used as one side of the corral, as shown in the overhead view.
- **a.** If the width of the corral is x, express the length and the area in terms of x. $\mathbf{l = 100 - 2x;\ A = 100x - 2x^2}$
- **b.** Make a graph showing values of x on the horizontal axis and the corresponding areas on the vertical axis.
- **c.** What dimensions give the corral the greatest possible area?

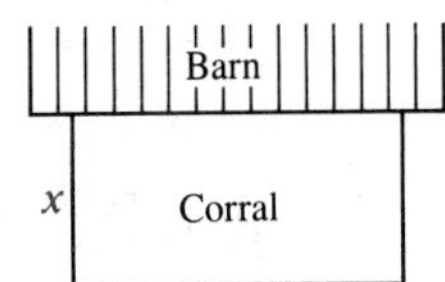

37. Draw a rectangle. Then construct a square with equal area.

36.c. 25 m × 50 m

Additional Answers Written Exercises

35.a. length $= \frac{1}{2}(40 - 2x)$
$= 20 - x$

Making Connections

The program in the Computer Key-In approximates the area under the graph of $y = x^2$ by adding the areas of rectangles. The notion of "area under a curve" will be important in more advanced mathematical study, especially calculus.

See also the Computer Key-In on pages 438 and 439. It approximates the area under the curve $y = x^2$ using trapezoids instead of rectangles.

♦ Computer Key-In

The shaded region shown is bounded by the graph of $y = x^2$, by the x-axis, and by the vertical line through the points (1, 0) and (1, 1). You can approximate the area of the shaded region by drawing ten rectangles having base vertices at $x = 0, 0.1, 0.2, 0.3, \ldots, 1.0$, as shown, and computing the sum of the areas of the ten rectangles. The base of each rectangle is 0.1, and the height of each rectangle is given by $y = x^2$.

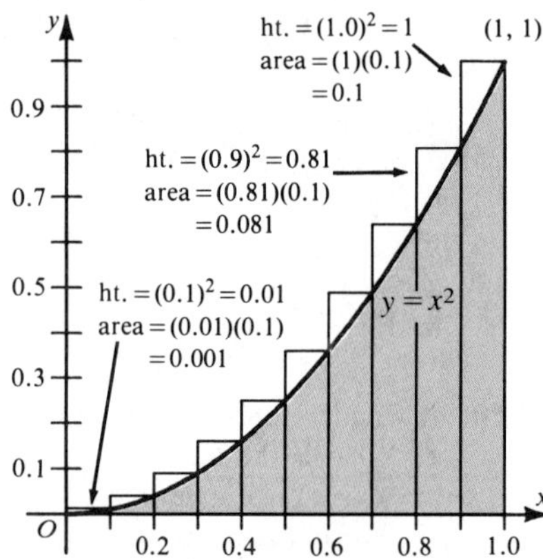

The following computer program will compute and add the areas of the ten rectangles shown in the diagram. In line 30, Y is the height of each rectangle. In line 40, A gives the current total of all the areas.

```
10 LET X = 0.1
20 FOR N = 1 TO 10
30 LET Y = X ↑ 2
40 LET A = A + Y * 0.1
50 LET X = X + 0.1
60 NEXT N
70 PRINT "AREA IS APPROXIMATELY ";A
80 END
```

If the program is run, the computer will print

```
AREA IS APPROXIMATELY 0.385
```

Exercises

1. A better approximation can be found by using 100 smaller rectangles with base vertices at 0, 0.01, 0.02, 0.03, . . . , 1.00. Change lines 10, 20, 40, and 50 as follows:

```
10 LET X = 0.01
20 FOR N = 1 TO 100
40 LET A = A + Y * 0.01
50 LET X = X + 0.01
```

RUN the program to approximate the area of the shaded region. **0.33835001**

2. Modify the given program so that it will use 1000 rectangles with base vertices at 0, 0.001, 0.002, 0.003, . . . , 1.000 to approximate the area of the shaded region. RUN the program. **0.333833494**

3. Is the actual area of the shaded region more or less than the value given by the computer program? Explain. **Less; each rectangle has more area than the shaded region below it.**

11-2 *Areas of Parallelograms, Triangles, and Rhombuses*

Although proofs of most area formulas are easy to understand, detailed formal proofs are long and time consuming. Therefore, we will show the key steps of each proof.

Theorem 11-2

The area of a parallelogram equals the product of a base and the height to that base. ($A = bh$)

Given: $\square PQRS$

Prove: $A = bh$

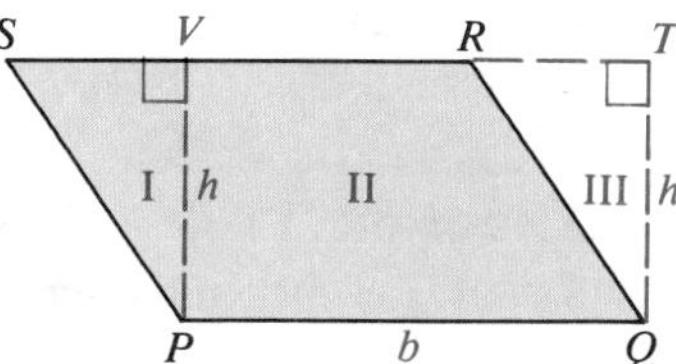

Key steps of proof:

1. Draw altitudes $\overline{PV}$ and $\overline{QT}$, forming two rt. $\triangle$s.
2. Area I = Area III ($\triangle PSV \cong \triangle QRT$ by HL or AAS)
3. Area of $\square PQRS$ = Area II + Area I
   = Area II + Area III
   = Area of rect. $PQTV$
   = bh

Example 1 Find the area of the parallelogram shown.

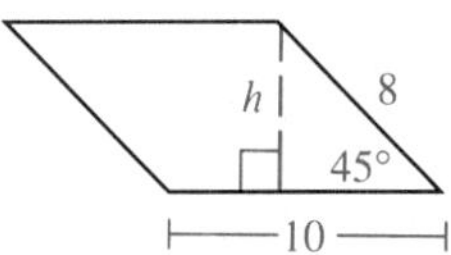

Solution Notice the 45°-45°-90° triangle.

$$h = \frac{8}{\sqrt{2}} = \frac{8}{\sqrt{2}} \cdot \frac{\sqrt{2}}{\sqrt{2}} = \frac{8\sqrt{2}}{2} = 4\sqrt{2}$$

$$A = bh = 10 \cdot 4\sqrt{2} = 40\sqrt{2}$$

Theorem 11-3

The area of a triangle equals half the product of a base and the height to that base. ($A = \frac{1}{2}bh$)

Given: $\triangle XYZ$

Prove: $A = \frac{1}{2}bh$

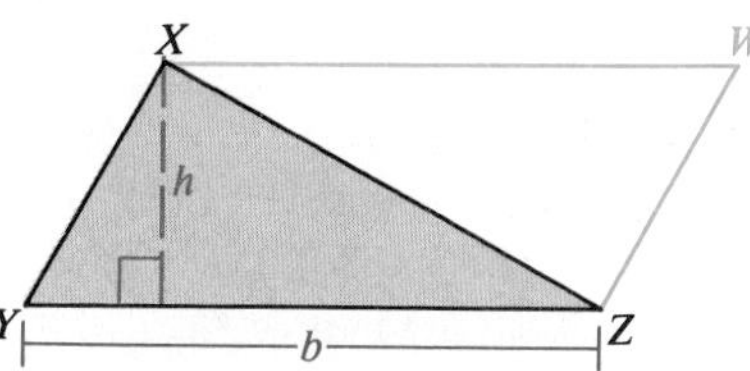

Key steps of proof:

1. Draw $\overline{XW} \parallel \overline{YZ}$ and $\overline{ZW} \parallel \overline{YX}$, forming $\square WXYZ$.
2. $\triangle XYZ \cong \triangle ZWX$ (SAS or SSS)
3. Area of $\triangle XYZ = \frac{1}{2} \cdot$ Area of $\square WXYZ$
   $= \frac{1}{2}bh$

Teaching Suggestions, p. T123

Objective
Presenting the Lesson
Using Technology

Supplementary Materials

Practice Master 64
Study Guide, pp. 139–140
Overhead Visual H

Lesson Focus

The purpose of this lesson is to state and prove the formulas for the areas of parallelograms, triangles, and rhombuses. Only the key steps of each proof are shown.

Suggested Assignments

Minimum
Day 1: 431/1–9
Day 2: 431–432/10–13, 18, 19, 22, 23, 25
S 427/26, 29

Average
Day 1: 431/2, 4, 5, 8, 9–11, 13–15, 17, 19
Day 2: 432–433/21, 22–26, 28, 30, 32, 34

Maximum
Day 1: 431–432/10, 11, 14, 15–21 odd
Day 2: 432–433/23–27 odd, 28, 30, 32, 33, 35, 37
S 427/36

Proof Note

The proof of Theorem 11-2 follows directly from the formula for the area of a rectangle, and the proof of Theorem 11-3 follows directly from the formula for the area of a parallelogram.

Chalkboard Examples

Find the area of each figure.

1. $24\sqrt{3}$

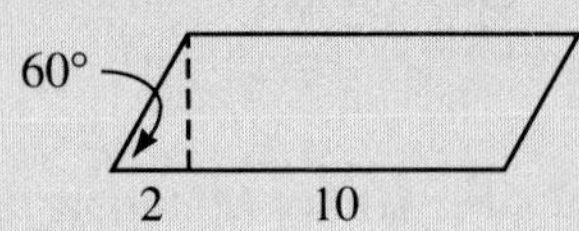

2. $27\sqrt{2}$

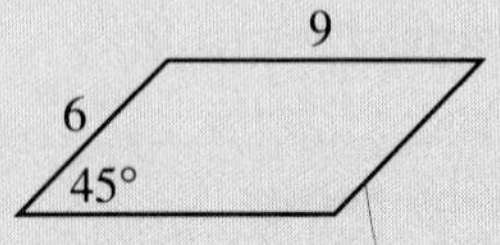

3. 276 mm²

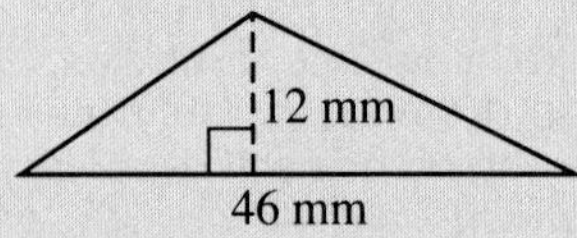

In rhombus $ABCD$, $AC = 20$ and $BD = 15$. The area can be found in more than one way.

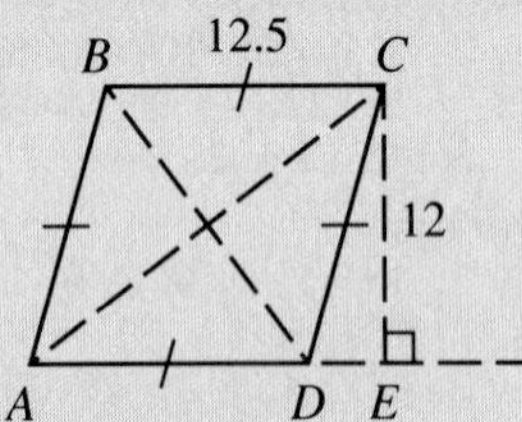

Complete.

4. $A = \underline{12.5} \cdot 12 = \underline{150}$

5. $A = \frac{1}{2} \cdot \underline{20} \cdot \underline{15} = \underline{150}$

6. $A = 4 \cdot \frac{1}{2} \cdot \underline{7.5} \cdot \underline{10} = \underline{150}$

Example 2 Find the area of a triangle with sides 8, 8, and 6.

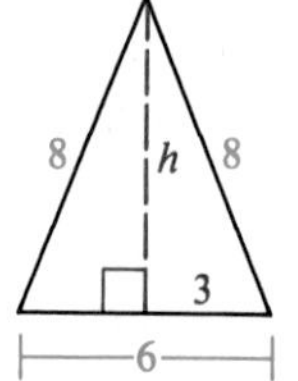

Solution Draw the altitude to the base shown. Since the triangle is isosceles, this altitude bisects the base.

$h^2 + 3^2 = 8^2$ (Pythagorean Theorem)
$h^2 = 64 - 9 = 55$
$h = \sqrt{55}$
$A = \frac{1}{2}bh = \frac{1}{2} \cdot 6 \cdot \sqrt{55} = 3\sqrt{55}$

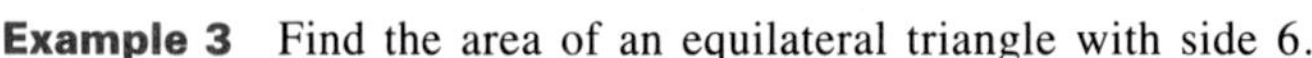

Example 3 Find the area of an equilateral triangle with side 6.

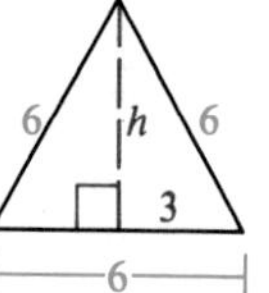

Solution Draw an altitude. Two 30°-60°-90° triangles are formed.

$h = 3\sqrt{3}$
$A = \frac{1}{2}bh = \frac{1}{2} \cdot 6 \cdot 3\sqrt{3} = 9\sqrt{3}$

Theorem 11-4

The area of a rhombus equals half the product of its diagonals. ($A = \frac{1}{2}d_1d_2$)

Given: Rhombus $ABCD$ with diagonals d_1 and d_2

Prove: $A = \frac{1}{2}d_1d_2$

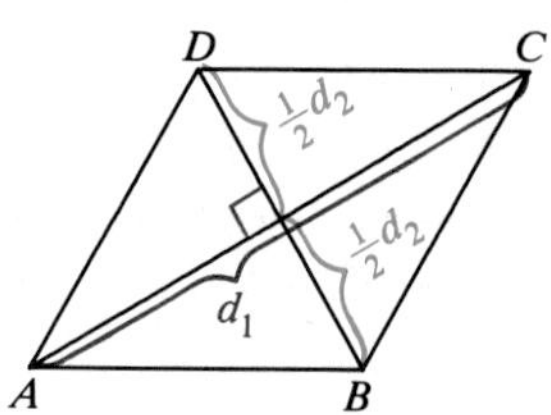

Key steps of proof:

1. $\triangle ADC \cong \triangle ABC$ (SSS)
2. Since $\overline{DB} \perp \overline{AC}$, the area of $\triangle ADC = \frac{1}{2}bh = \frac{1}{2} \cdot d_1 \cdot \frac{1}{2}d_2 = \frac{1}{4}d_1d_2$.
3. Area of rhombus $ABCD = 2 \cdot \frac{1}{4}d_1d_2 = \frac{1}{2}d_1d_2$

Classroom Exercises

1. The area of the parallelogram can be found in two ways:
  a. $A = 8 \cdot$ _?_ $=$ _?_ **3, 24**
  b. $A = 4 \cdot$ _?_ $=$ _?_ **6, 24**

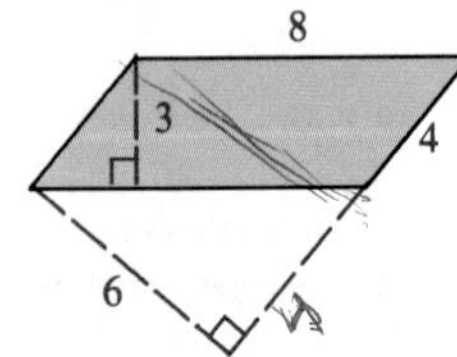

Each △ has area 18.

2. Find the areas of $\triangle ABC$, $\triangle DBC$, and $\triangle EBC$.

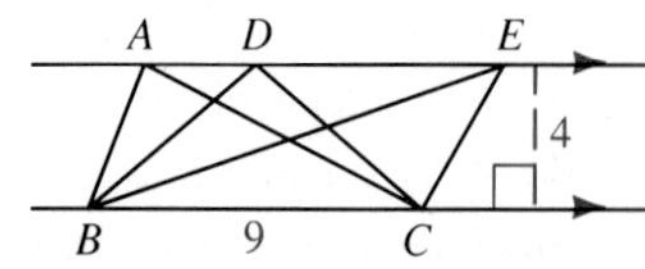

3. Give two formulas that can be used to find the area of a rhombus. (*Hint*: Every rhombus is also a _?_.) **parallelogram**

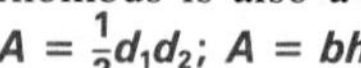

$A = \frac{1}{2}d_1d_2$; $A = bh$

Find the area of each figure.

4. **$4\sqrt{3}$**

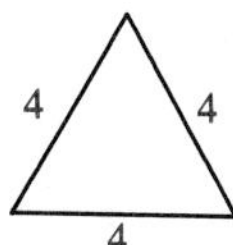

5. **$9\sqrt{3}$**

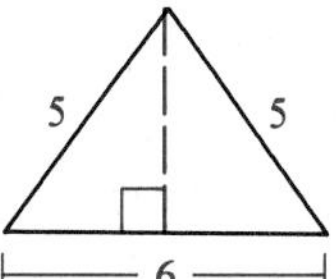

6. **12**

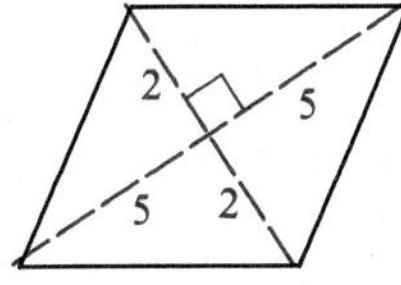

7. **20**

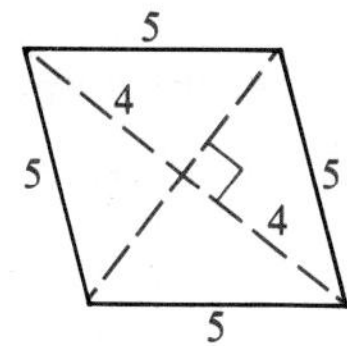

8. **24**

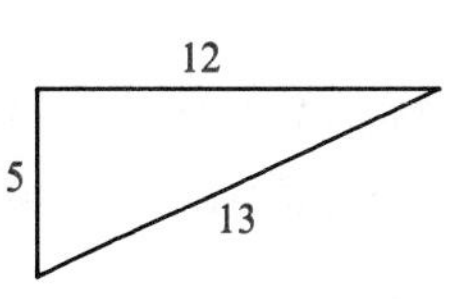

9. **30**

Written Exercises

In Exercises 1–20 find the area of each figure.

A 1. A triangle with base 5.2 m and corresponding height 11.5 m **29.9 m²**

2. A triangle with sides 3, 4, and 5 **6**
3. A parallelogram with base $3\sqrt{2}$ and corresponding height $2\sqrt{2}$ **12**
4. A rhombus with diagonals 4 and 6 **12**
5. An equilateral triangle with sides 8 ft **$16\sqrt{3}$ ft²**
6. An isosceles triangle with sides 10, 10, and 16 **48**

7. **40**

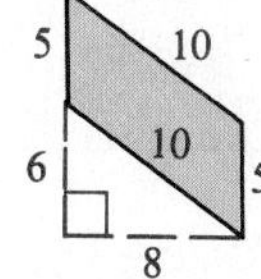

8. **44**

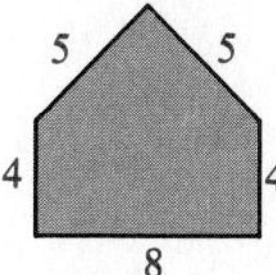

9. **84**

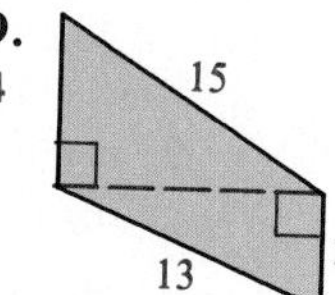

10. An isosceles triangle with base 10 and perimeter 36 **60**
11. An isosceles right triangle with hypotenuse 8 **16**
12. An equilateral triangle with perimeter 18 **$9\sqrt{3}$**

B 13. A parallelogram with a 45° angle and sides 6 and 10 **$30\sqrt{2}$**

14. A rhombus with a 120° angle and sides 6 cm **$18\sqrt{3}$ cm²**
15. A 30°-60°-90° triangle with hypotenuse 10   **15.** $\frac{25\sqrt{3}}{2}$
16. An equilateral triangle with height 9 **$27\sqrt{3}$**
17. A rhombus with perimeter 68 and one diagonal 30 **240**
18. A regular hexagon with perimeter 60 **$150\sqrt{3}$**
19. A square inscribed in a circle with radius r **$2r^2$**
20. A rectangle with length 16 inscribed in a circle with radius 10 **192**

Guided Practice

Find the area of each figure.

1. a triangle with base 6.3 cm and corresponding height 9.8 cm 30.87 cm²
2. a parallelogram with base $4\sqrt{3}$ and corresponding height $3\sqrt{5}$ $12\sqrt{15}$
3. a rhombus with diagonals 6 and 8 24
4. an isosceles triangle with sides 12, 12, 10 $5\sqrt{119}$
5. $80\sqrt{2} + 64$

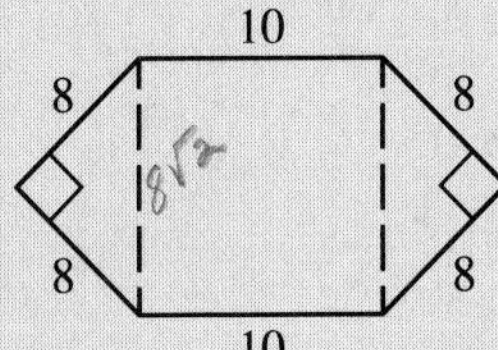

6. $\frac{81\sqrt{3}}{4}$

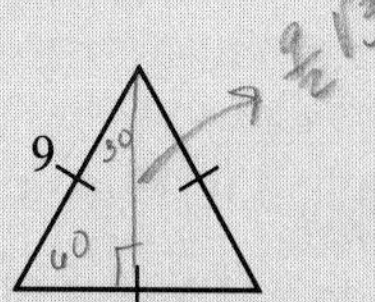

Exercise Note

You might want to review 30°-60°-90° and 45°-45°-90° triangle relationships with students before assigning the B exercises.

In Exercises 21–24 use a calculator or the trigonometry table on page 311 to find the area of each figure to the nearest tenth.

21. **18.2** (right triangle: 20°, 10)

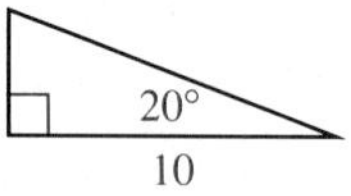

22. **34.2** (right triangle: 54°, 12)

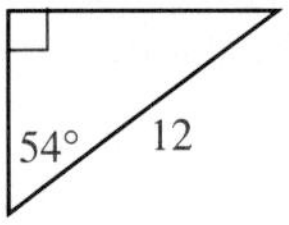

23. **73.5**

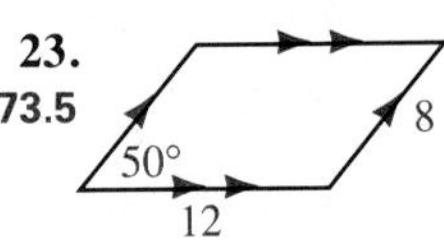

24. An isosceles triangle with a 32° vertex angle and a base of 8 cm **55.8 cm²**

25. $\overline{FG}$ is the altitude to the hypotenuse of $\triangle DEF$. Name three similar triangles and find their areas. (*Hint*: See Theorem 8-1 and Corollary 1 on pages 285–286.)

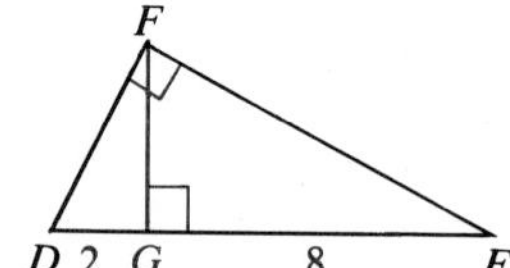

26. If the area of ▱$PQRS$ is 36 and T is a point on $\overline{PQ}$, find the area of $\triangle RST$. (*Hint*: Draw a diagram.) **18**

In Exercises 27 and 28, $\overline{AM}$ is a median of $\triangle ABC$.

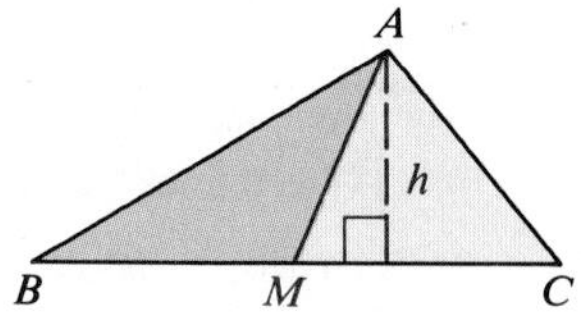

27. If $BC = 16$ and $h = 5$, find the areas of $\triangle ABC$ and $\triangle AMB$. **40; 20**

28. Prove: Area of $\triangle AMB = \frac{1}{2} \cdot$ Area of $\triangle ABC$

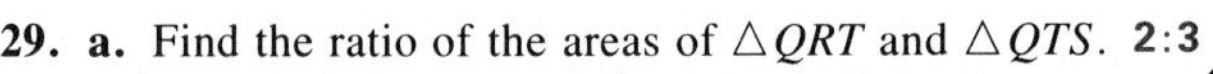

29. a. Find the ratio of the areas of $\triangle QRT$ and $\triangle QTS$. **2:3**

b. If the area of $\triangle QRS$ is 240, find the length of the altitude from S to $\overleftrightarrow{QR}$. **20**

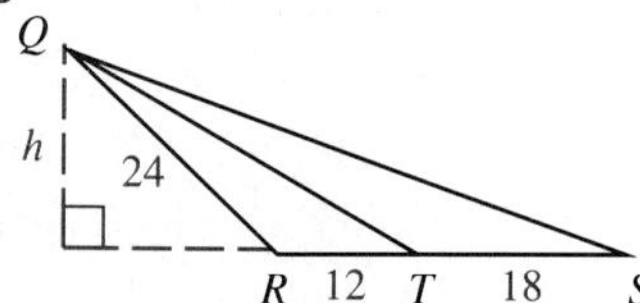

30. An isosceles triangle has sides that are 5 cm, 5 cm, and 8 cm long. Find its area and the lengths of the three altitudes. **12 cm²; 3 cm, 4.8 cm, 4.8 cm**

31. a. Find the area of the right triangle in terms of a and b.

b. Find the area of the right triangle in terms of c and h.

c. Solve for h in terms of the other variables.

d. A right triangle has legs 6 and 8. Find the lengths of the altitude and the median to the hypotenuse. **4.8; 5**

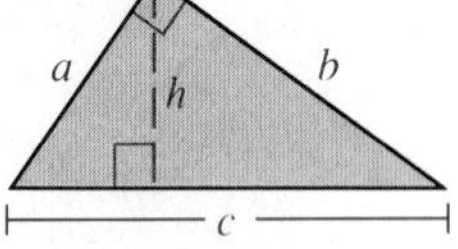

32. Use the diagram at the right.

a. Find the area of ▱$PQRS$. **480**

b. Find the area of $\triangle PSR$. **240**

c. Find the area of $\triangle OSR$. (*Hint*: Refer to $\triangle PSR$ and use Exercise 28.) **120**

d. What is the area of $\triangle PSO$? **120**

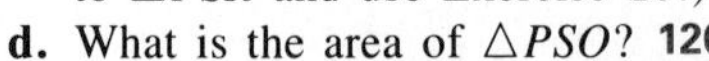

e. What must the area of $\triangle POQ$ be? Why? What must the area of $\triangle OQR$ be?

f. State what you have shown in parts (a)–(e) about how the diagonals of a parallelogram divide the parallelogram.

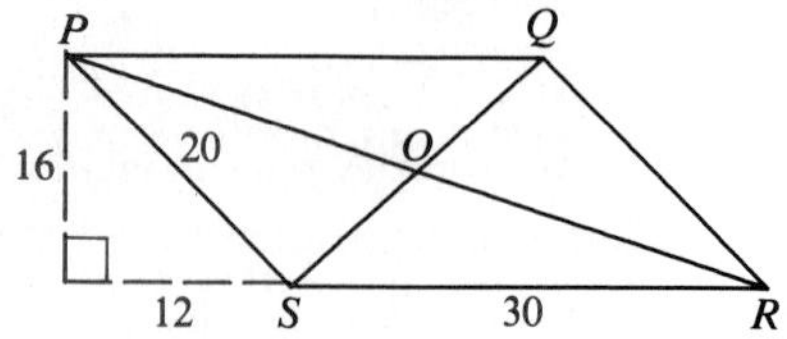

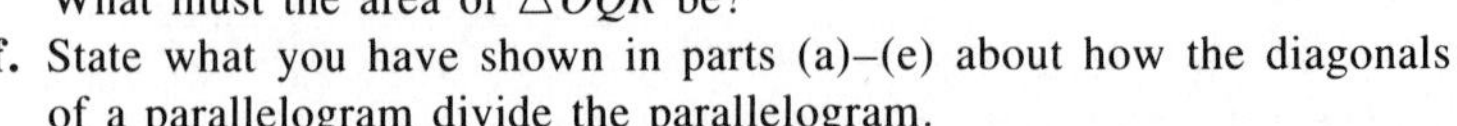

(Diagram: P, Q, O, S, R; 16, 20, 12, 30)

33. a. An equilateral triangle has sides of length s. Show that its area is $\frac{s^2}{4}\sqrt{3}$. $b = s, h = \frac{s\sqrt{3}}{2}; A = \frac{1}{2} \cdot s \cdot \frac{s\sqrt{3}}{2} = \frac{s^2\sqrt{3}}{4}$

b. Find the area of an equilateral triangle with side 7. $\frac{49\sqrt{3}}{4}$

Additional Answers
Written Exercises

25. $\triangle DFE$, $\triangle DGF$, $\triangle FGE$; 20, 4, 16

28. Area of $\triangle AMB = \frac{1}{2} \cdot MB \cdot h = \frac{1}{2} \cdot (\frac{1}{2} \cdot BC) \cdot h = \frac{1}{2} \cdot (\frac{1}{2} \cdot BC \cdot h) = \frac{1}{2} \cdot$ Area of $\triangle ABC$

31.a. $A = \frac{1}{2}ab$

b. $A = \frac{1}{2}ch$

c. $h = \frac{ab}{c}$

32.e. 120; $\triangle POQ \cong \triangle ROS$; 120

f. The diagonals of a ▱ divide the ▱ into four triangles with equal areas.

Exercise Note

Written Ex. 33 asks students to derive the area formula for an equilateral triangle, $\frac{s^2}{4}\sqrt{3}$. Students may add this formula to their list of area formulas or derive it as needed from the 30°-60°-90° triangle formed by drawing an altitude of an equilateral triangle.

34. Think of a parallelogram made with cardboard strips and hinged at each vertex so that the measure of $\angle C$ will vary. Find the area of the parallelogram for each measure of $\angle C$ given in parts (a)–(e). **See below.**

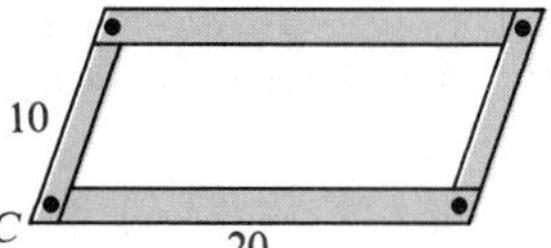

a. 30 **b.** 45 **c.** 60 **d.** 90 **e.** 120

f. Approximate your answers to parts (b), (c), and (e) by using $\sqrt{2} \approx 1.4$ and $\sqrt{3} \approx 1.7$. Then record your answers to parts (a)–(e) on a set of axes like the one below.

a. 100
b. $100\sqrt{2}$
c. $100\sqrt{3}$
d. 200
e. $100\sqrt{3}$

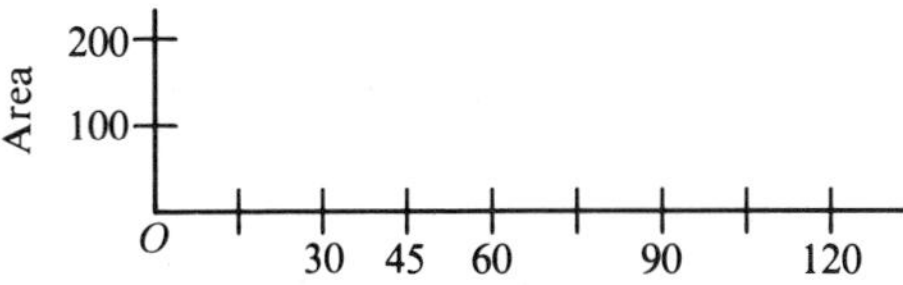

35. The area of a rhombus is 100. Find the length of the two diagonals if one is twice as long as the other. **10; 20**

36. The base of a triangle is 1 cm longer than its altitude. If the area of the triangle is 210 cm^2, how long is the altitude? **20 cm**

C 37. Find the area of quadrilateral $ABCD$ given $A(2, -2)$, $B(6, 4)$, $C(-1, 5)$, and $D(-5, 2)$. **41.5**

38. Two squares each with sides 12 cm are placed so that a vertex of one lies at the center of the other. Find the area of the shaded region. **36 cm^2**

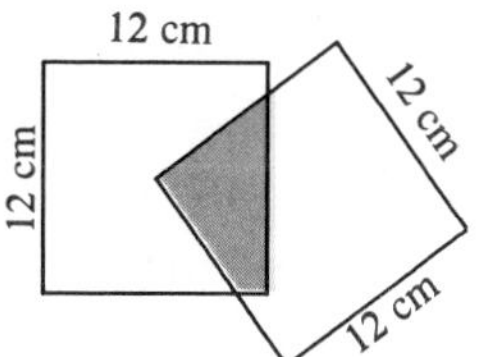

39. The diagonals of a parallelogram are 82 cm and 30 cm. One altitude is 18 cm long. Find the two possible values for the area. **936 cm^2; 504 cm^2**

For Exercises 40–42, draw a scalene triangle *ABC*.

40. Construct an isosceles triangle whose area is equal to the area of $\triangle ABC$.

41. Construct an isosceles right triangle whose area is equal to the area of $\triangle ABC$.

42. Construct an equilateral triangle whose area is equal to the area of $\triangle ABC$.

Explorations

These exploratory exercises can be done using a computer with a program that draws and measures geometric figures.

Draw any quadrilateral and connect the midpoints of its sides. You should get a parallelogram (see Exercise 11, page 186). Compare the area of the original quadrilateral and the area of this parallelogram. What do you notice? Can you explain why this is true? **Area of ▱ = $\frac{1}{2}$ · area of quad.**

Teaching Note

Ex. 34 involves graphing on a set of axes. You might want to review graphing briefly before assigning this exercise.

Exercise Note

Ex. 39 has two possible values for the area because two different parallelograms having the same diagonals and altitude can be drawn.

Using a Computer

This Exploration studies an interesting property of quadrilaterals. It extends the work in Lessons 11-1 and 11-2.

Making Connections

Heron's formula (also known as Hero's formula) can be derived by using right triangles or by using the Law of Cosines, which is studied in trigonometry.

Using a Computer

For an experiment that uses Heron's Formula with a computer program or spreadsheet, see page T123.

Cultural Note

Little is known about the mathematician and inventor Heron. It seems likely that he was Egyptian. His most important work in mathematics was in the measurement of plane figures and solids. He also helped advance knowledge of engineering and surveying. His inventions include a siphon and a fire engine.

Additional Answers Calculator Key-In

1. 42.4; 9.42; 8.48; 7.71
2. 17.3; 6.92; 4.94; 4.33
3. 32.9; 11.0; 5.98; 5.06
4. 110.0; 14.7; 13.8; 12.9
5. 22.5; 7.14; 6.25; 4.46
6. 2620; 77.1; 68.1; 49.9
7. 16.5; 6.00; 5.08; 3.30
8. 86.1; 14.4; 9.57; 6.38

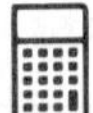

♦ Calculator Key-In

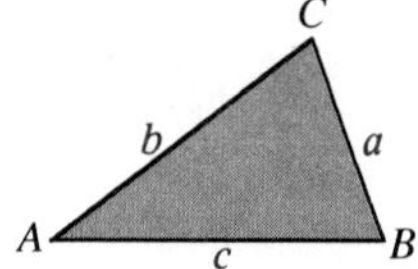

More than 2000 years ago, Heron, a mathematician from Alexandria, Egypt, derived a formula for finding the area of a triangle when the lengths of its sides are known. This formula is known as **Heron's Formula.** To find the area of $\triangle ABC$ using this formula:

Step 1 Find the *semiperimeter* $s = \frac{1}{2}(a + b + c)$.
Step 2 Area $= A = \sqrt{s(s - a)(s - b)(s - c)}$

Example If $a = 5$, $b = 6$, and $c = 7$, find the area of $\triangle ABC$.

Solution *Step 1* $s = \frac{1}{2}(5 + 6 + 7) = 9$
Step 2
$$\begin{aligned} A &= \sqrt{s(s - a)(s - b)(s - c)} \\ &= \sqrt{9(9 - 5)(9 - 6)(9 - 7)} \\ &= \sqrt{9 \cdot 4 \cdot 3 \cdot 2} \\ &= 6\sqrt{6} \end{aligned}$$

It is convenient to use a calculator when evaluating areas by using Heron's Formula. A calculator gives 14.7 as the approximate area of the triangle in the example above.

13. *a*, *b*, and *c* cannot be the sides of a △ since *a* + *b* = *c*.

Exercises

The lengths of the sides of a triangle are given. Use a calculator to find the area and the three heights of the triangle, each correct to three significant digits. (*Hint*: $h = \frac{2A}{b}$.)

1. 9, 10, 11 **2.** 5, 7, 8 **3.** 6, 11, 13 **4.** 15, 16, 17
5. 6.3, 7.2, 10.1 **6.** 68, 77, 105 **7.** 5.5, 6.5, 10 **8.** 12, 18, 27

Use two different methods to find the exact area of each triangle whose sides are given.

9. 3, 4, 5 **6** **10.** 6, 6, 6 **$9\sqrt{3}$** **11.** 13, 13, 10 **60** **12.** 29, 29, 42 **4**

13. Something strange happens when Heron's Formula is used with $a = 47$, $b = 38$, and $c = 85$. Why does this occur? **See above.**

14. Heron also derived the following formula for the area of an inscribed quadrilateral with sides a, b, c, and d:

$A = \sqrt{(s - a)(s - b)(s - c)(s - d)}$,
where the semiperimeter $s = \frac{1}{2}(a + b + c + d)$

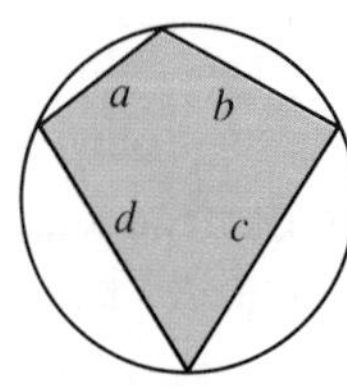

Use this formula to find the area of an isosceles trapezoid with sides 10, 10, 10, and 20 that is inscribed in a circle. **≈ 130**

11-3 *Areas of Trapezoids*

An **altitude** of a trapezoid is any segment perpendicular to a line containing a base from a point on the opposite base. Since the bases are parallel, all altitudes have the same length, called the *height* (h) of the trapezoid.

Theorem 11-5

The area of a trapezoid equals half the product of the height and the sum of the bases. ($A = \frac{1}{2}h(b_1 + b_2)$)

Key steps of proof:

1. Draw diagonal $\overline{BD}$ of trap. $ABCD$, forming two triangular regions, I and II, each with height h.
2. Area of trapezoid = Area I + Area II
$= \frac{1}{2}b_1h + \frac{1}{2}b_2h$
$= \frac{1}{2}h(b_1 + b_2)$

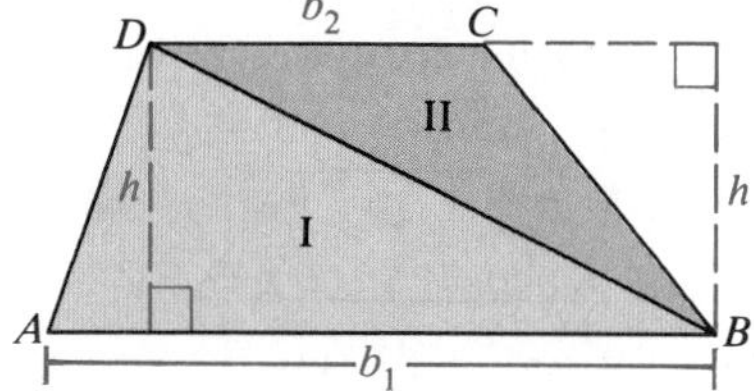

Example 1 Find the area of a trapezoid with height 7 and bases 12 and 8.

Solution $A = \frac{1}{2}h(b_1 + b_2) = \frac{1}{2} \cdot 7 \cdot (12 + 8) = 70$

Example 2 Find the area of an isosceles trapezoid with legs 5 and bases 6 and 10.

Solution When you draw the two altitudes shown, you get a rectangle and two congruent right triangles. The segments of the lower base must have lengths 2, 6, and 2. First find h:

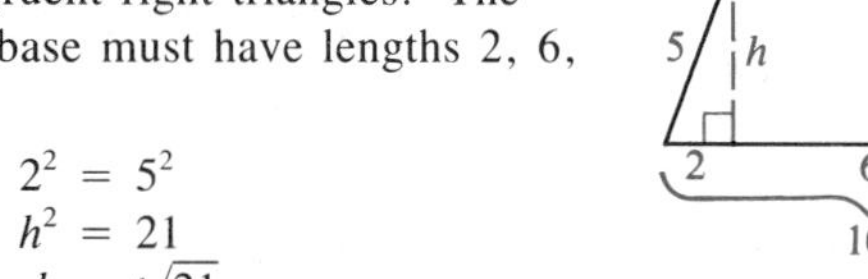

$$h^2 + 2^2 = 5^2$$
$$h^2 = 21$$
$$h = \sqrt{21}$$

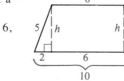

Then find the area: $A = \frac{1}{2}h(b_1 + b_2) = \frac{1}{2}\sqrt{21}(10 + 6) = 8\sqrt{21}$

Classroom Exercises

Find the area of each trapezoid and the length of the median.

1.

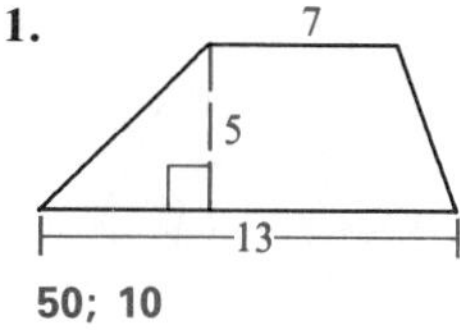

50; 10

2.

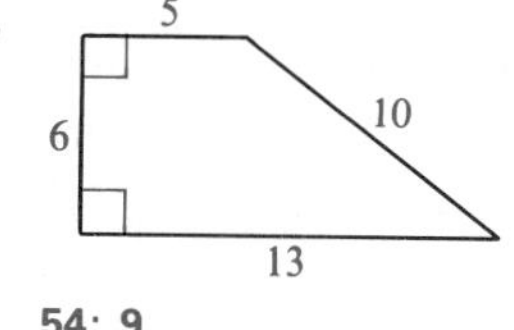

54; 9

3.

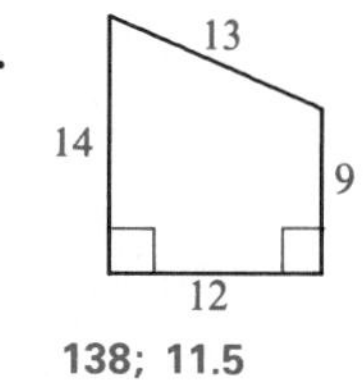

138; 11.5

Teaching Suggestions,
p. T123

Objective
Presenting the Lesson
Using Technology

Supplementary Materials

Practice Master 65
Study Guide, pp. 141–142
Overhead Visuals G, H

Lesson Focus

This lesson continues the study of areas of polygons by stating the formula for finding the area of a trapezoid.

Suggested Assignments

Minimum
Day 1: 436/1–7, 9–11
Day 2: 436–437/12–19
440/Mixed Review

Average
436–437/1, 2, 5, 10–12, 15, 17, 21, 24, 26
440/Mixed Review

Maximum
436–437/8, 10, 14, 16, 18, 21, 24, 26–28

Teaching Note

When discussing the formula for finding the area of a trapezoid, be sure to remind students that the bases are the sides that are parallel. Students frequently make errors identifying the bases for a trapezoid in nonstandard position, such as the one shown in Classroom Ex. 3.

Additional Answers Classroom Exercises

4. Area of trap.
$= \frac{1}{2}h(b_1 + b_2)$
$= h[\frac{1}{2}(b_1 + b_2)]$
$=$ height $\times$ median

Chalkboard Examples

1. In trapezoid *TRAP*, $\overline{RA} \parallel \overline{TP}$, $m\angle T = 60$, $RA = 10$, $TR = 8$ and $TP = 15$. Find the area of trapezoid *TRAP*. $50\sqrt{3}$
2. In isosceles trapezoid *ABCD*, the legs are 8 and the bases are 6 and 14. Find the area. $40\sqrt{3}$

Additional Answers Written Exercises

1. $A = 70$; $m = 10$
2. $A = 30.5$; $m = 5$
3. $A = 6$; $m = 3\frac{3}{4}$
4. $h = 10$; $m = 30$
5. $h = 5$; $m = 18$
6. $b_2 = 5$; $m = 4$
7. $b_2 = 1$; $m = 4$
8. $b_1 = 15k$; $m = 9k$

4. Use your answers from Exercises 1–3 to explain why the area of a trapezoid can be given by the formula

$$Area = height \times median.$$

5. Does the median of a trapezoid divide it into two regions of equal area? **No**
6. Does the segment joining the midpoints of the parallel sides of a trapezoid divide it into two regions of equal area? **Yes**
7. **a.** If the congruent trapezoids shown are slid together, what special quadrilateral is formed? **a ▱**
   b. Use your answer in part (a) to derive the formula $A = \frac{1}{2}h(b_1 + b_2)$.
   $A = \frac{1}{2} \cdot$ **Area of ▱** $= \frac{1}{2} \cdot h(b_1 + b_2)$

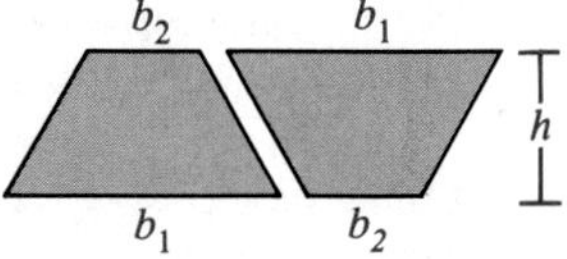

Find the area of each trapezoid.

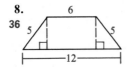

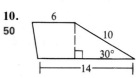

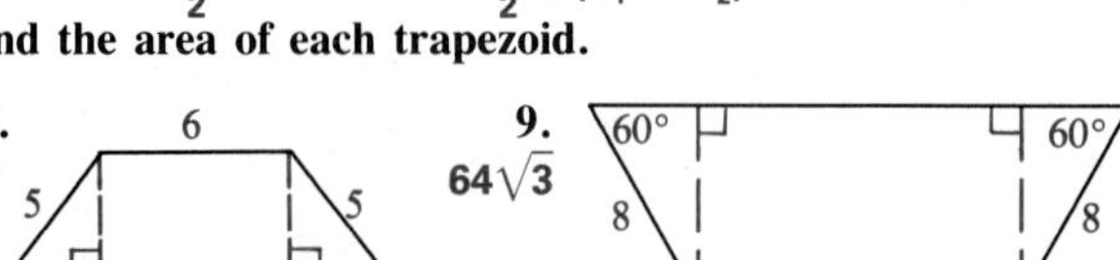

Written Exercises

Exercises 1–8 refer to trapezoids and *m* is the length of the median. Complete the table.

A

	1.	2.	3.	4.	5.	6.	7.	8.
b_1	12	6.8	$3\frac{1}{6}$	45	27	3	7	?
b_2	8	3.2	$4\frac{1}{3}$	15	9	?	?	$3k$
h	7	6.1	$1\frac{3}{5}$	?	?	3	$9\sqrt{2}$	$5k$
A	?	?	?	300	90	12	$36\sqrt{2}$	$45k^2$
m	?	?	?	?	?	?	?	?

9. A trapezoid has area 54 and height 6. How long is its median? **9**

In Exercises 10–18, find the area of each trapezoid.

10. **64**

11. **108**

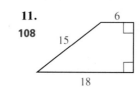

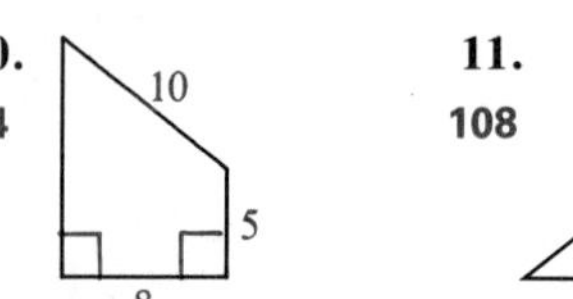

12. $21\sqrt{3}$

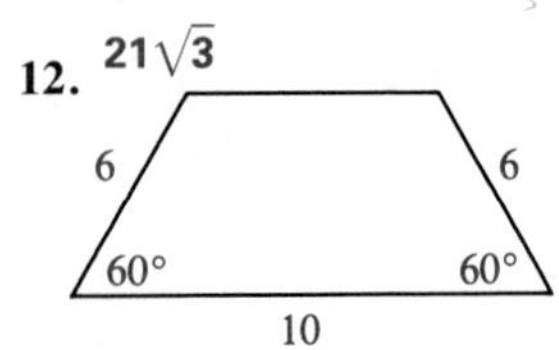

13. $\frac{27\sqrt{3}}{4}$

14. $94\frac{1}{2}$

15. 24

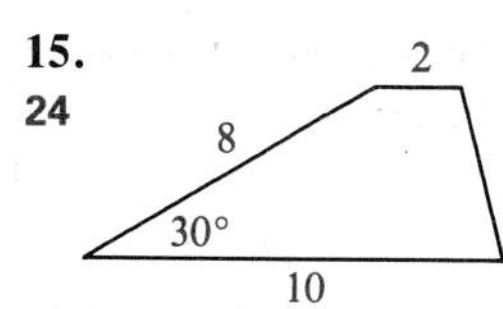

16. An isosceles trapezoid with legs 13 and bases 10 and 20 **180**

17. An isosceles trapezoid with legs 10 and bases 10 and 22 **128**

18. A trapezoid with bases 8 and 18 and 45° base angles **65**

Use a calculator or the trigonometry table on page 311 to find the area of each trapezoid to the nearest tenth. **Answers may vary.**

B **19.** **42.0**

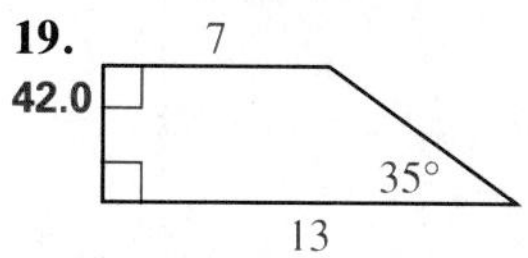

20. **71.0**

21. **87.8**

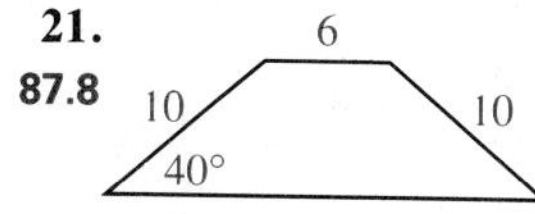

22. The legs of an isosceles trapezoid are 10 cm. The bases are 9 cm and 21 cm. Find the area of the trapezoid and the lengths of the diagonals. **120 cm²; 17 cm; 17 cm**

23. An isosceles trapezoid has bases 12 and 28. The area is 300. Find the height and the perimeter. **15; 74**

24. *ABCD* is a trapezoid with bases 4 cm and 12 cm, as shown. Find the ratio of the areas of:

a. $\triangle ABD$ and $\triangle ABC$ **1:1**

b. $\triangle AOD$ and $\triangle BOC$ **1:1**

c. $\triangle ABD$ and $\triangle ADC$ **3:1**

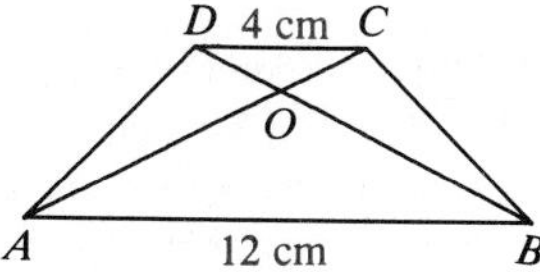

25. *ABCDEF* is a regular hexagon with side 12. Find the areas of the three regions formed when diagonals $\overline{AC}$ and $\overline{AD}$ are drawn. **See below.**

26. An isosceles trapezoid with bases 12 and 16 is inscribed in a circle of radius 10. The center of the circle lies in the interior of the trapezoid. Find the area of the trapezoid. **196**

27. A trapezoid of area 100 cm² has bases of 5 cm and 15 cm. Find the areas of the two triangles formed by extending the legs until they intersect. **12.5 cm²; 112.5 cm²**

C **28.** Draw a non-isosceles trapezoid. Then construct an isosceles trapezoid with equal area.

Find the exact area of each trapezoid. In Exercise 31, $\odot O$ is inscribed in quadrilateral *ABCD*.

29.

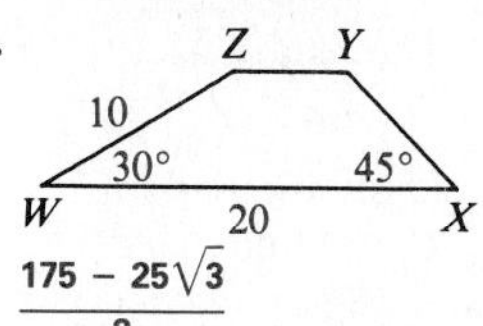

$\frac{175 - 25\sqrt{3}}{2}$

30. **204**

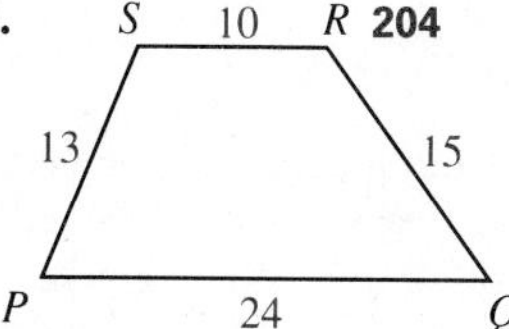

31. **156**

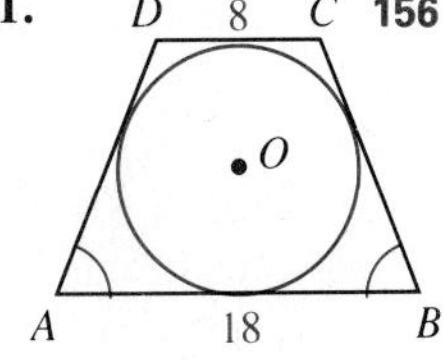

25. $\triangle ABC$: $36\sqrt{3}$; $\triangle ACD$: $72\sqrt{3}$; *ADEF*: $108\sqrt{3}$

Guided Practice

1. A trapezoid has an area of 75 cm² and a height of 5 cm. How long is the median? 15 cm

Find the area of each trapezoid.

2. $48\sqrt{3}$

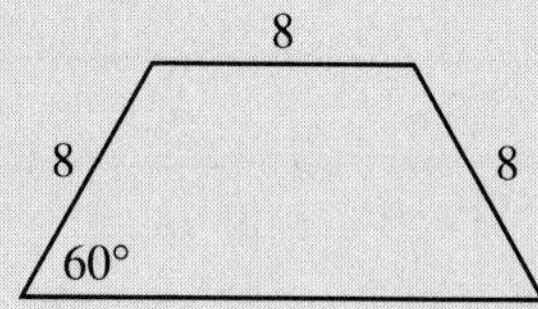

3. $\frac{33}{2}$

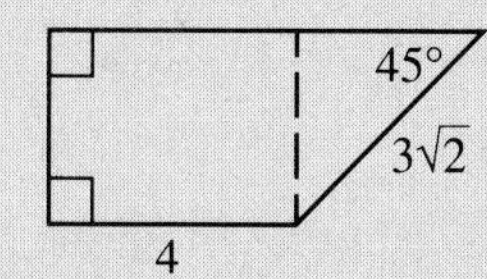

4. $63\sqrt{3}$

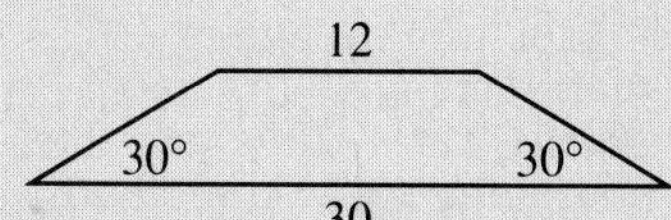

32. President James Garfield discovered a proof of the Pythagorean Theorem in 1876 that used a diagram like the one at the right. Refer to the diagram and write your own proof of the Pythagorean Theorem. (*Hint*: Express the area of quad. *MNOP* in two ways.)

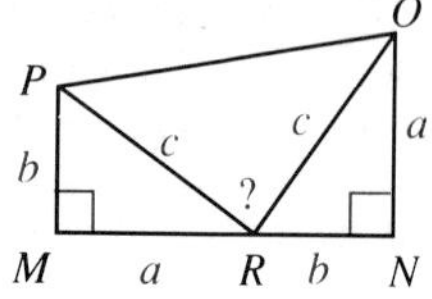
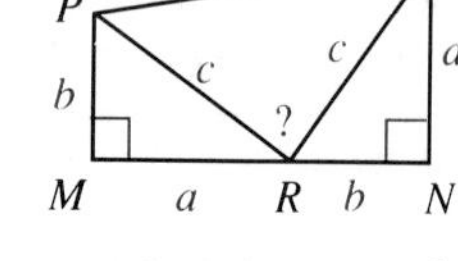

33. Show that the area of square *ABCD* equals the area of rectangle *EFGD*.

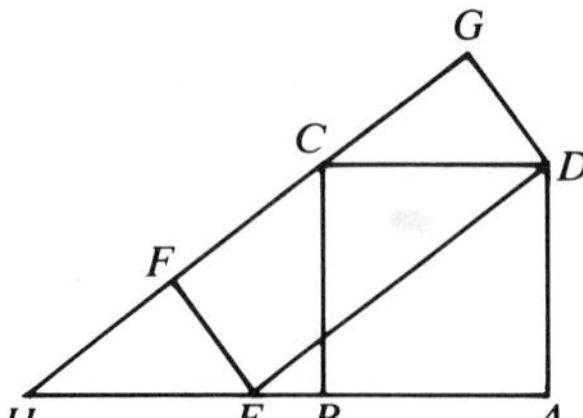

★ 34. If $NS = 16$, find the area of ▱*MNOP*. **122**

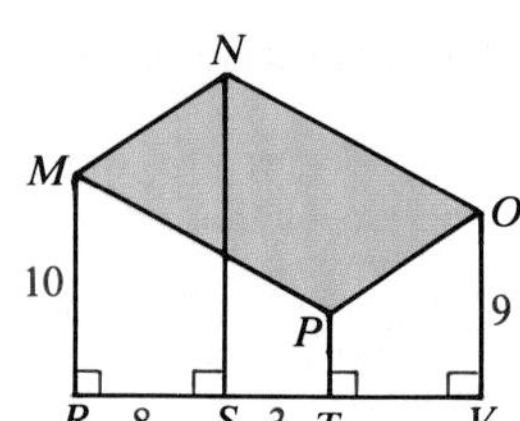

Using a Computer

This Computer Key-In extends the one on page 428. It uses trapezoids rather than rectangles to find the area under a curve and then compares the two methods. A spreadsheet can also be used to compare the methods.

Making Connections

Approximating the area under a curve by constructing trapezoids (see Computer Key-In) has important applications in advanced mathematics, especially calculus. This brief exposure to ideas studied in future courses will help students to grow mathematically.

◆ Computer Key-In

The shaded region shown below is bounded by the graph of $y = x^2$, the x-axis, and the vertical lines $x = 1$ and $x = 2$. The area of this region can be approximated by drawing rectangles. (See the Computer Key-In, page 428.) This area can also be approximated by drawing trapezoids. The curve $y = x^2$ has been exaggerated slightly to better show the trapezoids. The diagrams below suggest that you can obtain a closer approximation for the area by using trapezoids than by using rectangles.

Let us approximate the area using five rectangles and five trapezoids. The base of each rectangle is 0.2 and the height is given by $y = x^2$.

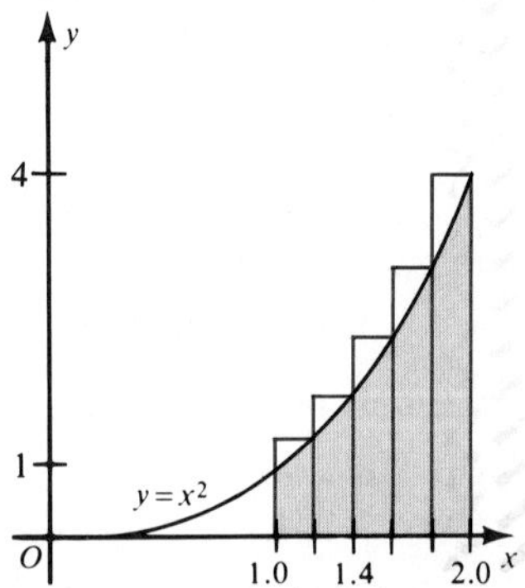

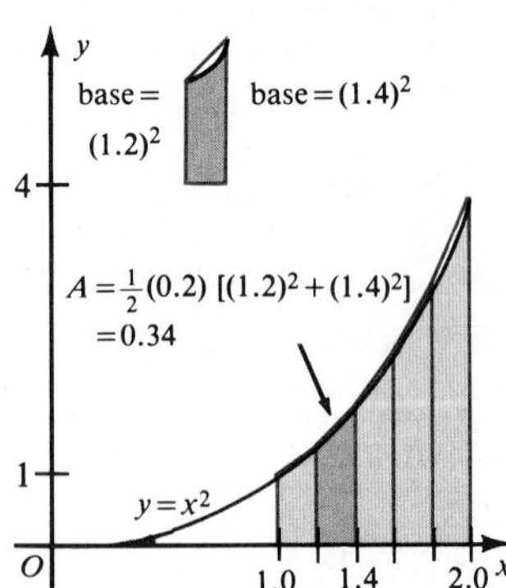

For each trapezoid in the diagram at the right above, the parallel bases are vertical segments from the x-axis to the curve $y = x^2$. The altitude is a horizontal segment with length 0.2. For example, in the second trapezoid, the bases are $(1.2)^2$ and $(1.4)^2$, respectively, and the height is 0.2.

The area of the shaded region is first approximated by the sum of the areas of the five rectangles and then by the sum of the areas of the five trapezoids. Compare these approximations. (Calculus can be used to prove that the exact area is $\frac{7}{3}$. Note that $\frac{7}{3} \approx 2.33$.)

Area approximated by five rectangles:
$A \approx (1.2)^2(0.2) + (1.4)^2(0.2) + (1.6)^2(0.2) + (1.8)^2(0.2) + (2.0)^2(0.2)$
$A \approx 2.64$

Area approximated by five trapezoids:

$$A \approx \tfrac{1}{2}(0.2)[(1.0)^2 + (1.2)^2] + \tfrac{1}{2}(0.2)[(1.2)^2 + (1.4)^2] + \tfrac{1}{2}(0.2)[(1.4)^2 + (1.6)^2] + \tfrac{1}{2}(0.2)[(1.6)^2 + (1.8)^2] + \tfrac{1}{2}(0.2)[(1.8)^2 + (2.0)^2]$$

$A \approx 2.34$

The following computer program will compute and add the areas of the five trapezoids shown in the diagram on the preceding page.

```
10 LET X = 1
20 FOR N = 1 TO 5
30 LET B1 = X ↑ 2
40 LET B2 = (X + 0.2) ↑ 2
50 LET A = A + 0.5 * 0.2 * (B1 + B2)
60 LET X = X + 0.2
70 NEXT N
80 PRINT "AREA IS APPROXIMATELY ";A
90 END
```

Exercises

1. A better approximation can be found by using 100 smaller trapezoids with base vertices at 1.00, 1.01, 1.02, . . . , 1.99, 2.00. Change lines 20, 40, 50, and 60 as follows:

```
20 FOR N = 1 TO 100
40 LET B2 = (X + 0.01) ↑ 2
50 LET A = A + 0.5 * 0.01 * (B1 + B2)
60 LET X = X + 0.01
```

   RUN the program to approximate the area of the shaded region. **2.33334996**

2. Modify the given computer program so that it will use 1000 trapezoids with base vertices at 1.000, 1.001, 1.002, . . . , 2.000 to approximate the area of the shaded region. RUN the program. **2.33333378**

3. Modify the given computer program so that it will use ten trapezoids to approximate the area of the region that is bounded by the graph of $y = x^2$, the x-axis, and *the vertical lines* $x = 0$ *and* $x = 1$. RUN the program. Compare your answer with that obtained on page 428, where ten rectangles were used. (*Note*: Calculus can be used to prove that the exact area is $\frac{1}{3}$.) **0.335**

Mixed Review Exercises

Complete.

1. In $\odot O$, if the measure of central angle AOB is 52, then the measure of arc AB is __?__. **52**
2. In $\odot P$, if the measure of inscribed angle RST is 73, then the measure of arc RT is __?__. **146**
3. The measure of each interior angle of a regular octagon is __?__. **135**
4. If the measure of each exterior angle of a regular polygon is 20, then the polygon has __?__ sides. **18**
5. In a 45°-45°-90° triangle with legs 20 cm long, the length of the altitude to the hypotenuse is __?__. **$10\sqrt{2}$ cm**
6. In a 30°-60°-90° triangle with hypotenuse 30 cm long, the lengths of the legs are __?__ and __?__. **15 cm, $15\sqrt{3}$ cm**
7. In an isosceles triangle with vertex angle of 60° and legs 10 m long, the length of the base is __?__. **10 m**
8. In $\triangle ABC$ if $m\angle C = 90$, $AC = 8$, and $AB = 17$, then $\cos B =$ __?__. **$\frac{15}{17}$**

11-4 *Areas of Regular Polygons*

The beautifully symmetrical designs of kaleidoscopes are produced by mirrors that reflect light through loose particles of colored glass. Since the body of a kaleidoscope is a tube, the designs always appear to be inscribed in a circle. The photograph of a kaleidoscope pattern at the right suggests a regular hexagon.

Given any circle, you can inscribe in it a regular polygon of any number of sides. The diagrams below show how this can be done.

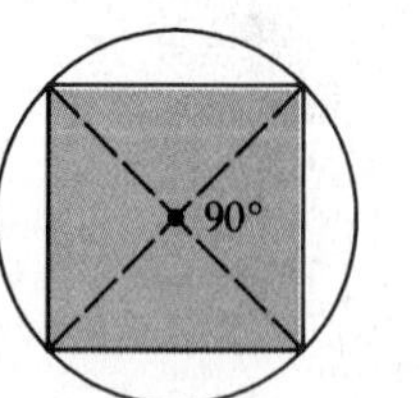

Square in circle: draw four 90° central angles.

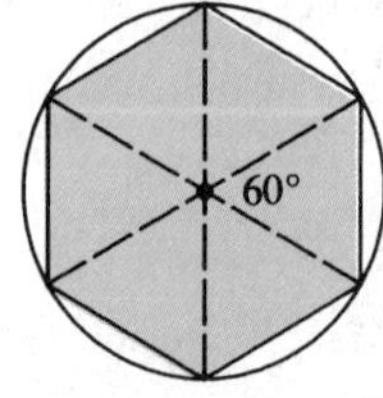

Regular hexagon in circle: draw six 60° central angles.

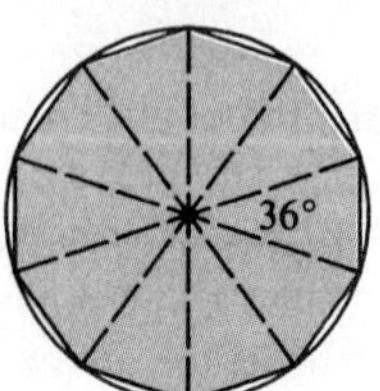

Regular decagon in circle: draw ten 36° central angles.

Teaching Suggestions, pp. T123–T124

Objective
Presenting the Lesson
Making Connections
Reinforcement
Extension

Cooperative Learning, p. T124

Supplementary Materials

Practice Master 66
Test 43
Resource Book, pp. 73, 152, 264
Study Guide, pp. 143–144

Lesson Focus

The focus of this lesson is on applying the formula for finding the area of a regular polygon.

Suggested Assignments

Minimum
Day 1: 443/1–12
Day 2: 443/13, 15
444/Self-Test 1

Average
Day 1: 443/1, 3, 5, 6, 10–13
Day 2: 443–444/14, 15, 18–22
444/Self-Test 1

Maximum
Day 1: 443–444/7, 10, 13–15, 17
S 437/25, 30
Day 2: 444/18–22

Teaching Note

You might need to review circumscribed circles, perimeter, 30°-60°-90° triangles, 45°-45°-90° triangles, and trigonometry for this lesson.

It is also true that if you are given any regular polygon, you can circumscribe a circle about it. This relationship between circles and regular polygons leads to the following definitions:

The **center of a regular polygon** is the center of the circumscribed circle.

The **radius of a regular polygon** is the distance from the center to a vertex.

A **central angle of a regular polygon** is an angle formed by two radii drawn to consecutive vertices.

The **apothem of a regular polygon** is the (perpendicular) distance from the center of the polygon to a side.

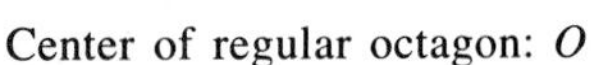

Center of regular octagon: O

Radius: OA, OB, OC, and so on

Central angle: $\angle AOB$, $\angle BOC$, and so on

Measure of central angle: $\frac{360}{8} = 45$

Apothem: OX

If you know the apothem and the perimeter of a regular polygon, you can use the next theorem to find the area of the polygon.

Theorem 11-6

The area of a regular polygon is equal to half the product of the apothem and the perimeter. ($A = \frac{1}{2}ap$)

Given: Regular n-gon $TUVW$ . . . ; apothem a; side s; perimeter p; area A

Prove: $A = \frac{1}{2}ap$

Key steps of proof:

1. If all radii are drawn, n congruent triangles are formed.
2. Area of each $\triangle = \frac{1}{2}sa$
3. $A = n(\frac{1}{2}sa) = \frac{1}{2}a(ns)$
4. Since $ns = p$, $A = \frac{1}{2}ap$.

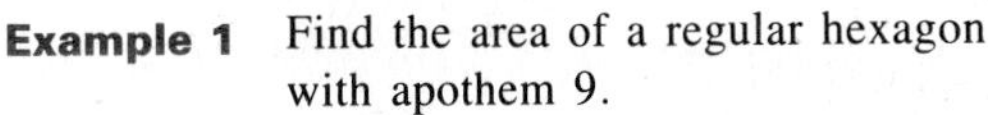

Example 1 Find the area of a regular hexagon with apothem 9.

Solution Use 30°-60°-90° $\triangle$ relationships.

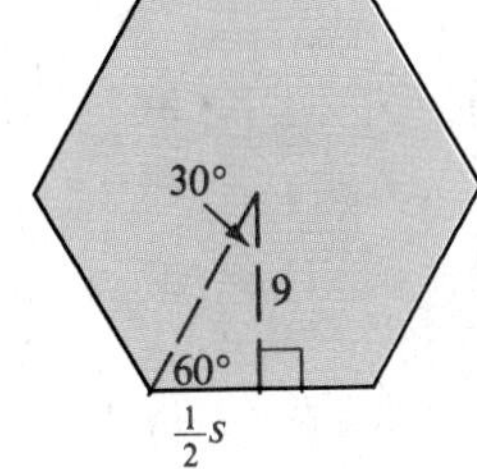

$$\frac{1}{2}s = \frac{9}{\sqrt{3}} = 3\sqrt{3}$$

$$s = 6\sqrt{3}; \quad p = 36\sqrt{3}$$

$$A = \frac{1}{2}ap = \frac{1}{2} \cdot 9 \cdot 36\sqrt{3} = 162\sqrt{3}$$

Chalkboard Examples

Find the measure of a central angle for each inscribed figure.

1. a square 90
2. a regular hexagon 60
3. a regular octagon 45
4. a regular dodecagon (12-sided polygon) 30

Find the perimeter and the area of each figure.

5. a regular hexagon with apothem 6 $24\sqrt{3}$; $72\sqrt{3}$
6. a regular octagon with side 5 and apothem 3 40; 60
7. an equilateral triangle with apothem 8 $48\sqrt{3}$; $192\sqrt{3}$
8. a regular hexagon with side 12 72; $216\sqrt{3}$
9. a square with diagonal 10 $20\sqrt{2}$; 50
10. Find the area of a regular pentagon inscribed in a circle of radius 8. 152.2

Thinking Skills

Students may think of regular triangles and hexagons as being composed of 30°-60°-90° triangles, as in Example 1.

Cultural Note

The word *kaleidoscope* is derived from the Greek words *kalos* (meaning *beautiful*), *eidos* (meaning *form*), and *skopein* (meaning to *see*).

Example 2 Find the area of a regular polygon with 9 sides inscribed in a circle with radius 10.

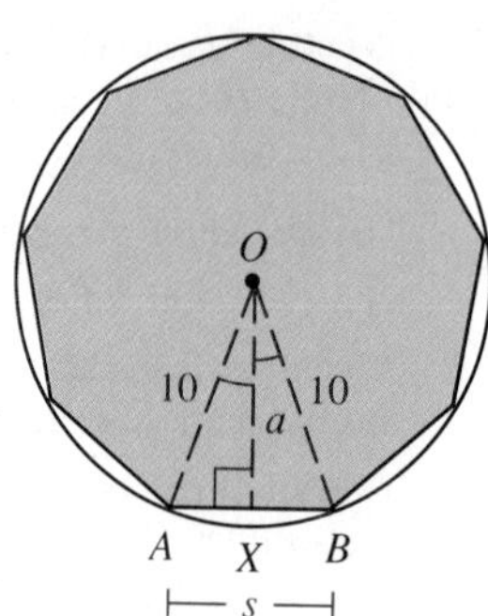

Solution $m\angle AOB = \frac{360}{9} = 40$; $m\angle AOX = 20$

Use trigonometry to find a and s:

$$\cos 20° = \frac{a}{10} \qquad \sin 20° = \frac{\frac{1}{2}s}{10}$$

$$a = 10 \cdot \cos 20° \qquad \tfrac{1}{2}s = 10 \sin 20°$$

$$a \approx 10(0.9397) \qquad s \approx 20(0.3420)$$

$$a \approx 9.397 \qquad s \approx 6.840$$

To find the area of the polygon, use either of two methods:

Method 1 Area of polygon $= 9 \cdot$ area of $\triangle AOB$

$= 9 \cdot \frac{1}{2}sa$

$\approx \frac{9}{2}(6.840)(9.397)$

≈ 289

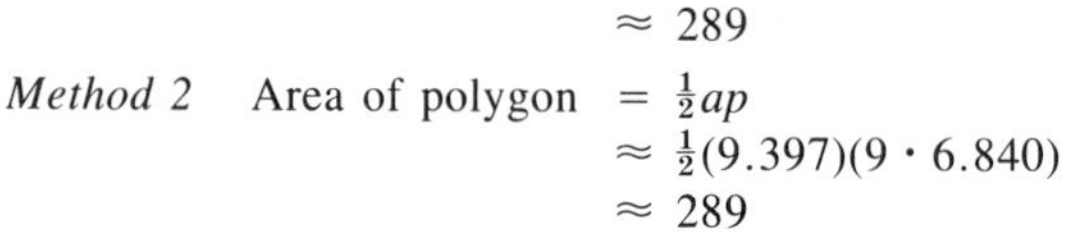

Method 2 Area of polygon $= \frac{1}{2}ap$

$\approx \frac{1}{2}(9.397)(9 \cdot 6.840)$

≈ 289

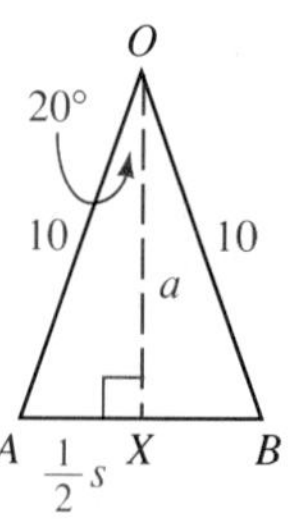

Guided Practice

Complete the tables for the regular polygons shown. In these tables, p represents the perimeter and A represents the area.

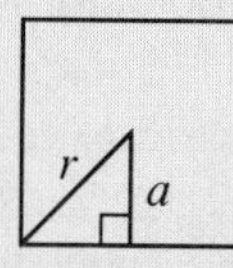

	r	a	p	A
1.	$5\sqrt{2}$	5	40	100
2.	$\sqrt{6}$	$\sqrt{3}$	$8\sqrt{3}$	12

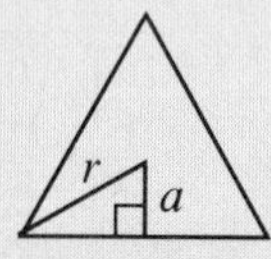

	r	a	p	A
3.	8	4	$24\sqrt{3}$	$48\sqrt{3}$
4.	2	1	$6\sqrt{3}$	$3\sqrt{3}$

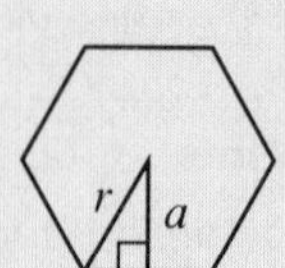

	r	a	p	A
5.	8	$4\sqrt{3}$	48	$96\sqrt{3}$
6.	$4\sqrt{3}$	6	$24\sqrt{3}$	$72\sqrt{3}$

Classroom Exercises

1. Find the measure of a central angle of a regular polygon with **(a)** 10 sides, **(b)** 15 sides, **(c)** 360 sides, and **(d)** n sides. **36; 24; 1;** $\frac{360}{n}$

Find the perimeter and the area of each regular polygon described.

2. A regular octagon with side 4 and apothem a **32; 16*a***
3. A regular pentagon with side s and apothem 3 **5*s*;** $\frac{15s}{2}$
4. A regular decagon with side s and apothem a **10*s*; 5*sa***
5. Explain why the apothem of a regular polygon must be less than the radius. **The apothem is a ⊥ segment so it is the shortest distance between the center and a side (Thm. 6-3, Cor. 1, p. 220).**

For each regular polygon shown, find (a) the perimeter, (b) the measure of a central angle, (c) the apothem *a*, (d) the radius *r*, and (e) the area *A*.

6. 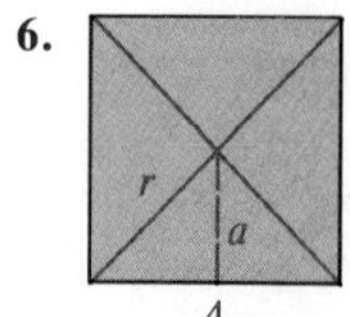

a. 16 **b.** 90 **c.** 2 **d.** $2\sqrt{2}$ **e.** 16

7. **a.** 12 **b.** 120 **c.** $\frac{2\sqrt{3}}{3}$ **d.** $\frac{4\sqrt{3}}{3}$ **e.** $4\sqrt{3}$

8. **a.** 24 **b.** 60 **c.** $2\sqrt{3}$ **d.** 4 **e.** $24\sqrt{3}$

9. *ABCDE* is a regular pentagon with radius 10.

a. Find the measure of $\angle AOB$. **72**

b. Explain why $m\angle AOX = 36$. **See below.**

Note: For parts (c)–(e), use a calculator or the table on page 311.

c. $\cos 36° = \frac{a}{?}$. To the nearest tenth, $a \approx$ _?_. **8.1**

d. $\sin 36° = \frac{\frac{1}{2}s}{?}$. To the nearest tenth, $s \approx$ _?_. **11.8**

e. Find the perimeter and area of the pentagon. **59; 238.95**

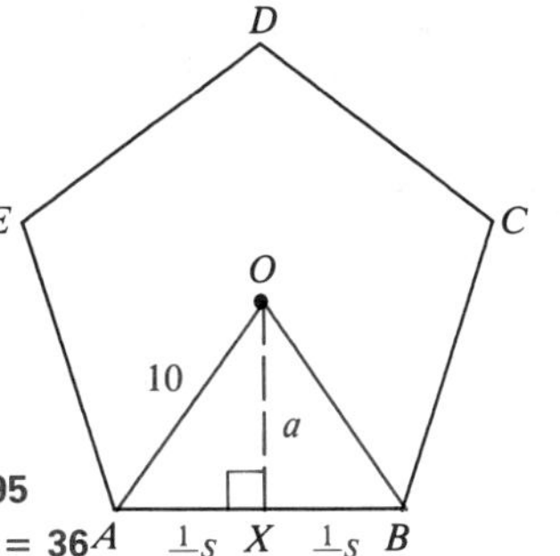

b. $\triangle AOX \cong \triangle BOX$ **so** $m\angle AOX = m\angle BOX = \frac{1}{2}m\angle AOB = 36$

Written Exercises

Copy and complete the tables for the regular polygons shown. In these tables, *p* represents the perimeter and *A* represents the area.

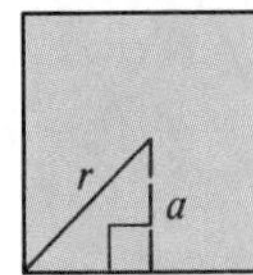

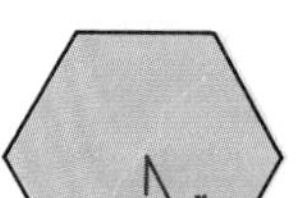

	r	*a*	*A*
A 1.	$8\sqrt{2}$	?	?
2.	?	5	?
3.	?	?	49
4.	?	$\sqrt{6}$	?

	r	*a*	*p*	*A*
5.	6	?	?	?
6.	?	4	?	?
7.	?	?	12	?
8.	?	?	$9\sqrt{3}$	?

	r	*a*	*p*	*A*
9.	4	?	?	?
10.	?	$5\sqrt{3}$	?	?
11.	?	6	?	?
12.	?	?	$12\sqrt{3}$	?

Find the area of each polygon. **13.** $36\sqrt{3}$ **15.** $216\sqrt{3}$

B 13. An equilateral triangle with radius $4\sqrt{3}$

14. A square with radius $8k$ $128k^2$

15. A regular hexagon with perimeter 72

16. A regular hexagon with apothem 4 $32\sqrt{3}$

17. A regular decagon is shown inscribed in a circle with radius 1.

a. Explain why $m\angle AOX = 18$. **See below.**

b. Use a calculator or the table on page 311 to evaluate *OX* and *AX* below.

$\sin 18° = \frac{AX}{1}$, so $AX \approx$ _?_. **0.3090**

$\cos 18° = \frac{?}{?}$, so $OX \approx$ _?_. $\frac{OX}{1}$; **0.9511**

c. Perimeter of decagon $\approx$ _?_ **6.18**

d. Area of $\triangle AOB \approx$ _?_ **0.2939**

e. Area of decagon $\approx$ _?_ **2.939**

a. $\triangle AOX \cong \triangle BOX$ **so** $m\angle AOX = \frac{1}{2}m\angle AOB = \frac{1}{2}\left(\frac{360}{10}\right) = \frac{1}{2}(36) = 18$

Additional Answers
Written Exercises

1. $a = 8$; $A = 256$
2. $r = 5\sqrt{2}$; $A = 100$
3. $r = \frac{7\sqrt{2}}{2}$; $a = \frac{7}{2}$
4. $r = 2\sqrt{3}$; $A = 24$
5. $a = 3$; $p = 18\sqrt{3}$; $A = 27\sqrt{3}$
6. $r = 8$; $p = 24\sqrt{3}$; $A = 48\sqrt{3}$
7. $r = \frac{4\sqrt{3}}{3}$; $a = \frac{2\sqrt{3}}{3}$; $A = 4\sqrt{3}$
8. $r = 3$; $a = \frac{3}{2}$; $A = \frac{27\sqrt{3}}{4}$
9. $a = 2\sqrt{3}$; $p = 24$; $A = 24\sqrt{3}$
10. $r = 10$; $p = 60$; $A = 150\sqrt{3}$
11. $r = 4\sqrt{3}$; $p = 24\sqrt{3}$; $A = 72\sqrt{3}$
12. $r = 2\sqrt{3}$; $a = 3$; $A = 18\sqrt{3}$

Additional Answers Written Exercises

18. $a = 0.5$; $p \approx 5.196$; $A \approx 1.299$

19. $a \approx 0.707$; $p \approx 5.656$; $A = 2$

20. $a \approx 0.866$; $p = 6$; $A \approx 2.598$

Quick Quiz

Find the area of each polygon.

1. a square with side $6\sqrt{3}$ 108
2. a rectangle with base $\sqrt{2}$ and diagonal $\sqrt{7}$ $\sqrt{10}$
3. $\square ABCD$ with $AB = 5\sqrt{2}$, $BC = 10$, and $m\angle A = 45$ 50
4. an equilateral triangle with perimeter 24 cm $16\sqrt{3}$ cm^2
5. an isosceles triangle with sides 9 cm, 9 cm, and 6 cm $18\sqrt{2}$ cm^2
6. a rhombus with side 17 and longer diagonal 30 240
7. an isosceles trapezoid with bases 4 and 8 and base angle of measure 45 12
8. a regular hexagon with perimeter 24 $24\sqrt{3}$
9. A regular dodecagon (12-sided polygon) with sides r and apothem s. $6rs$

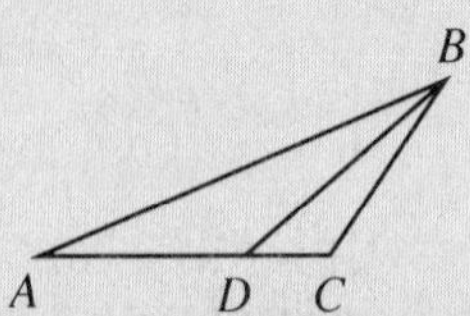

10. The area of $\triangle ABC$ is 56, $AC = 14$, and $DC = 4$. Find the areas of $\triangle ABD$ and $\triangle DBC$. 40; 16

Three regular polygons are inscribed in circles with radii 1. Find the apothem, the perimeter, and the area of each polygon. Use $\sqrt{3} \approx 1.732$ and $\sqrt{2} \approx 1.414$.

18.

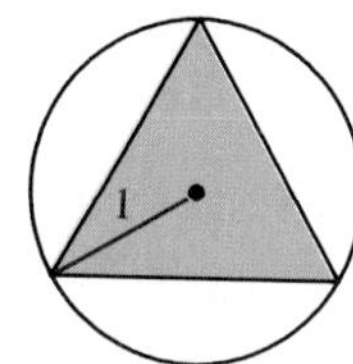

19.

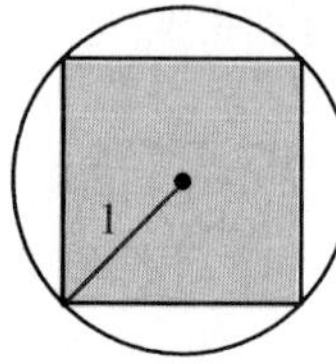

20.

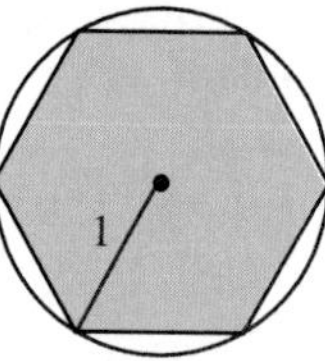

21. Find the perimeter and area of a regular dodecagon (12 sides) inscribed in a circle with radius 1. Use the procedure suggested by Exercise 17. **$A \approx 3$; $p \approx 6.2112$**

C **22.** A regular polygon with n sides is inscribed in a circle with radius 1.

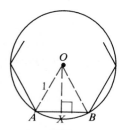

a. Explain why $m\angle AOX = \frac{180}{n}$. **See below.**

b. Show that $AX = \sin\left(\frac{180}{n}\right)^\circ$. $\sin\left(\frac{180}{n}\right)^\circ = \frac{AX}{1}$

c. Show that $OX = \cos\left(\frac{180}{n}\right)^\circ$. $\cos\left(\frac{180}{n}\right)^\circ = \frac{OX}{1}$

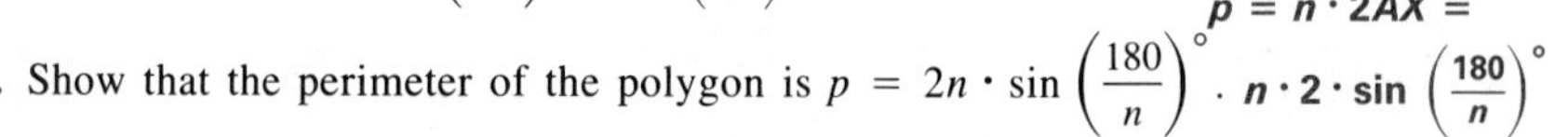

d. Show that the perimeter of the polygon is $p = 2n \cdot \sin\left(\frac{180}{n}\right)^\circ$. $p = n \cdot 2AX = n \cdot 2 \cdot \sin\left(\frac{180}{n}\right)^\circ$

e. Show that the area of the polygon is $A = n \cdot \sin\left(\frac{180}{n}\right)^\circ \cdot \cos\left(\frac{180}{n}\right)^\circ$.

$A = \frac{1}{2}ap = \frac{1}{2} \cdot \cos\left(\frac{180}{n}\right)^\circ \cdot 2n \cdot \sin\left(\frac{180}{n}\right)^\circ = n \cdot \sin\left(\frac{180}{n}\right)^\circ \cos\left(\frac{180}{n}\right)^\circ$

a. $\triangle AOX \cong \triangle BOX$ so $m\angle AOX = \frac{1}{2}m\angle AOB = \frac{1}{2}\left(\frac{360}{n}\right) = \frac{180}{n}$

Self-Test 1

Find the area of each polygon.

1. A square with diagonal $9\sqrt{2}$ **81**
2. A rectangle with base 12 and diagonal 13 **60**
3. A parallelogram with sides 8 and 10 and an angle of measure 60 **$40\sqrt{3}$**
4. An equilateral triangle with perimeter 12 cm **$4\sqrt{3}$ cm^2**
5. An isosceles triangle with sides 7 cm, 7 cm, and 12 cm **$6\sqrt{13}$ cm^2**
6. A rhombus with diagonals 8 and 10 **40**
7. An isosceles trapezoid with legs 5 and bases 9 and 17 **39**
8. A regular hexagon with sides 10 **$150\sqrt{3}$**
9. A regular decagon with sides x and apothem y **$5xy$**
10. The quadrilateral shown at the right **49**

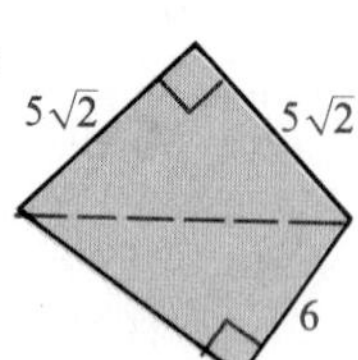

Ex. 10

♦ Calculator Key-In

If a regular polygon with n sides is inscribed in a circle with radius 1, then its perimeter and area are given by the formulas derived in Exercise 22 on the preceding page.

$$\text{Perimeter} = 2n \cdot \sin\left(\frac{180}{n}\right)^\circ \qquad \text{Area} = n \cdot \sin\left(\frac{180}{n}\right)^\circ \cdot \cos\left(\frac{180}{n}\right)^\circ$$

Exercises

1. Use the formulas and a calculator to complete the table at the right.
2. Use your answers in Exercise 1 to suggest approximations to the perimeter and the area of a *circle* with radius 1.
   Answers may vary.
   $p \approx 6.28318$; $A \approx 3.14159$

Number of sides	Perimeter	Area
18	?	?
180	?	?
1800	?	?
18000	?	?

Additional Answers Calculator Key-In

1. 18: 6.2513344; 3.0781813
   180: 6.2828663; 3.1409547
   1800: 6.2831821; 3.1415863
   18000: 6.2831853; 3.1415926

Circles, Similar Figures, and Geometric Probability

Objectives

1. Know and use the formulas for the circumferences and areas of circles.
2. Know and use the formulas for arc lengths and the areas of sectors of a circle.
3. Find the ratio of the areas of two triangles.
4. Understand and apply the relationships between scale factors, perimeters, and areas of similar figures.
5. Use lengths and areas to solve problems involving geometric probability.

Teaching Suggestions, pp. T124–T125

Objective
Presenting the Lesson
Reinforcement
Enrichment

Communication Skills, p. T125

Supplementary Materials

Practice Master 67
Study Guide, pp. 145–146
Computer Activity 23

11-5 *Circumferences and Areas of Circles*

When you think of the perimeter of a figure, you probably think of the distance around the figure. Since the word "around" is not mathematically precise, perimeter is usually defined in other ways. For example, the perimeter of a polygon is defined as the sum of the lengths of its sides. Since a circle is not a polygon, the perimeter of a circle must be defined differently.

Lesson Focus

In this lesson, the formulas for circumference and area of a circle are stated. These formulas can be understood by using facts that have been developed about areas of regular polygons.

Suggested Assignments

Minimum

Day 1: 448–449/1–8, 9–15 odd

Day 2: 448–449/10–16 even, 17, 18, 21

Average

Day 1: 448–449/2, 5–13 odd, 16–19, 21

Day 2: 449–450/23–27, 29, 30, 32

Maximum

Day 1: 448–450/7, 11, 12, 15, 17, 18, 20, 22–24, 26

Day 2: 450/27, 29–34

Teaching Note

Remind students that π is an irrational number and is not the ratio of two integers, as the quotient $\frac{22}{7}$ suggests.

In the expression, $\frac{C}{d}$, if d is rational, C is not, and vice versa.

Making Connections

The actual derivations of the formulas for the circumference and area of a circle require the concept of a limit. Students are introduced to the concept of a limiting process in an intuitive way. Stress the importance of studying the ideas of this lesson as a foundation for future work in mathematics.

First consider a sequence of regular polygons inscribed in a circle with radius r. Four such polygons are shown below. Imagine that the number of sides of the regular polygons continues to increase. As you can see in the diagrams, the more sides a regular polygon has, the closer it approximates (or "fits") the curve of the circle.

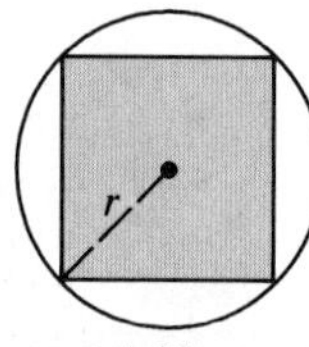

4 sides

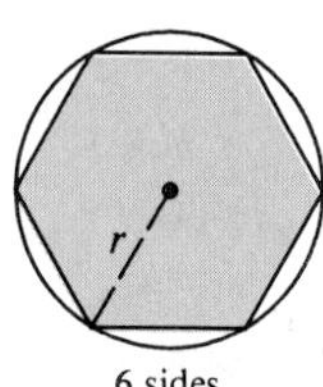

6 sides

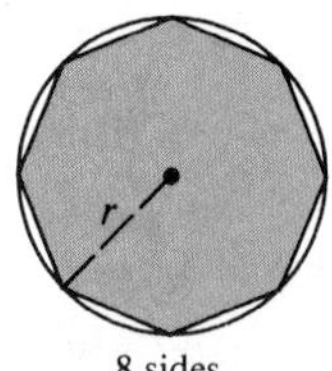

8 sides

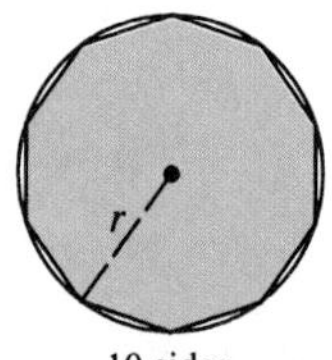

10 sides

Now consider the perimeters and the areas of this sequence of regular polygons. The table below contains values that are approximations (using trigonometry) of the perimeters and the areas of regular polygons in terms of the radius, r.

As the table suggests, these perimeters give us a sequence of numbers that get closer and closer to a limiting number. This limiting number is defined to be the perimeter, or **circumference,** of the circle.

The area of a circle is defined in a similar way. The areas of the inscribed regular polygons get closer and closer to a limiting number, defined to be the **area** of the circle.

The results in the table suggest that the circumference and the area of a circle with radius r are *approximately* $6.28r$ and $3.14r^2$.

Number of Sides of Polygon	Perimeter	Area
4	$5.66r$	$2.00r^2$
6	$6.00r$	$2.60r^2$
8	$6.12r$	$2.83r^2$
10	$6.18r$	$2.93r^2$
20	$6.26r$	$3.09r^2$
30	$6.27r$	$3.12r^2$
100	$6.28r$	$3.14r^2$

The exact values are given by the formulas below. (Proofs are suggested in Classroom Exercises 13 and 14 and Written Exercise 33.)

Circumference, C, of circle with radius r:	$C = 2\pi r$
Circumference, C, of circle with diameter d:	$C = \pi d$
Area, A, of circle with radius r:	$A = \pi r^2$

These formulas involve a famous number denoted by the Greek letter π (*pi*), which is the first letter in a Greek word that means "measure around." The number π is the ratio of the circumference of a circle to the diameter. This ratio is a constant for *all* circles. Because π is an irrational number, there isn't any decimal or fraction that expresses the constant number π exactly. Here are some common approximations for π:

$$3.14 \qquad \frac{22}{7} \qquad 3.1416 \qquad 3.14159$$

When you calculate the circumference and area of a circle, leave your answers in terms of π unless you are told to replace π by an approximation.

Example 1 Find the circumference and area of a circle with radius 6 cm.

Solution $C = 2\pi r = 2\pi \cdot 6 = 12\pi$ (cm)
$A = \pi r^2 = \pi \cdot 6^2 = 36\pi$ (cm^2)

Example 2 The photograph shows land that is supplied with water by an irrigation system. This system consists of a moving arm that sprinkles water over a circular region. If the arm is 430 m long, what is the area, correct to the nearest thousand square meters, of the irrigated region? (Use $\pi \approx 3.14$.)

Solution $A = \pi r^2 = \pi \cdot 430^2$
$A \approx 3.14 \cdot 184{,}900 = 580{,}586$
$A \approx 581{,}000$ m^2 (to the nearest 1000 m^2)

Example 3 Find the circumference of a circle if the area is 25π.

Solution Since $\pi r^2 = 25\pi$, $r^2 = 25$ and $r = 5$.
Then $C = 2\pi r = 2\pi \cdot 5 = 10\pi$.

Classroom Exercises

Complete the table. Leave answers in terms of π.

	1.	2.	3.	4.	5.	6.	7.	8.
Radius	3	4	0.8	?	?	?	?	?
Circumference	?	?	?	10π	18π	?	?	?
Area	?	?	?	?	?	36π	49π	144π

Find the circumference and area to the nearest tenth. Use $\pi \approx 3.14$.

9. $r = 2$
12.6; 12.6

10. $r = 6$
37.7; 113.0

11. $r = \frac{3}{2}$
9.4; 7.1

12. $r = 1.2$
7.5; 4.5

Teaching Note

Encourage students to leave answers in π form unless an approximation is specified. Emphasize that the exact circumference or exact area of a circle requires that π not be approximated.

Chalkboard Examples

Exs. 1–5 refer to circles. Complete the table. Leave the answers in terms of π.

	r	d	C	A
1.	15	30	30π	225π
2.	4	8	8π	16π
3.	13	26	26π	169π
4.	10	20	20π	100π
5.	$3\sqrt{2}$	$6\sqrt{2}$	$6\pi\sqrt{2}$	18π

For Exs. 6–8, the radius of ⊙O is three times the radius of ⊙R.

6. What is the ratio of the circumference to the diameter for each circle? π

7. Compare the circumferences of the two circles. The circumference of ⊙O is 3 times that of ⊙R.

8. Compare the areas of the two circles. The area of ⊙O is 9 times that of ⊙R.

Additional Answers Classroom Exercises

1. $C = 6\pi$; $A = 9\pi$
2. $C = 8\pi$; $A = 16\pi$
3. $C = 1.6\pi$; $A = 0.64\pi$
4. $r = 5$; $A = 25\pi$
5. $r = 9$; $A = 81\pi$
6. $r = 6$; $C = 12\pi$
7. $r = 7$; $C = 14\pi$
8. $r = 12$; $C = 24\pi$

13. The number π is defined to be the ratio of the circumference of a circle to the diameter. This ratio is the same for all circles. Supply the missing reasons for the key steps of proof below.

Given: $\odot O$ and $\odot O'$ with circumferences C and C' and diameters d and d'

Prove: $\frac{C}{d} = \frac{C'}{d'}$

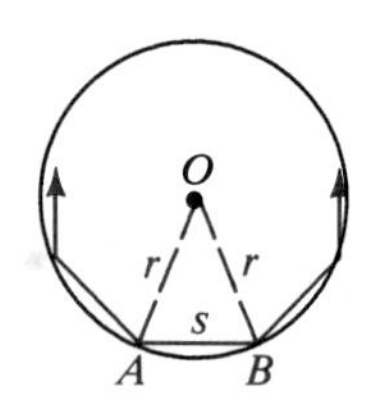

Key steps of proof:

1. Inscribe in each circle a regular polygon of n sides. Let p and p' be the perimeters.
2. $p = ns$ and $p' = ns'$ (Why?) **Def. of perimeter**
3. $\frac{p}{p'} = \frac{ns}{ns'} = \frac{s}{s'}$ (Why?) **By algebra**
4. $\triangle AOB \sim \triangle A'O'B'$ (Why?) **AA ~ Post.**
5. $\frac{s}{s'} = \frac{r}{r'} = \frac{d}{d'}$ (Why?) **Corr. sides of ~ △ are in proportion, and $d = 2r$.**
6. Thus $\frac{p}{p'} = \frac{d}{d'}$. (Steps 3 and 5)
7. Steps 2–5 hold for any number of sides n. We can let n be so large that p is practically the same as C, and p' is practically the same as C'. In advanced courses, you learn that C and C' can be substituted for p and p' in Step 6. This gives $\frac{C}{C'} = \frac{d}{d'}$, or $\frac{C}{d} = \frac{C'}{d'}$.

   (This constant ratio is the number π. Then, since $\frac{C}{d} = \pi$, $C = \pi d$.)

14. Use the formula $C = \pi d$ to derive the formula $C = 2\pi r$.
$C = \pi d = \pi(2r) = 2\pi r$

Written Exercises

Complete the table. Leave answers in terms of π.

A

	1.	2.	3.	4.	5.	6.	7.	8.
Radius	7	120	$\frac{5}{2}$	$6\sqrt{2}$	?	?	?	?
Circumference	?	?	?	?	20π	12π	?	?
Area	?	?	?	?	?	?	25π	50π

9. Use $\pi \approx \frac{22}{7}$ to find the circumference and area of a circle when the diameter is **(a)** 42 and **(b)** $14k$. **a. 132; 1386 b. $44k$; $154k^2$**

10. Use $\pi \approx 3.14$ to find the circumference and area of a circle when the diameter is **(a)** 8 (Answer to the nearest tenth.) and **(b)** $4t$. **a. 25.1; 50.2 b. $12.56t$; $12.56t^2$**

Additional Answers Written Exercises

1. $C = 14\pi$; $A = 49\pi$
2. $C = 240\pi$; $A = 14{,}400\pi$
3. $C = 5\pi$; $A = \frac{25}{4}\pi$
4. $C = 12\pi\sqrt{2}$; $A = 72\pi$
5. $r = 10$; $A = 100\pi$
6. $r = 6$; $A = 36\pi$
7. $r = 5$; $C = 10\pi$
8. $r = 5\sqrt{2}$; $C = 10\pi\sqrt{2}$

11. A basketball rim has diameter 18 in. Find the circumference of the rim and the area it encloses. Use $\pi \approx 3.14$. **$\approx$ 57 in.; $\approx$ 254 in.^{2}**

12. When a basketball player is shooting a free throw, the other players must stay out of the shaded region shown. This region consists of a semicircle together with a rectangle. Find the area of this region to the nearest square foot (ft^2). Use $\pi \approx 3.14$. **237 ft^2**

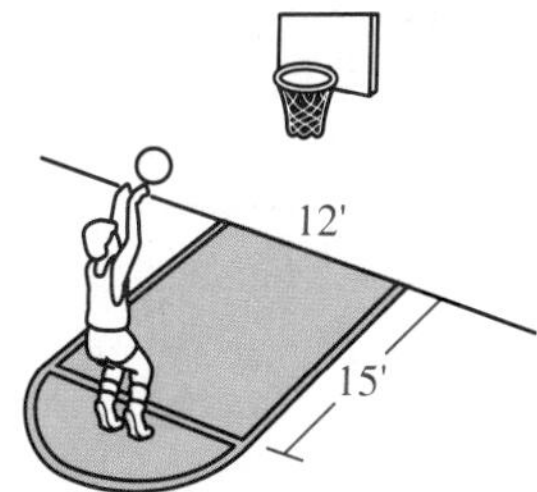

13. If 6 oz of dough are needed to make an 8-in. pizza, how much dough will be needed to make a 16-in. pizza of the same thickness? (*Hint*: Compare the areas of the pizza tops.) **24 oz**

14. One can of pumpkin pie mix will make a pie of diameter 8 in. If two cans of pie mix are used to make a larger pie of the same thickness, find the diameter of that pie. Use $\sqrt{2} \approx 1.414$. **11.3 in.**

15. A school's wrestling mat is a square with 40 ft sides. A circle 28 ft in diameter is painted on the mat. No wrestling is allowed outside the circle. Find the area of the part of the mat that is *not* used for wrestling. Use $\pi \approx \frac{22}{7}$. **984 ft^2**

16. An advertisement states that a Roto-Sprinkler can water a circular region with area 1000 ft^2. Find the diameter of this region to the nearest foot. Use $\pi \approx 3.14$. **36 ft**

17. Which is the better buy, a 10-in. pizza costing \$5 or a 15-in. pizza costing \$9? Use $\pi \approx 3.14$. **the 15-in. pizza**

18. Semicircles are constructed on the sides of the right triangle shown at the right. If $a = 6$ and $b = 8$, show that

Area I + Area II = Area III.

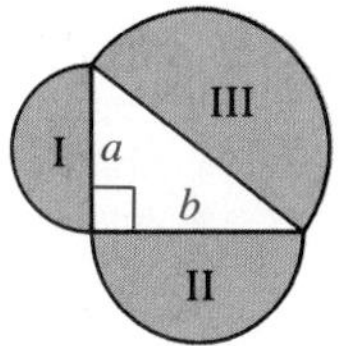

Exs. 18, 19

B **19.** Repeat Exercise 18 if the right triangle has legs a and b and hypotenuse c.

20. A Ferris wheel has diameter 42 ft. How far will a rider travel during a 4-min ride if the wheel rotates once every 20 seconds? Use $\pi \approx \frac{22}{7}$. **1584 ft**

21. The tires of a racing bike are approximately 70 cm in diameter.

a. How far does a bike racer travel in 5 min if the wheels are turning at a speed of 3 revolutions per second? Use $\pi \approx \frac{22}{7}$. **198,000 cm (or 1.98 km)**

b. How many revolutions does a wheel make in a 22 km race? Use $\pi \approx \frac{22}{7}$. **10,000**

22. A slide projector casts a circle of light with radius 2 ft on a screen that is 10 ft from the projector. If the screen is removed, the projector shines an even larger circle of light on the wall that was 10 ft behind the screen. Find the circumferences and areas of the circles of light on the screen and on the wall. Leave answers in terms of π. **screen: 4π ft; 4π ft^2 wall: 8π ft; 16π ft^2**

Guided Practice

Complete the table. Leave the answers in terms of π.

	1.	2.	3.	4.
Rad.	5	$3\sqrt{5}$	18	$5\sqrt{3}$
Cir.	10π	$6\pi\sqrt{5}$	36π	$10\pi\sqrt{3}$
Area	25π	45π	324π	75π

5. Use $\pi \approx \frac{22}{7}$ to find the circumference and area of a circle whose diameter is **(a)** 14, and **(b)** $7y$. (a) 44; 154 (b) $22y$; $\frac{77y^2}{2}$

6. Use $\pi \approx 3.14$ to find the circumference and area of a circle whose radius is **(a)** 12, and **(b)** $3x$. (a) 75.36; 452.16 (b) $18.84x$; $28.26x^2$

7. If a bicycle tire has a diameter of 26 in., how far does it travel in 1000 revolutions of the tire? Use $\pi \approx 3.14$. 81,640 in.

8. The rim of a satellite dish has a diameter of 7 ft. Find the circumference of the rim and the area of the circle defined by the rim. Use $\pi \approx 3.14$. 21.98 ft; 38.47 ft^2

9. The diameter of the world's largest optical telescope at the Zelenchukskaya Observatory in the USSR is 6 m. Find the circumference of the lens. Use $\pi \approx 3.14$. 18.84 m

10. What is the circumference of the earth at the equator if the radius of the earth is 6400 km? Use $\pi \approx 3.14$. 40,192 km

Group Activity

Exs. 24–28 can be done in a group environment if time permits. Divide the class into groups of four to five students and let them discuss how to find the areas of the shaded regions. Students should pay particular attention to the component parts of the regions and to which formulas are appropriate. Later, the class as a whole can discuss the solutions.

23. A target consists of four concentric circles with radii 1, 2, 3, and 4.

a. Find the area of the bull's eye and of each ring of the target. **π; 3π; 5π; 7π**

b. Find the area of the nth ring if the target contains n rings and a bull's eye. **$(2n + 1)\pi$**

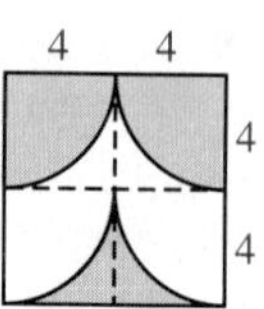

Ex. 24

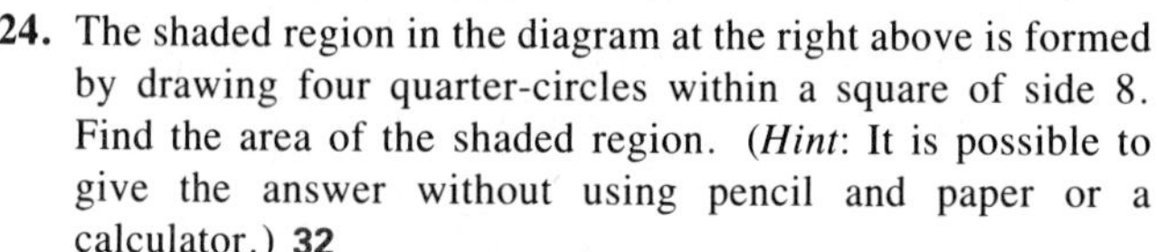

24. The shaded region in the diagram at the right above is formed by drawing four quarter-circles within a square of side 8. Find the area of the shaded region. (*Hint*: It is possible to give the answer without using pencil and paper or a calculator.) **32**

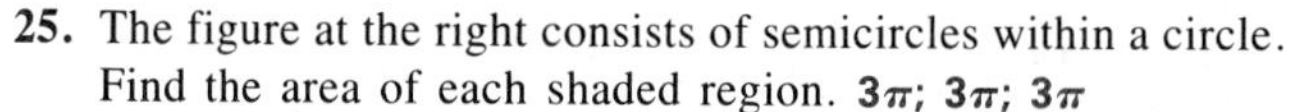

25. The figure at the right consists of semicircles within a circle. Find the area of each shaded region. **3π; 3π; 3π**

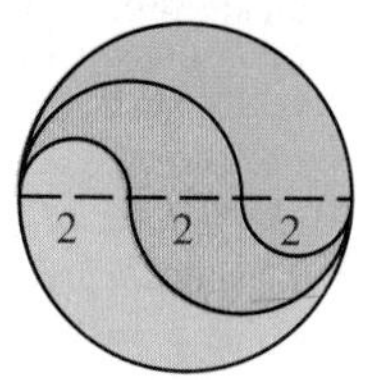

Ex. 25

Find the area of each shaded region. In Exercise 28, leave your answer in terms of *r*.

26.

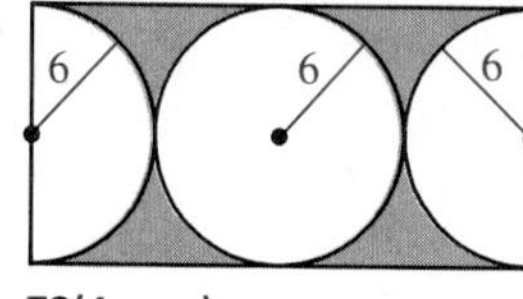

$72(4 - \pi)$

27. **32π**

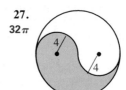

28. **$r^2\left(4 + \frac{3}{2}\pi\right)$**

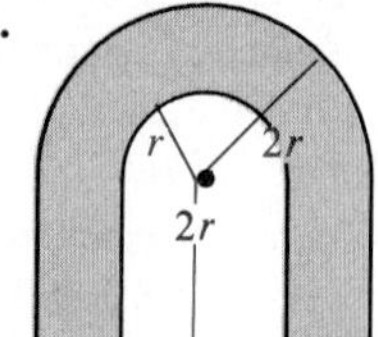

29. Draw a square and its inscribed and circumscribed circles. Find the ratio of the areas of these two circles. **1:2**

30. Draw an equilateral triangle and its inscribed and circumscribed circles. Find the ratio of the areas of these two circles. **1:4**

C **31.** The diagram shows part of a regular polygon of 12 sides inscribed in a circle with radius r. Find the area enclosed between the circle and the polygon in terms of r. Use $\pi \approx 3.14$. **$0.14r^2$**

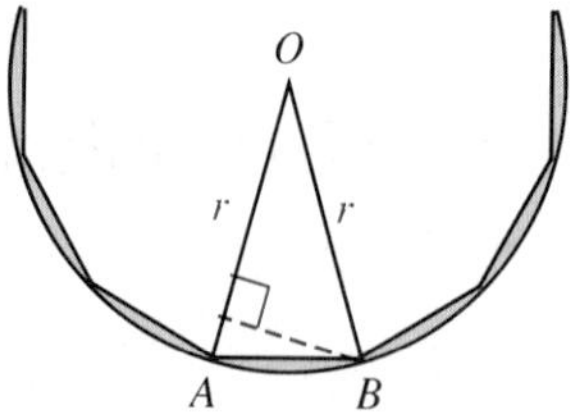

Ex. 31

32. A regular octagon is inscribed in a circle with radius r. Find the area enclosed between the circle and the octagon in terms of r. Use $\pi \approx 3.14$ and $\sqrt{2} \approx 1.414$. **$0.31r^2$**

33. A regular polygon with apothem a is inscribed in a circle with radius r.

a. Complete: As the number of sides increases, the value of a gets nearer to __?__ and the perimeter of the polygon gets nearer to $2\pi r$. ***r***

b. In the formula $A = \frac{1}{2}ap$, replace a by r, and p by $2\pi r$. What formula do you get? **$A = \pi r^2$, the formula for the area of a ⊙.**

34. Find the circumference of a circle inscribed in a rhombus with diagonals 12 cm and 16 cm. **9.6π cm**

35. Draw any circle O and any circle P. Construct a circle whose area equals the sum of the areas of circle O and circle P.

♦ Calculator Key-In

The number π is an irrational number. It cannot be expressed exactly as the ratio of two integers. Decimal *approximations* of π have been computed to thousands of decimal places. We can easily look up values in reference books, but such was not always the case. In the past, mathematicians had to rely on their cleverness to compute an approximate value of π. One of the earliest approximations was that of Archimedes, who found that $3\frac{1}{7} > \pi > 3\frac{10}{71}$.

Exercises

1. Find decimal approximations of $3\frac{1}{7}$ and $3\frac{10}{71}$. Did Archimedes approximate π correct to hundredths? **Yes**

2–4. Answers will vary depending on the number of terms used.

In Exercises 2–4, find approximations for π. The more terms or factors you use, the better your approximations will be.

2. $\pi \approx 2\sqrt{3}\left(1 - \frac{1}{3 \cdot 3} + \frac{1}{3^2 \cdot 5} - \frac{1}{3^3 \cdot 7} + \frac{1}{3^4 \cdot 9} - \frac{1}{3^5 \cdot 11} + \cdots\right)$ (Sharpe, 18th century)
3. $\pi \approx 2 \cdot \frac{2}{1} \cdot \frac{2}{3} \cdot \frac{4}{3} \cdot \frac{4}{5} \cdot \frac{6}{5} \cdot \frac{6}{7} \cdot \frac{8}{7} \cdot \frac{8}{9} \cdot \cdots$ (Wallis, 17th century)
4. This exercise is for calculators that have a square root function and a memory.

   $\pi \approx 2 \div \left(\sqrt{0.5} \cdot \sqrt{0.5 + 0.5\sqrt{0.5}} \cdot \sqrt{0.5 + 0.5\sqrt{0.5 + 0.5\sqrt{0.5}}} \cdot \ldots\right)$

   (Vieta, 16th century)

Cultural Note

Archimedes (ca. 287–212 B.C.) was a native of the Greek city of Syracuse. He is credited with many mathematical and scientific discoveries. His method for calculating π appears in a treatise on the measurement of circles.

You may want to have students research some of the many methods that have been used to calculate the value of π. Among those who investigated the value of π are Chinese mathematicians Wang Fan (ca. 3rd century A.D.), Liu Hui (ca. 3rd century A.D.), and Tsu Chongzhi (ca. 429–500 A.D.), Hindu mathematicians Aryabhata (ca. 475–500 A.D.) and Bhaskara (1114–ca. 1150 A.D.), and the Persian astronomer Jamshid al-Kashî (d. ca. 1436).

Algebra Review: *Evaluating Expressions*

Find the value of each expression using the given values of the variables.

Example $2\pi r$ when $r = \frac{5}{4}$

Solution $2 \cdot \pi \cdot \frac{5}{4} = \left(2 \cdot \frac{5}{4}\right)\pi = \frac{5}{2}\pi$

1. πr^2 when $r = \frac{2}{3}\sqrt{3}$ **$\frac{4}{3}\pi$**
2. $\pi r l$ when $r = 4\frac{1}{5}$ and $l = 15$ **63π**
3. $\frac{1}{3}\pi r^2 h$ when $r = 2\sqrt{6}$ and $h = 4$ **32π**
4. $\frac{4}{3}\pi r^3$ when $r = 6$ **288π**
5. $\pi r\sqrt{r^2 + h^2}$ when $r = h = \sqrt{5}$ **$5\pi\sqrt{2}$**
6. $2\pi r^2 + 2\pi rh$ when $r = 10$ and $h = 6$ **320π**
7. $\pi r^2 + \pi r\sqrt{r^2 + h^2}$ when $r = 2$ and $h = 2\sqrt{3}$ **12π**
8. $\pi(r_1^2 - r_2^2)$ when $r_1 = 6$ and $r_2 = 3\sqrt{2}$ **18π**

Teaching Suggestions, pp. T125–T126
Objective
Presenting the Lesson
Reinforcement

Cooperative Learning, pp. T125–T126

Supplementary Materials

Practice Master 68
Test 44
Resource Book, pp. 74, 153
Study Guide, pp. 147–148

Lesson Focus

This lesson shows how the length of an arc of a circle and the area of a region or sector of a circle can be calculated.

Suggested Assignments

Minimum
Day 1: 453–454/1–13 odd, 15–17
Day 2: 454/18, 19, 21

Average
453–455/3, 4, 6, 10, 11, 13, 14, 16–19, 21, 22, 25

Maximum
453–455/12, 14, 16–20, 22–26

Thinking Skills

Students sometimes confuse arc measure with arc length. Emphasize that an arc measure equals the measure of the corresponding central angle and is therefore independent of the size of the circle. Arc length does depend on the size of the circle because it is a part of the circumference of the circle.

11-6 *Arc Lengths and Areas of Sectors*

A *pie chart* is often used to analyze data or to help plan business strategy. The radii of a pie chart divide the interior of the circle into regions called sectors, whose areas represent the relative sizes of particular items. A **sector of a circle** is a region bounded by two radii and an arc of the circle. The shaded region of the diagram at the right below is called sector AOB. The unshaded region is also a sector.

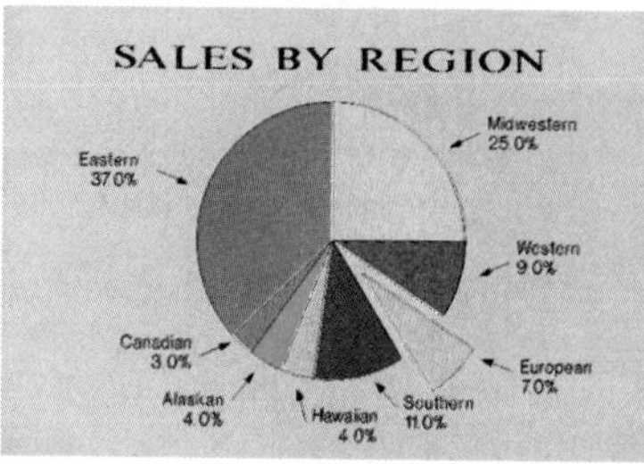

The length of $\widehat{AB}$ in circle O is part of the circumference of the circle. Since $m\widehat{AB} = 60$ and $\frac{60}{360} = \frac{1}{6}$, the length of $\widehat{AB}$ is $\frac{1}{6}$ of the circumference. Thus,

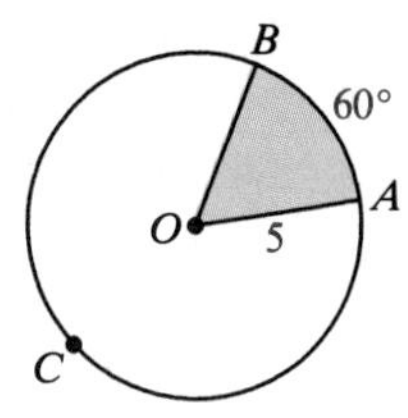

$$\text{Length of } \widehat{AB} = \frac{1}{6}(2\pi \cdot 5) = \frac{5}{3}\pi.$$

Similarly, the area of sector AOB is $\frac{1}{6}$ of the area of the circle. Thus,

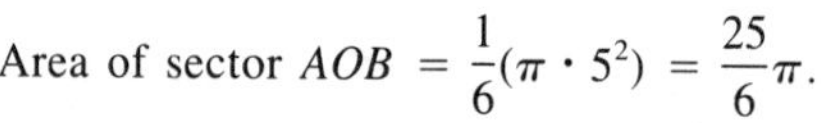

$$\text{Area of sector } AOB = \frac{1}{6}(\pi \cdot 5^2) = \frac{25}{6}\pi.$$

In general, if $m\widehat{AB} = x$:

$$\text{Length of } \widehat{AB} = \frac{x}{360} \cdot 2\pi r$$

$$\text{Area of sector } AOB = \frac{x}{360} \cdot \pi r^2$$

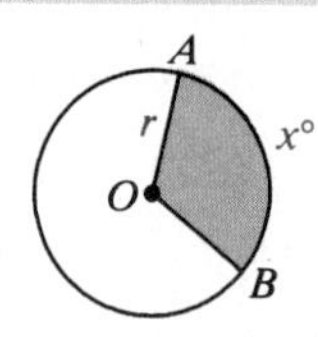

Example 1 In $\odot O$ with radius 9, $m\angle AOB = 120$. Find the lengths of the arcs $\widehat{AB}$ and $\widehat{ACB}$ and the areas of the two sectors shown.

Solution $m\widehat{AB} = 120$, and $m\widehat{ACB} = 240$.

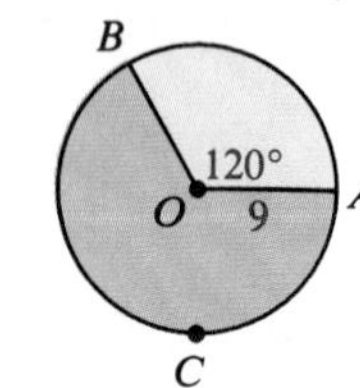

Minor arc $\widehat{AB}$:

$$\text{Length of } \widehat{AB} = \frac{120}{360} \cdot (2\pi \cdot 9) = \frac{1}{3}(18\pi) = 6\pi$$

$$\text{Area of sector } AOB = \frac{120}{360} \cdot (\pi \cdot 9^2) = \frac{1}{3}(81\pi) = 27\pi$$

Major arc $\widehat{ACB}$:

$$\text{Length of } \widehat{ACB} = \frac{240}{360} \cdot (2\pi \cdot 9) = \frac{2}{3}(18\pi) = 12\pi$$

$$\text{Area of sector} = \frac{240}{360} \cdot (\pi \cdot 9^2) = \frac{2}{3}(81\pi) = 54\pi$$

Example 2 Find the area of the shaded region bounded by $\overline{XY}$ and $\widehat{XY}$.

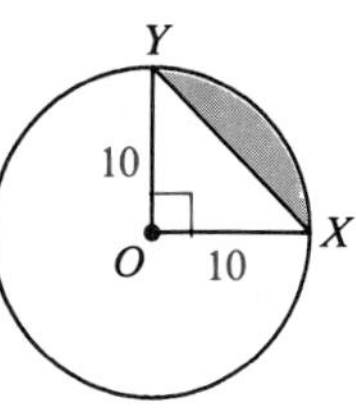

Solution Area of sector $XOY = \frac{90}{360} \cdot \pi \cdot 10^2 = 25\pi$

Area of $\triangle XOY = \frac{1}{2} \cdot 10 \cdot 10 = 50$

Area of shaded region $= 25\pi - 50$

Classroom Exercises

Find the arc length and area of each shaded sector.

1. 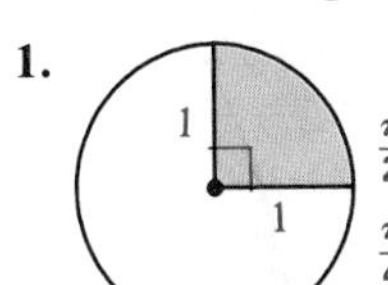

$\frac{\pi}{2}$; $\frac{\pi}{4}$

2. 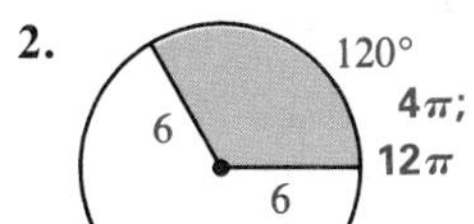

4π; 12π

3. 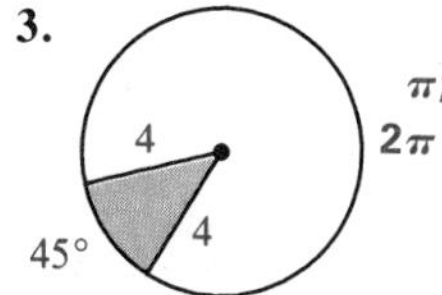

π; 2π

4. 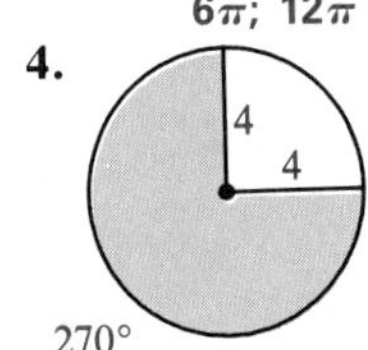

6π; 12π

5. In a circle with radius 6, $m\widehat{AB} = 60$. Make a sketch and find the area of the region bounded by $\overline{AB}$ and $\widehat{AB}$. **$6\pi - 9\sqrt{3}$**
6. A circle has area 160π cm^2. If a sector of the circle has area 40π cm^2, find the measure of the arc of the sector. **90**
7. Compare the areas of two sectors if
   a. they have the same central angle, but the radius of one is twice as long as the radius of the other. **Area of one sector = 4 × area of other sector**
   b. they have the same radius, but the central angle of one is twice as large as the central angle of the other. **Area of one sector = 2 × area of other sector**

Written Exercises

Sector AOB is described by giving $m\angle AOB$ and the radius of circle O. Make a sketch and find the length of $\widehat{AB}$ and the area of sector AOB.

A

	1.	2.	3.	4.	5.	6.	7.	8.	9.	10.
$m\angle AOB$	30	45	120	240	180	270	40	320	108	192
radius	12	4	3	3	1.5	0.8	$\frac{9}{2}$	$1\frac{1}{5}$	$5\sqrt{2}$	$3\sqrt{3}$

11. The area of sector AOB is 10π and $m\angle AOB = 100$. Find the radius of circle O. **6**

12. The area of sector AOB is $\frac{7\pi}{2}$ and $m\angle AOB = 315$. Find the radius of circle O. **2**

Chalkboard Examples

The radius of a circle is 3 cm. Find (a) the lengths of the given arcs, and (b) the areas of the sectors determined by the given arcs. Use $\pi \approx \frac{22}{7}$.

1. 50° (a) $\frac{55}{21}$ cm
   (b) $\frac{55}{14}$ cm^2
2. 20° (a) $\frac{22}{21}$ cm
   (b) $\frac{11}{7}$ cm^2
3. 140° (a) $\frac{22}{3}$ cm
   (b) 11 cm^2
4. 210° (a) 11 cm
   (b) $\frac{33}{2}$ cm^2
5. Find the area of the region bounded by $\overline{AB}$ and $\widehat{AB}$. $12\pi - 9\sqrt{3}$

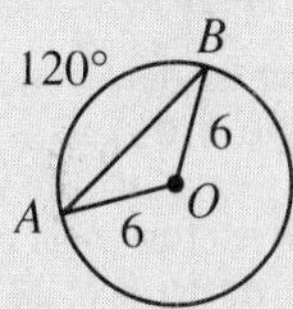

Additional Answers Written Exercises

1. 2π; 12π
2. π; 2π
3. 2π; 3π
4. 4π; 6π
5. $\frac{3\pi}{2}$; $\frac{9\pi}{8}$
6. 1.2π; 0.48π
7. π; $\frac{9\pi}{4}$
8. $\frac{32\pi}{15}$; $\frac{32\pi}{25}$
9. $3\pi\sqrt{2}$; 15π
10. $\frac{16\pi\sqrt{3}}{5}$; $\frac{72\pi}{5}$

Guided Practice

Sector XOY is described by giving $m\angle XOY$ and the radius of circle O. Make a sketch and find the length of $\overset{\frown}{XY}$ and the area of sector XOY.

	1.	2.	3.	4.	5.
$m\angle XOY$	90	45	120	200	270
radius	8	2	$6\sqrt{2}$	0.3	$\frac{8}{3}$

1. 4π; 16π
2. $\frac{\pi}{2}$; $\frac{\pi}{2}$
3. $4\pi\sqrt{2}$; 24π
4. $\frac{\pi}{3}$; 0.05π
5. 4π; $\frac{16}{3}\pi$
6. The area of a sector AOB is $\frac{5}{8}\pi$, and $m\angle AOB = 9$. Find the radius of $\odot O$. **5**

Exercise Note

Except for special cases, finding the area of a region bounded by a chord and its arc requires the use of trigonometry, as in Ex. 21.

Group Activity

Students can work in groups to discuss the solutions to Exs. 22–30. Listen to each group's discussion and offer assistance if needed. Encourage students to ask questions of other students in the group and to make comments when appropriate.

Find the area of each shaded region. Point O marks the center of a circle.

B **13.** 

$4\pi - 8$

14. 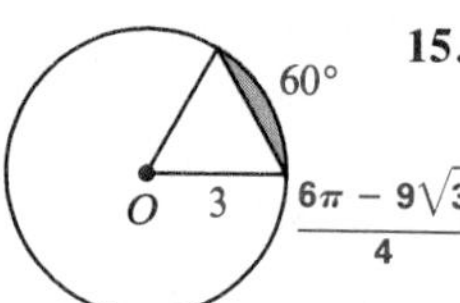

$\frac{6\pi - 9\sqrt{3}}{4}$

15. 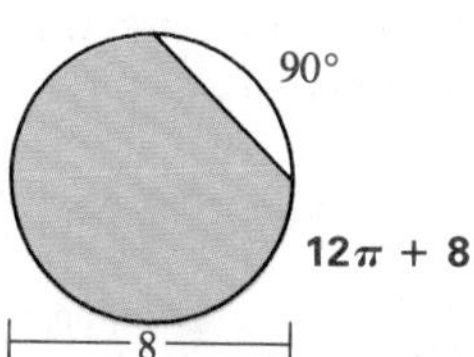

$12\pi + 8$

16. 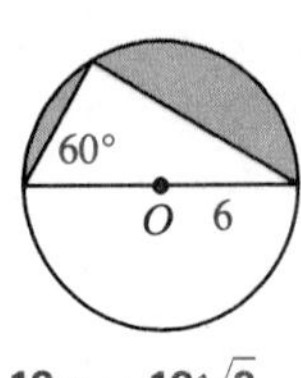

$18\pi - 18\sqrt{3}$

17. 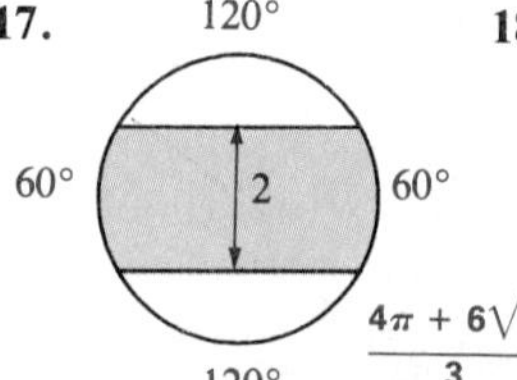

$\frac{4\pi + 6\sqrt{3}}{3}$

18. 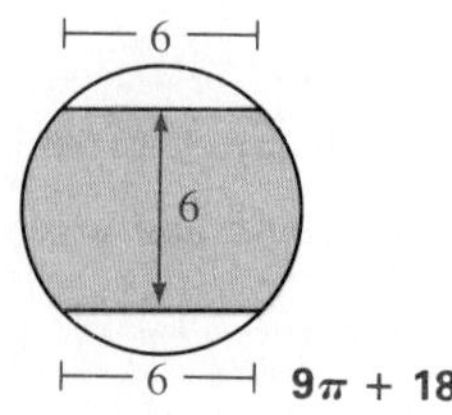

$9\pi + 18$

19. A rectangle with length 16 cm and width 12 cm is inscribed in a circle. Find the area of the region inside the circle but outside the rectangle. **$(100\pi - 192)$ cm^2**

20. From point P, $\overline{PA}$ and $\overline{PB}$ are drawn tangent to circle O at points A and B. If the radius of the circle is 6 and $m\angle APB = 60$, find the area of the region outside the circle but inside quadrilateral $AOBP$. **$36\sqrt{3} - 12\pi$**

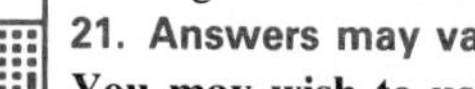

21. Answers may vary.

You may wish to use a calculator for Exercises 21–23. Use $\pi \approx 3.14$.

21. Chord AB is 18 cm long and the radius of the circle is 12 cm.
a. Use trigonometry to find the measures of $\angle AOX$ and $\angle AOB$, correct to the nearest integer. **49; 98**
b. Find the area of the shaded region to the nearest square centimeter. Use $\sqrt{7} \approx 2.646$. **52 cm^2**

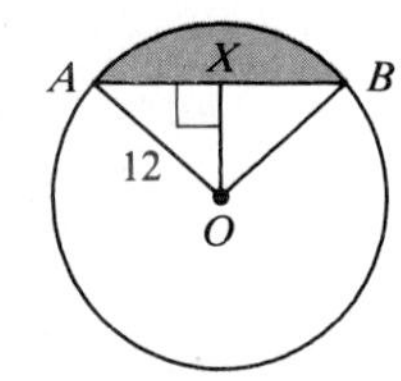

22. The diagram shows some dimensions in a baseball stadium. H represents home plate. Approximate the ratio of the areas of fair territory (shaded region) and foul territory (nonshaded region). **≈ 2:1**

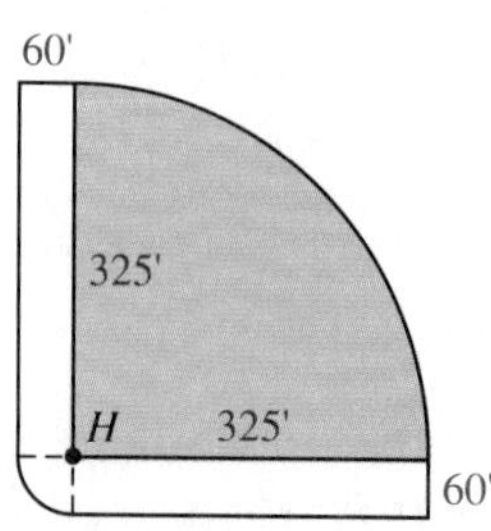

23. A cow is tied by a 25 m rope to the corner of a barn as shown. A fence keeps the cow out of the garden. Find, to the nearest square meter, the grazing area. Use $\sqrt{2} \approx 1.414$. **1343 m^2**

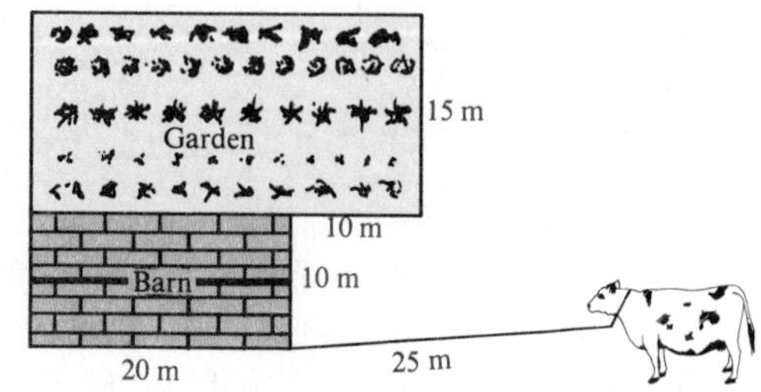

24. *ABCD* is a square with sides 8 cm long. Two circles each with radius 8 cm are drawn, one with center *A* and the other with center *C*. Find the area of the region inside both circles. **$(32\pi - 64)$ cm^2**

25. Two circles have radii 6 cm and their centers are 6 cm apart. Find the area of the region common to both circles. **$(24\pi - 18\sqrt{3})$ cm^2**

26. a. Draw a square. Then construct the figure shown at the right.
b. If the radius of the square is 2, find the area of the shaded region. **$4\pi - 8$**

C 27. a. Using only a compass, construct the six-pointed figure shown at the right. **b. $72\pi - 108\sqrt{3}$**
b. If the radius of the circle is 6, find the area of the shaded region.

28. Three circles with radii 6 are tangent to each other. Find the area of the region enclosed between them. **$36\sqrt{3} - 18\pi$**

★29. Circles *X* and *Y*, with radii 6 and 2, are tangent to each other. $\overline{AB}$ is a common external tangent. Find the area of the shaded region. (*Hint*: What kind of figure is *AXYB*? **trapezoid** What is the measure of $\angle AXY$? **60**) **$\frac{48\sqrt{3} - 22\pi}{3}$**

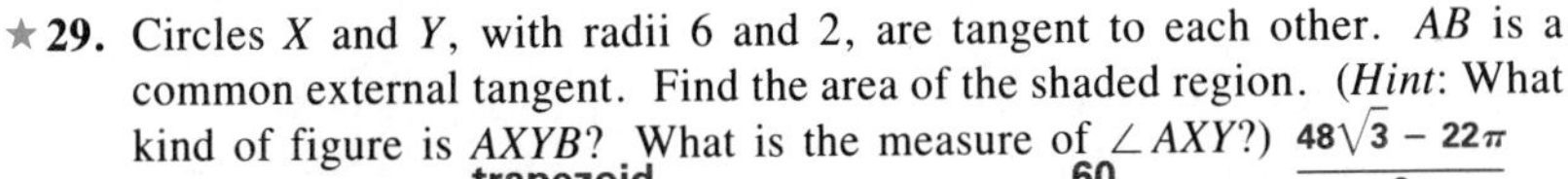

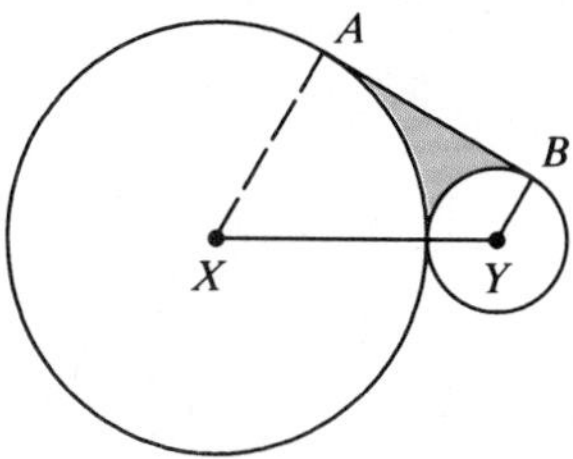

Ex. 29

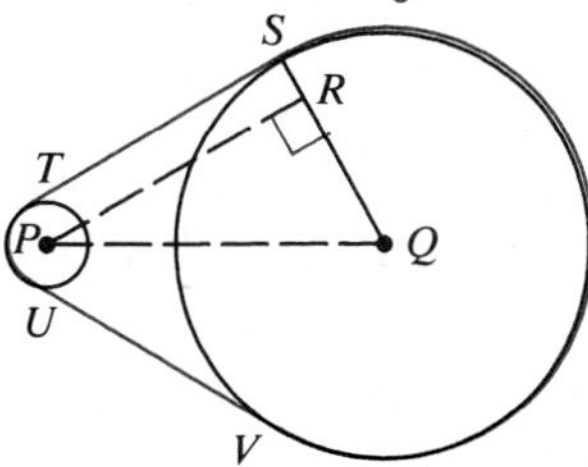

Ex. 30

★30. The diagram at the right above shows a belt tightly stretched over two wheels with radii 5 cm and 25 cm. The distance between the centers of the wheels is 40 cm. Find the length of the belt. **$\left(\frac{120\sqrt{3} + 110\pi}{3}\right)$ cm**

Challenge

Here $\overline{XY}$ has been divided into five congruent segments and semicircles have been drawn. But suppose $\overline{XY}$ were divided into millions of congruent segments and semicircles were drawn. What would the sum of the lengths of the arcs be?

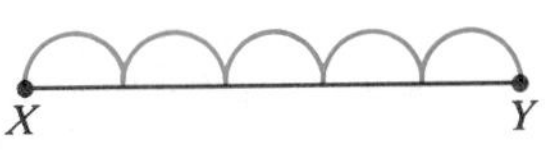

Sarah says, "*XY*, because all the points would be so close to $\overline{XY}$." Mike says, "A really large number, because there would be so many arc lengths to add up." What do you say? **No matter how many segments are used, the sum of the arc lengths is $\frac{\pi}{2}(XY)$. Proof: Let n = number of seg.; length of each arc $= \pi r = \pi\left(\frac{XY}{2n}\right)$; sum of arc lengths $= n(\pi)\left(\frac{XY}{2n}\right) = \frac{\pi}{2}(XY)$.**

Teaching Suggestions,
p. T126

Objectives
Presenting the Lesson
Enrichment

Communication Skills,
p. T126

Supplementary Materials

Practice Master 69

Study Guide, pp. 149–150

Lesson Focus

Areas of triangles can be compared by using ratios. This lesson studies triangles having equal heights or equal bases, and similar triangles. The ratios of the areas of pairs of triangles having any one of these properties are calculated.

Suggested Assignments

Minimum
Day 1: 458/1–8
Day 2: 458–459/9–12, 14, 15, 18
Day 3: 465/Self-Test 2, 1–8
471/Chapter Test 1–18

Average
Day 1: 458–459/1–15 odd
S 455/26
Day 2: 459–460/16, 18, 19–21, 23, 26, 30

Maximum
Day 1: 458–459/5, 8, 10, 13, 15, 17, 19, 20
S 455/27, 29
Day 2: 459–460/21–31 odd

Teaching Note

You might want to review similar triangles, ratio, and proportion before presenting this lesson.

11-7 *Ratios of Areas*

In this section you will learn to compare the areas of figures by finding ratios.

Example 1 Find the ratios of the areas of two triangles:

a. with equal heights
b. with equal bases
c. that are similar

Solution

a. $\dfrac{\text{area of } \triangle ABD}{\text{area of } \triangle DBC} = \dfrac{\frac{1}{2}ah}{\frac{1}{2}bh} = \dfrac{a}{b}$

ratio of areas = ratio of bases

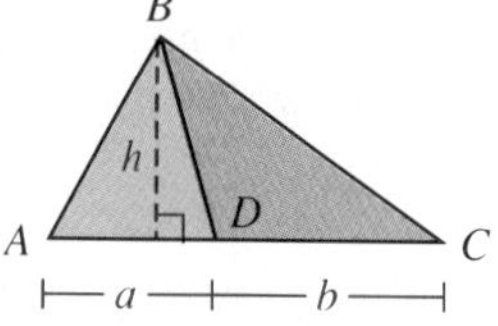

b. $\dfrac{\text{area of } \triangle ABC}{\text{area of } \triangle ADC} = \dfrac{\frac{1}{2}bh}{\frac{1}{2}bk} = \dfrac{h}{k}$

ratio of areas = ratio of heights

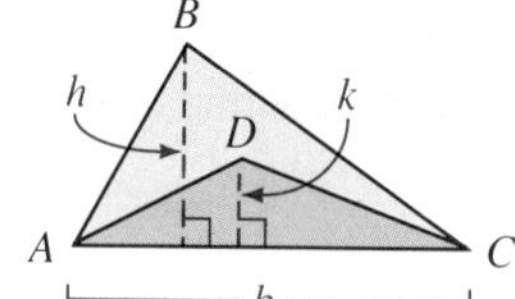

c. $\dfrac{\text{area of } \triangle ABC}{\text{area of } \triangle DEF} = \dfrac{\frac{1}{2}bh}{\frac{1}{2}ek} = \dfrac{bh}{ek} = \dfrac{b}{e} \cdot \dfrac{h}{k}$

It follows from Exercise 25 on page 259 that if

$\triangle ABC \sim \triangle DEF$, then $\dfrac{h}{k} = \dfrac{b}{e}$.

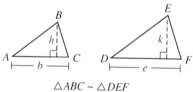

$\triangle ABC \sim \triangle DEF$

Thus, $\dfrac{\text{area of } \triangle ABC}{\text{area of } \triangle DEF} = \dfrac{b}{e} \cdot \dfrac{h}{k} = \dfrac{b}{e} \cdot \dfrac{b}{e} = \left(\dfrac{b}{e}\right)^2 = (\text{scale factor})^2.$

ratio of areas = square of scale factor

Example 1 justifies the following properties.

Comparing Areas of Triangles

1. If two triangles have equal heights, then the ratio of their areas equals the ratio of their bases.
2. If two triangles have equal bases, then the ratio of their areas equals the ratio of their heights.
3. If two triangles are similar, then the ratio of their areas equals the square of their scale factor.

Example 2 *ABCD* is a trapezoid. Find the ratio of the areas of:

a. $\triangle COD$ and $\triangle AOB$
b. $\triangle COD$ and $\triangle AOD$
c. $\triangle OAB$ and $\triangle DAB$

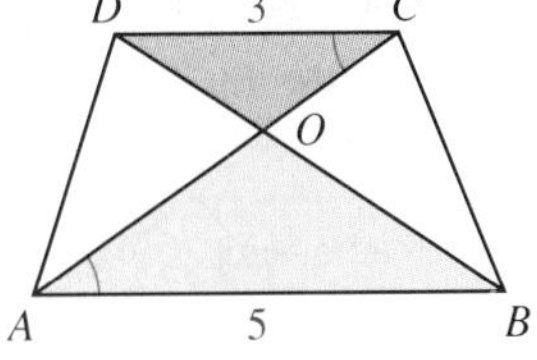

Solution $\triangle COD \sim \triangle AOB$ by the AA Similarity Postulate, with a scale factor of 3:5. Thus each of the corresponding sides and heights of these triangles has a 3:5 ratio.

a. Since $\triangle COD \sim \triangle AOB$,

$$\frac{\text{area of } \triangle COD}{\text{area of } \triangle AOB} = \left(\frac{3}{5}\right)^2 = \frac{9}{25}.$$

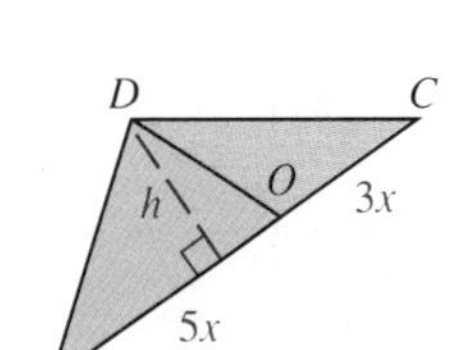

b. Since $\triangle COD$ and $\triangle AOD$ have the same height, h, their area ratio equals their base ratio.

$$\frac{\text{area of } \triangle COD}{\text{area of } \triangle AOD} = \frac{CO}{AO} = \frac{3x}{5x} = \frac{3}{5}$$

c. Since $\triangle OAB$ and $\triangle DAB$ have the same base, $\overline{AB}$, their area ratio equals their height ratio. Notice that the height of $\triangle DAB$ is $3y + 5y$, or $8y$.

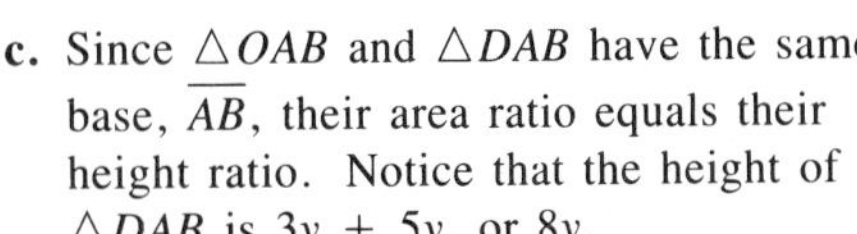

$$\frac{\text{area of } \triangle OAB}{\text{area of } \triangle DAB} = \frac{5y}{8y} = \frac{5}{8}$$

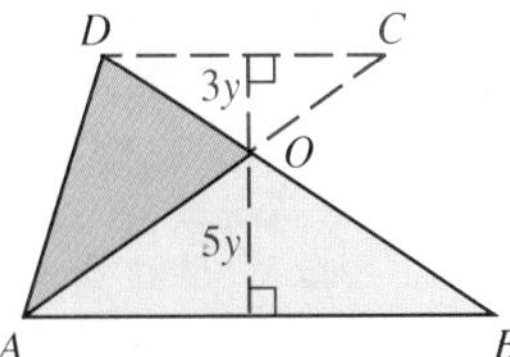

You know that the ratios of the perimeters and areas of two similar triangles are related to their scale factor. These relationships can be generalized to any two similar figures.

Theorem 11-7

If the scale factor of two similar figures is $a:b$, then

(1) the ratio of the perimeters is $a:b$.

(2) the ratio of the areas is $a^2:b^2$.

Example 3 Find the ratio of the perimeters and the ratio of the areas of the two similar figures.

Solution The scale factor is 8:12, or 2:3. Therefore, the ratio of the perimeters is 2:3. The ratio of the areas is $2^2:3^2$, or 4:9.

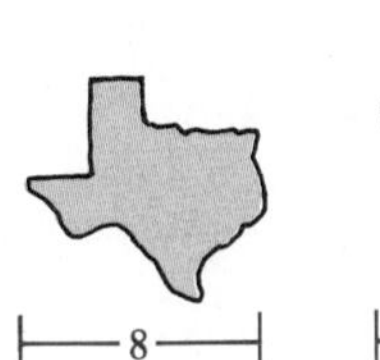

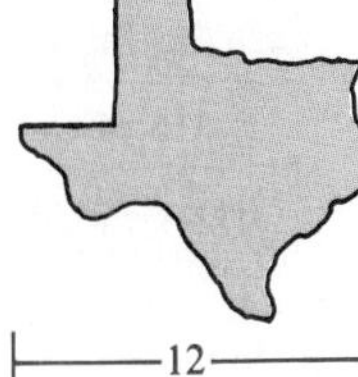

Chalkboard Examples

Find the ratio of the areas in each figure below.

1. $\triangle ABC : \triangle ADB$ 5:1

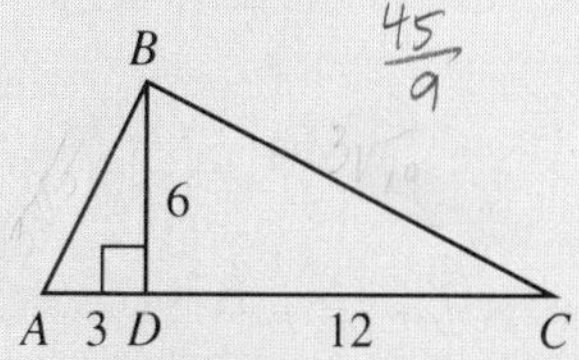

2. $\triangle ABD : \triangle BCD$ 4:9

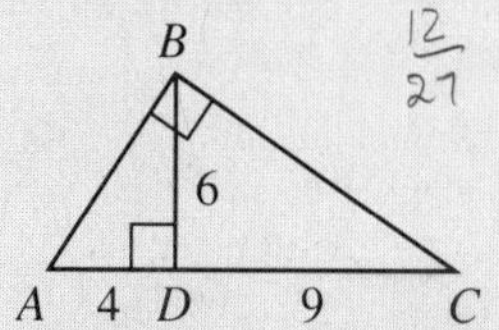

3. The ratio of the corresponding heights of two similar triangles is 3:5. What is the ratio of the corresponding sides? 3:5 of the perimeters? 3:5 of the areas? 9:25

Classify each statement as true or false.

4. If two quadrilaterals are similar, then their areas must be in the same ratio as the square of the ratio of their perimeters. T

5. If the ratio of the areas of two equilateral triangles is 1:3, then the ratio of the perimeters is $1:\sqrt{3}$. T

6. If the ratio of the perimeters of two rectangles is 4:7, then the ratio of their areas must be 16:49. F

7. If the ratio of the areas of two squares is 3:2, then the ratio of their sides must be $\sqrt{3}:\sqrt{2}$. T

Classroom Exercises

Find the ratio of the areas of $\triangle ABC$ and $\triangle ADC$.

1. $\frac{9}{5}$

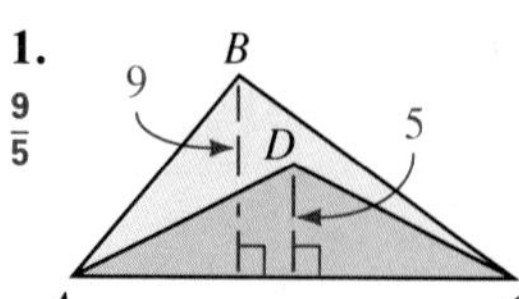

2. $\frac{9}{16}$

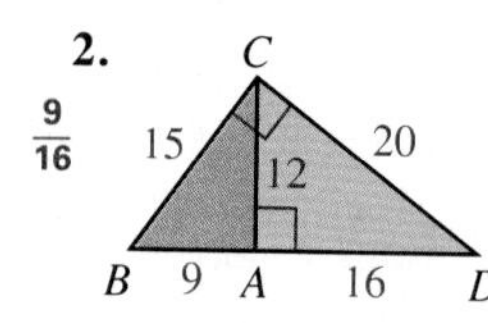

3. $\frac{5}{6}$

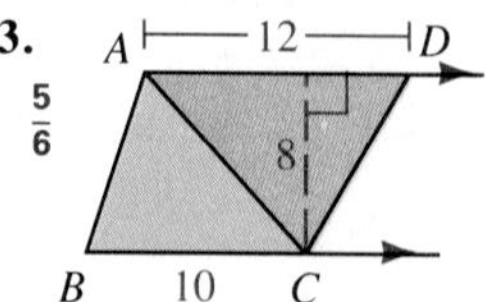

The table refers to similar figures. Complete the table.

	4.	5.	6.	7.	8.	9.	10.	11.
Scale factor	1:3	1:5	3:4	2:3	?	?	?	?
Ratio of perimeters	?	?	?	?	4:5	3:5	?	?
Ratio of areas	?	?	?	?	?	?	16:49	36:25

12. a. Are all circles similar? **Yes** **b. 3:4; 9:16**
    b. If two circles have radii 9 and 12, what is the ratio of the circumferences? of the areas?

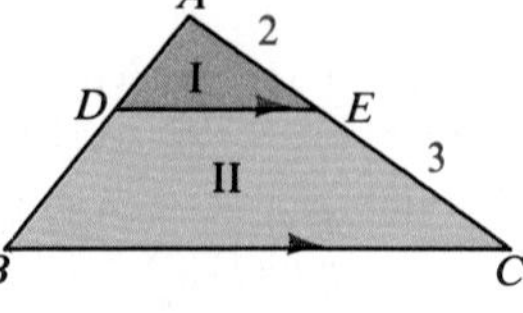

13. a. Are regions I and II similar? **No**
    b. Name two similar triangles. **$\triangle ADE \sim \triangle ABC$**
    c. What is the ratio of their areas? **4:25**
    d. What is the ratio of the areas of regions I and II? **4:21**

Find the ratio of the areas of triangles (a) I and II and (b) I and III.

14. **8:5; 8:15**

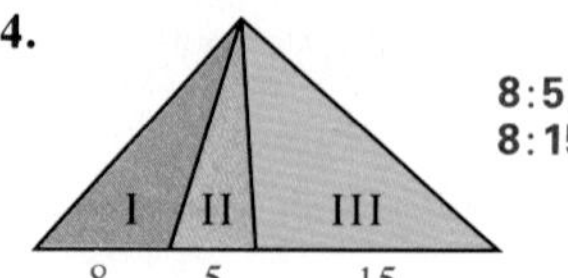

15. **7:4; 49:16**

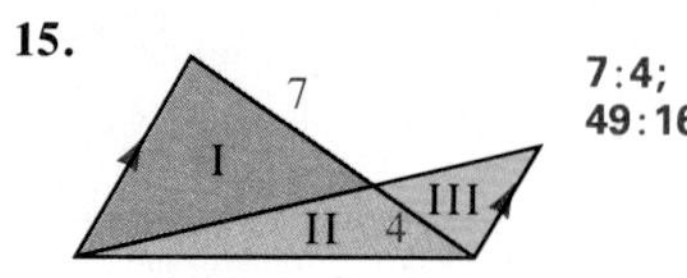

Written Exercises

The table refers to similar figures. Copy and complete the table.

A

	1.	2.	3.	4.	5.	6.	7.	8.
Scale factor	1:4	3:2	$r:2s$	?	?	?	?	?
Ratio of perimeters	?	?	?	9:5	3:13	?	?	?
Ratio of areas	?	?	?	?	?	25:1	9:64	2:1

9. On a map of California, 1 cm corresponds to 50 km. Find the ratio of the map's area to the actual area of California. **1:25,000,000,000,000**
(*Note*: students do not need to know the actual area of California to complete this exercise.)

Additional Answers Classroom Exercises

4. 1:3; 1:9
5. 1:5; 1:25
6. 3:4; 9:16
7. 2:3; 4:9
8. 4:5; 16:25
9. 3:5; 9:25
10. 4:7; 4:7
11. 6:5; 6:5

Using a Model

Using graph paper to draw different pairs of similar figures (such as rectangles, squares, triangles, and parallelograms) is a good way to reinforce the idea that the ratio of the areas of similar figures is the square of the ratio of their sides. Have students compare their areas by counting the unit squares.

Additional Answers Written Exercises

1. 1:4; 1:16
2. 3:2; 9:4
3. $r:2s$; $r^2:4s^2$
4. 9:5; 81:25
5. 3:13; 9:169
6. 5:1; 5:1
7. 3:8; 3:8
8. $\sqrt{2}:1$; $\sqrt{2}:1$

10. The areas of two circles are 36π and 64π. What is the ratio of the diameters? of the circumferences? **3:4; 3:4**

11. L, M, and N are the midpoints of the sides of $\triangle ABC$. Find the ratio of the perimeters and the ratio of the areas of $\triangle LMN$ and $\triangle ABC$. **1:2; 1:4**

12. The lengths of two similar rectangles are x^2 and xy, respectively. What is the ratio of the areas? **$x^2:y^2$**

Name two similar triangles and find the ratio of their areas. Then find *DE*.

13.

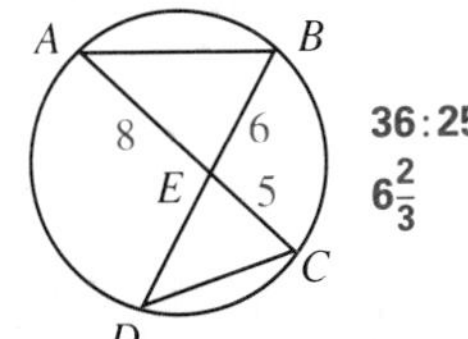

36:25; $6\frac{2}{3}$

$\triangle ABE \sim \triangle DCE$

14.

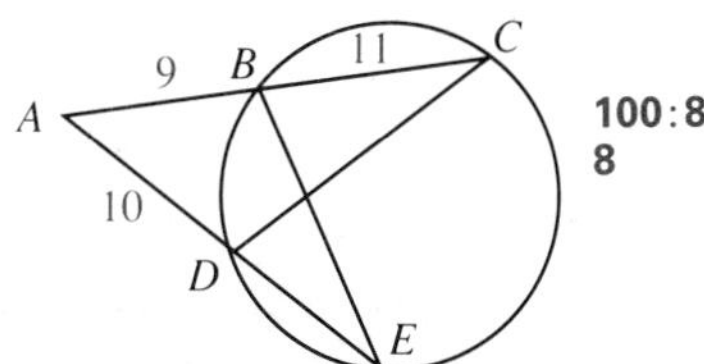

100:81; 8

$\triangle ACD \sim \triangle AEB$

15. A quadrilateral with sides 8 cm, 9 cm, 6 cm, and 5 cm has area 45 cm^2. Find the area of a similar quadrilateral whose longest side is 15 cm. **125 cm^2**

16. A pentagon with sides 3 m, 4 m, 5 m, 6 m, and 7 m has area 48 m^2. Find the perimeter of a similar pentagon whose area is 27 m^2. **$\frac{75}{4}$ m**

Find the ratio of the areas of triangles (a) I and II and (b) I and III. In Exercise 19(b), use the fact that Area I + Area II = Area III.

B **17.**

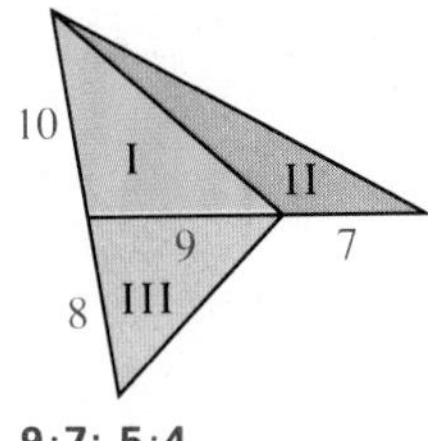

9:7; 5:4

18.

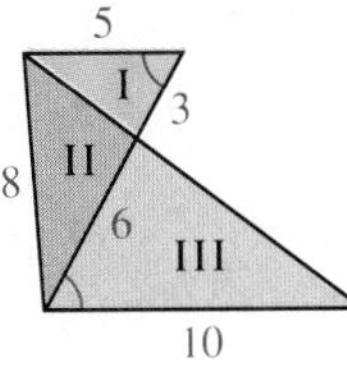

1:2; 1:4

19.

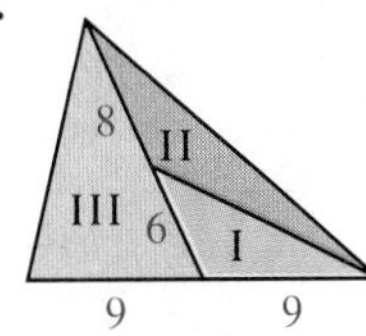

3:4; 3:7

20. In the diagram below, $PQRS$ is a parallelogram. Find the ratio of the areas for each pair of triangles.

a. $\triangle TOS$ and $\triangle QOP$ **4:9** **b.** $\triangle TOS$ and $\triangle TQR$ **4:25**

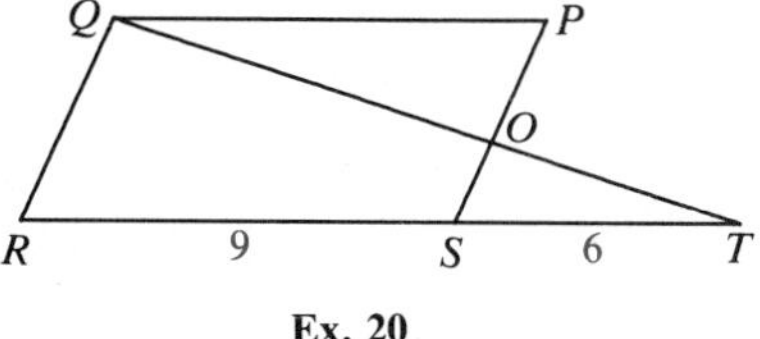

Ex. 20

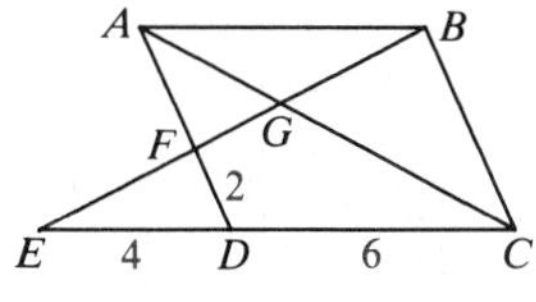

Ex. 21

21. In the diagram above, $ABCD$ is a parallelogram. Name *four pairs* of similar triangles and give the ratio of the areas for each pair. **Answers may vary. Examples: $\triangle ABC \sim \triangle CDA$, 1:1; $\triangle ABG \sim \triangle CEG$, 9:25; $\triangle ABF \sim \triangle DEF$, 9:4; $\triangle AGF \sim \triangle CGB$, 9:25; $\triangle EFD \sim \triangle EBC$, 4:25**

Guided Practice

The table refers to similar figures. Complete the table.

	1.	2.	3.	4.
Scale Factor	3:5	7:4	5:3	3:k
Ratio of Perimeters	3:5	7:4	5:3	3:k
Ratio of Areas	9:25	49:16	25:9	9:k^2

5. The diameters of two circles are 10 cm and 9 cm. What is the ratio of their circumferences? 10:9 of their areas? 100:81

6. A pentagon with sides 5 cm, 7 cm, 8 cm, 9 cm, and 11 cm has an area of 96 cm^2. Find the perimeter of a similar pentagon whose area is 24 cm^2. 20 cm

7. Find the ratio of the areas of triangles **(a)** I and II, and **(b)** I and III. (**a**) 1:1 (**b**) 1:2

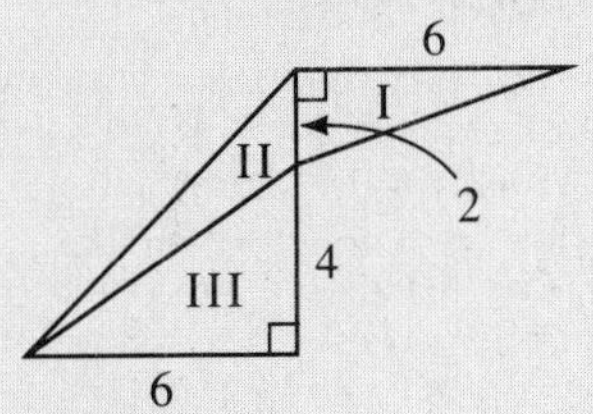

22. The area of parallelogram *ABCD* is 48 cm^2 and $DE = 2 \cdot EC$. Find the area of:

a. $\triangle ABE$ **24 cm^2** **b.** $\triangle BEC$ **8 cm^2** **c.** $\triangle ADE$ **16 cm^2**
d. $\triangle CEF$ **4 cm^2** **e.** $\triangle DEF$ **8 cm^2** **f.** $\triangle BEF$ **12 cm^2**

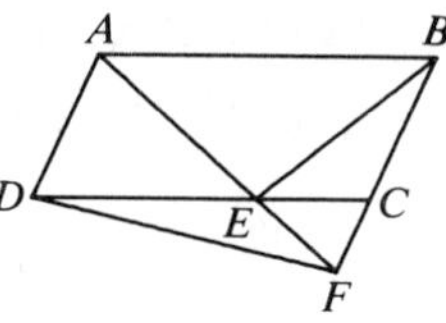

23. *ABCD* is a parallelogram. Find each ratio.

a. $\dfrac{\text{Area of } \triangle DEF}{\text{Area of } \triangle ABF}$ **1:9**

b. $\dfrac{\text{Area of } \triangle DEF}{\text{Area of } \triangle CEB}$ **1:4**

c. $\dfrac{\text{Area of } \triangle DEF}{\text{Area of trap. } DEBA}$ **1:8**

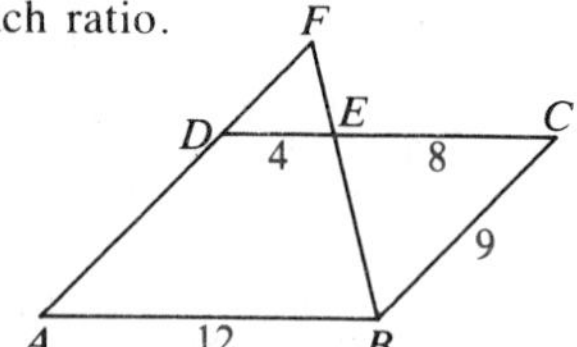

The figures in Exercises 24 and 25 are trapezoids. Find the ratio of the areas of (a) △I and △III, (b) △I and △II, (c) △I and △IV, (d) △II and △IV, and (e) △I and the trapezoid.

24.

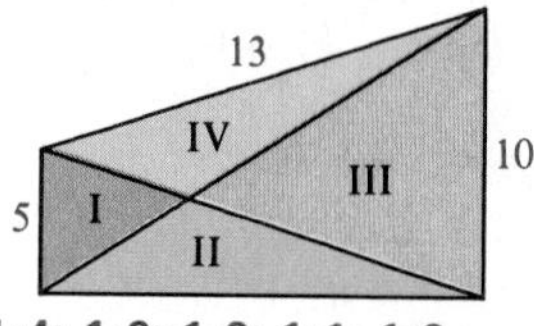

1:4; 1:2; 1:2; 1:1; 1:9

25.

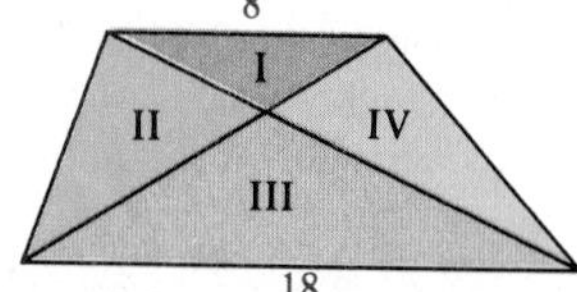

16:81; 4:9; 4:9; 1:1; 16:169

Find the ratio of the areas of regions I and II.

26. **16:65**

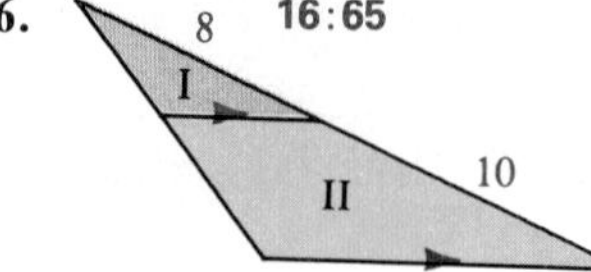

27. **9:40**

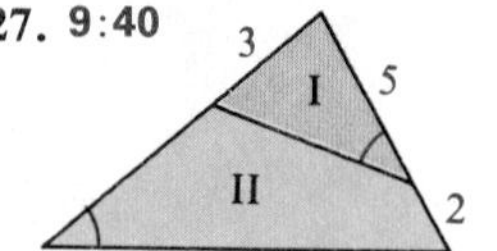

28. **1:3**

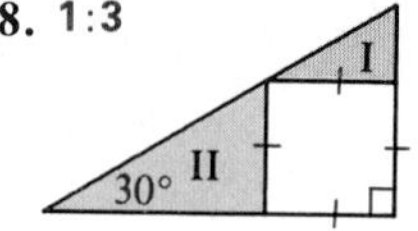

C **29.** *G* is the intersection point of the medians of $\triangle ABC$. A line through *G* parallel to $\overline{BC}$ divides the triangle into two regions. What is the ratio of their areas? (*Hint*: See Theorem 10-4, page 387.) **4:5**

30. In $\triangle LMN$, altitude $\overline{LK}$ is 12 cm long. Through point *J* of $\overline{LK}$ a line is drawn parallel to $\overline{MN}$, dividing the triangle into two regions with equal areas. Find *LJ*. **$6\sqrt{2}$ cm**

31. If you draw the three medians of a triangle, six small triangles are formed. Prove whatever you can about the areas of these six triangles. **See below.**

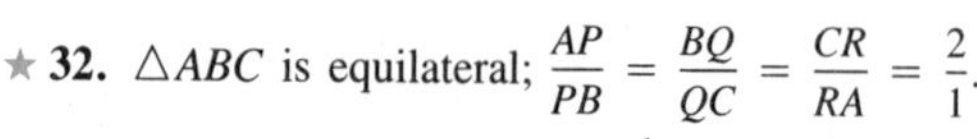

★ **32.** $\triangle ABC$ is equilateral; $\dfrac{AP}{PB} = \dfrac{BQ}{QC} = \dfrac{CR}{RA} = \dfrac{2}{1}$.

Prove: Area of $\triangle XYZ = \dfrac{1}{7}(\text{area of } \triangle ABC)$

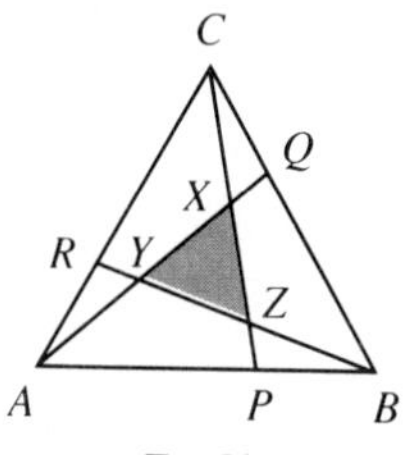

Ex. 32

31. Each of the small △s has area = $\frac{1}{6}$ · area of the orig. △.

11-8 *Geometric Probability*

The geometric probability problems in this section can be solved by using one of the following two principles.

1. Suppose a point P of $\overline{AB}$ is picked at random. Then:

$$\text{probability that } P \text{ is on } \overline{AC} = \frac{\text{length of } \overline{AC}}{\text{length of } \overline{AB}}$$

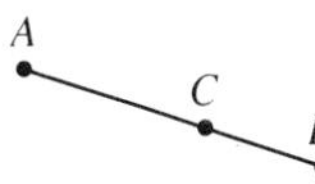

2. Suppose a point P of region S is picked at random. Then:

$$\text{probability that } P \text{ is in region } R = \frac{\text{area of } R}{\text{area of } S}$$

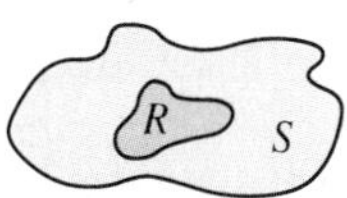

Example 1 Every ten minutes a bus pulls up to a hotel and waits for two minutes while passengers get on and off. Then the bus leaves. If a person walks out of the hotel front door at a random time, what is the probability that a bus is there?

Solution Think of a time line in which the colored segments represent times when the bus is at the hotel. For *any* ten-minute period, a two-minute subinterval is colored. Thus:

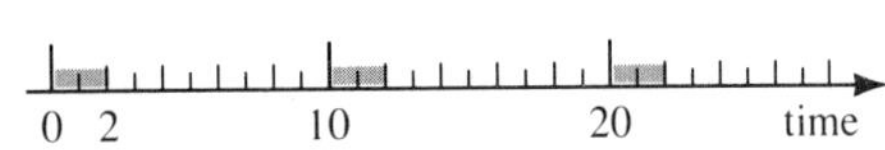

$$\text{probability that a bus will be there} = \frac{\text{length of colored segment}}{\text{length of whole segment}} = \frac{2}{10} = \frac{1}{5}$$

Example 2 A person who is just beginning archery lessons misses the target frequently. And when a beginner hits the target, each spot is as likely to be hit as another. If a beginner shoots an arrow and it hits the target, what is the probability that the arrow hits the red bull's eye?

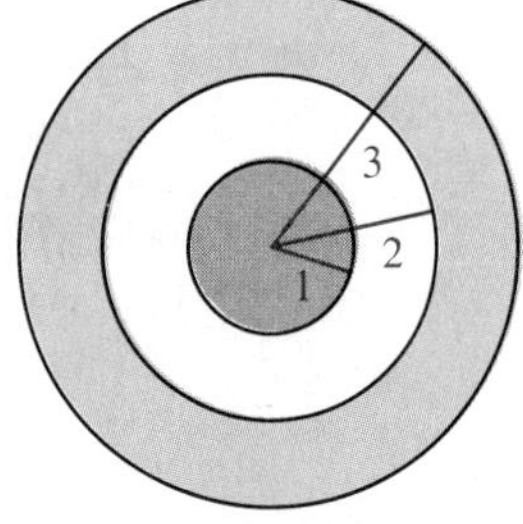

Solution probability arrow hits bull's eye if it hits target =

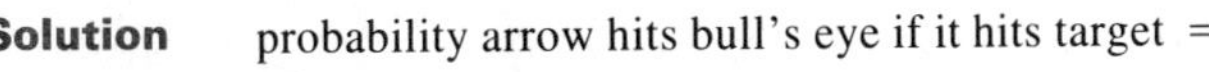

$$\frac{\text{area of bull's eye}}{\text{area of target}} = \frac{\pi \cdot 1^2}{\pi \cdot 3^2} = \frac{1}{9}$$

Teaching Suggestions, pp. T126–T127

Objective
Presenting the Lesson

Cooperative Learning, pp. T126–T127

Exploring Activity, p. 421c

Supplementary Materials

Practice Master 70
Test 45
Resource Book, pp. 75, 154
Study Guide, pp. 151–152
Computer Activity 24

Lesson Focus

The purpose of this lesson is to study the idea of geometric probability. Two principles are stated that can be used to solve problems.

Suggested Assignments

Average
463/1–7 odd
465/Self-Test 2
471/Chapter Test

Maximum
Day 1: 463/2–10 even, 11–17 odd
Day 2: 465/Self-Test 2
471/Chapter Test

Problem Solving

The geometric probability problems in the lesson are solved by using area or length. Encourage students to draw a diagram for each exercise and to label each one carefully. Students should also try to imagine performing the probability experiment as described in the problem.

Chalkboard Examples

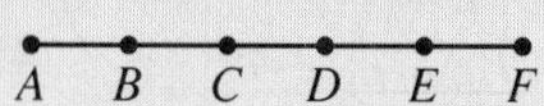

1. Suppose a point P on $\overline{AF}$ is picked at random. What is the probability that P is on $\overline{CF}$? $\frac{3}{5}$
2. At a carnival game, dishes are positioned on a table so that they do not overlap. You win a prize if you throw a nickel that lands in a dish. If the area of the table is 1.5 m^2 and the combined area of the dishes is 1 m^2, what is the probability that the nickel will not land in a dish? $\frac{1}{3}$

Example 3 At a carnival game, you can toss a coin on a large table that has been divided into squares 30 mm on a side. If the coin comes to rest without touching any line, you win. Otherwise you lose your coin. What are your chances of winning on one toss of a dime? (A dime has a radius of 9 mm.)

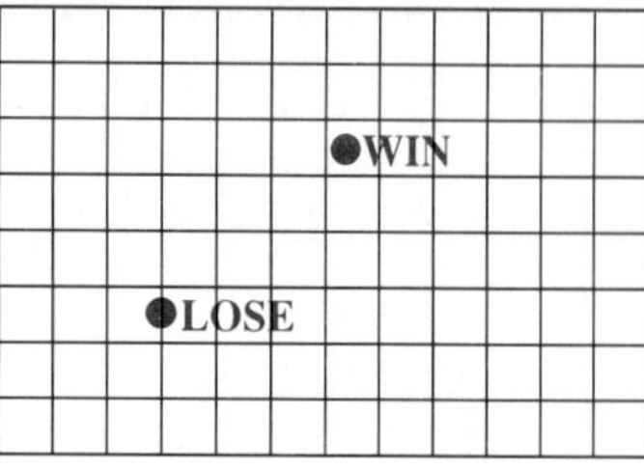

Solution Although there are many squares on the board, it is only necessary to consider the square in which the center of the dime lands. In order for the dime to avoid touching a line, the dime's center must be more than 9 mm from each side of the square. Its center must land in the shaded square shown. Thus the probability that the dime does not touch a line is equal to the probability that the center of the dime lies in the shaded region.

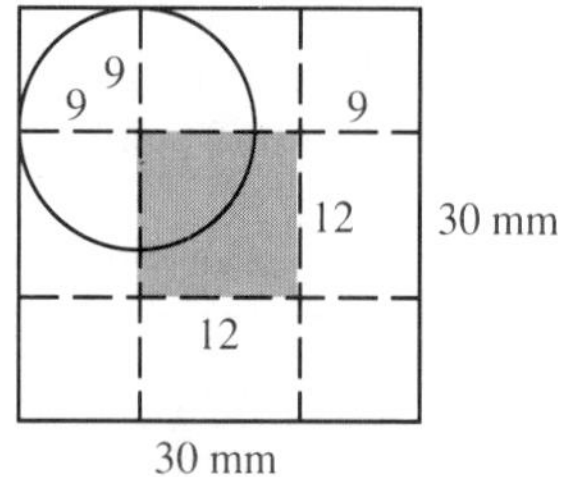

$$\text{probability of winning} = \frac{\text{area of shaded square}}{\text{area of larger square}} = \frac{12^2}{30^2} = 0.16$$

Note: In practice, your probability of winning would be less than 16% for several reasons. For example, a carnival might require you to toss a quarter instead of the smaller dime, as discussed in Written Exercise 9.

Classroom Exercises

1. A point P is picked at random on $\overline{RW}$. What is the probability that P is on:
   a. $\overline{RS}$? $\frac{1}{5}$ b. $\overline{SV}$? $\frac{3}{5}$ c. $\overline{SW}$? $\frac{4}{5}$
   d. $\overline{RW}$? **1** e. $\overline{XY}$? **0** f. $\overline{RY}$? **1**

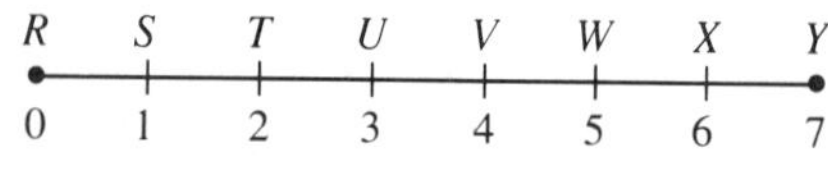

2. A friend promises to call you sometime between 4:00 and 4:30 P.M. If you are not home to receive the call until 4:10, what is the probability that you miss the first call that your friend makes to you? $\frac{1}{3}$

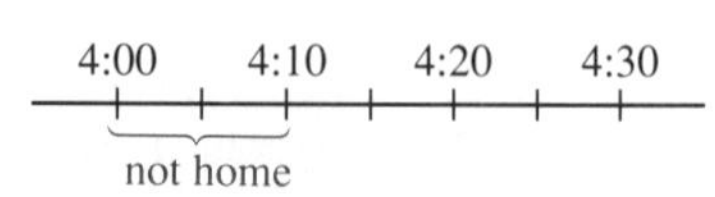

3. A dart lands at a random point on the square dartboard shown. What is the probability that the dart is within the outer circle? within the bull's eye? Use $\pi \approx 3.14$.
4. A ship is known to have sunk in the ocean in a square region 100 mi on a side. A salvage vessel anchors at a random spot in this square. Divers search 1 mi in all directions from the point on the ocean floor directly below the vessel. What is the approximate probability that they locate the sunken ship on the first try? Use $\pi \approx 3.14$.

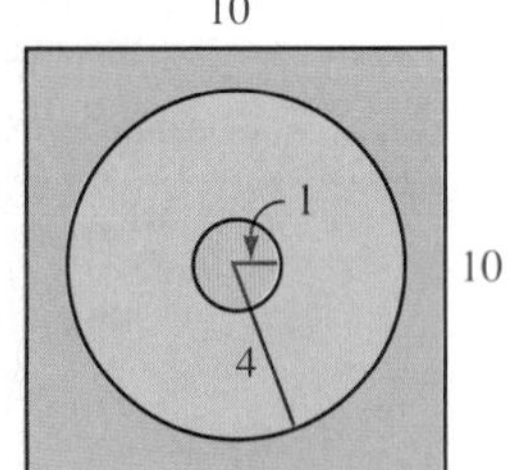

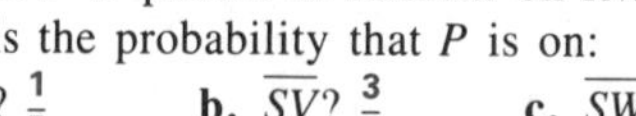

3. $\frac{16\pi - \pi}{100} \approx 0.471$; $\frac{\pi}{100} \approx 0.031$ **4.** $\frac{\pi}{10{,}000} \approx 0.0003$

Written Exercises

2. a. $\frac{1}{2}$ b. $\frac{1}{4}$ c. $\frac{3}{8}$

If a value of π is required in the following exercises, use $\pi \approx 3.14$.

A

1. M is the midpoint of $\overline{AB}$ and Q is the midpoint of $\overline{MB}$. If a point of $\overline{AB}$ is picked at random, what is the probability that the point is on $\overline{MQ}$? (*Hint:* Make a sketch.) $\frac{1}{4}$

2. In the diagram, $AC = CB$, $CD = DB$, and $DE = EB$. If a point X is selected at random from $\overline{AB}$, what is the probability that: **See above.**
   a. X is between A and C?
   b. X is between D and B?
   c. X is between C and E?

3. A friend promises to call you at home sometime between 3 P.M. and 4 P.M. At 2:45 P.M. you must leave your house unexpectedly for half an hour. What is the probability you miss the first call? $\frac{1}{4}$

4. a. At a subway stop, a train arrives every six minutes, waits one minute, and then leaves. If you arrive at a random time, what is the probability there will be a train waiting? $\frac{1}{6}$
   b. If you arrive and there is no train waiting, what is the probability that you will wait no more than two minutes before one arrives? $\frac{2}{5}$

5. A circular dartboard has diameter 40 cm. Its bull's eye has diameter 8 cm.
   a. If an amateur throws a dart and it hits the board, what is the probability that the dart hits the bull's eye? $\frac{1}{25}$
   b. After many throws, 75 darts have hit the target. Estimate the number hitting the bull's eye. **3**

6. Several hundred darts are thrown at the square dartboard shown. About what percentage of those hitting the board will land in the location described?
   a. Inside the inner square **50%**
   b. Outside the inner square but inside the circle **29%**

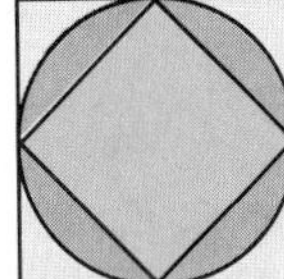

7. A dart is thrown at a board 12 m long and 5 m wide. Attached to the board are 30 balloons, each with radius 10 cm. Assuming each balloon lies entirely on the board, find the probability that a dart that hits the board will also hit a balloon. $\frac{\pi}{200} \approx 0.016$

8. Parachutists jump from an airplane and land in the rectangular field shown. What is the probability that a parachutist avoids the two trees represented by circles in the diagram? (Assume that the person is unable to control the landing point.) **See below.**

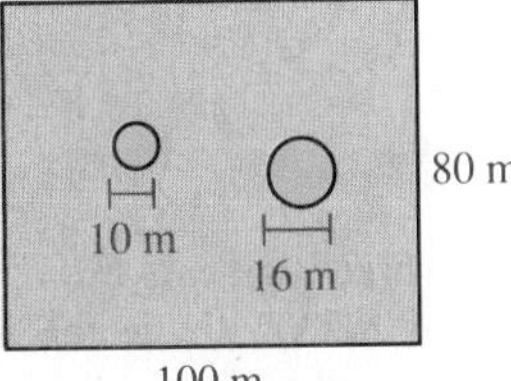

9. Refer to Example 3. Suppose that a quarter, instead of a dime, is tossed and lands on the table shown on the preceding page. What is the probability of winning on one toss? (The radius of a quarter is 12 mm.) **0.04**

8. $\frac{8000 - (\pi \cdot 5^2 + \pi \cdot 8^2)}{8000} = \frac{8000 - 89\pi}{8000} \approx 0.965$

Guided Practice

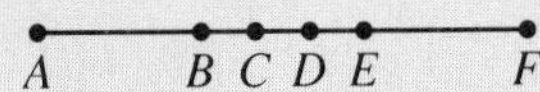

1. If $AB = BE = EF$ and $BC = CD = DE$ above, what is the probability that a point selected at random is between B and C? $\frac{1}{9}$ between C and F? $\frac{5}{9}$

2. In the diagram, $BC = 2AB$, $CD = AB$, and $CD = 2DE$. If a point X is selected at random from $\overline{AE}$, what is the probability that $AX > BC$? $\frac{5}{9}$

3. A different commuter train stops at a certain station every 20 minutes. The length of time each train stands at rest at the station is 3 minutes.
   a. If you arrive at a random time, what is the probability you will be able to board the train as soon as you arrive at the station? $\frac{3}{20}$
   b. If you arrive at the station and there is no train waiting, what is the probability that your wait will not exceed 10 minutes? $\frac{10}{17}$

Additional Answers
Written Exercises

15.a. To avoid a line, the coin's ctr. must be more than a dist. of R mm from each side of the square; that is, inside a square $(30 - 2R)$ mm on a side. Then prob. = $\frac{(30-2R)^2}{30^2} = \left(\frac{30-2R}{30}\right)^2$

Quick Quiz

Leave your answer in terms of π unless you are told to use an approximation.

1. Find the circumference and area of a circle with diameter 28. Use $\pi \approx \frac{22}{7}$. 88; 616
2. The area of a circle is 64π. Find its circumference. 16π
3. In $\odot O$ with radius 8, $m\overset{\frown}{XY} = 60$.
   a. Find the length of $\overset{\frown}{XY}$. $\frac{8}{3}\pi$
   b. Find the area of sector XOY. $\frac{32}{3}\pi$
   c. Find the area of the region bounded by $\overset{\frown}{XY}$ and $\overline{XY}$. $\frac{32}{3}\pi - 16\sqrt{3}$
4. Find the ratio of the circumferences of two circles whose areas are 100π and 64π. 5:4
5. The perimeters of two similar quadrilaterals are 15 cm and 20 cm. Find the ratio of their areas. 9:16

10. Repeat Exercise 9, using a nickel instead of a quarter. The radius of a nickel is 11 mm. $\approx$ **0.071**

B **11.** A piece of wire 6 in. long is cut into two pieces at a random point. What is the probability that both pieces of wire will be at least 1 in. long? $\frac{2}{3}$

12. A piece of string 8 cm long is cut at a random point. What is the probability that:
a. each piece is at least 2 cm long? $\frac{1}{2}$
b. the lengths of the two pieces differ by no more than 2 cm? $\frac{1}{4}$
c. the lengths of the two pieces total 8 cm? **1**

13. Darts are thrown at a 1-meter square which contains an irregular red region. Of 100 darts thrown, 80 hit the square. Of these, 10 hit the red region. Estimate the area of this region. **0.125 m²**

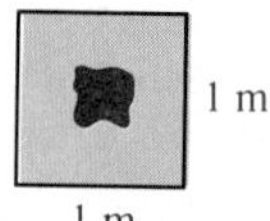

14. A carnival game has a white dartboard 5 m long and 2 m wide on which 100 red stars are painted. Each player tries to hit a star with a dart. Before trying it, you notice that only 3 shots out of the previous 50 hit a star. Estimate the area of one star. **0.006 m², or 60 cm²**

15. a. Suppose that a coin with radius R is tossed and lands on the table shown on page 462. Show that the probability the coin does not touch a line is $\left(\frac{30 - 2R}{30}\right)^2$.
b. Find the value of R for which the probability is 0.25. **7.5 mm**

16. A and B are the endpoints of a diameter. If C is a point chosen at random from the points on the circle (excluding A and B), what is the probability that:
a. $\triangle ABC$ is a right triangle? **1** **b.** $m\angle CAB \leq 30$? $\frac{1}{3}$

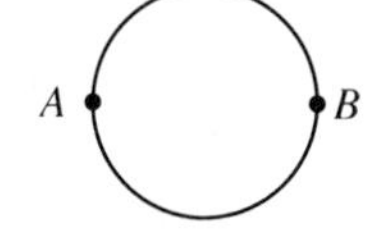

C **17.** A researcher was tape recording birdcalls. The tape recorder had a 1-hour tape in it. Eight minutes after the recorder was turned on, a 5-minute birdcall began. Unfortunately, the researcher accidentally erased 10 min of the tape. What is the probability that:
a. part of the birdcall was erased? **b.** all of the birdcall was erased?
(*Hint*: Draw a time line from 0 to 60 min and locate on this line when the birdcall took place. Also consider the possible starting times when the erasure could have occurred.) **a.** $\frac{13}{50}$ **b.** $\frac{5}{50} = \frac{1}{10}$

Challenge

Three segments through point P and parallel to the sides of $\triangle XYZ$ divide the whole region into six subregions. The three triangular subregions have the areas shown. Find the area of $\triangle XYZ$. **144**

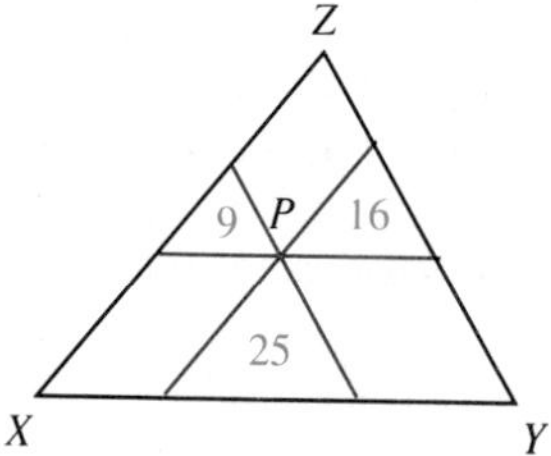

Self-Test 2

4. 16:49

Leave your answers in terms of π unless you are told to use an approximation.

1. Find the circumference and area of a circle with radius 14. Use $\pi \approx \frac{22}{7}$. **88; 616**
2. The circumference of a circle is 18π. What is its area? **81π**
3. In $\odot O$ with radius 12, $m\overset{\frown}{AB} = 90$.
   a. Find the length of $\overset{\frown}{AB}$. **6π**
   b. Find the area of sector AOB. **36π**
   c. Find the area of the region bounded by $\overline{AB}$ and $\overset{\frown}{AB}$. **$36\pi - 72$**
4. Find the ratio of the areas of two circles with radii 4 and 7.
5. The areas of two similar triangles are 36 and 81. Find the ratio of their perimeters. **2:3**

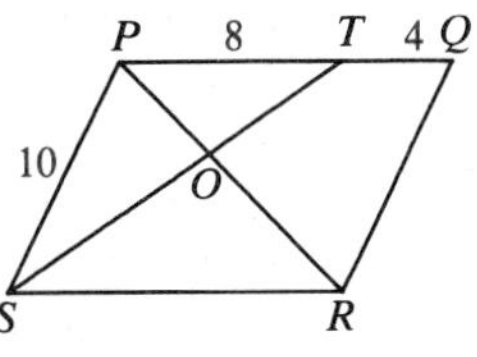

6. $PQRS$ is a parallelogram. Find the ratio of the areas of:
   a. $\triangle PTO$ and $\triangle RSO$ **4:9**
   b. $\triangle RPS$ and $\triangle TPS$ **3:2**

Each polygon is a regular polygon. Find the area of the shaded region.

7. **$64 - 16\pi$**

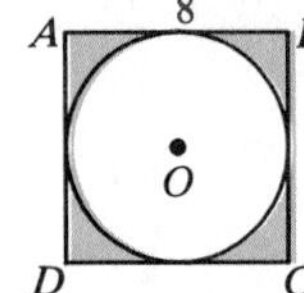

$\odot O$ is inscribed in square $ABCD$.

8. **$36\pi - 27\sqrt{3}$**

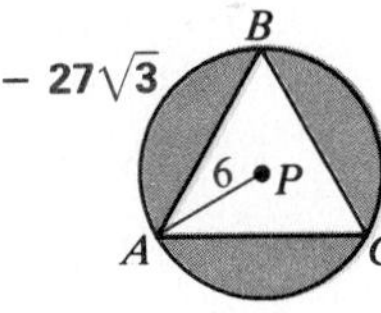

$\triangle ABC$ is inscribed in $\odot P$.

9. Refer to $\square PQRS$ in Exercise 6. A point is randomly chosen on $\overline{PR}$. Find the probability that the point is on $\overline{OR}$. **$\frac{3}{5}$**
10. Suppose that the figure in Exercise 7 is a dartboard. Imagine that someone with poor aim throws a dart and you *hear* it hit the dartboard. What is the probability that the dart landed inside the circle? **$\frac{\pi}{4}$**

Extra Congruence and Area

The SAS Postulate tells us that a triangle is *determined*, or fixed in size and shape, when two sides and the included angle are fixed. This means that the other parts of the triangle and its area can be determined from the given SAS information. Similarly, the area of a triangle can be determined when given ASA, SSS, AAS, or HL information. Computing the area of a triangle can often be simplified by using a calculator.

6. Find the ratio of the area of $\triangle ABC$ to the area of $\triangle BEC$. 3:1

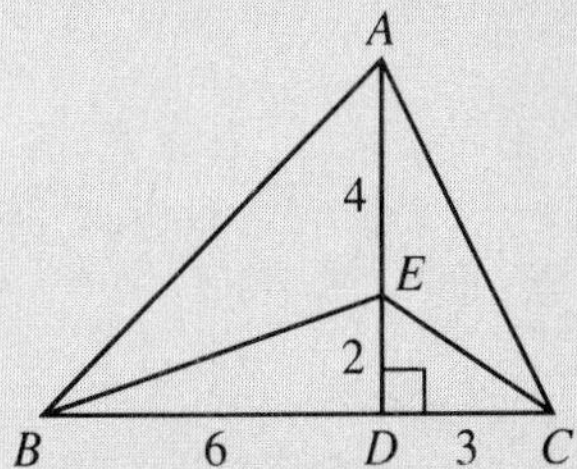

Refer to the diagram above.

7. A point is chosen at random on $\overline{AD}$. What is the probability that it is on $\overline{AE}$? $\frac{2}{3}$
8. Suppose you choose a random interior point of $\triangle ABC$. What is the probability it is in the interior of $\triangle BEC$? $\frac{1}{3}$

Each polygon is a regular polygon.

9. Find the area of the region inside the circle but outside the square. $64\pi - 128$

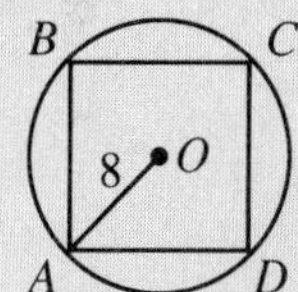

10. Find the area of the region inside the triangle but outside the circle. $27\sqrt{3} - 9\pi$

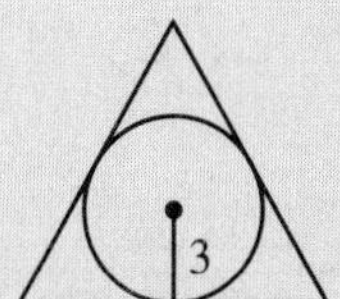

Example 1 Given the SAS information shown for $\triangle ABC$, find its area.

Solution Draw the altitude from C.

Then $\frac{h}{6} = \sin 53° \approx 0.7986$; $h \approx 4.79$.

Area $= \frac{1}{2}bh \approx \frac{1}{2}(10)(4.79) \approx 24.0$

Example 2 Given the ASA information shown for $\triangle ABC$, find its area.

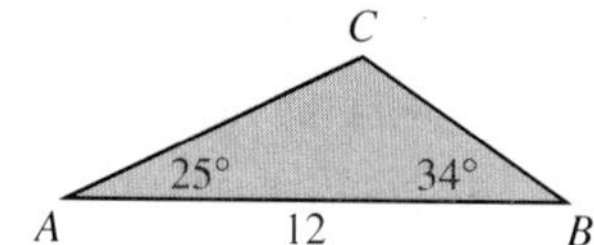

Solution

Step 1 Draw the altitude from C.

Then $\tan 25° = \frac{h}{12 - x}$ and $\tan 34° = \frac{h}{x}$.

$$(12 - x) \tan 25° = h \quad \text{and} \quad x \tan 34° = h$$
$$(12 - x) \tan 25° = x \tan 34°$$
$$(12 - x)(0.4663) \approx x(0.6745)$$
$$5.5956 - 0.4663x \approx 0.6745x$$
$$5.5956 \approx 1.1408x$$
$$4.905 \approx x$$

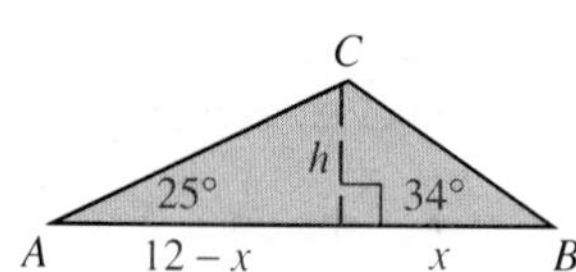

Step 2 Knowing x, we can find h:

$h = x \tan 34° \approx (4.905)(0.6745) \approx 3.308$

Step 3 Area $= \frac{1}{2}bh \approx \frac{1}{2}(12)(3.308) \approx 19.8$

Exercises

Use the given information to find the approximate area of $\triangle ABC$. In Exercises 6 and 7 the altitude from C lies outside the triangle. **Answers may vary.**

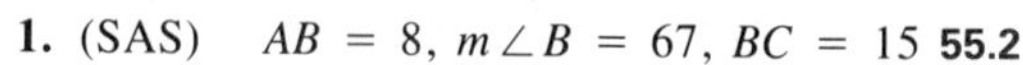

1. (SAS) $AB = 8$, $m\angle B = 67$, $BC = 15$ **55.2**
2. (HL) $m\angle C = 90$, $AB = 30$, $BC = 20$ (Use $\sqrt{5} \approx 2.236$.) **223.6**
3. (SSS) $AB = 10$, $BC = 12$, $CA = 8$ (*Hint*: Use Heron's Formula.) **39.7**
4. (ASA) $m\angle A = 28$, $AB = 10$, $m\angle B = 42$ **16.7**
5. (AAS) $m\angle A = 36$, $m\angle B = 80$, $BC = 10$ (*Hint*: Find the measure of $\angle C$. Then proceed as in Example 2.) **75.3**
6. (SAS) $AB = 12$, $m\angle A = 118$, $AC = 20$ **105.9**
7. (ASA) $m\angle A = 107$, $AB = 20$, $m\angle B = 35$ **178.2**

★ 8. The two triangles shown have two pairs of congruent corresponding sides and one pair of congruent corresponding non-included angles (SSA). Of course, they are *not* congruent. Find the area of each triangle.

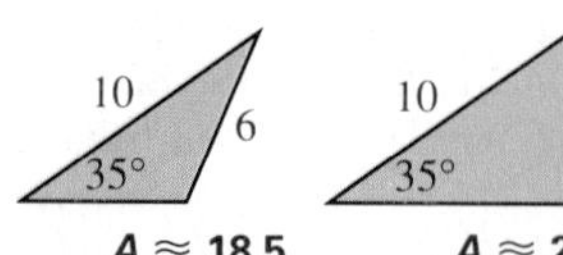

Application — Space Shuttle Landings

The space shuttle is launched vertically as a rocket but lands horizontally as a glider with no power and no second chance at the runway. NASA studied many different guidance systems for the final portion of entry and landing. The system that was selected for the first shuttle flights used a cylinder called the *Heading Alignment Cylinder* (HAC), shown in the diagram below. Notice that the projection of the flight path onto the Earth's surface is called the *ground track*.

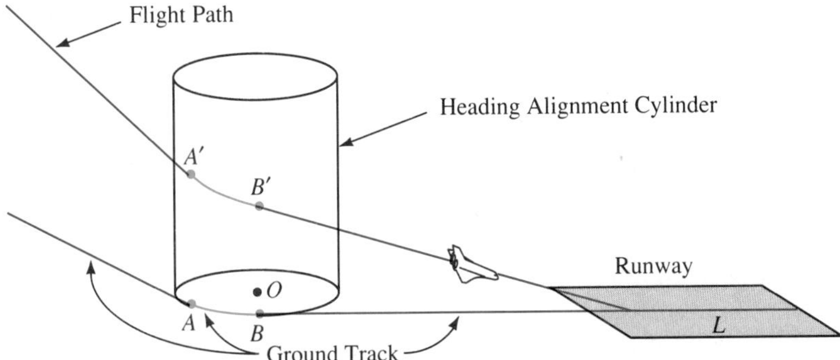

The shuttle followed a straight-line flight path to A' and then it followed a curved path along the Heading Alignment Cylinder to point B'. The shuttle continued to lose altitude so that it was closer to the Earth's surface at B' than at A'. From B' to landing at L the shuttle followed a straight path aligned with the center of the runway.

The points A' and B' where the shuttle's turn begins and ends can be determined by looking at the ground track. The figure at the right shows what you would see if you were high above the ground looking straight down on the ground track and runway. A' and B' are directly above A and B, which are located as follows: Extend the HAC acquisition line and the center line of the runway to meet at M. Bisect the angle at M and choose point O on the bisector so that a circle with center O and radius 20,000 ft will be tangent to the sides of the angle. Call the points of tangency A and B. $\odot O$ is the base of the Heading Alignment Cylinder and A' and B' are on the cylinder directly above A and B.

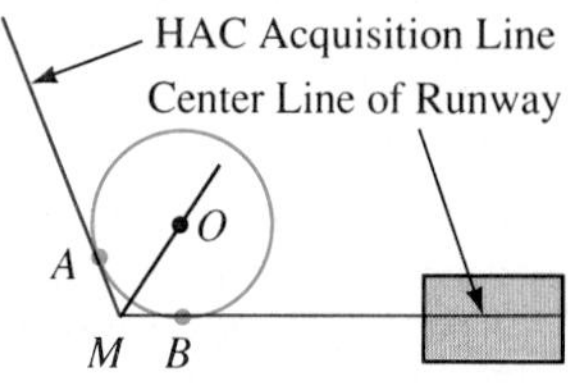

Normally the shuttle approached the cylinder at 800 ft/s and turned along its surface by lowering one wing tip so that the wings formed an angle of about 45° with the horizontal (called the *bank angle*). Under high-speed conditions the shuttle would have approached the cylinder at 1000 ft/s. This would have required a bank angle of about 57° to follow the surface of the cylinder. Unfortunately, at that bank angle, the shuttle would have lost lift, and the astronauts would have lost some of their control capability.

NASA has refined the guidance system so that the shuttle can be safely landed even under these adverse circumstances. Now, instead of following the surface of a cylinder, it spirals along the surface of a cone called the *Heading Alignment Cone*. Once every second during this part of the landing the shuttle's computers recompute the radius of turn necessary to keep the shuttle on the surface of the cone. Now even under most high-speed conditions the bank angle will not exceed approximately 42°. At point Q the shuttle is heading directly toward the runway; it leaves the cone and continues along a straight course to touchdown.

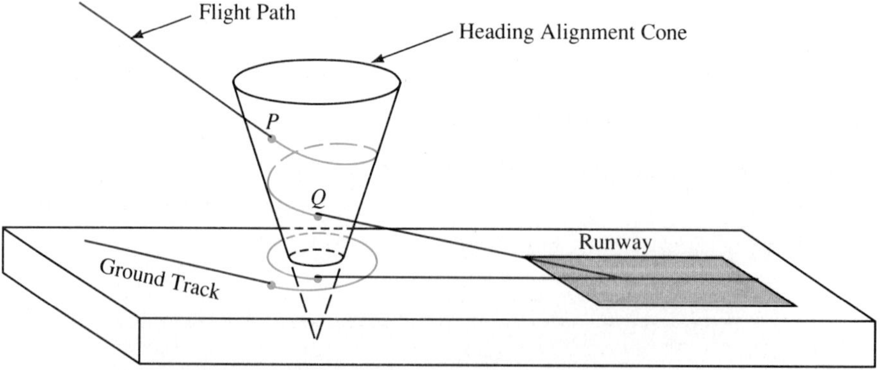

Exercises

1. Let T be any point on the bisector of $\angle AMB$. Show that if $\odot T$ is drawn tangent to $\overleftrightarrow{MA}$ it will also be tangent to $\overleftrightarrow{MB}$.

2. The radius of the Heading Alignment Cylinder was 20,000 ft, and a typical measure for $\angle AMB$ was 120. How long was the curved portion of the ground track, $\overset{\frown}{AB}$? (Use 3.1416 for π.) **20,944 ft**

3. The shuttle's turning radius changes as it moves along the surface of the Heading Alignment Cone. Is the radius larger near P or near Q? **near *P***

4. A good approximation of the detailed landing procedure uses a Heading Alignment Cone with vertex below the surface of the Earth. A typical radius of the cone at a height of 30,000 ft above the Earth's surface is 20,000 ft. At a height of 12,000 ft, which is a typical height for Q, the radius of the cone is 14,000 ft.
   a. How far below the surface of the Earth is the vertex of the cone? **30,000 ft**
   b. What is the radius of the cone at a height of 15,000 ft? **15,000 ft**
   c. At what height is the radius of the cone equal to 12,000 ft? **6000 ft**

Chapter Summary

1. If two figures are congruent, then they have the same area.
2. The area of a region is the sum of the areas of its non-overlapping parts.
3. The list below gives the formulas for areas of polygons.

Square:	$A = s^2$	Rectangle:	$A = bh$
Parallelogram:	$A = bh$	Triangle:	$A = \frac{1}{2}bh$
Rhombus:	$A = \frac{1}{2}d_1d_2$	Trapezoid:	$A = \frac{1}{2}h(b_1 + b_2)$

Regular polygon: $A = \frac{1}{2}ap$, where a is the apothem and p is the perimeter

4. The list below gives the formulas related to circles.

$C = 2\pi r$ Length of arc $= \frac{x}{360} \cdot 2\pi r$

$C = \pi d$

$A = \pi r^2$ Area of sector $= \frac{x}{360} \cdot \pi r^2$

(for the arc and sector formulas) where x is the measure of the arc

5. If two triangles have equal heights, then the ratio of their areas equals the ratio of their bases. If two triangles have equal bases, then the ratio of their areas equals the ratio of their heights.
6. If the scale factor of two similar figures is $a:b$, then
   (1) the ratio of the perimeters is $a:b$.
   (2) the ratio of the areas is $a^2:b^2$.
7. Two principles used in geometric probability problems are stated and illustrated on page 461.

Supplementary Materials

Practice Master 71

Test 46

Resource Book, pp. 76–77, 155

Chapter Review

1. Find the area of a square with perimeter 32. **64** 11–1
2. Find the area of a rectangle with length 4 and diagonal 6. **$8\sqrt{5}$**
3. Find the area of a square with side $3\sqrt{2}$ cm. **18 cm²**
4. Find the area of a rhombus with side 17 and longer diagonal 30. **240** 11–2
5. A parallelogram has sides 8 and 12. The shorter altitude is 6. Find the length of the other altitude. **9**
6. Find the perimeter and the area of the triangle shown. **$24 + 8\sqrt{3}$; $32\sqrt{3}$**

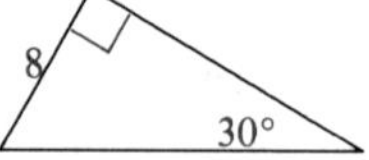

7. Find the height of a trapezoid with median 12 and area 84. **7** 11–3
8. Find the area of an isosceles trapezoid with legs 5 and bases 4 and 12. **24**
9. Find the perimeter and the area of the figure shown. **$30 + 4\sqrt{2}$; 52**

11
45°
15

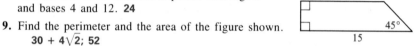

10. Find the area of a square with apothem 3 m. **36 m²** 11–4
11. Find the area of an equilateral triangle with radius $2\sqrt{3}$. **$9\sqrt{3}$**
12. Find the area of a regular hexagon with perimeter 12 cm. **$6\sqrt{3}$ cm²**
13. Find the circumference and area of a circle with radius 30. Use $\pi \approx 3.14$. **188.4; 2826** 11–5
14. The area of a circle is 121π cm². Find the diameter. **22 cm**
15. A square with side 8 is inscribed in a circle. Find the circumference and the area of the circle. **$8\pi\sqrt{2}$; 32π**
16. Find the length of a 135° arc in a circle with radius 24. **18π** 11–6

Find the area of each shaded region.

17.

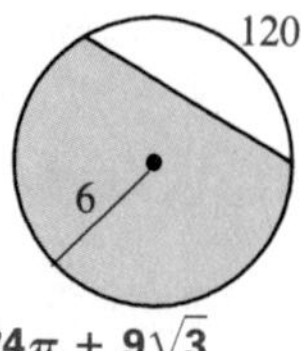

$24\pi + 9\sqrt{3}$

18.

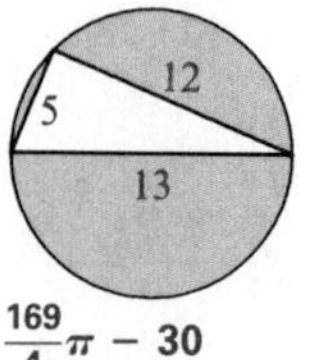

$\frac{169}{4}\pi - 30$

19.

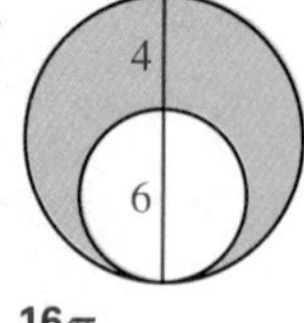

16π

20. If $AB = 9$ and $CD = 12$, find the ratio of the areas of: 11–7
    a. $\triangle AEB$ and $\triangle DEC$ **9:16** **b.** $\triangle AED$ and $\triangle DEC$
21. Two regular octagons have perimeters 16 cm and 32 cm, respectively. What is the ratio of their areas?

A B E D C

20.b. 3:4
21. 1:4

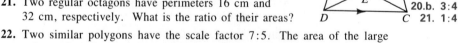

22. Two similar polygons have the scale factor 7:5. The area of the large polygon is 147. Find the area of the smaller polygon. **75**
23. A point is randomly chosen inside the larger circle of Exercise 19. What is the probability that the point is inside the smaller circle? **$\frac{9}{25}$** 11–8

Chapter Test

Teaching References

Alternate Test, p. T22

Find the area of each figure described.

1. A circle with diameter 10 **25π**

2. A square with diagonal 4 cm **8 cm^2**

3. An isosceles right triangle with hypotenuse $6\sqrt{2}$ **18**

4. A circle with circumference 30π m **225π m^2**

5. A rhombus with diagonals 5 and 4 **10**

6. An isosceles trapezoid with legs 10 and bases 6 and 22 **84**

7. A parallelogram with sides 6 and 10 that form a 30° angle **30**

8. A regular hexagon with apothem $2\sqrt{3}$ cm **$24\sqrt{3}$ cm^2**

9. Sector AOB of $\odot O$ with radius 4 and $m\widehat{AB} = 45$ **2π**

10. A rectangle with length 12 inscribed in a circle with radius 7.5 **108**

11. A sector of a circle with radius 12 and arc length 10π **60π**

12. A square with radius 9 **162**

Find the area of each shaded region.

13.

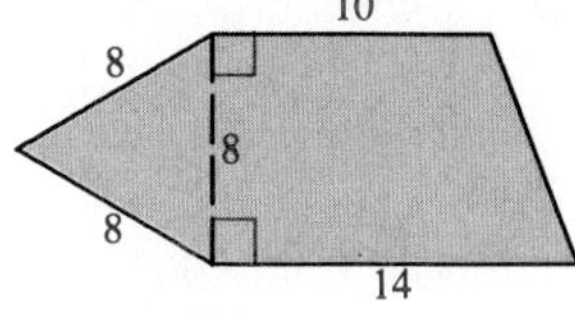

$96 + 16\sqrt{3}$

14.

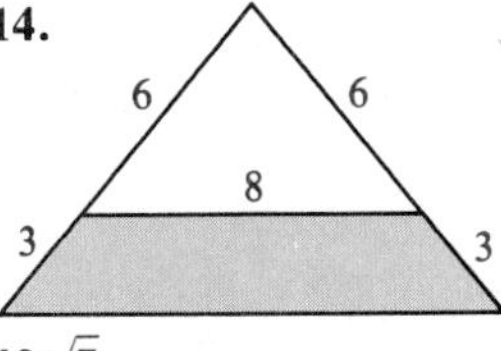

$10\sqrt{5}$

15.

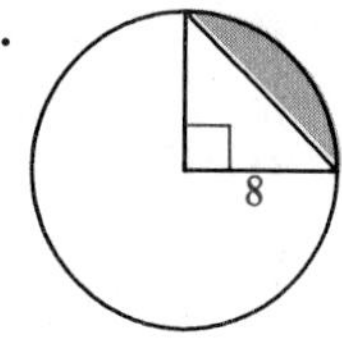

$16\pi - 32$

16. The areas of two circles are 100π and 36π. Find the ratio of their radii and the ratio of their circumferences. **5:3; 5:3**

17. Two regular pentagons have sides of 14 m and 3.5 m, respectively. Find their scale factor and the ratio of their areas. **4:1; 16:1**

18. In the diagram of $\odot Q$, $m\widehat{ABC} = 288$ and $QA = 10$.

a. Find the circumference of $\odot Q$. **20π**

b. Find the length of $\widehat{AC}$. **4π**

c. Find the area of sector AQC. **20π**

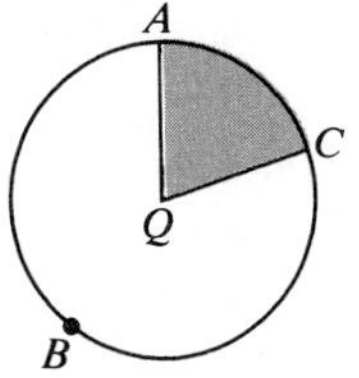

Ex. 18

19. A point is randomly chosen on $\overline{AD}$. Find the probability that the point is on $\overline{AE}$. **$\frac{3}{7}$**

20. A point is randomly chosen inside $\triangle ABC$. What is the probability that the point is inside:

a. $\triangle ABD$? **$\frac{1}{2}$** **b.** $\triangle BDE$? **$\frac{2}{7}$**

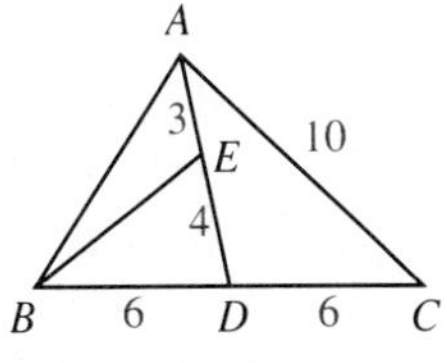

Exs. 19, 20

Supplementary Materials

Resource Book, p. 200

Cumulative Review: Chapters 1–11

In Exercises 1–12 classify each statement as true or false.

A

1. If point A lies on $\overrightarrow{BC}$, but not on $\overline{BC}$, then B is between A and C. **False**
2. A true conditional always has a true converse. **False**
3. The statement "If $ac = bc$, then $a = b$" is true for all real numbers a, b, and c. **False**
4. If two parallel lines are cut by transversal t and t is perpendicular to one of the lines, then t must also be perpendicular to the other line. **True**
5. If $\triangle ABC \cong \triangle DEF$ and $\angle A \cong \angle B$, then $\overline{DE} \cong \overline{EF}$. **False**
6. If the opposite sides of a quadrilateral are congruent and the diagonals are perpendicular, then the quadrilateral must be a square. **False**
7. If $\triangle GBS \sim \triangle JFK$, then $\frac{JF}{JK} = \frac{GB}{GS}$. **True**
8. The length of the altitude to the hypotenuse of a right triangle is always the geometric mean between the lengths of the legs. **False**
9. In any right triangle, the sine of one acute angle is equal to the cosine of the other acute angle. **True**
10. If an angle inscribed in a circle intercepts a major arc, then the measure of the angle must be between 180 and 360. **False**
11. The angle bisectors of an obtuse triangle intersect at a point that is equidistant from the three vertices. **False**
12. If $JK = 10$, then the locus of points in space that are 4 units from J and 5 units from K is a circle. **False**

13. Two lines that do not intersect are either _?_ or _?_. **parallel, skew**
14. In $\triangle RST$, $m\angle R = 2x + 10$, $m\angle S = 3x - 10$, and $m\angle T = 4x$.
    a. Find the numerical measure of each angle. **50; 50; 80**
    b. Is $\triangle RST$ scalene, isosceles, or right? Why? **isosceles; 2 ≅ ∠s**
15. Use inductive thinking to guess the next number: 10, 9, 5, -4, -20, _?_. **-45**
16. If a diagonal of an equilateral quadrilateral is drawn, what method could be used to show that the two triangles formed are congruent? **SSS**
17. A trapezoid has bases with lengths $x + 3$ and $3x - 1$ and a median of length 11. Find the value of x. **5**
18. If 4, 7, and x are the lengths of the sides of a triangle and x is an integer, list the possible values for x. **4, 5, 6, 7, 8, 9, 10**
19. Describe the locus of points in space that are 4 cm or less from a given point P. **a sphere with ctr. *P* and radius 4 cm, along with its interior**
20. Two similar rectangles have diagonals of $6\sqrt{3}$ and 9. Find the ratio of their perimeters and the ratio of their areas. **$2\sqrt{3}:3$; 4:3**

B **21.** Given: $\overline{AB} \perp \overline{BC}$; $\overline{DC} \perp \overline{BC}$; $\overline{AC} \cong \overline{BD}$
Prove: $\triangle BCE$ is isosceles.

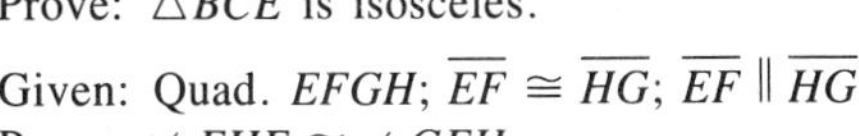

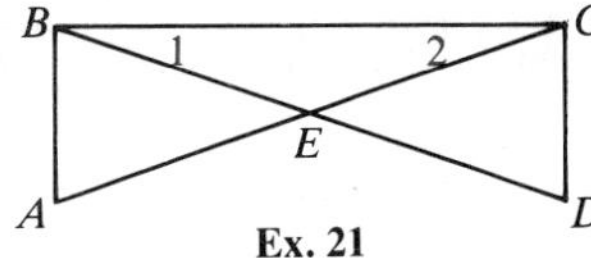

Ex. 21

22. Given: Quad. $EFGH$; $\overline{EF} \cong \overline{HG}$; $\overline{EF} \parallel \overline{HG}$
Prove: $\angle EHF \cong \angle GFH$

23. Use an indirect proof to show that no triangle has sides of length x, y, and $x + y$.

24. The legs of a right triangle are 4 cm and 8 cm long. What is the length of the median to the hypotenuse? **$2\sqrt{5}$ cm**

25. If a 45°-45°-90° triangle has legs of length $5\sqrt{2}$, find the length of the altitude to the hypotenuse. **5**

26. The altitude to the hypotenuse of a 30°-60°-90° triangle divides the hypotenuse into segments with lengths in the ratio __?__ : __?__. **1, 3**

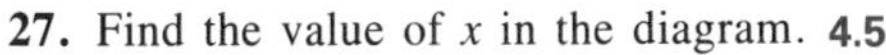

27. Find the value of x in the diagram. **4.5**

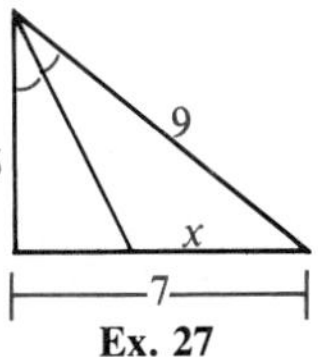

Ex. 27

28. In $\triangle DEF$, $m\angle F = 42$, $m\angle E = 90$, and $DE = 12$. Find EF to the nearest integer. (Use the table on page 311.) **13**

29. In right $\triangle XYZ$ with hypotenuse $\overline{XZ}$ if $\cos X = \frac{7}{10}$ and $XZ = 24$, then to the nearest integer $XY =$ __?__. **17**

30. If a tree is 20 m high and the distance from point P on the ground to the base of the tree is also 20 m, then the angle of elevation of the top of the tree from point P is __?__. **45°**

31. If $\overline{PQ}$ and $\overline{PR}$ are tangents to the circle and $m\angle 1 = 58$, find $m\angle 2$. **61**

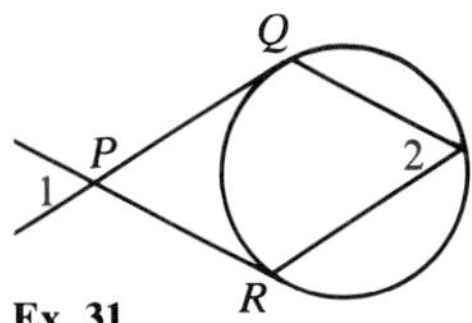

Ex. 31

32. $\triangle ABC$ is an isosceles right triangle with hypotenuse $\overline{AC}$ of length $2\sqrt{2}$. If medians $\overline{AD}$ and $\overline{BE}$ intersect at M, find AD and AM. **$\sqrt{5}$; $\frac{2}{3}\sqrt{5}$**

33. Draw two segments and let their lengths be x and y. Construct a segment of length t such that $t = \frac{2x^2}{y}$.

34. An equilateral triangle has perimeter 12 cm. Find its area. **$4\sqrt{3}$ cm²**

35. Find the area of an isosceles trapezoid with legs 7 and bases 11 and 21. **$32\sqrt{6}$**

36. a. Find the length of a 200° arc in a circle with diameter 24. **$\frac{40}{3}\pi$**
b. Find the area of the sector determined by this arc. **80π**

37. B and E are the respective midpoints of $\overline{AC}$ and $\overline{AD}$. Given that $AB = 9$, $BE = 6$, and $AE = 8$, find:
a. the perimeter of $\triangle ACD$ **46**
b. the ratio of the areas of $\triangle ABE$ and $\triangle ACD$ **$\frac{1}{4}$**

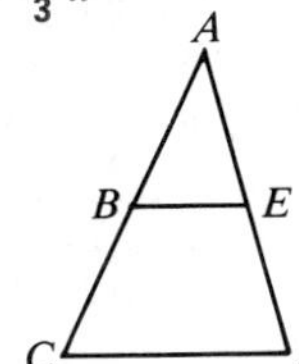

12 Areas and Volumes of Solids

Objectives

12-1 Identify the parts of prisms.

Find the lateral areas, total areas, and volumes of right prisms.

12-2 Identify the parts of pyramids.

Find the lateral areas, total areas, and volumes of regular polygons.

12-3 Find the lateral areas, total areas, and volumes of right cylinders and right cones.

12-4 Find the area and the volume of a sphere.

12-5 State and apply the properties of similar solids.

Assignment Guide

See page T40 for information about the Assignment Guide.

Day	Minimum Course	Average Course	Maximum Course
1	**12-1** 478/1–12	**12-1** 478/3, 5, 8, 9, 13, 15, 17, 18	**12-1** 478–479/4, 12, 13, 16, 18, 19, 21–24
2	**12-1** 478/13–18	**12-1** 478–480/19, 21–23, 25, 26, 28–30, 32	**12-1** 479–480/26, 27, 30–34
3	**12-1** 478–479/22, 24, 26	**12-2** 485/1, 4, 5, 7, 10–15	**12-2** 485/4, 10, 13, 15, 17
4	**12-2** 485/2, 4–10	**12-2** 485–486/16–18, 19–25 odd 487/Mixed Review 1–10	**12-2** 486/18, 23–25, 27 **S** 480/35, 37
5	**12-2** 485–486/11–15, 19, 20 487/Mixed Review 1–10	**12-3** 492–493/3, 5–8, 10, 11, 13, 16, 17	**12-3** 492–493/7, 8, 12–14, 16, 17 **S** 486/28, 30
6	**12-3** 492/1, 3, 5–8 **S** 486/18, 21	**12-3** 493–494/18–21, 23, 24, 26	**12-3** 493–494/19–21, 23, 25, 26
7	**12-3** 493/9–14, 16–19, 21	**12-3** 494/25, 27 496/Self-Test 1	**12-3** 494–495/27–39
8	**12-3** 493/15, 20 496/Self-Test 1	**12-4** 500/2, 3, 5, 8, 9, 11, 14, 15	**12-4** 500–501/6–14 even, 16–18
9	**12-4** 500/1–9	**12-4** 500–501/16–18, 20–23, 26 507/Mixed Review 1–6	**12-4** 501–502/19–25 odd, 26, 28, 29, 31
10	**12-4** 500/10–17 507/Mixed Review 1–6	**12-5** 511/1–6, 8, 10–12	**12-5** 511/4, 7, 9, 11–13 **S** 502/30
11	**12-5** 511/1–5 **S** 501/18–22	**12-5** 511–512/14–17, 19, 22, 23	**12-5** 511–512/14, 16–22
12	**12-5** 511/6, 8, 9, 11–13	**12-5** 513/Self-Test 2 519/Chapter Test 1–4	**12-5** 512–513/23–26, 28
13	**12-5** 512/15, 16 513/Self-Test 2	**12-5** 519/Chapter Test 5–16 Test, page T23	**12-5** 519/Chapter Test Test, page T23
14	**12-5** Chapter Test 1–15 odd Test, page T23		

Supplementary Materials Guide

For Use after Lesson	Practice Masters	Tests	Study Guide (Reteaching)	Resource Book: Tests	Resource Book: Practice Exercises	Resource Book: Mixed Review (MR) Prep. for College Entrance Exams (Col) Enrichment (E) Computer (C)	Computer Activities
12-1			pp. 153–154				
12-2	Sheet 72		pp. 155–156				Activity 25
12-3	Sheet 73	Test 47	pp. 157–158	pp. 78–79	p. 156		
12-4	Sheet 74		pp. 159–160				
12-5	Sheet 75	Test 48	pp. 161–162	p. 80	p. 157		Activity 26
Chapter 12	Sheet 76	Test 49		pp. 81–82	p. 158	p. 201 (Col) pp. 228–229 (E) p. 256 (C)	
Chapters 11–12	Sheets 77, 78	Test 50		pp. 83–85	pp. 159–160		
Chapters 1–12						pp. 183–185 (MR)	

Overhead Visuals

Guided Discovery Visuals (lettered) and Teaching Visuals (numbered) available for Chapter 12.

Lessons	Visual	Title
12-5	E	Similar Polygons in Space
12-4	I	Volume of a Sphere
12-4	J	A Volume Problem
12-4	K	The Five Possible Regular Polyhedrons
12-1, 12-2, 12-3	25	Volumes of Solids
12-4, 12-5	26	Similar Solids

Software Guide

Houghton Mifflin software for Chapter 12

Geometry Grapher (Apple or IBM)

Use with

p. 552 (Explorations)

Test Generator (Apple or IBM): 75 test items

Other software appropriate for Chapter 12

Spreadsheets

Guide to Integrated Curriculum

Teachers wishing to integrate coordinate and transformational geometry throughout the course can use the following lessons after Chapter 12. See pp. T56–T57 and p. 657 for more information.

14-5 Wr. Ex. 22, 23
14-6 all
14-7 all
14-8 all
13-8 all
13-9 all
14-2 Wr. Ex. 30, 31
Handbook: Deciding Which Method to Use in a Problem, pp. 672–675

Strategies for Teaching

Exploring Solids

When to Use

With or after Lesson 12-3

Overview

In this activity students predict which of two solids has the greater volume and which has the greater surface area. They then check their conjectures. A pattern emerges after several trials. This activity is related to Exercise 27 on page 494.

Materials

Construction paper, scissors, ruler, tape

Description of Activity

Cut out a rectangle $ABCD$ like the one shown below. Label the vertices and make sure AB is 8 units while AD is 6 units. You can form a cylinder by rotating the rectangle about side $\overline{AB}$. You can form a different cylinder by rotating the rectangle about side $\overline{AD}$.

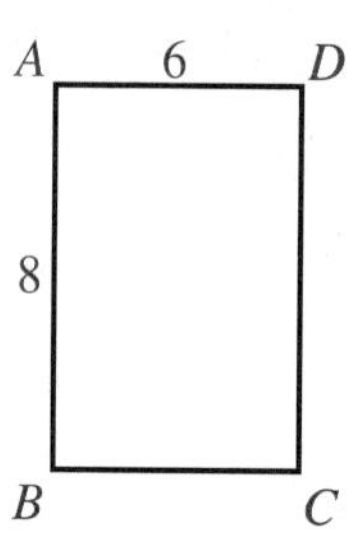

1. a. Which of the two cylinders do you think has the greater volume?
   b. Which cylinder has the greater surface area?
2. Check your predictions by finding each volume and surface area. Assume the two cylinders are open, without a top or bottom base. Then compute each of the following ratios.
   a. $\frac{\text{greater volume}}{\text{lesser volume}}$ b. $\frac{\text{greater surface area}}{\text{lesser surface area}}$
3. Repeat **1** and **2** of this activity for several other rectangles. Make a conjecture about the ratios obtained. Can you prove your conjecture?

Commentary

- **2.** Students may find it helpful to make a table of their results, then figure the ratios.

Cylinder	Volume	Surface Area
rotated about $\overline{AB}$ $(h = 8)$	288π	96π
rotated about $\overline{AD}$ $(h = 6)$	384π	96π

a. $\frac{\text{greater volume}}{\text{lesser volume}} = \frac{384\pi}{288\pi} = \frac{4}{3} = \frac{8}{6} = \frac{AB}{AD}$

b. $\frac{\text{greater surface area}}{\text{lesser surface area}} = \frac{96\pi}{96\pi} = \frac{1}{1} = 1$

- **3.** Students should summarize that the surface areas are in a ratio of 1 to 1, while the ratio of the volumes is $\frac{\text{length of longer side}}{\text{length of shorter side}}$.

Variations and Extensions

- The cylinders discussed in this activity were open cylinders. Would the same ratios hold true if the cylinders were closed? No
- Cut the rectangle in half, forming $\triangle ABC$. Then rotate the triangle about the hypotenuse, $\overline{AC}$. Predict the volume and surface area of this solid in relation to the solids formed by rotating the rectangles. Then find the volume (76.8π) and the surface area (67.2π), and compare with the other two solids. (This is similar to Exercise 39 on page 495.)

References to Strategies

PE: Pupil's Edition **TE:** Teacher's Edition **RB:** Resource Book

Problem Solving Strategies

PE: 480 (Challenge, Draw a diagram), 481 (Mathematical model), 482 (Choose a method of solution), 495 (Challenge, Visualize), 487 (Challenge, Generalize), 502 (Challenge, Apply a formula), 504, 514, 515 (Mathematical model)
TE: 479, 480 (Solve a simpler problem)

Applications

PE: 481 (Manufacturing), 497 (Air travel), 500–502, 505–506 (Geodesic domes), 511–512 (Similar solids), 514 (Maximizing area), 515 (Maximizing volume)
TE: T128, T131

Nonroutine Problems

PE: 480 (Challenge), 484 (Exs. 1, 16–18), 487 (Challenge), 494 (Ex. 28), 495 (Exs. 30, 31, 39, 40, Challenge), 502 (Challenge), 506 (Euler's formula), 513 (Challenge), 516–517 (Cavalieri's principle)
RB: 229

Communication

PE: 485, 492, 493 (Drawing geometric figures)
TE: T129, T130

Explorations

TE: 473c

Connections

PE: 506 (Euler), 507 (R. Buckminster Fuller), 516 (Cavalieri)
TE: T129, T130, 483 (Reference to Ch. 11), 515

Using Technology

PE: 481, 488–489, 496, 503, 504, 514, 515
TE: T128, T129, T130, 481, 488, 489, 491, 500, 503, 504, 515
RB: 240–241, 256
Computer Activities: 60–63

Using Manipulatives/Models

PE: 481, 485, 491 (Ex. 1), 492, 493, 502, 504, 513, 514–515
TE: T127, T128, T129, T130, T131, 477
RB: 228, 229
Overhead Visuals: E, I, J, K, 25, 26

Cooperative Learning

TE: T128, T129

Teaching Resources

For use in implementing the teaching strategies referenced on the previous page.

Using Manipulatives/Models
Resource Book, p. 228

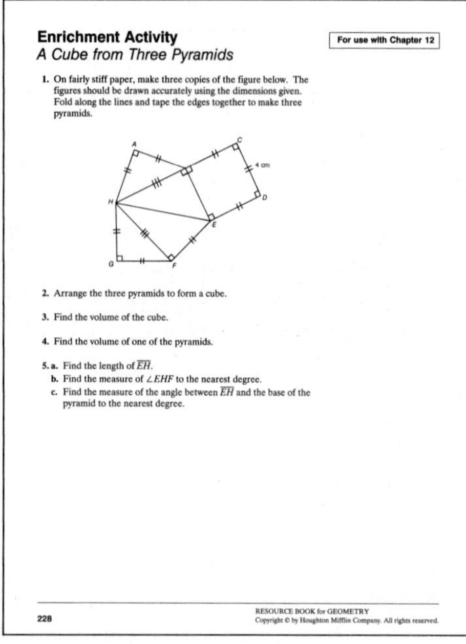

Enrichment Activity
A Cube from Three Pyramids

For use with Chapter 12

1. On fairly stiff paper, make three copies of the figure below. The figures should be drawn accurately using the dimensions given. Fold along the lines and tape the edges together to make three pyramids.

2. Arrange the three pyramids to form a cube.

3. Find the volume of the cube.

4. Find the volume of one of the pyramids.

5. a. Find the length of $\overline{EH}$.
   b. Find the measure of $\angle EHF$ to the nearest degree.
   c. Find the measure of the angle between $\overline{EH}$ and the base of the pyramid to the nearest degree.

228

RESOURCE BOOK for GEOMETRY

Using Manipulatives/Models
Resource Book, p. 229

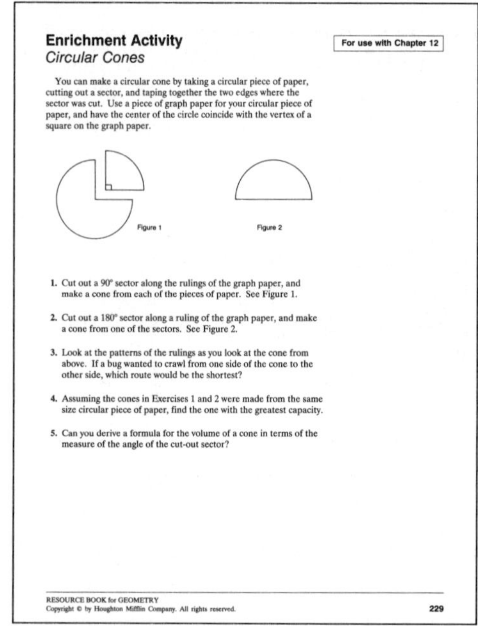

Enrichment Activity
Circular Cones

For use with Chapter 12

You can make a circular cone by taking a circular piece of paper, cutting out a sector, and taping together the two edges where the sector was cut. Use a piece of graph paper for your circular piece of paper, and have the center of the circle coincide with the vertex of a square on the graph paper.

Figure 1

Figure 2

1. Cut out a 90° sector along the rulings of the graph paper, and make a cone from each of the pieces of paper. See Figure 1.

2. Cut out a 180° sector along a ruling of the graph paper, and make a cone from one of the sectors. See Figure 2.

3. Look at the patterns of the rulings as you look at the cone from above. If a bug wanted to crawl from one side of the cone to the other side, which route would be the shortest?

4. Assuming the cones in Exercises 1 and 2 were made from the same size circular piece of paper, find the one with the greatest capacity.

5. Can you derive a formula for the volume of a cone in terms of the measure of the angle of the cut-out sector?

RESOURCE BOOK for GEOMETRY

229

Using Technology
Resource Book, p. 240

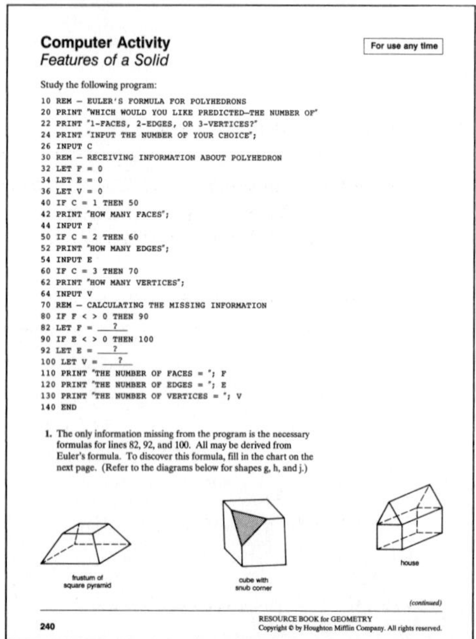

Computer Activity
Features of a Solid

For use any time

Study the following program:

```
10 REM — EULER'S FORMULA FOR POLYHEDRONS
20 PRINT "WHICH WOULD YOU LIKE PREDICTED—THE NUMBER OF"
22 PRINT "1-FACES, 2-EDGES, OR 3-VERTICES?"
24 PRINT "INPUT THE NUMBER OF YOUR CHOICE";
26 INPUT C
30 REM — RECEIVING INFORMATION ABOUT POLYHEDRON
32 LET F = 0
34 LET E = 0
36 LET V = 0
40 IF C = 1 THEN 50
42 PRINT "HOW MANY FACES";
44 INPUT F
50 IF C = 2 THEN 60
52 PRINT "HOW MANY EDGES";
54 INPUT E
60 IF C = 3 THEN 70
62 PRINT "HOW MANY VERTICES";
64 INPUT V
70 REM — CALCULATING THE MISSING INFORMATION
80 IF F < > 0 THEN 90
82 LET F = ___?___
90 IF E < > 0 THEN 100
92 LET E = ___?___
100 LET V = ___?___
110 PRINT "THE NUMBER OF FACES = "; F
120 PRINT "THE NUMBER OF EDGES = "; E
130 PRINT "THE NUMBER OF VERTICES = "; V
140 END
```

1. The only information missing from the program is the necessary formulas for lines 82, 92, and 100. All may be derived from Euler's formula. To discover this formula, fill in the chart on the next page. (Refer to the diagrams below for shapes g, h, and j.)

frustum of square pyramid

cube with snub corner

house

(continued)

240

RESOURCE BOOK for GEOMETRY

Using Technology
Resource Book, p. 241

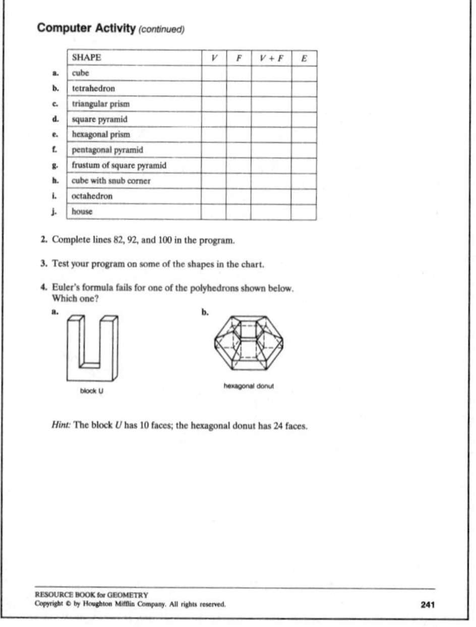

Computer Activity *(continued)*

	SHAPE	V	F	$V + F$	E
a.	cube				
b.	tetrahedron				
c.	triangular prism				
d.	square pyramid				
e.	hexagonal prism				
f.	pentagonal pyramid				
g.	frustum of square pyramid				
h.	cube with snub corner				
i.	octahedron				
j.	house				

2. Complete lines 82, 92, and 100 in the program.

3. Test your program on some of the shapes in the chart.

4. Euler's formula fails for one of the polyhedrons shown below. Which one?

a.

block U

b.

hexagonal donut

Hint: The block U has 10 faces; the hexagonal donut has 24 faces.

RESOURCE BOOK for GEOMETRY

241

Using Models

***Guided Discovery Visual* I, Sheet 1**

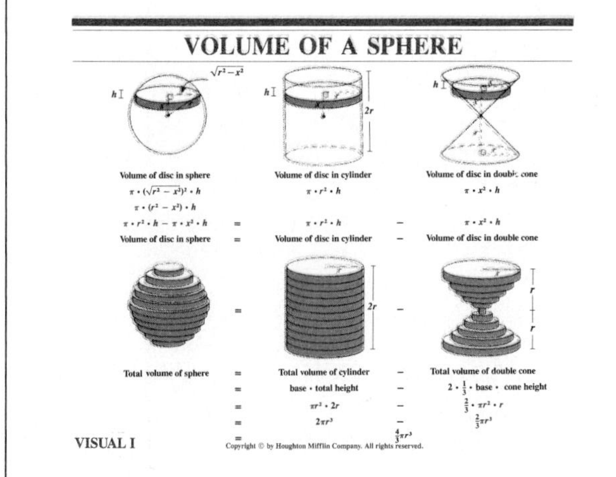

Using Models/Problem Solving

***Guided Discovery Visual* J, Sheets 1 and 2**

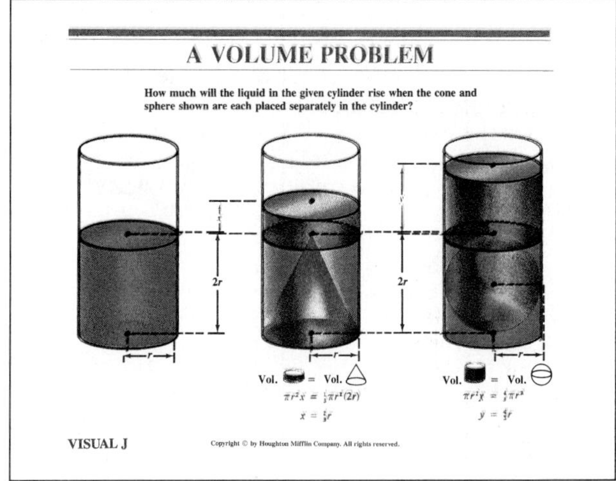

Using Models

***Guided Discovery Visual* K, Sheet 1**

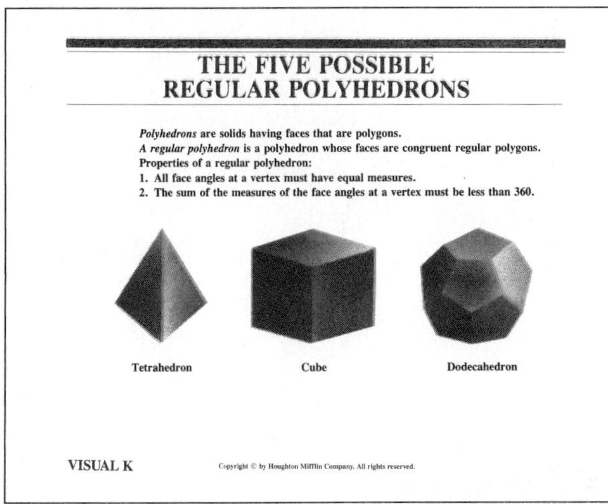

THE FIVE POSSIBLE
REGULAR POLYHEDRONS
Polyhedrons are solids having faces that are polygons.
A regular polyhedron is a polyhedron whose faces are congruent regular polygons.
Properties of a regular polyhedron:
1. All face angles at a vertex must have equal measures.
2. The sum of the measures of the face angles at a vertex must be less than 360.
Tetrahedron
Cube
Dodecahedron
VISUAL K
Copyright © by Houghton Mifflin Company. All rights reserved.

Using Models

***Guided Discovery Visual* K, Sheet 2**

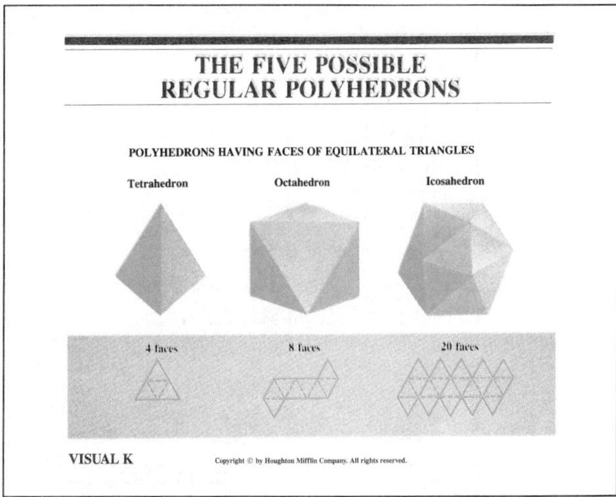

Teaching References

Lesson Commentary, pp. T127–T131

Assignment Guide, pp. T48–T51

Software Guide, p. T73

Alternate Test, p. T23

Supplementary Materials

Practice Masters 72–78

Tests 47–50

Resource Book
- Tests, pp. 78–85
- Practice, pp. 156–160
- Mixed Review, pp. 183–185
- Preparing for College Entrance Exams, p. 201
- Enrichment Activities, pp. 228–229
- Computer Activity, p. 256

Study Guide, pp. 153–162

Overhead Visuals E, I, J, K, 25, 26

Computer Activities
- 25 Lateral Area and Volume of a Square Pyramid
- 26 Changing Cylinders

Cultural Note

The Chinese mathematician Liu Hui (ca. 3rd century A.D.) calculated the volumes of relatively complicated solids using simpler solids such as cubes, prisms, pyramids, and tetrahedrons. His method involved grouping together the simpler solids of known volumes to form the more complicated solids.

12 AREAS AND VOLUMES OF SOLIDS

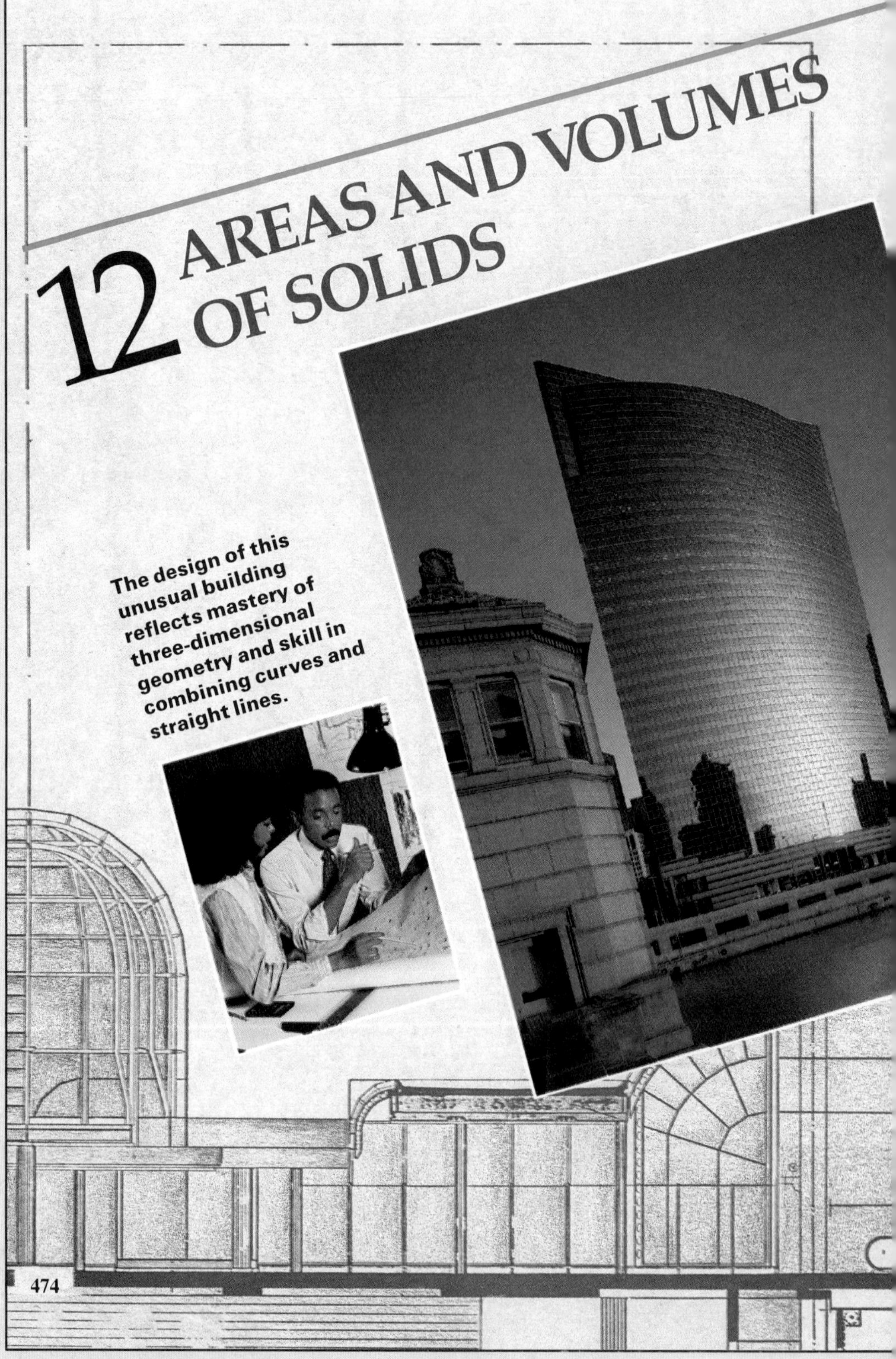

The design of this unusual building reflects mastery of three-dimensional geometry and skill in combining curves and straight lines.

Important Solids

Objectives

1. Identify the parts of prisms, pyramids, cylinders, and cones.
2. Find the lateral areas, total areas, and volumes of right prisms and regular pyramids.
3. Find the lateral areas, total areas, and volumes of right cylinders and right cones.

12-1 *Prisms*

In this chapter you will be calculating surface areas and volumes of special solids. It is possible to begin with some postulates and then prove as theorems the formulas for areas and volumes of solids, as we did for plane figures. Instead, the formulas for solids will be stated as theorems, and informal arguments will be given to show you that the formulas are reasonable.

The first solid we will study is the **prism.** The two shaded faces of the prism shown are its **bases.** Notice that the bases are congruent polygons lying in parallel planes. An **altitude** of a prism is a segment joining the two base planes and perpendicular to both. The length of an altitude is the *height*, *h*, of the prism.

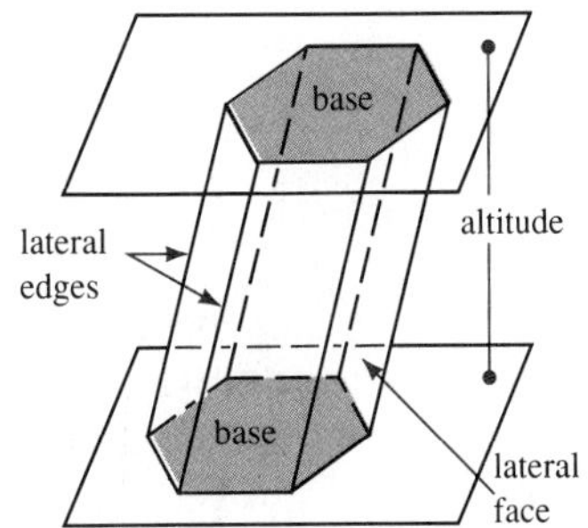

The faces of a prism that are not its bases are called **lateral faces.** Adjacent lateral faces intersect in parallel segments called **lateral edges.**

The lateral faces of a prism are parallelograms. If they are rectangles, the prism is a **right prism.** Otherwise the prism is an **oblique prism.** The diagrams below show that a prism is also classified by the shape of its bases. Note that in a right prism, the lateral edges are also altitudes.

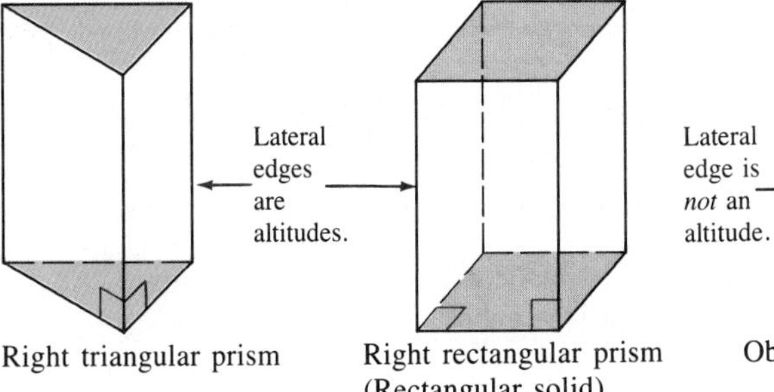

Right triangular prism

Right rectangular prism (Rectangular solid)

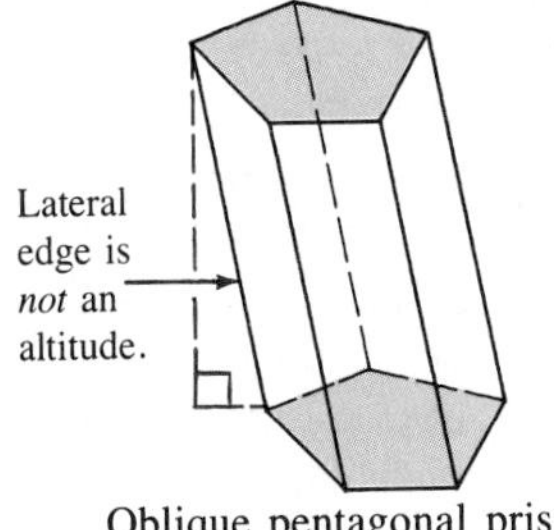

Oblique pentagonal prism

Teaching Suggestions, pp. T127–T128

Objectives
Presenting the Lesson
Application

Cooperative Learning, p. T128

Supplementary Materials

Study Guide, pp. 153–154

Lesson Focus

The purpose of this lesson is to study the properties of a solid figure called a prism. Two theorems present formulas for calculating the lateral area and volume of a right prism.

Suggested Assignments

Minimum
Day 1: 478/1–12
Day 2: 478/13–18
Day 3: 478–479/22, 24, 26

Average
Day 1: 478/3, 5, 8, 9, 13, 15, 17, 18
Day 2: 478–480/19, 21–23, 25, 26, 28–30, 32

Maximum
Day 1: 478–479/4, 12, 13, 16, 18, 19, 21–24
Day 2: 479–480/26, 27, 30–34

Chalkboard Examples

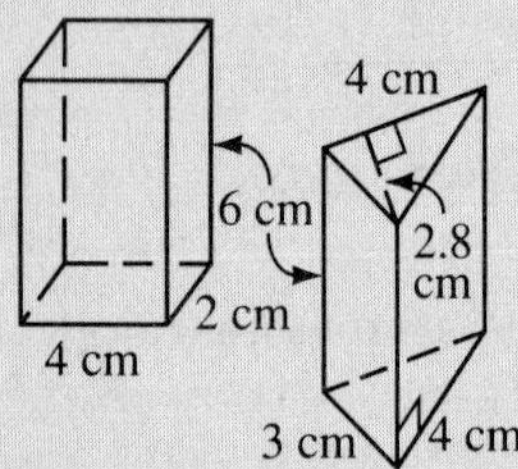

Refer to the diagrams above and complete the chart. (p denotes the perimeter of the base.)

		Rt. Rect. Prism	Rt. △ Prism
1.	p	12 cm	11 cm
2.	B	8 cm²	5.6 cm²
3.	L.A.	72 cm²	66 cm²
4.	V	48 cm³	33.6 cm³

A cube has volume 8 cm³. Complete each statement.

5. The length of each edge of the cube is 2 cm.
6. The total area of the cube is 24 cm².

Teaching Note

Stress the appropriate use of linear, square, and cubic units. Area is measured in square units, and volume in cubic units.

Assessment

Before proceeding to the next lesson, discuss the diagrams shown in the book to evaluate students' perceptions and understanding of these three-dimensional drawings.

The surface area of a solid is measured in square units. The **lateral area** (L.A.) of a prism is the sum of the areas of its lateral faces. The **total area** (T.A.) is the sum of the areas of all its faces. Using B to denote the area of a base, we have the following formula.

$$\text{T.A.} = \text{L.A.} + 2B$$

If a prism is a right prism, the next theorem gives us an easy way to find the lateral area.

Theorem 12-1

The lateral area of a right prism equals the perimeter of a base times the height of the prism. (L.A. = *ph*)

The formula for lateral area applies to any right prism. The right pentagonal prism can be used to illustrate the development of the formula:

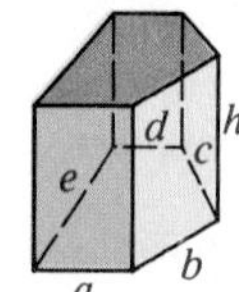

$$\begin{aligned}\text{L.A.} &= ah + bh + ch + dh + eh \\ &= (a + b + c + d + e)h \\ &= \text{perimeter} \cdot h \\ &= ph\end{aligned}$$

Prisms have *volume* as well as area. A rectangular solid with square faces is a **cube.** Since each edge of the blue cube shown is 1 unit long, the cube is said to have a volume of 1 cubic unit. The larger rectangular solid has 3 layers of cubes, each layer containing (4 · 2) cubes. Hence its volume is (4 · 2) · 3, or 24 cubic units.

$$\begin{aligned}\text{Volume} &= \text{Base area} \times \text{height} \\ &= (4 \cdot 2) \cdot 3 \\ &= 24 \text{ cubic units}\end{aligned}$$

The same sort of reasoning is used to find the volume of any right prism.

Theorem 12-2

The volume of a right prism equals the area of a base times the height of the prism. (*V* = *Bh*)

Volume is measured in cubic units. Some common units for measuring volume are the cubic centimeter (cm^3) and the cubic meter (m^3).

Example 1 A right trapezoidal prism is shown. Find the **(a)** lateral area, **(b)** total area, and **(c)** volume.

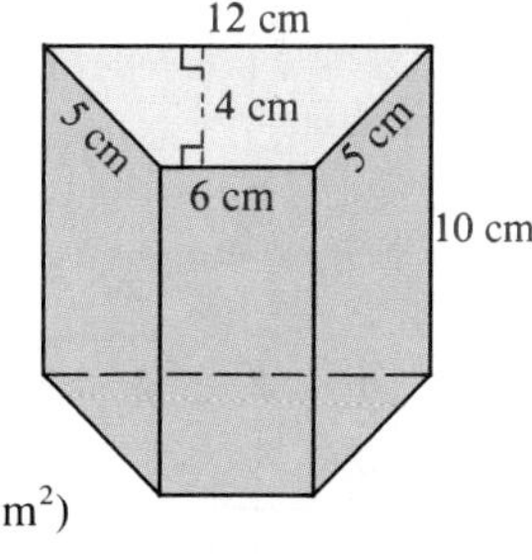

Solution **a.** First find the perimeter of a base.
$p = 5 + 6 + 5 + 12 = 28$ (cm)

Now use the formula for lateral area.
L.A. $= ph = 28 \cdot 10 = 280$ (cm^2)

b. First find the area of a base.
$B = \frac{1}{2} \cdot 4 \cdot (12 + 6) = 36$ (cm^2)

Now use the formula for total area.
T.A. $=$ L.A. $+ 2B = 280 + 2 \cdot 36 = 352$ (cm^2)

c. $V = Bh = 36 \cdot 10 = 360$ (cm^3)

Example 2 A right triangular prism is shown. The volume is 315. Find the total area.

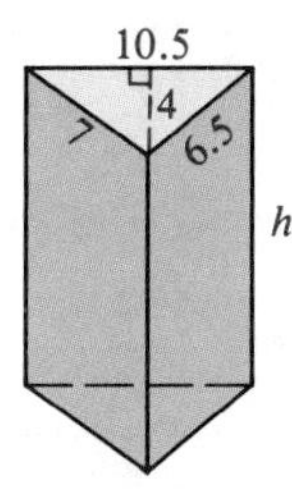

Solution First find the height of the prism.

$$V = Bh$$
$$315 = (\tfrac{1}{2} \cdot 10.5 \cdot 4)h$$
$$315 = 21h$$
$$15 = h$$

Next find the lateral area.
L.A. $= ph = (10.5 + 6.5 + 7) \cdot 15 = 24 \cdot 15 = 360$

Now use the formula for total area.
T.A. $=$ L.A. $+ 2B = 360 + 2 \cdot 21 = 402$

Classroom Exercises **4. $\overline{PA}$, $\overline{QB}$, $\overline{RC}$, $\overline{SD}$ are lateral edges and altitudes.**

Exercises 1–6 refer to the right prism shown.

U T P S Q R 5 cm A B C D

1. The prism is called a right __?__ prism. **hexagonal**
2. How many lateral faces are there? **6**
3. What kind of figure is each lateral face? **rectangle**
4. Name two lateral edges and an altitude. **See above.**
5. The length of an altitude is called the __?__ of the prism. **height**
6. Suppose the bases are regular hexagons with 4 cm edges.
   a. Find the lateral area. **b.** Find the base area.
   c. Find the total area. **See below.** **d.** Find the volume.

4 cm

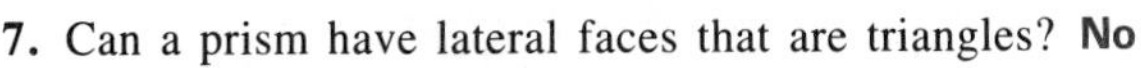

7. Can a prism have lateral faces that are triangles? **No**
8. What is the minimum number of faces a prism can have? **5**
9. If two prisms have equal volumes, must they also have equal total areas? **No**
10. **a.** Since 1 yd = 3 ft, 1 yd^2 = __?__ ft^2 and 1 yd^3 = __?__ ft^3. **9, 27**
    b. Since 1 ft = __?__ in., 1 ft^2 = __?__ in.^{2} and 1 ft^3 = __?__ in.^{3} **12, 144, 1728**
    c. Since 1 m = __?__ cm, 1 m^2 = __?__ cm^2 and 1 m^3 = __?__ cm^3. **100, 10,000, 1,000,000**

6. a. 120 **cm^2** **b.** $24\sqrt{3}$ **cm^2** **c.** $(120 + 48\sqrt{3})$ **cm^2** **d.** $120\sqrt{3}$ **cm^3**

Using a Model

Having models of solids available in the classroom will help students who have difficulty visualizing the three-dimensional figures of this chapter. If geometric models of plastic or wood are not available, perhaps you can have your students make models of the different solids when they are discussed in class.

Exercise Note

For Ex. 6(b), remind students that the diagonals of the base form six equilateral triangles. Also, another method is to use the formula $A = \frac{1}{2}ap$. For Ex. 9, you may wish to draw the following to help students answer the questions: (1) an 8 x 16 x 4 rectangular solid; (2) an 8 x 8 x 8 cube; and (3) a 6 x 13 x 6 rectangular solid. Have students compute T.A. and V for each.

Additional Answers Written Exercises

1. L.A. = 40; T.A. = 88; $V = 48$
2. L.A. = 2400; T.A. = 5400; $V = 22{,}500$
3. $h = 3$; L.A. = 54; T.A. = 90
4. $l = 9$; L.A. = 170; T.A. = 314
5. $w = 6$; T.A. = 168; $V = 108$
6. L.A. = $54x^2$; T.A. = $94x^2$; $V = 60x^3$
7. T.A. = 54; $V = 27$
8. T.A. = $6e^2$; $V = e^3$
9. $e = 10$; T.A. = 600
10. $e = 4$; T.A. = 96
11. $e = 5$; $V = 125$
12. T.A. = $24x^2$; $V = 8x^3$

Guided Practice

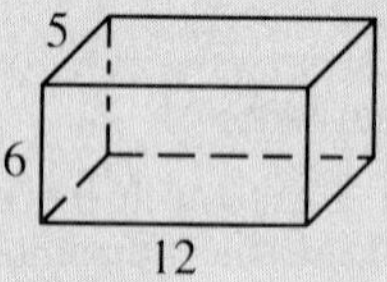

Use the figure above to find the following.

1. Lateral area 204
2. Total area 324
3. Volume 360

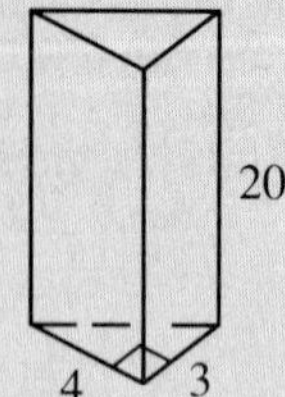

Use the figure above to find the following.

4. Lateral area 240
5. Total area 252
6. Volume 120

Written Exercises

Exercises 1–6 refer to rectangular solids with dimensions l, w, and h. Complete the table.

A

	1.	2.	3.	4.	5.	6.
l	6	50	6	?	9	$5x$
w	4	30	3	8	?	$4x$
h	2	15	?	5	2	$3x$
L.A.	?	?	?	?	60	?
T.A.	?	?	?	?	?	?
V	?	?	54	360	?	?

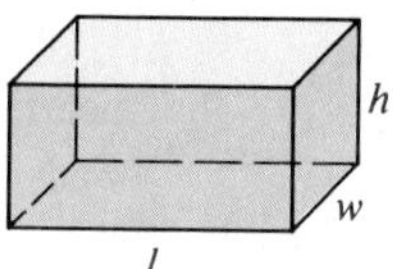

Exercises 7–12 refer to cubes with edges of length e. Complete the table.

	7.	8.	9.	10.	11.	12.
e	3	e	?	?	?	$2x$
T.A.	?	?	?	?	150	?
V	?	?	1000	64	?	?

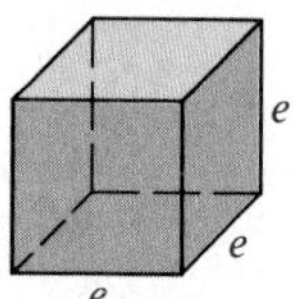

13. Find the lateral area of a right pentagonal prism with height 13 and base edges 3.2, 5.8, 6.9, 4.7, and 9.4. **390**
14. A right triangular prism has lateral area 120 cm^2. If the base edges are 4 cm, 5 cm, and 6 cm long, find the height of the prism. **8 cm**
15. If the edge of a cube is doubled, the total area is multiplied by __?__ and the volume is multiplied by __?__. **4, 8**
16. If the length, width, and height of a rectangular solid are all tripled, the lateral area is multiplied by __?__, the total area is multiplied by __?__, and the volume is multiplied by __?__. **9, 9, 27**

Facts about the base of a right prism and the height of the prism are given. Sketch each prism and find its lateral area, total area, and volume.

17. Equilateral triangle with side 8; $h = 10$ **240; $240 + 32\sqrt{3}$; $160\sqrt{3}$**
18. Triangle with sides 9, 12, 15; $h = 10$ **360; 468; 540**

B

19. Isosceles triangle with sides 13, 13, 10; $h = 7$ **252; 372; 420**
20. Isosceles trapezoid with bases 10 and 4 and legs 5; $h = 20$ **480; 536; 560**
21. Rhombus with diagonals 6 and 8; $h = 9$ **180; 228; 216**
22. Regular hexagon with side 8; $h = 12$ **576; $576 + 192\sqrt{3}$; $1152\sqrt{3}$**

23. The container shown has the shape of a rectangular solid. When a rock is submerged, the water level rises 0.5 cm. Find the volume of the rock. **675 cm³**

24. A driveway 30 m long and 5 m wide is to be paved with blacktop 3 cm thick. How much will the blacktop cost if it is sold at the price of $175 per cubic meter? **$787.50**

25. A brick with dimensions 20 cm, 10 cm, and 5 cm weighs 1.2 kg. A second brick of the same material has dimensions 25 cm, 15 cm, and 4 cm. What is its weight? **1.8 kg**

26. A drinking trough for horses is a right trapezoidal prism with dimensions shown below. If it is filled with water, about how much will the water weigh? (*Hint*: 1 m^3 of water weighs 1 metric ton.) **about 0.56 metric ton**

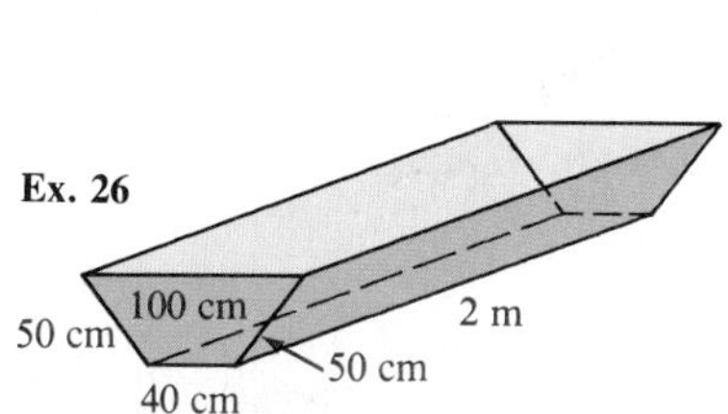

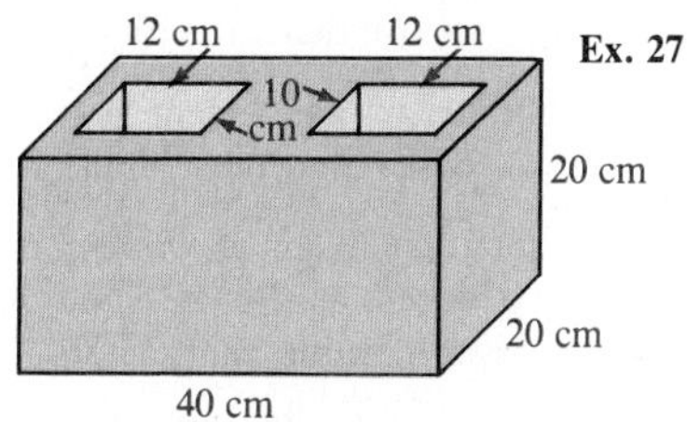

27. Find the weight, to the nearest kilogram, of the cement block shown. Cement weighs 1700 kg/m^3. **19 kg**

28. Find the weight, to the nearest 10 kg, of the steel **I**-beam shown below. Steel weighs 7860 kg/m^3. **3140 kg**

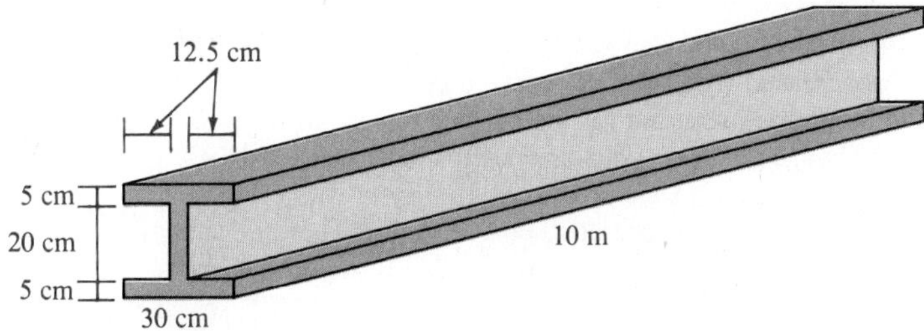

Find the volume and the total surface area of each solid in terms of the given variables.

29.

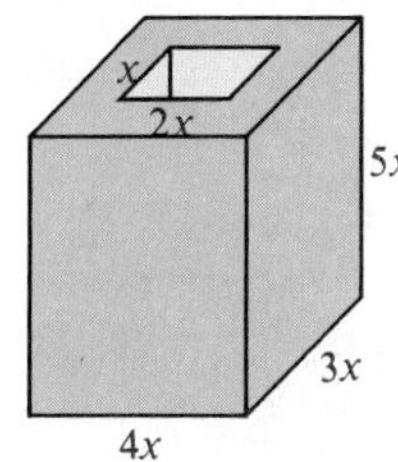

$V = 50x^3$; T.A. $= 120x^2$

30.

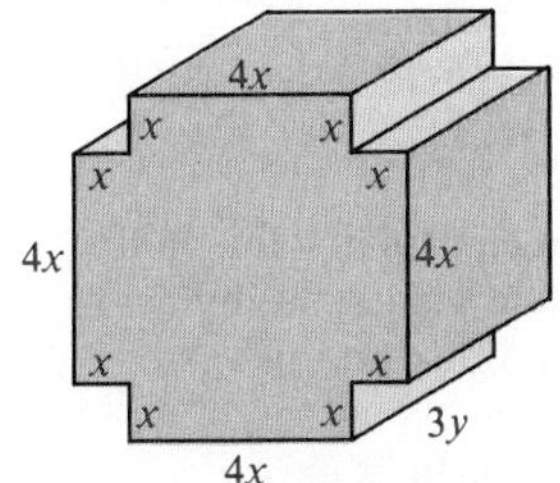

$V = 96x^2y$; T.A. $= 64x^2 + 72xy$

7. Find the volume of a rectangular solid with length 10 cm, width 3 cm, and height 12 cm. 360 cm³

8. Find the volume and total area of a cube with edge $5a$. $125a^3$; $150a^2$

9. A right triangular prism has base edges of 5, 12, and 13, and a volume of 450. Find the height of the prism. 15

10. The base of a triangular prism is an isosceles right triangle with legs of 3 cm. The height of the prism is 10 cm. Find the lateral area, total area, and volume of the prism.
$(60 + 30\sqrt{2})$ cm²;
$(69 + 30\sqrt{2})$ cm²;
45 cm³

Problem Solving

An additional problem that students can work on is the following.

A cube has volume 64. Find the length of its diagonal. $4\sqrt{3}$

31. The length of a rectangular solid is twice the width, and the height is three times the width. If the volume is 162 cm^3, find the total area of the solid. **198 cm^2**

32. A right prism has square bases with edges that are three times as long as the lateral edges. The prism's total area is 750 m^2. Find the volume. **1125 m^3**

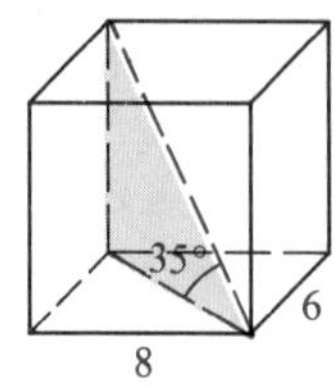

33. A diagonal of a box forms a 35° angle with a diagonal of the base, as shown. Use trigonometry to approximate the volume of the box. **≈ 336**

34. Refer to Exercise 33. Suppose another box has a base with dimensions 8 by 6 and a diagonal that forms a 70° angle with a diagonal of a base. Show that the ratio of the volumes of the two boxes is $\frac{\tan 35°}{\tan 70°}$. $\frac{Bh_1}{Bh_2} = \frac{48 \cdot 10 \cdot \tan 35°}{48 \cdot 10 \cdot \tan 70°} = \frac{\tan 35°}{\tan 70°}$

C **35.** A right prism has height x and bases that are equilateral triangles with sides x. Show that the volume is $\frac{1}{4}x^3\sqrt{3}$. $V = Bh = \frac{1}{2}aph = \frac{1}{2} \cdot \frac{x\sqrt{3}}{6} \cdot 3x \cdot x = \frac{1}{4}x^3\sqrt{3}$

36. A right prism has height h and bases that are regular hexagons with sides s. Show that the volume is $\frac{3}{2}s^2h\sqrt{3}$. $V = Bh = \frac{1}{2}aph = \frac{1}{2} \cdot \frac{s\sqrt{3}}{2} \cdot 6s \cdot h = \frac{3}{2}s^2h\sqrt{3}$

37. A rectangular beam of wood 3 m long is cut into six pieces, as shown. Find the volume of each piece in cubic centimeters. **See below.**

38. A diagonal of a cube joins two vertices not in the same face. If the diagonals are $4\sqrt{3}$ cm long, what is the volume? **64 cm^3**

39. All nine edges of a right triangular prism are congruent. Find the length of these edges if the volume is $54\sqrt{3}$ cm^3. **6 cm**

40. If the length and width of a rectangular solid are each decreased by 20%, by what percent must the height be increased for the volume to remain unchanged? Give your answer to the nearest whole percent. **56%**

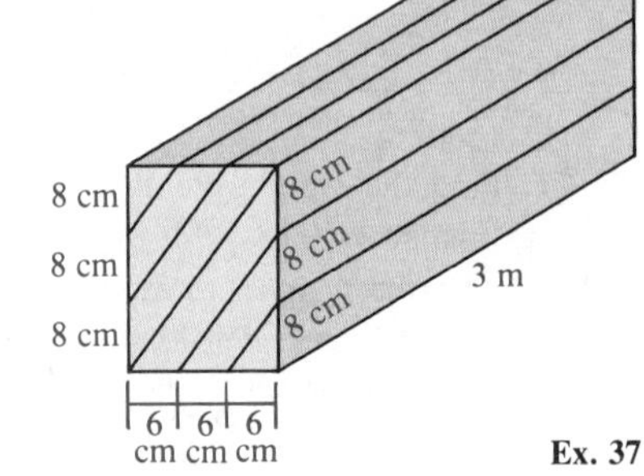

Ex. 37

37. 7200 cm^3, 21,600 cm^3, 36,000 cm^3, 36,000 cm^3, 21,600 cm^3, 7200 cm^3

Challenge

1. Given two rectangles, find one line that divides each rectangle into two parts of equal area.
Draw the diagonals of each rectangle to locate their centers, *A* and *B*. Draw $\overleftrightarrow{AB}$.

2. Given three rectangular solids, tell how to find one plane that divides each of these solids into two parts of equal volume.
Draw the diagonals of each solid to locate their centers, *A*, *B*, and *C*. Draw a plane containing *A*, *B*, and *C*. (If *A*, *B*, and *C* are not collinear, there is only one such plane.)

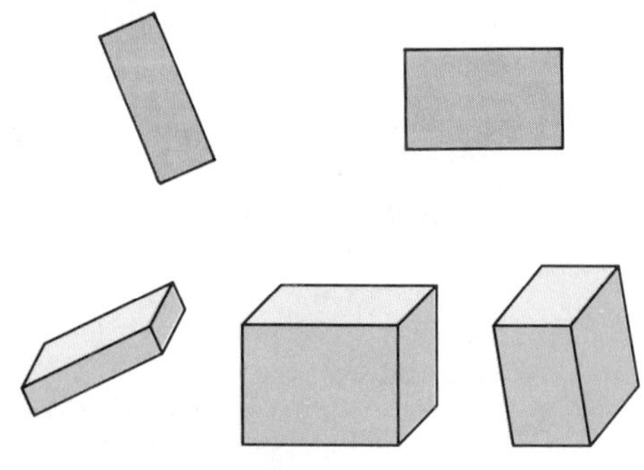

Problem Solving

Discussion of this Challenge can offer an insight into an important mathematical idea. That is, the solution of a problem in the plane often can be used to solve a similar problem involving a solid. Solving the first problem of the Challenge suggests an approach for solving the second problem. The second problem requires that students think about how to divide a rectangular solid into two parts of equal volume. One way to do this is to use the plane determined by the parallel diagonals of two opposite bases to form two wedges.

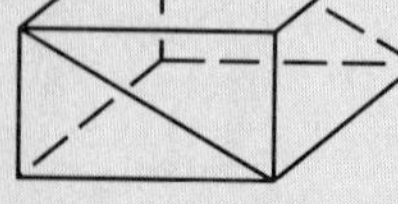

Using a Computer

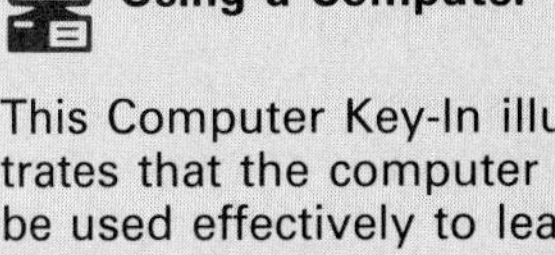

This Computer Key-In illustrates that the computer can be used effectively to learn about maximization, an important concept that has many applications. In the past, most students could not explore this topic until they had studied more advanced mathematics courses.

♦ Computer Key-In

A manufacturing company produces metal boxes of different sizes by cutting out square corners from rectangular pieces of metal that measure 9 in. by 12 in. The metal is then folded along the dashed lines to form a box without a top. If a customer requests the box with the greatest possible volume, what dimensions should be used?

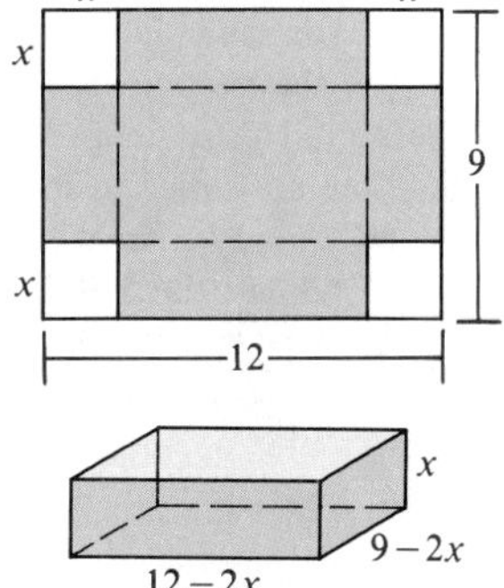

The volume, V, of the box can be expressed in terms of x.

$$\begin{aligned} V &= \text{length} \cdot \text{width} \cdot \text{height} \\ &= (12 - 2x) \cdot (9 - 2x) \cdot x \end{aligned}$$

To form a box, the possible values for x are $0 < x < \frac{9}{2}$.

The following computer program finds the volumes of the boxes produced for ten values of x from 0 to 4.5.

```
10 PRINT "X", "VOLUME"
15 PRINT
20 FOR X = 0 TO 4.5 STEP 0.5
30 LET V = (12 - 2 * X) * (9 - 2 * X) * X
40 PRINT X, V
50 NEXT X
60 END
```

X	VOLUME
0	0
.5	44
1	70
1.5	81
2	80
2.5	70
3	54
3.5	35
4	16
4.5	0

The print-out at the right shows that the maximum volume of the box probably occurs when the value of x is between 1 and 2. Also, the print-out shows that the maximum volume is about 81 in.^{3}

Exercises

1. To find a more accurate value for x, change line 20 to:

```
FOR X = 1 TO 2 STEP 0.1
```

Between what values of x does the maximum volume occur? **1.6 and 1.8**

2. Modify line 20 to find the maximum volume, correct to the nearest tenth of a cubic inch. What are the length, width, and height, correct to the nearest tenth of an inch, of the box with maximum volume? **See below.**

3. Suppose the manufacturing company cuts square corners out of pieces of metal that measure 8 in. by 15 in.

a. Express the volume in terms of x. $\mathbf{V = (15 - 2x) \cdot (8 - 2x) \cdot x}$

b. Find the maximum volume, correct to the nearest tenth of a cubic inch. **90.7 in.^{3}**

c. What are the length, width, and height of the box with maximum volume? Give each correct to the nearest tenth of an inch. **11.6 in., 4.6 in., 1.7 in.**

2. line 20: FOR X = 1.6 TO 1.8 STEP 0.01
Maximum volume is 81.9 in.^{3} when x = 1.7.
length = 8.6 in., width = 5.6 in., height = 1.7 in.

Teaching Suggestions,
pp. T128–T129

Objectives
Presenting the Lesson
Reinforcement
Using Technology

Supplementary Materials

Practice Master 72
Study Guide, pp. 155–156
Computer Activity 25

Lesson Focus

A common solid figure is the pyramid. This lesson studies the properties of regular pyramids and presents two methods for finding their lateral areas.

Suggested Assignments

Minimum
Day 1: 485/2, 4–10
Day 2: 485–486/11–15, 19, 20
487/Mixed Review 1–10

Average
Day 1: 485/1, 4, 5, 7, 10–15
Day 2: 485–486/16–18, 19–25 odd
487/Mixed Review 1–10

Maximum
Day 1: 485/4, 10, 13, 15, 17
Day 2: 486/18, 23–25, 27
S 480/35, 37

Teaching Note

Review the Pythagorean Theorem and stress its importance in working with pyramids. Show that the slant height of a pyramid is the hypotenuse of one right triangle but a leg of another.

12-2 *Pyramids*

The diagram shows the pentagonal **pyramid** V-$ABCDE$. Point V is the **vertex** of the pyramid and pentagon $ABCDE$ is the **base.** The segment from the vertex perpendicular to the base is the **altitude** and its length is the *height*, h, of the pyramid.

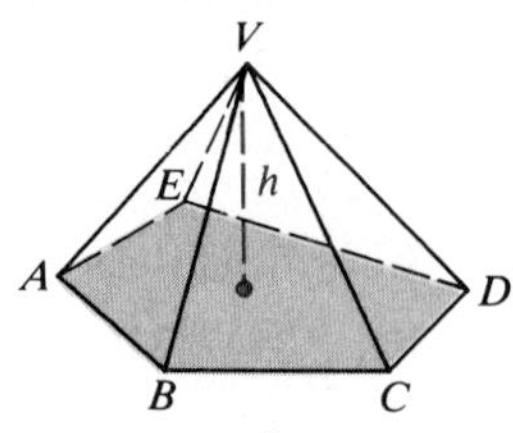

The five triangular faces with V in common, such as $\triangle VAB$, are **lateral faces.** These faces intersect in segments called **lateral edges.**

Most of the pyramids you'll study will be **regular pyramids.** These are pyramids with the following properties:

(1) The base is a regular polygon.
(2) All lateral edges are congruent.
(3) All lateral faces are congruent isosceles triangles. The height of a lateral face is called the **slant height** of the pyramid. It is denoted by l.
(4) The altitude meets the base at its center, O.

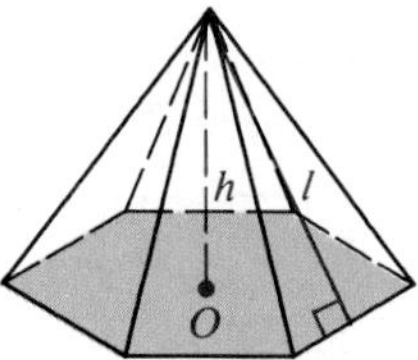

Regular hexagonal pyramid

Example 1 A regular square pyramid has base edges 10 and lateral edges 13. Find **(a)** its slant height and **(b)** its height.

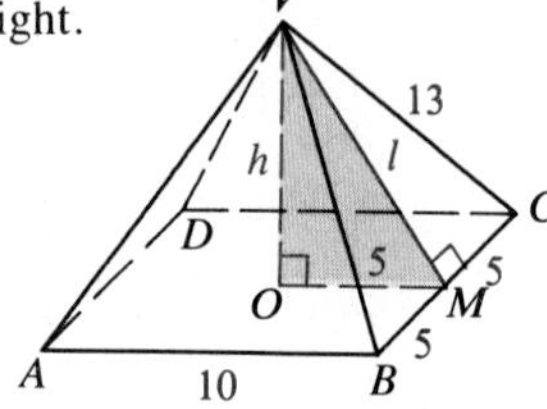

Solution Use the Pythagorean Theorem.

a. In rt. $\triangle VMC$,
$$l = \sqrt{13^2 - 5^2} = 12.$$

b. In rt. $\triangle VOM$,
$$h = \sqrt{12^2 - 5^2} = \sqrt{119}.$$

Example 2 Find the lateral area of the pyramid in Example 1.

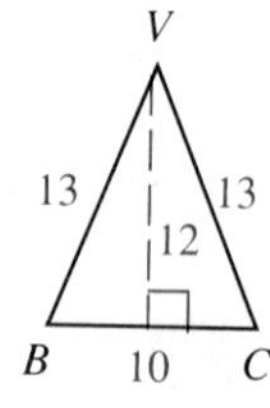

Solution The four lateral faces are congruent.

area of $\triangle VBC = \frac{1}{2} \cdot 10 \cdot 12 = 60$

lateral area = area of 4 lateral faces
= $4 \cdot$ area of $\triangle VBC$
= $4 \cdot 60 = 240$

Example 2 illustrates a simple method for finding the lateral area of a regular pyramid. It is Method 1, summarized below.

To find the lateral area of a **regular** pyramid with n lateral faces:

Method 1 Find the area of one lateral face and multiply by n.

Method 2 Use the formula L.A. $= \frac{1}{2}pl$, stated as the next theorem.

Theorem 12-3

The lateral area of a regular pyramid equals half the perimeter of the base times the slant height. (L.A. = $\frac{1}{2}pl$)

This formula is developed using Method 1 on the previous page. The area of one lateral face is $\frac{1}{2}bl$. Then:

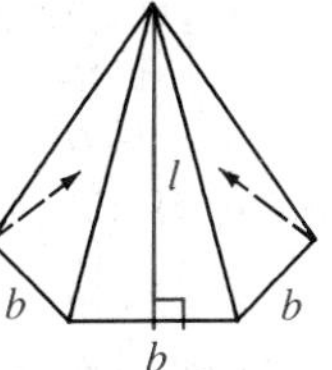

$$\text{L.A.} = (\tfrac{1}{2}bl)n = \tfrac{1}{2}(nb)l$$

Since $nb = p$, $\quad \text{L.A.} = \frac{1}{2}pl$

The prism and pyramid below have congruent bases and equal heights. Since the volume of the prism is Bh, the volume of the pyramid must be less than Bh. In fact, it is exactly $\frac{1}{3}Bh$. This result is stated as Theorem 12-4. Although no proof will be given, Classroom Exercise 1 and the Computer Key-In on pages 488–489 help justify the formula.

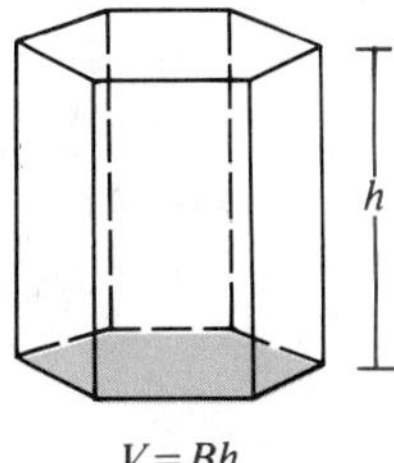

$V = Bh$

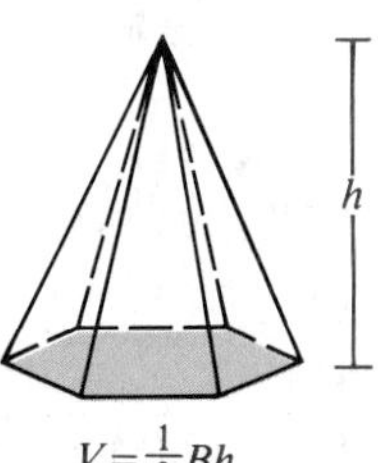

$V = \frac{1}{3}Bh$

Theorem 12-4

The volume of a pyramid equals one third the area of the base times the height of the pyramid. ($V = \frac{1}{3}Bh$)

Example 3 Suppose the regular hexagonal pyramid shown at the right above Theorem 12-4 has base edges 6 and height 12. Find its volume.

Solution Find the area of the hexagonal base.

Divide the base into six equilateral triangles. Find the area of one triangle and multiply by 6.

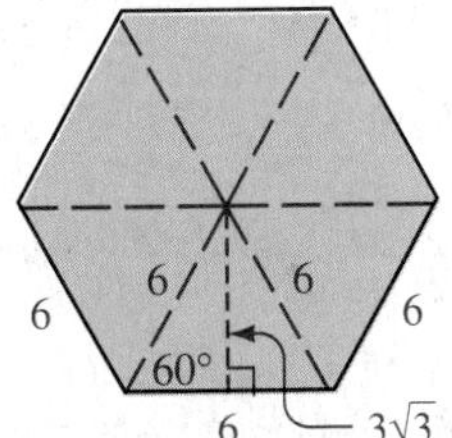

Base area $= B = 6(\frac{1}{2} \cdot 6 \cdot 3\sqrt{3}) = 54\sqrt{3}$

Then $V = \frac{1}{3}Bh = \frac{1}{3} \cdot 54\sqrt{3} \cdot 12 = 216\sqrt{3}$

Chalkboard Examples

A regular square pyramid has base edge 6 m and lateral edge 5 m. Complete.

1. Length of a slant height = 4 m
2. Lateral area = 48 m^2
3. Base area = 36 m^2
4. Total area = 84 m^2
5. Length of altitude = $\sqrt{7}$ m
6. Volume = $12\sqrt{7}$ m^3

A regular triangular pyramid has slant height 9 cm and base perimeter 12 cm.

7. Lateral area = 54 cm^2
8. Base area = $4\sqrt{3}$ cm^2
9. Total area = $(54 + 4\sqrt{3})$ cm^2
10. The height of a regular triangular pyramid is 6 cm, and the radius of the base is 8 cm. Find the base area and the volume of the pyramid. $48\sqrt{3}$ cm^2; $96\sqrt{3}$ cm^3

Making Connections

Point out the similarities between Theorem 12-3 and Theorem 11-6 on finding the area of a regular polygon. Ask students to justify the steps below Theorem 12-3.

Teaching Note

An alternate solution to Example 3 is the following. Notice that the apothem of the hexagon is $3\sqrt{3}$ and the perimeter of the hexagon is 36. Base area $= B = \frac{1}{2}ap = \frac{1}{2} \cdot 3\sqrt{3} \cdot 36 = 54\sqrt{3}$, the same value for B as in the Example.

Example 4 A regular triangular pyramid has lateral edge 10 and height 6. Find the **(a)** lateral area and **(b)** volume.

Solution

a. In rt. $\triangle VOA$, $AO = \sqrt{10^2 - 6^2} = \sqrt{64} = 8$.

Since $AO = \frac{2}{3}AM$ (why?), $\frac{2}{3}AM = 8$, $AM = 12$, and $OM = 4$.

$l = \sqrt{6^2 + 4^2} = \sqrt{52} = 2\sqrt{13}$

In 30°-60°-90° $\triangle AMC$, $CM = \frac{12}{\sqrt{3}} = \frac{12\sqrt{3}}{3} = 4\sqrt{3}$.

Base edge $= BC = 2 \cdot 4\sqrt{3} = 8\sqrt{3}$

L.A. $= \frac{1}{2}pl = \frac{1}{2}(3 \cdot 8\sqrt{3}) \cdot 2\sqrt{13} = 24\sqrt{39}$

b. Area of base $= B = \frac{1}{2} \cdot BC \cdot AM = \frac{1}{2} \cdot 8\sqrt{3} \cdot 12 = 48\sqrt{3}$

$V = \frac{1}{3}Bh = \frac{1}{3} \cdot 48\sqrt{3} \cdot 6 = 96\sqrt{3}$

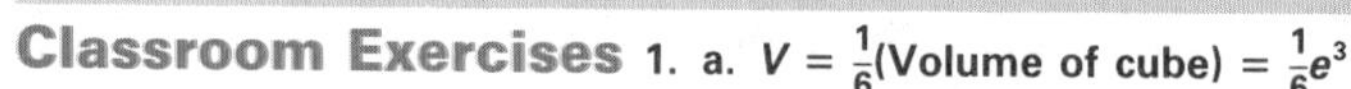

Classroom Exercises

1. a. $V = \frac{1}{6}$**(Volume of cube)** $= \frac{1}{6}e^3$

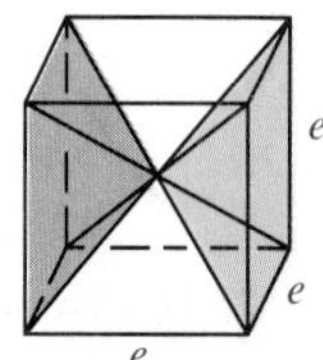

1. The diagonals of a cube intersect to divide the cube into six congruent pyramids as shown. The base of each pyramid is a face of the cube, and the height of each pyramid is $\frac{1}{2}e$.
   a. Use the formula for the volume of a cube to explain why the volume of each pyramid is $V = \frac{1}{6}e^3$. **See above.**
   b. Use the formula in part (a) to show that $V = \frac{1}{3}Bh$. (*Note*: This exercise shows that $V = \frac{1}{3}Bh$ gives the correct result for *these* pyramids.) $V = \frac{1}{6}e^3 = \frac{1}{3} \cdot \frac{1}{2} \cdot e^2 \cdot e = \frac{1}{3}(e^2)(\frac{1}{2}e) = \frac{1}{3}Bh$

***V-ABCD* is a regular square pyramid. Find numerical answers.**

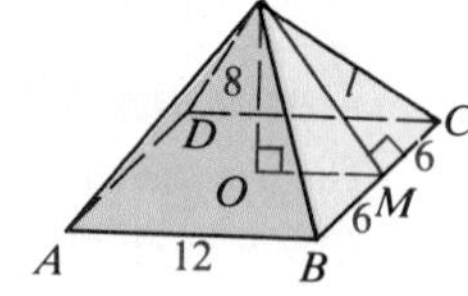

2. $OM = \underline{\ ?\ }$ **6**
3. $l = \underline{\ ?\ }$ **10**
4. Area of $\triangle VBC = \underline{\ ?\ }$ **60**
5. L.A. $= \underline{\ ?\ }$ **240**
6. Volume $= \underline{\ ?\ }$ **384**
7. $VC = \underline{\ ?\ }$ $\mathbf{2\sqrt{34}}$

Each edge of pyramid *V-XYZ* is 6 cm. Find numerical answers.

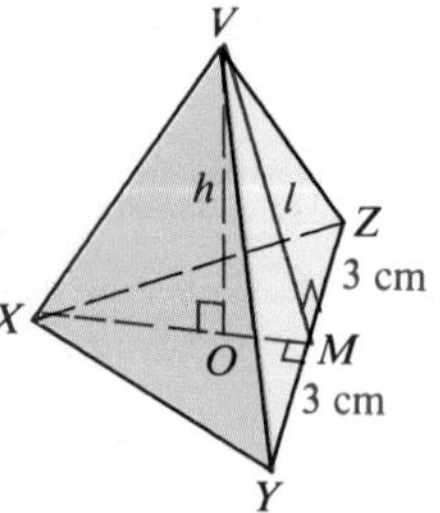

8. $XM = \underline{\ ?\ }$ $\mathbf{3\sqrt{3}}$ **cm**
9. $XO = \underline{\ ?\ }$ $\mathbf{2\sqrt{3}}$ **cm**
10. $h = \underline{\ ?\ }$ $\mathbf{2\sqrt{6}}$ **cm**
11. Base area $= \underline{\ ?\ }$ $\mathbf{9\sqrt{3}}$ **cm²**
12. Volume $= \underline{\ ?\ }$ $\mathbf{18\sqrt{2}}$ **cm³**
13. Slant height $= \underline{\ ?\ }$ $\mathbf{3\sqrt{3}}$ **cm**
14. L.A. $= \underline{\ ?\ }$ $\mathbf{27\sqrt{3}}$ **cm²**
15. T.A. $= \underline{\ ?\ }$ $\mathbf{36\sqrt{3}}$ **cm²**
16. Can the height of a regular pyramid be greater than the slant height? Explain. **No**
17. Can the slant height of a regular pyramid be greater than the length of a lateral edge? Explain. **No**
18. Can the area of the base of a regular pyramid be greater than the lateral area? Explain. **No; the apothem of the base is the leg of a rt. △ with hypotenuse *l*. Then $a < l$, $\frac{1}{2}ap < \frac{1}{2}pl$, and $B <$ L.A.**

Teaching Note

Review Theorem 10-4 concerning the concurrency of the medians of a triangle when discussing the explanation for $AO = \frac{2}{3}AM$. In a regular pyramid, the altitude meets the base at its center O. Since $\triangle ABC$ is equilateral, O is the point where its medians (which are also altitudes) meet. The medians of a △ intersect in a point that is $\frac{2}{3}$ of the distance from each vertex to the midpoint of the opposite side.

Additional Answers Classroom Exercises

16. The height is the length of a leg of a rt. △, and the slant height is the length of the hypotenuse. The length of the hypotenuse is always greater than the length of a leg.
17. The slant height is the length of a leg of a rt. △, and the lateral edge is the length of the hypotenuse. The length of the hypotenuse is always greater than the length of a leg.

Written Exercises

Copy and complete the table below for the regular square pyramid shown.

A

	1.	2.	3.	4.	5.	6.
height, *h*	4	12	24	?	?	6
slant height, *l*	5	13	?	12	5	?
base edge	?	?	14	?	8	?
lateral edge	?	?	?	15	?	10

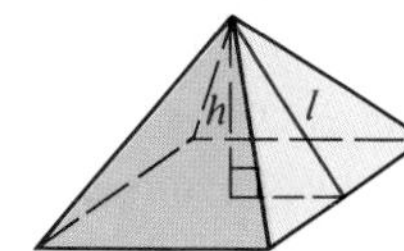

You can use the following three steps to sketch a square pyramid.

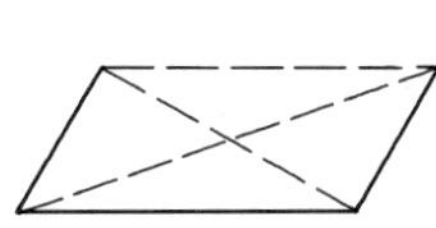

(1) Draw a parallelogram for the base and sketch the diagonals.

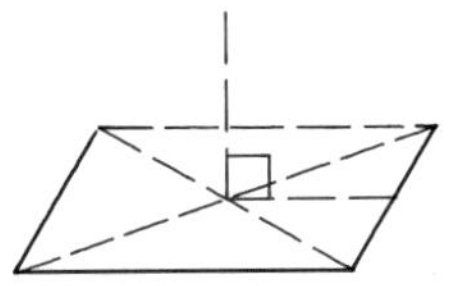

(2) Draw a vertical segment at the point where the diagonals intersect.

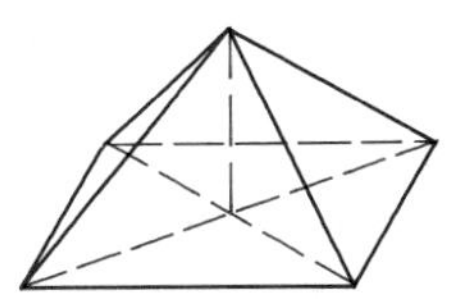

(3) Join the vertex to the base vertices.

Sketch each pyramid, as shown above. Then find its lateral area.

7. A regular triangular pyramid with base edge 4 and slant height 6 **36**
8. A regular pentagonal pyramid with base edge 1.5 and slant height 9 **33.75**
9. A regular square pyramid with base edge 12 and lateral edge 10 **192**
10. A regular hexagonal pyramid with base edge 10 and lateral edge 13 **360**

11. 60; 96; 48 13. 260; 360; 400 14. 480; 736; $\frac{256\sqrt{161}}{3}$

For Exercises 11–14 sketch each square pyramid described. Then find its lateral area, total area, and volume. See above.

320; 576; 512

11. base edge = 6, height = 4
12. base edge = 16, slant height = 10
13. height = 12, slant height = 13
14. base edge = 16, lateral edge = 17
15. A pyramid has a base area of 16 cm^2 and a volume of 32 cm^3. Find its height. **6 cm**
16. A regular octagonal pyramid has base edge 3 m and lateral area 60 m^2. Find its slant height. **5 m**

B

17. *V-ABCD* is a pyramid with a rectangular base 18 cm long and 10 cm wide. *O* is the center of the rectangle. The height, *VO*, of the pyramid is 12 cm.
    a. Find *VX* and *VY*. **15 cm; 13 cm**
    b. Find the lateral area of the pyramid. (Why can't you use the formula L.A. = $\frac{1}{2}pl$?) **384 cm^2 (*V-ABCD* is not regular.)**

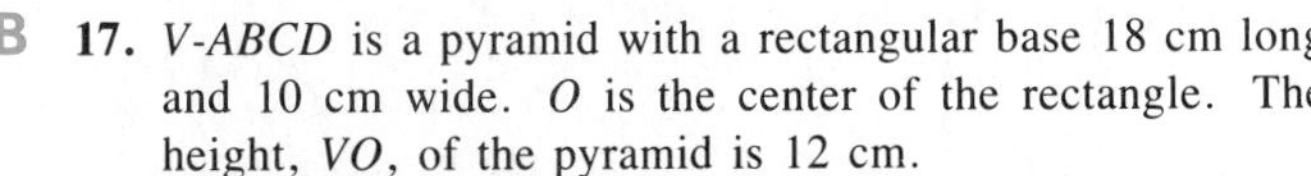

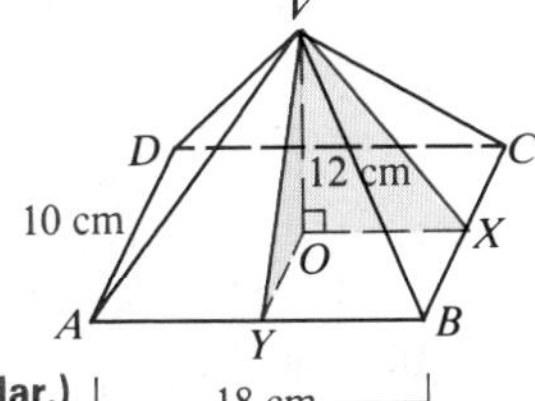

Additional Answers Written Exercises

1. base edge = 6; lat. edge = $\sqrt{34}$
2. base edge = 10; lat. edge = $\sqrt{194}$
3. l = 25; lat. edge = $\sqrt{674}$
4. $h = 3\sqrt{7}$; base edge = 18
5. h = 3; lat. edge = $\sqrt{41}$
6. $l = 2\sqrt{17}$; base edge = $8\sqrt{2}$

Guided Practice

Copy and complete the table for the regular triangular pyramid.

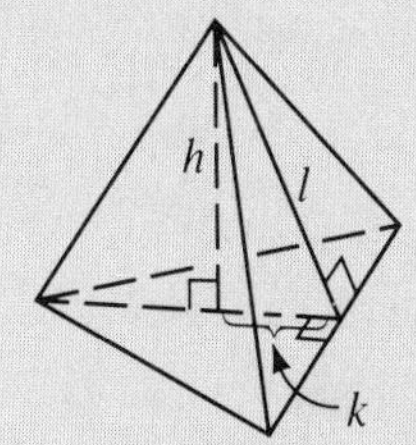

	1.	2.
k	3	5
height, h	4	12
slant height, l	5	13
base edge	$6\sqrt{3}$	$10\sqrt{3}$
lateral edge	$2\sqrt{13}$	$2\sqrt{61}$
lateral area	$45\sqrt{3}$	$195\sqrt{3}$
total area	$72\sqrt{3}$	$270\sqrt{3}$
volume	$36\sqrt{3}$	$300\sqrt{3}$

3. Find the lateral area, total area, and volume of a square pyramid with base edge 8 cm and height 4 cm.
   $64\sqrt{2}$ cm^2;
   $(64 + 64\sqrt{2})$ cm^2; $\frac{256}{3}$ cm^3

18. Find the height and the volume of a regular hexagonal pyramid with lateral edges 10 ft and base edges 6 ft. **8 ft; $144\sqrt{3}$ ft³**

19. The shaded pyramid in the diagram is cut from a rectangular solid. How does the volume of the pyramid compare with the volume of the rectangular solid? **See below.**

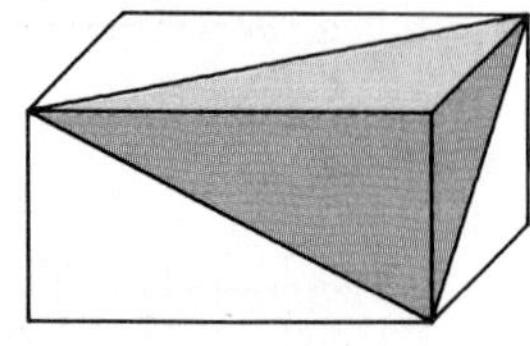

Ex. 19

20. A pyramid and a prism both have height 8.2 cm and congruent hexagonal bases with area 22.3 cm². Give the ratio of their volumes. (*Hint*: You do *not* need to calculate their volumes.) **1:3**

19. Volume of pyramid = $\frac{1}{6}$(volume of rectangular solid)

Exercises 21–25 refer to the regular triangular pyramid shown below.

21. If $AM = 9$ and $VA = 10$, find h and l. **8; $\sqrt{73}$**

22. a. If $BC = 6$, find AM and AO. **$3\sqrt{3}$; $2\sqrt{3}$**
    b. If $BC = 6$ and $VA = 4$, find h and l. **2; $\sqrt{7}$**

23. a. If $h = 4$ and $l = 5$, find OM, OA, and BC. **3; 6; $6\sqrt{3}$**
    b. Find the lateral area and the volume. **$45\sqrt{3}$; $36\sqrt{3}$**

24. If $VA = 5$ and $h = 3$, find the slant height, the lateral area, and the volume. **$\sqrt{13}$; $6\sqrt{39}$; $12\sqrt{3}$**

25. If $AB = 12$ and $VA = 10$, find the lateral area and the volume. **144; $24\sqrt{39}$**

V, h, l, C, A, O, M, B

26. Find the volume of a regular hexagonal pyramid with height 8 cm and base edges 6 cm. **$144\sqrt{3}$ cm³**

27. Use trigonometry to find the volume of the regular pyramid below to the nearest cubic unit. **about 66 cubic units**

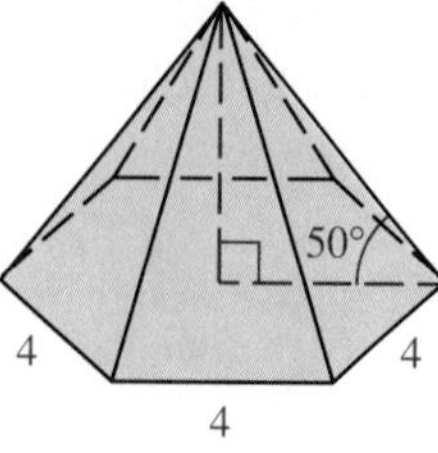

Ex. 27

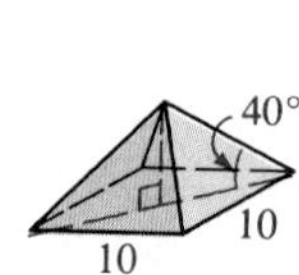

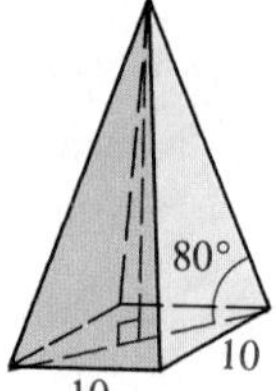

Ex. 28

28. Show that the ratio of the volumes of the two regular square pyramids shown above is $\frac{\tan 40°}{\tan 80°}$.

C 29. All the edges of a regular triangular pyramid are x units long. Find the volume of the pyramid in terms of x. **$\frac{x^3\sqrt{2}}{12}$**

30. The base of a pyramid is a regular hexagon with sides y cm long. The lateral edges are $2y$ cm long. Find the volume of the pyramid in terms of y. **$\frac{3y^3}{2}$ cm³**

31. Use a calculator and trigonometry to find the volume of the regular square pyramid shown to the nearest cubic unit. **246**

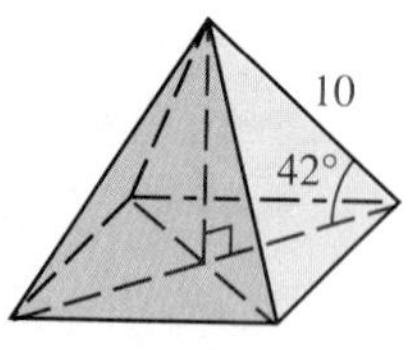

Ex. 31

Additional Answers
Written Exercises

28. $\frac{V_1}{V_2} = \frac{\frac{1}{3}10^2 \cdot h_1}{\frac{1}{3}10^2 \cdot h_2} = \frac{h_1}{h_2} = \frac{5\sqrt{2}\tan 40°}{5\sqrt{2}\tan 80°} = \frac{\tan 40°}{\tan 80°}$

★ **32.** Different pyramids are inscribed in two identical cubes, as shown below.
a. Which pyramid has the greater volume? **They have the same volume.**
b. Which pyramid has the greater total area? ***F-ABCD***

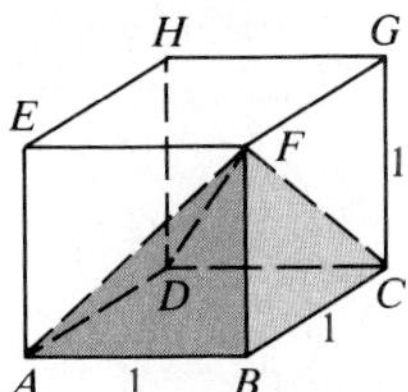

Pyramid *F-ABCD*

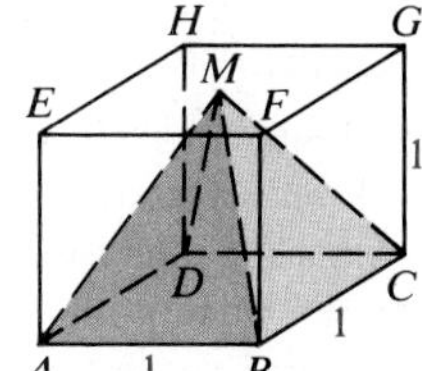

Pyramid *M-ABCD* has vertex *M* at the center of square *EFGH*.

Challenge **2.** $x + y + z = h$

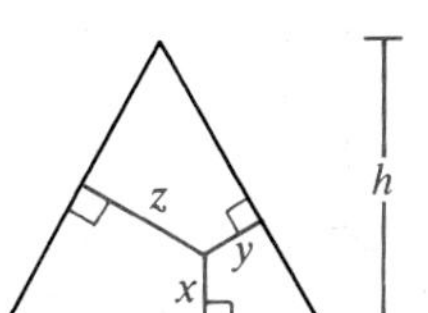

1. Accurately draw or construct a large equilateral triangle. Choose any point inside the triangle and carefully measure the distances x, y, z, and h. Then find $x + y + z$.

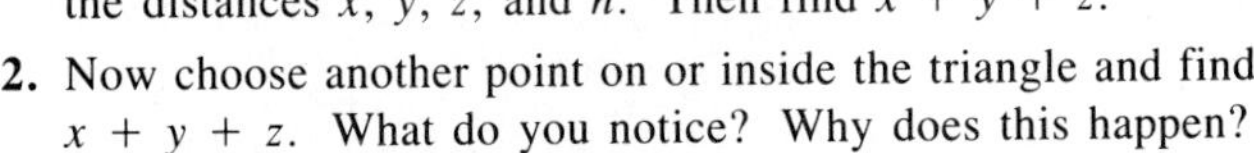

2. Now choose another point on or inside the triangle and find $x + y + z$. What do you notice? Why does this happen?

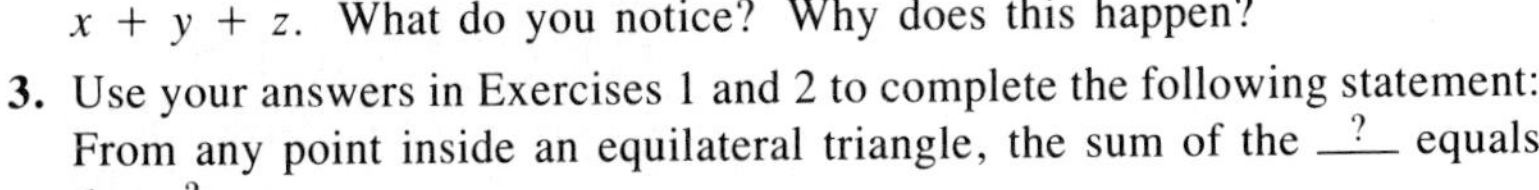

3. Use your answers in Exercises 1 and 2 to complete the following statement: From any point inside an equilateral triangle, the sum of the _?_ equals the _?_.

4. Generalize the statement in Exercise 3 from two dimensions to three dimensions.

Mixed Review Exercises

Copy and complete the table for circles.

	1.	2.	3.	4.	5.	6.	7.	8.
Radius	6	11	$\frac{1}{2}$	$3\sqrt{3}$	?	?	?	?
Circumference	?	?	?	?	10π	18π	?	?
Area	?	?	?	?	?	?	49π	15π

Draw a diagram for each exercise.

9. A circle is inscribed in a square with sides 24 mm. Find **(a)** the area of the circle and **(b)** the area of the square. **a.** 144π **mm²** **b. 576 mm²**

10. A square is inscribed in a circle with diameter $8\sqrt{2}$. Find **(a)** the perimeter of the square and **(b)** the circumference of the circle. **a. 32** **b.** $8\sqrt{2}\pi$

Additional Answers Challenge

3. lengths of the ⊥ segs. from the pt. to the sides; height of the △.
4. From any pt. inside a regular triangular pyramid with all edges ≅, the sum of the lengths of the ⊥ segs. to the faces = the height of the pyramid.

Additional Answers Mixed Review Exercises

1. $C = 12\pi$; $A = 36\pi$
2. $C = 22\pi$; $A = 121\pi$
3. $C = \pi$; $A = \frac{\pi}{4}$
4. $C = 6\pi\sqrt{3}$; $A = 27\pi$
5. $r = 5$; $A = 25\pi$
6. $r = 9$; $A = 81\pi$
7. $r = 7$; $C = 14\pi$
8. $r = \sqrt{15}$; $C = 2\pi\sqrt{15}$

♦ Calculator Key-In

The Great Pyramid of King Cheops has a square base with sides 755 feet long. The original height was 481 feet, but the top part of the pyramid, which was 31 feet in height, has been destroyed. Approximately what percent of the original volume remains? Answer to the nearest hundredth of a percent. $\approx$ **99.97%**

Using a Computer

The technique of analyzing slices of solids in order to solve more complex problems is historically important and interesting. Students who go on to study calculus will encounter this method again.

The computer allows students to explore this method and other methods that they could not otherwise explore since the calculations would be too unwieldy to do by hand.

Cultural Note

The Great Pyramid of King Cheops (or Khufu) was built over 4,500 years ago. The Egyptian builders of the pyramid were extremely exact in their measurements. For example, the right angles that make up the four corners of the base of the pyramid are never off by more than 12 seconds of a degree.

♦ Computer Key-In

The earliest pyramids, which were built about 2750 B.C., are called *step pyramids* because the lateral faces are not triangles but a series of great stone steps. To find the volume of such a pyramid it is necessary to find the sum of the volumes of the steps, or layers. Each layer is a rectangular solid with a square base.

Let us consider a pyramid with base edges 10 and height 10. Suppose that this pyramid is made up of 10 steps with equal heights. The top layer is a cube (base edges equal the height), and the base edge for each succeeding layer increases by an amount equal to the height of a layer. As the left side of the diagram at the bottom of this page shows, the height of each step is $\frac{10}{10} = 1$, and the volume of the top layer is $V_1 = Bh = (1^2) \cdot 1 = 1$. The volumes of the second and third layers are $V_2 = (2^2) \cdot 1 = 4$ and $V_3 = (3^2) \cdot 1 = 9$, respectively. Continuing in this way, the total volume of the pyramid is:

$$V = 1^2 \cdot 1 + 2^2 \cdot 1 + 3^2 \cdot 1 + 4^2 \cdot 1 + \cdots + 9^2 \cdot 1 + 10^2 \cdot 1 = 385$$

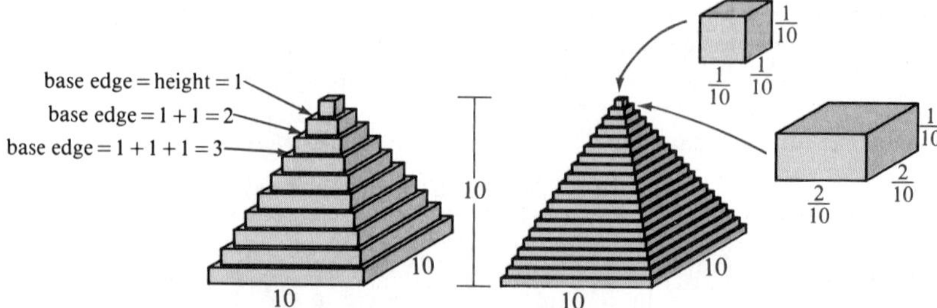

Now consider another pyramid with the same base and height but having 100 steps instead of 10 steps. The height of each layer is $\frac{10}{100} = \frac{1}{10}$, and the volume of each layer is computed using the formula $V = Bh$:

$$\text{Volume of top layer} = \left(\frac{1}{10}\right)^2 \cdot \frac{1}{10}$$

$$\text{Volume of second layer} = \left(2 \cdot \frac{1}{10}\right)^2 \cdot \frac{1}{10} = \left(\frac{2}{10}\right)^2 \cdot \frac{1}{10}$$

$$\text{Volume of third layer} = \left(3 \cdot \frac{1}{10}\right)^2 \cdot \frac{1}{10} = \left(\frac{3}{10}\right)^2 \cdot \frac{1}{10}$$

$$\vdots \qquad\qquad \vdots$$

$$\text{Volume of 99th layer} = \left(99 \cdot \frac{1}{10}\right)^2 \cdot \frac{1}{10} = \left(\frac{99}{10}\right)^2 \cdot \frac{1}{10}$$

$$\text{Volume of 100th layer} = \left(100 \cdot \frac{1}{10}\right)^2 \cdot \frac{1}{10} = \left(\frac{100}{10}\right)^2 \cdot \frac{1}{10}$$

Thus, the volume of the pyramid is:

$$V = \left(\frac{1}{10}\right)^2 \cdot \frac{1}{10} + \left(\frac{2}{10}\right)^2 \cdot \frac{1}{10} + \left(\frac{3}{10}\right)^2 \cdot \frac{1}{10} + \cdots + \left(\frac{99}{10}\right)^2 \cdot \frac{1}{10} + \left(\frac{100}{10}\right)^2 \cdot \frac{1}{10}$$

The following computer program finds the total volume for the given pyramid with N steps.

```
10  LET V = 0
20  PRINT "HOW MANY STEPS ARE THERE";
30  INPUT N
40  LET H = 10/N
50  FOR X = 1 TO N
60  LET V = V + (X * H) ↑2 * H
70  NEXT X
80  PRINT "VOLUME OF PYRAMID WITH ";N;" STEPS IS ";V
90  END
```

Exercises

1. RUN the given program to verify the volume of the 10-step pyramid and to find the volume of the 100-step pyramid. **338.35**

2. a. Suppose that another pyramid with the same base and height has 1000 steps. RUN the program to find the volume. **333.8335**

b. Make a chart that shows the volume for the given number of steps: 10, 100, 500, 750, 900, 1000.

c. As the number of steps increases, what value do the volumes seem to be approaching? **Answers may vary; $333.\overline{33}$**

d. What is the volume of a regular square pyramid with base edge of 10 and height 10? **$333.\overline{33}$**

e. What can you conclude from comparing the answers to parts (b)–(d)?
As the number of steps increase, the volume of the step pyramid approaches the volume of the regular square pyramid.

Cultural Note

The step pyramid shown on page 488 is the Pyramid of Kulkulkan, part of the ancient Mayan city of Chichen Itza. Chichen Itza was founded around the middle of the 5th century A.D. in what is now the Yucatan Peninsula in Mexico. The Mayan civilization is noted for its advancements in astronomy and mathematics. The Mayan number system, for example, made use of place value and had a symbol for zero. This number system proved instrumental in astronomical calculations and in developing a very precise calendar system.

Additional Answers
Computer Key-In

2.b.

No. of steps	Volume
10	385
100	338.35
500	334.334
750	334.000296
900	333.889095
1000	333.8335

Using a Computer

If the student has enough computer time (or a fast computer), extend the steps in Ex. 2(b) to also include 5000, 10,000, and 15,000. This will show better that the volume approaches the answer in Ex. 2(c).

Teaching Suggestions, pp. T129–T130

Objective
Presenting the Lesson
Making Connections
Using Technology

Communication Skills, p. T129

Cooperative Learning, pp. T129–T130

Exploring Activity, p. 473c

Supplementary Materials

Practice Master 73; Test 47
Resource Book, pp. 78, 156
Study Guide, pp. 157–158
Overhead Visual 8

Lesson Focus

Four theorems are stated that give formulas for finding the lateral area and volume of both cylinders and cones.

Suggested Assignments

Minimum
Day 1: 492/1, 3, 5–8
S 486/18, 21
Day 2: 493/9–14, 16–19, 21
Day 3: 493/15, 20
496/Self-Test 1

Average
Day 1: 492–493/3, 5–8, 10, 11, 13, 16, 17
Day 2: 493–494/18–21, 23, 24, 26
Day 3: 494/25, 27
496/Self-Test 1

Maximum
Day 1: 492–493/7, 8, 12–14, 16, 17
S 486/28, 30
Day 2: 493–494/19–21, 23, 25, 26
Day 3: 494–495/27–39

12-3 *Cylinders and Cones*

A **cylinder** is like a prism except that its bases are circles instead of polygons. In a **right cylinder,** the segment joining the centers of the circular bases is an **altitude.** The length of an altitude is called the *height*, h, of the cylinder. A radius of a base is also called a **radius,** r, of the cylinder.

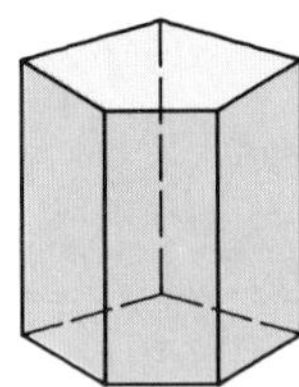
Right prism

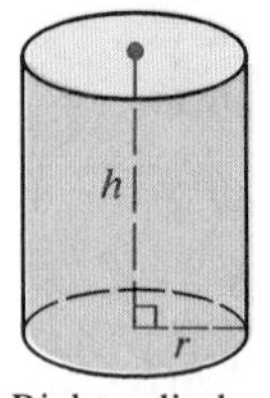

Right cylinder

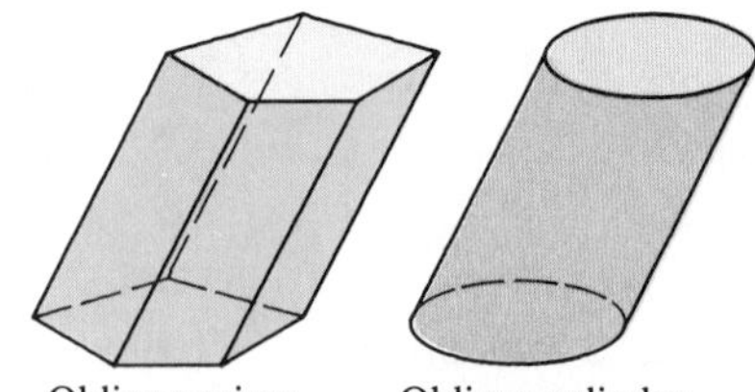
Oblique prism Oblique cylinder

The diagrams above show the relationship between prisms and cylinders. In the discussion and exercises that follow, the word "cylinder" will always refer to a right cylinder.

It is not surprising that the formulas for cylinders are related to those for prisms: L.A. $= ph$ and $V = Bh$. Since the base of a cylinder is a circle, we substitute $2\pi r$ for p and πr^2 for B and get the following formulas.

Theorem 12-5

The lateral area of a cylinder equals the circumference of a base times the height of the cylinder. (L.A. $= 2\pi rh$)

Theorem 12-6

The volume of a cylinder equals the area of a base times the height of the cylinder. ($V = \pi r^2 h$)

A **cone** is like a pyramid except that its base is a circle instead of a polygon. The relationship between pyramids and cones is shown in the diagrams below.

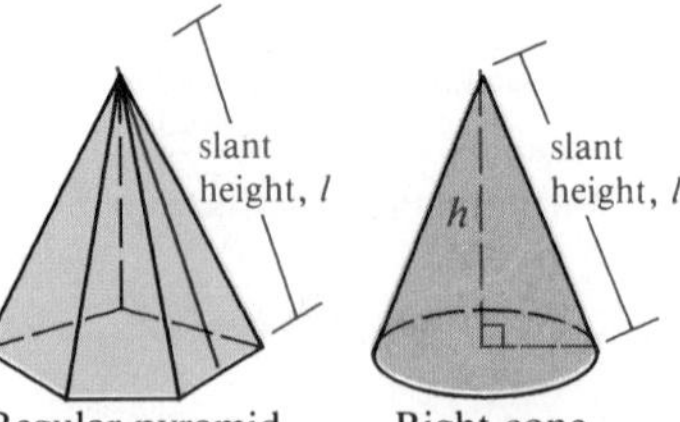

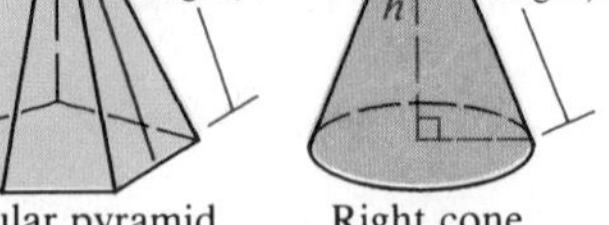
Regular pyramid Right cone

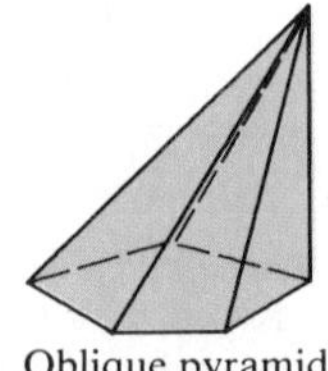
Oblique pyramid

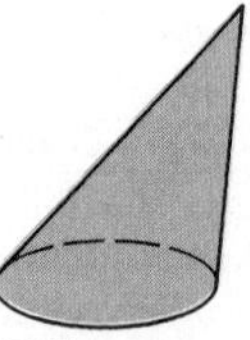
Oblique cone

Note that "slant height" applies only to a regular pyramid and a right cone. We will use the word "cone" to refer to a right cone.

The formulas for cones are related to those for pyramids: L.A. $= \frac{1}{2}pl$ and $V = \frac{1}{3}Bh$. Since the base of a cone is a circle, we again substitute $2\pi r$ for p and πr^2 for B and get the following formulas.

Theorem 12-7

The lateral area of a cone equals half the circumference of the base times the slant height. (L.A. $= \frac{1}{2} \cdot 2\pi r \cdot l$, or L.A. $= \pi rl$)

Theorem 12-8

The volume of a cone equals one third the area of the base times the height of the cone. ($V = \frac{1}{3}\pi r^2 h$)

So far our study of solids has not included formulas for oblique solids. The volume formulas for cylinders and cones, but *not* the area formulas, can be used for the corresponding oblique solids. (See the Extra on pages 516–517.)

Example 1 A cylinder has radius 5 cm and height 4 cm. Find the **(a)** lateral area, **(b)** total area, and **(c)** volume of the cylinder.

Solution

a. L.A. $= 2\pi rh = 2\pi \cdot 5 \cdot 4 = 40\pi$ (cm^2)

b. T.A. $=$ L.A. $+ 2B$
$= 40\pi + 2(\pi \cdot 5^2) = 90\pi$ (cm^2)

c. $V = \pi r^2 h = \pi \cdot 5^2 \cdot 4 = 100\pi$ (cm^3)

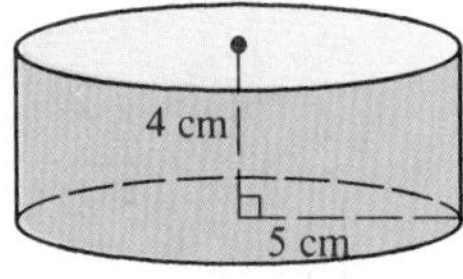

Example 2 Find the **(a)** lateral area, **(b)** total area, and **(c)** volume of the cone shown.

Solution

a. First use the Pythagorean Theorem to find l.
$l = \sqrt{6^2 + 3^2} = \sqrt{45} = 3\sqrt{5}$
L.A. $= \pi rl = \pi \cdot 3 \cdot 3\sqrt{5} = 9\pi\sqrt{5}$

b. T.A. $=$ L.A. $+ B = 9\pi\sqrt{5} + \pi \cdot 3^2 = 9\pi\sqrt{5} + 9\pi$

c. $V = \frac{1}{3}\pi r^2 h = \frac{1}{3}\pi \cdot 3^2 \cdot 6 = 18\pi$

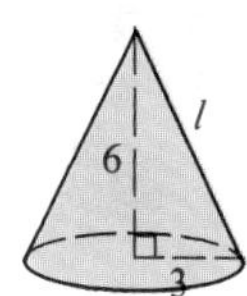

Classroom Exercises

1. **a.** When the label of a soup can is cut off and laid flat, it is a rectangular piece of paper. (See the diagram below.) How are the length and width of this rectangle related to r and h? **length = $2\pi r$; width = h**
   b. What is the area of this rectangle? **$2\pi rh$**

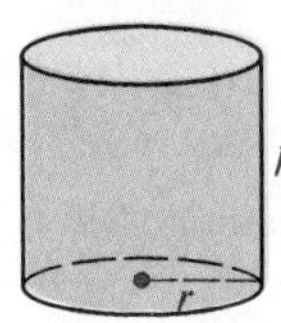

Chalkboard Examples

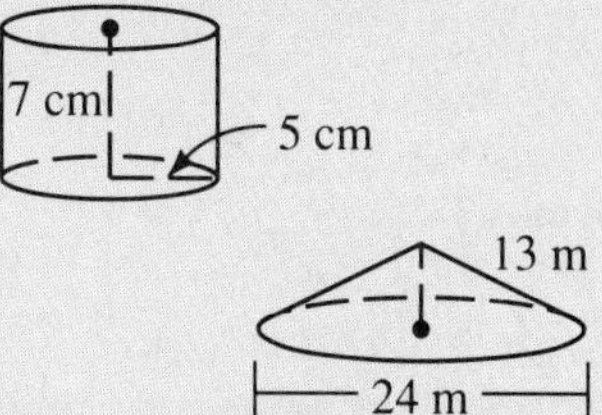

Refer to the diagrams above and complete the chart. Leave answers in terms of π.

		Cylinder	Cone
1.	B	25π cm^2	144π m^2
2.	L.A.	70π cm^2	156π m^2
3.	T.A.	120π cm^2	300π m^2
4.	V	175π cm^3	240π m^3

5. A cone with radius 6 cm and height 12 cm is filled to capacity with liquid. Find the minimum height of a cylinder with radius 4 cm that will hold the same amount of liquid. 9 cm

6. A right cone and a right cylinder have equal base areas. The height of the cylinder is four times the height of the cone. Compare their volumes. The volume of the cylinder is twelve times that of the cone.

Using a Calculator

See the Calculator Key-In on page 496 for an application and extension of the result in Classroom Ex. 1.

2. **a.** Find the lateral areas of cylinders I, II, and III. **24π; 48π; 48π**
   b. Notice that the height of II is twice the height of I. Is the lateral area of II twice the lateral area of I? **Yes**
   c. Notice that the radius of III is twice the radius of I. Is the lateral area of III twice the lateral area of I? **Yes**

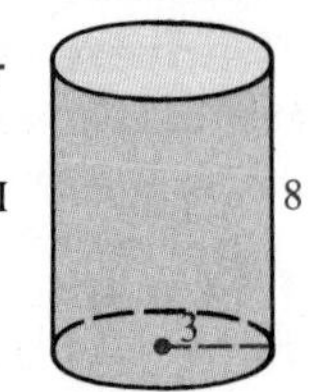

3. **a.** Find the total areas of cylinders I, II, and III. **42π; 66π; 120π**
   b. Are the ratios of the total areas the same as those of the lateral areas in Exercise 2? **No**
4. **a.** Find the volumes of cylinders I, II, and III. **36π; 72π; 144π**
   b. Notice that the height of II is twice the height of I. Is the volume of II twice the volume of I? **Yes**
   c. Notice that the radius of III is twice the radius of I. Is the volume of III twice the volume of I? **No**

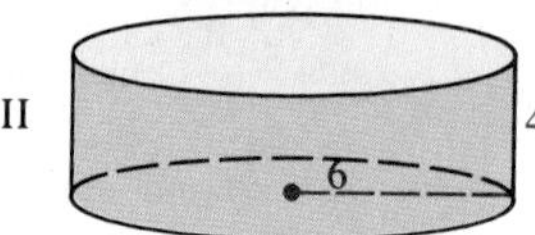

Complete the table for the cone shown.

	r	h	l	L.A.	T.A.	V
5.	3	4	?	?	?	?
6.	?	12	13	?	?	?
7.	6 cm	?	10 cm	?	?	?

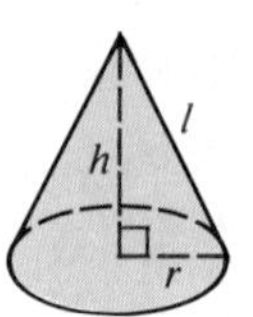

8. Describe the intersection of a plane and a cone if the plane is the perpendicular bisector of the altitude of the cone. **A ⊙ that is parallel to the base and has radius = $\frac{1}{2}$(radius of the base).**

Written Exercises

You can use the following three steps to sketch a cylinder.

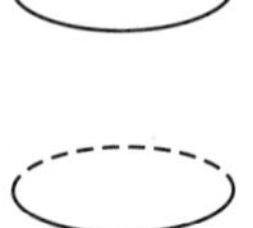

(1) Draw two congruent ovals, one above the other.

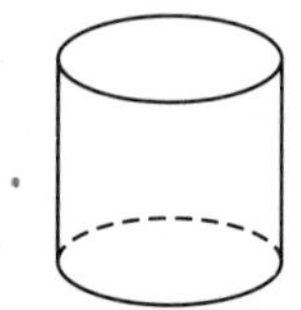

(2) Join the ovals with two vertical segments.

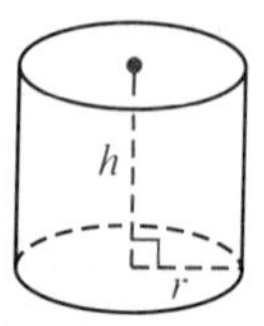

(3) Draw in the altitude and a radius.

Sketch each cylinder. Then find its lateral area, total area, and volume. See below.

A 1. $r = 4$; $h = 5$ 2. $r = 8$; $h = 10$ 3. $r = 4$; $h = 3$ 4. $r = 8$; $h = 15$

5. The volume of a cylinder is 64π. If $r = h$, find r. **4**
6. The lateral area of a cylinder is 18π. If $h = 6$, find r. **1.5**
7. The volume of a cylinder is 72π. If $h = 8$, find the lateral area. **48π**
8. The total area of a cylinder is 100π. If $r = h$, find r. **5**

1. 40π; 72π; 80π 2. 160π; 288π; 640π
3. 24π; 56π; 48π 4. 240π; 368π; 960π

Additional Answers
Classroom Exercises

5. $l = 5$; L.A. $= 15\pi$; T.A. $= 24\pi$; $V = 12\pi$
6. $r = 5$; L.A. $= 65\pi$; T.A. $= 90\pi$; $V = 100\pi$
7. $h = 8$ cm; L.A. $= 60\pi$ cm^2; T.A. $= 96\pi$ cm^2; $V = 96\pi$ cm^3

Guided Practice

Copy and complete the table for the cylinder shown.

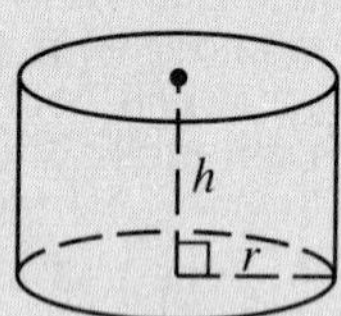

	r	h	L.A.	T.A.	V
1.	5	10	100π	150π	250π
2.	$\sqrt{7}$	3	$6\pi\sqrt{7}$	$(6\sqrt{7} + 14)\pi$	21π
3.	4	12	96π	128π	192π

Copy and complete the table for the cone shown.

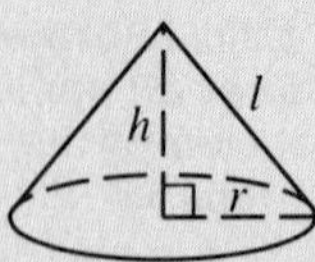

	r	h	l	L.A.	T.A.	V
4.	5	12	13	65π	90π	100π
5.	8	15	17	136π	200π	320π
6.	$\sqrt{2}$	3	$\sqrt{11}$	$\pi\sqrt{22}$	$(2 + \sqrt{22})\pi$	2π

You can use the following three steps to sketch a cone.

(1) Draw an oval and a vertex point over the center of the oval.

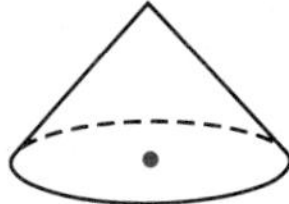

(2) Join the vertex to the oval, as shown.

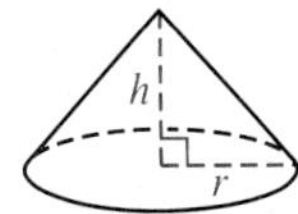

(3) Draw in the altitude and a radius.

Sketch each cone. Copy and complete the table.

	r	h	l	L.A.	T.A.	V
9.	4	3	?	?	?	?
10.	8	6	?	?	?	?
11.	12	?	13	?	?	?
12.	?	2	6	?	?	?
13.	?	?	15	180π	?	?
14.	21	?	?	609π	?	?
15.	15	?	?	?	?	600π
16.	9	?	?	?	?	324π

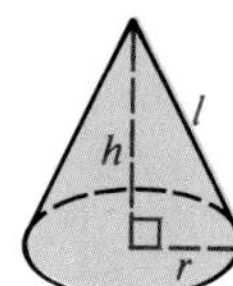

17. In Exercises 9 and 10, the ratio of the radii is $\frac{4}{8}$, or $\frac{1}{2}$, and the ratio of the heights is $\frac{3}{6}$, or $\frac{1}{2}$. Use the answers you found for these two exercises to determine the ratios of the following:
a. lateral areas **1:4** **b.** total areas **1:4** **c.** volumes **1:8**

18. A manufacturer needs to decide which container to use for packaging a product. One container is twice as wide as another but only half as tall. Which container holds more, or do they hold the same amount? Guess first and then calculate the ratio of their volumes. **Wider one holds more; 2:1**

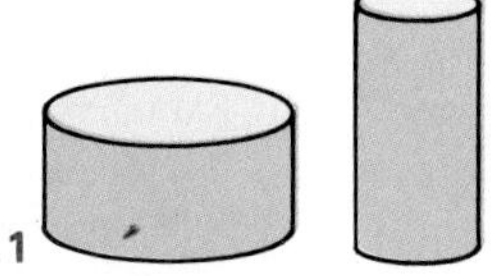

19. A cone and a cylinder both have height 48 and radius 15. Give the ratio of their volumes without calculating the two volumes. **1:3**

B **20. a.** Guess which contains more, the can or the bottle. (Assume that the top part of the bottle is a complete cone.) **can**

b. See if your guess is right by finding the volumes of both. **can: 62.5π cm³; bottle: 48π cm³**

21. A solid metal cylinder with radius 6 cm and height 18 cm is melted down and recast as a solid cone with radius 9 cm. Find the height of the cone. **24 cm**

Ex. 20

Additional Answers
Written Exercises

9. $l = 5$; L.A. $= 20\pi$; T.A. $= 36\pi$; $V = 16\pi$

10. $l = 10$; L.A. $= 80\pi$; T.A. $= 144\pi$; $V = 128\pi$

11. $h = 5$; L.A. $= 156\pi$; T.A. $= 300\pi$; $V = 240\pi$

12. $r = 4\sqrt{2}$; L.A. $= 24\pi\sqrt{2}$; T.A. $= 24\pi\sqrt{2} + 32\pi$; $V = \frac{64\pi}{3}$

13. $r = 12$; $h = 9$; T.A. $= 324\pi$; $V = 432\pi$

14. $h = 20$; $l = 29$; T.A. $= 1050\pi$; $V = 2940\pi$

15. $h = 8$; $l = 17$; L.A. $= 255\pi$; T.A. $= 480\pi$

16. $h = 12$; $l = 15$; L.A. $= 135\pi$; T.A. $= 216\pi$

22. A pipe is 2 m long and has inside radius 5 cm and outside radius 6 cm. Find the volume of metal contained in the pipe to the nearest cubic centimeter. Use $\pi \approx 3.14$. **6908 cm³**

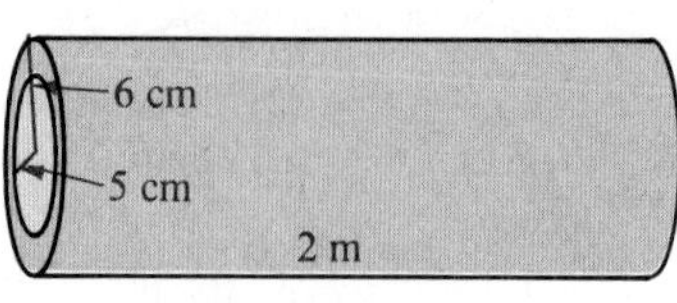

Ex. 22

5.2 m
6.8 m

Ex. 23

23. Water is pouring into a conical (cone-shaped) reservoir at the rate of 1.8 m^3 per minute. Find, to the nearest minute, the number of minutes it will take to fill the reservoir. Use $\pi \approx 3.14$. **25 minutes**

24. Two water pipes of the same length have inside diameters of 6 cm and 8 cm. These two pipes are replaced by a single pipe of the same length, which has the same capacity as the smaller pipes combined. What is the inside diameter of the new pipe? **10 cm**

25. The total area of a cylinder is 40π. If $h = 8$, find r. **2**

26. The total area of a cylinder is 90π. If $h = 12$, find r. **3**

27. In rectangle $ABCD$, $AB = 10$ and $AD = 6$.

a. The rectangle is rotated in space about $\overline{AB}$. Describe the solid that is formed and find its volume. **cylinder with $r = 6$, $h = 10$; $V = 360\pi$**

b. Answer part (a) if the rectangle is rotated about $\overline{AD}$. **See below.**

28. a. The segment joining (0, 0) and (4, 3) is rotated about the x-axis, forming the lateral surface of a cone. Find the lateral area and the volume of this cone. **15π; 12π**

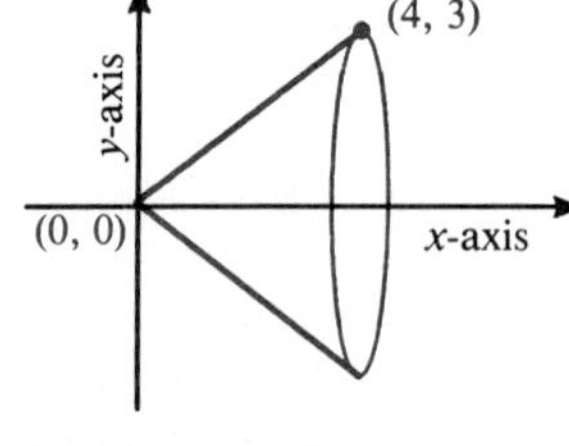

b. Sketch the cone that would be formed if the segment had been rotated about the y-axis. Find the lateral area and the volume of this cone. **20π; 16π**

c. Are your answers to parts (a) and (b) the same? **No**

Exercise Note

Ex. 29 is the first time that inscribed solids are discussed. Ask students how they would define such solids.

29. Each prism shown below is inscribed in a cylinder with height 10 and radius 6. Find the volume and lateral area of each prism.

a.

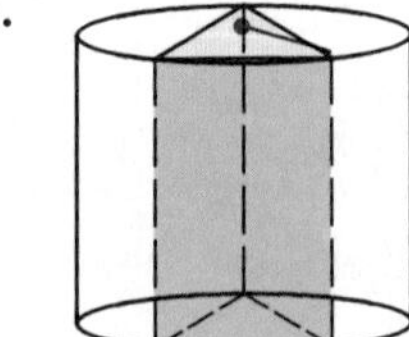

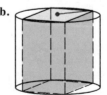

Base is an equilateral triangle.
$V = 270\sqrt{3}$; L.A. $= 180\sqrt{3}$

b.

Base is a square.
$V = 720$; L.A. $= 240\sqrt{2}$

c.

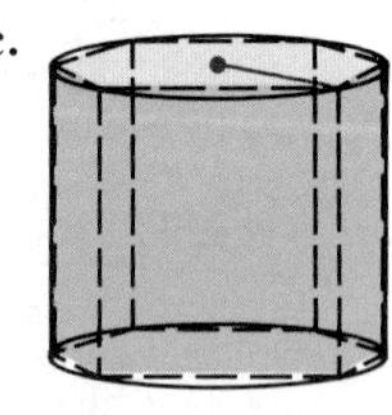

Base is a regular hexagon.
$V = 540\sqrt{3}$; L.A. $= 360$

27. b. cylinder with $r = 10$, $h = 6$; $V = 600\pi$

30. An equilateral triangle with 6 cm sides is rotated about an altitude. Draw a diagram and find the volume of the solid formed. **$9\sqrt{3}\pi$ cm^3**

31. A square is rotated in space about a side s. Describe the solid formed and find its volume in terms of s. **πs^3**

32. A cylinder with height 10 and radius 6 is inscribed in a square prism. Make a sketch. Then find the volume of the prism. **1440**

33. A regular square pyramid with base edge 4 cm is inscribed in a cone with height 6 cm. What is the volume of the cone? **16π cm^3**

34. A regular square pyramid is inscribed in a cone with radius 4 cm and height 4 cm.

a. What is the volume of the pyramid? **$42\frac{2}{3}$ cm^3**

b. Find the slant heights of the cone and the pyramid. **$4\sqrt{2}$ cm; $2\sqrt{6}$ cm**

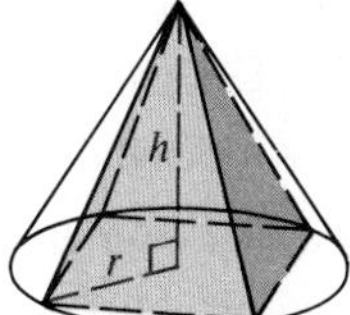

Exs. 33, 34

35. A cone is inscribed in a regular square pyramid with slant height 9 cm and base edge 6 cm. Make a sketch. Then find the volume of the cone. **$18\sqrt{2}\pi$ cm^3**

36. The lateral area of a cone is three-fifths the total area. Find the ratio of the radius and the slant height. **2:3**

C **37.** A regular hexagonal pyramid with base edge 6 and height 8 is inscribed in a cone. Find the lateral areas of the cone and the pyramid. **60π; $18\sqrt{91}$**

38. A 120° sector is cut out of a circular piece of tin with radius 6 in. and bent to form the lateral surface of a cone. What is the volume of the cone? **$\frac{16\sqrt{2}\pi}{3}$ in.^{3}**

39. In $\triangle ABC$, $AB = 15$, $AC = 20$, and $BC = 25$. The triangle is rotated in space about $\overline{BC}$. Find the volume of the solid formed. **1200π**

40. An equilateral triangle with sides of length s is rotated in space about one side. Show that the volume of the solid formed is $\frac{1}{4}\pi s^3$.

Challenge

A piece of wood contains a square hole, a circular hole, and a triangular hole, as shown. Explain how one block of wood in the shape of a cube with 2 cm edges can be cut down so that it can pass through, and exactly fit, all three holes.

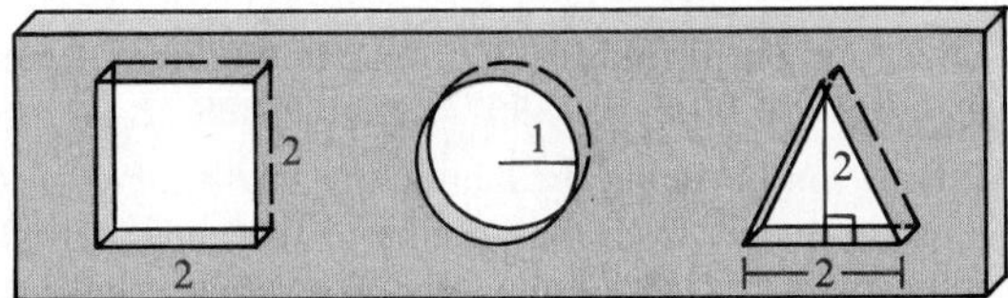

Quick Quiz

For 1–5, find the lateral area, total area, and volume of each solid.

1. a rectangular solid with length 10, width 5, and height 3 90, 190, 150
2. a regular square pyramid with base edge 12 and slant height 10 240, 384, 384
3. a cylinder with radius 20 cm and height 8 cm 320π cm^2, 1120π cm^2, 3200π cm^3
4. a right hexagonal prism with height 10 cm and base edge 3 cm 180 cm^2, $(180 + 27\sqrt{3})$ cm^2, $135\sqrt{3}$ cm^3
5. a cone with height $3\sqrt{3}$ cm and radius 3 cm 18π cm^2, 27π cm^2, $9\pi\sqrt{3}$ cm^3
6. The total area of a cube is 96 cm^2. Find the volume. 64 cm^3

Additional Answers Calculator Key-In

1.a. If the cylindrical layer of paint is cut and unrolled, it approx. a rect. solid with length = circumference of cylinder = $2\pi r$, width = height of cylinder = h, and height = thickness of paint layer = t. Thus, $V = 2\pi rht$.

b. Since the circumference of the cylinder is less than the circumference of the layer of paint, the figure is not a right prism. Therefore, $V \approx 2\pi rht$.

Self-Test 1

For Exercises 1–5 find the lateral area, total area, and volume of each solid.

1. A rectangular solid with length 10, width 8, and height 4.5 **162; 322; 360**
2. A regular square pyramid with base edge 24 and slant height 13 **624; 1200; 960**
3. A cylinder with radius 10 in. and height 7 in. **140π in.^{2}; 340π in.^{2}; 700π in.^{3}**
4. A right hexagonal prism with height 5 cm and base edge 6 cm **180 cm^2; $(180 + 108\sqrt{3})$ cm^2; $270\sqrt{3}$ cm^3**
5. A cone with height 12 and radius 9 **135π; 216π; 324π**
6. The total area of a cube is 2400 m^2. Find the volume. **8000 m^3**
7. A solid metal cylinder with radius 2 and height 2 is recast as a solid cone with radius 2. Find the height of the cone. **6**
8. A prism with height 2 m and a pyramid with height 5 m have congruent triangular bases. Find the ratio of their volumes. **6:5**

♦ Calculator Key-In

1. A cylinder has radius 10 and height 12. Suppose that the lateral surface of the cylinder is covered with a thin coat of paint having thickness 0.1. The volume of the paint can be calculated approximately or exactly.
   a. Use the diagrams below to explain the following formula.
   Approximate volume = (lateral area of cylinder) · (thickness of paint)
   $V \approx (2\pi rh) \cdot (t)$

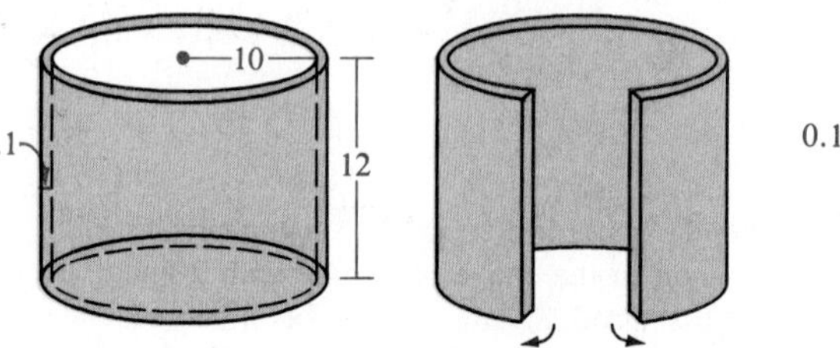

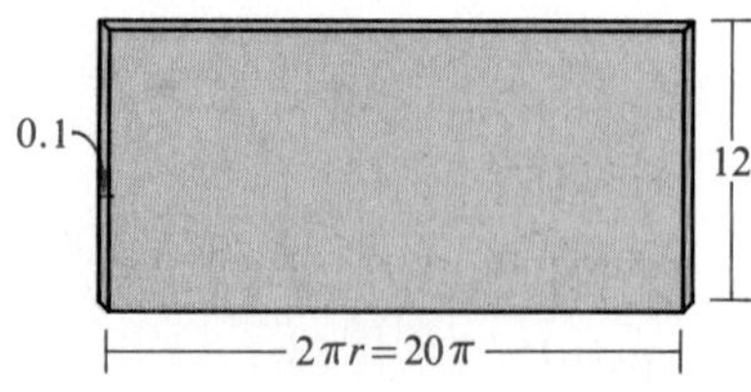

   b. Why is this formula only an approximation of the volume?
2. Use a calculator and the formula to find the approximate volume of paint for each thickness: 0.1, 0.01, 0.001. **75.398, 7.5398, 0.75398**
3. The exact volume of paint can be found by subtracting the volume of the inner cylinder (the given cylinder) from the volume of the outer cylinder (the given cylinder plus paint). Use a calculator to evaluate the exact volume of paint for each thickness: 0.1, 0.01, 0.001. **75.775, 7.5436, 0.75402**
4. Compare the values for the approximate volume and exact volume for each thickness in Exercises 2 and 3. What can you conclude? **The exact volume is greater than the approximate volume.**

Similar Solids

Objectives

1. Find the area and the volume of a sphere.
2. State and apply the properties of similar solids.

12-4 *Spheres*

Recall (page 329) that a sphere is the set of all points that are a given distance from a given point. The sphere has many useful applications. One recent application is the development of a spherical blimp. An experimental model of the blimp is shown in the photograph. A spherical shape was selected for this blimp because a sphere gives excellent mobility, stability, hovering capabilities, and lift. The rotation of the top of a sphere away from the direction in which the sphere is traveling provides lifting power.

The surface area and the volume of a sphere are given by the formulas below. After some examples showing how these formulas are used, justifications of the formulas will be presented.

Theorem 12-9

The area of a sphere equals 4π times the square of the radius. ($A = 4\pi r^2$)

Theorem 12-10

The volume of a sphere equals $\frac{4}{3}\pi$ times the cube of the radius. ($V = \frac{4}{3}\pi r^3$)

Example 1 Find the area and the volume of a sphere with radius 2 cm.

Solution

$$A = 4\pi r^2 = 4\pi \cdot 2^2 = 16\pi \text{ (cm}^2\text{)}$$

$$V = \frac{4}{3}\pi r^3 = \frac{4}{3}\pi \cdot 2^3 = \frac{32\pi}{3} \text{ (cm}^3\text{)}$$

Teaching Suggestions,
p. T130

Objective
Presenting the Lesson
Enrichment
Making Connections
Using Technology

Communication Skills,
p. T130

Supplementary Materials

Practice Master 74
Study Guide, pp. 159–160
Overhead Visuals I, J, K

Lesson Focus

Spheres are common figures in the real world. In this lesson, the formulas for calculating the area and volume of a sphere are used to solve problems.

Suggested Assignments

Minimum
Day 1: 500/1–9
Day 2: 500/10–17
507/Mixed Review 1–6

Average
Day 1: 500/2, 3, 5, 8, 9, 11, 14, 15
Day 2: 500–501/16–18, 20–23, 26
507/Mixed Review 1–6

Maximum
Day 1: 500–501/6–14 even, 16–18
Day 2: 501–502/19–25 odd, 26, 28, 29, 31

Example 2 The area of a sphere is 256π. Find the volume.

Solution To find the volume, first find the radius.

$$(1)\ A = 256\pi = 4\pi r^2 \qquad 64 = r^2 \qquad 8 = r$$

$$(2)\ V = \frac{4}{3}\pi r^3 = \frac{4}{3}\pi \cdot 8^3 = \frac{2048\pi}{3}$$

Example 3 A plane passes 4 cm from the center of a sphere with radius 7 cm. Find the area of the circle of intersection.

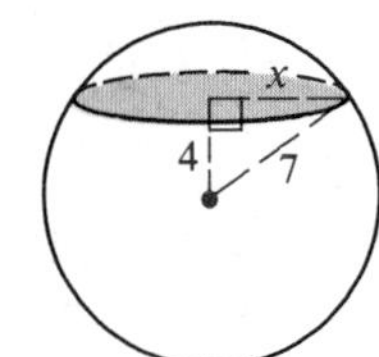

Solution Let x = radius of the circle.

$$x = \sqrt{7^2 - 4^2} = \sqrt{33}$$

$$\text{Area} = \pi x^2 = \pi(\sqrt{33})^2 = 33\pi\ (\text{cm}^2)$$

Teaching Note

Note that the justifications of the formulas for the volume and surface area of a sphere are considered optional. If you cover the justification of the formula for volume, you may want to point out to the students that the discs represented in the diagrams can be made as thin as possible so that they can approximate the solids closely. Another justification, using Cavalieri's Principle (pages 516–517), is similar to the one given on this page. Instead of very thin disks, circular cross sections are used.

Justification of the Volume Formula (Optional)

Any solid can be approximated by a stack of thin circular discs of equal thickness, as shown by the sphere drawn at the right. Each disc is actually a cylinder with height h.

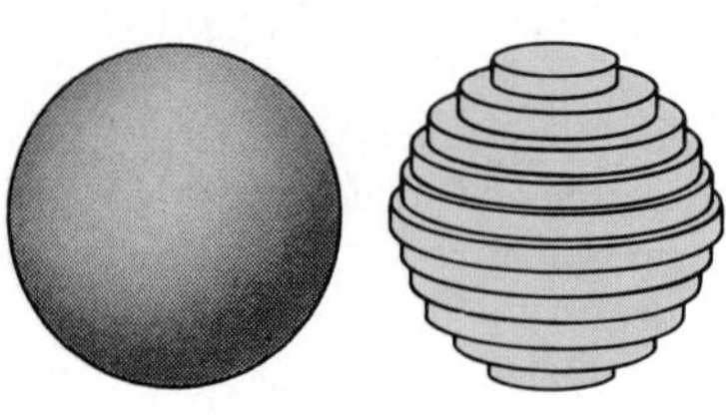

The sphere, the cylinder, and the double cone below all have radius r and height $2r$. Look at the disc that is x units above the center of each solid.

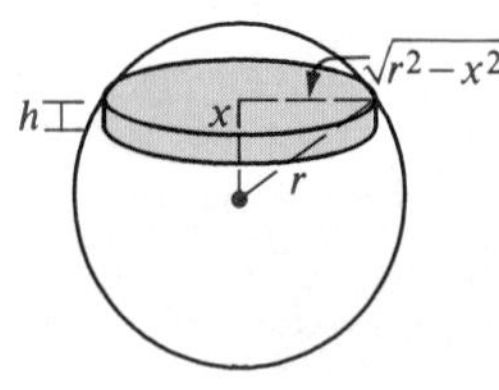

Disc volume:
$\pi(\sqrt{r^2 - x^2})^2 h = \pi(r^2 - x^2)h = \pi r^2 h - \pi x^2 h$

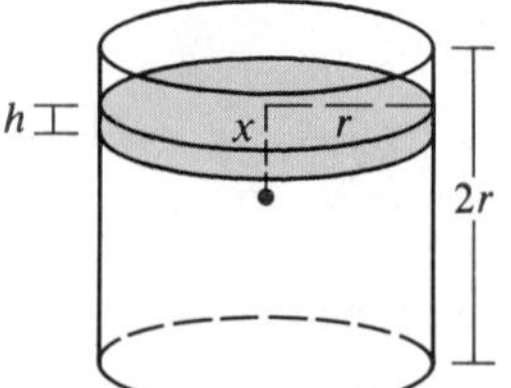

Disc volume: $\pi r^2 h$

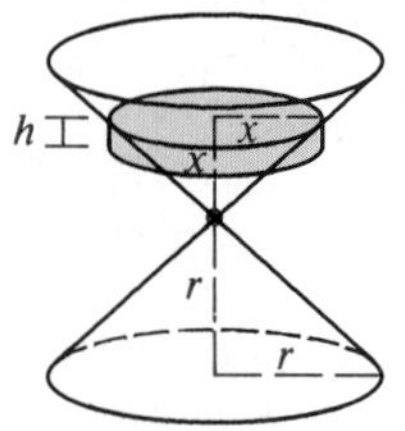

Disc volume: $\pi x^2 h$

Note from the calculations above that no matter what x is, the volume of the first disc equals the difference between the volumes of the other two discs.

Total volume of discs in sphere

=

Total volume of discs in cylinder

−

Total volume of discs in double cone

The relationship on the bottom of the previous page holds if there are just a few discs approximating each solid or very many discs. If there are very many discs, their total volume will be practically the same as the volume of the solid. Thus:

$$\begin{aligned}\text{Volume of sphere} &= \text{volume of cylinder} - \text{volume of double cone}\\ &= \pi r^2 \cdot 2r - 2(\tfrac{1}{3}\pi r^2 \cdot r)\\ &= 2\pi r^3 - \tfrac{2}{3}\pi r^3\\ &= \tfrac{4}{3}\pi r^3\end{aligned}$$

Justification of the Area Formula (Optional)

Imagine a rubber ball with inner radius r and rubber thickness t. To find the volume of the rubber, we can use the formula for the volume of a sphere. We just subtract the volume of the inner sphere from the volume of the outer sphere.

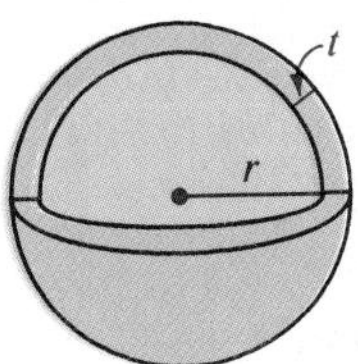

$$\begin{aligned}\text{Exact volume of rubber} &= \tfrac{4}{3}\pi(r + t)^3 - \tfrac{4}{3}\pi r^3\\ &= \tfrac{4}{3}\pi[(r + t)^3 - r^3]\\ &= \tfrac{4}{3}\pi[r^3 + 3r^2t + 3rt^2 + t^3 - r^3]\\ &= 4\pi r^2 t + 4\pi r t^2 + \tfrac{4}{3}\pi t^3\end{aligned}$$

The volume of the rubber can be found in another way as well. If we think of a small piece of the rubber ball, its approximate volume would be its outer area A times its thickness t. The same thing is true for the whole ball.

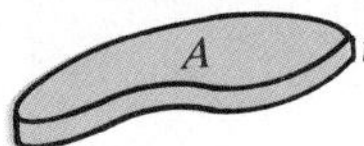

$$\text{Volume of rubber} \approx \text{Surface area} \cdot \text{thickness}$$
$$V \approx A \cdot t$$

Now we can equate the two formulas for the volume of the rubber:

$$A \cdot t \approx 4\pi r^2 t + 4\pi r t^2 + \tfrac{4}{3}\pi t^3$$

If we divide both sides of the equation by t, we get the following result:

$$A \approx 4\pi r^2 + 4\pi r t + \tfrac{4}{3}\pi t^2$$

This approximation for A gets better and better as the layer of rubber gets thinner and thinner. As t approaches zero, the last two terms in the formula for A also approach zero. As a result, the surface area gets closer and closer to $4\pi r^2$. Thus:

$$A = 4\pi r^2$$

This is exactly what we would expect, since the surface area of a ball clearly depends on the size of the radius, not on the thickness of the rubber.

Chalkboard Examples

Complete the table for spheres. Leave answers in terms of π.

	d	r	A	V
1.	12	6	144π	288π
2.	14	7	196π	$\frac{1372\pi}{3}$
3.	40	20	1600π	$\frac{32{,}000\pi}{3}$
4.	$2\sqrt{3}$	$\sqrt{3}$	12π	$4\pi\sqrt{3}$
5.	$2r$	r	$4\pi r^2$	$\frac{4\pi}{3}r^3$
6.	$4r$	$2r$	$16\pi r^2$	$\frac{32\pi}{3}r^3$

7. Compare the areas of the spheres in Exercises 5 and 6. 1:4

8. Compare the volumes of the spheres in Exercises 5 and 6. 1:8

9. The number of square centimeters in the area of a sphere is the same as the number of cubic centimeters in the volume of a sphere. Find the radius of the sphere. 3

Classroom Exercises

Copy and complete the table for spheres.

	1.	2.	3.	4.	5.	6.
Radius	1	8	$3t$	?	?	?
Area	?	?	?	36π	100π	?
Volume	?	?	?	?	?	$\frac{4000\pi}{3}$

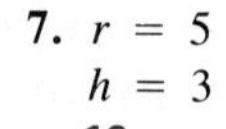

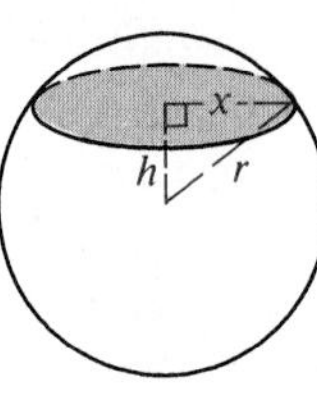

A plane passes h cm from the center of a sphere with radius r cm. Find the area of the circle of intersection, shaded in the diagram, for the given values.

7. $r = 5$, $h = 3$ **16π cm^2**

8. $r = 17$, $h = 8$ **225π cm^2**

9. $r = 7$, $h = 6$ **13π cm^2**

Written Exercises

Copy and complete the table for spheres.

A

	1.	2.	3.	4.	5.	6.	7.	8.
Radius	7	5	$\frac{1}{2}$	$\frac{3}{4}k$	?	?	$\sqrt{2}$	?
Area	?	?	?	?	64π	324π	?	?
Volume	?	?	?	?	?	?	?	288π

9. If the radius of a sphere is doubled, the area of the sphere is multiplied by _?_ and the volume is multiplied by _?_. **4, 8**

10. Repeat Exercise 9 if the radius of the sphere is tripled. **9, 27**

11. The area of a sphere is π cm^2. Find the diameter of the sphere. **1 cm**

12. The volume of a sphere is 36π m^3. Find its area. **36π m^2**

13. Find the area of the circle formed when a plane passes 2 cm from the center of a sphere with radius 5 cm. **21π cm^2**

14. Find the area of the circle formed when a plane passes 7 cm from the center of a sphere with radius 8 cm. **15π cm^2**

15. A sphere has radius 2 and a hemisphere (''half'' a sphere) has radius 4. Compare their volumes. **Vol. of hemisphere = 4 · vol. of sphere**

16. A scoop of ice cream with diameter 6 cm is placed in an ice-cream cone with diameter 5 cm and height 12 cm. Is the cone big enough to hold all the ice cream if it melts? **No; see below.**

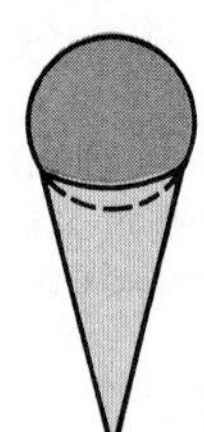

Ex. 16

17. Approximately 70% of the Earth's surface is covered by water. Use a calculator to find the area covered by water to the nearest million square kilometers. (The radius of the Earth is approximately 6380 km.) **358 million km^2**

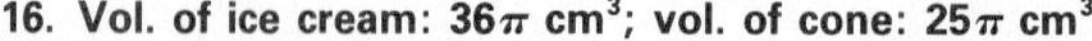

16. Vol. of ice cream: 36π cm^3; vol. of cone: 25π cm^3

Additional Answers Classroom Exercises

1. $A = 4\pi$; $V = \frac{4\pi}{3}$
2. $A = 256\pi$; $V = \frac{2048\pi}{3}$
3. $A = 36t^2\pi$; $V = 36t^3\pi$
4. $r = 3$; $V = 36\pi$
5. $r = 5$; $V = \frac{500\pi}{3}$
6. $r = 10$; $A = 400\pi$

Additional Answers Written Exercises

1. $A = 196\pi$; $V = \frac{1372\pi}{3}$
2. $A = 100\pi$; $V = \frac{500\pi}{3}$
3. $A = \pi$; $V = \frac{\pi}{6}$
4. $A = \frac{9k^2\pi}{4}$; $V = \frac{9k^3\pi}{16}$
5. $r = 4$; $V = \frac{256\pi}{3}$
6. $r = 9$; $V = 972\pi$
7. $A = 8\pi$; $V = \frac{8\pi\sqrt{2}}{3}$
8. $r = 6$; $A = 144\pi$

Using a Calculator

A calculator is suggested for Ex. 17.

18. a. Find the volume, correct to the nearest cubic centimeter, of a sphere inscribed in a cube with edges 6 cm long. Use $\pi \approx 3.14$. **113 cm^3**

b. Find the volume of the region inside the cube but outside the sphere. **103 cm^3**

B **19.** A silo of a barn consists of a cylinder capped by a hemisphere, as shown. Find the volume of the silo. $\frac{1750\pi}{3}$ **m^3**

20. About two cans of paint are needed to cover the hemispherical dome of the silo shown. Approximately how many cans are needed to paint the rest of the silo's exterior? **8 cans**

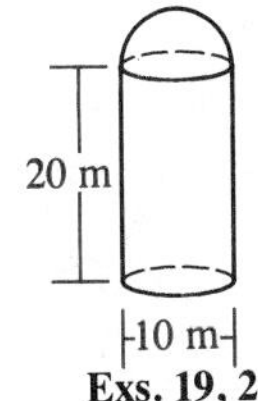

Exs. 19, 20

21. An experimental one-room house is a hemisphere with a floor. If three cans of paint are needed to cover the floor, how many cans will be needed to paint the ceiling? (Ignore door and windows.) **6 cans**

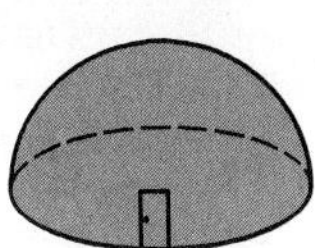

Ex. 21

22. A hemispheric bowl with radius 25 contains water whose depth is 10. What is the area of the water's surface? **400π**

23. A solid metal ball with radius 8 cm is melted down and recast as a solid cone with the same radius.

a. What is the height of the cone? **32 cm**

b. Use a calculator to show that the lateral area of the cone is about 3% more than the area of the sphere.

24. Four solid metal balls fit snugly inside a cylindrical can. A geometry student claims that two extra balls of the same size can be put into the can, provided all six balls can be melted and the molten liquid poured into the can. Is the student correct? (*Hint*: Let the radius of each ball be r.) **Yes; vol. of 6 balls = $6(\frac{4}{3}\pi r^3) = 8\pi r^3$ = vol. of can**

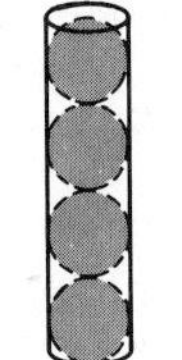

Ex. 24

25. A sphere with radius r is inscribed in a cylinder. Find the volume of the cylinder in terms of r. **$2\pi r^3$**

26. A sphere is inscribed in a cylinder. Show that the area of the sphere equals the lateral area of the cylinder. **See below.**

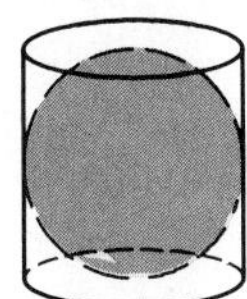

Exs. 25, 26

27. A double cone is inscribed in the cylinder shown. Find the volume of the space inside the cylinder but outside the double cone. **$\frac{4}{3}\pi r^3$**

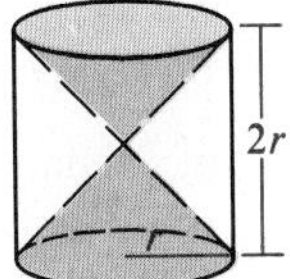

Ex. 27

28. A hollow rubber ball has outer radius 11 cm and inner radius 10 cm.

a. Find the exact volume of the rubber. Then evaluate the volume to the nearest cubic centimeter. **$\frac{1324\pi}{3}$ cm^3; 1386 cm^3**

b. The volume of the rubber can be approximated by the formula:

$V \approx$ inner surface area · thickness of rubber

Use this formula to approximate V. Compare your answer with the answer in part (a). **400$\pi \approx$ 1257 cm^3; approx. is less**

c. Is the approximation method used in part (b) better for a ball with a thick layer of rubber or a ball with a thin layer? **thin**

Ex. 28

26. Let r = radius; area of sphere = $4\pi r^2$; L.A. of cylinder = $2\pi rh = 2\pi r(2r) = 4\pi r^2$

Guided Practice

1. If the radius of a sphere is halved, the area of the sphere is multiplied by $\frac{1}{4}$ and the volume is multiplied by $\frac{1}{8}$.
2. If the surface area of a sphere is 16π, find the diameter and the volume. 4, $\frac{32\pi}{3}$
3. Find the area of the circle formed when a plane passes 9 cm from the center of a sphere with radius 15 cm. 144π
4. Betty made two wax candles, one in the shape of a sphere with radius 5 cm and another in the shape of a cylinder with radius 5 cm and height 6 cm. Which candle required more wax? Sphere: $166\frac{2}{3}\pi$ cm^3; Cylinder: 150π cm^3

5.a. Find the volume, correct to the nearest cubic centimeter, of a sphere inscribed in a cylinder with diameter and height each 5 cm. (Use $\pi \approx 3.14$.) 65 cm^3

b. Find the volume of the region outside the sphere but inside the cylinder. 33 cm^3

Additional Answers Written Exercises

23.b. cone: $\pi \cdot r \cdot \sqrt{1088} \approx$ 829

$1.03(4\pi \cdot 8^2) \approx 828$

29. A circle with diameter 9 in. is rotated about a diameter. Find the area and volume of the solid formed. **$A = 81\pi$ in.^{2}; $V = 121.5\pi$ in.^{3}**

30. A cylinder with height 12 is inscribed in a sphere with radius 10. Find the volume of the cylinder. **768π**

C **31.** A cylinder with height $2x$ is inscribed in a sphere with radius 10.

a. Show that the volume of the cylinder, V, is
$$2\pi x(100 - x^2).$$

b. By using calculus, one can show that V is maximum when $x = \frac{10\sqrt{3}}{3}$. Substitute this value for x to find the maximum volume V. **max. $V = \frac{4000\pi\sqrt{3}}{9}$**

c. (Optional) Use a calculator or a computer to evaluate $V = 2\pi x(100 - x^2)$ for various values of x between 0 and 10. Show that the maximum volume V occurs when $x \approx 5.77$.

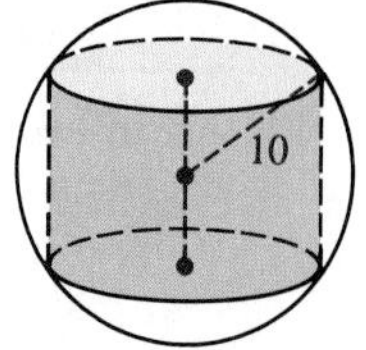

Exs. 30, 31

32. A cone is inscribed in a sphere with radius 10, as shown.

a. Show that the volume of the cone, V, is
$$\tfrac{1}{3}\pi(100 - x^2)(10 + x).$$

b. By using calculus, one can show that V is maximum when $x = \frac{10}{3}$. Substitute this value for x to find the maximum volume V. **max. $V = \frac{32{,}000\pi}{81}$**

c. (Optional) Use a calculator or a computer to evaluate the volume for various values of x between 0 and 10. Show that the maximum volume V occurs when $x = \frac{10}{3}$.

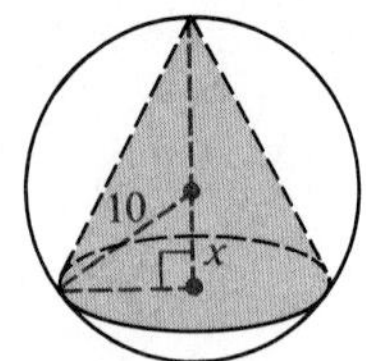

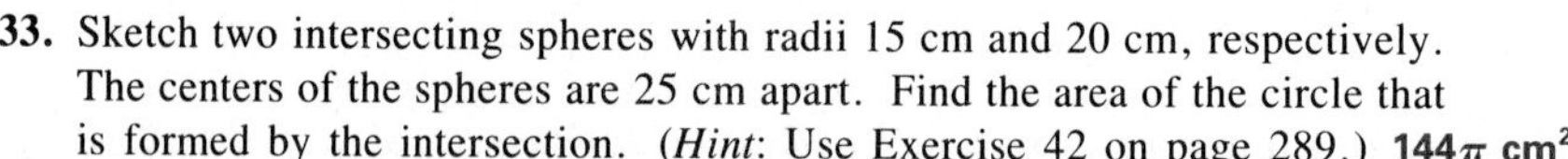

33. Sketch two intersecting spheres with radii 15 cm and 20 cm, respectively. The centers of the spheres are 25 cm apart. Find the area of the circle that is formed by the intersection. (*Hint*: Use Exercise 42 on page 289.) **144π cm^2**

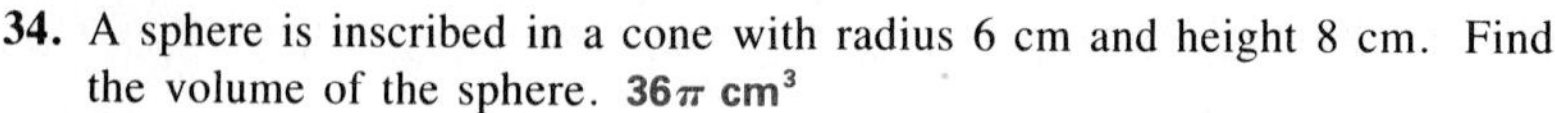

34. A sphere is inscribed in a cone with radius 6 cm and height 8 cm. Find the volume of the sphere. **36π cm^3**

Challenge

In a training exercise, two research submarines are assigned to take any two positions in the ocean at a depth between 100 m and 500 m and within a square area with 6000 m sides. If one submarine takes its position in the center of the square area at the 100-meter depth, what is the probability that the other submarine is within 400 m? Use $\pi \approx 3.14$. (*Hint*: Consider each submarine to be a point in a rectangular solid. Use the ideas of geometric probability.) **$\frac{8\pi}{2700} \approx 0.009$**

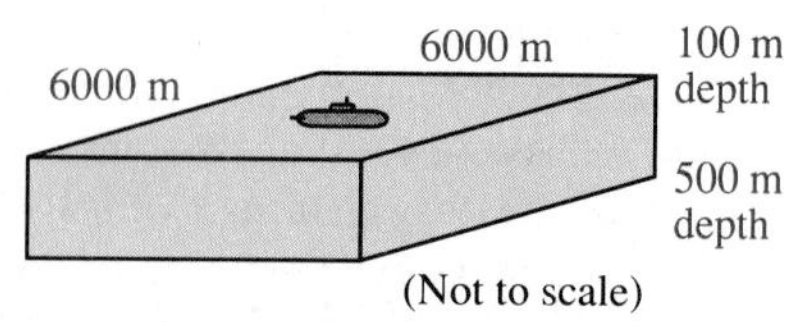

(Not to scale)

Additional Answers Written Exercises

31.a. radius of base of cylinder $= \sqrt{10^2 - x^2} = \sqrt{100 - x^2}$; $V = \pi(\sqrt{100 - x^2})^2 \cdot 2x = 2\pi x(100 - x^2)$

32.a. $h = 10 + x$; $r = \sqrt{10^2 - x^2} = \sqrt{100 - x^2}$; $V = \frac{1}{3}\pi(100 - x^2)(10 + x)$

♦ Calculator Key-In

1. The purpose of this exercise is to suggest the following statement: Of all figures in a plane with a fixed perimeter, the circle has the greatest possible area. If each regular polygon below has perimeter 60 mm and the circle has circumference 60 mm, find the area of each to the nearest square millimeter.

a.
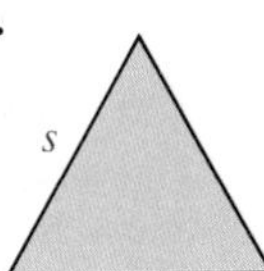

$s = \underline{?}$ **20 mm**
$A \approx \underline{?}$ **173 mm²**

b.
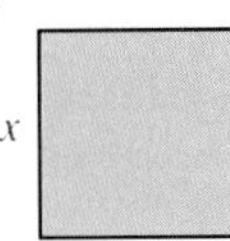

$x = \underline{?}$ **15 mm**
$A = \underline{?}$ **225 mm²**

c.
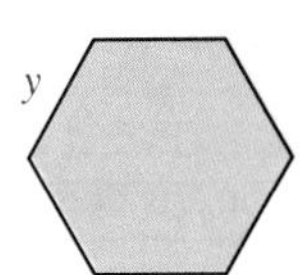

$y = \underline{?}$ **10 mm**
$A \approx \underline{?}$ **260 mm²**

d.
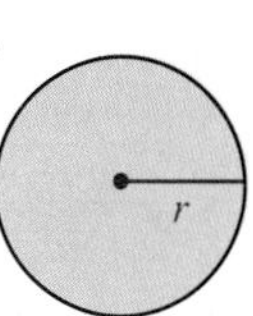

$r \approx \underline{?}$ **9.549 mm**
$A \approx \underline{?}$ **286 mm²**

2. The regular pyramid, the cube, and the sphere below all have total surface area 600 mm³. Find the volume of each to the nearest cubic millimeter.

a.
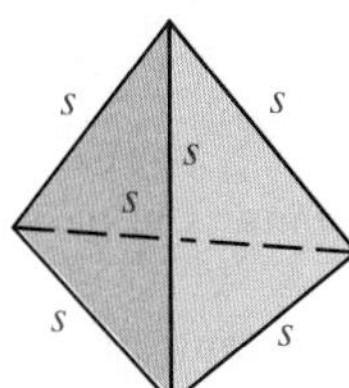

$\text{T.A.} = 4\left(\frac{s^2\sqrt{3}}{4}\right) = 600 \text{ mm}^2$
$s \approx \underline{?}$ **18.61 mm**
$V = \frac{s^3\sqrt{2}}{12} \approx \underline{?}$ **760 mm³**
(See Ex. 29, page 486.)

b.
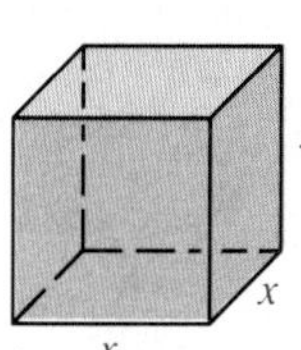

$\text{T.A.} = 6x^2 = 600 \text{ mm}^2$
$x = \underline{?}$ **10 mm**
$V = x^3 = \underline{?}$ **1000 mm³**

c.
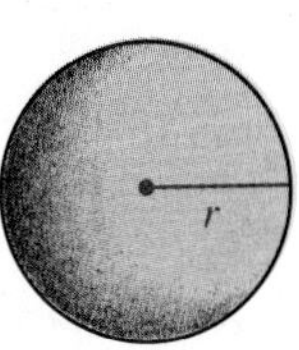

$\text{T.A.} = 4\pi r^2 = 600 \text{ mm}^2$
$r \approx \underline{?}$ **6.910 mm**
$V = \frac{4}{3}\pi r^3 \approx \underline{?}$ **1382 mm³**

d. Use the results of parts (a)–(c) to complete the following statement, which is similar to the one in Exercise 1: Of all solid figures with a fixed _?_, the _?_ has the _?_. **total surface area, sphere, greatest possible volume**

★ 3. Suppose the plane figures in Exercise 1 all have area 900 cm². Find the perimeter of each polygon and the circumference of the circle to the nearest centimeter. What do your answers suggest about all plane figures with a fixed area? **137 cm; 120 cm; 112 cm; 106 cm**

★ 4. Suppose the solid figures in Exercise 2 all have volume 1000 cm³. Find the total surface area of each to the nearest square centimeter. What do your answers suggest about all solid figures with a fixed volume? **721 cm²; 600 cm²; 484 cm²; of all solid figures with a fixed volume, the sphere has the least possible total surface area.**

Using a Calculator

Instead of doing calculations by hand, students can use a calculator and spend more time thinking about the important patterns and results of this Calculator Key-In.

Additional Answers Calculator Key-In

3. Of all plane figures with a fixed area, the circle has the least possible perimeter (circumference).

Using a Computer

Students may find it helpful if you discuss the difference between the discs outside the sphere and the discs inside the sphere as shown in the diagrams below.

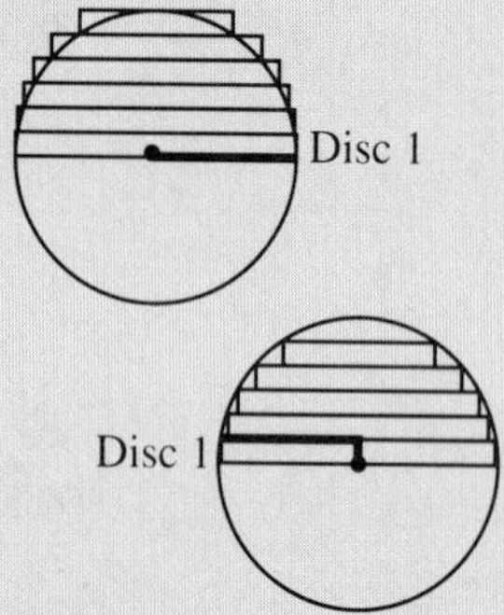

Line 40 in the program on this page indicates that the radius of each outside disc is determined by the distance that the disc is from the center of the sphere. The modified line 40 in Exercise 3 indicates that the radius of each inside disc is determined by the distance that the next disc above is from the center of the sphere.

♦ Computer Key-In

The volume of a sphere with radius 10 can be approximated by cylindrical discs with equal heights, as discussed on page 498. It is convenient to work with the upper half of the sphere, then double the result.

Suppose you use ten discs to approximate the upper hemisphere, as shown at the left below.

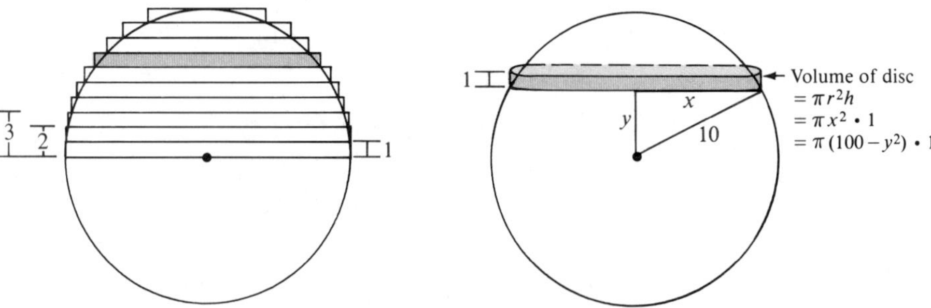

The diagram at the right above shows that the volume of a disc y units from the center of the sphere is $V = \pi(100 - y^2)$. You can substitute $y = 0, 1, 2, \ldots, 9$ to compute the volumes of the ten discs.

Now suppose you use n discs to approximate the upper hemisphere. Then the height of each disc equals $\frac{10}{n}$, and the volume of a disc y units from the center of the sphere is $V = \pi(100 - y^2) \cdot \frac{10}{n}$. The following computer program adds the volumes of the n discs, then doubles the result. Note that line 80 calculates the volume of the sphere using the formula $V = \frac{4}{3}\pi r^3$.

```
10 LET Y = 0
15 LET V = 0
20 PRINT "HOW MANY DISCS";
25 INPUT N
30 FOR I = 1 TO N
40 LET Y = (I - 1) * 10/N
50 LET V = V + 3.14159 * (100 - Y↑2) * (10/N)
60 NEXT I
70 PRINT "VOLUME OF DISCS IS ";2 * V
80 PRINT "VOLUME OF SPHERE IS ";4/3 * 3.14159 * 10↑3
90 END
```

Exercises

1. Use 10 for N and RUN the program. By about what percent does the disc method overapproximate the volume of the sphere? **≈ 7%**
2. RUN the program to find the total volume of n discs for each value of n.
   a. 20 **b.** 50 **c.** 100 **d.** 1000
   As n increases, does the approximate volume approach the actual volume? **Yes**
   a. 4343.24818 b. 4251.19959 c. 4220.09785 d. 4191.9272

3. The program uses discs that extend outside the sphere, so it yields approximations greater than the actual volume. To use discs that are inside the sphere, replace line 40 with: `LET Y = I * (10/N)`
   a. RUN the new program for `N = 100`. **$V \approx 4157.26605$**
   b. Find the average of the result in part (a) and the result in Exercise 2, part (c). Is the average close to the actual volume of the sphere? **Yes; average: 4188.68195; actual: 4188.7867**

Application — Geodesic Domes

A spherical dome is an efficient way of enclosing space, since a sphere holds a greater volume than any other container with the same surface area. (See Calculator Exercise 2 on page 503.) In 1947, R. Buckminster Fuller patented the *geodesic dome*, a framework made by joining straight pieces of steel or aluminum tubing in a network of triangles. A thin cover of aluminum or plastic is then attached to the tubing.

The segments forming the network are of various lengths, but the vertices are all equidistant from the center of the dome, so that they lie on a sphere. When we follow a chain of segments around the dome, we find that they approximate a circle on this sphere, often a great circle. It is this property that gives the dome design its name: A *geodesic* on any surface is a path of minimum length between two points on the surface, and on a sphere these shortest paths are arcs of great circles.

Though the geodesic dome is very light and has no internal supports, it is very strong, and standardized parts make construction of the dome relatively easy. Domes have been used with success for theaters, exhibition halls, sports arenas, and greenhouses.

The United States Pavilion that Fuller designed for Expo '67 in Montreal uses two domes linked together. The design of this structure is illustrated at the right. The red triangular network is the outer dome, the black hexagons form the inner dome, and the blue segments represent the trusses that tie the two domes together. The arrows mark one of the many chains of segments that form arcs of circles on the dome. You can see all of these features of the structure in the photograph at the right, which shows a view from inside the dome.

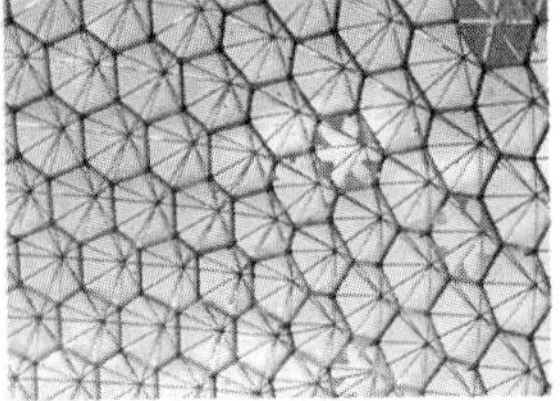

Although a grid of hexagons will interlock nicely to cover the plane, they cannot interlock to cover a sphere unless twelve of the hexagons are changed to pentagons. (The reason for this is given in the exercises on the next page.)

Exercises

For any solid figure with polygons for faces, Euler's formula, $F + V - E = 2$, must hold. In this formula, F, V, and E stand for the number of faces, vertices, and edges, respectively, that the figure has.

1. Verify Euler's formula for each figure below.

a. Cube

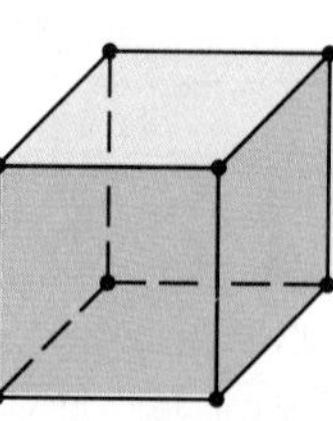

$\mathbf{F = 6,\ V = 8,\ E = 12;}$
$\mathbf{6 + 8 - 12 = 2}$

b. Octahedron

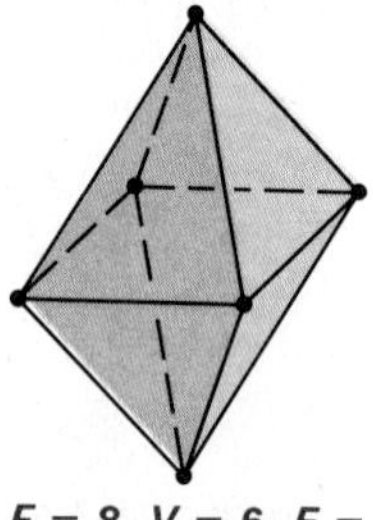

$\mathbf{F = 8,\ V = 6,\ E = 12;}$
$\mathbf{8 + 6 - 12 = 2}$

c. Icosahedron (20 faces)

$\mathbf{F = 20,\ V = 12,\ E = 30;}$
$\mathbf{20 + 12 - 30 = 2}$

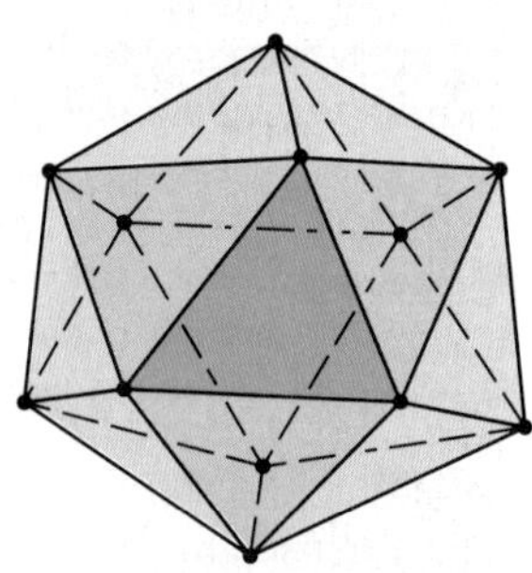

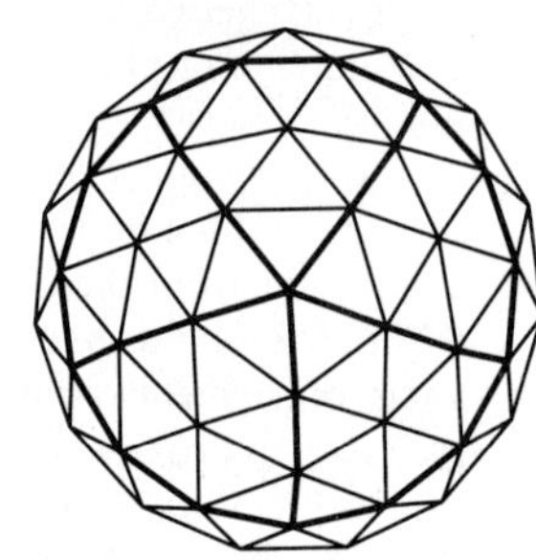

2. If each edge of the icosahedron above is trisected and the trisection points are "popped out" to the surface of the circumscribing sphere, one of the many possible geodesic domes is formed. By subdividing the edges of the icosahedron into more than three parts, the resulting geodesic dome is even more spherelike, as shown. In the diagram, find a group of equilateral triangles that cluster to form **(a)** a hexagon, and **(b)** a pentagon.

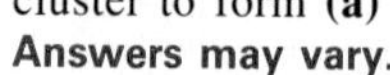

Answers may vary.

3. In this exercise, Euler's formula will be used to show that **(a)** the dome's framework *cannot* consist of hexagons only, and **(b)** the framework *can* consist of hexagons plus exactly 12 pentagons.

a. Use an indirect proof and assume that the framework has n faces, all hexagons. Thus $F = n$. To find V, the number of vertices on the framework, notice that each hexagon contributes 6 vertices, but each vertex is shared by 3 hexagons. Thus $V = \frac{6n}{3}$. To find E, the number of edges of the framework, notice that each hexagon contributes 6 edges, but each edge is shared by 2 hexagons. Thus $E = \frac{6n}{2}$. According to Euler's Formula: $F + V - E$ must equal 2. Does it? What does this contradiction tell you? **No; a framework of hexagons only is not possible.**

b. Suppose that 12 of the n faces of the framework are pentagons. Show that $V = \frac{6n - 12}{3}$ and that $E = \frac{6n - 12}{2}$. Then use algebra to show that $F + V - E = 2$. Since Euler's formula is satisfied, a dome framework can be constructed when n faces consist of 12 pentagons and $n - 12$ hexagons.

Additional Answers
Application

3.a. Suppose $F + V - E = 2$. Then $n + \frac{6n}{3} - \frac{6n}{2} = 2$, and $n + 2n - 3n = 2$. But $n + 2n - 3n = 0$, so $F + V - E \neq 2$.

b. 12 hexagon vertices are lost, but each is a vertex of 3 hexagons, so 4 vertices are lost and $V = \frac{6n}{3} - 4 = \frac{6n - 12}{3}$. 12 edges are lost, but each is an edge of 2 hexagons, so 6 edges are lost and $E = \frac{6n}{2} - 6 = \frac{6n - 12}{2}$. Then $F + V - E = n + 2n - 4 - 3n + 6 = 2$.

Biographical Note — *R. Buckminster Fuller*

The early curiosity shown by R. Buckminster Fuller (1895–1983) about the world around him led to a life of invention and philosophy. As a mathematician he made many contributions to the fields of engineering, architecture, and cartography. His ultimate goal was always "to do more with less." Thus his discoveries often had economic and ecological implications.

Fuller's inventions include the geodesic dome (see pages 505 and 506), the 3-wheeled Dymaxion car, and the Dymaxion Air-ocean World Map on which he was able to project the spherical earth as a flat surface without any visible distortions. He also designed other structures that were based upon triangles and circles instead of the usual rectangular surfaces.

Mixed Review Exercises

Trapezoid *ABCD* is similar to trapezoid *PQRS*.

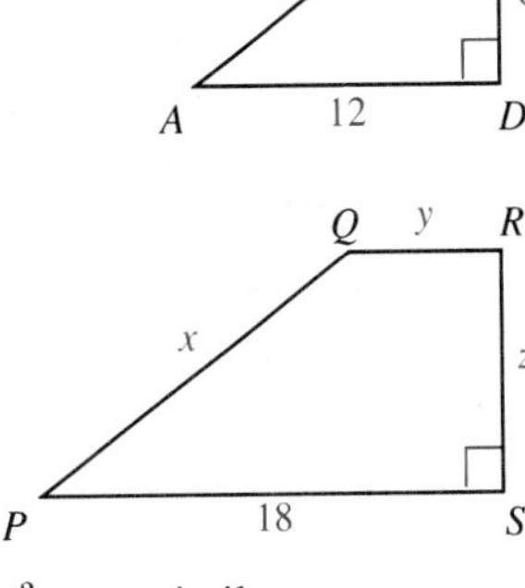

1. Find the scale factor of the trapezoids. **$\frac{2}{3}$**
2. Draw an altitude from point *B* and use the Pythagorean Theorem to find the value of *w*. **10**
3. Find the values of *x*, *y*, and *z*. **$x = 15$, $y = 6$, $z = 9$**
4. **a.** Find the perimeter of each trapezoid. **32, 48**
   b. Find the ratio of the perimeters. **$\frac{2}{3}$**
   c. Compare the ratio of the perimeters to the scale factor you found in Exercise 1. **They are both $\frac{2}{3}$.**
5. **a.** Find the area of each trapezoid. **48, 108**
   b. Find the ratio of the areas. **$\frac{4}{9}$**
   c. Compare the ratio of the areas to the scale factor you found in Exercise 1. **$\frac{4}{9} = \left(\frac{2}{3}\right)^2$**
6. For each of the following, complete the statement: All __?__ are similar. Classify the statement as true or false.

   a. squares **True**
   b. rectangles **False**
   c. circles **True**
   d. rhombuses **False**
   e. right triangles **False**
   f. equilateral triangles **True**
   g. regular pentagons **True**
   h. isosceles trapezoids **False**

Teaching Suggestions,
pp. T130–T131

Objective
Presenting the Lesson
Application

Supplementary Materials

Practice Master 75
Test 48
Resource Book, pp. 80, 157
Study Guide, pp. 161–162
Overhead Visual E
Computer Activity 26

Lesson Focus

The purpose of this lesson is to study solids that are similar. Similar solids have a scale factor that can be used to compare their perimeters, areas, and volumes.

Suggested Assignments

Minimum
Day 1: 511/1–5
S 501/18–22
Day 2: 511/6, 8, 9, 11–13
Day 3: 512/15, 16
513/Self-Test 2
Day 4: 519/Chapter Test
1–15 odd

Average
Day 1: 511/1–6, 8, 10–12
Day 2: 511–512/14–17, 19, 22, 23
Day 3: 513/Self-Test 2
519/Chapter Test 1–4
Day 4: 519/Chapter Test
5–16

Maximum
Day 1: 511/4, 7, 9, 11–13
S 502/30
Day 2: 511–512/14, 16–22
Day 3: 512–513/23–26, 28
Day 4: 519/Chapter Test

12-5 *Areas and Volumes of Similar Solids*

One of the best-known attractions in The Hague, the Netherlands, is a unique miniature city, Madurodam, consisting of five acres of carefully crafted reproductions done on a scale of 1:25. Everything in this model city works, including the two-mile railway network, the canal locks, the harbor fireboats, and the nearly 50,000 tiny street lights. In this section you will study the relationship between scale factors of *similar solids* and their areas and volumes.

Similar solids are solids that have the same shape but not necessarily the same size. It's easy to see that all spheres are similar. To decide whether two other solids are similar, determine whether bases are similar and corresponding lengths are proportional.

Right cylinders

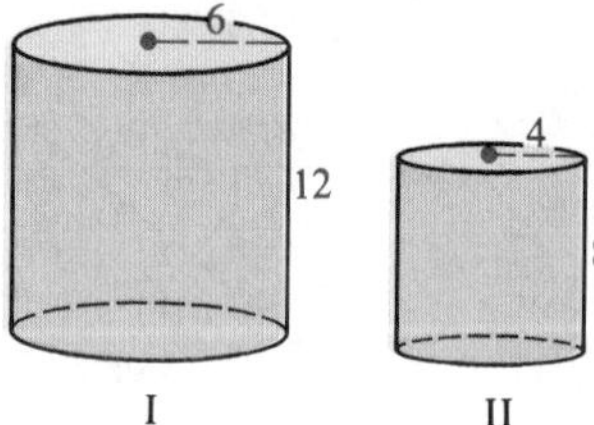

The bases are similar because all circles are similar. The lengths are proportional because $\frac{6}{4} = \frac{12}{8}$.

So the solids are similar with scale factor $\frac{3}{2}$.

Regular square pyramids

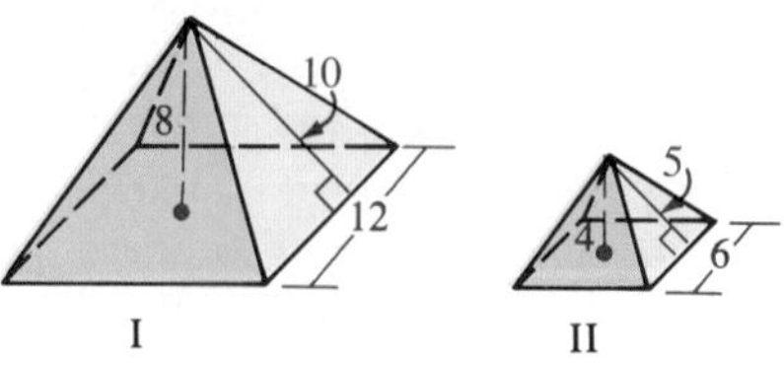

The bases are similar because all squares are similar. The lengths are proportional because $\frac{12}{6} = \frac{8}{4} = \frac{10}{5}$.

So the solids are similar with scale factor $\frac{2}{1}$.

The table below shows the ratios of the perimeters, areas, and volumes for both pairs of similar solids shown on page 508. Notice the relationship between the scale factor and the ratios in each column.

	Cylinders I and II	Pyramids I and II
Scale factor	$\frac{3}{2}$	$\frac{2}{1}$
$\frac{\text{Base perimeter (I)}}{\text{Base perimeter (II)}}$	$\frac{2\pi \cdot 6}{2\pi \cdot 4} = \frac{6}{4}$, or $\frac{3}{2}$	$\frac{4 \cdot 12}{4 \cdot 6} = \frac{12}{6}$, or $\frac{2}{1}$
$\frac{\text{L.A. (I)}}{\text{L.A. (II)}}$	$\frac{2\pi \cdot 6 \cdot 12}{2\pi \cdot 4 \cdot 8} = \frac{9}{4}$, or $\frac{3^2}{2^2}$	$\frac{\frac{1}{2} \cdot 48 \cdot 10}{\frac{1}{2} \cdot 24 \cdot 5} = \frac{4}{1}$, or $\frac{2^2}{1^2}$
$\frac{\text{Volume (I)}}{\text{Volume (II)}}$	$\frac{\pi \cdot 6^2 \cdot 12}{\pi \cdot 4^2 \cdot 8} = \frac{27}{8}$, or $\frac{3^3}{2^3}$	$\frac{\frac{1}{3} \cdot 12^2 \cdot 8}{\frac{1}{3} \cdot 6^2 \cdot 4} = \frac{8}{1}$, or $\frac{2^3}{1^3}$

The results shown in the table above are generalized in the following theorem. (See Exercises 22–27 for proofs.)

Theorem 12-11

If the scale factor of two similar solids is $a:b$, then

(1) the ratio of corresponding perimeters is $a:b$.

(2) the ratio of the base areas, of the lateral areas, and of the total areas is $a^2:b^2$.

(3) the ratio of the volumes is $a^3:b^3$.

Example For the similar solids shown, find the ratios of the **(a)** base perimeters, **(b)** lateral areas, and **(c)** volumes.

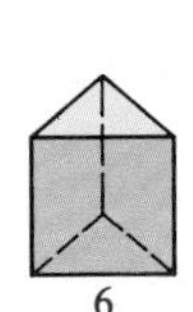

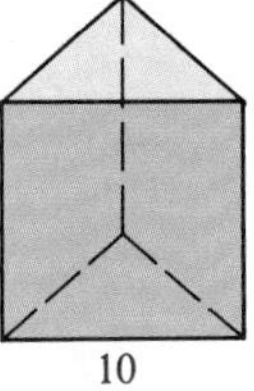

Solution The scale factor is 6:10, or 3:5.

a. Ratio of base perimeters = 3:5

b. Ratio of lateral areas = $3^2:5^2$ = 9:25

c. Ratio of volumes = $3^3:5^3$ = 27:125

Theorem 12-11 is the three-dimensional counterpart of Theorem 11-7 on page 457. (Take a minute to compare these theorems.) There is a similar relationship between the two cases shown below.

In two dimensions:

If $\overline{XY} \parallel \overline{AB}$, then $\triangle VXY \sim \triangle VAB$.

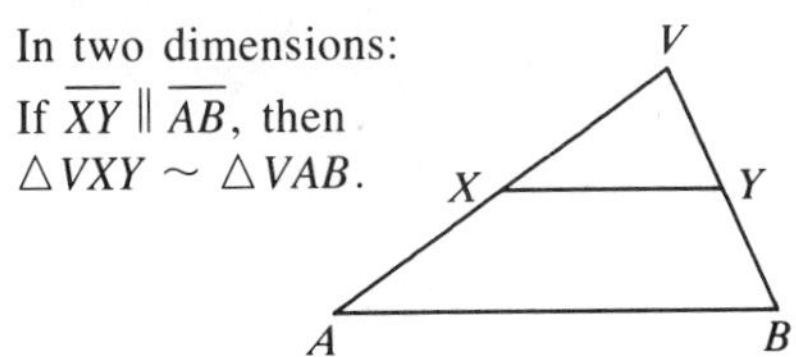

In three dimensions:

If plane $XYZ \parallel$ plane ABC, then $V\text{-}XYZ \sim V\text{-}ABC$.

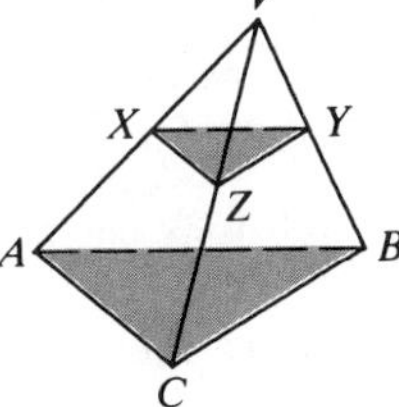

Chalkboard Examples

1. Are all spheres similar? yes
2. Are all right cylinders similar? no
3. Are all cubes similar? yes
4. Two cones have base radii 8 and 12 and heights 16 and 24, respectively. Are the cones similar? yes
5. Two similar square pyramids have base areas 4 m² and 36 m².
   a. Find the ratio of the heights of the pyramids. 1:3
   b. If the height of the larger pyramid is 27 m, what is the height of the smaller pyramid? 9 m

Teaching Note

Review with students the definition of similarity, reinforcing the fact that *all* corresponding lengths must be in the same proportion for two solids to be similar to each other.

Classroom Exercises

Tell whether the solids in each pair are similar. Explain your answer.

1. No; $\frac{6}{3} \neq \frac{12}{8}$

Right cylinders

2. Yes; bases are similar △s; $\frac{12}{8} = \frac{9}{6} = \frac{15}{10} = \frac{3}{2}$

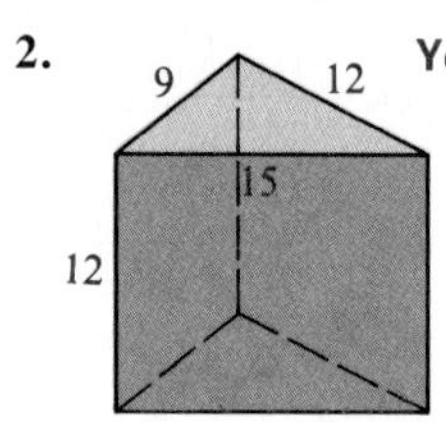

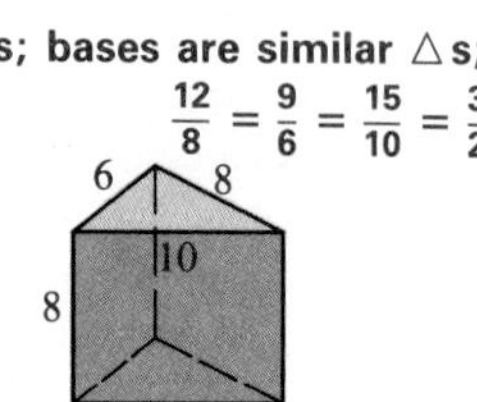

Right prisms

3. For the prisms in Exercise 2, find the ratios of:
 a. the lateral areas **9:4** **b.** the total areas **9:4** **c.** the volumes **27:8**

4. Two spheres have diameters 24 cm and 36 cm.
 a. What is the ratio of the areas? **4:9** **b.** What is the ratio of the volumes? **8:27**

5. Two spheres have volumes 2π m^3 and 16π m^3. Find the ratios of:
 a. the volumes **1:8** **b.** the diameters **1:2** **c.** the areas **1:4**

Complete the table below, which refers to two similar cones.

	6.	**7.**	**8.**	**9.**	**10.**	**11.**
Scale factor	3:4	5:7	2:? **1**	1:? **6**	2:? **3**	2:? **5**
Ratio of base circumferences	3:? **4**	5:? **7**	2:1	1:? **6**	2:? **3**	2:? **5**
Ratio of slant heights	3:? **4**	5:? **7**	2:? **1**	1:6	2:? **3**	2:? **5**
Ratio of lateral areas	9:? **16**	25:? **49**	4:? **1**	1:? **36**	4:9	4:? **25**
Ratio of total areas	9:? **16**	25:? **49**	4:? **1**	1:? **36**	4:? **9**	4:? **25**
Ratio of volumes	27:? **64**	?	8:? **1**	?	8:? **27**	8:125
		125:343		**1:216**		

12. Plane *PQR* is parallel to the base of the pyramid and bisects the altitude. Find the following ratios.
 a. The perimeter of △*PQR* to the perimeter of △*ABC* **1:2**
 b. The lateral area of the top part of the pyramid to the lateral area of the whole pyramid **1:4**
 c. The lateral area of the top part of the pyramid to the lateral area of the bottom part **1:3**
 d. The volume of the top part of the pyramid to the volume of the bottom part **1:7**

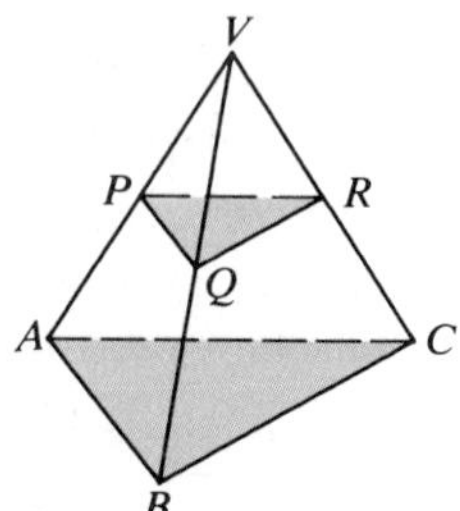

13. Find each ratio in Exercise 12 if the height of the top pyramid is 3 cm and the height of the whole pyramid is 5 cm.
a. 3:5 b. 9:25 c. 9:16 d. 27:98

Written Exercises **3. a. 3:4 b. 3:4 c. 9:16 d. 27:64**

A

1. Two cones have radii 6 cm and 9 cm. The heights are 10 cm and 15 cm, respectively. Are the cones similar? **Yes**
2. The heights of two right prisms are 18 ft and 30 ft. The bases are squares with sides 8 ft and 15 ft, respectively. Are the prisms similar? **No**
3. Two similar cylinders have radii 3 and 4. Find the ratios of the following: **See above.**
   a. heights **b.** base circumferences **c.** lateral areas **d.** volumes
4. Two similar pyramids have heights 12 and 18. Find the ratios of the following:
   a. base areas **4:9** **b.** lateral areas **4:9** **c.** total areas **4:9** **d.** volumes **8:27**
5. Assume that the Earth and the moon are smooth spheres with diameters 12,800 km and 3,200 km, respectively. Find the ratios of the following:
   a. lengths of their equators **4:1** **b.** areas **16:1** **c.** volumes **64:1**
6. Two similar cylinders have lateral areas 81π and 144π. Find the ratios of:
   a. the heights **3:4** **b.** the total areas **9:16** **c.** the volumes **27:64**
7. Two similar cones have volumes 8π and 27π. Find the ratios of:
   a. the radii **2:3** **b.** the slant heights **2:3** **c.** the lateral areas **4:9**
8. Two similar pyramids have volumes 3 and 375. Find the ratios of:
   a. the heights **1:5** **b.** the base areas **1:25** **c.** the total areas **1:25**
9. The package of a model airplane kit states that the scale is 1:200. Compare the amounts of paint required to cover the model and the actual airplane. (Assume the paint on the model is as thick as that on the actual airplane.) **See below.**
10. The scale for a certain model freight train is 1:48. If the model hopper car (usually used for carrying coal) will hold 90 in.^{3} of coal, what is the capacity in cubic feet of the actual hopper car? (*Hint*: See Exercise 10, page 477.) **5760 ft^3**

11. Two similar cones have radii of 4 cm and 6 cm. The total area of the smaller cone is 36π cm^2. Find the total area of the larger cone. **81π cm^2**

B

12. A diagonal of one cube is 2 cm. A diagonal of another cube is $4\sqrt{3}$ cm. The larger cube has volume 64 cm^3. Find the volume of the smaller cube. **$\frac{8\sqrt{3}}{9}$ cm^3**
13. Two balls made of the same metal have radii 6 cm and 10 cm. If the smaller ball weighs 4 kg, find the weight of the larger ball to the nearest 0.1 kg. **18.5 kg**
14. A snow man is made using three balls of snow with diameters 30 cm, 40 cm, and 50 cm. If the head weighs about 6 kg, find the total weight of the snow man. (Ignore the arms, eyes, nose and mouth.) **about 48 kg**

9. Paint for actual airplane = 40,000 × paint for model

Guided Practice

1. Two regular pyramids have equilateral triangular bases with sides 4 and 6. Their heights are 6 and 9, respectively. Are the two pyramids similar? yes
2. Two similar cones have bases with area ratios of 4:9. Find the ratios of the following:
   a. radii 2:3
   b. heights 2:3
   c. total areas 4:9
   d. volumes 8:27
3. The volumes of two spheres have a ratio of 27:64. Find the area of the larger sphere if the area of the smaller sphere is 18. 32
4. The radii of two similar cylinders are 2 and 5. Find the ratios of their volumes and of their lateral areas. 8:125, 4:25
5. The volumes of two similar rectangular solids are 125 cm^3 and 64 cm^3. Find the ratio of their base perimeters. 5:4

15. A certain kind of string is sold in a ball 6 cm in diameter and in a ball 12 cm in diameter. The smaller ball costs \$1.00 and the larger one costs \$6.50. Which is the better buy? **the larger ball**

16. Construction engineers know that the strength of a column is proportional to the area of its cross section. Suppose that the larger of two similar columns is three times as high as the smaller column.
   a. The larger column is ___?___ times as strong as the smaller column. **9**
   b. The larger column is ___?___ times as heavy as the smaller column. **27**
   c. Which can support more, *per pound of column material*, the larger or the smaller column? **the smaller column**

17. Two similar pyramids have lateral areas 8 ft^2 and 18 ft^2. If the volume of the smaller pyramid is 32 ft^3, what is the volume of the larger pyramid? **108 ft^3**

18. Two similar cones have volumes 12π and 96π. If the lateral area of the smaller cone is 15π, what is the lateral area of the larger cone? **60π**

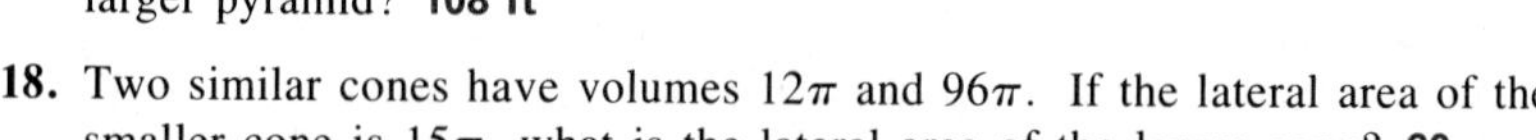

19. A plane parallel to the base of a cone divides the cone into two pieces. Find the ratios of the following:
   a. The areas of the shaded circles **9:16**
   b. The lateral area of the top part of the cone to the lateral area of the whole cone **9:16**
   c. The lateral area of the top part of the cone to the lateral area of the bottom part **9:7**
   d. The volume of the top part of the cone to the volume of the whole cone **27:64**
   e. The volume of the top part of the cone to the volume of the bottom part **27:37**

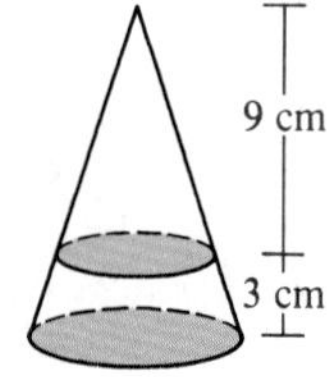

20. Redraw the figure for Exercise 19, changing the 9 cm and 3 cm dimensions to 10 cm and 4 cm, respectively. Then find the five ratios described in Exercise 19. **a. 25:49 b. 25:49 c. 25:24 d. 125:343 e. 125:218**

21. A pyramid with height 15 cm is separated into two pieces by a plane parallel to the base and 6 cm above it. What are the volumes of these two pieces if the volume of the original pyramid is 250 cm^3? **54 cm^3; 196 cm^3**

The purpose of Exercises 22–27 is to prove Theorem 12-11 for some similar solids.

$4\pi a^2 : 4\pi b^2 = a^2 : b^2$

22. Two spheres have radii a and b. Prove that the ratio of the areas is $a^2:b^2$.

23. Two spheres have radii a and b. Prove that the ratio of the volumes is $a^3:b^3$. **$\frac{4}{3}\pi a^3 : \frac{4}{3}\pi b^3 = a^3 : b^3$**

24. Two similar cones have radii r_1 and r_2 and heights h_1 and h_2. Prove that the ratio of the volumes is $h_1^3:h_2^3$.

25. Two similar cones have radii r_1 and r_2 and slant heights l_1 and l_2. Prove that the ratio of the lateral areas is $r_1^2:r_2^2$.

26. The bases of two similar right prisms are regular pentagons with base edges e_1 and e_2 and base areas B_1 and B_2. The heights are h_1 and h_2. Prove that the ratio of the lateral areas is $e_1^2 : e_2^2$.

27. Refer to Exercise 26. Prove that the ratio of the volumes of the prisms is $e_1^3 : e_2^3$.

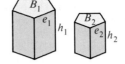

C **28.** The purpose of this exercise is to prove that if plane XYZ is parallel to plane ABC, then $V\text{-}XYZ \sim V\text{-}ABC$. To do this, suppose that $VA = k \cdot VX$ and show that every edge of $V\text{-}ABC$ is k times as long as the corresponding edge of $V\text{-}XYZ$. (*Hint*: Use Theorem 3-1.)

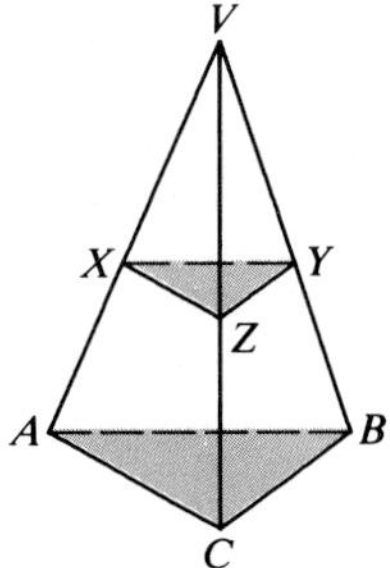

29. A plane parallel to the base of a pyramid separates the pyramid into two pieces with equal volumes. If the height of the pyramid is 12, find the height of the top piece. **$6\sqrt[3]{4}$**

Self-Test 2

1. Find the area and volume of a sphere with diameter 6 cm. **36π cm^2; 36π cm^3**
2. The volume of a sphere is $\frac{32}{3}\pi$ m^3. Find the area of the sphere. **16π m^2**
3. The students of a school decide to bury a time capsule consisting of a cylinder capped by two hemispheres. Find the volume of the time capsule shown. **$\frac{22{,}000\pi}{3}$ cm^3**
4. Find the area of the circle formed when a plane passes 12 cm from the center of a sphere with radius 13 cm. **25π cm^2**
5. One regular triangular pyramid has base edge 8 and height 6. A similar pyramid has height 4.
   a. Find the base edge of the smaller pyramid. **$\frac{16}{3}$**
   b. Find the ratio of the total areas of the pyramids. **9:4**
6. The base areas of two similar prisms are 32 and 200, respectively.
   a. Find the ratio of their heights. **2:5** **b.** Find the ratio of their volumes. **8:125**

60 cm
20 cm

Ex. 3

Challenge

square pyramid

A pattern for a model is shown. Can you tell what it is? To build it, make a large copy of the pattern on stiff paper. Cut along the solid lines, fold along the dashed lines, and tape the edges together.

If you want to make a pattern for a figure, think about the number of faces, their shapes, and how the edges are related. Try to create and build models for a triangular prism, a triangular pyramid, and a cone.

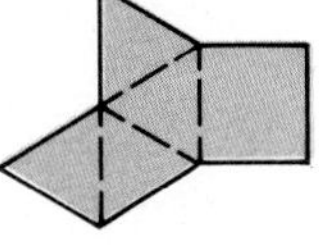

Quick Quiz

1. Find the area and volume of a sphere with diameter 8 cm.
   64π cm^2; $\frac{256}{3}\pi$ cm^3
2. The volume of a sphere is $\frac{500}{3}\pi$ m^3. Find the area of the sphere. 100π m^2
3. A capsule consists of a cylinder capped on each base by a hemisphere. If the cylinder has a base diameter of 2 m and a height of 5 m, find the volume of the capsule. $\frac{19}{3}\pi$ m^3
4. Find the area of the circle formed when a plane passes 6 cm from the center of a sphere with radius 10 cm. 64π cm^2
5. One regular triangular pyramid has a base edge of 9 and a height of 5. A similar pyramid has a height of 15.
   a. Find the base edge of the larger pyramid. 27
   b. Find the ratio of the total areas of the pyramids. 1:9
6. The base areas of two similar prisms are 75 and 300.
   a. Find the ratio of their heights. 1:2
   b. Find the ratio of their volumes. 1:8

♦ Calculator Key-In

Each diagram shows a rectangle inscribed in an isosceles triangle with legs 5 and base 6. There are many more such rectangles. Which one has the greatest area?

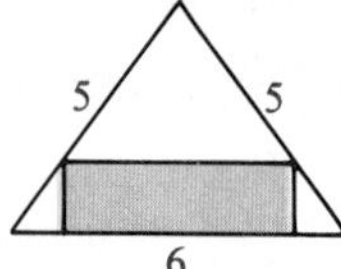

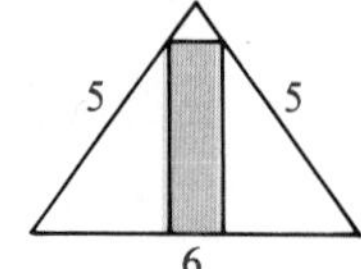

To solve the problem, let *CDEF* represent any rectangle inscribed in isosceles $\triangle ABV$ with legs 5 and base 6. If we let $OD = x$ and $ED = y$, then the area of the rectangle is $2xy$. Our goal is to express this area in terms of x alone. Then we can find out how the area changes as x changes.

1. In right $\triangle VOB$, $OB = 3$ and $VB = 5$. Thus $VO = 4$ by the Pythagorean Theorem.
2. $\triangle EDB \sim \triangle VOB$ (Why?) **AA Similarity Post.**
3. $\frac{ED}{VO} = \frac{DB}{OB}$ (Why?) **Corr. sides of ~ △s are in proportion.**
4. $\frac{y}{4} = \frac{3 - x}{3}$ (By substitution in Step 3)
5. $y = \frac{4}{3}(3 - x)$ (Multiplication Property of =)

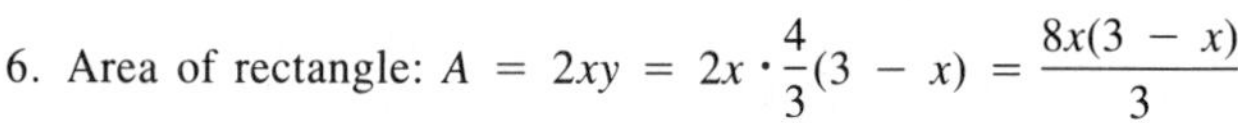

6. Area of rectangle: $A = 2xy = 2x \cdot \frac{4}{3}(3 - x) = \frac{8x(3 - x)}{3}$

Use the formula in Step 6 and a calculator to find the area for many values of x. Calculate $3 - x$ first, then multiply by x, then multiply by 8, and divide by 3.

x	Area
0	0
0.25	1.83333
0.5	3.33333
0.75	4.5
1	5.33333
1.25	5.83333
1.5	6
1.75	5.83333
2	5.33333
2.25	4.5
2.50	3.33333
2.75	1.83333
3	0

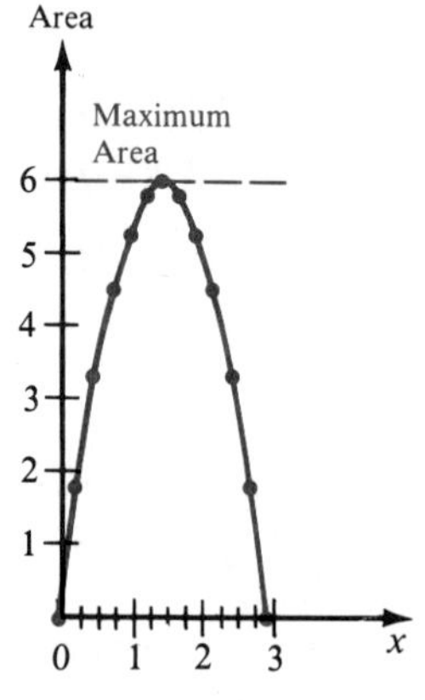

The table was used to make a graph showing how the area varies with x. Both the table and the graph suggest that the greatest area, 6 square units, occurs when $x = 1.5$.

Exercises

1. $VO = 3$; $DB = 4 - x$; $y = \frac{3}{4}(4 - x)$; $A = 2xy = 2x\left(\frac{3}{4}(4 - x)\right) = \frac{3x(4 - x)}{2}$

Suppose the original triangle had sides 5, 5, and 8 instead of 5, 5, and 6.

1. Draw a diagram. Then show that $A = \dfrac{3x(4 - x)}{2}$.
2. Find the value of x for which the greatest area occurs. **The greatest area, 6, occurs when $x = 2$.**

♦ Computer Key-In

A rectangle is inscribed in an isosceles triangle with legs 5 and base 6 and the triangle is rotated in space about the altitude to the base. The resulting figure is a cylinder inscribed in a cone with diameter 6 and slant height 5, as shown below. Which of the cylinders such as these has the greatest volume?

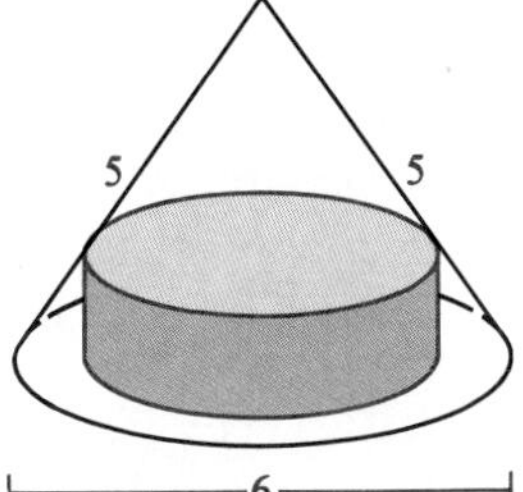

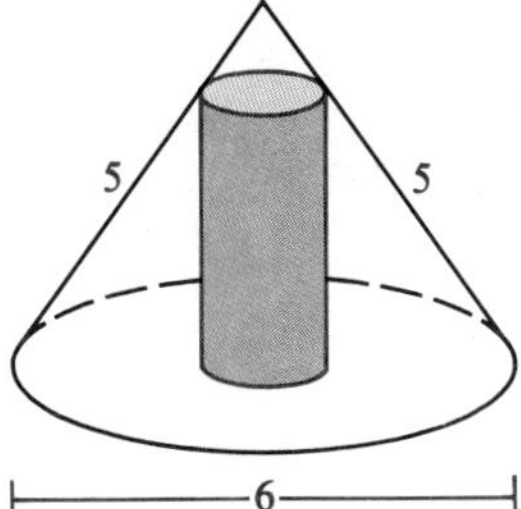

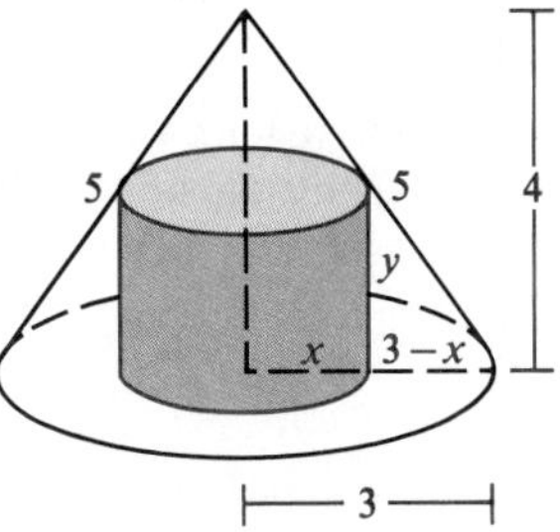

The diagram at the right above shows a typical inscribed cylinder. Using similar triangles, we have the proportion $\frac{y}{4} = \frac{3 - x}{3}$. Thus $y = \frac{4}{3}(3 - x)$.

The volume of the cylinder is found as follows:

$$V = \pi x^2 y = \pi x^2 \cdot \tfrac{4}{3}(3 - x) \approx \tfrac{4}{3}(3.14159)x^2(3 - x)$$

The following program in BASIC evaluates V for various values of x.

```
10  PRINT "X", "VOLUME"
20  FOR X = 0 TO 3 STEP 0.25
30  LET V = 4/3 * 3.14159 * X↑2 * (3 - X)
40  PRINT X, V
50  NEXT X
60  END
```

Exercises

1. RUN the program. Make a graph that shows how the volume varies with x. For what value of x did you find the greatest volume? **$x = 2$ ($V \approx 16.76$)**
2. Suppose the original triangle has sides 5, 5, and 8 instead of 5, 5, and 6. Rotate the triangle in space about the altitude to the base.
   a. Draw a diagram. Show that $V = \frac{3}{4}\pi x^2(4 - x)$.
   b. Change lines 20 and 30 of the program and RUN the revised program to find the value of x for which the greatest volume occurs. **$x = 2.75$ ($V \approx 22.27$)**

Using a Computer

Some students may want to write a computer program that will calculate the area of the rectangle for many values of x and generate a table of coordinates.

Making Connections

Point out the connection between the Key-In on this page and the one on the previous page (from two dimensions to three dimensions). Note also that the maximizing values of x are different in the two cases. Basically, $A = 2xy$ varies with x and $V = \pi x^2 y$ varies with x^2.

Extra

Cavalieri's Principle

Suppose you have a right rectangular prism and divide it horizontally into thin rectangular slices. The base of each rectangular slice, or *cross section*, has the same area as the base of the prism. If you rearrange the slices, the total volume of the slices does not change.

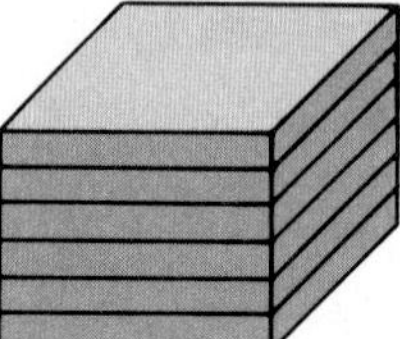

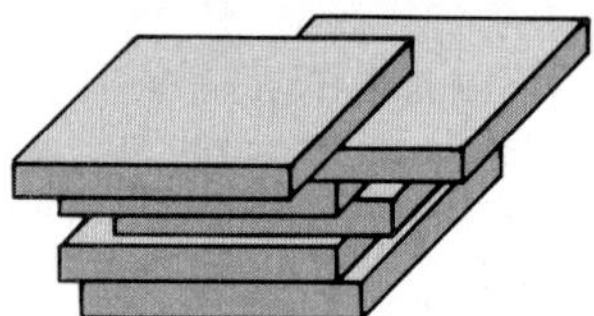

Bonaventura Cavalieri (1598–1647), an Italian mathematician, used this idea to compare the volumes of solids. His conclusion is known as *Cavalieri's Principle*.

Cavalieri's Principle

If two solids lying between parallel planes have equal heights and all cross sections at equal distances from their bases have equal areas, then the solids have equal volumes.

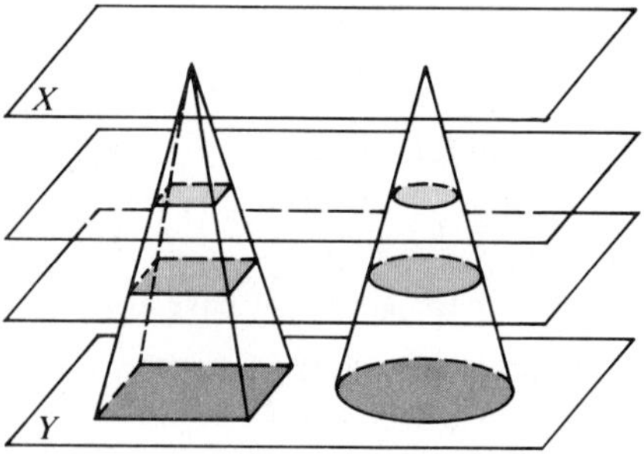

Using Cavalieri's Principle you can find the volume of an oblique prism. Consider a right triangular prism and an oblique prism that have the same base and height.

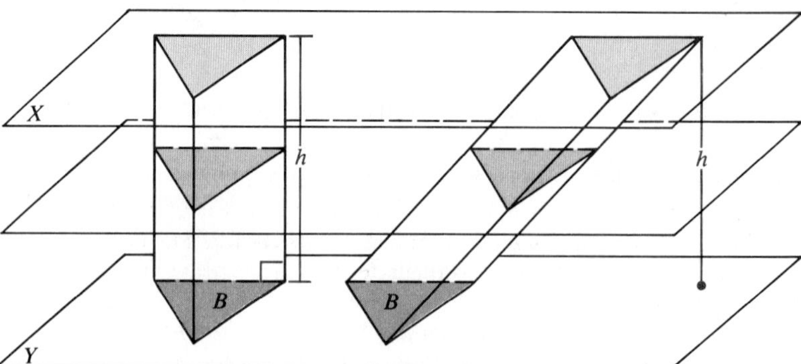

Teaching Note

Since Cavalieri's Principle is an important result in geometry, you may wish to cover this topic with your more advanced classes. Cavalieri's Principle uses the approach of taking slices, which is also the method used in the Computer Key-In on pages 488–489 (finding the volume of a pyramid) and the Computer Key-In on pages 504–505 (finding the volume of a sphere). By relating the Computer Key-Ins to Cavalieri's Principle, students can see the usefulness of the method of slicing.

Cultural Note

Bonaventura Cavalieri was a pupil of Galileo and a professor in Bologna, Italy. He published many works on mathematics, astronomy, and optics.

By Theorem 12-2, the volume of the right prism is $V = Bh$. Every cross section of each prism has the same area as that prism's base. Since the base areas are equal, the corresponding cross sections of the two prisms have equal areas. Therefore by Cavalieri's Principle, the volume of the oblique prism also is $V = Bh$.

You can use similar reasoning to show that the volume formulas given for a regular pyramid, right cylinder, and right cone hold true for the corresponding oblique solids.

$V = Bh$ for *any* prism or cylinder
$V = \frac{1}{3}Bh$ for *any* pyramid or cone

Exercises

Find the volume of the solid shown with the given altitude.

1. **22**

2. **200π**

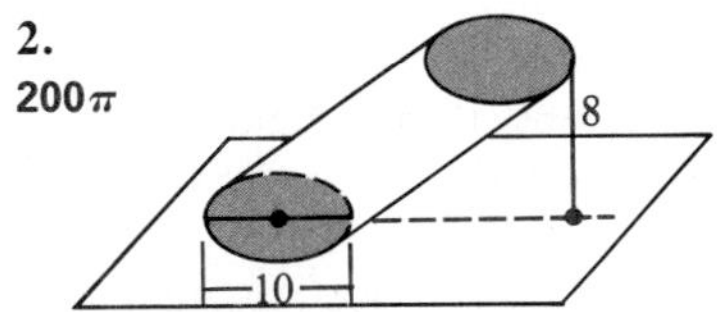

3. Find the volume of an oblique cone with radius 4 and height 3.5. $\mathbf{\frac{56\pi}{3}}$

4. The oblique square prism shown below has base edge 3. A lateral edge that is 15 makes a 60° angle with the plane containing the base. Find the exact volume. $\mathbf{\frac{135\sqrt{3}}{2}}$

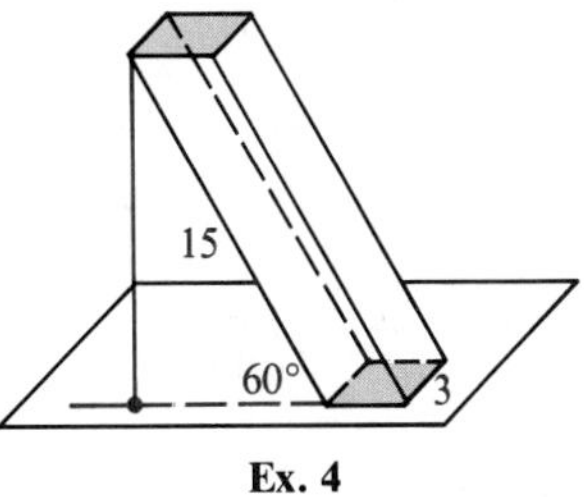

Ex. 4

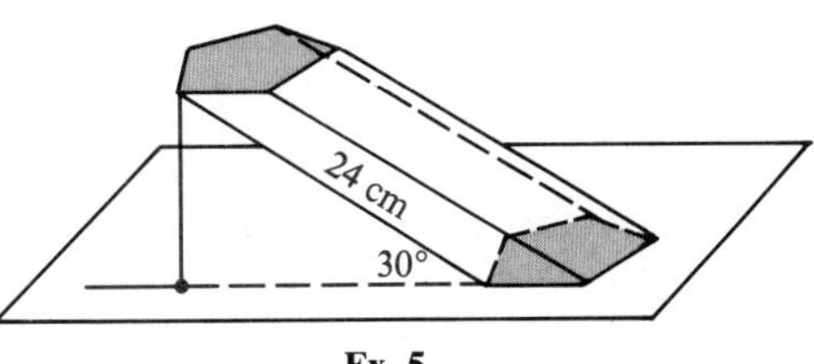

Ex. 5

5. The volume of the oblique pentagonal prism shown above is 96 cm^3. A lateral edge that is 24 cm makes a 30° angle with the plane containing the base. Find the area of the base. **8 cm^2**

6. Refer to the justification of the formula for the volume of a sphere given on pages 498–499. How does Cavalieri's Principle justify the statement that the volume of the sphere is equal to the difference between the volumes of the cylinder and the double cone?

Additional Answers
Extra

6. The area of each cross section of the sphere equals the difference of the areas of the corresponding cross sections of the cylinder and the double cone. All three solids have equal heights, namely, 2*r*. Then by Cavalieri's Principle, the volume of the sphere is equal to the difference between the volumes of the cylinder and the double cone.

Chapter Summary

1. The list below summarizes area and volume formulas for solids. The cylinder formulas are special cases of the prism formulas with $p = 2\pi r$ and $B = \pi r^2$. Also the cone formulas are special cases of the pyramid formulas with the same substitutions for p and B. To find the total area of each of the four solids, add lateral area to the area of the base(s).

Right prism	L.A. $= ph$	$V = Bh$
Right cylinder	L.A. $= 2\pi rh$	$V = \pi r^2 h$
Regular pyramid	L.A. $= \frac{1}{2}pl$	$V = \frac{1}{3}Bh$
Right cone	L.A. $= \pi rl$	$V = \frac{1}{3}\pi r^2 h$
Sphere	$A = 4\pi r^2$	$V = \frac{4}{3}\pi r^3$

2. If the scale factor of two similar solids is $a:b$, then
   a. the ratio of corresponding perimeters is $a:b$.
   b. the ratio of corresponding areas is $a^2:b^2$.
   c. the ratio of the volumes is $a^3:b^3$.

Supplementary Materials

Practice Master 76

Test 49

Resource Book, pp. 81–82, 158

Chapter Review

1. In a right prism, each __?__ is also an altitude. **lateral edge** 12–1
2. Find the lateral area of a right octagonal prism with height 12 and base edge 7. **672**
3. Find the total area and volume of a rectangular solid with dimensions 8, 6, and 5. **236; 240**
4. A right square prism has base edge 9 and volume 891. Find the total area. **558**
5. Find the volume of a regular triangular pyramid with base edge 8 and height 10. $\mathbf{\frac{160\sqrt{3}}{3}}$ 12–2
6. A regular pentagonal pyramid has base edge 6 and lateral edge 5. Find the slant height and the lateral area. **4; 60**

A regular square pyramid has base edge 30 and total area 1920.

7. Find the area of the base, the lateral area, and the slant height. **900; 1020; 17**
8. Find the height and the volume of the pyramid. **8; 2400**
9. Find the lateral area and the total area of a cylinder with radius 4 and height 3. **24π; 56π** 12–3
10. Find the lateral area, total area, and volume of a cone with radius 6 cm and slant height 10 cm. **60π cm^2; 96π cm^2; 96π cm^3**
11. A cone has volume 8π cm^3 and height 6 cm. Find its slant height. **$2\sqrt{10}$ cm**
12. The radius of a cylinder is doubled and its height is halved. How does the volume change? **The volume is doubled.**

13. A sphere has radius 7 m. Use $\pi \approx \frac{22}{7}$ to find the approximate area of the sphere. **616 m^2** 12–4

14. Find, in terms of π, the volume of a sphere with diameter 12 ft. **288π ft^3**

15. Find the volume of a sphere with area 484π cm^2. **$\frac{5324\pi}{3}$ cm^3**

Plane *RST* ∥ plane *XYZ* and *VS*:*VY* = 1:3.

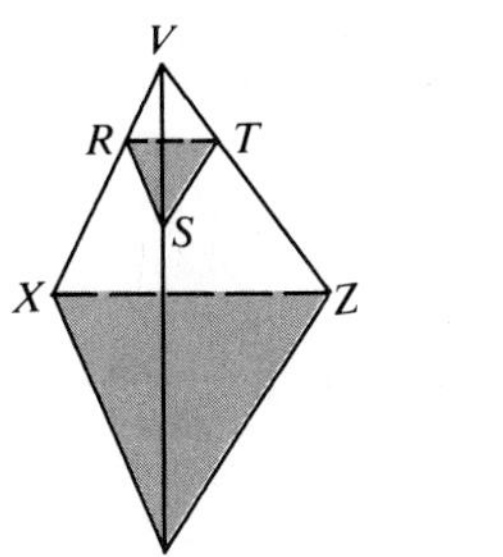

16. $\frac{\text{perimeter of } \triangle RST}{\text{perimeter of } \triangle XYZ} = \underline{\ ?\ }$ **1:3** 12–5

17. $\frac{\text{total area of small pyramid}}{\text{total area of large pyramid}} = \underline{\ ?\ }$ **1:9**

18. $\frac{\text{volume of small pyramid}}{\text{volume of bottom part}} = \underline{\ ?\ }$ **1:26**

19. Two similar cylinders have lateral areas 48π and 27π. Find the ratio of their volumes. **64:27**

Chapter Test

1. Find the volume and the total area of a cube with edge $2k$. **$8k^3$; $24k^2$**
2. A regular square pyramid has base edge 3 cm and volume 135 cm^2. Find the height. **45 cm**
3. A cone has radius 8 and height 6. Find the volume. **128π**
4. Find the lateral area and the total area of the cone in Exercise 3. **80π; 144π**
5. A right triangular prism has height 20 and base edges 5, 12, and 13. Find the total area. **660**
6. Find the volume of the prism in Exercise 5. **600**
7. A cylinder has radius 6 cm and height 4 cm. Find the lateral area. **48π cm^2**
8. Find the volume of the cylinder in Exercise 7. **144π cm^3**
9. A regular square pyramid has lateral area 60 m^2 and base edge 6 m. Find the volume. **48 m^3**
10. A sphere has radius 6 cm. Find the area and the volume. **144π cm^2; 288π cm^3**
11. Two cones have radii 12 cm and 18 cm, and have slant heights 18 cm and 24 cm. Are the cones similar? Explain. **No; $\frac{12}{18} \neq \frac{18}{24}$**
12. A regular pyramid has height 18 and total area 648. A similar pyramid has height 6. Find the total area of the smaller pyramid. **72**
13. The volumes of two similar rectangular solids are 1000 cm^3 and 64 cm^3. What is the ratio of their lateral areas? **25:4**
14. A cone and a cylinder each have radius 3 and height 4. Find the ratio of their volumes and of their lateral areas. **1:3; 5:8**
15. Find the volume of a sphere with area 9π. **$\frac{9\pi}{2}$**
16. A cylinder with radius 7 has total area 168π cm^2. Find its height. **5 cm**

Teaching References

Alternate Test, p. T23

Supplementary Materials

Practice Masters 77, 78

Test 50

Resource Book, pp. 83–85, 159–160, 183–185, 201

Preparing for College Entrance Exams

Strategy for Success

Questions on college entrance exams often require knowledge of areas and volumes. Be sure that you know all the important formulas developed in Chapters 11 and 12. To avoid doing unnecessary calculations, be sure to read the directions to find out whether answers may be expressed in terms of π.

Indicate the best answer by writing the appropriate letter.

A **1.** A cone has volume 320π and height 15. Find the total area.
(A) 200π **(B)** 368π **(C)** 264π **(D)** 136π **(E)** 320π

C **2.** Two equilateral triangles have perimeters 6 and $9\sqrt{3}$. The ratio of their areas is:
(A) $2:3\sqrt{3}$ **(B)** $2\sqrt{3}:9$ **(C)** $4:27$ **(D)** $4:9$ **(E)** $8:81\sqrt{3}$

E **3.** A sphere has volume 288π. Its diameter is:
(A) $12\sqrt{6}$ **(B)** $6\sqrt{2}$ **(C)** 6 **(D)** $12\sqrt{2}$ **(E)** 12

D **4.** *RSTW* is a rhombus with $m\angle R = 60$ and $RS = 4$. If X is the midpoint of $\overline{RS}$, find the area of trapezoid *SXWT*.
(A) 12 **(B)** 16 **(C)** $8\sqrt{3}$ **(D)** $6\sqrt{3}$ **(E)** $16 - 2\sqrt{2}$

B **5.** If *ABCD* is a square and $AE = y$, the area of *ABCDE* is
(A) $\frac{5}{4}y^2$ **(B)** $\frac{5}{2}y^2$ **(C)** $3y^2$
(D) $(4 + \frac{1}{2}\sqrt{3})y^2$ **(E)** $(\frac{1}{2} + \sqrt{2})y^2$

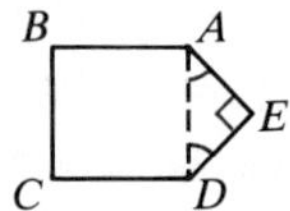

Compare the quantity in Column A with that in Column B. Select:
(A) if the quantity in Column A is greater;
(B) if the quantity in Column B is greater;
(C) if the two quantities are equal;
(D) if the relationship cannot be determined from the information given.

	Column A	**Column B**
C **6.**	volume of square pyramid	volume of square prism
B **7.**	area of triangle	area of sector

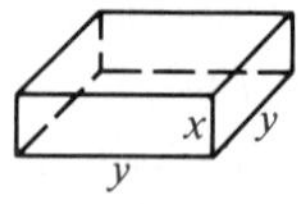

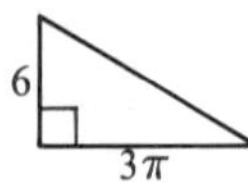

Cumulative Review: Chapters 1–12

For Exercises 1–9 classify each statement as true or false.

A 1. No more than one plane contains two given intersecting lines. **True**

2. The conditional "p only if q" is equivalent to "if p, then q." **True**

3. If the vertex angle of an isosceles triangle has measure j, then the measure of a base angle is $180 - 2j$. **False**

4. In $\triangle RST$, if $m\angle R = 48$ and $m\angle S = 68$, then $RT > RS$. **True**

5. If right $\triangle JEH$ has hypotenuse $\overline{JE}$, then $\tan J = \frac{JH}{EH}$. **False**

6. It is possible to construct an angle of measure 105. **True**

7. The area of a triangle with sides 3, 3, and 2 is $4\sqrt{2}$. **False**

8. When a square is circumscribed about a circle, the ratio of the areas is $4:\pi$. **True**

9. A triangle with sides of length $\sqrt{3}$, 2, and $\sqrt{7}$ is a right triangle. **True**

B 10. In $\square JKLM$, $m\angle J = \frac{3}{2}x$ and $m\angle L = x + 17$. Find the numerical measure of $\angle K$. **129**

11. Given: $\overline{WZ} \perp \overline{ZY}$; $\overline{WX} \perp \overline{XY}$; $\overline{WX} \cong \overline{YZ}$
Prove: $\overline{WZ} \parallel \overline{XY}$

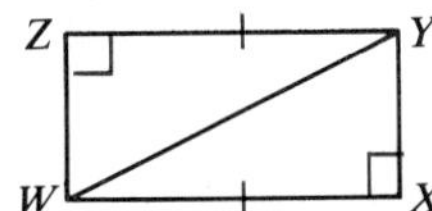

12. Prove: If the diagonals of a parallelogram are perpendicular, then the parallelogram must be a rhombus.

13. For $\triangle JKL$ and $\triangle XYZ$ use the following statement:
"If $\angle J \cong \angle X$ and $\angle K \cong \angle Y$, then $\triangle JKL \sim \triangle XYZ$."
   a. Name the postulate or theorem that justifies the statement. **AA ~ Post.**
   b. Write the converse of the statement. Is the converse true or false? **True**

14. Find the value of x in the diagram at the right. **8**

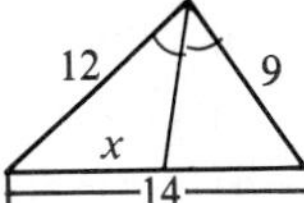

15. $\overline{AB}$ and $\overline{CD}$ are chords of $\odot P$ intersecting at X. If $AX = 7.5$, $BX = 3.2$, $CD = 11$, and $CX > DX$, find CX. **8**

16. Describe each possibility for the locus of points in space that are equidistant from the sides of a $\triangle ABC$ and 4 cm from A. **0, 1, or 2 points**

17. $\overset{\frown}{AB}$ lies on $\odot O$ with $m\overset{\frown}{AB} = 60$. $\odot O$ has radius 8. Find AB. **8**

18. A regular square pyramid has base edge 10 and height 12. Find its total area and volume. **360; 400**

19. A cylinder has a radius equal to its height. The total area of the cylinder is 100π cm^2. Find its volume. **125π cm^3**

20. A sphere has a diameter of 1.8 cm. Find its surface area to the nearest square centimeter. (Use $\pi \approx 3.14$.) **10 cm^2**

Additional Answers
Cumulative Review

13.b. If $\triangle JKL \sim \triangle XYZ$, then $\angle J \cong \angle X$ and $\angle K \cong \angle Y$.

13 Coordinate Geometry

Objectives

13-1 State and apply the distance formula.

State and apply the general equation of a circle.

13-2 State and apply the slope formula.

13-3 Determine whether two lines are parallel, perpendicular, or neither.

13-4 Understand the basic properties of vectors.

13-5 State and apply the midpoint formula.

13-6 Identify the slope and y-intercept of the line specified by a given equation.

Draw the graph of the line specified by a given equation.

Determine the intersection of two lines.

13-7 Write an equation of a line when given either one point and the slope of the line, or two points on the line.

13-8 Given a polygon, choose a convenient placement of coordinate axes and assign appropriate coordinates.

13-9 Prove statements by using coordinate geometry methods.

Assignment Guide

See page T40 for information about the Assignment Guide.

Day	Minimum Course	Average Course	Maximum Course
1		**13-1** 526–527/1–27 odd	**13-1** 526–527/2–40 even
2		**13-2** 532–533/1–5, 7, 8, 10, 11, 14, 16, 18, 19	**13-2** 532–533/5, 8, 11, 14–16, 18, 20–24
3		**13-3** 537/2, 3, 5, 7, 9	**13-2** 533–534/25–32
4		**13-4** 541–542/1–17 odd 543/Mix. Rev. 2–10 even	**13-3** 537–538/4, 5, 7, 10–12, 15
5		**13-5** 545–546/3, 5–7, 9, 12, 13 547/Self-Test 1	**13-3** 538/13, 17, 20, 21, 23
6		**13-6** 550–551/2, 5, 8, 15, 19, 25	**13-4** 541–542/8, 10, 16, 20, 26, 27, 31 **S** 538/19
7		**13-7** 555/1–25 odd	**13-5** 545–547/4, 5, 8, 12, 13, 15, 19, 23 **S** 542/29, 32
8		**13-8** 558–559/1–7 563/Self-Test 2, 1–6	**13-6** 550–551/3, 5, 8, 13, 16, 19, 24
9			**13-6** 551–552/25–37 odd
10			**13-7** 555/2, 6, 9, 15, 17–25 odd
11			**13-7** 555–556/27, 31, 34–36, 38
12			**13-8** 558–559/1–9

13		13-8 559/10–13 S 556/37	
14		13-9 562/1, 4, 5, 7–10	
15		13-9 562–563/3, 6, 11–14 568/Chapter Test Test, page T24	

Supplementary Materials Guide

For Use after Lesson	Practice Masters	Tests	Study Guide (Reteaching)	Resource Book			Computer Activities
				Tests	Practice Exercises	College Entrance (Col) Enrichment (E) Computer (C)	
13-1	Sheet 79		pp. 163–164				Activities 27, 28
13-2			pp. 165–166				
13-3	Sheet 80	Test 51	pp. 167–168	pp. 86–87	p. 161		Activity 29
13-4			pp. 169–170				
13-5	Sheet 81	Test 52	pp. 171–172	pp. 88–89	p. 162		Activity 30
13-6			pp. 173–174				
13-7	Sheet 82	Test 53	pp. 175–176	pp. 90–91	p. 163		Activities 31, 32
13-8			pp. 177–178				
13-9	Sheet 83	Test 54	pp. 179–180	pp. 92–93	p. 164		
Chapter 13	Sheet 84	Test 55		pp. 94–95	p. 165	p. 202 (Col) pp. 230–236 (E) pp. 243, 257–259 (C)	Activity 33

Overhead Visuals

Guided Discovery Visuals (lettered) and Teaching Visuals (numbered) available for Chapter 13.

Lessons	Visual	Title
13-5, 13-9	F	Diagonals of Prisms
13-2, 13-7	L	Slopes and Rotations
13-1, 13-2, 13-3, 13-4, 13-5	27	Coordinate Geometry Summary
Chapter 13	28a	Coordinate Plane
13-6, 13-7, 13-8, 13-9	28b	Placement of Grid on Shapes

Software Guide

Houghton Mifflin software for Chapter 13

Geometry Grapher (Apple or IBM)

Use with	Booklet
Ch. 13	Teaching Suggestions, pp. 5–10
Ch. 13	Activities 1–3, pp. 20–24

Test Generator (Apple or IBM): 135 test items

Other software appropriate for Chapter 13

GeoDraw (IBM)

Spreadsheets

Guide to Integrated Curriculum

Although the text presents coordinate and transformational geometry in Chapters 13 and 14, and in the Handbook on pp. 657–675, teachers wishing to integrate this material throughout the course may do so easily using the information on **pp. T56–T57.** The integration occurs throughout Chapters 3-12.

With this integrated curriculum, students learn concepts, solve problems, and prove theorems using alternate approaches. Students make connections between geometry and algebra, and they learn the valuable skill of deciding which method to use in a problem **(pp. 672–673).**

Strategies for Teaching

Exploring Taxi-Travel Geometry

When to Use

Anytime during Chapter 13

Overview

In this activity students locate points and measure distance in the coordinate plane using a way different from the distance formula. They are also presented with several optimization situations.

Materials

Coordinate graph paper

Description of Activity

Distances between points $P(x_1, y_1)$ and $Q(x_2, y_2)$ in the coordinate plane are measured "as the crow flies" using the distance formula $d(P, Q) = \sqrt{(x_1 - x_2)^2 + (y_1 - y_2)^2}$. Another way to measure distance is "as the taxi travels" using the formula $d^*(P, Q) = |x_1 - x_2| + |y_1 - y_2|$.
In the diagram below, $d(P, Q) = 5$ and $d^*(P, Q) = 4 + 3 = 7$.

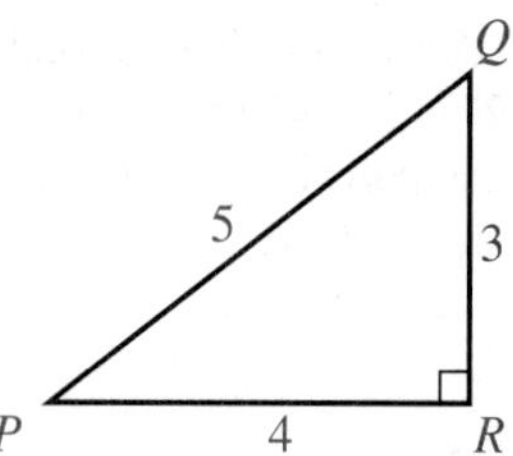

1. **a.** Find $d^*(P, Q)$ for $P(5, 4)$ and $Q(1, 2)$. 6
   b. Find $d^*(P, Q)$ for $P(3, -1)$ and $Q(-2, 4)$. 10
   c. What must be true of P and Q so that $d(P, Q) = d^*(P, Q)$? $\overline{PQ}$ must be horizontal or vertical.
   d. Prove $d(P, Q) \le d^*(P, Q)$ for all pairs of points (P, Q).
   e. Sketch the locus of all points Q for which $P(-3, 4)$ and $d^*(P, Q) = 5$.

2. **a.** Suppose Terry's house is located at $P(4, 4)$ and Chris's house is at $Q(8, 8)$. The distance between the houses is 8 "blocks," that is, $d^*(P, Q) = 8$. They want to meet at a point halfway between their houses so each will have to walk 4 blocks. Give the location of all possible meeting places. The 5 points along the diagonal of the square whose other diagonal is $\overline{PQ}$.
   b. There are some other points that are the same number of blocks from the two houses. Sketch the location of these points in the first quadrant.
   c. Repeat **a** and **b** for $P(3, 3)$ and $Q(10, 6)$. The 8 points along the diagonal of the parallelogram whose other diagonal is $\overline{PQ}$, vertices (3, 8) and (10, 1).

3. **a.** There are three grocery stores located at $P(-3, 3)$, $Q(4, 1)$, and $R(1, -3)$. As a planner for the grocery stores, where should you recommend that a central warehouse serving these three stores be built so the sum of the distances from the warehouse to the three stores is at most 15 blocks? (0, 0) to (2, 2)
   b. Where should you recommend that a central warehouse serving these three stores be built so the sum of the distances from the warehouse to the three stores is as small as possible?
   c. Generalize your solution to **b** and describe a procedure to locate the warehouse given the locations of three stores.
   d. If a new grocery store is built at $(-8, 1)$, where would you recommend that a central warehouse serving these four stores be built so the sum of the distances from the warehouse to the four stores is as small as possible?
   e. Generalize your solution to **d** and describe a procedure to locate the warehouse given the locations of four stores.

Commentary

- In **1c** and **1d** the "triangle inequality" is explored. **1d** offers a coordinate proof in the comparison of the two different algebraic expressions for the distance between two points. The idea of a "taxi-circle" is in **1e.**
- In **2,** the locus of points equidistant between two given points is explored.
- **3b.** The solution must be on the line $y = 1$ since if you move 1 unit off this line, you increase the distance to two of the stores by 1 unit and decrease the distance to the other store by 1 unit for a net increase of 1 unit. Similar reasoning applied to the line $x = 1$ shows the solution to be (1, 1).
- **3d.** Use reasoning similar to that in **3b** to establish that the warehouse could be anywhere on the segment from (-3, 1) to (1, 1).

References to Strategies

PE: Pupil's Edition **TE:** Teacher's Edition **RB:** Resource Book

Problem Solving Strategies

PE: 545 (Choose a method of solution), 552 (Challenge, Draw a diagram), 564 (Mathematical model), 672–675 (Choose a method of solution)
RB: 230–231 (Look for a pattern), 232 (Solve a simpler problem), 258–259 (Trial and error)

Applications

PE: 539–541 (Vectors), 564 (Network efficiency)
TE: T133, 564
RB: 235–236

Nonroutine Problems

PE: 527 (Exs. 41, 42), 532 (Ex. 7), 538 (Exs. 15–18), 541 (Ex. 8), 543 (Exs. 33, 34), 552 (Challenge), 564 (Application), 565 (Points in space), 674–675 (Exs. 1–20)
TE: T132, T136
RB: 230–236

Communication

TE: T132, T133, T136

Thinking Skills

TE: 527 (Analyze figures), 530 (Analyze figures)

Explorations

PE: 552
TE: 521c
RB: 230–234

Connections

PE: 523 (Coordinate plane), 525 (Equation of circle), 534 (Rules of exponents), 564 (Steiner), 672–675 (Coordinate and transformational geometry)
TE: T132, T137, 534, 535 (Reference to Ch. 13), 556 (Algebra), 564

Using Technology

PE: 528, 552
TE: T135, 527, 530, 533, 537, 546, 551, 552
RB: 243, 257–259
Using Geometry Grapher: 5–10, 20–24
Computer Activities: 64–81

Using Manipulatives/Models

PE: 539–541, 564
TE: T132, T134
Overhead Visuals: F, L, 27, 28a, 28b

Cooperative Learning

TE: T134, T137, 542

Teaching Resources

For use in implementing the teaching strategies referenced on the previous page.

Exploration
***Resource Book,* p. 230**

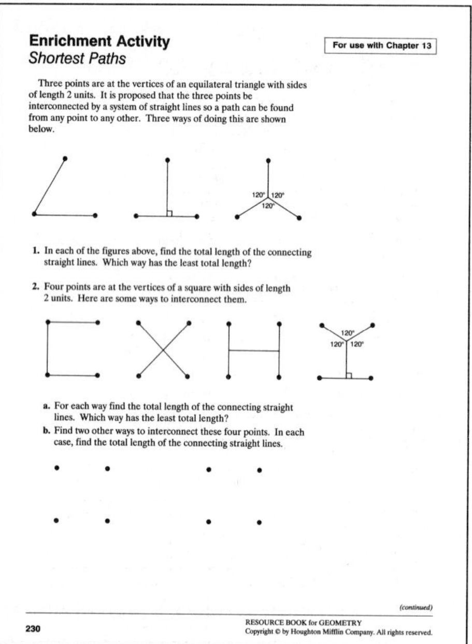

Enrichment Activity
Shortest Paths

For use with Chapter 13

Three points are at the vertices of an equilateral triangle with sides of length 2 units. It is proposed that the three points be interconnected by a system of straight lines so a path can be found from any point to any other. Three ways of doing this are shown below.

1. In each of the figures above, find the total length of the connecting straight lines. Which way has the least total length?

2. Four points are at the vertices of a square with sides of length 2 units. Here are some ways to interconnect them.

a. For each way find the total length of the connecting straight lines. Which way has the least total length?

b. Find two other ways to interconnect these four points. In each case, find the total length of the connecting straight lines.

(continued)

230 RESOURCE BOOK for GEOMETRY

Exploration
***Resource Book,* p. 232**

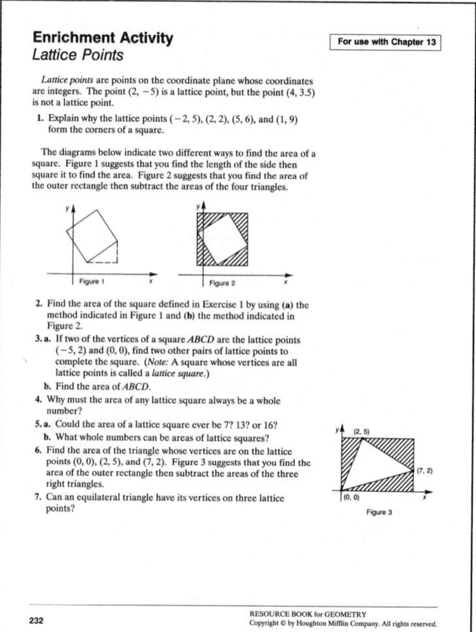

Enrichment Activity
Lattice Points

For use with Chapter 13

Lattice points are points on the coordinate plane whose coordinates are integers. The point $(2, -5)$ is a lattice point, but the point $(4, 3.5)$ is not a lattice point.

1. Explain why the lattice points $(-2, 5)$, $(2, 2)$, $(5, 6)$, and $(1, 9)$ form the corners of a square.

The diagrams below indicate two different ways to find the area of a square. Figure 1 suggests that you find the length of the side then square it to find the area. Figure 2 suggests that you find the area of the outer rectangle then subtract the areas of the four triangles.

2. Find the area of the square defined in Exercise 1 by using **(a)** the method indicated in Figure 1 and **(b)** the method indicated in Figure 2.
3. a. If two of the vertices of a square *ABCD* are the lattice points $(-5, 2)$ and $(0, 0)$, find two other pairs of lattice points to complete the square. (*Note:* A square whose vertices are all lattice points is called a *lattice square*.)
   b. Find the area of *ABCD*.
4. Why must the area of any lattice square always be a whole number?
5. a. Could the area of a lattice square ever be 7? 13? or 16?
   b. What whole numbers can be areas of lattice squares?
6. Find the area of the triangle whose vertices are on the lattice points $(0, 0)$, $(2, 5)$, and $(7, 2)$. Figure 3 suggests that you find the area of the outer rectangle then subtract the areas of the three right triangles.
7. Can an equilateral triangle have its vertices on three lattice points?

232 RESOURCE BOOK for GEOMETRY

Application/Problem Solving
***Resource Book,* p. 235**

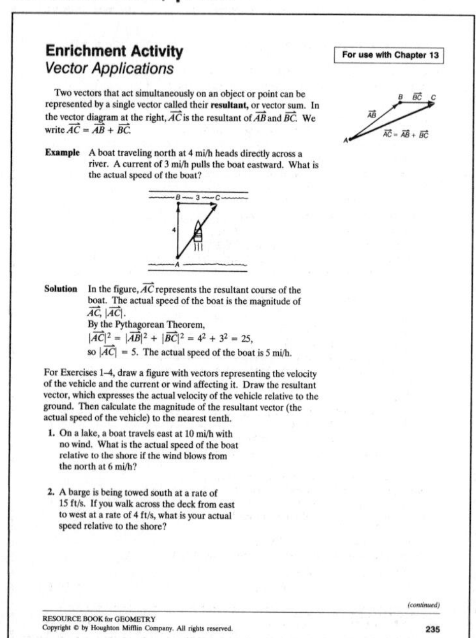

Enrichment Activity
Vector Applications

For use with Chapter 13

Two vectors that act simultaneously on an object or point can be represented by a single vector called their **resultant,** or vector sum. In the vector diagram at the right, $\overrightarrow{AC}$ is the resultant of $\overrightarrow{AB}$ and $\overrightarrow{BC}$. We write $\overrightarrow{AC} = \overrightarrow{AB} + \overrightarrow{BC}$.

Example A boat traveling north at 4 mi/h heads directly across a river. A current of 3 mi/h pulls the boat eastward. What is the actual speed of the boat?

Solution In the figure, $\overrightarrow{AC}$ represents the resultant course of the boat. The actual speed of the boat is the magnitude of $\overrightarrow{AC}$, $|\overrightarrow{AC}|$.
By the Pythagorean Theorem,
$|\overrightarrow{AC}|^2 = |\overrightarrow{AB}|^2 + |\overrightarrow{BC}|^2 = 4^2 + 3^2 = 25$,
so $|\overrightarrow{AC}| = 5$. The actual speed of the boat is 5 mi/h.

For Exercises 1–4, draw a figure with vectors representing the velocity of the vehicle and the current or wind affecting it. Draw the resultant vector, which expresses the actual velocity of the vehicle relative to the ground. Then calculate the magnitude of the resultant vector (the actual speed of the vehicle) to the nearest tenth.

1. On a lake, a boat travels east at 10 mi/h with no wind. What is the actual speed of the boat relative to the shore if the wind blows from the north at 6 mi/h?

2. A barge is being towed south at a rate of 15 ft/s. If you walk across the deck from east to west at a rate of 4 ft/s, what is your actual speed relative to the shore?

(continued)

RESOURCE BOOK for GEOMETRY 235

Problem Solving/Using Technology
***Resource Book,* p. 258**

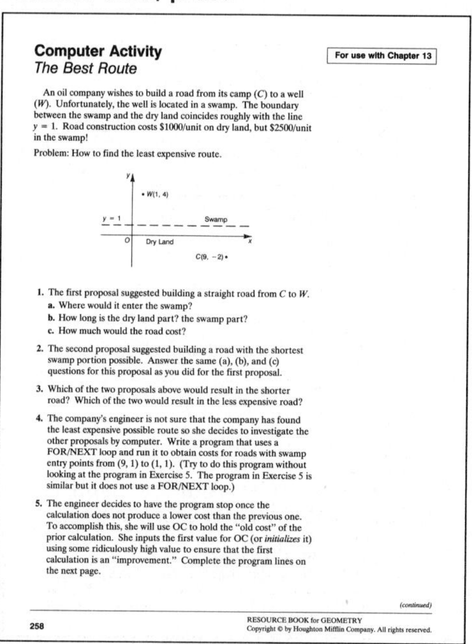

Computer Activity
The Best Route

For use with Chapter 13

An oil company wishes to build a road from its camp (*C*) to a well (*W*). Unfortunately, the well is located in a swamp. The boundary between the swamp and the dry land coincides roughly with the line $y = 1$. Road construction costs \$1000/unit on dry land, but \$2500/unit in the swamp!

Problem: How to find the least expensive route.

1. The first proposal suggested building a straight road from *C* to *W*.
   a. Where would it enter the swamp?
   b. How long is the dry land part? the swamp part?
   c. How much would the road cost?
2. The second proposal suggested building a road with the shortest swamp portion possible. Answer the same (a), (b), and (c) questions for this proposal as you did for the first proposal.
3. Which of the two proposals above would result in the shorter road? Which of the two would result in the less expensive road?
4. The company's engineer is not sure that the company has found the least expensive possible route so she decides to investigate the other proposals by computer. Write a program that uses a FOR/NEXT loop and run it to obtain costs for roads with swamp entry points from (9, 1) to (1, 1). (Try to do this program without looking at the program in Exercise 5. The program in Exercise 5 is similar but it does not use a FOR/NEXT loop.)
5. The engineer decides to have the program stop once the calculation does not produce a lower cost than the previous one. To accomplish this, she will use OC to hold the "old cost" of the prior calculation. She inputs the first value for OC (or *initializes* it) using some ridiculously high value to ensure that the first calculation is an "improvement." Complete the program lines on the next page.

(continued)

258 RESOURCE BOOK for GEOMETRY

Using Technology
Using Geometry Grapher, p. 5

Teaching Suggestions

Geometry Grapher can be used as a discovery tool to explore coordinate and transformational geometry in many ways. The following pages offer suggestions about how teachers can use *Geometry Grapher* to treat the material of Chapters 13 and 14 of Houghton Mifflin Company's *Geometry* (1990 edition).

For each lesson below, textbook exercises are listed that can be explored using *Geometry Grapher*. A sample textbook exercise is selected and step-by-step instructions are given for solving it using *Geometry Grapher*. In the paragraphs below and in the Activity Sheets that follow, the symbol (↵) is used to indicate pressing the Enter or Return key.

13-1 The Distance Formula

Geometry Grapher calculates lengths by using the distance formula. Once your students are proficient in using the distance formula, let them use *Geometry Grapher* to explore problems that would be tedious if solved by hand.

Suggested Textbook Exercises

pp. 525–528: Cl. Exs. 4–10; Wr. Exs. 5–16, 27–32, 39–42, 44

Sample Textbook Exercise

Page 528, Exercise 44: Find the coordinates of the point that is equidistant from (–2, 5), (8, 5), and (6, 7).

First, plot the points and connect them.

Type: C P C –2↵ 5↵ 8↵ 5↵ 6↵ 7↵↵ C S D ABC↵

Then draw the perpendicular bisectors of $\overline{AB}$, $\overline{BC}$, and $\overline{CA}$, lines 1, 2, and 3.

Type: C L B P AB↵ C L B P BC↵ C L B P CA↵

Find the point of intersection of lines 1 and 2, and the point of intersection of lines 2 and 3.

Type: C P I L 1↵ 2↵ C P I L 2↵ 3↵

The three perpendicular bisectors are concurrent at *D*(3, 2). This provides an illustration of Theorem 10-2. Verify that *D* is equidistant from *A*, *B*, and *C* by measuring *DA*, *DB*, and *DC*.

Type: M S DA↵ M S DB↵ M S DC↵

All three points are a distance 5.83 units away from *D*. A circle with center *D* and radius 5.83 could be circumscribed about $\triangle ABC$.

Type: C C D D↵ 5.83↵

Clear the screen after each demonstration by using the Erase/All feature.

Type: E A

USING GEOMETRY GRAPHER: TEACHING SUGGESTIONS

5

Using Technology
Using Geometry Grapher, p. 20

Geometry Grapher Activity 1

Lessons 13-2 and 13-3

1. Plot *A*(2, 2), *B*(8, 2), *C*(8, 4), *D*(8, 5), and *E*(8, –1) by typing C P C 2↵ 2↵ 8↵ 2↵ 8↵ 4↵ 8↵ 5↵ 8↵ –1↵↵. Use the Measure feature to fill in the blanks. For example, to find the length and slope of $\overline{CB}$, type M S CB↵.
   a. *CB* = ____ *AB* = ____ slope of $\overline{CA}$ = ____
   b. *DB* = ____ *AB* = ____ slope of $\overline{DA}$ = ____
   c. *EB* = ____ *AB* = ____ slope of $\overline{EA}$ = ____
   d. The slope of $\overline{CA}$ = *CB*/*AB*. Explain why the slope of $\overline{EA} \neq EB/AB$.

   ____

2. Plot *A*(2, 5), *B*(4, 1), *C*(6, 1), *D*(10, 7), *E*(10, 9), and *F*(6, 9). Construct shape *ABCDEF* by typing C S D ABCDEF↵. Find the slopes of the segments listed below. If the slope is not defined, write *undef.*

   slope of $\overline{AB}$ = ____ slope of $\overline{BC}$ = ____ slope of $\overline{CD}$ = ____
   slope of $\overline{DE}$ = ____ slope of $\overline{EF}$ = ____ slope of $\overline{FA}$ = ____
   slope of $\overline{CE}$ = ____ slope of $\overline{CF}$ = ____ slope of $\overline{DF}$ = ____

In Exercises 3–5, plot the triangles with the given vertices on the same screen. Record the slopes of the sides. Multiply slopes to decide whether each triangle is a right triangle.

3. *A*(–2, –4), *B*(4, –7), *C*(10, 4). Slopes: ____________ Right Δ? ____
4. *D*(–5, 9), *E*(–9, 8), *F*(–6, –4). Slopes: ____________ Right Δ? ____
5. *G*(–2, 6), *H*(–4, 1), *I*(2, –1). Slopes: ____________ Right Δ? ____
6. Verify your answers to Exercises 3–5 by using the Measure/Angle feature.

   $m\angle ABC$ = ____ $m\angle DEF$ = ____ $m\angle GHI$ = ____

Plot the quadrilaterals in Exercises 7–10 on the same screen. Measure the slopes and lengths of their sides, and complete the chart of properties by writing *yes* or *no* in each blank of the first three rows. Then find the best name for each quadrilateral.

7. *A*(–6, 6), *B*(2, 2), *C*(–2.5, –7), *D*(–10.5, –3)
8. *E*(8, 4), *F*(11, 0), *G*(8, –4), *H*(5, 0)
9. *I*(0, 9), *J*(5, 7), *K*(4, 2), *L*(–1, 4)
10. *M*(–3, 8), *N*(7, 2), *O*(1, –8), *P*(–9, –2)

Property	*ABCD*	*EFGH*	*IJKL*	*MNOP*
Opposite sides are parallel.				
Adjacent sides are perpendicular.				
All four sides are congruent.				
The best name for this shape is:				

20
USING GEOMETRY GRAPHER: ACTIVITY SHEETS

Using Technology
Using Geometry Grapher, p. 21

Geometry Grapher Activity 2

Lessons 13-1 and 13-5

1. Plot *A*(–2, 4), *B*(–4, –8), *C*(7, –1) and join the points to form $\triangle ABC$. Use the Ratio feature to find *D*, the midpoint of $\overline{AB}$, and *E*, the midpoint of $\overline{AC}$. For example, to find the midpoint of $\overline{AB}$, type: C P R AB↵ .5↵.
   a. midpoint of $\overline{AB}$ = *D*(___, ___); midpoint of $\overline{AC}$ = *E*(___, ___)
   b. Construct $\overline{DE}$ by typing C S D DE↵.
   c. Find the length and slope of $\overline{DE}$. *DE* = ____; slope of $\overline{DE}$ = ____
   d. Find the length and slope of $\overline{BC}$. *BC* = ____; slope of $\overline{BC}$ = ____
   e. State a theorem that this exercise suggests.

   ____

2. Plot *A*(–3, 9), *B*(–5, –5), *C*(6, –2) and join the points to form $\triangle ABC$. Use the Ratio feature to plot *D* on $\overline{AB}$ such that *AD*/*AB* = .3; plot *E* on $\overline{AC}$ such that *AE*/*AC* = .3; plot *F* on $\overline{AB}$ such that *AF*/*AB* = .7; and plot *G* on $\overline{AC}$ such that *AG*/*AC* = .7.
   a. Construct and measure $\overline{DE}$, $\overline{FG}$, and $\overline{BC}$. For example, to construct and measure $\overline{DE}$, type: C S D DE↵ M S DE↵. What do you notice about the slopes of $\overline{DE}$, $\overline{FG}$, and $\overline{BC}$?

   ____

   b. Construct $\overleftrightarrow{BE}$, $\overleftrightarrow{CD}$, $\overleftrightarrow{BG}$, and $\overleftrightarrow{CF}$. For example, to construct $\overleftrightarrow{BE}$, type: C L S BE↵.
   c. Type: C P I L 1↵ 2↵ to find *H*, the intersection of lines 1 and 2. Similarly, find *I*, the intersection of lines 3 and 4.
   d. How might you show that *A*, *H*, and *I* lie on a median of $\triangle ABC$?

   ____

   ____

   e. Choose ratios other than .3 and .7 and repeat the procedure. Do the intersection points you get also lie on the same median? ____
3. Plot *A*(–7, 3), *B*(–2, 8), *C*(4, 8), *D*(7, 1), *E*(0, –4), *F*(–4, –4), and *G*(–6, –2). Complete.
   a. Midpoint of $\overline{BE}$ = (___, ___); midpoint of $\overline{AD}$ = (___, ___);
      midpoint of $\overline{GC}$ = (___, ___); midpoint of $\overline{FC}$ = (___, ___).
   b. Name two segments with the same midpoint: ____, ____ .
   c. Name a quadrilateral that must be a parallelogram: ________ .

In Exercises 4–6, plot the points and join them in order to form a convex quadrilateral. Then find the midpoints of the diagonals.

4. *A*(4, 7), *B*(6, 1), *C*(–3, –4), *D*(–5, 3). Midpoint(s): ____________
5. *A*(–1, 8), *B*(2, 7), *C*(5, –2), *D*(2, –1). Midpoint(s): ____________
6. *A*(1, 1), *B*(–2, –2), *C*(–8, 3), *D*(–5, 6). Midpoint(s): ____________
7. How many of the quadrilaterals in Exercises 4–6 are parallelograms? ____

(continued)

USING GEOMETRY GRAPHER: ACTIVITY SHEETS

21

Using Technology
Using Geometry Grapher, p. 23

Geometry Grapher Activity 3

Lessons 13-6 and 13-7

1. Construct the vertical line *x* = –5 by typing C L E V –5↵. Construct the horizontal line *y* = 4 by typing C L E S 0↵4↵. Then construct a line with the slope-intercept equation $y = \frac{4}{5}x - 4$ by typing C L E S .8↵–4↵.
   a. To find the intersection of lines 1 and 2, type: C P I L 1↵2↵. In this way, find the intersection of lines 1 and 2, lines 2 and 3, and lines 3 and 1.

      A(___, ___) *B*(___, ___) *C*(___, ___)
   b. Find the area of $\triangle ABC$ by typing M R ABC↵. ____
2. Find the area of the triangle determined by the three lines whose equations are given.
   a. $y = x + 5$; $x = 4$; $y = -0.5x - 4$ area Δ = ____________
   b. $y = -0.5x + 7$; $y = x - 6$; $y = -4x$ area Δ = ____________
   c. $x = 4$; $y = 0.4x + 5$; $y = -x - 2$ area Δ = ____________
3. Plot *A*(0, 3), *B*(2, –1), and *C*(–2, 0), and construct $\overleftrightarrow{AB}$, $\overleftrightarrow{BC}$, and $\overleftrightarrow{CA}$.
   a. Read the slope-intercept equations of lines 1, 2, and 3 as they appear in the data window and record the slopes below.

      slope of $\overleftrightarrow{AB}$ = ____ slope of $\overleftrightarrow{BC}$ = ____ slope of $\overleftrightarrow{CA}$ = ____
   b. Complete the point-slope equations for the lines described below.

      The line through *A* and parallel to $\overleftrightarrow{BC}$: (y – ___) = ____(x – ___)
      The line through *B* and parallel to $\overleftrightarrow{CA}$: (y – ___) = ____(x – ___)
      The line through *C* and parallel to $\overleftrightarrow{AB}$: (y – ___) = ____(x – ___)
   c. Use the Point-slope feature (type: C L E P) to plot the three lines in part (b). Then find the intersection of lines 4 and 5, lines 5 and 6, and lines 6 and 4.

      D(___, ___) *E*(___, ___) *F*(___, ___)
   d. How is $\triangle ABC$ related to $\triangle DEF$? ____________
   e. Measure the areas of the triangles.

      area of $\triangle ABC$ = ____ area of $\triangle DEF$ = ____
4. The following exercise shows how to calculate the distance between a point and a line.
   a. Plot the line with equation *y* = 2*x* and the point *A*(6, 3).
   b. Complete the point-slope equation of the line through *A* and perpendicular to the line with equation *y* = 2*x*. (y – ___) = ____(x – ___)
   c. Plot this line as line 2. Find *B*, the intersection of lines 1 and 2, and measure $\overline{AB}$.

      B(___, ___) *AB* = ____
5. Repeat Exercise 4 with the line *y* = –0.25*x* – 3 and the point *A*(3, 7).

   Line 2: (y – ___) = ____(x – ___)

   B(___, ___) *AB* = ____

(continued)

USING GEOMETRY GRAPHER: ACTIVITY SHEETS

23

Teaching References

Lesson Commentary, pp. T131–T137

Assignment Guide, pp. T49–T50

Software Guide, p. T73

Alternate Test, p. T24

Supplementary Materials

Practice Masters 79–84

Tests 51–55

Resource Book
- Tests, pp. 86–95
- Practice, pp. 161–165
- Preparing for College Entrance Exams, p. 202
- Enrichment Activities, pp. 230–236
- Computer Activities, pp. 243, 257–259

Study Guide, pp. 163–180

Overhead Visuals F, L, 27, 28a, 28b

Computer Activities
- 27 Pythagorean Hideout
- 28 Lattice Points
- 29 Slope of a Line
- 30 Using the Distance and Midpoint Formulas
- 31 Equations of a Line
- 32 The Distance to a Line
- 33 Finding a Minimum

Handbook for Integrating Coordinate and Transformational Geometry

Deciding Which Method to Use in a Problem, pp. 672–675

Cultural Note

Arabian mathematicians working in the 8th and 9th centuries often used algebra to solve equations and geometry to justify their results.

13 COORDINATE GEOMETRY

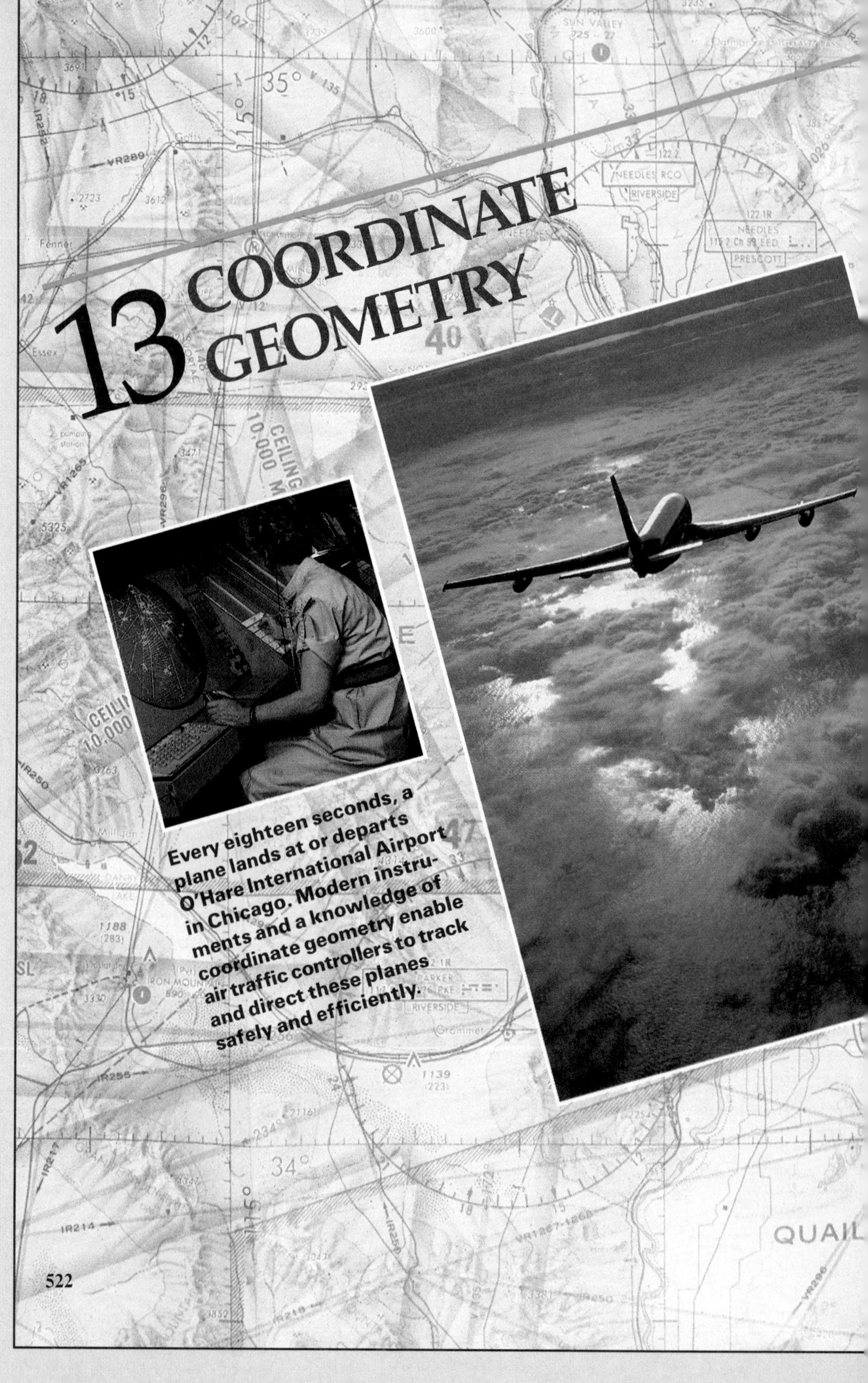

Every eighteen seconds, a plane lands at or departs O'Hare International Airport in Chicago. Modern instruments and a knowledge of coordinate geometry enable air traffic controllers to track and direct these planes safely and efficiently.

Geometry and Algebra

Objectives

1. State and apply the distance formula.
2. State and apply the general equation of a circle.
3. State and apply the slope formula.
4. Determine whether two lines are parallel, perpendicular, or neither.
5. Understand the basic properties of vectors.
6. State and apply the midpoint formula.

13-1 *The Distance Formula*

Some of the terms you have used in your study of graphs are reviewed below.

Origin: Point O

Axes: x-axis and y-axis

Quadrants: Regions I, II, III, and IV

Coordinate plane: The plane of the x-axis and the y-axis

The arrowhead on each axis shows the positive direction.

You can easily find the distance between two points that lie on a horizontal line or on a vertical line.

The distance between A and B is 4.
Using the x-coordinates of A and B:
$|3 - (-1)| = 4$, or $|(-1) - 3| = 4$

The distance between C and D is 3.
Using the y-coordinates of C and D:
$|1 - (-2)| = 3$, or $|(-2) - 1| = 3$

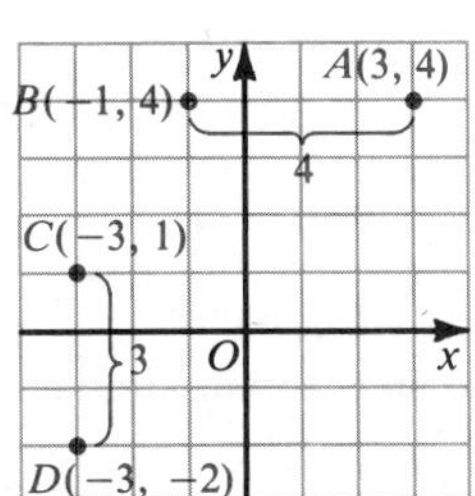

When two points do not lie on a horizontal or vertical line, you can find the distance between the points by using the Pythagorean Theorem.

Example 1 Find the distance between points $A(4, -2)$ and $B(1, 2)$.

Solution Draw the horizontal and vertical segments shown. The coordinates of T are $(1, -2)$. Then $AT = 3$, $BT = 4$, $(AB)^2 = 3^2 + 4^2 = 25$, and $AB = 5$.

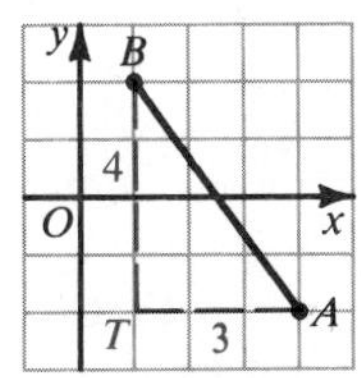

Teaching Suggestions, pp. T131–T132

Objectives
Presenting the Lesson
Making Connections
Extension
Enrichment

Communication Skills, p. T132

Exploring Activity, p. 521c

Supplementary Materials

Practice Master 79
Study Guide, pp. 163–164
Computer Activities 27, 28

Lesson Focus

The distance between any two points in a plane can be found by using the distance formula. This lesson develops and applies the distance formula.

Suggested Assignments

Average
526–527/1–27 odd

Maximum
526–527/2–40 even

Teaching Note

You may need to review plotting points, ordered pairs, the Pythagorean Theorem, the definition of collinear points, tangents, and the simplification of radicals before you do this lesson. See the Algebra Review on page 113.

Remind students that distance is always a positive number.

Teaching Note

Some students may need help in understanding how we go from $|x_2 - x_1|^2 + |y_2 - y_1|^2$ to $(x_2 - x_1)^2 + (y_2 - y_1)^2$. Also, mention to students that either point can be taken first because $(x_2 - x_1)^2 + (y_2 - y_1)^2 = (x_1 - x_2)^2 + (y_1 - y_2)^2$.

Chalkboard Examples

Find the distance between the origin and the point named.

1. $(0, -6)$ 6
2. $(8, 0)$ 8
3. $(7, 24)$ $\sqrt{7^2 + 24^2} = 25$

Find the distance between the points. Write the answer in simplest radical form.

4. $(2, 5), (8, 5)$ 6
5. $(-3, -8), (2, 4)$ 13
6. $(6, 0), (5, 1)$ $\sqrt{2}$
7. $(-1, 8), (5, -3)$ $\sqrt{157}$
8. $(9, -4), (1, -8)$ $4\sqrt{5}$

Find the equation of a circle with the given center and radius.

9. $(4, -3)$, radius 5
   $(x - 4)^2 + (y + 3)^2 = 25$
10. $(-1, -2)$, radius $\sqrt{3}$
    $(x + 1)^2 + (y + 2)^2 = 3$

Find the center and radius of each circle.

11. $(x - 8)^2 + (y - 1)^2 = 64$
    center $(8, 1)$; radius 8
12. $(x + 9)^2 + (y - 7)^2 = 25$
    center $(-9, 7)$; radius 5

Using a method suggested by Example 1, you can find a formula for the distance between points $P(x_1, y_1)$ and $Q(x_2, y_2)$. First draw a right triangle as shown. The coordinates of R are (x_2, y_1).

$$PR = |x_2 - x_1|;\ QR = |y_2 - y_1|$$
$$d^2 = (PR)^2 + (QR)^2$$
$$= |x_2 - x_1|^2 + |y_2 - y_1|^2$$
$$= (x_2 - x_1)^2 + (y_2 - y_1)^2$$
$$d = \sqrt{(x_2 - x_1)^2 + (y_2 - y_1)^2}$$

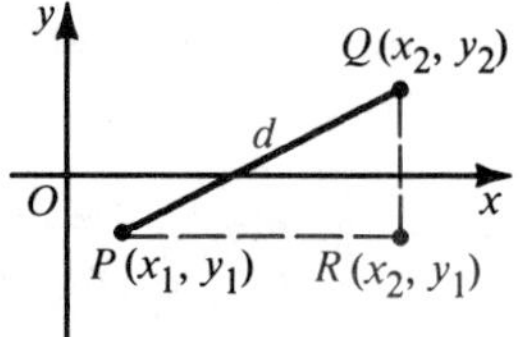

Since d represents distance, d cannot be negative.

Theorem 13-1 *The Distance Formula*

The distance d between points (x_1, y_1) and (x_2, y_2) is given by:

$$d = \sqrt{(x_2 - x_1)^2 + (y_2 - y_1)^2}$$

Example 2 Find the distance between points $(-4, 2)$ and $(2, -1)$.

Solution 1 Draw a right triangle. The legs have lengths 6 and 3.

$$d^2 = 6^2 + 3^2 = 36 + 9 = 45$$
$$d = \sqrt{45} = \sqrt{9} \cdot \sqrt{5} = 3\sqrt{5}$$

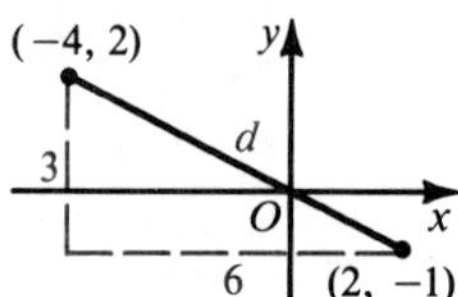

Solution 2 Let (x_1, y_1) be $(-4, 2)$ and (x_2, y_2) be $(2, -1)$.

Then $d = \sqrt{(x_2 - x_1)^2 + (y_2 - y_1)^2}$
$$= \sqrt{(2 - (-4))^2 + ((-1) - 2)^2}$$
$$= \sqrt{6^2 + (-3)^2} = \sqrt{36 + 9} = \sqrt{45} = 3\sqrt{5}$$

You can use the distance formula to find an equation of a circle. Example 3 shows how to do this.

Example 3 Find an equation of a circle with center $(5, 6)$ and radius 4.

Solution Let $P(x, y)$ represent any point on the circle. Since the distance from P to the center is 4,

$$\sqrt{(x - 5)^2 + (y - 6)^2} = 4,$$
$$\text{or } (x - 5)^2 + (y - 6)^2 = 16.$$

Either of these two equations is an equation of the circle, but the second equation is the one usually used.

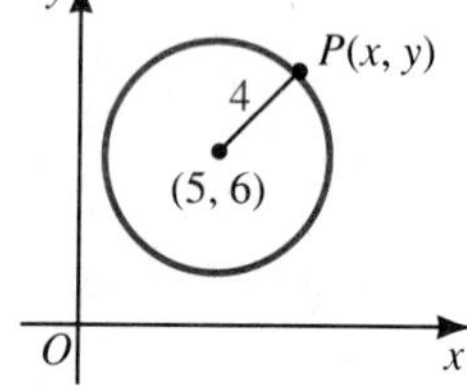

Example 3 can be generalized to give the theorem at the top of the next page.

Theorem 13-2

An equation of the circle with center (a, b) and radius r is

$$(x - a)^2 + (y - b)^2 = r^2.$$

Example 4 Find the center and the radius of the circle with equation $(x - 1)^2 + (y + 2)^2 = 9$. Sketch the graph.

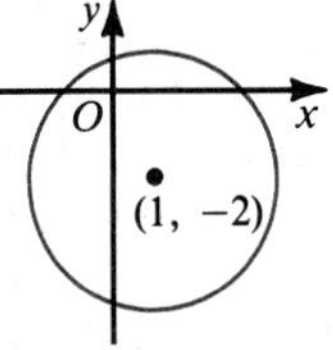

Solution 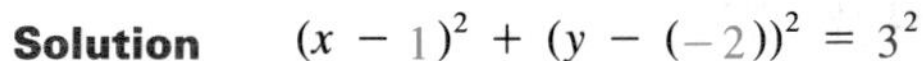
$(x - 1)^2 + (y - (-2))^2 = 3^2$
The center is point $(1, -2)$ and the radius is 3.
The graph is shown at the right.

Cultural Note

The word *geometry* comes from the Greek words *gē* (meaning *earth*) and *metron* (meaning *measure*). For example, the Greek word *geōmetrein* means to measure the earth. The word *algebra* comes from Arabic. The mathematician and astronomer al-Khowârizmî used the Arabic word *al-jabr* (meaning *restoring,* as in restoring the balance in an equation) in a book written in 830 A.D.

Classroom Exercises

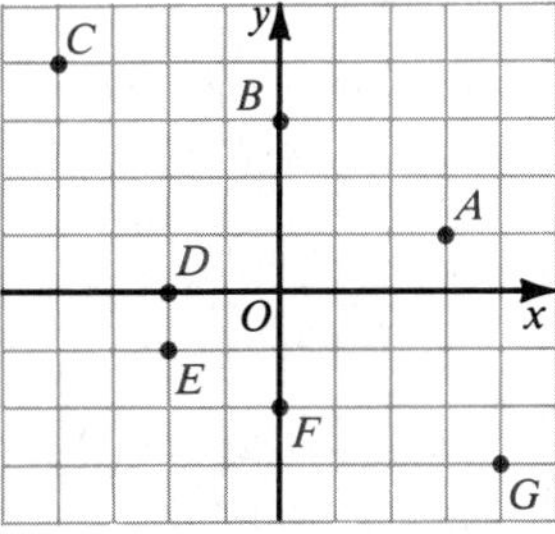

1. What is the x-coordinate of every point that lies on a vertical line through C? **−4**
2. Which of the following points lie on a horizontal line through C?

   (2, 4)   (2, −4)   (0, 4)
   (4, 3)   (15, 4)   (−4, 3)
3. Find OD and BF. **2; 5**

In Exercises 4–9 state: a. the coordinates of T
b. the lengths of the legs of the right triangle
c. the length of the segment shown

4. 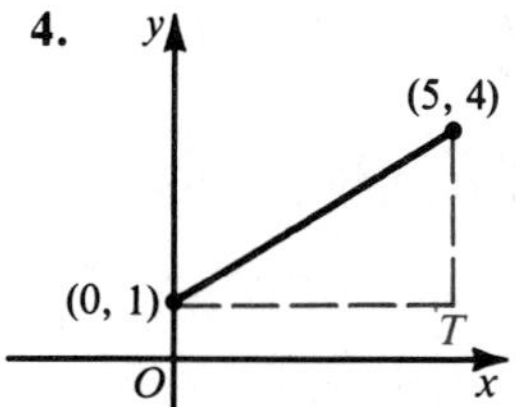

a. (5, 1) b. 5, 3 c. $\sqrt{34}$

5. 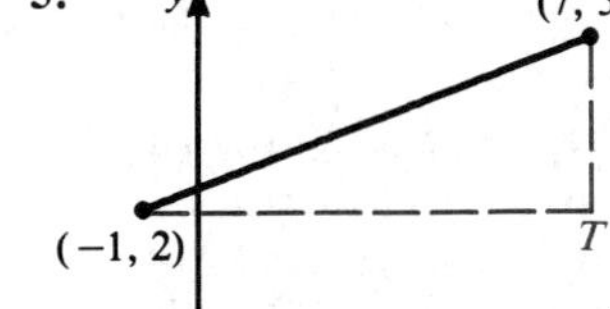

a. (7, 2) b. 8, 3 c. $\sqrt{73}$

6. 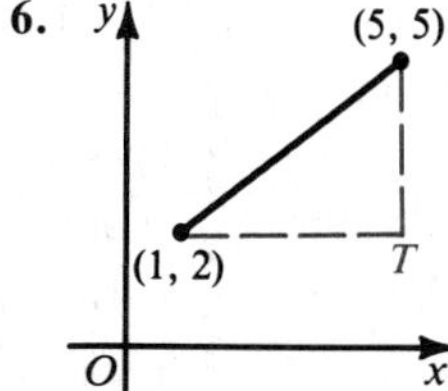

a. (5, 2) b. 4, 3 c. 5

7. 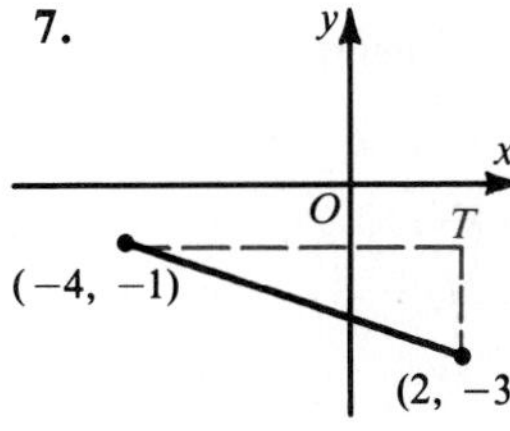

a. (2, −1) b. 6, 2
c. $2\sqrt{10}$

8. 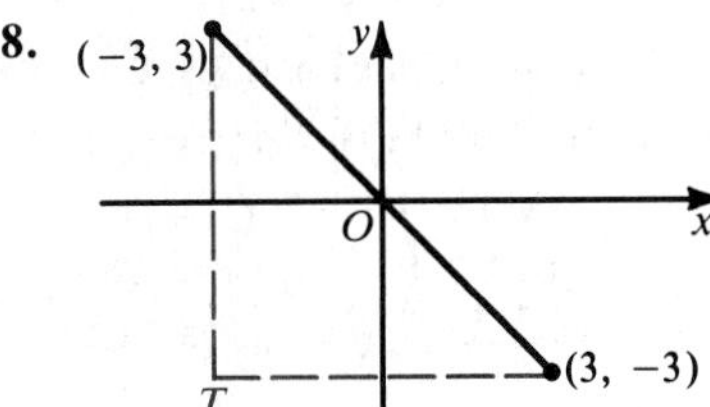

a. (−3, −3) b. 6, 6
c. $6\sqrt{2}$

9. 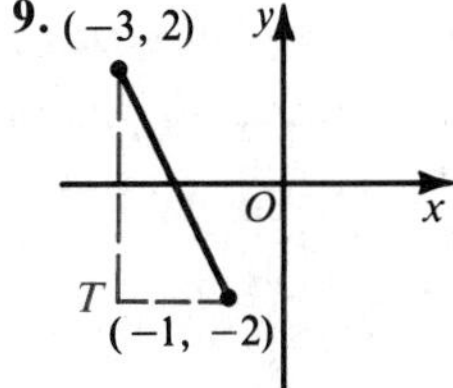

a. (−3, −2) b. 2, 4
c. $2\sqrt{5}$

Guided Practice

Find the distance between the two points named.

1. (8, −1), (−6, −1) 14
2. (0, 0), (8, 15) 17
3. (0, 0), (−5, −2) $\sqrt{29}$
4. (−6, 2), (2, −4) 10
5. (−1, 10), (−6, 1) $\sqrt{106}$
6. (5, −2), (−2, −3) $5\sqrt{2}$

Given points *R*, *S*, and *T*, find *RS*, *ST*, and *RT*. Are *R*, *S*, and *T* collinear? If so, which point lies between the other two?

7. *R*(6, −2), *S*(−4, −1), *T*(8, −1) $RS = \sqrt{101}$; $ST = 12$; $RT = \sqrt{5}$; not collinear
8. *R*(−3, −1), *S*(9, 8), *T*(5, 5) $RS = 15$; $ST = 5$; $RT = 10$; collinear; *T* between *R* and *S*

Find the center and radius of each circle.

9. $x^2 + (y + 5)^2 = 36$ (0, −5); 6
10. $(x - j)^2 + (y + k)^2 = r$ $(j, -k)$; $\sqrt{r}$

Write the equation of each circle and sketch its graph.

11. $C(-4, 0)$; $r = 5$ $(x + 4)^2 + y^2 = 25$

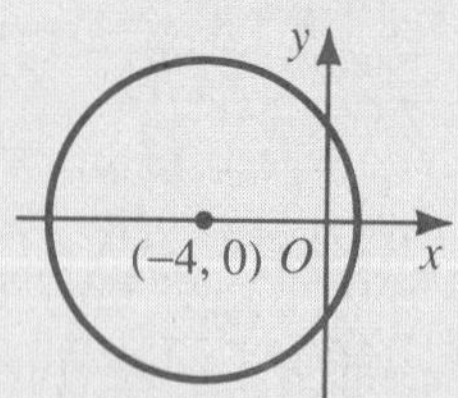

12. $C(2, -1)$; $r = 4$ $(x - 2)^2 + (y + 1)^2 = 16$

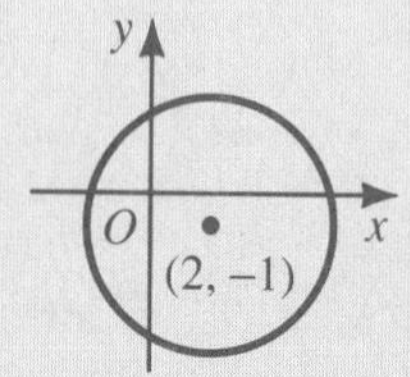

10. Find the distance between the points named. Give all answers in simplest form.
a. (0, 0) and (5, −3) **$\sqrt{34}$** **b.** (3, −2) and (−5, −2) **8** **c.** (4, 4) and (−3, −3) **$7\sqrt{2}$**

11. Find the center and the radius of each circle.
a. $(x - 2)^2 + y^2 = 1$ **(2, 0); 1** **b.** $(x + 2)^2 + (y - 8)^2 = 16$ **(−2, 8); 4**
c. $x^2 + (y + 5)^2 = 112$ **(0, −5); $4\sqrt{7}$** **d.** $(x + 3)^2 + (y + 7)^2 = 14$ **(−3, −7); $\sqrt{14}$**

12. Find an equation of the circle that has the given center and radius.
a. Center (2, 5); radius 3 **See below.** **b.** Center (−2, 0); radius 5 **See below.**
c. Center (−2, 3); radius 10 **d.** Center (j, k); radius n **$(x - j)^2 + (y - k)^2 = n^2$**

12. a. $(x - 2)^2 + (y - 5)^2 = 9$ b. $(x + 2)^2 + y^2 = 25$ c. $(x + 2)^2 + (y - 3)^2 = 100$

Written Exercises

Find the distance between the two points. If necessary, you may draw graphs but you shouldn't need to use the distance formula.

A **1.** (−2, −3) and (−2, 4) **7** **2.** (3, 3) and (−2, 3) **5**
3. (3, −4) and (−1, −4) **4** **4.** (0, 0) and (3, 4) **5**

Use the distance formula to find the distance between the two points.

5. (−6, −2) and (−7, −5) **$\sqrt{10}$** **6.** (3, 2) and (5, −2) **$2\sqrt{5}$**
7. (−8, 6) and (0, 0) **10** **8.** (12, −1) and (0, −6) **13**

Find the distance between the points named. Use any method you choose.

9. (5, 4) and (1, −2) **$2\sqrt{13}$** **10.** (−2, −2) and (5, 7) **$\sqrt{130}$**
11. (−2, 3) and (3, −2) **$5\sqrt{2}$** **12.** (−4, −1) and (−4, 3) **4**

Given points *A*, *B*, and *C*. Find *AB*, *BC*, and *AC*. Are *A*, *B*, and *C* collinear? If so, which point lies between the other two?

13. *A*(0, 3), *B*(−2, 1), *C*(3, 6) **Yes; *A*** **14.** *A*(5, −5), *B*(0, 5), *C*(2, 1) **Yes; *C***
15. *A*(−5, 6), *B*(0, 2), *C*(3, 0) **No** **16.** *A*(3, 4), *B*(−3, 0), *C*(−1, 1) **No**

Find the center and the radius of each circle.

17. $(x + 3)^2 + y^2 = 49$ **(−3, 0); 7** **18.** $(x + 7)^2 + (y - 8)^2 = \frac{36}{25}$ **(−7, 8); $\frac{6}{5}$**
19. $(x - j)^2 + (y + 14)^2 = 17$ **$(j, -14)$; $\sqrt{17}$** **20.** $(x + a)^2 + (y - b)^2 = c^2$ **$(-a, b)$; c**

Write an equation of the circle that has the given center and radius.

21. $C(3, 0)$; $r = 8$ **See below.** **22.** $C(0, 0)$; $r = 6$ **$x^2 + y^2 = 36$**
23. $C(-4, -7)$; $r = 5$ **24.** $C(-2, 5)$; $r = \frac{1}{3}$ **$(x + 2)^2 + (y - 5)^2 = \frac{1}{9}$**

25. Sketch the graph of $(x - 3)^2 + (y + 4)^2 = 36$.
26. Sketch the graph of $(x - 2)^2 + (y - 5)^2 \le 9$.

21. $(x - 3)^2 + y^2 = 64$ 23. $(x + 4)^2 + (y + 7)^2 = 25$

In Exercises 27–32 find and then compare lengths of segments.

B **27.** Show that the triangle with vertices $A(-3, 4)$, $M(3, 1)$, and $Y(0, -2)$ is isosceles. **$AM = AY = 3\sqrt{5}$**

28. Quadrilateral $TAUL$ has vertices $T(4, 6)$, $A(6, -4)$, $U(-4, -2)$, and $L(-2, 4)$. Show that the diagonals are congruent. **$TU = AL = 8\sqrt{2}$**

29. Triangles JAN and RFK have vertices $J(-2, -2)$, $A(4, -2)$, $N(2, 2)$, $R(8, 1)$, $F(8, 4)$, and $K(6, 3)$. Show that $\triangle JAN$ is similar to $\triangle RFK$.

30. The vertices of $\triangle KAT$ and $\triangle IES$ are $K(3, -1)$, $A(2, 6)$, $T(5, 1)$, $I(-4, 1)$, $E(-3, -6)$, and $S(-6, -1)$. What word best describes the relationship between $\triangle KAT$ and $\triangle IES$? **congruent**

31. Find the area of the rectangle with vertices $B(8, 0)$, $T(2, -9)$, $R(-1, -7)$, and $C(5, 2)$. **39**

32. Show that the triangle with vertices $D(0, 0)$, $E(3, 1)$, and $F(-2, 6)$ is a right triangle, then find the area of the triangle. **$(DE)^2 + (DF)^2 = 10 + 40 = 50 = (FE)^2$; 10**

33. There are twelve points, each with integer coordinates, that are 10 units from the origin. List the points. (*Hint*: Recall the 6, 8, 10 right triangle.)

34. a. List twelve points, each with integer coordinates, that are 5 units from $(-8, 1)$.

b. Find an equation of the circle containing these points. **$(x + 8)^2 + (y - 1)^2 = 25$**

In Exercises 35–38 find an equation of the circle described and sketch the graph.

35. The circle has center $(0, 6)$ and passes through point $(6, 14)$. **$x^2 + (y - 6)^2 = 100$**

36. The circle has center $(-2, -4)$ and passes through point $(3, 8)$. **$(x + 2)^2 + (y + 4)^2 = 169$**

37. The circle has diameter $\overline{RS}$ where R is $(-3, 2)$ and S is $(3, 2)$. **$x^2 + (y - 2)^2 = 9$**

38. The circle has center (p, q) and is tangent to the x-axis. **$(x - p)^2 + (y - q)^2 = q^2$**

39. a. Find the radii of the circles

$$x^2 + y^2 = 25 \text{ and } (x - 9)^2 + (y - 12)^2 = 100.$$ **5; 10**

b. Find the distance between the centers of the circles. **15**

c. Explain why the circles must be externally tangent. **dist. btwn. ctrs. = sum of radii**

d. Sketch the graphs of the circles.

40. a. Find the radii of the circles

$$x^2 + y^2 = 2 \text{ and } (x - 3)^2 + (y - 3)^2 = 32.$$ **$\sqrt{2}$; $4\sqrt{2}$**

b. Find the distance between the centers of the circles. **$3\sqrt{2}$**

c. Explain why the circles must be internally tangent. **dist. btwn. ctrs. = diff. of radii**

d. Sketch the graphs of the circles.

41. Discover and prove something about the quadrilateral with vertices $R(-1, -6)$, $A(1, -3)$, $Y(11, 1)$, and $J(9, -2)$. **Quad. *RAYJ* is a ▱.**

42. Discover and prove two things about the triangle with vertices $K(-3, 4)$, $M(3, 1)$, and $J(-6, -2)$. **$\triangle JKM$ is both an isos. △ and a rt. △.**

C **43.** It is known that $\triangle GHM$ is isosceles. G is point $(-2, -3)$, H is point $(-2, 7)$, and the x-coordinate of M is 4. Find all five possible values for the y-coordinate of M. **15, 5, 2, −1, −11**

Thinking Skills

Exs. 27–29 and 32 ask students to verify facts about given figures. Doing these exercises should help prepare students for the methods of coordinate proofs presented in the last lesson of this chapter.

Using a Computer

Exs. 27–30 and 32 can be done using a spreadsheet.

Additional Answers Written Exercises

29. $\frac{JA}{RF} = \frac{6}{3} = \frac{2}{1}$; $\frac{AN}{FK} = \frac{2\sqrt{5}}{\sqrt{5}} = \frac{2}{1}$; $\frac{JN}{RK} = \frac{4\sqrt{2}}{2\sqrt{2}} = \frac{2}{1}$; $\triangle JAN \sim \triangle RFK$ (SSS ~)

33. (6, 8), (8, 6), (−6, 8), (−8, 6), (−6, −8), (−8, −6), (6, −8), (8, −6), (10, 0), (0, 10), (−10, 0), (0, −10)

34.a. (−13, 1), (−3, 1), (−8, 6), (−8, −4), (−5, 5), (−5, −3), (−11, 5), (−11, −3), (−4, 4), (−4, −2), (−12, 4), (−12, −2)

Exercise Note

Exs. 39 and 40 review tangent circles from an algebraic viewpoint. Encourage students to sketch diagrams to determine if the circles are internally or externally tangent.

Proof Note

Exs. 41 and 42 preview some of the skills necessary to do coordinate proofs that are presented in the last lesson of the chapter.

44. Find the coordinates of the point that is equidistant from $(-2, 5)$, $(8, 5)$, and $(6, 7)$. **(3, 2)**

45. Find the center and the radius of the circle $x^2 + 4x + y^2 - 8y = 16$. (*Hint*: Express the given equation in the form
$(x - a)^2 + (y - b)^2 = r^2$.) **(−2, 4); 6**

♦ Computer Key-In

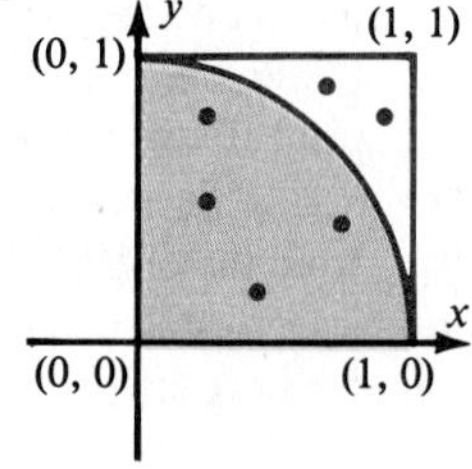

The graph shows a quarter-circle inscribed in a square with area 1. If points are picked at random inside the square, some of them will also be inside the quarter-circle. Let n be the number of points picked inside the square and let q be the number of these points that fall inside the quarter-circle. If many, many points are picked at random inside the square, the following ratios are approximately equal:

$$\frac{\text{Area of quarter-circle}}{\text{Area of square}} \approx \frac{q}{n}$$

$$\frac{\text{Area of quarter-circle}}{1} \approx \frac{q}{n}$$

$$\text{Area of whole circle} \approx 4 \times \frac{q}{n}$$

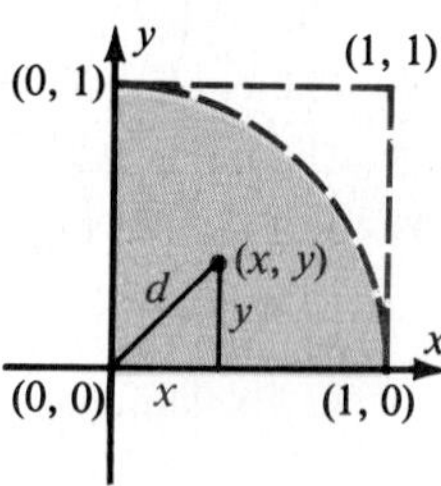

Any point (x, y) in the square region has coordinates such that $0 < x < 1$ and $0 < y < 1$. (Note that this restriction excludes points on the boundaries of the square.) A computer can pick a random point inside the unit square by choosing two random numbers x and y between 0 and 1. We let d be the distance from O to the point (x, y). By the Pythagorean Theorem, $d = \sqrt{x^2 + y^2}$. Do you see that if $d < 1$, the point lies inside the quarter-circle?

Exercises

1. Write a computer program to do all of the following:
   a. Choose n random points (x, y) inside the unit square.
   b. Using the distance formula test each point chosen to see whether it lies inside the quarter-circle.
   c. Count the number of points (q) which *do* lie inside the quarter-circle.
   d. Print out the value of $4 \times \frac{q}{n}$.

2. RUN your program for $n = 100$, $n = 500$, and $n = 1000$. **Answers will vary.**

3. Calculate the area of the circle, using the formula given on page 446. Compare this result with your computer approximations. **π; answers may vary.**

Additional Answers
Computer Key-In

1.
```
 10 INPUT "HOW MANY
      POINTS:"; N
 20 FOR I = 1 TO N
 30 LET X = RND(1)
 40 LET Y = RND(1)
 50 LET D = SQR(X ↑ 2 +
      Y ↑ 2)
 60 IF D < 1 THEN LET
      Q = Q + 1
 70 NEXT I
 80 PRINT Q; "POINTS
      INSIDE CIRCLE"
 90 PRINT "4 * Q/N =";
      4 * Q/N
100 END
```

13-2 *Slope of a Line*

The effect of steepness, or *slope*, must be considered in a variety of everyday situations. Some examples are the grade of a road, the pitch of a roof, the incline of a wheelchair ramp, and the tilt of an unloading platform, such as the one at a paper mill in Maine shown in the photograph at the right. In this section, the informal idea of steepness is generalized and made precise by the mathematical concept of *slope of a line through two points*.

Informally, slope is the ratio of the *change in y* (vertical change) to the *change in x* (horizontal change). The **slope,** denoted by m, of the nonvertical line through the points (x_1, y_1) and (x_2, y_2) is defined as follows:

$$\text{slope } m = \frac{y_2 - y_1}{x_2 - x_1}$$

$$= \frac{\text{change in } y}{\text{change in } x}$$

y
(x_2, y_2)
(x_1, y_1)
$y_2 - y_1$
$x_2 - x_1$
O
x

When you are given several points on a line you can use any two of them to compute the slope. Furthermore, the slope of a line does not depend on the order in which the points are chosen because $\frac{y_2 - y_1}{x_2 - x_1} = \frac{y_1 - y_2}{x_1 - x_2}$.

Example 1 Find the slope of each segment.

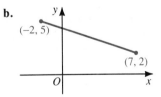

a.

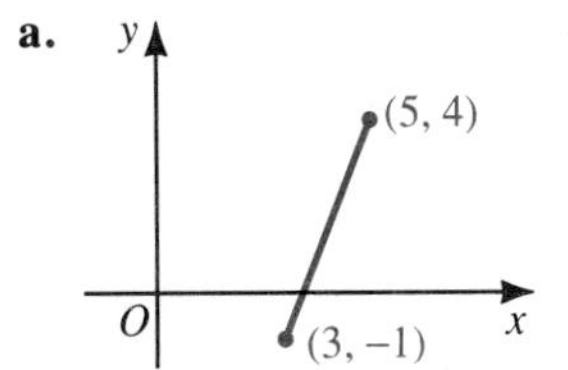

b.

y
(−2, 5)
(7, 2)
O
x

Solution **a.** $\frac{y_2 - y_1}{x_2 - x_1} = \frac{4 - (-1)}{5 - 3} = \frac{5}{2}$ **b.** $\frac{y_2 - y_1}{x_2 - x_1} = \frac{2 - 5}{7 - (-2)} = \frac{-3}{9} = -\frac{1}{3}$

Teaching Suggestions,
pp. T132–T133

Objective
Presenting the Lesson
Application
Reinforcement

Communication Skills,
p. T133

Supplementary Materials

Study Guide, pp. 165–166
Overhead Visual L

Lesson Focus

The purpose of this lesson is to introduce and study the slope of a line.

Suggested Assignments

Average
532–533/1–5, 7, 8, 10, 11, 14, 16, 18, 19

Maximum
Day 1: 532–533/5, 8, 11, 14–16, 18, 20, 21–24
Day 2: 533–534/25–32

Teaching Note

Some students may need to see examples of the equation $\frac{y_2 - y_1}{x_2 - x_1} = \frac{y_1 - y_2}{x_1 - x_2}$ in order to verify that the slope of a line does not depend on the order in which points are chosen. Point out that many different lines can have the same slope, and that unlike distance, slopes can be positive, negative, or zero.

Thinking Skills

Students should observe that the triangles formed in Example 2(a) are congruent, and that other right triangles formed along the same line will be similar to them since the ratio of the vertical leg to the horizontal leg is $\frac{3}{5}$.

Chalkboard Examples

Complete with *always*, *sometimes*, or *never.*

1. The slope of a vertical line is never zero.
2. The slope of a horizontal line is always zero.
3. The slope of a line that rises to the right is always positive.
4. The slope of a line that falls to the right is always negative.

Find the slope of the line through the two points named. If the slope is not defined, write *not defined.*

5. $(-3, 4), (-4, 5)$ -1
6. $(6, -3), (-1, -2)$ $-\frac{1}{7}$
7. $(8, -4), (-3, -4)$ 0
8. $(-6, -2), (-6, 9)$ not defined

Using a Computer

Use a computer graphing program to help students see how the value of the slope affects the graph of a straight line. Have students determine what happens to the line as a positive slope increases and what happens to a line as a slope becomes negative.

At this time, you may wish to assign the Explorations section on page 552, which deals with slopes of parallel and perpendicular lines.

Example 2 Sketch each line described, showing several points on the line.

a. The line passes through (1, 2) and has slope $\frac{3}{5}$.

b. The line passes through (0, 5) and has slope $-\frac{2}{3}$.

Solution

a. Since $\dfrac{\text{change in } y}{\text{change in } x} = \dfrac{3}{5}$, every horizontal change of 5 units is matched by a vertical change of 3 units. Start at (1, 2), move 5 units to the right and 3 units up.

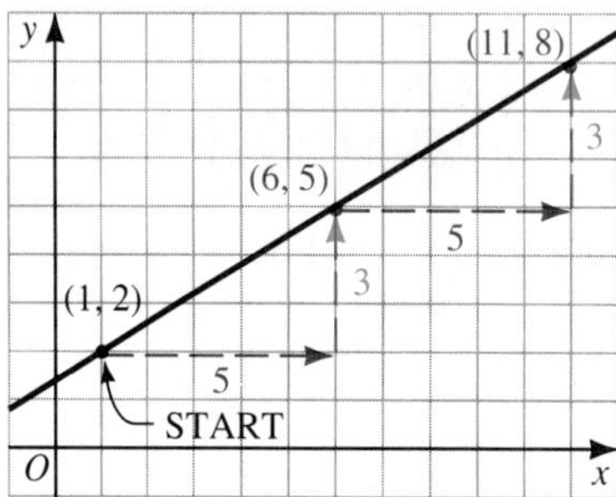

b. Since $\dfrac{\text{change in } y}{\text{change in } x} = -\dfrac{2}{3} = \dfrac{-2}{3}$, every horizontal change of 3 units is matched by a vertical change of 2 units. Start at (0, 5), move 3 units to the right and 2 units down.

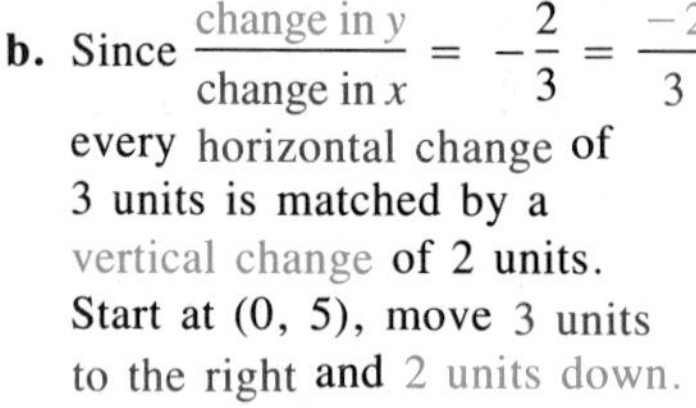

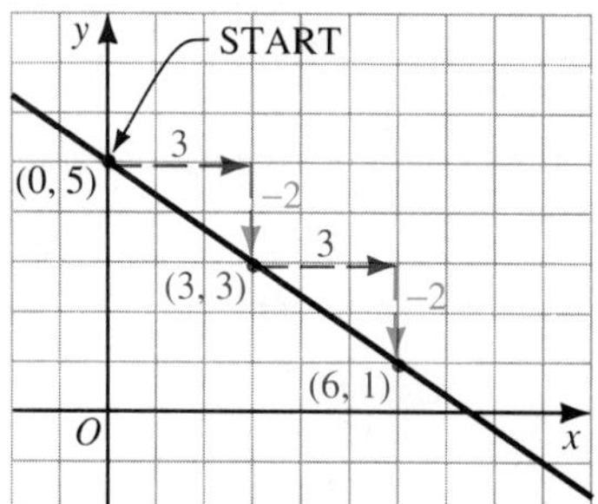

The examples above and the diagrams below illustrate the following facts.

Lines with positive slope rise to the right.

Lines with negative slope fall to the right.

The greater the absolute value of a line's slope, the steeper the line.

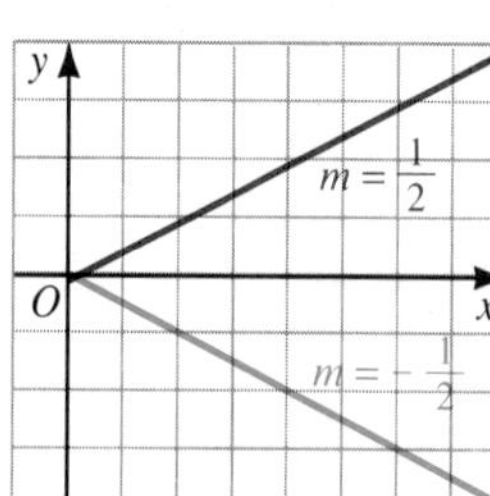

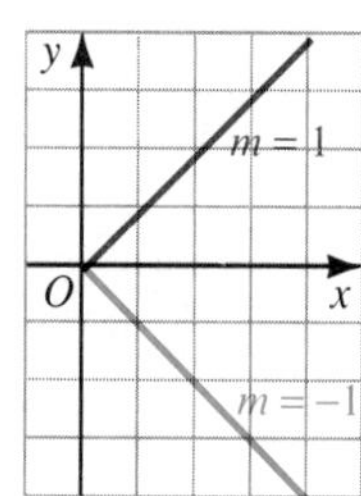

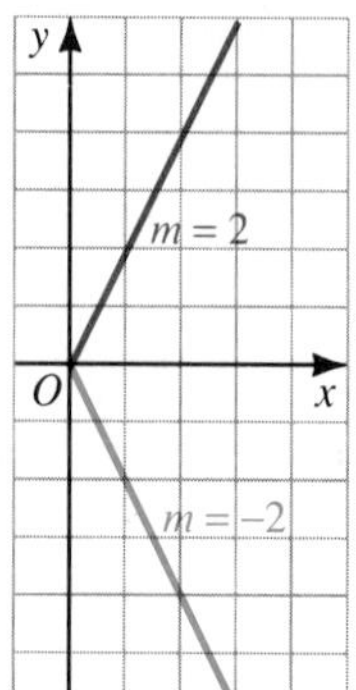

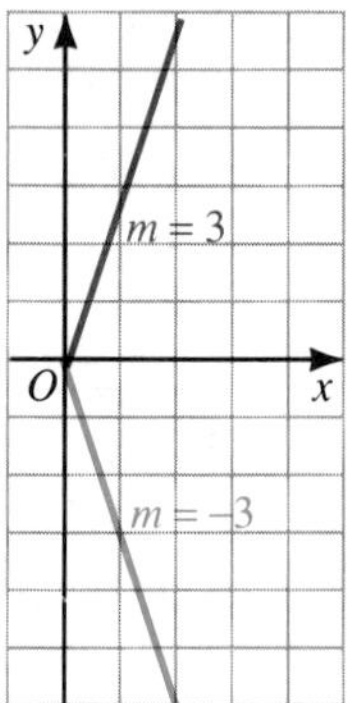

The diagrams below explain why the following are true.

The slope of a horizontal line is zero.

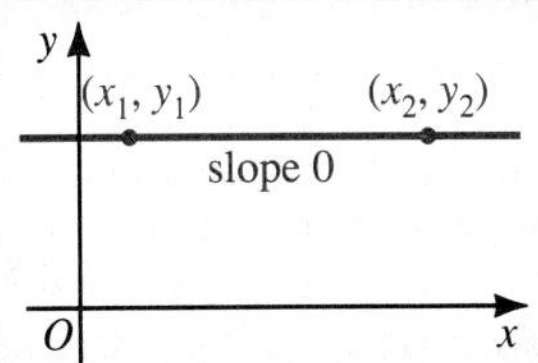

Since $y_1 = y_2$,
$$\frac{y_2 - y_1}{x_2 - x_1} = \frac{0}{x_2 - x_1} = 0.$$

The slope of a vertical line is not defined.

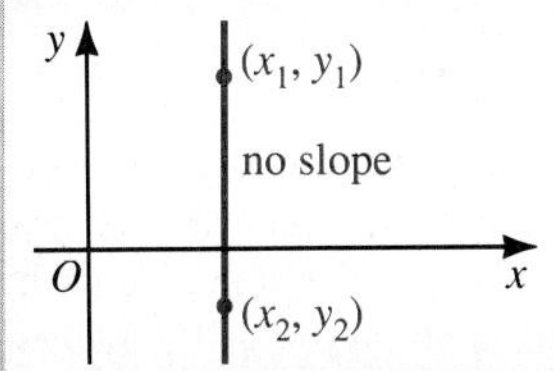

Since $x_1 = x_2$,
$$\frac{y_2 - y_1}{x_2 - x_1} = \frac{y_2 - y_1}{0},$$ which is not defined.

Classroom Exercises **1.** $\frac{1}{5}$ **2.** 0 **3.** −1

Find the slope of the line.

1.

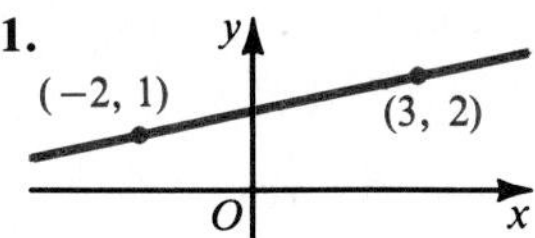

2.

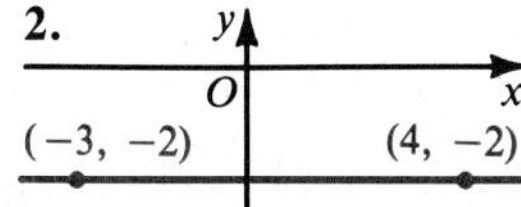

3.

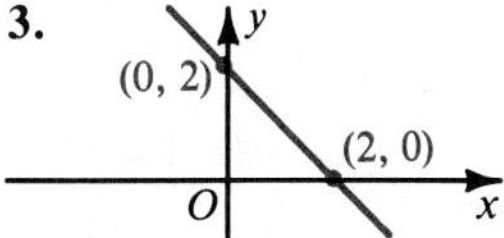

Tell whether each expression is positive or negative for the line shown:

a. $y_2 - y_1$ **b.** $x_2 - x_1$ **c.** $\dfrac{y_2 - y_1}{x_2 - x_1}$

4.

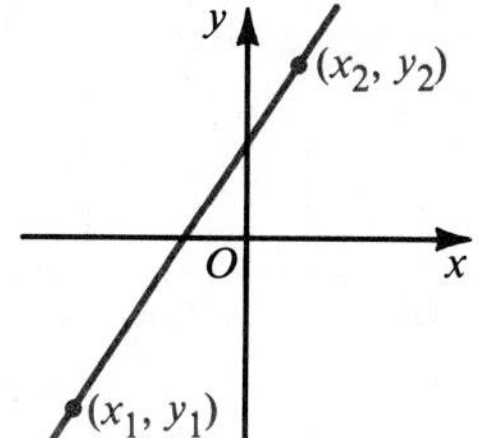

a. pos.
b. pos.
c. pos.

5. (x_1, y_1) y O x (x_2, y_2)

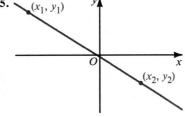

a. neg.
b. pos.
c. neg.

6. Does the slope of the line appear to be positive, negative, zero, or not defined?

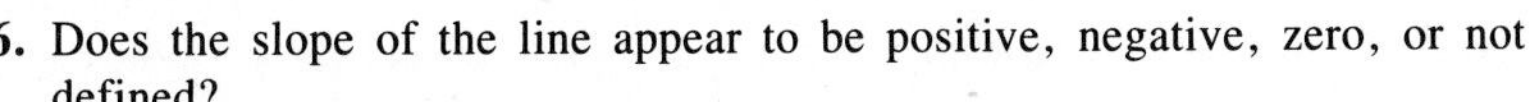

a. **pos.** **b.** **not defined** **c.** **neg.** **d.** **zero**

Teaching Note

Be sure to point out the distinction between a line that has slope 0 (horizontal) and a line that has no slope (vertical).

Additional Answers Classroom Exercises

7.c. $\tan n° = \frac{\text{Opp.}}{\text{Adj.}} = \frac{y_2 - y_1}{x_2 - x_1} =$ slope of $\overleftrightarrow{AB}$

Guided Practice

1. Name each line in the figure whose slope is (a) positive, (b) negative, (c) zero, (d) not defined.

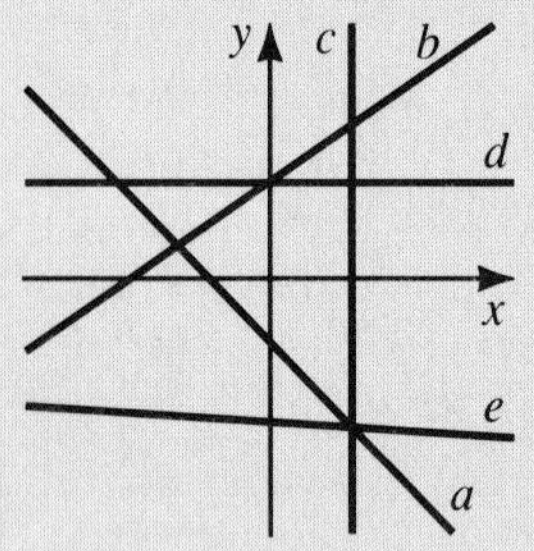

(a) *b* (b) *a*, *e* (c) *d* (d) *c*

Find the slope of the line through the points named. If the slope is not defined, write *not defined.*

2. (−4, 1); (3, 2) $\frac{1}{7}$
3. (6, −3); (2, −1) $-\frac{1}{2}$
4. (−1, 4); (−1, −3) not defined
5. (−2, −1); (−4, −3) 1
6. (−1, 7); (5, 7) 0
7. Find the slope and length of $\overline{AB}$ if $A = (-4, -3)$ and $B = (0, 5)$. slope = 2; $AB = 4\sqrt{5}$
8. Show that *R*, *S*, and *T* are collinear by showing $\overline{RS}$ and $\overline{ST}$ have the same slope. $R(4, -1)$, $S(-5, 2)$, $T(-2, 1)$ slope $\overline{RS} = -\frac{3}{9} = -\frac{1}{3}$; slope $\overline{ST} = -\frac{1}{3}$

7. **a.** Find the slope of $\overleftrightarrow{AB}$. $\frac{3}{2}$
   b. Find tan $n°$. $\frac{3}{2}$
   c. Consider the statement: If a line with positive slope makes an acute angle of $n°$ with the *x*-axis, then the slope of the line is tan $n°$. Do you think this statement is true or false? Explain. **True**

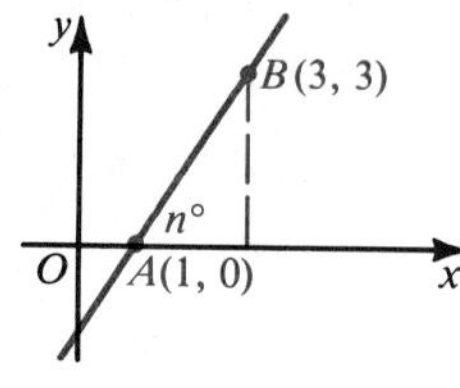

8. This exercise provides a geometric method of justifying the fact that you can use any two points on a line to determine the slope of the line. Horizontal and vertical segments have been drawn as shown. Supply the reason for each step. **2. If 2 ∥ lines are cut by a trans., corr. ∠s are ≅.**

Key steps of proof:

1. $\angle B \cong \angle A$ **def. of ⊥ lines; def. of ≅ ∠s**
2. $\angle 1 \cong \angle 2$ **See above.**
3. $\triangle LBN \sim \triangle DAJ$ **AA ~ Post.**
4. $\frac{BN}{AJ} = \frac{LB}{DA}$, or $\frac{BN}{LB} = \frac{AJ}{DA}$ **Corr. sides of ~ △s are in prop.**
5. The slope of $\overline{LN}$ equals $\frac{BN}{LB}$, and the slope of $\overline{DJ}$ equals $\frac{AJ}{DA}$. **def. of slope**
6. Slope of $\overline{LN}$ = slope of $\overline{DJ}$ **Substitution Prop.**

Written Exercises

A

1. Name each line in the figure whose slope is:
   a. positive ***k***
   b. negative ***n, r***
   c. zero ***l*, *x*-axis**
   d. not defined ***s*, *y*-axis**
2. What can you say about the slope of **(a)** the *x*-axis? and **(b)** the *y*-axis?
   a. slope = 0 b. slope is not defined

Find the slope of the line through the points named. If the slope is not defined, write *not defined*.

3. (1, 2); (3, 4) **1**
4. (1, 2); (−2, −5) $\frac{7}{3}$
5. (1, 2); (−2, 5) **−1**
6. (0, 0); (5, 1) $\frac{1}{5}$
7. (7, 2); (2, 7) **−1**
8. (3, 3); (3, 7) **not defined**
9. (6, −6); (−6, −6) **0**
10. (6, −6); (4, 3) $-\frac{9}{2}$
11. (−4, −3); (−6, −6) $\frac{3}{2}$

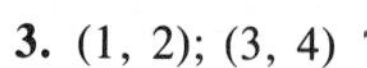

Find the slope and length of $\overline{AB}$.

12. $A(3, -1)$, $B(5, -7)$ **−3; $2\sqrt{10}$**
13. $A(-3, -2)$, $B(7, -6)$ $-\frac{2}{5}$; $2\sqrt{29}$
14. $A(8, -7)$, $B(-3, -5)$ $-\frac{2}{11}$; $5\sqrt{5}$
15. $A(0, -9)$, $B(8, -3)$ $\frac{3}{4}$; 10

In Exercises 16–19 a point P on a line and the slope of the line are given. Sketch the line and find the coordinates of two other points on the line. Answers may vary.

16. $P(-2, 1)$; slope $= \frac{1}{3}$ **(4, 3), (1, 2)** **17.** $P(-3, 0)$; slope $= \frac{2}{5}$ **(−8, −2), (2, 2)**

18. $P(2, 4)$; slope $= -\frac{3}{2}$ **(0, 7), (4, 1)** **19.** $P(0, -5)$; slope $= -\frac{1}{4}$ **(−4, −4), (4, −6)**

In Exercises 20 and 21 show that points P, Q, and R are collinear by showing that $\overline{PQ}$ and $\overline{QR}$ have the same slope.

20. $P(-1, 3)$ $Q(2, 7)$ $R(8, 15)$ **21.** $P(-8, 6)$ $Q(-5, 5)$ $R(4, 2)$

B **22.** A wheelchair ramp is to be built at the town library. If the entrance to the library is 18 in. above ground, and the slope of the ramp is $\frac{1}{15}$, how far out from the building will the ramp start? **$22\frac{1}{2}$ ft**

Complete.

23. A line with slope $\frac{3}{4}$ passes through points (2, 3) and (10, __?__). **9**

24. A line with slope $-\frac{5}{2}$ passes through points (7, −4) and (__?__, 6). **3**

25. A line with slope m passes through points (p, q) and $(r,$ __?__$)$. **$m(r - p) + q$**

26. a. Find the slopes of $\overline{OD}$ and $\overline{NF}$. **$\frac{2}{3}$**
b. Why is $\triangle OCD \cong \triangle NEF$? **SAS**
c. Why is $\angle DOC \cong \angle FNE$?
d. Why is $\overline{OD} \parallel \overline{NF}$?
e. What do you think is true about the slopes of parallel lines? **They are =.**

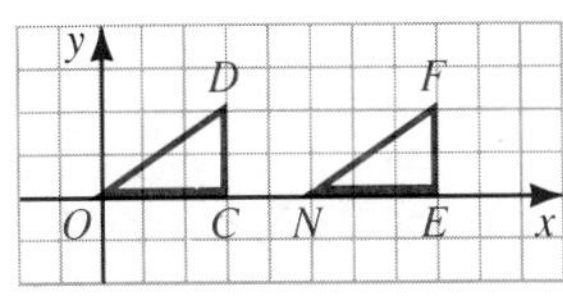

Ex. 26

27. a. Show that $\triangle OAB \cong \triangle ORS$. **SAS**
b. Why is $\overline{OB} \perp \overline{OS}$?
c. Find the product of the slopes of $\overline{OB}$ and $\overline{OS}$. **−1**

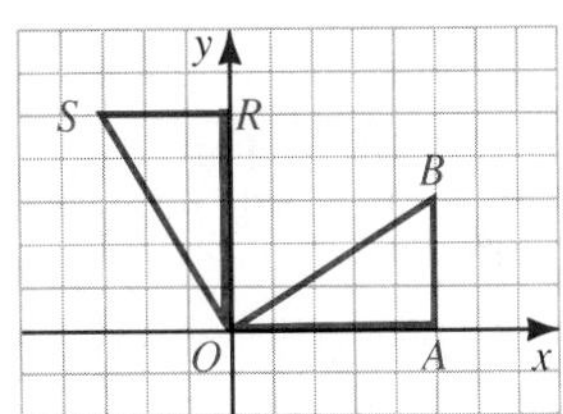

Ex. 27

In Exercises 28 and 29, (a) find the lengths of the sides of $\triangle RST$, (b) use the converse of the Pythagorean Theorem to show that $\triangle RST$ is a right triangle, and (c) find the product of the slopes of $\overline{RT}$ and $\overline{ST}$.

28. $R(4, 2)$, $S(-1, 7)$, $T(1, 1)$
a. $RS = 5\sqrt{2}$, $RT = \sqrt{10}$, $ST = 2\sqrt{10}$
c. −1

29. $R(4, 3)$, $S(-3, 6)$, $T(2, 1)$
a. $RS = \sqrt{58}$, $RT = 2\sqrt{2}$, $ST = 5\sqrt{2}$
c. −1

Exercise Note

Exs. 26 and 27 preview the slopes of parallel and perpendicular lines presented in the next lesson.

Additional Answers Written Exercises

20. slope $\overline{PQ}$ = slope $\overline{QR}$ = $\frac{4}{3}$

21. slope $\overline{PQ}$ = slope $\overline{QR}$ = $-\frac{1}{3}$

26.c. Corr. parts of ≅ △ are ≅.
d. If 2 lines are cut by a trans. and corr. ∠ are ≅, the lines are ∥.

27.b. $m\angle BOS = m\angle BOR + m\angle ROS = m\angle BOR + m\angle AOB = 90$

28.b. $(RT)^2 + (ST)^2 = 10 + 40 = 50 = (RS)^2$

29.b. $(RT)^2 + (ST)^2 = 8 + 50 = 58 = (RS)^2$

Using a Computer

Exs. 28, 29, and 32 can be done using a spreadsheet.

Additional Answers Written Exercises

30.a. tan $\angle A = \frac{BC}{AB} = \frac{4}{5}$

b. $m\angle A \approx 39$

Making Connections

In Exs. 30 and 31, the tangent of the angle formed by the intersection of a line with a horizontal line gives the slope of the line. That angle is known as the "angle of elevation."

30. **a.** Show that tan $\angle A$ = slope of $\overline{AC}$.
b. Use trigonometry to find $m\angle A$.

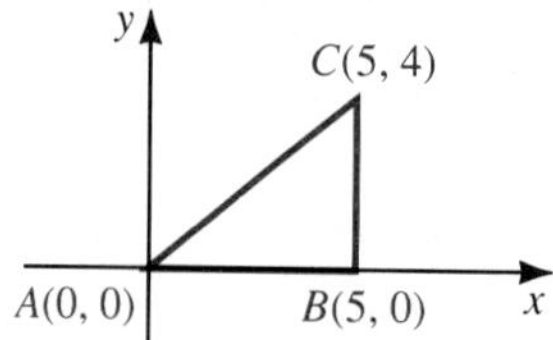

31. A line intersects the x-axis at a 45° angle. What is its slope? **1**

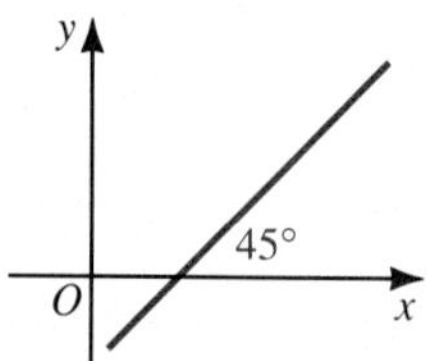

C **32.** A line passes through points $(-2, -1)$ and $(4, 3)$. Where does the line intersect the x-axis? the y-axis? $\left(-\frac{1}{2}, 0\right); \left(0, \frac{1}{3}\right)$

33. A line through $H(3, 1)$ and $J(5, a)$ has positive slope and makes a 60° angle measured counterclockwise with the positive x-axis. Find the value of a. $2\sqrt{3} + 1$

34. Find two values of k such that the points $(-3, 4)$, $(0, k)$, and $(k, 10)$ are collinear. **6, −5**

Algebra Review: *Exponents*

Rules of Exponents

When a and b are nonzero real numbers and m and n are integers:

	Examples
(1) $a^0 = 1$	$5^0 = 1$
(2) $a^m \cdot a^n = a^{m+n}$	$x^2 \cdot x^4 = x^{2+4} = x^6$
(3) $\frac{a^m}{a^n} = a^{m-n}$	$\frac{b^7}{b^3} = b^{7-3} = b^4$
(4) $(a^m)^n = a^{mn}$	$(y^3)^4 = y^{3 \cdot 4} = y^{12}$
(5) $a^{-m} = \frac{1}{a^m}$	$6^{-2} = \frac{1}{6^2} = \frac{1}{36}$

Simplify.

1. $(-6)^3$ **−216**
2. $(-5)^4$ **625**
3. 3^{-2} $\frac{1}{9}$
4. 2^{-3} $\frac{1}{8}$
5. $(-4)^{-3}$ $-\frac{1}{64}$
6. $\left(\frac{2}{3}\right)^{-2}$ $\frac{9}{4}$
7. $\left(\frac{5}{3}\right)^{-3}$ $\frac{27}{125}$
8. 15^0 **1**
9. $(-1)^{20}$ **1**
10. $(-1)^{99}$ **−1**
11. $2^3 \cdot 2^2 \cdot 2^{-4}$ **2**
12. $4^2 \cdot 3^3 \cdot 2^{-3}$ **54**

Simplify. Use only positive exponents in your answers.

13. $r^5 \cdot r^8$ r^{13}
14. $x^{-1} \cdot x^{-2}$ $\frac{1}{x^3}$
15. $\frac{r^9}{r^4}$ r^5
16. $\frac{t^3}{t^5}$ $\frac{1}{t^2}$
17. $a \cdot a^{-1}$ **1**
18. $(x^2)^{-2}$ $\frac{1}{x^4}$
19. $(b^4)^2$ b^8
20. $(s^5)^3$ s^{15}
21. $(3y^2)(2y^4)$ $6y^6$
22. $(4x^3y^2)(-3xy)$ $-12x^4y^3$
23. $(5a^2b^3)(a^{-2}b)$ $5b^4$
24. $(-2st^5)(-4st^{-3})$ $8s^2t^2$

13-3 *Parallel and Perpendicular Lines*

When you look at two parallel lines, you probably believe that the lines have equal slopes. This idea is illustrated by the photograph below. The parallel beams shown are needed to support a roof with a fixed pitch.

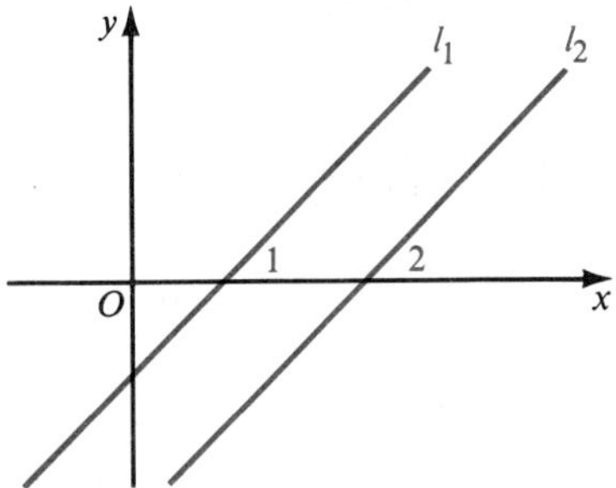

You can use trigonometry and properties of parallel lines to show the following for two nonvertical lines l_1 and l_2 (see the diagram at the right above):

1. $l_1 \parallel l_2$ if and only if $\angle 1 \cong \angle 2$
2. $\angle 1 \cong \angle 2$ if and only if $\tan \angle 1 = \tan \angle 2$
3. $\tan \angle 1 = \tan \angle 2$ if and only if slope of l_1 = slope of l_2

Therefore $l_1 \parallel l_2$ if and only if slope of l_1 = slope of l_2.

Although the diagram shows two lines with positive slope, this result can also be proved for two lines with negative slope. When the lines are parallel to the x-axis, both have slope zero.

Theorem 13-3

Two nonvertical lines are parallel if and only if their slopes are equal.

In Exercises 27–29 of the preceding section, you may have noticed that perpendicular lines, too, have slopes that are related in a special way. See Classroom Exercise 11 and Written Exercise 23 for proofs of the following theorem.

Theorem 13-4

Two nonvertical lines are perpendicular if and only if the product of their slopes is −1.

$$m_1 \cdot m_2 = -1, \text{ or } m_1 = -\frac{1}{m_2}$$

Teaching Suggestions,
pp. T133–T134

Objective
Presenting the Lesson
Reinforcement

Supplementary Materials

Practice Master 80
Test 51
Resource Book, pp. 86–87, 161
Study Guide, pp. 167–168
Computer Activity 29

Lesson Focus

The purpose of this lesson is to state and apply two theorems that can be used to determine if two lines are parallel or perpendicular by comparing their slopes.

Suggested Assignments

Average
537/2, 3, 5, 7, 9

Maximum
Day 1: 537–538/4, 5, 7, 10–12, 15
Day 2: 538/13, 17, 20, 21, 23

Making Connections

The relationships established in Theorems 13-3 and 13-4 will be important in the last lesson of this chapter, where coordinate proofs are done.

Teaching Note

Theorem 13-4 may be reworded as: Two nonvertical lines are perpendicular if and only if their slopes are *negative reciprocals* of each other.

Example Given points $S(5, -1)$ and $T(-3, 3)$, find the slope of every line (a) parallel to $\overleftrightarrow{ST}$ and (b) perpendicular to $\overleftrightarrow{ST}$.

Solution Slope of $\overleftrightarrow{ST} = \frac{3 - (-1)}{-3 - 5} = \frac{4}{-8} = -\frac{1}{2}$

a. Any line parallel to $\overleftrightarrow{ST}$ has slope $-\frac{1}{2}$. (Theorem 13-3)

b. Any line perpendicular to $\overleftrightarrow{ST}$ has slope

$$-\frac{1}{-\frac{1}{2}} = -1 \cdot (-2) = 2. \text{ (Theorem 13-4)}$$

Classroom Exercises

10. If 2 lines are ∥, their slopes are =. If 2 lines have = slopes, the lines are ∥.

1. Given: $l \perp n$. Find the slope of line n if the slope of line l is:

   a. 2 $-\frac{1}{2}$ **b.** $\frac{4}{5}$ $-\frac{5}{4}$ **c.** -4 $\frac{1}{4}$ **d.** not defined **0** **e.** 0 **not defined**

The slopes of two lines are given. Are the lines parallel, perpendicular, or neither?

2. $\frac{3}{4}; \frac{12}{16}$ **parallel**
3. $1; -1$ **⊥**
4. $3; -3$ **neither**
5. $-\frac{3}{4}; \frac{4}{3}$ **⊥**
6. $3; \frac{-1}{3}$ **⊥**
7. $\frac{-2}{3}; \frac{2}{-3}$ **parallel**
8. $0; -1$ **neither**
9. $\frac{5}{6}; \frac{6}{5}$ **neither**
10. State two conditionals that are combined in the biconditional of Theorem 13-3. **See above.**
11. The purpose of this exercise is to prove the statement: If two nonvertical lines are perpendicular, then the product of their slopes is -1. Supply the reason for each step.

Given: l_1 has slope m_1;
l_2 has slope m_2;
$l_1 \perp l_2$

Prove: $m_1 \cdot m_2 = -1$

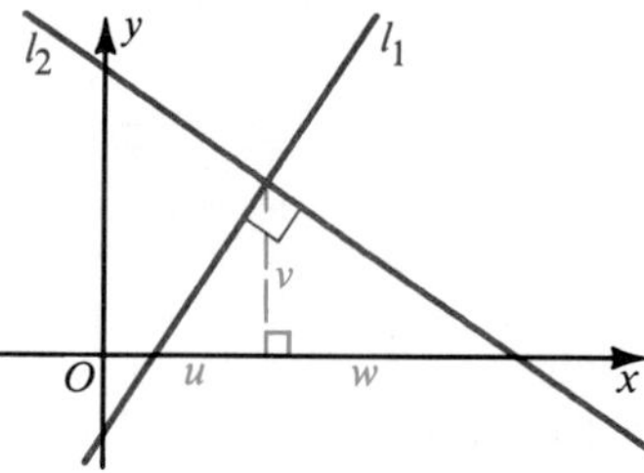

Key steps of proof:

1. Draw the vertical segment shown. **Through a pt. outside a line there is exactly 1 line ⊥ to the given line.**
2. $\frac{u}{v} = \frac{v}{w}$ **When the alt. is drawn to the hyp. of a rt. △, the length of the alt. is the geom. mean btwn. the segs. of the hyp.**
3. $m_1 = \frac{v}{u}$ **Def. of slope**
4. $m_2 = -\frac{v}{w}$ **Def. of slope**
5. $m_1 \cdot m_2 = \left(\frac{v}{u}\right) \cdot \left(-\frac{v}{w}\right)$ **Mult. Prop. of =**
6. $m_1 \cdot m_2 = \left(\frac{v}{u}\right) \cdot \left(-\frac{u}{v}\right) = -1$ **Substitution Prop.**

Proof Note

A proof of the "only if" part of Theorem 13-4 is outlined in Classroom Ex. 11. An alternate proof of both parts of Theorem 13-4 is suggested in Written Ex. 23 on page 538.

Chalkboard Examples

Complete the table below for $r \parallel s$ and $r \perp t$.

	Slope of r	Slope of s	Slope of t
1.	$-\frac{1}{2}$	$-\frac{1}{2}$	2
2.	-6	-6	$\frac{1}{6}$
3.	$\frac{1}{5}$	$\frac{1}{5}$	-5
4.	-4	-4	$\frac{1}{4}$
5.	$-\frac{1}{a}$	$-\frac{1}{a}$	a
6.	$-\frac{4}{3b}$	$-\frac{4}{3b}$	$\frac{3b}{4}$

7. If $r \parallel s$ and r is a horizontal line, what is the slope of s? 0
8. If $k \perp n$, and n has slope 0, what is the slope of k? not defined
9. Use slopes to show that a quadrilateral with vertices $A(-2, 7)$, $B(3, 7)$, $C(6, 11)$, and $D(1, 11)$ is a parallelogram.
   1. Slope $\overline{AB}$ = slope $\overline{CD} = 0$, so $\overline{AB} \parallel \overline{CD}$.
   2. Slope $\overline{AD}$ = slope $\overline{BC} = \frac{4}{3}$, so $\overline{AD} \parallel \overline{BC}$.
   3. Because the quad. has opposite sides parallel, it is a parallelogram.

Written Exercises 1. a. $\frac{2}{3}$ b. $\frac{2}{3}$ c. $-\frac{3}{2}$

Find the slope of (a) $\overleftrightarrow{AB}$, (b) any line parallel to $\overleftrightarrow{AB}$, and (c) any line perpendicular to $\overleftrightarrow{AB}$.

A 1. $A(-2, 0)$ and $B(4, 4)$

2. $A(-3, 1)$ and $B(2, -1)$ a. $-\frac{2}{5}$ b. $-\frac{2}{5}$ c. $\frac{5}{2}$

3. In the diagram at the left below, $OEFG$ is a parallelogram. What is the slope of $\overline{OE}$? of $\overline{GF}$? of $\overline{OG}$? of $\overline{EF}$? $\frac{7}{2}$; $\frac{7}{2}$; 0; 0

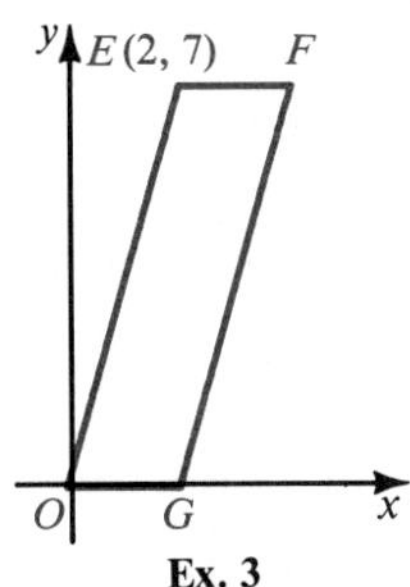

Ex. 3

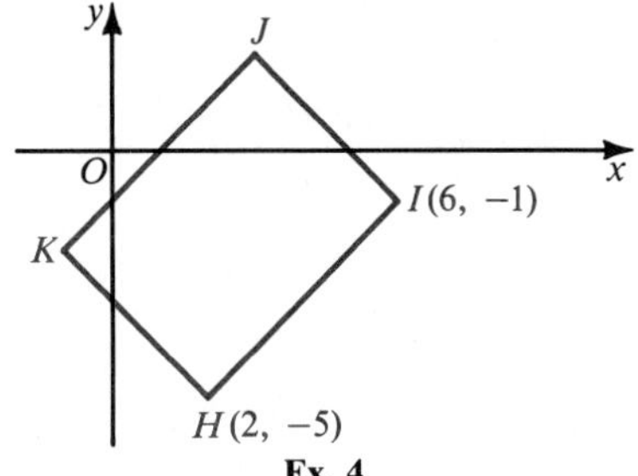

Ex. 4

4. In the diagram at the right above, $HIJK$ is a rectangle. What is the slope of $\overline{HI}$? of $\overline{JK}$? of $\overline{IJ}$? of $\overline{KH}$? 1; 1; −1; −1

5. a. What is the slope of $\overline{LM}$? of $\overline{PN}$? −3; −3
   b. Why is $\overline{LM} \parallel \overline{PN}$? Their slopes are =.
   c. What is the slope of $\overline{MN}$? of $\overline{LP}$? } See below.
   d. Why is $\overline{MN}$ not parallel to $\overline{LP}$? }
   e. What special kind of quadrilateral is $LMNP$? trapezoid

c. $\frac{1}{3}$; $-\frac{1}{7}$ d. Their slopes are not =.

6. Quadrilateral $RSTV$ is known to be a parallelogram.
   a. What is the slope of $\overline{RV}$? of $\overline{TV}$? −1; 1
   b. Why is $\overline{RV} \perp \overline{TV}$? Prod. of slopes = −1
   c. Why is ▱$RSTV$ a rectangle? One ∠ is a rt. ∠.
   d. Find the coordinates of S. (3, −1)

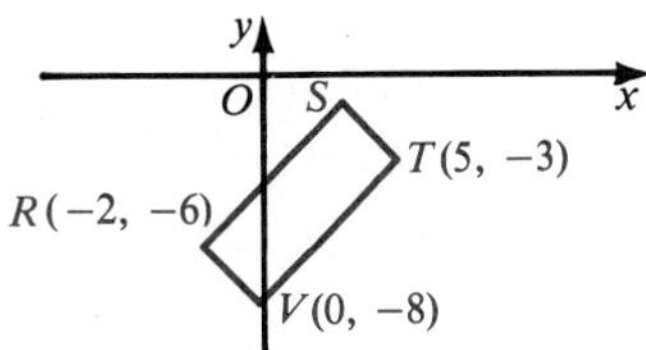

Find the slope of each side and each altitude of △ABC.

7. $A(0, 0)$ $B(7, 3)$ $C(2, -5)$

8. $A(1, 4)$ $B(-1, -3)$ $C(4, -5)$

Use slopes to show that △RST is a right triangle. See below.

9. $R(-3, -4)$ $S(2, 2)$ $T(14, -8)$

10. $R(-1, 1)$ $S(2, 4)$ $T(5, 1)$

B 11. Given the points $A(-6, -4)$, $B(4, 2)$, $C(6, 8)$, and $D(-4, 2)$ show that $ABCD$ is a parallelogram using two different methods.
   a. Show that opposite sides are parallel. b. Show that opposite sides are congruent.

9. $\overline{RS}$: $\frac{6}{5}$, $\overline{ST}$: $-\frac{5}{6}$; $\frac{6}{5}\left(-\frac{5}{6}\right) = -1$

10. $\overline{RS}$: 1, $\overline{ST}$: −1; 1(−1) = −1

Guided Practice

1. If $P(-3, 8)$ and $Q(4, 2)$, find the slope of (a) $\overline{PQ}$, (b) any line parallel to $\overline{PQ}$, and (c) any line ⊥ to $\overline{PQ}$.
   (a) $-\frac{6}{7}$; (b) $-\frac{6}{7}$; (c) $\frac{7}{6}$

2. In the diagram below, $RSTU$ is a rectangle. What is the slope of $\overline{RS}$? $-\frac{1}{2}$ of $\overline{RU}$? 2 of $\overline{ST}$? 2 of $\overline{UT}$? $-\frac{1}{2}$

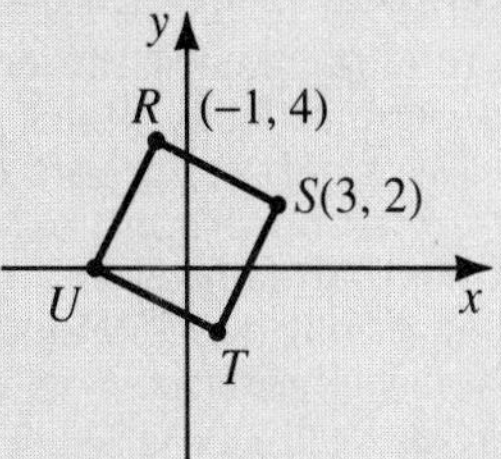

3. Use slopes to show that △ABC is a right triangle. $A(4, 0)$, $B(0, -8)$, $C(-16, 0)$
   Slope $\overline{AB}$ = 2, slope $\overline{BC}$ = $-\frac{1}{2}$, therefore $\overline{AB} \perp \overline{BC}$ and △ABC is a right △.

Additional Answers Written Exercises

7. $\overline{AB}$: $\frac{3}{7}$, alt. to $\overline{AB}$: $-\frac{7}{3}$; $\overline{AC}$: $-\frac{5}{2}$, alt. to $\overline{AC}$: $\frac{2}{5}$; $\overline{BC}$: $\frac{8}{5}$, alt. to $\overline{BC}$: $-\frac{5}{8}$

8. $\overline{AB}$: $\frac{7}{2}$, alt. to $\overline{AB}$: $-\frac{2}{7}$; $\overline{AC}$: −3, alt. to $\overline{AC}$: $\frac{1}{3}$; $\overline{BC}$: $-\frac{2}{5}$, alt. to $\overline{BC}$: $\frac{5}{2}$

11.a. slope $\overline{AB}$ = slope $\overline{CD}$ = $\frac{3}{5}$; slope $\overline{AD}$ = slope $\overline{BC}$ = 3
   b. $AB = CD = 2\sqrt{34}$; $AD = BC = 2\sqrt{10}$

Using a Computer

Exs. 9–14 can be done using a spreadsheet.

Additional Answers Written Exercises

12.b. Slope $\overline{EG} \cdot$ slope $\overline{HF} = 1(-1) = -1$

14.a. Slope $\overline{OP}$ = slope $\overline{NQ} = \frac{2}{3}$; $NO = QP = \sqrt{26}$; slope $\overline{NO} = 5 \neq -\frac{1}{5}$ = slope $\overline{QP}$.

Proof Note

Exs. 11–18 give students an opportunity to prove statements algebraically rather than geometrically. Point out that the algebraic proofs use theorems and properties that have already been presented about quadrilaterals and parallelograms.

Exercise Note

Ex. 23 previews methods of coordinate proof developed in the last lesson of this chapter.

12. Given: Points $E(-4, 1)$, $F(2, 3)$, $G(4, 9)$, and $H(-2, 7)$
- **a.** Show that *EFGH* is a rhombus. **$EF = FG = HG = EH = 2\sqrt{10}$**
- **b.** Use slopes to verify that the diagonals are perpendicular.

13. Given: Points $R(-4, 5)$, $S(-1, 9)$, $T(7, 3)$ and $U(4, -1)$
- **a.** Show that *RSTU* is a rectangle.
- **b.** Use the distance formula to verify that the diagonals are congruent. **$RT = US = 5\sqrt{5}$**

14. Given: Points $N(-1, -5)$, $O(0, 0)$, $P(3, 2)$, and $Q(8, 1)$
- **a.** Show that *NOPQ* is an isosceles trapezoid.
- **b.** Show that the diagonals are congruent. **$NP = QO = \sqrt{65}$**

Decide what special type of quadrilateral *HIJK* is. Then prove that your answer is correct.

15. $H(0, 0)$	$I(5, 0)$	$J(7, 9)$	$K(1, 9)$ **trapezoid**
16. $H(0, 1)$	$I(2, -3)$	$J(-2, -1)$	$K(-4, 3)$ **rhombus**
17. $H(7, 5)$	$I(8, 3)$	$J(0, -1)$	$K(-1, 1)$ **rectangle**
18. $H(-3, -3)$	$I(-5, -6)$	$J(4, -5)$	$K(6, -2)$ **parallelogram**

19. Point $N(3, -4)$ lies on the circle $x^2 + y^2 = 25$. What is the slope of the line that is tangent to the circle at N? (*Hint*: Recall Theorem 9-1.) **$\frac{3}{4}$**

20. Point $P(6, 7)$ lies on the circle $(x + 2)^2 + (y - 1)^2 = 100$. What is the slope of the line that is tangent to the circle at P? **$-\frac{4}{3}$**

In Chapter 3 parallel lines are defined as coplanar lines that do not intersect. It is also possible to define parallel lines *algebraically* as follows:

Lines *a* and *b* are *parallel* if and only if slope of *a* = slope of *b* (or both *a* and *b* are vertical).

21. Use the algebraic definition to classify each statement as true or false.
- **a.** For any line l in a plane, $l \parallel l$. **True**
- **b.** For any lines l and n in a plane, if $l \parallel n$, then $n \parallel l$. **True**
- **c.** For any lines k, l, and n in a plane, if $k \parallel l$ and $l \parallel n$, then $k \parallel n$. **True**

22. Refer to Exercise 21. Is parallelism of lines an equivalence relation? (See Exercise 15, page 43.) Explain. **Yes; the rel. is ref., sym., and trans.**

C **23.** This exercise shows another way to prove Theorem 13-4.
- **a.** Use the Pythagorean Theorem to prove:

  If $\overleftrightarrow{TU} \perp \overleftrightarrow{US}$, then the product of the slopes of $\overleftrightarrow{TU}$ and $\overleftrightarrow{US}$ equals -1. That is, prove $\left(-\frac{c}{a}\right) \cdot \left(-\frac{c}{b}\right) = -1$.

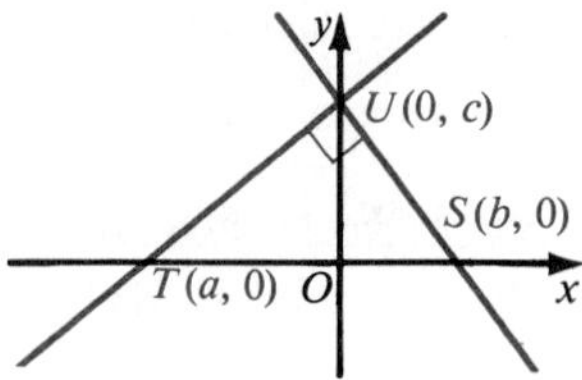

- **b.** Use the converse of the Pythagorean Theorem to prove:

  If $\left(-\frac{c}{a}\right) \cdot \left(-\frac{c}{b}\right) = -1$, then $\overleftrightarrow{TU} \perp \overleftrightarrow{US}$.

13-4 *Vectors*

The journey of a boat or airplane can be described by giving its speed and direction, such as 50 km/h northeast. Any quantity such as force, velocity, or acceleration, that has both *magnitude* (size) and *direction*, is a **vector.**

When a boat moves from point A to point B, its journey can be represented by drawing an arrow from A to B, $\overrightarrow{AB}$ (read "*vector AB*"). If $\overrightarrow{AB}$ is drawn in the coordinate plane, then the journey can also be represented as an ordered pair.

$$\overrightarrow{AB} = (\text{change in } x, \text{ change in } y)$$

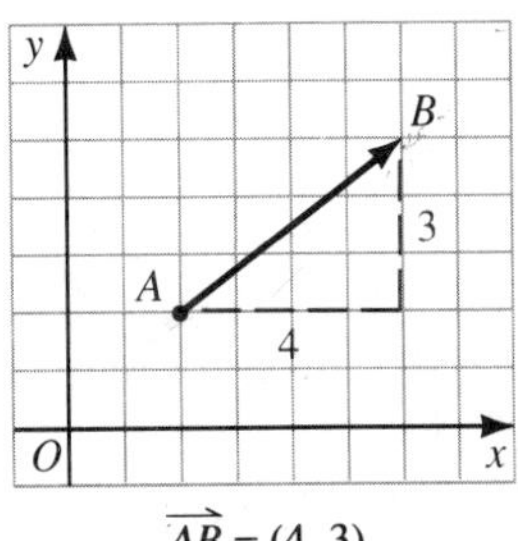

$\overrightarrow{AB} = (4, 3)$

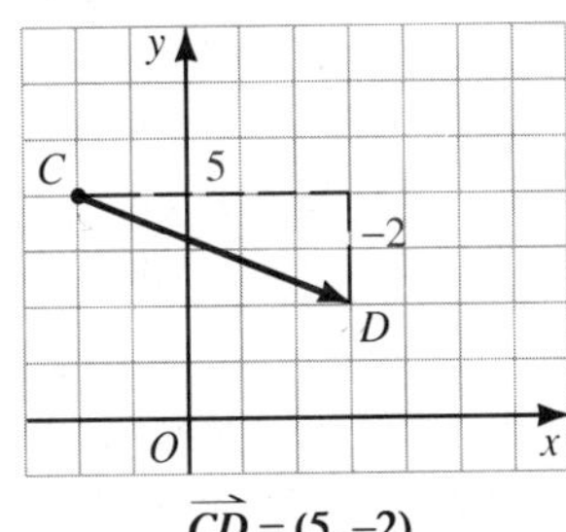

$\overrightarrow{CD} = (5, -2)$

The **magnitude** of a vector $\overrightarrow{AB}$ is the length of the arrow from point A to point B and is denoted by the symbol $|\overrightarrow{AB}|$. You can use the Pythagorean Theorem or the Distance Formula to find the magnitude of a vector. In the diagrams above,

$$|\overrightarrow{AB}| = \sqrt{4^2 + 3^2} = 5$$

and $|\overrightarrow{CD}| = \sqrt{5^2 + 2^2} = \sqrt{29}$.

Example 1 Given: Points $P(-5, 4)$ and $Q(1, 2)$

a. Sketch $\overrightarrow{PQ}$.

b. Find $\overrightarrow{PQ}$.

c. Find $|\overrightarrow{PQ}|$.

Solution **a.**

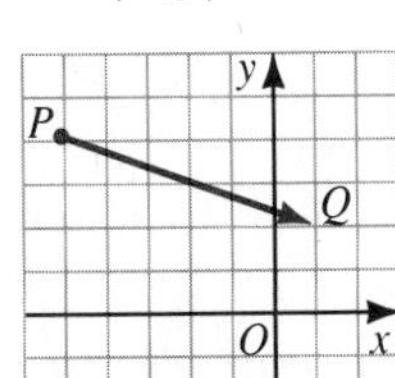

b. $\overrightarrow{PQ} = (1 - (-5), 2 - 4) = (6, -2)$

c. $|\overrightarrow{PQ}| = \sqrt{6^2 + (-2)^2} = \sqrt{40} = 2\sqrt{10}$

Teaching Suggestions, p. T134

Objective
Presenting the Lesson

Cooperative Learning, p. T134

Supplementary Materials

Study Guide, pp. 169–170

Lesson Focus

This lesson defines the concept of a vector. Vectors have important applications in physics, engineering, and other applied sciences.

Suggested Assignments

Average
541–542/1–17 odd
543/Mixed Review 2–10 even

Maximum
541–542/8, 10, 16, 20, 26, 27, 31
S 538/19

Teaching Note

Point out that the magnitude of a vector, $|\overrightarrow{AB}|$, is like the absolute value of a number. For example, on the number line, $|-7|$ is the distance from the origin to the point whose coordinate is -7. $|\overrightarrow{AB}|$ is the distance from point A to point B in the coordinate plane. Magnitude, like distance, is never negative.

Point out also that (3, 2) could be a *vector* or a *point*, and that the correct meaning of the symbol can be determined only from the context in which it is being used.

The symbol $2\overrightarrow{PQ}$ represents a vector that has twice the magnitude of $\overrightarrow{PQ}$ and has the same direction. If $\overrightarrow{PQ} = (3, 2)$, it should not surprise you that $2\overrightarrow{PQ} = (2 \cdot 3, 2 \cdot 2) = (6, 4)$. In general, if the vector $\overrightarrow{PQ} = (a, b)$, then $k\overrightarrow{PQ} = (ka, kb)$; $k\overrightarrow{PQ}$ is called a **scalar multiple** of $\overrightarrow{PQ}$. Multiplying a vector by a real number k multiplies the length of the vector by $|k|$. If $k < 0$, the direction of the vector reverses as well. This is illustrated in the diagrams below. What ordered pair represents $-3\overrightarrow{PQ}$?

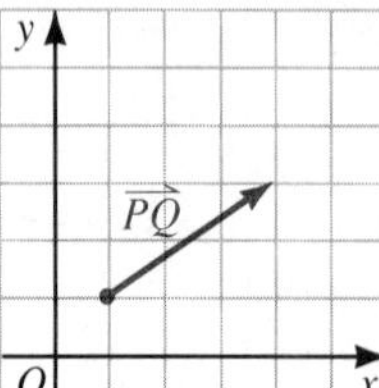

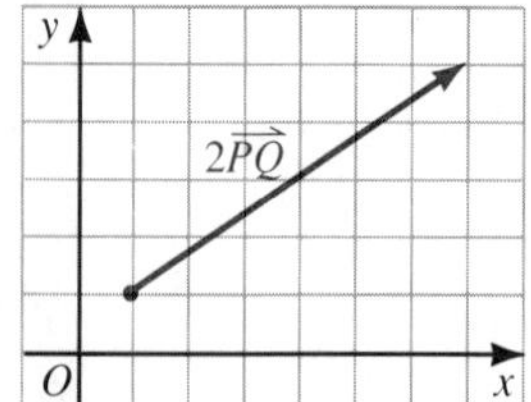

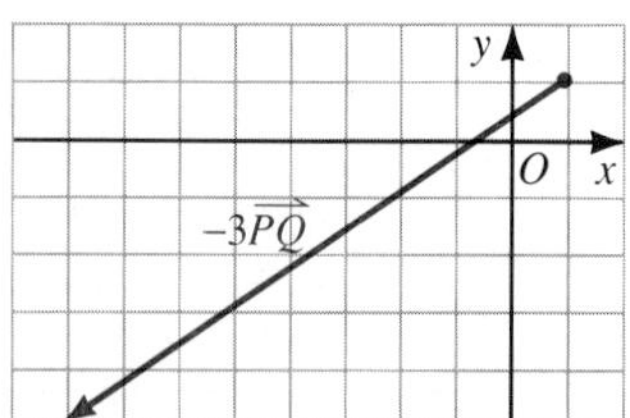

Two vectors are *perpendicular* if the arrows representing them have perpendicular directions. Two vectors are *parallel* if the arrows representing them have the same direction or opposite directions. All the vectors shown at the right are parallel. Notice that $\overrightarrow{OA}$ and $\overrightarrow{BC}$ are parallel even though the points O, A, B, and C are collinear.

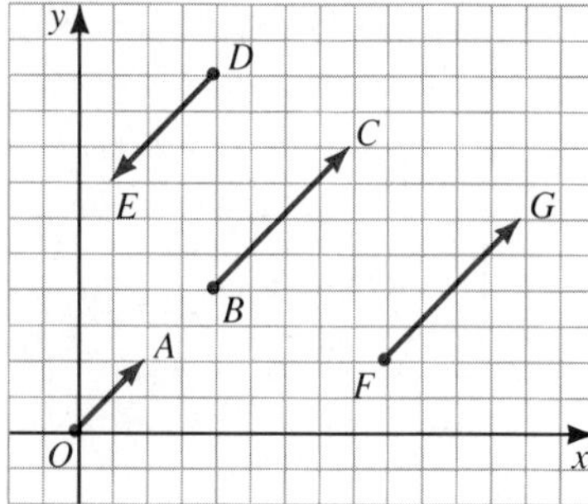

Two vectors are **equal** if they have the same magnitude and the same direction. In the diagram, $\overrightarrow{BC} = \overrightarrow{FG}$.

You can tell by using slopes whether nonvertical vectors are parallel or perpendicular. Example 2 shows how.

Example 2 **a.** Show that $(9, -6)$ and $(-6, 4)$ are parallel.
b. Show that $(9, -6)$ and $(2, 3)$ are perpendicular.

Solution **a.** Slope of $(9, -6)$ is $\frac{-6}{9} = -\frac{2}{3}$.

Slope of $(-6, 4) = \frac{4}{-6} = -\frac{2}{3}$.

Since the slopes are equal, the vectors are parallel.

b. Slope of $(9, -6)$ is $\frac{-6}{9} = -\frac{2}{3}$.

Slope of $(2, 3)$ is $\frac{3}{2}$.

Since $\frac{-2}{3} \cdot \frac{3}{2} = -1$, the vectors are perpendicular.

Chalkboard Examples

Given points P and Q, (a) sketch $\overrightarrow{PQ}$, (b) find $\overrightarrow{PQ}$, (c) find $|\overrightarrow{PQ}|$, (d) find $3\overrightarrow{PQ}$, and (e) find $-2\overrightarrow{PQ}$.

1. $P(-3, 4)$, $Q(-2, -2)$
(a)

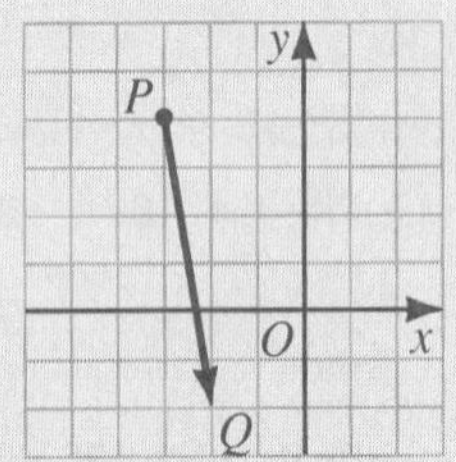

(b) $\overrightarrow{PQ} = (-2-(-3), -2-4) = (1, -6)$
(c) $|\overrightarrow{PQ}| = \sqrt{1^2 + (-6)^2}$ $\sqrt{1 + 36} = \sqrt{37}$
(d) $(3, -18)$
(e) $(-2, 12)$

2. $P(-1, -5)$, $Q(5, 3)$
(a)

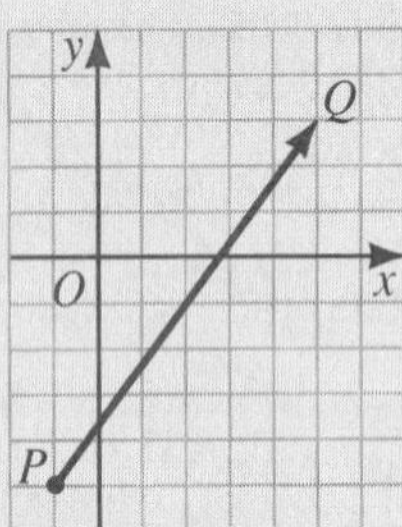

(b) $\overrightarrow{PQ} = (5-(-1), 3-(-5)) = (6, 8)$
(c) $|\overrightarrow{PQ}| = \sqrt{6^2 + 8^2}$ $\sqrt{36 + 64} = 10$
(d) $(18, 24)$
(e) $(-12, -16)$

3. Show that $(6, -3)$ and $(-4, 2)$ are parallel.
The slope of $(6, -3)$ is $-\frac{1}{2}$. The slope of $(-4, 2)$ is $-\frac{1}{2}$.

4. Show that $(6, -3)$ and $(2, 4)$ are perpendicular.
The slope of $(6, -3)$ is $-\frac{1}{2}$. The slope of $(2, 4)$ is 2. $-\frac{1}{2} \cdot 2 = -1$

Vectors can be added by the following simple rule:

$$(a, b) + (c, d) = (a + c, b + d)$$

To see an application of adding vectors, suppose that a jet travels from P to Q and then from Q to R. The jet could have made the same journey by flying directly from P to R. $\overrightarrow{PR}$ is the **sum** of $\overrightarrow{PQ}$ and $\overrightarrow{QR}$. We abbreviate this fact by writing

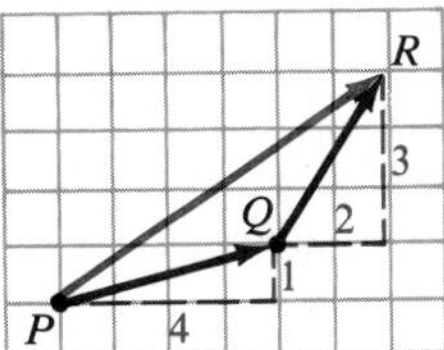

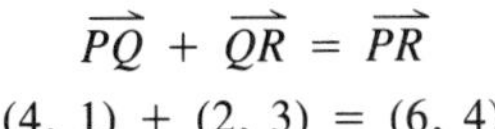

$$\overrightarrow{PQ} + \overrightarrow{QR} = \overrightarrow{PR}$$

$$(4, 1) + (2, 3) = (6, 4)$$

Classroom Exercises **2. a. 5 b. $\sqrt{17}$ c. 5 d. 2 e. $\sqrt{17}$ f. 5**

Exercises 1–4 refer to the figure at the right.

1. Name each vector as an ordered pair.
   a. $\overrightarrow{OB}$ **(4, −3)** b. $\overrightarrow{OD}$ **(1, 4)** c. $\overrightarrow{DE}$ **(−5, 0)**

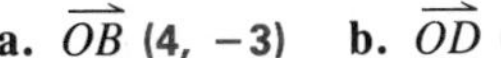

   d. $\overrightarrow{EF}$ **(0, −2)** e. $\overrightarrow{BC}$ **(1, 4)** f. $\overrightarrow{AG}$ **(−4, 3)**
2. Find the magnitude of each vector in Exercise 1.
3. a. Is $\overrightarrow{BC}$ parallel to $\overrightarrow{OD}$? Explain.
   b. Is $\overrightarrow{BC} = \overrightarrow{OD}$? Explain.
   c. What kind of figure is $OBCD$? Explain.
4. a. Is $\overrightarrow{AG}$ parallel to $\overrightarrow{OB}$? Explain.
   b. Is $\overrightarrow{AG} = \overrightarrow{OB}$? Explain.
5. Refer to the diagram. Find $|\overrightarrow{ST}|$ and tan $\angle S$. **$\frac{4}{9}$** **$\sqrt{97}$**
6. Find each sum.
   a. (3, 1) + (5, 6) **(8, 7)**
   b. (0, −6) + (7, 4) **(7, −2)**
   c. (−3, 10) + (−5, −12) **(−8, −2)**
7. Find each scalar multiple.
   a. 2(3, 1) **(6, 2)** b. 3(−5, 1) **(−15, 3)** c. $-\frac{1}{2}(-6, 0)$ **(3, 0)**
8. If $\overrightarrow{PQ}$ represents a wind blowing 45 km/h from the north, state two ways you could name the vector representing a wind blowing 45 km/h from the south. **$\overrightarrow{QP}$ or $-\overrightarrow{PQ}$**

Written Exercises **4. (−3, −3); $3\sqrt{2}$ 5. (−4, 2); $2\sqrt{5}$ 6. (−4, 2); $2\sqrt{5}$**

In Exercises 1–9 points A and B are given. Make a sketch. Then find $\overrightarrow{AB}$ and $|\overrightarrow{AB}|$.

A

1. $A(1, 1), B(5, 4)$ **(4, 3); 5**
2. $A(2, 0), B(8, 8)$ **(6, 8); 10**
3. $A(6, 1), B(4, 3)$ **(−2, 2); $2\sqrt{2}$**
4. $A(0, 5), B(-3, 2)$
5. $A(3, 5), B(-1, 7)$
6. $A(4, -2), B(0, 0)$
7. $A(0, 0), B(5, -9)$ **(5, −9); $\sqrt{106}$**
8. $A(-3, 5), B(3, 0)$ **(6, −5); $\sqrt{61}$**
9. $A(-1, -1), B(-4, -7)$ **(−3, −6); $3\sqrt{5}$**

Teaching Note

Point out the difference between a ray and a vector. For example, if B is between A and C, $\overrightarrow{AB}$ and $\overrightarrow{AC}$ are the same ray, but $\overrightarrow{AB} \neq \overrightarrow{AC}$. The magnitude of $\overrightarrow{AC}$ is greater than the magnitude of $\overrightarrow{AB}$.

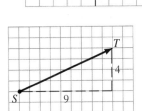

Additional Answers Classroom Exercises

3.a. Yes; the slopes are =.
b. Yes; they have the same magnitude and direction.
c. parallelogram; $\overline{OD}$ and $\overline{BC}$ are ∥ and ≅.

4.a. Yes; the slopes are =.
b. No; they do not have the same direction.

Guided Practice

In Exs. 1–4 points R and S are given. Make a sketch to find $\overrightarrow{RS}$ and $|\overrightarrow{RS}|$.

1. $R(1, 4)$, $S(-2, 3)$
   (−3, −1); $\sqrt{10}$
2. $R(0, 0)$, $S(4, -3)$
   (4, −3); 5
3. $R(-2, 0)$, $S(2, 4)$
   (4, 4); $4\sqrt{2}$
4. Name two vectors:
   parallel to (−2, 5)
   Answers will vary; (4, −10); (−6, 15)
   perpendicular to (−2, 5)
   Answers will vary; (5, 2); (−15, −6)

Find each vector sum.

5. (2, 1) + (3, 4) (5, 5)
6. (−1, 4) + 2(3, 1) (5, 6)

Use a grid and draw arrows to represent the following vectors. You can choose any starting point you like for each vector.

10. (3, 5) and 2(3, 5)
11. (4, −1) and 3(4, −1)
12. (−8, 4) and $\frac{1}{2}$(−8, 4)
13. (−6, −9) and $\frac{1}{3}$(−6, −9)
14. (4, 1) and −3(4, 1)
15. (6, −4) and $-\frac{1}{2}$(6, −4)

16. Name two vectors parallel to (3, −8). **Answers will vary. Examples: (6, −16), (−3, 8)**
17. The vectors (8, 6) and (12, *k*) are parallel. Find the value of *k*. **9**
18. Show that (4, −5) and (15, 12) are perpendicular. **See below.**
19. The vectors (8, *k*) and (9, 6) are perpendicular. Find the value of *k*. **−12**

18. $-\frac{5}{4}\cdot\frac{12}{15} = -1$

Find each vector sum. Then illustrate each sum with a diagram like that on page 541.

20. (2, 1) + (3, 6)
21. (3, −5) + (4, 5)
22. (−8, 2) + (4, 6)
23. (−3, −3) + (7, 7)
24. (1, 4) + 2(3, 1)
25. (7, 2) + 3(−1, 0)

B **26.** Two forces $\overrightarrow{AB}$ and $\overrightarrow{AC}$ are pulling an object at point *A*. The single force $\overrightarrow{AD}$ that has the same effect as these two forces is their sum $\overrightarrow{AB} + \overrightarrow{AC}$. This sum can be found by completing parallelogram *ABDC* as shown. Explain why the diagonal $\overrightarrow{AD}$ is the sum of $\overrightarrow{AB}$ and $\overrightarrow{AC}$.
$\overrightarrow{AD} = \overrightarrow{AC} + \overrightarrow{CD} = \overrightarrow{AC} + \overrightarrow{AB}$

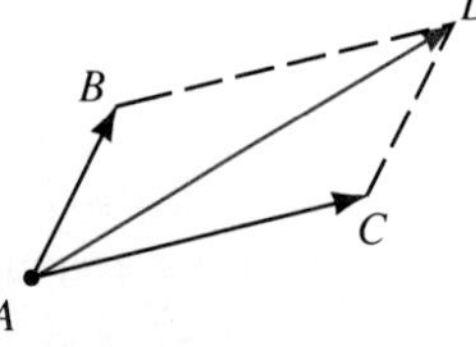

27. Make a drawing showing an object being pulled by the two forces $\overrightarrow{KX}$ = (−1, 5) and $\overrightarrow{KY}$ = (7, 3). What single force has the same effect as the two forces acting together? What is the magnitude of this force? **(6, 8); 10**

28. Repeat Exercise 27 for the forces $\overrightarrow{KX}$ = (2, −3) and $\overrightarrow{KY}$ = (−2, 3). **(0, 0); 0**

29. In the diagram, *M* is the midpoint of $\overline{AB}$ and *T* is a trisector point of $\overline{AB}$.
a. Complete: $\overrightarrow{AB}$ = (**18**, **18**), $\overrightarrow{AM}$ = (**9**, **9**) and $\overrightarrow{AT}$ = (_?_, _?_). **6, 6**
b. Find the coordinates of *M* and *T*. **(11, 12); (8, 9)**

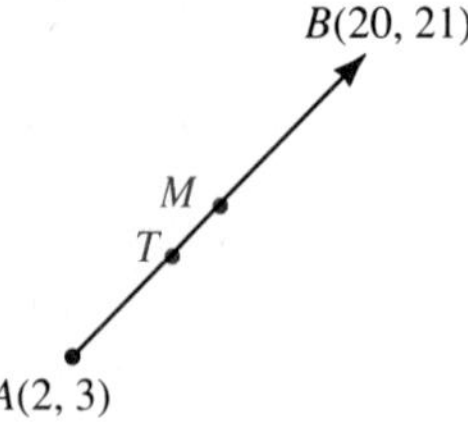

30. Repeat Exercise 29 given the points *A*(−10, 9) and *B*(20, −15). **See below.**

31. Use algebra to prove $|(ka, kb)| = |k|\cdot|(a, b)|$.

C **32.** **a.** Use definitions I and II below to prove that

$$k[(a, b) + (c, d)] = k(a, b) + k(c, d).$$

I. Definition of scalar multiple $\quad k(a, b) = (ka, kb)$
II. Definition of vector addition $\quad (a, b) + (c, d) = (a + c, b + d)$

b. Make a diagram illustrating what you proved in part (a).

30. a. $\overrightarrow{AB}$ **= (30, −24),** $\overrightarrow{AM}$ **= (15, −12),** $\overrightarrow{AT}$ **= (10, −8)**
b. ***M*(5, −3); *T*(0, 1)**

Additional Answers Written Exercises

20. (5, 7)
21. (7, 0)
22. (−4, 8)
23. (4, 4)
24. (7, 6)
25. (4, 2)
31. $|(ka, kb)| = \sqrt{(ka)^2 + (kb)^2} = \sqrt{k^2(a^2 + b^2)} = |k|\sqrt{a^2 + b^2} = |k|\cdot|(a, b)|$

Group Activity

Exs. 26–28 can be discussed in groups of two or three students. Have students first attempt to complete the parallelograms on their own; then have them explain their conclusions to the other members of the group.

33. a. Given: $\overrightarrow{AB} = 2\overrightarrow{DB}$ and $\overrightarrow{BC} = 2\overrightarrow{BE}$
Supply the reasons for each step.
1. $\overrightarrow{AC} = \overrightarrow{AB} + \overrightarrow{BC}$ **Def. of vector sum**
2. $= 2\overrightarrow{DB} + 2\overrightarrow{BE}$ **Substitution Prop.**
3. $= 2(\overrightarrow{DB} + \overrightarrow{BE})$ (*Hint*: See Exercise 32.)
4. $= 2\overrightarrow{DE}$ **Def. of vector sum**

b. What theorem about midpoints does part (a) prove?

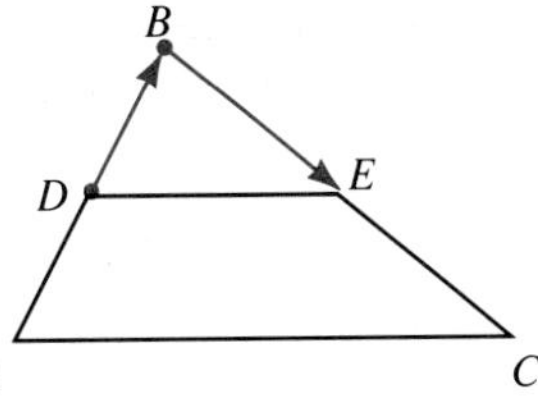

34. Suppose two nonvertical vectors (a, b) and (c, d) are perpendicular.
a. Use slopes to show that $\frac{bd}{ac} = -1$.
b. Show that $ac + bd = 0$.
c. The number $ac + bd$ is called the **dot product** of vectors (a, b) and (c, d). Complete: If (a, b) and (c, d) are perpendicular vectors, then their dot product __?__. **is zero**
d. Verify the statement in part (c) for the vectors in Example 2(b) on page 540 and in Exercise 18 on page 542.

33. Step 3: $k[(a, b) + (c, d)] = k(a, b) + k(c, d)$

Mixed Review Exercises

1. On a number line, point A has coordinate -11 and B has coordinate 7. Find the coordinate of the midpoint of $\overline{AB}$. **−2**
2. If M is the midpoint of the hypotenuse $\overline{AB}$ of right triangle ABC, and $AM = 6$, find MB and MC. **6; 6**
3. The lengths of the bases of a trapezoid are 12 and 20. Find the length of the median. **16**
4. If the length of one side of an equilateral triangle is $2a$, find the length of an altitude. **$a\sqrt{3}$**
5. Find the measure of each interior angle of a regular hexagon. **120**
6. Each side of a regular hexagon $ABCDEF$ has length x. Find AD and AC. **$2x$; $x\sqrt{3}$**
7. Find the measure of each exterior angle of a regular octagon. **45**
8. Find the coordinates of the fourth vertex of a rectangle that has three vertices at $(-3, -2)$, $(2, -2)$, and $(2, 5)$. **$(-3, 5)$**
9. The vertices of quad. $ABCD$ are $A(2, 0)$, $B(7, 0)$, $C(7, 5)$, and $D(2, 5)$. Find the area of quad. $ABCD$. **25**
10. The vertices of $\triangle PQR$ are $P(0, 0)$, $Q(-6, 0)$, and $R(-6, 6)$. Find the area of $\triangle PQR$. **18**
11. $\triangle DEF$ has vertices $D(-5, 1)$, $E(-2, -3)$, and $F(6, 3)$. **See below.**
    a. Use the distance formula to show that $\triangle DEF$ is a right triangle.
    b. Use slopes to show that $\triangle DEF$ is a right triangle. **slope $\overline{DE}$ · slope $\overline{EF}$ = $-\frac{4}{3} \cdot \frac{3}{4} = -1$**
12. $\triangle ABC$ has vertices $A(6, 0)$, $B(4, 8)$, and $C(2, 6)$.
    a. Find the slope of the altitude from B to $\overline{AC}$. **$\frac{2}{3}$**
    b. Find the slope of the perpendicular bisector of $\overline{AB}$. **$\frac{1}{4}$**

11. a. $(DE)^2 + (EF)^2 = 25 + 100 = 125$; $(DF)^2 = 121 + 4 = 125$

Additional Answers Written Exercises

33.b. The seg. that joins the midpts. of 2 sides of a △ is half as long as the third side.

Exercise Note

Ex. 33 uses vectors to prove that the segment that joins the midpoints of two sides of a triangle is half as long as the third side. (Theorem 5-11, part (2), page 178)

Teaching Suggestions,
pp. T134–T135

Objective
Presenting the Lesson
Enrichment

Supplementary Materials

Practice Master 81
Test 52
Resource Book, pp. 88–89, 162
Study Guide, pp. 171–172
Overhead Visual F
Computer Activity 30

Lesson Focus

In this lesson, the useful formula for finding the coordinates of the midpoint of a segment is stated and applied.

Suggested Assignments

Average
545–546/3, 5–7, 9, 12, 13
547/Self-Test 1

Maximum
545–547/4, 5, 8, 12, 13, 15, 19, 23
S 542/29, 32

Teaching Note

Point out that the midpoint formula shows that the coordinates of the midpoint of a segment are formed by taking the average of the x-coordinates and the average of the y-coordinates.

13-5 *The Midpoint Formula*

On a number line, if points A and B have coordinates x_1 and x_2, then the midpoint of $\overline{AB}$ has coordinate $\frac{x_1 + x_2}{2}$, the average of x_1 and x_2. (See Exercise 19 on page 47.)

This idea can be used to find the midpoint of any horizontal or vertical segment.

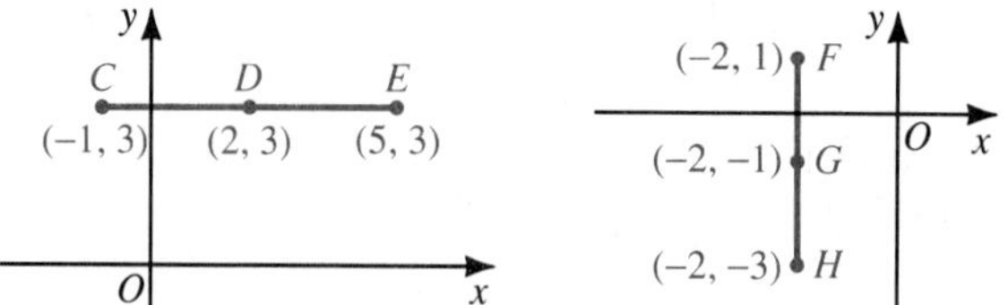

If a segment $\overline{PQ}$ is neither horizontal nor vertical, then the coordinates of its midpoint M can be found by drawing horizontal and vertical auxiliary lines as shown.

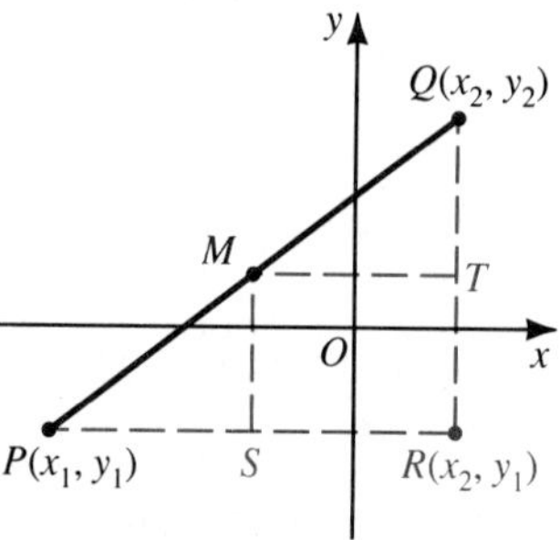

Since M is the midpoint of $\overline{PQ}$ and $\overline{MS} \parallel \overline{QR}$, S is the midpoint of $\overline{PR}$ (Theorem 5-10). Thus both S and M have x-coordinate $\frac{x_1 + x_2}{2}$.

Similarly, $\overline{MT} \parallel \overline{PR}$, so T is the midpoint of $\overline{QR}$. Thus both T and M have y-coordinate $\frac{y_1 + y_2}{2}$.

This discussion leads to the following theorem.

Theorem 13-5 *The Midpoint Formula*
The midpoint of the segment that joins points (x_1, y_1) and (x_2, y_2) is the point

$$\left(\frac{x_1 + x_2}{2}, \frac{y_1 + y_2}{2}\right).$$

Example 1 Find the midpoint of the segment that joins $(-11, 3)$ and $(8, -7)$.

Solution The x-coordinate of the midpoint is

$$\frac{x_1 + x_2}{2} = \frac{-11 + 8}{2} = \frac{-3}{2}, \text{ or } -\frac{3}{2}.$$

The y-coordinate of the midpoint is

$$\frac{y_1 + y_2}{2} = \frac{3 - 7}{2} = \frac{-4}{2} = -2.$$

The midpoint is $\left(-\frac{3}{2}, -2\right)$.

Example 2 Given points $A(2, 1)$ and $B(8, 5)$, show that $P(3, 6)$ is on the perpendicular bisector of $\overline{AB}$.

Solution 1 Join P to M, the midpoint of $\overline{AB}$ and show that $\overline{PM} \perp \overline{AB}$.

Step 1 $M = \left(\frac{2 + 8}{2}, \frac{1 + 5}{2}\right) = (5, 3)$

Step 2 Slope of $\overline{AB} = \frac{5 - 1}{8 - 2} = \frac{4}{6} = \frac{2}{3}$

Slope of $\overline{PM} = \frac{3 - 6}{5 - 3} = \frac{-3}{2}$

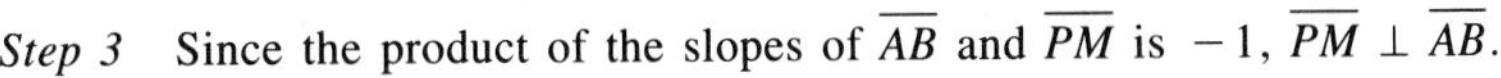

Step 3 Since the product of the slopes of $\overline{AB}$ and $\overline{PM}$ is -1, $\overline{PM} \perp \overline{AB}$.

Solution 2 Show that P is equidistant from A and B and apply Theorem 4-6, page 153.

Step 1 $PA = \sqrt{(3 - 2)^2 + (6 - 1)^2} = \sqrt{26}$

$PB = \sqrt{(3 - 8)^2 + (6 - 5)^2} = \sqrt{26}$

Step 2 Since $PA = PB$, P is on the perpendicular bisector of $\overline{AB}$.

Classroom Exercises

Find the coordinates of the midpoint of the segment that joins the given points.

1. $(3, 5)$ and $(7, 5)$ **(5, 5)**
2. $(0, 4)$ and $(4, 3)$ **$(2, \frac{7}{2})$**
3. $(-2, 2)$ and $(6, 4)$ **(2, 3)**
4. $(-3, 7)$ and $(-7, -5)$ **(−5, 1)**
5. $(-1, -3)$ and $(-3, 6)$ **$(-2, \frac{3}{2})$**
6. $(2b, 3)$ and $(4, -5)$ **$(b + 2, -1)$**
7. $(t, 2)$ and $(t + 4, -4)$ **$(t + 2, -1)$**
8. (a, n) and (d, p) **$\left(\frac{a + d}{2}, \frac{n + p}{2}\right)$**

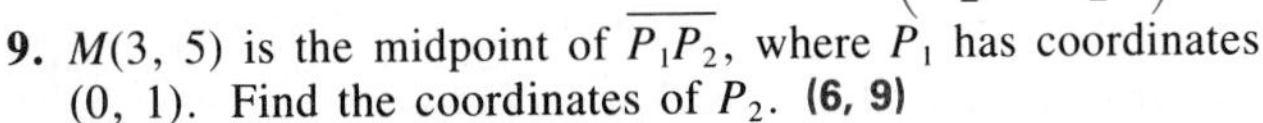

9. $M(3, 5)$ is the midpoint of $\overline{P_1P_2}$, where P_1 has coordinates $(0, 1)$. Find the coordinates of P_2. **(6, 9)**
10. Point $(1, -1)$ is the midpoint of $\overline{AB}$, where A has coordinates $(-1, 3)$. Find the coordinates of B. **(3, −5)**

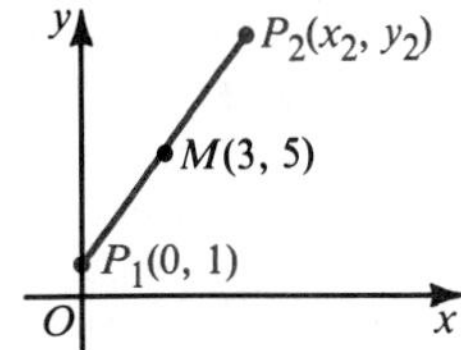

Written Exercises

Find the coordinates of the midpoint of the segment that joins the given points.

A

1. $(0, 2)$ and $(6, 4)$ **(3, 3)**
2. $(-2, 6)$ and $(4, 3)$ **$(1, \frac{9}{2})$**
3. $(6, -7)$ and $(-6, 3)$ **(0, −2)**
4. $(a, 4)$ and $(a + 2, 0)$ **$(a + 1, 2)$**
5. $(2.3, 3.7)$ and $(1.5, -2.9)$ **(1.9, 0.4)**
6. (a, b) and (c, d) **$\left(\frac{a + c}{2}, \frac{b + d}{2}\right)$**

Chalkboard Examples

Find the midpoint of $\overline{AB}$.

1. $A(6, 3)$, $B(-2, -5)$ $(2, -1)$
2. $A(a, b)$, $B(c, b)$ $\left(\frac{a + c}{2}, b\right)$
3. $A(-2k, 3m)$, $B(3k, -4m)$ $\left(\frac{k}{2}, -\frac{m}{2}\right)$
4. $M(4, -2)$ is the midpoint of $\overline{AB}$. A has coordinates $(2, -5)$. Find the coordinates of B. $(6, 1)$
5. Given points $A(5, 2)$ and $B(3, -6)$, show that $P(0, -1)$ is on the perpendicular bisector of $\overline{AB}$.
   Midpoint M is $(4, -2)$. Slope $\overline{AB} = 4$, slope $\overline{PM} = -\frac{1}{4}$, therefore $\overline{AB} \perp \overline{PM}$.
   Alternate solution:
   $PA = \sqrt{(0 - 5)^2 + (-1 - 2)^2} = \sqrt{25 + 9} = \sqrt{34}$
   $PB = \sqrt{(0 - 3)^2 + (-1 - (-6))^2} = \sqrt{9 + 25} = \sqrt{34}$
   Since $PA = PB$, P is on the $\perp$ bisector of $\overline{AB}$.

Guided Practice

Find the coordinates of the midpoint of the segment that joins the given points.

1. $(0, 4)$ and $(6, -2)$ $(3, 1)$
2. $(5, -2)$ and $(5, 8)$ $(5, 3)$
3. $(b + 2, 0)$ and $(3b, 6)$ $(2b + 1, 3)$
4. Find the length, slope, and midpoint of $\overline{PQ}$ for $P(6, -3)$ and $Q(4, -5)$. length $= 2\sqrt{2}$, slope $= 1$, midpoint $= (5, -4)$
5. If $M(6, 2)$ is the midpoint of $\overline{AB}$ where the coordinates of A are $(8, -7)$, find the coordinates of B. $(4, 11)$

Find the length, slope, and midpoint of $\overline{PQ}$.

7. $P(3, -8)$, $Q(-5, 2)$ **$2\sqrt{41}$; $-\frac{5}{4}$; $(-1, -3)$**
8. $P(-3, 4)$, $Q(7, 8)$ **$2\sqrt{29}$; $\frac{2}{5}$; $(2, 6)$**
9. $P(-7, 11)$, $Q(1, -4)$ **17; $-\frac{15}{8}$; $\left(-3, \frac{7}{2}\right)$**

In Exercises 10–12, M is the midpoint of $\overline{AB}$, where the coordinates of A are given. Find the coordinates of B.

10. $A(4, -2)$; $M(4, 4)$ **(4, 10)**
11. $A(1, -3)$; $M(5, 1)$ **(9, 5)**
12. $A(r, s)$; $M(0, 2)$ **$(-r, 4-s)$**

B

13. Given points $A(0, 0)$ and $B(8, 4)$, show that $P(2, 6)$ is on the perpendicular bisector of $\overline{AB}$ by using both of the methods in Example 2.
14. a. Given points $R(1, 0)$, $S(7, 4)$, and $T(11, -2)$, show that $\triangle RST$ is isosceles. **$RS = ST = 2\sqrt{13}$**
    b. The altitude from the vertex meets the base at K. Find the coordinates of K. **(6, −1)**
15. Find the midpoints of the legs, then the length of the median of the trapezoid with vertices $C(-4, -3)$, $D(-1, 4)$, $E(4, 4)$, and $F(7, -3)$.
16. Find the length of the longest median of the triangle with vertices $X(-2, 3)$, $Y(6, -3)$, and $Z(4, 7)$. **$\sqrt{89}$ (med. from Y)**
17. a. Verify that $\overline{OQ}$ and $\overline{PR}$ have the same midpoint. **$\left(\frac{9}{2}, \frac{9}{2}\right)$**
    b. Part (a) shows that the diagonals of $OPQR$ bisect each other. Therefore $OPQR$ is a __?__. **parallelogram**
    c. Use slopes to verify that the opposite sides of $OPQR$ are parallel.
    d. Use the distance formula to verify that the opposite sides are congruent.

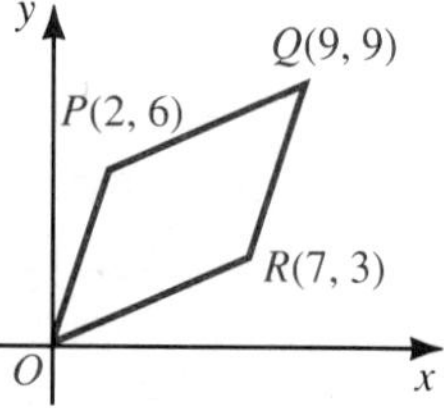

18. Graph the points $A(-5, 0)$, $B(3, 2)$, $C(5, 6)$, and $D(-3, 4)$. Then show that $ABCD$ is a parallelogram by two different methods.
    a. Show that one pair of opposite sides are both congruent and parallel.
    b. Show that the diagonals bisect each other (have the same midpoint).
19. In right $\triangle OAT$, M is the midpoint of $\overline{AT}$.
    a. M has coordinates (__?__, __?__). **−3, 4**
    b. Find, and compare, the lengths MA, MT, and MO. **5; 5; 5**
    c. State a theorem from Chapter 5 suggested by this exercise. **See below.**
    d. Find an equation of the circle that circumscribes $\triangle OAT$. **$(x+3)^2 + (y-4)^2 = 25$**

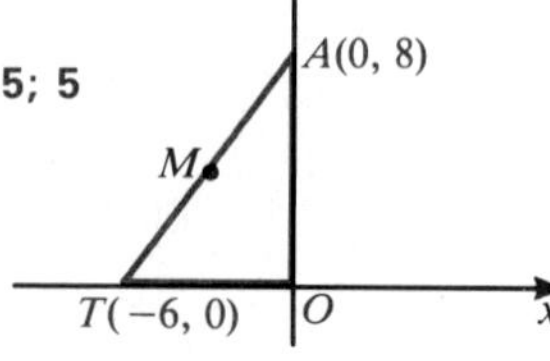

20. Given points $A(1, 1)$, $B(13, 9)$, and $C(3, 7)$. D is the midpoint of $\overline{AB}$, and E is the midpoint of $\overline{AC}$.
    a. Find the coordinates of D and E. **(7, 5); (2, 4)**
    b. Use slopes to show that $\overline{DE} \parallel \overline{BC}$.
    c. Use the distance formula to show that $DE = \frac{1}{2}BC$. **$DE = \sqrt{26}$, $BC = 2\sqrt{26}$**

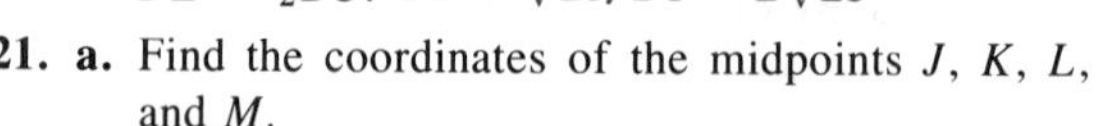

21. a. Find the coordinates of the midpoints J, K, L, and M.
    b. What kind of figure is $JKLM$? Prove it. **rhombus**

Ex. 21

19c. The midpt. of the hyp. of a rt. $\triangle$ is equidist. from the vertices.

Using a Computer

Exs. 13–16 and 20 can be done using a spreadsheet.

Additional Answers
Written Exercises

15. Midpt. of $\overline{CD}$: $\left(-\frac{5}{2}, \frac{1}{2}\right)$
    Midpt. of $\overline{EF}$: $\left(\frac{11}{2}, \frac{1}{2}\right)$
    length of median: 8

17.c. Slope $\overline{PQ}$ = slope $\overline{OR} = \frac{3}{7}$; slope $\overline{OP}$ = slope $\overline{RQ} = 3$
   d. $PQ = OR = \sqrt{58}$; $PO = QR = 2\sqrt{10}$

18.a. Slope $\overline{AD}$ = slope $\overline{BC} = 2$; $AD = BC = 2\sqrt{5}$
   b. midpt. of $\overline{AC}$ = (0, 3) = midpt. of $\overline{BD}$

20.b. Slope $\overline{DE}$ = slope $\overline{BC} = \frac{1}{5}$

21.a. $J\left(-\frac{1}{2}, \frac{3}{2}\right)$, $K(3, 6)$, $L\left(\frac{17}{2}, \frac{9}{2}\right)$, $M(5, 0)$

22. Suppose E is on $\overline{PQ}$ and $PE = \frac{1}{4}PQ$. If $P = (x_1, y_1)$ and $Q = (x_2, y_2)$, where $x_1 < x_2$, show that $E = \left(\frac{3}{4}x_1 + \frac{1}{4}x_2, \frac{3}{4}y_1 + \frac{1}{4}y_2\right)$.

C **23.** Suppose F is on $\overline{PQ}$ and $PF = \frac{3}{8}PQ$. If $P = (x_1, y_1)$ and $Q = (x_2, y_2)$, where $x_1 < x_2$, find the coordinates of F. (*Hint*: See Exercise 22.)

24. Given points $P(2, 1)$ and $D(7, 11)$, find the coordinates of a point T on $\overline{PD}$ such that $\frac{PT}{TD} = \frac{2}{3}$. **(4, 5)**

Self-Test 1

For each pair of points find (a) the distance between the two points and (b) the midpoint of the segment that joins the two points.

1. (5, 1) and (3, 1) **a. 2 b. (4, 1)**

2. (8, −6) and (0, 0) **a. 10 b. (4, −3)**

3. (−2, 7) and (8, −3) **a.** $10\sqrt{2}$ **b. (3, 2)**

4. (−3, 2) and (−5, 7) **a.** $\sqrt{29}$ **b.** $\left(-4, \frac{9}{2}\right)$

Write an equation of the circle described.

5. Center at the origin; radius 9 $x^2 + y^2 = 81$

6. Center (−1, 2); radius 5 $(x + 1)^2 + (y - 2)^2 = 25$

7. Find the center and the radius of the circle $(x + 2)^2 + (y - 3)^2 = 36$. **(−2, 3); 6**

Find the slope of the line through the points named.

8. (0, 0) and (7, 4) $\frac{4}{7}$

9. (−4, 2) and (1, −1) $-\frac{3}{5}$

10. For which is slope *not* defined, a horizontal line or a vertical line? **vertical**

11. Given $P(3, -2)$ and $Q(5, 2)$, find:

a. the slope of any line parallel to $\overleftrightarrow{PQ}$ **2**

b. the slope of any line perpendicular to $\overleftrightarrow{PQ}$ $-\frac{1}{2}$

12. Name each vector as an ordered pair.

a. $\overrightarrow{AB}$ **(6, −2)** **b.** $\overrightarrow{CD}$ **(−3, −3)** **c.** $\overrightarrow{FE}$ **(0, 4)**

13. Find the magnitude of each vector in Exercise 12. **See below.**

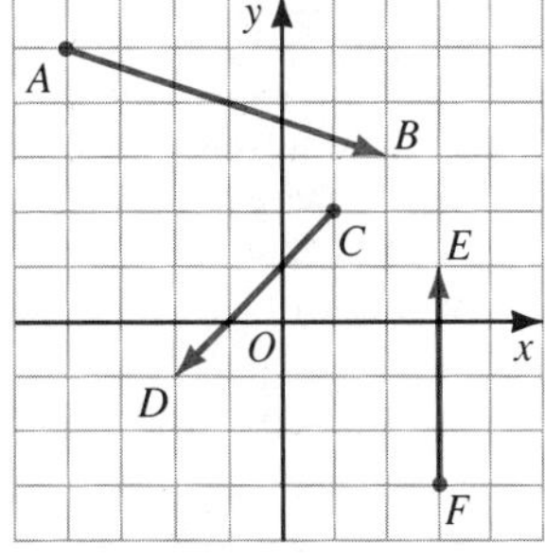

Exs. 12, 13

14. Complete.

a. (−3, 2) + (7, −11) = _?_ **(4, −9)**

b. 3(4, −1) + (−2)(−5, 3) = _?_ **(22, −9)**

15. If $M(-3, 7)$ is the midpoint of $\overline{PQ}$, where P has coordinates (9, −4), find the coordinates of Q. **(−15, 18)**

13. a. $2\sqrt{10}$ **b.** $3\sqrt{2}$ **c. 4**

Quick Quiz

For each pair of points, find (a) the distance between the points, and (b) the midpoint of the segment that joins the points.

1. (2, −3) and (2, 5)
(a) 8 (b) (2, 1)

2. (−4, 2) and (4, −2)
(a) $4\sqrt{5}$ (b) (0, 0)

3. (−3, −2) and (2, 10)
(a) 13 (b) $(-\frac{1}{2}, 4)$

4. (4, −2) and (−4, −8)
(a) 10 (b) (0, −5)

Write an equation of the circle described.

5. Circle with center (0, 0) and radius 7.
$x^2 + y^2 = 49$

6. Circle with center (4, −3) and radius 6.
$(x - 4)^2 + (y + 3)^2 = 36$

7. Find the center and radius of the circle with the equation $(x + 2)^2 + (y - 4)^2 = 5$.
(−2, 4); $\sqrt{5}$

Find the slope of the line through the points named.

8. (6, −3) and (0, 0) $-\frac{1}{2}$

9. (−1, −4) and (3, −2) $\frac{1}{2}$

10. Given $A(-4, -1)$ and $B(3, 5)$, find (a) the slope of any line parallel to $\overleftrightarrow{AB}$. $\frac{6}{7}$ (b) the slope of any line perpendicular to $\overleftrightarrow{AB}$. $-\frac{7}{6}$

11. Complete.

a. (−2, 6) + (8, 4) = (6, 10)

b. −2(4, −3) + $\frac{1}{3}$(6, −9) = (−6, 3)

12. If $M(4, -5)$ is the midpoint of $\overline{RS}$ where R has coordinates (0, −3), find the coordinates of S.
(8, −7)

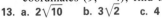

Teaching Suggestions,
p. T135

Objectives
Presenting the Lesson
Reinforcement
Using Technology

Supplementary Materials

Study Guide, pp. 173–174

Lesson Focus

The focus of this lesson is on the standard form and the slope-intercept form for the equation of a line. These forms are algebraic equations that describe geometric lines.

Suggested Assignments

Average
550–551/2, 5, 8, 15, 19, 25

Maximum
Day 1: 550–551/3, 5, 8, 13, 16, 19, 24
Day 2: 551–552/25–37 odd

Teaching Note

When discussing Example 1, you may want to explain that values other than $x = 0$ and $y = 0$ can be used to determine the points on a line. Also, note that after the graph has been sketched, a third point should be used to check the sketch.

Lines and Coordinate Geometry Proofs

Objectives

1. Identify the slope and y-intercept of the line specified by a given equation.
2. Draw the graph of the line specified by a given equation.
3. Write an equation of a line when given either one point and the slope of the line, or two points on the line.
4. Determine the intersection of two lines.
5. Given a polygon, choose a convenient placement of coordinate axes and assign appropriate coordinates.
6. Prove statements by using coordinate geometry methods.

13-6 *Graphing Linear Equations*

A **linear equation** is an equation whose graph is a line. As you will learn in this section and the next, linear equations can be written in different forms: *standard form*, *slope-intercept form*, and *point-slope form*. We state a theorem for the standard form, but omit the proof.

Theorem 13-6 *Standard Form*

The graph of any equation that can be written in the form

$$Ax + By = C$$

where A and B are not both zero, is a line.

The advantage of the standard form is that it is easy to determine the points where the line crosses the x-axis and the y-axis. If a line intersects the x-axis at the point $(a, 0)$, then its *x-intercept* is a; if it intersects the y-axis at the point $(0, b)$, then its *y-intercept* is b.

Example 1 Graph the line $2x - 3y = 12$.

Solution Since two points determine a line, begin by plotting two convenient points, such as the points where the line crosses the axes. Then draw the line through the points.

To find the x-intercept, let $y = 0$.

$$2x - 3(0) = 12$$
$$x = 6$$

Thus (6, 0) is a point on the line.

To find the y-intercept, let $x = 0$.

$$2(0) - 3y = 12$$
$$y = -4$$

Thus (0, −4) is a point on the line.

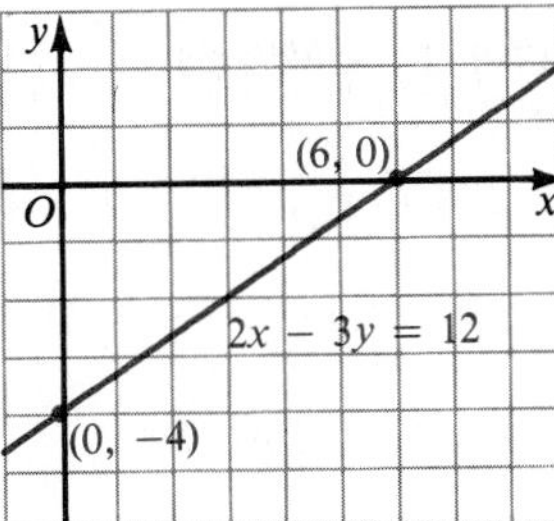

Example 2 Use algebra to find the intersection of the lines $2x - 3y = 9$ and $4x + y = 4$. Illustrate by drawing the graphs of the two lines.

Solution

$$\begin{array}{rll} 2x - 3y &= 9 & \text{(First equation)} \\ \underline{12x + 3y} &\underline{= 12} & \text{(Second equation} \times 3) \\ 14x &= 21 & \text{(Add to eliminate } y.) \\ x &= 1.5 & \\ 4(1.5) + y &= 4 & \text{(Substitution)} \\ y &= -2 & \end{array}$$

The point of intersection is (1.5, −2).

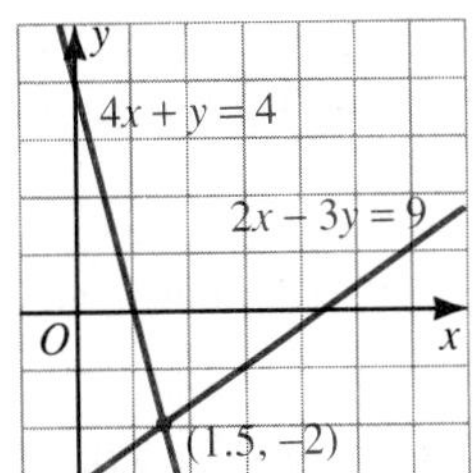

The equations in Examples 1 and 2 are all written in standard form. These equations can also be written in the *slope-intercept form* $y = mx + b$. This form tells you at a glance what the line's slope and y-intercept are.

standard form	*slope-intercept form*	*slope*	*y-intercept*
$2x - 3y = 12$	$y = \frac{2}{3}x - 4$	$\frac{2}{3}$	-4
$2x - 3y = 9$	$y = \frac{2}{3}x - 3$	$\frac{2}{3}$	-3
$4x + y = 4$	$y = -4x + 4$	-4	4

Theorem 13-7 *Slope-Intercept Form*

A line with the equation $y = mx + b$ has slope m and y-intercept b.

Proof:

When $x = 0$, $y = b$. So b is the y-intercept.

When $x = 1$, $y = m + b$.
Let $(x_1, y_1) = (0, b)$ and $(x_2, y_2) = (1, m + b)$.

Then the slope is $\frac{y_2 - y_1}{x_2 - x_1} = \frac{(m + b) - b}{1 - 0} = m$.

Chalkboard Examples

Find the x- and y-intercepts of each line.

1. $3x + 4y = 12$ 4; 3
2. $y = -2x + 4$ 2; 4

Find the point of intersection of the two lines.

3. $x + y = 6$; $x - y = 2$ (4, 2)
4. $5x + 3y = 21$; $2x + 2y = 10$ (3, 2)

Find the slope and y-intercept of each line.

5. $2x - 3y = 6$ slope $= \frac{2}{3}$; y-intercept $= -2$
6. $y = -\frac{1}{4}x + 2$ slope $= -\frac{1}{4}$; y-intercept $= 2$
7. $y = -3$ slope $= 0$; y-intercept $= -3$

Teaching Note

Since a vertical line has no slope, caution students about their use of the slope-intercept form. They cannot substitute a value for m into this equation if a line is vertical. Instead they should use the form $x = a$ (where a is the x-coordinate of a point on the line). Also, refer students to the Algebra Review (Systems of Equations) on page 69.

Example 3 Graph the line $y = -\frac{3}{4}x + 6$.

Solution The slope is $\frac{-3}{4}$ and the y-intercept is 6.

Step 1 Start at the point (0, 6).

Step 2 Use $\frac{\text{change in y}}{\text{change in x}} = \frac{-3}{4}$ to find other points of the line.
(See Example 2, page 530.)

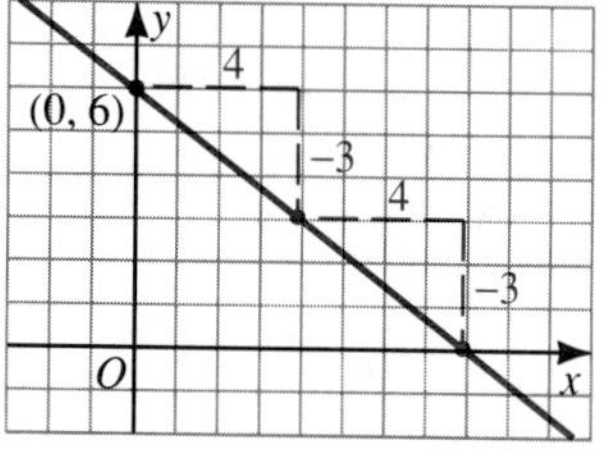

Guided Practice

1. On the same axes, graph $y = mx$ for $m = 3, -3, \frac{1}{3}$, and $-\frac{1}{3}$.

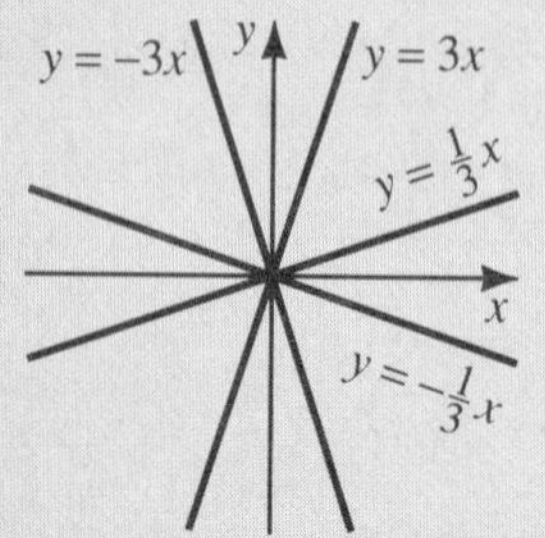

2. On the same axes, graph $y = -\frac{3}{4}x + b$ for $b = 0$, 2, and -3.

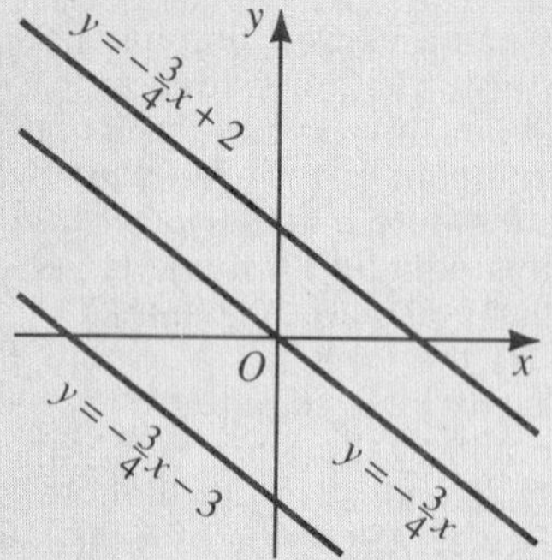

Find the x- and y-intercepts of each line.

3. $3x + 2y = 6$
x-intercept = 2,
y-intercept = 3
4. $2x - y = 4$
x-intercept = 2,
y-intercept = -4

Find the slope and y-intercept of each line.

5. $x - 2y = 8$
slope = $\frac{1}{2}$,
y-intercept = -4
6. $3x + 4y = 12$
slope = $-\frac{3}{4}$,
y-intercept = 3

Classroom Exercises

12. 0; Answers will vary: (1, 4), (−1, 4), (2, 4)

1. Which points lie on the line $3x - 2y = 12$?
   a. (0, 4) **(b.)** (2, −3) c. $\left(3, \frac{3}{2}\right)$ **(d.)** (0, −6)
2. Which point is the intersection of $x + 2y = 8$ and $2x + 3y = 10$?
   a. (−2, 5) **(b.)** (−4, 6) c. (2, 3) d. (−1, 4)

Find the x- and y-intercepts of each line.

3. $2x + 3y = 6$ **3; 2**
4. $3x - 5y = 15$ **5; −3**
5. $-4x + 3y = 24$ **−6; 8**
6. $x + 3y = 9$ **9; 3**
7. $y = 5x - 10$ **2; −10**
8. $y = 2x + 5$ **$-\frac{5}{2}$; 5**

Find the slope and y-intercept of each line.

9. $y = \frac{2}{5}x - 9$ **$\frac{2}{5}$; −9**
10. $2x + y = 8$ **−2; 8**
11. $3x - 4y = 6$ **$\frac{3}{4}$; $-\frac{3}{2}$**
12. What is the slope of the line $y = 4$? Name three points that lie on the line. **See above.**
13. The graph of $x = 5$ is a vertical line through (5, 0). Name three other points on the line and check to see if their coordinates satisfy the equation.
Answers will vary: (5, 1), (5, −1), (5, 4)

Written Exercises **1–6. Check students' graphs.**

A

1. On the same axes, graph $y = mx$ for $m = 2, -2, \frac{1}{2}$, and $-\frac{1}{2}$.
2. On the same axes, graph $y = mx + 2$ for $m = 3, -3, \frac{1}{3}$, and $-\frac{1}{3}$.
3. On the same axes, graph $y = \frac{1}{2}x + b$ for $b = 0, 2, 4, -2$, and -4.
4. On the same axes, graph $y = -\frac{2}{3}x + b$ for $b = 0, 3, 6, -3$, and -6.
5. On the same axes, graph the lines $y = 0$, $y = 3$, and $y = -3$.
6. On the same axes, graph the lines $x = 0$, $x = 2$, and $x = -2$.

Find the x-intercept and y-intercept of each line. Then graph the equation.

7. $3x + y = -21$ **−7; −21**
8. $4x - 5y = 20$ **5; −4**
9. $3x + 2y = 12$ **4; 6**
10. $3x - 2y = 12$ **4; −6**
11. $5x + 8y = 20$ **4; $\frac{5}{2}$**
12. $3x + 4y = -18$ **−6; $-\frac{9}{2}$**

Find the slope and y-intercept of each line. Plot the y-intercept. Then, using the slope, plot one more point. Finally, graph the line.

13. $y = 2x - 3$ **$m = 2$; $b = -3$**
14. $y = 2x + 3$ **$m = 2$; $b = 3$**
15. $y = -4x$ **$m = -4$; $b = 0$**
16. $y = \frac{3}{4}x + 1$ **$m = \frac{3}{4}$; $b = 1$**
17. $y = -\frac{2}{3}x - 4$ **$m = -\frac{2}{3}$; $b = -4$**
18. $y = \frac{5}{3}x - 2$ **$m = \frac{5}{3}$; $b = -2$**

Find the slope and y-intercept of each line.

Example $x + 3y = -6$

Solution Write the equation in slope-intercept form.

$$3y = -x - 6$$

$$y = -\frac{1}{3}x - 2$$

The slope is $-\frac{1}{3}$. The y-intercept is -2.

19. $4x + y = 10$ **$m = -4$; $b = 10$**
20. $2x - y = 5$ **$m = 2$; $b = -5$**
21. $5x - 2y = 10$ **$m = \frac{5}{2}$; $b = -5$**
22. $3x + 4y = 12$ **$m = -\frac{3}{4}$; $b = 3$**
23. $x - 4y = 6$ **$m = \frac{1}{4}$; $b = -\frac{3}{2}$**
24. $4x + 3y = 8$ **$m = -\frac{4}{3}$; $b = \frac{8}{3}$**

Solve each pair of equations algebraically. Then draw the graphs of the equations and label their intersection point.

25. $x + y = 3$, $x - y = -1$ **(1, 2)**
26. $2x + y = 7$, $3x + y = 9$ **(2, 3)**
27. $x + 2y = 10$, $3x - 2y = 6$ **(4, 3)**
28. $3x + 2y = -30$, $y = x$ **(−6, −6)**
29. $4x + 5y = -7$, $2x - 3y = 13$ **(2, −3)**
30. $3x + 2y = 8$, $-x + 3y = 12$ **(0, 4)**

B 31. a. Find the slopes of the lines $6x + 3y = 10$ and $y = -2x + 5$. **Both have slope −2.**
b. Do the lines intersect? **No**
c. What happens when you solve these equations algebraically? **There is no solution.**

32. Give a geometric reason and an algebraic reason why the lines $y = 3x - 5$ and $y = 3x + 5$ do not intersect. **(1) The lines are ∥. (2) The pair of eqs. has no sol.**

33. a. Find the slopes of the lines $2x - y = 7$ and $x + 2y = 4$. **2; $-\frac{1}{2}$**
b. What can you conclude about the lines? State the theorem that supports your answer. **They are ⊥. 2 nonvert. lines are ⊥ iff the prod. of their slopes is −1.**

34. a. On the same axes, graph $y = -2$, $x = -3$, and $2x + 3y = 6$.
b. Find the coordinates of the three points where the lines intersect. **(−3, 4), (−3, −2), (6, −2)**
c. Find the area of the triangle determined by the three lines. **27**

Solve each pair of equations algebraically. Then draw the graphs and label their intersection point.

7. $4x - 2y = -4$
$2x + 3y = 6$ (0, 2)

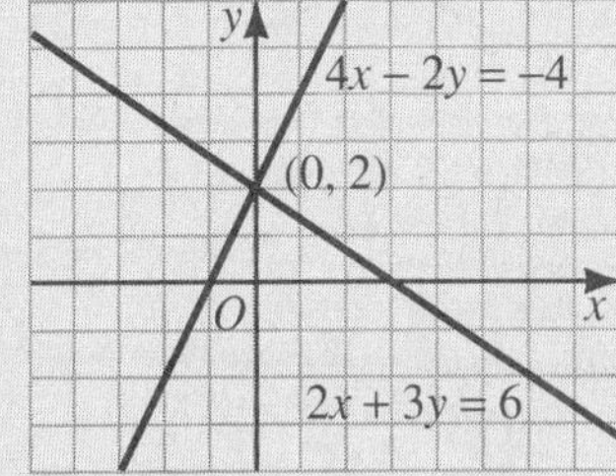

8. $y = 2x$
$4x + 3y = 10$ (1, 2)

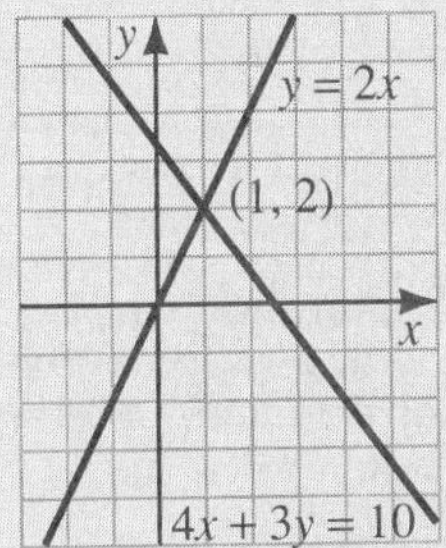

Using a Calculator

Have students graph the equations in Exs. 25–30 with a graphing calculator or a function plotting program.

Using a Computer

See page T135 for an Experiment in which students use spreadsheets or computer programs to review and apply distance, slope, midpoint, and y-intercept.

35. **a.** On the same axes, graph

$$y = \frac{1}{2}x - 2, \quad y = -2x + 3, \quad \text{and} \quad y = 3x + 8.$$

b. Find the coordinates of the three points where the lines intersect. **(2, −1), (−1, 5), (−4, −4)**

c. Find the area of the triangle determined by the three lines. **$22\frac{1}{2}$**

36. Find the area of the region inside the circle $x^2 + y^2 = 2$ *and* above the line $y = 1$. **$\frac{\pi}{2} - 1$**

C **37.** Use algebra to find each point at which the line $x - 2y = -5$ intersects the circle $x^2 + y^2 = 25$. Graph both equations to verify your answer. **(3, 4) and (−5, 0)**

38. **a.** Verify that the point $P(4, -2)$ is on the line $2x - y = 10$ and on the circle $x^2 + y^2 = 20$.

b. Show that the segment joining the center of the circle to P is perpendicular to the line.

c. What do parts (a) and (b) tell you about the line and the circle? **The line is tan. to the circle.**

39. Graph each equation.

a. $|x| = |y|$ **b.** $|x| + |y| = 6$ **c.** $|x| + 2|y| = 4$

Explorations

These exploratory exercises can be done using a graphing calculator.

Graph the lines $y = 2x$, $y = 2x + 1$, and $y = 2x + 3$ on the same screen. What do you notice about these lines? **They are parallel.**

What theorem does this illustrate? **Theorem 13-3**

Use what you have observed to write an equation of the line whose y-intercept is 7 and that is parallel to $y = 2x$. **$y = 2x + 7$**

Graph the lines $y = 2x$ and $y = -\frac{1}{2}x$ on the same screen.

Graph the lines $y = \frac{2}{3}x$ and $y = -\frac{3}{2}x$ on the same screen.

What do you notice about both pairs of lines? **They are perpendicular.**

What theorem does this illustrate? **Theorem 13-4**

Use what you have observed to write an equation of the line through the origin that is perpendicular to $y = \frac{4}{5}x$. **$y = -\frac{5}{4}x$**

Challenge

Draw segments that divide an obtuse triangle into acute triangles.

Additional Answers Written Exercises

38.a. $2(4) - (-2) = 10$, $4^2 + (-2)^2 = 20$

b. Center $C(0, 0)$, slope $\overline{PC} = -\frac{1}{2}$; slope of line $2x - y = 10$ is 2; $-\frac{1}{2} \cdot 2 = -1$

Using a Calculator

This Exploration can be done with a graphing calculator or a function plotting program.

Using a Computer

Computer graphing technology offers a powerful way to investigate the slopes of lines; it is especially suited to investigating the slopes of parallel and perpendicular lines, which is the purpose of the *Explorations* here.

13-7 *Writing Linear Equations*

In the previous section, you were given a linear equation and asked to draw its graph. In this section you will be given information about a graph and asked to find an equation of the line described.

Example 1 Find an equation of each line described.

a. Slope $= -\frac{5}{3}$, y-intercept $= 4$

b. x-intercept $= -6$, y-intercept $= 3$

Solution **a.** $y = mx + b$

$y = -\frac{5}{3}x + 4$

b. Because the y-intercept is 3, you have $b = 3$.
Because the points $(-6, 0)$ and $(0, 3)$ lie on the line,

$$\text{slope} = \frac{3 - 0}{0 - (-6)} = \frac{3}{6} = \frac{1}{2}.$$

Since the slope is $\frac{1}{2}$, you have $m = \frac{1}{2}$.

Now substitute into the equation $y = mx + b$ to get

$$y = \frac{1}{2}x + 3.$$

Both linear equations in Example 1 were written in slope-intercept form. This form is very easy to use if the y-intercept is given. If the y-intercept is not given, the *point-slope form* can be used.

Theorem 13-8 *Point-Slope Form*

An equation of the line that passes through the point (x_1, y_1) and has slope m is

$$y - y_1 = m(x - x_1).$$

Proof:

Let (x, y) be any point on the line. Since the line also contains the point (x_1, y_1) the slope must, by definition, equal $\frac{y - y_1}{x - x_1}$.

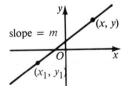

From $m = \frac{y - y_1}{x - x_1}$,

we get $y - y_1 = m(x - x_1)$.

Teaching Suggestions, pp. T135–T136

Objective
Presenting the Lesson
Reinforcement
Enrichment

Supplementary Materials

Practice Master 82
Test 53
Resource Book, pp. 90–91, 163
Study Guide, pp. 175–176
Overhead Visual L
Computer Activities 31, 32

Lesson Focus

The purpose of this lesson is to use information about the graph of a line to find an equation that represents the line.

Suggested Assignments

Average
555/1–25 odd

Maximum
Day 1: 555/2, 6, 9, 15, 17–25 odd
Day 2: 555–556/27, 31, 34–36, 38

Teaching Note

Be sure to emphasize that Theorem 13-8 assumes that the line is nonvertical (it has slope). Also, emphasize that (x, y) can be any point on the line with slope m passing through the point (x_1, y_1).

Chalkboard Examples

State the slope and a point on the line.

1. $y - 8 = -\frac{2}{3}(x - 3)$ $-\frac{2}{3}$; (3, 8)
2. $y = -(x + 4)$ -1; $(-4, 0)$
3. $y + 2 = 4(x + 7)$ 4; $(-7, -2)$
4. $x = 6$ undefined; (6, 0)
5. $y - r = m(x + s)$ m; $(-s, r)$

Find an equation of the line described.

6. the line through (6, 4) and parallel to the line $y = -2x + 4$ $y - 4 = -2(x - 6)$
7. the line through (6, 4) and perpendicular to the line $y = -2x + 4$ $y - 4 = \frac{1}{2}(x - 6)$
8. the line through the points $(3, -2)$ and $(4, 1)$ $y + 2 = 3(x - 3)$
9. the line with slope $-\frac{3}{4}$ and y-intercept -2. $y = -\frac{3}{4}x - 2$
10. the line with x-intercept 5 and y-intercept -3 $y = \frac{3}{5}x - 3$ or $3x - 5y = 15$
11. the line with slope 2 containing the point $(5, -2)$ $y + 2 = 2(x - 5)$

Additional Answers Classroom Exercises

Points may vary.

11. $m = -1$; $(0, -7)$, $(-7, 0)$
12. $m = \frac{1}{2}$; $(5, -2)$, $(7, -1)$
13. $m = \frac{a}{b}$; (d, c), $(b + d, a + c)$

Example 2 Find an equation of each line described.

a. The line through (1, 2) and parallel to the line $y = 3x - 7$
b. The line through (1, 2) and perpendicular to the line $y = 3x - 7$
c. The line through the points $(-3, 0)$ and $(1, 8)$

Solution

a. If the line is parallel to the line $y = 3x - 7$, its slope must be 3. Substituting in $y - y_1 = m(x - x_1)$ gives $y - 2 = 3(x - 1)$, or $y = 3x - 1$.

b. The required line has slope $-\frac{1}{3}$. (Why?) Thus an equation in point-slope form is $y - 2 = -\frac{1}{3}(x - 1)$, or $y = -\frac{1}{3}x + \frac{7}{3}$, or $x + 3y = 7$.

c. First find the slope: $m = \frac{8 - 0}{1 - (-3)} = 2$

Then use the point-slope form with *either* given point.
Using $(-3, 0)$, the equation is $y - 0 = 2[x - (-3)]$, or $y = 2x + 6$.
Using $(1, 8)$, the equation is $y - 8 = 2(x - 1)$, or $y = 2x + 6$.

Classroom Exercises 1–10. Form of equations may vary.

Give an equation of each line described. 1. $y = -\frac{1}{2}x + 5$ 3. $y = -2x + 4$ 4. $y = 3x - 6$

1. Slope $= -\frac{1}{2}$; y-intercept $= 5$
2. Slope $= \frac{3}{7}$; y-intercept $= 8$ $y = \frac{3}{7}x + 8$
3. x-intercept $= 2$; y-intercept $= 4$
4. x-intercept $= 2$; y-intercept $= -6$
5. The x-axis $y = 0$
6. The y-axis $x = 0$
7. y-intercept $= -3$; parallel to $y = -\frac{4}{5}x + 2$ $y = -\frac{4}{5}x - 3$
8. y-intercept $= 0$; perpendicular to $y = -\frac{7}{4}x + 9$ $y = \frac{4}{7}x$
9. Slope $= \frac{5}{8}$; passes through (3, 4) $y - 4 = \frac{5}{8}(x - 3)$
10. Slope $= -2$; passes through (8, 6) $y - 6 = -2(x - 8)$

State the slope of the line and name two points on the line.

11. $y = -(x + 7)$
12. $y + 2 = \frac{1}{2}(x - 5)$
13. $y - c = \frac{a}{b}(x - d)$

14. Line l is tangent to $\odot O$ at point $P(3, 4)$.
   a. Find the radius of the circle. 5
   b. Give an equation of the circle.
   c. Find the slope of line l. $-\frac{3}{4}$
   d. Give an equation of line l.
   b. $x^2 + y^2 = 25$
   d. $y - 4 = -\frac{3}{4}(x - 3)$

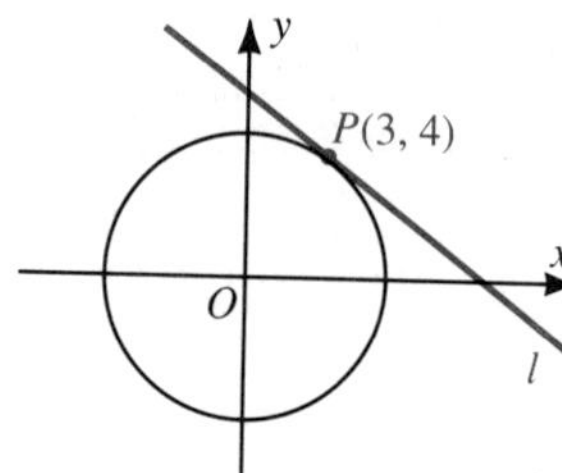

Written Exercises

Give an equation of each line described. Use the form specified by your teacher. 1. $y = 2x + 5$ 2. $y = -3x + 6$ 3. $y = \frac{1}{2}x - 8$ 4. $y = \frac{3}{4}x - 9$

A

	1.	2.	3.	4.	5.	6.
slope	2	−3	$\frac{1}{2}$	$\frac{3}{4}$	$-\frac{7}{5}$	$-\frac{3}{2}$
y-intercept	5	6	−8	−9	8	−7

5. $y = -\frac{7}{5}x + 8$
6. $y = -\frac{3}{2}x - 7$

	7.	8.	9.	10.
x-intercept	8	9	−8	−5
y-intercept	2	−3	4	−2

7. $y = -\frac{1}{4}x + 2$ 8. $y = \frac{1}{3}x - 3$ 9. $y = \frac{1}{2}x + 4$ 10. $y = -\frac{2}{5}x - 2$

	11.	12.	13.	14.	15.	16.
point	(1, 2)	(3, 8)	(−3, 5)	(6, −6)	(−4, 0)	(−10, 3)
slope	5	4	$\frac{1}{3}$	$-\frac{2}{3}$	$-\frac{1}{2}$	$-\frac{2}{5}$

17. $y = 2x - 1$ 18. $y = \frac{4}{3}x - \frac{5}{3}$ 19. $y = \frac{1}{3}x + 2$ 20. $y = x + 1$

17. line through (1, 1) and (4, 7)
18. line through (−1, −3) and (2, 1)
19. line through (−3, 1) and (3, 3)
20. line through (−2, −1) and (−6, −5)
21. vertical line through (2, −5) $x = 2$
22. horizontal line through (3, 1) $y = 1$
23. line through (5, −3) and parallel to the line $x = 4$ $x = 5$
24. line through (−8, −2) and parallel to the line $x = 5$ $x = -8$

B

25. line through (5, 7) and parallel to the line $y = 3x - 4$ $y - 7 = 3(x - 5)$
26. line through (−1, 3) and parallel to the line $3x + 5y = 15$ $3x + 5y = 12$
27. line through (−3, −2) and perpendicular to the line $8x - 5y = 0$ $5x + 8y = -31$
28. line through (8, 0) and perpendicular to the line $3x + 4y = 12$ $4x - 3y = 32$
29. perpendicular bisector of the segment joining (0, 0) and (10, 6) } See below.
30. perpendicular bisector of the segment joining (−3, 7) and (5, 1) }
31. the line through (5, 5) that makes a 45° angle measured counterclockwise from the positive x-axis $y = x$
32. the line through the origin that makes a 135° angle measured counterclockwise from the positive x-axis $y = -x$
33. Find each value of k for which the lines $y = 9kx - 1$ and $kx + 4y = 12$ are perpendicular. $\frac{2}{3}$ or $-\frac{2}{3}$
34. Quad. *BECK* is known to be a rhombus. Two of the vertices are *B*(3, 5) and *C*(7, −3).

a. Find the slope of diagonal $\overline{EK}$. $\frac{1}{2}$
b. Find an equation of $\overleftrightarrow{EK}$. $y = \frac{1}{2}x - \frac{3}{2}$

29. $y = -\frac{5}{3}x + \frac{34}{3}$ 30. $y = \frac{4}{3}x + \frac{8}{3}$

Guided Practice

Give an equation of each line described.

	1.	2.
slope	$\frac{1}{4}$	−3
y-intercept	5	−1

1. $y = \frac{1}{4}x + 5$
2. $y = -3x - 1$

	3.	4.
x-intercept	6	−4
y-intercept	−3	−2

3. $y = \frac{1}{2}x - 3$
4. $y = -\frac{1}{2}x - 2$

	5.	6.
point	(−4, 5)	(2, 5)
slope	$\frac{1}{2}$	4

5. $y - 5 = \frac{1}{2}(x + 4)$
6. $y - 5 = 4(x - 2)$

7. line through (2, 5) and (1, −2)
$y - 5 = 7(x - 2)$ or $y = 7x - 9$

8. line through (−2, −4) and (−3, −1)
$y + 4 = -3(x + 2)$ or $y = -3x - 10$

9. vertical line through (5, −3) $x = 5$

10. horizontal line through (−4, 7) $y = 7$

11. line through (−4, 2) and parallel to the line $x = 6$
$x = -4$

12. line through (5, 3) and perpendicular to the line $y = -2$ $x = 5$

Additional Answers Written Exercises

11. $y - 2 = 5(x - 1)$
12. $y - 8 = 4(x - 3)$
13. $y - 5 = \frac{1}{3}(x + 3)$
14. $y + 6 = -\frac{2}{3}(x - 6)$
15. $y = -\frac{1}{2}(x + 4)$
16. $y - 3 = -\frac{2}{5}(x + 10)$

Additional Answers Written Exercises

36.c. $QG = 4\sqrt{5}$ and $QM = 6\sqrt{5}$, where $M(6, 6)$ is the midpt. of $\overline{RS}$.

39.a. Slope $\overline{CG}$ = slope $\overline{GH}$ = slope $\overline{HC} = -1$

Making Connections

Exs. 36–39 make a very strong connection between algebra and geometry. Students who do these exercises will have excellent preparation for Exs. 12–14 on page 563.

Teaching Suggestions, pp. T136–T137

Objective
Presenting the Lesson

Communication Skills, pp. T136–T137

Supplementary Materials

Study Guide, pp. 177–178

Lesson Focus

This lesson provides an introduction to proving theorems by using coordinate geometry. A critical skill is placing the axes conveniently on a figure.

Suggested Assignments

Average
558–559/1–7
563/Self-Test 2, 1–6

Maximum
Day 1: 558–559/1–9
Day 2: 559/10–13
S 556/37

35. Find the center of the circle that passes through (2, 10), (10, 6), and (−6, −6). **(2, 0)**

Exercises 36–39 refer to $\triangle QRS$ with vertices $Q(-6, 0)$, $R(12, 0)$, and $S(0, 12)$.

C **36. a.** Find the equations of the three lines that contain the medians. $x - 2y = -6$, $4x + y = 12$, $2x + 5y = 24$

b. Show that the three medians meet in a point G (called the *centroid*). (*Hint*: Solve two equations simultaneously and show that their solution satisfies the third equation.) **$G(2, 4)$**

c. Show that the length QG is $\frac{2}{3}$ of the length of the median from Q.

37. a. Find the equations of the three perpendicular bisectors of the sides of $\triangle QRS$. $y = x$, $x = 3$, $x + 2y = 9$

b. Show that the three perpendicular bisectors meet in a point C (called the *circumcenter*). (See the hint from Exercise 36(b).) **$C(3, 3)$**

c. Show that C is equidistant from Q, R, and S by using the distance formula. $CQ = CR = CS = 3\sqrt{10}$

d. Find the equation of the circle that can be circumscribed about $\triangle QRS$. } **See below.**

38. a. Find the equations of the three lines that contain the altitudes of $\triangle QRS$. } **See below.**

b. Show that the three altitudes meet in a point H (called the *orthocenter*). **$H(0, 6)$**

39. a. Refer to Exercises 36, 37, and 38. Use slopes to show that the points C, G, and H are collinear. (The line through these points is called *Euler's Line*.)

b. Show that $GH = 2GC$. $GH = 2\sqrt{2}$, $GC = \sqrt{2}$

37. d. $(x - 3)^2 + (y - 3)^2 = 90$ **38. a.** $x = 0$, $y = x + 6$, $x + 2y = 12$

13-8 *Organizing Coordinate Proofs*

We will illustrate coordinate geometry methods by proving Theorem 5-15:

The midpoint of the hypotenuse of a right triangle is equidistant from the three vertices.

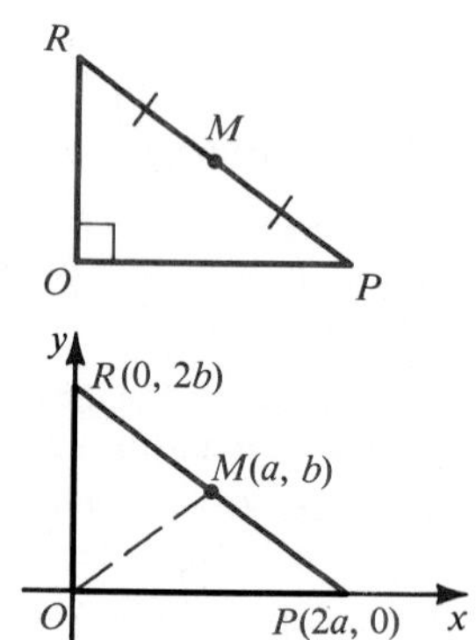

Proof:

Let $\overleftrightarrow{OP}$ and $\overleftrightarrow{OR}$ be the x-axis and y-axis.
Let P and R have the coordinates shown.

Then the coordinates of M are (a, b).

$MO = \sqrt{(a - 0)^2 + (b - 0)^2} = \sqrt{a^2 + b^2}$
$MP = \sqrt{(a - 2a)^2 + (b - 0)^2} = \sqrt{a^2 + b^2}$
Thus $MO = MP$.

By the definition of midpoint, $MP = MR$.

Hence $MO = MP = MR$.

Notice that $2a$ and $2b$ are convenient choices for coordinates since they lead to expressions that do not contain fractions for the coordinates of M.

If you have a right triangle, such as $\triangle POR$ on page 556, the most convenient place to put the x-axis and y-axis is usually along the legs of the triangle. If a triangle is not a right triangle, the two most convenient ways to place your axes are shown below. Notice that these locations for the axes maximize the number of times zero is a coordinate of a vertex.

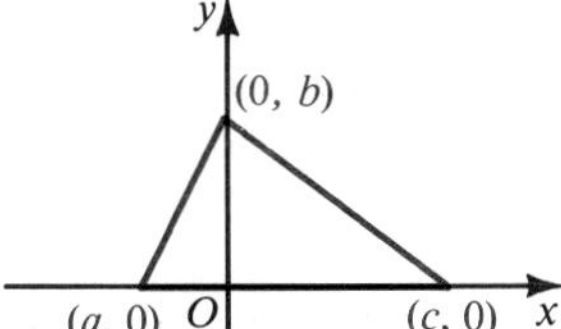

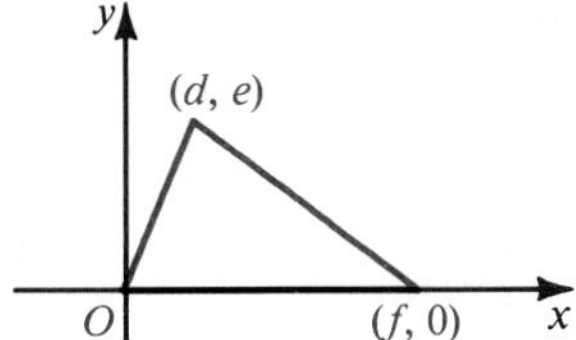

Some common ways of placing coordinate axes on other special figures are shown below.

$\triangle COD$ is isosceles; $CO = CD$.
Then C can be labeled (a, b).

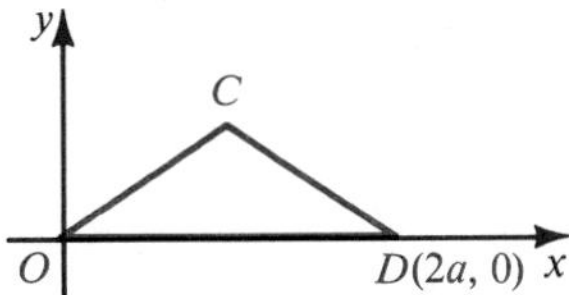

$\triangle EFG$ is isosceles; $EF = EG$.
Then F can be labeled $(-a, 0)$.

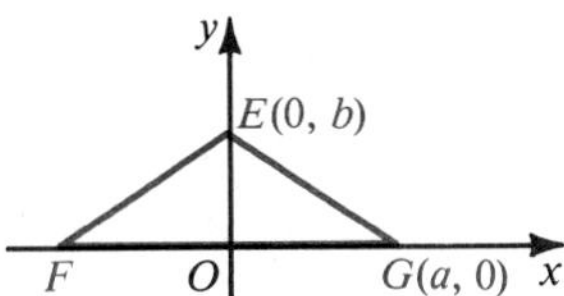

$HOJK$ is a rectangle.
Then K can be labeled (a, b).

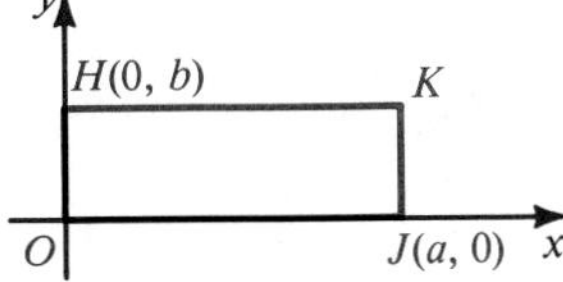

$MONP$ is a parallelogram.
Then P can be labeled $(a + b, c)$.

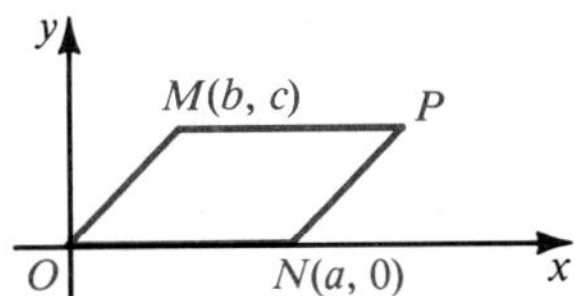

$ROST$ is a trapezoid.
Then T can be labeled (d, c).

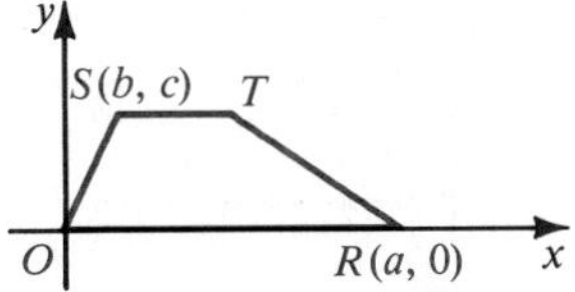

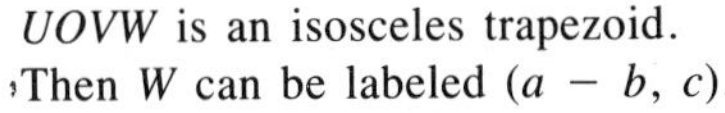
$UOVW$ is an isosceles trapezoid.
Then W can be labeled $(a - b, c)$.

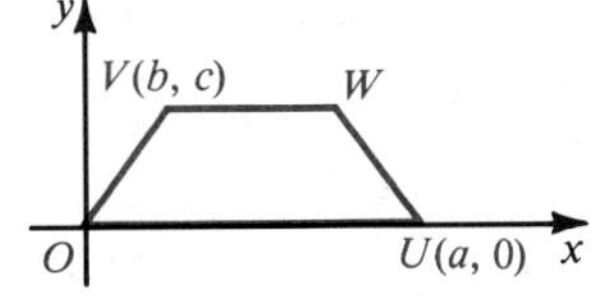

Chalkboard Examples

Supply the missing coordinates without introducing any new letters.

1. rectangle
   (a, b); $(-a, -b)$

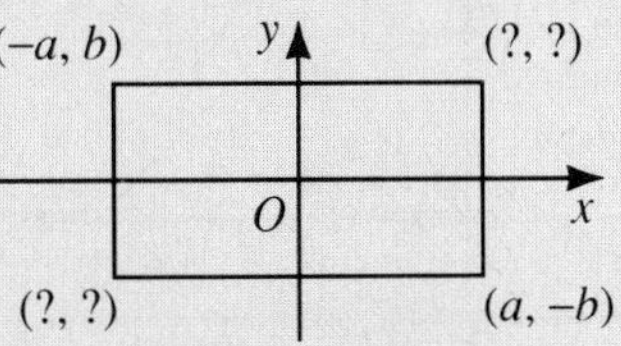

2. equilateral triangle
   $(2a, 0)$

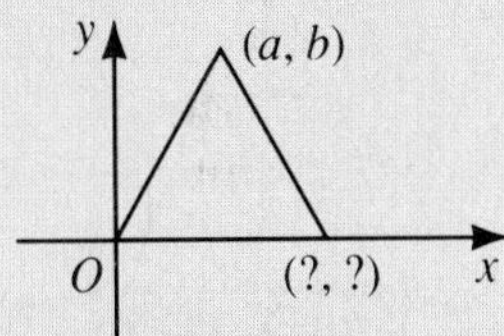

3. rhombus $(a + c, b)$

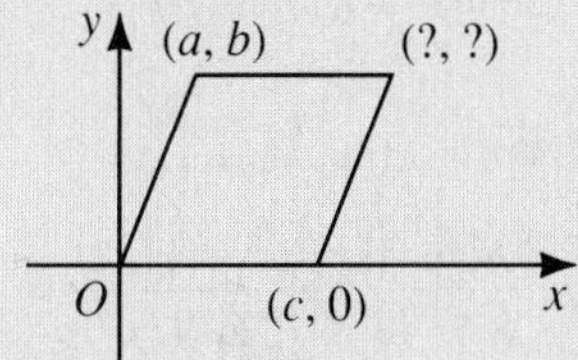

4. square $(3k, 6k)$, $(-3k, 6k)$, $(-3k, 0)$

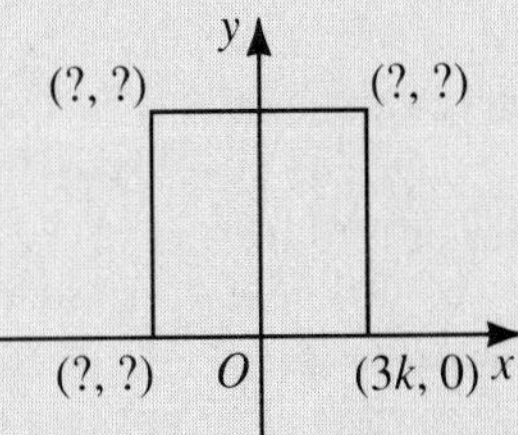

Determine which (if any) of the sides of quad. $WXYZ$ are perpendicular or parallel.

5. $W(0, 0)$; $X(a, 0)$; $Y(b, c)$; $Z(d, c)$ $\overline{WX} \parallel \overline{ZY}$
6. $W(0, 0)$; $X(-a, 0)$; $Y(-b, c)$; $Z(0, d)$ $\overline{XW} \perp \overline{ZW}$

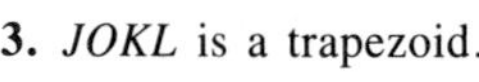

Guided Practice

Supply the missing coordinates without introducing any new letters.

1. isosceles triangle (a, b)

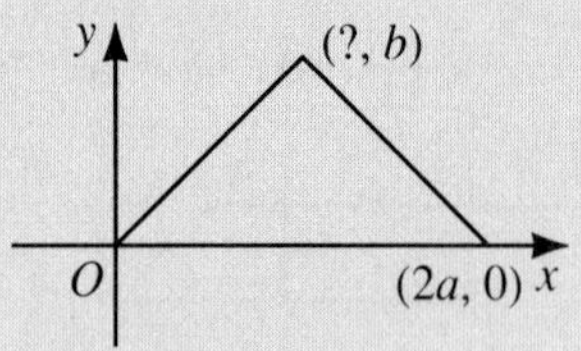

2. isosceles trapezoid $(-2e, f)$

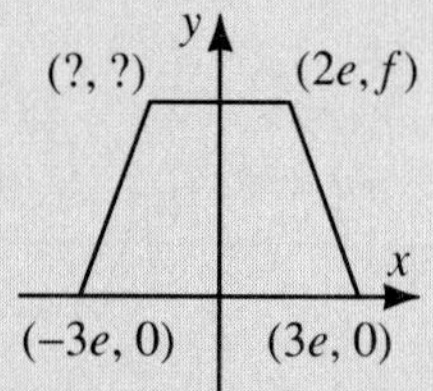

3. rectangle $(-3j, 2j)$; $(3j, 2j)$

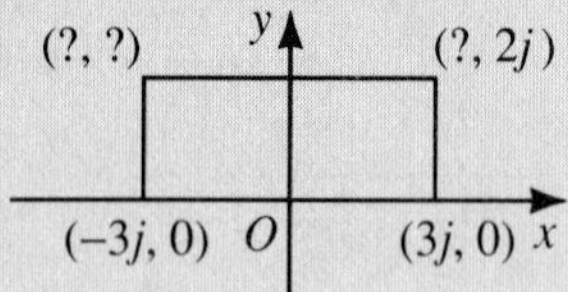

Classroom Exercises

Supply the missing coordinates without introducing any new letters.

1. *POST* is a square.

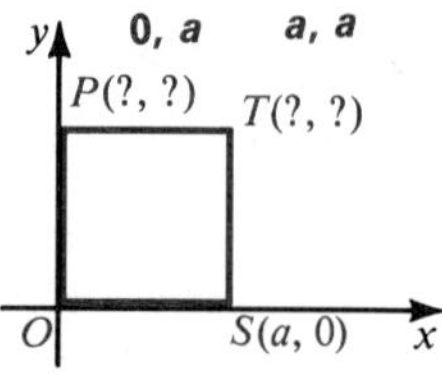
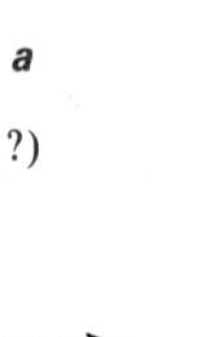

2. $\triangle MON$ is isosceles.

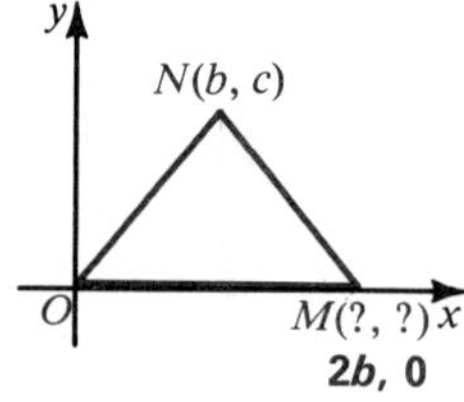

3. *JOKL* is a trapezoid.

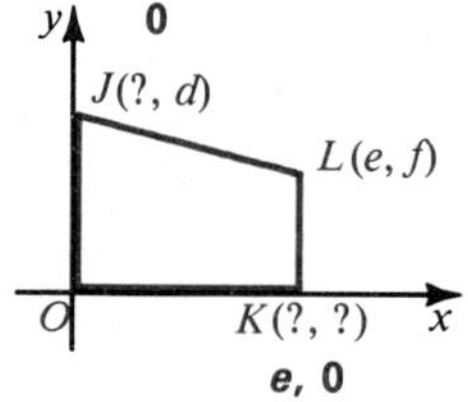

4. *GEOM* is a parallelogram.

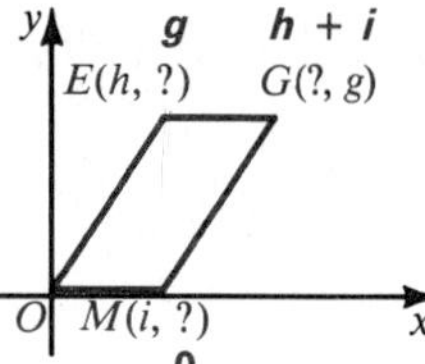

5. *GOLD* is a rectangle.

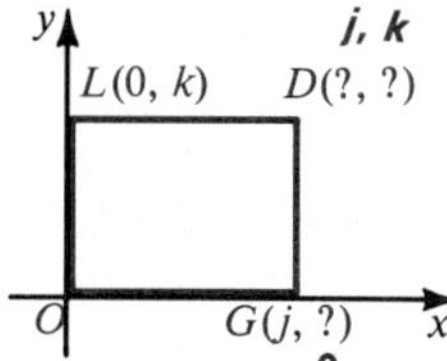

6. Rt. $\triangle TOP$ is isosceles.

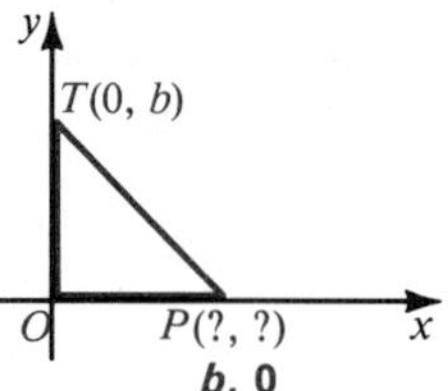

Written Exercises

Copy the figure. Supply the missing coordinates without introducing any new letters.

A

1. Rectangle

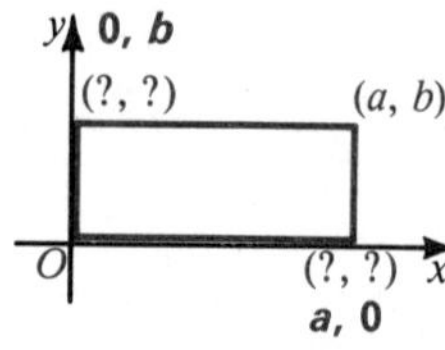

2. Parallelogram

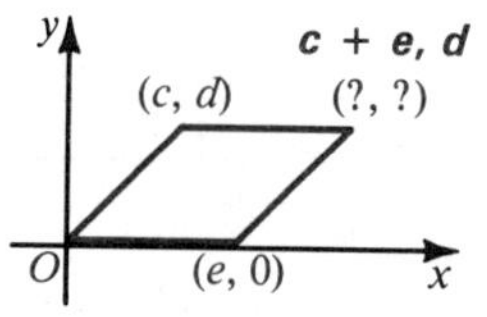

3. Square

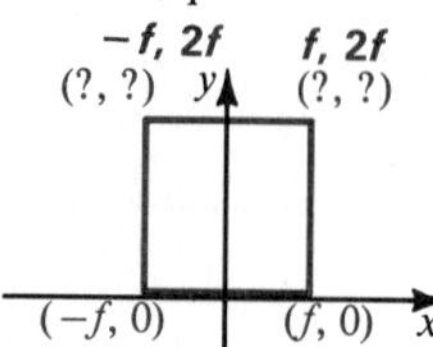

4. Isosceles triangle

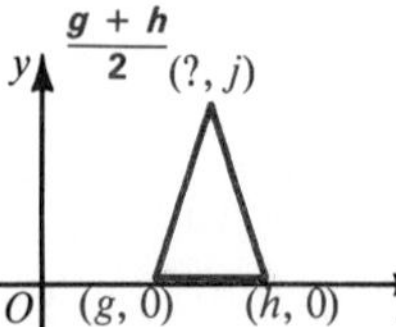

5. Parallelogram

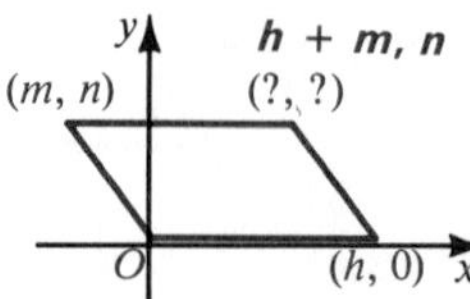

6. Isosceles trapezoid

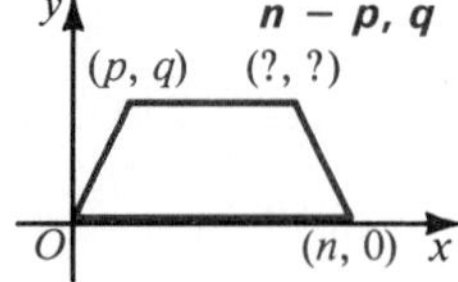

B **7.** An equilateral triangle is shown below. Express the missing coordinates in terms of s.

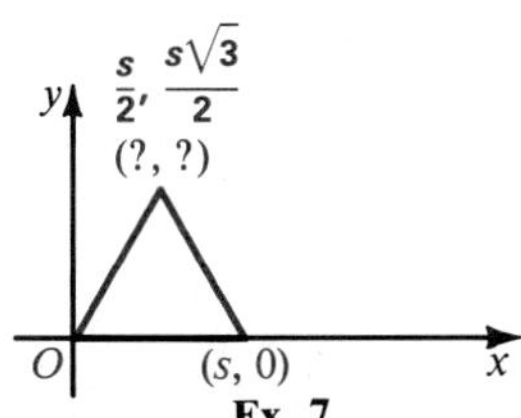

Ex. 7

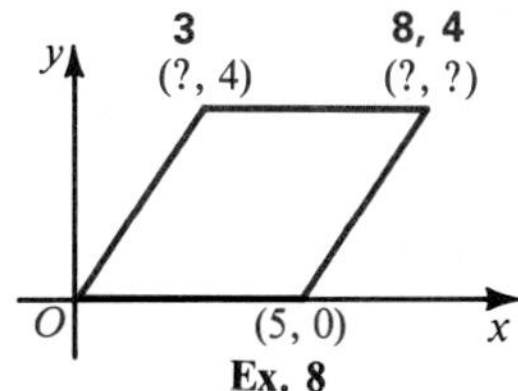

Ex. 8

8. A rhombus is shown above. Find the missing coordinates.

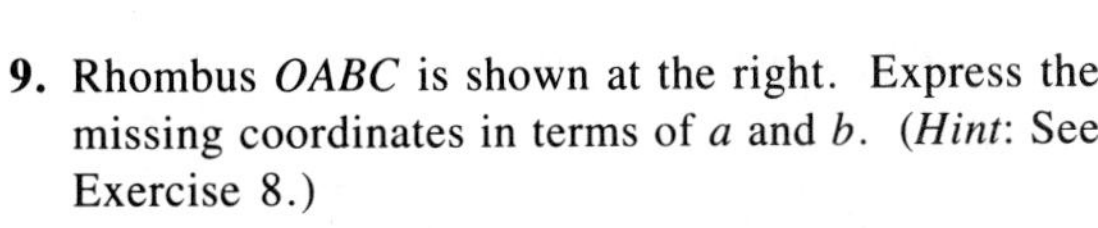
9. Rhombus $OABC$ is shown at the right. Express the missing coordinates in terms of a and b. (*Hint*: See Exercise 8.)

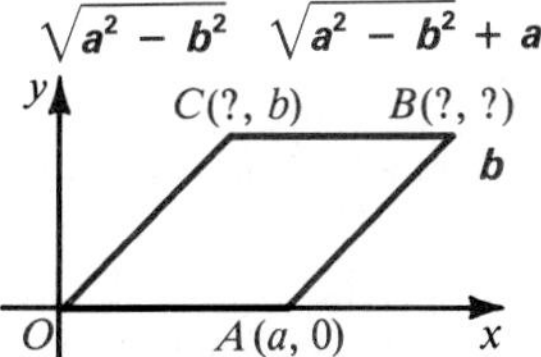

10. Supply the missing coordinates to prove: The segments that join the midpoints of opposite sides of any quadrilateral bisect each other. Let H, E, A, and R be the midpoints of the sides of quadrilateral $SOMK$. Choose axes and coordinates as shown.

a. R has coordinates (_?_, _?_). **w + t, z**
b. E has coordinates (_?_, _?_). **u, v**
c. The midpoint of $\overline{RE}$ has coordinates (_?_, _?_).
d. A has coordinates (_?_, _?_). **u + w, v + z**
e. H has coordinates (_?_, _?_). **t, 0**
f. The midpoint of $\overline{AH}$ has coordinates (_?_, _?_).
g. Because (_?_, _?_) is the midpoint of both $\overline{RE}$ and $\overline{AH}$, $\overline{RE}$ and $\overline{AH}$ bisect each other.

c, f, g. $\frac{w + t + u}{2}, \frac{z + v}{2}$

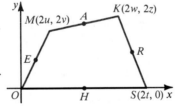

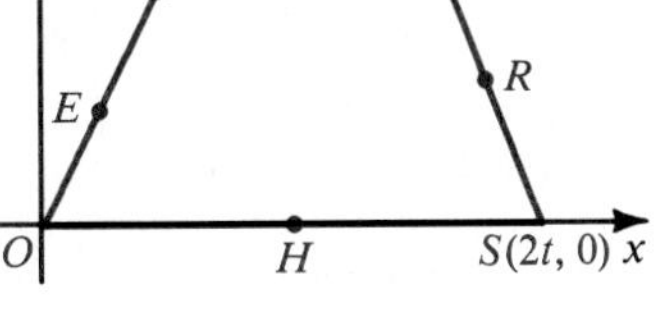

Draw the figure named. Select axes and label the coordinates of the vertices in terms of a single letter.

C **11.** a regular hexagon

12. a regular octagon

13. Given isosceles trapezoid $HOJK$ and the axes and coordinates shown, use the definition of an isosceles trapezoid to prove that $e = c$ and $d = a - b$.

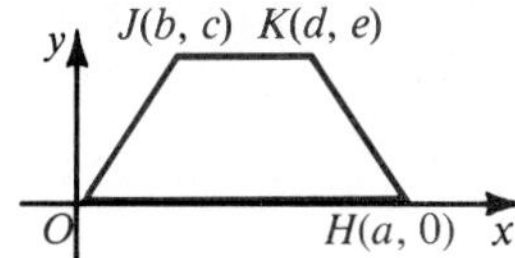

Teaching Suggestions,
p. T137

Objective
Presenting the Lesson
Making Connections

Cooperative Learning,
p. T137

Supplementary Materials

Practice Master 83
Test 54
Resource Book, pp. 92–93, 164
Study Guide, pp. 179–180
Overhead Visual F

Lesson Focus

Very often, a theorem is easier to prove by using coordinate geometry than by using synthetic geometry. This lesson shows how to apply coordinate geometry to proofs.

Suggested Assignments

Maximum
Day 1: 562/1, 4, 5, 7–10
Day 2: 562–563/3, 6, 11, 12–14
568/Chapter Test

Teaching Note

Students might need to review altitudes, slopes, medians, and perpendicular bisectors for this lesson.

In Example 1, the assignment of coordinates $(2a, 0)$ to point Q is not actually essential. You might want to emphasize that the algebra is made simpler by using these coordinates, rather than $(a, 0)$ for Q.

13-9 Coordinate Geometry Proofs

It is easy to verify that $\triangle OPQ$ is an isosceles triangle. Knowing this, we can deduce that medians $\overline{OR}$ and $\overline{QS}$ are congruent by using the midpoint and distance formulas.

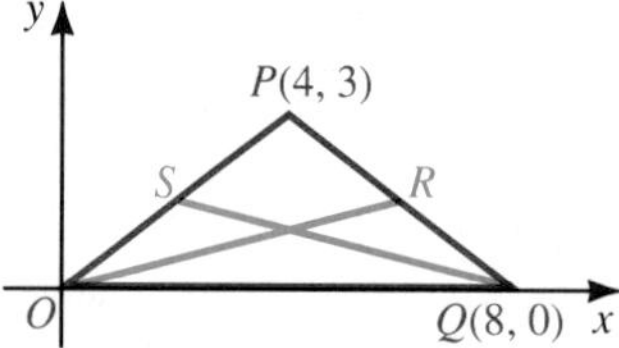

In order to give a coordinate proof that the medians to the legs are congruent for *any* isosceles triangle, and not just for the specific isosceles triangle above, you could use the figure below. Compare the general coordinates given in the figure below with the specific coordinates given for the triangle above. A coordinate proof follows.

Example 1

Prove that the medians to the legs of an isosceles triangle are congruent.

Proof:

Let OPQ be any isosceles triangle with $PO = PQ$. Choose convenient axes and coordinates as shown.

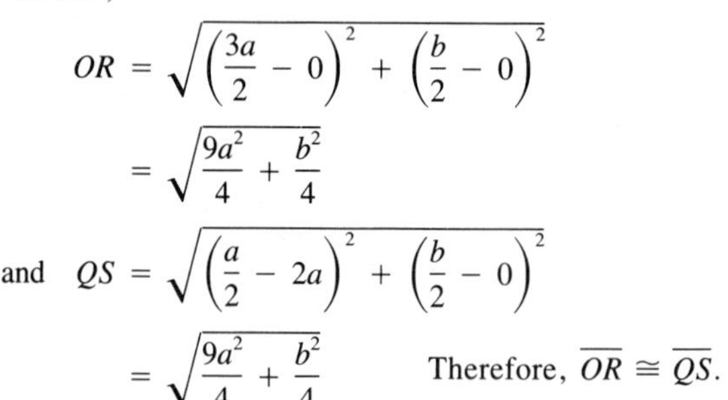

By the midpoint formula,

S has coordinates $\left(\frac{a}{2}, \frac{b}{2}\right)$ and R has coordinates $\left(\frac{3a}{2}, \frac{b}{2}\right)$.

By the distance formula,

$$OR = \sqrt{\left(\frac{3a}{2} - 0\right)^2 + \left(\frac{b}{2} - 0\right)^2} = \sqrt{\frac{9a^2}{4} + \frac{b^2}{4}}$$

$$\text{and} \quad QS = \sqrt{\left(\frac{a}{2} - 2a\right)^2 + \left(\frac{b}{2} - 0\right)^2} = \sqrt{\frac{9a^2}{4} + \frac{b^2}{4}}$$

Therefore, $\overline{OR} \cong \overline{QS}$.

It is possible to prove many theorems of geometry by using coordinate methods rather than the noncoordinate methods involving congruent triangles and angles formed by parallel lines. Coordinate proofs are sometimes, but not always, much easier than noncoordinate proofs. For example, compare the proof in Example 2 with the proof of Theorem 5-11 on page 178.

Example 2

Prove that the segment joining the midpoints of two sides of a triangle is parallel to the third side and is half as long as the third side.

Proof:

Let OPQ be any triangle. Choose convenient axes and coordinates as shown. By the midpoint formula, M has coordinates $\left(\frac{a}{2}, \frac{b}{2}\right)$ and N has coordinates $\left(\frac{a+c}{2}, \frac{b}{2}\right)$.

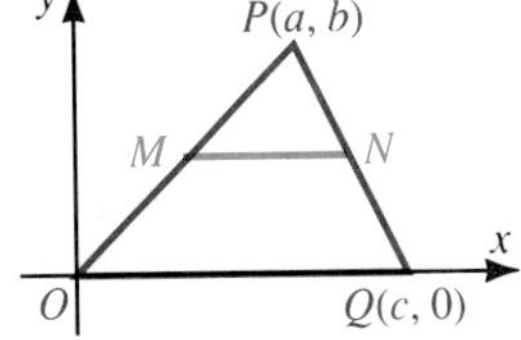

Slope of $\overline{MN} = 0$ and slope of $\overline{OQ} = 0$. (Why?)
Since $\overline{MN}$ and $\overline{OQ}$ have equal slopes, $\overline{MN} \parallel \overline{OQ}$.

Since $MN = \frac{a+c}{2} - \frac{a}{2} = \frac{c}{2}$ and $OQ = c - 0 = c$, $MN = \frac{1}{2}OQ$.

5d. Subst. b for x in the eq. in part (c). **5f. j has slope $-\frac{b}{c}$ and contains $(a, 0)$**

Classroom Exercises

4. midpt. of $\overline{OR}$: $\left(\frac{a}{2}, \frac{a}{2}\right)$, midpt. of $\overline{QS}$: $\left(\frac{a}{2}, \frac{a}{2}\right)$

In Exercises 1–4 use the diagram at the right.
$OQ = QR = RS = OS = a$; $m\angle QOS = 90$

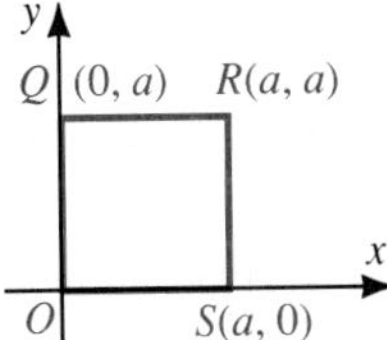

1. What kind of figure is quad. $OQRS$? Why? **square**
2. Show that $\overline{OR} \cong \overline{QS}$. **$OR = QS = a\sqrt{2}$**
3. Show that $\overline{OR} \perp \overline{QS}$. **slope $\overline{OR} = 1$, slope $\overline{QS} = -1$**
4. Show that $\overline{OR}$ bisects $\overline{QS}$. **See above.**
5. The purpose of this exercise is to prove that the lines that contain the altitudes of a triangle intersect in a point (called the *orthocenter*). **5c. l has slope $\frac{a-b}{c}$ and y-int. 0.**

   Given $\triangle ROM$, with lines j, k, and l containing the altitudes, we choose axes and coordinates as shown.

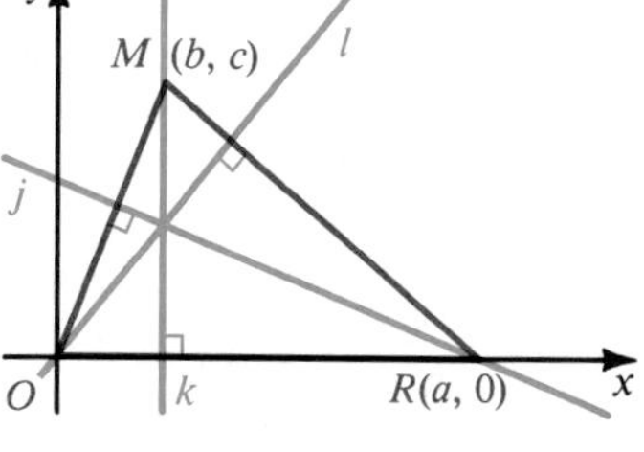

   a. The equation of line k is __?__. **$x = b$**
   b. Since the slope of $\overline{MR}$ is $\frac{c}{b-a}$, the slope of line l is __?__. **$\frac{a-b}{c}$**
   c. Show that an equation of line l is $y = \left(\frac{a-b}{c}\right)x$.
   d. Show that lines k and l intersect where $x = b$ and $y = \frac{ab-b^2}{c}$. **See above.**
   e. Since the slope of $\overline{OM}$ = __?__, the slope of line j is __?__. **$\frac{c}{b}$, $-\frac{b}{c}$**
   f. Show that an equation of line j is $y = -\frac{b}{c}(x - a)$. **See above.**
   g. Show that lines k and j intersect where $x = b$ and $y = \frac{ab-b^2}{c}$. **Subst. b for x in the eq. in part (f).**
   h. From parts (d) and (g) we see that the three altitude lines intersect in a point. Name the coordinates of that point. **$\left(b, \frac{ab-b^2}{c}\right)$**

Chalkboard Examples

1. Prove that the diagonals of an isosceles trapezoid are congruent.

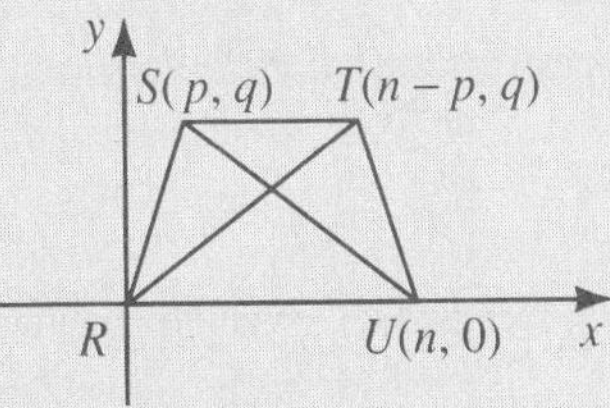

diagonal $RT = \sqrt{(n-p)^2 + q^2}$
diagonal $SU = \sqrt{(n-p)^2 + (0-q)^2} = \sqrt{(n-p)^2 + q^2}$
Since $RT = SU$, the diagonals are $\cong$.

2. Refer to the diagram below and complete the steps of the proof.
   Given: $\overline{RS} \cong \overline{RO}$; A is the midpoint of $\overline{RS}$; $\overline{AP} \perp \overline{OS}$
   Prove: $PS = \frac{1}{4} \cdot OS$

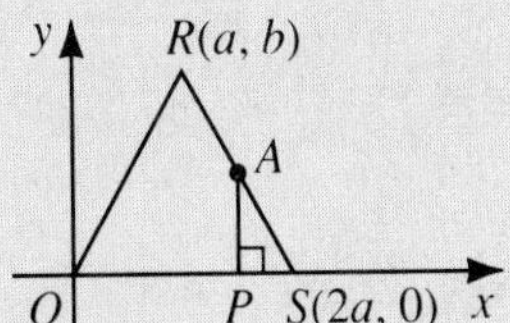

   a. Midpoint A has coordinates (?, ?). $\frac{3a}{2}, \frac{b}{2}$
   b. P has coordinates (?, ?). $\frac{3a}{2}, 0$
   c. OS = __?__ $2a$
   d. $PS = 2a$ − __?__ = __?__ $\frac{3a}{2}, \frac{a}{2}$
   e. In simplest form, $\frac{PS}{OS}$ = __?__. $\frac{1}{4}$
   f. Therefore, $PS = \frac{1}{4} \cdot$ __?__. OS

Written Exercises

Use coordinate geometry to prove each statement. First draw a figure and choose convenient axes and coordinates.

A

1. The diagonals of a rectangle are congruent. (Theorem 5-12)
2. The diagonals of a parallelogram bisect each other. (Theorem 5-3)
3. The diagonals of a rhombus are perpendicular. (Theorem 5-13) (*Hint*: Let the vertices be (0, 0), (*a*, 0), (*a* + *b*, *c*), and (*b*, *c*). Show that $c^2 = a^2 - b^2$.)

Exercises 4–6 refer to trapezoid *MNOP* at the right.

4. Prove that the median of a trapezoid:
   a. is parallel to the bases.
   b. has a length equal to the average of the base lengths. (Theorem 5-19)

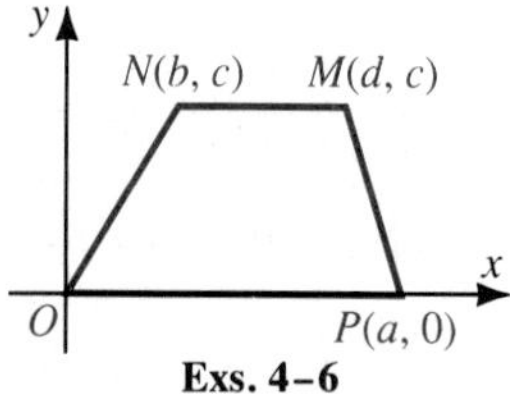

Exs. 4–6

5. Prove that the segment joining the midpoints of the diagonals of a trapezoid is parallel to the bases and has a length equal to half the difference of the lengths of the bases.
6. Assume that $a = b + d$.
   a. Show that the trapezoid is isosceles.
   b. Prove that its diagonals are congruent.

B

7. Prove that the figure formed by joining, in order, the midpoints of the sides of quadrilateral *ROST* is a parallelogram.

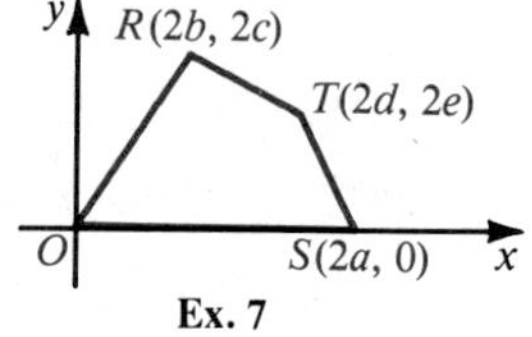

Ex. 7

8. Prove that the quadrilateral formed by joining, in order, the midpoints of the sides of an isosceles trapezoid is a rhombus.
9. Prove that an angle inscribed in a semicircle is a right angle. (*Hint*: The coordinates of *C* must satisfy the equation of the circle.)

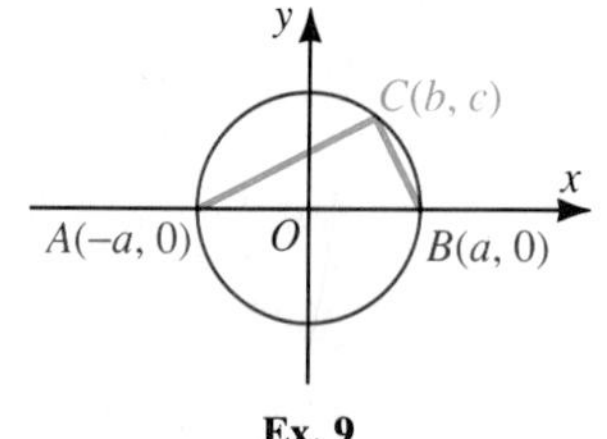

Ex. 9

10. Prove that the sum of the squares of the lengths of the sides of a parallelogram is equal to the sum of the squares of the lengths of the diagonals.

C

11. Use axes and coordinates as shown to prove: The medians of a triangle intersect in a point (called the *centroid*) that is two thirds of the distance from each vertex to the midpoint of the opposite side. (*Hint*: Find the coordinates of the midpoints, then the slopes of the medians, then the equations of the lines containing the medians.)

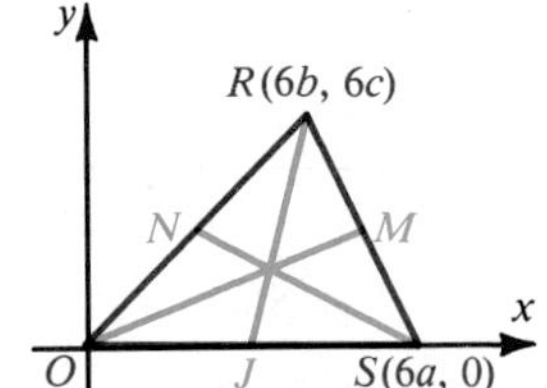

Additional Answers Written Exercises

2. Plan for Proof: Use the midpt. formula to show that midpt. of each diagonal is $\left(\frac{a+c}{2}, \frac{b}{2}\right)$

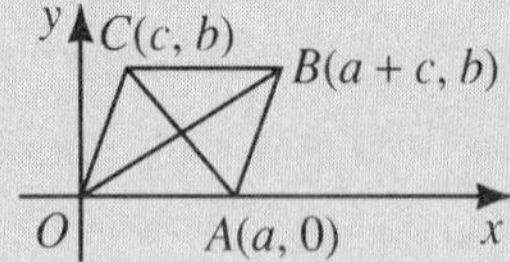

3. Plan for Proof: Show that the product of the slopes of the diagonals is −1.
5. Plan for Proof: Find the coords. of the midpts. *G* and *H* of $\overline{NP}$ and $\overline{OM}$, respectively. Show that $\overline{NM} \parallel \overline{GH} \parallel \overline{OP}$. Find *GH* and show that $GH = \frac{1}{2}(OP - NM)$.
8. Plan for Proof: Use the midpt. formula to find the coords. of *M, N, P,* and *O*. Use the dist. formula to show that *MN* = *NP* = *PO* = *OM*. Alternatively: By Ex. 7, *MNPO* is a ▱. Show that *MN* = *NP*.

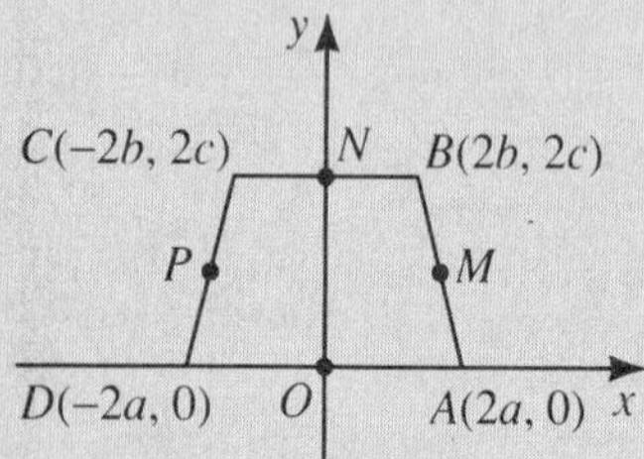

9. Plan for Proof: Use slopes to show that $\overline{AC} \perp \overline{CB}$.

Exercises 12, 13, and 14 refer to the diagram at the right.

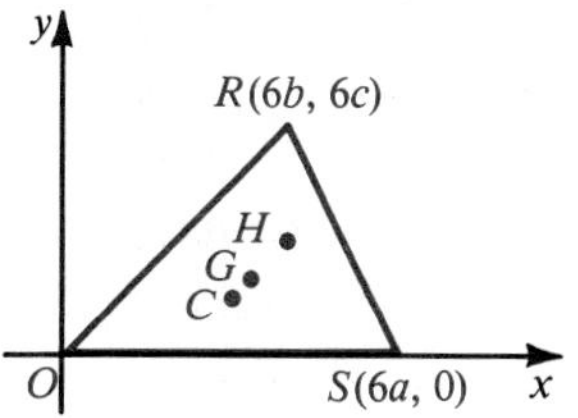

12. Prove that the perpendicular bisectors of the three sides of $\triangle ROS$ meet in a point C (called the *circumcenter*) whose coordinates are $\left(3a, \frac{3b^2 + 3c^2 - 3ab}{c}\right)$.
13. Prove that the lines containing the altitudes of $\triangle ROS$ intersect in a point $H\left(6b, \frac{6ab - 6b^2}{c}\right)$. (*Hint*: Use the procedure of Classroom Exercise 5.)
14. G, the intersection point of the medians of $\triangle ROS$, has coordinates $(2a + 2b, 2c)$. (See Exercise 11.) Prove each statement.
    a. Points C, G, and H are collinear. The line containing these points is called *Euler's Line*. (*Hint*: One way to prove this is to show that slope of $\overline{CG}$ = slope of $\overline{GH}$.)
    b. $CG = \frac{1}{3}CH$

Self-Test 2

1. Find the slope and y-intercept of the line $2x - 5y = 20$. **$\frac{2}{5}$; -4**
2. Graph the line $2x + 3y = 6$.
3. Write an equation of the line through $(1, 2)$ and $(5, 0)$. **$y = -\frac{1}{2}x + \frac{5}{2}$**
4. Write an equation of the horizontal line through $(-2, 5)$. **$y = 5$**
5. Find the intersection point of the lines $y = 3x - 4$ and $5x - 2y = 7$. **$(1, -1)$**

State the coordinates of point J without introducing any new letters.

6. Isosceles triangle **$(2e, 0)$**

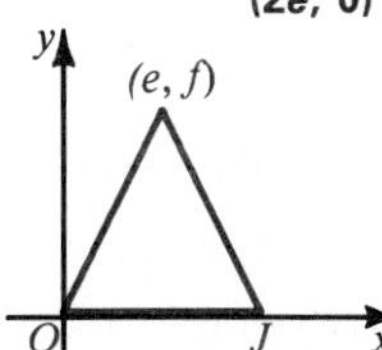

7. Parallelogram **$(c + g, h)$**

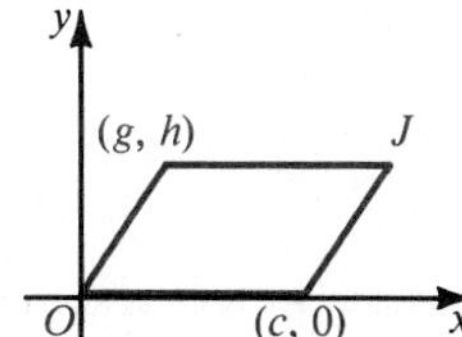

8. Isosceles trapezoid **$(c - g, h)$**

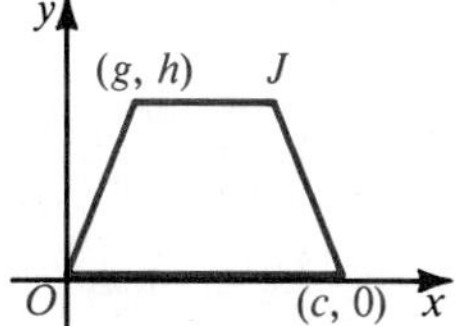

9. The vertices of a quadrilateral are $G(4, -1)$, $O(0, 0)$, $L(2, 6)$, and $D(6, 5)$. Show that quadrilateral $GOLD$ is a parallelogram.
   slope of $\overline{GO}$ = slope of $\overline{LD}$ = $-\frac{1}{4}$; slope of $\overline{OL}$ = slope of $\overline{DG}$ = 3

Guided Practice

1. Prove that if the diagonals of a parallelogram are congruent, then the parallelogram is a rectangle.

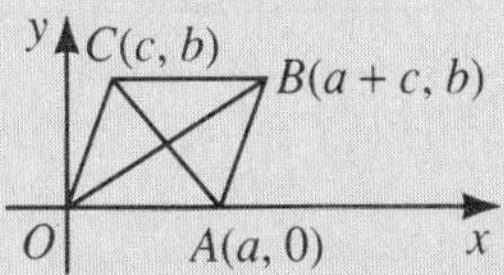

Give coordinates to points as shown.
$OB = \sqrt{(a + c)^2 + (b)^2}$
$CA = \sqrt{(a - c)^2 + (-b)^2}$
Since $OB = CA$,
$(a + c)^2 + (b)^2 = (a - c)^2 + (-b)^2$;
$(a + c)^2 = (a - c)^2$;
$a^2 + 2ac + c^2 = a^2 - 2ac + c^2$;
$2ac = -2ac$; $4ac = 0$,
So, $a = 0$ or $c = 0$. But $a \neq 0$ because point A is not point O. Therefore, $c = 0$. The points $O(0, 0)$, $A(a, 0)$, $B(a, b)$, and $C(0, b)$ form a rectangle.

Quick Quiz

1. Find the slope and y-intercept of the line $-3x + 2y = 6$. $\frac{3}{2}$; 3
2. Write the equation of the line through $(3, -1)$ and $(4, 2)$. $y + 1 = 3(x - 3)$
3. Write the equation of the vertical line through $(-4, -1)$. $x = -4$
4. Find the intersection point of the lines $y = -2x + 3$ and $4x + 3y = 8$. $(\frac{1}{2}, 2)$

(continued)

State the coordinates of point J without introducing any new letters.

5. $(a, -b)$

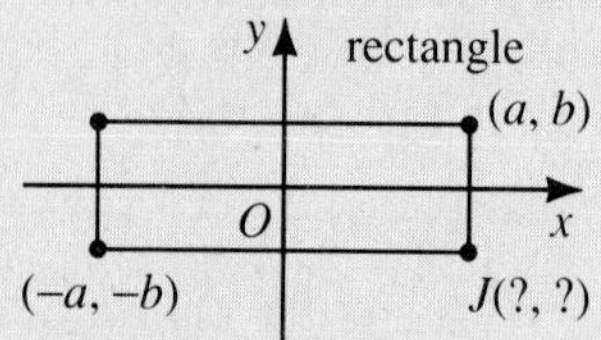

6. $(2b, a)$

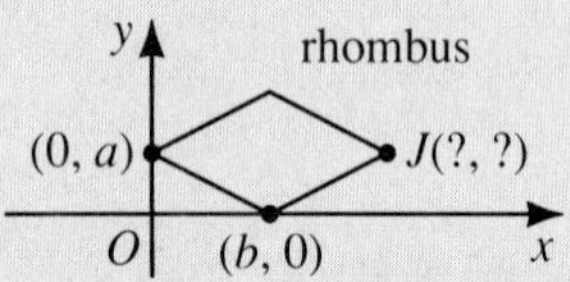

7. Show that $(-1, 1)$, $(2, 4)$, and $(5, 1)$ are the vertices of an isosceles right triangle.

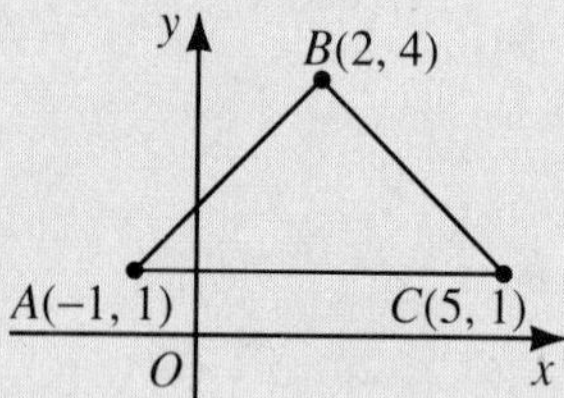

Plan for Proof: Use the distance formula to show that $AB = 3\sqrt{2}$, $BC = 3\sqrt{2}$, and $AC = 6$. Then use the Pythagorean Thm. to show that $(AC)^2 = (AB)^2 + (BC)^2$.

Making Connections

To gain an understanding of Steiner's problem, first consider a simple case with three villages, A, B, and C, that form a triangle with each angle less than 120°. By experimenting with soap films, you will find that the

Application — *Steiner's Problem*

Four villages plan to build a system of roads of minimum length that will connect them all. Shown below are some plans for how to build the roads. Which plan shows the shortest road? Is there another way to connect the villages by an even shorter system of roads?

This problem was first investigated by the German mathematician Jacob Steiner (1796–1863), and carried his name, *Steiner's problem*.

Because a soap film automatically minimizes its surface area you can build a model that will help you solve Steiner's problem. You will need:

a sheet of clear plastic
8 split-pin paper fasteners
a drinking straw cut into four 3-cm long pieces

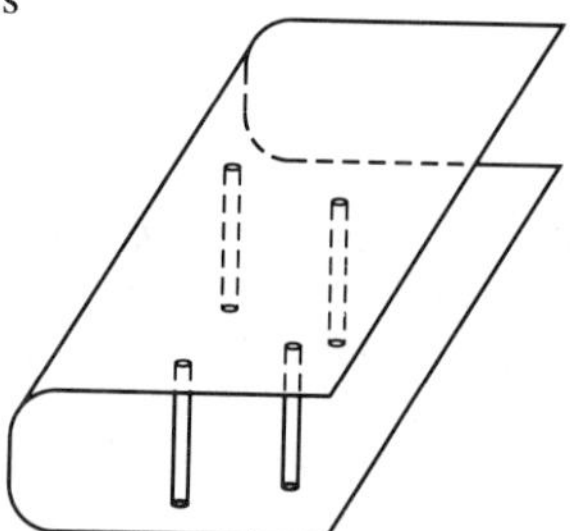

Bend the sheet of plastic without creasing it. Cut four small slits (to represent the location of the four villages) through both layers of the sheet. Insert the paper fasteners through all eight slits. Slip two fasteners through each of four straws, so that your model looks like the figure at the right. The halves of the plastic sheet should be parallel, and the straws perpendicular to them.

Dip the model in a soap solution and carefully lift it out. You should see a system of vertical soap films between the two sheets of plastic and joining the straws, revealing the solution to the problem. (Should any soap film adhere to the curved part of the plastic sheet, wet a drinking straw with the soap solution and push the straw through the soap films. You can suck air out through the straw to allow the films to form the minimum connection.)

Exercises

1. Gently place a protractor on top of the model and measure the angles where the soap films meet. What are the measures of these angles? **120**

Make other models to find the shortest connection between the vertices of the following polygons. In each model, find the measures of the angles where the soap films meet.

2. Triangle 3. Square 4. Pentagon

2–4. The measures of the ∡ where the soap films meet are 120.

Extra — *Points in Space*

To locate points in three-dimensional space, three coordinate axes are needed. Think of the *y-axis* and *z-axis* as lying in the plane of the paper with the *x-axis* perpendicular to the plane of the paper. The axes intersect at the *origin*, or zero point, of each axis. The arrowhead on each axis indicates the positive direction.

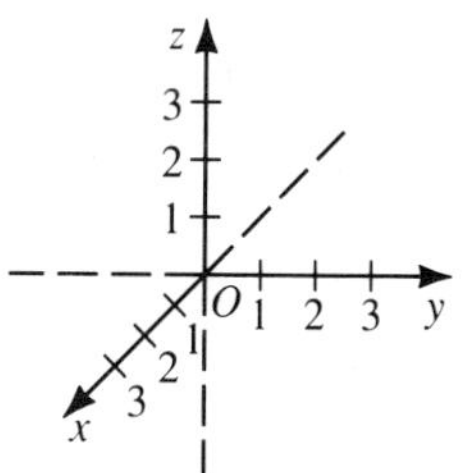

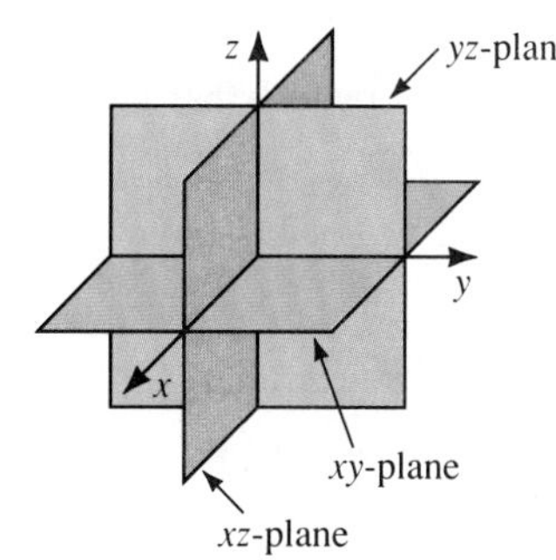

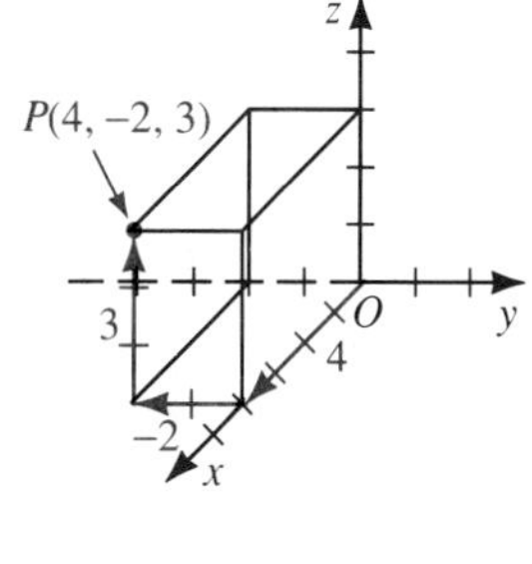

The coordinate axes determine three *coordinate planes*, as shown in the middle diagram above. Each point in space has three coordinates: the *x-coordinate*, *y-coordinate*, and *z-coordinate*. For example, point *P* in the diagram at the right above, has coordinates (**4**, **−2**, **3**). The red arrows in the figure show that to *graph P* you start at *O*, move **4** units in the positive direction on the *x*-axis, **−2** units parallel to the *y*-axis (that is 2 units in the negative direction parallel to the *y*-axis), and **3** units in the positive direction parallel to the *z*-axis.

Exercises

On which axis or axes does each point lie?

1. (0, 7, 0) **y-axis** **2.** (0, 0, −9) **z-axis** **3.** (5, 0, 0) **x-axis** **4.** (0, 0, 0) **all 3 axes**

On which coordinate plane or planes does each point lie?

5. (1, −3, 0) **xy-plane** **6.** (−7, 0, −1) **xz-plane** **7.** (0, 8, 5) **yz-plane** **8.** (0, 0, 0) **all 3 planes**

Graph each point on a coordinate system in space.

9. (−1, 4, 0) **10.** (2, 3, 1) **11.** (−2, −3, 4) **12.** (0, 1, −5)

Sketch the triangle in space whose vertices have the given coordinates.

13. (4, 0, 0), (0, 8, 0), (0, 0, 2) **14.** (1, 0, 0), (0, −5, 0), (0, 0, −5)

15. (−3, 0, 0), (0, −4, 0), (0, 0, 6) **16.** (0, 0, 0), (3, 0, 3), (0, −4, 5)

films meet at a point X such that $m\angle AXB = m\angle BXC = m\angle CXA = 120$. You will also find that as $m\angle A$, for example, approaches 120, the point X approaches A. If $m\angle A \geq 120$, X coincides with A. $AB + AC$ will be the shortest path.

To construct point X, draw two arcs of radius AB with centers A and B. Label the intersection of the two arcs P. Repeat these steps using radii BC and CA, and label the points of intersection Q and R. Point X is the intersection of $\overrightarrow{CP}$, $\overrightarrow{AQ}$, and $\overrightarrow{BR}$.

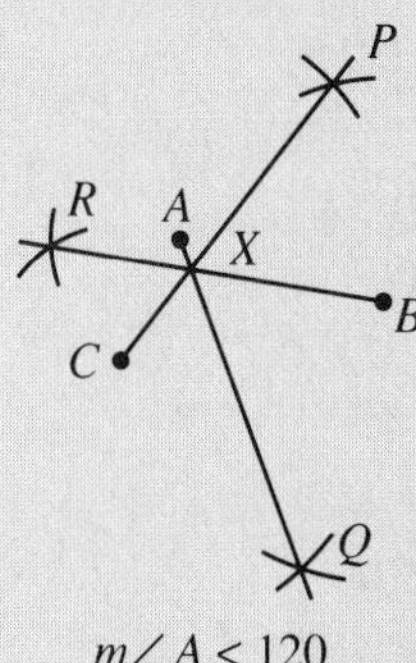

$m\angle A < 120$

If the number of villages is greater than 3, the solution may not be unique and will depend on the relative location of the points. For example, in the case where four villages, A, B, C, and D, form a square, there are two solutions. Again, as the measure of one angle of the quad. approaches 120, the intersection of the soap film approaches that point. The same theory applies for any number of villages.

Chapter Summary

1. The distance between points (x_1, y_1) and (x_2, y_2) is
$$\sqrt{(x_2 - x_1)^2 + (y_2 - y_1)^2}.$$
The midpoint of the segment joining these points is the point
$$\left(\frac{x_1 + x_2}{2}, \frac{y_1 + y_2}{2}\right).$$

2. The circle with center (a, b) and radius r has the equation
$$(x - a)^2 + (y - b)^2 = r^2.$$

3. The slope m of a line through two points (x_1, y_1) and (x_2, y_2), $x_1 \neq x_2$, is defined as follows: $m = \frac{y_2 - y_1}{x_2 - x_1}$. The slope of a horizontal line is zero. Slope is not defined for vertical lines.

4. Two nonvertical lines with slopes m_1 and m_2 are:
   a. parallel if and only if $m_1 = m_2$.
   b. perpendicular if and only if $m_1 \cdot m_2 = -1$.

5. Any quantity that has both magnitude and direction is called a vector. A vector can be represented by an arrow or by an ordered pair. The magnitude of $\overrightarrow{AB}$ equals the length of $\overline{AB}$. Two vectors are perpendicular if the arrows representing them are perpendicular. Two vectors are parallel if the arrows representing them have the same or opposite directions. Two vectors are equal if they have the same magnitude and direction.

6. Two operations with vectors were discussed: multiplication of a vector by a real number, and addition of vectors.

7. The graph of any equation that can be written in the form $Ax + By = C$, with A and B not both zero, is a line. An equation of the line through point (x_1, y_1) with slope m is $y - y_1 = m(x - x_1)$. An equation of the line with slope m and y-intercept b is $y = mx + b$. The coordinates of the point of intersection of two lines can be found by solving their equations simultaneously.

8. To prove theorems using coordinate geometry, proceed as follows:
   a. Place x- and y-axes in a convenient position with respect to a figure.
   b. Use known properties to assign coordinates to points of the figure.
   c. Use the distance formula, the midpoint formula, and the slope properties of parallel and perpendicular lines to prove theorems.

Chapter Review **8. Examples: (1, 3), (2, 8), (−1, −7)** **11.** $\frac{3}{4}, -\frac{4}{3}$

Exercises 1 and 2 refer to points $X(-2, -4)$, $Y(2, 4)$, and $Z(2, -6)$.

1. Graph X, Y, and Z on one set of axes, then find XY, YZ, and XZ. **$4\sqrt{5}$; 10; $2\sqrt{5}$** 13–1

2. Use the distance formula to show that $\triangle XYZ$ is a right triangle. **$(XY)^2 + (XZ)^2 = 80 + 20 = 100 = (YZ)^2$**

Find the center and radius of each circle. **5. $(x + 6)^2 + (y + 1)^2 = 9$**

3. $(x + 3)^2 + y^2 = 100$ **(−3, 0); 10** **4.** $(x - 5)^2 + (y + 1)^2 = 49$ **(5, −1); 7**

5. Write an equation of the circle that has center $(-6, -1)$ and radius 3. **See above.**

6. Find the slope of the line through $(-5, -1)$ and $(15, -6)$. **$-\frac{1}{4}$** 13–2

7. A line with slope $\frac{2}{3}$ passes through $(9, -13)$ and $(0, \underline{\ ?\ })$. **−19**

8. A line through $(0, -2)$ has slope 5. Find three other points on the line. **See above.**

9. What is the slope of a line that is parallel to the x-axis? **0**

10. Show that $QRST$ is a trapezoid. 13–3

11. Since the slope of $\overline{QT}$ is $\underline{\ ?\ }$, the slope of an altitude to $\overline{QT}$ is $\underline{\ ?\ }$. **See above.**

12. If U is a point on $\overline{QT}$ such that $\overline{UR} \parallel \overline{ST}$, then U has coordinates $(\underline{\ ?\ }, \underline{\ ?\ })$. **3, 1**

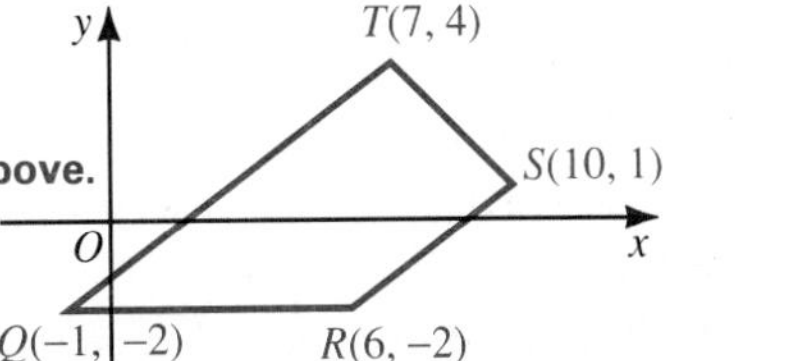

13. Given points $P(3, -2)$ and $Q(7, 1)$, find **(a)** $\overrightarrow{PQ}$, **(b)** $|\overrightarrow{PQ}|$, and **(c)** $-2\overrightarrow{PQ}$. 13–4

14. Find the vector sum $(2, 6) + 3(1, -2)$ and illustrate with a diagram. **(5, 0)**

13. a. (4, 3) b. 5 c. (−8, −6)

Find the coordinates of the midpoint of the segment that joins the given points.

15. $(7, -2)$ and $(1, -1)$ **$\left(4, -\frac{3}{2}\right)$** **16.** $(-4, 5)$ and $(2, -5)$ **(−1, 0)** **17.** (a, b) and $(-a, b)$ **(0, b)** 13–5

18. $M(0, 5)$ is the midpoint of $\overline{RS}$. If S has coordinates $(11, -1)$, then R is point $(\underline{\ ?\ }, \underline{\ ?\ })$. **(−11, 11)**

19. Graph the line $y = 2x - 3$. **20.** Graph the line $x + 2y = 4$. **See below.** 13–6

21. Find the point of intersection of the two lines in Exercises 19 and 20. **(2, 1)**

22. Find an equation of the line with slope 4 and y-intercept 7. **$y = 4x + 7$** 13–7

23. Find an equation of the line through $(-1, 2)$ and $(3, 10)$. **$y = 2x + 4$**

24. If $OPQR$ is a parallelogram, what are the coordinates of Q? **($a + b$, c)** 13–8

25. Let M be the midpoint of $\overline{RQ}$ and N be the midpoint of $\overline{OP}$. Use coordinate geometry to prove that $ONQM$ is a parallelogram. 13–9

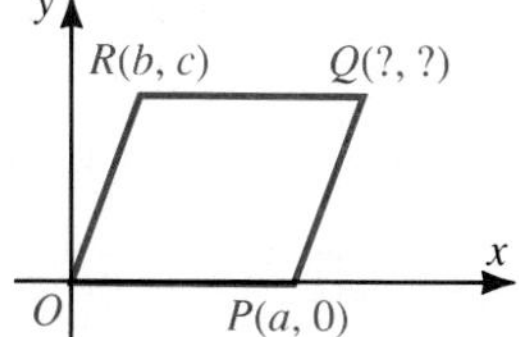

19. The line passes through (0, −3) and (2, 1).
20. The line passes through (4, 0) and (0, 2).

Supplementary Materials

Practice Master 84
Test 55
Resource Book, pp. 94–95, 165
Computer Activity 33

Additional Answers Chapter Review

10. Slope $\overline{TQ} = \frac{3}{4}$; slope $\overline{SR} = \frac{3}{4}$; slope $\overline{TS} = -1$; slope $\overline{QR} = 0$; $\overline{TQ} \parallel \overline{SR}$; $\overline{TS}$ is not $\parallel$ to $\overline{QR}$; thus $QRST$ is a trap.

25. $M(\frac{a}{2} + b, c)$, $N(\frac{a}{2}, 0)$; slope $\overline{ON}$ = slope $\overline{MQ}$ = 0; slope $\overline{OM}$ = slope $\overline{NQ} = \dfrac{2c}{a + 2b}$

Teaching References

Alternate Test, p. T24

Additional Answers Chapter Test

20. Plan for Proof: Use the midpt. formula to show that the midpt. of each diagonal is (a, b).

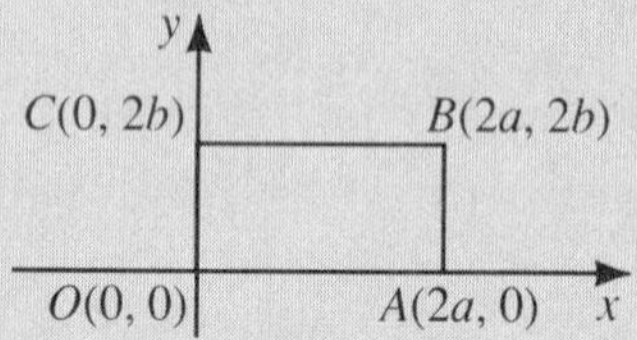

21. Plan for Proof: Use slopes and the dist. form. to show that $\overline{QM} \parallel \overline{PN}$ and $\overline{QM} \cong \overline{PN}$. Thus $MNPQ$ is a ▱. Then use dist. form. to show that $\overline{MN} \cong \overline{QM}$. Thus $MNPQ$ is a rhombus.

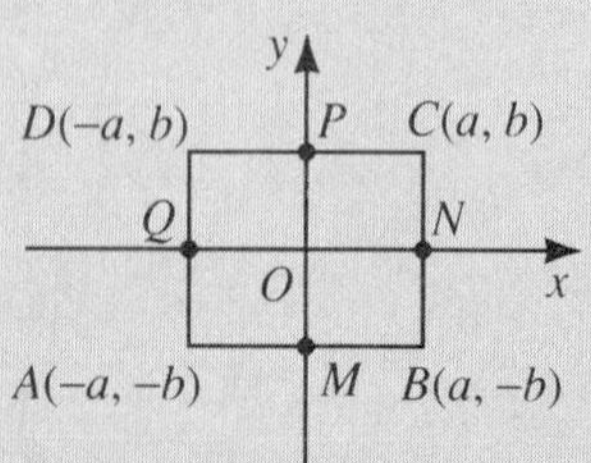

Chapter Test

Given: Points $M(-2, 1)$ and $N(2, 4)$

1. Find **(a)** MN, **(b)** the slope of $\overline{MN}$, and **(c)** the midpoint of $\overline{MN}$. **a. 5 b. $\frac{3}{4}$ c. $\left(0, \frac{5}{2}\right)$**
2. Write an equation of $\overleftrightarrow{MN}$. $\mathbf{y = \frac{3}{4}x + \frac{5}{2}}$
3. Write an equation of a circle with center M and radius MN. $\mathbf{(x + 2)^2 + (y - 1)^2 = 25}$
4. If M is the midpoint of $\overline{NZ}$, what are the coordinates of Z? **$(-6, -2)$**

In Exercises 5–8 write an equation of each line described. Form of eqs. may vary.

5. The line with slope $-\frac{3}{2}$ and y-intercept 4 $\mathbf{y = -\frac{3}{2}x + 4}$
6. The line with y-intercept 5 and x-intercept 3 $\mathbf{5x + 3y = 15}$
7. The line through $(-2, 5)$ and parallel to $3x + y = 6$ $\mathbf{y - 5 = -3(x + 2)}$
8. The line with y-intercept 7 and perpendicular to $y = -2x + 3$ $\mathbf{y = \frac{1}{2}x + 7}$
9. Given points $P(-2, 5)$ and $Q(4, 1)$, find **(a)** $\overrightarrow{PQ}$ and **(b)** $|\overrightarrow{PQ}|$. **a. $(6, -4)$ b. $2\sqrt{13}$**
10. The vectors $(3, 6)$ and $(-2, k)$ are parallel. Find the value of k. **-4**
11. The vectors $(3, -5)$ and $(c, 6)$ are perpendicular. Find the value of c. **10**
12. Evaluate the vector sum $(5, -3) + 4(-2, 1)$. **$(-3, 1)$**
13. Find the point of intersection of the lines $x + 2y = 8$ and $3x - y = 3$. **$(2, 3)$**

Draw the graph of each equation. **14. The line passes through $(3, 0)$ and $(0, -2)$.**

14. $2x - 3y = 6$
15. $y = 5$ **The line is horiz. and passes through $(0, 5)$.**
16. Name 3 points on the line through $(2, 2)$ with slope $\frac{4}{3}$.
    Answers may vary. Examples: $(5, 6)$, $(8, 10)$, $(-1, -2)$
17. An isosceles trapezoid is shown. Give the missing coordinates without introducing any new letters. **$(f - g, h)$**

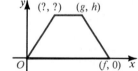

Use points $J(-12, 0)$, $K(0, 6)$, and $L(-3, -3)$.

18. Show that $\triangle JKL$ is isosceles. $\mathbf{JL = KL = 3\sqrt{10}}$
19. Use slopes to show that $\triangle JKL$ is a right triangle. **slope of $\overline{JL}$ · slope of $\overline{KL}$ = $-\frac{1}{3} \cdot 3 = -1$**

Use coordinate geometry to prove each statement.

20. The diagonals of a rectangle bisect each other.
21. The segments joining the midpoints of consecutive sides of a rectangle form a rhombus.

Supplementary Materials

Resource Book, p. 202

Cumulative Review: Chapters 1–13

A

1. $\overrightarrow{BD}$ bisects $\angle ABC$, $m\angle ABC = 5x - 4$, and $m\angle CBD = \frac{3}{2}x + 21$. Is $\angle ABC$ acute, obtuse, or right? **obtuse**
2. Name five ways to prove that two lines are parallel. **See page 85.**
3. If the diagonals of a quadrilateral are congruent and perpendicular, must the quadrilateral be a square? a rhombus? Draw a diagram to illustrate your answer. **No; no; draw a figure in which the diags. do not bisect each other.**
4. Write "$x = 1$ only if $x \neq 0$" in if-then form. Then write the contrapositive and classify the contrapositive as true or false. **If $x = 1$, then $x \neq 0$; if $x = 0$, then $x \neq 1$; true**
5. Refer to the diagram.
   a. Show that $\angle B \cong \angle D$.
   b. Find the value of x. **18**
   c. Find the ratio of the areas of the triangles. **4:9**

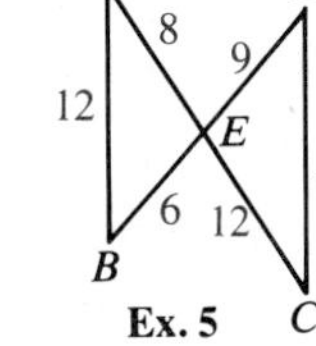

Ex. 5

6. Is a triangle with sides of lengths 12, 35, and 37 acute, right, or obtuse? **right**
7. In $\triangle ABC$, $\overline{AB} \perp \overline{BC}$, $AB = 1$, and $AC = 3$. Find:
   a. $\cos A$ $\frac{1}{3}$ b. $\sin C$ $\frac{1}{3}$ c. $\tan A$ $2\sqrt{2}$ d. $\cos C$ $\frac{2\sqrt{2}}{3}$
8. Find the perimeter and area of a regular hexagon with apothem $\sqrt{3}$ cm. **12 cm; $6\sqrt{3}$ cm^2**
9. Find the total area and volume of a cylinder with radius 10 and height 8.2. **364π; 820π**
10. Describe the locus of the centers of all circles tangent to each of two given parallel lines. **a line parallel to the 2 lines and halfway btwn. them**

Find the value of *x*.

11. $6\frac{2}{3}$

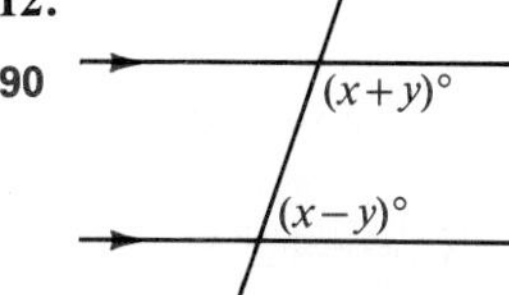

12. 90

13. 89

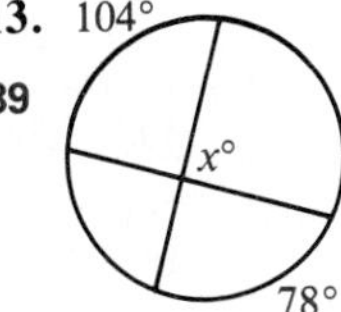

B

14. If x is the length of a tangent segment in the diagram, find the values of x and y. **$x = 6\sqrt{5}$, $y = 8$**

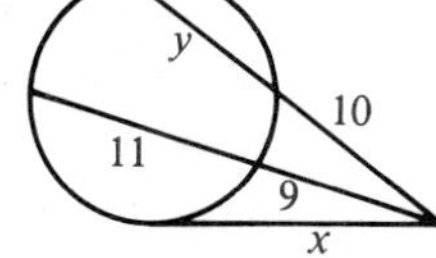

15. Prove: If the ray that bisects an angle of a triangle is perpendicular to the side that it intersects, then the triangle is an isosceles triangle.
16. Draw an obtuse triangle. Construct a circumscribed circle about the triangle. **Use Construction 10.**
17. Use coordinate geometry to prove that the median of a trapezoid is parallel to each base. **Plan for Proof: Show that the slope of the median = 0 = the slopes of the bases.**

14 Transformations

Objectives

14-1 Recognize and use the terms *image, preimage, mapping, one-to-one mapping, transformation, isometry,* and *congruence mapping*.

Recognize the properties of the basic mappings.

14-2 Locate images of figures by reflection.

14-3 Locate images of figures by translation and glide reflection.

14-4 Locate images of figures by rotation.

14-5 Locate images of figures by dilation.

14-6 Locate the images of figures by composites of mappings.

14-7 Recognize and use the terms *identity* and *inverse* in relation to mappings.

14-8 Describe the symmetry of figures and solids.

Assignment Guide

See page T40 for information about the Assignment Guide.

Day	Minimum Course	Average Course	Maximum Course
1		**14-1** 574–575/1–10	**14-1** 574–575/1–7, 10, 11, 14
2		**14-2** 580/1–15	**14-1** 575–576/12, 13, 15–19, 21
3		**14-3** 586/1–10 **S** 580/17	**14-2** 580–581/4–6, 8–18 even, 21, 23
4		**14-4** 590/1–23 odd 592/Mixed Review 1–7	**14-2** 581–582/25–30, 32–35, 38
5		**14-5** 596/2–8 even, 9–21 odd 597/Self-Test 1	**14-3** 586–587/2, 3, 6, 7, 9, 11, 14, 15, 17, 18, 21
6		**14-6** 603–604/1–4, 6–8, 10, 12	**14-4** 590/7–21 odd, 24–27
7		**14-7** 607–608/1–13 odd, 14–19 615/Self-Test 2, 1–10	**14-4** 590–592/28, 29, 31, 33, 35–38
8			**14-5** 596/2, 4, 7, 8, 10, 14, 16, 17, 19, 22
9			**14-5** 596–597/18, 21, 23–28
10			**14-6** 603–604/2, 4, 6, 7–19 odd
11			**14-7** 607–608/1–29 odd **S** 604–605/21–30
12			**14-7** 607–608/2–30 even
13			**14-8** 612–613/1–29 odd
14			**14-8** 613–614/20–28 even 620/Chapter Test Test, page T25

Supplementary Materials Guide

For Use after Lesson	Practice Masters	Tests	Study Guide (Reteaching)	Resource Book				Computer Activities
				Tests	Practice Exercises	Mixed Review (MR) Prep. for College Entrance Exams (Col)		
14-1	Sheet 85		pp. 181–182					Activity 34
14-2			pp. 183–184					
14-3	Sheet 86	Test 56	pp. 185–186	p. 96	p. 166			
14-4			pp. 187–188					
14-5	Sheet 87	Test 57	pp. 189–190	p. 97	p. 167			Activity 35
14-6			pp. 191–192					Activity 36
14-7	Sheet 88		pp. 193–194					
14-8	Sheet 89	Test 58	pp. 195–196	p. 98	p. 168			
Chapter 14	Sheet 90	Test 59		pp. 99–100	p. 169	p. 203 (Col)		
Chapters 13–14	Sheets 91, 92	Test 60		pp. 101–103	p. 170			
Chapters 8–14		Test 61		pp. 104–108	pp. 171–172			
Chapters 1–14						pp. 186–189 (MR)		

Overhead Visuals

Guided Discovery Visuals (lettered) and Teaching Visuals (numbered) available for Chapter 14.

Lessons	Visual	Title
14-4	L	Slopes and Rotation
14-2, 14-3, 14-4, 14-8	M	Symmetry in Tessellations
14-4	N	Which Method Is Easier?
14-1, 14-2, 14-3, 14-4, 14-5	29	Transformations Summary
14-6, 14-7, 14-8	30	Composition and Inverses of Transformations

Software Guide

Houghton Mifflin software for Chapter 14

Geometry Grapher (Apple or IBM)

Use with	Booklet
Ch. 14	Teaching Suggestions, pp. 10–13
Ch. 14	Class Demonstrations, pp. 17–19
Ch. 14	Activities 4–8, pp. 25–32
p. 576 (Explorations)	

Test Generator (Apple or IBM): 120 test items

Other software appropriate for Chapter 14

Geometric Supposer (Apple): Triangles

GeoDraw (IBM)

Spreadsheets

Guide to Integrated Curriculum

Although the text presents coordinate and transformational geometry in Chapters 13 and 14, and in the Handbook on pp. 657–675, teachers wishing to integrate this material throughout the course may do so easily using the information on **pp. T56–T57.** The integration occurs throughout Chapters 3–12.

With this integrated curriculum, students learn concepts, solve problems, and prove theorems using alternate approaches. Students make connections between geometry and algebra, and they learn the valuable skill of deciding which method to use in a problem **(pp. 672–673).**

Strategies for Teaching

Exploring Intersections

When to Use

With or after Lesson 14-4

Overview

In this activity students practice using rotations, especially half-turns, while reviewing some properties of polygons. The last exercise illustrates rotational symmetry and can be used to motivate Lesson 14-8.

Materials

Dot or grid paper, coordinate graph paper, 3 different colored pencils, or a geometric drawing program

Description of Activity

Let $\triangle A'B'C'$ be the image of $\triangle ABC$ under a half turn with center O. What figures are possible for the intersection of the two triangles?

1. Draw a blue $\triangle ABC$ with its vertices at grid points. Choose a point O at a grid point that is inside the triangle and "near" one of the vertices. Find the image of each vertex of $\triangle ABC$ under a half turn about O. Draw the image triangle $\triangle A'B'C'$ in red. Label the points of intersection of the two triangles that are not labeled and outline the intersection in green. What type of quadrilateral is the intersection? Justify your answer. parallelogram

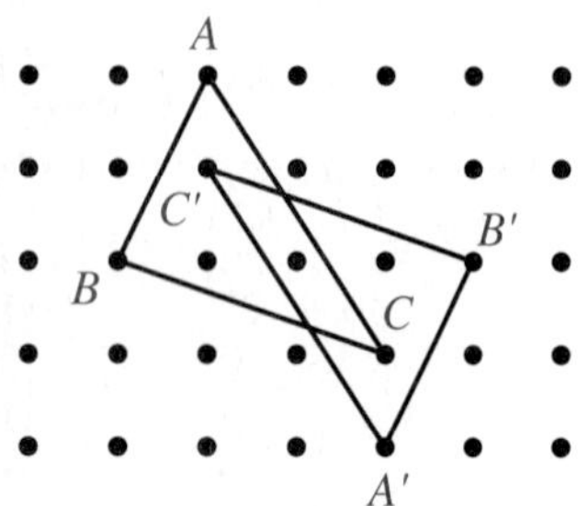

2. Show with a drawing how you can rotate a triangle so that each intersection listed can be obtained. Where can you place the center of the half turn?

a. the empty set (nothing) a point outside the $\triangle$

b. a point a vertex

c. a segment a point on a side

3. Suppose the intersection is a polygon that is not a quadrilateral. What type of polygon can it be? a hexagon

Where can you place the center of the half turn? Give an example of a drawing.

4. For $\triangle ABC$, where should you place the center of the half turn so that the area of the region formed by the intersection is as large as possible? at the centroid of $\triangle ABC$

5. Suppose you begin with a polygon that is not a triangle, and you place the center of the half turn so that the intersection of this polygon and its image is the original polygon. What type(s) of polygons could you have used? a polygon with a center of symmetry whose opposite sides are equal and parallel

Where could you have placed the center of the half turn? Give two examples (using different types of polygons) of drawings you could have made. parallelograms and regular $2n$-gons

Could you have used a triangle? no

Commentary

- The given description of the activity assumes the use of grid paper. Modifications in the directions should be made if coordinate graph paper or a geometric drawing program is used.

- **1.** If the students use grid paper or coordinate graph paper, they can check that the opposite sides of the quadrilateral are equal and parallel. On a geometric drawing program, they can check that the opposite sides are equal and perhaps draw a parallel to one of the sides through an opposite vertex to see that it coincides with the existing side.
- **3.** If the center of the half turn is inside the triangle whose vertices are the midpoints of the sides of the original triangle, the intersection is a hexagon; if it is outside this triangle, but inside the original triangle, it is a parallelogram as in Exercise **1.**
- **5.** Challenge the students to draw a non-regular hexagon that meets the given conditions.

References to Strategies

PE: Pupil's Edition **TE:** Teacher's Edition **RB:** Resource Book

Problem Solving Strategies

PE: 581, 582–583 (Exs. 24–29, Mathematical model), 614 (Challenge, Draw a diagram)

Applications

PE: 582–583 (Mirrors), 598 (Computer Animation)
TE: T139, T140, T141, T143

Nonroutine Problems

PE: 574 (Exs. 6–8), 576 (Exs. 16–19, 22), 581 (Exs. 26–29), 583 (Application), 587 (Exs. 16, 17), 598 (Fractal algorithm), 612 (Exs. 15; 8–11), 614 (Ex. 24, Challenges), 615–617 (Symmetry groups)
TE: T138, T139, T140, T142

Communication

TE: T138, T140, T142, 576, 579

Explorations

PE: 576
TE: 569c

Connections

PE: 521 (Function), 606 (Identity; inverse)
TE: T141, 571 (Mapping), 583 (Vectors), 584 (3-D coordinates), 606 (Comparing products of numbers and composites of mappings)

Using Technology

PE: 576
TE: 600
Using Geometry Grapher: 10–13, 17–19, 25–32
Computer Activities: 82–89

Using Manipulatives/Models

PE: 576 (Ex. 22), 581 (Exs. 24–29), 582–583, 598, 612 (Ex. 15), 615–616
TE: T138, T139, T140, T141, T142, T143, 615, 617
Overhead Visuals: L, M, N, 29, 30

Cooperative Learning

TE: T142, T143

Teaching Resources

For use in implementing the teaching strategies referenced on the previous page.

Using Technology

Using Geometry Grapher, p. 25

Geometry Grapher Activity 4

Lesson 14-2

1. Plot $A(0, 5)$, $B(4, 8)$, and $C(8, 3)$. Construct $\triangle ABC$. Reflect $\triangle ABC$ in the y-axis by typing T S 1↵ F Y.
   a. Show that $\triangle ABC \cong \triangle ADE$ by measuring corresponding angles and areas.
   b. Why can point A be called a *fixed point* of the reflection?

   ____

   c. Plot $F(1, -4)$, $G(-1, -1)$, $H(-9, -5)$, and $I(-2, -9)$. Construct $FGHI$. Reflect this shape in the y-axis. Show that quad. $FGHI \cong$ quad. $JKLM$ by measuring corresponding sides and angles.
   d. How many fixed points are there for this reflection? ____ What are their coordinates? ______________ (*Hint:* Define lines through the intersecting segments and find the points of intersection of these lines.)
2. Plot $A(-1, 3)$, $B(9, 5)$, $C(6, -6)$, $D(5, -1)$, $E(3, 9)$, $F(-6, 2)$ and construct $\triangle ABC$ and $\triangle DEF$.
   a. Construct the perpendicular bisectors of $\overline{AD}$, $\overline{BE}$, and $\overline{CF}$. To construct the perpendicular bisector of $\overline{AD}$, for example, type: C L B P AD↵. What do you notice about the equations that appear in the data window?

   ____

   b. Verify that $\triangle ABC$ can be mapped to $\triangle DEF$ by reflection in one of the three perpendicular bisectors. Type: T S 1↵ F L 1↵.

In Exercises 3–5, use the strategy of Exercise 2 to decide whether a reflection maps $\triangle ABC$ to $\triangle DEF$. If so, write the equation of the reflection line. If not, write *no reflection*.

3. $A(-5, 5)$, $B(6, 8)$, $C(4, 2)$; $D(3, 9)$, $E(-6, 2)$, $F(0, 0)$ ____________
4. $A(-5, 5)$, $B(4, -2)$, $C(4, 9)$; $D(-1, -7)$, $E(2, 4)$, $F(8, -4)$ ____________
5. $A(-9, 4)$, $B(1, 5)$, $C(-3, -1)$; $D(-9, -8)$, $E(1, -9)$, $F(-3, -3)$ ____________
6. Plot $A(-6, 5)$, $B(6, 3)$, $C(-6, 0)$, $D(-3, 0)$, $E(0, 0)$, $F(3, 0)$, and $G(6, 0)$. Construct the non-closed paths ACB, ADB, AEB, AFB, and AGB. For example, to construct path ACB, type: C S D ACBCA↵.
   a. Measure the paths and record your results below.
      $AC + CB =$ ____; $AD + DB =$ ____; $AE + EB =$ ____;
      $AF + FB =$ ____; $AG + GB =$ ____
   b. To find the point on the x-axis that will result in the shortest path that touches A, the line, and B, define the target point B as a shape and reflect it in the x-axis by typing C S D B↵ T S 6↵ F X. The coordinates of the image point are $H($___, ___$)$, and $AH =$ ____.
   c. Construct the lines $\overleftrightarrow{CG}$ and $\overleftrightarrow{AH}$. Find their intersection: $I($___, ___$)$.
   d. Measure $\overline{AI}$ and $\overline{IB}$. $AI + IB =$ ____.
   e. Draw the final path. Type: C S D AIBIA↵.
   f. Test whether the angle of incidence, $\angle AIC$, has the same measure as the angle of reflection, $\angle BIG$. $m\angle AIC =$ ____ and $m\angle BIG =$ ____.

(continued)

USING GEOMETRY GRAPHER: ACTIVITY SHEETS

25

Using Technology

Using Geometry Grapher, p. 27

Geometry Grapher Activity 5

Lesson 14-3

1. Plot $A(-9, 5)$, $B(-7, 8)$, and $C(-2, 4)$, and construct $\triangle ABC$.
   a. Translate this shape 12 units right and 5 units down by typing: T S 1↵ T C 12↵ –5↵. The result is $D($___, ___$)$, $E($___, ___$)$, and $F($___, ___$)$.
   b. Show that $\triangle ABC \cong \triangle DEF$ by measuring corresponding sides, angles, and areas.
   c. Measure $\overline{AD}$, $\overline{BE}$, and $\overline{CF}$, and state a conjecture about the segments joining corresponding points in a translation.

   ____

2. Construct the vertical lines $x = -6$ and $x = 2$. Construct a shape with vertices $A(-8, 8)$, $B(-11, 6)$, and $C(-9, 2)$.
   a. Reflect shape 1 in line 1 to get $\triangle DEF$. This results in $D($___, ___$)$, $E($___, ___$)$, and $F($___, ___$)$.
   b. Reflect $\triangle DEF$ in line 2 to get $\triangle GHI$. This results in $G($___, ___$)$, $H($___, ___$)$, and $I($___, ___$)$.
   c. The double reflection is equivalent to what single transformation?

   ____

   d. Measure $\overline{AG}$, $\overline{BH}$, and $\overline{CI}$, and compare these lengths to the distance between lines 1 and 2. What do you notice?

   ____

3. Construct the line $y = x$ and a triangle with vertices $A(-10, 0)$, $B(-6, 2)$, and $C(-5, -3)$. Perform a glide reflection that moves $\triangle ABC$ 4 units right and 4 units up and then reflects the resulting $\triangle DEF$ in line 1.
   a. The result is $\triangle GHI$ with vertices $G($___, ___$)$, $H($___, ___$)$, and $I($___, ___$)$.
   b. Construct the midpoints of $\overline{AG}$, $\overline{BH}$, and $\overline{CI}$. Their coordinates are $J($___, ___$)$, $K($___, ___$)$, and $L($___, ___$)$.
   c. Are the midpoints collinear? ____ What is their relationship to the reflection line?

   ____

In Exercises 4–6, use the strategy of Exercise 3(b) to decide if a glide reflection will map $\triangle ABC$ to $\triangle DEF$. If so, write the equation of the reflection line. If not, write *no glide reflection*. Test your answers by doing the reflection.

4. $A(1, 5)$, $B(-6, 9)$, $C(-7, 4)$; $D(0, 0)$, $E(1, -8)$, $F(-4, -7)$ ____________
5. $A(1, 9)$, $B(-4, 7)$, $C(1, 2)$; $D(3, 1)$, $E(8, -2)$, $F(3, -6)$ ____________
6. $A(1, 1)$, $B(3, 4)$, $C(6, 1)$; $D(2, -1)$, $E(5, -3)$, $F(2, -6)$ ____________
7. Show that a glide reflection has the same result as a reflection glide.

USING GEOMETRY GRAPHER: ACTIVITY SHEETS

27

Using Technology

Using Geometry Grapher, p. 28

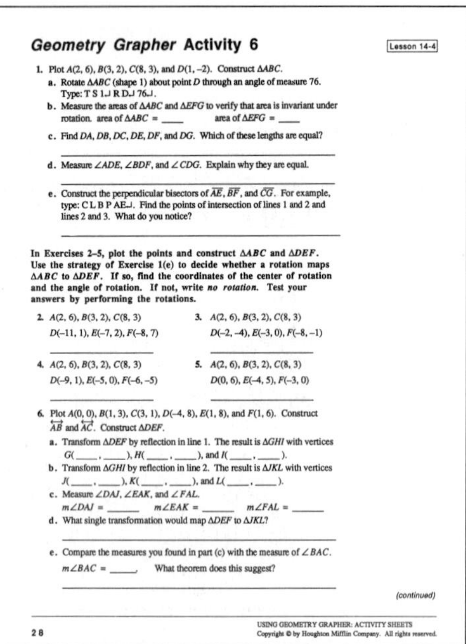

Geometry Grapher Activity 6

Lesson 14-4

1. Plot $A(2, 6)$, $B(3, 2)$, $C(8, 3)$, and $D(1, -2)$. Construct $\triangle ABC$.
   a. Rotate $\triangle ABC$ (shape 1) about point D through an angle of measure 76. Type: T S 1↵ R D↵ 76↵.
   b. Measure the areas of $\triangle ABC$ and $\triangle EFG$ to verify that area is invariant under rotation. area of $\triangle ABC =$ ____ area of $\triangle EFG =$ ____
   c. Find DA, DB, DC, DE, DF, and DG. Which of these lengths are equal?

   ____

   d. Measure $\angle ADE$, $\angle BDF$, and $\angle CDG$. Explain why they are equal.

   ____

   e. Construct the perpendicular bisectors of $\overline{AE}$, $\overline{BF}$, and $\overline{CG}$. For example, type: C L B P AE↵. Find the points of intersection of lines 1 and 2 and lines 2 and 3. What do you notice?

   ____

In Exercises 2–5, plot the points and construct $\triangle ABC$ and $\triangle DEF$. Use the strategy of Exercise 1(e) to decide whether a rotation maps $\triangle ABC$ to $\triangle DEF$. If so, find the coordinates of the center of rotation and the angle of rotation. If not, write *no rotation*. Test your answers by performing the rotations.

2. $A(2, 6)$, $B(3, 2)$, $C(8, 3)$; $D(-11, 1)$, $E(-7, 2)$, $F(-8, 7)$ ____________
3. $A(2, 6)$, $B(3, 2)$, $C(8, 3)$; $D(-2, -4)$, $E(-3, 0)$, $F(-8, -1)$ ____________
4. $A(2, 6)$, $B(3, 2)$, $C(8, 3)$; $D(-9, 1)$, $E(-5, 0)$, $F(-6, -5)$ ____________
5. $A(2, 6)$, $B(3, 2)$, $C(8, 3)$; $D(0, 6)$, $E(-4, 5)$, $F(-3, 0)$ ____________
6. Plot $A(0, 0)$, $B(1, 3)$, $C(3, 1)$, $D(-4, 8)$, $E(1, 8)$, and $F(1, 6)$. Construct $\overleftrightarrow{AB}$ and $\overleftrightarrow{AC}$. Construct $\triangle DEF$.
   a. Transform $\triangle DEF$ by reflection in line 1. The result is $\triangle GHI$ with vertices $G($___, ___$)$, $H($___, ___$)$, and $I($___, ___$)$.
   b. Transform $\triangle GHI$ by reflection in line 2. The result is $\triangle JKL$ with vertices $J($___, ___$)$, $K($___, ___$)$, and $L($___, ___$)$.
   c. Measure $\angle DAJ$, $\angle EAK$, and $\angle FAL$.
      $m\angle DAJ =$ ____ $m\angle EAK =$ ____ $m\angle FAL =$ ____
   d. What single transformation would map $\triangle DEF$ to $\triangle JKL$?

   ____

   e. Compare the measures you found in part (c) with the measure of $\angle BAC$.
      $m\angle BAC =$ ____. What theorem does this suggest?

   ____

(continued)

28
USING GEOMETRY GRAPHER: ACTIVITY SHEETS

Using Technology

Using Geometry Grapher, p. 30

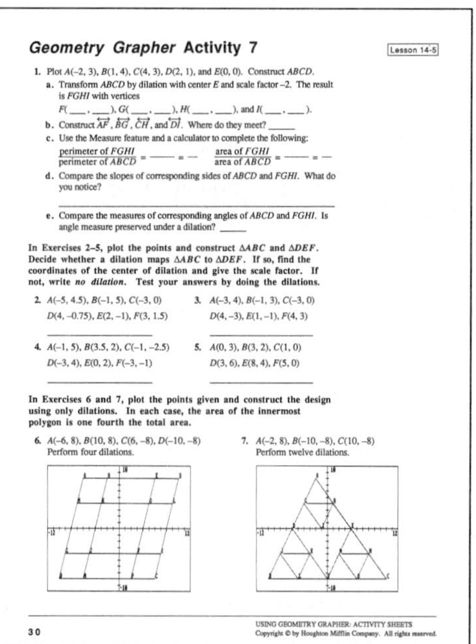

Geometry Grapher Activity 7

Lesson 14-5

1. Plot $A(-2, 3)$, $B(1, 4)$, $C(4, 3)$, $D(2, 1)$, and $E(0, 0)$. Construct $ABCD$.
   a. Transform $ABCD$ by dilation with center E and scale factor -2. The result is $FGHI$ with vertices $F($___, ___$)$, $G($___, ___$)$, $H($___, ___$)$, and $I($___, ___$)$.
   b. Construct $\overleftrightarrow{AF}$, $\overleftrightarrow{BG}$, $\overleftrightarrow{CH}$, and $\overleftrightarrow{DI}$. Where do they meet? ____
   c. Use the Measure feature and a calculator to complete the following:
      $\dfrac{\text{perimeter of } FGHI}{\text{perimeter of } ABCD} = \text{\_\_\_\_} = \text{\_\_}$ $\dfrac{\text{area of } FGHI}{\text{area of } ABCD} = \text{\_\_\_\_} = \text{\_\_}$
   d. Compare the slopes of corresponding sides of $ABCD$ and $FGHI$. What do you notice?

   ____

   e. Compare the measures of corresponding angles of $ABCD$ and $FGHI$. Is angle measure preserved under a dilation? ____

In Exercises 2–5, plot the points and construct $\triangle ABC$ and $\triangle DEF$. Decide whether a dilation maps $\triangle ABC$ to $\triangle DEF$. If so, find the coordinates of the center of dilation and give the scale factor. If not, write *no dilation*. Test your answers by doing the dilations.

2. $A(-5, 4.5)$, $B(-1, 5)$, $C(-3, 0)$; $D(4, -0.75)$, $E(2, -1)$, $F(3, 1.5)$ ____________
3. $A(-3, 4)$, $B(-1, 3)$, $C(-3, 0)$; $D(4, -3)$, $E(1, -1)$, $F(4, 3)$ ____________
4. $A(-1, 5)$, $B(3.5, 2)$, $C(-1, -2.5)$; $D(-3, 4)$, $E(0, 2)$, $F(-3, -1)$ ____________
5. $A(0, 3)$, $B(3, 2)$, $C(1, 0)$; $D(3, 6)$, $E(8, 4)$, $F(5, 0)$ ____________

In Exercises 6 and 7, plot the points given and construct the design using only dilations. In each case, the area of the innermost polygon is one fourth the total area.

6. $A(-6, 8)$, $B(10, 8)$, $C(6, -8)$, $D(-10, -8)$
   Perform four dilations.
7. $A(-2, 8)$, $B(-10, -8)$, $C(10, -8)$
   Perform twelve dilations.

30
USING GEOMETRY GRAPHER: ACTIVITY SHEETS

Using Models

***Guided Discovery Visual* L, Sheet 1**

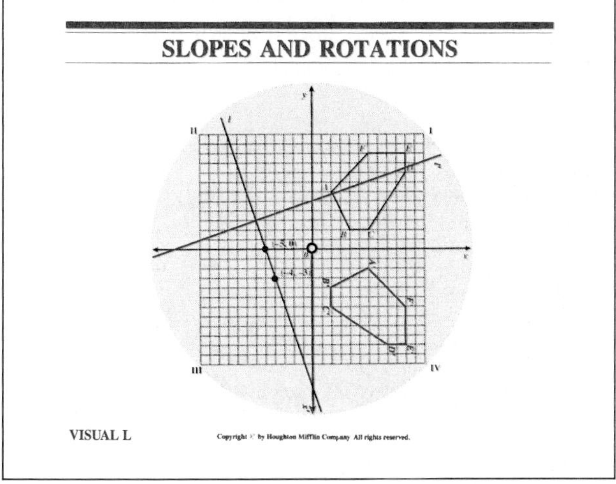
SLOPES AND ROTATIONS
VISUAL L
Copyright © by Houghton Mifflin Company. All rights reserved.

Using Models

***Guided Discovery Visual* M, Sheet 1**

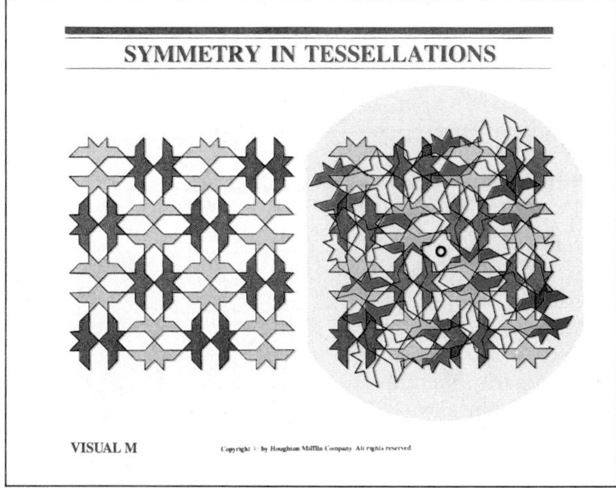
SYMMETRY IN TESSELLATIONS
VISUAL M
Copyright © by Houghton Mifflin Company. All rights reserved.

Connections

***Guided Discovery Visual* N, Sheet 1**

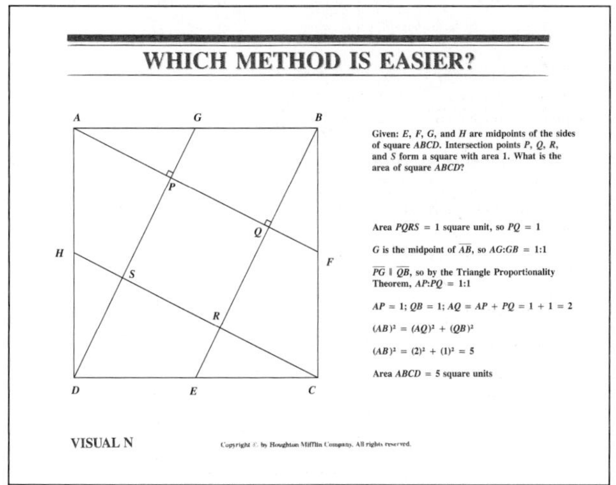
WHICH METHOD IS EASIER?
A
G
B
P
Q
H
F
S
R
D
E
C
Given: E, F, G, and H are midpoints of the sides of square ABCD. Intersection points P, Q, R, and S form a square with area 1. What is the area of square ABCD?
Area PQRS = 1 square unit, so PQ = 1
G is the midpoint of $\overline{AB}$, so AG:GB = 1:1
$\overline{PG} \parallel \overline{QB}$, so by the Triangle Proportionality Theorem, AP:PQ = 1:1
AP = 1; QB = 1; AQ = AP + PQ = 1 + 1 = 2
$(AB)^2 = (AQ)^2 + (QB)^2$
$(AB)^2 = (2)^2 + (1)^2 = 5$
Area ABCD = 5 square units
VISUAL N
Copyright © by Houghton Mifflin Company. All rights reserved.

Connections

***Guided Discovery Visual* N, Sheet 2**

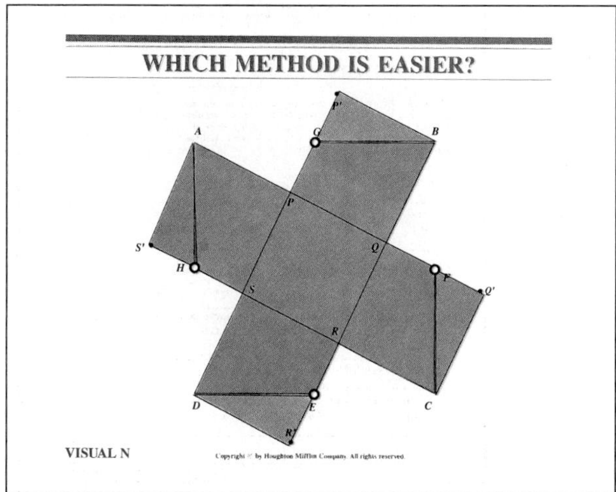
WHICH METHOD IS EASIER?
P'
A
G
B
P
S'
Q
H
F
Q'
S
R
D
E
C
R'
VISUAL N
Copyright © by Houghton Mifflin Company. All rights reserved.

Teaching References

Lesson Commentary, pp. T137–T143
Assignment Guide, pp. T50–T51
Software Guide, p. T73
Alternate Test, p. T25

Supplementary Materials

Practice Masters 85–92
Tests 56–61
Resource Book
Tests, pp. 96–108
Practice, pp. 166–172
Mixed Review, pp. 186–189
Preparing for College Entrance Exams, p. 203
Study Guide, pp. 181–196
Overhead Visuals L, M, N, 29, 30
Computer Activities
34 Transformations
35 The Chaos Game
36 Composites of Mappings

Cultural Note

Students may find it interesting to identify geometrical transformations in art and architecture. Traditional Native American designs used in weaving, for example, provide many examples of various kinds of symmetry. (For more on symmetry, see pages 609–617.)

14 TRANSFORMATIONS

This striking color photograph shows a repeated design, identical balconies on one face of a building. A mathematical operation that changes the position of a figure without changing its shape is called a *transformation*.

Some Basic Mappings

Objectives

1. Recognize and use the terms *image*, *preimage*, *mapping*, *one-to-one mapping*, *transformation*, *isometry*, and *congruence mapping*.
2. Locate images of figures by reflection, translation, glide reflection, rotation, and dilation.
3. Recognize the properties of the basic mappings.

14-1 *Mappings and Functions*

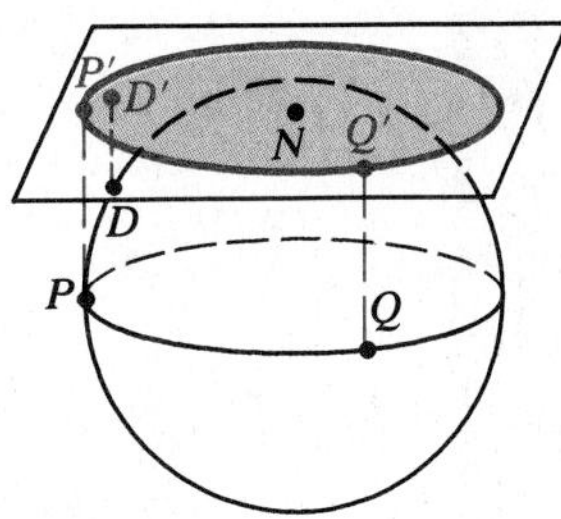

Have you ever wondered how maps of the round Earth can be made on flat paper? The diagram illustrates the idea behind a *polar map* of the northern hemisphere. A plane is placed tangent to a globe of the Earth at its North Pole N. Every point P of the globe is projected straight upward to exactly one point, called P', in the plane. P' is called the **image** of P, and P is called the **preimage** of P'. The diagram shows the images of two points P and Q on the globe's equator. It also shows D', the image of a point D not on the equator.

This correspondence between points of the globe's northern hemisphere and points in the plane is an example of a *mapping*. If we call this mapping M, then we could indicate that M maps P to P' by writing $M{:}P \rightarrow P'$. Notice that since the North Pole N is mapped to itself, we can write $M{:}N \rightarrow N$.

The word *mapping* is used in geometry as the word *function* is used in algebra. While a **mapping** is a correspondence between sets of points, a **function** is a correspondence between sets of numbers. Each number in the first set corresponds to exactly one number in the second set. For example, the squaring function f maps each real number x to its square x^2. We can write $f{:}x \rightarrow x^2$. Another way to indicate that the value of the function at x is x^2 is to write $f(x) = x^2$ (read "f of x equals x^2"). Similarly, for the mapping M, above, we can write $M(P) = P'$ to indicate that the image of P is P'. With all of these similarities, it should not surprise you that mathematicians often use the words *function* and *mapping* interchangeably.

A mapping (or a function) from set A to set B is called a **one-to-one mapping** (or a one-to-one function) if every member of B has exactly one preimage in A. The polar projection illustrated at the top of the page is a one-to-one mapping of the northern hemisphere of the globe onto a circular region in the tangent plane (the shaded area in the diagram). However, the squaring function $f{:}x \rightarrow x^2$ is *not* one-to-one because, for example, 9 has two preimages, 3 and -3.

Teaching Suggestions,
p. T138

Objectives
Presenting the Lesson
Reinforcement
Extension

Communication Skills,
p. T138

Supplementary Materials

Practice Master 85
Study Guide, pp. 181–182
Computer Activity 34

Lesson Focus

The purpose of this lesson is to introduce and define the concept of a mapping. The lesson also develops two other basic ideas, namely transformations of the plane and distance-preserving mappings called isometries.

Suggested Assignments

Average
574–575/1–10
Maximum
Day 1: 574–575/1–7, 10, 11, 14
Day 2: 575–576/12, 13, 15–19, 21

Making Connections

Review the ideas of domain, range, and one-to-one function from algebra. Emphasize the similarity between the use of the terms *mapping* in geometry and *function* in algebra.

Chalkboard Examples

1. Function k maps every number to a number that is two less than one-third of the number.
   a. Express this fact using function notation. $k:x \rightarrow \frac{1}{3}x - 2$
   b. Find the image of 9. 1
   c. Find the preimage of 16. 54
2. Mapping T maps each point (x, y) to the point $(x + 2, 3y)$.
   a. Express this fact using mapping notations. $T:(x, y) \rightarrow (x + 2, 3y)$
   b. Find P' and Q', the images of $P(2, 4)$ and $Q(-2, 6)$. $P'(4, 12)$, $Q'(0, 18)$
   c. Decide whether T maps M, the midpoint of $\overline{PQ}$, to M', the midpoint of $\overline{P'Q'}$. $M = (0, 5)$; $M' = (2, 15)$; yes; $T:(0, 5) \rightarrow (2, 15)$
   d. Decide whether $PQ = P'Q'$. $PQ = 2\sqrt{5}$; $P'Q' = 2\sqrt{13}$; no
3. Mapping S maps each point (x, y) to an image point $(x, -2y)$. Given: $A(-3, 1)$, $B(-1, 3)$, $C(4, 1)$ and $D(2, -1)$
   a. Decide whether:
      $AB = A'B'$. no
      $BC = B'C'$. no
      $AC = A'C'$. yes
      $CD = C'D'$. no
   b. Is S an isometry? Explain. No; the image distance $A'B'$ does not equal the preimage distance AB.

Example 1 Function g maps every number to a number that is six more than its double.

a. Express this fact using function notation.
b. Find the image of 7.
c. Find the preimage of 8.

Solution

a. $g:x \rightarrow 2x + 6$, or $g(x) = 2x + 6$
b. $g:7 \rightarrow 2 \cdot 7 + 6 = 20$. Thus the image of 7 is 20.
c. $g:x \rightarrow 2x + 6 = 8$. Therefore $x = 1$, so 1 is the preimage of 8.

Example 2 Mapping G maps each point (x, y) to the point $(2x, y - 1)$.

a. Express this fact using mapping notation.
b. Find P' and Q', the images of $P(3, 0)$ and $Q(1, 4)$.
c. Decide whether G maps M, the midpoint of $\overline{PQ}$, to M', the midpoint of $\overline{P'Q'}$.
d. Decide whether $PQ = P'Q'$.

Solution

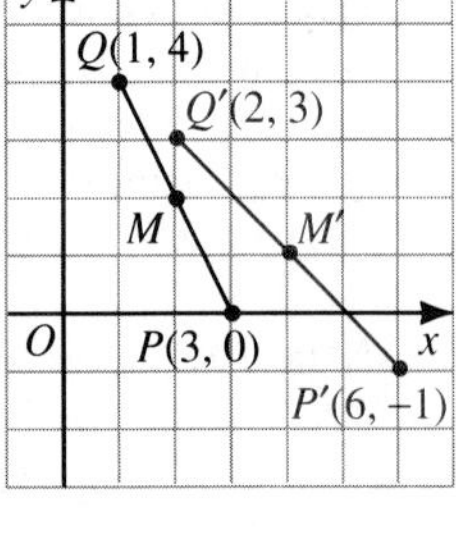

a. $G:(x, y) \rightarrow (2x, y - 1)$
b. $G:(3, 0) \rightarrow (2 \cdot 3, 0 - 1) = (6, -1) = P'$
   $G:(1, 4) \rightarrow (2 \cdot 1, 4 - 1) = (2, 3) = Q'$
c. $M = \left(\frac{3 + 1}{2}, \frac{0 + 4}{2}\right) = (2, 2)$

   $M' = \left(\frac{6 + 2}{2}, \frac{-1 + 3}{2}\right) = (4, 1)$

   $G:(2, 2) \rightarrow (2 \cdot 2, 2 - 1) = (4, 1)$
   Thus G does map midpoint M to midpoint M'.
d. Use the distance formula to show that

   $PQ = \sqrt{(1 - 3)^2 + (4 - 0)^2}$
   $= \sqrt{(-2)^2 + 4^2} = \sqrt{20} = 2\sqrt{5}$
   $P'Q' = \sqrt{(2 - 6)^2 + (3 - (-1))^2}$
   $= \sqrt{(-4)^2 + 4^2} = \sqrt{32} = 4\sqrt{2}$

   Thus $PQ \neq P'Q'$.

Although the diagram for Example 2 shows only points of $\overline{PQ}$ and their image points, you should understand that mapping G maps *every* point of the plane to an image point. Also, every point of the plane has a preimage point. A one-to-one mapping from the whole plane to the whole plane is called a **transformation.** Moreover, if a transformation maps every segment to a congruent segment, it is called an **isometry.** The transformation in Example 2 is *not* an isometry because $PQ \neq P'Q'$.

By definition, an isometry maps any segment to a congruent segment, so we can say that an isometry *preserves* distance. The next theorem states that an isometry also maps any triangle to a congruent triangle. For this reason, an isometry is sometimes called a **congruence mapping.**

Theorem 14-1

An isometry maps a triangle to a congruent triangle.

Given: Isometry $T: \triangle ABC \rightarrow \triangle A'B'C'$

Prove: $\triangle ABC \cong \triangle A'B'C'$

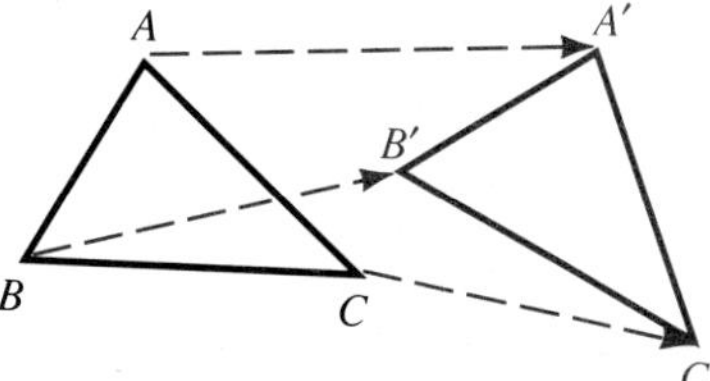

Proof:

Statements	Reasons
1. $\overline{AB} \cong \overline{A'B'}$, $\overline{BC} \cong \overline{B'C'}$, $\overline{AC} \cong \overline{A'C'}$	1. Definition of isometry
2. $\triangle ABC \cong \triangle A'B'C'$	2. SSS Postulate

Corollary 1

An isometry maps an angle to a congruent angle.

Corollary 2

An isometry maps a polygon to a polygon with the same area.

Example 3 Mapping R maps each point (x, y) to an image point $(-x, y)$.

a. Decide if $BA = B'A'$, $CB = C'B'$, and $CA = C'A'$.

b. Does R *appear* to be an isometry? Does part (a) *prove* that R is an isometry? Explain.

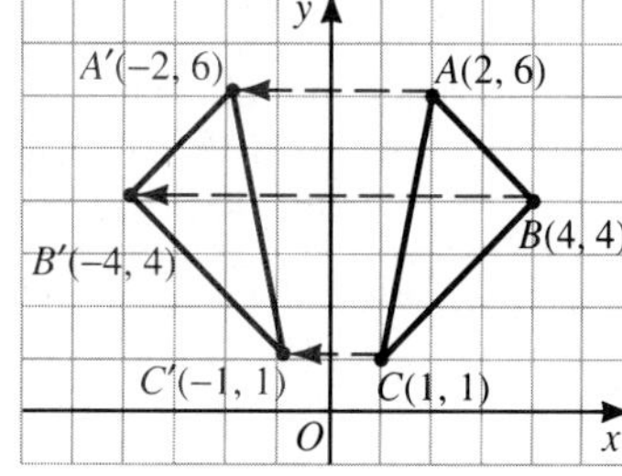

Solution **a.** Use the distance formula to show that

$BA = \sqrt{(2 - 4)^2 + (6 - 4)^2} = \sqrt{(-2)^2 + 2^2} = \sqrt{8} = 2\sqrt{2}$

$B'A' = \sqrt{(-2 - (-4))^2 + (6 - 4)^2} = \sqrt{2^2 + 2^2} = \sqrt{8} = 2\sqrt{2}$

$CB = \sqrt{(4 - 1)^2 + (4 - 1)^2} = \sqrt{3^2 + 3^2} = \sqrt{18} = 3\sqrt{2}$

$C'B' = \sqrt{(-4 - (-1))^2 + (4 - 1)^2} = \sqrt{(-3)^2 + 3^2} = \sqrt{18} = 3\sqrt{2}$

$CA = \sqrt{(2 - 1)^2 + (6 - 1)^2} = \sqrt{1^2 + 5^2} = \sqrt{26}$

$C'A' = \sqrt{(-2 - (-1))^2 + (6 - 1)^2} = \sqrt{(-1)^2 + 5^2} = \sqrt{26}$

We have $BA = B'A'$, $CB = C'B'$, and $CA = C'A'$.

b. R *appears* to be an isometry because part (a) shows that three segments are mapped to congruent segments. Part (a) *does not prove* that R is an isometry because a proof must show that the image of *every* segment is a congruent segment.

Teaching Note

By definition, an isometry preserves distance. Students can think of an isometry as keeping a figure rigid. Because the figure is kept rigid, its image will be a congruent figure.

Proof Note

Because an isometry maps a triangle to a congruent triangle, triangles can be proved to be congruent if there exists an isometry that maps one triangle to the other. It can be shown that if two congruent triangles have the same orientation, one can be mapped to the other by a single rotation or by a translation. If the triangles have opposite orientation, either a reflection or a glide reflection can map one triangle to the other.

Teaching Note

The triangles in the diagram for Example 3 are right triangles, so their areas can be calculated easily. Students will find that area is preserved under this isometry.

Additional Answers Classroom Exercises

1.a. One pt. in A has 2 images in B.
b. One pt. in B has no preimage in A.
c. One pt. in B has 2 preimages in A.
d. One pt. in A has no image in B.

2.b. No; every positive number y has 2 preimages, y and $-y$.

Exercise Note

Until it is proven that a given transformation maps *every* segment to a congruent segment, students should not claim that a transformation is an isometry. They may say that it *appears to be* an isometry based on their experiments with particular segments. (See Classroom Exs. 3 and 5.)

Guided Practice

1. If function $f:x \to 3 - 2x$, find the image of 5 and the preimage of 13. -7; -5
2. If $f(x) = 2x^2 - 1$, find $f(-3)$ and $f(3)$. 17; 17 Is f a one-to-one function? no

Given the mapping $T:(x, y) \to (2x, y)$.

3. Plot the following points and their images: $M(0, 0)$, $N(3, 0)$, $P(3, 6)$, $Q(0, 6)$. $M'(0, 0)$, $N'(6, 0)$, $P'(6, 6)$, $Q'(0, 6)$
4. Is $MNPQ$ a square? No Is $M'N'P'Q'$? Yes
5. Is T a transformation? an isometry? yes; no

Classroom Exercises

1. Explain why each of the correspondences pictured below is not a one-to-one mapping from set A to set B.

a. 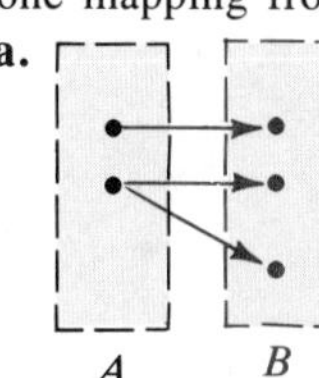

b. 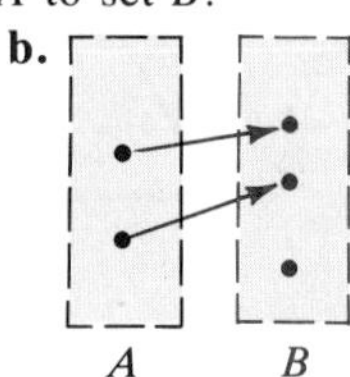

c. 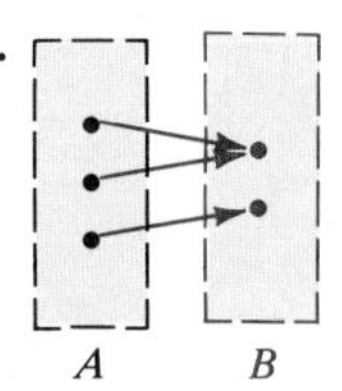

d. 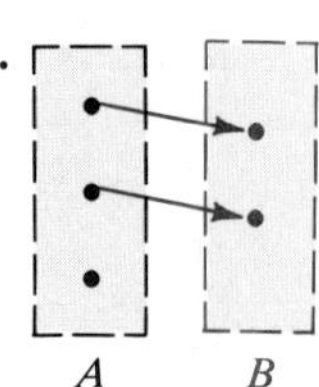

2. **a.** If $f:x \to |x|$, find the images of -3, 6, and -6. **3, 6, 6**
   b. Is f a one-to-one function? Explain. **No**
3. **a.** If mapping $M:(x, y) \to (2x, 2y)$, find the images of P and Q in the diagram. **(2, 6), (8, 2)**
   b. Is M a transformation? **Yes**
   c. Does M appear to be an isometry? **No; $PQ \neq P'Q'$.**
   d. Decide whether M maps the midpoint of $\overline{PQ}$ to the midpoint of $\overline{P'Q'}$. **Yes**

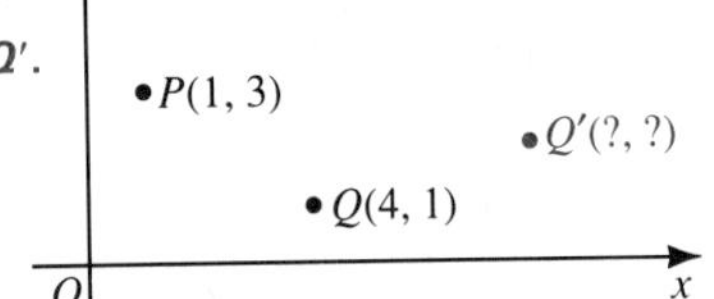

4. **a.** If $g(x) = 2x - 1$, find $g(8)$ and $g(-8)$. **15, −17**
   b. Find the image of 5. **9**
   c. Find the preimage of 7. **4**
5. Use the transformation $T:(x, y) \to (x + 1, y + 2)$ in this exercise.
   a. Plot the following points and their images on the chalkboard: $A(0, 0)$, $B(3, 4)$, $C(5, 1)$, and $D(-1, -3)$. **$A'(1, 2)$, $B'(4, 6)$, $C'(6, 3)$, $D'(0, -1)$**
   b. Find AB, $A'B'$, CD, and $C'D'$. **5, 5, $2\sqrt{13}$, $2\sqrt{13}$**
   c. Does this transformation appear to be an isometry? **Yes**
   d. What is the preimage of (0, 0)? of (4, 5)? **(−1, −2); (3, 3)**

Exercises 6–8 refer to the globe shown on page 571.

6. What is the image of point N? ***N***
7. Is the distance between N and P on the globe the same as the corresponding distance on the polar map? **No**
8. Does the polar map preserve or distort distances? **It distorts distances.**
9. Explain how Corollary 1 follows from Theorem 14-1.
10. Explain how Corollary 2 follows from Theorem 14-1.

Written Exercises

A

1. If function $f:x \to 5x - 7$, find the image of 8 and the preimage of 13. **33, 4**
2. If function $g:x \to 8 - 3x$, find the image of 5 and the preimage of 0. **$-7, \frac{8}{3}$**
3. If $f(x) = x^2 + 1$, find $f(3)$ and $f(-3)$. Is f a one-to-one function? **10, 10; no**
4. If $h(x) = 6x + 1$, find $h(\frac{1}{2})$. Is h a one-to-one function? **4; yes**

For each transformation given in Exercises 5–10:

a. Plot the three points $A(0, 4)$, $B(4, 6)$, and $C(2, 0)$ and their images A', B', and C' under the transformation. **Check students' graphs.**

b. State whether the transformation appears to be an isometry.

c. Find the preimage of (12, 6).

5. $T:(x, y) \rightarrow (x + 4, y - 2)$ **Yes; (8, 8)**

6. $S:(x, y) \rightarrow (2x + 4, 2y - 2)$ **No; (4, 4)**

7. $D:(x, y) \rightarrow (3x, 3y)$ **No; (4, 2)**

8. $H:(x, y) \rightarrow (-x, -y)$ **Yes; (−12, −6)**

9. $M:(x, y) \rightarrow (12 - x, y)$ **Yes; (0, 6)**

10. $G:(x, y) \rightarrow (-\frac{1}{2}x, -\frac{1}{2}y)$ **No; (−24, −12)**

11. O is a point equidistant from parallel lines l_1 and l_2. A mapping M maps each point P of l_1 to the point P' where $\overrightarrow{PO}$ intersects l_2.

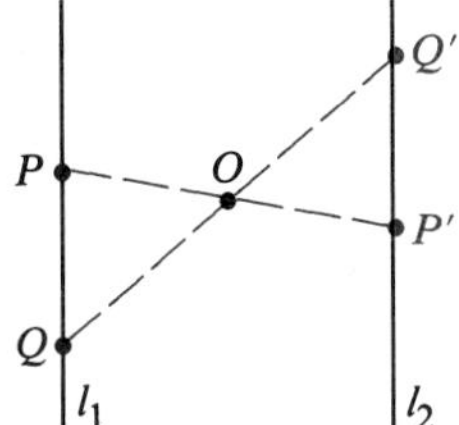

a. Is the mapping a one-to-one mapping of l_1 onto l_2? **Yes**

b. Does this mapping preserve or distort distance? **preserve**

c. If l_1 and l_2 were not parallel, would the mapping preserve distance? Illustrate your answer with a sketch. **No**

12. $\triangle XYZ$ is isosceles with $\overline{XY} \cong \overline{XZ}$. Describe a way of mapping each point of $\overline{XY}$ to a point of $\overline{XZ}$ so that the mapping is an isometry. **Map each pt. P on $\overline{XY}$ to the pt. P' where the line ∥ to $\overline{YZ}$ through P intersects $\overline{XZ}$.**

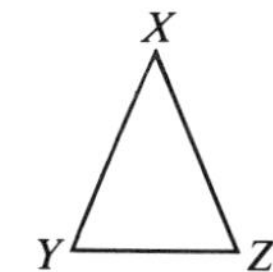

B **13.** $ABCD$ is a trapezoid. Describe a way of mapping each point of $\overline{DC}$ to a point of $\overline{AB}$ so that the mapping is one-to-one. Is your mapping an isometry? **Let X be the int. of $\overline{AC}$ and $\overline{DB}$. For each pt. P on $\overline{DC}$, map P to the pt. P' where $\overrightarrow{PX}$ int. $\overline{AB}$; no**

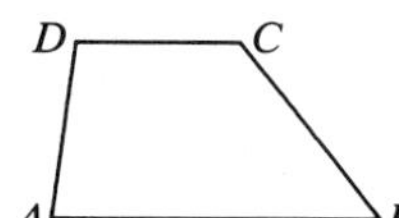

14. The red and blue squares are congruent and have the same center O. A mapping maps each point P of the red square to the point P' where $\overrightarrow{OP}$ intersects the blue square.

a. Is this mapping one-to-one? **Yes**

b. Copy the diagram and locate a point X that is its own image.

c. Locate two points R and S on the red square and their images R' and S' on the blue square that have the property that $RS \neq R'S'$. **Answers may vary.**

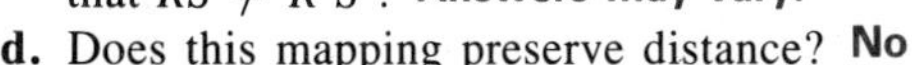

d. Does this mapping preserve distance? **No**

e. Describe a mapping from the red square onto the blue square that *does* preserve distance.

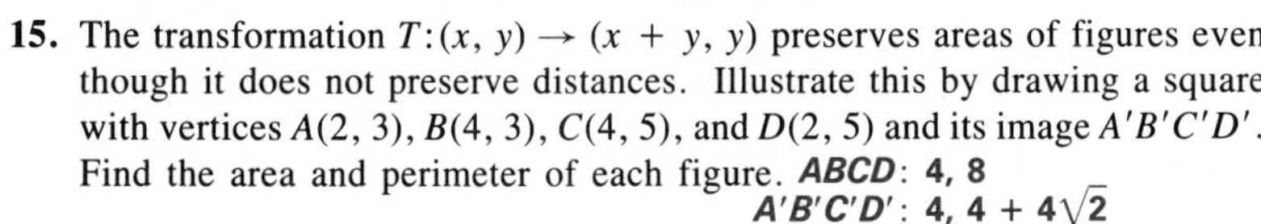

15. The transformation $T:(x, y) \rightarrow (x + y, y)$ preserves areas of figures even though it does not preserve distances. Illustrate this by drawing a square with vertices $A(2, 3)$, $B(4, 3)$, $C(4, 5)$, and $D(2, 5)$ and its image $A'B'C'D'$. Find the area and perimeter of each figure. **$ABCD$: 4, 8**
$A'B'C'D'$: 4, $4 + 4\sqrt{2}$

Additional Answers
Written Exercises

5.a. $A'(4, 2)$, $B'(8, 4)$, $C'(6, -2)$

6.a. $A'(4, 6)$, $B'(12, 10)$, $C'(8, -2)$

7.a. $A'(0, 12)$, $B'(12, 18)$, $C'(6, 0)$

8.a. $A'(0, -4)$, $B'(-4, -6)$, $C'(-2, 0)$

9.a. $A'(12, 4)$, $B'(8, 6)$, $C'(10, 0)$

10.a. $A'(0, -2)$, $B'(-2, -3)$, $C'(-1, 0)$

14.e. Answers may vary. For example, rotate $\overrightarrow{OP}$ clockwise through an angle of 45°. Let P' be the intersection of the rotated ray and the blue square.

Exercise Note

Ex. 22 can be used to prepare students for line symmetry, which is presented later in this chapter.

Communication Skills

The new term "reflection" is used here before it is more formally defined in the next lesson because this word is frequently used in computer construction programs.

A piece of paper is wrapped around a globe of the Earth to form a cylinder as shown. O is the center of the Earth and a point P of the globe is projected along $\overrightarrow{OP}$ to a point P' of the cylinder.

16. Describe the image of the globe's equator. **The equator is mapped to itself.**
17. Is the image of the Arctic Circle congruent to the image of the equator? **Yes**
18. Are distances near the equator distorted more than or less than distances near the Arctic Circle? **Less**
19. Does the North Pole (point N) have an image? **No**
20. Consider the mapping $S: (x, y) \rightarrow (x, 0)$. ***P*′(4, 0), *Q*′(−3, 0), *R*′(−3, 0)**
    a. Plot the points $P(4, 5)$, $Q(-3, 2)$, and $R(-3, -1)$ and their images.
    b. Does S appear to be an isometry? Explain. **No. $PQ \neq P'Q'$**
    c. Is S a transformation? Explain. **No; *S* maps the whole plane onto the *x*-axis.**
21. Mapping M maps points A and B to the same image point. Explain why the mapping M does not preserve distance. **$A'B' = 0$, but if *A* and *B* are diff. pts., $AB > 0$.**
22. Fold a piece of paper. Cut a design connecting the top and bottom point of the fold, as shown. Unfold the shape. Consider a mapping M of the points in the gray region to the corresponding points in the red region.

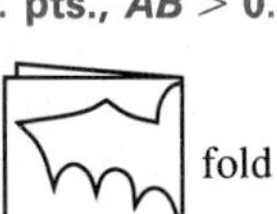

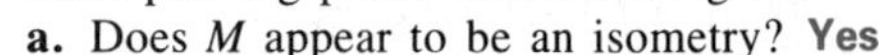

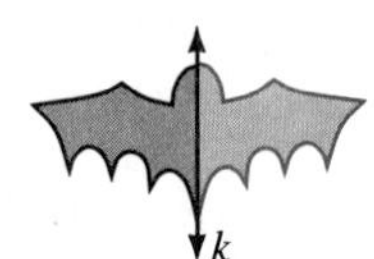

    a. Does M appear to be an isometry? **Yes**
    b. If a point P is on line k, what is the image of P? ***P***
    c. If a point Q is not on line k, and $M(Q) = Q'$, what is the relationship between line k and $\overline{QQ'}$? ***k* is the ⊥ bis. of $\overline{QQ'}$.**

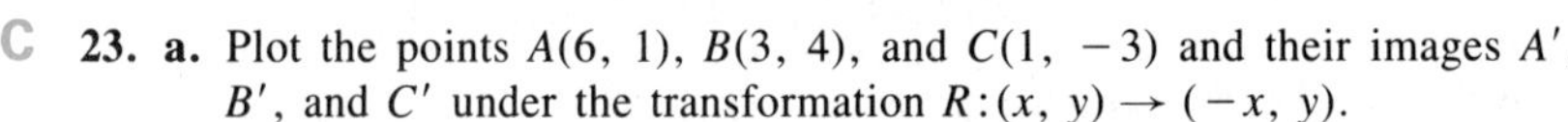

C 23. a. Plot the points $A(6, 1)$, $B(3, 4)$, and $C(1, -3)$ and their images A', B', and C' under the transformation $R: (x, y) \rightarrow (-x, y)$. **$A'(-6, 1)$ $B'(-3, 4)$ $C'(-1, -3)$**
    b. Prove that R is an isometry. (*Hint*: Let $P(x_1, y_1)$ and $Q(x_2, y_2)$ be any two points. Find P' and Q', and use the distance formula to show that $PQ = P'Q'$.)

Explorations

These exploratory exercises can be done using a computer with a program that draws and measures geometric figures.

As you will learn in the next lesson, a *reflection* is a mapping in the plane across a mirror line, just as your reflection in a mirror is a mapping in space across a mirror plane.

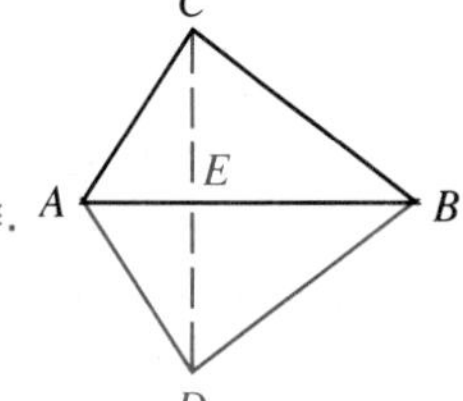

Draw any $\triangle ABC$. Reflect C in $\overleftrightarrow{AB}$ to locate point D. Draw $\overline{AD}$ and $\overline{BD}$. What do you notice about $\triangle ABC$ and $\triangle ABD$? **They are ≅.**

Draw $\overline{CD}$. Label the intersection of $\overleftrightarrow{AB}$ and $\overleftrightarrow{CD}$ as E. Compare CE and DE. What do you notice? Measure the angles with vertex E. What do you notice? **$CE = DE$; they are rt. ∠s.**

Repeat the construction with other types of triangles.

14-2 *Reflections*

When you stand before a mirror, your image appears to be as far behind the mirror as you are in front of it. The diagram shows a transformation in which a line acts like a mirror. Points P and Q are reflected in line m to their images P' and Q'. This transformation is called a *reflection*. Line m is called the *line of reflection* or the mirror line.

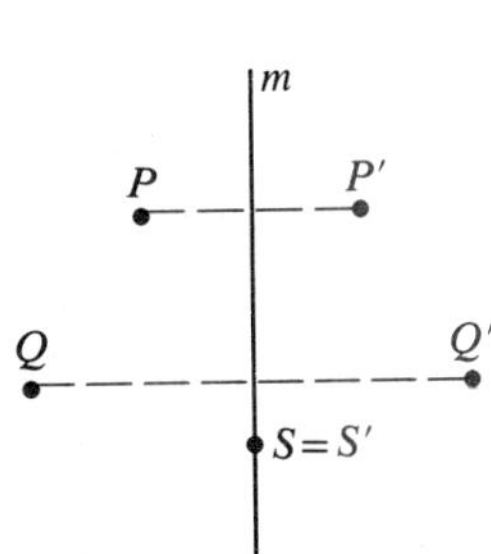

A **reflection** in line m maps every point P to a point P' such that:

(1) If P is not on the line m, then m is the perpendicular bisector of $\overline{PP'}$.
(2) If P is on line m, then $P' = P$.

To abbreviate *reflection in line m*, we write R_m. To abbreviate the statement *R_m maps P to P'*, we write $R_m: P \rightarrow P'$ or $R_m(P) = P'$. This may also be read as *P is reflected in line m to P'*.

Theorem 14-2
A reflection in a line is an isometry.

To prove Theorem 14-2 by using coordinates, we assign coordinates in the plane so that the line of reflection becomes the y-axis. Then in coordinate terms the reflection is $R: (x_1, y_1) \rightarrow (-x_1, y_1)$. In Exercise 23 on page 576 the distance formula was used to prove that $PQ = P'Q'$. Although the diagram shows P and Q on the same side of the y-axis, you should realize that the coordinates x_1, y_1, x_2, and y_2 can be positive, negative, or zero, thereby covering all cases.

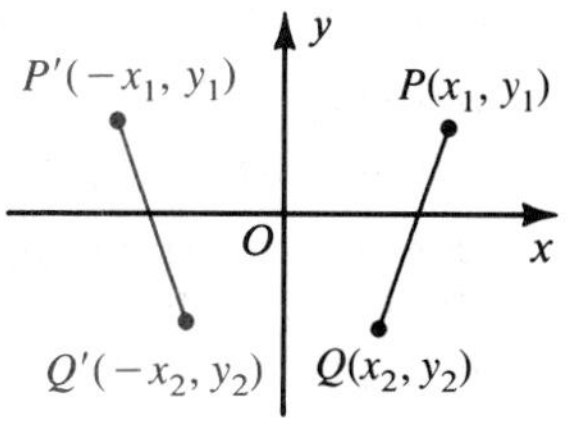

Teaching Suggestions,
pp. T138–T139

Objective
Presenting the Lesson
Applications
Extension
Enrichment

Supplementary Materials

Study Guide, pp. 183–184
Overhead Visual M

Lesson Focus

This second lesson discusses a basic distance-preserving mapping, namely a reflection in a line.

Suggested Assignments

Average
580/1–15
Maximum
Day 1: 580–581/4–6, 8–18 even, 21, 23
Day 2: 581–582/25–30, 32–35, 38

Chalkboard Examples

Classify each statement as true or false.

1. A reflection preserves angle measure. T
2. A reflection preserves segment length. T
3. A reflection preserves orientation. F
4. A reflection preserves the slopes of lines. F
5. A reflection preserves the area of polygons. T

For Exs. 6–8, give the coordinates of the indicated point.

6. Find P, if $R_x:(-2, 5) \rightarrow P$. $(-2, -5)$
7. Find P, if $R_y:(-3, 4) \rightarrow P$. $(3, 4)$
8. Find Q, if $R_x:(4, -1) \rightarrow P$, and $R_y:P \rightarrow Q$. $(-4, 1)$

Theorem 14-2 can also be proved without the use of coordinates. If coordinates are not used, we must show that $PQ = P'Q'$ for all choices of P and Q. Four of the possible cases are shown below. In Written Exercises 18–20 you will prove Theorem 14-2 for Cases 2–4, using the fact that the line of reflection, m, is the perpendicular bisector of $\overline{PP'}$ and $\overline{QQ'}$.

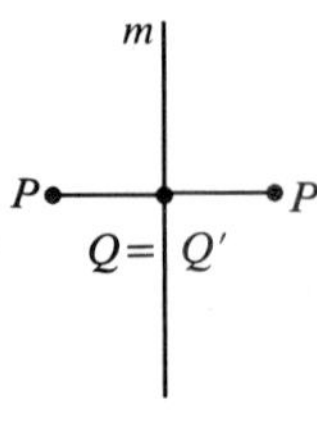

Case 1

m, $P = P'$, Q, Q'

Case 2

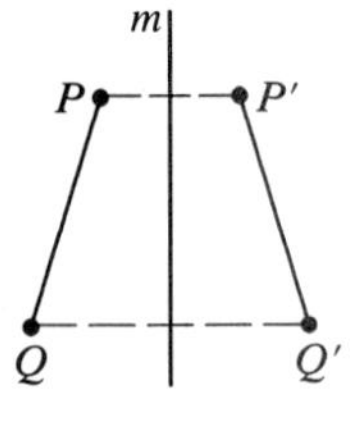

Case 3

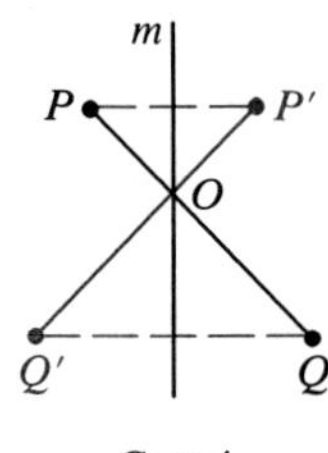

Case 4

Since a reflection is an isometry, it preserves distance, angle measure, and the area of a polygon. Another way to say this is that distance, angle measure, and area are *invariant* under a reflection. On the other hand, the orientation of a figure is *not* invariant under a reflection because a reflection changes a clockwise orientation to a counterclockwise one, as shown at the right.

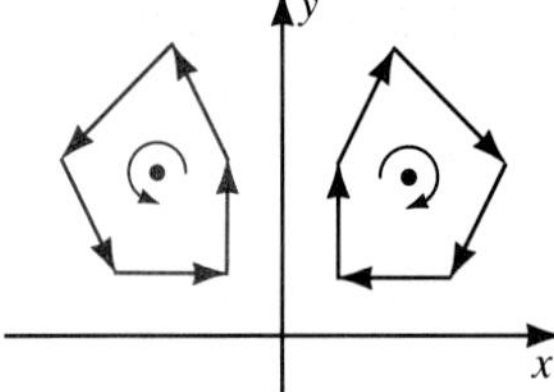

Example Find the image of point $P(2, 4)$ and $\triangle ABC$ under each reflection.

a. The line of reflection is the x-axis.

b. The line of reflection is the line $y = x$.

Solution The images are shown in red.

a.

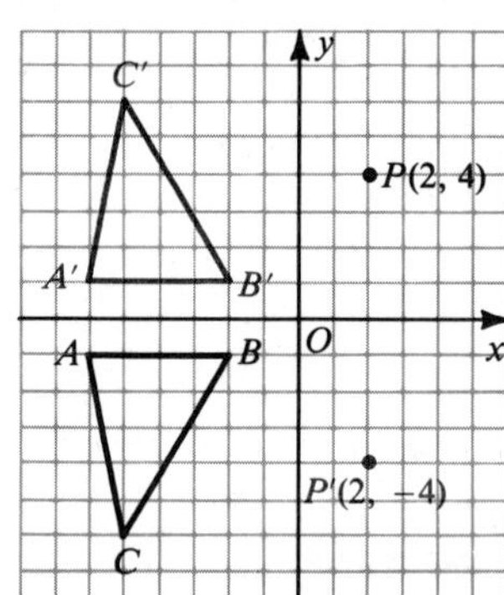

b.

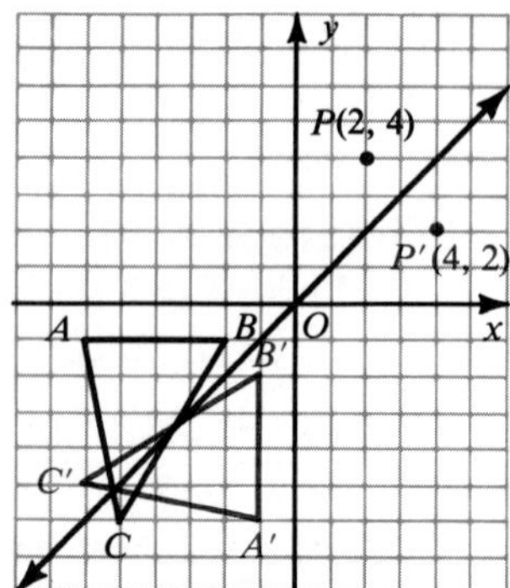

Notice that under reflection in the line $y = x$, the point (x, y) is mapped to the point (y, x).

Classroom Exercises

Complete the following. Assume points *D, C, U, W, X,* and *Y* are obtained by reflection in line *k* or *j*.

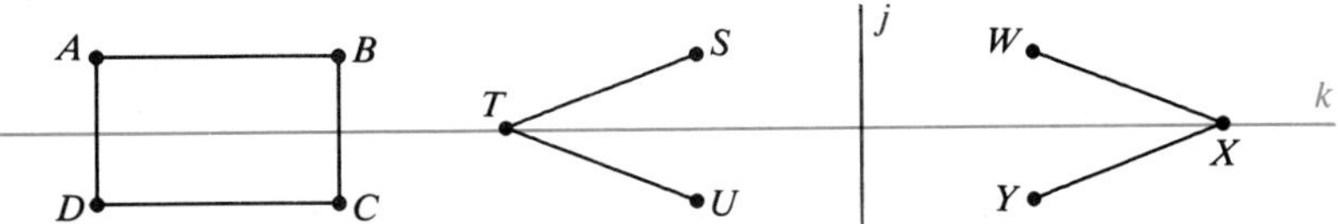

1. R_k stands for $\underline{?}$. **reflection in line *k***
2. $R_k: A \rightarrow \underline{?}$ **D**
3. $R_k(B) = \underline{?}$ **C**
4. $R_k: \overline{AB} \rightarrow \underline{?}$ **$\overline{DC}$**
5. $R_k(C) = \underline{?}$ **B**
6. $R_k: T \rightarrow \underline{?}$ **T**
7. $R_k: \overline{BC} \rightarrow \underline{?}$ **$\overline{CB}$**
8. $R_k: \angle STU \rightarrow \underline{?}$ **$\angle UTS$**
9. $R_j(S) = \underline{?}$ **W**
10. $R_j: \overline{ST} \rightarrow \underline{?}$ **$\overline{WX}$**
11. $R_j(\underline{?}) = \overline{XY}$ **$\overline{TU}$**
12. R_j: line $k \rightarrow \underline{?}$ **line *k***

Points *A–D* are reflected in the *x*-axis. Points *E–H* are reflected in the *y*-axis. State the coordinates of the images.

13.

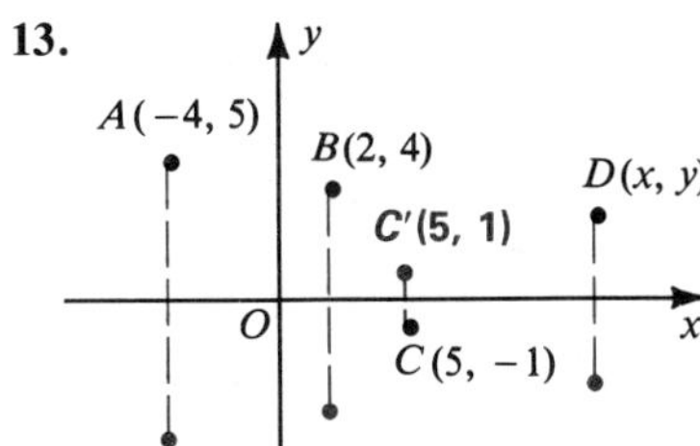

14.

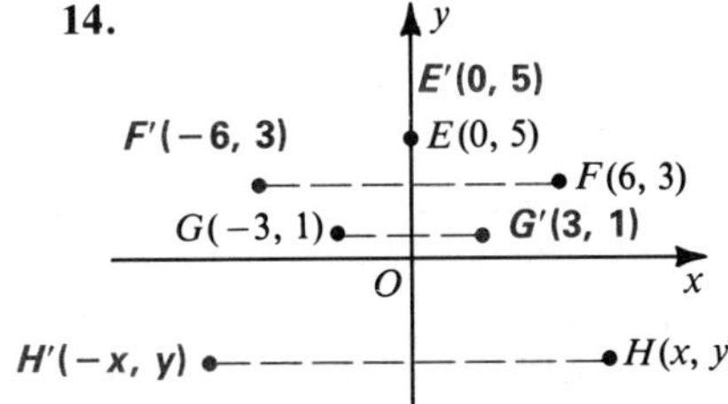

A′(−4, −5) B′(2, −4) D′(x, −y)

Sketch each figure on the chalkboard. With a different color, sketch its image, using the dashed line as the line of reflection.

15.

16.

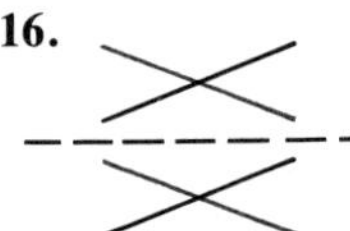

17.

18.

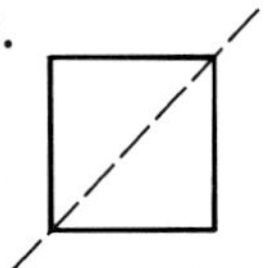

19. Under a reflection, is an angle always mapped to a congruent angle? Is a polygon always mapped to a polygon with the same area? Explain. **Yes; yes; by Thm. 14-2, a reflection is an isometry.**
20. Explain in your own words the meaning of each phrase.
    a. An isometry preserves distance.
    b. Area is invariant under a reflection.
    c. Orientation is not invariant under a reflection.

Communication Skills

Some students may have difficulty with the notation introduced in this lesson. A complete discussion of the Classroom Exercises should help those students. Stress that "*R*" stands for a reflection, and the subscript describes the line of reflection.

Exercise Note

The answer to Ex. 8 could also be $\angle STU$.

Guided Practice

Draw the image of each of the following figures by reflection in line *k*.
Answers are given as dashed lines.

1.

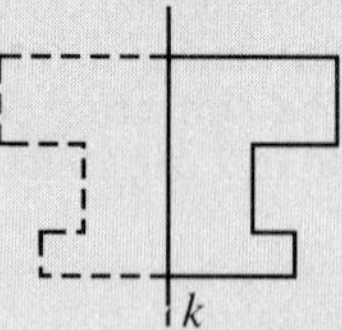

2.

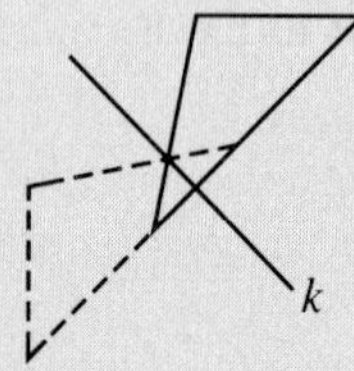

Write the coordinates of the image of each point by reflection in (a) the *x*-axis, (b) the *y*-axis, and (c) the line $y = -x$.

3. $R(-2, -3)$
(a) $(-2, 3)$
(b) $(2, -3)$
(c) $(3, 2)$

4. $T(4, 1)$
(a) $(4, -1)$
(b) $(-4, 1)$
(c) $(-1, -4)$

Written Exercises

Copy each figure on graph paper. Then draw the image by reflection in line *k*.

A

1. 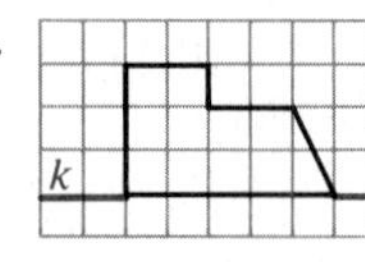

2. 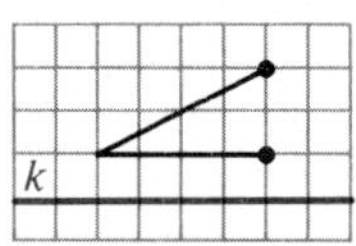

3. 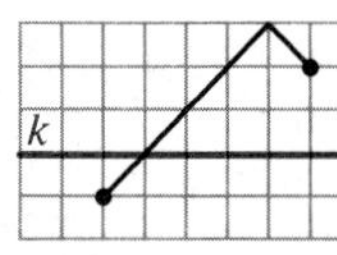

4. 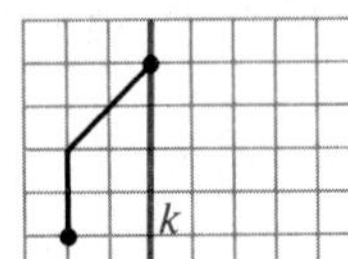

5. 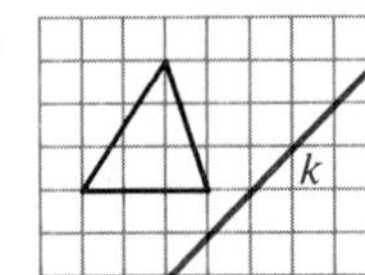

6. 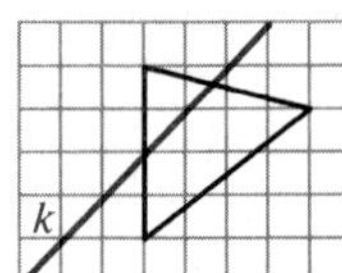

Write the coordinates of the image of each point by reflection in (a) the *x*-axis, (b) the *y*-axis, and (c) the line $y = x$. (*Hint*: Refer to the Example on page 578.)

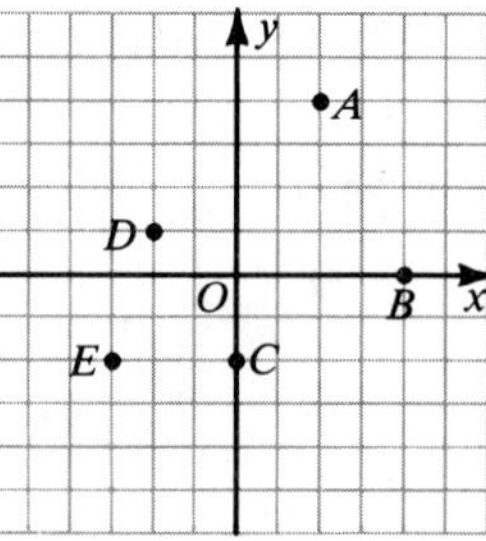

Exs. 7–12

7. *A*	8. *B*	9. *C*
10. *D*	11. *E*	12. *O*

13. When the word MOM is reflected in a vertical line, the image is still MOM. Can you think of other words that are unchanged when reflected in a vertical line? **See below.**

14. When the word HIDE is reflected in a horizontal line, the image is still HIDE. Can you think of other words that are unchanged when reflected in a horizontal line? **See below.**

B

15. Draw a triangle and a line *m* such that R_m maps the triangle to itself. What kind of triangle did you use? **isosceles**

16. Draw a pentagon and a line *n* such that R_n maps the pentagon to itself.

17. The sketch illustrates a *reflection in plane X*. Write a definition of this reflection similar to the definition of a reflection in line *m* on page 577. **If *P* is not on plane *X*, then *X* is ⊥ to and bisects $\overline{PP'}$. If *P* is on plane *X*, $P' = P$.**

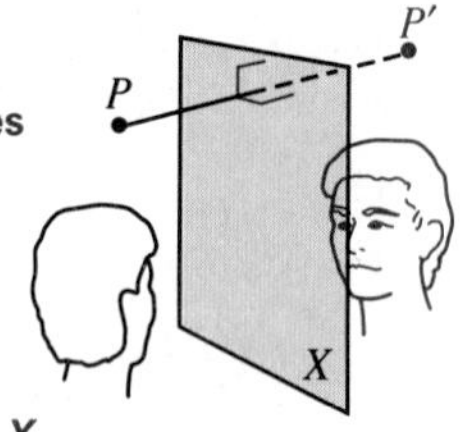

Ex. 17

In Exercises 18–20, refer to the diagrams on page 578. Given the reflection $R_m:\overline{PQ} \rightarrow \overline{P'Q'}$, write the key steps of a proof that $PQ = P'Q'$ for each case.

18. Case 2	19. Case 3	20. Case 4

21. Draw a line *t* and a point *A* not on *t*. Then use a straightedge and compass to construct the image of *A* under R_t.

22. Draw any two points *B* and *B'*. Then use a straightedge and compass to construct the line of reflection *j* so that $R_j(B) = B'$. **Const. the ⊥ bis. of $\overline{BB'}$.**

13. Answers may vary; for example: WOW, TOOT, AHA.
14. Answers may vary; for example: ICEBOX, DECIDE, OBOE.

Additional Answers Written Exercises

7.a. $(2, -4)$ b. $(-2, 4)$ c. $(4, 2)$

8.a. $(4, 0)$ b. $(-4, 0)$ c. $(0, 4)$

9.a. $(0, 2)$ b. $(0, -2)$ c. $(-2, 0)$

10.a. $(-2, -1)$ b. $(2, 1)$ c. $(1, -2)$

11.a. $(-3, 2)$ b. $(3, -2)$ c. $(-2, -3)$

12.a. $(0, 0)$ b. $(0, 0)$ c. $(0, 0)$

23. If a transformation maps two parallel lines to two image lines that are also parallel, we say that parallelism is invariant under the transformation. Is parallelism invariant under a reflection? **Yes**

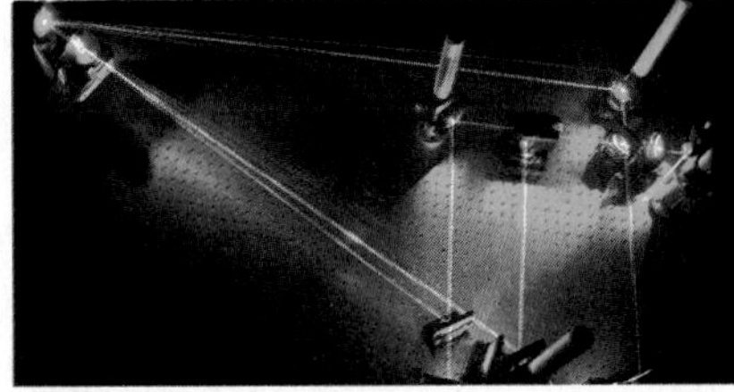

The photograph shows a reflected beam of laser light. Exercises 24–28 deal with the similar reflected path of a golf ball bouncing off the walls of a miniature golf layout. These exercises show how the geometry of reflections can be used to solve the problem of aiming a reflected path at a particular target.

24. A rolling ball that does not have much spin will bounce off a wall so that the two angles that the path forms with the wall are congruent. Thus, to roll the ball from B off the wall shown and into hole H, you need to aim the ball so that $\angle 1 \cong \angle 2$.

   a. Let H' be the image of H by reflection in the wall. $\overline{BH'}$ intersects the wall at P. Why is $\angle 1 \cong \angle 3$? Why is $\angle 3 \cong \angle 2$? Why is $\angle 1 \cong \angle 2$? You can conclude that if you aim for H', the ball will roll to H.

   b. Show that the distance traveled by the ball equals the distance BH'.

25. In the two-wall shot illustrated at the right, a reflection in one wall maps H to H', and a reflection in a second wall (extended) maps H' to H''. To roll the ball from B to H, you aim for H''. Show that the total distance traveled by the ball equals the distance BH''.

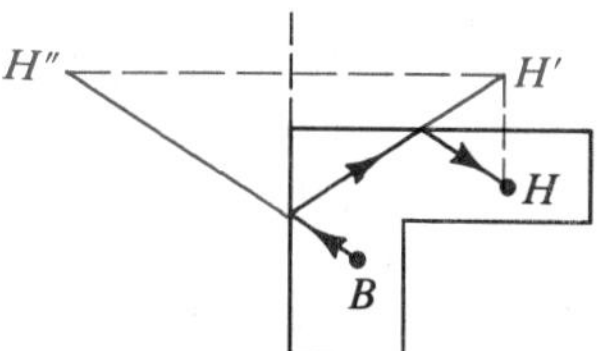

26.–28. Answers may vary.

26. Show how to score a hole in one on the fifth hole of the golf course shown by rolling the ball off one wall.

27. Repeat Exercise 26 but roll the ball off two walls.

28. Repeat Exercise 26 but roll the ball off three walls.

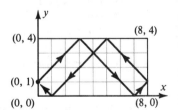

29. A ball rolls at a 45° angle away from one side of a billiard table that has a coordinate grid on it. If the ball starts at the point (0, 1) it will eventually return to its starting point. Would this happen if the ball started from other points on the y-axis between (0, 0) and (0, 4)? **Yes**

30. The line with equation $y = 2x + 3$ is reflected in the y-axis. Find an equation of the image line. $y = -2x + 3$

31. The line with equation $y = x + 5$ is reflected in the x-axis. Find an equation of the image line. $y = -x - 5$

Exercise Note

Exs. 24–28 will interest many students, particularly those who have played miniature golf. In Ex. 24, $\angle 1$ is called the *angle of incidence* in physics applications, and $\angle 2$ is called the *angle of reflection.*

Additional Answers Written Exercises

24.a. $\angle 1 \cong \angle 3$ since $\angle 1$ and $\angle 3$ are vert. $\angle$s. Let X be the pt. where $\overline{HH'}$ int. the wall; $\triangle PXH \cong \triangle PXH'$ (SAS), so $\angle 3 \cong \angle 2$. $\angle 1 \cong \angle 2$ by the Trans. Prop.

b. $BP + PH = BP + PH' = BH'$

25. Let P and Q be the pts. where $\overline{H'H''}$ and $\overline{HH'}$, resp., int. the walls. Let R and S be pts. where $\overline{BH''}$ and $\overline{RH'}$, resp., int. the walls. $\triangle RPH'' \cong \triangle RPH'$; $\triangle SQH \cong \triangle SQH'$ (SAS). Thus, $BR + RS + SH = BR + RS + SH' = BR + RH' = BR + RH'' = BH''$.

26. Find H' by reflecting H (the hole) in the line of the lower wall. Aim for H'.

27. Find H' as in Ex. 26. Find H'', the image of H' under the reflection in the line of the left side wall. Aim for H''.

28. Find H' and H'' as in Ex. 27. Find H''', the image of H'' under reflection in the upper wall. Aim for H'''.

In each exercise $R_k: A \to A'$. Find an equation of line k.

	32.	33.	34.	35.	36.	37.
A	(5, 0)	(1, 4)	(4, 0)	(5, 1)	(0, 2)	(−1, 2)
A′	(9, 0)	(3, 4)	(4, 6)	(1, 5)	(4, 6)	(4, 5)

32. $x = 7$ **33.** $x = 2$ **34.** $y = 3$ **35.** $y = x$ **36.** $y = -x + 6$ **37.** $y = -\frac{5}{3}x + 6$

C **38.** Draw the x- and y-axes and the line l with equation $y = -x$. Plot several points and their images under R_l. What is the image of (a, b)? **$(-b, -a)$**

39. Draw the x- and y-axes and the vertical line j with equation $x = 5$. Find the images under R_j of the following points.

a. $(4, 3)$ **(6, 3)** **b.** $(0, -2)$ **(10, −2)** **c.** $(-3, 1)$ **(13, 1)** **d.** (x, y) **$(10 - x, y)$**

40. Repeat Exercise 39 letting j be the horizontal line with equation $y = 6$.

a. (4, 9) **b. (0, 14)** **c. (−3, 11)** **d. $(x, 12 - y)$**

Application *Mirrors*

If a ray of light strikes a mirror at an angle of 40°, it will be reflected off the mirror at an angle of 40° also. The angle between the mirror and the reflected ray is always congruent to the angle between the mirror and the initial light ray. In the diagram at the left below, $\angle 2 \cong \angle 1$.

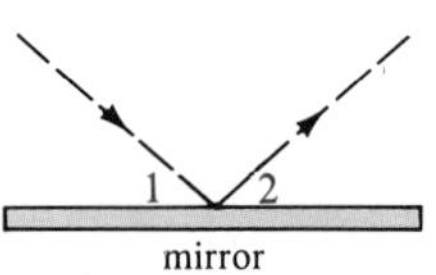

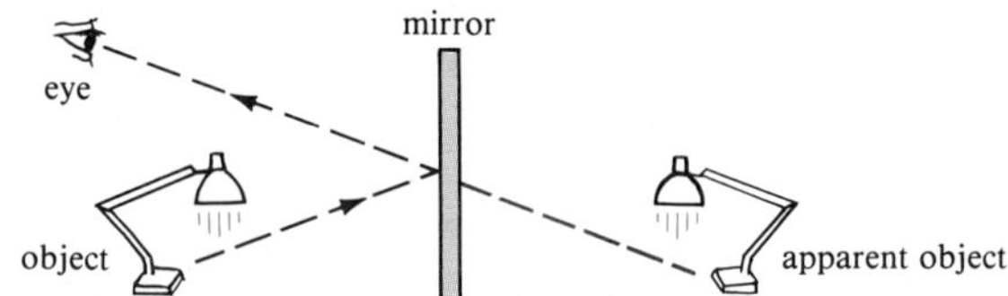

We see objects in a mirror when the reflected light ray reaches the eye. The object appears to lie behind the mirror as shown in the diagram at the right above.

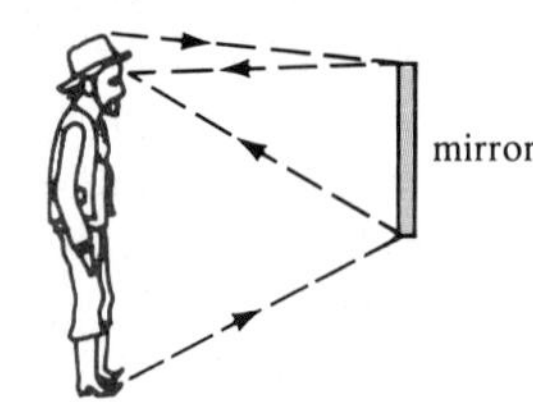

You don't need a full-length mirror to see all of yourself. A mirror that is only half as tall as you are will do if the mirror is in a position as shown. You see the top of your head at the top of the mirror and your feet at the bottom of the mirror. If the mirror is too high or too low, you will not see your entire body.

A periscope uses mirrors to enable a viewer to see above the line of sight. The diagram at the right is a simple illustration of the principle used in a periscope. It has two mirrors, parallel to each other, at the top and at the bottom. The mirrors are placed at an angle of 45° with the horizontal. Horizontal light rays from an object entering at the top are reflected down to the mirror at the bottom. They are then reflected to the eye of the viewer.

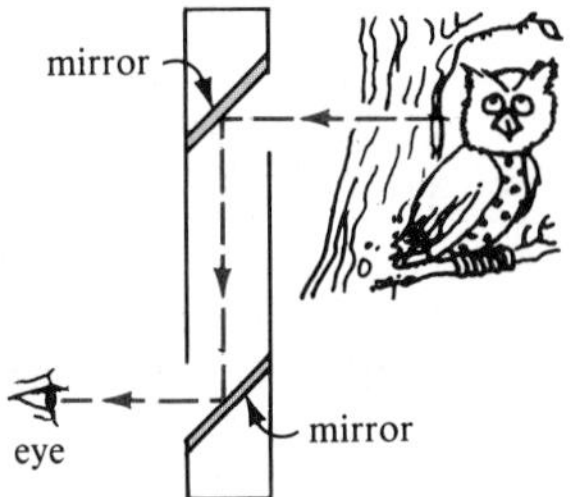

Exercises

1. What are the measures of the angles that the initial light ray and the reflected light rays make with the mirrors in the diagram of the periscope on the previous page? **45**
2. If you can see the eyes of someone when you look into a mirror, can the other person see your eyes in that same mirror? **Yes**
3. A person with eyes at A, 150 cm above the floor, faces a mirror 1 m away. The mirror extends 30 cm above eye level. How high can the person see on a wall 2 m behind point A? **270 cm**

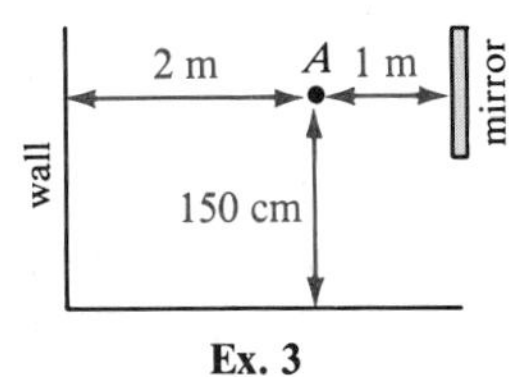

Ex. 3

4. Prove that you can see all of yourself in a mirror that is only half as tall as you are. (*Hint*: Study the diagram on page 582.)
5. Prove that the point D which is as far behind the mirror as the object A is in front of the mirror lies on $\overleftrightarrow{BC}$. (*Hint*: Show that $\angle CBE$ and $\angle EBD$ are supplementary.)
6. Show that the light ray follows the shortest possible path from A to C via the mirror by proving that for any point E on the mirror (other than B) $AE + EC > AB + BC$. (*Hint*: See the Application: Finding the Shortest Path, on page 224.)

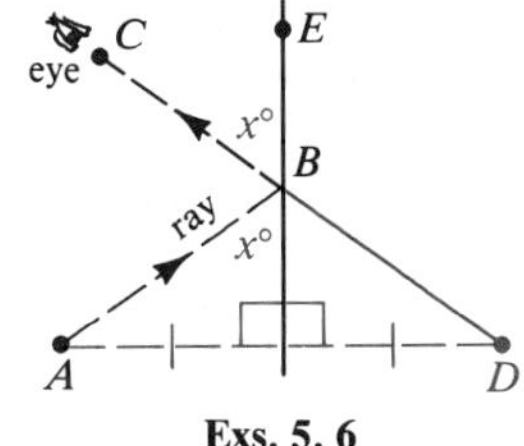

Exs. 5, 6

14-3 *Translations and Glide Reflections*

The photograph at the right suggests the transformation called a *translation*, or *glide*. The skate blades of the figure-skating pair move in identical ways when the pair is skating together. A transformation that glides all points of the plane the same distance in the same direction is called a **translation.**

If a transformation maps A to A', B to B', and C to C', points A, B, and C glide along parallel or collinear segments and $AA' = BB' = CC'$. Any of the vectors $\overrightarrow{AA'}$, $\overrightarrow{BB'}$, or $\overrightarrow{CC'}$ could describe this translation.

Each vector has the same magnitude of $\sqrt{1^2 + 3^2}$, or $\sqrt{10}$, and each vector has the same direction as indicated by its slope of $\frac{1}{3}$. Note that we don't need to know the coordinates of points A, B, or C to describe the translation. All that is important is the change in the x-coordinate and y-coordinate of each point.

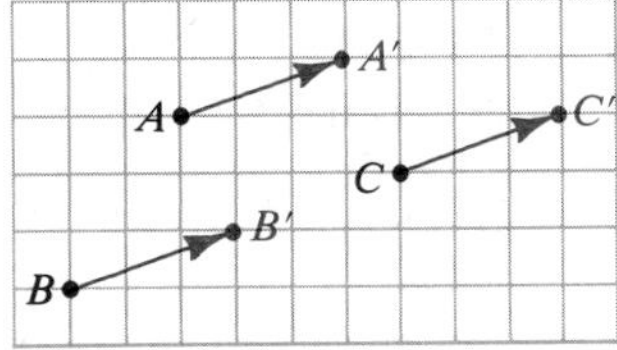

Teaching Suggestions,
pp. T139–T140

Objective
Presenting the Lesson

Communication Skills,
p. T140

Supplementary Materials

Practice Master 86
Test 56
Resource Book, pp. 96, 166
Study Guide, pp. 185–186
Overhead Visual M

Lesson Focus

The purpose of this lesson is to study two basic isometries, translations and glide reflections. A glide reflection combines two isometries, a translation and a reflection, to produce a new isometry.

Suggested Assignments

Average
586/1–10
S 580/17

Maximum
586–587/2, 3, 6, 7, 9, 11, 14, 15, 17, 18, 21

Making Connections

A translation is a transformation that corresponds to physical sliding without turning. It can be expressed by coordinates, vectors, parallelograms (the geometric method), or as a composite of reflections.

Chalkboard Examples

In Exs. 1–5, the translation T maps $A(1, -2)$ to $A'(4, 1)$.

1. Rewrite the translation by (a) using a vector, (3, 3) and by (b) using a coordinate expression.
   $T:(x, y) \rightarrow (x + 3, y + 3)$
2. Give the coordinates of B' and C' for $B(3, 2)$ and $C(-1, 2)$.
   $B'(6, 5)$; $C'(2, 5)$
3. What is the preimage of $D'(0, 3)$? $D(-3, 0)$
4. What is $|\overrightarrow{AA'}|$?
   $\sqrt{3^2 + 3^2} = 3\sqrt{2}$
5. Find the lengths $\overline{BC}$ and $\overline{B'C'}$. $BC = 4$; $B'C' = 4$
6. If $T:(2, 1) \rightarrow (4, -3)$, then $T(0, 0) \rightarrow$ (2, −4).

Making Connections

The mapping notation for translations can easily be expanded to show translation in space using x-, y-, and z-coordinates in ordered triples.

Consider a translation in which every point glides 8 units right and 2 units up. We could use the vector (8, 2) to indicate such a translation, or we could use the coordinate expression $T:(x, y) \rightarrow (x + 8, y + 2)$. The following diagram shows how $\triangle PQR$ is mapped by T to $\triangle P'Q'R'$. You can use the distance formula to check that each segment is mapped to a congruent segment so that T is an isometry.

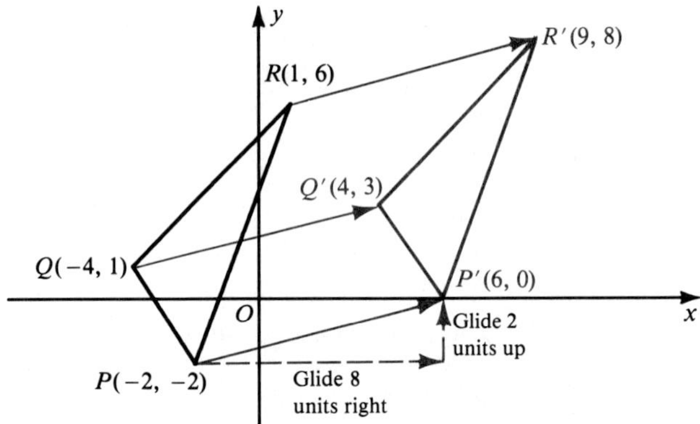

The illustration just presented should help you to understand why we use the following definition of a translation when working in the coordinate plane. A **translation,** or glide, in a plane is a transformation T which maps any point (x, y) to the point $(x + a, y + b)$ where a and b are constants. This definition makes it possible to give a simple proof of the following theorem.

Theorem 14-3

A translation is an isometry.

Plan for Proof: Label two points P and Q and their images P' and Q' as shown in the diagram. To show that T is an isometry, we need to show that $PQ = P'Q'$. Use the distance formula to show that:

$$PQ = P'Q' = \sqrt{(x_2 - x_1)^2 + (y_2 - y_1)^2}$$

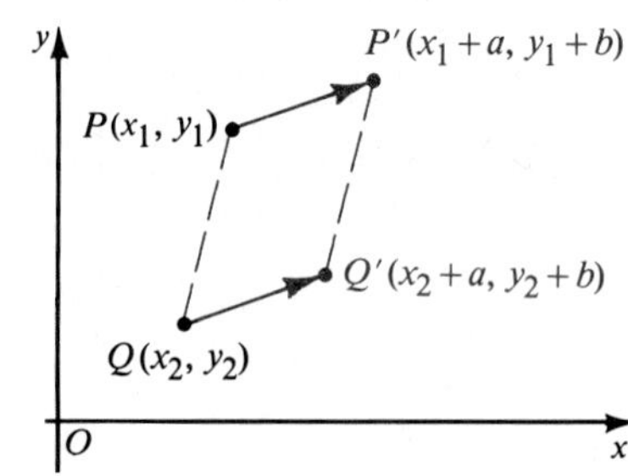

Of course, since a translation is an isometry, we know by the corollaries of Theorem 14-1, page 573, that a translation preserves angle measure and area.

A glide and a reflection can be carried out one after the other to produce a transformation known as a *glide reflection*. A **glide reflection** is a transformation in which every point P is mapped to a point P'' by these steps:

1. A glide maps P to P'.
2. A reflection in a line parallel to the glide line maps P' to P''.

A glide reflection combines two isometries to produce a new transformation, which is itself an isometry. The succession of footprints shown illustrates a glide reflection. Note that the reflection line is parallel to the direction of the glide.

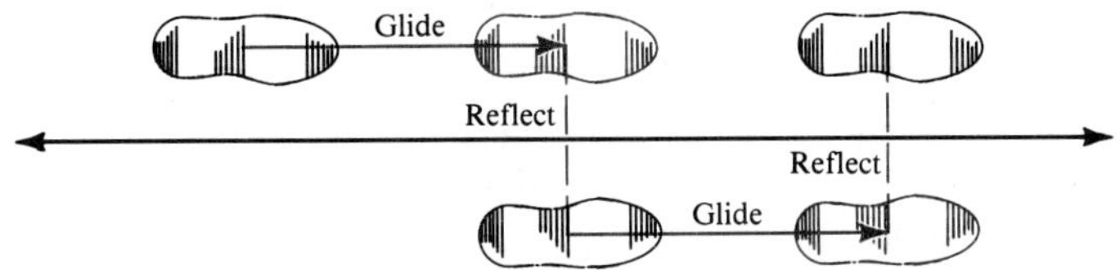

As long as the glide is parallel to the line of reflection, it doesn't matter whether you glide first and then reflect, or reflect first and then glide. For other combinations of mappings, the order in which you perform the mappings will affect the result. We will look further at such combinations of mappings in Section 14-6.

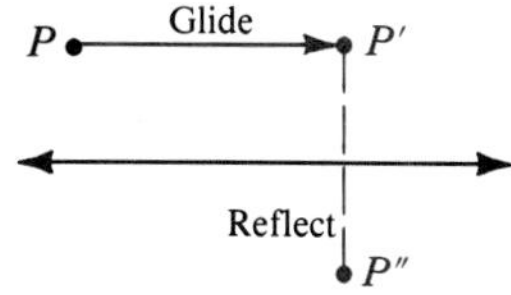

Classroom Exercises

1. Complete each statement for the translation $T:(x, y) \rightarrow (x + 3, y - 1)$.
   a. T glides points _?_ units right and 1 unit _?_. **3, down**
   b. The image of (4, 6) is (_?_, _?_). **(7, 5)**
   c. The preimage of (2, 3) is (_?_, _?_). **(−1, 4)**

Describe each translation in words, as in Exercise 1(a), and give the image of (4, 6) and the preimage of (2, 3). **2. 5 units left, 4 units up**

2. $T:(x, y) \rightarrow (x - 5, y + 4)$ **(−1, 10); (7, −1)**
3. $T:(x, y) \rightarrow (x + 1, y)$ **1 unit right** **(5, 6); (1, 3)**

Each diagram shows a point P on the coordinate plane and its image P' under a translation T. Complete the statement $T:(x, y) \rightarrow$ (_?_, _?_).

4. 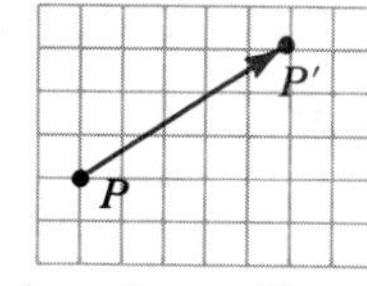

(x + 5, y + 3)

5. 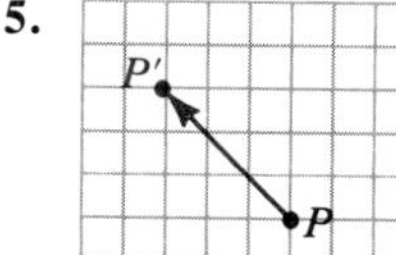

(x − 3, y + 3)

6. 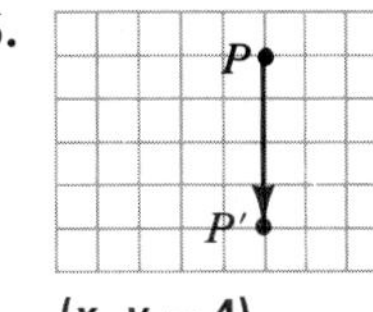

(x, y − 4)

7. For a given translation, the image of the origin is (5, 7). What is the preimage of the origin? **(−5, −7)**
8. A glide reflection has the glide translation $T:(x, y) \rightarrow (x + 2, y + 2)$. The line of reflection is line m with equation $y = x$.
   a. Find the image, point S', of $S(-1, 3)$ under T. **(1, 5)**
   b. Find the image, point S'', of S' under R_m. (*Hint*: Recall from the example on page 578 that $R_m:(x, y) \rightarrow (y, x)$.) **(5, 1)**
   c. Under the glide reflection, (x, y) is first mapped to (_?_, _?_) and then to (_?_, _?_). **(x + 2, y + 2); (y + 2, x + 2)**

Additional Answers Written Exercises

1.a. $A'(-4, 6)$, $B'(-2, 10)$, $C'(1, 5)$

2.a. $A'(0, 0)$, $B'(-6, 0)$, $C'(-4, -8)$

Guided Practice

1. The translation $T:(x, y) \rightarrow (x + 3, y - 1)$ maps $\triangle ABC$ to $\triangle A'B'C'$, $A(3, -1)$, $B(0, 2)$, $C(2, -3)$.
   a. Graph $\triangle ABC$ and its image.
   b. Draw arrows connecting A to A', B to B', and C to C'.
   c. Are the arrows the same length? yes parallel? yes

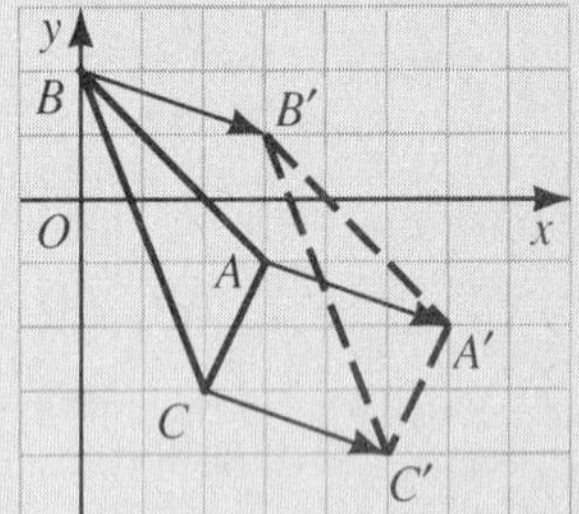

2. If $T:(2, 2) \rightarrow (-2, -2)$, then $T(4, 4) \rightarrow$ (0, 0).
3. The image of $R(4, -3)$ under a translation is $R'(0, -1)$. What is the preimage of $S'(2, -2)$? (6, −4)
4. A glide reflection moves all points down 3 units and reflects all points in the x-axis. Find the image of $A(2, -1)$, $B(1, 1)$ and $C(3, 3)$.
   $A'(2, 4)$, $B'(1, 2)$, $C'(3, 0)$

Written Exercises

In Exercises 1 and 2 a translation T is described. For each:
a. Graph $\triangle ABC$ and its image $\triangle A'B'C'$. Is $\triangle ABC \cong \triangle A'B'C'$? Yes
b. In color, draw arrows from A to A', B to B', and C to C'.
c. Are your arrows the same length? Are they parallel? Yes; yes

A

1. $T:(x, y) \rightarrow (x - 2, y + 6)$
$A(-2, 0)$, $B(0, 4)$, $C(3, -1)$

2. $T:(x, y) \rightarrow (x - 3, y - 6)$
$A(3, 6)$, $B(-3, 6)$, $C(-1, -2)$

3. If $T:(0, 0) \rightarrow (5, 1)$, then $T:(3, 3) \rightarrow$ (_?_, _?_). **(8, 4)**

4. If $T:(1, 1) \rightarrow (3, 0)$, then $T:(0, 0) \rightarrow$ (_?_, _?_). **(2, −1)**

5. If $T:$(_?_, _?_)$\rightarrow$ (2, 6), then $T:$(_?_, _?_) $\rightarrow (0, 0)$. **(−4, −3)**

6. The image of $P(-1, 5)$ under a translation is $P'(5, 7)$. What is the pre-image of P? **(−7, 3)**

In each exercise a glide reflection is described. Graph $\triangle ABC$ and its image under the glide, $\triangle A'B'C'$. Also graph $\triangle A''B''C''$, the image of $\triangle A'B'C'$ under the reflection.

7. Glide: All points move up 4 units. **$A'(1, 4)$, $B'(4, 6)$, $C'(5, 10)$**
Reflection: All points are reflected in the y-axis. **$A''(-1, 4)$, $B''(-4, 6)$, $C''(-5, 10)$**
$A(1, 0)$, $B(4, 2)$, $C(5, 6)$

8. Glide: All points move left 7 units. **$A'(-3, 2)$, $B'(0, 0)$, $C'(2, -3)$**
Reflection: All points are reflected in the x-axis. **$A''(-3, -2)$, $B''(0, 0)$, $C''(2, 3)$**
$A(4, 2)$, $B(7, 0)$, $C(9, -3)$

B

9. Where does the glide reflection in Exercise 7 map (x, y)? **$(-x, y + 4)$**

10. Where does the glide reflection in Exercise 8 map (x, y)? **$(x - 7, -y)$**

11. Which of the following properties are invariant under a translation? **a, b, c, d**
a. distance **b.** angle measure **c.** area **d.** orientation

12. Which of the properties listed in Exercise 11 are invariant under a glide reflection? **a, b, c**

In Exercises 13 and 14 translations R and S are described. R maps point P to P', and S maps P' to P''. Find T, the translation that maps P to P''.

13. $R:(x, y) \rightarrow (x + 1, y + 2)$
$S:(x, y) \rightarrow (x - 5, y + 7)$
$T:(x, y) \rightarrow$ (_?_, _?_) **$(x - 4, y + 9)$**

14. $R:(x, y) \rightarrow (x - 5, y - 3)$
$S:(x, y) \rightarrow (x + 4, y - 6)$
$T:(x, y) \rightarrow$ (_?_, _?_) **$(x - 1, y - 9)$**

15. If a translation T maps P to P', then T can be described by the vector $\overrightarrow{PP'}$. Suppose a translation T is described by the vector $(3, -4)$ because it glides all points 3 units right and 4 units down.
a. Graph points $A(-1, 2)$, $B(0, 6)$, A', and B', where $T(A) = A'$ and $T(B) = B'$. **$A'(2, -2)$, $B'(3, 2)$**
b. What kind of figure is $AA'B'B$? What is its perimeter? **parallelogram; $10 + 2\sqrt{17}$**

16. a. Graph $\triangle POQ$ with vertices $P(0, 3)$, $O(0, 0)$, and $Q(6, 0)$.
    b. $T_1:(x, y) \rightarrow (x + 2, y - 4)$ and $T_2:(x, y) \rightarrow (x + 5, y + 6)$. If $T_1:\triangle POQ \rightarrow \triangle P'O'Q'$ and $T_2:\triangle P'O'Q' \rightarrow \triangle P''O''Q''$, graph $\triangle P'O'Q'$ and $\triangle P''O''Q''$. **b. $P'(2, -1)$ $O'(2, -4)$ $Q'(8, -4)$; $P''(7, 5)$, $O''(7, 2)$, $Q''(13, 2)$**
    c. Find T_3, a translation that maps $\triangle POQ$ directly to $\triangle P''O''Q''$. **$T_3: (x, y) \rightarrow (x + 7, y + 2)$**
    d. Because T_1 glides all points 2 units right and 4 units down, the translation can be described by the vector $\overrightarrow{T_1} = (2, -4)$. Describe T_2 and T_3 by vectors. How are these three vectors related? **$\overrightarrow{T_2} = (5, 6)$ $\overrightarrow{T_3} = (7, 2)$ $\overrightarrow{T_1} + \overrightarrow{T_2} = \overrightarrow{T_3}$**

17. A glide reflection maps $\triangle ABC$ to $\triangle A'B'C'$. Copy the diagram and locate the midpoints of $\overline{AA'}$, $\overline{BB'}$, and $\overline{CC'}$. What seems to be true about these midpoints? Try to prove your conjecture. **The midpoints of $\overline{AA'}$, $\overline{BB'}$, and $\overline{CC'}$ are on the reflecting line.**

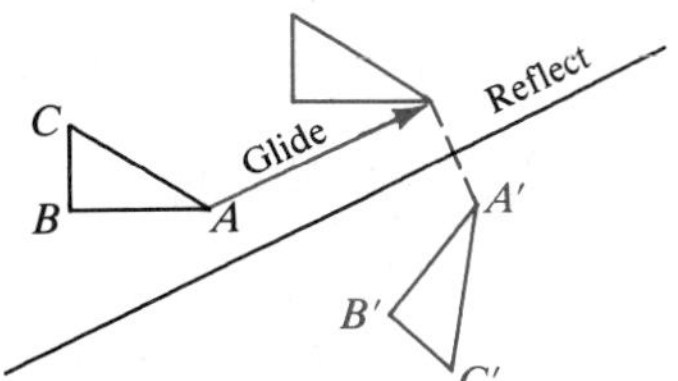

18. Copy the figure and use the result of Exercise 17 to construct the reflecting line of the glide reflection that maps $\triangle ABC$ to $\triangle A'B'C'$. Also construct the glide image of $\triangle ABC$. **The reflecting line is the line containing the midpts. of $\overline{AA'}$, $\overline{BB'}$, and $\overline{CC'}$.**

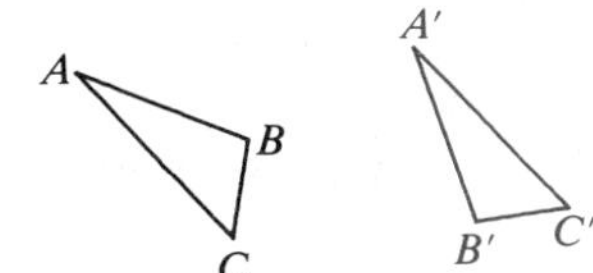

19. Explain why a glide reflection is an isometry.

20. Given $\odot A$ and $\odot B$ and $\overline{CD}$, construct a segment $\overline{XY}$ parallel to and congruent to $\overline{CD}$ and having X on $\odot A$ and Y on $\odot B$. (*Hint*: Translate $\odot A$ along a path parallel to and congruent to $\overline{CD}$.)

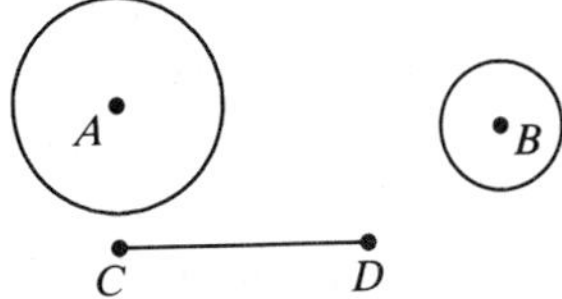

C 21. Describe how you would construct points X and Y, one on each of the lines shown, so that $\overline{XY}$ is parallel to and congruent to $\overline{EF}$.

22. Show by example that if a glide is not parallel to a line of reflection, then the image of a point when the glide is followed by the reflection will be different from the image of the same point when the reflection is followed by the glide.

23. Prove Theorem 14-3 (page 584).

Additional Answers
Written Exercises

18. Const. the ⊥ bis. of any 2 of $\overline{AA'}$, $\overline{BB'}$, and $\overline{CC'}$, to locate midpts. M and P; $\overleftrightarrow{MP}$ is the line of reflection. To find the glide image of A, const. the ⊥ to $\overleftrightarrow{MP}$ from pt. A', int. $\overleftrightarrow{MP}$ at X. Const. $\overrightarrow{XA''}$ on $\overrightarrow{A'X}$ such that $\overline{XA''} \cong \overline{XA'}$. Similarly, locate B'' and C''.

19. Let T be the translation and R_k the reflection. Let $T(P) = P'$, $T(Q) = Q'$, $R_k(P') = P''$, $R_k(Q') = Q''$. Since T and R_k are isometries, $PQ = P'Q'$ and $P'Q' = P''Q''$. Then $PQ = P''Q''$, so the glide reflection is an isometry.

20. Const. a ∥ to $\overline{CD}$ through A and const. $\overline{AA'}$ on the ∥ such that $\overline{AA'} \cong \overline{CD}$. Draw $\odot A' \cong \odot A$. $\odot A'$ int. $\odot B$ at 2 pts.; name 1 pt. Y. Const. a ∥ to $\overline{CD}$ through Y, int. $\odot A$ at X. Since Y is on $\odot A'$ and $\overline{XY} \parallel \overline{CD}$, Y is the image of X under the translation; $XY = CD$.

21. Let j and k be the upper and lower lines. Choose a pt. G on k and draw $\overline{GF}$. Const. a ∥ to $\overline{EF}$ through G and const. $\overline{HG}$ on the ∥ such that $\overline{HG} \cong \overline{EF}$. $EFGH$ is a ▱. Const. $\overleftrightarrow{HX} \parallel k$ with X on j, and $\overleftrightarrow{XY} \parallel \overleftrightarrow{GH}$ with Y on k. Two lines ∥ to the same line are ∥ to each other, so $\overline{XY} \parallel \overline{EF}$. Since $\overline{EF} \cong \overline{HG}$ and $\overline{XY} \cong \overline{HG}$, $\overline{XY} \cong \overline{EF}$.

Teaching Suggestions, p. T140

Objective
Presenting the Lesson
Applications
Extension
Enrichment

Exploring Activity, p. 569c

Supplementary Materials

Study Guide, pp. 187–188
Overhead Visuals L, M, N

Lesson Focus

In this lesson, the basic transformation called a rotation is studied. A rotation is an isometry.

Suggested Assignments

Average
590/1–23 odd
592/Mixed Review 1–7

Maximum
Day 1: 590/7–21 odd, 24–27
Day 2: 590–592/28, 29, 31, 33, 35–38

14-4 *Rotations*

A *rotation* is a transformation suggested by rotating a paddle wheel. When the wheel moves, each paddle rotates to a new position. When the wheel stops, the new position of a paddle (P') can be referred to mathematically as the image of the initial position of the paddle (P).

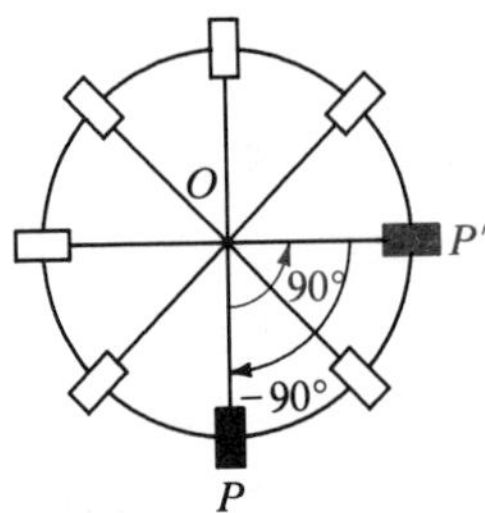

For the counterclockwise rotation shown about point O through 90°, we write $\mathcal{R}_{O,\,90}$. A counterclockwise rotation is considered positive, and a clockwise rotation is considered negative. If the red paddle is rotated about O clockwise until it moves into the position of the black paddle, the rotation is denoted by $\mathcal{R}_{O,\,-90}$. (Note that to avoid confusion with the R used for reflections we use a script $\mathcal{R}$ for rotations.)

A full revolution, or 360° rotation about point O, rotates any point P around to itself so that $P' = P$. The diagram at the left below shows a rotation of 390° about O. Since 390° is 30° more than one full revolution, the image of any point P under a 390° rotation is the same as its image under a 30° rotation, and the two rotations are said to be equal. Similarly, the diagram at the right below shows that a 90° counterclockwise rotation is equal to a 270° clockwise rotation because both have the same effect on any point P.

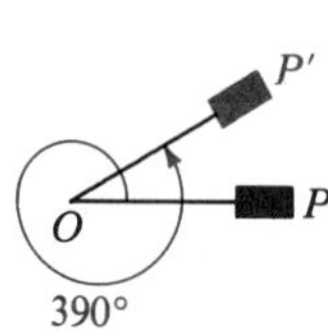

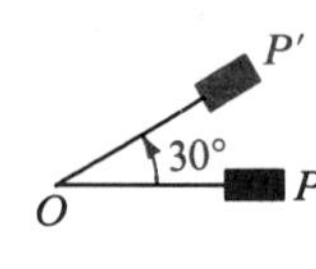

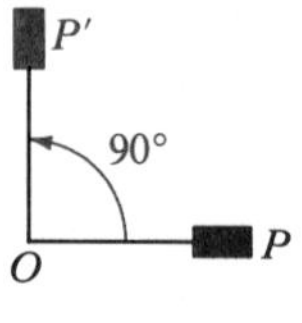

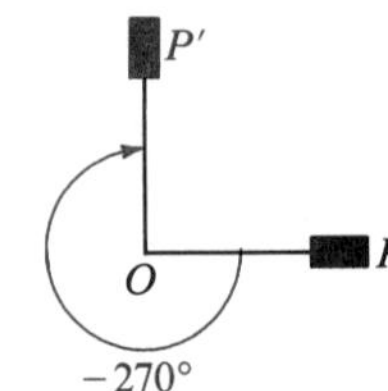

$\mathcal{R}_{O,\,390} = \mathcal{R}_{O,\,30}$
Notice: $390 - 360 = 30$

$\mathcal{R}_{O,\,90} = \mathcal{R}_{O,\,-270}$
Notice: $90 - 360 = -270$

In the following definition of a rotation, the angle measure x can be positive or negative and can be more than 180 in absolute value.

A **rotation** about point O through $x°$ is a transformation such that:

(1) If a point P is different from O, then $OP' = OP$ and $m\angle POP' = x$.
(2) If point P is the point O, then $P' = P$.

Theorem 14-4

A rotation is an isometry.

Given: $\mathcal{R}_{O,x}$ maps P to P' and Q to Q'.
Prove: $\overline{PQ} \cong \overline{P'Q'}$

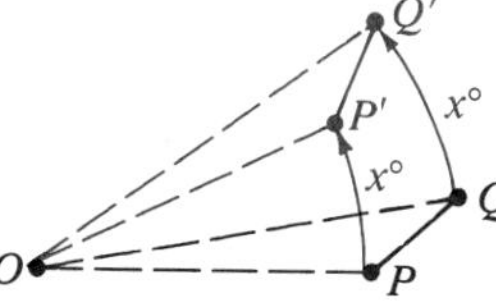

Key steps of proof:

1. $OP = OP'$, $OQ = OQ'$ (Definition of rotation)
2. $m\angle POP' = m\angle QOQ' = x$ (Definition of rotation)
3. $m\angle POQ = m\angle P'OQ'$ (Subtraction Property of $=$: subtract $m\angle QOP'$.)
4. $\triangle POQ \cong \triangle P'OQ'$ (SAS Postulate)
5. $\overline{PQ} \cong \overline{P'Q'}$ (Corr. parts of $\cong$ $\triangle$s are $\cong$.)

A rotation about point O through 180° is called a **half-turn** about O and is usually denoted by H_O. The diagram shows $\triangle PQR$ and its image $\triangle P'Q'R'$ by H_O. Notice that O is the midpoint of $\overline{PP'}$, $\overline{QQ'}$, and $\overline{RR'}$.

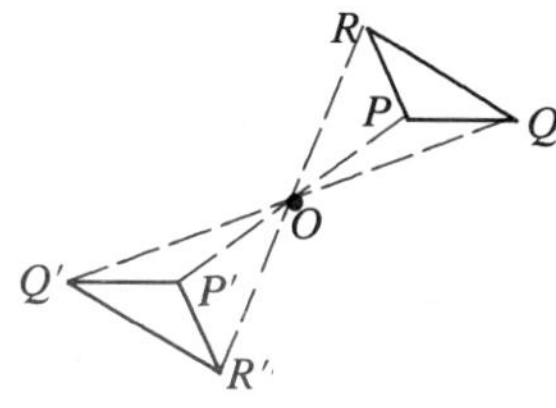

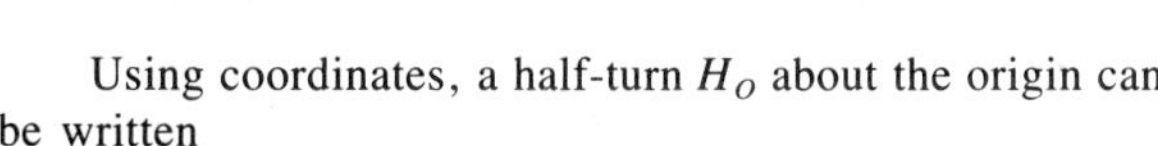
Using coordinates, a half-turn H_O about the origin can be written

$$H_O:(x, y) \rightarrow (-x, -y).$$

Classroom Exercises

State another name for each rotation. **Answers may vary. Examples are given.**

1. $\mathcal{R}_{O,50}$ $\mathcal{R}_{O,410}$
2. $\mathcal{R}_{O,-40}$ $\mathcal{R}_{O,320}$
3. $\mathcal{R}_{O,-90}$ $\mathcal{R}_{O,270}$
4. $\mathcal{R}_{O,400}$ $\mathcal{R}_{O,40}$
5. $\mathcal{R}_{O,-180}$ $\mathcal{R}_{O,180}$

In the diagram for Exercises 6–11, O is the center of equilateral $\triangle PST$. State the images of points P, S, and T for each rotation.

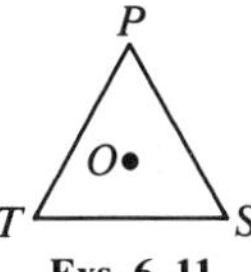

Exs. 6–11

6. $\mathcal{R}_{O,120}$ **T, P, S**
7. $\mathcal{R}_{O,-120}$ **S, T, P**
8. $\mathcal{R}_{O,360}$ **P, S, T**

Name each image point.

9. $\mathcal{R}_{T,60}(S)$ **P**
10. $\mathcal{R}_{T,-60}(P)$ **S**
11. $\mathcal{R}_{O,240}(P)$ **S**

12. Draw a coordinate grid on the chalkboard. Plot the origin and $A(4, 1)$. Give the coordinates of **(a)** $H_O(A)$, **(b)** $\mathcal{R}_{O,90}(A)$, and **(c)** $\mathcal{R}_{O,-90}(A)$. **a. (−4, −1) b. (−1, 4) c. (1, −4)**
13. Repeat Exercise 12 if A has coordinates $(-3, 5)$. **a. (3, −5) b. (−5, −3) c. (5, 3)**
14. Is congruence invariant under a half-turn mapping? Explain. **Yes; a half-turn is a rotation, and a rotation is an isometry.**
15. Read each expression aloud.
    a. $R_k(A) = A'$
    b. $H_O:(-2, 0) \rightarrow (2, 0)$
    c. $T:(x, y) \rightarrow (x - 1, y + 3)$
    d. $\mathcal{R}_{P,10}$

Teaching Note

Stress that a half-turn is a rotation and is therefore an isometry.

Chalkboard Examples

State another name for each rotation.

1. $\mathcal{R}_{O,-270}$ $\mathcal{R}_{O,90}$
2. $\mathcal{R}_{O,180}$ $\mathcal{R}_{O,-180}$
3. $\mathcal{R}_{O,450}$ $\mathcal{R}_{O,90}$
4. $\mathcal{R}_{O,135}$ $\mathcal{R}_{O,-225}$

The diagonals of square *ABCD* intersect at *O*. Complete each statement.

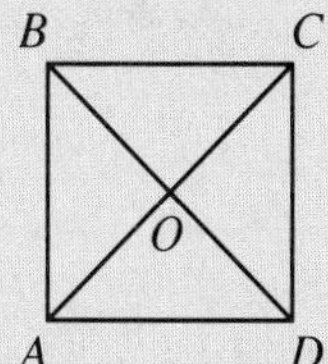

5. $\mathcal{R}_{O,-90}: B \rightarrow \underline{C}$
6. $\mathcal{R}_{O,-270}: C \rightarrow \underline{B}$
7. $\mathcal{R}_{O,180}: A \rightarrow \underline{C}$
8. $\mathcal{R}_{O,270}: C \rightarrow \underline{D}$
9. If $\mathcal{R}_{O,135}: D \rightarrow X$, then X lies on the $\underline{\perp \text{ bisector of } \overline{BC}}$.
10. $H_O: D \rightarrow \underline{B}$

Additional Answers Classroom Exercises

15. Answers may vary. Examples:
    a. Reflection in line *k* maps *A* to *A'*.
    b. A half-turn about the origin maps (−2, 0) to (2, 0).
    c. Translation *T* maps (*x*, *y*) to (*x* − 1, *y* + 3).
    d. Rotation about point *P* through 10°

Guided Practice

State another name for each rotation.

1. $\mathcal{R}_{O,-90}$ $\mathcal{R}_{O,270}$
2. $\mathcal{R}_{O,-200}$ $\mathcal{R}_{O,160}$
3. $\mathcal{R}_{O,540}$ $\mathcal{R}_{O,180}$

The diagonals of an octagon *ABCDEFGH* meet at *O* and form eight triangles. Complete Exs. 4–7 below.

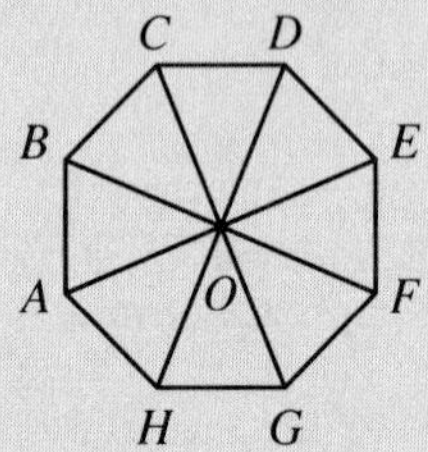

4. $\mathcal{R}_{O,-45}: D \to \underline{E}$
5. $\mathcal{R}_{O,270}: B \to \underline{D}$
6. $H_O(F) = \underline{B}$
7. A reflection in $\overleftrightarrow{AE}$ maps *B* to $\underline{H}$.

State whether the specified parallelogram is mapped to the other parallelogram by a reflection, translation, rotation, or half-turn.

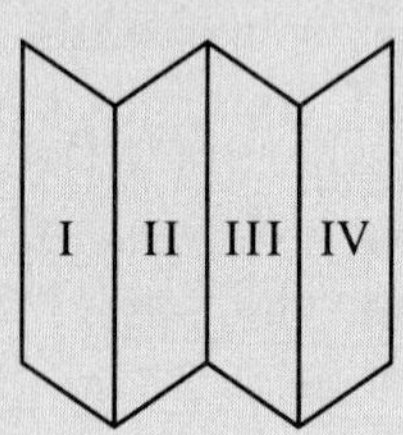

8. I to II reflection
9. II to IV translation

Written Exercises

State another name for each rotation. **Answers may vary; for example:**

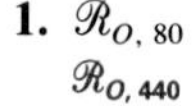

A 1. $\mathcal{R}_{O,80}$ **$\mathcal{R}_{O,440}$** 2. $\mathcal{R}_{O,-15}$ **$\mathcal{R}_{O,345}$** 3. $\mathcal{R}_{A,450}$ **$\mathcal{R}_{A,90}$** 4. $\mathcal{R}_{B,-720}$ **$\mathcal{R}_{B,0}$** 5. H_O **$\mathcal{R}_{O,180}$**

The diagonals of regular hexagon *ABCDEF* form six equilateral triangles as shown. Complete each statement below.

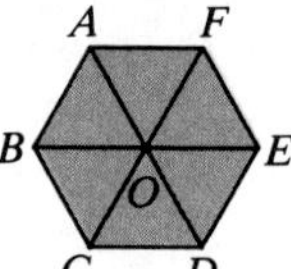

Exs. 6–14

6. $\mathcal{R}_{O,60}: E \to$ _?_ **F**
7. $\mathcal{R}_{O,-60}: D \to$ _?_ **C**
8. $\mathcal{R}_{O,120}: F \to$ _?_ **B**
9. $\mathcal{R}_{D,60}:$ _?_ $\to O$ **E**
10. $\mathcal{R}_{B,-60}(O) =$ _?_ **C**
11. $H_O(A) =$ _?_ **D**
12. A reflection in $\overleftrightarrow{FC}$ maps *B* to _?_ and *D* to _?_. **D, B**
13. If *k* is the perpendicular bisector of $\overline{FE}$, then $R_k(A) =$ _?_. **D**
14. If a translation maps *A* to *B*, then it also maps *O* to _?_ and *E* to _?_. **C, D**

State whether the specified triangle is mapped to the other triangle by a reflection, translation, rotation, or half-turn. **20. half-turn**

15. △(1) to △(2) **rotation**
16. △(1) to △(3) **reflection**
17. △(1) to △(4) **half-turn**
18. △(1) to △(5) **transl.**
19. △(2) to △(4) **rotation**
20. △(2) to △(7)
21. △(4) to △(6) **reflection**
22. △(4) to △(8) **transl.**

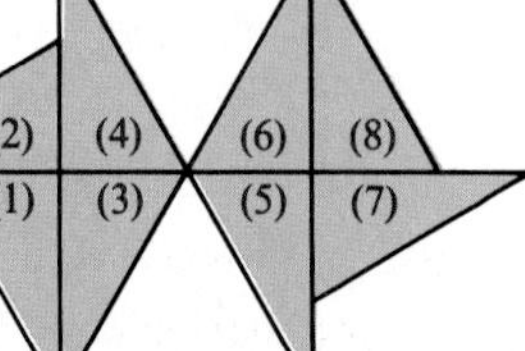

Exs. 15–24

B 23. In the diagram at the right there is a glide reflection that maps triangle (1) to triangle (_?_). **6**

24. Name another pair of triangles for which one triangle is mapped to another by a glide reflection. **(3) and (8)**

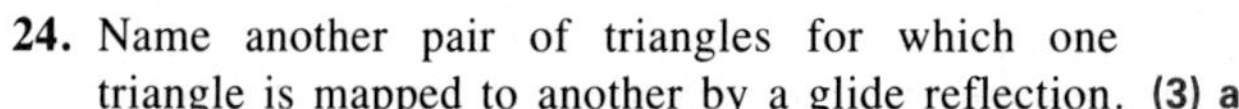

25. Which of the following properties are invariant under a half-turn? **a, b, c, d**
    a. distance **b.** angle measure **c.** area **d.** orientation
26. Which of the properties listed in Exercise 25 are invariant under the rotation $\mathcal{R}_{O,90}$? **a, b, c, d**

Copy the figure on graph paper. Draw the image by the specified rotation.

27. $\mathcal{R}_{O,90}$

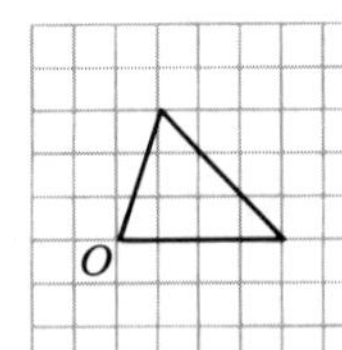

28. $\mathcal{R}_{O,-90}$

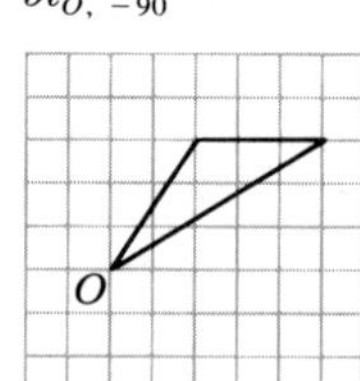

29. H_O

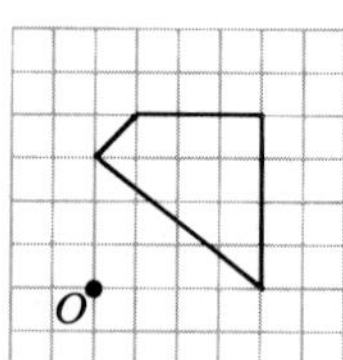

30. If $H_C: (1, 1) \to (7, 3)$, find the coordinates of *C*. **(4, 2)**

31. A rotation maps A to A' and B to B'. Construct the center of the rotation. (*Hint*: If the center is O, then $\overline{OA} = \overline{OA'}$ and $OB = OB'$.) **Const. the ⊥ bisectors of $\overline{AA'}$ and $\overline{BB'}$. Their intersection is O.**

32. a. Draw a coordinate grid with origin O and plot the points $A(0, 3)$ and $B(4, 1)$.

b. Plot A' and B', the images of A and B by $\mathcal{R}_{O, 90}$. **$A'(-3, 0)$, $B'(-1, 4)$**

c. Compare the slopes of $\overleftrightarrow{AB}$ and $\overleftrightarrow{A'B'}$. What does this tell you about these lines? **slope of $\overleftrightarrow{AB} = -\frac{1}{2}$, slope of $\overleftrightarrow{A'B'} = 2$; the lines are ⊥**

d. Without using the distance formula, you know that $A'B' = AB$. State the theorem that tells you this. **A rotation is an isometry.**

e. What reason supports the conclusion that $\triangle AOB$ and $\triangle A'OB'$ have the same area? **An isometry maps any △ to a ≅ △.**

f. Use your graph to find the image of (x, y) by $\mathcal{R}_{O, 90}$. **$(-y, x)$**

33. Repeat Exercise 32 using $\mathcal{R}_{O, 270}$. **a., c., d., e. same as Ex. 32**

33. b. $A'(3, 0)$
$B'(1, -4)$
f. $(y, -x)$

34. A half-turn about $(3, 2)$ maps P to P'. Where does this half-turn map the following points?

a. P' **P**   **b.** $(0, 0)$ **$(6, 4)$**   **c.** $(3, 0)$ **$(3, 4)$**

d. $(1, 4)$ **$(5, 0)$**   **e.** $(-2, 1)$ **$(8, 3)$**   **f.** (x, y) **$(6 - x, 4 - y)$**

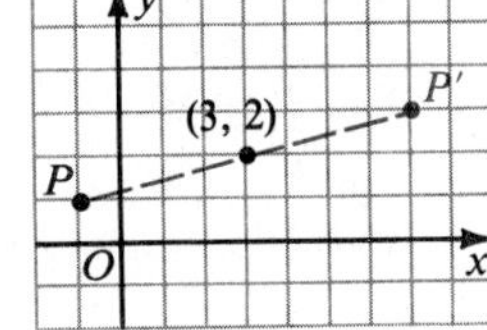

35. The rotation $\mathcal{R}_{O, x}$ maps line l to line l'. (You can think of rotating $\overline{OF}$, the perpendicular from O to l, through $x°$. Its image will be $\overline{OF'}$.) Show that one of the angles between l and l' has measure x. **Extend $\overrightarrow{OF}$ to int. l' at G and let H be the int. of l and l'. $m\angle F'GO = 90 - x$ so $m\angle GHF = 90 - (90 - x) = x$.**

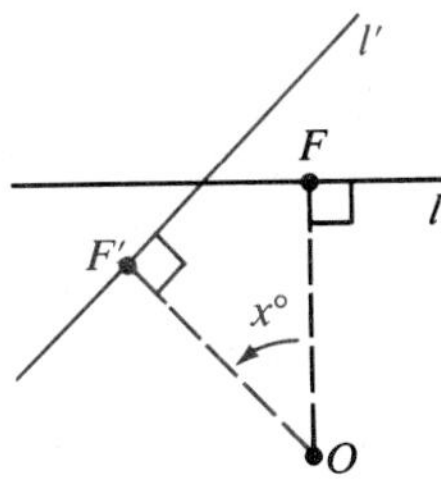

36. $\triangle ABC$ and $\triangle DCE$ are equilateral.

a. What rotation maps A to B and D to E? **$\mathcal{R}_{C, -60}$**

b. Why does $AD = BE$? **See below.**

c. Find the measure of an acute angle between $\overleftrightarrow{AD}$ and $\overleftrightarrow{BE}$. (*Hint*: See Exercise 35.) **60**

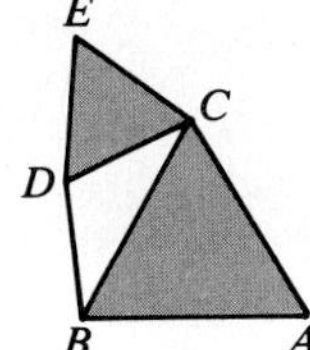

b. $\overline{BE}$ is the image of $\overline{AD}$ under an isometry.

37. $\triangle ABC$ and $\triangle DEC$ are isosceles right triangles.

a. What rotation maps B to A and E to D? **$\mathcal{R}_{C, 90}$**

b. Why does $AD = BE$? **See below.**

c. Explain why $\overline{AD} \perp \overline{BE}$. (*Hint*: See Exercise 35.) **If a rotation of 90° maps $\overline{BE}$ to $\overline{AD}$, then one of the angles betw. $\overline{BE}$ and $\overline{AD}$ has measure 90.**

b. $\overline{AD}$ is the image of $\overline{BE}$ under an isometry.

Exercise Note

You might want to point out that in Ex. 31 once the center of the rotation is found, the angle of rotation can be measured using a protractor.

C **38.** Given: Parallel lines l and k and point A.

a. Construct an equilateral $\triangle ABC$ with B on k and C on l using the following method.

Step 1. Rotate l through 60° about A and let B be the point on k where the image of l intersects k. (The diagram for Exercise 35 may be helpful in rotating l.)

Step 2. Let point C on l be the preimage of B.

b. Explain why $\triangle ABC$ is equilateral.

c. Are there other equilateral triangles with vertices at A and on l and k?

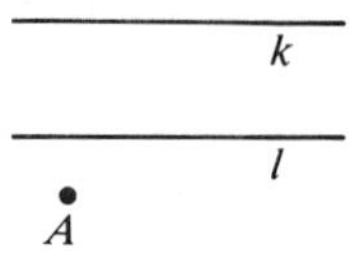

Exs. 38, 39

39. Given the figure for Exercise 38, construct a square $AXYZ$ with X on k and Z on l. **Locate X and Z as you did B and C in Ex. 38, using $\mathcal{R}_{A,90}$ instead of $\mathcal{R}_{A,60}$. With ctrs. X and Z and radius AX, draw arcs int. at Y.**

Mixed Review Exercises **3. $x = \frac{9}{2}$, $y = \frac{10}{3}$, $z = 5$, $w = \frac{9}{2}$**

Given $\overline{ED} \parallel \overline{BC} \parallel \overline{FG}$. Complete the statements.

1. $\triangle OBC$ is similar to $\triangle$ _?_ and $\triangle$ _?_. ***ODE, OFG***
2. The scale factor of $\triangle OBC$ to $\triangle ODE$ is _?_. **2:3**
3. Find the values of x, y, z, and w. **See above.**
4. The scale factor of $\triangle ODE$ to $\triangle OFG$ is _?_. **3:5**
5. The ratio of the areas of $\triangle OBC$ and $\triangle ODE$ is _?_. **4:9**
6. The ratio of the areas of $\triangle ODE$ and $\triangle OFG$ is _?_. **9:25**
7. The ratio of the areas of $\triangle OBC$ and $\triangle OFG$ is _?_. **4:25**

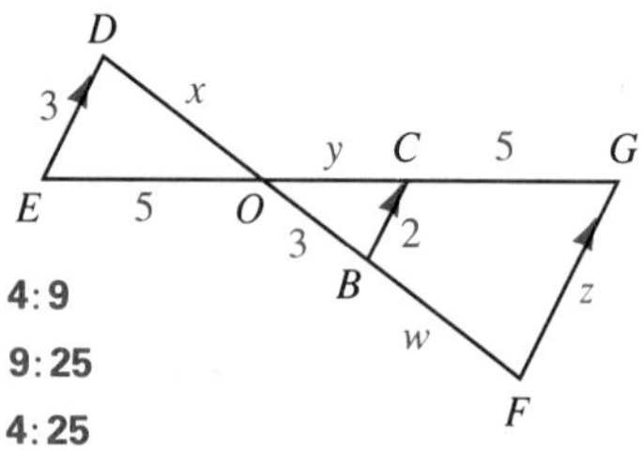

14-5 *Dilations*

Reflections, translations, glide reflections, and rotations are isometries, or *congruence* mappings. In this section we consider a transformation related to *similarity* rather than congruence. It is called a **dilation.** The dilation $D_{O,k}$ has *center O* and nonzero *scale factor k*. $D_{O,k}$ maps any point P to a point P' determined as follows:

(1) If $k > 0$, P' lies on $\overrightarrow{OP}$ and $OP' = k \cdot OP$.

(2) If $k < 0$, P' lies on the ray opposite $\overrightarrow{OP}$ and $OP' = |k| \cdot OP$.

(3) The center O is its own image.

If $|k| > 1$, the dilation is called an **expansion.**
If $|k| < 1$, the dilation is called a **contraction.**

A developing leaf undergoes an expansion, keeping approximately the same shape as it grows in size.

Teaching Suggestions, pp. T140–T141

Objective
Presenting the Lesson
Applications
Reinforcement
Extension

Supplementary Materials

Practice Master 87
Test 57
Resource Book, pp. 97, 167
Study Guide, pp. 189–190
Computer Activity 35

Lesson Focus

There are transformations that do not preserve distance. This lesson introduces one such transformation, called a dilation.

Suggested Assignments

Average
596/2–8 even, 9–21 odd
597/Self-Test 1

Maximum
Day 1: 596/2, 4, 7, 8, 10, 14, 16, 17, 19, 22
Day 2: 596–597/18, 21, 23–28

Example 1 Find the image of $\triangle ABC$ under the expansion $D_{O,\,2}$.

Solution $D_{O,\,2}: \triangle ABC \rightarrow \triangle A'B'C'$

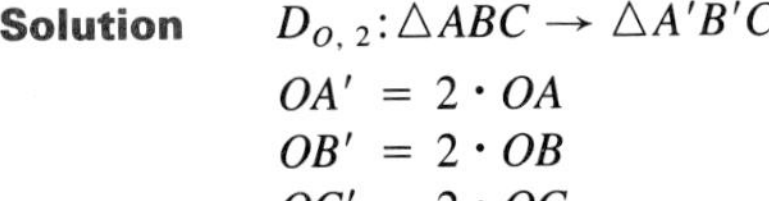

$OA' = 2 \cdot OA$
$OB' = 2 \cdot OB$
$OC' = 2 \cdot OC$

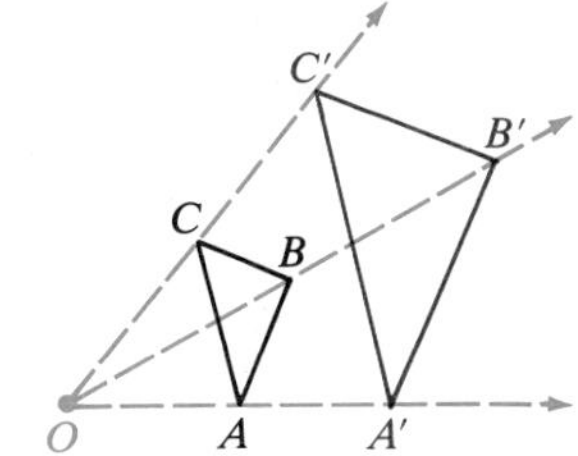

Example 2 Find the image of $\triangle RST$ under the contraction $D_{O,\,\frac{2}{3}}$.

Solution $D_{O,\,\frac{2}{3}}: \triangle RST \rightarrow \triangle R'S'T'$

$OR' = \frac{2}{3} \cdot OR$
$OS' = \frac{2}{3} \cdot OS$
$OT' = \frac{2}{3} \cdot OT$

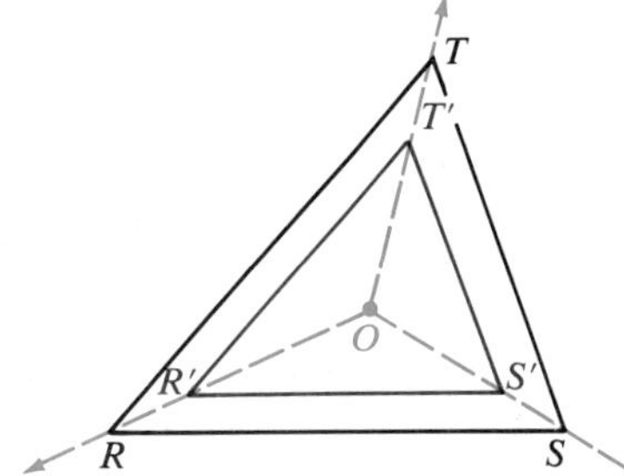

In the examples above, can you prove that the two triangles are similar? **Yes** How are the areas of each pair of triangles related? **1:4, 9:4**

Example 3 Find the image of figure F under the contraction $D_{O,\,-\frac{1}{2}}$.

Solution $D_{O,\,-\frac{1}{2}}$: figure $F \rightarrow$ figure F'
$\overrightarrow{OP}$ is opposite to $\overrightarrow{OP'}$.
$OP' = |-\frac{1}{2}| \cdot OP = \frac{1}{2} \cdot OP$

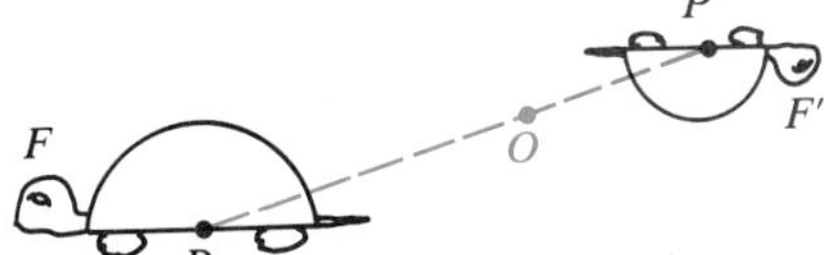

If the scale factor in Example 3 was -1 instead of $-\frac{1}{2}$, the figure F' would be congruent to the figure F, and the transformation would be an isometry, equivalent to a half-turn. In general, however, as these examples illustrate, dilations do not preserve distance. Therefore a dilation is not an isometry (unless $k = 1$ or $k = -1$).

But a dilation always maps any geometric figure to a similar figure. In the examples above, $\triangle ABC \sim \triangle A'B'C'$, $\triangle RST \sim \triangle R'S'T'$ and the figure F is similar to the figure F'. For this reason, a dilation is an example of a **similarity mapping.**

Chalkboard Examples

1. Find the image of $\triangle RST$ under the expansion $D_{O,3}$.

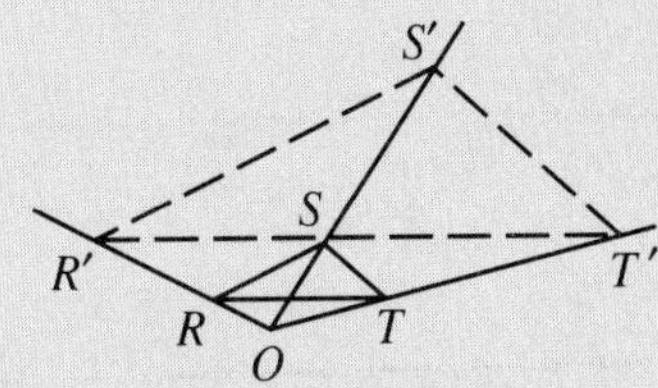

2. Find the image of $WXYZ$ under the contraction $D_{O,\frac{1}{2}}$.

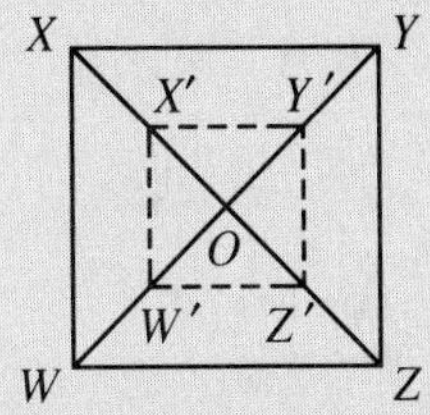

3.a. Find the image of $\triangle ABC$ under $D_{O,\,-2}$.

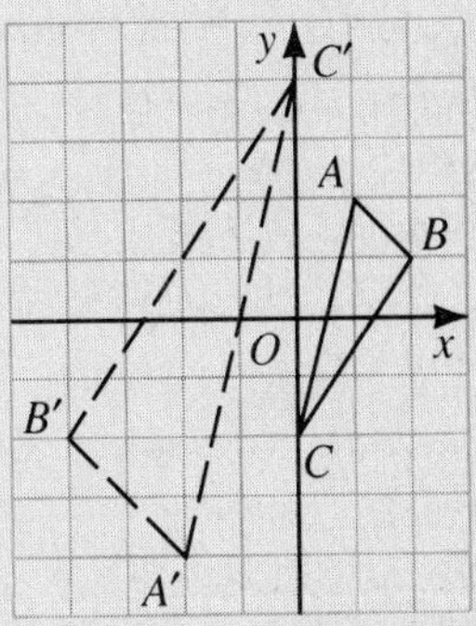

b. What is the ratio of the perimeters of $\triangle ABC$ and $\triangle A'B'C'$? 1:2

c. What is the ratio of the areas of $\triangle ABC$ and $\triangle A'B'C'$? 1:4

4. If $D_{O,\,-\frac{1}{2}}$ maps R to R', then $OR' = \frac{1}{2}\,OR$.

Theorem 14-5

A dilation maps any triangle to a similar triangle.

Given: $D_{O,k}: \triangle ABC \rightarrow \triangle A'B'C'$

Prove: $\triangle ABC \sim \triangle A'B'C'$

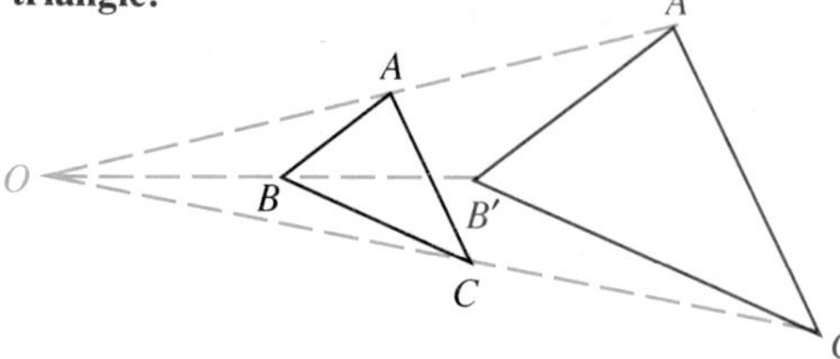

Key steps of proof:

1. $OA' = |k| \cdot OA$, $OB' = |k| \cdot OB$ (Definition of dilation)
2. $\triangle OAB \sim \triangle OA'B'$ (SAS Similarity Theorem)
3. $\frac{A'B'}{AB} = \frac{OA'}{OA} = |k|$ (Corr. sides of ~ ≜ are in proportion.)
4. Similarly, $\frac{B'C'}{BC} = \frac{A'C'}{AC} = |k|$ (Repeat Steps 1–3 for $\triangle OBC$ and $\triangle OB'C'$ and for $\triangle OAC$ and $\triangle OA'C'$.)
5. $\triangle ABC \sim \triangle A'B'C'$ (SSS Similarity Theorem)

Corollary 1

A dilation maps an angle to a congruent angle.

Corollary 2

A dilation $D_{O,k}$ maps any segment to a parallel segment $|k|$ times as long.

Corollary 3

A dilation $D_{O,k}$ maps any polygon to a similar polygon whose area is k^2 times as large.

The diagram for the theorem above shows the case in which $k > 0$. You should draw the diagram for $k < 0$ and convince yourself that the proof is the same.

Theorem 14-5 can also be proved by using coordinates (see Exercise 28). To do this, you set the center of dilation at the origin, and describe $D_{O,k}$ in terms of coordinates by writing $D_{O,k}: (x, y) \rightarrow (kx, ky)$. You can see that this description satisfies the definition of a dilation because O, P, and P' are collinear (use slopes) and $OP' = |k| \cdot OP$ (use the distance formula).

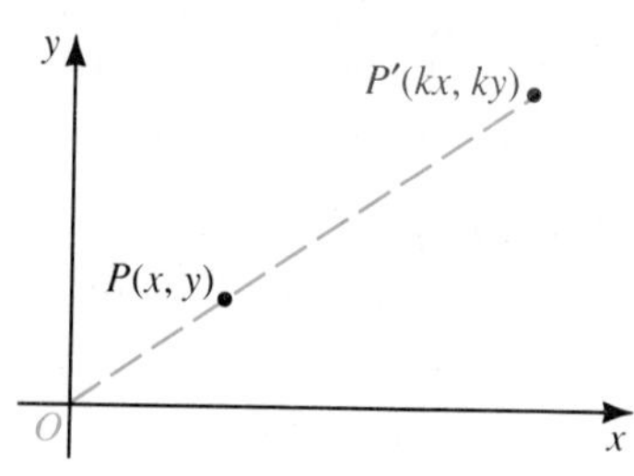

Classroom Exercises **1.–4. Check students' drawings.**

Sketch each triangle on the chalkboard. Then sketch its image under the given dilation.

1. $D_{O,3}$

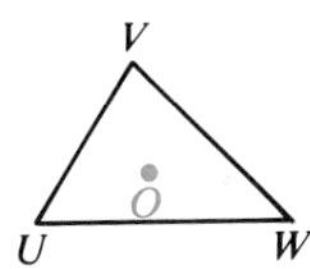

2. $D_{S,\frac{1}{2}}$

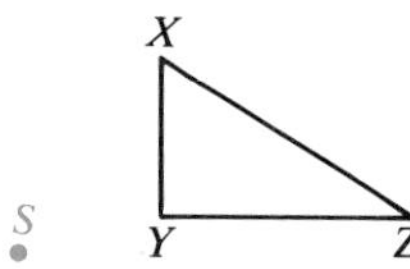

3. $D_{E,-2}$

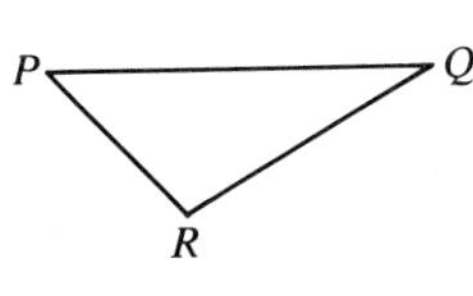

4. $D_{N,-\frac{1}{3}}$

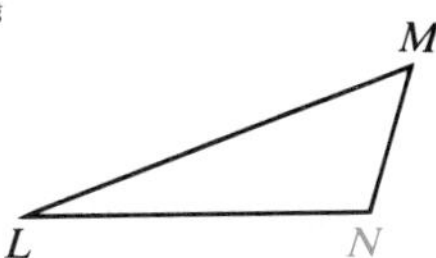

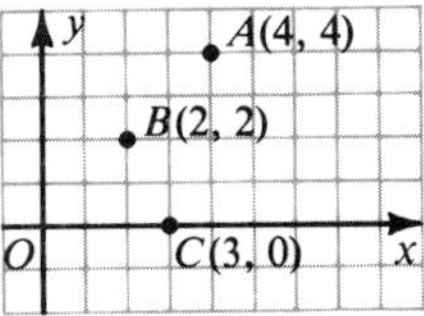

Exs. 5–10

5. Find the coordinates of the images of points A, B, and C under the dilation $D_{O,2}$. **$A'(8, 8)$, $B'(4, 4)$, $C'(6, 0)$**
6. Find the image of (x, y) under $D_{O,2}$. **$(2x, 2y)$**
7. What dilation with center O maps A to B? **$D_{O,\frac{1}{2}}$**
8. What dilation with center O maps C to the point $(-6, 0)$? **$D_{O,-2}$**
9. Find the coordinates of the image of A under $D_{B,2}$. **(6, 6)**
10. Find the coordinates of the image of B under $D_{C,3}$. **(0, 6)**
11. Match each scale factor in the first column with the name of the corresponding dilation in the second column.

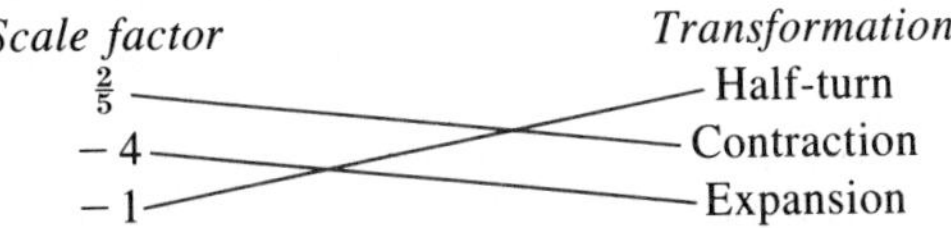

12. Describe the dilation $D_{O,1}$. **It maps every point onto itself.**
13. If $\odot S$ has radius 4, describe the image of $\odot S$ under $D_{S,5}$ and under $D_{S,-1}$. **$D_{S,5}$: $\odot$ with ctr. S, rad. 20; $D_{S,-1}$: $\odot S$**
14. If point A is on line k, what is the image of line k under $D_{A,2}$? **k**
15. The dilation $D_{O,3}$ maps P to P' and Q to Q'.
    a. If $OQ = 2$, find OQ'. **6**
    b. If $PQ = 7$, find $P'Q'$. **21**
    c. If $PP' = 10$, find OP. **5**
16. Explain how Corollary 1 follows from Theorem 14-5.
17. Explain how Corollary 3 follows from Corollaries 1 and 2.

Exercise Note

The center O is specified in Exs. 7 and 8 because there are many different dilations (each with a different center) that could achieve the required mapping.

Proof Note

Note that because of its difficulty, the proof of Corollary 2 appears later, in Written Exs. 25 and 26, rather than accompanying Classroom Exs. 16 and 17. The proof does not use Corollary 3.

Additional Answers Classroom Exercises

16. A dilation maps any △ to a ~ △; corr. ∠s of ~ △s are ≅.
17. By Cor. 1, the image poly. has ∠s ≅ to those of the orig. poly. By Cor. 2, the sides are in prop., so the figs. are ~ with scale factor k, and the ratio of the areas is $|k|^2:1 = k^2:1$, since $|k|^2 = k^2$ for all real k.

Written Exercises

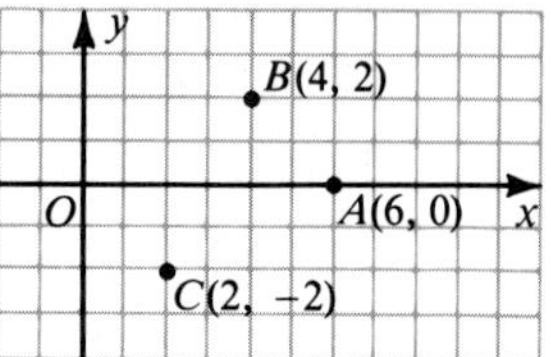

Find the coordinates of the images of A, B, and C by the given dilation.

A

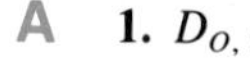

1. $D_{O,2}$ **2.** $D_{O,3}$ **3.** $D_{O,\frac{1}{2}}$ **4.** $D_{O,-\frac{1}{2}}$

5. $D_{O,-2}$ **6.** $D_{O,1}$ **7.** $D_{A,-\frac{1}{2}}$ **8.** $D_{A,2}$

A dilation with the origin, O, as center maps the given point to the image point named. Find the scale factor of the dilation. Is the dilation an expansion or a contraction?

9. (2, 0) → (8, 0) **4; exp.** **10.** (2, 3) → (4, 6) **2; exp.** **11.** (3, 9) → (1, 3) **$\frac{1}{3}$; contr.**

12. (4, 10) → (−2, −5) **12. $-\frac{1}{2}$; contraction** **13.** $(0, \frac{1}{6}) \to (0, \frac{2}{3})$ **4; exp.** **14.** (−6, 2) → (18, −6) **−3; exp.**

B **15.** Which of the following properties are invariant under any dilation? **b, d**

  a. distance **b.** angle measure **c.** area **d.** orientation

16. Is parallelism invariant under a dilation? (*Hint*: See Exercise 23 on page 581.) **Yes**

17. If A', B', C', and D' are the images of any four points A, B, C, and D, then we say the ratio of distances is invariant under the transformation if $\frac{AB}{CD} = \frac{A'B'}{C'D'}$. For which of the following transformations is the ratio of distances invariant? **a, b, c**

  a. reflection **b.** rotation **c.** dilation

Graph quad. $PQRS$ and its image by the dilation given. Find the ratio of the perimeters and the ratio of the areas of the two quadrilaterals.

18.	$P(-1, 1)$	$Q(0, -1)$	$R(4, 0)$	$S(2, 2)$	$D_{O,3}$ **1:3; 1:9**
19.	$P(12, 0)$	$Q(0, 15)$	$R(-9, 6)$	$S(3, -9)$	$D_{O,\frac{2}{3}}$ **3:2; 9:4**
20.	$P(3, 0)$	$Q(3, 4)$	$R(6, 6)$	$S(5, -1)$	$D_{O,-2}$ **1:2; 1:4**
21.	$P(-2, -2)$	$Q(0, 0)$	$R(4, 0)$	$S(6, -2)$	$D_{O,-\frac{1}{2}}$ **2:1; 4:1**

22. The diagram illustrates a dilation of three-dimensional space. $D_{O,2}$ maps the smaller cube to the larger cube.

  a. What is the ratio of the surface areas of these cubes? **1:4**

  b. What is the ratio of the volumes of these cubes? **1:8**

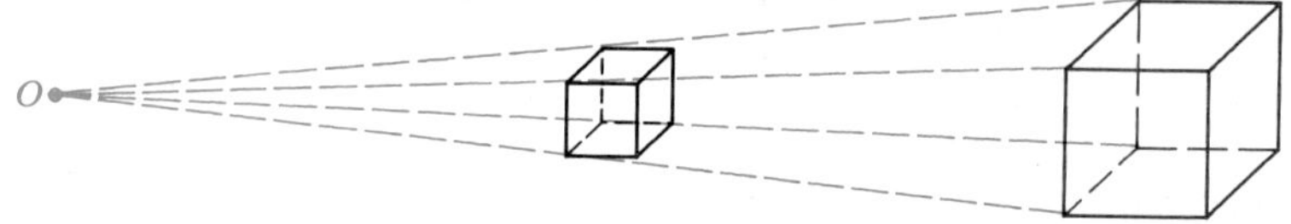

23. A dilation with scale factor $\frac{3}{4}$ maps a sphere with center C to a concentric sphere.

  a. What is the ratio of the surface areas of these spheres? **16:9**

  b. What is the ratio of the volumes of these spheres? **64:27**

Additional Answers Written Exercises

1. $A'(12, 0)$, $B'(8, 4)$, $C'(4, -4)$
2. $A'(18, 0)$, $B'(12, 6)$, $C'(6, -6)$
3. $A'(3, 0)$, $B'(2, 1)$, $C'(1, -1)$
4. $A'(-3, 0)$, $B'(-2, -1)$, $C'(-1, 1)$
5. $A'(-12, 0)$, $B'(-8, -4)$, $C'(-4, 4)$
6. $A'(6, 0)$, $B'(4, 2)$, $C'(2, -2)$
7. $A'(6, 0)$, $B'(7, -1)$, $C'(8, 1)$
8. $A'(6, 0)$, $B'(2, 4)$, $C'(-2, -4)$

18. $P'(-3, 3)$; $Q'(0, -3)$; $R'(12, 0)$; $S'(6, 6)$
19. $P'(8, 0)$; $Q'(0, 10)$; $R'(-6, 4)$; $S'(2, -6)$
20. $P'(-6, 0)$; $Q'(-6, -8)$; $R'(-12, -12)$; $S'(-10, 2)$
21. $P'(1, 1)$; $Q'(0, 0)$; $R'(-2, 0)$; $S'(-3, 1)$

Guided Practice

Find the coordinates of the images of $A(3, 6)$, $B(-3, -3)$ and $C(-6, 0)$ by the given dilation.

1. $D_{O,2}$ $A'(6, 12)$, $B'(-6, -6)$, $C'(-12, 0)$
2. $D_{O,-\frac{1}{3}}$ $A'(-1, -2)$, $B'(1, 1)$, $C'(2, 0)$
3. A dilation with the origin, O, as center maps (3, 4) to (9, 12). Find the scale factor. Is the dilation an expansion or contraction? 3; expansion
4. A dilation with the origin, O, as center maps $(-3, 4) \to (1, -\frac{4}{3})$. Find the scale factor. Is the dilation an expansion or contraction? $-\frac{1}{3}$; contraction

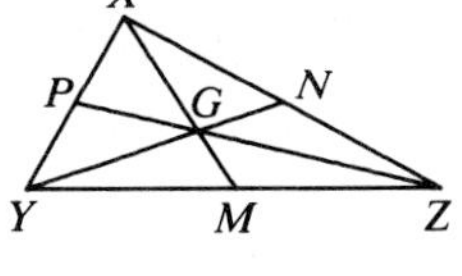

24. G is the intersection of the medians of $\triangle XYZ$. Complete the following statements. (*Hint*: Use Theorem 10-4 on page 387.)

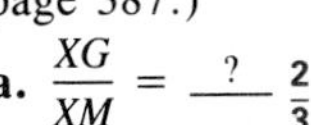

a. $\frac{XG}{XM} = \underline{\ ?\ }$ **$\frac{2}{3}$** b. $\frac{GM}{GX} = \underline{\ ?\ }$ **$\frac{1}{2}$**

c. What dilation maps X to M? **$D_{G, -\frac{1}{2}}$**

d. What is the image under this dilation of Y? of Z? **N; P**

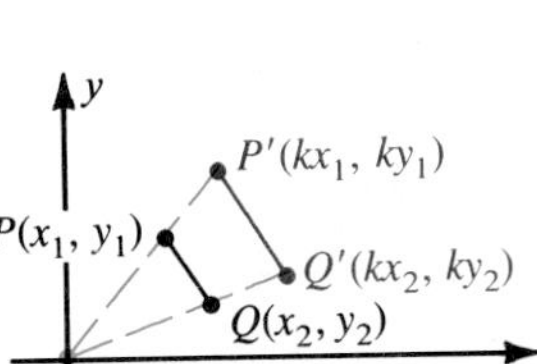
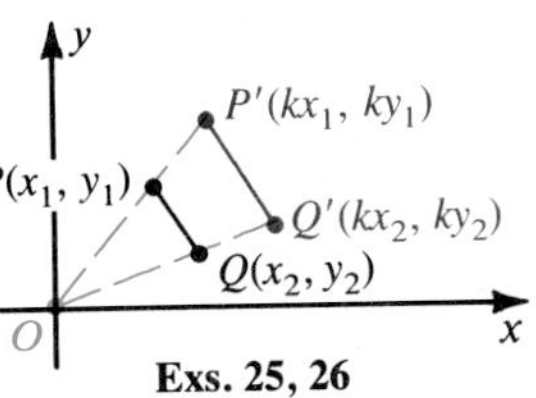

Exs. 25, 26

25. $D_{O,k}$ maps $\overline{PQ}$ to $\overline{P'Q'}$.

a. Show that the slopes of $\overline{PQ}$ and $\overline{P'Q'}$ are equal.

b. Part (a) proves that $\overline{PQ}$ and $\overline{P'Q'}$ are $\underline{\ ?\ }$. **parallel**

C 26. Use the distance formula to show that $P'Q' = |k|\sqrt{(x_1 - x_2)^2 + (y_1 - y_2)^2} = |k| \cdot PQ$.

27. A dilation with center (a, b) and scale factor k maps $A(3, 4)$ to $A'(1, 8)$, and $B(3, 2)$ to $B'(1, 2)$. Find the coordinates of the center (a, b) and the value of k. **(4, 2), $k = 3$**

28. Prove Theorem 14-5 using the coordinate definition of a dilation, $D_{O,k}:(x, y) \rightarrow (kx, ky)$. (*Hint*: Let A, B, and C have coordinates (p, q), (r, s), and (t, u) respectively.)

Self-Test 1

1. Define an isometry. **An isometry is a one-to-one mapping from the whole plane onto the whole plane that maps every segment to a ≅ segment.**

2. If $f(x) = 3x - 7$, find the image of 2 and the preimage of 2. **−1, 3**

3. If $T:(x, y) \rightarrow (x + 1, y - 2)$, find the image and preimage of the origin. **(1, −2), (−1, 2)**

4. Find the image of (3, 5) when reflected in each line.

a. the x-axis **(3, −5)** b. the y-axis **(−3, 5)** c. the line $y = x$. **(5, 3)**

5. A dilation with scale factor 3 maps $\triangle ABC$ to $\triangle A'B'C'$. Which of the following are true? **a, b**

a. $\overline{AB} \parallel \overline{A'B'}$ b. $\frac{A'B'}{AB} = 3$ c. $\frac{\text{area of } \triangle A'B'C'}{\text{area of } \triangle ABC} = 3$

6. Give two other names for the rotation $\mathcal{R}_{O,-30}$. **Examples: $\mathcal{R}_{O,330}$ and $\mathcal{R}_{O,-390}$**

Complete. R_x and R_y denote reflections in the x- and y-axes, respectively.

7. $R_y:A \rightarrow \underline{\ ?\ }$ **B**

8. $R_x:B \rightarrow \underline{\ ?\ }$ **C**

9. $R_x:\overline{DC} \rightarrow \underline{\ ?\ }$ **$\overline{AB}$**

10. $R_y:\underline{\ ?\ } \rightarrow \overline{OA}$ **$\overline{OB}$**

11. $H_O:K \rightarrow \underline{\ ?\ }$ **M**

12. $H_O:\underline{\ ?\ } \rightarrow \overline{CO}$ **$\overline{AO}$**

13. $\mathcal{R}_{O,90}$ maps M to $\underline{\ ?\ }$. **L**

14. $\mathcal{R}_{O,-90}$ maps $\triangle MCO$ to $\triangle\underline{\ ?\ }$. **NDO**

15. $D_{O,2}$ maps P to $\underline{\ ?\ }$. **C**

16. $D_{M,-\frac{1}{2}}$ maps B to $\underline{\ ?\ }$. **Q**

17. A translation that maps A to L maps N to $\underline{\ ?\ }$. **C**

18. The glide reflection in $\overleftrightarrow{BD}$ that maps K to M maps N to $\underline{\ ?\ }$. **L**

Additional Answers Written Exercises

25.a. slope of $\overline{PQ} = \frac{y_2 - y_1}{x_2 - x_1}$; slope of $\overline{P'Q'} = \frac{ky_2 - ky_1}{kx_2 - kx_1} = \frac{k(y_2 - y_1)}{k(x_2 - x_1)} = \frac{y_2 - y_1}{x_2 - x_1}$

26. $P'Q' = \sqrt{(kx_1 - kx_2)^2 + (ky_1 - ky_2)^2} = \sqrt{[k(x_1 - x_2)]^2 + [k(y_1 - y_2)]^2} = \sqrt{k^2(x_1 - x_2)^2 + k^2(y_1 - y_2)^2} = \sqrt{k^2[(x_1 - x_2)^2 + (y_1 - y_2)^2]} = |k|\sqrt{(x_1 - x_2)^2 + (y_1 - y_2)^2} = |k| \cdot PQ$

Quick Quiz

1. Which transformations are isometries? reflection, translation, glide reflection, rotation, half-turn
2. If $g(x) = 7 - 2x$, find the image of 3 and the preimage of −5. 1; 6
3. If $R:(x, y) \rightarrow (x - 2, y + 3)$, find the image of (−3, 1). (−5, 4)
4. Find the image of (−1, 4) when reflected in each line.
   a. the x-axis (−1, −4)
   b. the y-axis (1, 4)
   c. the line $y = x$ (4, −1)
5. A dilation with scale factor $\frac{1}{2}$ maps $\triangle RST$ to $\triangle R'S'T'$. Which of the following are true?
   a. $\overline{RS} \parallel \overline{R'S'}$ T
   b. $\frac{R'S'}{RS} = \frac{1}{2}$ T

(continued)

c. $\frac{\text{perimeter of } \triangle R'S'T'}{\text{perimeter of } \triangle RST} = \frac{1}{2}$
T

d. $\frac{\text{area of } \triangle R'S'T'}{\text{area of } \triangle RST} = \frac{1}{4}$ T

6. Give two other names for $\mathcal{R}_{O,-90}$.
$\mathcal{R}_{O,270}$; $\mathcal{R}_{O,-450}$

Complete. R_x and R_y denote reflections in the x- and y-axes, respectively.

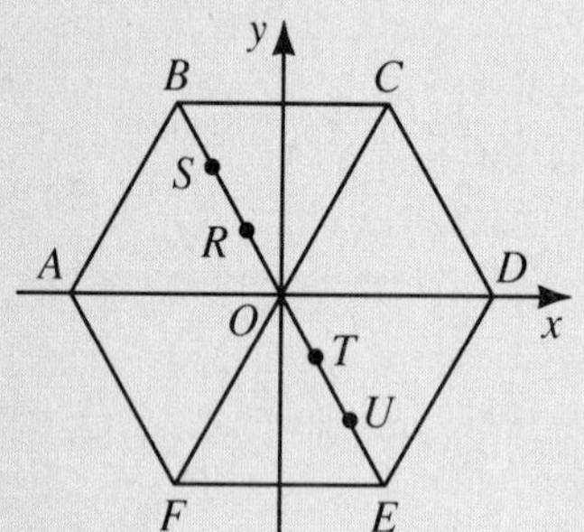

7. $R_y: A \to \underline{D}$
8. $R_x: A \to \underline{A}$
9. $R_y: \overline{DE} \to \underline{\overline{AF}}$
10. $R_x: \underline{\overline{AB}} \to \overline{AF}$
11. $H_O: B \to \underline{E}$
12. $H_O: \underline{\overline{AB}} \to \overline{DE}$
13. $\mathcal{R}_{O,120}$ maps E to $\underline{C}$.
14. $\mathcal{R}_{O,-120}$ maps $\triangle BOC$ to $\underline{\triangle DOE}$.
15. $D_{O,3}$ maps R to $\underline{B}$.
16. $D_{O,-\frac{2}{3}}$ maps B to $\underline{U}$.
17. A translation that maps F to A maps D to $\underline{C}$.
18. The glide reflection in $\overline{AD}$ that maps B to E maps F to $\underline{C}$.

Career

Computer Animation Programmer

One problem computer animation programmers have encountered is how to produce natural-looking landscapes. The structures of trees, mountains, clouds, and coastlines are complex. To create them in a computer landscape can require storing a great deal of information. Also, since animations often include moving through space, data about the landscape features needs to be provided at many levels of detail. (If you specified the appearance of a mountain from only one viewpoint, say, then "zooming in" for a close-up would reveal that details are missing, a problem known as *loss of resolution*.)

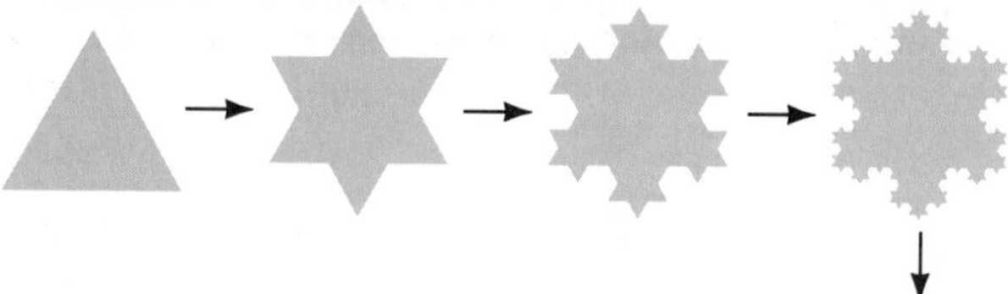

One new approach involves using fractals. A *fractal* is a complex shape that looks more or less the same at all magnifications. Fractals are made by following simple rules, called *algorithms*. The snowflake shape in the diagram at right is an example. Its algorithm is: Start with an equilateral triangle. Divide each side of the polygon in thirds; add an equilateral triangle to each center third; repeat. No matter how much you magnify a piece of this polygon, it will retain the overall pattern and complexity of the original. When you "zoom in" on a fractal shape, there is no loss of resolution.

Computer programmers are taking advantage of this property of fractals to approximate many items in nature, such as the mountains in the photograph above. Programming a computer to follow these algorithms uses less memory than specifying the exact shape of each element from many different viewpoints and distances.

Composition and Symmetry

Objectives

1. Locate the images of figures by composites of mappings.
2. Recognize and use the terms *identity* and *inverse* in relation to mappings.
3. Describe the symmetry of figures and solids.

14-6 *Composites of Mappings*

Suppose a transformation T maps point P to P' and then a transformation S maps P' to P''. Then T and S can be combined to produce a new transformation that maps P directly to P''. This new transformation is called the **composite** of S and T and is written $S \circ T$. Notice in the diagram that $P'' = S(P') = S(T(P)) = (S \circ T)(P)$.

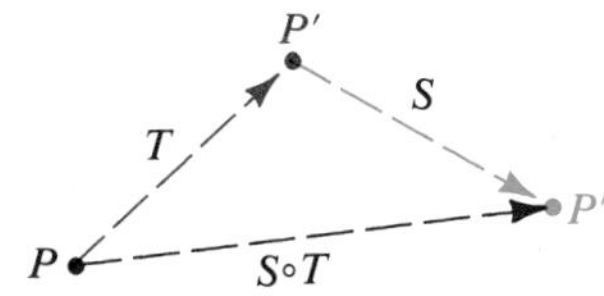

We reduce the number of parentheses needed to indicate that the composite of S and T maps P to P'' by writing $S \circ T: P \rightarrow P''$. Notice that T, the transformation that is applied first, is written closer to P, and S, the transformation that is applied second, is written farther from P. For this reason, the composite $S \circ T$ is often read "S after T," or "T followed by S."

The operation that combines two mappings (or functions) to produce the composite mapping (or composite function) is called *composition*. We shall see that composition has many characteristics similar to multiplication, but there is one important exception. For multiplication, it makes no difference in which order you multiply two numbers. For composition, however, the order of the mappings or functions usually *does* make a difference. Examples 1 and 2 illustrate this.

Example 1 If $f(x) = x^2$ and $g(x) = 2x$, find **(a)** $(g \circ f)(x)$ and **(b)** $(f \circ g)(x)$.

Solution

a. $(g \circ f)(x) = g(f(x))$
$= g(x^2)$
$= 2x^2$

b. $(f \circ g)(x) = f(g(x))$
$= f(2x)$
$= (2x)^2$, or $4x^2$

In mapping notation, we could write that $g \circ f: x \rightarrow 2x^2$ and $f \circ g: x \rightarrow 4x^2$. Note that since $2x^2 \neq 4x^2$, $g \circ f \neq f \circ g$.

Teaching Suggestions,
pp. T141–T142

Objective
Presenting the Lesson
Making Connections
Reinforcement
Extension

Cooperative Learning,
p. T142

Supplementary Materials

Study Guide, pp. 191–192
Computer Activity 36

Lesson Focus

Two transformations can be combined to produce a new transformation called a composite. The focus of this lesson is to study composites of transformations.

Suggested Assignments

Average
603–604/1–4, 6–8, 10, 12

Maximum
603–604/2, 4, 6, 7–19 odd

Teaching Note

In Example 1, the parentheses in $(g \circ f)(x)$ are retained because writing $g \circ f(x)$ would be a nonsensical composition of the function g and the number $f(x)$. When using the mapping notation, these parentheses are no longer needed because the colon serves as a grouping symbol, as in $g \circ f: x \rightarrow 2x^2$.

Example 2 Show that $H_O \circ R_j \neq R_j \circ H_O$.

Solution Study the two diagrams below.

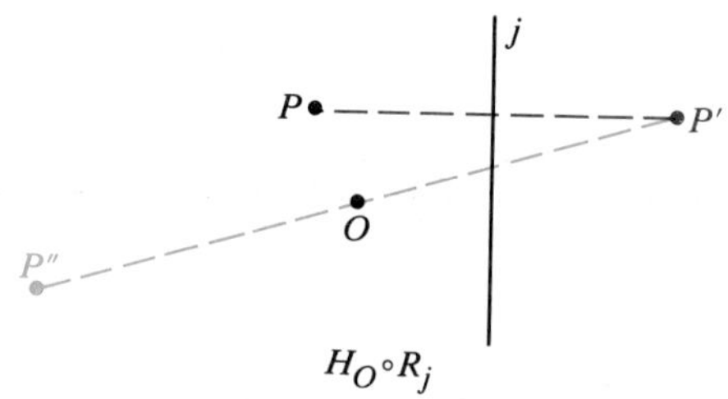

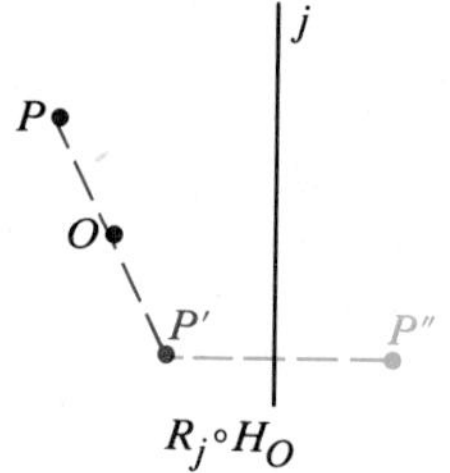

Here R_j, the reflection of P in line j, is carried out first, mapping P to P'. Then H_O maps P' to P''. Thus P'' is the image of P under the composite $H_O \circ R_j$.

With the order changed in the composite, the half-turn is carried out first, followed by the reflection in line j. The image point P'' is now in a different place.

Notice that the two composites map P to different image points, so the composites are not equal.

Example 2 shows that the order in a composite of transformations can be very important, but this is not always true. For example, if S and T are two translations, then order is not important, since $S \circ T = T \circ S$ (see Exercise 10).

Example 2 above shows the effect of a composite of mappings on a single point P. The diagram below shows a composite of reflections acting on a whole figure, F. F is reflected in line j to F', and F' is reflected in line k to F''. Thus $R_k \circ R_j$ maps F to F''. Again notice that the first reflection, R_j, is written on the right.

The final image F'' is the same size and shape as F. Also, F'' is the image of F under a translation. This illustrates our next two theorems. First, the composite of any two isometries is an isometry. Second, the composite of reflections in two parallel lines is a translation.

Teaching Note

Example 2 shows that the composition of a half-turn and a reflection is not commutative.

Chalkboard Examples

1. If $f(x) = 3x + 1$ and $g(x) = x^2$, find
   a. $(g \circ f)(x)$
      $9x^2 + 6x + 1$
   b. $(f \circ g)(x)$
      $3x^2 + 1$

Give a single transformation that is equal to the composition, if $T:(x, y) \to (x + 2, y - 1)$, and R_x and R_y are reflections in the x- and y-axes.

2. $\mathcal{R}_{O, 30} \circ \mathcal{R}_{O, 60}$
   $\mathcal{R}_{O, 90}$
3. $H_O \circ R_x$ R_y
4. $R_x \circ R_y$ H_O
5. $R_x \circ T$
   $M:(x, y) \to (x + 2, -y + 1)$
6. $R_y \circ R_y$ Answers may vary. For example, $M:(x, y) \to (x, y)$; $\mathcal{R}_{O, 0}$; and so on.

Using a Computer

Use the LOGO graphing language to demonstrate the composition of mappings. Have students perform various composite rotations (LEFT and RIGHT commands) and translations (FORWARD and BACK commands) of the screen turtle to develop an intuitive understanding of the composition of mappings and to test associativity and commutativity.

Theorem 14-6

The composite of two isometries is an isometry.

Theorem 14-7

A composite of reflections in two parallel lines is a translation. The translation glides all points through twice the distance from the first line of reflection to the second.

Although we will not present a formal proof of Theorem 14-7, the following argument should convince you that it is true. Assume that $j \parallel k$ and that R_j maps P to P' and Q to Q', and that R_k maps P' to P'' and Q' to Q''. To show that the composite $R_k \circ R_j$ is a translation we will demonstrate that $PP'' = QQ''$ and that $\overleftrightarrow{PP''}$ and $\overleftrightarrow{QQ''}$ are parallel.

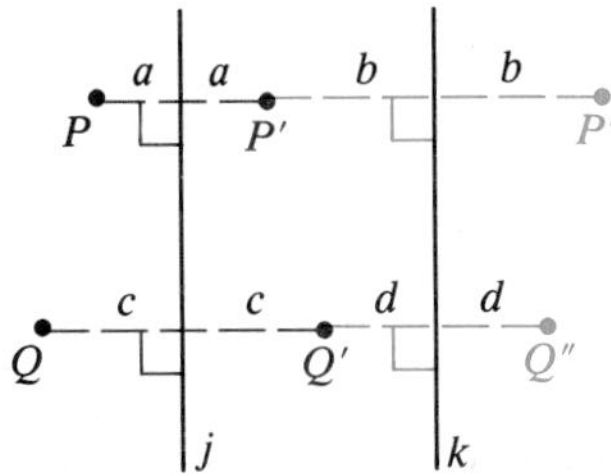

The letters a, b, c, and d in the diagram label pairs of distances that are equal according to the definition of a reflection. P, P', and P'' are collinear and

$$PP'' = 2a + 2b = 2(a + b)$$

Similarly,

$$QQ'' = 2c + 2d = 2(c + d)$$

But $(a + b) = (c + d)$, since by Theorem 5-8, the distance between the parallel lines j and k is constant. Therefore $PP'' = QQ'' =$ twice the distance from j to k.

That $\overleftrightarrow{PP''}$ and $\overleftrightarrow{QQ''}$ are parallel follows from the fact that both lines are perpendicular to j and k. Theorem 3-7 guarantees that if two lines in a plane are perpendicular to the same line, then the two lines are parallel.

You should make diagrams for the case when P is on j or k, when P is located between j and k, and when P is to the right of k. Convince yourself that $PP'' = 2(a + b)$ in these cases also. In every case, the glide is perpendicular to j and k and goes in the direction from j to k (that is, from the first line of reflection toward the second line of reflection).

Theorem 14-7 shows that when lines j and k are parallel, $R_k \circ R_j$ translates points through twice the distance between the lines. If lines j and k intersect, $R_k \circ R_j$ rotates points through twice the measure of the angle between the lines. This is our next theorem.

Teaching Note

If a translation $T: \triangle ABC \rightarrow \triangle A'B'C'$ is already done, students can find a pair of parallel reflecting lines by the following procedure. Draw $\overline{AA'}$ and then find its midpoint, M, by constructing the perpendicular bisector of $\overline{AA'}$. Then construct the perpendicular bisectors of $\overline{AM}$ and $\overline{MA'}$. These two lines are parallel reflecting lines that translate $\triangle ABC$ to $\triangle A'B'C'$.

Teaching Note

Emphasize that a rotation is a transformation, so that the image of any point can be found by using the center, the magnitude, and the direction of rotation (clockwise or counterclockwise).

Teaching Note

If $\triangle ABC \rightarrow \triangle A'B'C'$ under a rotation is already done, students can find a pair of intersecting reflecting lines by the following procedure. Draw $\overline{AA'}$ and $\overline{BB'}$. Construct their perpendicular bisectors. The intersection of the perpendicular bisectors gives the center of the rotation, O. Now draw $\overline{OA}$ and $\overline{OA'}$. (Measuring $\angle AOA'$ gives the magnitude of the rotation.) To find the reflecting lines, bisect $\angle AOA'$ to get $\angle AOX$ and $\angle XOA'$. Then bisect $\angle AOX$ and $\angle XOA'$. These angle bisectors are the intersecting reflecting lines that rotate $\triangle ABC$ to $\triangle A'B'C'$.

Theorem 14-8

A composite of reflections in two intersecting lines is a rotation about the point of intersection of the two lines. The measure of the angle of rotation is twice the measure of the angle from the first line of reflection to the second.

Given: j intersects k, forming an angle of measure y at O.

Prove: $R_k \circ R_j = \mathcal{R}_{O,\,2y}$

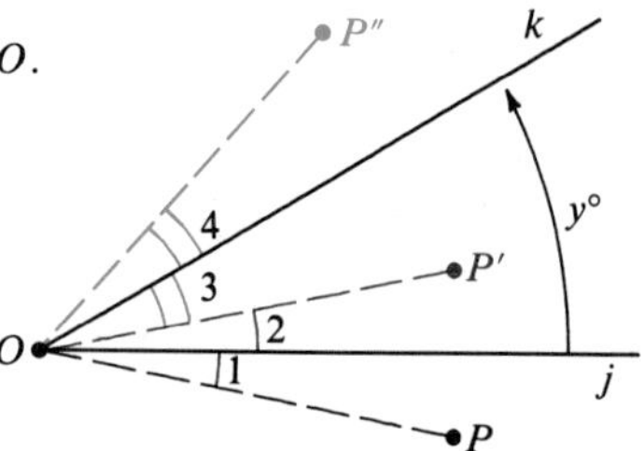

Proof:

The diagram shows an arbitrary point P and its image P' by reflection in j. The image of P' by reflection in k is P''. According to the definition of a rotation we must prove that $OP = OP''$ and $m\angle POP'' = 2y$.

R_j and R_k are isometries, so they preserve both distance and angle measure. Therefore $OP = OP'$, $OP' = OP''$, $m\angle 1 = m\angle 2$, and $m\angle 3 = m\angle 4$. Thus $OP = OP''$ and the measure of the angle of rotation equals

$$m\angle 1 + m\angle 2 + m\angle 3 + m\angle 4 = 2m\angle 2 + 2m\angle 3 = 2y.$$

Corollary

A composite of reflections in perpendicular lines is a half-turn about the point where the lines intersect.

Classroom Exercises

1. If $f(x) = x + 1$ and $g(x) = 3x$, find the following.
   a. $f(4)$ **5** **b.** $(g \circ f)(4)$ **15** **c.** $(g \circ f)(x)$ **3(x + 1)**
   d. $g(2)$ **6** **e.** $(f \circ g)(2)$ **7** **f.** $(f \circ g)(x)$ **3x + 1**
2. Repeat Exercise 1 if $f: x \rightarrow \sqrt{x}$ and $g: x \rightarrow x + 7$.
   a. 2 b. 9 c. $\sqrt{x} + 7$ d. 9 e. 3 f. $\sqrt{x + 7}$

Complete the following. R_x and R_y are reflections in the x- and y-axes.

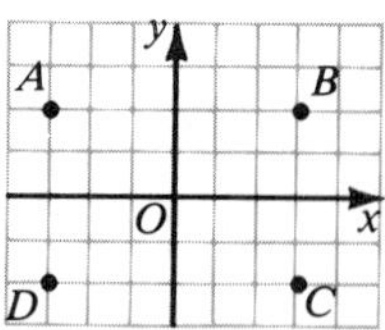

3. $R_x \circ R_y : A \rightarrow$ __?__ **C**
4. $R_x \circ R_y : D \rightarrow$ __?__ **B**
5. $H_O \circ R_y : B \rightarrow$ __?__ **C**
6. $R_y \circ H_O : B \rightarrow$ __?__ **C**
7. $H_O \circ H_O : A \rightarrow$ __?__ **A**
8. $R_y \circ R_y : C \rightarrow$ __?__ **C**

Copy the figure on the chalkboard and find its image by $R_k \circ R_j$. Then copy the figure again and find its image by $R_j \circ R_k$. **Check students' drawings.**

9.

10.

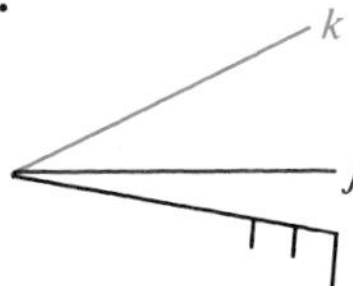

11. Prove Theorem 14-6. (*Hint*: Let S and T be isometries. Consider a $\overline{PQ}$ under $S \circ T$.)

12. Explain how the Corollary follows from Theorem 14-8.

Written Exercises **2. a. −2 b. 3x − 8 c. −20 d. 3x − 26**

A

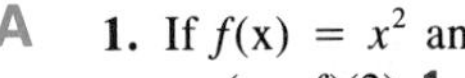

1. If $f(x) = x^2$ and $g(x) = 2x - 7$, evaluate the following.
 a. $(g \circ f)(2)$ **1** **b.** $(g \circ f)(x)$ **$2x^2 - 7$** **c.** $(f \circ g)(2)$ **9** **d.** $(f \circ g)(x)$ **$(2x - 7)^2$**

2. Repeat Exercise 1 if $f(x) = 3x + 1$ and $g(x) = x - 9$.

3. If $h{:}x \to \frac{x+1}{2}$ and $k{:}x \to x^3$, complete the following.
 a. $k \circ h{:}3 \to$ __?__ **8** **b.** $k \circ h{:}5 \to$ __?__ **27** **c.** $k \circ h{:}x \to$ __?__ **$\left(\frac{x+1}{2}\right)^3$**
 d. $h \circ k{:}3 \to$ __?__ **14** **e.** $h \circ k{:}5 \to$ __?__ **63** **f.** $h \circ k{:}x \to$ __?__ **$\frac{x^3+1}{2}$**

4. Repeat Exercise 3 if $h{:}x \to x^2 - 1$ and $k{:}x \to 2x + 7$.
 a. 23 b. 55 c. $2x^2 + 5$ d. 168 e. 288 f. $4x^2 + 28x + 48$

Copy each figure and find its image under $R_k \circ R_j$. Then copy the figure again and find its image under $R_j \circ R_k$. **5.–9. Check students' drawings.**

5.

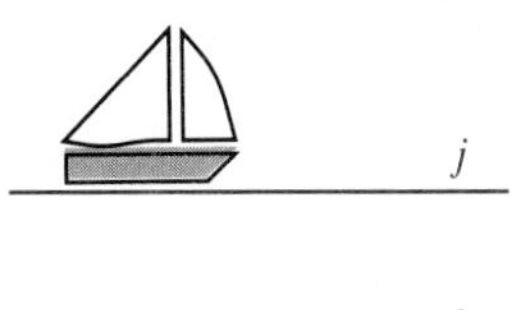

6.

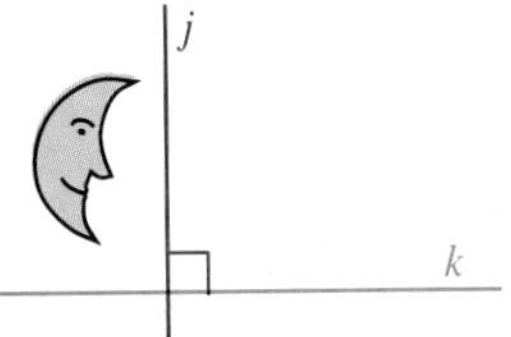

Copy each figure twice and show the image of the red flag under each of the composites given.

7. a. $H_B \circ H_A$
 b. $H_A \circ H_B$

8. a. $R_j \circ H_C$
 b. $H_C \circ R_j$

9. a. $H_E \circ D_{E,\frac{1}{3}}$
 b. $D_{E,\frac{1}{3}} \circ H_E$

A B

C j

E

Additional Answers Classroom Exercises

11. Let $T(P) = P'$, $T(Q) = Q'$, $S(P') = P''$, and $S(Q') = Q''$. Then $(S \circ T)(P) = P''$ and $(S \circ T)(Q) = Q''$. Since S and T are isometries, $PQ = P'Q'$ and $P'Q' = P''Q''$. Thus $PQ = P''Q''$; $S \circ T$ preserves distance, so it is an isometry.

12. Since ⊥ lines form rt. ∠s, the meas. of the ∠ of rotation is $2 \cdot 90 = 180$. A rotation of 180° about a point is a half-turn.

Guided Practice

1. If $f(x) = x^2$ and $g(x) = 1 - x$, evaluate the following.
 a. $(g \circ f)(3)$ -8
 b. $(g \circ f)(x)$ $1 - x^2$
 c. $(f \circ g)(3)$ 4
 d. $(f \circ g)(x)$ $1 - 2x + x^2$

2. Given $A(-2, 1)$, $B(1, 4)$, and $C(3, -2)$. S and T are translations, with $S{:}(x, y) \to (x - 2, y + 3)$ and $T{:}(x, y) \to (x + 1, y - 1)$. Draw $\triangle ABC$ and its images under $S \circ T$ and $T \circ S$.

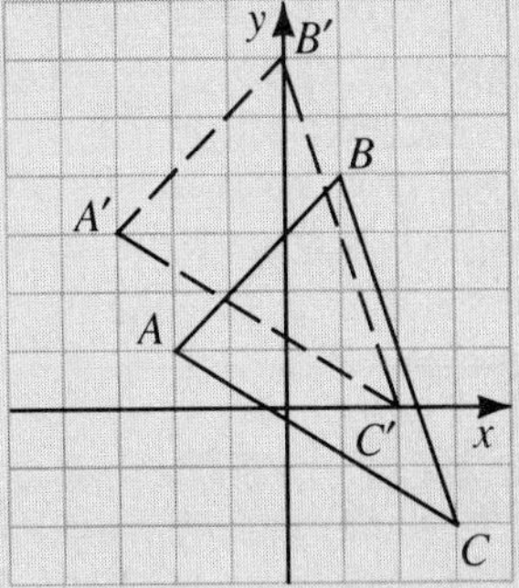

 a. Does $S \circ T$ appear to be a translation? yes
 b. Is $S \circ T = T \circ S$? yes
 c. $S \circ T{:}(x, y) \to (x - 1, y + 2)$
 d. $T \circ S{:}(x, y) \to (x - 1, y + 2)$

10. Given $A(4, 1)$, $B(1, 5)$, and $C(0, 1)$. S and T are translations. $S:(x, y) \rightarrow (x + 1, y + 4)$ and $T:(x, y) \rightarrow (x + 3, y - 1)$. Draw $\triangle ABC$ and its images under $S \circ T$ and $T \circ S$. **A″(8, 4) B″(5, 8) C″(4, 4)**

a. Does $S \circ T$ appear to be a translation? **Yes**

b. Is $S \circ T$ equal to $T \circ S$? **Yes**

c. $S \circ T:(x, y) \rightarrow (\underline{?}, \underline{?})$ **x + 4, y + 3** and $T \circ S:(x, y) \rightarrow (\underline{?}, \underline{?})$ **x + 4, y + 3**

11. L, M, and N are midpoints of the sides of $\triangle QRS$.

a. $H_N \circ H_M:S \rightarrow \underline{?}$ **Q**
b. $H_M \circ H_N:Q \rightarrow \underline{?}$ **S**
c. $D_{S, \frac{1}{2}} \circ H_N:Q \rightarrow \underline{?}$ **M**
d. $H_N \circ D_{S, 2}:M \rightarrow \underline{?}$ **Q**
e. $H_L \circ H_M \circ H_N:Q \rightarrow \underline{?}$ **Q**

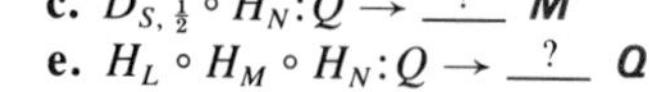

S L M Q R N

Exs. 11, 12

B **12.** If T is a translation that maps R to N, then:

a. $T:M \rightarrow \underline{?}$ **L**
b. $T \circ D_{S, \frac{1}{2}}:R \rightarrow \underline{?}$ **L**
c. $T \circ T:R \rightarrow \underline{?}$ **Q**

In Exercises 13–16 tell which of the following properties are invariant under the given transformation.

a. distance **b. angle measure** **c. area** **d. orientation**

13. The composite of a reflection and a dilation **b**

14. The composite of two reflections **a, b, c, d**

15. The composite of a rotation and a translation **a, b, c, d**

16. The composite of two dilations **b, d**

For each exercise draw a grid and find the coordinates of the image point. O is the origin and A is the point (3, 1). R_x and R_y are reflections in the x- and y-axes. **20. (−5, −1) 22. (−1, 2) 23. (3, −3)**

17. $R_x \circ R_y:(3, 1) \rightarrow (\underline{?}, \underline{?})$ **(−3, −1)**

18. $R_y \circ H_O:(1, -2) \rightarrow (\underline{?}, \underline{?})$ **(1, 2)**

19. $H_A \circ H_O:(3, 0) \rightarrow (\underline{?}, \underline{?})$ **(9, 2)**

20. $H_O \circ H_A:(1, 1) \rightarrow (\underline{?}, \underline{?})$

21. $R_x \circ D_{O, 2}:(2, 4) \rightarrow (\underline{?}, \underline{?})$ **(4, −8)**

22. $\mathcal{R}_{O, 90} \circ R_y:(-2, 1) \rightarrow (\underline{?}, \underline{?})$

23. $\mathcal{R}_{A, 90} \circ \mathcal{R}_{O, -90}:(-1, -1) \rightarrow (\underline{?}, \underline{?})$

24. $D_{O, -\frac{1}{3}} \circ D_{A, 4}:(3, 0) \rightarrow (\underline{?}, \underline{?})$ **(−1, 1)**

25. Let R_l be a reflection in the line $y = x$ and R_y be a reflection in the y-axis. Draw a grid and label the origin O.

a. Plot the point $P(5, 2)$ and its image Q under the mapping $R_y \circ R_l$. **Q(−2, 5)**

b. According to Theorem 14-8, $m\angle POQ = \underline{?}$. **90**

c. Use the slopes of $\overline{OP}$ and $\overline{OQ}$ to verify that $\overline{OP} \perp \overline{OQ}$.

d. Find the images of (x, y) under $R_y \circ R_l$ and $R_l \circ R_y$. **(−y, x), (y, −x)**

26. Let R_k be a reflection in the line $y = -x$ and R_x be a reflection in the x-axis.

a. Plot $P(-6, -2)$ and its image Q under the mapping $R_k \circ R_x$. **Q(−2, 6)**

b. Use slopes to show that $m\angle POQ = 90$ where O is the origin. (Do you see that this result agrees with Theorem 14-8?)

c. Find the images of (x, y) under $R_k \circ R_x$ and $R_x \circ R_k$. **(y, −x), (−y, x)**

C **27.** Explain how you would construct line j so that $R_k \circ R_j:A \rightarrow B$.

Exercise Note

You might point out that distance and area (properties (a) and (c)) can be invariant for certain special cases of Exs. 13 and 16. In Ex. 13, this will occur if the absolute value of the scale factor of the dilation is 1. In Ex. 16, this will occur if the absolute values of the scale factors of the dilations are reciprocals.

Additional Answers Written Exercises

25.c. slope of $\overline{OP} = \frac{2 - 0}{5 - 0} = \frac{2}{5}$; slope of $\overline{OQ} = \frac{5 - 0}{-2 - 0} = \frac{5}{-2} = -\frac{5}{2}$; $\frac{2}{5}\left(-\frac{5}{2}\right) = -1$

26.b. Slope of $\overline{OP} = \frac{1}{3}$; slope of $\overline{OQ} = -3$; since $(\frac{1}{3})(-3) = -1$, $\overline{OP} \perp \overline{OQ}$ and $m\angle POQ = 90$.

27. Const. B' so that $R_k:B \rightarrow B'$. Const. line j, the $\perp$ bis. of $\overline{AB'}$.

28. The figure shows that $H_B \circ H_A : P \to P''$.

a. Copy the figure and verify by measuring that $PP'' = 2 \cdot AB$. What theorem about the midpoints of the sides of a triangle does this suggest? **Thm. 5-11**

b. Choose another point Q and carefully locate Q'', the image of Q under $H_B \circ H_A$. Does $QQ'' = 2 \cdot AB$? **Yes**

c. Measure PQ and $P''Q''$. Are they equal? What kind of transformation does $H_B \circ H_A$ appear to be? **Yes; transl.**

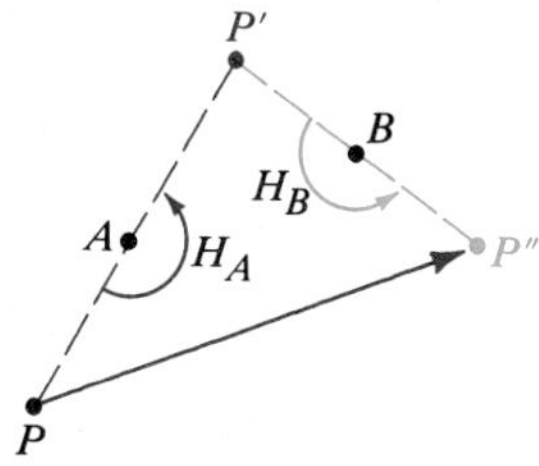

29. $D_{A,2} : \overline{PQ} \to \overline{P'Q'}$ and $D_{B,\frac{1}{2}} : \overline{P'Q'} \to \overline{P''Q''}$. What kind of transformation is the composite $D_{B,\frac{1}{2}} \circ D_{A,2}$? Explain. **translation**

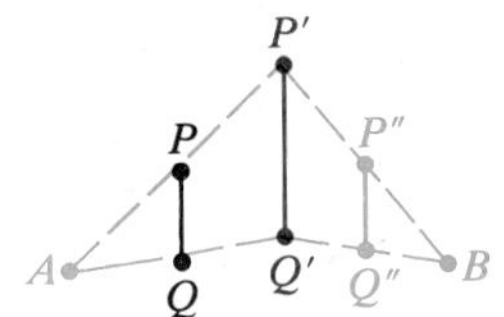

30. The point P is called a *fixed point* of the transformation T if $T : P \to P$.

a. How many fixed points does each of the following have: $\mathcal{R}_{O,90}$? R_y? $D_{O,3}$? the translation $T : (x, y) \to (x - 3, y + 2)$? **1 (the origin); infinitely many (the y-axis); 1 (the origin); none**

b. O is the origin and A is the point $(1, 0)$. Find the coordinates of a fixed point of the composite $D_{O,2} \circ D_{A,\frac{1}{4}}$. **(3, 0)**

14-7 *Inverses and the Identity*

Suppose that the pattern below continues indefinitely to both the left and the right. The translation T glides each runner one place to the right. The translation that glides each runner one place to the *left* is called the *inverse* of T, and is denoted T^{-1}. Notice that T followed by T^{-1} keeps *all* points fixed:

$$T^{-1} \circ T : P \to P$$

The composite $T \circ T$, also written $T \cdot T$, and usually denoted by T^2, glides each runner two places to the right.

The mapping that maps every point to itself is called the **identity** transformation I. The words "identity" and "inverse" are used for mappings in much the same way that they are used for numbers. In fact, the composite of two mappings is very much like the product of two numbers. For this reason, the composite $S \circ T$ is often called the **product** of S and T.

Additional Answers
Written Exercises

29. $\overline{P'Q'} \parallel \overline{PQ}$ and $\overline{P''Q''} \parallel \overline{P'Q'}$, so $\overline{PQ} \parallel \overline{P''Q''}$; $P'Q' = 2 \cdot PQ$ and $P''Q'' = \frac{1}{2} \cdot P'Q'$, so $P''Q'' = PQ$; then $PP''Q''Q$ is a ▱, and $D_{B,\frac{1}{2}} \circ D_{A,2}$ is a translation.

Teaching Suggestions,
p. T142

Objective
Presenting the Lesson

Communication Skills,
p. T142

Supplementary Materials

Practice Master 88
Study Guide, pp. 193–194

Lesson Focus

Two fundamental transformations, the inverse of a transformation and the identity transformation, are defined and applied in this lesson.

Suggested Assignments

Average
607–608/1–13 odd, 14–19
615/Self-Test 2, 1–10

Maximum
Day 1: 607–608/1–29 odd
S 604–605/21–30
Day 2: 607–608/2–30 even

Relating Algebra and Geometry

For products of numbers	*For composites of mappings*
1 is the identity.	I is the identity.
$a \cdot 1 = a$ and $1 \cdot a = a$	$S \circ I = S$ and $I \circ S = S$
The inverse of a is written a^{-1}, or $\frac{1}{a}$.	The inverse of S is written S^{-1}.
$a \cdot a^{-1} = 1$ and $a^{-1} \cdot a = 1$	$S \circ S^{-1} = I$ and $S^{-1} \circ S = I$

In general, the **inverse** of a transformation T is defined as the transformation S such that $S \circ T = I$. The inverses of some other transformations are illustrated below.

Example 1 Find the inverses of **(a)** translation $T:(x, y) \to (x + 5, y - 4)$, **(b)** rotation $\mathcal{R}_{O,\,x}$, and **(c)** dilation $D_{O,\,2}$.

Solution

a. $T^{-1}:(x, y) \to (x - 5, y + 4)$

$T:(0, 6) \to (5, 2)$
$T^{-1}:(5, 2) \to (0, 6)$

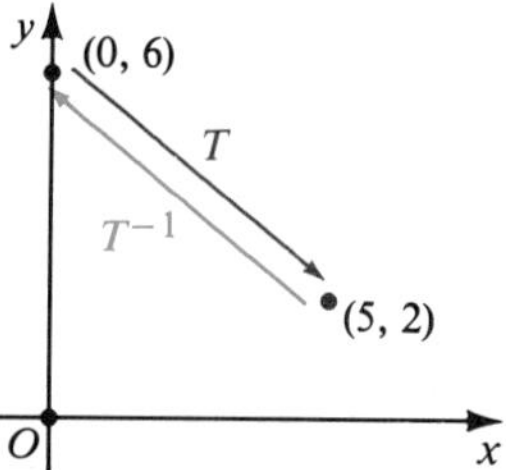

b. The inverse of $\mathcal{R}_{O,\,x}$ is $\mathcal{R}_{O,\,-x}$.

$\mathcal{R}_{O,\,x}:F \to G$
$\mathcal{R}_{O,\,-x}:G \to F$

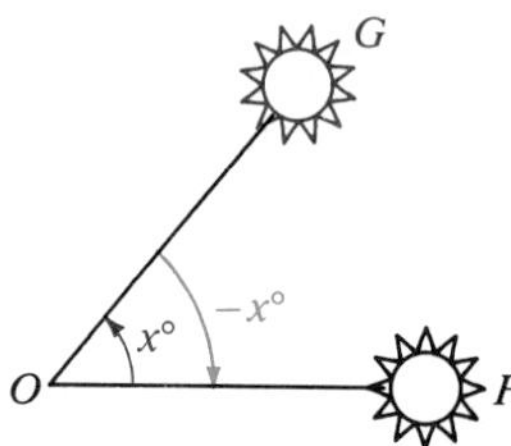

c. The inverse of $D_{O,\,2}$ is $D_{O,\,\frac{1}{2}}$.

$D_{O,\,2}:(3, 2) \to (6, 4)$
$D_{O,\,\frac{1}{2}}:(6, 4) \to (3, 2)$

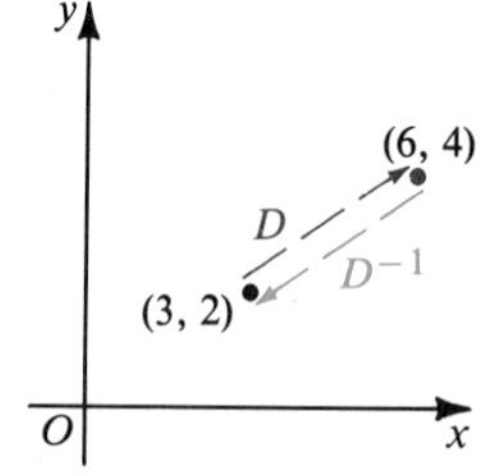

Example 2 What is the inverse of R_j? (Refer to the diagram at right.)

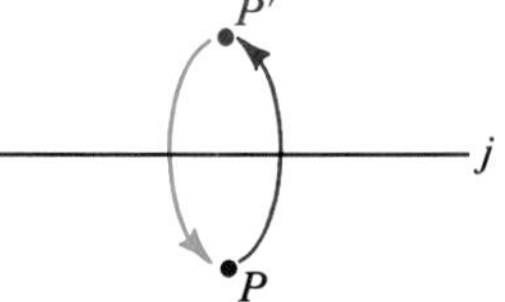

Solution Since $R_j \circ R_j = I$, the inverse of R_j is R_j itself. In symbols, $R_j^{-1} = R_j$. Do you see that the inverse of any reflection is that same reflection?

Making Connections

"Relating Algebra and Geometry" is an excellent way to show connections between algebra and geometry. Give some examples to illustrate the statements in the table. Students should note that the last line in the table shows that the product of a number and its inverse is the identity for multiplication (1), while the composite of a mapping and its inverse is the identity for composition (I).

Teaching Note

Discuss the informal notion that the inverse of a transformation "undoes" the effect of the transformation. For example, in the translation given, adding 5 to an x-coordinate can be "undone" by subtracting 5 from the x-coordinate. Adding 4 will "undo" subtracting 4.

Chalkboard Examples

Find the inverses of the following transformations.

1. Reflection R_x R_x
2. Translation $T:(x, y) \to (x - 2, y + 3)$ $T^{-1}:(x, y) \to (x + 2, y - 3)$
3. Rotation $\mathcal{R}_{O,\,a}$ $\mathcal{R}_{O,\,-a}$
4. Dilation $D_{O,\,3}$ $D_{O,\,\frac{1}{3}}$

Which pairs of transformations are inverses?

5. $\mathcal{R}_{O,\,180}$ and $\mathcal{R}_{O,\,-180}$ inverses
6. $\mathcal{R}_{O,\,270}$ and $\mathcal{R}_{O,\,-90}$ not inverses
7. $T:(x, y) \to (x + 1, y - 2)$ and $U:(x, y) \to (x - 2, y - 1)$ not inverses
8. $R_x \circ R_y$ and $R_y \circ R_x$ inverses

Classroom Exercises

The symbol 2^{-1} stands for the multiplicative inverse of 2, or $\frac{1}{2}$. Give the value of each of the following.

1. 3^{-1} $\frac{1}{3}$
2. 7^{-1} $\frac{1}{7}$
3. $(\frac{4}{5})^{-1}$ $\frac{5}{4}$
4. $(2^{-1})^{-1}$ 2

The translation T maps all points five units to the right. Describe each of the following transformations.

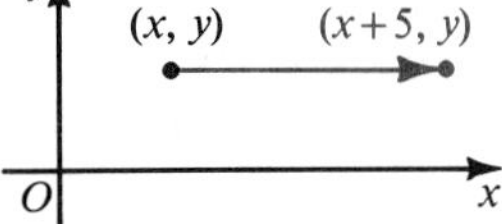

5. T^2 10 right
6. T^3 15 right
7. T^{-1} 5 left
8. T^{-2} 10 left
9. $T \circ T^{-1}$ identity
10. $(T^{-1})^{-1}$ T

The rotation $\mathcal{R}$ maps all points 120° about G, the center of equilateral $\triangle ABC$. Give the image of A under each rotation.

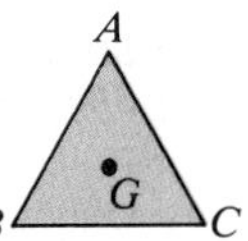

11. $\mathcal{R}$ B
12. $\mathcal{R}^2$ C
13. $\mathcal{R}^3$ A
14. $\mathcal{R}^6$ A
15. $\mathcal{R}^{-1}$ C
16. $\mathcal{R}^{-2}$ B
17. $\mathcal{R}^2 \circ \mathcal{R}^{-2}$ A
18. $\mathcal{R}^2 \circ \mathcal{R}^{-3}$ C
19. $\mathcal{R}^{100}$ B
20. What number is the identity for multiplication? 1
21. The product of any number t and the identity for multiplication is _?_. t
22. The product of any transformation T and the identity is _?_. T
23. State the inverse of each transformation.
    a. R_l R_l
    b. $\mathcal{R}_{O,\ 30}$ $\mathcal{R}_{O,\ -30}$
    c. $T:(x, y) \rightarrow (x - 4, y + 1)$ $T^{-1}:(x, y) \rightarrow (x + 4, y - 1)$
    d. $D_{O,\ -1}$ $D_{O,\ -1}$
24. Name an important difference between products of numbers and products of transformations. For all real numbers, $ab = ba$, but for transformations in general, $T \circ S \neq S \circ T$.

Written Exercises

Give the value of each of the following.

A

1. 4^{-1} $\frac{1}{4}$
2. 9^{-1} $\frac{1}{9}$
3. $(\frac{2}{3})^{-1}$ $\frac{3}{2}$
4. $(5^{-1})^{-1}$ 5

The rotation $\mathcal{R}$ maps all points 90° about O, the center of square $ABCD$. Give the image of A under each rotation.

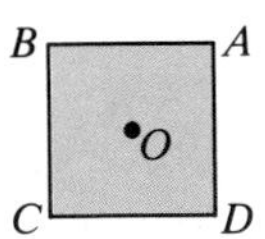

5. $\mathcal{R}^2$ C
6. $\mathcal{R}^3$ D
7. $\mathcal{R}^4$ A
8. $\mathcal{R}^{-1}$ D
9. $\mathcal{R}^{-2}$ C
10. $\mathcal{R}^{-3}$ B
11. $\mathcal{R}^{-3} \circ \mathcal{R}^3$ A
12. $\mathcal{R}^5$ B
13. $\mathcal{R}^{50}$ C

Complete.

14. By definition, the identity mapping I maps every point P to _?_. P
15. $H_O{}^2$ is the same as the mapping _?_. I
16. The inverse of H_O is _?_. H_O
17. $H_O{}^3$ is the same as the mapping _?_. H_O

Exercise Note

Point out that in Classroom Ex. 5, T is a translation 5 units to the right, and T^2 is a translation of 10 units, not 25 units.

Guided Practice

Give the value of each of the following.

1. 6^{-1} $\frac{1}{6}$
2. $(\frac{1}{4})^{-1}$ 4

The rotation $\mathcal{R}$ maps all points 120° about O, the center of hexagon $ABCDEF$. Give the image of point A under each rotation.

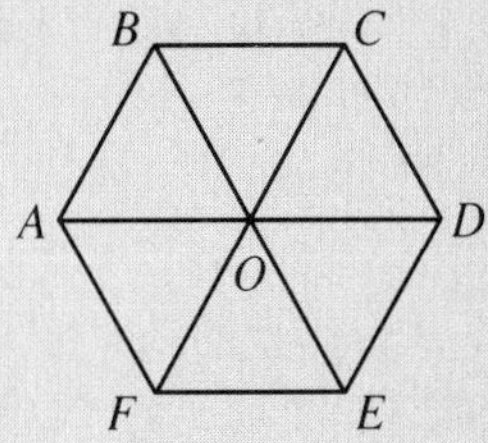

3. $\mathcal{R}^2$ C
4. $\mathcal{R}^{-1}$ C
5. $\mathcal{R}^{-2} \circ \mathcal{R}^2$ A
6. The identity transformation maps every point to itself.
7. The inverse of $\mathcal{R}_{O,\ -60}$ is $\mathcal{R}_{O,\ 60}$.
8. If $T:(x, y) \rightarrow (x - 1, y - 2)$, then $T^2:(x, y) \rightarrow (x - 2, y - 4)$.

Additional Answers Written Exercises

21. $S^{-1}: (x, y) \rightarrow (x - 5, y - 2)$
22. $S^{-1}: (x, y) \rightarrow (x + 3, y + 1)$
23. $S^{-1}: (x, y) \rightarrow (\frac{1}{3}x, -2y)$
24. $S^{-1}: (x, y) \rightarrow (4x, 4y)$
25. $S^{-1}: (x, y) \rightarrow (x + 4, \frac{1}{4}y)$
26. $S^{-1}: (x, y) \rightarrow (y, x)$

18. If $T:(x, y) \rightarrow (x + 2, y)$, then $T^2:(x, y) \rightarrow (\underline{\ ?\ }, \underline{\ ?\ })$. **$(x + 4, y)$**

19. If $T:(x, y) \rightarrow (x + 3, y - 4)$, then $T^2:(x, y) \rightarrow (\underline{\ ?\ }, \underline{\ ?\ })$. **$(x + 6, y - 8)$**

20. If R_x is reflection in the x-axis, then $(R_x)^2:P \rightarrow \underline{\ ?\ }$. **$P$**

In each exercise, a rule is given for a mapping S. Write the rule for S^{-1}.

B

21. $S:(x, y) \rightarrow (x + 5, y + 2)$

22. $S:(x, y) \rightarrow (x - 3, y - 1)$

23. $S:(x, y) \rightarrow (3x, -\frac{1}{2}y)$

24. $S:(x, y) \rightarrow (\frac{1}{4}x, \frac{1}{4}y)$

25. $S:(x, y) \rightarrow (x - 4, 4y)$

26. $S:(x, y) \rightarrow (y, x)$

27. If $S:(x, y) \rightarrow (x + 12, y - 3)$, find a translation T such that $T^6 = S$. **$T:(x, y) \rightarrow (x + 2, y - \frac{1}{2})$**

28. Find a transformation S (other than the identity) for which $S^5 = I$. **$\mathcal{R}_{O,72}$**

C

29. a. j and k are vertical lines 1 unit apart. According to Theorem 14-7, $R_k \circ R_j$ and $R_j \circ R_k$ are both translations. Describe in words the distance and direction of each translation. **2 units rt., 2 units left**

1 unit
j
k

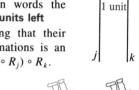

b. Show that $R_k \circ R_j$ and $R_j \circ R_k$ are inverses by showing that their composite is I. Note: Forming composites of transformations is an associative operation, so $(R_k \circ R_j) \circ (R_j \circ R_k) = R_k \circ (R_j \circ R_j) \circ R_k$.
$R_k \circ (R_j \circ R_j) \circ R_k = R_k \circ I \circ R_k = R_k \circ R_k = I$

30. The blue lines in the diagram illustrate the statement $H_B \circ H_A$ = translation T. The red lines show that $H_A \circ H_B$ = translation S. **S and T are inverses.**

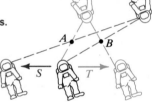

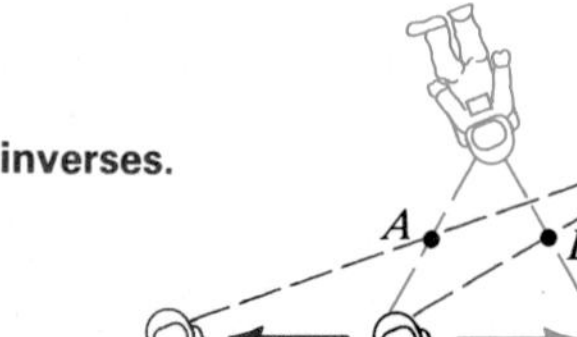

a. How is translation S related to translation T?

b. Prove your answer correct by showing that $(H_A \circ H_B) \circ (H_B \circ H_A) = I$. (*Hint*: See Exercise 29, part (b).)
$(H_A \circ H_B) \circ (H_B \circ H_A) = H_A \circ (H_B \circ H_B) \circ H_A = H_A \circ I \circ H_A = H_A \circ H_A = I$

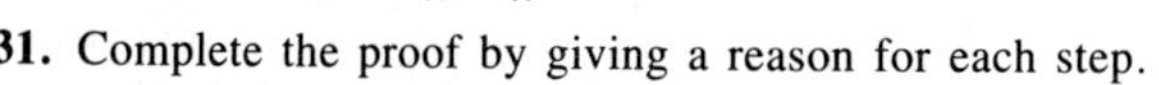

31. Complete the proof by giving a reason for each step.

Given: $l_1 \perp l_2$; $l_3 \perp l_2$; R_1, R_2, and R_3 denote reflections in l_1, l_2, and l_3.

Prove: $H_B \circ H_A$ is a translation.

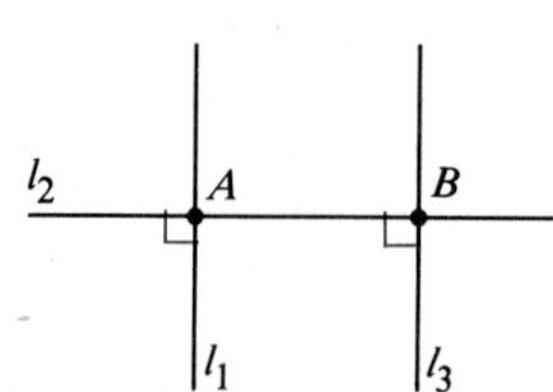

Proof:

Statements	Reasons
1. $H_A = R_2 \circ R_1$	1. ? **A comp. of refl. in ⊥ lines is a half-turn about the pt. where the lines intersect.**
2. $H_B = R_3 \circ R_2$	2. ?
3. $H_B \circ H_A = (R_3 \circ R_2) \circ (R_2 \circ R_1)$	3. ? **Subst. Prop.**
4. $H_B \circ H_A = (R_3 \circ (R_2 \circ R_2)) \circ R_1$	4. Composition is associative.
5. $H_B \circ H_A = (R_3 \circ I) \circ R_1$	5. ? **$R_2 \circ R_2 = I$; Subst. Prop.**
6. $H_B \circ H_A = R_3 \circ R_1$	6. ? **Def. identity mapping**
7. $H_B \circ H_A$ is a translation.	7. ? **A comp. of refl. in 2 ∥ lines is a translation.**

14-8 *Symmetry in the Plane and in Space*

A figure in the plane has **symmetry** if there is an isometry, other than the identity, that maps the figure onto itself. We call such an isometry a *symmetry* of the figure.

Both of the figures below have **line symmetry.** This means that for each figure there is a symmetry line k such that the reflection R_k maps the figure onto itself. The pentagon at the left has one symmetry line. The regular pentagon at the right has five symmetry lines.

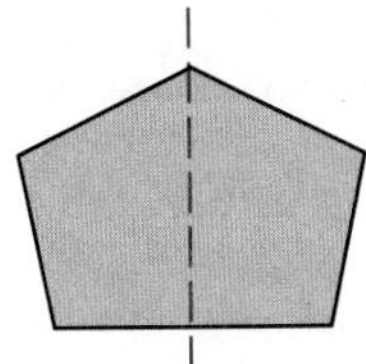

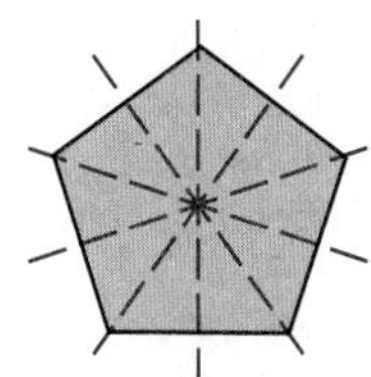

Each figure below has **point symmetry.** This means that for each figure there is a symmetry point O such that the half-turn H_O maps the figure onto itself.

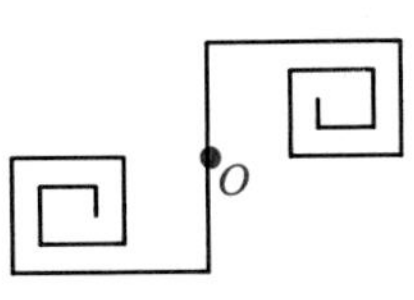

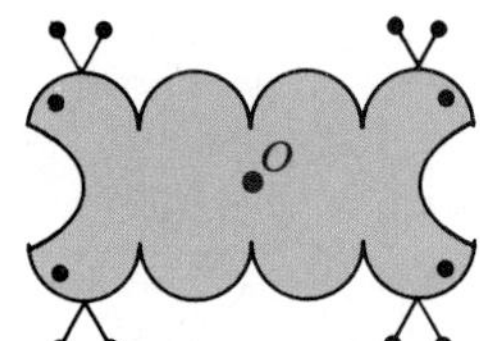

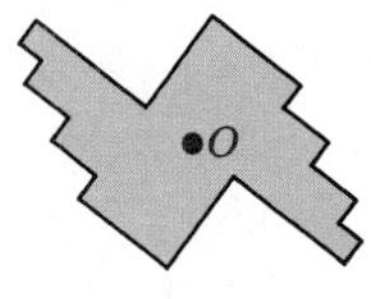

Besides having a symmetry point, the middle figure above has a vertical symmetry line and a horizontal symmetry line.

A third kind of symmetry is **rotational symmetry.** The figure below has the four rotational symmetries listed. Each symmetry has center O and rotates the figure onto itself. Note that 180° rotational symmetry is another name for point symmetry.

(1) 90° rotational symmetry: $\mathcal{R}_{O,\,90}$
(2) 180° rotational symmetry: $\mathcal{R}_{O,\,180}$ (or H_O)
(3) 270° rotational symmetry: $\mathcal{R}_{O,\,270}$
(4) 360° rotational symmetry: the identity I

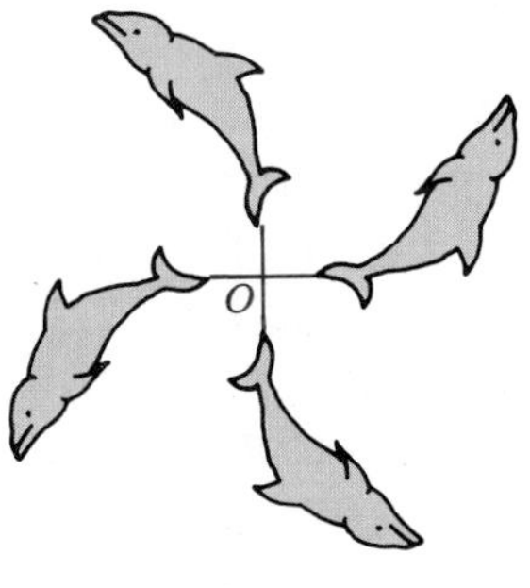

The identity mapping always maps a figure onto itself, and we usually include the identity when listing the symmetries of a figure. However, we do not call a figure *symmetric* if the identity is its only symmetry.

Teaching Suggestions,
pp. T142–T143

Objective
Presenting the Lesson
Applications

Cooperative Learning,
p. T143

Supplementary Materials

Practice Master 89
Test 58
Resource Book, pp. 98, 168
Study Guide, pp. 195–196
Overhead Visual M

Lesson Focus

The purpose of this lesson is to study the concept of symmetry in the plane and in space.

Suggested Assignments

Maximum
Day 1: 612–613/1–29 odd
Day 2: 613–614/20–28 even
620/Chapter Test

A figure can also have **translational symmetry** if there is a translation that maps the figure onto itself. For example, imagine that the design at the right extends in all directions to fill the plane. If you consider the distance between the eyes of adjacent blue fish as a unit, then a translation through one or more units right, left, up, or down maps the whole pattern onto itself. Do you see that you can also translate the pattern along diagonal lines?

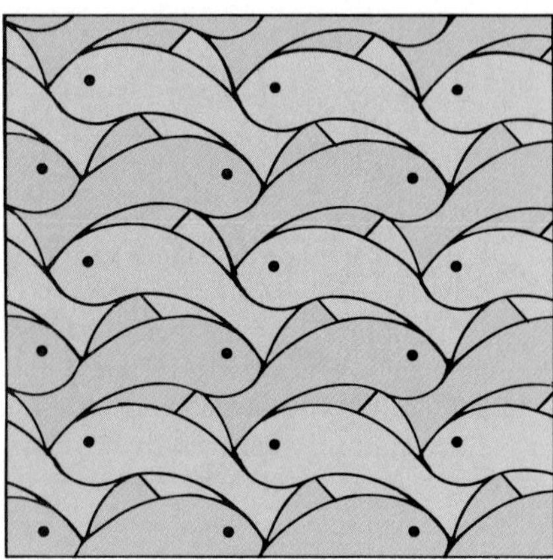

It is also possible to map the blue fish, which all face to the left, onto the right-facing green fish by translating the whole pattern a half unit up and then reflecting it in a vertical line. Thus, if we ignore color differences, the pattern has **glide reflection symmetry.**

A design like this pattern of fish, in which congruent copies of a figure completely fill the plane without overlapping, is called a *tessellation*. Tessellations can have any of the kinds of symmetry we have discussed. Here are two more examples.

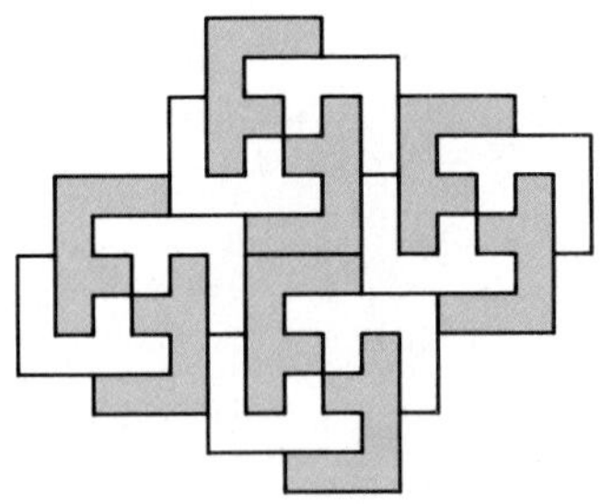

A tessellation of the letter *F*. This pattern has point symmetry and translational symmetry.

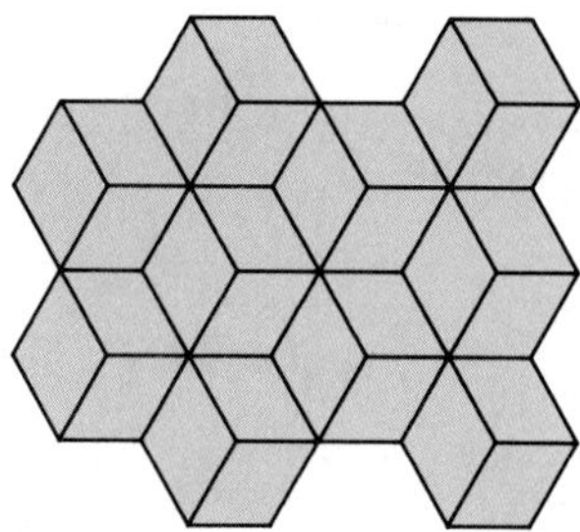

This tessellation has line, point, rotational, translational, and glide reflection symmetry.

Coloring a tessellation often changes its symmetries. For example, if the green were removed from the tessellation of the letter *F*, the pattern would also have 90° and 270° rotational symmetry.

A figure in space has **plane symmetry** if there is a symmetry plane *X* such that reflection in the plane maps the figure onto itself. (See Exercise 17, page 580.) Most living creatures have a single plane of symmetry. Such symmetry is called *bilateral symmetry*. The photographs on the next page illustrate bilateral symmetry.

Chalkboard Examples

For each regular polygon, describe (a) all line symmetries and (b) all rotational symmetries.

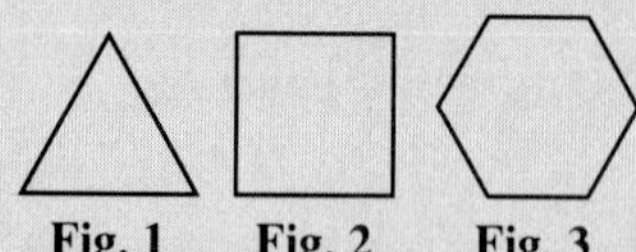

Fig. 1: (a) Altitudes are lines of symmetry. (3)
(b) Rotational symmetry about the intersection of the altitudes: 120°, 240°, 360°

Fig. 2: (a) Diagonals are lines of symmetry. (2)
⊥ bisectors of sides are lines of symmetry. (2)
(b) Rotational symmetry about the center: 90°, 180°, 270°, 360°

Fig. 3: (a) Lines of symmetry are drawn. (6)

(b) Rotational symmetry about the center: 60°, 120°, 180°, 240°, 300°, 360°

Some geometric solids have more than one symmetry plane. For example, the regular hexagonal prism shown has seven symmetry planes, two of which are shown. It also has six-fold rotational symmetry because rotating it 60°, 120°, 180°, 240°, 300°, or 360° about the line k (called the *axis of symmetry*) maps the prism onto itself.

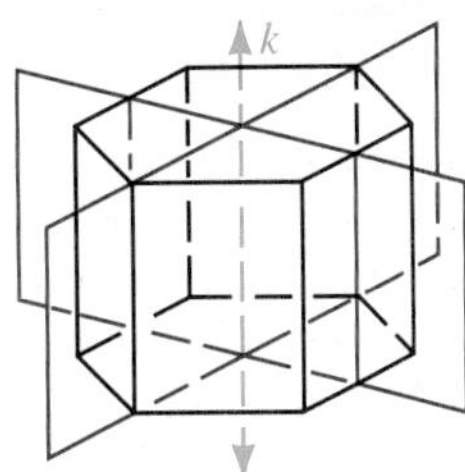

Teaching Note

The hexagonal prism has other axes of rotational symmetry besides line k. It has 180° rotational symmetry about any line that contains the midpoints of opposite lateral edges, as well as 180° rotational symmetry about any line that contains the centers of opposite lateral faces.

Classroom Exercises

Tell how many symmetry lines each figure has. In Exercise 2, O is the center of the equilateral triangle.

1. 1

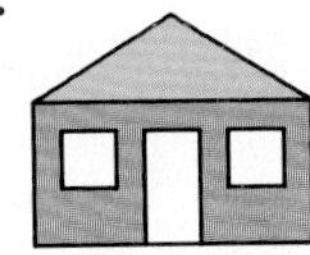

2. 3

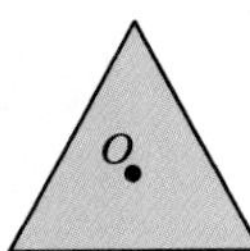

3. 4

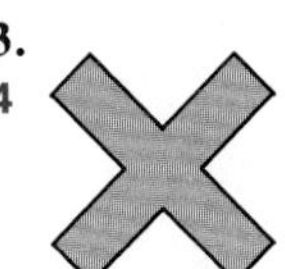

4. 0

5. Which figures above have point symmetry? **3 and 4**
6. Describe all of the rotational symmetries of the figure in Exercise 2. $\mathcal{R}_{O,120}$, $\mathcal{R}_{O,240}$, $\mathcal{R}_{O,360}$
7. Describe all of the rotational symmetries of the figure in Exercise 3.
   $\mathcal{R}_{P,90}$, $\mathcal{R}_{P,180}$, $\mathcal{R}_{P,270}$, $\mathcal{R}_{P,360}$ **where P is int. of sym. lines (the "center" of the X)**

Draw each figure on the chalkboard and describe all of its symmetries.

8. isosceles triangle
9. parallelogram
10. rectangle
11. rhombus
12. Imagine that the pattern shown fills the entire plane. Does the pattern have the symmetry named?
    a. translational symmetry **Yes** **b.** line symmetry **Yes**
    c. point symmetry **No** **d.** rotational symmetry **Yes**
13. How many planes of symmetry does the given solid have?
    a. a rectangular solid **3** **b.** a sphere **infinitely many** **c.** a regular square pyramid **4**

Additional Answers Classroom Exercises

8. line sym. about the ⊥ bis. of the base
9. pt. sym. about the int. of the diag.
10. pt. sym. about the int. of the diag.; line sym. about the lines joining the midpts. of the opp. sides
11. pt. sym. about the int. of the diag.; line sym. about the diag.

Additional Answers Classroom Exercises

14. Symmetry points for the tessellation of F's are shown below.

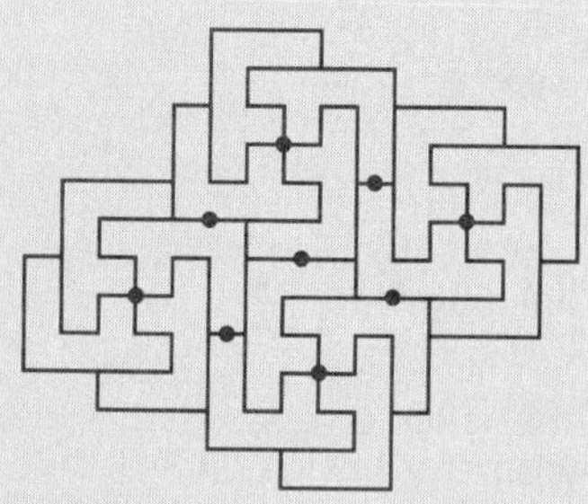

Symmetry points for the tessellation of rhombuses are at every vertex and in the centers of the rhombuses.

Additional Answers Written Exercises

1.a. 5 **b.** No
c. $\mathcal{R}_{O,72}$, $\mathcal{R}_{O,144}$, $\mathcal{R}_{O,216}$, $\mathcal{R}_{O,288}$

2.a. 6 **b.** Yes
c. $\mathcal{R}_{O,60}$, $\mathcal{R}_{O,120}$, $\mathcal{R}_{O,180}$, $\mathcal{R}_{O,240}$, $\mathcal{R}_{O,300}$

3.a. 4 **b.** Yes
c. $\mathcal{R}_{O,90}$, $\mathcal{R}_{O,180}$, $\mathcal{R}_{O,270}$

4.a. 13 **b.** No
c. $\mathcal{R}_{O,\frac{360n}{13}}$ for $n = 1, 2, 3, \ldots, 12$

Guided Practice

Draw in all lines of symmetry for each figure.

1.

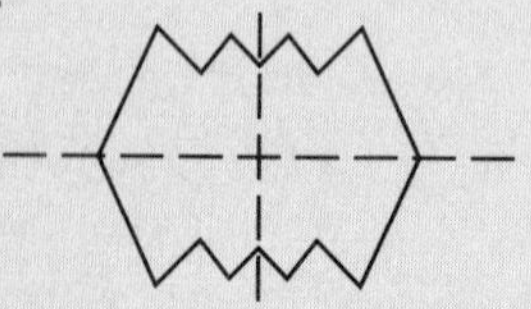

14. Where are the centers of the rotational symmetries for the tessellations in the middle of page 610?

15. Fold a piece of paper into quarters as shown. Cut out a scalene triangle that does not touch any of the edges. Unfold the paper. Describe the symmetries of the design. **pt. symm; line symm. about both fold lines**

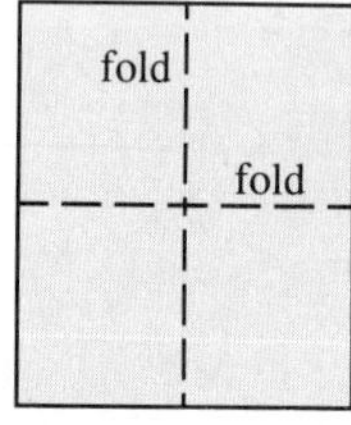

Written Exercises

Consider the object shown in each photograph as a plane figure.
a. State how many symmetry lines each figure has.
b. State whether or not the figure has a symmetry point.
c. List all the rotational symmetries of each figure between 0° and 360°.

A **1.**

2.

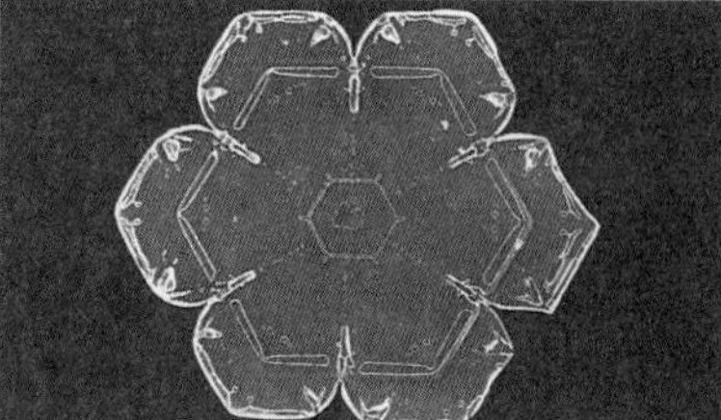

3.

4.

5. Which capital letters of the alphabet have just one line of symmetry? (One answer is "D".) **A, B, C, D, E, K, M, T, U, V, W, Y**

6. Which capital letters of the alphabet have two lines of symmetry?

7. Which capital letters of the alphabet have a point of symmetry?

6. H, I, O, X **7. H, I, N, O, S, X, Z**

5.–7. Answers may vary depending on the way in which the letters are formed.

Make a tessellation of the given figure.

8. 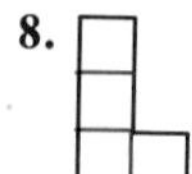

9. 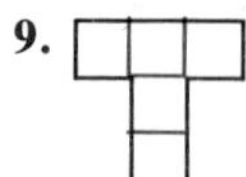

10. 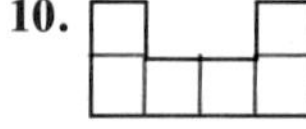

11. 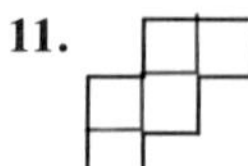

Copy the figure shown. Then complete the figure so that it has the specified symmetries.

12. 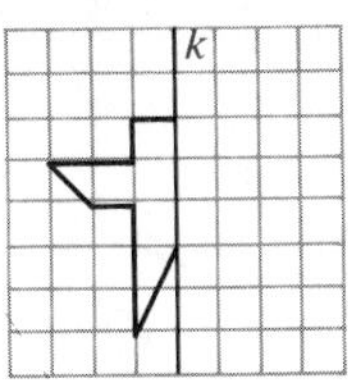

symmetry in line k

13. 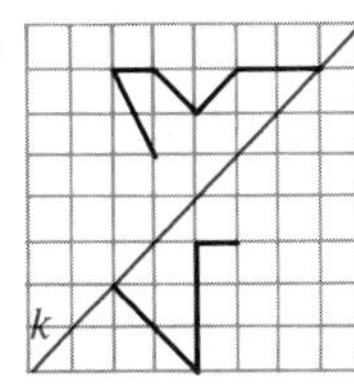

symmetry in line k

14. 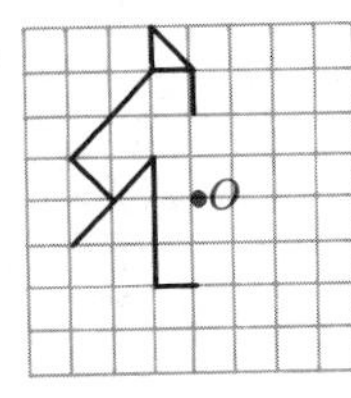

symmetry in point O

Copy the figure shown. Then complete the figure so that it has the specified symmetries.

B **15.** 

60°, 120°, and 180° rotational symmetry

16. 

90°, 180°, and 270° rotational symmetry

17. 

2 symmetry lines and 1 symmetry point

18. **a.** An octopus has one symmetry. Describe it.
b. If you disregard the eyes and mouth of an octopus, it has many symmetries. Describe them.

19. **a.** Describe the symmetries of the ellipse shown.
b. If the ellipse is rotated in space about one of its symmetry lines, an ellipsoid (an egg-like figure) is formed. Its volume is $V = \frac{4}{3}\pi a^2 b$. Interpret this formula when $a = b$.
c. Describe the symmetries of an ellipsoid.

20. Tell whether a tessellation can be made with the given figure.
a. A regular hexagon **Yes** **b.** A scalene triangle **Yes**
c. A regular pentagon **No** **d.** A nonisosceles trapezoid **Yes**

In Exercises 21–23 draw the figure if there is one that meets the conditions. Otherwise write *not possible*.

21. A trapezoid with **(a)** no symmetry, **(b)** one symmetry line, **(c)** a symmetry point. **a. non-isos. trap. b. isos. trap. c. not possible**

22. A parallelogram with **(a)** four symmetry lines, **(b)** just two symmetry lines, **(c)** just one symmetry line. **a. square b. rect. or rhombus c. not poss.**

23. An octagon with **(a)** eight rotational symmetries, **(b)** just four rotational symmetries, **(c)** only point symmetry. **a. regular octagon**

2. 

3. 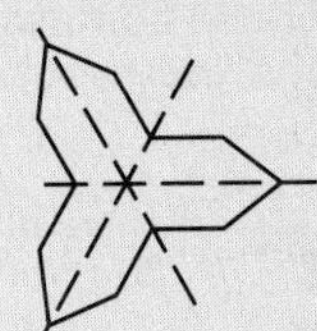

Additional Answers
Written Exercises

18.a. bilateral symmetry
b. 8 sym. planes (4 through pairs of opp. legs, 4 between pairs of adj. legs); rotational symmetry of 45°, 90°, 135°, 180°, 225°, 270°, 315°, 360°

19.a. The ellipse has line sym. about each of its axes and pt. sym. about the int. of the axes.
b. If $a = b$, the original fig. is a circle and the solid formed is a sphere with vol. $\frac{4}{3}\pi a^3$.
c. The ellipsoid shown has plane symmetry about the infinitely many planes that contain the major axis b; plane symmetry about the single plane that contains the minor axis a and is ⊥ to the major axis; infinitely many rotational symmetries about the major axis; 180° rotational symmetry about any line ⊥ to the major axis and containing the intersection of the axes.

Exercise Note

In Ex. 24, the hinged mirror is the principle behind the abstract symmetrical designs seen in kaleidoscopes. Hinged mirrors are also used to create confusion in a carnival's "house of mirrors."

Additional Answers Written Exercises

24.b. In general, the number of coins visible when mirrors are arranged at $x°$ is $\frac{360}{x}$. Whenever this is an even integer, half of these coins will have words reading backwards.

26. Let P be a pt. on the figure and P' be its image under $\mathcal{R}_{O,60}$. Let P'' be the image of P' under $\mathcal{R}_{O,60}$. P'' is also the image of P under $\mathcal{R}_{O,120}$. Thus the figure has 120° rotational symmetry. Similarly, it has 180°, 240°, 300°, and 360° rotational symmetries.

27. Let $ABCDEF$ be a hexagon with symmetry pt. O. H_O maps $\overline{AB}$ to $\overline{DE}$. Since a rotation is an isometry, $AB = DE$. By def. of a rotation, $OA = OD$; $OB = OE$. Thus $\triangle OAB \cong \triangle ODE$; $\angle OAB \cong \angle ODE$. Hence, $\overline{AB} \parallel \overline{DE}$.

28. $(50 \cdot n)°$ rotational symmetry for all integers n. Since the figure has 350° symmetry and 360° − 350° = 10°, this answer is equiv. to $(10 \cdot n)°$ rotational symmetry for all integers n.

24. If you use tape to hinge together two pocket mirrors as shown and place the mirrors at a 120° angle, then a coin placed between the mirrors will be reflected, giving a pattern with 120° and 240° rotational symmetry.

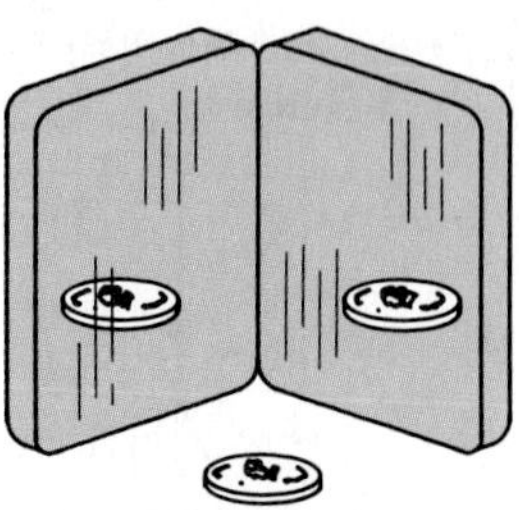

a. What kinds of symmetries occur when the mirrors are at a right angle? **90°, 180°, 270° rot. symm.**

b. Experiment by forming various angles with two mirrors. Be sure to try 60°, 45°, and 30° angles. Record the number of coins you see, including the actual coin. **60°: 6, 45°: 8, 30°: 12**

25. You can make a tessellation by tracing around *any* quadrilateral, placing copies of the quadrilateral systematically as shown.

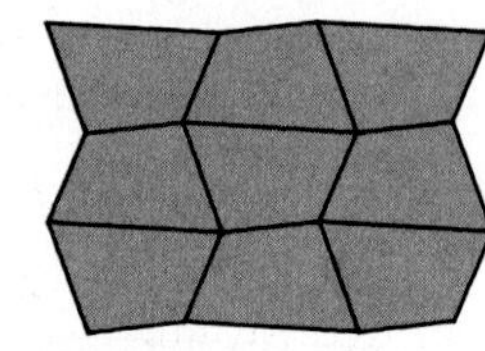

a. The tessellation shown has many symmetry points but none of these are at vertices of the quadrilateral. Where are they? **at the midpts. of the sides**

b. What other kind of symmetry does this mosaic have? **translational**

26. A figure has 60° rotational symmetry. What other rotational symmetries *must* it have? Explain your answer.

C **27.** Show that if a hexagon has point symmetry, then its opposite sides must be parallel.

28. A figure has 50° rotational symmetry. What other rotational symmetries *must* it have? Explain your answer.

★ **29.** Tell how many planes of symmetry and axes of rotation each solid has.

a. a right circular cone **b.** a cube

c. a regular tetrahedron (a pyramid formed by four equilateral triangles)

a. inf. many, 1 **b. 9, 13** **c. 6, 7**

Challenges

1. A mouse moves along $\overline{AJ}$. For any position M of the mouse, X and Y are such that $\overline{AX} \perp \overline{AJ}$ with $AX = AM$, and $\overline{JY} \perp \overline{AJ}$ with $JY = JM$. The cat is at C, the midpoint of $\overline{XY}$. Describe the locus of the cat as the mouse moves from A to J. **The point C**

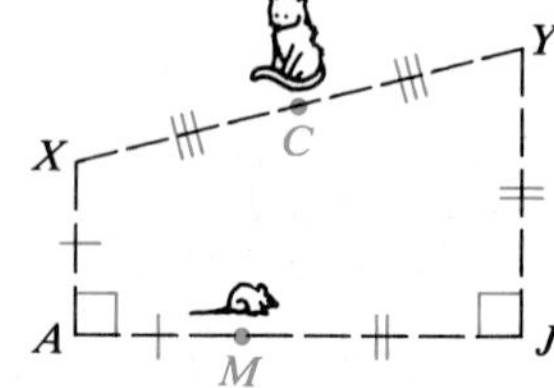

2. Points O, A, B, and C lie on a number line with coordinates 0, 8, 12, and 26. Take any point P not on the line. Draw $\overline{PA}$ and label its midpoint Q. Draw $\overline{QB}$ and label its midpoint R. Draw $\overline{PC}$ and label its midpoint S. Draw $\overrightarrow{SR}$. What is the coordinate of the point where $\overrightarrow{SR}$ intersects the number line? **3**

Self-Test 2

For Exercises 1–6, refer to the figure.

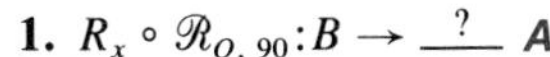

1. $R_x \circ \mathcal{R}_{O,\,90}: B \to$ _?_ **A**
2. $R_x \circ H_O: A \to$ _?_ **A**
3. $\mathcal{R}_{O,\,110} \circ \mathcal{R}_{O,\,70}: C \to$ _?_ **B**
4. $D_{O,\,\frac{1}{2}} \circ D_{R,\,\frac{1}{2}}: P \to$ _?_ **P**
5. What is the symmetry line of $\triangle ABC$? **y-axis**
6. Does $\triangle ABC$ have point symmetry? **No**

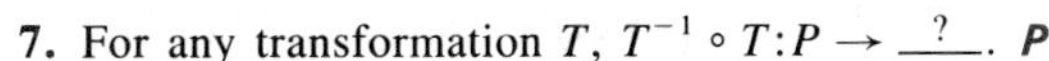

7. For any transformation T, $T^{-1} \circ T: P \to$ _?_. **P**
8. The composite of any transformation T and the identity is _?_. **T**
9. If line a is parallel to line b, then the composite $R_a \circ R_b$ is a _?_. **translation**
10. Give the inverse of each transformation.
    a. $D_{O,\,5}$ **$D_{O,\,\frac{1}{5}}$** b. $\mathcal{R}_{O,\,-70}$ **$\mathcal{R}_{O,\,70}$** c. R_y **R_y** d. $S:(x, y) \to (x + 2, y - 3)$ **$S^{-1}:(x, y) \to (x - 2, y + 3)$**
11. How many lines of symmetry does a regular hexagon have? **6**

Extra — *Symmetry Groups*

Cut out a cardboard or paper rectangle and color each corner with a color of its own on both front and back. Also on the front and back draw symmetry lines j and k and label symmetry point O. The rectangle has four symmetries: I, R_j, R_k, and H_O. The effect of each of these on the original rectangle is shown below.

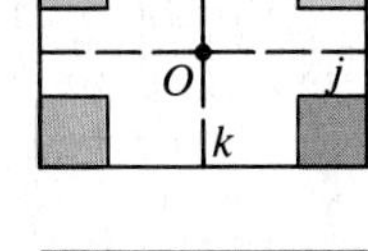

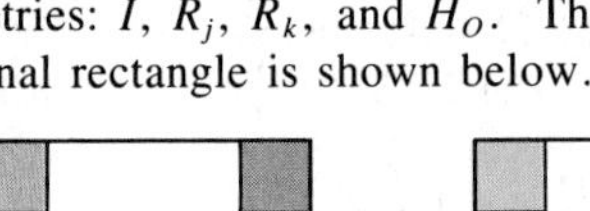

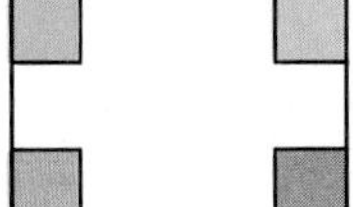

Effect of I:
Rectangle unchanged

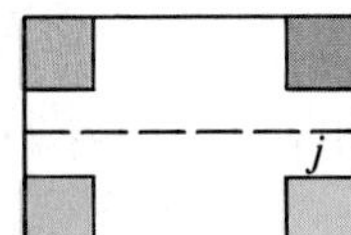

Effect of R_j

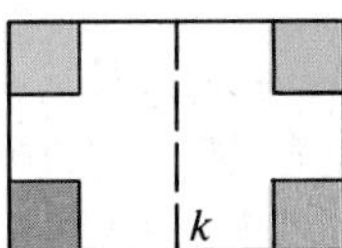

Effect of R_k

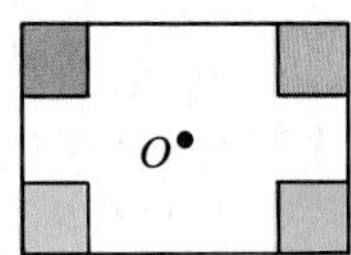

Effect of H_O

Our goal is to see how the four symmetries of the rectangle combine with each other. For example, if the original rectangle is mapped first by R_j and then by H_O, the images look like this:

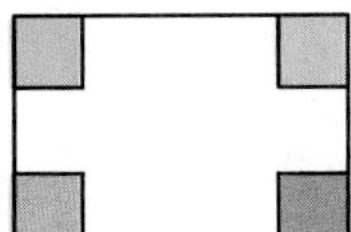

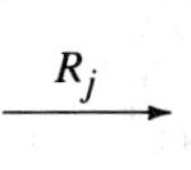

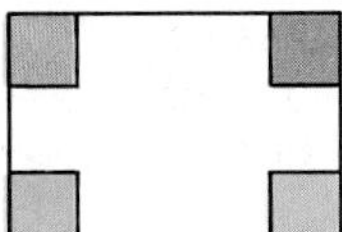

$\xrightarrow{H_O}$

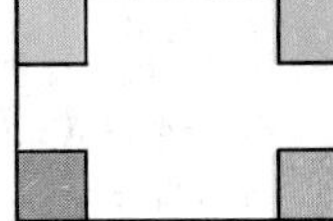

Using a Model

In Ex. 29 on page 614, the symmetries of the cube and regular tetrahedron can be interrelated by demonstrating a model of a tetrahedron inscribed inside a cube as shown.

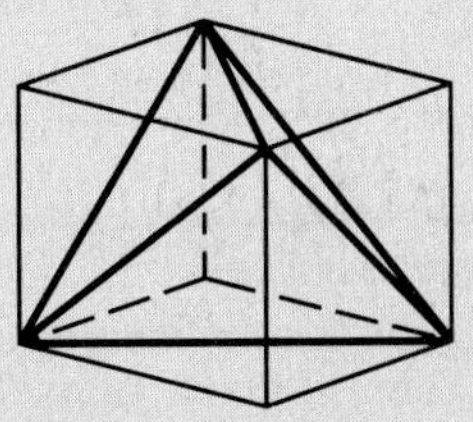

The symmetry planes of the tetrahedron will also be symmetry planes of the cube. Use this model to show that the line containing the midpoints of two skew tetrahedron edges is an axis of 180° rotational symmetry for the tetrahedron.

Quick Quiz

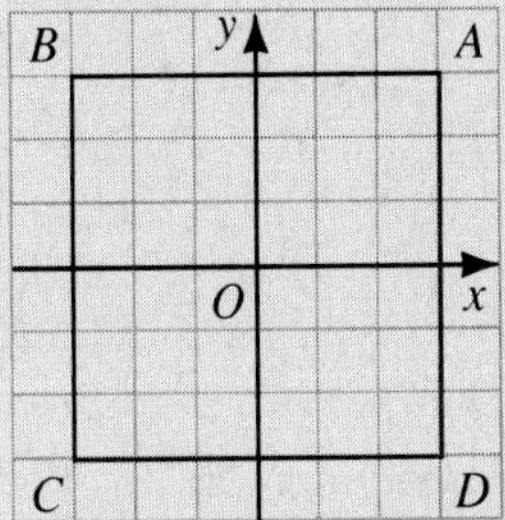

Refer to the diagram above for Exs. 1–6. Complete.

1. $\mathcal{R}_{O,\,135} \circ \mathcal{R}_{O,\,-45}: B \to$ C
2. $R_x \circ \mathcal{R}_{O,\,180}: A \to$ B
3. $D_{O,\,2} \circ R_y: C \to$ (6, −6)
4. $R_x \circ R_y: D \to$ B
5. $\mathcal{R}_{O,\,90} \circ R_x: D \to$ B
6. Name all symmetry lines for *ABCD*.
   x-, *y*-axes; $\overleftrightarrow{AC}$, $\overleftrightarrow{BD}$

(continued)

Mapping the rectangle by R_j and then by H_O has the same effect as the single symmetry R_k, so $H_O \circ R_j = R_k$. We can record this fact in a table resembling a multiplication table. Follow the row for R_j to where it meets the column for H_O, and enter the product $H_O \circ R_j$, which is R_k.

$\circ$	I	R_j	R_k	H_O
I				
R_j				R_k
R_k				
H_O				

We can determine other products of symmetries in the same way, but sometimes short cuts can be used. For example, we know that

(1) $R_j \circ R_j = I$ and $R_k \circ R_k = I$ (Why?) **See below.**
(2) $H_O \circ H_O = I$ (Why?)
(3) $R_j \circ R_k = H_O$ and $R_k \circ R_j = H_O$
(Corollary to Theorem 14-8)

Also we know that the product of any symmetry and the identity is that same symmetry. The completed table is shown at the right.

$\circ$	I	R_j	R_k	H_O
I	I	R_j	R_k	H_O
R_j	R_j	I	H_O	R_k
R_k	R_k	H_O	I	R_j
H_O	H_O	R_k	R_j	I

By studying the table you can see that the symmetries of the rectangle have these four properties, similar to the properties of nonzero real numbers under multiplication:

(1) The product of two symmetries is another symmetry.
(2) The set of symmetries contains the identity.
(3) Each symmetry has an inverse that is also a symmetry. (In this example each symmetry is its own inverse.)
(4) Forming products of transformations is an associative operation: $A \circ (B \circ C) = (A \circ B) \circ C$ for any three symmetries A, B, and C.

A set of symmetries with these four properties is called a symmetry *group*. Symmetry groups are used in crystallography, and more general groups are important in physics and advanced mathematics. The exercises that follow illustrate the fact that the symmetries of any figure form a group.

A reflection is its own inverse. A half-turn is its own inverse.

Exercises

1. An isosceles triangle has just two symmetries, including the identity. Make a 2 by 2 group table showing how these symmetries combine.

2. a. List the four symmetries of the rhombus shown. (Include the identity.) ***I*, R_j, R_k, H_O**
   b. Make a group table showing all products of two symmetries.
   c. Is your table in part (b) identical to the table of symmetries for the rectangle? **Yes**

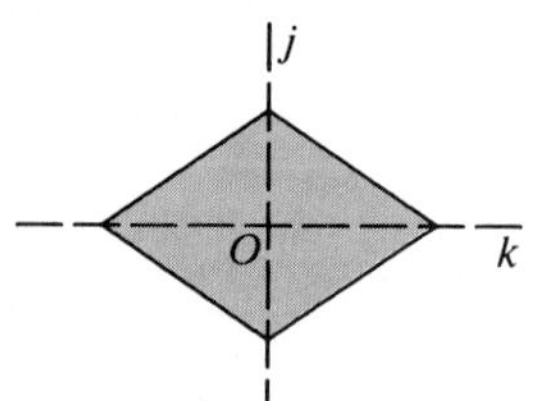

7. Are $\mathcal{R}_{O,180}$ and $D_{O,-1}$ inverse transformations? yes
8. If line a intersects line b, then the composite of $R_a \circ R_b$ is a rotation.
9. Give the inverse of each transformation.
   a. $T:(x, y) \to (x + 4, y - 3)$ $T:(x, y) \to (x - 4, y + 3)$
   b. $D_{O,\frac{1}{4}}$ $D_{O,4}$
   c. $\mathcal{R}_{O,-270}$ $\mathcal{R}_{O,270}$
   d. R_x R_x
10. How many lines of symmetry does a regular octagon have? 8

Teaching Note

Point out to students that the transformations written in the left column of the multiplication table are carried out first and those written along the top are carried out second. This distinction is important for noncommutative groups, such as the group of the equilateral triangle and the group of the square.

Additional Answers
Extra Exercises

1. Let k be the alt. to the base.

$\circ$	I	R_k
I	I	R_k
R_k	R_k	I

2.b.

$\circ$	I	R_j	R_k	H_O
I	I	R_j	R_k	H_O
R_j	R_j	I	H_O	R_k
R_k	R_k	H_O	I	R_j
H_O	H_O	R_k	R_j	I

3. Make a group table for the three symmetries of this figure.

4. Make a group table for the four symmetries of this figure.

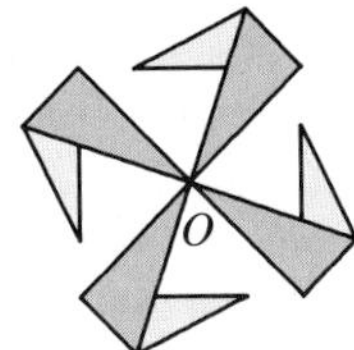

5. A transformation that is its own inverse is called a *self-inverse*.

a. How many of the four symmetries of the figure in Exercise 4 are self-inverses? **2: H_O, I**

b. How many of the four symmetries of the rectangle are self-inverses? **all 4**

6. A symmetry group is called *commutative* if $A \circ B = B \circ A$ for every pair of symmetries A and B in the group. The symmetry group of the rectangle is commutative, as you can see from the completed table. (For example, $H_O \circ R_j$ and $R_j \circ H_O$ are both equal to R_k.) Tell whether the groups in Exercises 3 and 4 are commutative or not. **Yes; yes**

7. An equilateral triangle has three rotational symmetries (I, $\mathcal{R}_{O,\,120}$, and $\mathcal{R}_{O,\,240}$) and three line symmetries (R_j, R_k, and R_l).

a. Make a group table for these six symmetries.

b. Give an example which shows that this group is *not* commutative. **Answers may vary.**

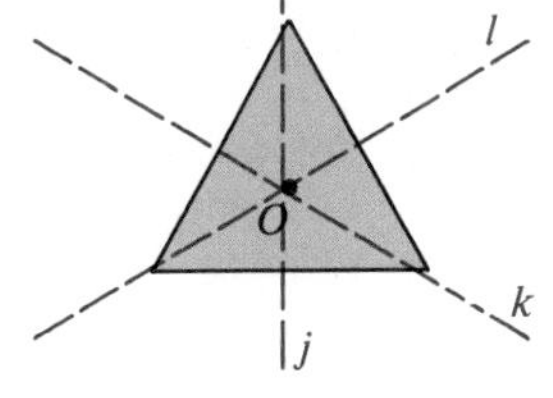

8. A square has four rotational symmetries (including the identity) and four line symmetries. Make a group table for these eight symmetries. Is this a commutative group? **No**

9. The four rotational symmetries of the square satisfy the four requirements for a group, and so they are called a *subgroup* of the full symmetry group. (Notice that the identity is one of these rotational symmetries and that the product of two rotations is another rotation in the subgroup.)

a. Do the four line symmetries of the square form a subgroup? **No; there is no identity.**

b. Does the symmetry group of the equilateral triangle have a subgroup? **Yes; the rot. symm.**

c. Which two symmetries of the figure in Exercise 4 form a subgroup? ***I*, H_O**

10. The tessellation with fish on page 610 has translational symmetry. Let S be the horizontal translation mapping each fish to the fish of the same color to its right, and let T be the vertical translation mapping each fish to the fish of the same color directly above. **a.–c. Each fish is mapped:**

a. Describe the mapping S^3. Is it a symmetry of the pattern? **3 fish to the right; yes**

b. Describe T^{-1}. Is it a symmetry? **directly below; yes**

c. Describe $S \circ T$. Is it a symmetry? **above and to the right; yes**

d. How many symmetries does the tessellation have? **infinitely many**

e. Does this set of symmetries satisfy the four requirements for a group? **Yes**

Exercise Note

Ex. 5 can be used to point out that although the symmetry groups of the rectangle and the figure in Ex. 4 have four elements, the structures of their multiplication tables are different. In group theory, such groups are called nonisomorphic. There are only two nonisomorphic groups with four elements: the group of the rectangle and the rotation group of Ex. 4. The group of the rhombus is isomorphic to the group of the rectangle.

Using a Model

Students may find that using cardboard cutouts or paper models will be helpful in doing Exs. 7 and 8. The vertices should be labeled on the front and back, and the lines of reflection should be marked on an additional sheet of paper placed under the cutout so that their positions are fixed.

Chapter Summary

1. A transformation is a one-to-one mapping from the whole plane to the whole plane. If the transformation S maps P to P', we write $S: P \rightarrow P'$ or $S(P) = P'$.
2. The word "mapping" is used in geometry as the word "function" is used in algebra. If the function f maps every number to its square we write $f: x \rightarrow x^2$ or $f(x) = x^2$.
3. An isometry is a transformation that preserves distance. An isometry maps any figure to a congruent figure.
4. Some basic isometries are:

   Reflection in a line. R_j is a reflection in line j.

   Translation or glide. $T: (x, y) \rightarrow (x + a, y + b)$ is a translation.

   Rotation about a point. $\mathcal{R}_{O, x}$ is a rotation counterclockwise about O through $x°$. H_O is a half-turn about O.

   Glide reflection. A glide followed by a reflection in a line parallel to the glide yields a glide reflection.
5. A dilation maps any figure to a similar figure. $D_{O, k}$ is a dilation with center O and nonzero scale factor k. A dilation is an isometry if $|k| = 1$.
6. Properties of figures that are preserved by a transformation are said to be invariant under that transformation. Invariant properties are checked in the table below.

	Distance	Angle Measure	Parallelism	Ratio of distances	Area
Isometry:	√	√	√	√	√
Dilation:		√	√	√	

7. The combination of one mapping followed by another is called a composite or product of mappings. The mapping A followed by B is written $B \circ A$.
8. A composite of isometries is an isometry.
   A composite of reflections in two parallel lines is a translation.
   A composite of reflections in two intersecting lines is a rotation.
   A composite of reflections in two perpendicular lines is a half-turn.
9. The identity transformation I keeps all points fixed. A transformation S followed by its inverse S^{-1} is equal to the identity.
10. A symmetry of a figure is an isometry that maps the figure onto itself. Figures can have line symmetry, point symmetry, and rotational symmetry. A tessellation, or covering of the plane with congruent figures, may also have translational and glide reflection symmetry. Solid figures in space can have planes of symmetry and rotational symmetry about an axis.

Chapter Review

1. If isometry S maps A to A' and B to B', then $\overline{AB}$ _?_ $\overline{A'B'}$. ≅ 14–1
2. If $f(x) = 3x$, find the image and preimage of 6. **18, 2**
3. **a.** If $S:(x, y) \to (2x, y - 2)$, find the image and preimage of (3, 3). **(6, 1), $\left(\frac{3}{2}, 5\right)$**
   b. Is S an isometry? **No**
4. Find the image of (−7, 5) when reflected in **(a)** the x-axis, **(b)** the y-axis, and **(c)** the line $y = x$. **a. (−7, −5) b. (7, 5) c. (5, −7)** 14–2
5. Draw the line $y = 2x + 1$ and its image under reflection in the y-axis. **$y = -2x + 1$**
6. **a.** If translation $T:(5, 5) \to (7, 1)$, then $T:(x, y) \to$ (_?_, _?_) **$(x + 2, y - 4)$** 14–3
   b. Is distance invariant under T? **Yes**
   c. Is angle measure invariant under T? **Yes**
   d. Is area invariant under T? **Yes**
7. Find the image of (7, −2) under the glide reflection that moves all points 5 units to the right and then reflects all points in the x-axis. **(12, 2)**
8. Plot the points $A(3, 2)$, $B(-1, 1)$, and $C(1, -3)$. Label the origin O. Draw $\triangle ABC$ and its images under **(a)** $\mathcal{R}_{O, 90}$ and **(b)** H_O. **See below.** 14–4
9. Which of the given rotations are equal to $\mathcal{R}_{O, 140}$? **a, c**
   a. $\mathcal{R}_{O, 500}$ **b.** $\mathcal{R}_{O, -140}$ **c.** $\mathcal{R}_{O, -220}$
10. If O is the origin then the dilation $D_{O, 2}:(3, -2) \to$ (_?_, _?_). **(6, −4)** 14–5
11. Find the image of (3, 1) under a dilation with center (0, 4) and scale factor $\frac{1}{3}$. **(1, 3)**
12. Find the image of (3, 1) under the following transformations: 14–6
    a. $R_x \circ R_y$ **(−3, −1)** **b.** $R_y \circ H_O$ **(3, −1)** **c.** $R_x \circ \mathcal{R}_{O, -90}$ **(1, 3)**

Complete.

13. If $T:(x, y) \to (x - 1, y + 6)$, then $T^{-1}:(x, y) \to$ (_?_, _?_). **$(x + 1, y - 6)$** 14–7
14. The inverse of $D_{O, 4}$ is $D_{?, ?}$. **$D_{O, \frac{1}{4}}$**
15. $R_j \circ R_j$ = _?_ **I** 16. $\mathcal{R}_{O, 75} \circ \mathcal{R}_{O, ?} = I$ **−75 (or 285)**
17. Does a scalene triangle have line symmetry? **No** 14–8
18. Does a rectangle have point symmetry? **Yes**
19. Does a regular octagon have 90° rotational symmetry? **Yes**
20. Name a figure that has 72° rotational symmetry. **a regular pentagon**

8. a. $A'(-2, 3)$, $B'(-1, -1)$, $C'(3, 1)$ b. $A'(-3, -2)$, $B'(1, -1)$, $C'(-1, 3)$

Supplementary Materials

Practice Master 90

Test 59

Resource Book, pp. 99–100, 169

Teaching References

Alternate Test, p. T25

Chapter Test

State whether the transformation mapping the black triangle to the red triangle is a reflection, a translation, a glide reflection, or a rotation.

1.  translation
2. 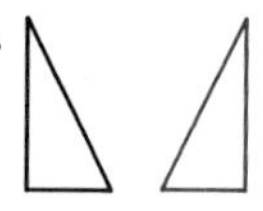 reflection
3. 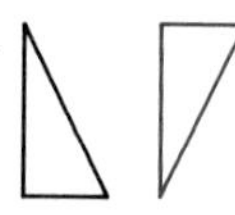 glide ref.
4.  rotation

5. If $f(x) = \frac{1}{2}x + 3$, find the image and preimage of 4. **5, 2**

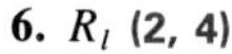

Give the coordinates of the image of point P under the transformation specified.

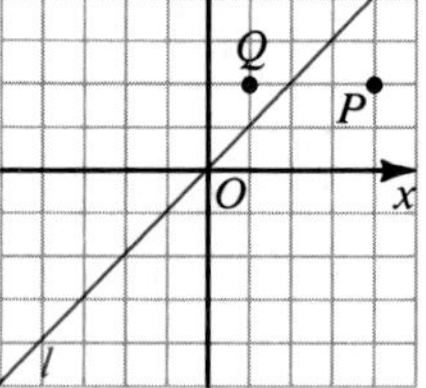

6. R_l (2, 4)
7. $\mathcal{R}_{O, -90}$ (2, −4)
8. $D_{O, \frac{1}{2}}$ (2, 1)
9. $H_O \circ R_x$ (−4, 2)
10. $\mathcal{R}_{O, 90} \circ \mathcal{R}_{O, 90}$ (−4, −2)
11. $D_{Q, \frac{1}{3}}$ (2, 2)
12. $R_l \circ D_{Q, -2}$ (2, −5)
13. $R_l \circ (R_y \circ R_x)$ (−2, −4)

Give the inverse of each transformation.

14. H_O H_O
15. R_x R_x
16. $D_{O, -2}$ $D_{O, -\frac{1}{2}}$

***T* is the translation mapping (4, 1) to (6, 2). Find the coordinates of the image of the origin under each mapping.**

17. T (2, 1)
18. T^3 (6, 3)
19. T^{-1} (−2, −1)

Classify each statement as true or false.

20. All regular polygons have rotational symmetry. **True**
21. 180° rotational symmetry is the same as point symmetry. **True**
22. All regular n-gons have exactly n symmetry lines. **True**
23. A figure that has two intersecting lines of symmetry must have rotational symmetry. **True**

24. **a.** Is a half-turn a transformation? Is it an isometry? **Yes; yes**
    b. Name three properties that are invariant under a half-turn. **dist., ∠ meas., area**
25. A line has slope 2. What is the slope of the image of the line under a:
    a. reflection in the x-axis? **−2**
    b. reflection in the line $y = x$? $\frac{1}{2}$
    c. dilation $D_{O, 3}$? **2**

Preparing for College Entrance Exams

Strategy for Success
Try to work quickly and accurately on exam questions. Do not take time to double-check your answers unless you finish all the questions before the deadline. Skip questions that are too difficult for you, and spend no more than a few minutes on each question.

Indicate the best answer by writing the appropriate letter.

B **1.** Find an equation of the perpendicular bisector of the segment joining $(3, -1)$ and $(-1, 7)$.
(A) $x + 2y = 7$ **(B)** $x - 2y = -5$ **(C)** $2x + y = -5$
(D) $2x + y = 5$ **(E)** $2x - y = -1$

A **2.** A circle has a diameter with endpoints $(0, -8)$ and $(-6, -16)$. An equation of the circle is:
(A) $(x + 3)^2 + (y + 12)^2 = 25$ **(B)** $(x + 3)^2 + (y + 12)^2 = 100$
(C) $(x - 3)^2 + (y - 12)^2 = 25$ **(D)** $(x - 3)^2 + (y - 12)^2 = 100$
(E) $(x + 6)^2 + (y + 24)^2 = 100$

E **3.** The point $(\frac{1}{2}, -\frac{1}{2})$ lies on line t. Which of the following allow you to find an equation for t?
I. slope of t is -3 II. x-intercept of t is 7 III. t is parallel to $4x - 5y = 7$
(A) I only **(B)** III only **(C)** I and III only **(D)** II only **(E)** I, II, and III

C **4.** Given $A(-3, 5)$, $B(0, -4)$, $C(2, 5)$, and $D(-6, -1)$, find the intersection point of $\overleftrightarrow{AB}$ and $\overleftrightarrow{CD}$.
(A) $(6, 23)$ **(B)** $(2, -10)$ **(C)** $(-2, 2)$ **(D)** $(-18, 5)$ **(E)** cannot be determined

C **5.** What is the best name for quadrilateral $WXYZ$ with vertices $W(-3, -2)$, $X(-5, 2)$, $Y(1, 5)$, and $Z(3, 1)$?
(A) isosceles trapezoid **(B)** parallelogram **(C)** rectangle
(D) rhombus **(E)** square

E **6.** Two vertices of an isosceles right triangle are $(0, 0)$ and $(j, 0)$. The third vertex cannot be:
(A) $(0, j)$ **(B)** $(0, -j)$ **(C)** (j, j) **(D)** $\left(\frac{j}{2}, \frac{j}{2}\right)$ **(E)** $\left(\frac{j}{2}, j\right)$

A **7.** What is the image of $(-2, 3)$ under reflection in the line $y = x$?
(A) $(3, -2)$ **(B)** $(2, 3)$ **(C)** $(-2, -3)$ **(D)** $(2, -3)$ **(E)** $(-3, 2)$

E **8.** Find the preimage of $(0, 0)$ under $D_{P, \frac{1}{4}}$, where P is the point $(-1, 1)$.
(A) $(-4, 4)$ **(B)** $(-\frac{3}{4}, \frac{3}{4})$ **(C)** $(-\frac{1}{4}, \frac{1}{4})$ **(D)** $(4, -4)$ **(E)** $(3, -3)$

B **9.** A regular pentagon does *not* have:
(A) line symmetry **(B)** point symmetry **(C)** 360° rotational symmetry
(D) 216° rotational symmetry **(E)** 72° rotational symmetry

D **10.** If $CDEF$ is a square with vertices labeled counterclockwise, then $\mathcal{R}_{C, -450}: \overline{CF} \rightarrow$ ___?___.
(A) $\overline{FE}$ **(B)** $\overline{ED}$ **(C)** $\overline{CF}$ **(D)** $\overline{CD}$ **(E)** none of these

Supplementary Materials

Practice Masters 91, 92
Tests 60, 61
Resource Book, pp. 101–108, 170–172, 186–189, 203

Cumulative Review: Chapters 1-14

True-False Exercises

Classify each statement as true or false.

A **1.** Three given points are always coplanar. **True**

2. Each interior angle of a regular n-gon has measure $\frac{(n - 2)180}{n}$. **True**

3. If $\triangle RST \cong \triangle RSV$, then $\angle SRT \cong \angle SRV$. **True**

4. The contrapositive of a true conditional is sometimes false. **False**

5. Corresponding parts of similar triangles must be congruent. **False**

6. An acute angle inscribed in a circle must intercept a minor arc. **True**

7. In a plane the locus of points equidistant from M and N is the midpoint of $\overline{MN}$. **False**

8. If a cylinder and a right prism have equal base areas and equal heights, then they have equal volumes. **True**

9. A triangle with vertices $(a, 0)$, $(-a, 0)$, and $(0, a)$ is equilateral. **False**

10. If the slopes of two lines have opposite signs, the lines are perpendicular. **False**

11. $R_k \circ R_k = I$ **True**

12. If a figure has 90° rotational symmetry, then it also has point symmetry. **True**

B **13.** A point lies on the bisector of $\angle ABC$ if and only if it is equidistant from A and C. **False**

14. In $\triangle RST$, if $RS < ST$, then $\angle R$ must be the largest angle of the triangle. **False**

15. A triangle with sides of length $2x$, $3x$, and $4x$ must be obtuse. **True**

16. In a right triangle, the altitude to the hypotenuse is always the shortest of the three altitudes. **True**

17. Given a segment of length t, it is possible to construct a segment of length $t\sqrt{3}$. **True**

18. If an equilateral triangle and a regular hexagon are inscribed in a circle, then the ratio of their areas is 1:2. **True**

19. The lateral area of a cone can be equal to the area of the base of the cone. **False**

20. The circle $(x + 3)^2 + (y - 2)^2 = 4$ is tangent to the line $x = -1$. **True**

Multiple-Choice Exercises

Write the letter that indicates the best answer.

A **1.** The measure of an interior angle of a regular decagon is:
a. 36 **b.** 108 **c.** 72 **(d.)** 144

2. Which of the following is *not* a method for proving two triangles congruent?
a. HL **b.** AAS **(c.)** SSA **d.** SAS

3. The median to the hypotenuse of a right triangle divides the triangle into two triangles that are both:
a. similar **(b.)** isosceles **c.** scalene **d.** right

4. Which proportion is *not* equivalent to $\frac{a}{b} = \frac{c}{d}$?
a. $\frac{a}{c} = \frac{b}{d}$ **b.** $\frac{b}{a+b} = \frac{d}{c+d}$ **c.** $\frac{b}{a} = \frac{d}{c}$ **(d.)** $\frac{a}{d} = \frac{c}{b}$

5. For every acute angle X:
a. $\cos X < \sin X$ **b.** $\cos X > \tan X$ **c.** $\tan X > 1$ **(d.)** $\cos X < 1$

B **6.** If A, B, and C are points on $\odot O$, $\overline{AC}$ is a diameter, and $m\angle AOB = 60$, then $m\angle ACB =$
(a.) 30 **b.** 60 **c.** 90 **d.** 120

7. A rectangle with perimeter 30 and area 44 has length:
a. $2\sqrt{11}$ **b.** 8 **(c.)** 11 **d.** 10

8. A regular hexagon with perimeter 24 has area:
(a.) $24\sqrt{3}$ **b.** $16\sqrt{3}$ **c.** $48\sqrt{3}$ **d.** $32\sqrt{3}$

9. In $\odot O$, $m\widehat{AB} = 90$ and $OA = 6$. The region bounded by $\overline{AB}$ and $\widehat{AB}$ has area:
a. $3\pi - 6$ **b.** $9\pi - 36$ **(c.)** $9\pi - 18$ **d.** $36\pi - 6\sqrt{2}$

10. Two regular octagons have sides of length $6\sqrt{3}$ and 9. The ratio of their areas is:
a. $2\sqrt{3}:3$ **(b.)** $4:3$ **c.** $2:3$ **d.** $8\sqrt{3}:9$

11. If F is the point $(-3, 5)$ and G is the point $(0, -4)$, then an equation of $\overleftrightarrow{FG}$ is:
a. $y = -\frac{1}{3}x + 4$ **(b.)** $y = -3x - 4$ **c.** $y = \frac{1}{3}x + 4$ **d.** $y = -3x + 4$

Completion Exercises

Write the correct word, number, phrase, or expression.

A **1.** If $5x - 1 = 14$, then the statement $5x = 15$ is justified by the __?__. **Add. Prop. of =**

2. If two parallel lines are cut by a transversal, then __?__ angles are congruent, __?__ angles are congruent, and __?__ angles are supplementary. **corr.; alt. int.; s-s int.**

3. The measures of two angles of a triangle are 56 and 62. The measure of the largest exterior angle of the triangle is __?__. **124**

4. In $\triangle BEV$ with $m\angle B = 53$ and $m\angle E = 63$, the longest side is __?__. $\overline{BE}$

5. The area of a triangle with vertices $(-2, 0)$, $(9, 0)$, and $(3, 6)$ is __?__. **33**

6. The distance between $(-5, -2)$ and $(1, -6)$ is __?__. $2\sqrt{13}$

7. If $j \perp k$ and line j has slope $\frac{2}{3}$, then k has slope __?__. $-\frac{3}{2}$

8. If A is $(-8, 3)$ and B is $(-4, -1)$, then the midpoint of $\overline{AB}$ is (__?__, __?__). **(−6, 1)**

B **9.** If O is the origin, then $R_x \circ \mathcal{R}_{O,\,90}:(-2, 5) \to$ (__?__, __?__). **(−5, 2)**

10. If $RX = 18$, $XS = 10$, and $RT = 35$, then $YT =$ __?__. **12.5**

11. If $RX = 16$, $XS = 8$, and $XY = 15$, then $ST =$ __?__. **22.5**

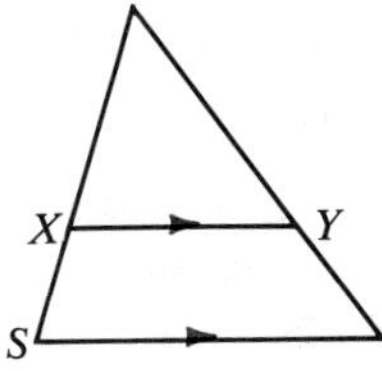

Exs. 10, 11

12. If a dart thrown at a 64-square checkerboard lands on the board, the probability that it lands on a black square is _?_. The probability that it lands on one of the four central squares is _?_. **$\frac{1}{2}$; $\frac{1}{16}$**
13. In $\triangle ABC$, $\overline{AB} \perp \overline{BC}$, $AB = 15$, and $BC = 8$. Then the exact value of $\sin C$ is _?_. **$\frac{15}{17}$**
14. A tree 5 m tall casts a shadow 8 m long. To the nearest degree, the angle of elevation of the sun is _?_. (Use the table on page 311.) **32°**
15. A trapezoid with sides 8, 8, 8, and 10 has area _?_. **$27\sqrt{7}$**
16. A circle with area 100π has circumference _?_. **20π**
17. A cone with radius 9 and slant height 15 has volume _?_ and lateral area _?_. **324π, 135π**
18. A sphere with surface area 144π cm^2 has volume _?_. **288π cm^3**
19. If $B = (2, 0)$, then $D_{B,\,-2}:(1, 1) \to$ (_?_, _?_). **(4, −2)**

C 20. If each edge of a regular triangular pyramid is 6 cm, then the pyramid has total area _?_ and volume _?_. **$36\sqrt{3}$ cm^2, $18\sqrt{2}$ cm^3**

21. A plane parallel to the base of a cone and bisecting the altitude divides the cone into two parts whose volumes have the ratio _?_. **1:7**

Always-Sometimes-Never Exercises

Write A, S, or N to indicate your answer.

A 1. Vertical angles are _?_ adjacent angles. **N**

2. If J is a point outside $\odot P$ and $\overline{JA}$ and $\overline{JB}$ are tangents to $\odot P$ with A and B on $\odot P$, then $\triangle JAB$ is _?_ scalene. **N**
3. A conclusion based on inductive reasoning is _?_ correct. **S**
4. Two right triangles with congruent hypotenuses are _?_ congruent. **S**
5. If the diagonals of a quadrilateral are perpendicular bisectors of each other, then the quadrilateral is _?_ a rhombus. **A**
6. If $\triangle RST$ is a right triangle with hypotenuse $\overline{RS}$, then $\sin R$ and $\cos S$ are _?_ equal. **A**
7. A circle _?_ contains three collinear points. **N**
8. A lateral edge of a regular pyramid is _?_ longer than the slant height. **A**
9. Transformations are _?_ isometries. **S**
10. Under a half-turn about point O, point O is _?_ mapped onto itself. **A**

B 11. If the measures of three consecutive angles of a quadrilateral are 58, 122, and 58, then the diagonals _?_ bisect each other. **A**

12. A triangle with sides of length x, $x + 2$, and $x + 4$ is _?_ an acute triangle. **S**
13. If $\widehat{RS}$ and $\widehat{XY}$ are arcs of $\odot O$ and $m\widehat{RS} < m\widehat{XY}$, then RS and XY are _?_ equal. **N**

14. The center of the circle that can be circumscribed about a given triangle is _?_ outside the triangle. **S**
15. Given two segments with lengths r and s, it is _?_ possible to construct a segment of length $\frac{3}{4}\sqrt{2rs}$. **A**
16. A median of a triangle _?_ separates the triangle into two triangles with equal areas. **A**
17. A composite of reflections in two lines is _?_ a translation. **S**

Construction Exercises

A 1. Construct an angle of measure $22\frac{1}{2}$. **Construction 3**

2. Draw a circle O and choose a point T on $\odot O$. Construct the tangent to $\odot O$ at T. **Construction 8**
3. Draw a large triangle. Inscribe a circle in the triangle. **Construction 11**

For Exercises 4–7, draw two long segments. Let their lengths be x and y, with $x > y$.

4. Construct a segment of length $\frac{1}{2}(x + y)$.

B 5. Construct a rectangle with width y and diagonal x.

6. Construct any triangle with area xy.
7. Construct a segment with length $\sqrt{3xy}$.
8. Draw a very long $\overline{AB}$. Construct a rectangle with perimeter AB and sides in the ratio 3:2.

Proof Exercises

A 1. Given: $\overline{PQ} \parallel \overline{RS}$
Prove: $\frac{PO}{RO} = \frac{PQ}{RS}$

2. Given: $\overline{PR} \perp \overline{QS}$; $\overline{PS} \cong \overline{QR}$; $\overline{OS} \cong \overline{OR}$
Prove: $\angle PSO \cong \angle QRO$

Exs. 1–3

B 3. Given: $\angle OSR \cong \angle ORS$; $\angle OPQ \cong \angle OQP$
Prove: $\triangle PSR \cong \triangle QRS$

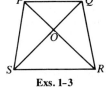

4. Prove: The diagonals of a rectangle intersect to form four congruent segments.
5. Use coordinate geometry to prove that the triangle formed by joining the midpoints of the sides of an isosceles triangle is an isosceles triangle.

C 6. Use an indirect proof to show that a trapezoid cannot have two pairs of congruent sides.

7. Prove: If two coplanar circles intersect in two points, then the line joining those points bisects a common tangent segment.

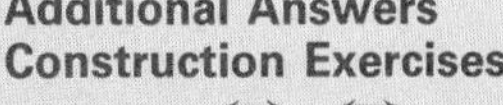

Additional Answers
Construction Exercises

1. Const. $\overleftrightarrow{AC} \perp \overleftrightarrow{BD}$ at E. Const. $\overrightarrow{EF}$, the bis. of $\angle DEC$; then const. $\overrightarrow{EG}$, the bis. of $\angle FEC$. $m\angle GEC = 22\frac{1}{2}$
4. On a line, mark off $AB = x$, $BC = y$. Construct the $\perp$ bis. of $\overline{AC}$ int. $\overline{AC}$ at D. $AD = \frac{1}{2}(x + y)$
5. Const. $AB = y$. Const. the $\perp$ to $\overline{AB}$ at A and the $\perp$ to $\overline{AB}$ at B. With ctr. B and rad. x, draw an arc int. the first $\perp$ at D. With ctr. A and rad. x, draw an arc int. the second $\perp$ at C. Draw $\overline{DC}$.
6. On a line, mark off $AB = x$, $BC = x$. Const. a $\perp$ to $\overline{AC}$ at C and const. $\overline{CD}$ on the $\perp$ with length y. Draw $\overline{AD}$.
7. On a line, mark off $AB = x$, $BC = x$, and $CD = x$. Use Const. 14 to const. the geom. mean of AD and y.
8. Const. the $\perp$ bis. of $\overline{AB}$, int. $\overline{AB}$ at C. Use Const. 12 to divide $\overline{AC}$ into 5 $\cong$ parts, $\overline{AW}$, $\overline{WX}$, $\overline{XY}$, $\overline{YZ}$, and $\overline{ZC}$. Const. $\overline{DE} \cong \overline{AY}$. Const. a $\perp$ to $\overline{DE}$ at D and one at E. Const. $\overline{DG}$ and $\overline{EF}$ both $\cong$ to $\overline{YC}$ on the $\perp$s. Draw $\overline{GF}$.

Examinations

Chapter 1

Indicate the best answer by writing the appropriate letter.

b **1.** Which of the following sets of points are *not* coplanar?
a. E, H, O, G **b.** K, O, G, E
c. E, O, F, J **d.** H, K, O, J

d **2.** Which of the following sets of points are contained in *more* than one plane?
a. G, O, J **b.** E, O, G
c. H, E, G **d.** G, O, H

b **3.** How many planes contain point E and $\overleftrightarrow{JK}$?
a. 0 **b.** exactly 1
c. unlimited **d.** unknown

Exs. 1–4

a **4.** If $\overleftrightarrow{GH}$ bisects $\overline{EF}$, which statement is *not necessarily* true?
a. O is the midpoint of $\overline{GH}$. **b.** $\overline{EO} \cong \overline{OF}$
c. E, F, G, H, and O are coplanar. **d.** $GO + OH = GH$

a **5.** Points A, B, C are collinear, but they do not necessarily lie on a line in the order named. If $AB = 5$ and $BC = 3$, what is the length of $\overline{AC}$?
a. either 2 or 8 **b.** either 2 or 4 **c.** 2 **d.** 8

b **6.** On a number line, point R has coordinate -5 and point S has coordinate 3. Point X lies on $\overrightarrow{SR}$ and $SX = 5$. Find the coordinate of X.
a. -10 **b.** -2 **c.** 8 **d.** 0

d **7.** Which angle appears to be obtuse?
a. $\angle AEB$ **b.** $\angle DEB$
c. $\angle CEA$ **d.** $\angle AED$

c **8.** If $\overrightarrow{EC}$ bisects $\angle DEB$, $\overrightarrow{EB}$ bisects $\angle DEA$, and $m\angle BEC = 28$, find the measure of $\angle CEA$.
a. 28 **b.** 56
c. 84 **d.** 112

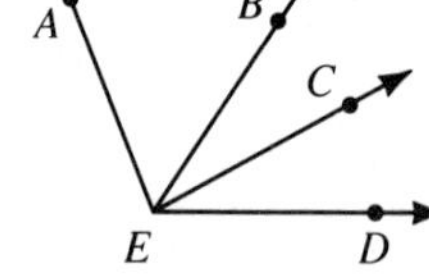

Exs. 7–9

a **9.** Which two angles are adjacent angles?
a. $\angle DEB$ and $\angle BEA$ **b.** $\angle DEB$ and $\angle CEA$
c. $\angle DEC$ and $\angle BEA$ **d.** $\angle DEA$ and $\angle DEC$

b **10.** M is the midpoint of $\overline{YZ}$. If $YM = r + 3$ and $YZ = 3r - 1$, find MZ.
a. 7 **b.** 10 **c.** 20 **d.** 4

a **11.** Which of the following is *not always* true when lines j and k intersect?
a. Exactly one plane contains line j.
b. The lines intersect in exactly one point.
c. All points on j and k are coplanar points.
d. Given any point P on j and any point Q on k, P and Q are collinear points.

Chapter 2

Indicate the best answer by writing the appropriate letter.

c **1.** If $m\angle 1 = 60$ and $m\angle 2 = 30$, then $\angle 1$ and $\angle 2$ *cannot* be which of the following?
a. acute $\angle$s **b.** adjacent $\angle$s
c. vertical $\angle$s **d.** complementary $\angle$s

a **2.** Given: If q, then r. Which of the following is the converse of the given conditional?
a. r implies q. **b.** r if q.
c. q only if r. **d.** r if and only if q.

b **3.** What are basic mathematical assumptions called?
a. theorems **b.** postulates **c.** conditionals **d.** conclusions

d **4.** Which of the following *cannot* be used as a reason in a proof?
a. a definition **b.** a postulate
c. yesterday's theorem **d.** tomorrow's theorem

d **5.** $\angle A$ and $\angle B$ are supplements, $m\angle A = 2x - 14$, and $m\angle B = x + 8$. Find the measure of $\angle B$.
a. 62 **b.** 30 **c.** 40 **d.** 70

a **6.** If $\angle 1$ and $\angle 2$ are complements, $\angle 2$ and $\angle 3$ are complements, and $\angle 3$ and $\angle 4$ are supplements, what are $\angle 1$ and $\angle 4$?
a. supplements **b.** complements **c.** congruent angles **d.** can't be determined

b **7.** The statement "If $m\angle A = m\angle B$ and $m\angle D = m\angle A + m\angle C$, then $m\angle D = m\angle B + m\angle C$" is justified by what property?
a. Transitive **b.** Substitution **c.** Symmetric **d.** Reflexive

b **8.** If $\overline{TQ} \perp \overline{QR}$, which angles *must* be complementary angles?
a. $\angle 2$ and $\angle 3$ **b.** $\angle 3$ and $\angle 4$
c. $\angle 5$ and $\angle 8$ **d.** $\angle 3$ and $\angle 7$

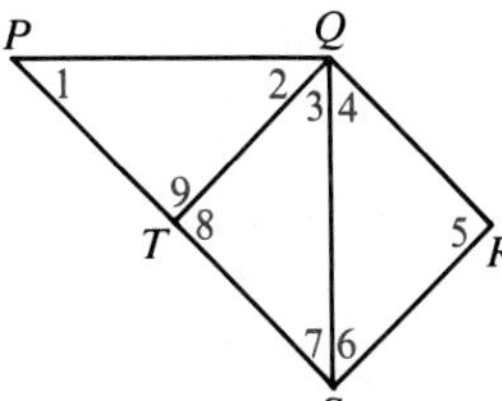

Exs. 8–11

a **9.** If $m\angle 8 = x + 80$, what is the measure of $\angle 9$?
a. $100 - x$ **b.** $100 + x$
c. $x - 80$ **d.** $x - 180$

b **10.** If $\overline{QT} \perp \overline{PS}$, which statement is *not* always true?
a. $\angle 8 \cong \angle 9$ **b.** $\angle 2 \cong \angle 3$
c. $\angle 8$ is a rt. $\angle$. **d.** $\angle 8$ and $\angle 9$ are supp. $\angle$s.

a **11.** If $\overrightarrow{SQ}$ bisects $\angle RST$, which statement *must* be true?
a. $2 \cdot m\angle 6 = m\angle RST$ **b.** $\frac{1}{2}m\angle 7 = m\angle RST$
c. $\angle 4 \cong \angle 6$ **d.** $\angle RST \cong \angle RQT$

Chapter 3

Indicate the best answer by writing the appropriate letter.

d **1.** If $\overrightarrow{BE}$ bisects $\angle ABC$, what is the measure of $\angle AEB$?
a. 30 **b.** 35 **c.** 40 **d.** 45

a **2.** If $m\angle ABE = 40$, what is the measure of $\angle DEB$?
a. 140 **b.** 40 **c.** 75 **d.** 135

b **3.** If $\overline{AB} \parallel \overline{DC}$, what is the measure of $\angle D$?
a. 70 **b.** 80 **c.** 90 **d.** 100

a **4.** Which of the following would allow you to conclude that $\overline{AD} \parallel \overline{BC}$?
a. $\angle DEC \cong \angle BCE$ **b.** $\angle ABE \cong \angle BEC$
c. $\angle BEC \cong \angle BCE$ **d.** $m\angle A + m\angle AEC = 180$

Exs. 1–4

d **5.** What is the measure of each interior angle of a regular octagon?
a. 150 **b.** 144 **c.** 140 **d.** 135

b **6.** The plane containing Q, S, A, U appears to be parallel to the plane containing which points?
a. Q, E, K, S **b.** E, K, C, R
c. R, E, Q, U **d.** U, R, C, A

d **7.** Which of the following appear to be skew lines?
a. $\overleftrightarrow{QE}$ and $\overleftrightarrow{AC}$ **b.** $\overleftrightarrow{QU}$ and $\overleftrightarrow{KC}$
c. $\overleftrightarrow{AC}$ and $\overleftrightarrow{UR}$ **d.** $\overleftrightarrow{QS}$ and $\overleftrightarrow{AC}$

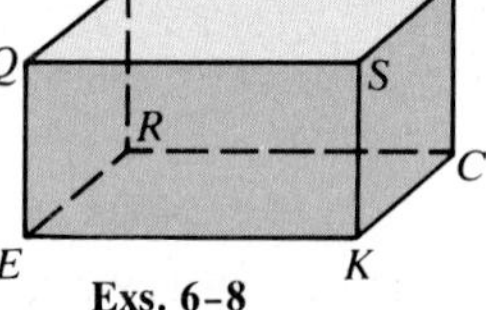

Exs. 6–8

c **8.** $\overleftrightarrow{EK}$ does *not* appear to be parallel to the plane containing which points?
a. U, A, C **b.** Q, U, A **c.** Q, U, R **d.** Q, S, C

a **9.** The sum of the measures of the interior angles of a certain polygon is the same as the sum of the measures of its exterior angles. How many sides does the polygon have?
a. four **b.** six **c.** eight **d.** ten

c **10.** What is the next number in the sequence 1, 2, 4, 7, 11, . . . ?
a. 17 **b.** 13 **c.** 16 **d.** 15

c **11.** $\overline{AC}$ is a diagonal of regular pentagon $ABCDE$. What is the measure of $\angle ACD$?
a. 36 **b.** 54 **c.** 72 **d.** 108

a **12.** A, B, C, and D are coplanar points. $\overleftrightarrow{AB} \parallel \overleftrightarrow{CD}$, $\overleftrightarrow{AB} \perp \overleftrightarrow{AC}$, and $m\angle ACD = 2x + 8$. Find the value of x.
a. 41 **b.** 49 **c.** 90 **d.** 180

d **13.** What is the *principal* basis for inductive reasoning?
a. definitions **b.** previously proved theorems
c. postulates **d.** past observations

Chapter 4

In Exercises 1–8 write a method (SSS, SAS, ASA, AAS, or HL) that can be used to prove the two triangles congruent.

1.

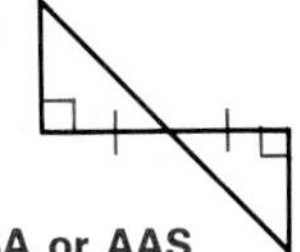

ASA or AAS

2. AAS

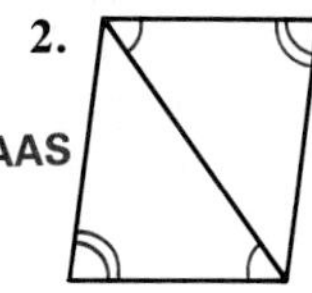

3.

ASA or AAS

4.

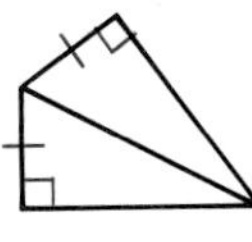

HL

5. SSS

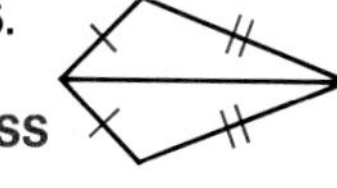

6. AAS

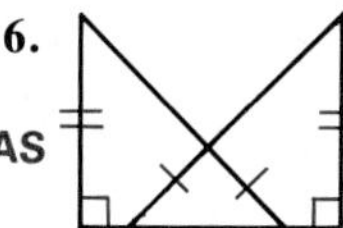

7. Given: $\overline{PO} \perp$ plane X; $OT = OS$ SAS

8. Given: $\overline{PO} \perp$ plane X; $PT = PS$ HL

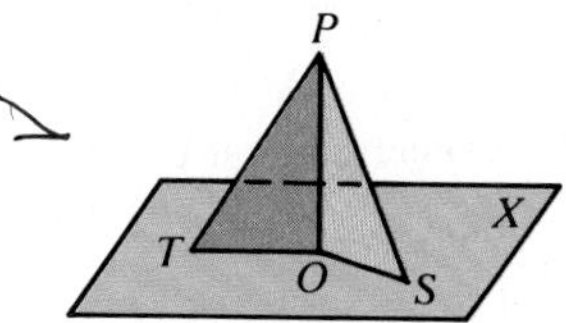

Exs. 7, 8

Indicate the best answer by writing the appropriate letter.

d **9.** In $\triangle RXT$, $\angle R \cong \angle T$, $RT = 2x + 5$, $RX = 5x - 7$, and $TX = 2x + 8$. What is the perimeter of $\triangle RXT$?

a. 5 **b.** 15 **c.** 18 **d.** 51

a **10.** If $\triangle DEF \cong \triangle PRS$, which of these congruences *must* be true?

a. $\overline{DF} \cong \overline{PS}$ **b.** $\overline{EF} \cong \overline{PR}$ **c.** $\angle E \cong \angle S$ **d.** $\angle F \cong \angle R$

a **11.** In $\triangle ABC$, $AB = AC$, $m\angle A = 46$, and $\overline{BD}$ is an altitude. What is the measure of $\angle CBD$?

a. 23 **b.** 44 **c.** 67 **d.** 134

c **12.** An equiangular triangle *cannot* be which of the following?

a. equilateral **b.** isosceles **c.** scalene **d.** acute

b **13.** Point X is equidistant from vertices T and N of scalene $\triangle TEN$. Point X *must* lie on which of the following?

a. bisector of $\angle E$ **b.** perpendicular bisector of $\overline{TN}$

c. median to $\overline{TN}$ **d.** the altitude to $\overline{TN}$

c **14.** Given: $\overline{AB} \parallel \overline{DC}$; $\overline{AB} \cong \overline{CD}$; $\angle 1 \cong \angle 2$

To prove that $\overline{DE} \cong \overline{BF}$, what would you prove first?

a. $\triangle ADE \cong \triangle CBF$ **b.** $\triangle ABF \cong \triangle CDE$

c. $\triangle ABC \cong \triangle CDA$ **d.** cannot be proved

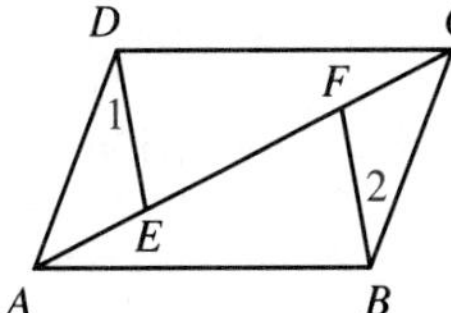

Chapter 5

Indicate the best answer by writing the appropriate letter.

a **1.** Both pairs of opposite sides of a quadrilateral are parallel. Which special kind of quadrilateral *must* it be?
a. parallelogram **b.** rectangle **c.** rhombus **d.** trapezoid

d **2.** The diagonals of a certain quadrilateral are congruent. Which term could *not* be used to describe the quadrilateral?
a. isosceles trapezoid **b.** rectangle
c. rhombus **d.** parallelogram with a 60° angle

a **3.** M is the midpoint of hypotenuse $\overline{TK}$ of right $\triangle TAK$. $AM = 13$. What is the length of $\overline{TK}$?
a. 26 **b.** $19\frac{1}{2}$ **c.** 13 **d.** none of these

d **4.** In $\square$ $WXYZ$, $WX = 10$. What does ZW equal?
a. 16 **b.** YZ **c.** WY **d.** none of these

b **5.** A diagonal of a parallelogram bisects one of its angles. Which special kind of parallelogram *must* it be?
a. rectangle **b.** rhombus
c. square **d.** parallelogram with a 60° angle

b **6.** The lengths of the bases of a trapezoid are 18 and 26. What is the length of the median?
a. 8 **b.** 22 **c.** 44 **d.** 34

a **7.** In quad. $PQRS$, $PQ = SR$, $QR = PS$, and $m\angle P = m\angle Q$. Which of the following is *not necessarily* true?
a. $\overline{PR} \perp \overline{QS}$ **b.** $\overline{PR} \cong \overline{QS}$ **c.** $\angle P \cong \angle R$ **d.** $\angle R \cong \angle S$

c **8.** In $\triangle ABC$, $AB = 8$, $BC = 10$, and $AC = 12$. M is the midpoint of $\overline{AB}$, and N is the midpoint of $\overline{BC}$. What is the length of $\overline{MN}$?
a. 4 **b.** 5 **c.** 6 **d.** 9

b **9.** If $EFGH$ is a parallelogram, which of the following *must* be true?
a. $\angle E \cong \angle F$ **b.** $\angle F \cong \angle H$
c. $\overline{FG} \parallel \overline{GH}$ **d.** $m\angle E + m\angle G = 180$

c **10.** Which information does *not* prove that quad. $ABCD$ is a parallelogram?
a. $\overline{AC}$ and $\overline{BD}$ bisect each other. **b.** $\overline{AD} \parallel \overline{BC}$; $\overline{AD} \cong \overline{BC}$
c. $\overline{AB} \parallel \overline{CD}$; $\overline{AD} \cong \overline{BC}$ **d.** $\angle A \cong \angle C$; $\angle B \cong \angle D$

c **11.** In the figure, $\overline{RU} \cong \overline{US}$ and $\angle 1 \cong \angle 2$. Which of the following *cannot* be proved?
a. $\angle 3 \cong \angle 4$ **b.** $\overline{RV} \cong \overline{VT}$
c. $\overline{US} \cong \overline{VT}$ **d.** $ST = 2 \cdot UV$

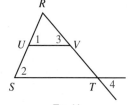

R
U 1 3 V
2
S T 4

Ex. 11

b **12.** Which of the following *must* be true for any trapezoid?
a. Any two consecutive angles are supplementary.
b. At least one angle is obtuse.
c. The diagonals bisect each other.
d. The median bisects each base.

Chapter 6

Indicate the best answer by writing the appropriate letter.

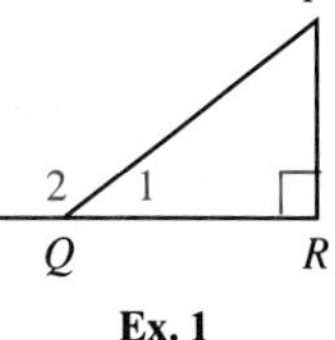

Ex. 1

b **1.** Which of the following statements *must* be false?
a. $QR + PR > PQ$ **b.** $m\angle 2 > m\angle P + m\angle R$
c. $\frac{1}{2}m\angle 2 > \frac{1}{2}m\angle 1$ **d.** $PQ > PR$

d **2.** You don't need a figure to do this exercise. Given that $m\angle A = m\angle B$, you want to prove that $m\angle 3 = m\angle 4$. To write an an indirect proof, you should begin by temporarily assuming which statement?
a. $m\angle A \neq m\angle B$ **b.** $m\angle A = m\angle B$
c. $m\angle 3 = m\angle 4$ **d.** $m\angle 3 \neq m\angle 4$

a **3.** In quadrilateral $MNPQ$, $MN = 5$, $NP = 6$, $PQ = 7$, and $QM = 9$. Which of the following might possibly be the length of $\overline{NQ}$?
a. 12.5 **b.** 14 **c.** 2 **d.** all of these

c **4.** Given: (1) If A is white, then B is red.
(2) B is not red.
Which of the following *must* be true?
a. B is white. **b.** B is not white. **c.** A is not white. **d.** A is red.

b **5.** If a conditional is known to be true, then which of the following *must* also be true?
a. its converse **b.** its contrapositive
c. its inverse **d.** none of these

c **6.** In $\triangle DEF$, $m\angle D = 50$, and an exterior angle with vertex F has measure 120. What is the longest side of $\triangle DEF$?
a. $\overline{DE}$ **b.** $\overline{EF}$ **c.** $\overline{DF}$ **d.** unknown

a **7.** In $\triangle MNP$, $MN = 8$ and $NP = 10$. Which of these *must* be true?
a. $MP > 2$ **b.** $MP < 2$ **c.** $MP > 10$ **d.** $MP < 10$

b **8.** What is the inverse of "If $x = 3$, then $x > 0$"?
a. If $x > 0$, then $x = 3$. **b.** If $x \neq 3$, then $x \leq 0$.
c. If $x \leq 0$, then $x \neq 3$. **d.** If $x = 3$, then $x \leq 0$.

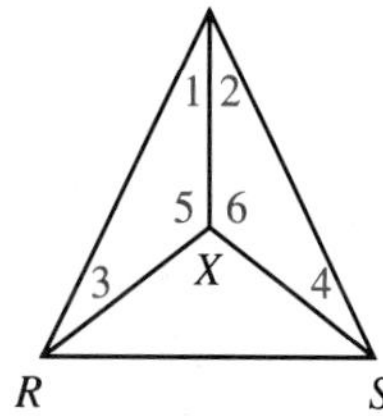

a **9.** If $RT = ST$ and $RX > SX$, what can you conclude?
a. $m\angle 1 > m\angle 2$ **b.** $m\angle XRS > m\angle XSR$
c. $m\angle 3 = m\angle 4$ **d.** $m\angle 5 > m\angle 6$

a **10.** If $RX = SX$ and $m\angle 5 > m\angle 6$, what can you conclude?
a. $m\angle TRS < m\angle TSR$ **b.** $RT < ST$
c. $m\angle 1 > m\angle 2$ **d.** $m\angle 3 > m\angle 4$

d **11.** Which of the following is an important part of an indirect proof?
a. Proving that the hypothesis *cannot* be deduced from the conclusion
b. Proving that the temporary assumption must be true
c. Assuming temporarily that the conclusion must be true
d. Finding a contradiction of a known fact

Chapter 7

Indicate the best answer by writing the appropriate letter.

c **1.** If the measures of the angles of a triangle are in the ratio 3:3:4, what is the measure of the largest angle of the triangle?
a. 40 **b.** 54 **c.** 72 **d.** 90

d **2.** If $\triangle ABC \sim \triangle JOT$, which of these is a correct proportion?
a. $\frac{BC}{AC} = \frac{JT}{OT}$ **b.** $\frac{AB}{JT} = \frac{AC}{JO}$ **c.** $\frac{AB}{BC} = \frac{OT}{JT}$ **d.** $\frac{AC}{JT} = \frac{BC}{OT}$

a **3.** If $\frac{a}{b} = \frac{x}{y}$, what does $\frac{y}{b}$ equal?
a. $\frac{x}{a}$ **b.** $\frac{a}{x}$ **c.** $\frac{y}{x}$ **d.** $\frac{b}{y}$

d **4.** $\triangle ABC \sim \triangle DEF$, $AB = 8$, $BC = 12$, $AC = 16$, and $DE = 12$. What is the perimeter of $\triangle DEF$?
a. 36 **b.** 40 **c.** 48 **d.** 54

b **5.** Which of the following pairs of polygons *must* be similar?
a. two rectangles **b.** two regular hexagons
c. two isosceles triangles **d.** two parallelograms with a 60° angle

b **6.** Quad. $GHJK \sim$ quad. $RSTU$, $GH = JK = 10$, $HJ = KG = 14$, and $RS = TU = 16$. What is the scale factor of quad. $GHJK$ to quad. $RSTU$?
a. $\frac{5}{7}$ **b.** $\frac{5}{8}$ **c.** $\frac{7}{8}$ **d.** $\frac{16}{10}$

b **7.** Which of the following can you use to prove that the two triangles are similar?
a. SAS Similarity Theorem **b.** AA Similarity Postulate
c. SSS Similarity Theorem **d.** Def. of similar triangles

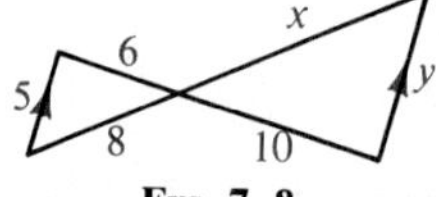

Exs. 7, 8

a **8.** Which statement is correct?
a. $\frac{6}{10} = \frac{8}{x}$ **b.** $\frac{6}{8} = \frac{x}{10}$ **c.** $6 \cdot 10 = 8x$ **d.** $\frac{5}{y} = \frac{8}{10}$

b **9.** What is the value of u?
a. 8 **b.** 10 **c.** 16 **d.** 25

d **10.** What is the value of z?
a. 25 **b.** 28 **c.** $\frac{28}{3}$ **d.** $\frac{70}{3}$

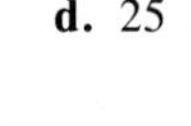

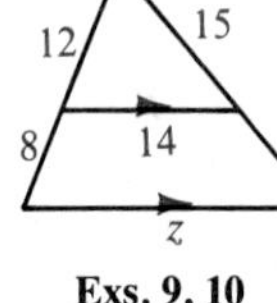

Exs. 9, 10

c **11.** In $\triangle APC$, the bisector of $\angle P$ meets $\overline{AC}$ at B. $PA = 30$, $PC = 50$, and $AB = 12$. What is the length of $\overline{BC}$?
a. $\frac{36}{5}$ **b.** 12 **c.** 20 **d.** 32

b **12.** If $\triangle RST \sim \triangle XYZ$, what is the ratio of $m\angle S$ to $m\angle Y$?
a. $m\angle R : m\angle Z$ **b.** 1:1 **c.** $RS:XY$ **d.** not enough information

Chapter 8

Indicate the best answer by writing the appropriate letter.

a **1.** The shorter leg of a 30°-60°-90° triangle has length 7. Find the length of the hypotenuse.
a. 14 **b.** $7\sqrt{2}$ **c.** $7\sqrt{3}$ **d.** $\sqrt{14}$

c **2.** The altitude to the hypotenuse of a right triangle divides the hypotenuse into segments 25 cm and 30 cm long. How long is the altitude?
a. $15\sqrt{3}$ cm **b.** $15\sqrt{5}$ cm **c.** $5\sqrt{30}$ cm **d.** $5\sqrt{55}$ cm

c **3.** The hypotenuse and one leg of a right triangle have lengths 61 and 11. Find the length of the other leg.
a. 36 **b.** $5\sqrt{2}$ **c.** 60 **d.** $\sqrt{3842}$

d **4.** Each side of an equilateral triangle has length 12. Find the length of an altitude.
a. 6 **b.** 12 **c.** $6\sqrt{2}$ **d.** $6\sqrt{3}$

b **5.** One side of a square has length s. Find the length of a diagonal.
a. $2\sqrt{s}$ **b.** $s\sqrt{2}$ **c.** $\frac{s}{2}\sqrt{3}$ **d.** $s\sqrt{3}$

a **6.** What kind of triangle has sides of lengths 12, 13, and 18?
a. an obtuse triangle **b.** a right triangle
c. an acute triangle **d.** an impossibility

c **7.** In $\triangle RST$, $m\angle S = 90$. What is the value of $\sin T$?
a. $\frac{ST}{RT}$ **b.** $\frac{RS}{ST}$ **c.** $\frac{RS}{RT}$ **d.** $\frac{RT}{RS}$

d **8.** What is the geometric mean between 2 and 24?
a. 48 **b.** $16\sqrt{3}$ **c.** $4\sqrt{6}$ **d.** $4\sqrt{3}$

c **9.** One acute angle of a certain right triangle has measure n. If $\sin n° = \frac{3}{5}$, what is the value of $\tan n°$?
a. $\frac{4}{3}$ **b.** $\frac{4}{5}$ **c.** $\frac{3}{4}$ **d.** $\frac{5}{3}$

a **10.** Which equation could be used to find the value of x?

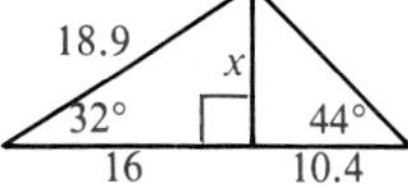

a. $\cos 58° = \frac{x}{18.9}$ **b.** $\sin 32° = \frac{x}{16}$
c. $\cos 44° = \frac{x}{10.4}$ **d.** $\tan 46° = \frac{x}{10.4}$

c **11.** In rt. $\triangle ABC$, $\overline{AB} \perp \overline{BC}$, $\overline{BD} \perp \overline{AC}$ at point D, $BC = 9$, and $AC = 12$. Find the ratio of AD to DC.
a. $\frac{9}{16}$ **b.** $\frac{16}{9}$ **c.** $\frac{7}{9}$ **d.** $\frac{9}{7}$

b **12.** For what value(s) of x is a triangle with sides of lengths x, $x + 7$, and $x + 8$ a right triangle?
a. $x = -7$ **b.** $x = 5$ **c.** $x = -7$ or $x = 5$ **d.** $-7 < x < 5$

Chapter 9

Indicate the best answer by writing the appropriate letter.
In Exercises 1–3, $\overline{PT}$ is tangent to $\odot M$ at T.

Exs. 1–4

c **1.** If $m\angle TMA = 80$, what is the measure of $\widehat{TBA}$?
a. 100 **b.** 80 **c.** 280 **d.** 145

a **2.** If $m\angle M = 80$, $m\angle P = 50$, what is the measure of $\angle MAP$?
a. 140 **b.** 150 **c.** 160 **d.** 170

c **3.** If $PA = 9$ and $AB = 16$, what does PT equal?
a. 12 **b.** $\frac{25}{2}$ **c.** 15 **d.** 20

c **4.** Suppose $\overline{PS}$ were drawn tangent to $\odot M$ at point S. If $m\angle SPT = 62$, find $m\widehat{ST}$.
a. 62 **b.** 236 **c.** 118 **d.** 242

c **5.** How many common tangents can be drawn to two circles that are externally tangent?
a. one **b.** two **c.** three **d.** four

c **6.** Points A, B, and C lie on a circle in the order named. $m\widehat{AB} = 110$ and $m\widehat{BC} = 120$. What is the measure of $\angle BAC$?
a. 130 **b.** 65 **c.** 60 **d.** 55

a **7.** Refer to Exercise 6. If point D lies on $\widehat{AC}$, what is the sum of the measures of $\angle ABC$ and $\angle ADC$?
a. 180 **b.** 170 **c.** 160 **d.** 130

b **8.** R and S are points on a circle. $\overline{RS}$ could be which of these?
a. radius **b.** diameter **c.** secant **d.** tangent

Exs. 9–11

b **9.** If $m\widehat{BC} = 120$ and $m\widehat{AD} = 50$, what is the measure of $\angle X$?
a. 25 **b.** 35 **c.** 60 **d.** 70

d **10.** If $m\widehat{BC} = 120$ and $m\widehat{AD} = 50$, what is the measure of $\angle 1$?
a. 60 **b.** 85 **c.** 90 **d.** 95

a **11.** If $AY = j$, $YC = k$, and $YD = 7$, what does BY equal?
a. $\frac{jk}{7}$ **b.** $\frac{7j}{k}$ **c.** $\frac{7k}{j}$ **d.** $\frac{k}{7j}$

In Exercises 12–14, $\overleftrightarrow{XA}$ is tangent to $\odot O$ at X.

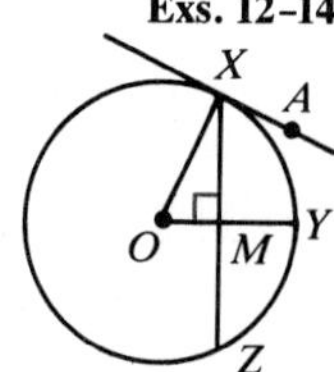

Exs. 12–14

d **12.** Which of these equals $m\angle AXZ$?
a. $m\widehat{XYZ}$ **b.** $m\angle OXM$ **c.** $\frac{1}{2}m\widehat{XY}$ **d.** $\frac{1}{2}m\widehat{XZ}$

a **13.** If the radius of $\odot O$ is 13 and $XZ = 24$, what is the distance from O to chord $\overline{XZ}$?
a. 5 **b.** 8 **c.** 11 **d.** $\sqrt{407}$

d **14.** If $OM = 8$ and $MY = 9$, what does XZ equal?
a. $6\sqrt{2}$ **b.** $2\sqrt{17}$ **c.** $\sqrt{145}$ **d.** 30

Chapter 10

Indicate the best answer by writing the appropriate letter.

c **1.** In a plane, what is the locus of points equidistant from two given points?
a. a point **b.** a circle **c.** a line **d.** a pair of lines

d **2.** Point P lies on line l in a plane. What is the locus of points, in that plane, that lie 8 cm from P and 2 cm from l?
a. no points **b.** two points **c.** three points **d.** four points

b **3.** To inscribe a circle in a triangle, what should you construct first?
a. two medians **b.** two angle bisectors
c. two altitudes **d.** the perpendicular bisectors of two sides

b **4.** The lengths of two segments are r and s, with $r > s$. It is *not* possible to construct a segment with which of these lengths?
a. $\frac{1}{5}(r + s)$ **b.** rs **c.** $\sqrt{3rs}$ **d.** $\sqrt{r^2 + s^2}$

c **5.** It *is* possible to construct an angle with which of these measures?
a. 10 **b.** 20 **c.** 30 **d.** 40

d **6.** You are to construct a tangent to a given $\odot O$ from a point P outside the circle. In the process, it would be useless to construct which of these?
a. $\overline{OP}$ **b.** the perpendicular bisector of $\overline{OP}$
c. a circle with O and P on it **d.** a line parallel to $\overline{OP}$

a **7.** You are given points R and S. Which of the following could *not* be the locus of points in space that are equidistant from R and S and also 4 cm from point S?
a. a pair of circles **b.** a circle **c.** a point **d.** the empty set

d **8.** Where *must* the perpendicular bisectors of the sides of a triangle meet?
a. inside the triangle **b.** on the triangle
c. outside the triangle **d.** none of these

d **9.** In space, what is the locus of points 3 cm from a given point A?
a. a line **b.** a plane
c. a circle **d.** a sphere

d **10.** In a plane, what is the locus of points equidistant from the sides of a square?
a. a square **b.** a line
c. a circle **d.** a point

a **11.** In $\triangle ABC$, $\overline{AD}$ and $\overline{BE}$ are medians. If $AG = 8$, find AD.
a. 12 **b.** 32
c. 4 **d.** 16

c **12.** You are to construct a perpendicular to a line l at a given point X on l. In how many places on l will you need to position the point of your compass in order to do this construction?
a. one **b.** two **c.** three **d.** four

Chapter 11

Indicate the best answer by writing the appropriate letter.

a **1.** One side of a rectangle is 14 and the perimeter is 44. What is the area?
a. 112 **b.** 210 **c.** 224 **d.** 420

d **2.** What is the area of a square inscribed in a circle with radius 8?
a. 32 **b.** 64 **c.** $64\sqrt{2}$ **d.** 128

b **3.** The area of a circle is 25π. What is its circumference?
a. 5π **b.** 10π **c.** 12.5π **d.** 50π

c **4.** What is the area of a trapezoid with bases 7 and 8 and height 6?
a. 90 **b.** 336 **c.** 45 **d.** 168

b **5.** A parallelogram and a triangle have equal areas. The base and height of the parallelogram are 12 and 9. If the base of the triangle is 36, find its height.
a. 3 **b.** 6 **c.** 9 **d.** 12

a **6.** What is the area of trapezoid $ABCD$?
a. 96 **b.** 120 **c.** 144 **d.** 192

d **7.** What is the ratio of the areas of $\triangle AOB$ and $\triangle COD$?
a. $\sqrt{3}:1$ **b.** $\sqrt{3}:3$ **c.** $3:1$ **d.** $9:1$

b **8.** What is the ratio of the areas of $\triangle AOB$ and $\triangle AOD$?
a. $\sqrt{3}:1$ **b.** $3:1$ **c.** $9:1$ **d.** cannot be determined

Exs. 6–8

b **9.** What is the area of a regular hexagon inscribed in a circle with radius 8?
a. $16\sqrt{3}$ **b.** $96\sqrt{3}$ **c.** $128\sqrt{3}$ **d.** $192\sqrt{3}$

c **10.** In the diagram, what is the length of $\widehat{AB}$?
a. $6\sqrt{2}$ **b.** 6π **c.** 3π **d.** 36π

c **11.** In the diagram, what is the area of the shaded region?
a. $9\pi - 36$ **b.** $12\pi - 36$ **c.** $9\pi - 18$ **d.** $12\pi - 18$

d **12.** If a point is chosen at random in the interior of $\odot O$, what is the probability that the point is inside $\triangle AOB$?
a. 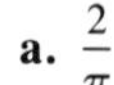 $\frac{2}{\pi}$ **b.** $\frac{1}{4}$ **c.** $\frac{3}{2\pi}$ **d.** $\frac{1}{2\pi}$

Exs. 10–12

b **13.** A rhombus has diagonals 6 and 8. What is its area?
a. 12 **b.** 24 **c.** 36 **d.** 48

d **14.** What is the area of a circle with diameter 12?
a. $24\pi^2$ **b.** 12π **c.** 144π **d.** 36π

d **15.** What is the area of an equilateral triangle with perimeter 24?
a. $64\sqrt{3}$ **b.** $32\sqrt{3}$ **c.** $\frac{32\sqrt{3}}{3}$ **d.** $16\sqrt{3}$

b **16.** What is the area of a triangle with sides 15, 15, and 24?
a. 54 **b.** 108 **c.** 180 **d.** 216

Chapter 12

Indicate the best answer by writing the appropriate letter.

d **1.** What is the volume of a rectangular solid with dimensions 12, 9, and 6?
a. 108 **b.** 216 **c.** 432 **d.** 648

b **2.** What is the total surface area of the solid in Exercise 1?
a. 234 **b.** 468 **c.** 252 **d.** 360

a **3.** Two similar cones have heights 5 and 20. What is the ratio of their volumes?
a. 1:64 **b.** 1:4 **c.** 1:16 **d.** 4:16

c **4.** What is the volume of a regular square pyramid with base edge 16 and height 6?
a. 128 **b.** 256 **c.** 512 **d.** 1536

b **5.** What is the lateral area of the pyramid in Exercise 4?
a. 256 **b.** 320 **c.** 576 **d.** 640

b **6.** A sphere has area 16π. What is its volume?
a. $\frac{8\pi}{3}$ **b.** $\frac{32\pi}{3}$ **c.** $\frac{64\pi}{3}$ **d.** $\frac{256\pi}{3}$

a **7.** A cone has radius 5 and height 12. A cylinder with radius 10 has the same volume as the cone. What is the cylinder's height?
a. 1 **b.** 2 **c.** 3 **d.** 4

b **8.** A cube is inscribed in a cylinder with radius 5. What is the volume of the cube?
a. $15\sqrt{2}$ **b.** $250\sqrt{2}$ **c.** 125 **d.** 100

a **9.** A plane passes 2 cm from the center of a sphere with radius 4 cm. What is the area of the circle of intersection?
a. 12π cm^2 **b.** 16π cm^2 **c.** 18π cm^2 **d.** 20π cm^2

d **10.** Find the total surface area of a cylinder with radius 4 and height 6.
a. 16π **b.** 32π **c.** 48π **d.** 80π

c **11.** Two similar pyramids have volumes 27 and 125. If the smaller has lateral area 18, what is the lateral area of the larger?
a. 30 **b.** $83\frac{1}{3}$ **c.** 50 **d.** 25

a **12.** The base of a right prism is a regular hexagon with side 4. The height of the prism is 6. What is the volume of the prism?
a. $144\sqrt{3}$ **b.** $72\sqrt{3}$ **c.** $48\sqrt{3}$ **d.** $36\sqrt{3}$

d **13.** What is the lateral area of the prism in Exercise 12?
a. 24 **b.** 36 **c.** 72 **d.** 144

b **14.** Find the total surface area of a cone with radius 9 and slant height 12.
a. 108π **b.** 189π **c.** $81\pi\sqrt{7}$ **d.** 216π

Chapter 13

Indicate the best answer by writing the appropriate letter.

d **1.** Given $P(-2, 0)$ and $Q(2, 5)$, find $\overrightarrow{PQ}$.
a. (0, 2.5) **b.** (0, 5) **c.** (−4, −5) **d.** (4, 5)

d **2.** Refer to Exercise 1. Find $|\overrightarrow{PQ}|$.
a. 5 **b.** 3 **c.** $\sqrt{29}$ **d.** $\sqrt{41}$

a **3.** A line with slope $\frac{2}{5}$ passes through point (1, 4). What is an equation of the line?
a. $y - 4 = \frac{2}{5}(x - 1)$ **b.** $y - 4 = \frac{5}{2}(x - 1)$
c. $y + 4 = \frac{2}{5}(x + 1)$ **d.** $y - 1 = \frac{5}{2}(x - 4)$

c **4.** The midpoint of $\overline{AB}$ is (3, 4). If the coordinates of B are (6, 6), what are the coordinates of A?
a. (9, 10) **b.** (4.5, 5) **c.** (0, 2) **d.** (9, 10)

d **5.** What is an equation of the line through (−4, 7) and perpendicular to $y = \frac{2}{3}x + 5$?
a. $y = \frac{3}{4}x + 10$ **b.** $y = -\frac{3}{2}x - 5$ **c.** $y = -\frac{7}{4}x$ **d.** $y = -\frac{3}{2}x + 1$

b **6.** What is an equation of the circle with center (3, 0) and radius 8?
a. $x^2 + y^2 = 64$ **b.** $(x - 3)^2 + y^2 = 64$
c. $(x + 3)^2 + y^2 = 8$ **d.** $(x - 3)^2 + y^2 = 8$

b **7.** Find an equation of the line through points (−3, 5) and (2, 8).
a. $5x + 3y = 16$ **b.** $3x - 5y = -34$
c. $5x - 3y = -30$ **d.** $5x + 3y = 0$

c **8.** Three consecutive vertices of a parallelogram are $(j, 5)$, (0, 0), and (7, 0). Which is the fourth vertex?
a. (7, 5) **b.** (5, 7) **c.** $(j + 7, 5)$ **d.** $(j + 5, 7)$

c **9.** Points (2, 2) and $(8, v)$ lie on a line with slope $\frac{1}{2}$. What is the value of v?
a. −10 **b.** −1 **c.** 5 **d.** 14

a **10.** What is the *best* term for a triangle with vertices (1, −3), (6, 2), and (0, 4)?
a. isosceles triangle **b.** equilateral triangle
c. right triangle **d.** none of these

b **11.** Which point is the intersection of lines $3x + 2y = 17$ and $x - 4y = 1$?
a. (1, 5) **b.** (5, 1) **c.** (−1, 5) **d.** $\left(\frac{33}{5}, \frac{7}{5}\right)$

b **12.** $\triangle ABC$ is equilateral with vertices $A(r, 0)$ and $B(-r, 0)$. Which of the following could be the coordinates of point C?
a. $(r\sqrt{3}, 0)$ **b.** $(0, r\sqrt{3})$ **c.** $(0, r)$ **d.** $(0, 2r)$

Chapter 14

Indicate the best answer by writing the appropriate letter.

c **1.** A regular hexagon does *not* have which symmetry?
a. line **b.** point **c.** 30° rotational **d.** 120° rotational

c **2.** What is the image of the point (2, 3) by reflection in the x-axis?
a. (3, 2) **b.** (−2, 3) **c.** (2, −3) **d.** (−2, −3)

b **3.** $T:(x, y) \rightarrow (x, y - 2)$. What is the preimage of (3, 5)?
a. (5, 7) **b.** (3, 7) **c.** (3, 3) **d.** (5, 3)

c **4.** If O is the point (0, 0), what is the image of (3, 6) by $D_{O,\frac{1}{3}}$?
a. (9, 18) **b.** (2, 4) **c.** (1, 2) **d.** (−1, −2)

a **5.** What is the image of (−1, 3) by a half-turn about (1, 2)?
a. (3, 1) **b.** (1, −3) **c.** (−1, −2) **d.** (3, −1)

d **6.** $T:(x, y) \rightarrow (x, y - 2)$. What is the image of (5, 3) by T^{-1}?
a. (3, 3) **b.** (5, 1) **c.** (3, 5) **d.** (5, 5)

b **7.** Isometry $S: \square ABCD \rightarrow \square JKLM$. Which statement *must* be true?
a. $\angle DAB \cong \angle JKL$ **b.** $AC = JL$
c. $S: C \rightarrow M$ **d.** $CD = MJ$

c **8.** What is the line of reflection for a transformation that maps (−2, 1) to (2, 1)?
a. the x-axis **b.** the line $y = x$
c. the y-axis **d.** the origin

c **9.** How many lines of symmetry does a rhombus with a 60° angle have?
a. none **b.** one **c.** two **d.** four

d **10.** If k is the line $y = x$, find the image of J by $R_k \circ R_y$.
a. J **b.** K **c.** L **d.** M

b **11.** T is a translation that maps K to N. What is the image of J under T?
a. K **b.** O **c.** N **d.** L

b **12.** What is the image of J under $R_x \circ H_O$?
a. J **b.** K **c.** L **d.** M

d **13.** What is the image of $\triangle LMJ$ by $\mathcal{R}_{O,90}$?
a. $\triangle JKL$ **b.** $\triangle KLM$ **c.** $\triangle LMJ$ **d.** $\triangle MJK$

Exs. 10–13

c **14.** Which mapping is *not* an isometry?
a. glide reflection **b.** translation
c. dilation **d.** the identity transformation

b **15.** Which of the following is *not* invariant under a glide reflection?
a. angle measure **b.** orientation of points
c. parallelism of lines **d.** areas of polygons

College Entrance Exams

If you are planning to attend college, you will probably be required to take college entrance exams. Some of these exams test your knowledge of specific subject areas; others are more general exams that attempt to measure the extent to which your verbal and mathematical reasoning abilities have been developed. These abilities are ones that can be improved through study and practice. Generally the best preparation for college entrance exams is to follow a strong academic program in high school and to read as extensively as possible.

At the end of every even-numbered chapter in this book are tests called "Preparing for College Entrance Exams." These tests contain questions similar to the questions asked on college entrance exams.

The following test-taking strategies may be useful:

- Familiarize yourself with the test you will be taking well in advance of the test date. Sample tests, with accompanying explanatory material, are available for many standardized tests. By working through this sample material, you become comfortable with the types of questions and directions that will appear on the test and you develop a feeling for the pace at which you must work in order to complete the test.
- Find out how the test is scored so that you know whether it is advantageous to guess.
- Skim sections of the test before starting to answer the questions, to get an overview of the questions. You may wish to answer the easiest questions first. Correctly answering the easy questions earns you the same credit as correctly answering the difficult ones, so do not waste time on questions you do not understand; go on to those that you do.
- Mark your answer sheet carefully, checking the numbering on the answer sheet about every five questions to avoid errors caused by misplaced answer markings.
- Write in the test booklet if it is helpful; for example, cross out incorrect alternatives and do mathematical calculations. Do *not* make extra marks on the answer sheet.
- Work carefully, but do not take time to double-check your answers unless you finish before the deadline and have extra time.
- Arrive at the test center early and come well prepared with any necessary supplies such as sharpened pencils and a watch.

College entrance exams that test general reasoning abilities, such as the Scholastic Aptitude Test, frequently include questions relating to basic geometric concepts and skills. The following topics often appear on such exams. For each topic, page references have been given to the places in your textbook where the topic is discussed.

Properties of Parallel and Perpendicular Lines (pages 56, 73–74, 78–79, 535)

If two parallel lines are cut by a transversal, then alternate interior angles are congruent, corresponding angles are congruent, and same-side interior angles are supplementary.

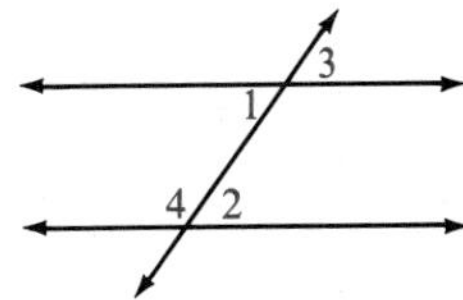

$$m\angle 1 = m\angle 2$$

$$m\angle 3 = m\angle 2$$

$$m\angle 1 + m\angle 4 = 180$$

If two lines are perpendicular, they form congruent adjacent angles.

Angle Measure Relationships (pages 51, 94–95, 102, 204)

Vertical angles are congruent.

$$m\angle 3 = m\angle 5$$

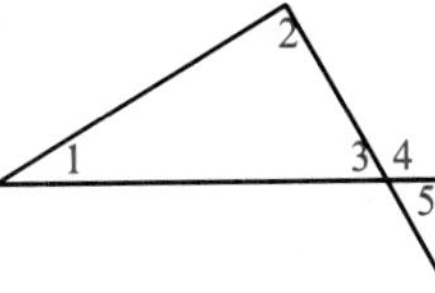

The sum of the measures of the angles of a triangle is 180.

$$m\angle 1 + m\angle 2 + m\angle 3 = 180$$

The measure of an exterior angle of a triangle equals the sum of the measures of the two remote interior angles.

$$m\angle 4 = m\angle 1 + m\angle 2$$

The measure of an exterior angle of a triangle is greater than the measure of either remote interior angle.

The sum of the measures of the angles of a convex polygon with n sides is $(n - 2)180$.

For example, the sum of the measures of the angles of the pentagon at the right is $3 \cdot 180 = 540$.

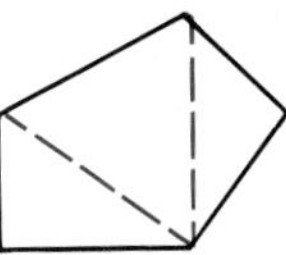

Triangle Side Relationships (pages 219–220, 228–229)

The sum of the lengths of any two sides of a triangle is greater than the length of the third side.

For example, $AB + BC > AC$.

If one side of a triangle is longer than a second side, then the angle opposite the first side is larger than the angle opposite the second side. The converse is also true.

For example, if $AC > BC$, then $m\angle B > m\angle A$;
if $m\angle C < m\angle B$, then $AB < AC$.

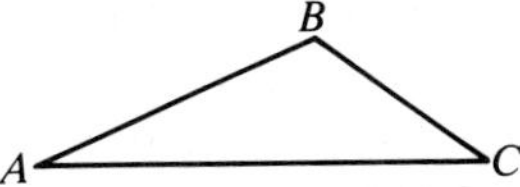

Special Triangle Relationships (pages 93, 135–136, 290, 295, 300)

Isosceles Triangle

At least 2 sides are congruent.

Angles opposite congruent sides are congruent.

Equilateral Triangle

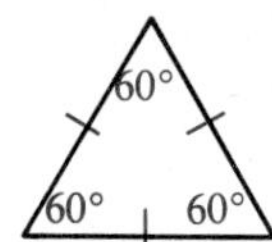

All sides are congruent.

All angles are congruent.

By the Pythagorean Theorem, in $\triangle ABC$

$$c^2 = a^2 + b^2.$$

Since $\angle C$ is a right angle,

$$m\angle A + m\angle B = 90.$$

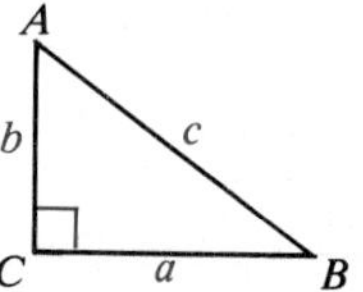

45°-45°-90° Triangle

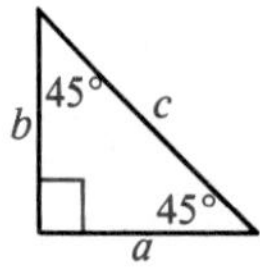

$a = b$
$c = \sqrt{2}\,a$
$= \sqrt{2}\,b$

Legs are congruent.

Hypotenuse $= \sqrt{2} \cdot$ leg

30°-60°-90° Triangle

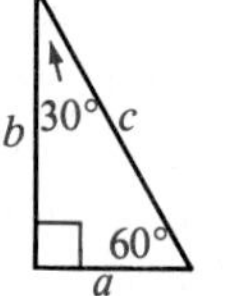

$c = 2a$
$b = \sqrt{3}\,a$

Hypotenuse $= 2 \cdot$ shorter leg

Longer leg $= \sqrt{3} \cdot$ shorter leg

Perimeter, Area, and Volume Formulas (pages 424, 429, 447, 469, 476, 518)

Rectangle

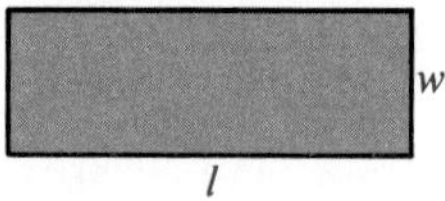

Perimeter $= 2l + 2w$

Area $= lw$

Triangle

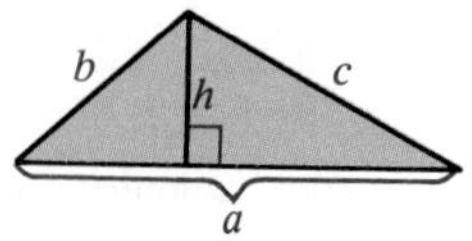

Perimeter $= a + b + c$

Area $= \frac{1}{2}(\text{base} \times \text{height})$
$= \frac{1}{2}ah$

Circle

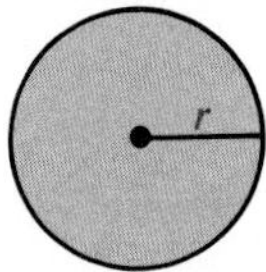

Circumference $= 2\pi r$

Area $= \pi r^2$

Rectangular Solid

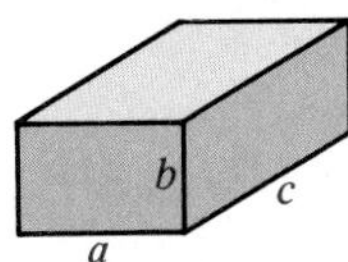

Total area $= 2ab + 2bc + 2ac$

Volume $= abc$

Locating Points on a Grid (pages 113, 523–525)

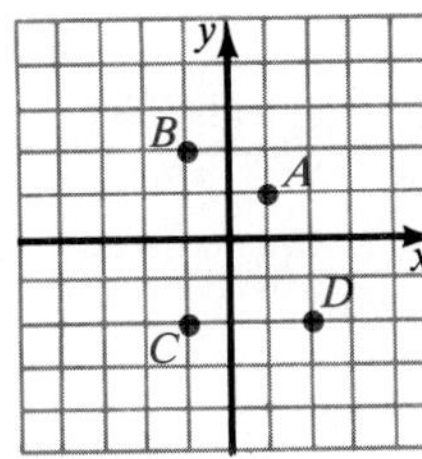

The points shown are $A(1, 1)$, $B(-1, 2)$, $C(-1, -2)$, and $D(2, -2)$.

The distance d between points (x_1, y_1) and (x_2, y_2) is given by

$$d = \sqrt{(x_2 - x_1)^2 + (y_2 - y_1)^2}.$$

An equation of the circle with center at the origin and radius r is $x^2 + y^2 = r^2$.

Supplementary Materials

Computer Activity 37

Logic

Statements and Truth Tables

In algebra, you have used letters to represent numbers. In logic, letters are used to represent statements that are either true or false. For example, p might represent the statement "Paris is the capital city of France," and q might represent the statement "The moon is made of green cheese." Deciding whether statements are true or false involves investigating the real world, not the "logic" of an argument.

Statements can be joined to form **compound statements.** Two important compound statements are defined below.

A **conjunction** is a compound statement composed of two statements joined by the word "and." The symbol $\wedge$ is used to represent the word "and."

A **disjunction** is a compound statement composed of two statements joined by the word "or." The symbol $\vee$ is used to represent the word "or."

Example 1

Statements:	p	Inez plays the flute.
	q	Sue Yin plays the cello.
Conjunction:	$p \wedge q$	Inez plays the flute and Sue Yin plays the cello.
Disjunction:	$p \vee q$	Inez plays the flute or Sue Yin plays the cello.

The table at the left below is called a **truth table.** It tells you the conditions under which a conjunction is a true statement. "T" stands for "true" and "F" for "false." The first row of the table shows that when statement p is true and statement q is true, the conjunction $p \wedge q$ is true. The other rows of the table show that $p \wedge q$ is false when either of its statements is false.

Truth table for conjunction

p	q	$p \wedge q$
T	T	T
T	F	F
F	T	F
F	F	F

Truth table for disjunction

p	q	$p \vee q$
T	T	T
T	F	T
F	T	T
F	F	F

A disjunction is true if either of its statements is true or both are true. This corresponds to what is called the *inclusive use* of "or." (The *exclusive use* of "or" would imply that one of the statements is true, but not both. We deal only with the inclusive use of "or" in this course.) The first row of the truth table for disjunction shows that when both p and q are true, $p \vee q$ is true. The next two rows show that the compound statement $p \vee q$ is true when either of its statements is true. The last row shows that a disjunction is false when both of its statements are false.

In addition to the words "and" and "or," the word "not" is an important word in logic. If p is a statement, then the statement "p is not true," usually shortened to "not p" and written $\sim p$, is called the **negation** of p.

Example 2 Statement: p Will is sleeping in class.
Negation: $\sim p$ It is not true that Will is sleeping in class.
or $\sim p$ Will is not sleeping in class.

Truth table for negation

p	$\sim p$
T	F
F	T

The truth table for negation shows that when p is true, $\sim p$ is false. When p is false, $\sim p$ is true. Note that it is impossible for a statement and its negation to be both true or both false at the same time. The conjunction $p \wedge \sim p$ would have Fs in both rows of its truth table. Such a statement is called a *contradiction*.

An example will show how to make truth tables for some other compound statements.

Example 3 Make a truth table for $\sim p \vee \sim q$.

p	q	$\sim p$	$\sim q$	$\sim p \vee \sim q$
T	T	F	F	F
T	F	F	T	T
F	T	T	F	T
F	F	T	T	T

Solution

1. Make a column for p and a column for q. Write all possible combinations of T and F in the standard pattern shown.
2. Since $\sim p$ is a part of the given statement, add a column for $\sim p$. To fill out this column, use the first column and refer to the truth table for negation above. Similarly, add a column for $\sim q$.
3. Using the columns for $\sim p$ and $\sim q$, refer to the truth table for disjunction on the preceding page in order to fill out the column for $\sim p \vee \sim q$. Remember that a disjunction is false only when both of its statements are false.

To make a truth table for a compound statement involving three simple statements p, q, and r, you would need an eight-row table to show all possible combinations of T and F. The standard pattern across the three columns headed p, q, and r is as follows: TTT, TTF, TFT, TFF, FTT, FTF, FFT, FFF.

Exercises

Suppose p stands for "I like the city," and q stands for "You like the country." Express in words each of the following statements.

1. $p \wedge q$
2. $\sim p$
3. $\sim q$
4. $p \vee q$
5. $p \vee \sim q$
6. $\sim(p \wedge q)$
7. $\sim p \vee \sim q$
8. $\sim p \wedge q$
9. $\sim(p \vee q)$
10. $\sim p \wedge \sim q$

Additional Answers
Exercises

1. I like the city and you like the country.
2. I don't like the city.
3. You don't like the country.
4. I like the city or you like the country.
5. I like the city or you don't like the country.
6. It is not true that I like the city and you like the country.
7. I don't like the city or you don't like the country.
8. I don't like the city and you like the country.
9. It is not true that I like the city or you like the country.
10. I don't like the city and you don't like the country.

Suppose p stands for "Hawks swoop," and q stands for "Gulls glide." Express in symbolic form each of the following statements.

11. Hawks swoop or gulls glide. $p \vee q$
12. Gulls do not glide. $\sim q$
13. It is not true that "Hawks swoop or gulls glide." $\sim(p \vee q)$
14. Hawks do not swoop and gulls do not glide. $\sim p \wedge \sim q$
15. It is not true that "Hawks swoop and gulls glide." $\sim(p \wedge q)$
16. Hawks do not swoop or gulls do not glide. $\sim p \vee \sim q$
17. Do the statements in Exercises 13 and 14 mean the same thing? **Yes**
18. Do the statements in Exercises 15 and 16 mean the same thing? **Yes**

Make a truth table for each of the following statements.

19. $p \vee \sim q$ **T, T, F, T**
20. $\sim p \vee q$ **T, F, T, T**
21. $\sim(\sim p)$ **T, F**
22. $\sim(p \wedge q)$ **F, T, T, T**
23. $p \vee \sim p$ **T, T**
24. $p \wedge \sim p$ **F, F**
25. $p \wedge (q \vee r)$ **T, T, T, F, F, F, F, F**
26. $(p \wedge q) \vee (p \wedge r)$ **T, T, T, F, F, F, F, F**

Truth Tables for Conditionals

The conditional statement "If p, then q," which is discussed in Lesson 2–1, is symbolized as $p \to q$. This is also read as "p implies q" and as "q follows from p." The truth table for $p \to q$ is shown at the right. Notice that the only time a conditional is false is when the hypothesis p is true and the conclusion q is false. The example below will show why this is a reasonable way to make out the truth table.

Truth table for conditionals

p	q	$p \to q$
T	T	T
T	F	F
F	T	T
F	F	T

Example Mom promises, "If I catch the early train home I'll take you swimming." Consider the four possibilities of the truth table.

1. Mom catches the early train home and takes you swimming. She kept her promise; her statement was *true*.
2. Mom catches the early train home but does not take you swimming. She broke her promise; her statement was *false*.
3. Mom does not catch the early train home but still takes you swimming. She has not broken her promise; her statement was *true*.
4. Mom does not catch the early train home and does not take you swimming. She has not broken her promise; her statement was *true*.

The tables on the next page show the converse and contrapositive of $p \to q$. Make sure that you understand how these tables were made. Notice that the last column of the table for the contrapositive $\sim q \to \sim p$ is identical with the last column of the table for the conditional on this page. In other words, the contrapositive of a statement is true (or false) if and only if the statement itself is true (or false). This is what we mean when we say that a statement and its contrapositive are logically equivalent (see Lesson 6–2). On the other hand, a statement and its converse are not logically equivalent. Can you see why?

Converse of $p \rightarrow q$

p	q	$q \rightarrow p$
T	T	T
T	F	T
F	T	F
F	F	T

Contrapositive of $p \rightarrow q$

p	q	$\sim q$	$\sim p$	$\sim q \rightarrow \sim p$
T	T	F	F	T
T	F	T	F	F
F	T	F	T	T
F	F	T	T	T

Exercises

Suppose p represents "You like to paint," q represents "You are an artist," and r represents "You draw landscapes." Express in words each of the following statements.

1. $p \rightarrow q$ **2.** $q \rightarrow r$ **3.** $\sim q \rightarrow \sim r$ **4.** $\sim(p \rightarrow q)$

5. $(p \land q) \rightarrow r$ **6.** $p \land (q \rightarrow r)$ **7.** $(r \lor q) \rightarrow p$ **8.** $r \lor (q \rightarrow p)$

Let b, s, and k represent the following statements.
b: Bonnie bellows. s: Sheila shouts. k: Keiko cackles.
Express in symbolic form each of the following statements.

9. If Bonnie bellows, then Keiko cackles. $b \rightarrow k$

10. If Keiko cackles, then Sheila does not shout. $k \rightarrow \sim s$

11. If Bonnie does not bellow or Keiko does not cackle, then Sheila shouts. $(\sim b \lor \sim k) \rightarrow s$

12. Sheila shouts, and if Bonnie bellows, then Keiko cackles. $s \land (b \rightarrow k)$

13. It is not true that Sheila shouts if Bonnie bellows. $\sim(b \rightarrow s)$

14. If Bonnie does not bellow, then Keiko cackles and Sheila shouts. $\sim b \rightarrow (k \land s)$

15. a. Make a truth table for $\sim p \rightarrow \sim q$ (the inverse of $p \rightarrow q$). Your first two columns should be the same as the first two columns of the table for $p \rightarrow q$. The last columns of the two tables should be different. Are they? Is $\sim p \rightarrow \sim q$ logically equivalent to $p \rightarrow q$? **Yes; No**

b. Compare the truth table for $\sim p \rightarrow \sim q$ (the inverse of $p \rightarrow q$) with the truth table for $q \rightarrow p$ (the converse of $p \rightarrow q$). Are the last columns the same? Are the inverse and the converse logically equivalent? **Yes; Yes**

Make truth tables for the following statements.

16. $p \rightarrow \sim q$ **F, T, T, T** **17.** $\sim(p \rightarrow q)$ **F, T, F, F** **18.** $p \land \sim q$ **F, T, F, F**

19. By comparing the truth tables in Exercises 16–18, you should find that two of the three statements are logically equivalent. Which two? $\sim(p \rightarrow q)$, $p \land \sim q$

20. The biconditional statement "p if and only if q" is defined as $(p \rightarrow q) \land (q \rightarrow p)$. Make a truth table for this statement. **T, F, F, T**

Additional Answers Exercises

1. If you like to paint, then you are an artist.

2. If you are an artist, then you draw landscapes.

3. If you aren't an artist, then you don't draw landscapes.

4. It is not true that if you like to paint, then you are an artist.

5. If you like to paint and you are an artist, then you draw landscapes.

6. You like to paint, and if you are an artist, then you draw landscapes.

7. If you draw landscapes or are an artist, then you like to paint.

8. You draw landscapes, or if you are an artist, then you like to paint.

Some Rules of Inference

Four rules for making logical inferences are symbolized below. A horizontal line separates the given information, or premises, from the conclusion. If you accept the given statement or statements as true, then you must accept as true the conclusions shown.

1. Modus Ponens

   $p \rightarrow q$
   p
   ―――――
   Therefore, q

2. Modus Tollens

   $p \rightarrow q$
   $\sim q$
   ―――――
   Therefore, $\sim p$

3. Simplification

   $p \wedge q$
   ―――――
   Therefore, p

4. Disjunctive Syllogism

   $p \vee q$
   $\sim p$
   ―――――
   Therefore, q

You should convince yourself that these rules make good sense. For example, Rule 4 says that if you know that "p or q" is true and then you find out that p is not true, you must conclude that q is true.

Example 1 If today is Tuesday, then tomorrow is Wednesday.
Today is Tuesday.
―――――
Therefore, tomorrow is Wednesday. (Rule 1)

Example 2 If a figure is a triangle, then it is a polygon.
This figure is not a polygon.
―――――
Therefore, this figure is not a triangle. (Rule 2)

Example 3 It is Tuesday and it is April.
―――――
Therefore, it is Tuesday. (Rule 3)

Example 4 It is a square or it is a triangle.
It is not a square.
―――――
Therefore, it is a triangle. (Rule 4)

Example 5 Given: $p \rightarrow q$; $p \vee r$; $\sim q$
Prove: r

Proof:

Statements	Reasons
1. $p \rightarrow q$	1. Given
2. $\sim q$	2. Given
3. $\sim p$	3. Steps 1 and 2 and Modus Tollens
4. $p \vee r$	4. Given
5. r	5. Steps 3 and 4 and Disj. Syllogism

Exercises

Supply the reasons to complete each proof.

1. Given: $p \wedge q$; $p \rightarrow s$
Prove: s

Statements
1. $p \wedge q$
2. p
3. $p \rightarrow s$
4. s

2. Given: $r \rightarrow s$; r; $s \rightarrow t$
Prove: t

Statements
1. $r \rightarrow s$
2. r
3. s
4. $s \rightarrow t$
5. t

Write two-column proofs for the following.

3. Given: $p \vee q$; $\sim p$; $q \rightarrow s$
Prove: s

4. Given: $a \rightarrow b$; $a \vee c$; $\sim b$
Prove: c

5. Given: $a \wedge b$; $a \rightarrow \sim c$; $c \vee d$
Prove: d

6. Given: $p \wedge q$; $p \rightarrow \sim s$; $r \rightarrow s$
Prove: $\sim r$

Symbolize the statements using the letters indicated, accept the statements as true, and write two-column proofs.

7. If Jorge wins the marathon, then he will receive a gold medal. **$w \rightarrow g$**
If Jorge receives a gold medal, then his country will be proud. **$g \rightarrow p$**
Jorge wins the marathon and Yolanda wins the javelin contest. **$w \wedge y$**
Prove that Jorge's country will be proud. **p**

(Use the letter w for "Jorge wins the marathon," g for "Jorge receives a gold medal," p for "Jorge's country will be proud," and y for "Yolanda wins the javelin contest.")

8. The sides of $ABCD$ are not all the same length, and $ABCD$ is a plane figure. $ABCD$ is a square or a rectangle. If the sides of $ABCD$ are not all the same length, then it is not a square.

Prove that $ABCD$ is a rectangle. (Use the letters l, p, s, and r.)

$\sim l \wedge p$
$s \vee r$
$\sim l \rightarrow \sim s$
r

Valid Arguments and Mistaken Premises

A statement whose truth table contains only Ts in the last column is called a *tautology*. An example is the disjunction $p \vee \sim p$ ("p or not p"). This is always true, no matter whether p is true (and $\sim p$ is false) or p is false (in which case $\sim p$ is true).

Tautology

p	$\sim p$	$p \vee \sim p$
T	F	T
F	T	T

Valid argument

p	p	$p \rightarrow p$
T	T	T
F	F	T

Additional Answers
Exercises

1. 1. Given 2. Step 1 and Simplification 3. Given 4. Steps 2 and 3 and Modus Ponens

2. 1. Given 2. Given 3. Steps 1 and 2 and Modus Ponens 4. Given 5. Steps 3 and 4 and Modus Ponens

A conditional whose truth table contains only Ts in the last column is a tautology that represents a **valid argument.** A valid argument is true no matter what the truth or falsity of the components is. Its validity is independent of the real world. For example, the conditional "If p, then p" is always true, even if p stands for "Unicorns exist."

The geometrical theorems in this text are all valid (if you accept the Postulates), and you can use them with confidence in any logical argument. Every theorem in this text can be written as a tautology in the form of a conditional whose hypothesis is a conjunction of givens, definitions, and theorems, and whose conclusion is the statement that is to be proved.

Theorem: $[a \wedge b \wedge (c \rightarrow d) \wedge (e \rightarrow f)] \rightarrow g$
givens + definition + theorem = conclusion

In everyday situations, though, you must be careful to inspect the logic of arguments. Even though the reasoning is logically correct, the conclusion may be wrong. The problem is usually that some of the given premises or conditionals are wrong.

Example The following is a logically valid argument. Is the conclusion true?

1. The weather is sunny.
2. If the weather is sunny, the plane will arrive on time.
3. If the plane arrives on time, we will be able to ski today.
4. Therefore, we will be able to ski today.

Solution We cannot evaluate the truth of the conclusion unless we investigate all the premises. The first statement, a given, may not be accurate. Perhaps it is cloudy. Also, one or more of the remaining conditional statements might be wrong. Perhaps the plane will malfunction and be late even though the weather is sunny. Perhaps we won't be able to get to the ski area, even if the plane lands on time. Or maybe we don't even know how to ski! It is important to investigate the truth of every premise before you can draw meaningful conclusions.

Exercises

1. Make a truth table for each statement. Which is a tautology?

a. $(p \vee q) \rightarrow p$ **T, T, F, T** **b.** $(p \rightarrow q) \rightarrow p$ **T, T, F, F**

c. $(p \wedge q) \rightarrow p$ **T, T, T, T** **d.** $(p \rightarrow q) \rightarrow q$ **T, T, T, F**

2. Show that $(p \vee q \vee r) \vee \sim(p \wedge q \wedge r)$ is a tautology by making an eight-row truth table.

3. Show that the argument $(p \wedge q \wedge r) \rightarrow (p \vee q \vee r)$ is valid by making an eight-row truth table.

4. A chain of deductive reasoning is often used in geometric proofs. For example, if you are given three premises: p; $p \rightarrow q$; and $q \rightarrow r$, then you can conclude r. Prove the validity of this argument by filling in the truth table for $[p \wedge (p \rightarrow q) \wedge (q \rightarrow r)] \rightarrow r$.

5. The following argument is not logically valid, because it is missing a premise.
"I have $5.00 to spend for lunch. If the sandwich I want to buy costs $3.50, then I'll have enough money left over to buy a beverage. If milk costs less than $1.50, I'll buy it. The price of milk is $1.00. Therefore, I'll buy milk with my sandwich." **a. "The sandwich costs $3.50."**
   a. Add a premise that would make this argument complete and valid.
   b. Can you think of any reasons why I still might not buy milk?

6. The following argument is logically valid. But the conclusion that two equals one is nonsensical. Can you find the mistake in one of the conditionals below? **Step 5 involves dividing by zero.**
   1. Let $x = 1$. (Given.)
   2. If $x = 1$, then $x - 2 = -1$. (Subtract 2.)
   3. If $x - 2 = -1$, then $x^2 + x - 2 = x^2 - 1$. (Add x^2.)
   4. If $x^2 + x - 2 = x^2 - 1$, then $(x + 2)(x - 1) = (x + 1)(x - 1)$. (Factor.)
   5. If $(x + 2)(x - 1) = (x + 1)(x - 1)$, then $(x + 2) = (x + 1)$. (Divide by $x - 1$.)
   6. If $(x + 2) = (x + 1)$, then $2 = 1$. (Subtract x.)
   7. Therefore, if $x = 1$, then $2 = 1$.

Some Rules of Replacement

The symbol $\equiv$ means "is logically equivalent to." Thus Rule 5 below states that the conditional statement $p \rightarrow q$ is logically equivalent to its contrapositive, $\sim q \rightarrow \sim p$. Rules 6–10 give other logical equivalences. These can be verified by comparing the truth tables of the statements on both sides of the $\equiv$ sign.

5. Contrapositive Rule
   $p \rightarrow q \equiv \sim q \rightarrow \sim p$

6. Double Negation
   $\sim(\sim p) \equiv p$

7. Commutative Rules
   $p \wedge q \equiv q \wedge p$
   $p \vee q \equiv q \vee p$

8. Associative Rules
   $(p \wedge q) \wedge r \equiv p \wedge (q \wedge r)$
   $(p \vee q) \vee r \equiv p \vee (q \vee r)$

9. Distributive Rules
   $p \wedge (q \vee r) \equiv (p \wedge q) \vee (p \wedge r)$
   $p \vee (q \wedge r) \equiv (p \vee q) \wedge (p \vee r)$

10. DeMorgan's Rules
   $\sim(p \wedge q) \equiv \sim p \vee \sim q$
   $\sim(p \vee q) \equiv \sim p \wedge \sim q$

Any logically equivalent expressions can replace each other wherever they occur in a proof.

Additional Answers Exercises

5.b. Perhaps it's not true that if I have enough money I'll buy milk. Maybe I'm allergic to milk. Or maybe milk costs more than a dollar.

Example Given: $p \wedge q$; $q \rightarrow \sim(r \vee s)$
Prove: $\sim r \wedge \sim s$

Proof:

Statements	Reasons
1. $p \wedge q$	1. Given
2. $q \wedge p$	2. Step 1 and Commutative Rule
3. q	3. Step 2 and Simplification
4. $q \rightarrow \sim(r \vee s)$	4. Given
5. $\sim(r \vee s)$	5. Steps 3 and 4 and Modus Ponens
6. $\sim r \wedge \sim s$	6. Step 5 and DeMorgan's Rule

Additional Answers Exercises

1. 1. Given 2. Step 1 and Double Negation 3. Given 4. Steps 2 and 3 and Modus Tollens

2. 1. Given 2. Step 1 and Distributive Rule 3. Step 2 and Simplification 4. Step 3 and Commutative Rule 5. Given 6. Steps 4 and 5 and Disjunctive Syllogism

Exercises

Supply the reasons to complete each proof.

1. Given: $a \rightarrow \sim b$; b
Prove: $\sim a$

Statements
1. b
2. $\sim(\sim b)$
3. $a \rightarrow \sim b$
4. $\sim a$

2. Given: $a \vee (b \wedge c)$; $\sim b$
Prove: a

Statements
1. $a \vee (b \wedge c)$
2. $(a \vee b) \wedge (a \vee c)$
3. $a \vee b$
4. $b \vee a$
5. $\sim b$
6. a

Write two-column proofs for the following.

3. Given: $a \wedge (b \wedge c)$
Prove: c

4. Given: $(p \wedge q) \rightarrow s$; $\sim s$
Prove: $\sim p \vee \sim q$

5. Given: $p \vee \sim q$; q
Prove: p

6. Given: $\sim q \rightarrow \sim p$; $q \rightarrow r$; p
Prove: r

7. Given: $p \vee (q \wedge s)$
Prove: $p \vee s$

8. Given: $t \vee (r \vee s)$; $\sim r \wedge \sim s$
Prove: t

Assume the given statements are true, symbolize the statements, and write a two-column proof.

9. If solid X is a cube, then it has twelve edges. If solid X is not a cube, then it does not have all square faces. Solid X has all square faces. Prove that solid X has twelve edges. (Use the letters c, t, and s.)

$c \rightarrow t$
$\sim c \rightarrow \sim s$
s
———
t

10. Pat loves me or Jean loves me. Pat sent me a valentine or Pat sent Kevin a valentine. If Pat sent me a valentine, I would have received it by now. If Pat sent Kevin a valentine, then Pat doesn't love me. I have received no valentines.
Prove that Jean loves me. (Use the letters p, j, v, k, r.)

$p \vee j$
$v \vee k$
$v \rightarrow r$
$k \rightarrow \sim p$
$\sim r$
———
j

Application of Logic to Circuits

The diagram at the right represents part of an electrical circuit. When switch p is open, the electricity that is flowing from A will not reach B. When switch p is closed, as in the second diagram, the electricity flows through the switch to B.

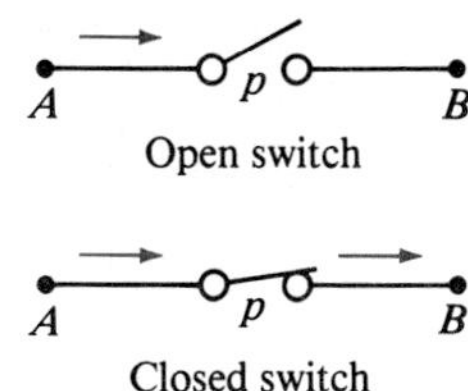

The diagram at the left below represents two switches p and q that are *connected in series*. Notice that current will flow if and only if both switches are closed. The diagram at the right below represents the switches p and q *connected in parallel*. Notice that current will flow if either switch is closed or if both switches are closed. If switches p and q are both open, the current cannot flow.

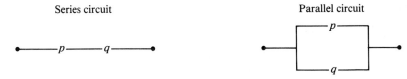

In order to understand how circuits are related to truth tables, let us do the following:

(1) If a switch is closed, label it T. If it is open, label it F.

(2) If current will flow in a circuit, label the circuit T. If the current will not flow, label the circuit F.

With these agreements, we can use truth tables to show what happens in the series circuit and the parallel circuit illustrated above.

Series circuit

p	q	Circuit
T	T	T
T	F	F
F	T	F
F	F	F

Parallel circuit

p	q	Circuit
T	T	T
T	F	T
F	T	T
F	F	F

The truth table for the series circuit is just like the truth table for $p \wedge q$. Also, the truth table for the parallel circuit is just like the table for $p \vee q$.

Now study the circuit shown at the right. Notice that one of the switches is labeled $\sim q$. This means that this switch is open if switch q is closed, and vice versa. The circuit shown is basically a parallel circuit, but in each branch of the circuit there are two switches connected in series. This explains why the circuit is labeled $(p \wedge q) \vee (p \wedge \sim q)$. A truth table for this circuit is given on the next page.

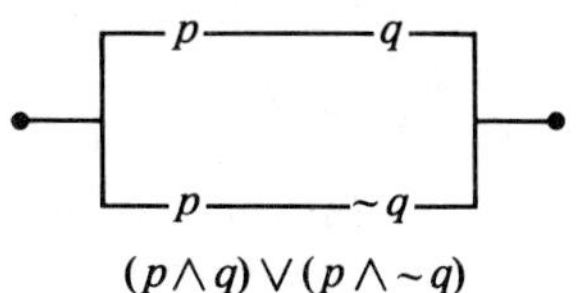

$(p \wedge q) \vee (p \wedge \sim q)$

p	q	$\sim q$	$p \wedge q$	$p \wedge \sim q$	$(p \wedge q) \vee (p \wedge \sim q)$
T	T	F	T	F	T
T	F	T	F	T	T
F	T	F	F	F	F
F	F	T	F	F	F

Notice that the first and last columns of the truth table are identical. This means that the complicated circuit shown can be replaced by a simpler circuit that contains just switch p! In other words, logic can be used to replace a complex electrical circuit by a simpler one.

Exercises

Symbolize each circuit using $\wedge$, $\vee$, $\sim$, and letters given for the switches in each diagram.

1. 

2. 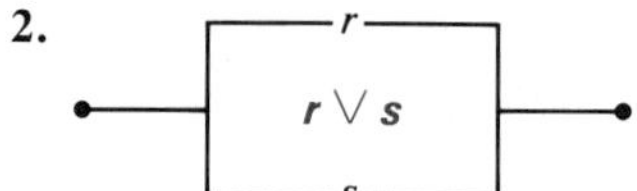

3.

4. 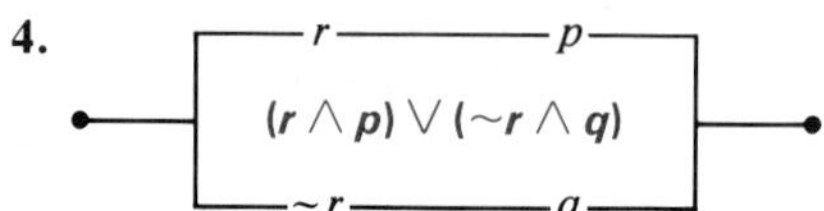

5. 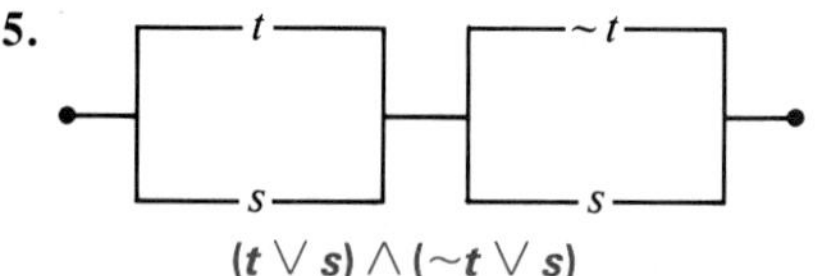

6. 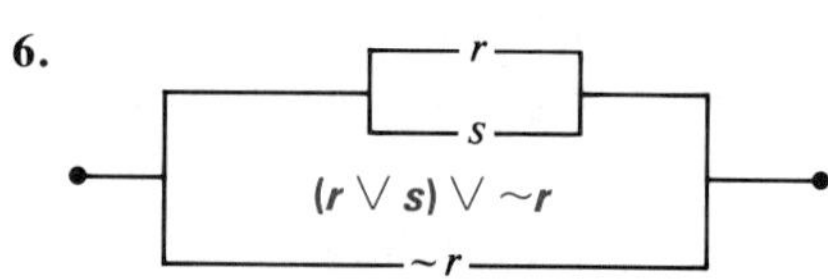

7. Draw a diagram for the circuit $p \wedge \sim p$; also for the circuit $p \vee \sim p$. Electricity can always pass through one of these circuits and can never pass through the other. Which is which? **always: $p \vee \sim p$; never: $p \wedge \sim p$**
8. According to the commutative rule, $p \wedge q \equiv q \wedge p$. This means that the circuit $p \wedge q$ does the same thing as the circuit $q \wedge p$. Make a diagram of each circuit.
9. According to the associative rule, $(p \vee q) \vee r \equiv p \vee (q \vee r)$. Draw diagrams for each circuit.
10. The distributive rule says that $p \wedge (q \vee r) \equiv (p \wedge q) \vee (p \wedge r)$. Draw diagrams for each circuit.
11. Make both a diagram and a truth table for the circuit $(p \vee q) \vee \sim q$. Notice that the last column of your table is always T so that current always flows. This means that all of the switches could be eliminated.
12. Make both a diagram and a truth table for the circuit $(p \vee q) \wedge (p \vee \sim q)$. Describe a simpler circuit equivalent to this circuit. **The circuit is equivalent to one that contains just switch p.**

Flow Proofs

Proofs can be written in a variety of forms, including: (1) two-column form, (2) paragraph form, and (3) flow form. In a *flow proof*, a diagram with implication arrows (→) shows the logical flow of the statements of a proof. The statements in the diagram are numbered and the reasons for each are given below the flow diagram.

Example 1 Given: $\angle 1 \cong \angle 2$; $\angle 3 \cong \angle 4$

Prove: $\angle 5 \cong \angle 6$

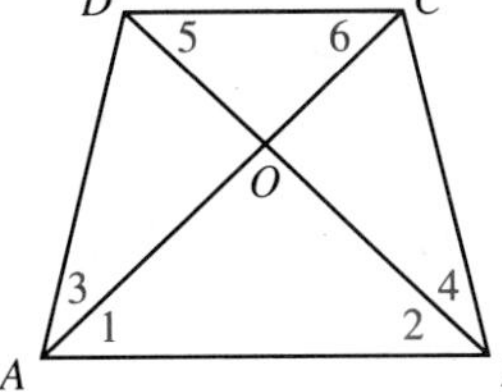

Flow Proof:

1. $\angle 1 \cong \angle 2$ → 2. $\overline{AO} \cong \overline{BO}$

3. $\angle 3 \cong \angle 4$

4. $\angle AOD \cong \angle BOC$

(2, 3, 4) → 5. $\triangle AOD \cong \triangle BOC$ → 6. $\overline{DO} \cong \overline{CO}$ → 7. $\angle 5 \cong \angle 6$

Reasons

1. Given
2. If 2 $\angle$s of a $\triangle$ are $\cong$, the sides opp. them are $\cong$.
3. Given
4. Vertical $\angle$s are $\cong$.
5. ASA Postulate
6. Corr. parts of $\cong$ $\triangle$s are $\cong$.
7. Isosceles $\triangle$ Theorem

Because this flow proof is long, we have drawn an arrow connecting steps 5 and 6 to show that the proof continues below. You can do this or turn your paper sideways to accommodate a long proof.

One advantage of flow proof is that it shows clearly which steps depend on other steps. In the example above, for instance, we see that step 5 (whose justification is ASA) depends on steps 2, 3, and 4, each of which provides one of the three congruences needed for ASA. The next example shows how a complex proof can be understood more easily by organizing it into a flow proof.

Example 2 Given: $\overline{QS} \perp \overline{PR}$;
$\overrightarrow{PR}$ bisects $\angle QPS$.
Prove: $\overrightarrow{RP}$ bisects $\angle QRS$.

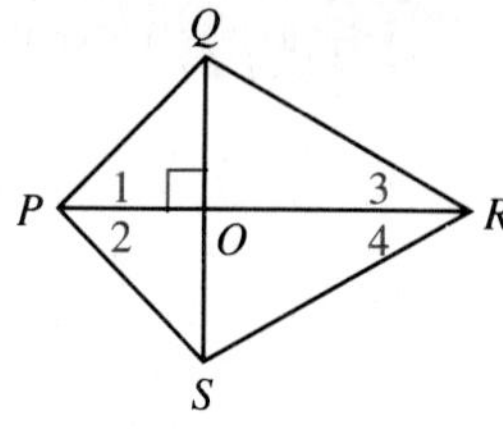

Flow Proof:

1. $\overline{QS} \perp \overline{PR}$ → 3. $\angle POQ \cong \angle POS$
2. $\overrightarrow{PR}$ bis. $\angle QPS$ → 4. $\angle 1 \cong \angle 2$
5. $\overline{PO} \cong \overline{PO}$

(3, 4, 5) → 6. $\triangle POQ \cong \triangle POS$ →

7. $\overline{PQ} \cong \overline{PS}$
8. $\overline{PR} \cong \overline{PR}$
9. $\angle 1 \cong \angle 2$

(7, 8, 9) → 10. $\triangle PQR \cong \triangle PSR$ → 11. $\angle 3 \cong \angle 4$ → 12. $\overrightarrow{RP}$ bis. $\angle QRS$.

Reasons

1. Given
2. Given
3. If two lines are ⊥, then they form ≅ adj. ∠s.
4. Def. of ∠ bisector
5. Reflexive Prop.
6. ASA Postulate
7. Corr. parts of ≅ △s are ≅.
8. Reflexive Prop.
9. See Step 4. (Repeating this makes Step 10 easier to follow.)
10. SAS Postulate
11. Corr. parts of ≅ △s are ≅.
12. Def. of ∠ bisector

When you are working on a flow proof, you may find it helpful to wait until you have completed the structure of the proof before numbering the steps. You might work backwards from the statement you wish to prove, for example, filling in the intermediate steps until you arrive at given statements. Then you can number the steps and give the reasons underneath. Sometimes there will be more than one correct way to do this; just make sure that the number at the head of each arrow is always greater than the number(s) at the tail of the arrow.

Exercises

Write a flow proof for each exercise referred to below.

1. Exercise 3, page 130
2. Exercise 16, page 125
3. Exercise 15, page 145
4. Exercise 13, page 81
5. Exercise 17, page 126
6. Exercise 2, page 143
7. Exercise 7, page 149
8. Exercise 24, page 82
9. Exercise 20, page 145

Handbook for Integrating Coordinate and Transformational Geometry

The purpose of the following sections is to enable students to study coordinate geometry and transformational geometry throughout the year, interspersed with their study of traditional (synthetic) geometry. Teachers will need to present Lessons 13-1 through 13-7 after Chapter 4 and Lessons 14-1 through 14-4 after Chapter 5. (Complete instructions are provided in the Teacher's Edition.) The sections presented here are to follow each of Chapters 3 through 11, and a final section, called ''Deciding Which Method to Use in a Problem,'' provides guidance in selecting the approach that best suits a problem. Each section is intended for use *after* the chapter listed with its title.

Translation and Rotation **(Chapter 3)**

Objective: Study the effect of the basic transformations of translation and rotation upon polygons.

You may have noticed from putting a jigsaw puzzle together that the size and shape of a piece do not change if you slide or spin it around on the table. The same is true of polygons in the plane. Consider the pattern of identical triangles shown below. A pattern of identical shapes that fills the plane in this way is called a *tiling*, or *tessellation*.

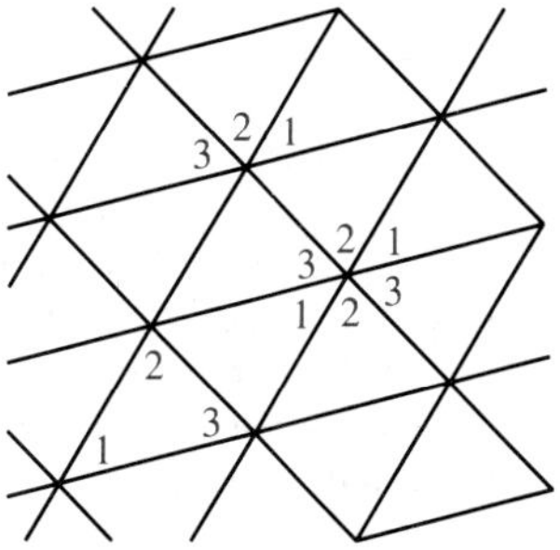

You could create this pattern by first sliding a triangle and leaving copies of it across the plane. If you then put your finger on a vertex of one triangle and spin the triangle 180 degrees, the result is an ''upside-down'' triangle that fills in the rest of the pattern. Notice that the angle measures of the triangles are not altered by these movements, so we can number the angles in the diagram.

The movements of sliding and spinning are known in geometry as *translations* and *rotations*. They are examples of *transformations* that preserve length and angle measure.

Example

a. In the diagram above, find three numbered angles whose measures add up to a straight angle.

b. What does this tell you about the sum of the measures of the angles of a triangle?

c. There are 3 sets of lines that *look* parallel. What theorem or postulate tells you that they *must be* parallel?

Solution a. Every straight angle is made up of one $\angle 1$, one $\angle 2$, and one $\angle 3$.

b. Since each triangle in the diagram is also made up of one $\angle 1$, one $\angle 2$, and one $\angle 3$, the sum of the measures of a triangle must equal the measure of a straight angle, or 180.

c. Postulate 11

Exercises

2. the upper left, upper right, and center quads.
4.b. The sum of the meas. of the ext. ∠s of a △ is 360.

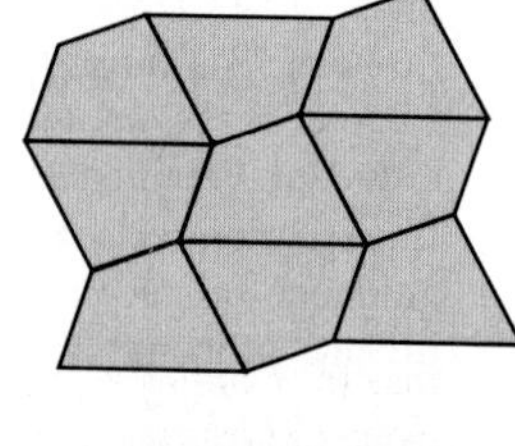

1. The repetitive pattern at the right is a tiling of the plane with identical quadrilaterals (four-sided polygons). What does it tell you about the sum of the angle measures in a quadrilateral? Explain. **The sum is 360.**

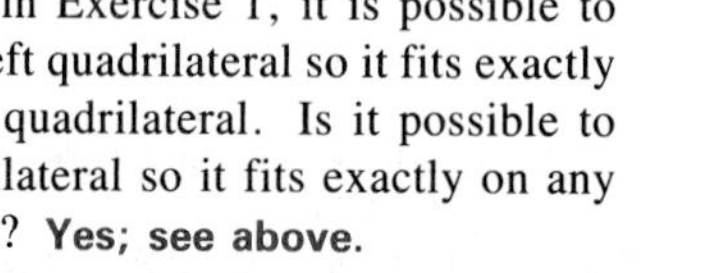

2. In the tessellation shown in Exercise 1, it is possible to slide, or glide, the lower left quadrilateral so it fits exactly on top of the lower right quadrilateral. Is it possible to glide the lower left quadrilateral so it fits exactly on any of the other quadrilaterals? **Yes; see above.**

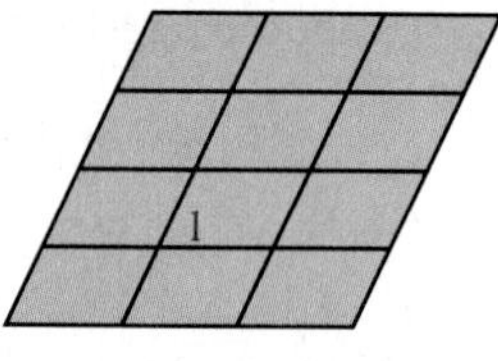

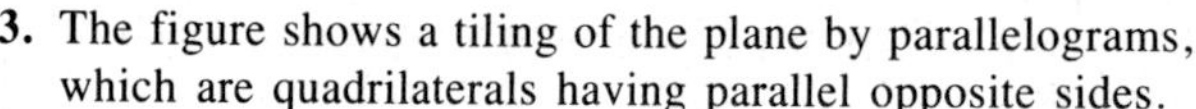

3. The figure shows a tiling of the plane by parallelograms, which are quadrilaterals having parallel opposite sides.
   a. Copy the diagram and mark all angles that must be congruent to $\angle 1$ if you reason from Postulate 10.
   b. Mark any additional angles on the diagram that are also congruent to $\angle 1$, and tell why they are congruent to $\angle 1$.
   c. This exercise suggests a theorem about the opposite angles of a parallelogram. State this theorem. **c. Opp. ∠s of a ▱ are ≅.**

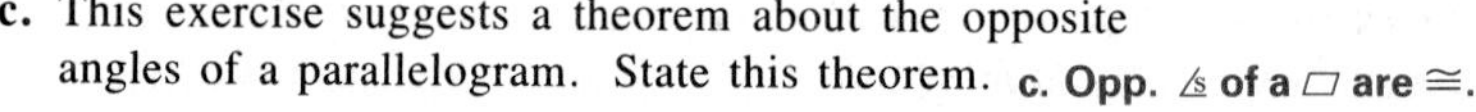

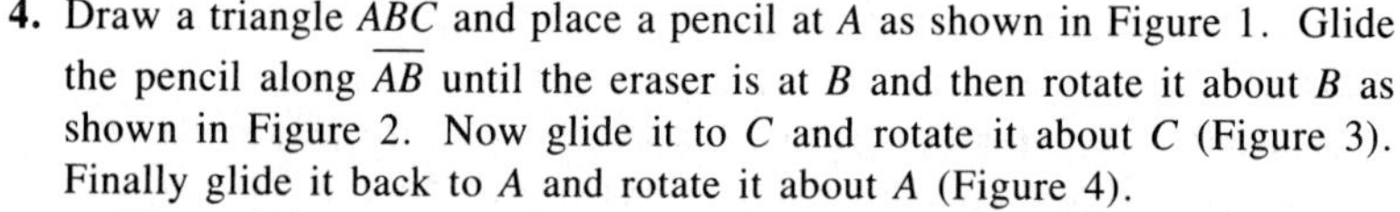

4. Draw a triangle ABC and place a pencil at A as shown in Figure 1. Glide the pencil along $\overline{AB}$ until the eraser is at B and then rotate it about B as shown in Figure 2. Now glide it to C and rotate it about C (Figure 3). Finally glide it back to A and rotate it about A (Figure 4).
   a. Through how many degrees has your pencil rotated? **360**
   b. What theorem is suggested by this exercise? **See above.**

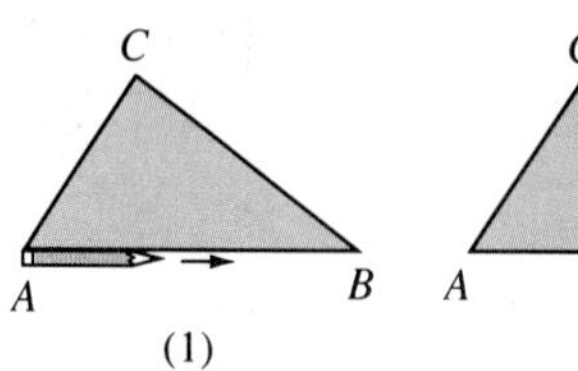

(1)

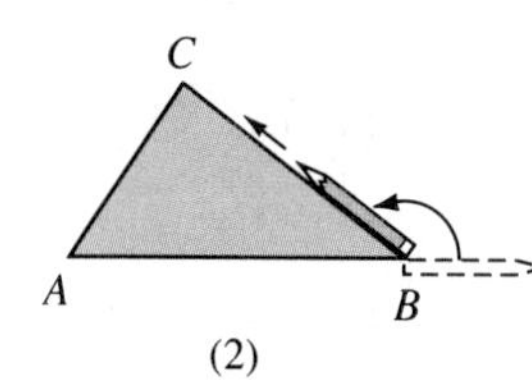

(2)

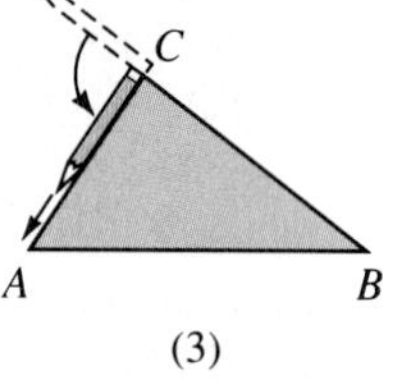

(3)

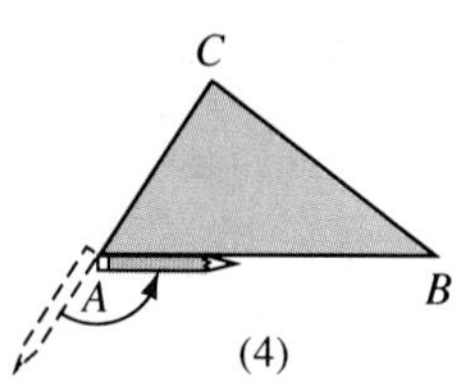

(4)

5. Suppose you follow these instructions: Walk 1 m north, then walk 1 m northeast. As the diagram shows, you turn through a 45° angle.
   a. Copy the diagram and continue according to these additional instructions: Walk 1 m east, 1 m southeast, 1 m south, 1 m southwest, 1 m west, and 1 m northwest.
   b. What is the total number of degrees through which you turned? **360**

45°

Additional Answers
Exercises

3.a. All corr. ∠s of the transversals are ≅.

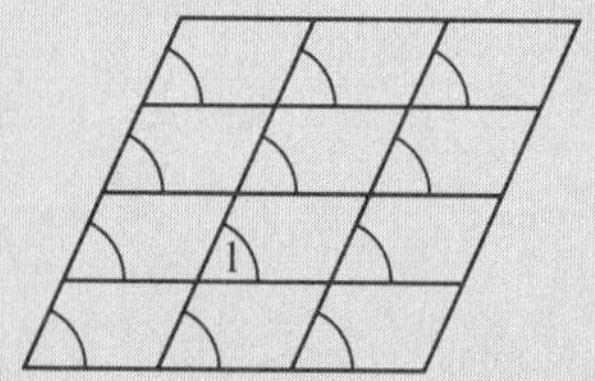

b. Vertical ∠s are ≅; Postulate 10

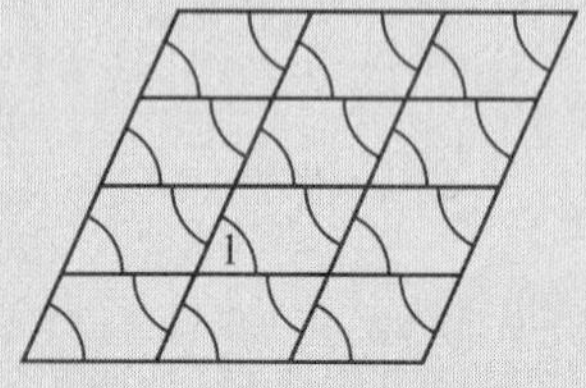

Exercise Note

A variation of Ex. 4 is to slide the pencil and rotate it around the interior, not exterior, angles of the △. At the end, the pencil will point in the opposite direction, indicating a rotation of 180°.

6. Create another closed path as in Exercise 5, but this time use a variety of different distances. What is the total number of degrees through which you turned? **360**

7. Create a third closed path, but this time vary the angles at which you turn. What is the total number of degrees through which you turned? What theorem does this exercise suggest? **The sum of the meas. of the ext. ∠s of a conv. polygon, one ∠ at each vertex, is 360.**

Reflection and Symmetry (Chapter 4)

Objective: Study the concepts of reflection and symmetry by using paper cutouts.

Flipping a jigsaw puzzle piece over exposes the cardboard back and makes it unusable in a puzzle. In geometry, however, the front and back of a polygon share many important features. We say that the original and the flipped versions are *congruent*. The two figures are called *mirror images* of each other because each looks like the other's reflection in a mirror. In fact, this type of transformation is called a *reflection*.

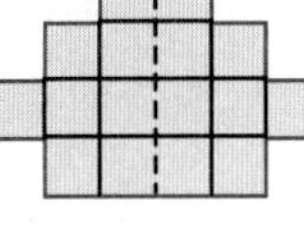

You can investigate reflections by folding graph paper along one of its lines and cutting along a path that begins on the fold line and ends somewhere else on the fold line. The resulting cutouts will have *mirror symmetry* across the fold line. The exercises will help you develop your skills in visualizing mirror symmetry.

Exercises

For each figure, (a) sketch on graph paper the figure you would obtain if you were to cut out the figure along the red lines shown and open it up, and (b) test your predictions by actually cutting out the shapes.

1.

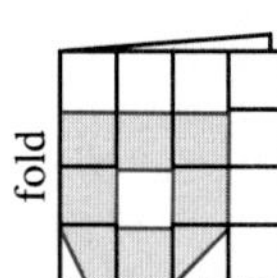

2.

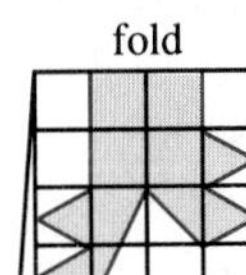

3.

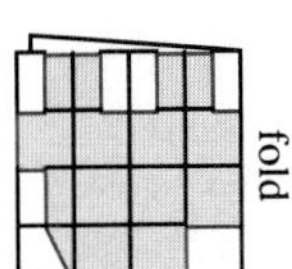

4.

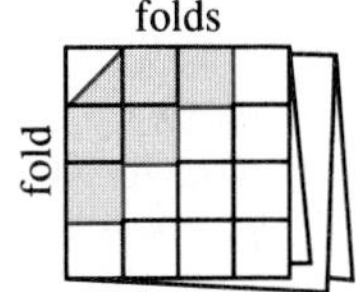

5. a. Draw a line segment $\overline{AB}$ on a sheet of paper and then fold the paper so that A lies on top of B.
   b. Cut the paper so that when it is opened an isosceles triangle is formed with $\overline{AB}$ as its base.
   c. What does your cut-out triangle tell you about the angles at A and B? Explain. **$\angle A \cong \angle B$**

Additional Answers
Exercises

2.

4.

6. Lines l and m are perpendicular at O. Figure I is reflected across line l to figure II and figure II is reflected across line m to figure III.
   a. What single transformation moves figure I directly to figure III? **rotation**
   b. Join the eye of figure I to the eye of figure III. How is O related to these two points? ***O* is the midpt. of the seg. joining the eyes.**

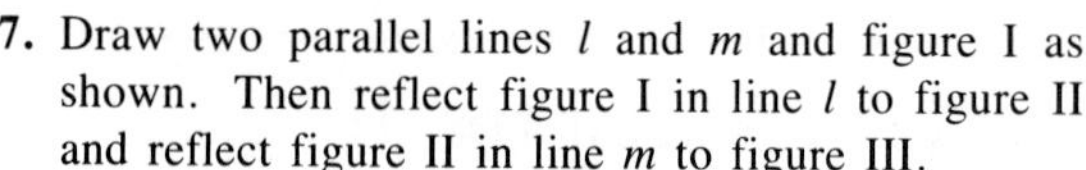

7. Draw two parallel lines l and m and figure I as shown. Then reflect figure I in line l to figure II and reflect figure II in line m to figure III.
   a. What single transformation moves figure I directly to figure III? **translation**
   b. How does the distance between corresponding points in figures I and III compare with the distance between l and m? **Twice as great.**

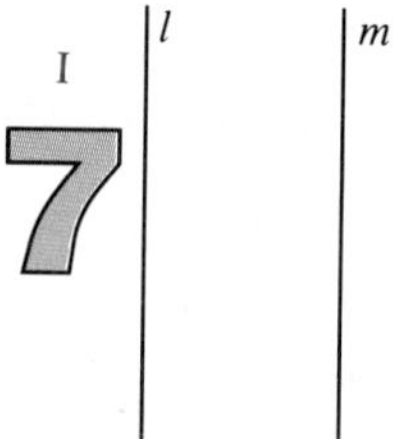

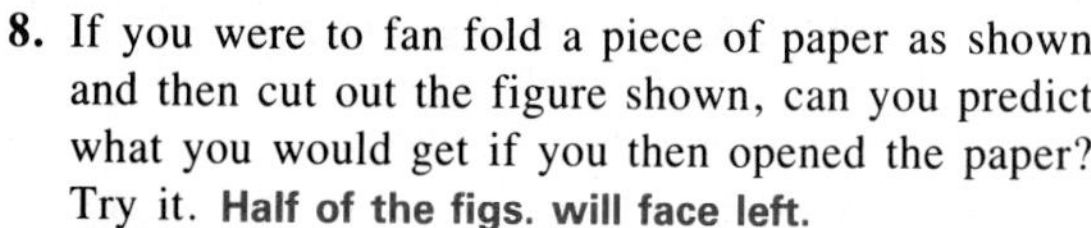

8. If you were to fan fold a piece of paper as shown and then cut out the figure shown, can you predict what you would get if you then opened the paper? Try it. **Half of the figs. will face left.**

★ 9. Can you modify the design cut out in Exercise 8 to create four figures all facing in the same direction? **Cut a symmetric figure; or fan fold paper from top to bottom.**

Quadrilaterals (Chapter 5)

Objective: Investigate the properties of various quadrilaterals and classify them using coordinate methods. (Requires understanding of Lessons 13-1 through 13-7.)

At the bottom of page 172, five ways are shown for proving that a quadrilateral is a parallelogram. At this stage of your learning, coordinate geometry methods can be used for all but the fourth of these methods.

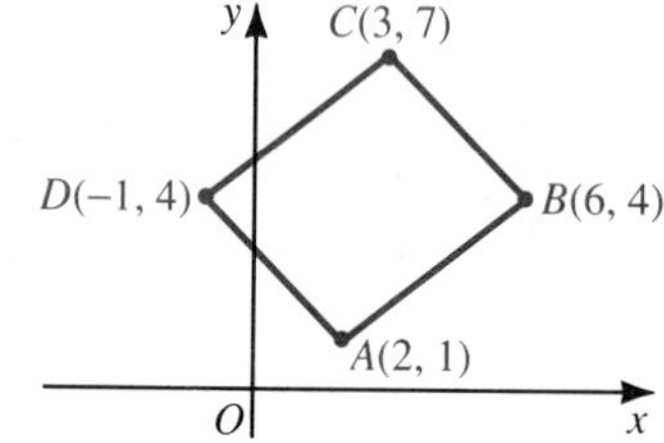

Example Prove that quad. $ABCD$ is a $\square$.

Solution

Method 1 *Show that both pairs of opposite sides are congruent.*

$$AB = \sqrt{(6-2)^2 + (4-1)^2} = \sqrt{4^2 + 3^2} = \sqrt{25} = 5$$

$$DC = \sqrt{(3-(-1))^2 + (7-4)^2} = \sqrt{4^2 + 3^2} = \sqrt{25} = 5$$

$$AD = \sqrt{(-1-2)^2 + (4-1)^2} = \sqrt{(-3)^2 + 3^2} = \sqrt{18} = 3\sqrt{2}$$

$$BC = \sqrt{(3-6)^2 + (7-4)^2} = \sqrt{(-3)^2 + 3^2} = \sqrt{18} = 3\sqrt{2}$$

Method 2 *Show that both pairs of opposite sides are parallel.*

$$\text{Slope of } \overline{AB} = \frac{4-1}{6-2} = \frac{3}{4};$$

$$\text{slope of } \overline{DC} = \frac{7-4}{3-(-1)} = \frac{3}{4}.$$

$$\text{Slope of } \overline{AD} = \frac{4-1}{-1-2} = \frac{3}{-3} = -1;$$

$$\text{slope of } \overline{BC} = \frac{7-4}{3-6} = \frac{3}{-3} = -1.$$

Method 3 *Show that the diagonals bisect each other.*

$$\text{Midpoint of } \overline{AC} = \left(\frac{3+2}{2}, \frac{1+7}{2}\right) = \left(\frac{5}{2}, 4\right);$$

$$\text{midpoint of } \overline{BD} = \left(\frac{-1+6}{2}, \frac{4+4}{2}\right) = \left(\frac{5}{2}, 4\right).$$

Since the diagonals have the same midpoint, they bisect each other.

You could also use the work in Methods 1 and 2 to show that one pair of opposite sides is both congruent and parallel.

Exercises

8.b. $M\left(\frac{b}{2}, \frac{c}{2}\right)$, $N\left(\frac{a+b}{2}, \frac{c}{2}\right)$

The coordinates of the vertices of quadrilateral *ABCD* are given. Show that *ABCD* is a parallelogram by using each of the three methods shown in the example.

1. $A(5, 7)$, $B(0, 3)$, $C(1, -3)$, $D(6, 1)$

2. $A(-2, 6)$, $B(-3, 2)$, $C(2, -4)$, $D(3, 0)$

Decide whether quadrilateral *DEFG* is a parallelogram.

3. $D(3, 5)$, $E(5, 7)$, $F(3, 4)$, $G(0, 1)$ **No**

4. $D(3, -2)$, $E(-2, 5)$, $F(5, 6)$, $G(10, -1)$ **Yes**

The coordinates of three vertices of ▱*PQRS* are given. Find the coordinates of the missing vertex.

5. $P(0, 0)$, $Q(5, 2)$, $R(8, 4)$ ***S*(3, 2)**

6. $P(-2, 0)$, $Q(2, 1)$, $S(0, 5)$ ***R*(4, 6)**

7. **a.** Draw the triangle with vertices $O(0, 0)$, $I(4, 2)$, and $J(2, 6)$.

b. Find the coordinates of M and N, the midpoints of $\overline{OJ}$ and $\overline{IJ}$, respectively. ***M*(1, 3), *N*(3, 4)**

c. Find the slopes of $\overline{MN}$ and $\overline{OI}$. What do your results tell you about $\overline{MN}$ and $\overline{OI}$? What kind of quadrilateral is *OMNI*? **$\frac{1}{2}, \frac{1}{2}$; *OMNI* is a trap.**

8. Repeat Exercise 7 for the general triangle with vertices $O(0, 0)$, $I(a, 0)$, and $J(b, c)$. **b. See above. c. 0, 0; *OMNI* is a trap.**

9. Given the quadrilateral *ABCD* with vertices $A(-4, 5)$, $B(4, -1)$, $C(7, 3)$, and $D(-1, 9)$. **9.a. slope of $\overline{AB}$ = slope of $\overline{DC}$ = $-\frac{3}{4}$, slope of $\overline{AD}$ = slope of $\overline{BC}$ = $\frac{4}{3}$**

a. Use slopes to show that opposite sides are parallel and adjacent sides are perpendicular.

b. What kind of quadrilateral is *ABCD*? **rectangle**

Exercise Note

In Exs. 5 and 6, students may find three points that seem to work as missing vertices that complete a ▱. Only one point, however, will give the correct order of vertices (*PQRS*).

Additional Answers Exercises

10.a. slope $\overline{RS}$ = slope $\overline{UT} = \frac{3}{4}$; slope $\overline{RU}$ = slope $\overline{ST} = \frac{-4}{3}$; $\frac{3}{4} \cdot \frac{-4}{3} = -1$, so $\overline{RS} \perp \overline{RU}$.
b. $RT = SU = 5\sqrt{5}$

11.a. $DE = EF = FG = GD = 2\sqrt{10}$
b. slope $\overline{DF} = 1$, slope $\overline{EG} = -1$

12. The resulting fig. is a ▱ with base length $a + b$. Its median, twice that of the trap., has length $a + b$. Length of med. of trap. is $\frac{a+b}{2}$.

10. Given the quadrilateral *RSTU* with vertices $R(5, -3)$, $S(9, 0)$, $T(3, 8)$, and $U(-1, 5)$.
a. Show that *RSTU* is a rectangle.
b. Use the distance formula to verify that the diagonals are congruent.

11. Given the quad. *DEFG* with vertices $D(-4, 1)$, $E(2, 3)$, $F(4, 9)$, and $G(-2, 7)$.
a. Use the distance formula to show that *DEFG* is a rhombus.
b. Use slopes to verify that the diagonals are perpendicular.

12. Suppose two congruent trapezoids glide together as shown. Explain how you can deduce the length of the median, shown in red, of a trapezoid.

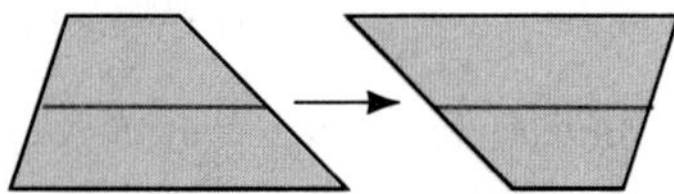

13–34. Work Exercises 28 and 41 on page 527; Exercises 3–6 and 11–18 on pages 537–538; Classroom Exercise 3 on page 541 and Exercises 26, 33 on pages 542–543; Exercises 15, 18, 19, and 21 on page 546; and Exercise 34 on page 555.

Minimal Paths (Chapter 6)

Objective: Solve "shortest distance" problems using translations and coordinate geometry. (Requires understanding of Lessons 13-1 through 13-7 and 14-1 through 14-4.)

The Application found on page 224 shows how to find the shortest path from point *A* to line *l* to point *B*. The solution is found by using a reflection of *B* in line *l*. Example 1 shows a different kind of shortest-path problem. It is solved by another kind of transformation: a *translation*.

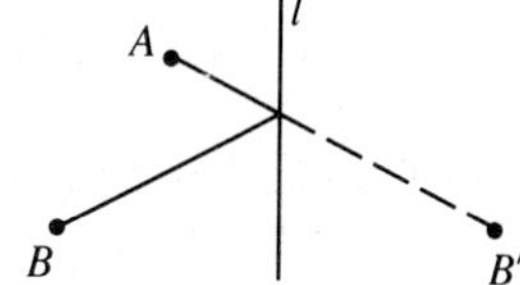

Example 1 Where should a bridge perpendicular to two parallel river banks be built if the total distance from *A* to *B*, including the distance across the bridge, is to be minimum?

Solution Translate *B* toward the river a distance equal to the width of the river. Draw $\overline{AB'}$ and build the bridge at the point *X* where $\overline{AB'}$ intersects the river on *A*'s side.

Here is why this method works: We want to minimize $AX + XY + YB$, but since XY is fixed, we need to minimize $AX + YB$, which equals $AX + XB'$ because $XYBB'$ is a parallelogram. This sum is minimum when *X* is on $\overline{AB'}$. In effect, translating *B* to *B'* "sews up" the gap of the river.

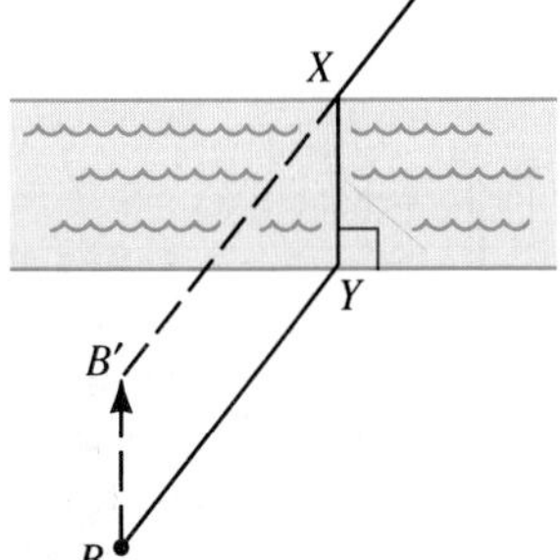

Example 2 Find the shortest distance from $P(0, 5)$ to the line l with equation $y = 2x$.

Solution The shortest segment is the perpendicular $\overline{PQ}$.
Its length can be found in three steps.

Step 1 *Find the equation of* $\overleftrightarrow{PQ}$.

Slope of line $y = 2x$ is 2.

Then the slope of $\overleftrightarrow{PQ}$ is $-\frac{1}{2}$.

The equation of $\overleftrightarrow{PQ}$ is $y = -\frac{1}{2}x + 5$.

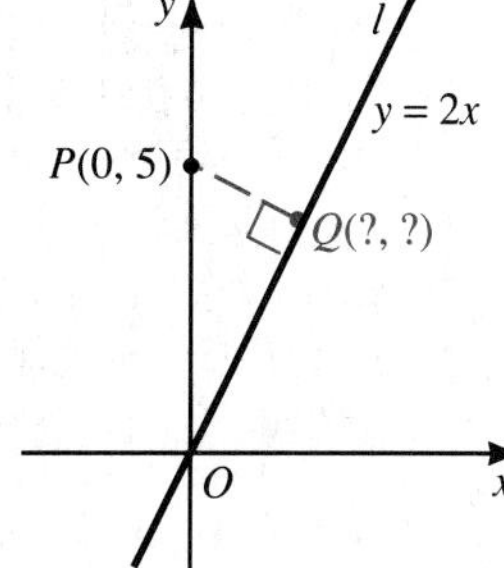

Step 2 *Find Q by solving the equations for l and* $\overleftrightarrow{PQ}$ *simultaneously.*

$y = 2x$ and $y = -\frac{1}{2}x + 5$

$2x = -\frac{1}{2}x + 5$

$\frac{5}{2}x = 5$

$x = 2$

If $x = 2$, then $y = 2x = 4$. Thus Q is $(2, 4)$.

Step 3 *Find PQ by using the distance formula.*

$PQ = \sqrt{(0 - 2)^2 + (5 - 4)^2} = \sqrt{5}$

Exercises

In Exercises 1–5 assume that each bridge must be perpendicular to the two river banks it joins.

1. Copy the figure shown and find the location of a bridge across the river that will allow the path from A to B to be minimum.

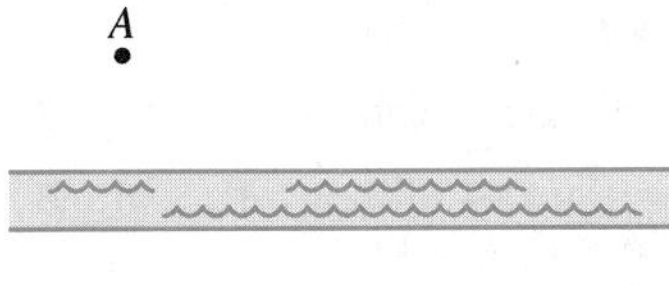

★ **2.** Two bridges are to be built over the parallel rivers shown. Find where they should be built if the total distance from C to D, including the distances across the bridges, is to be minimum.

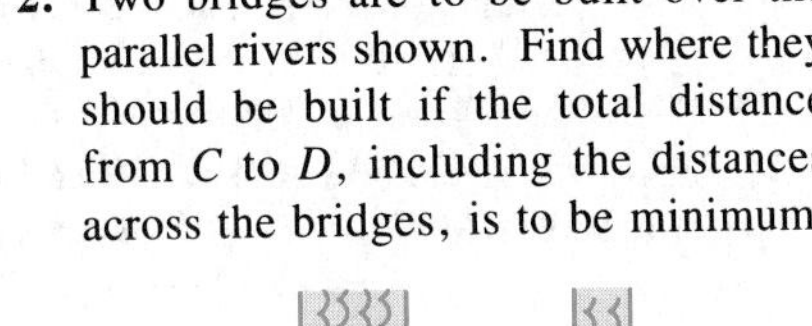

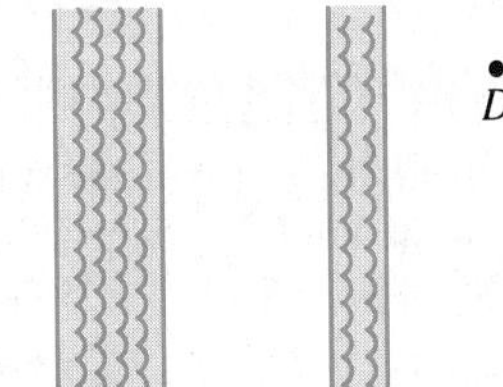

3. A river flows between the lines $x = 3$ and $x = 4$. Where should a bridge be constructed to minimize the path from $O(0, 0)$ to $P(5, 4)$? **Connect (3, 3) and (4, 3).**

4. A river flows between the lines $y = x$ and $y = x + 2$. Where should a bridge be constructed to minimize the path from $Q(0, 6)$ to $R(8, 5)$? **Connect (4, 6) and (5, 5).**

Additional Answers
Exercises

2. Translate C toward the wide river a distance equal to the river width, and translate D toward the narrow river a distance equal to the narrow river width. Connect the images to find the path across the strip of land between the rivers.

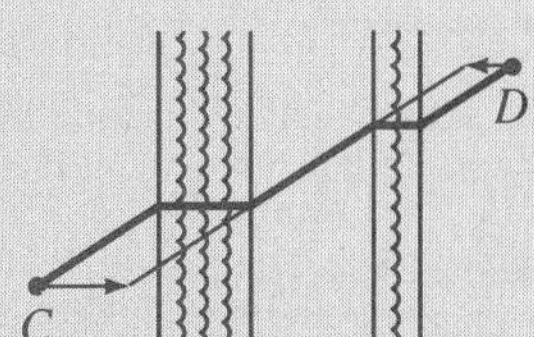

★ **5.** Two bridges are to be built over the river forks shown. Find where they should be built if the total distance from E to F via the island, including the distances across the bridges, is to be minimum. What do you notice about the three non-bridge portions of your path? **They are parallel.**

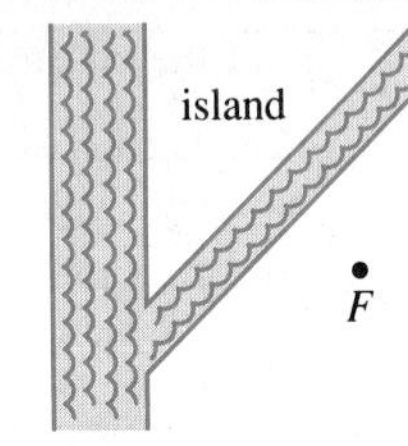

Find the shortest distance from the given point to the line whose equation is given.

6. $N(0, 10)$; $y = \frac{1}{3}x$ **$3\sqrt{10}$**

7. $O(0, 0)$; $y = 2x + 5$ **$\sqrt{5}$**

★ **8.** $P(2, -1)$; $y = \frac{2}{3}x + 2$ **$\sqrt{13}$**

Dilations and Similarity (Chapter 7)

Objective: Understand the close relationship between dilation transformations and the similar figures they produce. (Requires understanding of Lessons 13-6, 13-7, and 14-1 through 14-5.)

If a transformation maps a figure to a similar figure, it is called a similarity mapping. Every similarity mapping can be broken into two components: (1) a dilation and (2) a congruence mapping.

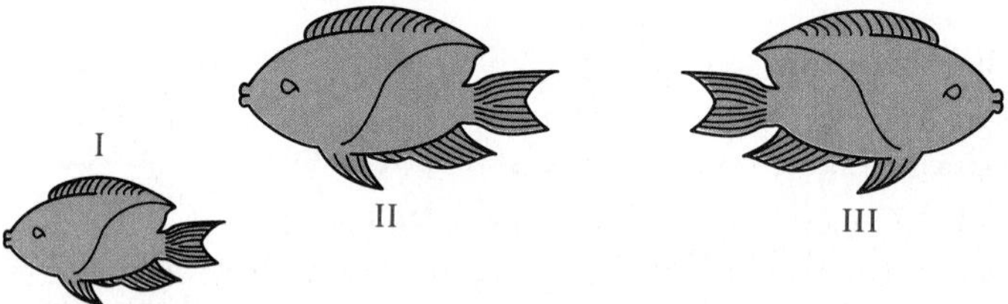

In the figure, a dilation maps fish I to the similar fish II, and a reflection maps fish II to a congruent fish III. If you perform these two mappings consecutively, the result is a similarity mapping that maps fish I to fish III.

Exercises **1. scale factor about $\frac{2}{3}$; rot. 90° 2. scale factor $-\frac{1}{2}$; rot. 180°**

Give the scale factor for the dilation that maps figure I to figure II, and tell what kind of congruence mapping maps figure II to figure III.

1. **2.**

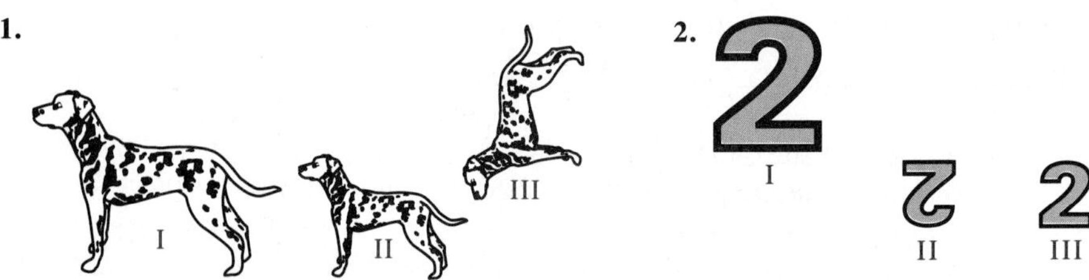

3. $D_{O, 2}$ maps $\triangle RST$ to $\triangle R'S'T'$. How are $\overrightarrow{RS}$ and $\overrightarrow{R'S'}$ related? **$\overrightarrow{RS} \parallel \overrightarrow{R'S'}$, same direction**

4 $D_{O, -3}$ maps $\triangle JKL$ to $\triangle J'K'L'$. How are $\overrightarrow{JK}$ and $\overrightarrow{J'K'}$ related? **$\overrightarrow{JK} \parallel \overrightarrow{J'K'}$, opp. directions**

5. A dilation maps square I to square II, and another dilation maps square II to square III. If the areas of these three squares are 25, 100, and 900, respectively, find the scale factor of each dilation. **2, 3**

6. The square *WXYZ* has three vertices on the sides of $\triangle ABC$. How can you find a square with all four vertices on $\triangle ABC$? (*Hint:* Consider a dilation.)
Dilate *WXYZ* with ctr. *B* until *Z* hits $\overline{AC}$.

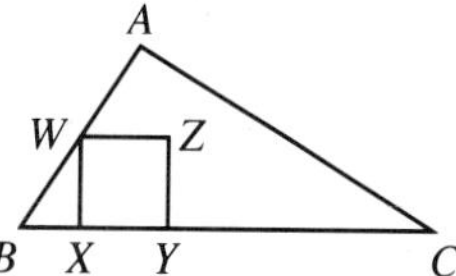

7. *O* is the origin and the dilation $D_{O, 3}$ maps line *l* to line *l'*. If the equation of *l* is $y = 2x + 1$, what is the equation of *l'*? **$y = 2x + 3$**

8. a. Draw a figure like the one shown, in which the dilation $D_{P, 2}$ maps $\triangle ABC$ to $\triangle A'B'C'$ and the dilation $D_{Q, 2}$ maps $\triangle A'B'C'$ to $\triangle A''B''C''$.
b. There is a single dilation that will map $\triangle ABC$ directly to $\triangle A''B''C''$. What is its scale factor? **4**
c. Draw lines $\overleftrightarrow{AA''}$, $\overleftrightarrow{BB''}$, and $\overleftrightarrow{CC''}$ to locate the center of the single dilation. How is this point related to points *P* and *Q*? **See below.**

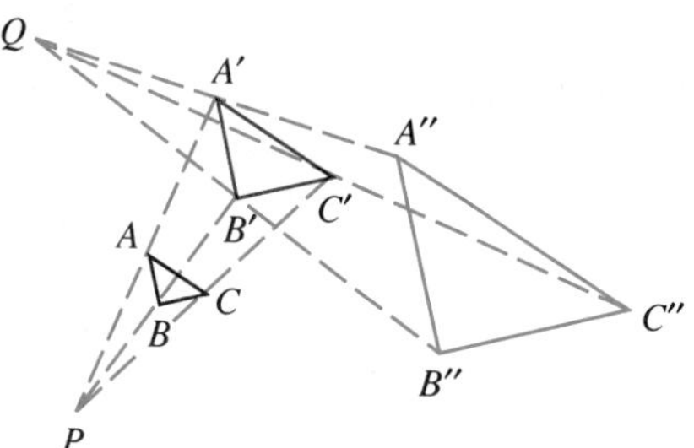

9–10. Work Exercise 29 on page 527 and Classroom Exercise 8 on page 532.
8.c. Between *P* and *Q*, $\frac{1}{3}$ of the way from *P* to *Q*.

Exercise Note

Capable students may wish to explore Ex. 8 with different scale factors. If the two scale factors are reciprocals, the double-dilation is equiv. to a translation. Otherwise, the ctr. of the single equiv. dilation is on $\overleftrightarrow{PQ}$. Coordinate methods can be used to show that an expansion with ctr. *P*, scale factor *k*, followed by an exp. with ctr. *Q*, scale factor *j*, is equiv. to a single exp. whose ctr. is $\frac{j-1}{jk-1}$ of the way between *P* and *Q*.

Right Triangles (Chapter 8)

Objective: Explore the properties of right triangles and other special triangles by using coordinate, vector, and transformational approaches. (Requires understanding of Lessons 13-1 through 13-7 and 14-1 through 14-5.)

The example below shows how to use coordinates, the distance formula, and Theorems 8-3, 8-4, and 8-5 to tell whether a triangle is acute, right, or obtuse.

Example Is $\triangle OPQ$ acute, right, or obtuse?

Solution First find the lengths of the sides of the triangle by using the distance formula.

$OP = \sqrt{6^2 + 3^2} = \sqrt{45}$

$OQ = \sqrt{4^2 + 5^2} = \sqrt{41}$

$PQ = \sqrt{(6-4)^2 + (3-5)^2} = \sqrt{8}$

y
Q(4, 5)
P(6, 3)
O
x

(Solution continued on next page.)

Since $\overline{OP}$ is the longest side of the triangle, we compare as follows:

$$(OP)^2 \ \underline{\ ?\ }\ (OQ)^2 + (PQ)^2$$
$$(\sqrt{45})^2 \ \underline{\ ?\ }\ (\sqrt{41})^2 + (\sqrt{8})^2$$
$$45 \ \underline{\ ?\ }\ 41 + 8$$
$$45 < 49$$

Thus the triangle is acute by Theorem 8-4.

Exercises

The vertices of a triangle are given. Decide whether the triangle is acute, right, or obtuse.

1. $O(0, 0)$, $P(8, 4)$, $Q(6, 8)$ **right**

2. $O(0, 0)$, $R(-1, 5)$, $S(-6, 0)$ **acute**

3. $A(1, 1)$, $B(3, -2)$, $C(8, 1)$ **obtuse**

4. $D(-5, 0)$, $E(0, 7)$, $F(3, -3)$ **acute**

5. Given vertices $A(3, 0)$, $B(5, 3)$, $C(-1, 7)$. Show that $\triangle ABC$ is a right triangle
a. by using slopes. **b.** by using Theorem 8-3.

6. In Exercise 5, $\triangle ABC$ has a right angle at B.
a. Find the coordinates of M, the midpoint of the hypotenuse. **$M(1, \frac{7}{2})$**
b. Use the distance formula to show that $MB = \frac{1}{2}AC$.
c. What theorem does part (b) illustrate?

7. Describe how to map $\triangle PNQ$ to $\triangle QNR$ with a rotation followed by a dilation. Give the scale factor of the dilation.
$\mathcal{R}_{N,-90}$ followed by $D_{N,2}$; scale factor is 2

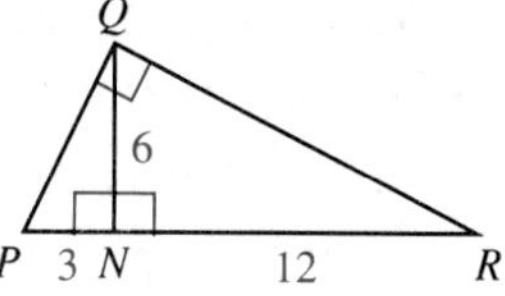

8. **a.** Draw $\triangle OPQ$ where O is the origin, $\overrightarrow{OP} = (4, 3)$ and $\overrightarrow{PQ} = (-2, 11)$.
b. Find $\overrightarrow{OQ}$. **(2, 14)**
c. Find $|\overrightarrow{OP}|$, $|\overrightarrow{PQ}|$, and $|\overrightarrow{OQ}|$. **$5, 5\sqrt{5}, 10\sqrt{2}$**
d. Is $\triangle OPQ$ a right triangle? Explain. **No; $(OQ)^2 > (OP)^2 + (PQ)^2$ so $\triangle OPQ$ is obtuse.**

9. Four right triangles and a small square are arranged to form a larger square as shown at the left below. What is the area of the large square? If two of the triangles are rotated about P and Q as shown, we get the figure at the right below. Show that this figure can be considered as the sum of two squares. Find the dimensions of the two squares. What theorem does this exercise suggest? **c^2; b^2, a^2; the Pythagorean Theorem**

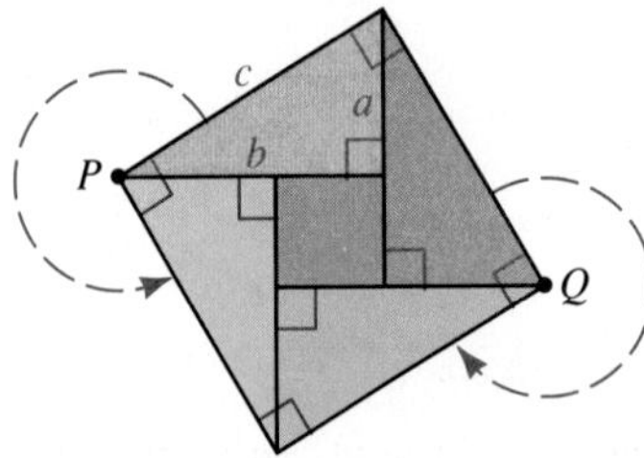

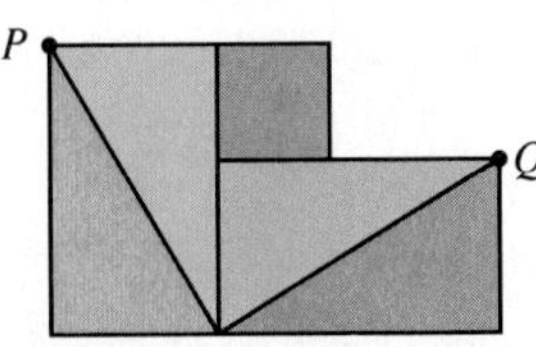

Additional Answers Exercises

6.c. Thm. 5-15: The midpt. of the hyp. of a rt. △ is equidistant from the three vertices.

9. The dashed line divides the area into two squares of area b^2 and a^2.

10. The inner square in the diagram is formed by connecting the midpoints of the outer square. It is possible to map the outer square to the inner square by performing a rotation followed by a dilation.

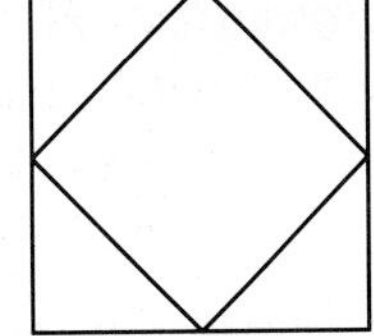

a. Give the center of the rotation and the amount of the rotation. **ctr. of square, 45°** **See below.**

b. Give the center of the dilation and the scale factor.

11–21. Work Exercises 32, 42 on page 527; Classroom Exercise 7 on page 532; Exercises 28–31, 33 on pages 533–534; Classroom Exercise 11 on page 536; Exercise 23 on page 538; and Classroom Exercise 5 on page 541.

10.b. ctr. of square, $\frac{\sqrt{2}}{2}$

Exercise Note

Some students may suggest that for Ex. 10(a), any odd multiple of 45 is a correct answer for the measure of the required rotation.

Circles (Chapter 9)

Objective: Write the equations of tangent lines, and make observations about circles and their symmetry. (Requires understanding of Lessons 13-1 through 13-7 and 14-1 through 14-5.)

Many relationships among circles and their chords and tangents can be investigated by using coordinates and transformations. Before studying the example below, you should understand how the equation of a circle is used in Examples 3 and 4 of Lesson 13-1.

Example

a. Sketch the circle $x^2 + y^2 = 10$ and the line $y = 3x + 10$.

b. Solve the two equations simultaneously and show that there is just one solution for x.

c. Find the corresponding value for y. Label the solution point, T, on your sketch. What does this tell you about the line and the circle?

d. Use the slopes to show that $\overline{OT}$ is perpendicular to the line $y = 3x + 10$.

Solution

a. The circle has center O and radius $\sqrt{10}$.

b.
$$\begin{aligned} x^2 + y^2 &= 10 \\ x^2 + (3x + 10)^2 &= 10 \\ x^2 + 9x^2 + 60x + 100 &= 10 \\ 10x^2 + 60x + 90 &= 0 \\ x^2 + 6x + 9 &= 0 \\ (x + 3)(x + 3) &= 0 \\ x + 3 &= 0 \\ x &= -3 \end{aligned}$$

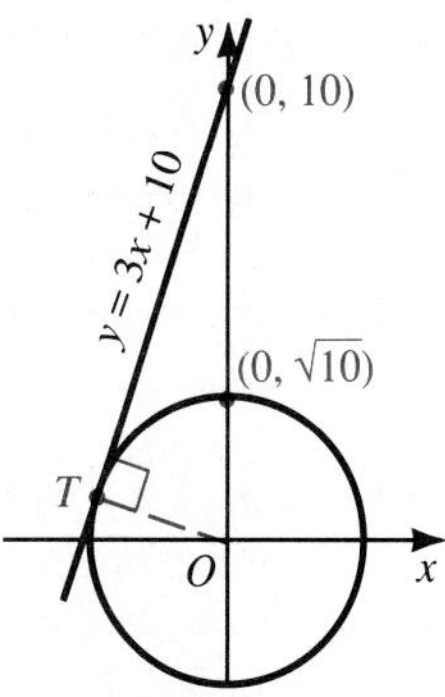

c. $y = 3x + 10$; $y = 3(-3) + 10$; $y = 1$. Point T is $(-3, 1)$. The line is tangent to the circle at point T.

d. The slope of $\overline{OT}$ is $\frac{1 - 0}{-3 - 0} = -\frac{1}{3}$. The slope of $y = 3x + 10$ is 3. Since the slopes are negative reciprocals, the lines are perpendicular.

Exercises

1. **a.** What is the equation of a circle with center (6, 0) and radius 5? **$(x - 6)^2 + y^2 = 25$**
   b. Is the point $Q(2, 3)$ on the circle? **Yes**
   c. Plot $P(12, 8)$. Is $\overline{PQ}$ tangent to the circle? **No**

In Exercises 2–4, (a) verify that points A and B lie on circle O, (b) make a sketch and find M, the midpoint of $\overline{AB}$, and (c) use slopes to verify that $\overline{OM} \perp \overline{AB}$.

2. Circle O has radius 5. The points are $A(0, 5)$ and $B(4, 3)$.
3. Circle O has radius 10. The points are $A(6, 8)$ and $B(-8, 6)$.
4. Circle O has radius $5\sqrt{2}$. The points are $A(5, 5)$ and $B(-7, 1)$.
5. Sketch the circles $x^2 + y^2 = 225$ and $(x - 6)^2 + (y - 8)^2 = 25$ and explain why the circles must be internally tangent. (*Hint:* Find the two radii and the distance between the centers of the circles.)
6. **a.** Sketch the circle $x^2 + y^2 = 25$ and the line $y = 2x - 5$.
   b. Solve the two equations simultaneously by substituting $2x - 5$ for y in the equation $x^2 + y^2 = 25$. Solve the resulting quadratic equation by factoring. For each value of x, find the corresponding value of y by substituting into the equation $y = 2x - 5$.
   c. Your two solutions in part (b) correspond to two points on the circle. Show them on your sketch. **(0, −5), (4, 3)**
7. $\overleftrightarrow{PA}$ is tangent to circle O at A.
   a. If the figure shown is reflected in $\overleftrightarrow{PO}$, what is the image of circle O? of $\overline{PA}$? **⊙O; the other tan.**
   b. Since a reflection is an isometry, what do you know about $\overline{PA}$ and its image? **They are ≅.**
   c. State the corollary that part (b) proves. **Tangents to a ⊙ from a pt. are ≅.**
8. Circles P and Q intersect at A and B.
   a. What is the image of A when reflected in $\overleftrightarrow{PQ}$? **B**
   b. What does part (a) tell you about $\overline{AB}$ and $\overline{PQ}$?
   c. Sketch the image of $\overline{XY}$ when reflected in $\overleftrightarrow{PQ}$.
   d. What can you deduce from part (c) about the common external tangents of two circles?

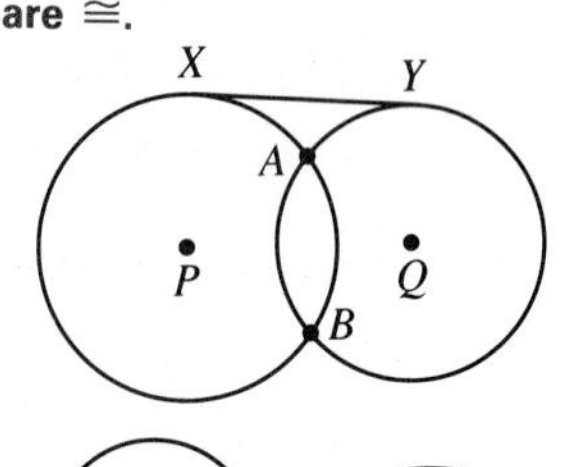

★ 9. Find an equilateral triangle ABC with vertex B on ⊙P and vertex C on ⊙Q. (*Hint:* Rotate ⊙P 60° about A. Its image will intersect ⊙Q in two points. Either of these points can be the desired vertex C. How do you find B?)
Rotate C −60° about A to find B.

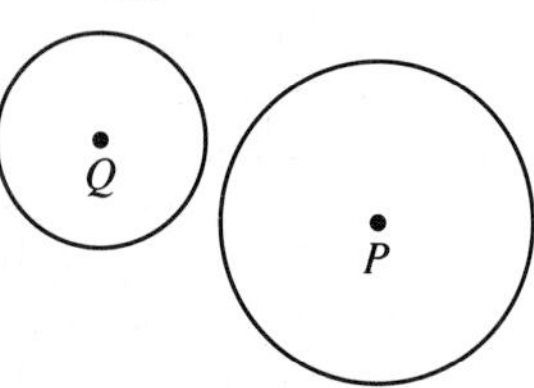

8.b. $\overline{AB} \perp \overline{PQ}$
8.d. Common external tangents of two circles are ≅.

10–18. Work Exercises 19, 20 on page 538; Exercises 36–39 on page 552; Classroom Exercise 14 on page 554 and Exercise 35 on page 556; and Classroom Exercise 13 on page 595.

Constructions (Chapter 10)

Objective: Use transformations with concurrency and construction problems. (Requires understanding of Lessons 14-1 through 14-5.)

Concurrency Theorems 10-1 and 10-2 are proved by synthetic methods, while the proofs of concurrency Theorems 10-3 and 10-4 are delayed until coordinate methods can be used. However, all four theorems can be proved with coordinates or without. The following theorem states that three of the four concurrency points are collinear. A proof of this theorem with coordinates is quite involved. (See Exercises 11–14 of Lesson 13-9.) However, the transformational proof below is much shorter and more elegant.

Theorem: The orthocenter, centroid, and circumcenter of a triangle are collinear. (The line on which they lie is called *Euler's line.*)

Given: $\triangle RST$ with orthocenter H, centroid G, and circumcenter C.

Prove: H, G, and C are collinear.

Proof: Consider the dilation $D_{G,\ -\frac{1}{2}}$.

Because G divides each median in a 2:1 ratio, this dilation maps R to R', the midpoint of $\overline{TS}$. Also this dilation maps altitude $\overline{RK}$ to a parallel line through R'. But since $\overline{RK}$ is perpendicular to $\overline{TS}$, the image of $\overline{RK}$ must be perpendicular to $\overline{TS}$. Thus the image of altitude $\overline{RK}$ is the perpendicular bisector of $\overline{TS}$.

We have just proved that $D_{G,\ -\frac{1}{2}}$ maps an altitude to a perpendicular bisector. Similar reasoning shows that the dilation also maps the other two altitudes to perpendicular bisectors. Therefore the dilation maps the orthocenter H, which is on all three altitudes, to the circumcenter C, which is on all three perpendicular bisectors. And since the dilation $D_{G,\ -\frac{1}{2}}$ also maps G to itself, then H, G, and C must be collinear by the definition of a dilation.

Proof Note

Some students may find it difficult to see how the dilation maps altitude $\overline{RK}$ to a perpendicular through R'. You may wish to make a large copy of the diagram and add S' (the midpoint of $\overline{RT}$) and T' (the midpoint of $\overline{RS}$). Then show that the dilation involves mapping $\triangle RST$ to $\triangle R'S'T'$.

Just as $\overline{RK} \perp \overline{TS}$, so too will the image of $\overline{RK}$ be perpendicular to $\overline{T'S'}$. And since $\overline{T'S'} \parallel \overline{TS}$ (by Thm. 5-11), the image of $\overline{RK}$ must be perpendicular to $\overline{TS}$ as well.

If your diagram is large enough, you may be able to demonstrate how the other altitudes of $\triangle RST$ are mapped to the other altitudes of $\triangle R'S'T'$. Since each altitude of $\triangle R'S'T'$ is also a perpendicular bisector of $\triangle RST$, it is clear that the orthocenter H is mapped to the circumcenter C.

Exercises

Carefully draw a *large* $\triangle RST$ and construct its centroid G, its orthocenter H, and its circumcenter C.

1. G, H, and C should be collinear. Are they? **Yes**
2. Measure the lengths of $\overline{HG}$ and $\overline{GC}$ and find the ratio $HG:GC$. Does your result agree with what you would expect if you were using the dilation $D_{G,\,-\frac{1}{2}}$? **$HG:GC = 2:1$**
3. Draw $\triangle R'S'T'$, the image of $\triangle RST$ by the dilation $D_{G,\,-\frac{1}{2}}$. What is the ratio of the areas of these two triangles? **1:4**
4. Locate Q, the midpoint of $\overline{HC}$. Put the point of your compass on Q and draw a circle through R'. This is the famous *nine-point circle*. See page 414.
5. Draw a sketch that shows the locus of points in the coordinate plane whose distance to the x-axis and distance to the y-axis have a sum of 10.
6. Given line l, $\odot P$ and point M, construct a segment $\overline{XY}$ with X on $\odot P$, Y on l, and M as the midpoint of $\overline{XY}$. (*Hint:* Consider a half-turn.) You may find two answers.
7. Construct an isosceles right $\triangle ABC$ with B on $\odot P$, C on line l, and right angle at A. (*Hint:* Consider a rotation. What will be the magnitude and center of the rotation?) You may find two answers.

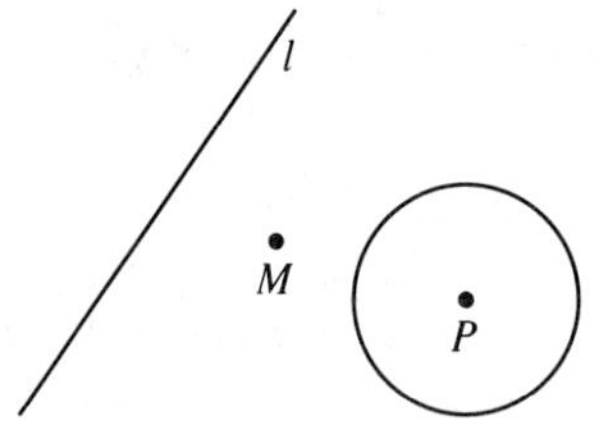

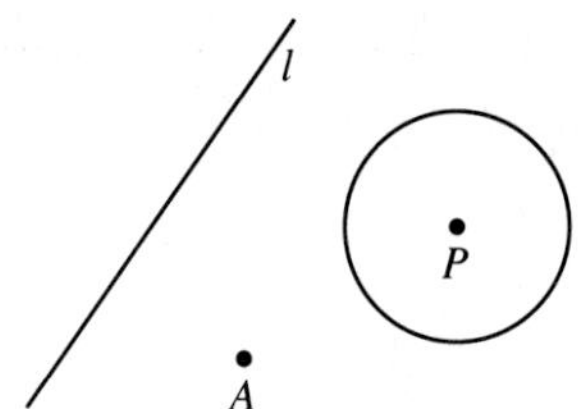

8–16. Work Exercises 21, 22 on page 580; Exercises 18, 20, 21 on page 587; Exercises 31, 38, 39 on pages 591–592; and Exercise 24 on page 597.

Additional Answers Exercises

6. The image of $\odot P$ under a half-turn about M int. l at two pts.: Y_1 and Y_2. The preimages are the required X_1, X_2.

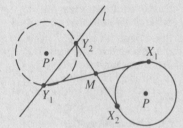

Areas (Chapter 11)

Objective: Calculate complex areas by dividing them into portions and using transformations to rearrange the pieces into simpler shapes. (Requires understanding of Lessons 14-1 through 14-5.)

The proof of Theorem 11-2 uses a translation of a triangular portion of a parallelogram to show that a parallelogram and a rectangle have the same area if they have the same base and height. Other transformations, such as rotation, can be used to find areas that would be more difficult without transformations.

An unfamiliar figure can sometimes be divided into pieces that can be rearranged to form a familiar figure whose area is easier to calculate. This method is called *dissection*.

Example Find the area of the "goblet" that is constructed in a square by drawing one semicircle and two quarter circles, as shown in the diagram at the left below.

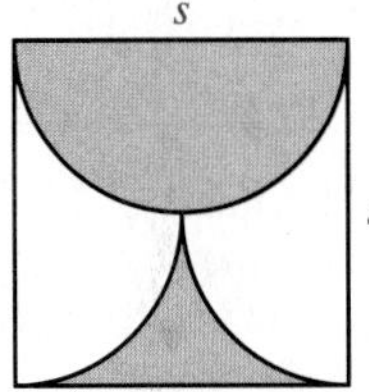

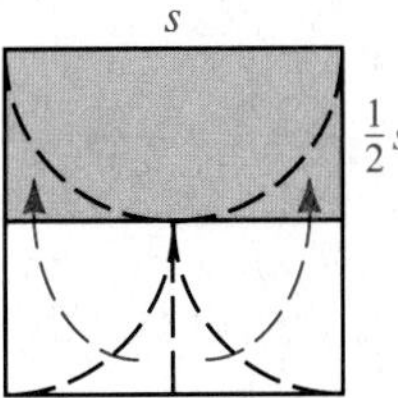

Solution Divide the bottom of the goblet into halves and rotate them upward as shown in the diagram at the right above. Thus the shaded area is $\frac{1}{2}s^2$.

Exercises

Each figure below is drawn with arcs of radius 4. Use rotations to find the area of each.

1. **32**

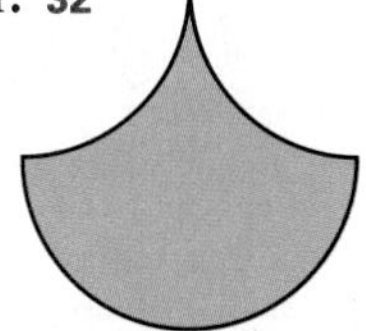

2. **32**

3. **64**

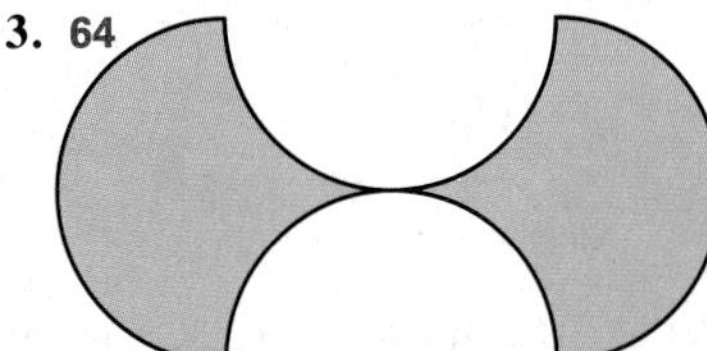

4. The figure shows a series of squares inscribed within each other. Transformation T, which maps region I to region II is achieved by performing a rotation followed by a dilation.

a. Give the number of degrees in the rotation and the scale factor of the dilation. **See below.**

b. What is the image of region I by the transformation T^2 (T performed twice)? by the transformation T^3?

c. Give the areas of regions I, II, III, IV and V.

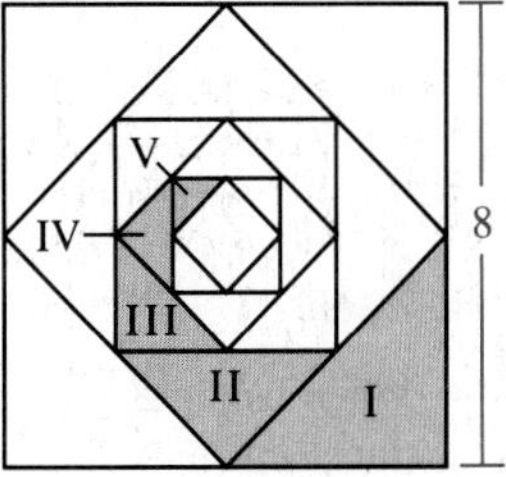

4.a. $-45, \frac{\sqrt{2}}{2}$ **b.** **III, IV** **c.** $8, 4, 2, 1, \frac{1}{2}$

Making Connections

Students can explore the concept of the sum of a series by copying the diagram for Ex. 4 and coloring in regions I through V to reveal a "spiral arm."

Ask students to imagine continuing this process inward forever. By using three other colors, students can find that four congruent spiral arms fill the square completely. Thus, the area of one spiral arm is one-fourth the area of the square, or 16.

But the area of one spiral arm is also the sum of the endless series whose first terms were calculated in Ex. 4(c). Thus: $8 + 4 + 2 + 1 + \frac{1}{2} + \frac{1}{4} + \cdots = 16$.

Using a Model

Students may find that Exs. 6 and 7 are easier to accomplish by constructing the diagrams on heavy paper, cutting out the pieces required for each dissection, and manipulating them on their desktops.

Additional Answers Exercises

6.

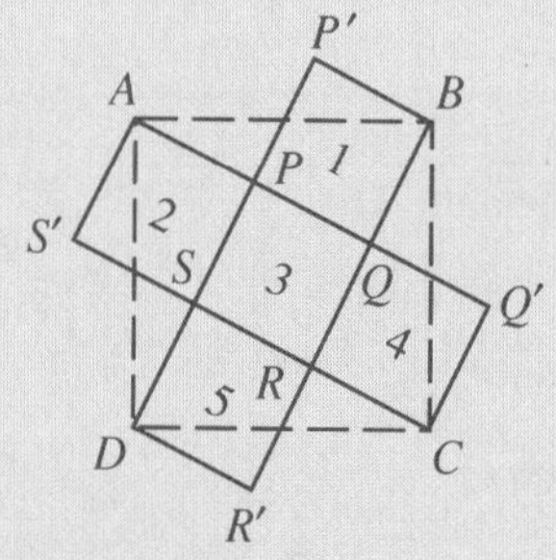

7.

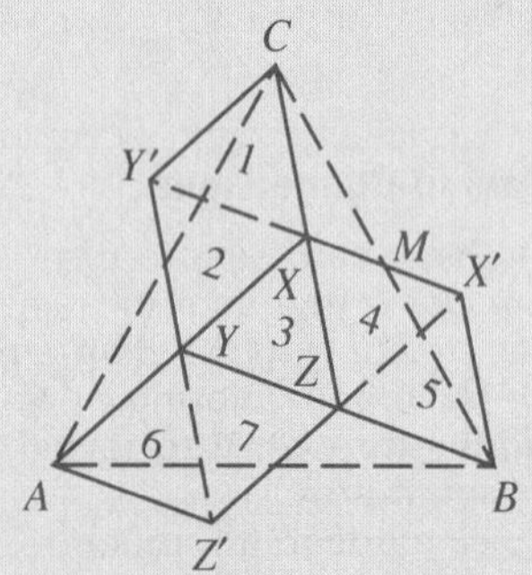

Supplementary Materials

Overhead Visual N

5. The figure shows a series of equilateral triangles and circles inscribed within each other. Transformation T, which maps region I to region II, is the result of performing a rotation followed by a dilation.
   a. Give the number of degrees in the rotation and the scale factor of the dilation. **See below.**
   b. What is the image of region I by the transformation T? T^2? T^3? **II, III, IV**
   c. If region I has area 1, give the areas of regions II, III, and IV. $\frac{1}{4}, \frac{1}{16}, \frac{1}{64}$

5.a. $-60, \frac{1}{2}$

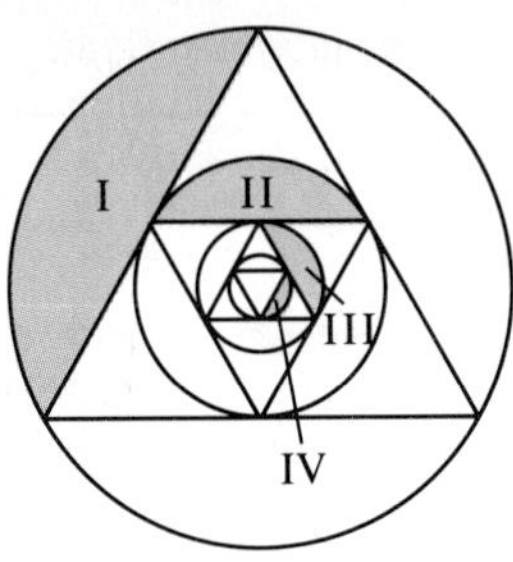

6. E, F, G, and H are midpoints of the sides of square $ABCD$. If the area of square $PQRS$ is 1, what is the area of square $ABCD$? (*Hint:* Rotate $\triangle APG$ 180° about G. Rotate in a similar manner $\triangle$s BQF, CRE, and DSH.) **5**

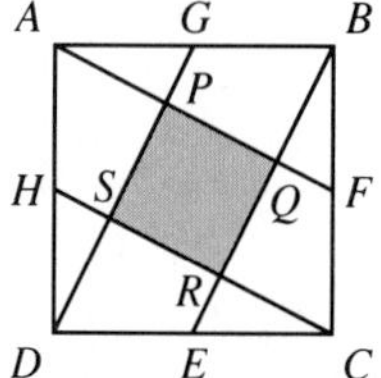

★ 7. Exercise 32 on page 460 is difficult to prove synthetically. Recall that points P, Q, and R divide the sides of $\triangle ABC$ into 2:1 ratios. Follow the strategy of Exercise 6 above to prove that the area of equilateral $\triangle ABC$ is seven times the area of equilateral $\triangle XYZ$. (*Hint:* Draw an auxiliary line from X to the midpoint, M, of $\overline{CB}$. Rotate $\triangle CXM$ 180° about M. Repeat for the other two sides of $\triangle ABC$.)

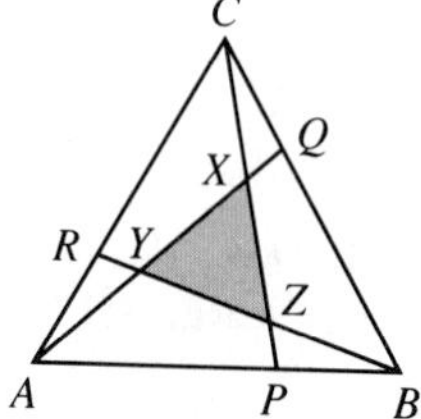

8–10. Work Exercise 31 on page 527, and Exercises 34, 35 on pages 551–552.

Deciding Which Method to Use in a Problem (Chapter 13)

Objective: Learn to recognize clues that indicate whether a coordinate, transformational, or synthetic approach is most suitable for a problem. (Requires completion of Chapters 13 and 14)

When facing a geometry problem, how do you know when to use a coordinate, transformational, or traditional (usually called *synthetic*) approach? Many problems can be solved in more than one way, but often one approach is simpler than another. Here are some tips to help you decide which method may be most suitable for a given problem.

Synthetic Approach

Usually a synthetic approach is best when at least one of the following is true.

1. The lengths of the sides of a figure are given, rather than the coordinates of its vertices.
2. Angle measures other than 90 are given or asked for in the problem. (If lines are parallel or form right angles, however, then a coordinate approach using slopes may be appropriate.)
3. The given information or diagram involves transversals and corresponding angles; congruent lengths, angles, or figures; the areas of similar figures; or the volumes of solids.

Coordinate Approach

1. Usually a coordinate approach is easiest when the problem uses coordinates to name points.
   a. To calculate lengths, use the distance formula.
   b. To locate midpoints, use the midpoint formula.
   c. To show lines are parallel or perpendicular, use the slopes of the lines.
   d. To prove that lines are concurrent, show that their equations have a common solution.
2. Even if a problem does not use coordinates to name points, you can place the coordinate axes on the figure and assign coordinates to the vertices as was shown in Lessons 13-8 and 13-9.
   a. If the figures involved are symmetric, place the axes so that one of them is a line of symmetry. Such a placement reduces the number of variables needed to describe the vertices.
   b. If the figures involved are not symmetric, place the axes so that as many vertices and edges of the figures lie on the x- and y-axes as possible. Distance calculations are simplified whenever zeros appear in the coordinate pairs.

Transformational Approach

1. If the figure has line symmetry, try using a reflection.
2. If the figure has rotational symmetry, try using a rotation.
3. If there are congruent figures placed some distance apart, try using a translation, rotation, glide reflection or a composite of any number of such congruence mappings to map one figure onto the other.
4. If the problem involves similar figures, look for a center of a dilation that would map one figure onto the other. You may first have to rotate one figure so that corresponding sides of similar figures are parallel.
5. If the problem involves calculating the area of an unfamiliar figure, try dissecting the figure and moving the pieces around by transformations until the result is a figure whose area is easy to calculate.
6. Some construction problems can be solved by using reflections (constructing perpendicular bisectors) or by using rotations of angles you can construct, such as 45°, 60°, 90°, or 180°.

Exercises

For Exercises 1–4 complete proofs using the strategies listed, then state which approach is easiest for you.

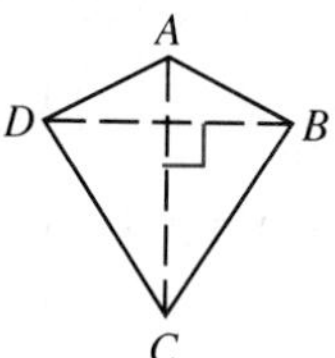

1. Given: $\overline{AC}$ is the perpendicular bisector of $\overline{BD}$.
   Prove: $AD = AB$ and $CD = CB$.
   a. Use a synthetic proof.
   b. Use a reflection.
   c. Use a coordinate proof.

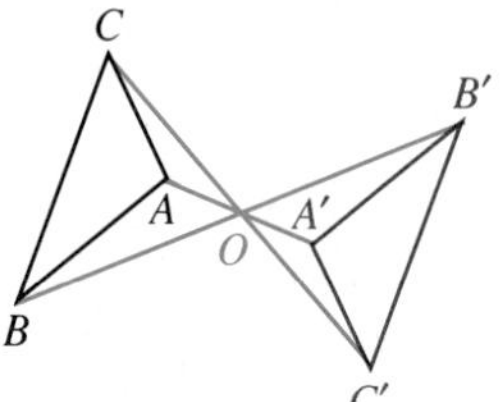

2. Given: O is the midpoint of $\overline{AA'}$, $\overline{BB'}$, and $\overline{CC'}$.
   Prove: $\triangle ABC \cong \triangle A'B'C'$
   a. Use a synthetic proof.
   b. Use a 180° rotation.

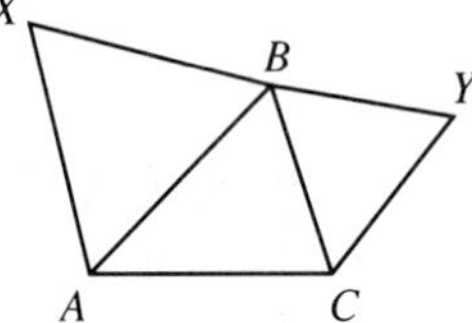

3. Equilateral triangles ABX and BCY are constructed on two sides of $\triangle ABC$ as shown. Prove that $AY = XC$.
   a. Use a synthetic proof.
   b. Find the image of $\overline{AY}$ under the rotation $\mathcal{R}_{B,\,-60}$.
   $\overline{XC}$

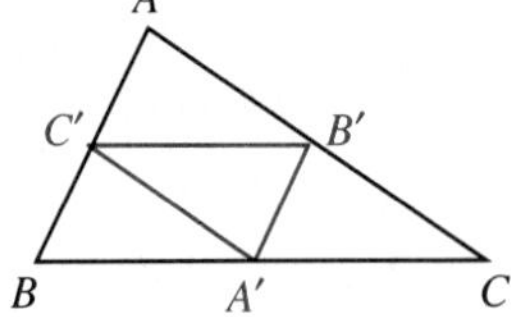

4. A', B', and C' are the midpoints of the sides of $\triangle ABC$. Find the ratio of the areas of $\triangle ABC$ and $\triangle A'B'C'$.
   a. Use a synthetic argument. **ratio of areas is 4:1**
   b. Use a dilation to map $\triangle ABC$ to $\triangle A'B'C'$. Where is the center of the dilation? What is the scale factor?
   Ctr. is int. of $\overline{AA'}$, $\overline{BB'}$, and $\overline{CC'}$. Scale factor is $-\frac{1}{2}$.

For Exercises 5–20 choose the approach that you feel is best suited to each problem.

5. What kind of figure do you get if you join the midpoints of successive sides of a square? Prove your conjecture. **square**
6. What kind of figure do you get if you join the midpoints of successive sides of a rhombus? Prove your conjecture. **rectangle**
7. The successive midpoints of the sides of quadrilateral $ABCD$ are P, Q, R, and S. Prove that $\overline{PR}$ and $\overline{QS}$ bisect each other.
8. You are given the points $A(-4, 1)$, $B(2, 3)$, $C(4, 9)$, and $D(-2, 7)$.
   a. Show that $ABCD$ is a parallelogram with perpendicular diagonals.
   b. What special name is given to $ABCD$? **rhombus**

9. P is an arbitrary point inside rectangle $ABCD$. Prove the following: $(PA)^2 + (PC)^2 = (PB)^2 + (PD)^2$

10. Find the area of a quadrilateral with vertices $A(-1, -1)$, $B(9, 4)$, $C(20, 6)$, and $D(10, 1)$. **35**

11. $ABCD$ is a quadrilateral such that if sides $\overline{AB}$ and $\overline{CD}$ are extended they will meet at a right angle. Prove that $(AC)^2 + (BD)^2 = (AD)^2 + (BC)^2$.

12. A ray of light is reflected successively in two perpendicular mirrors. Prove that the final ray is parallel to the initial ray.

★ 13. Find a point X on l and a point Y on m so that $\overline{XY}$ is parallel and congruent to $\overline{AB}$.

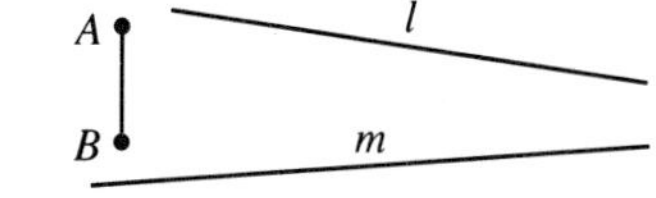

★ 14. Find a point X on the triangle and a point Y on line l so that M is the midpoint of $\overline{XY}$.

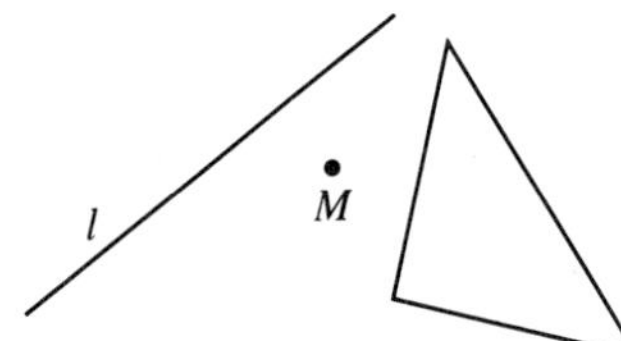

★ 15. Construct three parallel lines so that the middle line is not equidistant from the other two. Then construct an equilateral triangle with one vertex on each of the three lines.

16. Find the length of the tangent line segment from (9, 13) to the circle $x^2 + y^2 = 25$. **15**

17. Given: $\overline{MN}$ is the median of trapezoid $ABCD$; $\overline{MN}$ intersects the diagonals at X and Y.
Prove: $XY = \frac{1}{2}(AB - DC)$

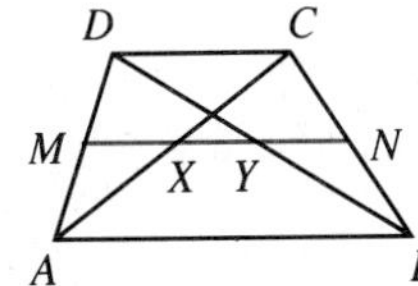

18. Given: $ABCD$ is a parallelogram whose diagonals meet at O; P and Q are midpoints of $\overline{AB}$ and $\overline{CD}$; R and S are midpoints of $\overline{AO}$ and $\overline{CO}$.
Prove: $PRQS$ is a parallelogram.

★ 19. Graph the circles whose equations are $(x + 9)^2 + (y - 5)^2 = 25$ and $(x - 2)^2 + (y - 4)^2 = 25$. Find a point X on one circle and a point Y on the other such that the y-axis is the perpendicular bisector of $\overline{XY}$.

★ 20. A and B are fixed points 12 units apart. P is an arbitrary point. Once P is chosen, find points X and Y such that $PA = AX$, $\overline{PA} \perp \overline{AX}$, $PB = BY$, and $\overline{PB} \perp \overline{BY}$ as shown. Now locate M, the midpoint of $\overline{XY}$. Show that the position of M does not depend on the position of P.

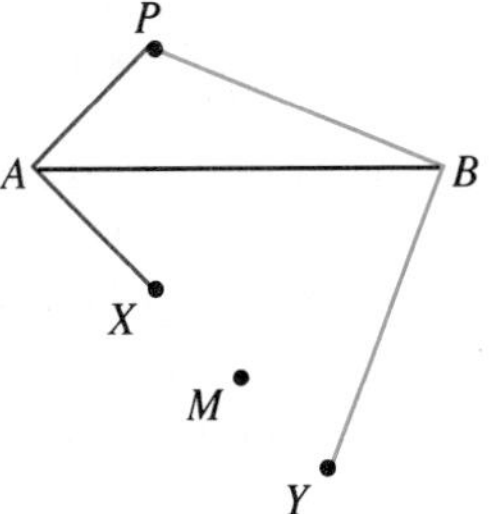

Exercise Note

Ex. 20 is an elaboration on the cat-and-mouse Challenge problem presented on page 614. In this case, M stands for the location of the cat, while P is the location of the moving mouse. Although in the Challenge problem the mouse is restricted to moving along a line (represented by $\overline{AB}$ in Ex. 20), this exercise demonstrates that the mouse can in fact move anywhere in the plane without changing the location of the cat.

Teaching Note

A question students may raise regarding an Euler circuit is whether one can pass a particular point more than once. The diagrams of the river help to show that it is acceptable, and probably necessary, to travel over a land mass such as A more than once. When land mass A is represented by point A in the graph, then, it is still fine to pass through the point more than once.

Additional Answers Exercises

1.

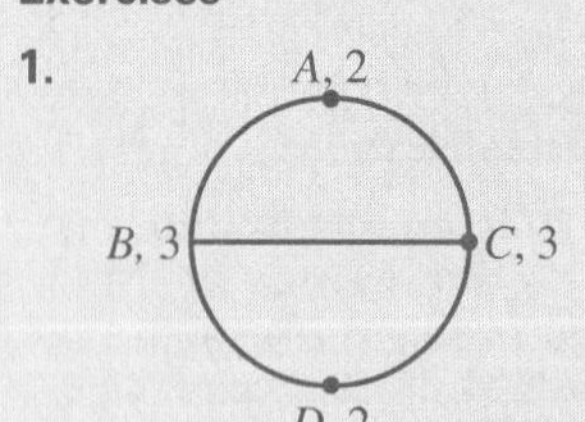

2.

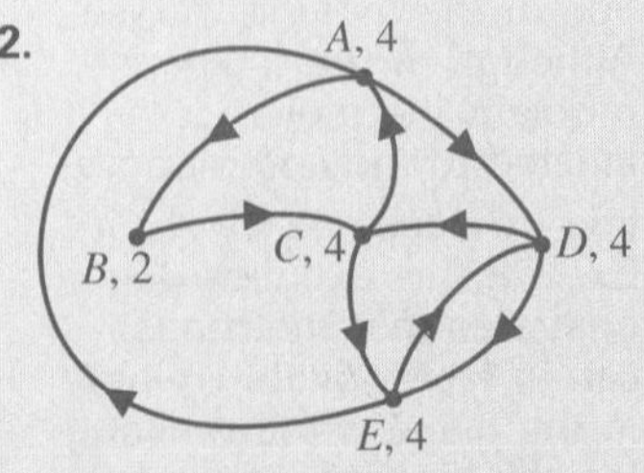

Discrete Mathematics

A Famous Bridge Problem

In the 1700's the European city of Koenigsberg (now called Kaliningrad) had seven bridges connecting both banks of the Pregel River to two islands in the river. Villagers of the city developed this problem: Is it possible to start at some point in the city, travel over each of the seven bridges exactly once, and return to your starting point? Do you think it is possible?

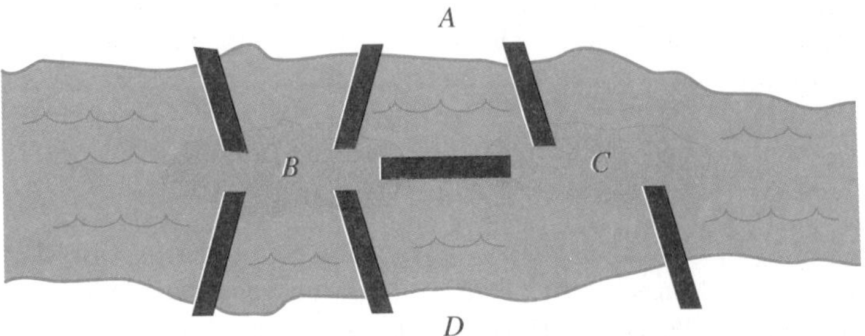

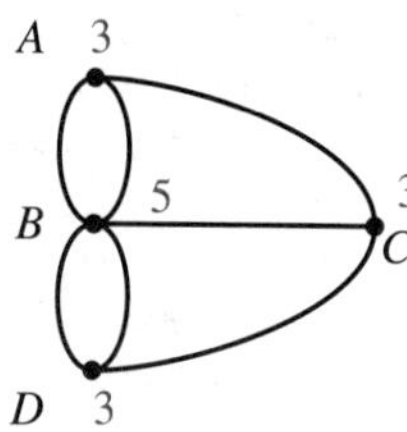

To analyze this problem, the Swiss mathematician Leonhard Euler (1707–1783) drew a *graph* like the one at the right. This graph is not like the graphs you have studied in algebra. It is a diagram in which the 4 land masses of the city (A, B, C, and D) are represented by *vertices* (points), and the 7 bridges are represented by *edges* (lines and arcs). Next to each vertex is a number indicating how many edges are attached to the vertex. This number is called the *valence* of the vertex.

Euler reasoned that in order for a person to travel over every bridge once and return to the starting point, every vertex must have an even valence. This is because a person traveling *into* a vertex must also *leave* it. So the edges must be paired, one "in" with one "out."

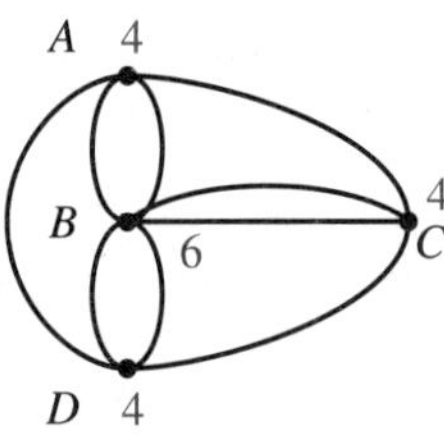

In the 7-bridges problem, none of the vertices has an even valence, so a circuit over all 7 bridges is impossible. However, if two more bridges are added, giving the 9 bridges shown at the right, then every vertex has an even valence, and a circuit over all 9 bridges is possible. Such a circuit, which traces every edge of a graph exactly once and returns to its starting point, is called an *Euler circuit*. Can you find an Euler circuit for the graph of the 9-bridges problem? **Yes**

Exercises

Draw a graph for each bridge problem below. Find the valence of each vertex and decide whether an Euler circuit is possible. If possible, find an Euler circuit for the graph.

1. 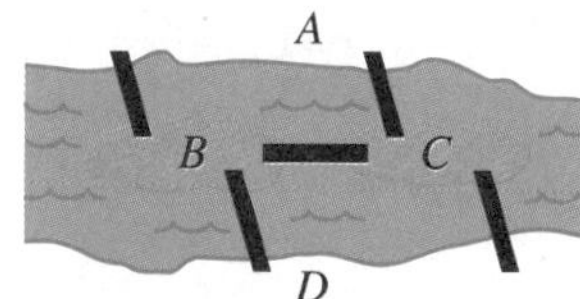

2. 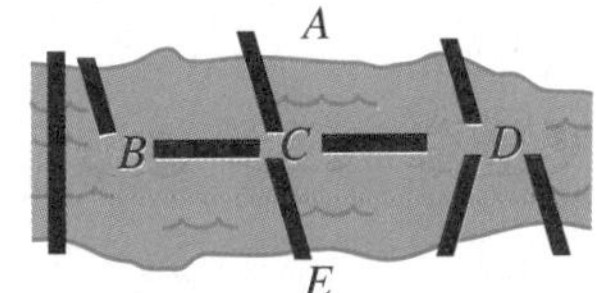

3. An Euler circuit is not possible for the bridge problem in Exercise 1. But it *is* possible to start at one point of the city, travel over each bridge once, and end at a point of the city other than the starting point. Show how this is possible. **Possible answer: *CBDCAB***

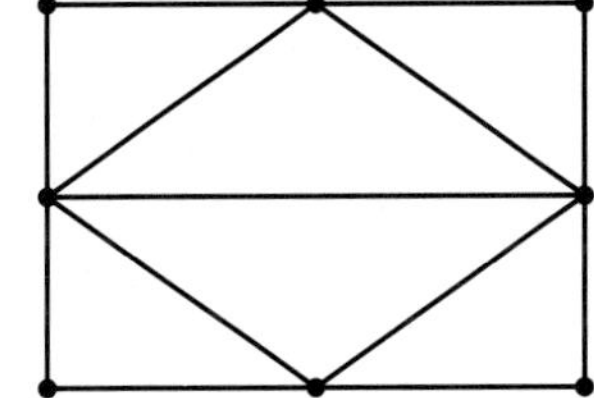

4. A network of city streets is shown at the right.
   a. Could a member of the highway department start at an intersection, inspect each street, and return to the starting point without traveling over any portion of a street twice? **No**
   b. Can part **a** be done if the inspector starts and ends at different points? **Yes**

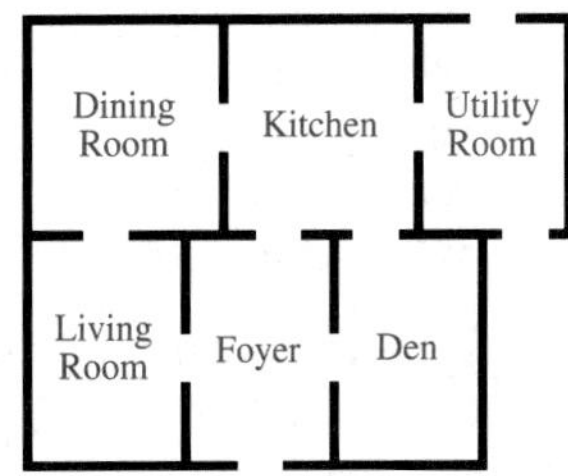

5. The first floor plan of a house is shown at the right.
   a. Can you enter the house from outside, travel through each doorway exactly once, and return to your starting point? Make a graph in which the outdoors is represented by one vertex and each room is represented by a vertex. **No**
   b. Can you travel through each door exactly once and end at a place different from where you started? **Yes**
   c. Examine your answers to Exercises **1–4** more closely. Can you make some conjectures about what is or is not possible with different numbers of vertices with odd valences?

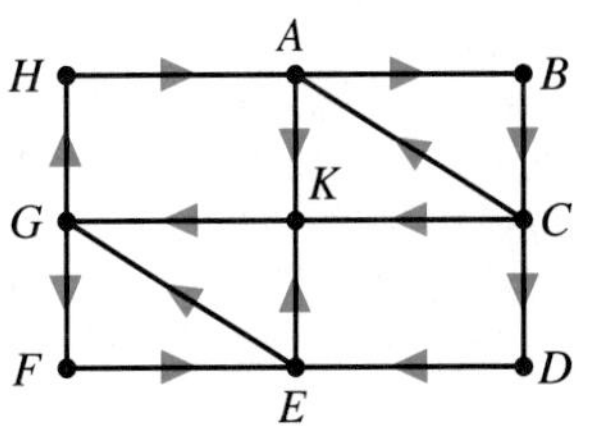

6. The graph at the right represents a network of one-way streets. The arrowheads indicate the direction of travel. Since two streets lead into vertex A, we say that the *invalence* of A is 2. Since two streets lead out of vertex A, we say that the *outvalence* of A is 2.
   a. Find the invalence and outvalence of each of the other vertices.
   b. Is an Euler circuit possible? Why or why not? **No**
   c. Can you change the direction of just one arrowhead so that an Euler circuit is possible? Name the vertices in one order in which they could be visited. **Yes**

Additional Answers
Exercises

3. 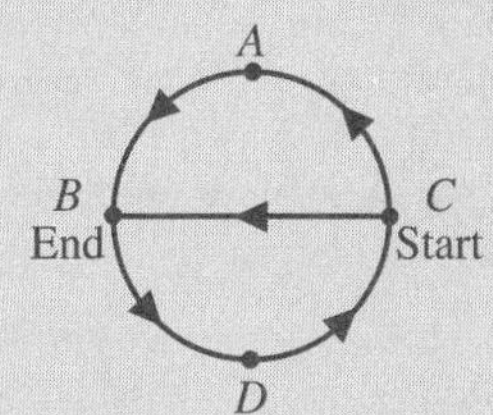

5. a. 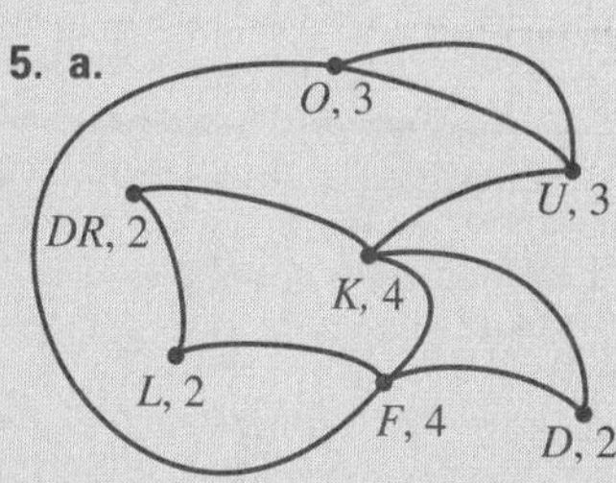

b. Yes. Possible answer: Outside, Foyer, Den, Kitchen, Foyer, Living Room, Dining Room, Kitchen, Utility Room, Outside, Utility Room
c. It is possible to travel a path starting at one vertex with an odd valence and ending at another vertex with an odd valence, only if the graph contains exactly two vertices with odd valences.

6. a.

Point	In	Out
A	2	2
B	1	1
C	1	3
D	1	1
E	2	2
F	1	1
G	2	2
H	1	1
K	3	1

b. No; the invalence must equal the outvalence for every vertex, and this is not true for C or K.
c. Yes; change the arrowhead between K and C. Possible answer: *KGHABCAKCDEGFEK*

Additional Answers Exercises

7. b.

c. Bears should be ranked first since they have three wins, no losses, and a victory over the other team with three wins (Lions). Eagles should be ranked last since they have no wins, three losses, and a loss to the only other team with three losses (Panthers).

Additional Answers A Traveler's Puzzle

Possible Hamilton circuit: Denver, Portland, Los Angeles, Boston, Tampa, Washington D.C., Nashville, St. Louis, New Orleans, Dallas, Denver

7. Five teams in a tournament play each of the other four teams exactly once. The results after a few games are shown in the graph. An arrow from one team to another indicates that the first team defeated the second.

a. Which two teams have the most wins? **Bears, Tigers**

b. Copy the graph and add arrows to show that the Lions beat both the Eagles and the Tigers, while the Panthers lost to the Bears.

c. At the end of the competition, which team do you think should be ranked first, and which team last? Why? **Bears first; Eagles last**

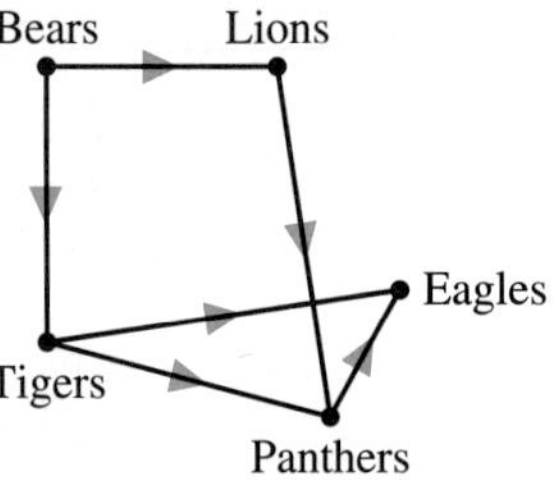

A Traveler's Puzzle

A business traveler located in Denver must travel to each of the cities shown in the graph below. The airline that the traveler prefers to use connects certain pairs of cities, but not all pairs. Is it possible to make a circuit that starts and ends in Denver and visits each of the other cities exactly once?

This kind of circuit is called a *Hamilton circuit* in honor of William Rowan Hamilton (1805–1865), an Irish mathematician who worked on such circuits. In a Hamilton circuit, each *vertex* is visited once while in an Euler circuit each *edge* is traveled once.

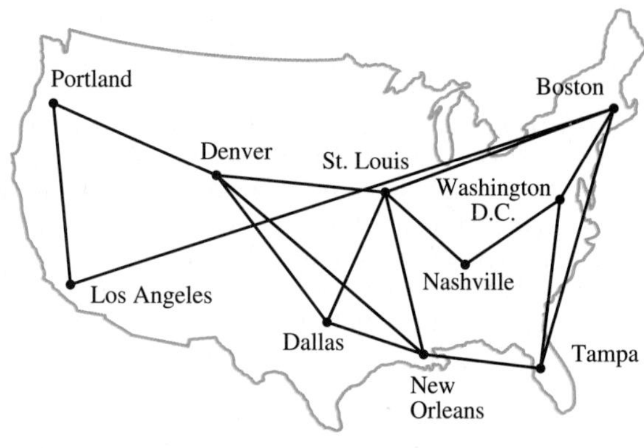

In the graph there are 10 vertices representing the 10 cities. Any other points where two edges intersect are not vertices. The graph has a Hamilton circuit. Can you find it?

The next example is a specific case of the *traveling salesperson problem*.

Example The graph shows the distances between four cities, A, B, C, and D. A traveling salesperson is to leave city A to visit the three other cities exactly once, and return to city A. What is the shortest circuit?

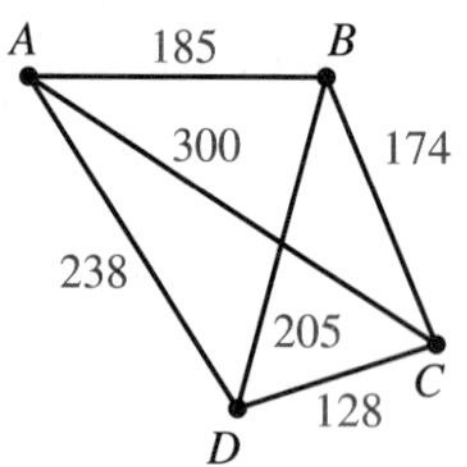

Solution The salesperson can visit any of the 3 cities first, then go to either of the 2 remaining cities, then go to the 1 unvisited city. So there are $3 \times 2 \times 1 = 6$ possible circuits. The total distance for each circuit is shown on the next page.

Circuit	Total Distance
ABCDA	185 + 174 + 128 + 238 = 725
ABDCA	185 + 205 + 128 + 300 = 818
ACBDA	300 + 174 + 205 + 238 = 917
ACDBA	300 + 128 + 205 + 185 = 818
ADBCA	238 + 205 + 174 + 300 = 917
ADCBA	238 + 128 + 174 + 185 = 725

The shortest circuit is *ABCDA*, or its reverse, *ADCBA*.

There is no known general rule for deciding when a Hamilton circuit is possible. For a small number of cities, you can use the trial-and-error method as in the Example. For a larger number of cities, a computer can be programmed to use trial and error. For 10 cities, there are $9! = 9 \times 8 \times 7 \times 6 \times 5 \times 4 \times 3 \times 2 \times 1 = 362{,}880$ possible circuits to consider. A computer can check all of these circuits and tell you the shortest one in less than a second. However, with 15 cities, the computation time is about $1\frac{1}{2}$ minutes, and with 20 cities it is almost 4 years! The exercises will help you to understand why even a fast computer will need so much time.

Although the shortest circuit can be found only by testing all circuits, it is possible to get a very good circuit, even though it might not be the shortest, by using the *nearest neighbor algorithm*. With this method, you travel from each city to the nearest city you haven't yet visited. For the traveling salesperson graph, you would go from *A* to *B* to *C* to *D* and back to *A*. This gives a total distance of 725 mi, which in this case *is* the shortest circuit.

Teaching Note

Suggest that students use their calculators to compute 9!, 15!, and 20! so that they get a sense of these large values.

Exercises

Tell whether a Hamilton circuit is possible for each graph below. If it is possible, name the vertices in the order visited. (More than one answer may be possible.)

1. **No**

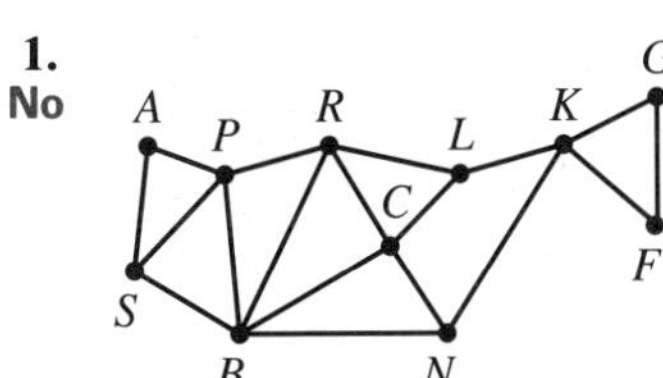

2.

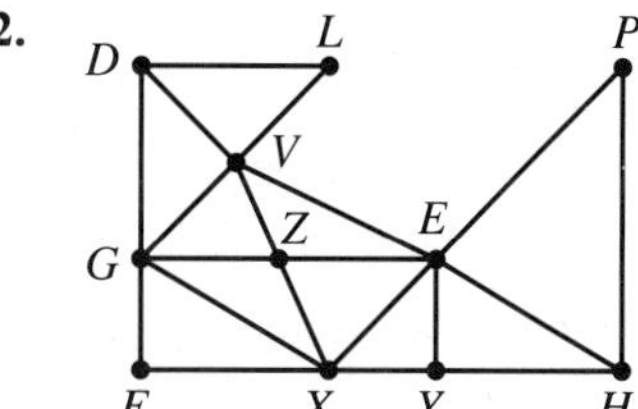

Yes; *LDGFXYHPEZVL*

Group Activity

Have students work together in pairs or small groups on Exercise 3. They can experiment with more rectangular dot patterns to formulate and then support a hypothesis in part (c).

Additional Answers Exercises

3. b. 2-by-3, 2-by-8, 4-by-6
   c. At least one of x or y must be even.
8. a. $25! = 1.551121004 \times 10^{25}$
   b. 25
   c. $25 \cdot 25!$
   d. about 12,296,431,097 years

9. a.

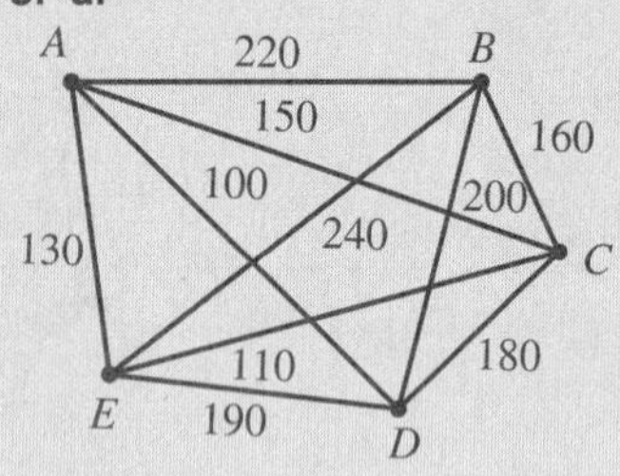

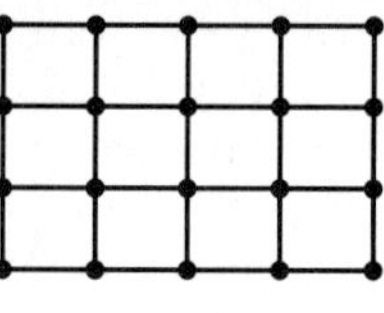

3. a. Is a Hamilton circuit possible for the 4-by-5 rectangular dot pattern shown at the right? **Yes**
   b. For which of these dot patterns is a Hamilton circuit possible: 2-by-3, 2-by-8, 3-by-5, 4-by-6, 5-by-7?
   c. Given an x-by-y dot pattern, what must be true about x and y if a Hamilton circuit is possible?

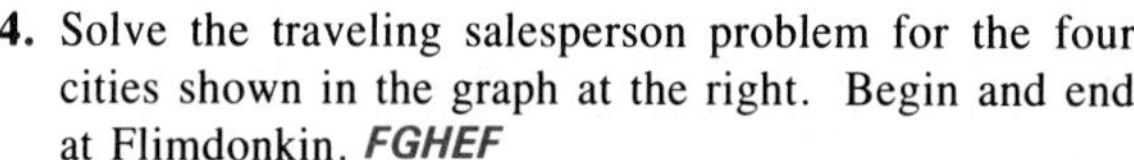

4. Solve the traveling salesperson problem for the four cities shown in the graph at the right. Begin and end at Flimdonkin. ***FGHEF***

Etnola 140 Flimdonkin 130 80 100 200 Huffington 150 Greenbrook

5. Use the nearest neighbor algorithm for the graph in Exercise **4**. Begin and end at Flimdonkin. Does this algorithm give you the shortest circuit? **Yes**

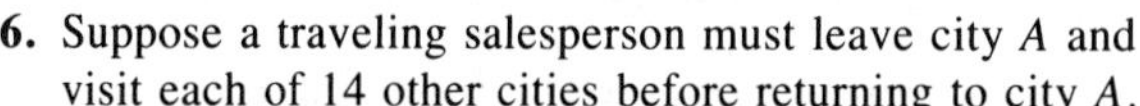

6. Suppose a traveling salesperson must leave city A and visit each of 14 other cities before returning to city A.

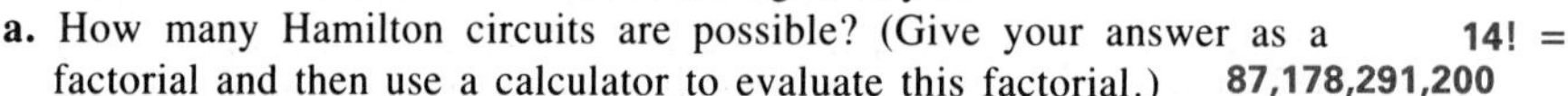

   a. How many Hamilton circuits are possible? (Give your answer as a factorial and then use a calculator to evaluate this factorial.) **14! = 87,178,291,200**
   b. Since each circuit involves adding 15 numbers, there are 14 additions per circuit. So the total number of additions to check all 14! circuits is $14 \times 14!$. If a computer can do one addition per nanosecond (one billionth of a second), how long will it take a computer to compute the distances for all circuits? **about 20 min, 20 s**
7. Suppose a traveling salesperson must leave city A and visit each of 20 other cities before returning to city A.
   a. How many Hamilton circuits are possible? **20! = 2,432,902,008,176,640,000**
   b. How many additions per circuit are there to compute the distance traveled? **20**
   c. What is the total number of additions required to find the distance traveled for each circuit? **$20 \times 20!$ = 48,658,040,163,532,800,000**
   d. How long would it take a computer to do all the additions given in part **c** if the computer can do one billion additions per second? **about 1543 years**
8. Repeat Exercise **7** if 25 cities are to be visited before returning to city A.
9. The table gives the cost of transportation between 5 cities, A, B, C, D, and E.

To/From	A	B	C	D	E
A	—	$220	$150	$100	$130
B	$220	—	$160	$200	$240
C	$150	$160	—	$180	$110
D	$100	$200	$180	—	$190
E	$130	$240	$110	$190	—

   a. Make a graph similar to the one in the Example on page 678 showing these costs.
   b. Use the nearest neighbor algorithm to find a circuit beginning and ending at city A. (Note that the nearest neighbor in this problem means the city which is the least expensive to reach.) ***ADCEBA* = $850**
   c. Find a circuit that is less expensive than the circuit the nearest neighbor algorithm produced. ***AECBDA* = $700**

10. A salesperson in Boston has to make a sales trip to 8 cities and return to Boston. If all flights are made on one airline, the salesperson's frequent-flier mileage will be increased a maximum amount. The table shows which places the airline reaches from each city, indicated by an "X." Make a graph from this information, and decide whether or not only the one airline can be used. **Yes**

	Boston	Albany	Newark	Buffalo	Pittsburgh	D.C.	Raleigh	Charlotte	Memphis
Boston		X	X		X	X	X		
Albany	X		X	X		X			
Newark	X	X			X	X	X	X	
Buffalo		X			X	X			
Pittsburgh	X		X	X			X		X
Washington D.C.	X	X	X	X			X	X	
Raleigh	X		X		X	X		X	
Charlotte			X			X	X		X
Memphis					X			X	

11. There are many real-life problems like the traveling salesperson problem. For example, the telephone company must decide on the most efficient route for a worker to collect the money from public telephones. Give another example. **The postal service collecting mail from mailboxes, or delivering packages to specific destinations.**

Minimizing the Cost of a Network

The graph at the left below gives the costs, in thousands of dollars, of joining several locations with roads. The total cost of all fourteen roads is $179,000. For far less money, just the roads shown at the right below could be built, and people could still get from any location to any other. The cost of this network is $72,000, the sum of the costs for the seven roads. Can you find another network of roads that includes every location and costs less than this?

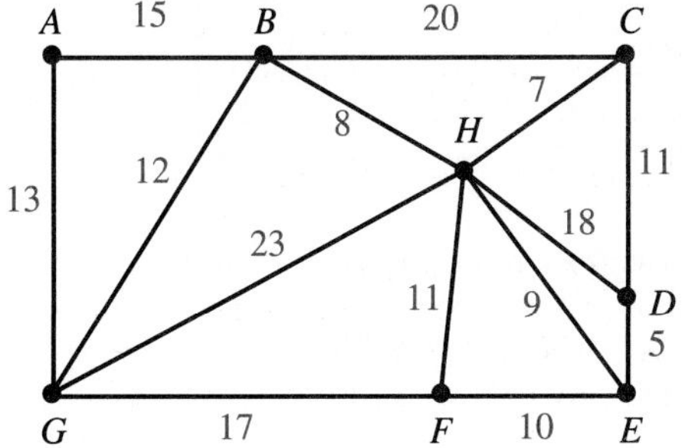

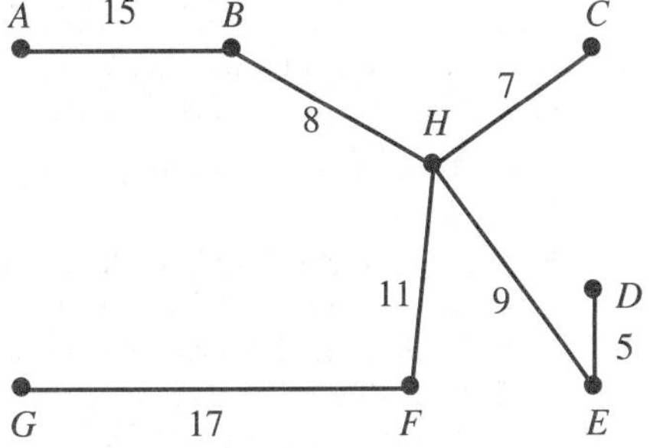

Additional Answers
Exercises

10.

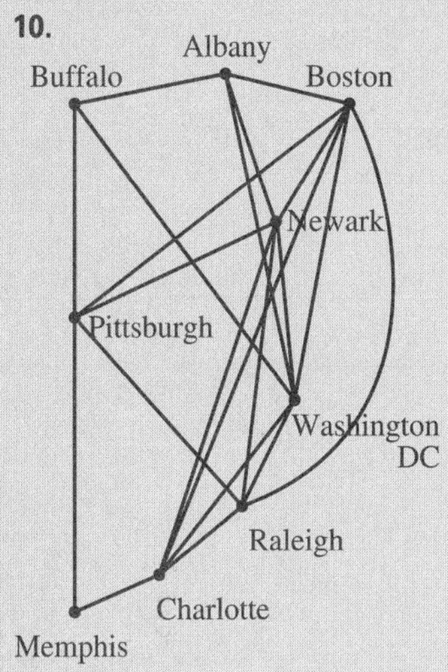

A network of least possible cost that permits travel from each vertex to any other vertex is called a *minimal spanning tree*. It is called "minimal" because the cost is least; it is called "spanning" because the network spans out to touch every vertex; and it is called a "tree" because it resembles a tree with branches.

Finding a Minimal Spanning Tree

1. Build the least expensive road (edge) first.
2. Then build the road next lowest in cost.
3. At each stage, build the road that is next lowest in cost and *does not form any circuit*. Stop when all vertices have been reached.

Example Use the steps above to find the minimal spanning tree for the roads in the left-hand graph on page 681.

Solution

1. The least expensive road is DE.
2. The roads next lowest in cost are HC, HB, HE, and EF.
3. The road next lowest in cost is HF or CD. These roads are not built because they form circuits. Therefore, go to the road next lowest in cost, BG, and finally to GA.

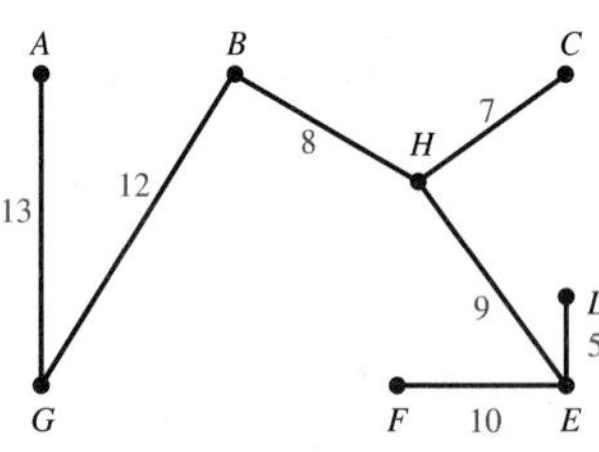

The total cost of the minimal spanning tree is \$5000 + \$7000 + \$8000 + \$9000 + \$10,000 + \$12,000 + \$13,000 = \$64,000.

Exercises

Find a minimal spanning tree for each graph.

1. **32**

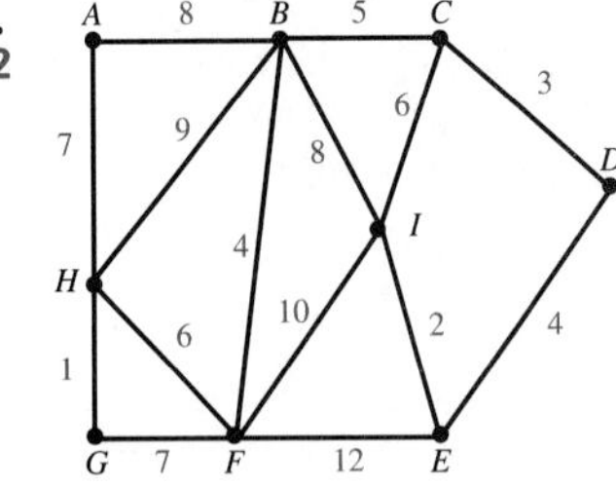

2. **108**

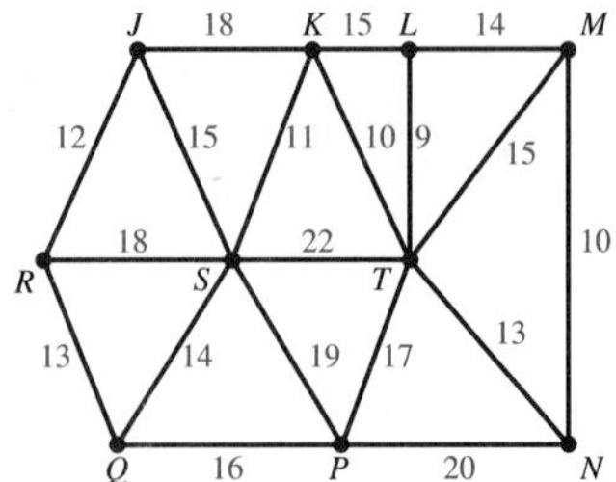

3. If a graph has n vertices, how many edges does a minimal spanning tree have? $\boldsymbol{n - 1}$

Additional Answers
Exercises

1.

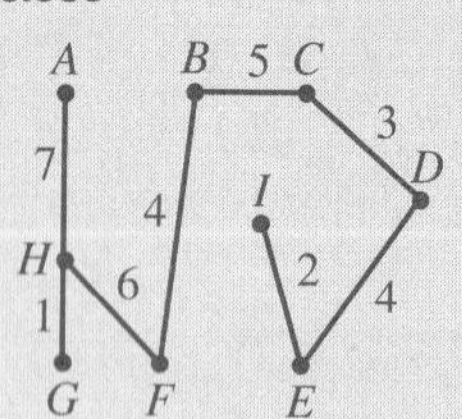

2.

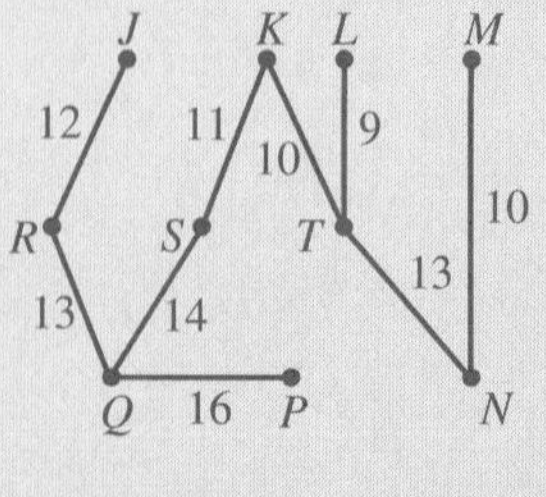

4. **a.** Give an example of a situation in which a person or a company might want to find a *maximal* spanning tree. **To make the greatest profit on options.**
   b. Copy the graph in Exercise **1** and find a maximal spanning tree. Remember that a tree has no circuits.
   c. If the numbers in Exercise **1** indicate cost in hundreds of dollars, find the difference in the costs of the network formed by the *minimal* spanning tree and the network formed by the *maximal* spanning tree. **$3200**

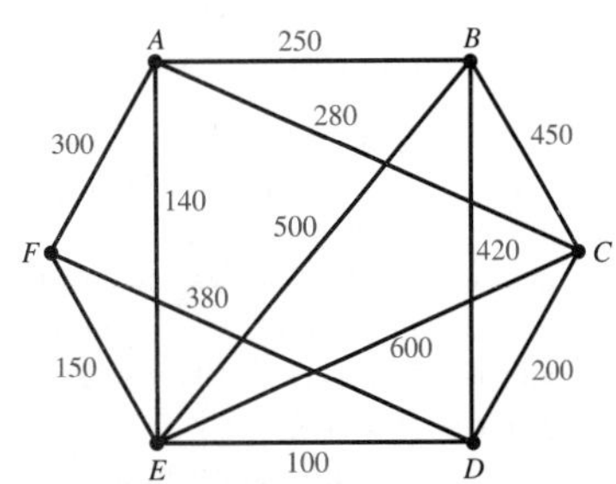

5. The graph at the right shows the dollar costs required to connect various computers (vertices A–F) to form a computer network. What is the minimal cost of a network that links the six computers? **$840**

6. A real estate developer wants to connect locations A, B, C, D, E, and F with roads, keeping costs to a minimum. The table at the right gives estimates of the costs, in thousands of dollars, for building roads between each pair of locations. Draw a graph and find the minimum cost of connecting the six locations. **$50,000**

	A	*B*	*C*	*D*	*E*	*F*
A		18	21	30	15	9
B			10	18	13	22
C				8	12	18
D					16	24
E						11
F						

7. **a.** The graph at the right shows the costs, in thousands of dollars, of building sidewalks between buildings on a college campus. Although a sidewalk between the Administration Building and the college president's home is the most expensive, the president insists that it be built. What then is the minimum cost of joining the locations? **$99,000**
   b. How much more does this cost than the least expensive network that does not include the sidewalk between the Administration Building and the president's home? **$34,000**

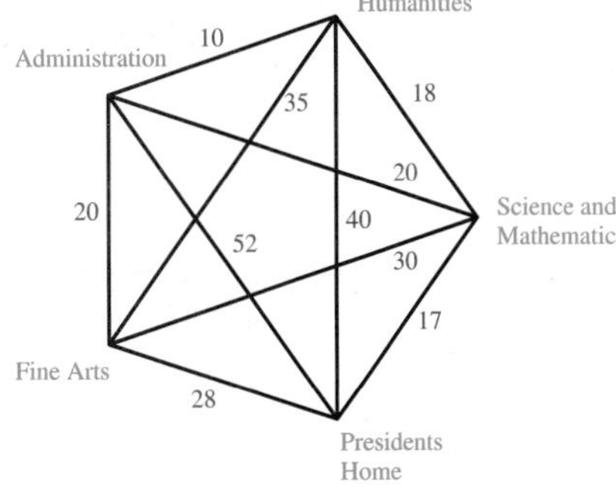

Additional Answers Exercises

4. b.

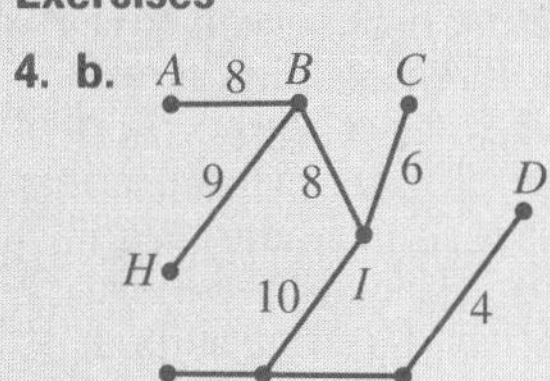

6.

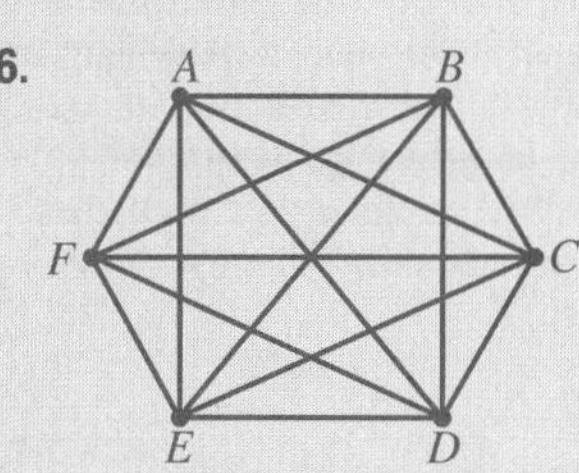

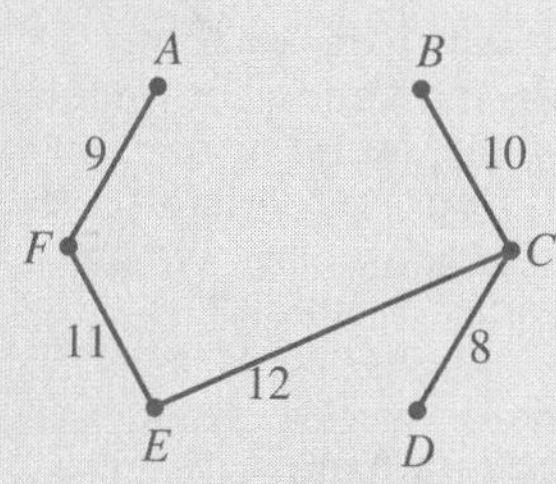

7. a.

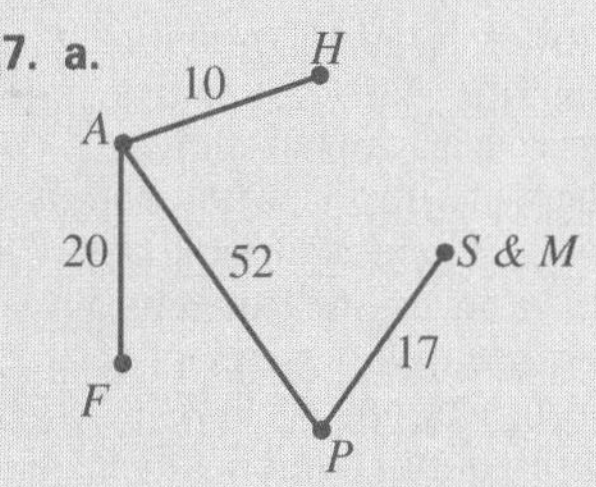

b.

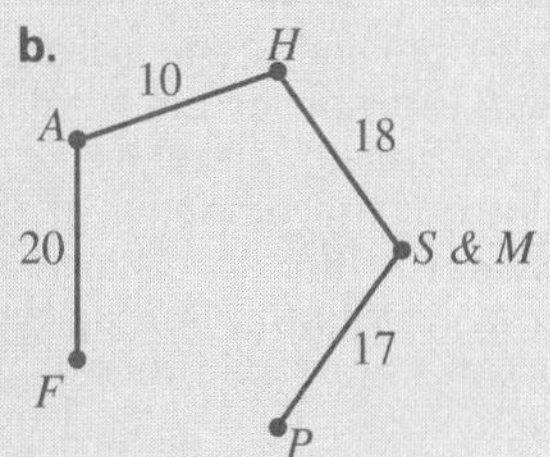

Fractal Geometry

Length of a Coastline

While doing some research on the nature of conflict between nations, the British scientist Lewis F. Richardson (1881–1953) discovered that the common borders between two countries were often given significantly different lengths by each country. After seeing Richardson's work, the French mathematician Benoit Mandelbrot (b. 1924) began to study the geometry of borders and coastlines and other naturally occurring shapes. He named this new branch of geometry **fractal geometry.**

Mandelbrot showed that the lengths of coastlines are virtually unmeasurable because the smaller the unit of measure becomes, the longer the total length becomes. The following steps, diagram, and table show the compass method of measuring the coastline of Great Britain.

Example **The Compass Method of Measuring a Coastline**

1. Set the compass points a distance L_1, called the *ruler length*, apart.
2. Fix one point of the compass at P_0, and swing the compass counterclockwise until it meets the coastline at P_1.
3. Use P_1 as the next fixed point, and swing the compass counterclockwise until it meets the coastline at P_2.
4. Repeat this procedure until you reach a point P_k, with a distance from P_0 that is less than the ruler length.
5. Find the perimeter of polygon $P_0P_1P_2...P_k$ to approximate the length of the coastline. (Estimate P_kP_0.)
6. Repeat this procedure (steps 1–5) for a sequence of decreasing ruler lengths. The result should be a sequence of increasing approximations for the length of the coastline.

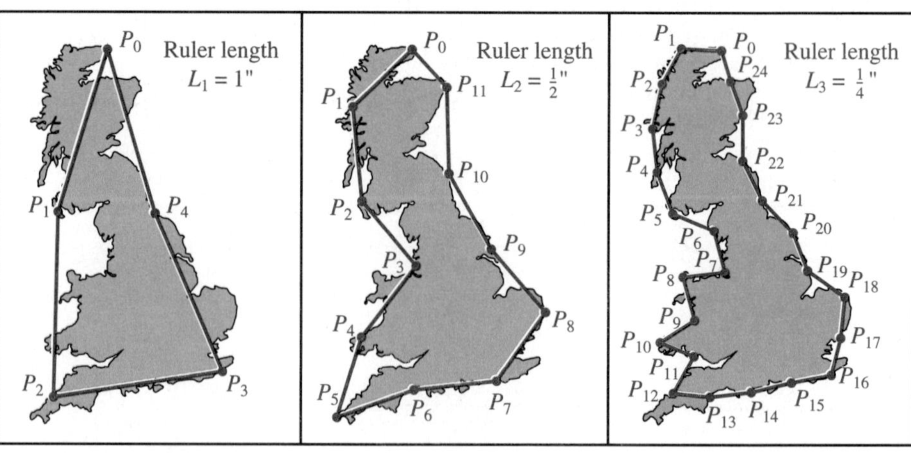

Teaching Note

Richardson observed that if he plotted coastline length versus ruler length on log-log graph paper, the graphs were close to linear. Mandelbrot noticed that these lines had different slopes, and that the more twisted and broken the coastline, the steeper the slope. For a fractal, the slope of such a line is equal to the self-similarity dimension minus 1 (see Making Connections, p. 687).

Communication Skills

The word *fractal* comes from the Latin root *fractus*, the root found in *fraction* and *fragment*. It is also related to *frangere*, which means "to break."

Teaching Note

Another way to measure a coastline is to cover the curve with a transparent piece of graph paper which uses a scale of 1 box per inch and count how many boxes contain parts of the curve. Repeat this with graph paper which has 2 boxes per inch, then 4 boxes per inch, and so on. Make a graph of the number of boxes versus the length of the diagonal of the box used. Plotted on log-log paper, the graph will approximate a straight line.

Ruler Length	Number of Sides	Perimeter
$L_1 = 1$ in.	5	5 in.
$L_2 = \frac{1}{2}$ in.	12	$5\frac{3}{4}$ in.
$L_3 = \frac{1}{4}$ in.	25	$6\frac{1}{4}$ in.

Table 1. Data for the coastline length

Exercises

Measure each coastline using the ruler lengths given. Copy and complete each table. Does the coastline get longer as the ruler length gets shorter?

1. Yes

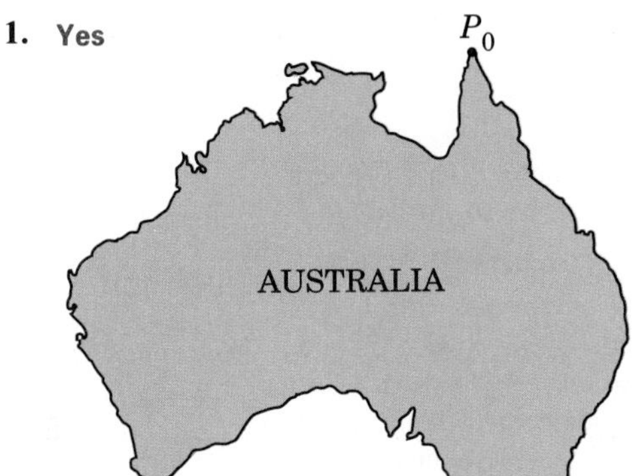

Ruler Length	Number of Sides	Perimeter
$L_1 = 1$ in.	7	7 in.
$L_2 = \frac{1}{2}$ in.	15	$7\frac{1}{4}$ in.
$L_3 = \frac{1}{4}$ in.	30	$7\frac{1}{2}$ in.

2. Yes

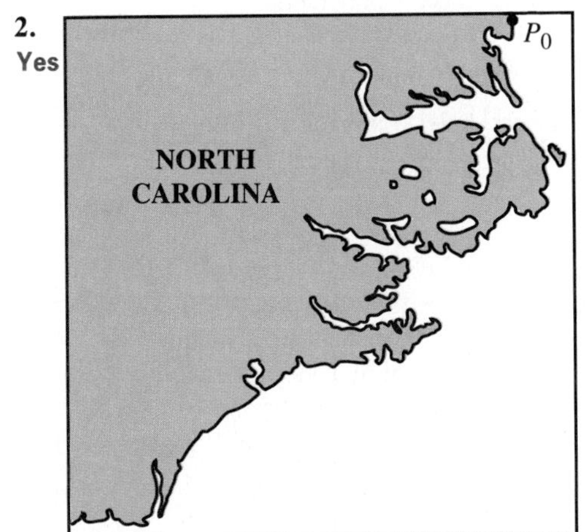

Ruler Length	Number of Segments	Length
$L_1 = 1$ in.	4	$3\frac{1}{2}$ in.
$L_2 = \frac{1}{2}$ in.	12	$5\frac{1}{2}$ in.
$L_3 = \frac{1}{4}$ in.	30	$7\frac{1}{2}$ in.

Exercise Note

When students use the "compass method" to measure coastlines, their results may differ depending on whether they spin the compass around the outside or the inside of the coastline, especially if the coastline has many inlets. You may wish to discuss this with students.

Thinking Skills

Students may argue that they should not be allowed to estimate the length of the last segment of coastline (the piece that is smaller than a full ruler length). Strictly, this is true, since the "compass method" assumes a fixed ruler length as the smallest measurable unit. That is, the ruler length represents the "resolution" at which we can distinguish details. If you wish, you may instruct students to ignore the last segment and consider the length of the coastline to be approximated by a nonclosed figure.

Exercise Note

In Exercise 3, students see how the series of approximations has a limiting value (the circumference of the circle). Like a fractal, the circle is a limit curve, but unlike a fractal, its length is measurable.

Making Connections

If you use the "compass method" to calculate the length of the Koch curve fractal with ruler lengths of 3, 1, $\frac{1}{3}$, and $\frac{1}{9}$ units, the polygons formed will be the first four pre-fractals.

Communication Skills

The term *curve* is used to describe a connected sequence of line segments.

3. Draw a circle of radius 3 in. Use the compass method with rulers 4 in., 2 in., and 1 in. to approximate the circumference as if the circle were a coastline. Create a table of data.

a. Does the approximate length of the circumference increase as the ruler length decreases? **Yes**

b. Will it continue to increase, or will it stop at a certain length? **It will stop before 6π.**

c. How is a circle's circumference different from a jagged coastline's length?
The circumference of a circle has a measurable length; a jagged coastline does not.

How to Generate Fractals

The study of real-world irregular forms led Mandelbrot to explore some curves of infinite length that were easy to generate and describe mathematically, using a process called *iteration*. The process of iteration is used to generate the three examples of fractals that follow.

Example 1 The Koch Curve

1. Draw a segment three units long. This figure is called the *level 0 pre-fractal*, or an *initiator*.

level 0 pre-fractal

2. Trisect the segment and erase the middle third.
3. Construct two sides of an equilateral triangle with vertices at the inner ends of the two remaining pieces. This is called the *level 1 pre-fractal*, or a *generator*. Notice that a segment of length 3 has been replaced by four connected segments, each with length 1 unit. Each of the four segments is $\frac{1}{3}$ as long as the original segment.

level 1 pre-fractal

4. To construct a level 2 pre-fractal, replace every segment of length 1 unit in the level 1 pre-fractal by using the process described in steps 2 and 3.

level 2 pre-fractal

5. To construct a level 3 pre-fractal, replace every segment of length $\frac{1}{3}$ unit in the level 2 pre-fractal by again using the process described in steps 2 and 3.

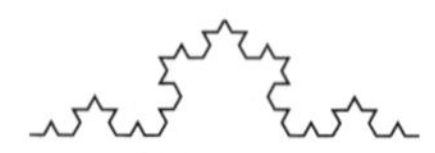

level 3 pre-fractal

As the level n gets larger, the pre-fractal curves approach a curve that is called a *fractal*. The fractal in the example above is called the *Koch*, or "snowflake," *curve*. It was created in 1904 by the Swedish mathematician Helge von Koch. The following table gives the length of an edge, the number of edges, and the total length of each pre-fractal for the Koch curve.

Level Number	Edge Length	Number of edges	Total length
0	3	1	3
1	1	4	4
2	$\frac{1}{3}$	16	$\frac{16}{3} = 5.\overline{3}$
3	$\frac{1}{9}$	64	$\frac{64}{9} = 7.\overline{1}$

Table 2. Data for the Koch curve pre-fractals

The table shows that as the level increases by 1, the edge length decreases by a factor of $\frac{1}{3}$, the number of edges increases by a factor of 4, and the perimeter increases by a factor of $\frac{4}{3}$. This suggests that the lengths of the pre-fractals become larger and larger, and so the total length of the fractal itself is infinite, even though the distance between the endpoints of the fractal is just 3 units.

Example 2 The Sierpiński gasket

Instead of using a segment for an initiator, start with an equilateral triangle. Replace the triangle with three triangles similar to the original with a scale factor of $\frac{1}{2}$. The sequence of pre-fractals is shown below. This fractal is called the *Sierpiński gasket*. Table 3 gives data for pre-fractals of the Sierpiński gasket.

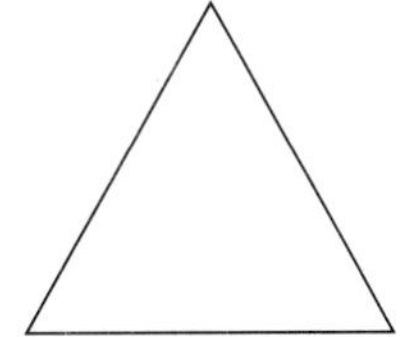
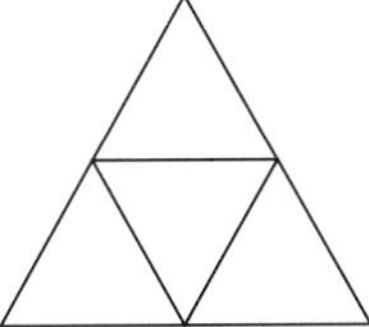
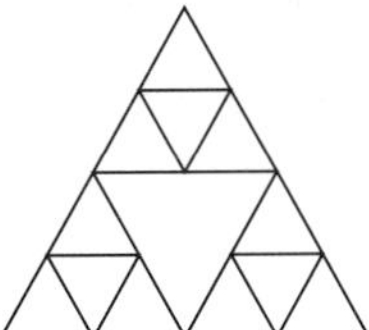

Level Number	Edge Length	Number of edges	Sum of lengths
0	1	3	3
1	$\frac{1}{2}$	9	$\frac{9}{2} = 4.5$
2	$\frac{1}{4}$	27	$\frac{27}{4} = 6.75$
3	$\frac{1}{8}$	81	$\frac{81}{8} = 10.125$

Table 3. Data for the Sierpiński gasket pre-fractals

Making Connections

Mandelbrot's idea of self-similarity dimension (p. 690) is related to Richardson's observations about coastlines (p. 684).

Richardson observed that if P is the perimeter of the coastline when measured with a ruler of length $\frac{1}{R}$, then

$$\log P = k \log R.$$

That is, the log-log graph of P versus R is linear.

On p. 690, we learn that for a self-similar fractal,

$$N = R^D.$$

This implies that

$$N\left(\frac{1}{R}\right) = R^D\left(\frac{1}{R}\right) = R^{D-1}.$$

But the perimeter of the coastline P is equal to $N\left(\frac{1}{R}\right)$, so $P = R^{D-1}$.

Applying logs to both sides, we get

$$\log P = (D - 1)\log R.$$

Therefore, $k = D - 1$, and the slope of the line Richardson found is equal to the Mandelbrot self-similarity dimension minus 1.

Additional Answers
Exercises

1. a.

b.

2. a.

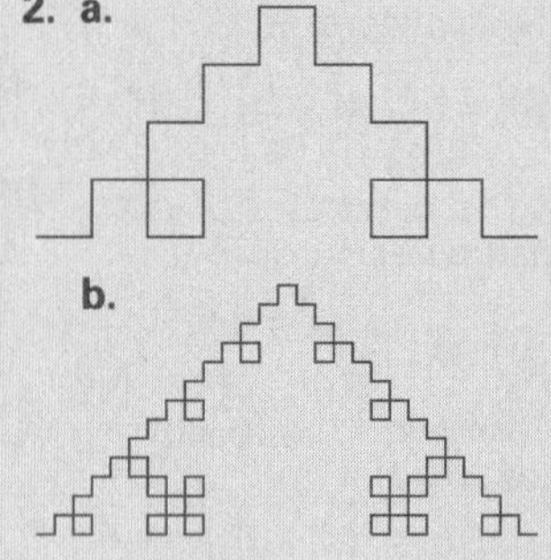

b.

c. For levels 0, 1, 2, 3:
edge lengths $1, \frac{1}{3}, \frac{1}{9}, \frac{1}{27}$;
number of edges 1, 5, 25, 125;
total lengths $1, 1\frac{2}{3}, 2\frac{7}{9}, 4\frac{17}{27}$

3. a.

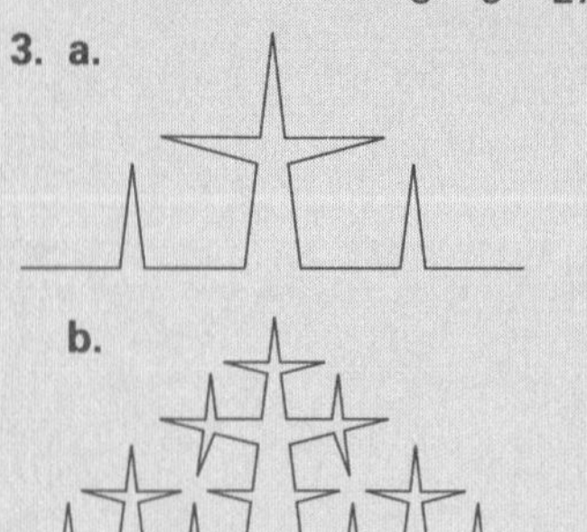

b.

Example 3 The Cantor Set

Use a segment for an initiator and replace it with 2 copies of itself, each $\frac{1}{3}$ as long. This creates a set of disjointed segments that get shorter and shorter with each new level. This fractal is called the *Cantor set* in honor of its creator, Georg Cantor (1845–1918). It is one of the most important sets in mathematics. The data in Table 4 suggests that this fractal has an infinite number of points, yet its length is zero.

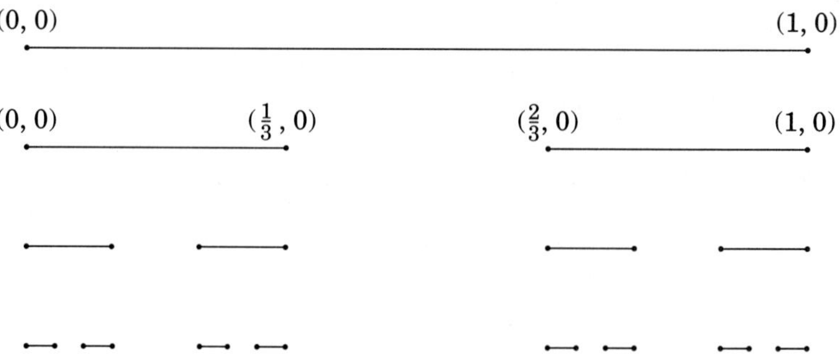

Level Number	Edge Length	Number of edges	Sum of lengths
0	1	1	1
1	$\frac{1}{3}$	2	$\frac{2}{3} = 0.\overline{6}$
2	$\frac{1}{9}$	4	$\frac{4}{9} = 0.\overline{4}$
3	$\frac{1}{27}$	8	$\frac{8}{27} \approx 0.3$

Table 4. Data for the Cantor set pre-fractals

Exercises

In Exercises 1–5, level 1 pre-fractals are shown. Assume that the level 0 pre-fractal for each is a segment of length 1. For each exercise, (a) draw the level 2 pre-fractal, (b) draw the level 3 pre-fractal (or a portion of it), and (c) construct a table showing edge length, number of edges, and total length for pre-fractals 0 through 3.

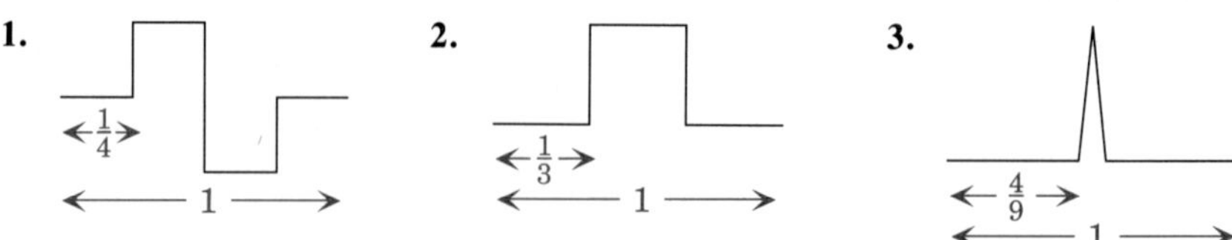

4.

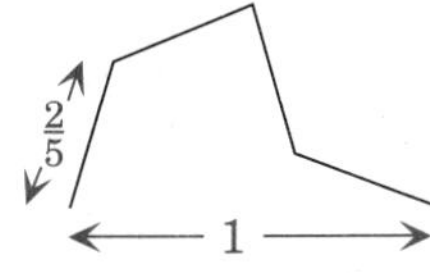

5.

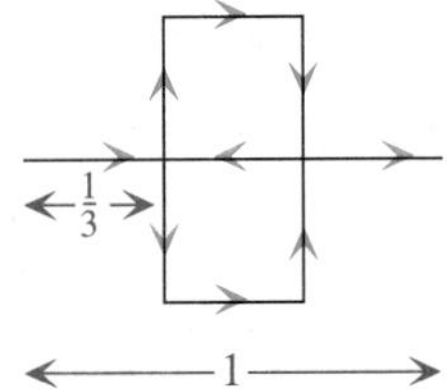

6. Look at the data for the Sierpiński gasket. As the pre-fractal level increases, describe what happens to each of the following.
 a. edge length **b.** number of edges **c.** sum of the lengths

7. Look at the data for the Cantor set. As the pre-fractal level increases, describe what happens to each of the following.
 a. edge length **b.** number of edges **c.** sum of the lengths

8. A variety of interesting fractals can be generated by applying a generator first one way, then another. The level 2 pre-fractals below were created by applying the generator to itself first right side up, then upside down. For each set of pre-fractals below, draw the next level.

a.

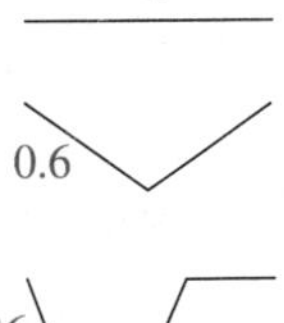

b.

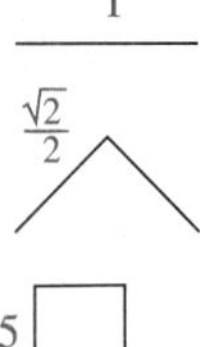

9. Assume that the initiator for the construction of the Cantor set is the segment $\overline{AB}$ where $A = (0, 0)$ and $B = (1, 0)$. The generator then consists of the segments $\overline{AC}$ and $\overline{DB}$ where $C = (\frac{1}{3}, 0)$ and $D = (\frac{2}{3}, 0)$. The endpoints of every pre-fractal are included in the Cantor set. So $(0, 0)$, $(\frac{1}{3}, 0)$, $(\frac{2}{3}, 0)$, and $(1, 0)$ all belong to the Cantor set. Construct the next two pre-fractals, and find 12 more endpoints belonging to the Cantor set.

10. An alternate way to construct the Sierpiński gasket is to start with a solid triangle and delete the mid-triangle, then delete the mid-triangles of the resulting triangles, and so on. Construct a table and show that the resulting fractal is indeed the Sierpiński gasket. Add an area column to your data table and show that the resulting sequence of pre-fractals have areas that approach zero.

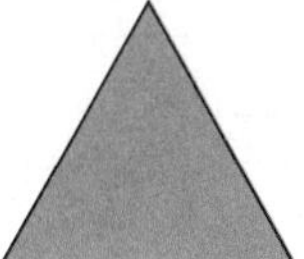
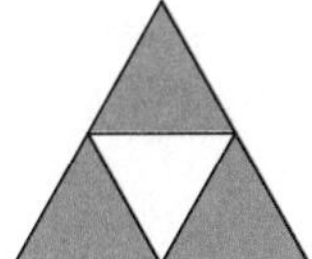

Additional Answers
Exercises

4. a.

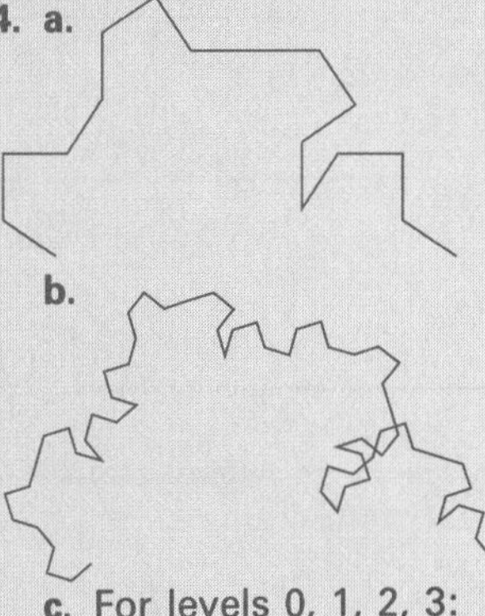

b.

c. For levels 0, 1, 2, 3: edge lengths $1, \frac{2}{5}, \frac{4}{25}, \frac{8}{125}$; number of edges 1, 4, 16, 64; total lengths $1, 1\frac{3}{5}, 2\frac{14}{25}, 4\frac{12}{125}$

6. a. decreases by a factor of $\frac{1}{2}$ **b.** increases by a factor of 3 **c.** increases by a factor of $\frac{3}{2}$

8. a.

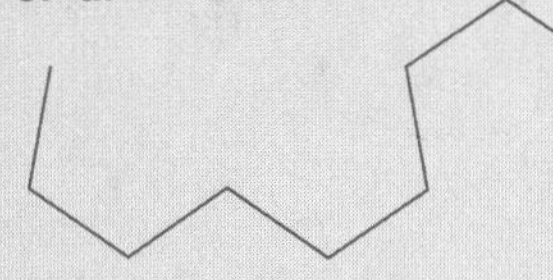

b.

10. The sequence of areas $1, \frac{3}{4}, \frac{9}{16}, \frac{27}{64}, \ldots$ tends to zero.

Additional Answers Exercises

11. The area of the snowflake fractal is $1 + \frac{1}{3} + \frac{4}{27} + \frac{16}{243} + \ldots = 1 + \frac{3}{5} = 1.6$ times the area of the original equilateral triangle.

★ **11.** If you apply the Koch curve construction to an equilateral triangle, you get the sequence of pre-fractals shown below. Calculate the area of each pre-fractal. If you can, calculate the area of the fractal. (*Hint*: Let the area of the original equilateral triangle be 1 square unit.)

Dimension of Fractals

The dimension of a fractal is usually not an integer. Measuring the dimension of a fractal involves finding its *self-similarity dimension*, defined below.

In general, if a shape can be replaced, or covered, by N shapes similar to itself with scale factor $\frac{1}{R}$, then it has **self-similarity dimension** D, where $N = R^D$.

The example below demonstrates the use of this definition with shapes whose dimensions you already know.

Example 1 **a.** A *segment* can be replaced by 2 segments similar to itself with scale factor $\frac{1}{2}$. In this case, $N = 2$ and $R = 2$. Since $2 = (2)^1$, we will say that the segment has self-similarity dimension 1.

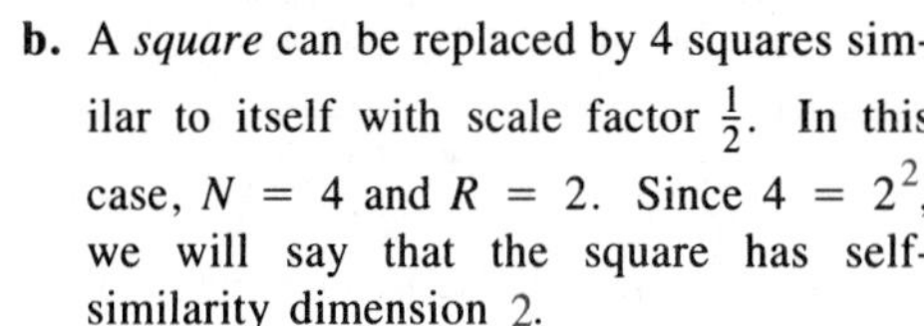

Dimension 1

b. A *square* can be replaced by 4 squares similar to itself with scale factor $\frac{1}{2}$. In this case, $N = 4$ and $R = 2$. Since $4 = 2^2$, we will say that the square has self-similarity dimension 2.

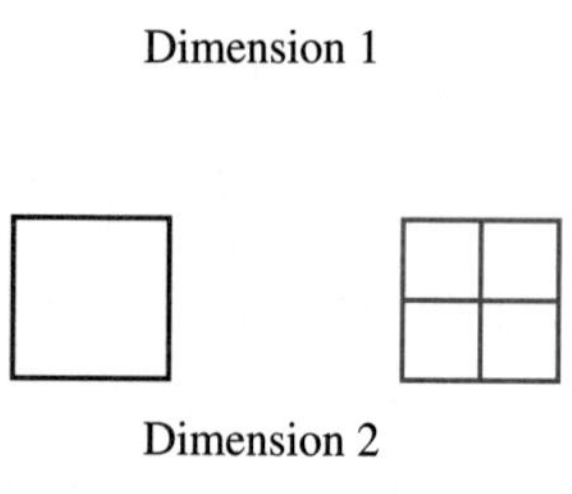

Dimension 2

c. A *cube* can be replaced by 8 cubes similar to itself with scale factor $\frac{1}{2}$. In this case, $N = 8$ and $R = 2$. Since $8 = 2^3$, we will say that the cube has self-similarity dimension 3.

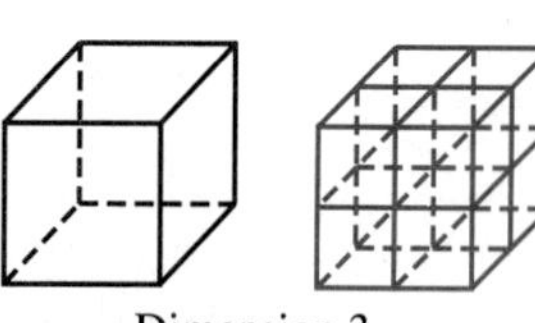

Dimension 3

A fractal will not have dimension of 1, 2, or 3. But you can use your knowledge of shapes having these dimensions to form an idea of the dimension of a fractal. You can estimate that the dimension of a curve (or a coastline) that looks almost like a line will have dimension close to 1, while the dimension of a very jagged curve (or a coastline) that tends toward filling a plane will have dimension closer to 2.

In this next example, the dimension of the Koch curve is found.

Example 2 A Koch curve can be replaced with 4 curves similar to itself with scale factor $\frac{1}{3}$. In this case, $N = 4$ and $R = 3$. Then we must solve $4 = 3^D$, where D is the self-similarity dimension.

Solution 1 Find an approximation by using a calculator and the y^x key.
Since $3^1 = 3 \le 4 \le 9 = 3^2$, $1 \le D \le 2$.
Since $3^{1.2} = 3.73 \le 4 \le 4.17 = 3^{1.3}$, $1.2 \le D \le 1.3$.
Since $3^{1.26} = 3.99 \le 4 \le 4.04 = 3^{1.27}$, $1.26 \le D \le 1.27$.
Thus $D = 1.26$ to two decimal places.

Solution 2 Find a more accurate answer using a calculator and logarithms. If $4 = 3^D$, then $D = \frac{\log 4}{\log 3}$. Using the log key on a calculator, you will find that D is approximately 1.2618595071429.

Fractals are geometric shapes that are often defined by the following ideas of similarity and dimension:
1. the shape is "similar to itself," or self-similar;
2. the shape has self-similarity dimension that is not an integer.

Exercises

Find the self-similarity dimension of the fractals defined in Exercises 1–5 on pages 688–689. Values for N and R are listed below. Express your answer to the nearest hundredth.

1. $N = 8$, $R = 4$ **1.5**
2. $N = 5$, $R = 3$ **1.46**
3. $N = 4$, $R = \frac{9}{4}$ **1.71**
4. $N = 4$, $R = \frac{5}{2}$ **1.51**
5. $N = 9$, $R = 3$ **2**
6. Find the self-similarity dimension of the Sierpiński gasket. First try to predict between which two integers the dimension will be. **$N = 3$, $R = 2$, $D \approx 1.58$**
7. Find the self-similarity dimension of the Cantor set. First try to predict between which two integers the dimension will be. **$N = 2$, $R = 3$, $D \approx 0.63$**
8. Create your own fractal and find its self-similarity dimension. **Answers will vary.**

Teaching Note

Students may not be familiar with logarithms. Sucessive approximations with a calculator will be sufficient. If students know logs, show them this:

$$4 = 3^D$$
$$\log 4 = \log (3^D)$$
$$\log 4 = D \log 3$$
$$D = \frac{\log 4}{\log 3}$$

You may wish to introduce the idea of a geometric sequence if students are unfamiliar with it.

R: 1, a, a^2, a^3, a^4 ... is a geometric sequence with ratio a.

$N = R^D$: 1, a^D, a^{2D}, a^{3D} ... is a geometric sequence with ratio a^D.

Thus, if the rulers form a geometric sequence, then the coastline lengths will also form a geometric sequence. In this case, the graph of N vs. R on log-log paper will be a straight line.

Postulates

Postulate 1 **(Ruler Postulate)**

1. The points on a line can be paired with the real numbers in such a way that any two points can have coordinates 0 and 1.
2. Once a coordinate system has been chosen in this way, the distance between any two points equals the absolute value of the difference of their coordinates. (p. 12)

Postulate 2 **(Segment Addition Postulate)** If B is between A and C, then

$$AB + BC = AC. \quad \text{(p. 12)}$$

Postulate 3 **(Protractor Postulate)** On $\overleftrightarrow{AB}$ in a given plane, choose any point O between A and B. Consider $\overrightarrow{OA}$ and $\overrightarrow{OB}$ and all the rays that can be drawn from O on one side of $\overleftrightarrow{AB}$. These rays can be paired with the real numbers from 0 to 180 in such a way that:

a. $\overrightarrow{OA}$ is paired with 0, and $\overrightarrow{OB}$ with 180.

b. If $\overrightarrow{OP}$ is paired with x, and $\overrightarrow{OQ}$ with y, then $m\angle POQ = |x - y|$. (p. 18)

Postulate 4 **(Angle Addition Postulate)** If point B lies in the interior of $\angle AOC$, then $m\angle AOB + m\angle BOC = m\angle AOC$. If $\angle AOC$ is a straight angle and B is any point not on $\overleftrightarrow{AC}$, then $m\angle AOB + m\angle BOC = 180$. (p. 18)

Postulate 5 A line contains at least two points; a plane contains at least three points not all in one line; space contains at least four points not all in one plane. (p.23)

Postulate 6 Through any two points there is exactly one line. (p. 23)

Postulate 7 Through any three points there is at least one plane, and through any three noncollinear points there is exactly one plane. (p. 23)

Postulate 8 If two points are in a plane, then the line that contains the points is in that plane. (p. 23)

Postulate 9 If two planes intersect, then their intersection is a line. (p. 23)

Postulate 10 If two parallel lines are cut by a transversal, then corresponding angles are congruent. (p. 78)

Postulate 11 If two lines are cut by a transversal and corresponding angles are congruent, then the lines are parallel. (p. 83)

Postulate 12 **(SSS Postulate)** If three sides of one triangle are congruent to three sides of another triangle, then the triangles are congruent. (p. 122)

Postulate 13 **(SAS Postulate)** If two sides and the included angle of one triangle are congruent to two sides and the included angle of another triangle, then the triangles are congruent. (p. 122)

Postulate 14 **(ASA Postulate)** If two angles and the included side of one triangle are congruent to two angles and the included side of another triangle, then the triangles are congruent. (p. 123)

Postulate 15 **(AA Similarity Postulate)** If two angles of one triangle are congruent to two angles of another triangle, then the triangles are similar. (p. 255)

Postulate 16 **(Arc Addition Postulate)** The measure of the arc formed by two adjacent arcs is the sum of the measures of these two arcs. (p. 339)

Postulate 17 The area of a square is the square of the length of a side. ($A = s^2$) (p. 423)

Postulate 18 **(Area Congruence Postulate)** If two figures are congruent, then they have the same area. (p. 423)

Postulate 19 **(Area Addition Postulate)** The area of a region is the sum of the areas of its non-overlapping parts. (p. 424)

Theorems

Points, Lines, Planes, and Angles

1-1 If two lines intersect, then they intersect in exactly one point. (p. 23)

1-2 Through a line and a point not in the line there is exactly one plane. (p. 23)

1-3 If two lines intersect, then exactly one plane contains the lines. (p. 23)

Deductive Reasoning

2-1 **(Midpoint Theorem)** If M is the midpoint of $\overline{AB}$, then
$$AM = \frac{1}{2}AB \text{ and } MB = \frac{1}{2}AB.$$
(p. 43)

2-2 **(Angle Bisector Theorem)** If $\overrightarrow{BX}$ is the bisector of $\angle ABC$, then
$$m\angle ABX = \frac{1}{2}m\angle ABC \text{ and } m\angle XBC = \frac{1}{2}m\angle ABC.$$
(p. 44)

2-3 Vertical angles are congruent. (p. 51)

2-4 If two lines are perpendicular, then they form congruent adjacent angles. (p. 56)

2-5 If two lines form congruent adjacent angles, then the lines are perpendicular. (p. 56)

2-6 If the exterior sides of two adjacent acute angles are perpendicular, then the angles are complementary. (p. 56)

2-7 If two angles are supplements of congruent angles (or of the same angle), then the two angles are congruent. (p. 61)

2-8 If two angles are complements of congruent angles (or of the same angle), then the two angles are congruent. (p. 61)

Parallel Lines and Planes

3-1 If two parallel planes are cut by a third plane, then the lines of intersection are parallel. (p. 74)

3-2 If two parallel lines are cut by a transversal, then alternate interior angles are congruent. (p. 78)

3-3 If two parallel lines are cut by a transversal, then same-side interior angles are supplementary. (p. 79)

3-4 If a transversal is perpendicular to one of two parallel lines, then it is perpendicular to the other one also. (p. 79)

3-5 If two lines are cut by a transversal and alternate interior angles are congruent, then the lines are parallel. (p. 83)

3-6 If two lines are cut by a transversal and same-side interior angles are supplementary, then the lines are parallel. (p. 84)

3-7 In a plane two lines perpendicular to the same line are parallel. (p. 84)

3-8 Through a point outside a line, there is exactly one line parallel to the given line. (p. 85)

3-9 Through a point outside a line, there is exactly one line perpendicular to the given line. (p. 85)

3-10 Two lines parallel to a third line are parallel to each other. (p. 85)

3-11 The sum of the measures of the angles of a triangle is 180. (p. 94)

Corollary 1 If two angles of one triangle are congruent to two angles of another triangle, then the third angles are congruent. (p. 94)

Corollary 2 Each angle of an equiangular triangle has measure 60. (p. 94)

Corollary 3 In a triangle, there can be at most one right angle or obtuse angle. (p. 94)

Corollary 4 The acute angles of a right triangle are complementary. (p. 94)

3-12 The measure of an exterior angle of a triangle equals the sum of the measures of the two remote interior angles. (p. 95)

3-13 The sum of the measures of the angles of a convex polygon with n sides is $(n - 2)180$. (p. 102)

3-14 The sum of the measures of the exterior angles of any convex polygon, one angle at each vertex, is 360. (p. 102)

Congruent Triangles

4-1 **(The Isosceles Triangle Theorem)** If two sides of a triangle are congruent, then the angles opposite those sides are congruent. (p. 135)

Corollary 1 An equilateral triangle is also equiangular. (p. 135)

Corollary 2 An equilateral triangle has three 60° angles. (p. 135)

Corollary 3 The bisector of the vertex angle of an isosceles triangle is perpendicular to the base at its midpoint. (p. 135)

4-2 If two angles of a triangle are congruent, then the sides opposite those angles are congruent. (p. 136)

Corollary An equiangular triangle is also equilateral. (p. 136)

4-3 **(AAS Theorem)** If two angles and a non-included side of one triangle are congruent to the corresponding parts of another triangle, then the triangles are congruent. (p. 140)

4-4 **(HL Theorem)** If the hypotenuse and a leg of one right triangle are congruent to the corresponding parts of another right triangle, then the triangles are congruent. (p. 141)

4-5 If a point lies on the perpendicular bisector of a segment, then the point is equidistant from the endpoints of the segment. (p. 153)

4-6 If a point is equidistant from the endpoints of a segment, then the point lies on the perpendicular bisector of the segment. (p. 153)

4-7 If a point lies on the bisector of an angle, then the point is equidistant from the sides of the angle. (p. 154)

4-8 If a point is equidistant from the sides of an angle, then the point lies on the bisector of the angle. (p. 154)

Quadrilaterals

5-1 Opposite sides of a parallelogram are congruent. (p. 167)

5-2 Opposite angles of a parallelogram are congruent. (p. 167)

5-3 Diagonals of a parallelogram bisect each other. (p. 167)

5-4 If both pairs of opposite sides of a quadrilateral are congruent, then the quadrilateral is a parallelogram. (p. 172)

5-5 If one pair of opposite sides of a quadrilateral are both congruent and parallel, then the quadrilateral is a parallelogram. (p. 172)

5-6 If both pairs of opposite angles of a quadrilateral are congruent, then the quadrilateral is a parallelogram. (p. 172)

5-7 If the diagonals of a quadrilateral bisect each other, then the quadrilateral is a parallelogram. (p. 172)

5-8 If two lines are parallel, then all points on one line are equidistant from the other line. (p. 177)

5-9 If three parallel lines cut off congruent segments on one transversal, then they cut off congruent segments on every transversal. (p. 177)

5-10 A line that contains the midpoint of one side of a triangle and is parallel to another side passes through the midpoint of the third side. (p. 178)

5-11 The segment that joins the midpoints of two sides of a triangle
(1) is parallel to the third side.
(2) is half as long as the third side. (p. 178)

5-12 The diagonals of a rectangle are congruent. (p. 185)

5-13 The diagonals of a rhombus are perpendicular. (p. 185)

5-14 Each diagonal of a rhombus bisects two angles of the rhombus. (p. 185)

5-15 The midpoint of the hypotenuse of a right triangle is equidistant from the three vertices. (p. 185)

5-16 If an angle of a parallelogram is a right angle, then the parallelogram is a rectangle. (p. 185)

5-17 If two consecutive sides of a parallelogram are congruent, then the parallelogram is a rhombus. (p. 185)

5-18 Base angles of an isosceles trapezoid are congruent. (p. 190)

5-19 The median of a trapezoid
(1) is parallel to the bases.
(2) has a length equal to the average of the base lengths. (p. 191)

Inequalities in Geometry

6-1 **(The Exterior Angle Inequality Theorem)** The measure of an exterior angle of a triangle is greater than the measure of either remote interior angle. (p. 204)

6-2 If one side of a triangle is longer than a second side, then the angle opposite the first side is larger than the angle opposite the second side. (p. 219)

6-3 If one angle of a triangle is larger than a second angle, then the side opposite the first angle is longer than the side opposite the second angle. (p. 220)

Corollary 1 The perpendicular segment from a point to a line is the shortest segment from the point to the line. (p. 220)

Corollary 2 The perpendicular segment from a point to a plane is the shortest segment from the point to the plane. (p. 220)

6-4 **(The Triangle Inequality)** The sum of the lengths of any two sides of a triangle is greater than the length of the third side. (p. 220)

6-5 **(SAS Inequality Theorem)** If two sides of one triangle are congruent to two sides of another triangle, but the included angle of the first triangle is larger than the included angle of the second, then the third side of the first triangle is longer than the third side of the second triangle. (p. 228)

6-6 **(SSS Inequality Theorem)** If two sides of one triangle are congruent to two sides of another triangle, but the third side of the first triangle is longer than the third side of the second, then the included angle of the first triangle is larger than the included angle of the second. (p. 229)

Similar Polygons

7-1 **(SAS Similarity Theorem)** If an angle of one triangle is congruent to an angle of another triangle and the sides including those angles are in proportion, then the triangles are similar. (p. 263)

7-2 **(SSS Similarity Theorem)** If the sides of two triangles are in proportion, then the triangles are similar. (p. 263)

7-3 **(Triangle Proportionality Theorem)** If a line parallel to one side of a triangle intersects the other two sides, then it divides those sides proportionally. (p. 269)

Corollary If three parallel lines intersect two transversals, then they divide the transversals proportionally. (p. 270)

7-4 **(Triangle Angle-Bisector Theorem)** If a ray bisects an angle of a triangle, then it divides the opposite side into segments proportional to the other two sides. (p. 270)

Right Triangles

8-1 If the altitude is drawn to the hypotenuse of a right triangle, then the two triangles formed are similar to the original triangle and to each other. (p. 285)

Corollary 1 When the altitude is drawn to the hypotenuse of a right triangle, the length of the altitude is the geometric mean between the segments of the hypotenuse. (p. 286)

Corollary 2 When the altitude is drawn to the hypotenuse of a right triangle, each leg is the geometric mean between the hypotenuse and the segment of the hypotenuse that is adjacent to that leg. (p. 286)

8-2 **(Pythagorean Theorem)** In a right triangle, the square of the hypotenuse is equal to the sum of the squares of the legs. (p. 290)

8-3 If the square of one side of a triangle is equal to the sum of the squares of the other two sides, then the triangle is a right triangle. (p. 295)

8-4 If the square of the longest side of a triangle is less than the sum of the squares of the other two sides, then the triangle is an acute triangle. (p. 296)

8-5 If the square of the longest side of a triangle is greater than the sum of the squares of the other two sides, then the triangle is an obtuse triangle. (p. 296)

8-6 **(45°-45°-90° Theorem)** In a 45°-45°-90° triangle, the hypotenuse is $\sqrt{2}$ times as long as a leg. (p. 300)

8-7 **(30°-60°-90° Theorem)** In a 30°-60°-90° triangle, the hypotenuse is twice as long as the shorter leg, and the longer leg is $\sqrt{3}$ times as long as the shorter leg. (p. 300)

Circles

9-1 If a line is tangent to a circle, then the line is perpendicular to the radius drawn to the point of tangency. (p. 333)

Corollary Tangents to a circle from a point are congruent. (p. 333)

9-2 If a line in the plane of a circle is perpendicular to a radius at its outer endpoint, then the line is tangent to the circle. (p. 333)

9-3 In the same circle or in congruent circles, two minor arcs are congruent if and only if their central angles are congruent. (p. 340)

9-4 In the same circle or in congruent circles,
(1) congruent arcs have congruent chords.
(2) congruent chords have congruent arcs. (p. 344)

9-5 A diameter that is perpendicular to a chord bisects the chord and its arc. (p. 344)

9-6 In the same circle or in congruent circles,
(1) chords equally distant from the center (or centers) are congruent.
(2) congruent chords are equally distant from the center (or centers). (p. 345)

9-7 The measure of an inscribed angle is equal to half the measure of its intercepted arc. (p. 350)

Corollary 1 If two inscribed angles intercept the same arc, then the angles are congruent. (p. 351)

Corollary 2 An angle inscribed in a semicircle is a right angle. (p. 351)

Corollary 3 If a quadrilateral is inscribed in a circle, then its opposite angles are supplementary. (p. 351)

9-8 The measure of an angle formed by a chord and a tangent is equal to half the measure of the intercepted arc. (p. 352)

9-9 The measure of an angle formed by two chords that intersect inside a circle is equal to half the sum of the measures of the intercepted arcs. (p. 357)

9-10 The measure of an angle formed by two secants, two tangents, or a secant and a tangent drawn from a point outside a circle is equal to half the difference of the measures of the intercepted arcs. (p. 358)

9-11 When two chords intersect inside a circle, the product of the segments of one chord equals the product of the segments of the other chord. (p. 362)

9-12 When two secant segments are drawn to a circle from an external point, the product of one secant segment and its external segment equals the product of the other secant segment and its external segment. (p. 362)

9-13 When a secant segment and a tangent segment are drawn to a circle from an external point, the product of the secant segment and its external segment is equal to the square of the tangent segment. (p. 363)

Constructions and Loci

10-1 The bisectors of the angles of a triangle intersect in a point that is equidistant from the three sides of the triangle. (p. 386)

10-2 The perpendicular bisectors of the sides of a triangle intersect in a point that is equidistant from the three vertices of the triangle. (p. 387)

10-3 The lines that contain the altitudes of a triangle intersect in a point. (p. 387)

10-4 The medians of a triangle intersect in a point that is two thirds of the distance from each vertex to the midpoint of the opposite side. (p. 387)

Areas of Plane Figures

11-1 The area of a rectangle equals the product of its base and height. ($A = bh$) (p. 424)

11-2 The area of a parallelogram equals the product of a base and the height to that base. ($A = bh$) (p. 429)

11-3 The area of a triangle equals half the product of a base and the height to the base. ($A = \frac{1}{2}bh$) (p. 429)

11-4 The area of a rhombus equals half the product of its diagonals. ($A = \frac{1}{2}d_1d_2$) (p. 430)

11-5 The area of a trapezoid equals half the product of the height and the sum of the bases. ($A = \frac{1}{2}h(b_1 + b_2)$) (p. 435)

11-6 The area of a regular polygon is equal to half the product of the apothem and the perimeter. ($A = \frac{1}{2}ap$) (p. 441)

Related Formulas In a circle: $C = 2\pi r = \pi d$ $\quad A = \pi r^2$ (p. 447)

11-7 If the scale factor of two similar figures is $a:b$, then
(1) the ratio of the perimeters is $a:b$.
(2) the ratio of the areas is $a^2:b^2$. (p. 457)

Areas and Volumes of Solids

12-1 The lateral area of a right prism equals the perimeter of a base times the height of the prism. (L.A. $= ph$) (p. 476)

12-2 The volume of a right prism equals the area of a base times the height of the prism. ($V = Bh$) (p. 476)

12-3 The lateral area of a regular pyramid equals half the perimeter of the base times the slant height. (L.A. $= \frac{1}{2}pl$) (p. 483)

12-4 The volume of a pyramid equals one third the area of the base times the height of the pyramid. ($V = \frac{1}{3}Bh$) (p. 483)

12-5 The lateral area of a cylinder equals the circumference of a base times the height of the cylinder. (L.A. $= 2\pi rh$) (p. 490)

12-6 The volume of a cylinder equals the area of a base times the height of the cylinder. ($V = \pi r^2h$) (p. 490)

12-7 The lateral area of a cone equals half the circumference of the base times the slant height. (L.A. $= \frac{1}{2} \cdot 2\pi r \cdot l$ or L.A. $= \pi rl$) (p. 491)

12-8 The volume of a cone equals one third the area of the base times the height of the cone. ($V = \frac{1}{3}\pi r^2h$) (p. 491)

12-9 The area of a sphere equals 4π times the square of the radius. ($A = 4\pi r^2$) (p. 497)

12-10 The volume of a sphere equals $\frac{4}{3}\pi$ times the cube of the radius. ($V = \frac{4}{3}\pi r^3$) (p. 497)

12-11 If the scale factor of two similar solids is $a:b$, then
(1) the ratio of corresponding perimeters is $a:b$.
(2) the ratio of the base areas, of the lateral areas, and of the total areas is $a^2:b^2$.
(3) the ratio of the volumes is $a^3:b^3$. (p. 509)

Coordinate Geometry

13-1 **(The Distance Formula)** The distance d between points (x_1, y_1) and (x_2, y_2) is given by $d = \sqrt{(x_2 - x_1)^2 + (y_2 - y_1)^2}$. (p. 524)

13-2 An equation of the circle with center (a, b) and radius r is $(x - a)^2 + (y - b)^2 = r^2$. (p. 525)

13-3 Two nonvertical lines are parallel if and only if their slopes are equal. (p. 535)

13-4 Two nonvertical lines are perpendicular if and only if the product of their slopes is -1. (p. 535)

$$m_1 \cdot m_2 = -1, \text{ or } m_1 = -\frac{1}{m_2}$$

13-5 **(The Midpoint Formula)** The midpoint of the segment that joins points (x_1, y_1) and (x_2, y_2) is the point $\left(\frac{x_1 + x_2}{2}, \frac{y_1 + y_2}{2}\right)$. (p. 544)

13-6 **(Standard Form)** The graph of any equation that can be written in the form $Ax + By = C$, with A and B not both zero, is a line. (p. 548)

13-7 **(Slope-Intercept Form)** A line with the equation $y = mx + b$ has slope m and y-intercept b. (p. 549)

13-8 **(Point-Slope Form)** An equation of the line that passes through the point (x_1, y_1) and has slope m is $y - y_1 = m(x - x_1)$. (p. 553)

Transformations

14-1 An isometry maps a triangle to a congruent triangle. (p. 573)

Corollary 1 An isometry maps an angle to congruent angle. (p. 573)

Corollary 2 An isometry maps a polygon to a polygon with the same area. (p. 573)

14-2 A reflection in a line is an isometry. (p. 577)

14-3 A translation is an isometry. (p. 584)

14-4 A rotation is an isometry. (p. 589)

14-5 A dilation maps any triangle to a similar triangle. (p. 594)

Corollary 1 A dilation maps an angle to a congruent angle. (p. 594)

Corollary 2 A dilation $D_{O,k}$ maps any segment to a parallel segment $|k|$ times as long. (p. 594)

Corollary 3 A dilation $D_{O,k}$ maps any polygon to a similar polygon whose area is k^2 times as large. (p. 351)

14-6 The composite of two isometries is an isometry. (p. 601)

14-7 A composite of reflections in two parallel lines is a translation. The translation glides all points through twice the distance from the first line of reflection to the second. (p. 601)

14-8 A composite of reflections in two intersecting lines is a rotation about the point of intersection of the two lines. The measure of the angle of rotation is twice the measure of the angle from the first line of reflection to the second. (p. 602)

Corollary A composite of reflections in perpendicular lines is a half-turn about the point where the lines intersect. (p. 602)

Constructions

Portfolio Projects

In the side columns you will find a combination of hints, comments, answers, and ideas for extensions.

Chapter 1

1.

2. a.

b.

c. Regular nonagon

3. 60°: regular hexagon
120°: equilateral triangle
180°: line segment
240°: equilateral triangle
300°: regular hexagon

4. 45°: regular octagon
90°: square
135°: eight-pointed star
180°: line segment
225°: eight-pointed star
270°: square
315°: regular octagon

5. Write the turning angle as $(m/n) \cdot 360°$, where m/n is a reduced fraction and $m/n < 1$. If $m = 1$ and $n = 2$, a line segment results. If $n > 2$, there are two cases: (1) If $m = 1$ or $m = n - 1$, the figure is a regular n-gon, or (2) if $1 < m < n - 1$, the figure is an n-pointed star.

Portfolio Projects

To make a portfolio, an artist selects a variety of original work to represent the range of his or her skills. Each of the following projects will give you a chance to create a finished product that you will be proud to add to your geometry portfolio.

The projects will help you develop your ability to present and communicate your ideas. They will also help you develop your problem-solving and reasoning abilities as you make connections between what you know and what is new. Your individual insight and creativity will help shape the mathematics you discover.

Let these projects be springboards for further exploration. Feel free to expand them to include new questions or areas of interest that arise. Most of all, have fun!

Drawing a Star (Chapter 1)

Materials: Ruler, protractor

1. Following the directions given below, draw a five-pointed star. Use a ruler and a protractor.
   a. Mark a starting point on a piece of paper, and choose a starting direction. Move in that direction for 2 in., drawing the line segment that marks your path.
   b. Change your direction by turning clockwise through an angle of $\frac{2}{5}(360°) = 144°$, as shown. Move in the new direction for 2 in., again drawing your path.

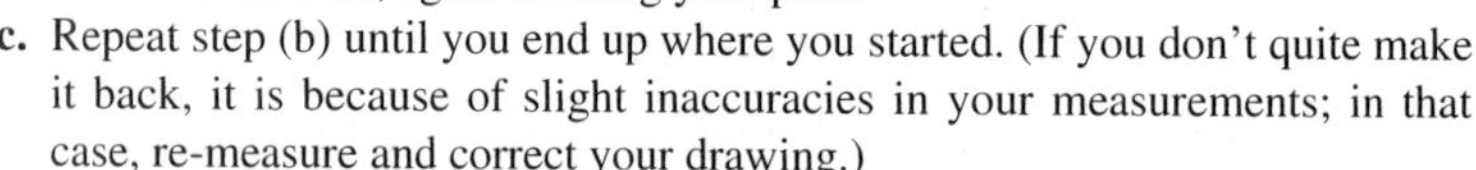

   c. Repeat step (b) until you end up where you started. (If you don't quite make it back, it is because of slight inaccuracies in your measurements; in that case, re-measure and correct your drawing.)
2. What figure do you think will result if you follow the star-drawing directions given above using each of the following turning angles? Draw each figure and see if your predictions are correct.
   a. $\frac{2}{9}(360°) = 80°$ **b.** $\frac{4}{9}(360°) = 160°$ **c.** $\frac{1}{9}(360°) = 40°$
3. Follow the star-drawing directions using a turning angle of $\frac{n}{6}(360°)$ for $n = 1, 2, 3, 4$, and 5. For each turning angle, describe the resulting figure. Do any of these turning angles produce six-pointed stars?
4. Analyze the shapes produced by following the star-drawing directions using turning angles of $\frac{n}{8}(360°)$ for $n = 1, 2, 3, \ldots, 7$.
5. Based on your work in Exercises 1–4, write a paragraph in which you discuss how to predict the shape that will result from following the star-drawing directions using any turning angle expressed as a fraction times 360°.

Territorial Monkeys (Chapter 2)

Materials: Ruler, protractor, compass

Imagine that scientists have placed two small troops of territorial monkeys in a rectangular enclosure containing two trees. By means of threat and some physical conflict, each troop stakes out its territory, with one of the trees serving as the troop's home tree. The final result is that each troop's territory is the set of all points inside the enclosure that are nearer to its home tree than to the other troop's home tree.

1. Make a diagram of the enclosure and the two trees. Figure out where to place the boundary between the two territories, making measurements with a ruler if you need to. You may also wish to use a protractor and/or a compass. Describe an efficient method for finding and drawing the boundary.
2. Suppose that a third home tree and a third monkey troop are added to the enclosure. Assuming that territories for three troops are established in the same way as for two troops, draw the new boundary. Describe a systematic method of determining the location of the boundary. Apply your method to one or two other arrangements of three trees. Write down anything interesting you notice about the shape of the boundary.
3. Extend your method to four or more trees. Draw at least two examples.

Tessellations (Chapter 3)

Materials: Ruler, protractor, compass

A *tessellation* is a repeating pattern of one or more shapes that covers the plane completely without any overlap. Tessellations often use regular polygons. A simple tessellation of squares is shown, along with a more complex tessellation that uses regular hexagons and dodecagons (12-gons), as well as squares.

Because a tessellation is a repeating pattern, the same number and type of polygons must meet at each vertex. In both tessellations shown above, notice that the sum of the angles that share each vertex is 360°, as it must be if the polygons are to cover the plane completely without any overlap.

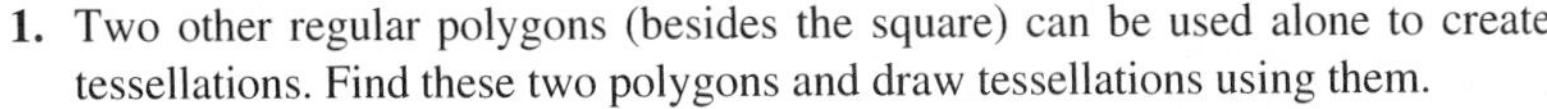

1. Two other regular polygons (besides the square) can be used alone to create tessellations. Find these two polygons and draw tessellations using them.
2. Create several other tessellations that use a combination of regular polygons. Remember, you must find a *repeating* pattern that covers the plane.
3. Not all tessellations use regular polygons. Draw a tessellation that uses a *scalene* triangle.

Chapter 2

Students have not yet learned the theorem that states that points on the perpendicular bisector of a segment are equidistant from the endpoints of the segment (see p. 153). Exercise 1 should help them to discover and describe this fact, though they might not use the term "perpendicular bisector."

Encourage students who have trouble with Exercise 2 to approach it systematically. Determine troop 1's territory by first eliminating all points closer to troop 2's tree. Then, of the remaining points eliminate all points closer to troop 3's tree. Finally, divide the space outside troop 1's territory between troop 2 and troop 3. Students should find that the three boundary lines meet at a point, which is the circumcenter (see p. 387) of the triangle that joins the three trees.

Chapter 3

Students may want to cut one copy of each regular polygon out of cardboard and then make their tessellations by repeatedly tracing these templates. The regular polygons must all have the same side length.

Students can develop their tessellations into art works to display in the classroom.

1. Equilateral triangles, regular hexagons
2. There are 8 semiregular tessellations that use 2 or more regular polygons.
3. 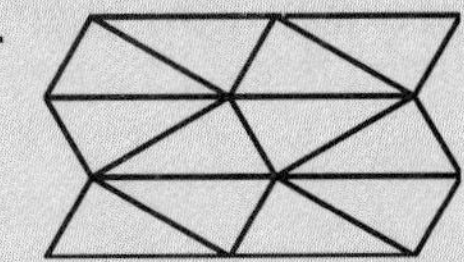

Chapter 4

1. Not necessarily ≅
2. a. Not necessarily ≅
   b. Congruent
   c. Not necessarily ≅
   d. Congruent
3. Other methods that work include ASASA and SSAAA.

Chapter 5

Numbers on the diagram below refer to these steps for drawing a checkerboard from one-point perspective:

1. Draw the board's front horizontal edge. Divide it into eight equal segments.
2. Choose a vanishing point. Join it to the endpoints of the equal segments.
3. Draw the board's back horizontal edge—you can vary the sense of depth with this line's position.
4. Draw the diagonal.
5. Draw a horizontal line through each intersection point of the diagonal and the lines drawn in Step 2.

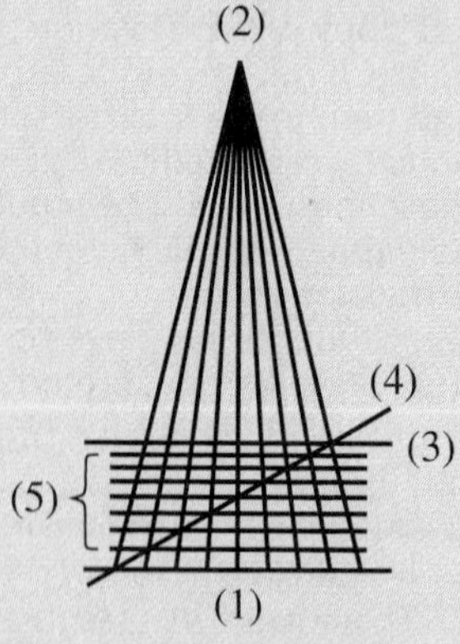

To finish the checkerboard, erase the diagonal and the extra lines behind the board. Color the squares.

Congruence of Quadrilaterals (Chapter 4)

Use the following exercises to investigate methods of proving congruence of quadrilaterals similar to the ASA, SAS, SSS congruence postulates for triangles.

1. Does the SAS method of proving congruence work for quadrilaterals? That is, if two quadrilaterals $ABCD$ and $EFGH$ have $\overline{AB} \cong \overline{EF}$, $\angle ABC \cong \angle EFG$, and $\overline{BC} \cong \overline{FG}$, must the two quadrilaterals be congruent? If so, give a proof. If not, draw a diagram that shows that the method does not work.
2. For each of the following possible methods of proving congruence of quadrilaterals, either prove that the method works, or draw a picture that shows it does not imply congruence. As with triangles, the parts represented by the letters in each abbreviation are consecutive as you move in one direction around the quadrilateral.

   a. SASA **b.** SASAS **c.** SSSS **d.** SASSS
3. Find at least two more methods of proving congruence of quadrilaterals. Prove that your methods work.

Perspective Drawing (Chapter 5)

The diagram at the right is a view of a checkerboard. Although you know that a checkerboard is composed of congruent squares, here the squares appear distorted in both size and shape. The checkerboard has been drawn *in perspective*, giving the figure a sense of depth.

Research and write a report on perspective drawing. The following suggestions may help you decide what to include in your report.

- Explain what is meant by a *vanishing point*.
- The checkerboard shown above is drawn from a *one-point* perspective, while the cereal box shown at the right is drawn from a *two-point* persepective. Discuss the differences between one- and two-point perspective drawing.

- Describe how to draw the checkerboard shown above from a one-point perspective. Use your knowledge of parallel lines and transversals to explain why the method works. That is, why do the 64 quadrilaterals represent 64 *congruent squares*?
- Illustrate your report with pictures you have drawn from one- or two-point perspective and describe the steps involved in drawing them.
- Give a brief history of the use of perspective drawing in art.

Elliptic Geometry (Chapter 6)

Read the *Extra*, pages 233–234, on non-Euclidean geometry. As discussed there, the surface of a sphere provides a model of elliptic geometry: a point is any point on the surface of the sphere, and a line is a *great circle* of the sphere, that is, the intersection of the surface of the sphere and a plane that passes through the center of the sphere (see the diagram on page 234).

The following exercises will help you investigate some of the differences between Euclidean geometry and elliptic geometry.

1. Use the diagram at the right to explain why the following theorem from Euclidean geometry is not true in elliptic geometry.

   Theorem 3-9: Through a point outside a line, there is exactly one line perpendicular to the given line.

2. Decide whether the given postulate or theorem of Euclidean geometry appears to be true or false in elliptic geometry. Support your conclusion about each statement with one or more diagrams.
   a. *Postulate 6*: Through any two points there is exactly one line.
   b. *Theorem 3-7*: In a plane two lines perpendicular to the same line are parallel.
   c. *Theorem 3-11*: The sum of the measures of the angles of a triangle is 180°.
   d. *Theorem 6-1*: The measure of an exterior angle of a triangle is greater than the measure of either remote interior angle.

Human Similarity (Chapter 7)

Materials: Tape measure

In this project you will investigate the following conjectures.

(1) Human beings in the same broad age group (such as small children, adolescents, or adults) are approximately similar in basic shape. For example, the ratio of head size to height is about the same for most adults.

(2) Human beings in different broad age groups are not similar. For example, an infant's arms are shorter relative to its height than are an adult's arms.

1. Plan and carry out an investigation to test the conjectures stated above. For example, you could measure height, length of head, and length of arms for members of several age groups, such as infants (under 6 months), 2–5 year-old children, students your own age, and adults. Then develop a method of using the data you gather to draw conclusions about conjectures (1) and (2).
2. Design a report to present your data, your methods, and your conclusions. Include a scale drawing of an average person in each group. Draw all of your diagrams the same height, adjusting the relative size of heads and arms to reflect the average ratios of lengths that you found. See if people outside of your class can identify the ages of the people you have drawn.

Chapter 6

Visualizing relationships between lines in elliptic geometry may be easier for students if they have access to a globe or ball on which they can draw. Also, large rubber bands can be stretched around a globe to represent great circles.

You may want to point out to students that this is a model of *two-dimensional* elliptic geometry—the surface of the sphere corresponds to a *plane* in Euclidean geometry.

Note that the geometry of Earth's surface is elliptic. You may want to ask students why we study and use primarily Euclidean geometry. Under what circumstances would it be appropriate to use elliptic geometry?

2. All are false. In part (c), you may want to ask students if they can find an upper, as well as a lower, limit to the sum of the angles of a triangle. ($180° < S < 540°$—the larger the angle sum S, the closer the triangle is to being a full hemisphere.)

Chapter 7

Results may vary. The chart below shows approximate ratios you might expect to find in a large population sample. Note that while the ratio of head length to height changes gradually over an individual's years of growth, the ratio of arm length to height remains fairly constant after infancy.

age (yrs)	head:hgt	arm:hgt
under 1	1:3 to 1:4	1:3
2–5	1:5	2:5
11–14	1:6	2:5
over 16	1:7	2:5

Chapter 8

In order to give students a concrete understanding of how the same object can appear to be in two different places, have them consider the following phenomenon:

Hold up your index finger and stretch your arm out in front of you at shoulder height. By alternately closing your left and right eyes, look at your finger first with one eye and then with the other. You will see the position of your finger shift relative to the background. Your finger seems to move because your two eyes are viewing it from slightly different positions.

1. $AC = AB \tan B$
2. The shortest measurable distance is $12 \tan 1° \approx 0.21$ in., and the longest measurable distance is $12 \tan 89° \approx 687.48$ in., or about 57.29 ft.
3. See *parallax* in most general and science encyclopedias.

Chapter 9

1. Since the chords are all the same length, they are all the same distance d from the center of the circle. d is the length of the perpendicular segment joining the center of the circle to a chord; therefore, each chord is tangent to the concentric circle with radius d. Thus, the chords outline a circle of radius d.
2. As the length of the chords increases, the inner circle becomes smaller. Drawing all the chords produces a set of concentric circles. Connecting n to $2n$ gives a heart-shaped *cardiod.*

Rangefinders and Stellar Parallaxes (Chapter 8)

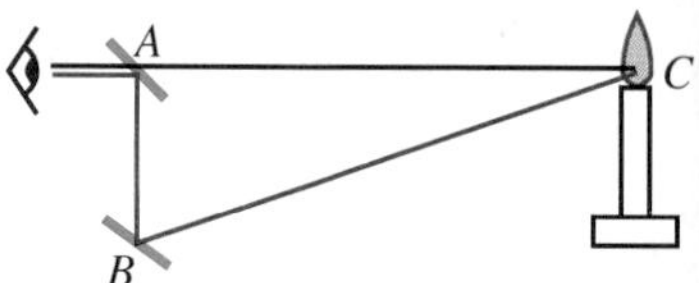

A *rangefinder* is an instrument used to find the distance from a viewer to an object. The rangefinder modeled in the diagram has a mirror at B and a semi-transparent mirror at A that allows light from the distant object to combine with light from mirror B. The length AB is fixed.

An operator looking through the eyepiece at A sees two images of the candle—one from the light following the straight-line path from C to A, and the other from light traveling along the angled path from C to B to A. The operator adjusts the angle of the mirror at B until the two images of the candle appear to merge. The distance to the candle can then be read from a scale on the instrument.

1. Show how to calculate AC from the fixed distance AB and the measure of $\angle B$.
2. Suppose that $AB = 12$ inches. Assuming you can measure $\angle B$ to the nearest degree, for what distances is the rangefinder is useful?
3. Read about *stellar parallax* and write a description, with diagrams, of how astronomers can use a stellar parallax to measure the distance from Earth to a nearby star. In what ways is this method of finding distances to stars similar to the method of finding distances using a rangefinder?

Chord Designs (Chapter 9)

Materials: You will need some or all of the following items: compass, protractor, ruler, colored pens or pencils, cardboard, tacks, and string.

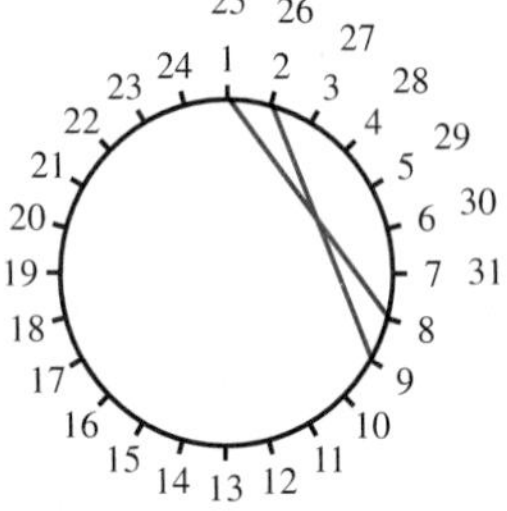

1. Divide a large circle into 24 equal arcs and number their endpoints consecutively, as shown. Draw a chord joining points 1 and 8 and a second chord joining points 2 and 9. Continue this pattern, drawing chords until each point n is connected to point $n + 7$.
2. What shape is outlined by all the intersecting chords? Explain why.
3. Experiment with the chord-drawing process. For example, you could change the number of points between points joined by a chord. Or you could draw *all* possible chords joining the points. Or try drawing chords by connecting point n to point $2n$.
4. Choose one of the designs you have created and develop it into an art piece. You may want to emphasize different aspects of the design by varying the colors of the chords. You might make your design into *string art*: draw the circle on a piece of cardboard, use tacks to mark the points around the circle, and tie string (of different colors if you like) to the tacks to make the chords.

The Problem of Appolonius (Chapter 10)

Materials: Compass and straightedge

In the third century B.C., the Greek geometer Appolonius gave a complete solution of the following famous construction problem:

Given three coplanar circles, construct a fourth circle tangent to all three.

1. Three coplanar circles have up to *eight* circles tangent to all three. In the diagram, the red circle is tangent to the three black circles. Copy the diagram and sketch (don't construct) as many other circles as you can that appear to be tangent to all three black circles.

2. Draw three *congruent* circles whose centers are not collinear. Devise a compass and straightedge construction of two different circles tangent to the three congruent circles. Explain the steps of your construction. Demonstrate that your method works for other configurations of three congruent circles.

Covering the Plane (Chapter 11)

In this project you will investigate the percentage of the plane that can be covered by different arrangements of non-overlapping circles.

1. The diagram below shows a *square arrangement* of congruent circles.
   a. Given that the radius of each circle is 1 unit, find the area of the small square and the area of the portion of the small square that is covered by the circles. Then find the percentage of the small square's interior that is covered by the circles. Repeat these calculations for the larger square.

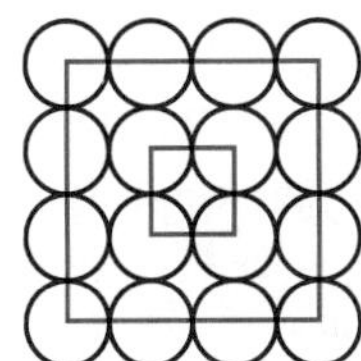

   b. Repeat part (a) given that the radius of each circle is 2 units.
   c. Make a conjecture about the percentage of the plane that would be covered if the square arrangement of circles extended without end in all directions.
2. Find the percentage of the plane covered by a *hexagonal arrangement* of congruent circles, as shown at the right. Show that you get the same percentage regardless of the radius of the circles. How does this percentage compare with the percentage of the plane covered by the square arrangement of circles in Exercise 1?

3. Suppose you fit one smaller circle into each existing gap in the square and hexagonal arrangements shown above. Find the largest percentage of the plane that can be covered in each case. Show your method.

Chapter 10

1. Students may want to use a computer with drawing software. Encourage students to consider every possible way that a circle can be tangent to the three given circles. As long as three given circles are mutually external, there will be eight circles tangent to all three.
2. Let the congruent circles have centers A, B, and C, and radius r. Follow Construction 10 on p. 393 to locate the circumcenter O of $\triangle ABC$. Then the circles with center O and radii $OA + r$ and $|OA - r|$ will be tangent to the three congruent circles.

Chapter 11

Be sure students show and explain their work. This project can lead to a discussion of the limiting process hinted at in Exercise 3.

1. a. Small square: 4; π; about 78.5%
   Larger square: 9π; 36; about 78.5%
   b. Small square: 16; 4π; about 78.5%
   Larger square: 144; 36π; about 78.5%
   c. about 78.5%
2. $\frac{3r^2\pi}{6r^2\sqrt{3}} \approx 0.907$; about 90.7%. The hexagonal arrangement covers a much higher percentage of the plane.
3. Square arrangement: about 92.0%; hexagonal arrangement: about 91.4%. Note that the square arrangement gives the higher percentage now.

Chapter 12

1.

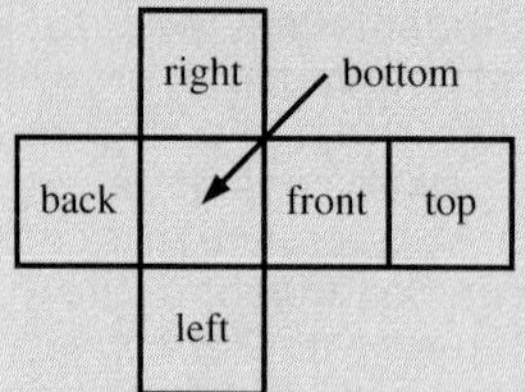

2. Cut along the red edges:

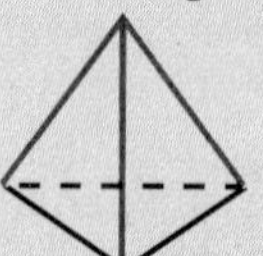

Unfolded tetrahedron:

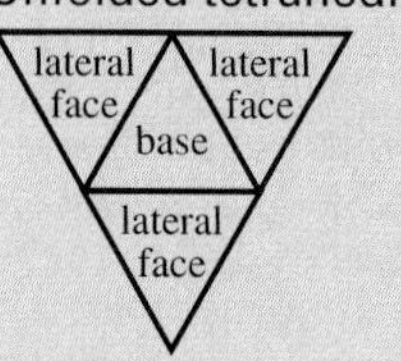

3. Octahedron:

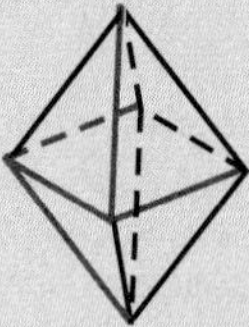

Icosahedron (left)
Dodecahedron (right)

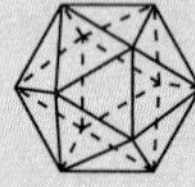
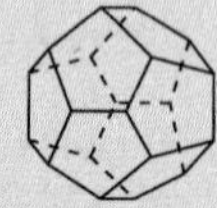

If you cut the octahedron shown above along the red edges, it will unfold to look like the figure below.

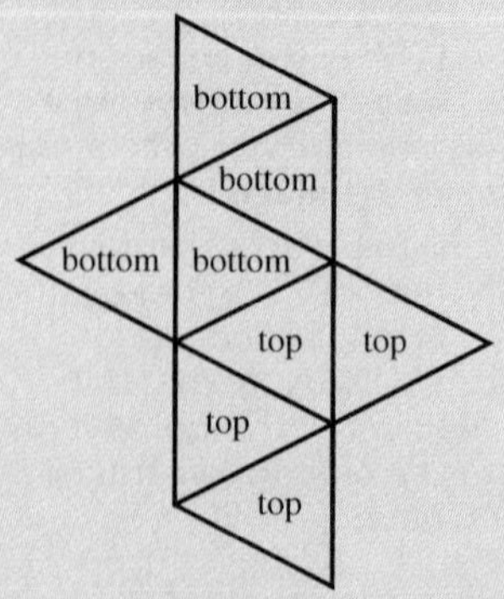

Regular Polyhedra (Chapter 12)

Materials: Ruler, protractor, construction paper, scissors, tape

A regular polyhedron is a solid figure whose faces are congruent regular polygons, with the same number of polygons joined at each vertex (or corner). One example of a regular polyhedron is a cube. If the cube shown at the right is cut along each red edge, it will unfold into the two-dimensional cross shape shown next to it.

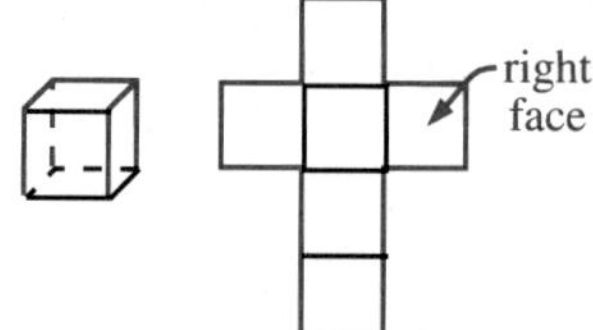

1. Copy the diagram of the unfolded cube and label the other faces: top, bottom, front, back, and left. Then draw the cross-shaped figure on a piece of construction paper, cut it out, and fold it into a cube. Tape the edges together.
2. A regular *tetrahedron*, as shown at the right, is made of four equilateral triangles. Copy the tetrahedron and mark the edges you would cut to unfold it. Sketch what it will look like unfolded. Check your sketch by making a tetrahedron out of a piece of construction paper.

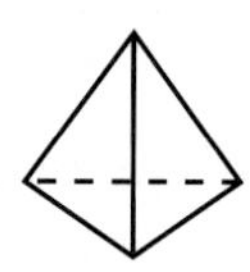

3. In a book, find pictures of the three other regular polyhedra: the *octahedron* (8 equilateral triangles), the *icosahedron* (20 equilateral triangles), and the *dodecahedron* (12 pentagons). Repeat Exercise 2 for the octahedron.

Pixel Lines (Chapter 13)

Materials: Graph paper with a fine grid (at least 16 squares per inch)

A computer screen is made up of small squares called *pixels*, which are used to display all graphics and text. The pixels are arranged in a rectangular grid. If you were to magnify a "line" displayed on a computer screen, you would see that it is actually a jagged collection of pixels, rather than a smooth, straight line. Computers use the three rules given below to create a jagged approximation of a line that looks as smooth as possible.

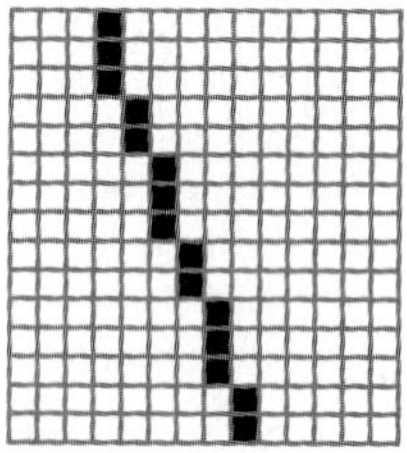

(1) Every pixel on a line, except for the first and last, touches *exactly two* other pixels on the line, either vertically, horizontally, or diagonally.

(2) A line is made by repeating a pattern of horizontal or vertical "runs" of pixels.

(3) The number of pixels in the different "runs" used in one copy of the pattern must be as close to equal as possible.

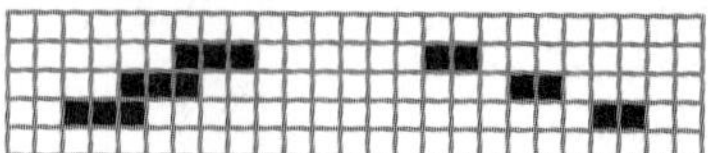

Notice that the pixel line shown in the example above meets condition (1), but that the two examples shown at the left do not meet condition (1).

To understand condition (2), look at the line shown in the first example on page 708. The basic pattern is: move down 3 pixels, shift diagonally to the right, move down 2 pixels, shift diagonally to the right. The notation *3d, r, 2d, r* designates this pattern, which is used repeatedly to form the line.

In moving from the first pixel in one copy of the pattern to the first pixel of the next copy of the pattern, you move down a total of 5 pixels and to the right a total of 2 pixels. In other words, the "line" has

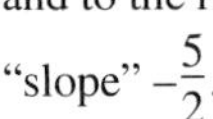

"slope" $-\frac{5}{2}$.

1. To understand condition (3), note that in the pattern for the line with slope $-\frac{5}{2}$ shown above, the lengths of the two vertical runs of pixels differ by one pixel. Draw the line produced by the pattern *4d, r, 1d, r* and confirm that it also has slope $-\frac{5}{2}$. By how much do the lengths of the two vertical runs of pixels differ for this pattern? Which pattern gives a smoother line with slope $-\frac{5}{2}$?
2. Draw a line with the pattern *2r, u, 1r, u*, where *r* indicates a move to the right and *u* indicates a diagonal shift up. What is the slope of this line?
3. Draw the smoothest line with the given slope, and state the pattern you used.

   a. 1 **b.** -2 **c.** $-\frac{3}{5}$ **d.** $\frac{7}{4}$ **e.** $\frac{5}{8}$

Creating a Tessellating Figure (Chapter 14)

Materials: Posterboard, ruler, protractor, compass, scissors

To create a figure that tessellates, such as the fish on page 610, you can modify any polygon that tessellates. Here is an example.

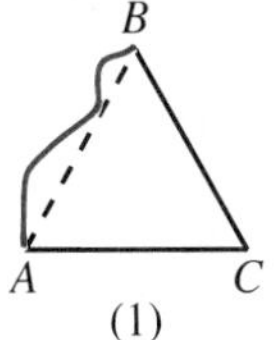

(1)

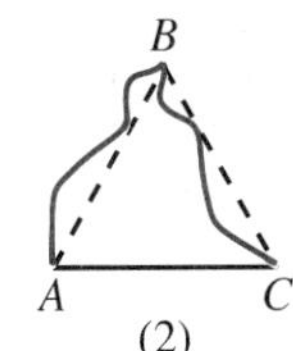

(2)

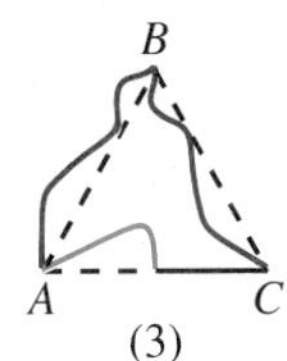

(3)

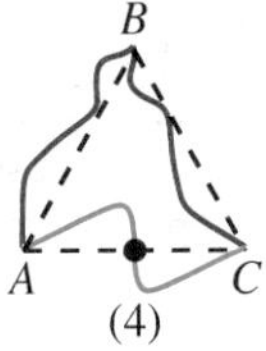

(4)

(1) Draw equilateral $\triangle ABC$, and then alter the shape of side $\overline{AB}$.
(2) Rotate the curve AB about point B through 60°, creating a curve BC that will interlock with the curve AB.
(3) Alter the left half of $\overline{AC}$.
(4) Rotate the shape drawn in step (3) through 180° about the midpoint of $\overline{AC}$. The curve AC will interlock with itself.
(5) Cut out the shape and trace copies of it to make a tessellation. The shape looks like a bird, so add an eye and feathers!

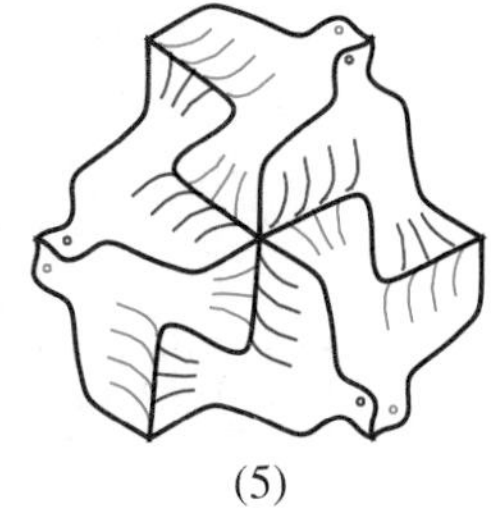

(5)

Experiment with the process demonstrated above. Use other shapes and transformations. Develop one tessellation into an art piece.

Chapter 13

1.

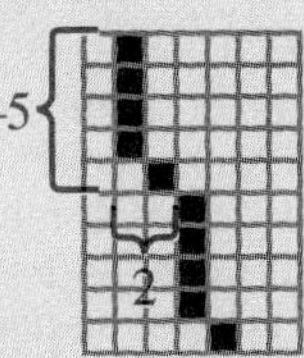

The lengths differ by 3. The pattern *3d, r, 2d, r* gives a smoother line.

2.

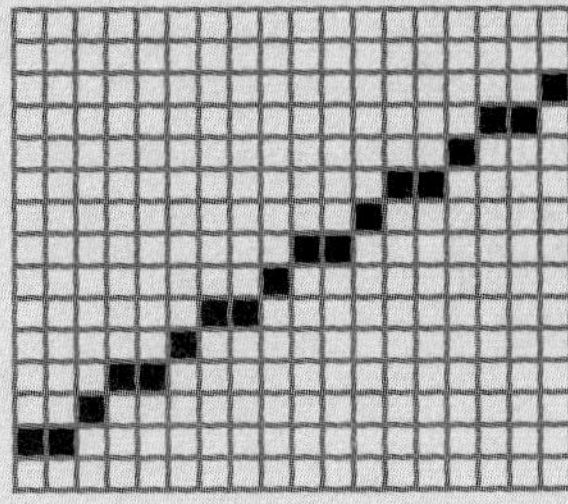

The slope is $\frac{\pi}{4}$.

3. Patterns may vary. Examples are given.
   a. *1r, u*
   b. *2d, r*
   c. *2r, d, 1r, d, 2r, d*
   d. *2u, r, 2u, r, 2u, r, 1u, r*
   e. *2r, u, 1r, u, 2r, u, 1r, u, 2r, u*

Chapter 14

Students may find it easier to begin with a square or a parallelogram. After altering one side, the opposite side should be altered in the same way, so that it becomes a *translation* of the first side that was altered.

Some students may want to research the complex tessellations created by the famous artist Maurits C. Escher (1898–1972).

Teaching Note

The ideal type of paper to use in paper folding constructions is hamburger patty paper. Used in fast food restaurants to separate hamburger patties, patty papers are waxed and come in small squares (approximately 6 in. on a side). Patty papers are carried by companies that sell restaurant equipment and supplies. If patty papers are not available, students can use waxed paper or any other transparent or translucent paper, cut into squares $5\frac{1}{2}$ in. to 6 in. on a side.

Constructions Using Paper Folding

Basic Constructions

Chapter 10 teaches geometric constructions using a straightedge and a compass. Constructions can also be done using paper folding and tracing. Constructions 1–7 below and in the exercises are the same as Constructions 1–7 in Chapter 10, but the procedures here use paper folding and tracing.

Use paper you can see through. *Every time you fold the paper, make a crease and draw a dashed line along the crease.*

You will learn how to do Constructions 1, 2, and 7 in Exercises 1, 2, and 7, respectively.

Construction 3 *Bisector of an angle*

Given an angle, construct the bisector of the angle.

Given: $\angle ABC$

Construct: The bisector of $\angle ABC$

Procedure: Fold the paper so that $\overrightarrow{BC}$ is on top of $\overrightarrow{BA}$

The crease is the bisector of $\angle ABC$.

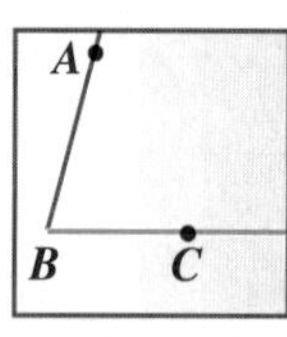

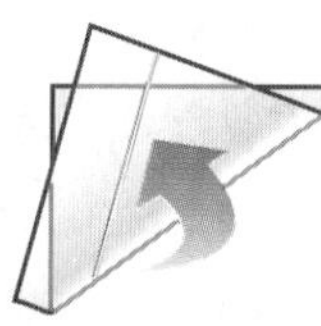

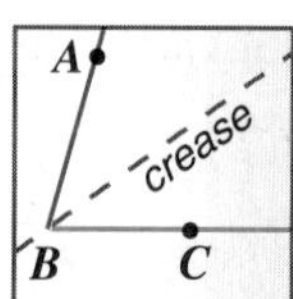

Construction 4 *Perpendicular bisector of a segment*

Given a segment, construct the perpendicular bisector of the segment.

Given: $\overline{AB}$

Construct: The perpendicular bisector of $\overline{AB}$

Procedure: Fold the paper so that B is on top of A.

The crease is the perpendicular bisector of $\overline{AB}$

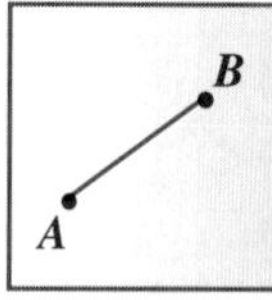

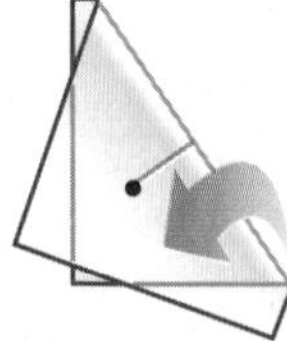

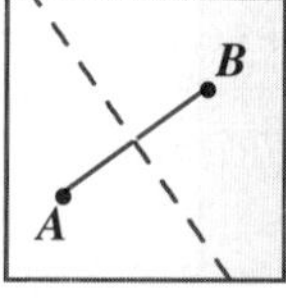

Construction 5 *Perpendicular at a point on a line*

Given a point on a line, construct the perpendicular to the line at the given point.

Given: Point P on line m

Construct: The perpendicular to m at P

Procedure: Fold the paper so that one side of line m is on top of the other and the crease goes through P.

The crease is perpendicular to m at P.

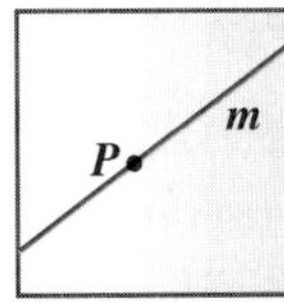

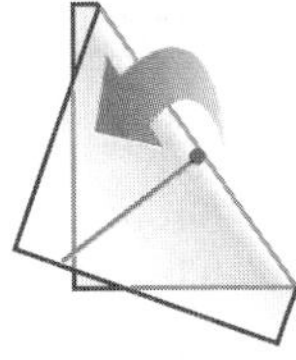
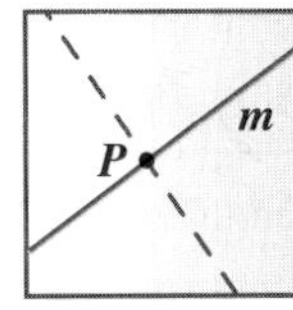

Construction 6 *Perpendicular from a point outside a line*

Given a point outside a line, construct the perpendicular to the line from the given point.

Given: Point Q outside line k

Construct: The perpendicular to k from Q

Procedure: Fold the paper so that one side of line k is on top of the other and the crease goes through Q.

The crease is the perpendicular to k from Q.

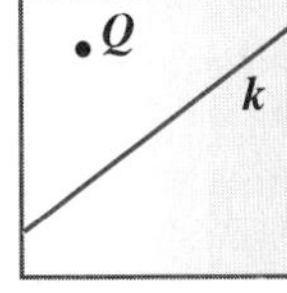

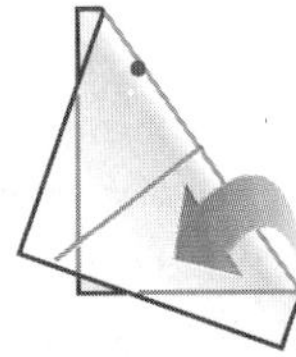
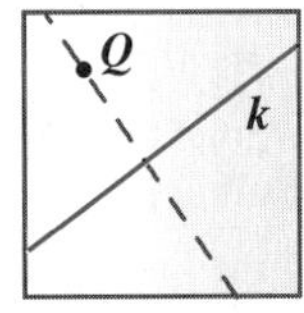

Exercises

1. Draw any $\overline{AB}$. Use Construction 1, below, to construct $\overline{YZ}$ congruent to $\overline{AB}$.

> **Construction 1** *Congruent segment*
>
> **Given a segment, construct a segment congruent to the given segment.**
>
> Given: $\overline{AB}$
>
> Construct: A segment congruent to $\overline{AB}$
>
> Procedure: Place a piece of paper over $\overline{AB}$ and trace $\overline{AB}$ onto the piece of paper. Label the endpoints of the new segment Y and Z.
>
> $\overline{YZ}$ is congruent to $\overline{AB}$.

Additional Answers
Exercises

1. Check students' work.

Additional Answers
Exercises

2. Check students' work.
3. Const. 3
4. Const. 4
5. Const. 5
6. Const. 6
7. Check students' work.
8. Constructions 5 and 6
9. *m* and *n* are both ⊥ to *k*, so by Theorem 3-7, *m* and *n* are ∥.
10. **a.** Const. 4
    b. Construction 4
11. **a.** Check students' work.
    b. Use Const. 4 to const. the midpt. *M* of $\overline{AB}$. Use Const. 4 two more times to const. the midpt. *P* of $\overline{AM}$ and the midpt. *Q* of $\overline{MB}$. $AP = PM = MQ = QB$.

2. Draw any ∠*ABC*. Use Construction 2, below, to construct ∠*DEF* congruent to ∠*ABC*.

> ### Construction 2 *Congruent angle*
> **Given an angle, construct an angle congruent to the given angle.**
>
> Given: ∠*ABC*
> Construct: An angle congruent to ∠*ABC*
> Procedure: Place a piece of paper over ∠*ABC* and trace ∠*ABC* onto the piece of paper. Label the new angle ∠*DEF*.
> ∠*DEF* is congruent to ∠*ABC*.

Draw the figure described. Then use paper folding to do the indicated construction.

3. Given: Any obtuse ∠*JKL*
Construct: The bisector of ∠*JKL*

4. Given: Any segment $\overline{HM}$
Construct: The perpendicular bisector of $\overline{HM}$

5. Given: Any point *D* on a line *l*
Construct: The perpendicular to *l* at *D*

6. Given: Any point *R* outside a line *n*
Construct: The perpendicular to *n* from *R*

For Exercises 7–9, refer to Construction 7 below.

> ### Construction 7 *Parallel through a point outside a line*
> **Given a point outside a line, construct the parallel to the line through the given point.**
>
> Given: Point *P* outside line *n*
> Construct: The line through *P* parallel to *n*
> Procedure: Construct the perpendicular to *n* from *P*. Label it *k*.
> Construct the perpendicular to *k* at *P*. Label it *m*.
> *m* is the line through *P* parallel to *n*.

7. Draw a line *n* and a point *P* outside the line. Construct the line through *P* that is parallel to *n*.

8. Which of Constructions 1–6 are used in Construction 7?

9. Write an explanation to justify that *m* is parallel to *n*.

For each of Exercises 10 and 11, trace $\overline{AB}$ onto a new piece of paper. Then use paper folding.

10. a. Divide $\overline{AB}$ into two congruent parts.
b. Which construction did you use in part (a)?

11. a. Divide $\overline{AB}$ into four congruent parts.
b. Explain the method you used in part (a).

12. Which of the following do you *not* construct when you do Construction 4? Choose one letter A–F.

A. midpoint B. perpendicular lines C. median
D. right angles E. supplementary angles F. congruent segments

For each of Exercises 13 and 14, trace the circle shown onto a piece of paper.

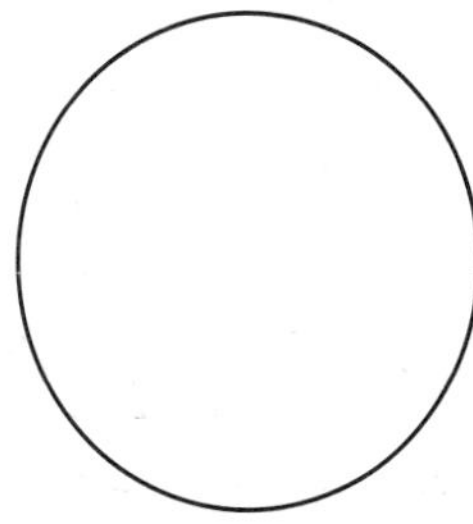

13. **a.** Use paper folding to find a diameter of the circle.
b. Describe the method you used in part (a).

14. **a.** Use paper folding to find the center of the circle.
b. Describe the procedure you used in part (a).
c. Explain how you know that the point you found is the center of the circle.

15. Use a compass to draw a $\odot O$. Choose a point on the circle and label it A.
a. Use paper folding to construct the tangent to $\odot O$ at A. Label the tangent t. (*Hint:* See Construction 8 on page 392.)
b. Describe the procedure you used in part (a).
c. Write an explanation to justify that t is the tangent to $\odot O$ at A.

Applications of Basic Constructions

Constructions 1–7 can be used to produce polygons and other geometric figures. In the examples and exercises below, you will use paper folding and tracing to construct geometric figures and explore geometric properties.

Example 1 Given $\angle EFG$ and $\angle JKL$, construct an angle whose measure equals $m\angle EFG + m\angle JKL$.

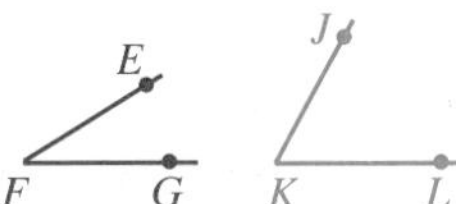

Solution

Step 1 Trace each given angle onto a different piece of paper.

Position the two pieces of paper so that $\overrightarrow{FG}$ is on top of $\overrightarrow{KJ}$.

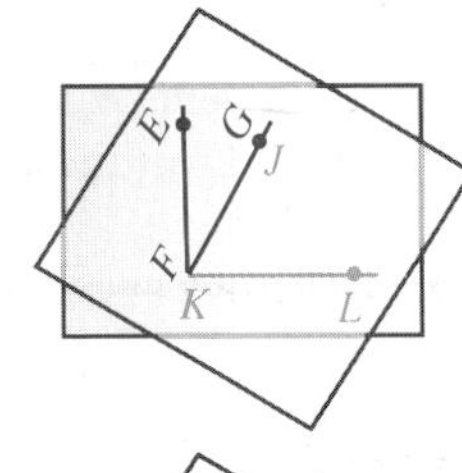

Step 2 Use Construction 2 (on page 712) to construct $\angle GFZ$ congruent to $\angle JKL$.

$$m\angle EFZ = m\angle EFG + m\angle GFZ$$
$$= m\angle EFG + m\angle JKL$$

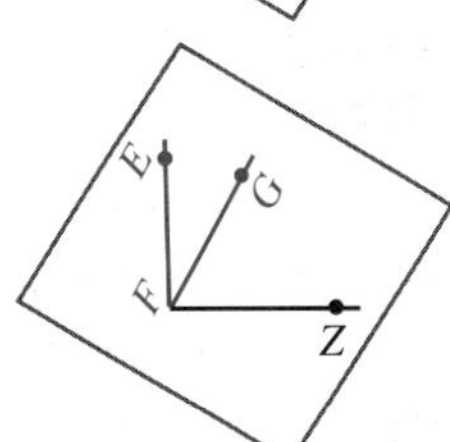

Additional Answers Exercises

12. C (median)

13. a. Check students' work.
b. Fold the $\odot$ onto itself so that one side is exactly on top of the other. The crease is a diameter of the $\odot$.

14. a. Check students' work.
b. Use the method in Exercise 13 to find two different diameters of the $\odot$. Their point of intersection is the center of the $\odot$.
c. Every diameter of a $\odot$ contains the center, so the intersection point of two diameters must be the center.

15. a. Check students' work.
b. Fold or draw $\overleftrightarrow{OA}$. Use Const. 5 to construct t, the $\perp$ to $\overleftrightarrow{OA}$ at A.
c. Since t is $\perp$ to radius $\overline{OA}$ at A, t is tangent to $\odot O$ (Theorem 9-2).

Example 2 Construct a parallelogram with diagonals of lengths AB and CD.

A B C D

Solution Recall that if the diagonals of a quadrilateral bisect each other, the quadrilateral is a parallelogram.

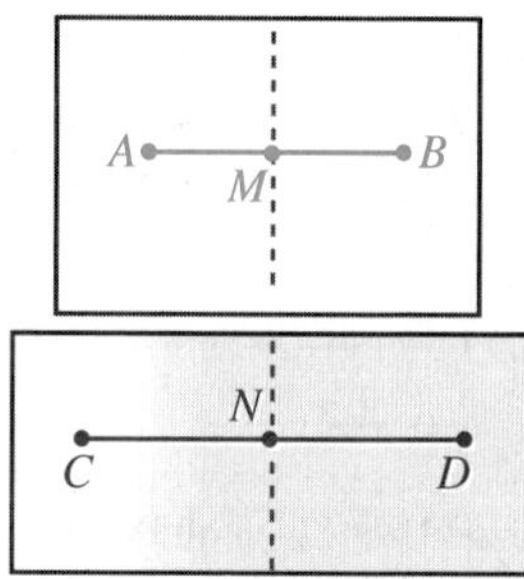

Step 1 Trace each given segment onto a different piece of paper. Use Construction 4 to construct the midpoint M of $\overline{AB}$ and the midpoint N of $\overline{CD}$.

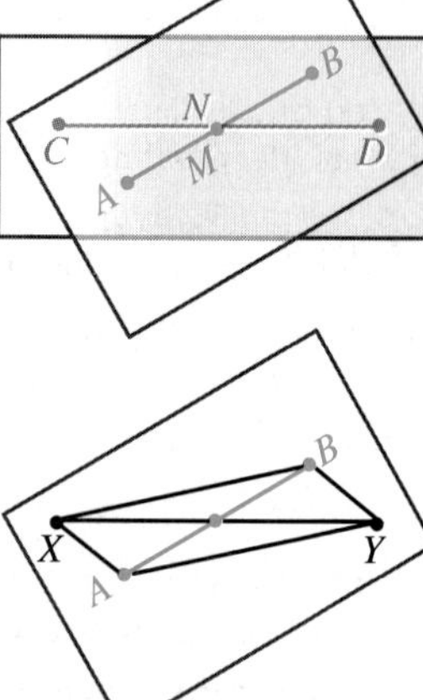

Step 2 Position the two pieces of paper so that M is on top of N and the two segments are not lined up.

Step 3 Use Construction 1 (on page 711) to construct $\overline{XY}$ congruent to $\overline{CD}$. Draw $\square AXBY$.

Since $\overline{AB}$ and $\overline{XY}$ bisect each other, $AXBY$ is a parallelogram.

Exercises

Use the angles shown to construct an angle having the indicated measure.

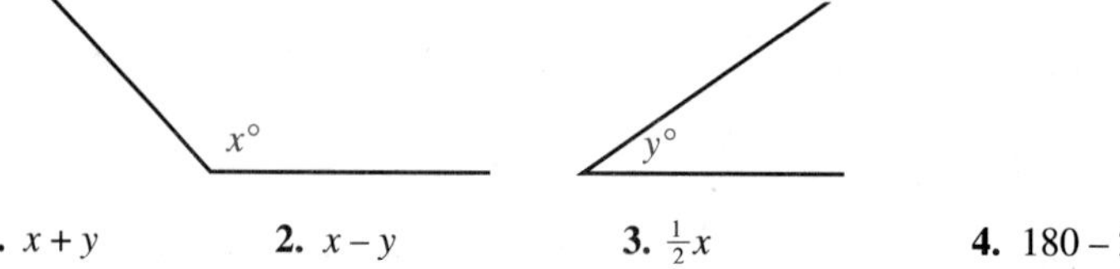

1. $x + y$ **2.** $x - y$ **3.** $\frac{1}{2}x$ **4.** $180 - 2y$

Additional Answers Exercises

1. Check students' work.
2. Check students' work.
3. Const. 3
4. Methods may vary.

Construct an angle with the indicated measure.

5. 90 **6.** 45 **7.** 135 **8.** your choice

Use the segments shown to construct a segment having the indicated length.

9. $a + b$ **10.** $b - a$ **11.** $3a - b$ **12.** $a + 2b$

13. Use the given segments and angle to construct a triangle in which an angle congruent to $\angle 1$ is included between segments of lengths q and r.

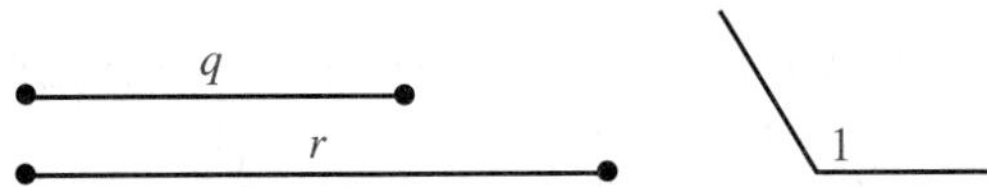

Use the segments shown below. Perform each construction using paper folding and tracing.

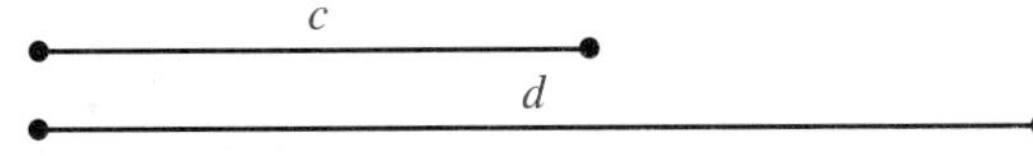

14. Construct a rectangle with diagonals of length d. (*Hint:* A quadrilateral is a rectangle if its diagonals are congruent and bisect each other.)

15. Construct a rhombus with diagonals of lengths c and d. (*Hint:* A quadrilateral is a rhombus if its diagonals are perpendicular and bisect each other.)

16. Construct a square with diagonals of length c. (*Hint:* A quadrilateral is a square if its diagonals are perpendicular, are congruent, and bisect each other.)

17. Construct a square with sides of length c.

18. Construct a rectangle with sides of lengths c and d.

For each of Exercises 19 and 20, trace $\triangle ABC$ onto a piece of paper. Then use paper folding.

19. a. Construct the perpendicular bisectors of all three sides of $\triangle ABC$. Label their point of intersection P. Recall that P is the circumcenter of $\triangle ABC$.

b. Use a compass to draw the circle that circumscribes $\triangle ABC$. (*Hint:* The circle has center P and radius PA.)

20. a. Construct the incenter of $\triangle ABC$ (the point at which the three angle bisectors meet).

b. Use a compass to draw the circle that is inscribed in $\triangle ABC$. (*Hint:* Construct the perpendicular to one of the sides from the incenter.)

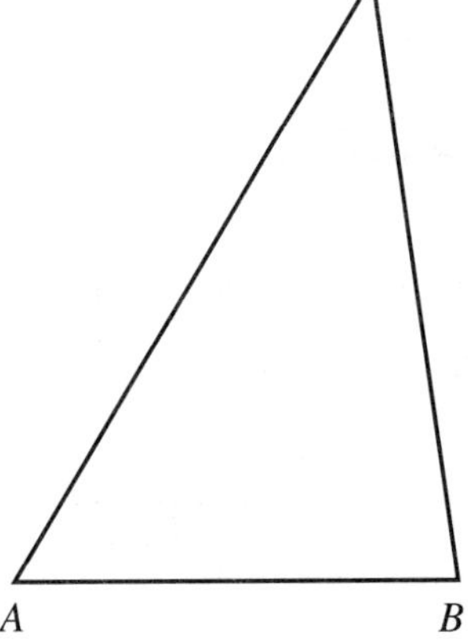

Additional Answers Exercises

5–8. Methods may vary.

9–12. Check students' work. (Repeated use of Const. 1.)

13. Const. $\angle B \cong \angle 1$. Along one ray of $\angle B$, const. $\overline{AB}$ with length q. Along the other ray, const. $\overline{BC}$ with length r. $\triangle ABC$ is the required triangle.

14. Check students' work. (Same procedure as in Example 2, but here the diagonals are $\cong$.)

15. Const. $\overline{EF}$ with length c on one piece of paper and $\overline{GH}$ with length d on another. Const. the midpt. P of $\overline{EF}$ and the $\perp$ bisector k of $\overline{GH}$. Label Q, the midpt. of $\overline{GH}$. Position the pieces of paper so that P is on top of Q and $\overleftrightarrow{EF}$ is on top of k. Const. $\overline{XY} \cong \overline{GH}$. $EXFY$ is the required quadrilateral.

16. Check students' work. (Same procedure as in Ex. 15, but both diagonals have length c.)

17. Const. $\overline{AB}$ with length c. Const. k, the $\perp$ to $\overleftrightarrow{AB}$ at A. Along k, const. $\overline{AC}$ with length c. Const. m, the $\perp$ to $\overleftrightarrow{AB}$ at B, and n, the $\perp$ to $\overleftrightarrow{AC}$ at C. m and n intersect at D. $ABCD$ is the required square.

18. Check students' work. (Similar procedure to Ex. 17.)

19. Check students' work.

20. a. Check students' work.

b. Check students' work. (The $\perp$ to a side from the incenter is a radius of the circle.)

Glossary

acute angle: An angle with measure between 0 and 90. (p. 17)

acute triangle: A triangle with three acute angles. (p. 93)

adjacent angles: Two angles in a plane that have a common vertex and a common side but no common interior points. (p. 19)

adjacent arcs: Arcs of a circle that have exactly one point in common. (p. 339)

alternate interior angles: Two nonadjacent interior angles on opposite sides of a transversal. Angles 1 and 2 are alternate interior angles. (p. 74)

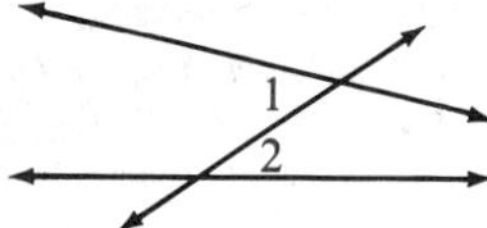

altitude of a parallelogram: Any segment perpendicular to the line containing a base from any point on the opposite side. (p. 424)

altitude of a solid: *See* prism, pyramid, cone, cylinder.

altitude of a trapezoid: Any segment perpendicular to a line containing one base from a point on the opposite base. (p. 435)

altitude of a triangle: The perpendicular segment from a vertex to the line containing the opposite side. In the figure, $\overline{BD}$ and $\overline{AD}$ are altitudes. (p. 152)

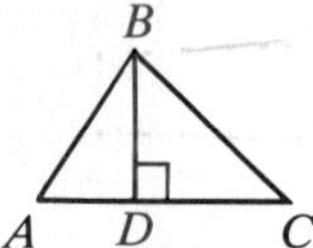

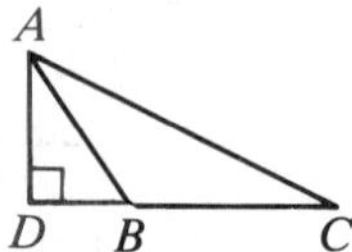

angle: A figure formed by two rays that have the same endpoint. The two rays are called the *sides* of the angle. Their common endpoint is the *vertex*. (p. 17)

angle of depression: When a point B is viewed from a higher point A, as shown by the diagram below, $\angle 1$ is the angle of depression. (p. 317)

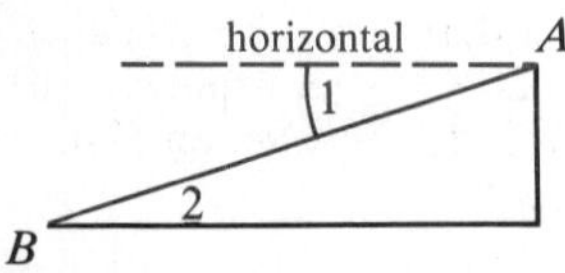

angle of elevation: When a point A is viewed from a lower point B, as shown by the diagram at the left below, $\angle 2$ is the angle of elevation. (p. 317)

apothem: The (perpendicular) distance from the center of a regular polygon to a side. (p. 441)

auxiliary line: A line (or ray or segment) added to a diagram to help in a proof. (p. 94)

axes: Usually, two perpendicular lines used to establish a coordinate system. (p. 523)

axiom: A statement that is accepted without proof. (p. 12)

base of an isosceles triangle: *See* legs of an isosceles triangle.

base of a parallelogram: Any side of a parallelogram can be considered its base. The term *base* may refer to the line segment or its length. (p. 424)

base of a pyramid: *See* pyramid.

bases of a prism: *See* prism.

bases of a trapezoid: *See* trapezoid.

biconditional: A statement that contains the words "if and only if." (p. 34)

bisector of an angle: The ray that divides the angle into two congruent adjacent angles. (p. 19)

bisector of a segment: A line, segment, ray, or plane that intersects the segment at its midpoint. (p. 13)

center of a circle: *See* circle.

center of a regular polygon: The center of the circumscribed circle. (p. 441)

central angle of a circle: An angle with its vertex at the center of the circle. (p. 339)

central angle of a regular polygon: An angle formed by two radii drawn to consecutive vertices. (p. 441)

chord: A segment whose endpoints lie on a circle. (p. 329)

circle: The set of points in a plane that are a given distance from a given point in the plane. The given point is the *center*, and the given distance is the *radius*. (p. 329)

circumference of a circle: The perimeter of a circle given by the limiting number approached by the perimeters of a sequence of regular inscribed polygons. For radius r, $C = 2\pi r$. (p. 446)

circumscribed circle: A circle is circumscribed about a polygon when each vertex of the polygon lies on the circle. The polygon is *inscribed* in the circle. (p. 330)

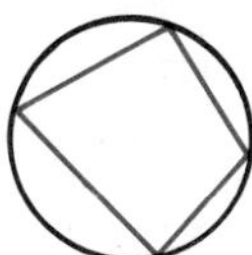

circumscribed polygon: A polygon is *circumscribed* about a circle when each side of the polygon is tangent to the circle. The circle is *inscribed* in the polygon. (p. 334)

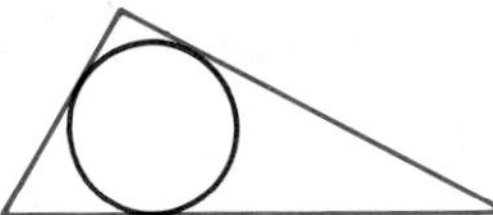

collinear points: Points all in one line. (p. 6)
common tangent: A line that is tangent to each of two coplanar circles. A common *internal* tangent intersects the segment joining the centers. A common *external* tangent does not intersect that segment. (p. 334)
complementary angles: Two angles whose measures have the sum 90. (p. 50)
composite of mappings: A transformation that combines two mappings. The composite of mappings S and T maps P to P'' where $T(P) = P'$ and $S(P') = P''$. Also called a product of mappings. (pp. 599, 605)
concentric circles: Circles that lie in the same plane and have the same center. (p. 330)
concentric spheres: Spheres that have the same center. (p. 330)
conclusion: *See* if-then statement.
concurrent lines: Two or more lines that intersect in one point. (p. 386)
conditional statement: *See* if-then statement.
cone: The diagrams illustrate a *right cone* and an *oblique cone*. Both have circular *bases* and a *vertex* V. In the right cone, h is the length of the *altitude*, l is the *slant height*, and r is the *radius*. (p. 490)

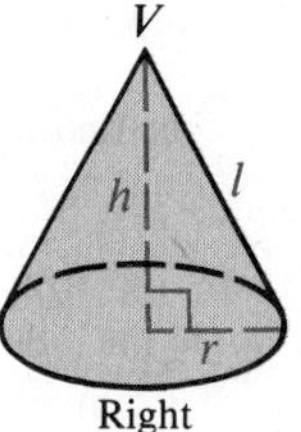

Right

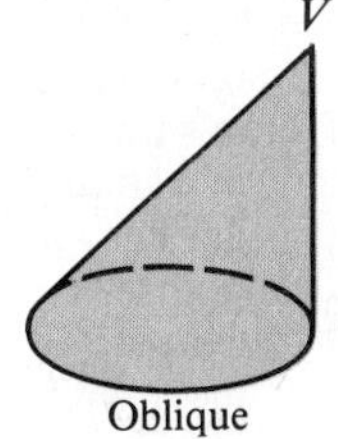

Oblique

congruence mapping: *See* isometry.
congruent angles: Angles that have equal measures. (p. 19)
congruent arcs: Arcs, in the same circle or in congruent circles, that have equal measures. (p. 340)
congruent circles (or spheres): Circles (or spheres) that have congruent radii. (p. 330)
congruent figures: Figures having the same size and shape. (p. 117)
congruent polygons: Polygons whose vertices can be matched up so that the corresponding parts (angles and sides) of the polygons are congruent. (p. 118)
congruent segments: Segments that have equal lengths. (p. 13)
contraction: *See* dilation.
contrapositive of a conditional: The contrapositive of the statement *If p, then q* is the statement *If not q, then not p.* (p. 208)
converse: The converse of the statement *If p, then q* is the statement *If q, then p.* (p. 33)
convex polygon: A polygon such that no line containing a side of the polygon contains a point in the interior of the polygon. (p. 101)
coordinate plane: The plane of the x-axis and the y-axis. (p. 523)
coplanar points: Points all in one plane. (p. 6)
corollary of a theorem: A statement that can be proved easily by applying the theorem. (p. 94)
corresponding angles: Two angles in corresponding positions relative to two lines. In the figure, $\angle$s 2 and 6 are corresponding angles. (p. 74)

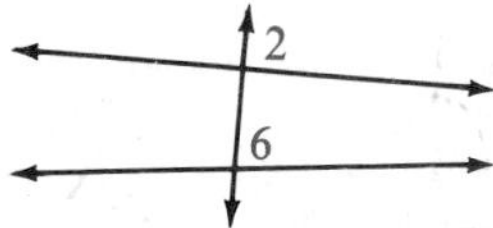

cosine (cos):

cosine of $\angle A = \frac{AC}{AB}$

or $\cos A = \frac{\text{adjacent}}{\text{hypotenuse}}$

(p. 312)

B
A C

counterexample: An example used to prove that an if-then statement is false. For that counterexample, the hypothesis is true and the conclusion is false. (p. 33)

cube: A rectangular solid with square faces. (p. 476)

cylinder: The diagrams illustrate a *right cylinder* and an *oblique cylinder*. In a right cylinder, the segment joining the centers of the circular *bases* is an *altitude*. The length of an altitude is the *height*, h, of the cylinder. A radius of a base is a *radius*, r, of the cylinder. (p. 490)

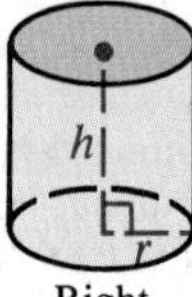

Right

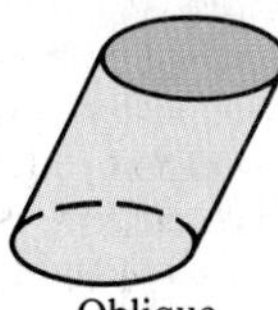
Oblique

decagon: A 10-sided polygon. (p. 101)

deductive reasoning: Proving statements by reasoning from accepted postulates, definitions, theorems, and given information. (p. 45)

diagonal: A segment joining two non-consecutive vertices of a polygon. (p. 102)

diameter: A chord that contains the center of a circle. (p. 329)

dilation: A dilation with center O and nonzero scale factor k maps any point P to a point P' determined as follows:

(1) If $k > 0$, P' lies on $\overrightarrow{OP}$ and $OP' = k \cdot OP$.

(2) If $k < 0$, P' lies on the ray opposite $\overrightarrow{OP}$ and $OP' = |k| \cdot OP$.

(3) The center O is its own image.

If $|k| > 1$, the dilation is an *expansion*.

If $|k| < 1$, the dilation is a *contraction*.

(p. 592)

distance from a point to a line (or plane): The length of the perpendicular segment from the point to the line (or plane). (p. 154)

dot product: For vectors (a, b) and (c, d), the number $ac + bd$. The dot product of perpendicular vectors is zero. (p. 543)

equal vectors: Vectors with the same magnitude and the same direction. (p. 540)

equiangular triangle: A triangle with all angles congruent. (p. 93)

equilateral triangle: A triangle with all sides congruent. (p. 93)

expansion: *See* dilation.

exterior angle of a triangle: The angle formed when one side of the triangle is extended. $\angle DAC$ is an exterior angle of $\triangle ABC$, and $\angle$s B and C are *remote interior angles* with respect to $\angle DAC$. *Exterior angle* is also applied to other polygons. (p. 95)

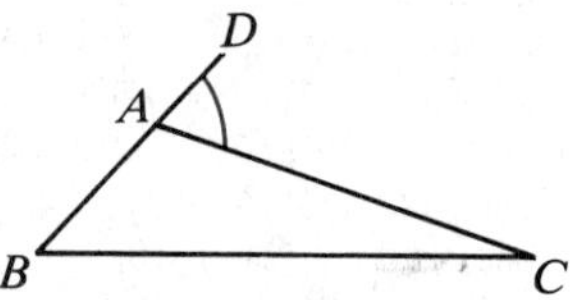

function: A correspondence between sets of numbers in which each number in the first set corresponds to exactly one number in the second set. (p. 571)

geometric mean: If a, b, and x are positive numbers with $\frac{a}{x} = \frac{x}{b}$, then x is the geometric mean between a and b. (p. 285)

glide: *See* translation.

glide reflection: A transformation in which every point P is mapped to a point P'' by these steps: (1) a glide maps P to P', and (2) a reflection in a line parallel to the glide line maps P' to P''. (p. 584)

glide reflection symmetry: A figure has glide reflection symmetry if there is a glide reflection that maps the figure onto itself. (p. 610)

golden ratio: *See* golden rectangle.

golden rectangle: A rectangle such that its length l and width w satisfy the equation $\frac{l}{w} = \frac{l + w}{l}$. The ratio $l:w$ is called the *golden ratio*. (p. 253)

great circle: The intersection of a sphere with any plane passing through the center of the sphere. (p. 331)

half-turn: A rotation through 180°. (p. 589)

height: The length of an altitude of a polygon or solid. (p. 424)

Heron's formula: A formula for finding the area of a triangle when the lengths of its sides are known. (p. 434)

hexagon: A 6-sided polygon. (p. 101)

hypotenuse: In a right triangle the side opposite the right angle. The other two sides are called *legs*. (p. 141)

hypothesis: *See* if-then statement.

identity transformation: The mapping that maps every point to itself. (p. 605)
if-then statement: A statement whose basic form is *If p, then q*. Statement p is the *hypothesis* and statement q is the *conclusion*. (p. 33)
image: *See* mapping.
indirect proof: A proof in which you assume temporarily that the conclusion is not true, and then deduce a contradiction. (p. 214)
inductive reasoning: A kind of reasoning in which the conclusion is based on several past observations. (p. 106)
inscribed angle: An angle whose vertex is on a circle and whose sides contain chords of the circle. (p. 349)
inscribed circle: *See* circumscribed polygon.
inscribed polygon: *See* circumscribed circle.
intersection of two figures: The set of points that are in both figures. (p. 6)
inverse of a conditional: The inverse of the statement *If p, then q* is the statement *If not p, then not q*. (p. 208)
inverse of a transformation: The inverse of T is the transformation S such that $S \circ T = I$. (p. 606)
isometry: A transformation that maps every segment to a congruent segment. Also called a *congruence mapping*. (p. 572)
isosceles trapezoid: A trapezoid with congruent legs. (p. 190)
isosceles triangle: A triangle with at least two sides congruent. (p. 93)

kite: A quadrilateral that has two pairs of congruent sides, but opposite sides are not congruent. (p. 193)

lateral area of a prism: The sum of the areas of its lateral faces. (p. 476)
lateral edges of a prism: *See* prism.
lateral edges of a pyramid: *See* pyramid.
lateral faces of a prism: *See* prism.
lateral faces of a pyramid: *See* pyramid.
legs of an isosceles triangle: The two congruent sides. The third side is the *base*. (p. 134)
legs of a right triangle: *See* hypotenuse.
legs of a trapezoid: *See* trapezoid.
length of a segment: The distance between its endpoints. (p. 11)
linear equation: An equation whose graph is a line. (p. 548)
line symmetry: A figure has line symmetry if there is a symmetry line k such that the reflection R_k maps the figure onto itself. (p. 609)
locus: The set of all points, and only those points, that satisfy one or more conditions. (p. 401)
logically equivalent statements: Statements that are either both true or both false. (p. 208)

magnitude of a vector $\overrightarrow{AB}$: The length AB. (p. 539)
major arc: *See* minor and major arcs.
mapping: A correspondence between points. Each point P in a given set is *mapped* to exactly one point P' in the same or a different set. P' is called the *image* of P, and P is called the *preimage* of P'. (p. 571)
measure of a major arc: *See* minor and major arcs.
measure of a minor arc: *See* minor and major arcs.
measure of an angle: A unique positive number, less than or equal to 180, that is paired with the angle. (p. 17)
measure of a semicircle: *See* semicircles.
median of a trapezoid: The segment that joins the midpoints of the legs. (p. 191)
median of a triangle: A segment from a vertex to the midpoint of the opposite side. (p. 152)
midpoint of a segment: The point that divides the segment into two congruent segments. (p. 13)
minor and major arcs: $\overparen{YZ}$ is a minor arc of $\odot O$. $\overparen{YXZ}$ is a major arc. The *measure of a minor arc* is the measure of its central angle, here $\angle YOZ$. The *measure of a major arc* is found by subtracting the measure of the minor arc from 360. (p. 339)

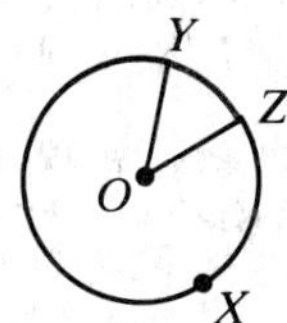

***n*–gon:** A polygon of n sides. (p. 101)

oblique solid: *See* cone, cylinder, prism.
obtuse angle: An angle with measure between 90 and 180. (p. 17)
obtuse triangle: A triangle with one obtuse angle. (p. 93)
octagon: An 8-sided polygon. (p. 101)

one-to-one mapping (or function): A mapping (or function) from set A to set B in which every member of B has exactly one preimage in A. (p. 571)

opposite rays: Given three collinear points R, S, T: If S is between R and T, then $\overrightarrow{SR}$ and $\overrightarrow{ST}$ are opposite rays. (p. 11)

origin: The intersection point, denoted $O(0, 0)$, of the x-axis and the y-axis in a coordinate plane. (p. 523)

parallel line and plane: A line and a plane that do not intersect. (p. 73)

parallel lines: Coplanar lines that do not intersect. (p. 73)

parallelogram: A quadrilateral with both pairs of opposite sides parallel. (p. 167)

parallel planes: Planes that do not intersect. (p. 73)

pentagon: A 5-sided polygon. (p. 101)

perimeter of a polygon: The sum of the lengths of its sides. (p. 445)

perpendicular bisector of a segment: A line (or ray or segment) that is perpendicular to the segment at its midpoint. (p. 153)

perpendicular line and plane: A line and a plane are perpendicular if and only if they intersect and the line is perpendicular to all lines in the plane that pass through the point of intersection. (p. 128)

perpendicular lines: Two lines that intersect to form right angles. (p. 56)

plane symmetry: A figure in space has plane symmetry if there is a symmetry plane X such that reflection in the plane maps the figure onto itself. (p. 610)

point of tangency: *See* tangent to a circle.

point symmetry: A figure has point symmetry if there is a symmetry point O such that the half-turn H_O maps the figure onto itself. (p. 609)

polygon: A plane figure formed by coplanar segments (*sides*) such that (1) each segment intersects exactly two other segments, one at each endpoint; and (2) no two segments with a common endpoint are collinear. (p. 101)

postulate: A statement that is accepted without proof. (p. 12)

preimage: *See* mapping.

prism: The solids shown are *prisms*. The shaded faces are the *bases* (congruent polygons lying in parallel planes). The other faces are *lateral faces* and all are parallelograms. Adjacent lateral faces intersect in parallel segments called *lateral edges*. An *altitude* of a prism is a segment joining the two base planes and perpendicular to both. The length of an altitude is the *height*, h, of the prism. Figure (A), in which the lateral faces are rectangles, is called a *right prism*. Figure (B) is an *oblique prism*. (p. 475)

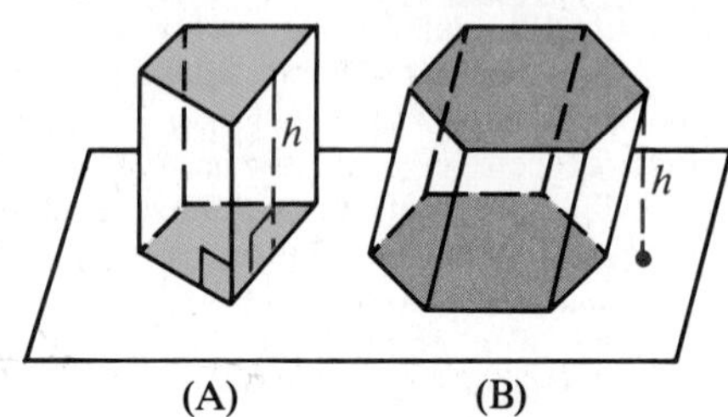

product of mappings: *See* composite of mappings.

proportion: An equation stating that two ratios are equal. The first and last terms are the *extremes*; the middle terms are the *means*. (pp. 242, 245)

pyramid: The diagram shows a pyramid. Point V is its *vertex*; the pentagon $ABCDE$ is its *base*. The five triangular faces meeting at V are *lateral faces*; they intersect in segments called *lateral edges*. The segment from the vertex perpendicular to the base is the *altitude*, and its length is the *height*, h, of the pyramid.

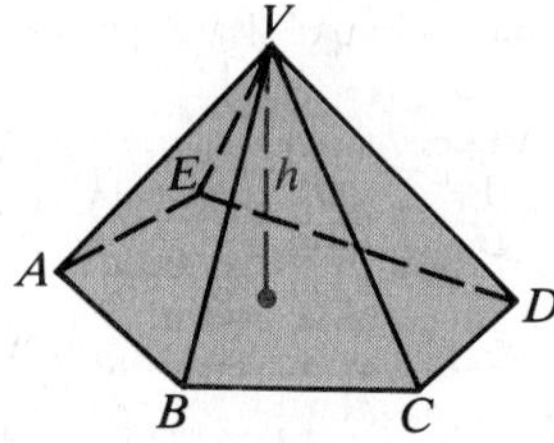

In a *regular pyramid*, the base is a regular polygon, all lateral edges are congruent, all lateral faces are congruent isosceles triangles, and the altitude meets the base at its center. The height of a lateral face is the *slant height* of the pyramid. (p. 482)

Pythagorean triple: Any triple of positive integers a, b, and c, such that $a^2 + b^2 = c^2$. (p. 299)

quadrant: Any one of the four regions into which the plane is divided by the coordinate axes. (p. 523)

quadrilateral: A 4-sided polygon. (p. 101)

radius of a circle: *See* circle.

radius of a regular polygon: The distance from the center to a vertex. (p. 441)

radius of a right cylinder: *See* cylinder.

ratio: The ratio of x to y ($y \neq 0$) is $\frac{x}{y}$ and is sometimes written $x:y$. (pp. 241, 242)

ray: The ray AC ($\overrightarrow{AC}$) consists of segment $\overline{AC}$ and all other points P such that C is between A and P. The point named first, here A, is the *endpoint of* $\overrightarrow{AC}$. (p. 11)

rectangle: A quadrilateral with four right angles. (p. 184)

rectangular solid: A right rectangular prism. (p. 475) *See also* prism.

reflection: A transformation in which a *line of reflection* acts like a mirror, reflecting points to their images. A reflection in a line m maps every point P to a point P' such that: (1) if P is not on line m, then m is the perpendicular bisector of $\overline{PP'}$; and (2) if P is on line m, then $P' = P$. (p. 577)

regular polygon: A polygon that is both equiangular and equilateral. (p. 103)

regular pyramid: *See* pyramid.

remote interior angles: *See* exterior angle of a triangle.

rhombus: A quadrilateral with four congruent sides. (p. 184)

right angle: An angle with measure 90. (p. 17)

right solid: *See* cone, cylinder, prism.

right triangle: A triangle with one right angle. (p. 93)

rotation: A rotation about point O through $x°$ is a transformation such that: (1) if point P is different from O, then $OP' = OP$ and $m\angle POP' = x$; and (2) if point P is the same as O, then $P' = P$. (p. 588)

rotational symmetry: A figure has rotational symmetry if there is a rotation that maps the figure onto itself. (p. 609)

same-side interior angles: Two interior angles on the same side of a transversal. (p. 74)

scalar multiple of a vector: The product of the vector (a, b) and the real number k is the scalar multiple (ka, kb). (p. 540)

scale factor: For similar polygons, the ratio of the lengths of two corresponding sides. (p. 249)

scalene triangle: A triangle with no sides congruent. (p. 93)

secant of a circle: A line that contains a chord. (p. 329)

sector of a circle: A region bounded by two radii and an arc of the circle. (p. 452)

segment of a line: Two points on the line and all points between them. The two points are called the *endpoints* of the segment. (p. 11)

segments divided proportionally: $\overline{AB}$ and $\overline{CD}$ are divided proportionally if points L and M lie on $\overline{AB}$ and $\overline{CD}$, respectively, and $\frac{AL}{LB} = \frac{CM}{MD}$. (p. 269)

semicircles: The two arcs of a circle that are cut off by a diameter. The *measure of a semicircle* is 180. (p. 339)

sides of an angle: *See* angle.

sides of a triangle: *See* triangle.

similarity mapping: A transformation that maps any figure to a similar figure. *See also* dilation. (p. 593)

similar polygons: Two polygons are similar if their vertices can be paired so that corresponding angles are congruent and corresponding sides are in proportion. (p. 249)

similar solids: Solids that have the same shape but not necessarily the same size. (p. 508)

simplest form of a radical: No perfect square factor other than 1 is under the radical sign, no fraction is under the radical sign, and no fraction has a radical in its denominator. (p. 287)

sine (sin):

sine of $\angle A = \frac{BC}{AB}$

or $\sin A = \frac{\text{opposite}}{\text{hypotenuse}}$

(p. 312)

skew lines: Lines that are not coplanar. (p. 73)

slant height of a regular pyramid: *See* pyramid.

slant height of a right cone: *See* cone.

slope of a line: The steepness of a nonvertical line, defined by $m = \frac{y_2 - y_1}{x_2 - x_1}$, $x_1 \neq x_2$, where $P_1(x_1, y_1)$ and $P_2\ (x_2, y_2)$ are two points on the line. (p. 529)

space: The set of all points. (p. 6)

sphere: The set of all points in space that are a given distance from a given point. (p. 329)
square: A quadrilateral with four right angles and four congruent sides. (p. 184)
straight angle: An angle with measure 180. (p. 17)
sum of two vectors: The sum of the vectors (a, b) and (c, d) is the vector $(a + c, b + d)$. (p. 541)
supplementary angles: Two angles whose measures have the sum 180. (p. 50)
symmetry: A figure in the plane has symmetry if there is an isometry, other than the identity, that maps the figure onto itself. (p. 609)

tangent (tan):

tangent of $\angle A = \frac{BC}{AC}$

or $\tan A = \frac{\text{opposite}}{\text{adjacent}}$

(p. 305)

tangent circles: Coplanar circles that are tangent to the same line at the same point. (p. 334)
tangent to a circle: A line in the plane of the circle that intersects the circle in exactly one point, called the *point of tangency*. (p. 329)
tessellation: A pattern in which congruent copies of a figure completely fill the plane without overlapping. (p. 610)
theorem: A statement that can be proved. (p. 23)
total area of a prism: The sum of the areas of all its faces. (p. 476)
transformation: A one-to-one mapping from the whole plane to the whole plane. (p. 572)
translation: A transformation that glides all points of the plane the same distance in the same direction, and maps any point (x, y) to the point $(x + a, y + b)$ where a and b are constants. Also called a *glide*. (pp. 583, 584)
translational symmetry: A figure has translational symmetry if there is a translation that maps the figure onto itself. (p. 610)
transversal: A line that intersects two or more coplanar lines in different points. (p. 74)
trapezoid: A quadrilateral with exactly one pair of parallel sides, called *bases*. The other sides are *legs*. (p. 190)
triangle: The figure formed by three segments joining three noncollinear points. Each of the three points is a *vertex* of the triangle and the segments are the *sides*. (p. 93)

vector: Any quantity that has both magnitude and direction. (p. 539)
Venn diagram: A circle diagram that may be used to represent a conditional. (p. 208)
vertex angle of an isosceles triangle: The angle opposite the base. (p. 134)
vertex of an angle: *See* angle.
vertex of a pyramid: *See* pyramid.
vertex of a triangle: *See* triangle.
vertical angles: Two angles whose sides form two pairs of opposite rays. $\angle$s 1 and 2 are vertical angles, as are $\angle$s 3 and 4. (p. 51)

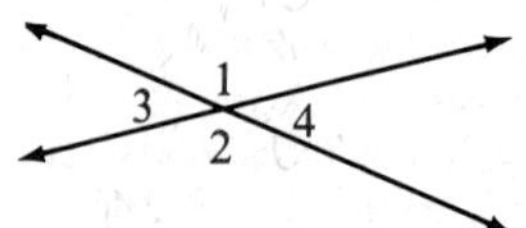

Index

Selected Answers

The answers in this answer section have been written in condensed form. Key steps are given for certain proofs, and abbreviations, such as CPCT for "corresponding parts of congruent triangles are congruent," are used. Check with your teacher regarding the form in which you should give answers in your own work.

Chapter 1

Written Exercises, Pages 3–4

1. X and F, 14 m; X and T, 7 cm, 14 m; Y and F, 9.5 cm; F and T, 24 m
3. a, b. See diagram. **c.** none
5. the distance from R to S
7. It is twice the area of the inner square.
9. $ab = cd$

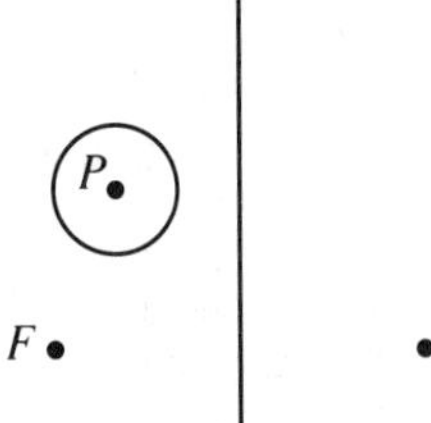

Written Exercises, Pages 7–9

1. True **3.** True **5.** True **7.** True **9.** False **11.**

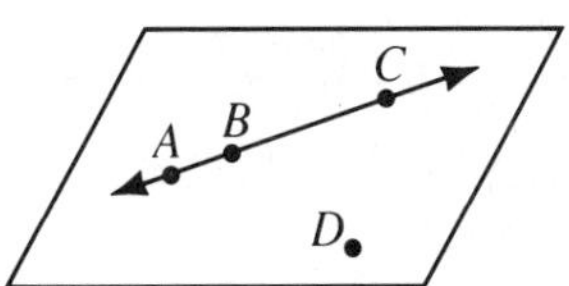

13. VWT, VST, VRS, VWR, $WRST$ **15.** $\overleftrightarrow{RW}$, $\overleftrightarrow{RV}$, $\overleftrightarrow{RS}$ **17.** VRS, VST, $WRST$ **21.** $RSGF$ and $FGCB$
23. $ABCD$, $REABF$, $GFBC$ **25. a.** Yes **b.** No **27.** No

29.

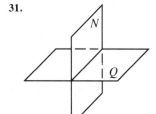

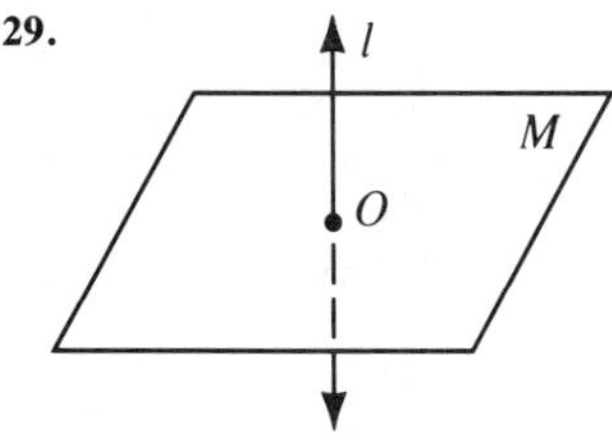

31. **35.**

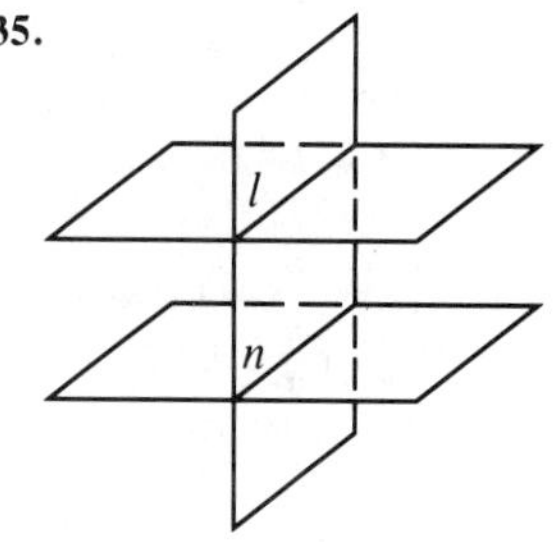

Self-Test 1, Page 10

1. T **2.** T **3.** V **4.** True **5.** True **6.** False **7.**

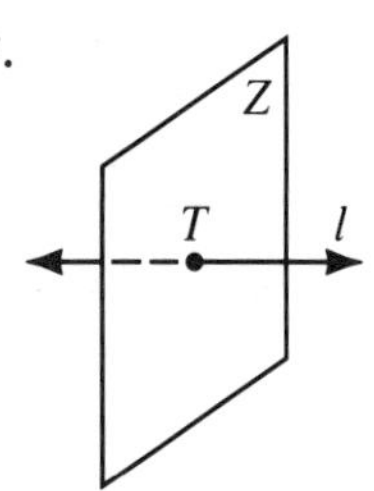

Algebra Review, Page 10

1. $c = 7$ **3.** $c = 17$ **5.** $z = 15$ **7.** $x = 5$ **9.** $x = 1$ **11.** $a = 12$ **13.** $b = -3$ **15.** $b = -\frac{2}{9}$ **17.** $k = \frac{1}{2}$ **19.** $e = 24$ **21.** $e = -15$ **23.** $p = 6$ **25.** $t = 8$ **27.** $s = 9$ **29.** $x = 15$ **31.** $g = 8$ **33.** $w = 8$ **35.** $y = 13$ **37.** $b = 5$ **39.** $h = 20$ **41.** $f = 15$ **43.** $d = -1$ **45.** $x = 45$

Written Exercises, Pages 15–16

1. 15 **3.** 4.5 **5.** True **7.** True **9.** False **11.** False **13.** True **15.** True **17.** False **19.** B **21.** C, G **23.** D **25.** -1 **31. a.** 5 **b.** 10 **c.** 10 **d.** 6 **33.** $x = 6$ **35.** $x = 3$ **37.** $y = 6$ **39.** $z = 8$; $GE = 10$; $EH = 10$; yes **41.** $\overline{HN}$ **43.** $\overline{GT}$ **45.** M **47.** 2 if $AB \geq 3$ cm, 1 if $AB < 3$ cm

Written Exercises, Pages 21–22

1. E; $\overrightarrow{EL}$, $\overrightarrow{EA}$ Answers may vary in Exs. 3–7. **3.** $\angle DLT$ **5.** $\angle AEL$ **7.** $\angle 7$ **9.** acute **11.** right **13.** straight **15.** LAS **17.** $\overrightarrow{LE}$, $\angle ALS$ **19.** **21.** **23.** 2

25. Yes; the sum of the measures of the angles is 180. **27.** $180 - t$, t, $180 - t$ **29.** $x = 18$ **31.** $x = 9$ **33.** $x = 20$ **35. a.** 6; 10 **b.** 15 **c.** $\frac{n(n-1)}{2}$

Written Exercises, Pages 25–26

1. If there is a line and a pt. not on the line, then one and only one plane contains them. **3. a.** a line **b.** If two planes intersect, then their intersection is a line. **5.** Through any 2 pts. there is exactly one line. **7.** $ACGE$ **9.** $\overleftrightarrow{AB}$, $\overleftrightarrow{CD}$, $\overleftrightarrow{AD}$, $\overleftrightarrow{BC}$ **11.** $ABCD$, $DCGH$, $ABGH$ **13.** No **15.** No **17. a.** Through any 3 pts. there is at least one plane. **b.** **c.** Yes; if 2 pts. are in a plane, then the line that contains the pts. is in that plane.

d. Through any 2 pts. there is exactly one line. **e.** If 2 pts. are in a plane, then the line that contains the pts. is in that plane. **19. a.** 3 **b.** 6 **c.** 10 **d.** 15 **e.** 21 **f.** $\frac{n(n-1)}{2}$

Self-Test 2, Page 29

1. $\overleftrightarrow{RN}$, $\overleftrightarrow{RC}$, $\overleftrightarrow{NC}$ **2.** $\overrightarrow{NR}$ **3.** No **4.** $x = 2$ **5.** JOT **6.** $\overrightarrow{OK}$, JOT **7.** 180, straight **8.** c **9.** there is exactly one line **10.** then $\overleftrightarrow{AB}$ is in Z **11.** their intersection is a line **12.** there is exactly one plane that contains j and P

Chapter Review, Page 30

1. infinitely many **3.** 2 **5.**

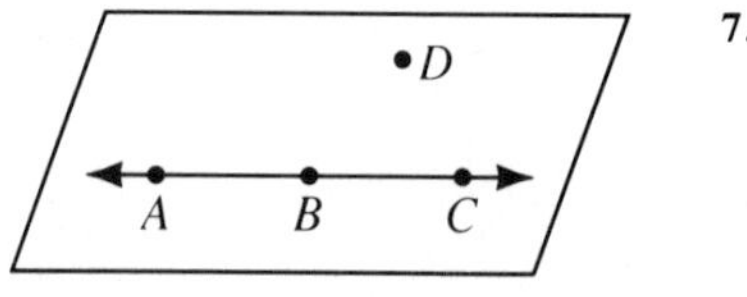

7.

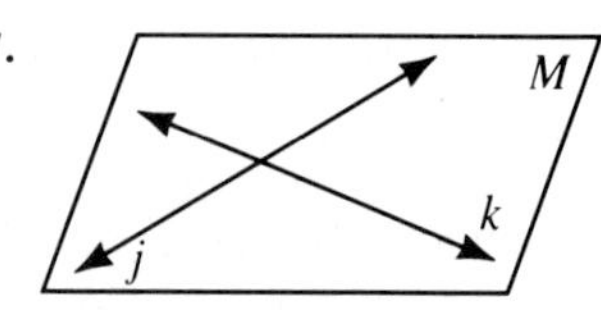

9. U or V **11.** congruent **13.** $\angle 1$, $\angle 2$, $\angle ADC$; $\angle 1$, $\angle 2$ **15.** obtuse **17.** True **19.** False

Chapter 2

Written Exercises, Page 35

1. H: $3x - 7 = 32$, C: $x = 13$ **3.** H: you will, C: I'll try **5.** H: $a + b = a$, C: $b = 0$ **7.** B is between A and C if and only if $AB + BC = AC$. **9.** If points are collinear, then they all lie in 1 line. If points lie in 1 line, then they are collinear. Answers may vary in Exs. 11–15. **11.** $a = 1, b = -1$

13. 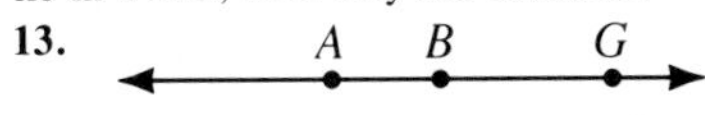

15. 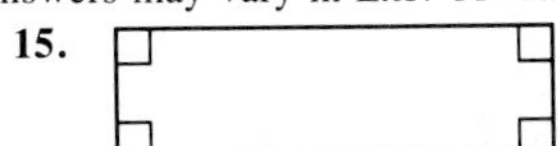

17. True. If $|x| = 6$, then $x = -6$; false. **19.** True. If $5b > 20$, then $b > 4$; true. **21.** True. If Pam lives in Illinois, then she lives in Chicago; false. **23.** True. If $a^2 > 9$, then $a > 3$; false. **25.** False. If $n > 7$, then $n > 5$; true. **27.** False. If $DE + EF = DF$, then points D, E, and F are collinear; true. **29.** Two ∠s are ≅ if and only if their measures are =. **31.** Possible conclusions are: q, not r, s.

Mixed Review Exercises, Page 37

1. $\overline{AM}$; $\overline{MB}$ **2.** $\angle ABX$; $\angle XBC$ **3.** AOB; BOC; AOC **4.** POR; ROQ; 180

Written Exercises, Pages 41–43

1. Given; Add. Prop. of =; Div. Prop. of = **3.** Given; Mult. Prop. of =; Subtr. Prop. of = **5.** Given; Mult. Prop. of =; Dist. Prop.; Add. Prop. of =; Div. Prop. of = **7.** 1. ∠ Add. Post 2. ∠ Add. Post. 3. $m\angle AOD = m\angle 1 + m\angle 2 + m\angle 3$; Substitution Prop. **9.** 1. Given 2. OW, WN; Seg. Add. Post. 3. $DO + OW = OW + WN$ 4. Refl. Prop. 5. $DO = WN$; Subtr. Prop. of = **11.** 1. $m\angle 1 = m\angle 2$; $m\angle 3 = m\angle 4$ (Given) 2. $m\angle 1 + m\angle 3 = m\angle 2 + m\angle 4$ (Add. Prop. of =) 3. $m\angle 1 + m\angle 3 = m\angle SRT$; $m\angle 2 + m\angle 4 = m\angle STR$ (∠ Add. Post.) 4. $m\angle SRT = m\angle STR$ (Substitution Prop.) **13.** 1. $RQ = TP$; (Given) 2. $RZ + ZQ = RQ$; $TZ + ZP = TP$ (Seg. Add. Post.) 3. $RZ + ZQ = TZ + ZP$ (Substitution Prop.) 4. $ZQ = ZP$ (Given) 5. $RZ = TZ$ (Subtr. Prop. of =) **15.** b

Written Exercises, Pages 46–47

1. Def. of midpt. **3.** Def. of ∠ bis. **5.** Def. of midpt. **7.** ∠ Add. Post. **9.** 60 **11.** 70 **13. a.** 12 **b.** 28 **c.** 6 **d.** 22 **15. a.** $\overline{LM}$ and $\overline{MK}$, $\overline{GN}$ and $\overline{NH}$ **b.** Answers may vary; for example, $\overline{LK} \cong \overline{GH}$ **17.** $AC = BD$ **19.** 1. Given 2. Ruler Post. 3. Given 4. Def. of Midpt. 5. Substitution Prop. 6. $a + b$; Add. Prop. of = 7. Div. Prop. of = **21.** $Q: \frac{3a + b}{4}$; $T: \frac{5a + 3b}{8}$

Self-Test 1, Page 49

1. H: $\overline{AB}$ and $\overline{CD}$ intersect; C: $\overrightarrow{AB}$ and $\overrightarrow{CD}$ intersect **2.** If $\overrightarrow{AB}$ and $\overrightarrow{CD}$ intersect, then $\overline{AB}$ and $\overline{CD}$ intersect. False **3.** $\overline{AB} \cong \overline{CD}$ if and only if $AB = CD$. **4.** Answers may vary; $m\angle A = 95$ **5.** Substitution Prop. **6.** $x = 3$ **7.** 81 **8.** definitions, postulates

Written Exercises, Pages 52–54

1. 70, 160 **3.** $90 - x$, $180 - x$ **5.** 45, 45 **7.** $\angle AFD$ **9.** $\angle AFD$ and $\angle AFB$ **11.** $\angle BFC$ and $\angle EFD$ **13.** 35 **15.** 25 **17.** 60 **19.** 25 **21.** 25 **23.** 1. Vertical ∠s are ≅. 2. Given 3. Vert. ∠s are ≅. 4. $\angle 1 \cong \angle 4$ **25.** $x = 60$, $m\angle A = 76$, $m\angle B = 104$ **27.** $y = 24$, $m\angle C = 16$, $m\angle D = 74$ **29.** $x = \frac{1}{2}(90 - x)$; 30 **31.** $180 - x = 6(90 - x)$; 72; 108; 18 **33.** $x = 33$, $y = 66$

Written Exercises, Pages 58–60

1. a. $90 - x$ **b.** $180 - x$ **3.** Def. of ⊥ lines **5.** If the ext. sides of 2 adj. ∠s are ⊥, then the ∠s are comp. **7.** Def. of ⊥ lines **9.** 35 **11.** 20 **13.** 1. Given 3. ∠ Add. Post. 4. $m\angle AOB + m\angle BOC = 90$ 5. $\angle AOB$ and $\angle BOC$ are comp. ∠s. **15.** $180 - y$ **17.** $90 - (x + y)$ **19.** No **21.** No **23.** Yes **25.** No **27.** Answers may vary. $m\angle 2 = m\angle 3$; $m\angle DAC = 90$; $m\angle ECA = 90$ **29.** $\overleftrightarrow{XD} \perp \overleftrightarrow{XF}$

Mixed Review Exercises, Page 60

Answers may vary in Exs. 1–7. **1.** $\angle CBF \cong \angle BCG$ **2.** $AC = BD$ **3.** $\angle 3 \cong \angle 4$ **4.** $m\angle 1 = m\angle 2 = 45$ **5.** $CE = BE$ **6.** $\overleftrightarrow{AB} \perp \overleftrightarrow{BF}$ **7.** $m\angle 5 = 90$

Written Exercises, Pages 63–65

1. Seg. Add. Post. **3.** Vertical ∠s are ≅. **5.** Def. of ∠ bis. **7.** Def. of ⊥ lines **9.** Def. of comp. ∠s **11.** If 2 lines are ⊥, then they form ≅ adj. ∠s. **13.** Def. of ⊥ lines **15.** 1. ∠5 are supplementary; Given 2. Def. of supp. ∠s 3. Substitution Prop. 5. Subtr. Prop. of = **17. a.** 1. Given 2. If the ext. sides of 2 adj. acute ∠s are ⊥, then the ∠s are comp. 3. Given 4. If 2 ∠s are comp. of ≅ ∠s, then the 2 ∠s are ≅. **b.** Show that ∠3 and ∠6 are supps. of ≅ ∠s. **19.** 1. ∠2 ≅ ∠3 (Given) 2. ∠1 ≅ ∠2 (Vert. ∠s are ≅.) 3. ∠1 ≅ ∠3 (Substitution Prop.) 4. ∠3 ≅ ∠4 (Vert. ∠s are ≅.) 5. ∠1 ≅ ∠4 (Trans. Prop.) **21.** 1. $\overline{AC} \perp \overline{BC}$ (Given) 2. ∠2 is comp. to ∠1. (If the ext. sides of 2 adj. acute ∠s are ⊥, then the 2 ∠s are comp.) 3. ∠3 is comp. to ∠1 (Given) 4. ∠3 ≅ ∠2 (If 2 ∠s are comp. of the same ∠, then the 2 ∠s are ≅.) **23.** $\overrightarrow{OF}$ bisects ∠*COD*. Proof: 1. $\overrightarrow{OE}$ bisects ∠*AOB*. (Given) 2. ∠1 ≅ ∠2 (Def. of ∠ bis.) 3. ∠2 ≅ ∠3 (Vert. ∠s are ≅.) 4. $m\angle 1 = m\angle 3$ (Trans. Prop.) 5. $m\angle 1 = m\angle 4$ (Vert. ∠s are ≅.) 6. $m\angle 3 = m\angle 4$ (Substitution Prop.) 7. $\overrightarrow{OF}$ bisects ∠*COD*. (Def. of ∠ bis.)

Self-Test 2, Page 65

1. Answers may vary; $90 \le m\angle HOK < 180$ **2. a.** 15 **b.** 40 **3.** 53; 37; 53 **4.** $m\angle 4 = 90 - t$, $m\angle 5 = t$, $m\angle 6 = 90 - t$ **5.** Def. of ⊥ lines **6.** Vert. ∠s are ≅. **7.** If the ext. sides of 2 adj. ∠s are ⊥, then the ∠s are comp. **8.** Show that ∠1 ≅ ∠2, so $j \perp k$. **9.** 1. ∠1 is supp. to ∠3; ∠2 is supp. to ∠3 (Given) 2. ∠1 ≅ ∠2 (If 2 ∠s are supp. of the same ∠, the 2 ∠s are ≅.) 3. $j \perp k$ (If 2 lines form ≅ adj. ∠s, then the lines are ⊥.)

Extra, Page 66

1. None of it; one **3.** 2; the result is 2 non-Möbius (2-sided) bands linked together. **5.** The result is a rectangular frame.

Chapter Review, Pages 67–68

1. H: $m\angle 1 = 120$, C: ∠1 is obtuse **3.** Answers may vary; $m\angle 1 = 100$ **5.** Substitution Prop. **7.** Div. Prop. of = **9.** Def. of midpt. **11.** ∠ Bis. Thm. **13.** ∠*BOA* or ∠*DOE* **15.** Def. of ⊥ lines **17.** If 2 lines are ⊥, then they form ≅ adj. ∠s. **19.** Show that ∠3 and ∠4 are supp. of ≅ ∠s.

Algebra Review, Page 69

1. $x = 3, y = 9$ **3.** $x = -16, y = -8$ **5.** $x = 28, y = 4$ **7.** $x = 1, y = 6$ **9.** $x = 5, y = 4$ **11.** $x = -2, y = 3$ **13.** $x = 4, y = 1$ **15.** $x = 6, y = 2$ **17.** $x = 11, y = 16$

Preparing for College Entrance Exams, Page 70

1. C **2.** C **3.** D **4.** E **5.** D **6.** B **7.** E **8.** C

Cumulative Review, Page 71

1. Div. Prop. of = **3.** Def. of ⊥ lines **5.** Subtr. Prop. of = **7.** If 2 planes int., then their int. is a line. **9.** Seg. Add. Post. **11.** True **13.** False **15.** False; 3 collinear pts. **17.** True **19.** True **21.** $x = 36$ **23.** $x = 10$ **25.** $x = 31$

Chapter 3

Written Exercises, Pages 76–77

1. alt. int. ∠s **3.** s-s. int. ∠s **5.** corr. ∠s **7.** $\overleftrightarrow{PQ}$, $\overleftrightarrow{SR}$; $\overleftrightarrow{SQ}$ **9.** $\overleftrightarrow{PQ}$, $\overleftrightarrow{SR}$; $\overleftrightarrow{PS}$ **11.** $\overleftrightarrow{PQ}$, $\overleftrightarrow{SR}$; $\overleftrightarrow{QR}$ **13.** corr. ∠s **15.** s-s. int. ∠s **17.** corr. ∠s **19.** Alt. int. ∠s are ≅. **21. a.** Answers may vary. **b.** Same as $m\angle 1 + m\angle 2$ **c.** Same as $m\angle 1 + m\angle 2$ **d.** When 2 nonparallel lines are cut by trans., the sum of the meas. of s-s. int. ∠s is a constant. **23.** $\overleftrightarrow{BH}$, $\overleftrightarrow{CI}$, $\overleftrightarrow{DJ}$, $\overleftrightarrow{EK}$, $\overleftrightarrow{FL}$ **25.** Answers may vary. $\overleftrightarrow{FL}$, $\overleftrightarrow{EK}$, $\overleftrightarrow{DJ}$, $\overleftrightarrow{CI}$, $\overleftrightarrow{GL}$, $\overleftrightarrow{LK}$, $\overleftrightarrow{JI}$, $\overleftrightarrow{IH}$ **27.** *ABHG*, *BCIH*, *CDJI*, *DEKJ* **29.** If the top and bottom lie in ∥ planes, then $\overline{CD}$ and $\overline{IJ}$ are the lines of intersection of *DCIJ* with 2 ∥ planes, and are therefore ∥. **31.** sometimes **33.** always **35.** sometimes **37.** always **39.** sometimes

Written Exercises, Pages 80–82

1. ∠3, ∠6, ∠8 **3.** ∠4, ∠5, ∠7, ∠10, ∠12, ∠13, ∠15 **5.** 110, 70 **7.** $x = 60, y = 61$ **9.** $x = 60, y = 18$ **11.** $x = 14, y = 9$ **13.** 1. Given 2. Def. of ⊥ lines 3. $l \parallel n$ 4. If 2 ∥ lines are cut by a trans., then corr. ∠s are ≅. 5. $m\angle 2 = 90$ 6. Def. of ⊥ lines **15.** $x = 70, y = 12, z = 38$

17. a. $m\angle DAB = 64$, $m\angle KAB = 32$, $m\angle DKA = 32$ **b.** More information is needed. **19.** $x = 30$, $y = 5$ **21.** 1. $k \parallel l$ (Given) 2. $\angle 1 \cong \angle 8$ or $m\angle 1 = m\angle 8$ (If 2 $\parallel$ lines are cut by a trans., then alt. int. $\angle$s are $\cong$.) 3. $m\angle 8 + m\angle 7 = 180$ ($\angle$ Add. Post.) 4. $m\angle 1 + m\angle 7 = 180$ (Substitution Prop.) 5. $\angle 1$ is supp. to $\angle 7$ (Def. of supp. $\angle$s) **23. a.** 1. $\overline{AB} \parallel \overline{DC}$; $\overline{AD} \parallel \overline{BC}$ (Given) 2. $\angle A$ is supp. to $\angle B$; $\angle C$ is supp. to $\angle B$ (If 2 $\parallel$ lines are cut by a trans., then s-s. int. $\angle$s are supp.) 3. $\angle A \cong \angle C$ (If 2 $\angle$s are supp. of the same $\angle$, then the 2 $\angle$s are $\cong$.) **b.** Yes, by the same reasoning as in part (a) **25.** 60

Mixed Review Exercises, Page 82

1. a. True **b.** If 2 lines form $\cong$ adj. $\angle$s, then the lines are $\perp$. **c.** True **2. a.** True **b.** If 2 lines are not skew, then they are $\parallel$. **c.** False **3. a.** True **b.** If two $\angle$s are supp., then the sum of their meas. is 180. **c.** True **4. a.** True **b.** If 2 planes do not intersect, then they are $\parallel$. **c.** True

Written Exercises, Pages 87–88

1. $\overline{AB} \parallel \overline{FC}$ **3.** $\overline{AB} \parallel \overline{FC}$ **5.** none **7.** none **9.** $\overline{AE} \parallel \overline{BD}$ **11.** $\overline{AE} \parallel \overline{BD}$ **13.** $\overline{AE} \parallel \overline{BD}$ **15.** $\overline{FB} \parallel \overline{EC}$; $\overline{AE} \parallel \overline{BD}$ **17.** 1. Given 2. Vert. $\angle$s are $\cong$. 3. Trans. Prop. 4. If 2 lines are cut by a trans. and corr. $\angle$s are $\cong$, then the lines are $\parallel$. **19.** $x = 35$, $y = 20$ **21.** $\angle 1 \cong \angle 4$; $\angle 2 \cong \angle 5$
23. 1. $k \perp t$; $n \perp t$ (Given) 2. $m\angle 1 = 90$; $m\angle 2 = 90$ (Def. of $\perp$ lines) 3. $m\angle 1 = m\angle 2$ or $\angle 1 \cong \angle 2$ (Substitution Prop.) 4. $k \parallel n$ (If 2 lines are cut by a trans. and corr. $\angle$s are $\cong$, then the lines are $\parallel$.)
25. 1. $\overline{BE} \perp \overline{DA}$; $\overline{CD} \perp \overline{DA}$ (Given) 2. $\overline{CD} \parallel \overline{BE}$ (In a plane, 2 lines $\perp$ to the same line are $\parallel$.) 3. $\angle 1 \cong \angle 2$ (If 2 $\parallel$ lines are cut by a trans., then alt. int. $\angle$s are $\cong$.) **27.** $m\angle RST = 110$ **29.** $x = 50$, $y = 20$
31. $x = 12$

Self-Test 1, Page 89

1. sometimes **2.** never **3.** always **4.** sometimes **5.** always **6.** $\angle 3$, $\angle 6$; $\angle 4$, $\angle 5$ **7.** Answers may vary; $\angle 1$, $\angle 5$; $\angle 2$, $\angle 6$; $\angle 3$, $\angle 7$; $\angle 4$, $\angle 8$ **8.** $\angle 3$, $\angle 5$ or $\angle 4$, $\angle 6$ **9.** $\angle 4$; $\angle 3$ **10.** $\angle 2$, $\angle 8$; $\angle 4$, $\angle 7$ **11.** $\angle 2$, $\angle 8$ **12.** 65, 115 **13.** $\overline{EB} \parallel \overline{DC}$ **14.** none **15.** $\overline{AE} \parallel \overline{BD}$ **16.** one, one

Written Exercises, Pages 97–99

1. a.

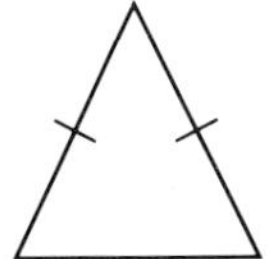

b.

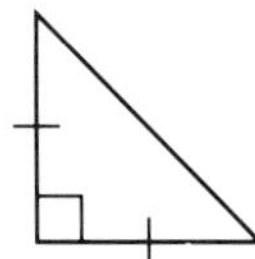

c.

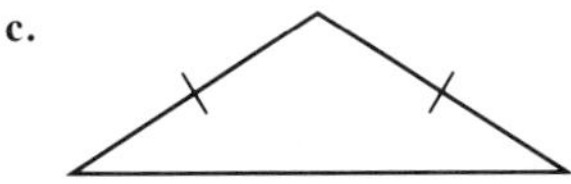

3. not possible **5.** 180

7. 95 **9.** 25 **11.** $x = 30$, $y = 80$ **13.** $x = 40$, $y = 50$ **15.** $x = 40$, $y = 50$ **17.** Yes, $n = 5$ **19.** 30, 60, 90 **21.** $m\angle C > 60$ **23. a.** 22 **b.** 23 **c.** $\angle ABD$ and $\angle C$ are comps. of $\angle CBD$.
25. 1. $\angle ABD \cong \angle AED$ (Given) 2. $\angle A \cong \angle A$ (Refl. Prop.) 3. $\angle C \cong \angle F$ (If 2 $\angle$s of one $\triangle$ are $\cong$ to 2 $\angle$s of another $\triangle$, then the third $\angle$s are $\cong$.) **27.** Given: $\triangle ABC$. Prove: $m\angle 1 + m\angle 2 + m\angle 3 = 180$. Proof: 1. Draw $\overrightarrow{CD}$ through $C \parallel$ to $\overleftrightarrow{AB}$. (Through a pt. outside a line, there is exactly 1 $\parallel$ to a given line.) 2. $\angle 2 \cong \angle 5$ or $m\angle 2 = m\angle 5$ (If 2 $\parallel$ lines are cut by a trans., alt. int. $\angle$s are $\cong$.) 3. $\angle 1 \cong \angle 4$ or $m\angle 1 = m\angle 4$ (If 2 $\parallel$ lines are cut by trans., corr. $\angle$s $\cong$.) 4. $m\angle ACD + m\angle 4 = 180$; $m\angle ACD = m\angle 3 + m\angle 5$ ($\angle$ Add. Post.) 5. $m\angle 1 + m\angle 2 + m\angle 3 = 180$ (Subst.) **29.** $x = 25$, $y = 5$ **31.** $\angle 1 \cong \angle 2 \cong \angle 5$; $\angle 3 \cong \angle 4 \cong \angle 6$

Written Exercises, Pages 104–105

1. 360; 360 **3.** 720; 360 **5.** 1440; 360 **7.** 360; yes **9.** 135 **11.** 120 **15.** not possible **17.** 24 **21.** $x = 36$; $\overline{AB} \parallel \overline{CD}$ **23.** 108 **25.** 14
27. a. Sketches may vary.
b. Yes

Written Exercises, Pages 107–109

1. 256, 1024 **3.** $\frac{1}{81}, \frac{1}{243}$ **5.** 17, 23 **7.** 15, 4 **9.** 500, 250 **11.** none **13.** none **15.** $1234 \times 9 + 5 = 11111$ **17.** $9999^2 = 99980001$ **21.** True.

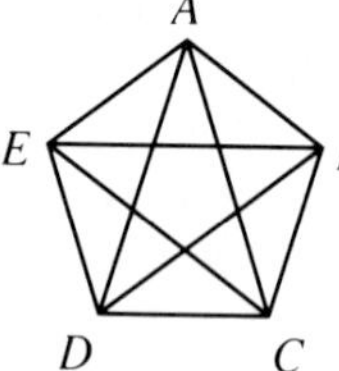

Given: $ABCDE$ is a reg. pentagon.
Prove: $\overline{AC} \cong \overline{AD} \cong \overline{BE} \cong \overline{BD} \cong \overline{CE}$

23. False.

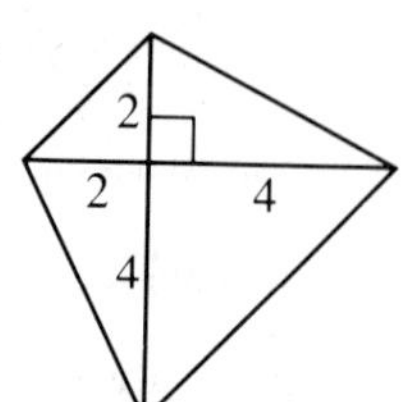

27. a. Opp. $\angle$s are $\cong$. **b.** If both pairs of opp. $\angle$s of a quad. are $\cong$, then opp. sides are $\parallel$. Given: $ABCD$ is a quad.; $m\angle A = m\angle C$; $m\angle B = m\angle D$ Prove: $\overline{AD} \parallel \overline{BC}$; $\overline{AB} \parallel \overline{CD}$ Proof: 1. $m\angle A + m\angle B + m\angle C + m\angle D = 360$ (The sum of the meas. of the int. $\angle$s of a quad. is 360.) 2. $m\angle A = m\angle C$; $m\angle D = m\angle B$ (Given) 3. $2m\angle A + 2m\angle B = 360$; $2m\angle B + 2m\angle C = 360$ (Substitution Prop.) 4. $m\angle A + m\angle B = 180$; $m\angle B + m\angle C = 180$ (Div. Prop. of =) 5. $\angle A$ and $\angle B$ are supp.; $\angle B$ and $\angle C$ are supp. (Def. of supp. $\angle$s) 6. $\overline{AD} \parallel \overline{BC}$; $\overline{AB} \parallel \overline{CD}$ (If 2 lines are cut by a trans. and s-s. int. $\angle$s are supp., then the lines are $\parallel$.) **c.** Both pairs of opp. $\angle$s of a quad. are $\cong$ if and only if opp. sides are $\parallel$. **29.** 5; 9; 14; 20; $\frac{n(n-3)}{2}$

Self-Test 2, Page 110

1. acute **2.** scalene **3.** 60 **4.** 105, 35 **5.** 19 **6.** $y = 50$, $z = 60$ **7.** $x = 1$, $x = 7$ **8.** 8 **9.** equilateral, equiangular **10.** 360, 144 **11.** 6, 60 **12.** 32 **13.** 32 **14.** 36 **15.** 16

Chapter Review, Pages 111–112

1. 2 **3.** alt. int. **5.** 105, 105 **7.** $y = 20$ **9.** $\overleftrightarrow{DE}$; $\angle A$ is supp. to $\angle ADE$. **11.** See page 85. **13.** 180 **15.** $\angle 3 \cong \angle 6$; If 2 $\angle$s are supp. of $\cong$ $\angle$s, then the 2 $\angle$s are $\cong$. $\angle 2 \cong \angle 8$; If 2 $\angle$s of one $\triangle$ are $\cong$ to 2 $\angle$s of another $\triangle$, then the third $\angle$s are $\cong$. **17.** 160 **19.** 12 **21.** $\frac{1}{100}, -\frac{1}{1000}$

Algebra Review, Page 113

1. 3 **3.** (0, 0) **5.** (3, 5) **7.** (4, 0) **9.** (−5, 0) **11.** (−2, 2) **13.** (−2, −3) **15.** K, O, S **17.** 3 **19.** M, N, P **21.** V, W **23–34.**

y, x, O, A, B, C, D, E, F, G, H, I, J, K

35. (2, 1) **37.** (0, 3) **39.** (−4, −2)

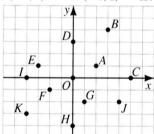

Cumulative Review, Pages 114–115

1. sometimes **3.** sometimes **5.** always **7.**

9. not possible **11.** $x = 13$; $m\angle PQR = 156$ **13.** 15, 75, 90 **15.** 90 **17.** 90 **19.** 60 **21.** 60 **23.** False. If 2 lines are $\parallel$, then they do not intersect; true. **25.** True. If an $\angle$ is not obtuse, then it is acute; false. **27.** Vert. $\angle$s are $\cong$. **29.** $\angle$ Add. Post. **31.** The meas. of an ext. $\angle$ of a $\triangle$ = the sum of the meas. of the 2 remote int. $\angle$s. **33.** The sum of the meas. of the $\angle$s of a $\triangle$ is 180. **35.** X **37.** pentagon **39.** $\cong$ **41.** biconditional **43.** 1080 **45.** 1. $\overline{WX} \perp \overline{XY}$ (Given) 2. $\angle 1$ is comp. to $\angle 2$. (If the ext. sides of adj. $\angle$s are $\perp$, then the $\angle$s are comp.) 3. $\angle 1$ is comp. to $\angle 3$. (Given) 4. $\angle 2 \cong \angle 3$ (Comps. of same $\angle$ are $\cong$.)

Chapter 4

Written Exercises, Pages 120–121

1. $\angle T$ **3.** CA **5.** $\triangle ATC$ **7.** $\angle E, \angle F, \angle S, \angle T$ **9.** $\angle L \cong \angle F, \angle X \cong \angle N, \angle R \cong \angle E, \overline{LX} \cong \overline{FN}, \overline{XR} \cong \overline{NE}, \overline{LR} \cong \overline{FE}$ **11. a.** $\triangle RLA$ **b.** $\overline{RL}$ **c.** $\angle 3$, CPCT; $\overline{LR}$, If 2 lines are cut by a trans. and alt. int. ∠s are ≅, then the lines are ∥. **d.** $\angle 4$, CPCT; $\overline{PL}, \overline{AR}$, If 2 lines are cut by a trans. and alt. int. ∠s are ≅, then the lines are ∥. **13.** $C(7, -1)$ **15.** $\triangle ABC \cong \triangle EDF$ **17.** $\triangle ABC \cong \triangle FDE$ **19.** $F(2, 5)$, $F(6, 1)$ **21. a.** Since $NERO \cong MARO$, $\overline{NO} \cong \overline{OM}$. By the def. of midpt., O is the midpt. of $\overline{NM}$. **b.** $\angle NOR$ and $\angle MOR$ are corr. ∠s of ≅ quads. **c.** If 2 lines form ≅ adj. ∠s, then the lines are ⊥. **23.** Yes; yes; yes

Mixed Review Exercises, Page 121

1. 1. $\overline{AD} \perp \overline{BC}$; $\overline{BA} \perp \overline{AC}$ (Given) 2. $\angle BDA$ and $\angle BAC$ are rt. ∠s. (Def. of ⊥ lines) 3. $\triangle ABC$ and $\triangle DBA$ are rt. △s. (Def. of rt. △) 4. $\angle 1$ and $\angle B$ are comp.; $\angle 2$ and $\angle B$ are comp. (The acute ∠s of a rt. △ are comp.) 5. $\angle 1 \cong \angle 2$ (If 2 ∠s are comp. of the same ∠, then the 2 ∠s are ≅.) **2.** 1. $\overline{FC}$ and $\overline{SH}$ bis. each other at A. (Given) 2. A is the midpt. of $\overline{FC}$ and $\overline{SH}$. (Def. of bis.) 3. $SA = \frac{1}{2}SH$ and $AC = \frac{1}{2}FC$ (Midpt. Thm.) 4. $FC = SH$ (Given) 5. $\frac{1}{2}FC = \frac{1}{2}SH$ (Mult. Prop. of =.) 6. $SA = AC$ (Substitution Prop.)

Written Exercises, Pages 124–127

1. $\triangle ABC \cong \triangle NPY$; ASA **3.** $\triangle ABC \cong \triangle CKA$; SSS **5.** No ≅ can be deduced. **7.** $\triangle ABC \cong \triangle PQC$; SAS **9.** $\triangle ABC \cong \triangle AGC$; ASA **11.** $\triangle ABC \cong \triangle BST$; ASA **13.** No ≅ can be deduced. **15.** $\triangle ABC \cong \triangle MNC$; ASA **17.** 1. Given 2. T; Def. of ⊥ lines 3. Def. of ≅ ∠s 4. Given 5. $\overline{VT}$; Def. of midpt. 6. UVT; Vert. ∠s are ≅. 7. RSV, UTV; ASA Post. **19.** 1. E is the midpt. of $\overline{TP}$ and $\overline{MR}$. (Given) 2. $\overline{TE} \cong \overline{PE}$; $\overline{ME} \cong \overline{RE}$ (Def. of midpt.) 3. $\angle TEM \cong \angle PER$ (Vert. ∠s are ≅.) 4. $\triangle TEM \cong \triangle PER$ (SAS Post.) **21.** 1. Plane M bis. $\overline{AB}$. (Given) 2. $\overline{AO} \cong \overline{BO}$ (Def. of bis.) 3. $\overline{PO} \perp \overline{AB}$ (Given) 4. $\angle POA \cong \angle POB$ (If 2 lines are ⊥, then they form ≅ adj. ∠s.) 5. $\overline{PO} \cong \overline{PO}$ (Refl. Prop.) 6. $\triangle POA \cong \triangle POB$ (SAS Post.)

23. Given: Isos. $\triangle ABC$ with $\overline{AC} \cong \overline{AB}$; D is the midpt. of $\overline{CB}$.
Prove: $\triangle ACD \cong \triangle ABD$
Proof: 1. $\overline{AC} \cong \overline{AB}$; D is the midpt. of $\overline{CB}$. (Given)
2. $\overline{CD} \cong \overline{BD}$ (Def. of midpt.)
3. $\overline{AD} \cong \overline{AD}$ (Refl. Prop.)
4. $\triangle ACD \cong \triangle ABD$ (SSS Post.)

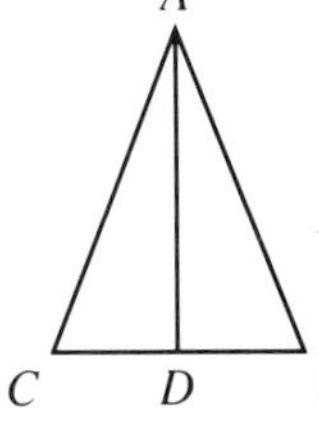

27. SSS

Written Exercises, Pages 130–132

1. 1. Given 2. Given 3. Def. of midpt. 4. Vert. ∠s are ≅. 5. ASA Post. 6. CPCT 7. Def. of midpt. **3.** 1. $\overline{WO} \cong \overline{ZO}$; $\overline{XO} \cong \overline{YO}$ (Given) 2. $\angle WOX \cong \angle ZOY$ (Vert. ∠s are ≅.) 3. $\triangle WOX \cong \triangle ZOY$ (SAS Post.) 4. $\angle W \cong \angle Z$ (CPCT) **5.** 1. $\overline{SK} \parallel \overline{NR}$; $\overline{SN} \parallel \overline{KR}$ (Given) 2. $\angle 1 \cong \angle 3$; $\angle 2 \cong \angle 4$ (If 2 ∥ lines are cut by a trans., then alt. int. ∠s are ≅.) 3. $\overline{SR} \cong \overline{SR}$ (Refl. Prop.) 4. $\triangle SKR \cong \triangle RNS$ (ASA Post.) 5. $\overline{SK} \cong \overline{NR}$; $\overline{SN} \cong \overline{KR}$ (CPCT) **7.** 1. $\overline{AD} \parallel \overline{ME}$; $\overline{MD} \parallel \overline{BE}$ (Given) 2. $\angle A \cong \angle EMB$; $\angle DMA \cong \angle B$ (If 2 ∥ lines are cut by a trans., then corr. ∠s are ≅.) 3. M is the midpt. of $\overline{AB}$. (Given) 4. $\overline{AM} \cong \overline{MB}$ (Def. of midpt.) 5. $\triangle ADM \cong \triangle MEB$ (ASA Post.) 6. $\overline{MD} \cong \overline{BE}$ (CPCT) **9.** Either (a) $\angle 1 \cong \angle 2$ or (b) $\overline{QR} \cong \overline{SR}$ can be omitted. **a.** 1. $\overline{PQ} \cong \overline{PS}$; $\overline{QR} \cong \overline{SR}$ (Given) 2. $\overline{PR} \cong \overline{PR}$ (Refl. Prop.) 3. $\triangle PQR \cong \triangle PSR$ (SSS Post.) 4. $\angle 3 \cong \angle 4$ (CPCT) **b.** 1. $\overline{PQ} \cong \overline{PS}$; $\angle 1 \cong \angle 2$ (Given) 2. $\overline{PR} \cong \overline{PR}$ (Refl. Prop.) 3. $\triangle PQR \cong \triangle PSR$ (SAS Post.) 4. $\angle 3 \cong \angle 4$ (CPCT) **11.** 1, 2 **13.** 1. $\overline{RS} \perp$ plane Y (Given) 2. $\overline{RS} \perp \overline{ST}$; $\overline{RS} \perp \overline{SV}$ (Def. of a line ⊥ to a plane.) 3. $m\angle RST = 90$; $m\angle RSV = 90$ (Def. of ⊥ lines) 4. $\angle RST \cong \angle RSV$ (Def. of ≅ ∠s) 5. $\angle TRS \cong \angle VRS$ (Given) 6. $\overline{RS} \cong \overline{RS}$ (Refl. Prop.) 7. $\triangle RST \cong \triangle RSV$ (ASA Post.) 8. $\overline{RT} \cong \overline{RV}$ (CPCT) 9. $\triangle RTV$ is isos. (Def. of isos. △) **15.** The wires are of equal length, so $PA = PB = PC$. The stakes are equidistant from the base of the tree, so $TA = TB = TC$. $PT = PT = PT$ by the Refl. Prop. and $\triangle PTA \cong \triangle PTB \cong \triangle PTC$ by SSS. The ∠s that 3 wires make with the ground are ≅ parts of ≅ △s.

Self-Test 1, Pages 132–133

1. $\angle P \cong \angle T$; CPCT **2.** $\overline{KO}$, $\overline{MA}$; $\overline{OP}$, $\overline{AT}$; $\overline{KP}$, $\overline{MT}$ **3.** $\triangle JKX \cong \triangle JKY$; SAS **4.** No $\cong$ can be deduced. **5.** $\triangle TRP \cong \triangle TRS$; ASA **6.** 1. $\angle 1 \cong \angle 2$; $\angle 3 \cong \angle 4$ (Given) 2. $\overline{DB} \cong \overline{DB}$ (Refl. Prop.) 3. $\triangle ADB \cong \triangle CBD$ (ASA Post.) **7.** 1. $\overline{CD} \cong \overline{AB}$; $\overline{CB} \cong \overline{AD}$ (Given) 2. $\overline{DB} \cong \overline{DB}$ (Refl. Prop.) 3. $\triangle ADB \cong \triangle CBD$ (SSS Post.) 4. $\angle 1 \cong \angle 2$ (CPCT) **8.** 1. $\overline{AD} \parallel \overline{BC}$ (Given) 2. $\angle 4 \cong \angle 3$ (If 2 $\parallel$ lines are cut by a trans., then alt. int. $\angle$s are $\cong$.) 3. $\overline{AD} \cong \overline{CB}$ (Given) 4. $\overline{DB} \cong \overline{DB}$ (Refl. Prop.) 5. $\triangle ADB \cong \triangle CBD$ (SAS Post.) 6. $\angle 1 \cong \angle 2$ (CPCT) 7. $\overline{DC} \parallel \overline{AB}$ (If 2 lines are cut by a trans. and alt. int. $\angle$s are $\cong$, then the lines are $\parallel$.)

Written Exercises, Pages 137–139

1. 80 **3.** 53 **5.** 5 **7.** 41 **9.** Answers may vary; c, d, b, a **11.** 1. $\overline{AB} \cong \overline{AC}$ (Given) 2. Let the bis. of $\angle A$ int. $\overline{BC}$ at D. (By the Protractor Post., an $\angle$ has exactly one bis.) 3. $\angle BAD \cong \angle CAD$ (Def. of $\angle$ bis.) 4. $\overline{AD} \cong \overline{AD}$ (Refl. Prop.) 5. $\triangle BAD \cong \triangle CAD$ (SAS Post.) 6. $\angle B \cong \angle C$ (CPCT) **13.** 1. $\angle 1 \cong \angle 2$ (Given) 2. $\overline{JG} \cong \overline{JM}$ (If 2 $\angle$s of a $\triangle$ are $\cong$, then the sides opp. those $\angle$s are $\cong$.) 3. M is the midpt. of $\overline{JK}$. (Given) 4. $\overline{JM} \cong \overline{MK}$ (Def. of midpt.) 5. $\overline{JG} \cong \overline{MK}$ (Trans. Prop.) **15.** 1, 3 **17.** 1. $\overline{XY} \cong \overline{XZ}$ (Given) 2. $\angle XYZ \cong \angle XZY$ or $m\angle XYZ = m\angle XZY$ (Isos. $\triangle$ Thm.) 3. $m\angle XYZ = m\angle 1 + m\angle 2$; $m\angle XZY = m\angle 3 + m\angle 4$ ($\angle$ Add. Post.) 4. $m\angle 1 + m\angle 2 = m\angle 3 + m\angle 4$ (Substitution Prop.) 5. $\overline{OY} \cong \overline{OZ}$ (Given) 6. $\angle 2 \cong \angle 3$ or $m\angle 2 = m\angle 3$ (Isos. $\triangle$ Thm.) 7. $m\angle 1 = m\angle 4$ (Subtr. Prop. of $=$)
19. 1. $\overline{AB} \cong \overline{AC}$ (Given) 2. $\angle B \cong \angle C$ (Isos. $\triangle$ Thm.) 3. $\overline{AL}$ and $\overline{AM}$ trisect $\angle BAC$, so $\angle 1 \cong \angle 3$. (Given) 4. $\triangle BLA \cong \triangle CMA$ (ASA Post.) 5. $\overline{AL} \cong \overline{AM}$ (CPCT) **21.** 1. $\overline{OP} \cong \overline{OQ}$; $\angle 3 \cong \angle 4$ (Given) 2. $\angle POS \cong \angle QOR$ (Vert. $\angle$s are $\cong$.) 3. $\triangle POS \cong \triangle QOR$ (ASA Post.) 4. $\overline{OS} \cong \overline{OR}$ (CPCT) 5. $\angle 5 \cong \angle 6$ (Isos. $\triangle$ Thm.) **23. a.** 40, 40, 60 **b.** $2x$, $2x$, $3x$ **25. a.** 90 **b.** 90 **27.** $x = 2$, $y = 1$
29. $x = 30$, $y = 10$ **31. a.** Key steps of proof: 1. $\triangle JKM \cong \triangle JKN$ and $\triangle LKM \cong \triangle LKN$ (SAS Post.) 2. $\overline{JM} \cong \overline{JN}$ and $\overline{LM} \cong \overline{LN}$ (CPCT) 3. $\triangle JMN$ and $\triangle LMN$ are isos. (Def. of isos. $\triangle$) **b.** No. They are $\cong$ if and only if $\overline{KJ} \cong \overline{KL}$. **33.** $m\angle EAF = 9$, $m\angle AFD = 54$, $m\angle DAF = 45$

Written Exercises, Pages 143–145

1. 1. Given 2. Def. of rt. $\triangle$ 3. Given 4. $\overline{XZ} \cong \overline{XZ}$ 5. $\triangle XYZ$; HL 6. $\overline{WZ} \cong \overline{YZ}$; CPCT **3.** 1. $\overline{EF} \perp \overline{EG}$; $\overline{HG} \perp \overline{EG}$ (Given) 2. $\angle HGE$ and $\angle FEG$ are rt. $\angle$s. (Def. of $\perp$ lines) 3. $\triangle HGE$ and $\triangle FEG$ are rt. $\triangle$s. (Def. of rt. $\triangle$) 4. $\overline{EH} \cong \overline{GF}$ (Given) 5. $\overline{EG} \cong \overline{EG}$ (Refl. Prop.) 6. $\triangle HGE \cong \triangle FEG$ (HL) 7. $\angle H \cong \angle F$ (CPCT) **5.** SAS **7.** HL **9. a.** 1. $\overline{PR} \cong \overline{PQ}$ (Given) 2. $\angle PQR \cong \angle PRQ$ (Isos. $\triangle$ Thm.) 3. $\overline{SR} \cong \overline{TQ}$ (Given) 4. $\overline{RQ} \cong \overline{RQ}$ (Refl. Prop.) 5. $\triangle RQS \cong \triangle QRT$ (SAS Post.) 6. $\overline{QS} \cong \overline{RT}$ (CPCT) **b.** 1. $\overline{PR} \cong \overline{PQ}$ or $PR = PQ$; $\overline{SR} \cong \overline{TQ}$ or $SR = TQ$ (Given) 2. $PR = PS + SR$; $PQ = PT + TQ$ (Seg. Add. Post.) 3. $PS + SR = PT + TQ$ (Substitution Prop.) 4. $PS = PT$ or $\overline{PS} \cong \overline{PT}$ (Subtr. Prop. of $=$) 5. $\angle P \cong \angle P$ (Refl. Prop.) 6. $\triangle PQS \cong \triangle PRT$ (SAS Post.) 7. $\overline{QS} \cong \overline{RT}$ (CPCT) **11.** $\overline{PR} \cong \overline{PS}$, $\overline{PQ} \cong \overline{PT}$, $\overline{QR} \cong \overline{TS}$; SSS **13.** $\angle 3 \cong \angle 4$, $\overline{PQ} \cong \overline{PT}$, $\angle 6 \cong \angle 5$; AAS **15.** 1. $\angle 1 \cong \angle 2 \cong \angle 3$ (Given) 2. $\overline{ME} \cong \overline{MD}$ (If 2 $\angle$s of a $\triangle$ are $\cong$, then the sides opp. those $\angle$s are $\cong$.) 3. $\overline{EN} \cong \overline{DG}$ (Given) 4. $\triangle MEN \cong \triangle MDG$ (SAS Post.) 5. $\angle 4 \cong \angle 5$ (CPCT)

17. Given: Isos. $\triangle XYZ$ with $\overline{XY} \cong \overline{XZ}$;
$\overline{ZA} \perp \overline{XY}$; $\overline{YB} \perp \overline{XZ}$
Prove: $\overline{ZA} \cong \overline{YB}$

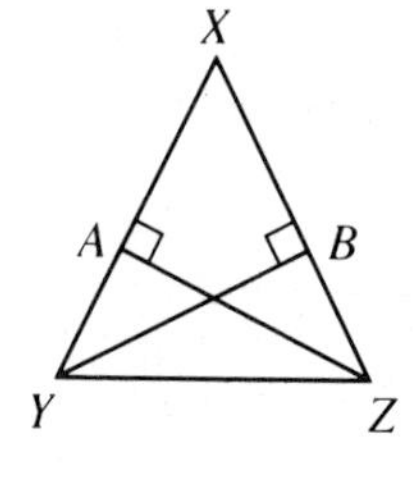

Proof: 1. $\overline{ZA} \perp \overline{XY}$; $\overline{YB} \perp \overline{XZ}$ (Given) 2. $m\angle XBY = 90$; $m\angle XAZ = 90$ (Def. of $\perp$ lines) 3. $\angle XBY \cong \angle XAZ$ (Def. of $\cong$ $\angle$s) 4. $\angle X \cong \angle X$ (Refl. Prop.) 5. $\overline{XY} \cong \overline{XZ}$ (Given) 6. $\triangle XBY \cong \triangle XAZ$ (AAS Thm.) 7. $\overline{ZA} \cong \overline{YB}$ (CPCT)

Self-Test 2, Page 146

1. 70 **2.** 7 **3.** 30 **4.** $\overline{AB} \cong \overline{AC}$, $\angle A \cong \angle A$, $\angle ANB \cong \angle AMC$, so $\triangle ABN \cong \triangle ACM$ by AAS.
5. 1. $\overline{BN} \perp \overline{AC}$; $\overline{CM} \perp \overline{AB}$ (Given) 2. $\angle BMC$ and $\angle CNB$ are rt. $\angle$s. (Def. of $\perp$ lines) 3. $\triangle BMC$ and $\triangle CNB$ are rt. $\triangle$s. (Def. of rt. $\triangle$) 4. $\overline{MB} \cong \overline{NC}$ (Given) 5. $\overline{BC} \cong \overline{BC}$ (Refl. Prop.) 6. $\triangle BMC \cong \triangle CNB$ (HL)
7. $\overline{CM} \cong \overline{BN}$ (CPCT)

Written Exercises, Pages 148–151

1. a. SSS **b.** CPCT **c.** SAS **d.** CPCT **3. a.** AAS **b.** CPCT **c.** SAS **d.** CPCT **5. a.** SAS **b.** CPCT **c.** HL **d.** CPCT **7. a.** 1. $\triangle FLA \cong \triangle FKA$ (SSS) 2. $\angle 1 \cong \angle 2$ (CPCT) 3. $\triangle FLJ \cong \triangle FKJ$ (SAS) 4. $\overline{LJ} \cong \overline{KJ}$ (CPCT) **b.** 1. $\overline{LF} \cong \overline{KF}$; $\overline{LA} \cong \overline{KA}$ (Given) 2. $\overline{FA} \cong \overline{FA}$ (Refl. Prop.) 3. $\triangle FLA \cong \triangle FKA$ (SSS) 4. $\angle 1 \cong \angle 2$ (CPCT) 5. $\overline{FJ} \cong \overline{FJ}$ (Refl. Prop.) 6. $\triangle FLJ \cong \triangle FKJ$ (SAS) 7. $\overline{LJ} \cong \overline{KJ}$ (CPCT) **9.** Key steps of proof: 1. $\overline{ST} \cong \overline{YZ}$; $\angle T \cong \angle Z$; $\angle RST \cong \angle XYZ$ (CPCT) 2. $m\angle KST = \frac{1}{2}m\angle RST$; $m\angle LYZ = \frac{1}{2}m\angle XYZ$ ($\angle$ Bis. Thm.) 3. $m\angle KST = m\angle LYZ$ (Substitution Prop.) 4. $\triangle KST \cong \triangle LYZ$ (ASA) 5. $\overline{SK} \cong \overline{YL}$ (CPCT) **11.** Key steps of proof: 1. $\triangle GDE \cong \triangle EFG$ (SSS) 2. $\angle DEH \cong \angle FGK$ (CPCT) 3. $\triangle HDE \cong \triangle KFG$ (ASA) 4. $\overline{DH} \cong \overline{FK}$ (CPCT) **17.** isos.; $\overline{AX} \cong \overline{AY}$, $\overline{AZ} \cong \overline{AZ}$, and $\angle XAZ \cong \angle YAZ$, so $\triangle XAZ \cong \triangle YAZ$ by SAS. Then $\overline{XZ} \cong \overline{YZ}$ (CPCT) and $\triangle XYZ$ is isos.

Mixed Review Exercises, Page 151

1. Two sides of a $\triangle$ are $\cong$ if and only if the $\angle$s opp. those sides are $\cong$. **2.** sometimes **3.** sometimes **4.** always **5. a.** A M B **b.** A M B

6. a. Y C D X

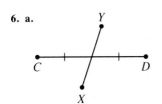

b.

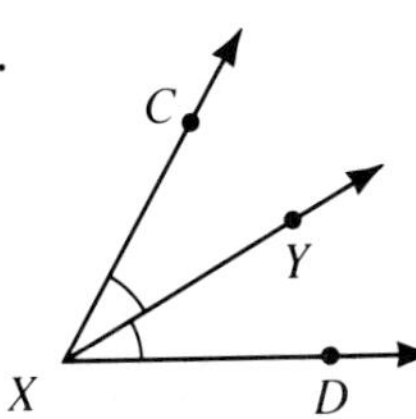

7. a.

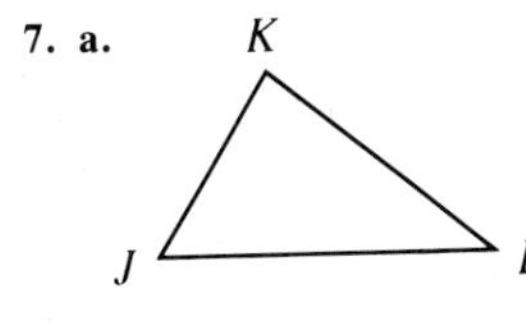

b.

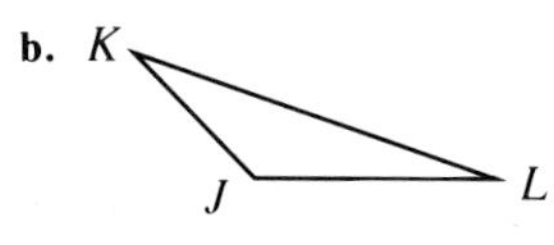

8. a.

b.

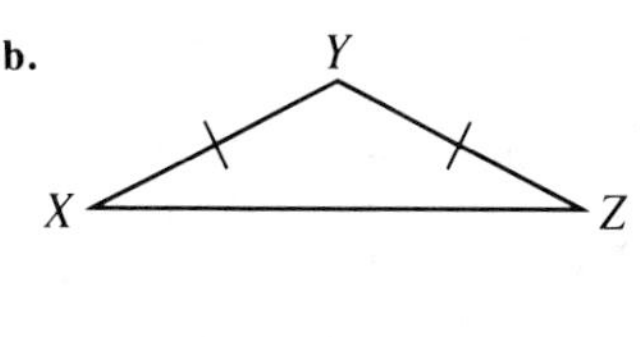

9. a.

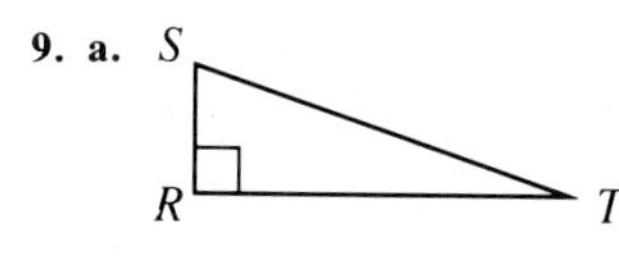

b.

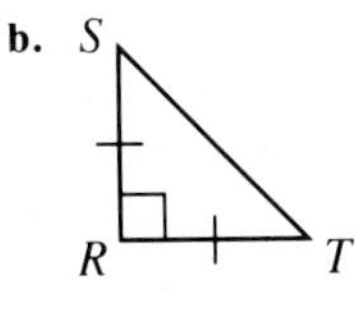

10. a.

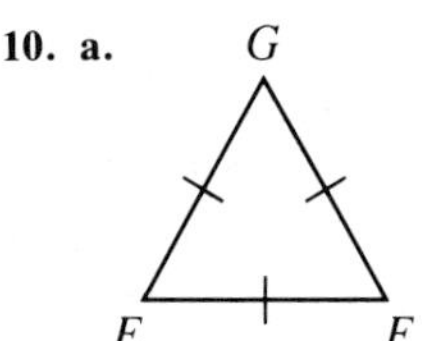

b.

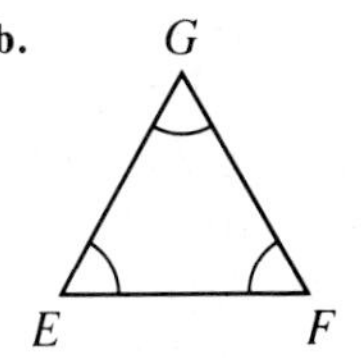

11. 1. $\overline{BE} \cong \overline{CD}$; $\overline{BD} \cong \overline{CE}$ (Given) 2. $\overline{BC} \cong \overline{BC}$ (Refl. Prop.) 3. $\triangle EBC \cong \triangle DCB$ (SSS) 4. $\angle EBC \cong \angle DCB$ (CPCT) 5. $\overline{AB} \cong \overline{AC}$ (If 2 $\angle$s of a $\triangle$ are $\cong$, then the sides opp. those $\angle$s are $\cong$.) 6. $\triangle ABC$ is isos. (Def. of isos. $\triangle$)

Written Exercises, Pages 156–158

Sketches may vary in Exs. 1–5. **1. b.** No **5.** Yes; at the midpt. of the hyp. **7.** $\overrightarrow{KS}$, $\overrightarrow{KN}$ **9.** bis. of $\angle S$ **11.** A, F **13.** 1. P is on the $\perp$ bisectors of $\overline{AB}$ and $\overline{BC}$. (Given) 2. $PA = PB$; $PB = PC$ (If a pt. lies on the $\perp$ bis. of a seg., then it is equidistant from the end pts. of the seg.) 3. $PA = PC$ (Trans. Prop.) **15.** Key steps of proof: 1. Let X be the midpt. of $\overline{BC}$. (Ruler Post.) 2. $\triangle AXB \cong \triangle AXC$ (SSS) 3. $\angle 1 \cong \angle 2$ (CPCT) 4. $\overline{AX} \perp \overline{BC}$ (If 2 lines form $\cong$ adj. $\angle$s, then the lines are $\perp$.) 5. $\overline{AX}$ is the $\perp$ bis. of $\overline{BC}$. (Def. of $\perp$ bis.) **17.** Key steps of proof: 1. $\overline{PX} \perp \overrightarrow{BA}$; $\overline{PY} \perp \overrightarrow{BC}$; $PX = PY$ (Given) 2. $\triangle PXB \cong \triangle PYB$ (HL) 3. $\angle PBX \cong \angle PBY$ (CPCT) 4. $\overrightarrow{BP}$ bis. $\angle ABC$. (Def. of $\angle$ bis.)

21. a. Key steps of proof: 1. $\overline{AB} \cong \overline{AC}$; $\overline{BD} \perp \overline{AC}$; $\overline{CE} \perp \overline{AB}$ (Given) 2. $\triangle ADB \cong \triangle AEC$ (AAS) 3. $\overline{BD} \cong \overline{CE}$ (CPCT) **b.** The altitudes drawn to the legs of an isos. △ are ≅. **23.** Q is on the ⊥ bis. of $\overline{PS}$, so $PQ = SQ$. S is on the ⊥ bis. of $\overline{QT}$, so $QS = TS$. Then $PQ = TS$ by the Trans. Prop. **25. a.** $\overline{OD}$ is a ⊥ bis. of $\overline{AB}$, so $\overline{AD} \cong \overline{BD}$. **b.** $\overline{OC}$ is a ⊥ bis. of $\overline{AB}$, so $\overline{AC} \cong \overline{BC}$. **c.** By parts (a) and (b) above, $\overline{AD} \cong \overline{BD}$ and $\overline{AC} \cong \overline{BC}$. Then since $\overline{CD} \cong \overline{CD}$, $\triangle CAD \cong \triangle CBD$ by SSS and $\angle CAD \cong \angle CBD$ (CPCT).

Self-Test 3, Page 159

1. $\overline{EA} \cong \overline{DB}$ and $\angle AEB \cong \angle BDA$ **2.** 1. $\triangle MPQ \cong \triangle PMN$ (Given) 2. $\overline{MN} \cong \overline{QP}$; $\angle MPQ \cong \angle PMN$ (CPCT) 3. $\overline{MS} \cong \overline{PR}$ (Given) 4. $\triangle MSN \cong \triangle PRQ$ (SAS) **3. a.** $\overline{LJ}$ or $\overline{KJ}$ **b.** $\overline{KZ}$ **4.** No **5.** If a pt. lies on the bis. of an ∠, then the pt. is equidistant from the sides of the ∠. **6.** If a pt. is equidistant from the endpts. of a seg., then the pt. lies on the ⊥ bis. of the seg.

Chapter Review, Pages 160–161

1. $\triangle QPR$ **3.** $\angle W$ **5.** Yes; SSS **7.** Yes; ASA **9.** 1. $\overline{JM} \cong \overline{LM}$; $\overline{JK} \cong \overline{LK}$ (Given) 2. $\overline{MK} \cong \overline{MK}$ (Refl. Prop.) 3. $\triangle MJK \cong \triangle MLK$ (SSS) 4. $\angle MJK \cong \angle MLK$ (CPCT) **11.** $\overline{ER}$, $\overline{EV}$ **13.** 25
15. 1. $\overline{GH} \perp \overline{HJ}$; $\overline{KJ} \perp \overline{HJ}$ (Given) 2. $m\angle GHJ = 90$; $m\angle KJH = 90$ (Def. of ⊥ lines) 3. $\angle GHJ \cong \angle KJH$ (Def. of ≅ ∠s) 4. $\angle G \cong \angle K$ (Given) 5. $\overline{HJ} \cong \overline{HJ}$ (Refl. Prop.) 6. $\triangle GHJ \cong \triangle KJH$ (AAS)
17. 1. ASA 2. CPCT 3. HL 4. CPCT 5. If 2 lines are cut by a trans. and alt. int. ∠s are ≅, then the lines are ∥. **19.** If a pt. lies on the ⊥ bis. of a seg., then the pt. is equidistant from the endpts. of the seg.

Algebra Review, Page 163

1. −6, 1 **3.** −2, 9 **5.** 0, 13 **7.** −13, 13 **9.** −0.2, 0.2 **11.** 3 **13.** −6, −2 **15.** 5 **17.** −4, 5 **19.** $\frac{-3 \pm \sqrt{57}}{6}$ **21.** $\frac{-5 \pm \sqrt{17}}{2}$ **23.** $\frac{5 \pm \sqrt{13}}{2}$ **25.** 1, 9 **27.** −7, 2 **29.** 20 **31.** 1 **33.** 1.5

Preparing for College Entrance Exams, Page 164

1. A **2.** C **3.** D **4.** C **5.** B **6.** C **7.** E **8.** D **9.** B

Cumulative Review, Page 165

1. Seg. Add. Post. **3.** obtuse **5.** 16 **7.** 10 **9.** SSS **11.** $m\angle 5 = 90$, $m\angle 6 = 54$, $m\angle 7 = 36$, $m\angle 8 = 54$ **13.** No **15.** Yes; $a \parallel b$ **17.** Key steps of proof: 1. $\overline{MO} \perp \overline{NP}$, $\overline{NO} \cong \overline{PO}$ (Given) 2. $\triangle NQO \cong \triangle PQO$ (HL) 3. $\angle NOQ \cong \angle POQ$ (CPCT) 4. $\triangle MNO \cong \triangle MPO$ (SAS) 5. $\overline{MN} \cong \overline{MP}$ (CPCT)

Chapter 5

Written Exercises, Pages 169–171

1. $\overline{CR}$, $\overline{CE}$ **3.** $\overline{ER}$, $\overline{RC}$, $\overline{CW}$ **5.** $a = 8$, $b = 10$, $x = 118$, $y = 62$ **7.** $a = 5$, $b = 3$, $x = 120$, $y = 22$ **9.** $a = 8$, $b = 8$, $x = 56$, $y = 68$ **11.** 60 **17.** (3, 2) **19.** $x = 3$, $y = 5$ **21.** $x = 13$, $y = 5$ **23.** $x = 5$, $y = 4$ **25.** 5, 2 **27.** 10, 70 **29.** 1. $PQRS$ is a ▱; $\overline{PJ} \cong \overline{RK}$ (Given) 2. $\angle P \cong \angle R$ (Thm. 5-2) 3. $\overline{SP} \cong \overline{QR}$ (Thm. 5-1) 4. $\triangle SPJ \cong \triangle QRK$ (SAS) 5. $\overline{SJ} \cong \overline{QK}$ (CPCT)
31. 1. $ABCD$ is a ▱; $\overline{CD} \cong \overline{CE}$ (Given) 2. $\overline{AB} \parallel \overline{CD}$ (Def. of ▱) 3. $\angle CDE \cong \angle A$ (If lines ∥, corr. ∠s ≅.) 4. $\angle CDE \cong \angle E$ (Isos. △ Thm.) 5. $\angle A \cong \angle E$ (Subst.) **35.** (6, 0), (0, 8), (12, 8)

Written Exercises, Pages 174–176

1. Def. of ▱ **3.** Thm. 5-5 **5.** Thm. 5-6 **7.** Thm. 5-7 **9. a.** Thm. 5-4 **b.** Thm. 5-6 **c.** Thm. 5-7 **15.** $m\angle DAB = m\angle BCD$, so $m\angle NAM = \frac{1}{2}m\angle DAB = \frac{1}{2}m\angle BCD = m\angle NCM$. $m\angle DNA = m\angle NAM = m\angle NCM$, so $\overline{AN}$ and $\overline{CM}$ are ∥. $\overline{CN}$ and $\overline{AM}$ are ∥ because $ABCD$ is a ▱. Then $AMCN$ is a ▱, by def. of ▱. **17.** Draw $\overline{AC}$ int. $\overline{DB}$ at Z. Since $DZ = ZB$ and $DE = FB$, $EZ = DZ - DE = ZB - FB = ZF$. Also, $AZ = ZC$. If the diags. of a quad. bis. each other, then the quad. is a ▱. So $AFCE$ is a ▱.
19. $x = 18$, $y = 14$ **21.** $x = 10$, $y = 2$ **23.** Key steps of proof: 1. $\triangle DAE \cong \triangle BCF$ (AAS) 2. $\overline{DE} \cong \overline{BF}$ (CPCT) 3. $\overline{DE} \parallel \overline{BF}$ (Thm. 3-7) 4. $DEBF$ is a ▱. (Thm. 5-5)

Written Exercises, Pages 180–182

1. 12, 12 **3.** 4 **5. a.** 40 **b.** 20 **c.** 26 **d.** 34 **7.** D, E **9.** D, F **11.** 6 **13.** 11 **15.** 3, 2 **17.** $x = 4$, $y = 2$ **19.** 1. $\overline{BE} \parallel \overline{MD}$; M is the midpt. of $\overline{AB}$. (Given) 2. D is the midpt. of $\overline{AE}$. (Thm. 5-10) 3. $\overline{DE} \cong \overline{AD}$ (Def. of midpt.) 4. $ABCD$ is a ▱. (Given) 5. $\overline{AD} \cong \overline{BC}$ (Thm. 5-1) 6. $DE = BC$ (Trans. Prop.)

23. Given: X, Y, and Z are the midpts. of $\overline{AB}$, $\overline{AC}$, and $\overline{BC}$, resp.; P and Q are midpts. of $\overline{BZ}$ and $\overline{CZ}$, resp.

Prove: $PX = QY$

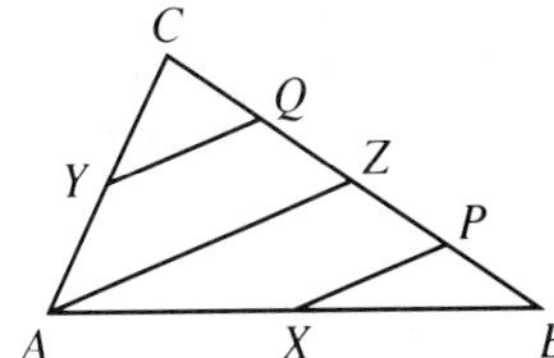

Key steps of proof: 1. $PX = \frac{1}{2}AZ$; $QY = \frac{1}{2}AZ$ (Thm. 5-11, part (2))

2. $PX = QY$ (Subst.)

Self-Test 1, Page 182

1. may be **2.** must be **3.** must be **4.** cannot be **5.** See page 172. **6. a.** If 3 ∥ lines cut off ≅ seg. on one trans., then they cut off ≅ seg. on every trans. **b.** $x = 6$, $y = 19$ **7.** 1. $ABCD$ is a ▱. (Given) 2. $\overline{AC}$ and $\overline{BD}$ bis. each other. (Diags. ▱ bis. each other.) 3. O is the midpt. of $\overline{BD}$. (Def. of bis.) 4. M is the midpt. of $\overline{AB}$. (Given) 5. $MO = \frac{1}{2}AD$ (Thm. 5-11) **8.** 1. $PQRS$ is a ▱. (Given) 2. $\overline{SR} \parallel \overline{PQ}$; $\overline{SP} \parallel \overline{RQ}$ (Def. of ▱) 3. $m\angle QPR = m\angle SRP$ (If lines ∥, alt. int. ∠s ≅.) 4. $\overrightarrow{PX}$ bis. $\angle QPR$; $\overrightarrow{RY}$ bis. $\angle SRP$. (Given) 5. $m\angle RPX = \frac{1}{2}m\angle QPR$; $m\angle PRY = \frac{1}{2}m\angle SRP$ (∠ Bis. Thm.) 6. $\frac{1}{2}m\angle QPR = \frac{1}{2}m\angle SRP$ (Mult. Prop. of =) 7. $m\angle RPX = m\angle PRY$ (Subst.) 8. $\overline{YR} \parallel \overline{PX}$ (If alt. int. ∠s ≅, lines ∥.) 9. $RYPX$ is a ▱. (Def. of ▱)

Written Exercises, Pages 187–189

1. all **3.** all **5.** all **7.** rhom., sq. **9.** rect., sq. **11.** 25, 65, 65, 90 **13.** 10 **15.** $13\frac{1}{2}$ **17.** 32, 58, 58 **19.** $\frac{1}{2}$ **21.** (2, 5); no **23.** (4, 6); yes **25.** 15 **27.** 60 **29.** 1. $ABZY$ is a ▱. (Given) 2. $\overline{BZ} \cong \overline{AY}$ (Thm. 5-1) 3. $\overline{AY} \cong \overline{BX}$ (Given) 4. $\overline{BZ} \cong \overline{BX}$ (Trans. Prop.) 5. $\angle 1 \cong \angle 2$ (Isos. △ Thm.) 6. $\overline{BZ} \parallel \overline{AY}$ (Def. of ▱) 7. $\angle 2 \cong \angle 3$ (If lines ∥, corr. ∠s are ≅.) 8. $\angle 1 \cong \angle 3$ (Trans. Prop.) **31.** 1. $QRST$ is a rect.; $RKST$ and $JQST$ are ▱s. (Given) 2. $\overline{KS} \cong \overline{RT}$; $\overline{JT} \cong \overline{QS}$ (Thm. 5-1) 3. $\overline{RT} \cong \overline{QS}$ (Diags. of rect. ≅.) 4. $\overline{JT} \cong \overline{KS}$ (Subst.) **37.** square **39.** 6, 8

Mixed Review Exercises, Page 189

1. 13 **2.** 20 **3.** 11 **4.** 9 **5.** 8.2 **6.** −1.5 **7.** 1 **8.** 3.45 **9. a.** 23 **b.** 2 **c.** 4 **d.** −6

Written Exercises, Pages 192–194

1. 12 **3.** 15 **5.** 9 **7.** 4 **9.** 6 **11.** $x = 10$; 40, 40, 140, 140 **13.** $BE = \frac{1}{2}(AD + CF)$ **15.** 13, 39 **17.** 9, 15 **19.** $CF = 3 \cdot AD$, but $17 \neq 3 \cdot 5$. **21.** rect. **23.** rhom. **25.** ▱

27. Given: Trap. $ABXY$ with $\overline{BX} \cong \overline{AY}$

Prove: $\angle 1 \cong \angle 3$; $\angle ABX \cong \angle A$

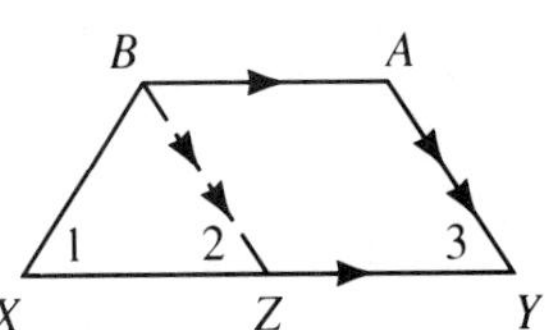

Key steps of proof: 1. $ABZY$ is a ▱. (Def. of ▱) 2. $\angle 1 \cong \angle 2$ (Isos. △ Thm.) 3. $\angle 2 \cong \angle 3$ (If lines ∥, corr. ∠s ≅.) 4. $\angle 1 \cong \angle 3$ (Trans. Prop.) 5. $\angle ABX \cong \angle A$ (Supps. of ≅ ∠s are ≅.) **29. a.** rect. **b.** rect. **33.** rhom. **35. a.** Drawings may vary. **b.** The diags. must be ≅.

Self-Test 2, Page 195

1. ▱ **2.** trap. **3.** rect. **4.** sq. **5.** 11 **6.** 17, 67 **7.** 1. $\angle 1 \cong \angle 2 \cong \angle 3 \cong \angle 4$ (Given) 2. $\overline{HG} \parallel \overline{EF}$; $\overline{HE} \parallel \overline{GF}$ (If alt. int. ∠s $\cong$, lines ∥.) 3. $EFGH$ is a ▱. (Def. of ▱) 4. $\overline{HG} \cong \overline{HE}$ (If 2 ∠s of a $\triangle$ are $\cong$, sides opp. the ∠s are $\cong$.) 5. $HGFE$ is a rhom. (Thm. 5-17) **8. a.** ▱ **b.** 1. $PQRS$ is a ▱. (Given) 2. $\overline{PQ} \parallel \overline{SR}$ (Def. of ▱) 3. X is the midpt. of $\overline{PQ}$; Y is the midpt. of $\overline{SR}$. (Given) 4. $XQ = \frac{1}{2}PQ$; $YR = \frac{1}{2}SR$ (Midpt. Thm.) 5. $PQ = SR$ (Thm. 5-1) 6. $\frac{1}{2}PQ = \frac{1}{2}SR$ (Mult. Prop. of =) 7. $XQ = YR$ (Subst.) 8. $XQRY$ is a ▱. (Thm. 5-5) **c.** trap.

Chapter Review, Pages 197–198

1. 110 **3.** 28 **5.** $GS = 5$ or $\overline{SA} \parallel \overline{GN}$ **7.** $\overline{AZ} \cong \overline{GZ}$ **9.** Thm. 5-10 **11.** Thm. 5-11, part (2) **13.** ▱ **15.** rect. **17.** Key steps of proof: 1. $DO = BO$; $AO = CO$ (Diags. ▱ bis. each other.) 2. $EO = FO$ (Subtr. Prop. =) 3. $AECF$ is a ▱. (Thm. 5-7) 4. $\overline{BD} \perp \overline{AC}$ (Diags. of rhom. $\perp$.) 5. $\triangle COE \cong \triangle COF$ (SAS) 6. $\overline{CE} \cong \overline{CF}$ (CPCT) 7. $AECF$ is a rhom. (Thm. 5-17) **19.** $\overline{ZO}$, $\overline{DI}$ **21.** 4

Cumulative Review, Pages 200–201

1. one **3.** If you enjoy winter weather, then you are a member of the skiing club. **5.** Trans. Prop. **7.** 180; $\angle$ Add. Post. **9.** $\angle 1$; If lines ∥, corr. ∠s are $\cong$. **11.** bis., $\perp$ **13. a.** $\triangle RTA$ **b.** $\overline{DB}$ **c.** $m\angle E$ **15.** 150, 150 **17.** $3r - s$ **19.** bis. **21.** 72, 36 **23.** ABC, BAC, ACD, CFD **25.** $m\angle 1 = m\angle 4 = k$, $m\angle 2 = m\angle 3 = 45 - k$ **27.** $\angle NOM$, $\angle LMO$, $\angle NMO$; Thm. 5-14 **29.** PQ, ON; Thm. 5-19 **31.** 1. $\overline{AD} \cong \overline{BC}$; $\overline{AD} \parallel \overline{BC}$ (Given) 2. $ABCD$ is a ▱. (Thm. 5-5) 3. $\overline{DF} \cong \overline{BF}$ (Diags. ▱ bis. each other.) 4. $\angle DFG \cong \angle BFE$ (Vert. ∠s $\cong$.) 5. $\overline{DC} \parallel \overline{AB}$ (Def. of ▱) 6. $\angle CDB \cong \angle ABD$ (If ∥ lines, alt. int. ∠s $\cong$.) 7. $\triangle DFG \cong \triangle BFE$ (ASA) 8. $\overline{EF} \cong \overline{FG}$ (CPCT)

Chapter 6

Written Exercises, Pages 206–207

1. a. No **b.** Yes **c.** Yes **d.** No **e.** Yes **f.** No **3. a.** No **b.** No **c.** Yes **d.** Yes **5.** $j = 2, k = 1, l = 4, m = 3$ **7.** 1. Vert. ∠s $\cong$. 2. $\angle$ Add Post. 3. A Prop. of Ineq. 4. Subst. **9.** 1. $m\angle ROS > m\angle TOV$ (Given) 2. $m\angle SOT = m\angle SOT$ (Reflex.) 3. $m\angle ROS + m\angle SOT > m\angle TOV + m\angle SOT$ (A Prop. of Ineq.) 4. $m\angle ROS + m\angle SOT = m\angle ROT$; $m\angle TOV + m\angle SOT = m\angle SOV$ ($\angle$ Add. Post.) 5. $m\angle ROT > m\angle SOV$ (Subst.) **11.** 1. $m\angle 1 > m\angle 2$; $m\angle 2 > m\angle 3$ (Ext. $\angle$ Ineq. Thm.) 2. $m\angle 1 > m\angle 3$ (A Prop. of Ineq.) 3. $m\angle 3 = m\angle 4$ (Vert. ∠s $\cong$.) 4. $m\angle 1 > m\angle 4$ (Subst.)

Written Exercises, Pages 210–212

1. a. If $4n \neq 68$, then $n \neq 17$. **b.** If $n \neq 17$, then $4n \neq 68$. **3. a.** If $x + 1$ is odd, then x is even. **b.** If x is even, then $x + 1$ is odd. **5.** True. If I don't live in Calif., then I don't live in L.A.; true. If I live in Calif., then I live in L.A.; false. If I don't live in L.A., then I don't live in Calif.; false. **7.** False. If M is not the midpt. of $\overline{AB}$, then $AM \neq MB$; false. If M is the midpt. of $\overline{AB}$, then $AM = MB$; true. If $AM \neq MB$, then M is not the midpt. of $\overline{AB}$; true. **9.** True. If $n \leq -3$, then $-2n \geq 6$; true. If $n > -3$, then $-2n < 6$; true. If $-2n \geq 6$, then $n \leq -3$; true. **11.** If you are a senator, then you are at least 30 years old. **a.** No concl. **b.** She is at least 30 years old. **c.** No concl. **d.** He is not a senator. **13. a.** It is raining. **b.** I am happy. **c.** No concl. **d.** No concl. **15. a.** No concl. **b.** $\angle ABC$ and $\angle DBF$ are not vert. ∠s. **c.** No concl. **d.** $\angle RVU \cong \angle SVT$, $\angle RVT \cong \angle SVU$ **17. a.** Diags. are $\cong$. **b.** No concl. **c.** No concl. **d.** $STAR$ is not a rect. **19.** contrapositive **21.** Statement: If $m\angle A + m\angle B \neq 180$, then $m\angle D + m\angle C \neq 180$. Contrapositive: If $m\angle D + m\angle C = 180$, then $m\angle A + m\angle B = 180$. Given: $m\angle D + m\angle C = 180$ Prove: $m\angle A + m\angle B = 180$ Proof: 1. $m\angle D + m\angle C = 180$ (Given) 2. $\overleftrightarrow{AD} \parallel \overleftrightarrow{BC}$ (If s-s. int. ∠s supp., lines ∥.) 3. $m\angle A + m\angle B = 180$ (If ∥ lines, s-s. int. ∠s supp.)

Mixed Review Exercises, Page 212

1. sometimes **2.** sometimes **3.** always **4.** never **5.** always **6.** always **7.** sometimes **8.** $m\angle 1 = 60$, $m\angle 2 = 75$, $m\angle 3 = 45$, $m\angle 4 = 60$ **9.** 95

Written Exercises, Pages 216–217

1. Assume temp. that $m\angle B \neq 40$. **3.** Assume temp. that $a - b = 0$. **5.** Assume temp. that $\overleftrightarrow{EF} \parallel \overleftrightarrow{GH}$. **7.** Assume temp. that $\angle Y$ is a rt. $\angle$. Since $m\angle X = 100$, this contradicts Thm. 3-11 Cor. 3. The temp. assumption must be false. It follows that $\angle Y$ is not a rt. $\angle$. **11.** Assume temp. that planes P and Q do not intersect, that is, they are $\parallel$. The lines in which plane N intersects planes P and Q, $\overleftrightarrow{AB}$ and $\overleftrightarrow{CD}$, must be $\parallel$. This contradicts the given info. that $\overleftrightarrow{AB} \nparallel \overleftrightarrow{CD}$. The temp. assumption must be false. It follows that planes P and Q intersect. **15.** Assume temp. that n does not int. k. Since n and k are coplanar, n and k must be $\parallel$. Then P is on n and l, and n and l are both $\parallel$ to k. This contradicts the thm. which states that through a pt. outside a line there is exactly 1 line $\parallel$ to the given line. The temp. assumption must be false. It follows that n does int. k. **17.** Assume temp. that there is an n-sided reg. polygon with an interior $\angle$ of meas. 155. Then the meas. of each ext. $\angle$ is 25 and $25n = 360$. This contradicts the fact that there is no whole number n such that $25n = 360$. The temp. assumption must be false. It follows that there is no reg. polygon with an interior $\angle$ of meas. 155.

Self-Test 1, Page 218

1. True **2.** True **3.** False **4.** False **5.** If $\triangle ABC$ is not acute, then $m\angle C = 90$. False **6.** If $m\angle C = 90$, then $\triangle ABC$ is not acute. True **7.** C **8. a.** $ABCD$ is not a rhom. **b.** No concl. **c.** No concl. **d.** $GHIJ$ is a ▱. **9.** Assume temp. that $AC \neq 14$. **10.** d, b, a, c

Written Exercises, Pages 222–223

1. 3, 15 **3.** 0, 200 **5.** $a - b$, $a + b$ **7.** $\angle 2$ **9.** $\angle 3$ **11.** $\overline{WT}$ **13.** $\overline{WY}$ **15.** $c > d > e > b > a$ **17.** $m\angle 2 > m\angle X > m\angle XZY > m\angle Y > m\angle 1$ **19.** 1. $EFGH$ is a ▱; $EF > FG$ (Given) 2. $HG > EH$ (Thm. 5-1 and Subst.) 3. $m\angle 1 > m\angle 2$ (Thm. 6-2)

Written Exercises, Pages 231–232

1. $m\angle 1 > m\angle 2$; SSS Ineq. **3.** $>$; $>$ **5.** $<$; $>$ **7.** $<$ **9.** $>$ **11.** 1. $m\angle SUV > m\angle STU$ (Ext. $\angle$ Ineq. Thm.) 2. $\overline{TU} \cong \overline{US} \cong \overline{SV}$ (Given) 3. $m\angle SVU = m\angle SUV$ (Isos. $\triangle$ Thm.) 4. $m\angle SVU > m\angle STU$ (Subst.) 5. $ST > SV$ (Thm. 6-3) **13.** Key steps of proof: 1. $m\angle P > m\angle Q$ (SSS Ineq. Thm.) 2. $m\angle PCA + m\angle A + m\angle P = 180$; $m\angle QCB + m\angle QBC + m\angle Q = 180$ (Thm. 3-11) 3. $m\angle PCA = m\angle A$; $m\angle QCB = m\angle QBC$ (Isos. $\triangle$ Thm.) 4. $m\angle PCA < m\angle QCB$ (Subst.)

Self-Test 2, Page 233

1. $\overline{XY}$ **2.** $\overline{OD}$ **3.** $<$ **4.** $=$ **5.** $>$ **6.** 1, 11 **7.** cannot be **8.** must be **9.** may be

Chapter Review, Pages 235–236

1. $>$ **3.** $=$ **5.** $>$ **7.** No concl. **9.** Barbara is at least 18 years old. **11.** $m\angle T$ **13.** $<$ **15.** $>$ **17.** $=$

Algebra Review, Page 237

1. $\frac{1}{5}$ **3.** $\frac{a}{2}$ **5.** $\frac{1}{3}$ **7.** $-4y^2$ **9.** $\frac{ab}{2c}$ **11.** $3x - 2y$ **13.** $\frac{1}{3}$ **15.** $t + 1$ **17.** $\frac{b+5}{b-7}$ **19.** $\frac{3(x-4)}{3x-4}$

Preparing for College Entrance Exams, Page 238

1. A **2.** A **3.** B **4.** B **5.** B **6.** E **7.** E **8.** C

Cumulative Review, Page 239

1. 57 **3. a.** Yes; SAS **b.** Yes; ASA **c.** No **d.** Yes; AAS **5. a.** $\overline{YZ}$ **b.** $\overline{XZ}$ **7.** 109, 71 **9.** Assume temp. that $\angle Q$, $\angle R$, and $\angle S$ are all 120° angles. Then $m\angle P > 0$ and $m\angle Q + m\angle R + m\angle S + m\angle P > 360$. This contradicts the thm. that states the sum of the int. ∡ of a quad. $= 360$. Therefore, the temp. assumption must be false. It follows that $\angle Q$, $\angle R$, and $\angle S$ are not all 120° angles.

Chapter 7

Written Exercises, Pages 243–244

1. 5:3 **3.** 1:5 **5.** 3:16 **7.** 2 to 1 **9.** $\frac{1}{3}$ **11.** $\frac{17}{1}$ **13.** 12:6:5 **15.** 1:9 **17.** 3:4 **19.** 8:5 **21.** $\frac{3}{4b}$ **23.** $\frac{3}{a}$ **25.** 132, 48 **27.** 37.5, 52.5 **29.** 72, 90, 90, 144, 162, 162 **31.** 50, 70, 110, 130; 2 s-s. int. ∠s are supp. **33. a.** 104 **b.** 0.310 **35.** 52.5

Written Exercises, Pages 247–248

1. 6 **3.** 21 **5.** $\frac{4}{7}$ **7.** $\frac{y+3}{3}$ **9.** $2\frac{2}{5}$ **11.** $\frac{14}{15}$ **13.** −3 **15.** 2 **17.** 11 **19.** 3 **21.** 21; 12; 28 **23.** 8; 24; 20 **25.** 8; 4; 15 **27.** 27; 36; 12 **29.** By the means-ext. prop., $\frac{a+b}{b} = \frac{c+d}{d}$ is equiv. to $ad + bd = bc + bd$, or $ad = bc$. **33.** 20 **35.** $\frac{1}{2}$ **37.** 4 or $-\frac{9}{5}$ **39.** $x = 16$, $y = 4$ **43.** 3:2

Written Exercises, Pages 250–252

1. always **3.** sometimes **5.** always **7.** sometimes **9.** always **11.** never **13.** sometimes **15.** 4:5 **17.** 135 **19.** 12 **21.** $4k$ **23.** Prop. 2 **25.** $x = 8$, $y = 18$, $z = 12$ **27.** $x = 6\frac{1}{4}$, $y = 6\frac{2}{3}$, $z = 5$ **29.** **31.** $RS = RS$, but $ZR > XR$, so $\frac{RS}{RS} = 1 \neq \frac{ZR}{XR}$. **33.** $C'(9, 1)$, $D'(8, 2)$, or $C'(5, 1)$, $D'(6, 2)$ **35.** 90; sq. **37. a.** $-3 + 3\sqrt{5}$ **b.** $\frac{1+\sqrt{5}}{2}$; 1.62

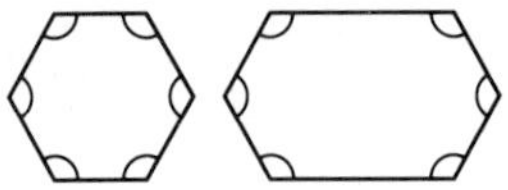

Self-Test 1, Page 252

1. 3:5 **2.** 3 to 10 **3.** $\frac{2a}{3b}$ **4.** 6 **5.** 10 **6.** 3 **7.** No **8.** Yes **9.** Yes **10.** 45, 60, 75 **11.** 2:3 **12.** 12 **13.** 15 **14.** 12 **15.** 100, 100, 100, 120, 140, 160

Written Exercises, Pages 257–260

1. ~ **3.** ~ **5.** No concl. **7.** ~ **9.** No concl. **11.** $x = 6$, $y = 4$ **13.** $x = 9$, $y = 5$ **15.** 27 m **17.** 0.55 cm **19.** $x = 2$, $y = 6$ **21. a.** 1. $\overline{EF} \parallel \overline{RS}$ (Given) 2. $\angle XFE \cong \angle XSR$; $\angle XEF \cong \angle XRS$ (If lines ∥, corr. ∠s ≅.) 3. $\triangle FXE \sim \triangle SXR$ (AA ~) **b.** 1. $\triangle FXE \sim \triangle SXR$ (Part (a), above) 2. $\frac{FX}{SX} = \frac{EF}{RS}$ (Corr. sides of ~ △s are in prop.) **23.** 1. $\angle B \cong \angle C$ (Given) 2. $\angle 1 \cong \angle 2$ (Vert. ∠s ≅.) 3. $\triangle MLC \sim \triangle MNB$ (AA ~) 4. $\frac{NM}{LM} = \frac{BM}{CM}$ (Corr. sides of ~ △s are in prop.) 5. $NM \cdot CM = LM \cdot BM$ (means-ext. prop.) **25.** Key steps of proof: 1. $\angle B \cong \angle Y$ (Corr. ∠s of ~ △s are ≅.) 2. $\triangle ADB \sim \triangle XWY$ (AA ~) 3. $\frac{AD}{XW} = \frac{AB}{XY}$ (Corr. sides of ~ △s are in prop.) **27.** Key steps of proof: 1. $\triangle AHE \sim \triangle ADG$ (AA ~) 2. $\frac{AE}{AG} = \frac{HE}{DG}$ (Corr. sides of ~ △s are in prop.) 3. $AE \cdot DG = AG \cdot HE$ (means-ext. prop.) **29.** Key steps of proof: 1. $\triangle ABC \sim \triangle ADB$ (AA ~) 2. $\frac{AB}{AD} = \frac{AC}{AB}$ (Corr. sides of ~ △s are in prop.) 3. $(AB)^2 = AD \cdot AC$ (means-ext. prop.) **31.** 20

Written Exercises, Pages 266–267

1. $\triangle BAC \sim \triangle EDC$; SAS ~ **3.** $\triangle LKM \sim \triangle NPO$; SAS ~ **5.** $\triangle ABC \sim \triangle AEF$; AA ~ **7.** $\triangle ABC \sim \triangle TRI$; 2:3 **9.** $\triangle ABC \sim \triangle ITR$; 2:5 **11.** 1. $\frac{DE}{GH} = \frac{DF}{GI} = \frac{EF}{HI}$ (Given)

2. $\triangle DEF \sim \triangle GHI$ (SSS $\sim$) 3. $\angle E \cong \angle H$ (Corr. $\angle$s of $\sim \triangle$s are $\cong$.) **13.** 1. $\frac{VW}{VX} = \frac{VZ}{VY}$ (Given) 2. $\angle V \cong \angle V$ (Reflex.) 3. $\triangle VWZ \sim \triangle VXY$ (SAS $\sim$) 4. $\angle 1 \cong \angle 2$ (Corr. $\angle$s of $\sim \triangle$s are $\cong$.) 5. $\overline{WZ} \parallel \overline{XY}$ (If corr. $\angle$s $\cong$, lines $\parallel$.) **15.** 1. $\frac{JL}{NL} = \frac{KL}{ML}$ (Given) 2. $\angle MLN \cong \angle KLJ$ (Vert. $\angle$s $\cong$.) 3. $\triangle MLN \sim \triangle KLJ$ (SAS $\sim$) 4. $\angle J \cong \angle N$ (Corr. $\angle$s of $\sim \triangle$s are $\cong$.)

17. Given: $\triangle ABC \sim \triangle DEF$; $\overline{AM}$ and $\overline{DN}$ are medians.

Prove: $\frac{AM}{DN} = \frac{AB}{DE}$

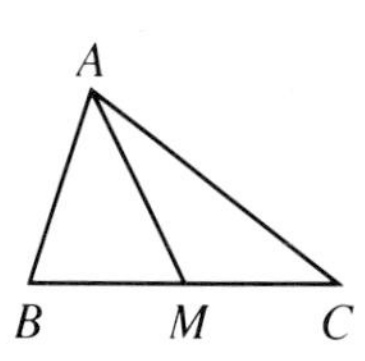

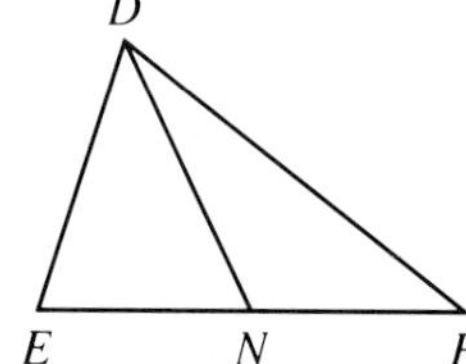

Key steps of proof: 1. $BM = \frac{1}{2}BC$; $EN = \frac{1}{2}EF$ (Midpt. Thm.) 2. $\frac{BC}{EF} = \frac{AB}{DE}$ (Corr. sides of $\sim \triangle$s are in prop.) 3. $\frac{BM}{EN} = \frac{AB}{DE}$ (Subst.) 4. $\triangle ABM \sim \triangle DEN$ (SAS $\sim$) 5. $\frac{AM}{DN} = \frac{AB}{DE}$ (Corr. sides of $\sim \triangle$s are in prop.)

Mixed Review Exercises, Page 268

1. a. $\overline{GC}$; $\overline{EF}$ **b.** 18 **c.** 3 **d.** 90 **2. a.** Midpt., $\overline{RV}$ **b.** 2 **c.** 4

Written Exercises, Pages 272–273

1. a. No **b.** Yes **c.** Yes **d.** No **e.** Yes **f.** Yes **3.** 7.5 **5.** 26 **7.** 18 **9.** 14.5 **11.** 4 **13.** $AN = 10$ **15.** $RT = 8$; $AN = 18$; $NP = 12$; $TP = 25$ **17.** $AR = 8$; $NP = 6$; $AP = 12$ **21.** 22.5 **23.** 78 **25.** 0.5

Self-Test 2, Page 274

1. SSS $\sim$ **2.** AA $\sim$ **3.** SAS $\sim$ **4. a.** $\triangle EDC$ **b.** ED; EC; DC **c.** 10; x; 14 **d.** 10; y; 18 **5.** r **6.** p **7.** h **8.** a **9.** 12 **10.** 14 **11.** $6\frac{2}{3}$

Extra, Page 276

1. c **3.** b **5.** d

Chapter Review, Pages 277–278

1. 3:5 **3.** $\frac{2y}{3x}$ **5.** No **7.** Yes **9.** $\angle J$ **11. a.** 12 **b.** 50 **13. a.** $\triangle UVH$ **b.** AA $\sim$ **15.** UH; $\frac{RT}{UV}$ **17.** $\triangle NCD \sim \triangle NAB$; AA $\sim$ **19.** No **21.** 2 **23.** 14.4

Algebra Review, Page 280

1. 6 **3.** $2\sqrt{6}$ **5.** $10\sqrt{3}$ **7.** $\frac{\sqrt{15}}{3}$ **9.** 1 **11.** 13 **13.** 12 **15.** 162 **17.** $12\sqrt{3}$ **19.** $10\sqrt{2}$ **21.** 5 **23.** 12 **25.** $\sqrt{65}$ **27.** $2\sqrt{2}$ **29.** 7

Cumulative Review, Pages 281–283

True-False Exercises 1. F **3.** F **5.** T **7.** F **9.** F **11.** F **Multiple-Choice Exercises 1.** d **3.** d **5.** c **Always-Sometimes-Never Exercises 1.** S **3.** S **5.** N **7.** A **9.** S **11.** A **13.** A **15.** S **Completion Exercises 1.** 120 **3.** obtuse **5.** 108 **7.** rect. **9.** 36 **Algebraic Exercises 1.** 6 **3.** 84 **5.** 20 **7.** 7 **9.** 6 **11.** 15 **13.** 16 cm, 20 cm, 28 cm **15.** $x = 6$, $y = 3.5$ **Proof Exercises 1.** 1. $\overline{SU} \cong \overline{SV}$; $\angle 1 \cong \angle 2$ (Given) 2. $\overline{QS} \cong \overline{QS}$ (Reflex.) 3. $\triangle QUS \cong \triangle QVS$ (SAS) 4. $\overline{UQ} \cong \overline{VQ}$ (CPCT) **3.** Key steps of proof: 1. $\overline{QR} \cong \overline{QT}$; $\angle R \cong \angle T$; $\overline{RU} \cong \overline{TV}$ (CPCT) 2. $\overline{RS} \cong \overline{TS}$ (Seg. Add. Post and Add. Prop. =) 3. $\triangle QRS \cong \triangle QTS$ (SAS) **5.** 1. $\overline{EF} \parallel \overline{JK}$; $\overline{JK} \parallel \overline{HI}$ (Given) 2. $\overline{EF} \parallel \overline{HI}$ (Thm. 3-10) 3. $\angle 2 \cong \angle 3$; $\angle F \cong \angle H$ (If lines $\parallel$, alt. int. $\angle$s $\cong$.) 4. $\triangle EFG \sim \triangle IHG$ (AA $\sim$)

Chapter 8

Written Exercises, Pages 288–290

1. $2\sqrt{3}$ **3.** $3\sqrt{5}$ **5.** $20\sqrt{2}$ **7.** $18\sqrt{10}$ **9.** $6\sqrt{5}$ **11.** $\frac{\sqrt{21}}{7}$ **13.** $6\sqrt{3}$ **15.** $\frac{\sqrt{3}}{9}$ **17.** 9 **19.** $10\sqrt{10}$ **21.** $11\sqrt{10}$ **23.** 9 **25.** $3\sqrt{5}$ **27.** 9 **29.** 3 **31.** $x = 10, y = 2\sqrt{29}, z = 5\sqrt{29}$ **33.** $x = \frac{\sqrt{2}}{6}, y = \frac{\sqrt{3}}{6}, z = \frac{\sqrt{6}}{6}$ **35.** $x = 5.4, y = 9.6, z = 7.2$ **37.** $x = \sqrt{2}, y = 2, z = \sqrt{2}$ **39.** $x = 4, y = 2\sqrt{5}, z = 3\sqrt{5}$ **41. a.** cd, ce **b.** $a^2 + b^2 = cd + ce = c(d + e) = c^2$ **43.** Key steps of proof: 1. $\triangle PST \sim \triangle TRQ$ (SAS~) 2. $m\angle PTS = m\angle TQR$ (Corr. ∠s of ~ △s are ≅.) 3. $m\angle QTR + m\angle TQR = 90$ (Thm. 3-11 Cor. 4) 4. $m\angle PTS + m\angle QTR = 90$ (Subst.) 5. $m\angle PTQ + m\angle PTS + m\angle QTR = 180$ and $m\angle PTQ = 90$ (∠ Add. Post.)

Written Exercises, Pages 292–294

1. 5 **3.** 8 **5.** $10\sqrt{3}$ **7.** 8 **9.** 25 **11.** $8\sqrt{2}$ **13.** 3 **15.** $4\sqrt{2}$ **17.** 68 **19.** 3 **21.** $3\sqrt{5}$ **23.** 12 **25.** 10 **27.** 17 **29.** 20 **31. a.** 5 **b.** 4.8 **33.** 13 **35.** $e\sqrt{3}$ **37.** 12 **39.** 12

Mixed Review Exercises, Page 294

1. *AC* **2.** >, *A* **3.** > **4.** $\overline{AB}$ **5.** *B*, *C* **6.** *AB* **7.** *BX*, *CX*

Written Exercises, Pages 297–298

1. acute **3.** rt. **5.** obt. **7. a.** rt. **b.** rt. **9.** $(ST)^2 = 13^2 - 12^2 = 25$; $(ST)^2 = (RS)^2 + (RT)^2 = 25$. By the conv. of the Pythag. Thm., $\triangle RST$ is a rt. △. **11.** acute **13.** obt. **15.** $12 < x \le 16$ **17.** $\overline{RM}$; $\angle RST$ is obt. and $\angle STU$ is acute, so $RT > SU$. **19. a.** is greater than the sum of the squares of the other 2 sides, then the △ is an obt. △. **b.** 1. $n^2 = j^2 + k^2$ (Pythag. Thm.) 2. $l^2 > j^2 + k^2$ (Given) 3. $l^2 > n^2$ and $l > n$ (Subst.) 4. $m\angle S > m\angle V = 90$ (SSS Ineq. Thm.) 5. $\triangle RST$ is obt. △. (Def. of obt. △)

Written Exercises, Pages 302–303

1. 4; $4\sqrt{2}$ **3.** $\sqrt{5}$; $\sqrt{10}$ **5.** $3\sqrt{2}$; $3\sqrt{2}$ **7.** $4\sqrt{2}$; 8 **9.** $7\sqrt{3}$; 14 **11.** 5; 10 **13.** 5; $5\sqrt{3}$ **15.** $\sqrt{3}$; $2\sqrt{3}$ **17.** $12\sqrt{2}$ **19.** 36 **21.** $x = 4, y = \frac{4\sqrt{3}}{3}$ **23.** $x = 6\sqrt{2}, y = 12$ **25.** $x = 8\sqrt{2}, y = 4\sqrt{6}$ **27.** $OB = \sqrt{2}, OC = 2, OD = 2\sqrt{2}, OE = 4$ **29.** 16, $16\sqrt{3}$ **31.** A 30°–60°–90° △ with hyp. 2 has legs 1 and $\sqrt{3}$. Any △ with sides in ratio $1:\sqrt{3}:2$ is ~ to this 30°–60°–90° △ and thus is a 30°–60°–90° △. **33.** $GH = GI = 6, JG = 6\sqrt{3}, HI = 6\sqrt{2}, JH = 12$ **35. a.** $4\sqrt{2} + 4\sqrt{6}$ **b.** $(1 + \sqrt{3}):2$ **37.** $\frac{3j + j\sqrt{3}}{4}$ **39.** $4\sqrt{2}$

Self-Test 1, Page 304

1. $3\sqrt{5}$ **2. a.** 4 **b.** $2\sqrt{5}$ **c.** $4\sqrt{5}$ **3. a.** rt. **b.** acute **c.** obtuse **4.** $4\sqrt{5}$ **5.** $20\sqrt{2}$ cm **6.** $6\sqrt{3}$ cm **7.** 12

Written Exercises, Pages 308–310

1. 13.7 **3.** 48.3 **5.** 55.4 **7.** 57° **9.** 27° **11.** 31° **13.** $w = 60, z \approx 54$ **15.** $w = 75, z \approx 89$ **17.** $w = 160, z \approx 117$ **19.** about 4° **21.** 65° **23.** 174 cm **25. a.** 0.7002, 0.4663, 1.1665 **b.** 60°, 1.7321 **c.** No **d.** No **27. a.** 5 **b.** 22° **29.** about 136 ft

Written Exercises, Pages 314–316

1. $x \approx 21, y \approx 28$ **3.** $x \approx 89, y \approx 117$ **5.** $x \approx 28, y \approx 10$ **7.** $v° \approx 26°$ **9.** $x \approx 9, v° \approx 63°$ **11.** $v° \approx 37°, w° \approx 106°$ **13. a.** $\sqrt{115}$ **b.** $y \approx 40, x \approx 10.7$ **c.** Yes; $\sqrt{115} \approx 10.7$ **15.** about 149 m **17.** 0.4 m **19. a.** $AB = AC \approx 16$ **b.** ≈ 15 **21.** length ≈ 17 cm, width ≈ 5 cm **23.** about 12 cm

Written Exercises, Pages 318–320

1. about 32 m **3.** about 50 m **5.** about 2.3 km **7.** Heidi; ≈ 63 cm longer **9.** about 440 m **11.** ≈ 14° **13. a.** ∠*A* **b.** *A*; a player at *A* has a wider ∠ over which to aim at the goal.

Self-Test 2, Page 320

1. $\frac{7}{24}$ **2.** $\frac{24}{25}$ **3.** $\frac{7}{25}$ **4.** $\frac{24}{7}$ **5.** 74 **6.** 74 **7.** 109 **8.** 113 **9.** about 45 m

Chapter Review, Pages 323–324

1. 6 **3.** $5\sqrt{6}$ **5.** $3\sqrt{5}$ **7.** $7\sqrt{2}$ **9.** acute **11.** rt. **13.** $5\sqrt{3}$ **15.** 16 **17. a.** 1.5 **b.** $\frac{2}{3}$ **c.** 34 **19. a.** $\frac{12}{13}$ **b.** $\frac{12}{13}$ **c.** 67 **21.** 57 **23.** 23

Preparing for College Entrance Exams, Page 326

1. A **2.** C **3.** B **4.** C **5.** E **6.** A **7.** C **8.** A **9.** B **10.** C

Cumulative Review, Page 327

1. Seg. Add. Post. **3.** corollary **5.** contrapositive **7.** $1:\sqrt{2}$ **9. a.** If a △ is equiangular, then it is isos. **b.** If a △ is isos., then it is equiangular. **11.** 36 **13.** 20 **15.** Since $\overline{AX}$ is a median, $\overline{BX} \cong \overline{CX}$. Since $\overline{AX}$ is an altitude, $\angle AXB \cong \angle AXC$. Thus, $\triangle AXB \cong \triangle AXC$ (SAS) and $\overline{AB} \cong \overline{AC}$ (CPCT). By def., $\triangle ABC$ is isos. **17.** 1. $\angle WXY \cong \angle XZY$ (Given) 2. $\angle Y \cong \angle Y$ (Reflex.) 3. $\triangle XYW \sim \triangle ZYX$ (AA~) 4. $\frac{XY}{ZY} = \frac{WY}{XY}$ or $(XY)^2 = WY \cdot ZY$ (Corr. sides of ~ ⚠ are in prop.)

Chapter 9

Written Exercises, Pages 330–331

1. The midpts. lie on a diam. ⊥ to the given chords. **3. b.** It is equidist. from the vertices. **c.** at the midpt. of the hyp. **d.** 5 **5.** 8, 22 **9.** **13.** 24 **15.** $12\sqrt{3}$ **17. a.** rhom.; ⊙$Q \cong$ ⊙R so $\overline{QC}$, $\overline{QD}$, $\overline{RC}$, and $\overline{RD}$ are ≅. **b.** Diags. of rhom. are ⊥ bis. of each other. **c.** 16 **19.** $4\sqrt{6}$

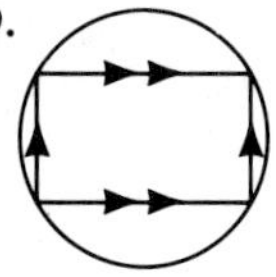

Extra, Page 332

1. 4 odd, 1 even; cannot be traced **3.** 2 odd, 6 even; can be traced **5.** There are more than 2 odd vertices.

Written Exercises, Pages 335–337

1. 8 **3.** 12 **5.** 8.2 **7. a.** $\overline{AB} \cong \overline{CD}$ Proof: 1. Draw $\overleftrightarrow{AB}$ and $\overleftrightarrow{CD}$ int. at Z. (Through any 2 pts. there is ex. 1 line.) 2. $ZA + AB = ZB$; $ZC + CD = ZD$ (Seg. Add. Post.) 3. $ZB = ZD$ (Thm. 9-1 Cor.) 4. $ZA + AB = ZC + CD$ (Subst.) 5. $ZA = ZC$ (Thm. 9-1 Cor.) 6. $\overline{AB} \cong \overline{CD}$ (Subtr. Prop. =) **b.** Yes **9. a.** square; $\overline{XZ} \perp \overline{OX}$, so $\overline{XZ} \parallel \overline{OY}$. Similarly, $\overline{ZY} \parallel \overline{OX}$, so $OXZY$ is a rect. Since $OX = OY$, $OXZY$ is a square. **b.** $5\sqrt{2}$ **11.** $\overline{AR} \perp \overline{RS}$ and $\overline{BS} \perp \overline{RS}$ (Thm. 9-1) so $\overline{AR} \parallel \overline{BS}$. Then $\angle A \cong \angle B$ and $\triangle ARC \sim \triangle BSC$ (AA~), so $\frac{AC}{BC} = \frac{RC}{SC}$. (Corr. sides of ~ ⚠ are in prop.) **13.** Two planes tan. to a sphere at the endpts. of a diam. are ∥. **15.** $RA = RC$ and $SB = SC$ (Thm. 9-1 Cor.), so $PR + RS + SP = PA + PB$ (Subst.) **17.** 15 (trapezoid) **19. a.** G is the midpt. of $\overline{EF}$. Key steps of proof: 1. $GE = GH$; $GH = GF$ (Thm. 9-1 Cor.) 2. $GE = GF$ (Trans. Prop.) **b.** $m\angle EHF = 90$. Key steps of proof: 1. $m\angle E = m\angle GHE$; $m\angle F = m\angle GHF$ (Isos. △ Thm.) 2. $m\angle E + m\angle GHE + m\angle F + m\angle GHF = 180$ (Thm. 3-11) 3. $2m\angle GHE + 2m\angle GHF = 180$ (Subst.) 4. $m\angle EHF = 90$ (Div. Prop. =) **21. a.** 8 **b.** infinitely many **23.** $2\sqrt{2}$

Mixed Review Exercises, Page 337

1. 15 **2.** $9\sqrt{2}$ **3.** $2\sqrt{7}$

Written Exercises, Pages 341–343

1. 85 **3.** 150 **5.** 52 **7.** 30 **9. a.**

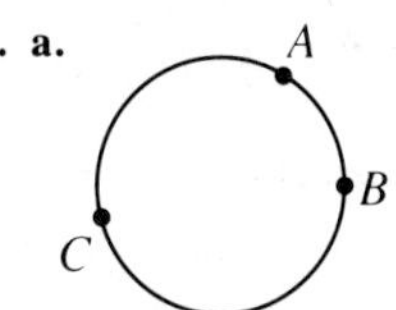

b. No

11. $m\overset{\frown}{BD}$: 34, 44; $m\angle COD$: 100, 88, 104, $p + q$; $m\angle CAD$: 50, 44, 50, $\frac{1}{2}(p + q)$

13. d. The opp. ∠s of inscr. quad. are supp.

15. Key steps of proof: 1. Draw $\overline{OY}$. (Through any 2 pts. there is ex. 1 line.) 2. $m\angle WOY = m\overset{\frown}{WY} = 2n$ (Def. meas. of arc, Arc Add. Post.) 3. $m\angle WOY = m\angle Z + m\angle OYZ$ (Thm. 3-12) 4. $m\angle Z = m\angle OYZ$ (Isos. △ Thm.) 5. $m\angle Z = n$ (Subst. and Div. Prop. =) **17.** $r \approx 4700$ km **19.** $r \approx 5300$ km **23.** ≈ 3800 km

Written Exercises, Pages 347–348

1. 8 **3.** $9\sqrt{2}$ **5.** 80 **7.** 24 **9.** $10\sqrt{5}$ **11.** $2\sqrt{21}$ cm **13.** $2\sqrt{21}$ cm **15.** 1. $\angle J \cong \angle K$ (Given) 2. $\overline{JZ} \cong \overline{KZ}$ (If 2 ∠s of △ ≅, sides opp. the ∠s are ≅.) 3. $\overset{\frown}{JZ} \cong \overset{\frown}{KZ}$ (In same ⊙, ≅ chords have ≅ arcs.) **17.** $10\sqrt{3}$ **19.** 26 cm **21.** ≈ 74 **23.** If 2 ⊙s are concentric and a chord of the outer ⊙ is tan. to the inner circle, then the pt. of tan. is the midpt. of the chord. **25.** $18\sqrt{3}$ **27.** 2.8 cm

Self-Test 1, Page 349

1. a. $\overline{QB}$, $\overline{QC}$ **b.** $\overline{BC}$ **c.** $\overline{AC}$ or $\overline{BC}$, $\overleftrightarrow{AC}$ **2. a.**

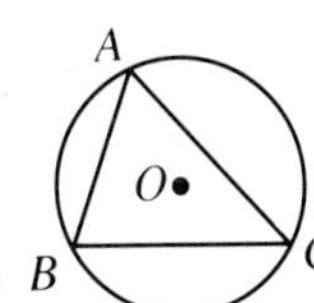

b.

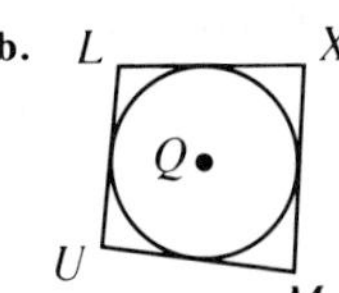

3. 15 **4.** two concentric ⊙s
5. $4\sqrt{10}$ cm **6. a.** 50, 310
b. In same ⊙, ≅ chords have ≅ arcs.

Written Exercises, Pages 354–356

1. $x = 30$, $y = 25$, $z = 15$ **3.** $x = 110$, $y = 100$, $z = 100$ **5.** $x = 50$, $y = 130$, $z = 65$ **7.** $x = 104$, $y = 104$, $z = 52$ **9.** $x = 50$, $y = 100$, $z = 35$ **11. a.** If the arcs between 2 chords are ≅, then the chords are ∥. **b.** False, the chords may int. **13.** 1. Thm. 9-1; def. of ⊥ lines 2. Def. of semicircle 3. Subst. **17.** $\triangle ADE \sim \triangle BCE$, $\triangle EDC \sim \triangle EAB$ **19.** $x = 80$, $m\angle D = 20$ **21.** $x = 10$, $m\angle A = 55$ **23.** rect.; $m\overset{\frown}{AB} = 120$ and $m\overset{\frown}{AQ} = 60$, so $\overset{\frown}{BAQ}$ is semicir. and $\angle BAQ$ is rt. ∠. Similarly, $\angle AQP$, $\angle QPB$, and $\angle PBA$ are rt. ∠s, so $AQPB$ is rect. **29.** $\frac{ab}{c}$

Mixed Review Exercises, Page 357

1. $\overline{LM}$ **2.** $\overleftrightarrow{LM}$ **3.** $\overline{NP}$ **4.** 14 **5.** $360 - x$ **6.** 6

Written Exercises, Pages 359–361

1. 90 **3.** 25 **5.** 55 **7.** 35 **9.** 90 **11.** 60 **13.** 30 **15.** 30 **17.** 40 **19.** 90 **21.** 115 **23.** 100, 90, 86, 84 **27.** $b - a = c$ **29.** Key steps of proof: 1. $m\angle ABP = \frac{1}{2}m\overset{\frown}{AP}$ (Thm. 9-7) 2. $m\angle Q = \frac{1}{2}(m\overset{\frown}{AB} - m\overset{\frown}{PC})$ (Thm. 9-10) 3. $m\angle Q = \frac{1}{2}(m\overset{\frown}{AC} - m\overset{\frown}{PC})$ (Subst.) 4. $m\angle Q = \frac{1}{2}m\overset{\frown}{AP}$ (Arc Add. Post.) **31.** $m\overset{\frown}{CE} = 3m\overset{\frown}{BD}$

Written Exercises, Pages 364–366

1. 10 **3.** $\sqrt{21}$ **5.** 6 **7.** 8 **9.** 5 **11.** 1. $\overline{UT}$ is tan. to ⊙O and ⊙P. (Given) 2. $UV \cdot UW = (UT)^2$, $UX \cdot UY = (UT)^2$ (Thm. 9-13) 3. $UV \cdot UW = UX \cdot UY$ (Subst.) **13.** 4 or 12 **15.** 6 **17.** 9 **19.** 4 **21. a.** Pythag. Thm. **c.** Thm. 9-13 **23.** 20 m **25.** 1. $AX \cdot XB = PX \cdot XQ$, $CX \cdot XD = PX \cdot XQ$ (Thm. 9-11) 2. $AX \cdot XB = CX \cdot XD$ (Trans. Prop.) **27.** $2\sqrt{10}$

Self-Test 2, Page 367

1. 40 **2.** 150 **3.** 82 **4.** 9 **5.** $x = 70$, $y = 50$ **6.** 35 **7.** 10 **8.** 12

Chapter Review, Pages 369–370

1. chord, secant **3.** diam. **5.** tan. **7.** 10 **9.** 100 **11.** $\angle YPW$ **13.** 120 **15.** In same ⊙, ≅ chords are equally distant from the center. **17.** 50, 50 **19.** 105 **21.** 40 **23.** 9

Cumulative Review, Pages 372–373

1. 3, $2x + 3$ **3.** 1. $\overline{MN}$ is median of trap. (Given) 2. $\overline{MN} \parallel \overline{ZY} \parallel \overline{WX}$ (Thm. 5-19) 3. V is the midpt. of $\overline{WY}$. (Thm. 5-10) 4. $\overline{MN}$ bis. $\overline{WY}$. (Def. of bis.) **5.** 7, $7\sqrt{3}$ **7.** 9, 81, 90 **9.** $2\sqrt{2}$ **11.** 1. $\angle 1 \cong \angle 2$, $\angle 2 \cong \angle 3$ (Given) 2. $\overline{AB} \parallel \overline{DC}$ (If alt. int. ∠s ≅, lines ∥.) 3. $\overline{AD} \parallel \overline{BC}$ (If corr. ∠s ≅, lines ∥.) 4. $ABCD$ is a ▱. (Def. of ▱) 5. $\overline{AB} \cong \overline{DC}$ (Opp. sides of a ▱ are ≅.) **13. a.** If $\angle A \not\cong \angle C$, then quad. $ABCD$ is not a ▱. **b.** If quad. $ABCD$ is not a ▱, then $\angle A \not\cong \angle C$. **15.** 20 **17. a.** inside **b.** on **c.** on **19. a.** Janice likes to dance. **b.** no concl. **c.** no concl. **d.** Kim is not Bill's sister. **21.** always **23.** always **25.** sometimes **27.** 0, 1 **29.** 1. $AB > AC$ (Given) 2. $m\angle ACB > m\angle ABC$ (Thm. 6-2) 3. $BD = EC$ (Given) 4. $BC = BC$ (Reflex.) 5. $BE > CD$ (SAS Ineq. Thm.)

Chapter 10

Written Exercises, Pages 378–379

9.

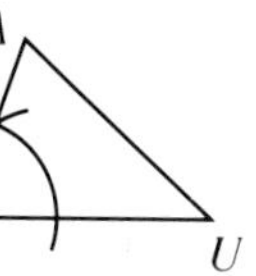

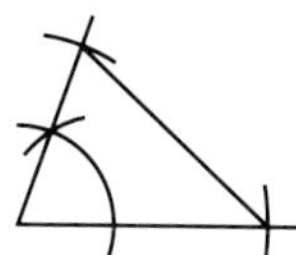

13.

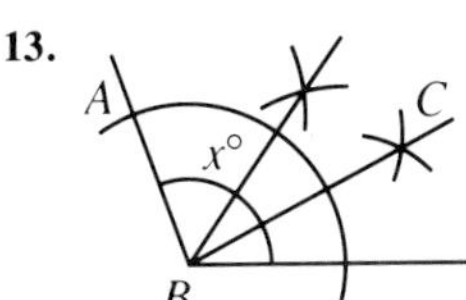

$m\angle ABC = \frac{3}{4}x$

15. c. They are the same pt., which is equidistant from the sides of the △. **19.** Methods may vary; for example, see the figure at the right.

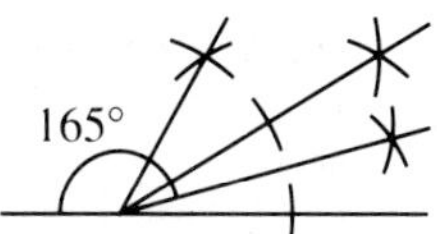

Mixed Review Exercises, Page 380

1. midpt. **2.** ▱ **3.** rect. **4.** rhom. **5.** $5\sqrt{2}$ **6.** 108

Written Exercises, Pages 383–385

1. Const. 5 **3.** Const. 4 **5.** Const. 7 **7.** Extend $\overrightarrow{HJ}$; use Const. 6. **11.** Methods may vary; for example, see the figure at the right. **15. b, c.** Yes; yes **19.** Const. $\overline{AB}$ so that $AB = a$. Const. the ⊥ bis. of $\overline{AB}$ int. $\overline{AB}$ at M, so that $AM = \frac{1}{2}a$. Const. $\overline{MC} \perp \overline{AB}$ so that $MC = \frac{1}{2}a$. With ctrs. A and C and radius AM, draw arcs int. at D. Draw $\overline{AD}$ and $\overline{CD}$. **23.** Const. a square with sides of length b.

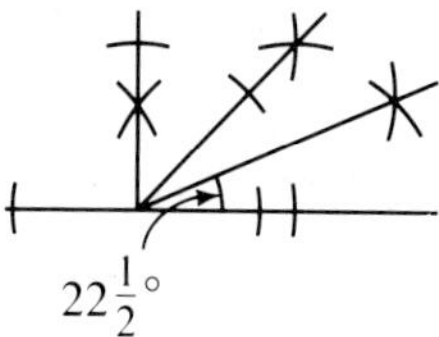

Written Exercises, Pages 388–389

1. a. any acute △ **b.** any obt. △ **c.** any rt. △ **3.** 2, 4 **5.** 3.8, 5.7 **7.** Const. 3 **9.** The pt. of int. of the ⊥ bis. of $\overline{XY}$, $\overline{XZ}$, and $\overline{YZ}$ is equidistant from all 3 towns. It would be wiser to build it equidistant from X and Z, near Y. **11. a.** $GD = \frac{1}{3} \cdot AD = \frac{1}{3} \cdot BE = GE$ **b.** GB **c.** $\angle GBA$, $\angle GED$, $\angle GDE$ **13.** 3, −1 **15.** Key steps of proof: 1. Draw $\overline{BD}$ int. $\overline{AC}$ at Y. (Through any 2 pts. there is ex. 1 line.) 2. $\overline{BM}$ and $\overline{CY}$ are medians of $\triangle BDC$. (Def. of median) 3. $CX = \frac{2}{3}CY$ (The medians of a △ int. in a pt. that is $\frac{2}{3}$ of the dist. from each vertex to the opp. side.) 4. $CX = \frac{2}{3} \cdot \frac{1}{2} \cdot AC = \frac{1}{3}AC$ (Subst.) **17. a.** pts. in the interior of $\angle XPY$ **b.** pts. in the interior of the ∠ vert. to $\angle XPY$

Self-Test 1, Page 390

1. Const. 4 **2.** Draw $\overline{ST}$. With ctrs. S and T, and radius ST, draw arcs int. at R. Draw $\overrightarrow{SR}$; $m\angle RST = 60$. Use Const. 3. **3.** Const. 6 **4.** Const. 7 **5.** Methods may vary. Const. $\overline{JK}$ such that $JK = 2AB$ (Const. 1). Const. lines $\perp$ to $\overline{JK}$ at J and K. Const. $\overline{JM} \cong \overline{KL} \cong \overline{AB}$. Draw $\overline{ML}$. **6.** lines that contain the altitudes, medians, $\angle$ bis., $\perp$ bis. of the sides **7.** midpt. of the hyp. **8.** $4\sqrt{3}$, $2\sqrt{3}$

Mixed Review Exercises, Page 391

1. 12 **2.** tan., 10 **3.** 3 **4.** 141

Written Exercises, Pages 395–396

1. Const. 8 **3.** Const. 10 **5.** Const. 10 **7.** Const. 11 **9.** Draw $\odot O$ with radius r. Choose pt. A on $\odot O$, and with ctr. A and radius r, mark off $\overset{\frown}{AB}$. With ctr. B and radius r, mark off $\overset{\frown}{BC}$. Similarly, mark off $\overset{\frown}{CD}$, $\overset{\frown}{DE}$, and $\overset{\frown}{EF}$. Draw $\overline{AC}$, $\overline{EC}$, and $\overline{AE}$. **11. a.** Draw $\odot O$. Draw diam. $\overline{AE}$. Const. $\perp$ diam. $\overline{CG}$. Bis. 2 adj. rt. $\angle$s to form 8 $\cong$ arcs. Connect consec. pts. to form octagon $ABCDEFGH$. **b.** Draw overlapping squares $ACEG$ and $BDFH$. **13.** Draw the diags. of the square int. at O. Draw the $\odot$ with ctr. O and radius $=$ half the length of a diag. **15.** Divide the $\odot$ into 6 $\cong$ arcs as in Ex. 9. At every other pt., const. a tan. to the $\odot$.
17. Const. a $\parallel$ to l through O, int. $\odot O$ at P. Const. a tan. to $\odot O$ at P.

Written Exercises, Page 399

1. Const. 12 **3. b.** No **c.** Let the 5 $\cong$ seg. from Ex. 3(a) be $\overline{AW}$, $\overline{WX}$, $\overline{XY}$, $\overline{YZ}$, and $\overline{ZB}$. $AX:XB = 2:3$ **5.** Const. 13 **7.** Const. 14 **9.** Use $\frac{z}{w} = \frac{y}{x}$ or $\frac{z}{y} = \frac{w}{x}$ with Const. 13. **11.** Const. 14, 12 **13.** Const. 1, 14 **15.** Draw a line and const. $\overline{AB}$ so that $AB = 3$ and $\overline{BC}$ so that $BC = 5$. Use Const. 14. **17.** Divide $\overline{CD}$ into 7 $\cong$ parts: $\overline{CU}$, $\overline{UV}$, $\overline{VW}$, $\overline{WX}$, $\overline{XY}$, $\overline{YZ}$, and $\overline{ZD}$. Then $CV:VX:XD = 2:2:3$. Use SSS to const. a $\triangle$.

Self-Test 2, Page 401

1. Const. 9 **2.** Const. 11 **3.** Use Const. 12 to divide a seg. $\overline{AB}$ into 3 $\cong$ parts, $\overline{AX}$, $\overline{XY}$, and $\overline{YB}$. Then $AY:YB = 2:1$. **4.** Const. 13 **5.** Const. 14 **6.** $\perp$, F, $\perp$, G **7.** Const. the $\perp$ bis. of 2 sides of $\triangle TRI$, int. at O. Draw a $\odot$ with ctr. O and radius OT.

Written Exercises, Pages 404–405

1. the $\perp$ bis. of $\overline{AB}$ **3.** 2 $\parallel$ lines 4 cm apart with h halfway between them **5.** the seg. joining the midpts. of $\overline{AD}$ and $\overline{BC}$ **7.** diag. $\overline{BD}$ **9.** a plane $\parallel$ to both planes and halfway between them **11.** a sphere with ctr. E and radius 3 cm **13. a.** Use Const. 3 to bis. $\angle HEX$. **b.** Use Const. 3 to bis. the $\angle$s formed by j and k; locus is 2 $\perp$ lines. **15.** Const. the $\odot$ with diameter AB, and exclude pts. A and B. **17.** Const. 2 $\odot$s with radius EF, one with ctr. E and one with ctr. F, and exclude pts. E and F and the other 2 pts. of the int. of the $\odot$s with $\overleftrightarrow{EF}$. **19.** a line $\perp$ to the plane of the square at the int. of the diags.

Written Exercises, Pages 407–410

1. a. $\perp$ bis. of $\overline{AB}$ int. $\odot O$ in 2 pts. **b.** $\perp$ bis. of $\overline{AB}$ doesn't int. $\odot O$. **c.** $\perp$ bis. of $\overline{AB}$ is tan. to $\odot O$.
3. a. a $\odot$ with ctr. D and radius 1 cm **b.** a $\odot$ with ctr. E and radius 2 cm
c.

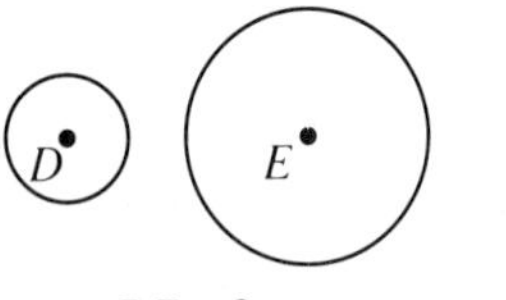

$DE > 3$ cm

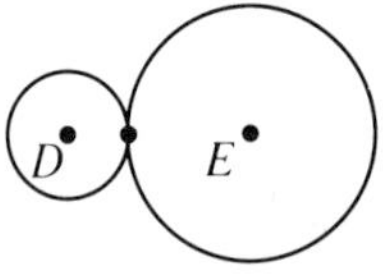

$DE = 3$ cm

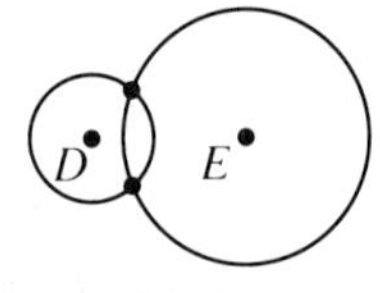

$DE < 3$ cm

d. The locus is 0, 1, or 2 pts., depending on the int. of $\odot D$ and $\odot E$.

5. the int. of $\odot P$, with radius 3 cm, and l (2 pts.) **7.** the int. of $\odot A$, with radius 2 cm, and $\odot B$, with radius 2 cm (2 pts.) **9.** the int. of $\odot A$, with radius 2 cm, and the bis. of $\angle A$ (1 pt.) **11.** 0, 1, or 2 pts. **13.** 0, 1, or 2 pts. **15.** 0 pts., 1 pt., or a $\odot$ **17.** 2 $\odot$s **19.** 0 pts. ($d > 5$), 2 pts. ($d = 5$), 2 $\odot$s ($d < 5$)
21. a. the $\perp$ bis. plane of $\overline{RS}$ **b.** the $\perp$ bis. plane of $\overline{RT}$ **c.** line, line **d.** the $\perp$ bis. plane of $\overline{RW}$ **e.** pt., pt.
23. a. infinitely many **b.** 2 **c.** none

Written Exercises, Pages 412–413

1. The locus is the 2 $\parallel$ lines. **3.** The $\odot$, of radius a, has ctr. at the int. pt. of the bis. of $\angle XYZ$ and a line that is $\parallel$ to $\overrightarrow{YZ}$ and a units from $\overrightarrow{YZ}$. **5.** The locus is a pair of lines, both $\parallel$ to $\overline{AB}$ and r units from $\overline{AB}$. Const. may vary in Exs. 7-17. **7.** Const. $j \perp k$ at M. Const. $\overline{MA}$ on j so that $MA = s$ and then $\cong$ segs. $\overline{AB}$ and $\overline{AC}$, B and C on k, so that $AB = AC = t$. **9.** Const. $\overline{AB}$ so that $AB = t$. Const. the $\perp$ bis. of $\overline{AB}$ to locate midpt. M of $\overline{AB}$. Draw an arc with ctr. M and radius r, and an arc with ctr. A and radius s intersecting at C. Draw $\overline{AC}$ and $\overline{BC}$.

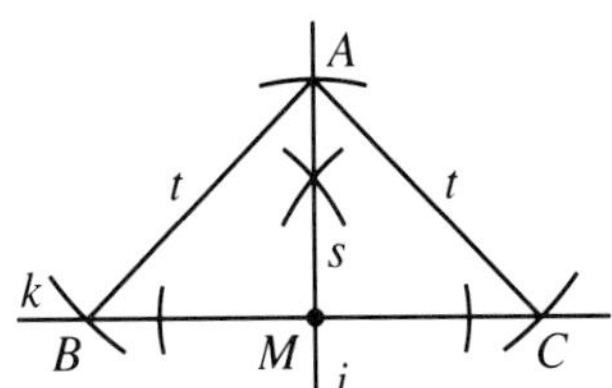

Ex. 7

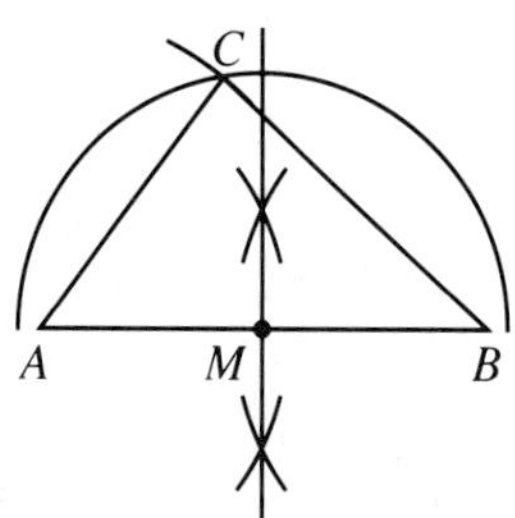

Ex. 9

11. Const. $\angle A$ with meas. n. Const. a line $\parallel$ to and s units from $\overrightarrow{AX}$ in order to locate point C. Const. $\overline{BC} \perp \overline{AC}$. **13.** Const. $\overline{AB}$ such that $AB = t$. Const. the $\perp$ bis. of $\overline{AB}$ to locate midpt. M of $\overline{AB}$. Const. line k, $\parallel$ to and r units from, $\overleftrightarrow{AB}$. With ctr. M and radius s, draw an arc int. k at pt. C. Draw $\overline{AC}$ and $\overline{BC}$.

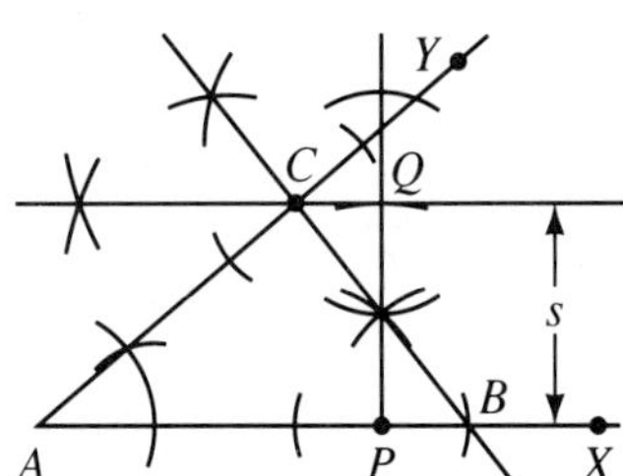

Ex. 11

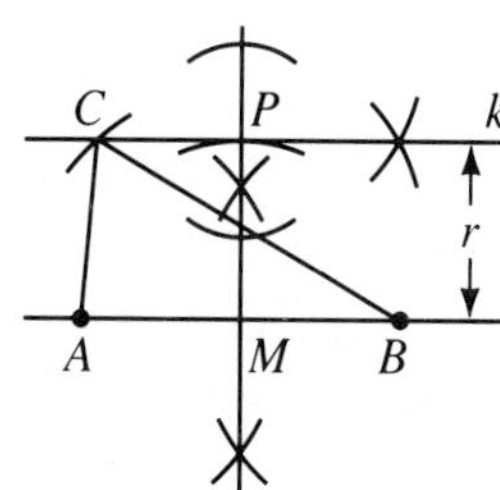

Ex. 13

Self-Test 3, Page 414

1. the bis. of the vert. $\measuredangle$s formed by j and k (2 lines) **2.** the sphere with ctr. P and radius t **3.** the $\perp$ bis. plane of $\overline{WX}$ **4.** the int. of the bis. of $\angle DEF$ and a pair of rays $\parallel$ to $\overrightarrow{EF}$ and each 4 cm from $\overrightarrow{EF}$ (1 pt.) **5.** the int. of $\odot A$ with radius 4 cm and a line $\parallel$ to s and t halfway between them. (0, 1, or 2 pts.) **6.** Use Const. 4 to const. the $\perp$ bis. of 2 sides of $\triangle RST$. The locus is the pt. of int. of the $\perp$ bis. **7.** Const. may vary; for example, const. $\angle X \cong \angle 1$. Const. $\overline{XY} \cong \overline{BC}$ on one side of $\angle X$. Const. a line from $Y \perp$ to the other side of $\angle X$.

Extra, Pages 414–415

3. Some of the pts. are the same: L and R, M and S, N and T. The $\odot$ has ctr. H. **5.** Key steps of proof: $\overline{NM} \parallel \overline{AB}$; $\overline{XY} \parallel \overline{AB}$; $NM = \frac{1}{2}AB$; $XY = \frac{1}{2}AB$ (Thm. 5-11) 2. $XYMN$ is a $\square$. (Thm. 5-5) 3. $\overline{NX} \parallel \overline{CH}$ (Thm. 5-11) 4. $\overline{NM} \perp \overline{NX}$ (Thm. 3-4) 5. $XYMN$ is a rect. (Thm. 5-16)

Chapter Review, Pages 416–417

1. Const. 1 **3.** Const. 3 **5.** Const. 5 **7.** Const. 7 **9.** $\angle$ bis. **11.** 1:2 **13.** Const. 9 **15.** Const. 10 **17.** Const. 13 **19.** a line $\parallel$ to l and m and halfway between them **21.** a plane $\parallel$ to both planes and halfway between them **23.** the int. of the $\perp$ bis. of $\overline{PQ}$ and $\odot P$ with radius 8 cm (2 pts.) **25.** 0 pts., 1 pt., a $\odot$, a $\odot$ and a pt., or 2 $\odot$s, dep. on the int. of 2 planes $\parallel$ to Q and 1 m from Q and a sphere with ctr. Z and radius 2 m.

27. Const. $\overline{RS}$ so that $RS = a$. Const. the ⊥ bis. of $\overline{RS}$ to locate midpt. M. Draw an arc with ctr. M and radius b and an arc with ctr. R and radius c, int. at T. Draw $\overline{TR}$ and $\overline{TS}$.

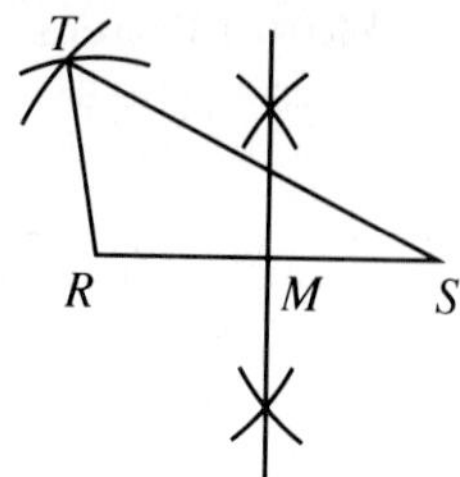

Algebra Review, Page 419

1. 1.69 **3.** $\frac{19}{3}$ **5.** $18\sqrt{2}$ **7.** 2826 **9.** 42 **11.** $-\frac{1}{2}$ **13.** 54 **15.** $15\sqrt{2}$ **17.** 96 **19.** cd **21.** πrl **23.** πd^2 **25.** $x = \frac{c - by}{a}, a \neq 0$ **27.** $n = \frac{S}{180} + 2$ **29.** $h = \pm\sqrt{xy}$ **31.** $h = \frac{2A}{b}, b \neq 0$

Preparing for College Entrance Exams, Page 420

1. B **2.** C **3.** E **4.** A **5.** B **6.** C **7.** A **8.** C **9.** E

Cumulative Review, Page 421

1. never **3.** sometimes **5.** always **7.** never **9.** 107 **11.** 15 **13.** Methods may vary: SSS, SAS, ASA **15. a.** 3.6 **b.** $4\frac{2}{7}$ **17.** 1. $m\angle 1 = 45$ (Given) 2. $m\widehat{PQ} = 90$ (Thm. 9-7) 3. $m\angle O = 90$ (Def. meas. of arc) 4. $\overline{OP} \cong \overline{OQ}$ (All radii of a ⊙ are ≅.) 5. $m\angle OQP = m\angle OPQ$ (Isos. △ Thm.) 6. $m\angle OQP + m\angle OPQ = 90$; $2m\angle OPQ = 90$; $m\angle OPQ = m\angle OQP = 45$ (Thm. 3-11 Cor. 4, algebra) 7. $\triangle OPQ$ is a 45°–45°–90° △. (Def. of 45°–45°–90° △) **19.** Methods may vary. Draw line k and pts. P and Q on k so that $PQ < AB$. Const. line l ⊥ to k at P and line m ⊥ to k at Q. Draw an arc with ctr. Q and radius AB int. l at S. Draw an arc with ctr. P and radius AB int. m at R. Draw $\overline{RS}$.

Chapter 11

Written Exercises, Pages 426–427

1. 60 cm² **3.** 5 cm **5.** 24 **7.** $2x^2 - 6x$ **9.** 36 cm²; 26 cm **11.** 5 cm; 80 cm² **13.** $a^2 - 9$; $4a$ **15.** $x - 3$; $4x - 6$ **17.** 130 **19.** 48 **21.** 39.4 **23.** $40xy$ **25.** $\frac{d^2}{2}$ **27.** 144 m² **29. a.** 768 ft² **b.** 3 cans **31.** 14 m × 28 m **35. a.** length $= \frac{1}{2}(40 - 2x) = 20 - x$ **b.** $20x - x^2$ **c.** See figure at right. **d.** 10 m × 10 m

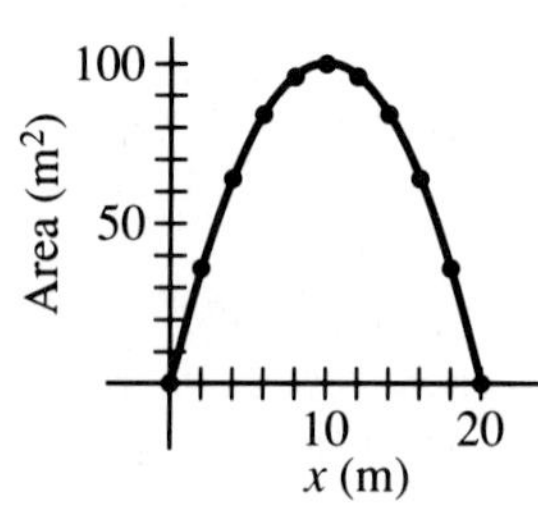

Written Exercises, Pages 431–433

1. 29.9 m² **3.** 12 **5.** $16\sqrt{3}$ **7.** 40 **9.** 84 **11.** 16 **13.** $30\sqrt{2}$ **15.** $\frac{25\sqrt{3}}{2}$ **17.** 240 **19.** $2r^2$ **21.** 18.2 **23.** 73.5 **25.** $\triangle DFE \sim \triangle DGF \sim \triangle FGE$; 20, 4, 16 **27.** 40; 20 **29. a.** 2:3 **b.** 20 **31. a.** $A = \frac{1}{2}ab$ **b.** $A = \frac{1}{2}ch$ **c.** $h = \frac{ab}{c}$ **d.** 4.8; 5 **33. a.** $b = s$, $h = \frac{s\sqrt{3}}{2}$; $A = \frac{1}{2} \cdot s \cdot \frac{s\sqrt{3}}{2} = \frac{s^2\sqrt{3}}{4}$ **b.** $\frac{49\sqrt{3}}{4}$ **35.** 10; 20 **37.** 41.5 **39.** 936 cm²; 504 cm²

Written Exercises, Pages 436–438

1. 70; 10 **3.** 6; $3\frac{3}{4}$ **5.** 5; 18 **7.** 1; 4 **9.** 9 **11.** 108 **13.** $\frac{27\sqrt{3}}{4}$ **15.** 24 **17.** 128 Answers may vary in Exs. 19–21. **19.** 42.0 **21.** 87.8 **23.** 15; 74 **25.** $\triangle ABC$: $36\sqrt{3}$; $\triangle ACD$: $72\sqrt{3}$; $ADEF$: $108\sqrt{3}$ **27.** 12.5 cm²; 112.5 cm² **29.** $\frac{175 - 25\sqrt{3}}{2}$ **31.** 156

Mixed Review Exercises, Page 440

1. 52 **2.** 146 **3.** 135 **4.** 18 **5.** $10\sqrt{2}$ cm **6.** 15 cm, $15\sqrt{3}$ cm **7.** 10 m **8.** $\frac{15}{17}$

Written Exercises, Pages 443–444

1. 8; 256 **3.** $\frac{7\sqrt{2}}{2}$; $\frac{7}{2}$ **5.** 3; $18\sqrt{3}$; $27\sqrt{3}$ **7.** $\frac{4\sqrt{3}}{3}$; $\frac{2\sqrt{3}}{3}$; $4\sqrt{3}$ **9.** $2\sqrt{3}$; 24; $24\sqrt{3}$ **11.** $4\sqrt{3}$; $24\sqrt{3}$; $72\sqrt{3}$ **13.** $36\sqrt{3}$ **15.** $216\sqrt{3}$ **17. a.** $m\angle AOX = \frac{1}{2}m\angle AOB = \frac{1}{2}\left(\frac{360}{10}\right) = \frac{1}{2}(36) = 18$ **b.** 0.3090; $\frac{OX}{1}$, 0.9511 **c.** 6.18 **d.** 0.2939 **e.** 2.939 **19.** $a \approx 0.707$; $p \approx 5.656$; $A = 2$ **21.** $p \approx 6.2112$; $A \approx 3$

Self-Test 1, Page 444

1. 81 **2.** 60 **3.** $40\sqrt{3}$ **4.** $4\sqrt{3}$ cm^2 **5.** $6\sqrt{13}$ cm^2 **6.** 40 **7.** 39 **8.** $150\sqrt{3}$ **9.** $5xy$
10. 49

Written Exercises, Pages 448–450

1. 14π; 49π **3.** 5π; $\frac{25}{4}\pi$ **5.** 10; 100π **7.** 5; 10π **9. a.** 132; 1386 **b.** $44k$; $154k^2$

11. ≈ 57 in.; ≈ 254 in.^{2} **13.** 24 oz **15.** 984 ft^2 **17.** 15-in. pizza **19.** Area I $= \frac{a^2\pi}{8}$, Area II $= \frac{b^2\pi}{8}$, Area III $= \frac{c^2\pi}{8}$. Since $a^2 + b^2 = c^2$, Area I + Area II = Area III. **21. a.** 198,000 cm (or 1.98 km) **b.** 10,000 **23. a.** π; 3π; 5π; 7π **b.** $(2n + 1)\pi$ **25.** 3π; 3π; 3π **27.** 32π **29.** 1:2
31. $0.14r^2$ **33. a.** r **b.** $A = \pi r^2$ **35.** Radius is hypot. of rt. △ in which radii of ⊙O and ⊙P are legs.

Algebra Review, Page 451

1. $\frac{4}{3}\pi$ **3.** 32π **5.** $5\pi\sqrt{2}$ **7.** 12π

Written Exercises, Pages 453–455

1. 2π; 12π **3.** 2π; 3π **5.** $\frac{3}{2}\pi$; $\frac{9}{8}\pi$ **7.** π; $\frac{9}{4}\pi$ **9.** $3\pi\sqrt{2}$; 15π **11.** 6 **13.** $4\pi - 8$

15. $12\pi + 8$ **17.** $\frac{4\pi + 6\sqrt{3}}{3}$ **19.** $(100\pi - 192)$ cm^2 **21. a.** 49; 98 **b.** 52 cm^2 **23.** 1343 m^2

25. $(24\pi - 18\sqrt{3})$ cm^2 **27. b.** $72\pi - 108\sqrt{3}$ **29.** $\frac{48\sqrt{3} - 22\pi}{3}$; trapezoid; 60

Written Exercises, Pages 458–460

1. 1:4; 1:16 **3.** $r:2s$; $r^2:4s^2$ **5.** 3:13; 9:169 **7.** 3:8; 3:8 **9.** 1:25,000,000,000,000

11. 1:2; 1:4 **13.** $\triangle ABE \sim \triangle DCE$; 36:25; $6\frac{2}{3}$ **15.** 125 cm^2 **17. a.** 9:7 **b.** 5:4

19. a. 3:4 **b.** 3:7 **21.** Answers may vary. $\triangle ABC \sim \triangle CDA$, 1:1; $\triangle ABG \sim \triangle CEG$, 9:25; $\triangle ABF \sim \triangle DEF$, 9:4; $\triangle AGF \sim \triangle CGB$, 9:25; $\triangle EFD \sim \triangle EBC$, 4:25; $\triangle ABF \sim \triangle CEB$, 9:25
23. a. 1:9 **b.** 1:4 **c.** 1:8 **25. a.** 16:81 **b.** 4:9 **c.** 4:9 **d.** 1:1 **e.** 16:169 **27.** 9:40
29. 4:5

31. Each of the small △s has area $= \frac{1}{6} \cdot$ area of the orig. △.

Written Exercises, Pages 463–464

1. $\frac{1}{4}$ **3.** $\frac{1}{4}$ **5. a.** $\frac{1}{25}$ **b.** 3 **7.** $\frac{\pi}{200} \approx 0.016$ **9.** 0.04 **11.** $\frac{2}{3}$ **13.** 0.125 m^2 **15. b.** 7.5 mm

17. a. $\frac{13}{50}$ **b.** $\frac{1}{10}$

Self-Test 2, Page 465

1. 88; 616 **2.** 81π **3. a.** 6π **b.** 36π **c.** $36\pi - 72$ **4.** 16:49 **5.** 2:3 **6. a.** 4:9 **b.** 3:2 **7.** $64 - 16\pi$ **8.** $36\pi - 27\sqrt{3}$ **9.** $\frac{3}{5}$ **10.** $\frac{\pi}{4}$

Extra, Page 466

Answers may vary in Exs. 1–8. **1.** 55.2 **3.** 39.7 **5.** 75.3 **7.** 178.2

Chapter Review, Page 470

1. 64 **3.** 18 cm^2 **5.** 9 **7.** 7 **9.** $30 + 4\sqrt{2}$; 52 **11.** $9\sqrt{3}$ **13.** 188.4; 2826 **15.** $8\pi\sqrt{2}$; 32π **17.** $24\pi + 9\sqrt{3}$ **19.** 16π **21.** 1:4 **23.** $\frac{9}{25}$

Cumulative Review, Pages 472–473

1. False **3.** False **5.** False **7.** True **9.** True **11.** False **13.** $\parallel$, skew **15.** -45 **17.** 5 **19.** a sphere with ctr. P and radius 4 cm, along with its interior **21.** Key steps of proof: 1. $\triangle ABC \cong \triangle DCB$ (HL) 2. $\angle 1 \cong \angle 2$ (CPCT) 3. $\overline{CE} \cong \overline{BE}$ (Thm. 4-2) 4. $\triangle BCE$ is isos. (Def. isos. $\triangle$) **23.** Assume temp. that there is a $\triangle$ whose sides have lengths x, y, and $x + y$, then the length of the longest side equals the sum of the lengths of the other two sides. This contradicts the $\triangle$ Ineq. Thm., if 2 sides of a triangle have lengths x and y, then the third side must be greater than $x + y$. Therefore, the temp. assumption must be false. It follows that no $\triangle$ has sides of length x, y, and $x + y$. **25.** 5 **27.** 4.5 **29.** 17 **31.** 61 **33.** Const. a seg. of length $2x$. Use Const. 13 with $a = y$, $b = 2x$, and $c = x$ to find a seg. with length t; $\frac{y}{2x} = \frac{x}{t}$; $ty = 2x^2$; $t = \frac{2x^2}{y}$. **35.** $32\sqrt{6}$ **37. a.** 46 **b.** $\frac{1}{4}$

Chapter 12

Written Exercises, Pages 478–480

1. 40; 88; 48 **3.** 3; 54; 90 **5.** 6, 168, 108 **7.** 54; 27 **9.** 10; 600 **11.** 5; 125 **13.** 390 **15.** 4; 8 **17.** 240; $240 + 32\sqrt{3}$; $160\sqrt{3}$ **19.** 252; 372; 420 **21.** 180; 228; 216 **23.** 675 cm^3 **25.** 1.8 kg **27.** 19 kg **29.** $50x^3$; $120x^2$ **31.** 198 cm^2 **33.** ≈ 336 **35.** $V = Bh = \frac{1}{2}aph = \frac{1}{2} \cdot \frac{x\sqrt{3}}{6} \cdot 3x \cdot x = \frac{1}{4}x^3\sqrt{3}$ **39.** 6 cm

Written Exercises, Pages 485–487

1. 6; $\sqrt{34}$ **3.** 25; $\sqrt{674}$ **5.** 3; $\sqrt{41}$ **7.** 36 **9.** 192 **11.** 60; 96; 48 **13.** 260; 360; 400 **15.** 6 cm **17. a.** 15 cm; 13 cm **b.** 384 cm^2 (V-$ABCD$ is not reg.) **19.** Vol. pyr. $= \frac{1}{6} \cdot$ vol. rect. solid **21.** 8; $\sqrt{73}$ **23. a.** 3; 6; $6\sqrt{3}$ **b.** $45\sqrt{3}$; $36\sqrt{3}$ **25.** 144; $24\sqrt{39}$ **27.** ≈ 66 cubic units **29.** $\frac{x^3\sqrt{2}}{12}$ **31.** 246

Mixed Review Exercises, Page 487

1. 12π; 36π **2.** 22π; 121π **3.** π; $\frac{\pi}{4}$ **4.** $6\pi\sqrt{3}$; 27π **5.** 5; 25π **6.** 9; 81π **7.** 7; 14π **8.** $\sqrt{15}$; $2\pi\sqrt{15}$ **9. a.** 144π mm^2 **b.** 576 mm^2 **10. a.** 32 **b.** $8\pi\sqrt{2}$

Written Exercises, Pages 492–495

1. 40π; 72π; 80π **3.** 24π; 56π; 48π **5.** 4 **7.** 48π **9.** 5; 20π; 36π; 16π **11.** 5; 156π; 300π; 240π **13.** 12; 9; 324π; 432π **15.** 8; 17; 255π; 480π **17. a.** 1:4 **b.** 1:4 **c.** 1:8 **19.** 1:3 **21.** 24 cm **23.** 25 min **25.** 2 **27. a.** cyl. with $r = 6$, $h = 10$; $V = 360\pi$ **b.** cyl. with $r = 10$, $h = 6$; $V = 600\pi$ **29. a.** $270\sqrt{3}$; $180\sqrt{3}$ **b.** 720; $240\sqrt{2}$ **c.** $540\sqrt{3}$; 360 **31.** cyl. with $r = s$, $h = s$; $V = \pi s^3$ **33.** 16π cm^3 **35.** $18\pi\sqrt{2}$ cm^3 **37.** 60π; $18\sqrt{91}$ **39.** 1200π

Self-Test 1, Page 496

1. 162; 322; 360 **2.** 624; 1200; 960 **3.** 140π in.^{2}; 340π in.^{2}; 700π in.^{3} **4.** 180 cm^2; $(180 + 108\sqrt{3})$ cm^2; $270\sqrt{3}$ cm^3 **5.** 135π; 216π; 324π **6.** 8000 m^3 **7.** 6 **8.** 6:5

Written Exercises, Pages 500–502

1. 196π; $\frac{1372\pi}{3}$ **3.** π; $\frac{\pi}{6}$ **5.** 4; $\frac{256\pi}{3}$ **7.** 8π; $\frac{8\pi\sqrt{2}}{3}$ **9.** 4, 8 **11.** 1 cm **13.** 21π cm^2 **15.** Vol. of hemisphere = 4 • Vol. of sphere **17.** 358 million km^2 **19.** $\frac{1750\pi}{3}$ m^3 **21.** 6 cans **23. a.** 32 cm **b.** cone: $8\pi\sqrt{1088} \approx 829$; sphere: $4\pi \cdot 8^2 \approx 804$ **25.** $2\pi r^3$ **27.** $\frac{4}{3}\pi r^3$ **29.** 81π in.^{2}; 121.5π in.^{3} **31. a.** $h = 2x$; $r^2 = 10^2 - x^2 = 100 - x^2$; $V = \pi r^2 h = \pi(100 - x^2)(2x) = 2\pi x(100 - x^2)$ **b.** $\frac{4000\pi\sqrt{3}}{9}$ **33.** 144π cm^2

Mixed Review Exercises, Page 507

1. $\frac{2}{3}$ **2.** 10 **3.** $x = 15$; $y = 6$; $z = 9$ **4. a.** 32; 48 **b.** $\frac{2}{3}$ **c.** They are both $\frac{2}{3}$. **5. a.** 48; 108 **b.** $\frac{4}{9}$ **c.** $\frac{4}{9} = \left(\frac{2}{3}\right)^2$ **6. a.** True **b.** False **c.** True **d.** False **e.** False **f.** True **g.** True **h.** False

Written Exercises, Pages 511–513

1. Yes **3. a.** 3:4 **b.** 3:4 **c.** 9:16 **d.** 27:64 **5. a.** 4:1 **b.** 16:1 **c.** 64:1 **7. a.** 2:3 **b.** 2:3 **c.** 4:9 **9.** Paint for actual airplane = 40,000 times paint for model **11.** 81π cm^2 **13.** 18.5 kg **15.** the larger ball **17.** 108 ft^3 **19. a.** 9:16 **b.** 9:16 **c.** 9:7 **d.** 27:64 **e.** 27:37 **21.** 54 cm^3; 196 cm^3 **23.** $\frac{4}{3}\pi a^3 : \frac{4}{3}\pi b^3 = a^3 : b^3$ **25.** $r_1 : r_2 = l_1 : l_2$; L.A.$_1$:L.A.$_2$ $= \pi r_1 l_1 : \pi r_2 l_2 = r_1^2 : r_2^2$ **27.** $B_1 : B_2 = e_1^2 : e_2^2$; $h_1 : h_2 = e_1 : e_2$; $V_1 : V_2 = B_1 h_1 : B_2 h_2 = e_1^2 e_1 : e_2^2 e_2 = e_1^3 : e_2^3$ **29.** $6\sqrt[3]{4}$

Self-Test 2, Page 513

1. 36π cm^2; 36π cm^3 **2.** 16π m^2 **3.** $\frac{22{,}000\pi}{3}$ cm^3 **4.** 25π cm^2 **5. a.** $\frac{16}{3}$ **b.** 9:4 **6. a.** 2:5 **b.** 8:125

Extra, Page 517

1. 22 **3.** $\frac{56\pi}{3}$ **5.** 8 cm^2

Chapter Review, Pages 518–519

1. lateral edge **3.** 236; 240 **5.** $\frac{160\sqrt{3}}{3}$ **7.** 900; 1020; 17 **9.** 24π; 56π **11.** $2\sqrt{10}$ cm **13.** 616 m^2 **15.** $\frac{5324\pi}{3}$ cm^3 **17.** 1:9 **19.** 64:27

Preparing for College Entrance Exams, Page 520

1. A **2.** C **3.** E **4.** D **5.** B **6.** C **7.** B

Cumulative Review, Page 521

1. True **3.** False **5.** False **7.** False **9.** True **11.** Key steps of proof: 1. $\triangle WXY \cong \triangle YZW$ (HL) 2. $\angle XYW \cong \angle ZWY$ (CPCT) 3. $\overline{WZ} \parallel \overline{XY}$ (If alt. int. $\angle$s $\cong$, lines $\parallel$.) **13. a.** AA~ **b.** If $\triangle JKL \sim \triangle XYZ$, then $\angle J \cong \angle X$ and $\angle K \cong \angle Y$. True **15.** 8 **17.** 8 **19.** 125π cm^3

Chapter 13

Written Exercises, Pages 526–528

1. 7 **3.** 4 **5.** $\sqrt{10}$ **7.** 10 **9.** $2\sqrt{13}$ **11.** $5\sqrt{2}$ **13.** Yes; A **15.** No **17.** $(-3, 0)$; 7 **19.** $(j, -14)$; $\sqrt{17}$ **21.** $(x - 3)^2 + y^2 = 64$ **23.** $(x + 4)^2 + (y + 7)^2 = 25$ **27.** $AM = AY = 3\sqrt{5}$ **29.** $\frac{JA}{RF} = \frac{6}{3} = \frac{2}{1}$; $\frac{AN}{FK} = \frac{2\sqrt{5}}{\sqrt{5}} = \frac{2}{1}$; $\frac{JN}{RK} = \frac{4\sqrt{2}}{2\sqrt{2}} = \frac{2}{1}$. The △ are ~ by SSS ~ Thm. **31.** 39 **33.** $(10, 0)$, $(6, 8)$, $(8, 6)$, $(0, 10)$, $(-6, 8)$, $(-8, 6)$, $(-10, 0)$, $(6, -8)$, $(8, -6)$, $(0, -10)$, $(-6, -8)$, $(-8, -6)$ **35.** $x^2 + (y - 6)^2 = 100$ **37.** $x^2 + (y - 2)^2 = 9$ **39. a.** 5; 10 **b.** 15 **c.** Dist. between ctrs. = sum of radii. **41.** Quad. $RAYJ$ is a ▱. **43.** 15, 5, 2, −1, −11 **45.** $(-2, 4)$; 6

Written Exercises, Pages 532–534

1. a. k **b.** n, r **c.** l, x-axis **d.** s, y-axis **3.** 1 **5.** −1 **7.** −1 **9.** 0 **11.** $\frac{3}{2}$ **13.** $-\frac{2}{5}$; $2\sqrt{29}$ **15.** $\frac{3}{4}$; 10 Answers will vary in Exs. 17–19. Examples are given. **17.** $(-8, -2)$, $(2, 2)$ **19.** $(-4, -4)$, $(4, -6)$ **21.** Slope of $\overline{PQ}$ = slope of $\overline{QR}$ = $-\frac{1}{3}$ **23.** 9 **25.** $m(r - p) + q$ **27. a.** SAS **b.** $m\angle BOS = m\angle BOR + m\angle ROS = m\angle BOR + m\angle AOB = 90$ **c.** −1 **29. a.** $RS = \sqrt{58}$; $RT = 2\sqrt{2}$; $ST = 5\sqrt{2}$ **b.** $(RT)^2 + (ST)^2 = 8 + 50 = 58 = (RS)^2$ **c.** −1 **31.** 1 **33.** $a = 2\sqrt{3} + 1$

Algebra Review, Page 534

1. −216 **3.** $\frac{1}{9}$ **5.** $-\frac{1}{64}$ **7.** $\frac{27}{125}$ **9.** 1 **11.** 2 **13.** r^{13} **15.** r^5 **17.** 1 **19.** b^8 **21.** $6y^6$ **23.** $5b^4$

Written Exercises, Pages 537–538

1. a. $\frac{2}{3}$ **b.** $\frac{2}{3}$ **c.** $-\frac{3}{2}$ **3.** $\frac{7}{2}$; $\frac{7}{2}$; 0; 0 **5. a.** −3; −3 **b.** Slope of $\overline{LM}$ = slope of $\overline{PN}$ **c.** $\frac{1}{3}$; $-\frac{1}{7}$ **d.** Slope of $\overline{MN} \neq$ slope of $\overline{LP}$ **e.** trap. **7.** Slope of $\overline{AC} = -\frac{5}{2}$, slope of $\overline{AB} = \frac{3}{7}$, slope of $\overline{BC} = \frac{8}{5}$; slope of alt. to $\overline{AC} = \frac{2}{5}$, slope of alt. to $\overline{AB} = -\frac{7}{3}$, slope of alt. to $\overline{BC} = -\frac{5}{8}$ **9.** Slope of $\overline{RS} = \frac{6}{5}$, slope of $\overline{ST} = -\frac{5}{6}$; $\frac{6}{5}\left(-\frac{5}{6}\right) = -1$ **11. a.** Slope of $\overline{AB} = \frac{2 - (-4)}{4 - (-6)} = \frac{3}{5}$, and slope of $\overline{DC} = \frac{8 - 2}{6 - (-4)} = \frac{3}{5}$; $\overline{AB} \parallel \overline{DC}$. Slope of $\overline{AD} = \frac{2 - (-4)}{-4 - (-6)} = 3$, slope of $\overline{BC} = \frac{8 - 2}{6 - 4} = 3$; $\overline{AD} \parallel \overline{BC}$. **b.** $AB = 2\sqrt{34} = DC$, $AD = 2\sqrt{10} = BC$ **13. a.** Slope of $\overline{RS}$ = slope of $\overline{UT} = \frac{4}{3}$; slope of $\overline{RU}$ = slope of $\overline{ST} = -\frac{3}{4}$; $RSTU$ is a ▱. $\overline{RS} \perp \overline{RU}$, so $RSTU$ is a rect. **b.** $RT = US = 5\sqrt{5}$ **15.** trap. **17.** rect. **19.** $\frac{3}{4}$ **21. a.** True **b.** True **c.** True

Written Exercises, Pages 541–543

1.

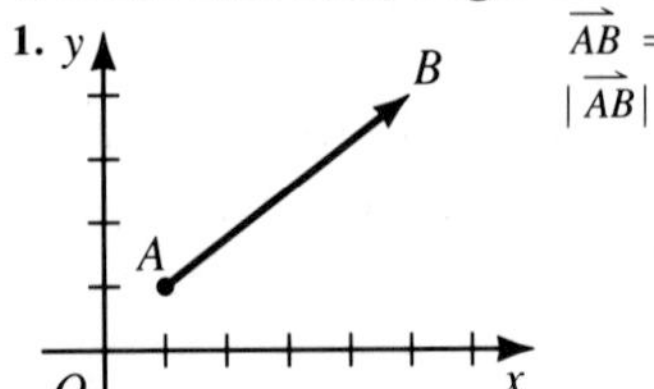

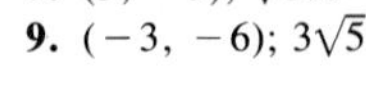
$\overrightarrow{AB} = (4, 3)$
$|\overrightarrow{AB}| = 5$

3. $(-2, 2)$; $2\sqrt{2}$ **5.** $(-4, 2)$; $2\sqrt{5}$ **7.** $(5, -9)$; $\sqrt{106}$ **9.** $(-3, -6)$; $3\sqrt{5}$

15.

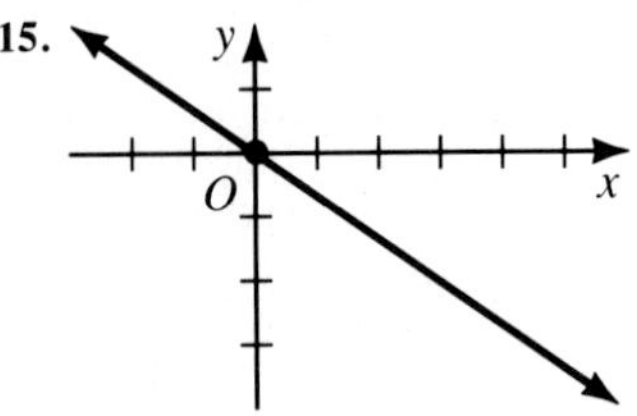

17. 9 **19.** -12 **21.** (7, 0) **23.** (4, 4) **25.** (4, 2) **27.** (6, 8); 10 **29. a.** (18, 18), (9, 9), (6, 6) **b.** (11, 12), (8, 9) **31.** $|(ka, kb)| = \sqrt{(ka)^2 + (kb)^2} = \sqrt{k^2(a^2 + b^2)} = |k|\sqrt{a^2 + b^2} = |k| \cdot |(a, b)|$
33. a. 1. Def. of vector sum 2. Subst. 3. $k[(a, b) + (c, d)] = k(a, b) + k(c, d)$ 4. Def. of vector sum
b. Thm. 5-11

Mixed Review, Page 543

1. -2 **2.** 6; 6 **3.** 16 **4.** $a\sqrt{3}$ **5.** 120 **6.** $2x$; $x\sqrt{3}$ **7.** 45 **8.** $(-3, 5)$ **9.** 25
10. 18 **11. a.** $(DE)^2 + (EF)^2 = 25 + 100 = 125$; $(DF)^2 = 121 + 4 = 125$ **b.** Slope of $\overline{DE}$ · slope of $\overline{EF} = -\frac{4}{3} \cdot \frac{3}{4} = -1$ **12. a.** $\frac{2}{3}$ **b.** $\frac{1}{4}$

Written Exercises, Pages 545–547

1. (3, 3) **3.** $(0, -2)$ **5.** (1.9, 0.4) **7.** $2\sqrt{41}$; $\frac{-5}{4}$; $(-1, -3)$ **9.** 17; $-\frac{15}{8}$; $\left(-3, \frac{7}{2}\right)$ **11.** (9, 5)
13. 1. The midpt. of $\overline{AB}$ is $M(4, 2)$. Slope of $\overline{AB} = \frac{4 - 0}{8 - 0} = \frac{1}{2}$, slope of $\overline{PM} = \frac{2 - 6}{4 - 2} = -2$; $\frac{1}{2}(-2) = -1$, so $\overline{PM} \perp \overline{AB}$. 2. $PA = 2\sqrt{10} = PB$, so P is on the ⊥ bis. of $\overline{AB}$. **15.** $\left(-\frac{5}{2}, \frac{1}{2}\right), \left(\frac{11}{2}, \frac{1}{2}\right)$; 8
17. a. $\left(\frac{9}{2}, \frac{9}{2}\right)$ **b.** ▱ **c.** slope of $\overline{PQ}$ = slope of $\overline{OR} = \frac{3}{7}$; slope of $\overline{PO}$ = slope of $\overline{QR} = 3$ **d.** $PQ = OR = \sqrt{58}$; $PO = QR = 2\sqrt{10}$ **19. a.** $(-3, 4)$ **b.** 5; 5; 5 **c.** Thm. 5-15 **d.** $(x + 3)^2 + (y - 4)^2 = 25$
21. a. $J\left(-\frac{1}{2}, \frac{3}{2}\right)$, $K(3, 6)$, $L\left(\frac{17}{2}, \frac{9}{2}\right)$; $M(5, 0)$ **b.** rhom.; $JK = KL = LM = JM = \frac{\sqrt{130}}{2}$
23. $\left(\frac{5}{8}x_1 + \frac{3}{8}x_2, \frac{5}{8}y_1 + \frac{3}{8}y_2\right)$

Self-Test 1, Page 547

1. a. 2 **b.** (4, 1) **2. a.** 10 **b.** $(4, -3)$ **3. a.** $10\sqrt{2}$ **b.** (3, 2) **4. a.** $\sqrt{29}$ **b.** $\left(-4, \frac{9}{2}\right)$
5. $x^2 + y^2 = 81$ **6.** $(x + 1)^2 + (y - 2)^2 = 25$ **7.** $(-2, 3)$; 6 **8.** $\frac{4}{7}$ **9.** $-\frac{3}{5}$ **10.** vertical
11. a. 2 **b.** $-\frac{1}{2}$ **12. a.** $(6, -2)$ **b.** $(-3, -3)$ **c.** (0, 4) **13. a.** $2\sqrt{10}$ **b.** $3\sqrt{2}$ **c.** 4
14. a. $(4, -9)$ **b.** $(22, -9)$ **15.** $(-15, 18)$

Written Exercises, Pages 550–552

1.
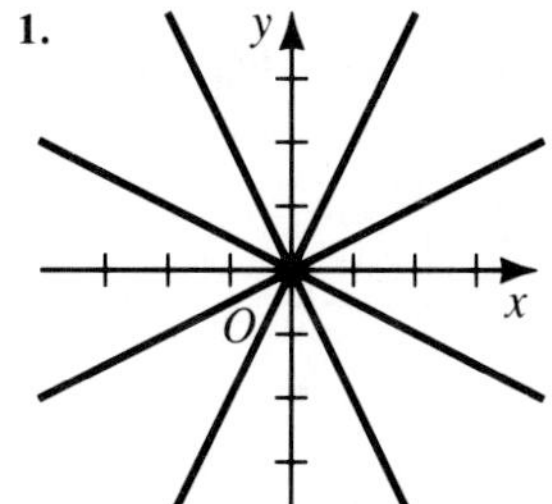

7. -7; -21
9. 4; 6
11. 4; $\frac{5}{2}$

13.
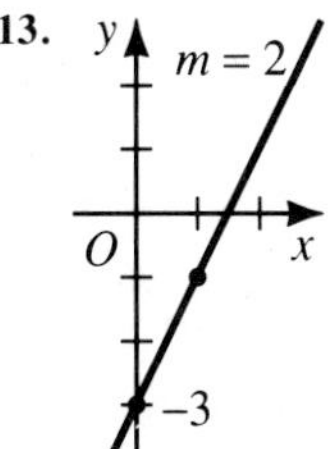

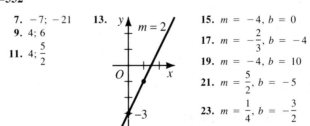

15. $m = -4$, $b = 0$
17. $m = -\frac{2}{3}$, $b = -4$
19. $m = -4$, $b = 10$
21. $m = \frac{5}{2}$, $b = -5$
23. $m = \frac{1}{4}$, $b = -\frac{3}{2}$

25. (1, 2) **27.** (4, 3) **29.** $(2, -3)$ **31. a.** Both have slope -2. **b.** No **c.** There is no sol.
33. a. 2; $-\frac{1}{2}$ **b.** They are ⊥; 2 nonvert. lines are ⊥ iff the prod. of their slopes is -1. **35. b.** $(2, -1)$, $(-1, 5)$, $(-4, -4)$ **c.** $22\frac{1}{2}$ **37.** (3, 4), $(-5, 0)$

Written Exercises, Pages 555–556

1. $y = 2x + 5$ **3.** $y = \frac{1}{2}x - 8$ **5.** $y = -\frac{7}{5}x + 8$ **7.** $y = -\frac{1}{4}x + 2$ **9.** $y = \frac{1}{2}x + 4$

11. $y - 2 = 5(x - 1)$ **13.** $y - 5 = \frac{1}{3}(x + 3)$ **15.** $y = -\frac{1}{2}(x + 4)$ **17.** $y = 2x - 1$

19. $y = \frac{1}{3}x + 2$ **21.** $x = 2$ **23.** $x = 5$ **25.** $y - 7 = 3(x - 5)$ **27.** $5x + 8y = -31$

29. $y = -\frac{5}{3}x + \frac{34}{3}$ **31.** $y = x$ **33.** $\frac{2}{3}$ or $-\frac{2}{3}$ **35.** $(2, 0)$ **37. a.** $y = x, x = 3, x + 2y = 9$
b. $C(3, 3)$ **c.** $CQ = CR = CS = 3\sqrt{10}$ **d.** $(x - 3)^2 + (y - 3)^2 = 90$ **39. a.** slope of $\overline{CG} = -1 =$ slope of $\overline{GH}$ **b.** $GH = 2\sqrt{2}$, $GC = \sqrt{2}$

Written Exercises, Pages 558–559

1. $(0, b), (a, 0)$ **3.** $(-f, 2f), (f, 2f)$ **5.** $(h + m, n)$ **7.** $\left(\frac{s}{2}, \frac{s\sqrt{3}}{2}\right)$ **9.** $(\sqrt{a^2 - b^2}, b)$, $(\sqrt{a^2 - b^2} + a, b)$

Written Exercises, Pages 562–563

1. Plan for proof: Use the distance formula twice to show that the length of each diag. is $\sqrt{a^2 + b^2}$. **5.** Plan for proof: Find the coords. of the midpts. G and H of $\overline{NP}$ and $\overline{MO}$, resp. Use slopes to show that $\overline{NM} \parallel \overline{GH} \parallel \overline{OP}$. Use the Dist. Formula to show that $GH = \frac{1}{2}(OP - NM)$. **9.** Plan for proof: Use the eq. of the ⊙ to show that $b^2 - a^2 = -c^2$. Then use slopes to show that $\overline{CA} \perp \overline{CB}$.

Ex. 1

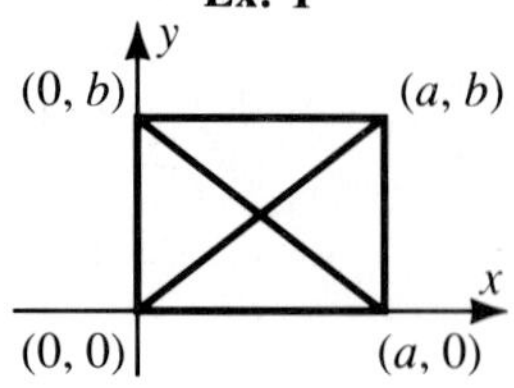

Self-Test 2, Page 563

1. $\frac{2}{5}$; -4 **2.**

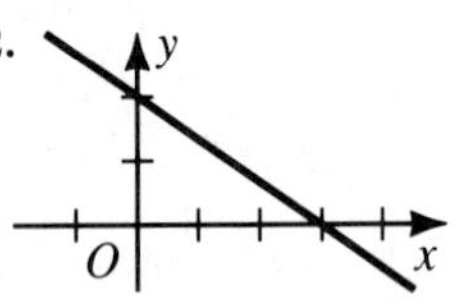

3. $y = -\frac{1}{2}x + \frac{5}{2}$ **4.** $y = 5$ **5.** $(1, -1)$ **6.** $(2e, 0)$
7. $(c + g, h)$ **8.** $(c - g, h)$ **9.** slope of $\overline{GO} =$ slope of $\overline{LD} = -\frac{1}{4}$; slope of $\overline{OL} =$ slope of $\overline{DG} = 3$

Extra, Page 565

1. y-axis **3.** x-axis **5.** xy-plane **7.** yz-plane

Chapter Review, Page 567

1. $4\sqrt{5}$; 10; $2\sqrt{5}$ **3.** $(-3, 0)$; 10 **5.** $(x + 6)^2 + (y + 1)^2 = 9$ **7.** -19 **9.** 0 **11.** $\frac{3}{4}, -\frac{4}{3}$

13. a. $(4, 3)$ **b.** 5 **c.** $(-8, -6)$ **15.** $\left(4, -\frac{3}{2}\right)$ **17.** $(0, b)$ **19.**

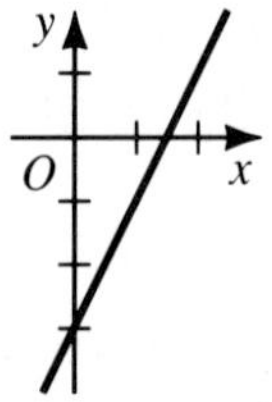

21. $(2, 1)$ **23.** $y = 2x + 4$ **25.** $M\left(\frac{a}{2} + b, c\right), N\left(\frac{a}{2}, 0\right)$; slope of $\overline{ON} = 0 =$ slope of $\overline{MQ}$, $\overline{ON} \parallel \overline{MQ}$; slope of $\overline{OM} = \frac{2c}{a + 2b} =$ slope of $\overline{NQ}$, $\overline{OM} \parallel \overline{NQ}$

Cumulative Review, Page 569

1. obtuse **3.** No; no; draw a fig. in which the diags. do not bis. each other. **5. a.** Since $\angle AEB \cong \angle CED$ (Vert. ∠s ≅.) and $\frac{AE}{CE} = \frac{BE}{DE}$, $\triangle AEB \sim \triangle CED$ (SAS~); therefore $\angle B \cong \angle D$ (Corr. ∠s of ~ △s are ≅.).
b. $x = 18$ **c.** 4:9 **7. a.** $\frac{1}{3}$ **b.** $\frac{1}{3}$ **c.** $2\sqrt{2}$ **d.** $\frac{2\sqrt{2}}{3}$ **9.** 364π; 820π **11.** $6\frac{2}{3}$ **13.** 89

15. Given: $\overrightarrow{BD}$ bis. $\angle ABC$; $\overrightarrow{BD} \perp \overline{AC}$
Prove: $\triangle ABC$ is isos.
Key steps of proof: 1. $\triangle ABD \cong \triangle CBD$ (ASA)
2. $\overline{AB} \cong \overline{CB}$ (CPCT)

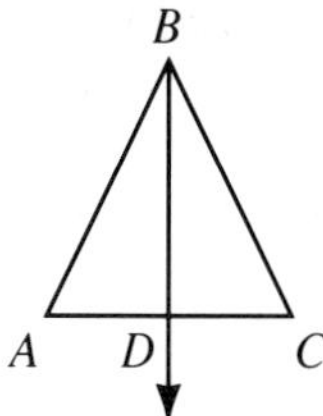

17. Plan for proof: Show that the slopes of the bases = 0, and that the slope of the median = 0.

Chapter 14

Written Exercises, Pages 574–576

1. 33, 4 **3.** 10, 10; no **5. a.** $A'(4, 2)$, $B'(8, 4)$, $C'(6, -2)$ **b.** Yes **c.** (8, 8) **7. a.** $A'(0, 12)$, $B'(12, 18)$, $C'(6, 0)$ **b.** No **c.** (4, 2) **9. a.** $A'(12, 4)$, $B'(8, 6)$, $C'(10, 0)$ **b.** Yes **c.** (0, 6) **11. a.** Yes **b.** preserves **c.** No **13.** Let X be int. of $\overline{AC}$ and $\overline{DB}$. P on $\overline{DC}$ maps to pt. P', where $\overrightarrow{PX}$ int. $\overline{AB}$. Not an isom. **15.** $A'(5, 3)$, $B'(7, 3)$, $C'(9, 5)$, $D'(7, 5)$. Area $ABCD = 4$, perimeter $ABCD = 8$; Area $A'B'C'D' = 4$, perimeter $A'B'C'D' = 4 + 4\sqrt{2}$ **17.** Yes **19.** No **21.** If A and B are diff. pts., $AB > 0$. But $A'B' = 0$. **23. a.** $A'(-6, 1)$, $B'(-3, 4)$, $C'(-1, -3)$

Written Exercises, Pages 580–582

1.

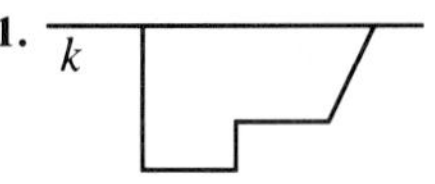

3.

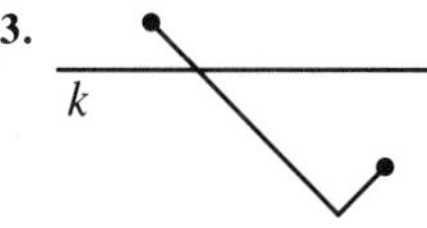

5.

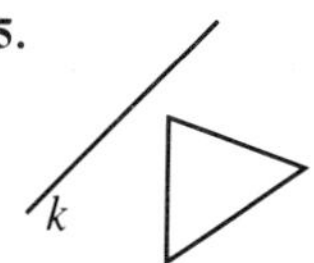

7. a. (2, −4) **b.** (−2, 4) **c.** (4, 2) **9. a.** (0, 2) **b.** (0, −2) **c.** (−2, 0) **11. a.** (−3, 2) **b.** (3, −2) **c.** (−2, −3)

13. Examples: WOW, AHA. **15.** An isos. $\triangle$ with m the $\perp$ bis. of the base. **17.** If P is not on plane X, then X is $\perp$ to and bis. $\overline{PP'}$. If P is on plane X, $P' = P$. **19.** Let X and Y be the pts. where $\overline{PP'}$ and $\overline{QQ'}$ int. m, resp. $\triangle XYQ \cong \triangle XYQ'$, so $XQ = XQ'$ and $\angle QXY \cong \angle Q'XY$. Then $\angle PXQ \cong \angle P'XQ'$ and since $XP = XP'$, $\triangle XPQ \cong \triangle XP'Q'$ by SAS. Then $PQ = P'Q'$. **21.** Const. k, the $\perp$ to t through A, int. t at P; const. $\overline{PA'}$ on k so that $AP = PA'$; $A' = R_t(A)$. **23.** Yes **25.** Path from B to H hits walls first at X, then at Y. Because reflect. is isom., $YH = YH'$, $XH' = XH''$. Thus $BX + XY + YH = BX + XY + YH' = BX + XH' = BX + XH'' = BH''$. **27.** Aim for image of hole under reflect. in two walls, as in Ex. 25. **29.** Yes **31.** $y = -x - 5$ **33.** $x = 2$ **35.** $y = x$ **37.** $y = -\frac{5}{3}x + 6$ **39. a.** (6, 3) **b.** (10, −2) **c.** (13, 1) **d.** $(10 - x, y)$

Written Exercises, Pages 586–587

1. a. $A'(-4, 6)$, $B'(-2, 10)$, $C'(1, 5)$; yes **c.** Yes; yes **3.** (8, 4) **5.** (−4, −3) **7.** $A'(1, 4)$, $B'(4, 6)$, $C'(5, 10)$; $A''(-1, 4)$, $B''(-4, 6)$, $C''(-5, 10)$ **9.** $(-x, y + 4)$ **11.** a, b, c, d **13.** $(x - 4, y + 9)$ **15. a.** $A'(2, -2)$, $B'(3, 2)$ **b.** ▱; $10 + 2\sqrt{17}$ **17.** The midpts. of $\overline{AA'}$, $\overline{BB'}$, and $\overline{CC'}$ lie on the reflecting line. **19.** Let translation T map P to P' and Q to Q'. Let reflection R_k map P' to P'' and Q' to Q''. Since T and R_k are isom., $PQ = P'Q'$ and $P'Q' = P''Q''$. By trans. $PQ = P''Q''$, so the glide reflection is also an isom.

Written Exercises, Pages 590–592

Answers may vary in Exs. 1–5. **1.** $\mathcal{R}_{O, 440}$ **3.** $\mathcal{R}_{A, 90}$ **5.** $\mathcal{R}_{O, 180}$ **7.** C **9.** E **11.** D **13.** D **15.** rotation **17.** half-turn **19.** rotation **21.** reflection **23.** 6 **25.** a, b, c, d

27.

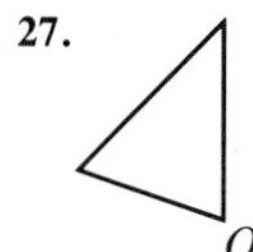

29.

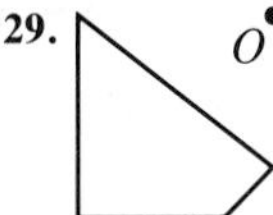

31. Const. the $\perp$ bis. of $\overline{AA'}$ and $\overline{BB'}$. They int. at O. **33. b.** $A'(3, 0)$, $B'(1, -4)$ **c.** slope of $\overleftrightarrow{AB} = -\frac{1}{2}$, slope of $\overleftrightarrow{A'B'} = 2$; the lines are $\perp$ **d.** A rotation is an isom. **e.** An isom. maps any $\triangle$ to a $\cong \triangle$. **f.** $(y, -x)$

35. Extend $\overrightarrow{OF}$ to int. l' at G and let H be the int. of l and l'. $m\angle F'GO = 90 - x$ so $m\angle GHF = 90 - (90 - x) = x$. **37. a.** $\mathcal{R}_{C,\,90}$ **b.** $\overline{AD}$ is the image of $\overline{BE}$ under an isom. **c.** If a rotation of 90° maps $\overline{BE}$ to $\overline{AD}$, then one of the ∠s between $\overline{BE}$ and $\overline{AD}$ has meas. 90. (Result from Ex. 35.) **39.** Locate X and Z as you did B and C in Ex. 38, using $\mathcal{R}_{A,\,90}$ instead of $\mathcal{R}_{A,\,60}$. With ctrs. X and Z and radius AX, draw arcs int. at Y.

Mixed Review Exercises, Page 592

1. *ODE*, *OFG* **2.** 2:3 **3.** $x = \frac{9}{2}$, $y = \frac{10}{3}$, $z = 5$, $w = \frac{9}{2}$ **4.** 3:5 **5.** 4:9 **6.** 9:25 **7.** 4:25

Written Exercises, Pages 596–597

1. $A'(12, 0)$, $B'(8, 4)$, $C'(4, -4)$ **3.** $A'(3, 0)$, $B'(2, 1)$, $C'(1, -1)$ **5.** $A'(-12, 0)$, $B'(-8, -4)$, $C'(-4, 4)$ **7.** $A'(6, 0)$, $B'(7, -1)$, $C'(8, 1)$ **9.** 4; expansion **11.** $\frac{1}{3}$; contraction **13.** 4; expansion **15.** b, d **17.** a, b, c **19.** 3:2, 9:4 **21.** 2:1, 4:1 **23. a.** 16:9 **b.** 64:27 **25. a.** Slope of $\overline{PQ} = \frac{y_2 - y_1}{x_2 - x_1}$ = slope of $\overline{P'Q'}$. **b.** ∥ **27.** (4, 2), $k = 3$

Self-Test 1, Page 597

1. An isom. is a one-to-one mapping from the whole plane onto the whole plane that maps every seg. to a ≅ seg. **2.** −1, 3 **3.** (1, −2), (−1, 2) **4. a.** (3, −5) **b.** (−3, 5) **c.** (5, 3) **5.** a, b **6.** Answers may vary; for example, $\mathcal{R}_{O,\,330}$ **7.** *B* **8.** *C* **9.** $\overline{AB}$ **10.** $\overline{OB}$ **11.** *M* **12.** $\overline{AO}$ **13.** *L* **14.** *NDO* **15.** *C* **16.** *Q* **17.** *C* **18.** *L*

Written Exercises, Pages 603–605

1. a. 1 **b.** $2x^2 - 7$ **c.** 9 **d.** $(2x - 7)^2$ **3. a.** 8 **b.** 27 **c.** $\left(\frac{x+1}{2}\right)^3$ **d.** 14 **e.** 63 **f.** $\frac{x^3 + 1}{2}$ **11. a.** *Q* **b.** *S* **c.** *M* **d.** *Q* **e.** *Q* **13.** b **15.** a, b, c, d **17.** (−3, −1) **19.** (9, 2) **21.** (4, −8) **23.** (3, −3) **25. a.** $Q(-2, 5)$ **b.** 90 **c.** slope of $\overline{OP} = \frac{2}{5}$, slope of $\overline{OQ} = -\frac{5}{2}$; $\frac{2}{5}\left(-\frac{5}{2}\right) = -1$ **d.** $(-y, x)$, $(y, -x)$ **27.** Construct B' so that k is the ⊥ bisector of $\overline{BB'}$. Construct line j, the ⊥ bis. of $\overline{AB'}$. **29.** translation

Written Exercises, Pages 607–608

1. $\frac{1}{4}$ **3.** $\frac{3}{2}$ **5.** *C* **7.** *A* **9.** *C* **11.** *A* **13.** *C* **15.** *I* **17.** H_O **19.** $(x + 6, y - 8)$ **21.** $S^{-1}:(x, y) \to (x - 5, y - 2)$ **23.** $S^{-1}:(x, y) \to \left(\frac{1}{3}x, -2y\right)$ **25.** $S^{-1}:(x, y) \to \left(x + 4, \frac{1}{4}y\right)$ **27.** $T:(x, y) \to \left(x + 2, y - \frac{1}{2}\right)$ **29. a.** 2 units rt., 2 units left

Written Exercises, Pages 612–614

1. a. 5 **b.** No **c.** $\mathcal{R}_{O,\,72}$, $\mathcal{R}_{O,\,144}$, $\mathcal{R}_{O,\,216}$, $\mathcal{R}_{O,\,288}$ **3. a.** 4 **b.** Yes **c.** $\mathcal{R}_{O,\,90}$, $\mathcal{R}_{O,\,180}$, $\mathcal{R}_{O,\,270}$ **5.** A, B, C, D, E, K, M, T, U, V, W, Y **7.** H, I, N, O, S, X, Z

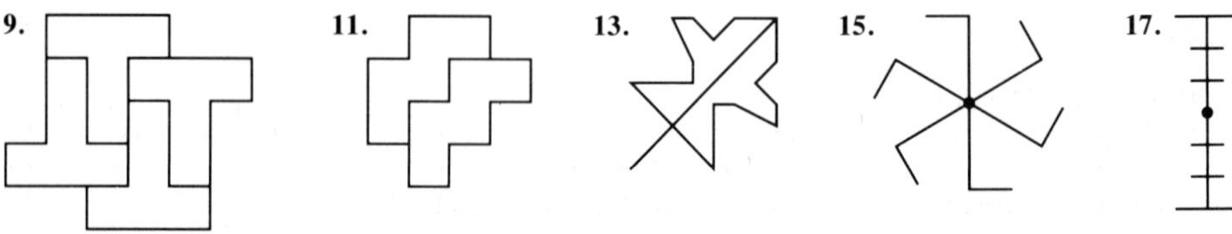

19. a. The ellipse has line symm. about two axes and pt. symm. about the int. of the axes. **b.** If $a = b$, the ellipse becomes a ⊙ and the solid formed is a sphere with vol. $\frac{4}{3}\pi a^3$. **c.** The ellipsoid has plane symm. about the

inf. many planes that contain b; plane symm. about the single plane that contains a and is $\perp$ to b; inf. many rot. symmetries about b; 180° rot. symm. about the inf. many lines $\perp$ to b and containing the int. of the axes.

21. a. non-isos. trap. **b.** isos. trap. **c.** not poss. **23. a.** reg. octagon **b.**  **c.** 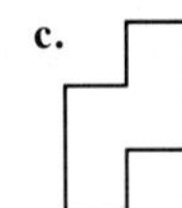
25. a. at the midpts. of the sides **b.** translational

Self-Test 2, Page 615

1. A **2.** A **3.** B **4.** P **5.** y-axis **6.** No **7.** P **8.** T **9.** translation **10. a.** $D_{O,\frac{1}{5}}$ **b.** $\mathcal{R}_{O,70}$ **c.** R_y **d.** $S^{-1}:(x, y) \to (x - 2, y + 3)$

Extra, Pages 616–617

1. Let t be the $\perp$ bis. of the base.

$\circ$	I	R_t
I	I	R_t
R_t	R_t	I

3.

$\circ$	I	$\mathcal{R}_{O,120}$	$\mathcal{R}_{O,240}$
I	I	$\mathcal{R}_{O,120}$	$\mathcal{R}_{O,240}$
$\mathcal{R}_{O,120}$	$\mathcal{R}_{O,120}$	$\mathcal{R}_{O,240}$	I
$\mathcal{R}_{O,240}$	$\mathcal{R}_{O,240}$	I	$\mathcal{R}_{O,120}$

5. a. 2 **b.** 4 **9. a.** No; there is no identity. **b.** Yes; the rot. symmetries **c.** I, H_O

Chapter Review, Page 619

1. $\cong$ **3. a.** (6, 1), $\left(\frac{3}{2}, 5\right)$ **b.** No **5.** $y = -2x + 1$ **7.** (12, 2) **9.** a, c **11.** (1, 3)
13. $(x + 1, y - 6)$ **15.** I **17.** No **19.** Yes

Preparing for College Entrance Exams, Page 621

1. B **2.** A **3.** E **4.** C **5.** C **6.** E **7.** A **8.** E **9.** B **10.** D

Cumulative Review, Pages 622–625

True-False Exercises **1.** T **3.** T **5.** F **7.** F **9.** F **11.** T **13.** F **15.** T **17.** T **19.** F **Multiple-Choice Exercises** **1.** d **3.** b **5.** d **7.** c **9.** c **11.** b

Completion Exercises **1.** Add. Prop. = **3.** 124 **5.** 33 **7.** $-\frac{3}{2}$ **9.** $(-5, 2)$ **11.** 22.5 **13.** $\frac{15}{17}$ **15.** $27\sqrt{7}$ **17.** 324π, 135π **19.** $(4, -2)$ **21.** 1:7 **Always-Sometimes-Never Exercises** **1.** N **3.** S **5.** A **7.** N **9.** S **11.** A **13.** N **15.** A **17.** S
Construction Exercises **1.** Const. 3 **3.** Const. 11 **5.** Const. $l \perp m$ at A; on m mark off $AB = y$; from B, locate D on l such that $BD = x$; const. $n \perp l$ at D; on n mark off $DC = y$; draw $\overline{BC}$. **7.** On a line, mark off $AB = x$, $BC = x$, $CD = x$. Use Const. 14 to const. the geom. mean of AD and y. **Proof Exercises** **1.** Key steps of proof: 1. $\triangle OQP \sim \triangle OSR$ (AA~) 2. $\frac{PO}{RO} = \frac{PQ}{RS}$ (Corr. sides of ~ $\triangle$s are in prop.) **3.** Key steps of proof: 1. $OS = OR$; $OP = OQ$ (If 2 $\angle$s of a $\triangle$ are $\cong$, sides opp. those $\angle$s are $\cong$.) 2. $PR = QS$ (Add. Prop. =, Seg. Add. Post.) 3. $\triangle PSR \cong \triangle QRS$ (SAS) **5.** Plan for proof: Let the coords. be $R(-2a, 0)$, $S(2a, 0)$, and $T(0, 2b)$. Midpts. of the segs. are $M(-a, b)$, $N(0, 0)$, and $P(a, b)$. Use the Dist. Form. to show that $NM = NP = \sqrt{a^2 + b^2}$.

Logic

Exercises, Pages 645–646

1. I like the city and you like the country. **3.** You don't like the country. **5.** I like the city or you don't like the country. **7.** I don't like the city or you don't like the country. **9.** It is not true that "I like the city or you like the country." **11.** $p \vee q$ **13.** $\sim(p \vee q)$ **15.** $\sim(p \wedge q)$ **17.** Yes

19.

p	q	$\sim q$	$p \vee \sim q$
T	T	F	T
T	F	T	T
F	T	F	F
F	F	T	T

Exercises, Page 647

1. If you like to paint, then you are an artist. **3.** If you are not an artist, then you do not draw landscapes. **5.** If you like to paint and you are an artist, then you draw landscapes. **7.** If you draw landscapes or you are an artist, then you like to paint. **9.** $b \rightarrow k$ **11.** $(\sim b \vee \sim k) \rightarrow s$ **13.** $\sim(b \rightarrow s)$ **15. a.** Yes; no **b.** Yes; yes **17.**

p	q	$p \rightarrow q$	$\sim(p \rightarrow q)$
T	T	T	F
T	F	F	T
F	T	T	F
F	F	T	F

19. $\sim(p \rightarrow q)$ and $p \wedge \sim q$

Exercises, Page 649

1. 1. Given 2. Step 1, Simplification 3. Given 4. Steps 2, 3, Modus Ponens **5.** 1. $a \wedge b$ (Given) 2. a (Step 1, Simplification) 3. $a \rightarrow \sim c$ (Given) 4. $\sim c$ (Steps 2, 3, Modus Ponens) 5. $c \vee d$ (Given) 6. d (Steps 4, 5, Disj. Syllogism) **7.** Given: $w \rightarrow g$; $g \rightarrow p$; $w \wedge y$. Prove: p.

Exercises, Pages 650–651

1. a. T, T, F, T **b.** T, T, F, F **c.** T, T, T, T (tautology) **d.** T, T, T, F **5. a.** The sandwich costs \$3.50. **b.** Perhaps it's not true that if I have enough money I'll buy milk. Maybe I'm allergic to milk. Or maybe the statement that milk costs a dollar is wrong.

Exercises, Page 652

1. 1. Given 2. Step 1, Double Neg. 3. Given 4. Steps 2, 3, Modus Tollens **5.** 1. $p \vee \sim q$ (Given) 2. $\sim q \vee p$ (Step 1, Comm. Rule) 3. q (Given) 4. $\sim(\sim q)$ (Step 3, Double Neg.) 5. p (Steps 2, 4, Disj. Syllogism) **9.** Given: $c \rightarrow t$; $\sim c \rightarrow \sim s$; s. Prove: t

Exercises, Page 654

1. $p \wedge r$ **3.** $s \wedge (t \vee p)$ **5.** $(t \vee s) \wedge (\sim t \vee s)$ **7.** Electricity passes through $p \vee \sim p$ but never through $p \wedge \sim p$.

Handbook

Exercises, Pages 658–659

1. The sum is 360. **3. b.** Vert. ∠s are ≅. **c.** Opp. ∠s of a ▱ are ≅. **5. b.** 360 **7.** 360; Thm. 3-14

Exercises, Pages 659–660

5. c. $\angle A \cong \angle B$ because the 2 ∠s overlap exactly. **7. a.** A trans. maps fig. I to fig. III. **b.** The distance bet. corr. pts. in figures I and III is twice the distance bet. l and m.

Exercises, Pages 661–662

3. No **5.** $S(3, 2)$ **7. b.** $M(1, 3)$, $N(3, 4)$ **c.** slope of $\overline{MN}$ = slope of $\overline{OI} = \frac{1}{2}$; $\overline{MN} \parallel \overline{OI}$; $OMNI$ is a trap.

9. a. slope of $\overline{AB}$ = slope of $\overline{DC} = -\frac{3}{4}$, slope of $\overline{AD}$ = slope of $\overline{BC} = \frac{4}{3}$; Thm. 13-4 **b.** rect.

11. a. $DE = EF = FG = GD = \sqrt{40} = 2\sqrt{10}$ **b.** slope of $\overline{DF} = 1$, slope of $\overline{EG} = -1$ **13–33.** Refer to Sel. Ans. of specified pages.

Exercises, Pages 663–664

1. A

B

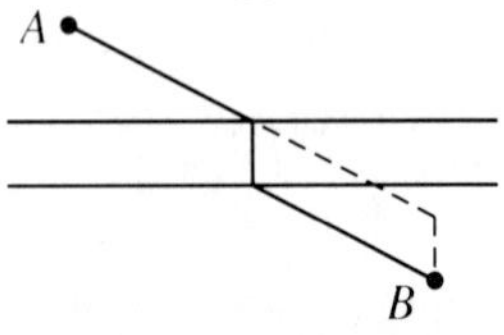

3. Construct the bridge between (3, 3) and (4, 3). **7.** $\sqrt{5}$

Exercises, Pages 664–665

1. about $\frac{2}{3}$; rotation 90° **3.** $\overrightarrow{RS} \parallel \overrightarrow{R'S'}$ **5.** 2; 3 **7.** $y = 2x + 3$ **9.** Refer to Sel. Ans. for p. 527.

Exercises, Pages 666–667

1. rt. **3.** obt. **5. a.** slope of $\overline{AB} = \frac{3}{2}$, slope of $\overline{BC} = -\frac{2}{3}$; $\overline{AB} \perp \overline{BC}$ **b.** $(AB)^2 = 13$, $(BC)^2 = 52$, $(AC)^2 = 65$ **7.** $\mathcal{R}_{N,\,-90}$ followed by $D_{N,\,2}$; 2 **9.** The left fig. has area c^2; the right fig. has area $b^2 + a^2$. This suggests the Pyth. Thm. **11–21.** Refer to Sel. Ans. of specified pages.

Exercises, Pages 668–669

1. a. $(x - 6)^2 + y^2 = 25$ **b.** Yes **c.** No **3. b.** $M(-1, 7)$ **c.** slope of $\overline{OM} = -7$; slope of $\overline{AB} = \frac{1}{7}$; Thm. 13-4 **5.** radius of outer ⊙ = $\sqrt{225} = 15$, radius of inner ⊙ = $\sqrt{25} = 5$, dist. bet. ctrs. of ⊙s is 10; $10 + 5 = 15$ **7. a.** ⊙O; the other tan. to ⊙O from P **b.** $\overline{PA}$ and its image are ≅. **c.** Thm. 9-1 Cor. **9.** To find B, rotate C $-60°$ about A. **11–17.** Refer to Sel. Ans. of specified pages.

Exercises, Page 670

3. 1:4 **5.** $|x| + |y| = 10$

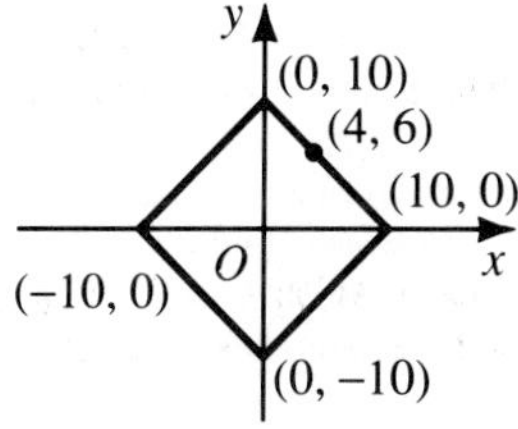

7. Rotate ⊙P 90° about A to locate two points, C_1 and C_2, then rotate each $-90°$ about A to get B_1 and B_2.

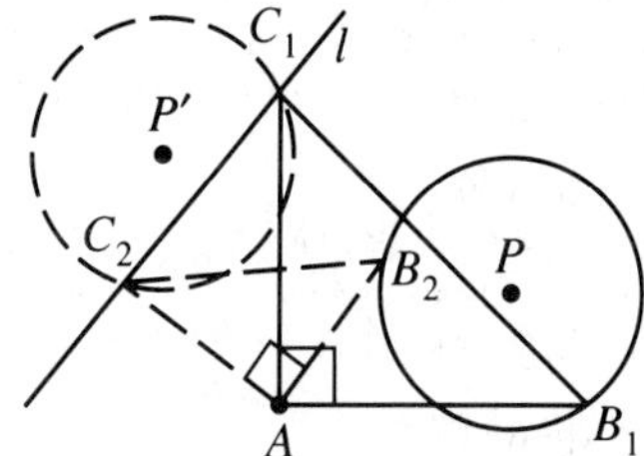

9–15. Refer to Sel. Ans. of specified pages.

Exercises, Pages 671–672

1. 32 **3.** 64 **5. a.** $-60°$, $\frac{1}{2}$ **b.** reg. II; reg. III; reg. IV **c.** $\frac{1}{4}, \frac{1}{16}, \frac{1}{64}$

Exercises, Pages 674–675

1. Plans for proofs: **a.** Use Thm. 4-5 **b.** Reflect $\triangle ADC$ to $\triangle ABC$. The isom. preserves dist. **c.** Assign coords. $A(0, a)$, $B(b, 0)$, $C(0, -c)$, $D(-b, 0)$ and use the dist. form. **3. a.** Plan for proof: Use SAS to prove $\triangle XBC \cong \triangle ABY$. **b.** $\overline{XC}$ Answers may vary in Exs. 5–17. **5.** square; use a coord. approach. **7.** Use a syn. or coord. approach. **9.** Use a syn. approach. Draw $\overline{XY} \parallel \overline{BC}$ through P with X on $\overline{AB}$ and Y on $\overline{DC}$. **11.** Use a syn. approach. Extend $\overrightarrow{AB}$ and $\overrightarrow{DC}$ to int. at rt. $\angle X$. Then use the Pyth. Thm. **13.** Use a transf. approach. Trans. l toward m a dist. AB. **15.** Use a transf. approach. See the figure at the right. Const. ∥ lines j, k, l. Choose A on k. Rotate l 60° about A to get B on j. Rotate B $-60°$ about A to get C on l. **17.** Use a syn. approach. Note that $XN = \frac{1}{2}AB$ and $YN = \frac{1}{2}DC$.

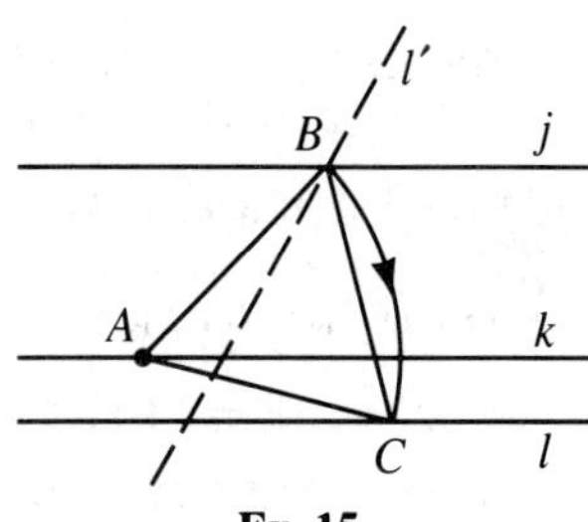

Ex. 15

Discrete Mathematics

Exercises, pages 677–678

1. No Euler circuit is possible.

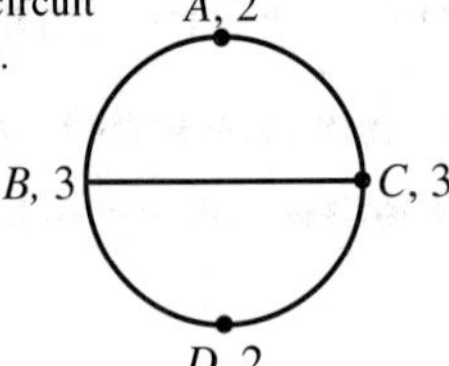

3.

A
B End
C Start
D

5. a. no

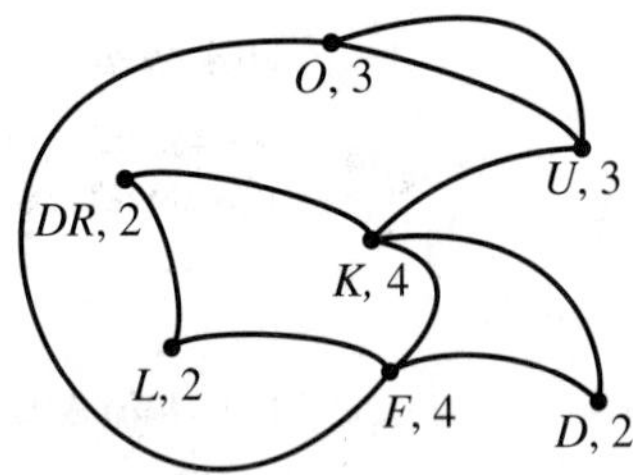

b. yes **c.** It is possible to travel a path starting at one odd vertex and ending at another, only if the graph contains exactly two odd vertices.

7. a. Bears, Tigers **b.**

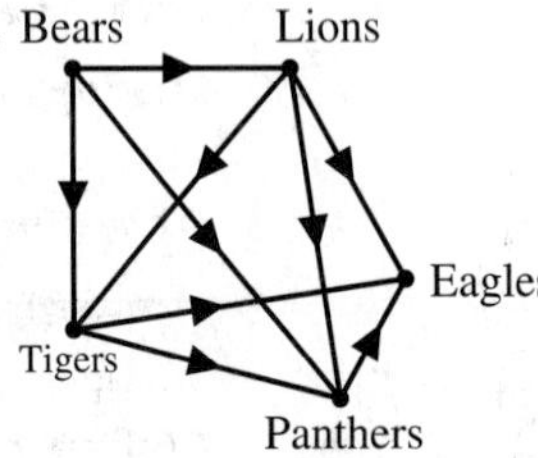

c. Bears should be ranked first since they have three wins, no losses, and a victory over the other team with three wins (Lions). Eagles should be ranked last since they have no wins, three losses, and a loss to the only other team with three losses (Panthers).

Exercises, pages 679–681

1. no **3. a.** yes **b.** 2-by-3, 2-by-8, 4-by-6 **c.** At least one of x or y must be even. **5.** yes **7. a.** $20! = 2{,}432{,}902{,}008{,}176{,}640{,}000$ **b.** 20 **c.** $20 \times 20! = 48{,}658{,}040{,}163{,}532{,}800{,}000$ **d.** about 1543 years

9. a.

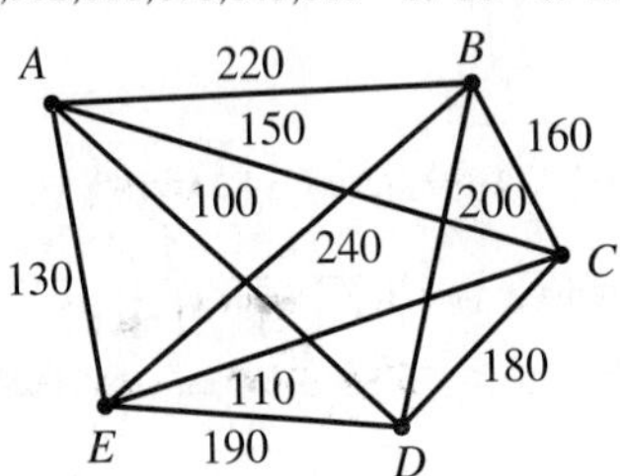

b. $ADCEBA$ = \$850 **c.** $AECBDA$ = \$700

11. The postal service collecting mail from mailboxes, or delivering packages to specific destinations.

Exercises, pages 682–683

1. 32;

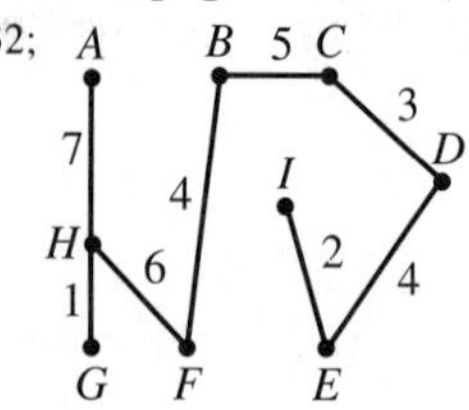

3. $n - 1$

5. \$840

7. a. \$99,000 **b.** \$34,000

Fractal Geometry

Exercises, Pages 685–686

1. For ruler lengths 1 in., $\frac{1}{2}$ in., $\frac{1}{4}$ in.: number of sides 7, 15, 30; perimeters 7 in., $7\frac{1}{4}$ in., $7\frac{1}{2}$ in. **3. a.** Yes; a typical sequence of approximations is: 17 in., $18\frac{1}{4}$ in., $18\frac{3}{4}$ in. **b.** The approximate length of the circumference will always be less than 6π, or 18.85, in. **c.** The circumference of a circle has a measurable length; a jagged coastline does not.

Exercises, Pages 688–690

1. a.

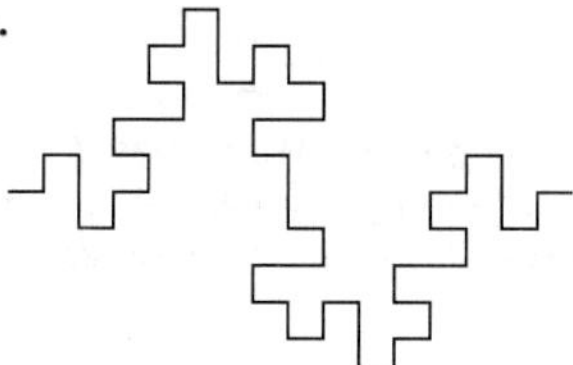

b.

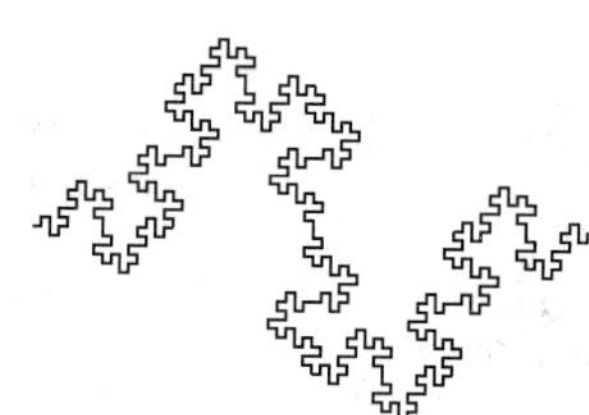

c. For levels 0, 1, 2, 3: edge lengths $1, \frac{1}{4}, \frac{1}{16}, \frac{1}{64}$; number of edges 1, 8, 64, 512; total lengths 1, 2, 4, 8

3. a.

b.

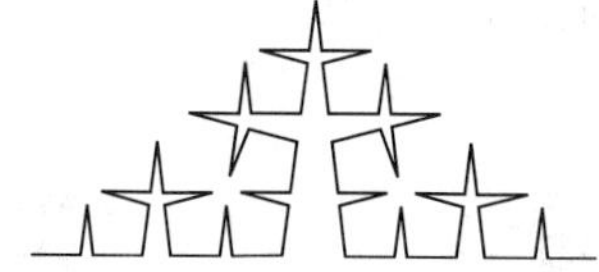

c. For levels 0, 1, 2, 3: edge lengths $1, \frac{4}{9}, \frac{16}{81}, \frac{64}{729}$; number of edges 1, 4, 16, 64; total lengths $1, 1\frac{7}{9}, 3\frac{13}{81}, 5\frac{451}{729}$

5. a.

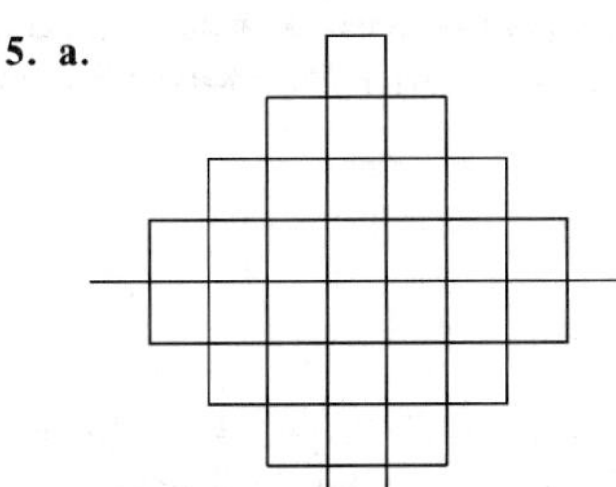

b.

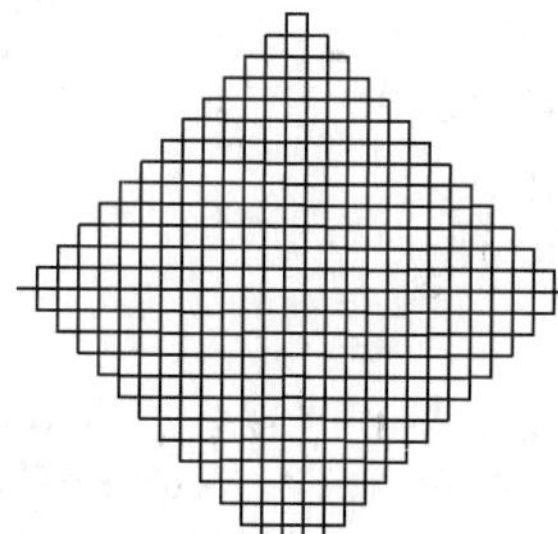

c. For levels 0, 1, 2, 3: edge lengths $1, \frac{1}{3}, \frac{1}{9}, \frac{1}{27}$; number of edges 1, 9, 81, 729; total lengths 1, 3, 9, 27

7. a. As the pre-fractal level increases, the edge length for the Cantor set decreases by a factor of $\frac{1}{3}$. **b.** The number of edges increases by a factor of 2. **c.** The sum of the lengths decreases by a factor of $\frac{2}{3}$.
9. The level 3 pre-fractal for the Cantor set is defined by the following 16 endpoints. (The boldface points were given as endpoints of the level 1 pre-fractal.)
$\mathbf{(0, 0)}, \left(\frac{1}{27}, 0\right), \left(\frac{2}{27}, 0\right), \left(\frac{1}{9}, 0\right), \left(\frac{2}{9}, 0\right), \left(\frac{7}{27}, 0\right), \left(\frac{8}{27}, 0\right), \mathbf{\left(\frac{1}{3}, 0\right)}, \mathbf{\left(\frac{2}{3}, 0\right)}, \left(\frac{19}{27}, 0\right), \left(\frac{20}{27}, 0\right), \left(\frac{7}{9}, 0\right), \left(\frac{8}{9}, 0\right), \left(\frac{25}{27}, 0\right), \left(\frac{26}{27}, 0\right), \mathbf{(1, 0)}$. **11.** The area of the snowflake fractal is $1 + \frac{1}{3} + \frac{4}{27} + \frac{16}{243} + \ldots = 1.6$ times the area of the original equilateral triangle.

Exercises, Page 691

1. 1.5 **3.** 1.71 **5.** 2 **7.** $N = 2, R = 3, D \approx 0.63$

Acknowledgments

Book designed by Ligature, Inc.
Cover concept and design by Ligature, Inc.
Technical art: Precision Graphics, ANCO/Boston

Cover photographs: John Payne Photo, Ltd., (background) Jim Brandenburg/Westlight

Photographs

xvi *(background)* Astromedia, division of Kalmbach Publishing Co. and The Press Syndicate of the University of Cambridge, *(left)* Jim Richardson/Westlight, *(right)* Chuck O'Rear/Westlight **4** Tad Goodale **5** Paul Von Stroheim **9** Lou Jones **11** Tad Goodale **24** Chuck O'Rear/Westlight **27** Landslides **32** *(left)* Rene Sheret/Marilyn Gartman Agency, *(right)* Hank Morgan/Rainbow **36** *(top)* David Muench, *(bottom)* Yoram Kahana/Peter Arnold, Inc. **43** Seth Resnick/Picture Group **49** *(left)* Margaret Berg/Berg and Associates, *(right)* University of California, Berkeley **54** Tad Goodale **56** Landslides **72** *(background)* courtesy of Spieth-Anderson International Inc. and American Athletic, Inc., *(left)* David Madison, *(right)* Roland Weber/Masterfile **75** Cary Wolinsky/Stock Boston **100** *(top left)* Dan McCoy/Rainbow, *(top right)* Larry Lee/Westlight, *(bottom)* Index Stock **101** The Flag Research Center **104** Shostal **116** *(left)* Robert Carr/Stock Boston, *(right)* America Hurrah **128** Thomas Russell **133** *(left)* FPG, *(middle)* Steve Elmore/Stock Market, *(right)* Swanke, Hayden, Connell Architects **134** Tom and Michelle Grimm/After Image **140** Barbara Burten **166** *(top)* Hans Hofmann, 1961, oil on canvas, 151 × 182 cm, Mr. and Mrs. Frank G. Logan Prize Fund, 1962.775, The Art Institute of Chicago. All Rights Reserved. *(bottom)* Richard Hirneisen/The Stock Shop **171** *(left)* Stephen R. Brown/Stock Market **179** Owen Franken/Stock Boston **190** Rob Outlaw **196** *(top)* Rob Outlaw, *(bottom)* Peter Chapman **202** *(left)* Breck Kent, *(right)* Jim Olive/Uniphoto Picture Agency **209, 210** FPG **213** *(left)* NASA, *(right)* Ken Lax/Stock Shop, *(bottom)* NASA **214** Peter Chapman **224** FPG **240** *(background)* U. S. Geological Survey, *(left)* Kathleen Norris Cook, *(right)* Jim Richardson/Westlight **242** Lee Boltin **244** Peter Chapman **253** *(left)* Gail Page, *(right)* The Dallas Museum of Art, Foundation for the Arts Collection, gift of the James H. and Lillian Clark Foundation **262** Eric Kroll/Taurus **284** *(background)* Bruce Roberts-Goodson, A.M.S.N.A.M.E., *(left)* John Terence Turner/FPG, *(right)* Sharon Green/Sportschrome, Inc. **303** Ed Brunette **304** *(left)* Department of Mathematics, Massachusetts Institute of Technology, *(right)* Sovfoto **315** Dominique Berretty/Black Star **317** Karl Hentz/Image Bank **320** Cameramann International **321** Charles F. Norton/Deck House, Inc. **328** *(left)* Lou Jones, *(right)* Jeffrey L. Cook/The Stock Broker **334** Jonathan Barkin/Picture Cube **338** *(left)* Alfred Borcover, *(right)* Culver Pictures **343** NASA **368** Rothwell/FPG **374** *(background)* Chilton Book Company/Chrysler Plymouth Company, *(left)* Takeshi Takahara/Photo Researchers, *(right)* Jay Freis/Image Bank **379** *(bottom)* courtesy of Cruft Photo Lab, Harvard University/Paul Donaldson, *(left)* Department of the Navy **390** Collection of Whitney Museum of American Art, New York, gift of the Howard and Jean Lipman Foundation, Inc., photo by Geoffrey Clements **400** *(top)* Ellis Herwig/Picture Cube, *(right)* Tom Tracey/Stock Shop, *(left)* Sepp Seitz/Woodfin Camp and Associates **401** Seth Goltzer/Stock Market **403, 409** Richard Haynes, Jr. **410** Brian Milne/Animals, Animals **422** *(left)* Gerrit Rietvald, *Red-Blue Chair*, 1918, Acc #L1884.139, Milwaukee Art Museum, *(right)* Cecile Brunswick/Peter Arnold **440** Wayne Sorce **447** Landslides **452** FPG **467** NASA **474** *(background)* courtesy of Anthony Belluschi Architects, Ltd., *(left)* Tom Grill/Comstock, Inc., *(right)* © Greg Murphy **488** *(top)* M. Timothy O'Keefe/Tom Stack and Associates, *(bottom)* Christopher Crowley/Tom Stack and Associates **497** Van Dusen Corporation **501** Judy Gibbs **505** *(top)* Owen Franken/Stock Boston, *(bottom)* City of Montreal, Archives Division **507** *(left)* Buckminster Fuller Institute, *(right)* DeClan Haun/Black Star **508** FPG **511** Barbara Burten **522** *(background)* U. S. Department of Commerce, NOAA, *(left)* Milton and Joan Mann/Cameramann International, *(right)* James Warren/Westlight **529** Story Litchfield/Stock Boston **533** Richard Haynes, Jr. **535** Grant Haller/Leo deWys, Inc. **539** Dick Luria/Folio Inc. **570** *(background, left)* © Wayne Eastep, *(right)* Tom Campbell/FPG **577** Larry Sutton/FPG **581** Kay Chernush/Image Bank **583** Focus on Sports **588** Braniff/FPG **592** Eric Neurath/Stock Boston **598** IBM **611** *(left)* Philip A. Savoie/Bruce Coleman, Inc., *(right)* Robert P. Carr/Bruce Coleman, Inc. **612** *(top left)* Carl Roessler/Animals, Animals, *(top right)* Bruce Coleman, Inc., *(bottom left)* Steve Solum/Bruce Coleman, Inc., *(bottom right)* David Stone